The Wonderful world of Non-League Football

as seen through the lense of our photographers

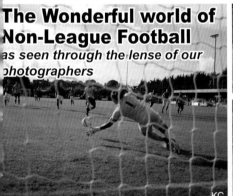

...and that'll be a Cup hat-trick - 1

2

3

KC

R

GV

PB

KC

RT

BW

PB

AC

RT

PB

GW

AC

RT

Once again a huge mention to Peter Barnes (PB), Keith Clayton (KC), Alan Coomes (AC), Roger Turner (RT), Bill Wheatcroft (BW) and Gordon Whittington (GW), *thank you* so much for your support of our Directory.

Again I haven't captioned the photographs so as to fit more action shots in. However, each photographer as been credited with their photo and so should you be interested in obtaining a copy we can put you in touch with the photographer in question.

NON-LEAGUE CLUB DIRECTORY 2017-18

(40th Edition)

EDITORS
MIKE & TONY WILLIAMS

NON-LEAGUE CLUB DIRECTORY 2017-18
ISBN 978-1-869833-74-9

Editors
Mike Williams
(Tel: 01548 531 339)
mwpublishing@btconnect.com
Tony Williams
(Tel: 01823 490 684)
Email: t.williams320@btinternet.com

Published by MW Publishing
(Tel: 01548 531 339)
Email: mwpublishing@btconnect.com

Printed and bound by
CPI Group (UK) Ltd, Croydon, CR0 4YY

Sales & Distribution
MWPublishing (01548 531 339)

Front Cover: York City's Simon Heslop and Macclesfield Town's Ollie Norburn
challenge for the ball during the FA Trophy final at Wembley.
Photo: Alan Coomes.

THE NON-LEAGUE CLUB DIRECTORY 2017-18
FOREWORD

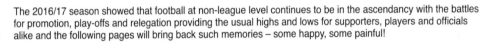

I t gives me great pleasure to welcome you to the 40th Anniversary edition of The Non-League Club Directory, the must read reference book for all non-league football aficionado's, and I congratulate Tony and Mike Williams for once again putting this comprehensive publication together.

The directory started as a small pocket book back in 1977 and has expanded over the past 40 years into the sizeable volume it is today, which faithfully records the past seasons statistics for many of the league and cup competitions that operate nationwide, thus making its publication eagerly anticipated.

The non-league game is the heartbeat of football in the United Kingdom and the contribution that clubs make to their local communities should not be under estimated. As ever, the game is reliant on the dedicated service given by a largely volunteer workforce who work tirelessly for their league or club every week and it is appropriate to use this page to say a big 'THANK YOU' to each and every one of them.

The 2016/17 season showed that football at non-league level continues to be in the ascendancy with the battles for promotion, play-offs and relegation providing the usual highs and lows for supporters, players and officials alike and the following pages will bring back such memories – some happy, some painful!

In the FA Cup section we will particularly recall the exploits of Lincoln City and Sutton United in reaching the Quarter-Finals and 5th Round respectively, with both clubs being knocked out by Arsenal – the eventual winners.

The second FA Non-League Finals Day proved a great success with an attendance of just over 38,000 seeing York City lift the FA Trophy for the second time and South Shields winning the FA Vase to continue the recent dominance of teams from the Northern League. Congratulations also to Hardwick Social from Stockton on winning the FA Sunday Cup for the first time.

Lincoln City capped an outstanding season by winning the National League title, thus earning a return to the English Football League after suffering relegation at the end of the 2010/11 season; and congratulations to 'the little club on the hill' Forest Green Rovers on gaining promotion to the English Football League for the first time in their history.

The England C team is an important feature of the non-league scene, giving players at non-league level the opportunity to proudly represent their country, and congratulations go to Paul Fairclough and the squad on reaching the Final of the International Challenge Trophy and we wish them success when they travel to play Slovakia in the Final later this year.

For The Football Association, and both the Professional Game and National Game, Safeguarding has been one of the highest priorities in recent months and all in the game have a collective responsibility to ensure that football provides a safe environment for all participants as well as ensuring that Fair Play and Respect remain at the fore.

Good news for clubs entering the FA Trophy and FA Vase is that the National Game Board have approved a 21% increase in prize funds for both competitions for the 2017/18 season.

In 12 months' time the structure of the National League System will further evolve with the implementation of another division at both Step 3 (Southern League) and Step 4 (Isthmian League), thus adding to the importance of the coming season for a number of clubs.

As a new season beckons, may I wish everyone involved in non-league football an enjoyable and successful season and may The Non-League Club Directory continue to prosper.

Mervyn Leggett
Chairman – FA National Game Board

CONTENTS

Being Chairman of The Football Association, I am extremely fortunate to be present at incredible sporting events across the world, seeing top players shine and great teams performing at the highest levels. Whilst a privilege that I will never take for granted, as a lifelong football fan that started in the professional game selling programmes at Leicester City matches, I am similarly delighted at being afforded the opportunity to attend matches at every level of our game, up and down the country.

The non-league pyramid, in my opinion, is one of the best things about English football. Put me by a pitch at a non-league ground, whether in shirt-sleeves during late summer or wrapped in layers on a cold winter's night, and I am in my element. The opportunity to feel the passion and pride of a loyal band of supporters, get up close and personal to the action and meet the men and women who devote their spare time to keeping clubs alive is a truly unique experience. Last season, my travels have ranged from South Park in Surrey to Blue Flame Walking Football Team in Northumbria and Devon County FA v the Navy in Newton Abbot to Loughborough Dynamo FC.

Although there are many things to be proud of in our national game, the volunteer spirit is integral to the success of non-league football and should be celebrated. At The FA we firmly believe that the game belongs to everyone and it is the collective responsibility of all those working in football to ensure that the right to take part – regardless of ability level, ethnicity or gender – is protected and promoted for all.

The 40th edition of this wonderful directory is a remarkable resource and typifies the sheer size and nature of non-league football within this country. Well done to all those involved, I hope to see it continue for many years to come.

Greg Clarke
Chairman
The FA

FROM BULLPITT TO BUTT LANE

I can't remember exactly what age I was when I first sampled Non-League football, I'm guessing about six or seven. To be honest I don't remember much about the actual football being played, my memories were of the sausage, chips and beans at the Three Swans Pub for lunch, walking in through the gates of Bullpit Lane (Hungerford Town), ball in hand, and disappearing for the next three hours or so behind the top goal to play football with whoever turned up. The day would then be completed with a bottle of coke and a packet crisps - the type that came with their own navy blue sachet of salt - as Dad entertained the traveling officials and players. It was a year or so later that I started to care more about the Crusaders' actual result and looked up to my footballing heros such as Ian Farr and Nevarda Phillips - one day I was going to play for Hungerford!

Alas that never happened but the club will always have a place in my heart and I look forward to visiting again next season - I still smile whenever I see their name on the vidiprinter, my little Hungerford in the National South.

Now, 40 years later, and I'm the one running a football club, Loddiswell Athletic in the South Devon League. We're not looking to climb the 'Pyramid' but the enjoyment of being involved is just the same as at any other non-League club. I won't lie times are hard for little clubs like mine as the 'pool' of players gets smaller and smaller, the bigger problem however, is the lack of today's players moving on into the running of clubs when they hang up their boots.

Things could change dramatically in the lower levels of our game in the future but until then, I'm going to enjoy everything that non-League football brings you on a match day - although, nobody does sausage, chips and beans quite like the Three Swans did!

SPECIAL ACKNOWLEDGMENTS

'OUR TEAM' OF PHOTOGRAPHERS
Peter Barnes, Keith Clayton, Alan Coomes,
'Uncle Eric' Marsh, Roger Turner, Bill Wheatcroft and Gordon Whittington.

FA COMPETITIONS DEPARTMENT
Chris Darnell and Scott Bolton

CONTRIBUTORS
Arthur Evans (Photographer & reports).
Richard Rundle (Football Club History Database).
The many league and club officials that have been kind enough to supply the necessary information.

And last but not least, Dad, whose passion for the game
(albeit waning slightly in recent years when watching the so called 'professional level' our game)
is second to none.
Over the 40 years, and more, he has put so much in to the sport he loves, and taken very little.

Thank you one and all

Mike Williams

In Memory of Maurice
" I'm going to miss our chats about Crawley Town"

40 YEARS OF PROMOTING THE GAME I LOVE

It's difficult to accept that this years Non-League Directory is the 40th since we produced the first little pocket book as The Non-League Annual in 1976. Having helped the Football Association with programmes and magazines, their chief executive Ted Croker had suggested that we should compile an annual for the huge world of Non-League football. As we had been responsible for the first Rothmans Football Yearbooks featuring Football League clubs, why didn't we provide a similar annual for the semi-professional and amateur senior leagues?

So, with the encouragement of The Football Association, which was full of true football lovers, the idea developed year by year and grew from a 168 page pocket book to an annual with over a thousand pages, before settling down with a 872 pagination. The help of a number of sponsors has been appreciated over the years and there were times when our publications topped the national lists of sports book sales.

Some of the most enjoyable days for me have been when invited by Steve Clark and The Competitions Department of the Football Association, to attend the FA Trophy and FA Vase Finals at Wembley Stadium. The lunch at these wonderful non-league occasions brings together many real non-league workers who love the game and have promoted the competitions throughout the season.

The Wembley Finals also give us a chance to thank all the wonderful Photographers who have sent in photos and copy to Michael all season, in all weathers, without ever asking for, or expecting payments. They love the game and the also enjoy the spirit in which they all work through the season before meeting to work together at the wonderful Wembley Stadium. Our special thanks go to: Peter Barnes, Graham Brown, Keith Clayton, Alan Coomes, Arthur Evans, 'Uncle' Eric Marsh, Roger Turner, Bill Wheatcroft and Gordon Whittington

Throughout the 38 years that we hope 'The Non-League Club Directory' has promoted non-league football, the co-operation and help from Mike Appleby, David Barber, Steve Clark and Graham Noakes plus their colleagues in their offices at the Football Association, have been greatly appreciated.

Michael has worked incredibly hard to keep the book 'alive.' His dedication to the game is immense but sadly he has had to battle at a time when books have become less popular, and non-league football is not exactly fashionable. Encouragement and support from the higher ranks at The Football Association is obviously important as it's an uphill battle to compile, design, print and distribute an annual that features 95% of the national game.

The character of the senior non-league football world has been influenced by the all important automatic promotion to The Football league and quite incredible money is now available for successful clubs. Understandably, the massive amount of football on television, as well as a superb coverage of all sports in general, may make the idea of a visit to your local non-league club less appealing.

However, a good local club can offer exciting competition, friendship on and off the field, an enjoyable chance to mix with, and possibly help the players and officials. Being involved with a good non-league club, can give you the exciting and satisfying chance of feeling part of a sporting community and enjoying all the good things involved with team spirit and a sport that you love.

My special thanks to Adrian Titcombe and Brian Lee whose dedication to, and obvious love for the game, has inspired and helped me throughout my lifetime involved with non-league football. Their special messages and the support from the FA Executives in our special 40th edition are greatly appreciated.

Looking back to recent editorials in the Directories its interesting to note that we have already warned against the increased 'diving' , holding at corners and free kicks, plus the fact that the strong but fair tackle is being driven out of the game as many confused referees are bullied into giving yellow cards for more and more honest tackles.

It is very difficult for two determined players to commit an honest, but physical tackle and arrive at exactly the same time. One will get the ball and the other may be a fraction late, but surely this doesn't deserve so many yellow cards. If a player is booked for miss timing a tackle, he might just as stupidly be booked for hitting a shot off target. Its just a mistake and not deliberate! Timing and technique cannot always be perfect! Its not necessarily planned aggression which would be worth a red or yellow card.

After a deliberate foul or basic cheating, pundits are heard to say 'he took one for the team" when the culprit is booked. Is cheating really to be admired and encouraged ? Should all youngsters be taught to cheat if they cannot be successful legally? Is winning by cheating really more important than honesty and sportsmanship? I wonder whether these players teach their youngsters to cheat at home, at school and at work throughout life in general? Where do they stop?

If you respect the game you love and are proud of your sport's principles of fair play and sportsmanship, every incident of deliberate cheating is sickening to see and of course does no good at all to the spirit and image of 'our national game'. I'm proud of football and hate to see trends creeping in that will bring the modern game and its image into disrepute. Hopefully, improvements to football are considered regularly by the game's administrators. So, if they seriously care for the national sport, we will be able to enjoy a more honest, but still competitive game, in the seasons ahead.

We obviously realise that the popularity of books in general has dropped in the modern world. But hopefully, a full review of each year's Non-league clubs and their competitions can still be considered an enjoyable possession and a valuable annual record featuring the level of football you love.

Michael and I have been lucky to have been involved with non-league football all our lives and although we hear, and sometimes agree, that times are changing. Just think of the improvements we have seen over the years regarding playing surfaces, club facilities and possible financial rewards

Congratulations and thanks to the Lincoln City club and their wonderful leaders, Danny and Nick Cowley, who gave the sporting world an uplifting example of a quality sporting non-league football club on and off the field in their wonderful FA Cup run.

In 1986 the Football Association presented us with an award inscribed 'for continued promotion of all that's good in football'. Hopefully we have continued with that promotion. The publication is now forty years old and its certainly been a labour of love!

Tony Williams

TIME TO CELEBRATE!

As another season of optimism and expectations dawn, the latest Edition of the Non-League Directory is anxiously awaited and the game at this level owes Tony and Mike Williams a massive 'thank you' for this 40th Edition.

Their knowledge and enthusiasm together with the high respect in which Tony is held, by all levels of the game, has benefitted and enthused many, many people over the years.

We live in a constantly changing world where football plays its part. We change Competitions, move Clubs, change boundaries and IFAB (International Football Association Board) change the Laws of the Game, increase the number of substitutes – but have we got it right yet?

Why is the game so arrogant and not prepared to look at other sports? The use of Sin Bins and Rolling Substitutes are examples. If United are playing City and a United player receives a Yellow Card, he has clearly offended the City team, does a Free Kick equate to the Card? No - but 10 minutes in the Sin Bin would give an immediate benefit to City.

IFAB have also expressed their concern about wasting time and possibly reducing each 45 minute Half, well Rolling Substitutes (making a Player Substitution whilst the game is in play) that operate in some other countries, would at least help the 'time wasting' at all levels of the game.

The synthetic grass surface continues to present a challenge for the English Football League but as demonstrated at Sutton United in particular, the correct FIFA Standard surface can be a benefit for the GAME as well as the Clubs and their Communities.

Another concern as we approach the new season is the role of Fourth Officials, has the game benefitted from their introduction? They could be just as effective sitting next to the TV Camera in the Stand, for it looks as though more Decisions are coming from there in the future. After all, it will not be long before the 'new' Referee takes over – the Video Assisted Referee (VAR) , which did not receive any plaudits for its performance in the Confederation Cup.

In the National League (and above) Fourth Officials at present are often figures for abuse from people in the Technical Areas and can become an unnecessary focal point.

Whilst Central Funding and Sponsorship are often blamed for the ills in the game, how can we live without them? It is also important to remember the early role Rothmans – and again Tony Williams – played in Sponsor development with the Isthmian League. Now, most if not all, Non-League clubs enjoy sponsorship at various levels and they also play a much wider role in bringing their Communities into their clubs as well as taking their Clubs into the Community.

One sad struggle at the moment is the fight to preserve Representative Football and in particular, the England C team, where Paul Fairclough has led the team to the Final of the International Challenge Trophy in Slovakia in November. Nothing can replace the honour of being selected to represent your Country. I hope The FA remember the huge benefits the player makes on behalf of the Governing Body in promoting the game on their behalf.

There is a lot happening and our level is the heartbeat of the game where Clubs run by Volunteers for both men and women continues to grow. Tony Williams is one of those Volunteers but a special and exceptional one. In thanking him (and not forgetting Mike) may I wish you all an enjoyable and successful season as we look forward to the '50th' Non-League Club Directory!

Brian Lee

The Seventies saw a number of changes and developments which were to have significant impact upon the face of the game below the Football League. The abolition of the amateur status meant that from season 1974/75 instead of playing in the FA Amateur Cup or the professional FA Trophy, the top two hundred or so non-League clubs now entered the revamped Trophy, while those from the leagues below entered an entirely new competition, the FA Vase.

Amateur internationals were naturally a thing of the past and the opportunity for international recognition now lay with the England Semi-Professional team with the first Four Nation Tournament being staged in 1979, featuring teams from England, Scotland, Italy and The Netherlands.

The strength of the non-League game meant there were always clubs who believed (with good cause) that they could more than hold their own in the Football League but entry rested in the hands of the FL clubs themselves when the bottom clubs offered themselves annually for re-election. The likelihood of success was diminished by the ambitious non-Leaguers splitting the vote and to have a single non-League candidate would clearly improve that club's chances. It was agreed that a single league producing a champion would be a better option and discussions between the Northern Premier and Southern Leagues in the late Seventies saw the establishment of the Alliance Premier League in 1979/80. At the same time the then FA Secretary agreed that I should meet with leagues and clubs throughout the country to gauge the strength of support for a promotion and relegation system between leagues below the APL. The Isthmian League joined soon after and the Pyramid of Football (now National League System) was born.

I had met with Tony Williams early in my career at The FA and, if there was a more enthusiastic advocate of the non-League game, I never came across him. A staunch believer in the need to play the game in a fair and sporting manner, he was (and still is) an endless source of ideas. One of these was for an annual to provide a reference point for the many fans of the non-League game whose needs were largely ignored by the mainstream media. Of course, I was delighted to support the project and I am pleased to say The FA felt similarly. Looking at the first edition, I see my name on the Editorial Committee but, as I recall it, my contribution was minimal.

Last season's FA Vase competition saw 592 clubs aspiring to a Wembley Final appearance and, of all the many and varied FA projects in which I have been involved, setting this up is probably the one which gives me most satisfaction.

In 1987 automatic promotion to the Football League for the APL champions was agreed (subject to stadium criteria) and from 2003 a second place was made available to the play-off winners. The National League, to use its current name, now tops a National League System consisting of seven tiers. Forest Green Rovers, the most recent addition to the EFL ranks, worked their way up through the leagues, having won the FA Vase in 1982.

Through the Directory and his other publications, Tony Williams provided enthusiastic backing for this evolution of the non-League game. He was actively involved with FA XI matches and also the England Semi-Pro team whose very existence was threatened after the completion of two cycles of the Four Nation Tournament. The vociferous support from Tony and other liked minded persons help to ensure the team's continuation, albeit in a limited fashion, and was fundamental to its development into today's England C team.

Of course, I was delighted to support the project and I am pleased to say The FA felt similarly.

In recent years, the mantle of editor has passed to son, Mike, and the original pocket sized Annual of 250 pages has swelled to a Directory of over 900. Only those close to the pair of them know what a battle it has been to ensure its continued production in this IT dominated age and, indeed, the amount of work involved. However, whatever the future holds, the Non-League Directory, in always steadfastly championing the need to maintain standards, has made a major contribution to this vital area of the English game.

Adrian Titcombe

Non-League Pyramid (Steps 1-7) 2017-18 and it's 2016-17 Champions

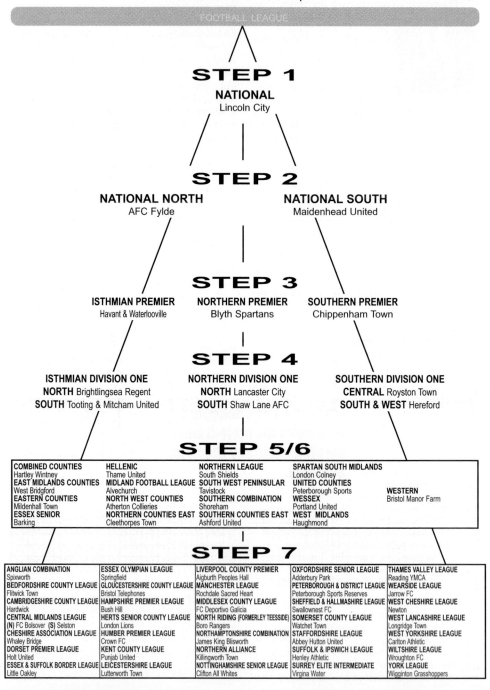

FOOTBALL LEAGUE

STEP 1
NATIONAL
Lincoln City

STEP 2
NATIONAL NORTH
AFC Fylde

NATIONAL SOUTH
Maidenhead United

STEP 3
ISTHMIAN PREMIER
Havant & Waterlooville

NORTHERN PREMIER
Blyth Spartans

SOUTHERN PREMIER
Chippenham Town

STEP 4
ISTHMIAN DIVISION ONE
NORTH Brightlingsea Regent
SOUTH Tooting & Mitcham United

NORTHERN DIVISION ONE
NORTH Lancaster City
SOUTH Shaw Lane AFC

SOUTHERN DIVISION ONE
CENTRAL Royston Town
SOUTH & WEST Hereford

STEP 5/6

COMBINED COUNTIES
Hartley Wintney
EAST MIDLANDS COUNTIES
West Bridgford
EASTERN COUNTIES
Mildenhall Town
ESSEX SENIOR
Barking

HELLENIC
Thame United
MIDLAND FOOTBALL LEAGUE
Alvechurch
NORTH WEST COUNTIES
Atherton Collieries
NORTHERN COUNTIES EAST
Cleethorpes Town

NORTHERN LEAGUE
South Shields
SOUTH WEST PENINSULAR
Tavistock
SOUTHERN COMBINATION
Shoreham
SOUTHERN COUNTIES EAST
Ashford United

SPARTAN SOUTH MIDLANDS
London Colney
UNITED COUNTIES
Peterborough Sports
WESSEX
Portland United
WEST MIDLANDS
Haughmond

WESTERN
Bristol Manor Farm

STEP 7

ANGLIAN COMBINATION
Spixworth
BEDFORDSHIRE COUNTY LEAGUE
Flitwick Town
CAMBRIDGESHIRE COUNTY LEAGUE
Hardwick
CENTRAL MIDLANDS LEAGUE
(N) FC Bolsover (S) Selston
CHESHIRE ASSOCIATION LEAGUE
Whaley Bridge
DORSET PREMIER LEAGUE
Holt United
ESSEX & SUFFOLK BORDER LEAGUE
Little Oakley

ESSEX OLYMPIAN LEAGUE
Springfield
GLOUCESTERSHIRE COUNTY LEAGUE
Bristol Telephones
HAMPSHIRE PREMIER LEAGUE
Bush Hill
HERTS SENIOR COUNTY LEAGUE
London Lions
HUMBER PREMIER LEAGUE
Crown FC
KENT COUNTY LEAGUE
Punjab United
LEICESTERSHIRE LEAGUE
Lutterworth Town

LIVERPOOL COUNTY PREMIER
Aigburth Peoples Hall
MANCHESTER LEAGUE
Rochdale Sacred Heart
MIDDLESEX COUNTY LEAGUE
FC Deportivo Galicia
NORTH RIDING (FORMERLEY TEESSIDE)
Boro Rangers
NORTHAMPTONSHIRE COMBINATION
James King Blisworth
NORTHERN ALLIANCE
Killingworth Town
NOTTINGHAMSHIRE SENIOR LEAGUE
Clifton All Whites

OXFORDSHIRE SENIOR LEAGUE
Adderbury Park
PETERBOROUGH & DISTRICT LEAGUE
Peterborough Sports Reserves
SHEFFIELD & HALLMASHIRE LEAGUE
Swallownest FC
SOMERSET COUNTY LEAGUE
Watchet Town
STAFFORDSHIRE LEAGUE
Abbey Hutton United
SUFFOLK & IPSWICH LEAGUE
Henley Athletic
SURREY ELITE INTERMEDIATE
Virgina Water

THAMES VALLEY LEAGUE
Reading YMCA
WEARSIDE LEAGUE
Jarrow FC
WEST CHESHIRE LEAGUE
Newton
WEST LANCASHIRE LEAGUE
Longridge Town
WEST YORKSHIRE LEAGUE
Carlton Athletic
WILTSHIRE LEAGUE
Wroughton FC
YORK LEAGUE
Wigginton Grasshoppers

CONFERENCE LEAGUE TABLE 2016-17

		P	W	D	L	F	A	GD	Pts
1	Lincoln City	46	30	9	7	83	40	43	99
2	Tranmere Rovers	46	29	8	9	79	39	40	95
3	Forest Green Rovers	46	25	11	10	88	56	32	86
4	Dagenham & Redbridge	46	26	6	14	79	53	26	84
5	Aldershot Town	46	23	13	10	66	37	29	82
6	Dover Athletic	46	24	7	15	85	63	22	79
7	Barrow	46	20	15	11	72	53	19	75
8	Gateshead	46	19	13	14	72	51	21	70
9	Macclesfield Town	46	20	8	18	64	57	7	68
10	Bromley	46	18	8	20	59	66	-7	62
11	Boreham Wood	46	15	13	18	49	48	1	58
12	Sutton United	46	15	13	18	61	63	-2	58
13	Wrexham	46	15	13	18	47	61	-14	58
14	Maidstone United	46	16	10	20	59	75	-16	58
15	Eastleigh	46	14	15	17	56	63	-7	57
16	Solihull Moors	46	15	10	21	62	75	-13	55
17	Torquay United	46	14	11	21	54	61	-7	53
18	Woking	46	14	11	21	66	80	-14	53
19	Chester	46	14	10	22	63	71	-8	52
20	Guiseley	46	13	12	21	50	67	-17	51
21	York City	46	11	17	18	55	70	-15	50
22	Braintree Town	46	13	9	24	51	76	-25	48
23	Southport	46	10	9	27	52	97	-45	39
24	North Ferriby United	46	12	3	31	32	82	-50	39

Play-Off Semi Finals: Aldershot Town 0-3 Tranmere Rovers / Tranmere Rovers 2-2 Aldershot Town
Dagenham & Redbridge 1-1 Forest Green Rovers / Forest Green Rovers 2-0 Dagenham & Redbridge
Final: Tranmere Rovers 1-3 Forest Green Rovers

		1	2	3	4	5	6	7	8	9	10	11	12	13	14	15	16	17	18	19	20	21	22	23	24
1	Aldershot Town		2-2	2-0	2-0	4-0	0-0	3-1	1-0	0-1	0-4	3-0	1-0	0-0	1-2	1-0	2-0	2-0	2-1	2-0	1-1	3-1	4-0	2-0	0-0
2	Barrow	1-0		1-1	2-1	1-1	3-2	2-1	2-3	4-0	2-3	0-0	3-0	3-0	1-1	3-0	3-1	2-1	0-1	0-0	0-0	2-1	2-2	1-1	2-0
3	Boreham Wood	1-1	1-1		0-1	0-0	1-1	1-3	5-0	0-1	1-0	0-4	0-0	2-0	2-4	0-1	1-0	0-0	2-0	1-0	2-0	0-1	2-1	0-1	1-1
4	Braintree Town	2-0	0-2	1-2		2-2	1-2	3-2	1-2	1-1	0-1	1-4	2-0	0-4	1-3	0-0	1-0	0-1	2-0	1-0	1-3	0-1	1-3	1-2	3-0
5	Bromley	2-2	4-1	1-0	0-5		0-1	1-3	0-2	0-5	1-5	3-2	1-1	1-1	0-1	2-0	1-0	3-1	1-0	1-0	0-2	2-1	4-3	3-0	
6	Chester	2-0	1-2	0-2	1-0	1-1		3-0	5-0	1-0	1-2	1-2	2-0	2-5	2-3	1-3	3-0	0-3	2-2	4-0	1-0	2-3	2-3	1-1	0-2
7	Dagenham & Redbridge	1-0	1-4	0-2	3-0	2-1	3-2		2-0	4-0	2-1	0-5	1-2	1-0	1-1	0-2	2-0	4-4	3-0	2-2	0-1	0-0	1-1	3-0	1-0
8	Dover Athletic	1-2	3-1	1-4	6-1	1-0	3-1	1-2		3-0	4-3	2-0	2-0	2-0	2-2	1-1	2-0	0-0	3-0	3-1	1-2	1-4	3-1	1-1	2-2
9	Eastleigh	1-1	2-0	2-2	0-2	2-1	0-3	0-1	2-4		1-1	1-1	2-1	0-1	0-1	3-0	2-0	2-0	1-1	2-1	5-5	2-2	4-3	3-0	2-1
10	Forest Green Rovers	2-1	0-0	2-0	1-1	1-0	2-0	1-1	1-1	1-1		1-0	3-0	2-3	3-0	2-2	0-1	2-1	5-1	1-1	0-0	0-1	2-1	2-2	6-1
11	Gateshead	1-1	4-1	1-1	1-1	0-2	3-0	1-0	4-2	2-2	3-1		1-1	1-2	1-1	1-2	0-1	0-0	3-0	1-0	0-0	0-1	2-1	2-2	6-1
12	Guiseley	1-0	1-0	3-1	0-0	1-4	1-1	0-2	0-4	1-1	0-1	1-1		2-1	1-2	2-1	1-2	1-1	2-1	2-1	2-0	1-2	1-1	2-3	6-1
13	Lincoln City	3-3	1-2	2-0	3-0	1-0	1-0	2-0	2-0	0-0	3-1	3-0	3-1		2-1	2-0	6-1	0-0	4-0	1-3	2-1	2-1	3-2	1-0	1-1
14	Macclesfield Town	0-2	0-1	0-2	2-0	1-2	0-0	1-4	2-1	0-1	0-1	1-1	1-2	1-2		3-0	1-0	1-3	3-1	0-0	2-0	4-2	3-1	3-0	1-3
15	Maidstone United	0-2	2-1	1-0	2-1	0-2	4-2	0-1	1-4	0-2	1-4	0-2	1-1	0-0	2-1		1-2	2-4	4-2	1-1	2-1	0-1	0-3	2-2	0-1
16	North Ferriby United	0-2	0-1	2-4	0-0	1-2	0-1	0-4	1-2	2-1	0-3	1-0	3-2	0-1	0-2	0-2		1-4	4-0	3-0	0-1	0-3	2-2	0-1	1-2
17	Solihull Moors	0-2	2-4	1-1	3-3	1-0	3-2	2-5	2-3	2-0	0-1	0-2	3-2	0-1	2-3	2-0	2-0		1-1	1-2	1-1	2-1	3-2	2-0	
18	Southport	1-1	1-4	1-0	4-5	1-2	0-1	1-4	0-1	4-3	2-0	0-3	0-1	1-1	1-2	3-2	2-4	0-0		1-1	1-2	1-1	2-1	3-2	2-0
19	Sutton United	2-0	0-0	1-0	1-2	2-0	5-2	1-0	0-6	1-1	1-2	3-0	1-0	1-1	2-0	2-2	5-1	1-3	2-2		2-0	1-0	4-1	1-0	2-2
20	Torquay United	0-0	1-1	1-0	3-1	1-0	0-1	1-0	2-1	3-1	4-3	3-1	1-2	1-2	1-1	2-3	2-0	3-0	1-2	2-3		0-0	1-2	1-1	2-0
21	Tranmere Rovers	2-2	2-0	2-1	1-0	2-2	2-2	0-2	1-0	2-1	0-1	0-1	1-0	0-1	1-0	2-1	1-0	9-0	4-1	3-2	2-1		3-1	2-0	1-0
22	Woking	1-2	1-1	0-0	2-3	2-1	3-1	1-3	1-0	3-3	0-1	3-0	0-0	1-3	1-0	2-4	1-1	2-1	0-0	2-1	3-1	0-3		2-0	1-1
23	Wrexham	0-2	2-2	2-1	0-1	2-1	0-0	0-1	0-0	0-0	3-1	0-2	3-1	1-2	0-3	1-3	1-0	1-0	1-0	1-1	0-1	0-1	2-1		2-1
24	York City	0-1	2-1	1-1	3-0	0-2	1-1	0-2	0-1	3-1	2-2	1-3	1-1	1-4	1-0	1-1	0-1	4-0	5-3	2-2	0-0	0-0	4-1	1-3	

NATIONAL NORTH LEAGUE TABLE 2016-17

		P	W	D	L	F	A	GD	Pts
1	AFC Fylde	42	26	10	6	109	60	49	88
2	Kidderminster Harriers	42	25	7	10	76	41	35	82
3	FC Halifax Town	42	24	8	10	81	43	38	80
4	Salford City	42	22	11	9	79	44	35	77
5	Darlington 1883	42	22	10	10	89	67	22	76
6	Chorley	42	20	14	8	60	41	19	74
7	Brackley Town	42	20	13	9	66	43	23	73
8	Stockport County	42	19	16	7	59	41	18	73
9	Tamworth	42	21	6	15	73	67	6	69
10	Gloucester City	42	18	10	14	69	61	8	64
11	Harrogate Town	42	16	11	15	71	63	8	59
12	Nuneaton Town	42	14	13	15	67	69	-2	55
13	FC United of Manchester	42	14	12	16	69	68	1	54
14	Curzon Ashton	42	14	10	18	63	72	-9	52
15	Boston United	42	12	11	19	54	72	-18	47
16	Bradford (Park Avenue)	42	12	7	23	46	74	-28	43
17	AFC Telford United	42	10	12	20	38	57	-19	42
18	Alfreton Town	42	11	9	22	62	95	-33	42
19	Gainsborough Trinity	42	8	12	22	51	84	-33	36
20	Worcester City	42	7	14	21	44	63	-19	35
21	Stalybridge Celtic	42	8	5	29	40	89	-49	29
22	Altrincham	42	4	9	29	39	91	-52	21

Play-Off Semi Finals: Chorley 0-1 Kidderminster Harriers / Kidderminster Harriers 0-2 Chorley
Salford City 1-1 FC Halifax Town / FC Halifax Town 1-1 Salford City (FC Halifax won on penalty kicks)
Final: FC Halifax Town 2-1 Chorley

		1	2	3	4	5	6	7	8	9	10	11	12	13	14	15	16	17	18	19	20	21	22
1	AFC Fylde		1-1	2-0	4-1	9-2	1-1	1-1	0-2	4-1	4-1	3-2	3-1	3-1	2-2	2-1	2-2	2-1	3-3	5-0	0-0	3-1	4-2
2	AFC Telford United	0-1		1-1	1-0	1-2	0-6	1-3	0-0	3-1	2-0	1-2	1-0	1-1	0-2	0-0	1-0	2-4	0-2	2-0	0-0	1-0	1-0
3	Alfreton Town	3-5	3-2		3-2	1-0	0-0	0-1	2-2	0-1	0-3	1-0	2-1	4-0	0-2	1-0	3-3	3-3	1-1	0-2	1-1	2-5	0-0
4	Altrincham	0-6	0-2	1-1		0-1	1-3	2-3	2-2	2-4	2-2	0-1	0-3	2-3	0-1	0-0	1-4	1-3	0-2	0-0	2-3	1-2	2-0
5	Boston United	0-3	3-0	3-2	0-1		2-3	1-0	3-1	3-1	1-2	1-4	2-3	1-1	1-2	0-3	1-1	1-3	2-0	0-1	0-2	3-0	0-0
6	Brackley Town	1-3	2-1	2-3	1-1	0-0		2-0	0-1	2-0	2-2	0-0	1-0	0-0	3-0	2-1	2-0	2-1	0-1	5-2	0-3	0-0	0-2
7	Bradford (Park Avenue)	1-4	1-1	1-0	2-1	0-2	2-1		0-3	4-4	1-2	1-3	0-0	5-1	0-1	2-3	1-3	1-1	0-2	0-1	0-2	0-0	0-3
8	Chorley	1-3	2-1	2-1	2-0	2-0	1-1	3-0		0-3	1-1	0-2	3-3	4-0	4-1	1-0	2-1	1-0	2-1	1-0	0-1	1-1	1-0
9	Curzon Ashton	3-2	1-1	5-0	2-3	4-2	0-0	1-2	1-1		1-2	4-2	1-2	1-2	0-0	1-0	1-6	2-1	0-2	0-0	1-2	1-5	1-1
10	Darlington 1883	1-1	1-0	3-4	3-1	4-1	1-0	2-0	1-3	1-3		3-2	4-2	5-2	2-0	2-3	0-1	1-2	2-2	4-1	2-1	3-2	5-1
11	FC Halifax Town	0-1	1-1	1-0	2-2	0-0	1-3	4-0	2-1	3-0	2-2		3-1	2-1	0-1	0-1	2-0	2-0	4-2	1-0	0-0	4-0	3-0
12	FC United of Manchester	2-3	0-0	4-3	1-1	1-1	1-2	2-3	3-3	0-0	2-3	0-3		5-1	2-4	2-2	1-0	3-0	0-3	2-2	2-0	1-0	1-1
13	Gainsborough Trinity	1-2	3-1	0-2	2-0	1-2	1-1	1-1	0-2	0-1	3-3	3-2	1-2		1-1	0-2	1-1	2-2	1-0	2-2	0-1	3-2	1-1
14	Gloucester City	1-5	3-0	4-0	5-0	3-1	1-3	1-0	2-2	0-2	1-2	0-2	2-3	4-1		1-1	1-2	2-2	3-2	2-1	0-1	2-0	3-0
15	Harrogate Town	3-3	2-1	6-3	2-2	2-0	1-2	1-0	2-1	2-2	1-4	0-3	3-1	1-3	3-1		0-2	3-1	3-3	3-1	0-1	3-4	3-0
16	Kidderminster Harriers	3-3	1-0	3-0	1-0	1-0	1-2	3-1	0-0	3-2	2-1	1-2	0-2	3-0	3-0	1-0		4-0	1-0	2-1	2-0	6-0	2-1
17	Nuneaton Town	4-1	1-1	4-1	4-1	2-2	2-2	1-2	1-1	0-1	1-1	2-3	1-4	2-1	1-1	2-1	0-2		0-1	2-1	1-1	1-0	1-1
18	Salford City	5-0	2-1	4-1	2-1	3-1	1-0	1-1	1-0	1-1	1-0	1-0	3-2	1-0	3-0	4-0		1-0		1-1	1-2	3-0	
19	Stalybridge Celtic	2-1	0-2	2-3	0-2	3-3	0-1	4-3	0-1	1-2	0-1	1-0	2-4	3-2	1-3	2-4	1-0	0-4	0-4		1-3	0-4	0-1
20	Stockport County	1-2	1-1	4-3	3-0	1-1	2-4	1-2	0-0	3-1	3-3	1-1	2-1	1-0	1-1	1-1	0-1	1-1	2-1	3-1		2-1	1-0
21	Tamworth	1-0	2-1	4-1	2-1	1-0	2-1	5-1	0-1	3-2	2-1	2-6	1-1	1-0	3-1	3-2	3-4	1-2	2-0	2-1	2-2		1-0
22	Worcester City	1-2	2-1	5-3	3-0	0-2	1-2	0-1	0-1	1-1	2-2	1-2	0-0	2-2	2-3	2-2	0-0	2-3	1-2	4-0	0-0	1-1	

NATIONAL SOUTH LEAGUE TABLE 2016-17

		P	W	D	L	F	A	GD	Pts
1	Maidenhead United	42	30	8	4	93	29	64	98
2	Ebbsfleet United	42	29	9	4	96	30	66	96
3	Dartford	42	25	9	8	83	45	38	84
4	Chelmsford City	42	23	13	6	89	47	42	82
5	Poole Town	42	20	11	11	63	49	14	71
6	Hungerford Town	42	19	13	10	67	49	18	70
7	Hampton & Richmond Borough	42	19	12	11	81	56	25	69
8	Wealdstone	42	18	12	12	62	58	4	66
9	Bath City	42	18	8	16	71	52	19	62
10	St Albans City	42	16	11	15	72	66	6	59
11	Eastbourne Borough	42	16	10	16	82	70	12	58
12	Hemel Hempstead Town	42	15	12	15	74	83	-9	57
13	East Thurrock United	42	14	14	14	73	65	8	56
14	Oxford City	42	15	7	20	48	73	-25	52
15	Weston-super-Mare	42	14	6	22	63	69	-6	48
16	Welling United	42	12	7	23	64	69	-5	43
17	Whitehawk	42	12	7	23	51	72	-21	43
18	Concord Rangers	42	10	12	20	57	75	-18	42
19	Truro City	42	11	7	24	53	99	-46	40
20	Gosport Borough	42	9	9	24	45	101	-56	36
21	Bishop's Stortford	42	8	3	31	29	104	-75	27
22	Margate	42	7	4	31	26	81	-55	25

Play-Off Semi Finals: Chelmsford City 0-0 Dartford / Dartford 1-2 Chelmsford City
Hampton & Richmond Borough 1-2 Ebbsfleet United / Ebbsfleet United 2-1 Hampton & Richmond Borough
Final: Ebbsfleet United 2-1 Chelmsford City

		1	2	3	4	5	6	7	8	9	10	11	12	13	14	15	16	17	18	19	20	21	22
1	Bath City		2-0	2-2	2-2	0-1	2-1	1-1	0-1	4-0	1-1	6-0	1-1	1-5	2-0	1-3	3-0	3-0	4-0	1-2	2-1	1-2	2-1
2	Bishop's Stortford	0-1		1-3	1-0	0-3	0-4	1-4	0-3	0-2	0-1	0-4	1-2	0-2	0-2	0-2	1-4	1-5	4-0	0-3	2-2	2-1	0-3
3	Chelmsford City	3-1	4-0		4-3	1-1	2-2	5-1	2-1	5-1	2-2	4-4	3-3	0-1	2-0	2-0	3-0	1-1	2-0	4-1	3-1	1-0	1-0
4	Concord Rangers	0-5	0-0	2-2		1-1	1-1	3-1	0-1	2-2	2-1	2-0	2-4	0-1	0-0	3-3	3-2	3-2	0-2	0-1	0-5	1-3	3-0
5	Dartford	2-0	4-0	0-1	2-1		6-1	4-3	2-1	0-0	3-1	2-0	2-0	0-0	4-0	1-0	2-1	0-2	5-3	2-2	2-1	3-2	3-1
6	East Thurrock United	2-0	2-2	1-2	1-1	1-1		1-1	1-1	5-1	2-1	2-3	0-1	0-0	1-2	1-1	5-1	1-1	1-1	1-1	5-1	2-3	
7	Eastbourne Borough	1-2	1-0	1-5	2-1	2-3	4-0		0-0	2-2	2-2	3-0	2-2	1-2	2-1	4-0	0-0	3-2	2-0	5-1	7-3	3-4	4-2
8	Ebbsfleet United	1-0	8-0	2-0	4-0	1-0	6-1	4-1		2-0	1-1	2-2	1-0	2-3	4-0	1-0	4-0	3-1	4-2	4-1	5-1	2-1	1-1
9	Gosport Borough	1-0	0-1	0-6	2-5	0-4	1-5	3-1	1-0		1-1	0-6	1-4	0-2	1-0	0-1	0-2	4-0	3-1	1-3	1-1	1-1	2-3
10	Hampton & Richmond Borough	2-1	4-1	0-2	1-0	4-1	1-2	3-1	1-1	2-2		3-3	2-0	2-3	1-0	0-1	0-2	4-0	2-2	1-1	3-1	0-2	0-2
11	Hemel Hempstead Town	3-3	3-2	2-2	2-1	2-2	1-1	0-4	1-1	1-2	1-0		2-0	2-1	3-2	2-0	2-4	2-2	0-1	1-3	2-0	0-5	2-0
12	Hungerford Town	2-2	2-0	1-1	2-1	2-0	3-0	0-2	1-1	3-3	1-3	3-0		1-1	1-0	2-0	0-1	0-0	5-0	2-0	1-0	2-1	3-1
13	Maidenhead United	2-1	6-0	1-0	2-0	5-0	2-1	2-1	1-2	3-0	0-0	5-0	2-2		2-0	6-1	1-1	1-1	2-0	2-0	3-0	3-0	2-1
14	Margate	1-0	0-3	0-2	1-5	0-2	2-1	1-1	0-1	2-0	2-4	2-1	1-1	0-3		0-5	0-2	0-2	2-1	0-1	0-3	3-1	0-2
15	Oxford City	1-1	3-1	2-0	2-2	1-1	0-1	1-0	1-3	1-2	0-5	1-0	0-6	1-3	1-0		0-1	2-1	1-1	0-3	2-1	0-0	1-0
16	Poole Town	1-0	1-0	4-0	2-1	2-3	1-1	1-1	0-2	7-0	3-3	1-1	1-1	1-0	1-0	1-3		1-0	2-0	1-1	2-1	2-0	3-1
17	St Albans City	1-4	0-1	2-1	2-0	1-0	2-2	1-0	0-3	2-1	2-4	2-2	5-0	2-2	1-1	2-4	4-0		5-0	0-3	3-2	3-0	3-1
18	Truro City	1-3	1-2	2-2	1-2	0-5	0-6	2-2	1-1	2-0	0-3	2-1	2-0	0-3	2-0	3-2	0-0	3-2		1-2	1-1	1-2	4-2
19	Wealdstone	0-1	5-0	1-1	1-1	0-4	1-0	1-4	2-4	2-1	2-4	1-1	3-0	2-1	2-1	1-1	2-2	2-2	1-2		0-1	1-0	0-0
20	Welling United	3-1	1-2	0-2	3-1	0-0	2-0	3-1	1-2	4-0	1-2	2-3	0-0	1-2	5-1	4-0	2-1	0-1	3-2	0-1		0-2	1-2
21	Weston-super-Mare	1-2	5-0	0-0	1-2	1-2	1-3	2-0	0-2	1-1	1-3	3-5	0-1	1-3	3-1	3-0	0-0	0-3	4-2	1-2	2-2		3-1
22	Whitehawk	0-2	1-0	0-1	0-0	1-0	2-3	1-1	0-3	4-4	1-3	1-4	1-2	1-2	2-0	3-0	2-0	1-1	2-4	0-0	1-0	0-2	

AFC FYLDE

Club Contact Details
Mill Farm, Coronation Way, Wesham, Preston PR4 3JZ
01772 682 593
info@afcfylde.co.uk

Ground Capacity: 6,000   **Seats:** 6,000   **Covered:** Yes   **Clubhouse:** Yes   **Shop:** Yes

Record Attendance
3,858 v Chorley, National League North, 26/12/2016.
Previous Grounds
Coronation Road > 2006. Kellamergh Park 2006-2016.

10 YEAR RECORD

07-08		08-09		09-10		10-11		11-12		12-13		13-14		14-15		15-16		16-17	
NWC2	2	NWCP	1	NP1N	13	NP1N	5	NP1N	1	NP P	5	NP P	2	Conf N	2	Nat N	3	Nat N	1
FAC	N/A	FAC	Pr	FAC	2Q	FAC	P	FAC	2Qr	FAC	1P	FAC	2Q	FAC	1P	FAC	1P	FAC	2Q
FAV	F	FAV	4P	FAT	3Qr	FAT	P	FAT	1Q	FAT	3Q	FAT	3Q	FAT	3P	FAT	3P	FAT	1Pr

Club Factfile

Founded: 1988   **Nickname:** The Coasters   **Manager:** Dave Challinor - Nov 2011

Previous Names: Wesham FC and Kirkham Town amalgamated in 1988 to form Kirkham & Wesham > 2008.

Previous Leagues: West Lancashire > 2007. North West Counties 2007-09. Northern Premier 2009-14.

Club Colours (change): White (Orange)

RECORDS
Victory: 8-1 v Oxford City, Conference North, 06/09/14. 9-2 v (H) Boston United, Conference North, 19/11/16.

HONOURS
FA Comps: FA Vase 2007-08.

League: West Lancashire League 1999-2000, 00-01, 01-02, 03-04, 04-05, 05-06, 06-07.
North West Counties League 2008-09. Northern Premier Division One North 2011-12. National North 2016-17.

County FA: Lancashire FA Challenge Trophy 2010-11, 12-13, 13-14. Lancashire Amateur Shield 2000-01, 03-04, 04-05, 05-06.
Northern Inter Counties Cup 2004-05, 05-06, 06-07.

BEST PERFORMANCES
FA Cup: First Round Proper 2012-13, 14-15, 15-16.
FA Trophy: Third Round Proper 2014-15, 15-16.
FA Vase: Final 2007-08.

AFC FYLDE MATCH RESULTS 2016-17

Date	Comp	H/A	Opponents	Att:	Result	Goalscorers	Pos	No.
Aug 6	Nat N	A	AFC Telford United	1139	W 1 - 0	Rowe 47	4	1
13	Nat N	H	Brackley Town	1365	D 1 - 1	Williams 81	11	2
16	Nat N	A	Altrincham	850	W 6 - 0	Dixon 12 37 Rowe 7 Daniels 16 Hardy 31 Bond 47	3	3
20	Nat N	A	Alfreton Town	440	W 5 - 3	ROWE 4 (8 16 53 69) Hardy 83	3	4
22	Nat N	H	Saltford City	1832	D 3 - 3	Finley 10 Rowe 67 Williams 90	1	5
27	Nat N	H	FC Halifax Town	1905	W 3 - 2	Hughes 32 Hone 51 (og) Dixon 79	1	6
29	Nat N	A	Bradford PA	347	W 4 - 1	ROWE 3(32 43 74) Williams 54	1	7
Sept 3	Nat N	H	Gloucester City	1425	D 2 - 2	Rowe 11 Williams 80	2	8
6	Nat N	H	Curzon Ashton	1362	W 4 - 1	ROWE 3 (12 69 90) Dixon 51	1	9
10	Nat N	A	FC Utd of Manchester	2284	W 3 - 2	Rowe 14 51 Dixon 19	1	10
17	**FAC2Q**	**A**	**Alfreton Town**	**263**	**L 0 - 1**			11
24	Nat N	H	Gainsborough Trinity	1385	W 3 1	Rowe 60 Hardy 63 Bradley 80	1	12
27	Nat N	A	Stockport County	2206	W 2 - 1	Bradley 21 Rowe 90	1	13
Oct 8	Nat N	A	Kldderminster Harriers	1970	D 3 - 3	Rowe 44 Hardy 62 72	1	14
15	Nat N	H	Nuneaton Town	1627	W 2 - 1	Langley 35 Rowe 75	1	15
22	Nat N	H	Harogate Town	1935	W 2 - 1	Finley 62 Hardy 68	1	16
29	Nat N	A	Tamworth	807	L 0 - 1		1	17
Nov 5	Nat N	H	Stalybridge Celtic	1647	W 5 - 0	Bradley 13 ROWE 3 (21 34 55) Williams 25	1	18
12	Nat N	A	Darlington 1883	2001	D 1 - 1	Rowe 27	1	19
19	Nat N	H	Boston United	1503	W 9 - 2	Daniels 15 63 Bond 24 ROWE 4 (31 44 4 56) Hardy 39		20
						Langley 78	1	
26	**FAT 3Q**	**A**	**Gloucester City**	**240**	**W 3 - 2**	**ROWE 3 (18 pen 88 90)**		21
Dec 3	Nat N	A	Worcester City	585	W 2 - 1	Rowe 39 45	1	22
10	**FAT 1**	**H**	**Brackley Town**	**641**	**D 1 - 1**	**Daniels 51**		23
13	**FAT1r**	**A**	**Brackley Town**	**1647**	**L 0 - 4**			24
!7	Nat N	A	Gloucester City	342	W 5 - 1	Bradley 13 Rowe 40 66 Hardy 57 Daniels 59	1	25
26	Nat N	H	Chorley	3858	L 0 - 2		1	26
Jan 1	Nat N	A	Chorley	3128	W 3 - 1	Collins 51 Bradley 64 Bond 90	1	27
7	Nat N	A	FC Utd of Manchester	2821	W 3 - 1	Daniels 28 Bradley 36 Hughes 86	1	28
21	Nat N	A	Curzon Ashton	2341	L 2 - 3	Daniels 10 Rowe 68	1	29
24	Nat N	H	Alfreton Town	1503	W 2 - 0	Bradley 69 Hughes 77	1	30
28	Nat N	H	Altrincham	1735	W 4 - 1	Rowe 10 18 Wilson 28 Hughes 74	1	31
Feb 4	Nat N	A	Salford City	1485	L 0 - 5		1	32
	Nat N	H	AFC Telford United	1502	D 1 - 1	Bradley 17	1	33
18	Nat N	A	Brackley Town	396	W 3 - 1	Rowe 21 85 Wiilliams 67	1	34
25	Nat N	H	Tamworth	1572	W 3 - 1	Williams 2 Rowe 18 Bond 66	1	35
Mar 4	Nat N	A	Harrogate Town	1018	D 3 - 3	Rowe 26 (pen) Bradley 62 Hughes 87	1	36
11	Nat N	A	Gainsborough Trinity	469	W 2 - 1	Rowe 41 Evans 76 (og)	1	37
18	Nat N	H	Kldderminster Harriers	2359	D 2 - 2	Bradley 82 Blinkhorn 90	1	38
21	Nat N	H	Stockport County	2489	D 0 - 0		1	39
25	Nat N	A	Nuneaton Town	480	L 1 - 4	Dixon 86	1	40
April 1	Nat N	H	Darlington 1883	2365	W 4 - 1	Finley 8 Rowe 59 86 (pen) Bradley 80	1	41
8	Nat N	A	Stalybridge Celtic	551	L 1 - 2	Rowe 26	1	42
15	Nat N	H	FC Halifax Town	2368	W 1 - 0	Rowe 72	1	43
17	Nat N	H	Bradford PA	2321	D 1 - 1	Blinkhorn 90	1	44
22	Nat N	A	Boston United	1255	W 3 0	Rowe 41 (pen) 61 Hughes 74	1	45
29	Nat N	H	Worcester City	2684	W 4 - 2	Blinkhorn 22 Rowe 36 Bond 58 Baker 85	1	46

GOALSCORERS	SG	CSG	Pens	Hat tricks	Total		SG	CSG	Pens	Hat tricks	Total
2015-16 Rowe					**34**	Finley	3				3
Rowe	29	5,4,4,4	4	6	50	Langley	2				2
Bradley	11	2			11	Opponents	2				2
Hardy	7	2			8	Baker	1				1
Daniels	6	0			7	Collins	1				1
Williams	6	2			7	Wilson	1				1
Bond	5				6						
Dixon	6	2			6						
Hughes	5				5						
Blinkhoen	3				3						

ALDERSHOT TOWN
Club Contact Details
EBB Stadium, High street, Aldershot, GU11 1TW
01252 320 211
admin@theshots.co.uk

Ground Capacity: 7,500 **Seats:** 1,800 **Covered:** 6,850 **Clubhouse:** Yes **Shop:** Yes

Record Attendance
7,500 v Brighton & Hove Albion, FA Cup 1st Round, 18/11/2000
Previous Grounds
None

10 YEAR RECORD

07-08		08-09		09-10		10-11		11-12		12-13		13-14		14-15		15-16		16-17	
Conf	1	FL 2	15	FL 2	6	FL 2	14	FL 2	11	FL 2	24	Conf	19	Conf	18	Conf	15	Nat	5
FAC	1P	FAC	2P	FAC	2Pr	FAC	2P	FAC	2P	FAC	4P	FAC	4Qr	FAC	2Pr	FAC	1Pr	FAC	4Q
FAT	SF	FLC	1P	FLC	1P	FLC	1P	FLC	4P	FLC	1P	FAT	QF	FAT	1P	FAT	1P	FAT	1Pr

Club Factfile

Founded: 1992   **Nickname:** Shots   **Manager:** Gary Waddock

Previous Names: None

Previous Leagues: Isthmian 1992-2003. Conference 2003-2008. Football League 2008-13.

Club Colours (change): Red & blue

RECORDS
Victory: 8-0 v Bishop's Stortford (A) Isthmian Premier 05/09/1998
Defeat: 0-6 v Worthing (A) Isthmian League Cup 02/03/99
Goalscorer: Mark Butler - 155 (1992-98)
Appearances: Jason Chewings - 489 (August 1994 - May 2004)
Additional: Paid an undisclosed record fee to Woking for Marvin Morgan (05/2008)
Received £130,000 from Crewe Alexandra for Grant Payne (11/2008)

HONOURS
FA Comps: N/A

League: Isthmian League Division Three 1992-93, Division One 97-98, Premier Division 2002-03.
Conference 2007-08.

County FA: Hampshire Senior Cup 1998-99, 99-2000, 01-02, 02-03, 06-07.

BEST PERFORMANCES	**FA Cup:** (As a non-League side) Third Round Proper - 2006-07. (Football League side) Fourth Round Proper - 2012-13.
	FA Trophy: Semi-Finals 2003-04, 07-08.
	FA Vase: Quarter-Finals 1993-94.

ALDERSHOT TOWN MATCH RESULTS 2016-17

Date	Comp	H/A	Opponents	Att:	Result	Goalscorers	Pos	No.
Aug 6	Nat Lg	H	Barrow	1664	L	0 - 1		17	1
9	Nat Lg	A	Maidstone United	2355	W	1 - 0	Mensah 88	12	2
13	Nat Lg	A	Wrexham	1907	W	2 - 0	Fenelon 3 Rendell 58	8	3
16	Nat Lg	H	Bromley	906	D	2 - 2	Rendell 15 McClure 21	9	4
20	Nat Lg	A	Braintree Town	677	L	0 - 2		13	5
27	Nat Lg	H	North Ferriby United	1527	W	2 - 0	Mensah 15 Bellamy 26	8	6
29	Nat Lg	A	Dover Athletic	1093	W	2 - 1	Fenelon 21 Bellamy 41	5	7
Sept 3	Nat Lg	H	Tranmere Rovers	2585	W	3 - 1	Mensah 3 Rendell 79 Evans 82	3	8
10	Nat Lg	H	Chester	2445	D	0 - 0		5	9
13	Nat Lg	A	Boreham Wood	544	D	1 - 1	McClure 66	6	10
17	Nat Lg	A	Southport	772	D	1 - 1	Evans 79	7	11
24	Nat Lg	H	Gateshead	1647	W	3 - 0	Allen 50 McClure 69 (pen) Walker 90	7	12
Oct 1	Nat Lg	A	York City	2188	W	1 - 0	Mensah 29	5	13
4	Nat Lg	H	Forest Green Rovers	2195	L	0 - 4		7	14
8	Nat Lg	H	Solihull Moors	1712	W	2 - 0	Fenelon 84 Rendell 82	6	15
15	FAC4Q	H	Eastbourne Borough	1443	L	1 - 2	Kanu 69		16
22	Nat Lg	A	Torquay United	1788	D	0 - 0		7	17
25	Nat Lg	A	Dagenham & Redbridge	1371	L	0 - 1		9	18
29	Nat Lg	H	Guiseley	1731	W	1 - 0	Walker 74	6	19
Nov 5	Nat Lg	A	Forest Green Rovers	1638	L	1 - 2	Gallagher 88	6	20
12	Nat Lg	A	Lincoln City	3461	D	3 - 3	Kanu 10 Alexander 51 Rendell 72	8	21
19	Nat Lg	H	Macclesfield Town	1636	L	1 - 2	Evans 69	10	22
22	Nat Lg	H	Eastleigh	1609	L	0 - 1		11	23
26	Nat Lg	A	Sutton United	1847	L	0 - 2		11	24
Dec 3	Nat Lg	H	Boreham Wood	1390	W	2 - 0	Rendell 35 Kanu 76	12	25
10	FAT1	A	East Thurrock United	321	D	1 - 1	Mensah 27		26
12	FAT1r	H	East Thurrock United	566	L	3 - 4	McClure 28 Walker 53 Mensah 90 (aet)		27
17	Nat Lg	A	Chester	1937	L	0 - 2		10	28
26	Nat Lg	H	Woking	3456	W	4 - 0	Fenelon 10 RENDELL 3 (8 21 45)	10	29
Jan 1	Nat Lg	A	Woking	3224	W	2 - 1	Rendell 63 Gallagher 90	7	30
7	Nat Lg	H	Southport	1772	W	2 - 1	Fenelon 45 Gallagher 75	7	31
21	Nat Lg	A	Gateshead	653	D	1 - 1	Rendell 41	7	32
28	Nat Lg	H	York City	2230	D	0 - 0		7	33
Feb 4	Nat Lg	A	Maidstone United	2293	W	2 - 0	Benyu 19 Gallagher 86	6	34
11	Nat Lg	H	Barrow	1858	D	2 - 2	McClure 1 Evans 26	6	35
18	Nat Lg	A	Wrexham	4308	W	2 - 0	Rendell 71 Kellerman 81	7	36
25	Nat Lg	H	Bromley	2014	W	4 - 0	Arnold 37 Fenelon 45 Gallagher 47 McClure 87	6	37
28	Nat Lg	A	Eastleigh	2522	D	1 - 1	Kanu 42	6	38
Mar 4	Nat Lg	H	Lincoln United	3595	D	0 - 0		6	39
11	Nat Lg	A	Guiseley	1009	L	0 - 1		7	40
18	Nat Lg	H	Sutton United	2197	W	2 - 0	Puddy (og) 42 Mensah 90	7	41
21	Nat Lg	H	Dagenham & Redbridge	2113	W	3 - 1	Fenelon 17 Mensah 37 McClure 83	6	42
25	Nat Lg	A	Macclesfield Town	1586	W	2 - 0	Benyu 59 McClure 83	6	43
Apr 1	Nat Lg	A	Solihull Moors	1248	W	2 - 0	Benyu 27 61	5	44
8	Nat Lg	H	Torquay United	3007	D	1 - 1	Benyu 76	5	45
14	Nat Lg	A	Tranmere Rovers	6324	D	2 - 2	McClure 3 Mensah 40	6	46
17	Nat Lg	H	Dover Athletic	3857	W	1 - 0	McClure 73 (pen)	5	47
22	Nat Lg	A	North Ferriby United	552	W	3 - 0	Mensah 31 62 Rendell 82	5	48
29	Nat Lg	H	Braintree Town	3977	W	2 - 0	Evans 55 Mensah 59	5	49
May 3	P.O S-F 1	H	Tranmere Rovers	5614	L	0 - 3			50
6	P.O.S-F 2	A	Tranmere Rovers	10,241	D	2 - 2	Mensah 44 Hughes (og) 50		51

GOALSCORERS	SG	CSG	Pens	Hat tricks	Total		SG	CSG	Pens	Hat tricks	Total
2015-16 C. Walker					15	Bellamy	2	2			2
Mensah	12	2			13	Opponents	2				2
Rendell	11	2	1		13	Alexander	1				1
McClure	10		2		10	Allen	1				1
Fenelon	7	2			7	Arnold	1				1
Benyu	4				5	Kellerman	1				1
Evans	5				5						
Gallagher	5	2			5						
Kanu	4				4						
Walker	3				3						

BARROW

Club Contact Details
Furness Building Society Stadium, Wilkie Road, Barrow-in-Furness LA14 5UW
01299 823 061
office@barrowafc.com

Ground Capacity: 5,045   **Seats:** 1,000   **Covered:** 2,200   **Clubhouse:** Yes   **Shop:** Yes

Record Attendance
16,854 v Swansea Town - FA Cup 3rd Round 1954
Previous Grounds
Strawberry & Little Park, Roose.

10 YEAR RECORD

07-08		08-09		09-10		10-11		11-12		12-13		13-14		14-15		15-16		16-17	
Conf N	5	Conf	20	Conf	15	Conf	18	Conf	13	Conf	22	Conf N	11	Conf N	1	Nat	11	Nat	7
FAC	1Pr	FAC	3P	FAC	3P	FAC	4Q	FAC	1P	FAC	2Pr	FAC	4Qr	FAC	2Q	FAC	4Q	FAC	3P
FAT	3Q	FAT	2P	FAT	F	FAT	1P	FAT	2P	FAT	QF	FAT	2P	FAT	3Q	FAT	2P	FAT	QF

Club Factfile

Founded: 1901   **Nickname:** Bluebirds   **Manager:** Paul Cox - 23.11.15

Previous Names: None

Previous Leagues: Lancashire Combination 1901-21. Football League 1921-72. Northern Premier 1972-79, 83-84, 86-89, 92-98, 99-04.
Conference 1979-83, 84-86, 89-92, 98-99.

Club Colours (change): White/royal blue/white (Royal blue/white/royal blue)

RECORDS
Victory: 12-0 v Cleator - FA Cup 1920
Defeat: 1-10 v Hartlepool United - Football League Division 4 1959
Goalscorer: Colin Cowperthwaite - 282 (December 1977 - December 1992)
Appearances: Colin Cowperthwaite - 704
Additional: Paid £9,000 to Ashton United for Andy Whittaker (07/94)
Received £40,000 from Barnet for Kenny Lowe (01/91)

HONOURS
FA Comps: FA Trophy 1989-90, 2009-10.

League: Northern Premier League 1983-84, 88-89, 97-98.
Conference North 2014-15.

County FA: Lancashire Senior Cup 1954-55.
Lancashire Challenge Trophy 1980-81.

BEST PERFORMANCES	**FA Cup:** Third Round Proper - 1945-46, 53-54(r), 55-56, 58-59, 63-64, 66-67(r), 67-68, 90-91, 2008-09, 09-10, 16-17
	FA Trophy: Final - 1989-90, 2009-10
	FA Vase: N/A

BARROW MATCH RESULTS 2016-17

Date	Comp	H/A	Opponents	Att:	Result		Goalscorers	Pos	No.
Aug 6	Nat Lg	H	Aldershot Town	1664	W	1 - 0	Hughes 7	8	1
9	Nat Lg	A	Tranmere Rovers	4977	L	0 - 2		13	2
13	Nat Lg	A	Torquay United	2207	D	1 - 1	Bennett 90	16	3
16	Nat Lg	H	Chester	1351	W	3 - 2	Hannah 37 Williams 38 59	12	4
20	Nat Lg	A	Dover Athletic	826	L	1 - 3	Hannah 89 (pen)	14	5
27	Nat Lg	H	Braintree Town	966	W	2 - 1	Bennett 42 Hannah 87	10	6
29	Nat Lg	A	North Ferriby United	581	W	1 - 0	Bennett 90	7	7
Sept 3	Nat Lg	H	Bromley	1096	D	1 - 1	Harrison	8	8
10	Nat Lg	H	Boreham Wood	1041	D	1 - 1	Harrison 69 (pen)	9	9
13	Nat Lg	A	Southport	848	W	4 - 1	Harrison 4 27 (pen) Bennett 51 Hughes 59	7	10
17	Nat Lg	A	Lincoln City	3578	W	2 - 1	Bennett 14 Harrison 85	4	11
24	Nat Lg	H	York City	1628	W	2 - 0	Livesey 56 Fry (og) 63	3	12
Oct 1	Nat Lg	A	Forest Green Rovers	2236	D	0 - 0		6	13
4	Nat Lg	H	Macclesfield Town	1442	D	1 - 1	Livesey 76	6	14
8	Nat Lg	H	Maidstone United	1402	W	3 - 0	Turnbull 38 Williams 57 Bennett 60	4	15
15	FAC4Q	H	Tranmere Rovers	2133	W	2 - 1	Bennett 16 Turnbull 64		16
22	Nat Lg	A	Woking	1351	D	1 - 1	Harrison 20	5	17
25	Nat Lg	A	Wrexham	3616	D	2 - 2	Harrison 9 Yates 89	5	18
29	Nat Lg	H	Eastleigh	1795	W	4 - 0	HARRISON 3 (47 (pen) 72 90) Anderton 62	5	19
Nov 5	FAC1	A	Taunton Town	2297	D	2 - 2	Harrison 35 (pen) Bennett 43		20
12	Nat Lg	A	Sutton United	1588	D	0 - 0		5	21
15	FAC1r	H	Taunton Town	1717	W	2 - 1	Williams 48 Yates 75		22
19	Nat Lg	H	Solihull Moors	1184	W	2 - 1	Diarra 13 Harrison 16	5	23
22	Nat Lg	H	Guiseley	1070	W	3 - 0	Williams 41 Harrison 44 64 (pen)	4	24
26	Nat Lg	A	Dagenham & Redbridge	1228	W	4 - 1	Hughes 41 77 Harrison 45 Bennett 63	3	25
Dec 3	FAC2	A	Bristol Rovers	4570	W	2 - 1	Harrison 16 62		26
10	FAT1	A	Harrogate Town	441	D	3 - 3	Williams 2 Bennett 8 89		27
13	FAT1r	H	Harrogate Town	816	W	4 - 2	Hannah 16 Wright 90 109 Meikle 91 (aet)		28
17	Nat Lg	A	Boreham Wood	401	D	1 - 1	Harrison 75 (pen)	5	29
26	Nat Lg	H	Gateshead	2123	D	0 - 0		4	30
Jan 1	Nat Lg	A	Gateshead	871	L	1 - 4	Livesey 7	4	31
7	FAC3	H	Rochdale	4414	L	0 - 2			32
10	Nat Lg	H	Southport	956	L	0 - 1		6	33
14	FAT2	H	Matlock Town	976	W	3 - 2	Bennett 64 70 Livesey 73		34
21	Nat Lg	A	York City	2430	L	1 - 2	Williams 72	6	35
24	Nat Lg	H	Lincoln City	1152	W	3 - 0	Harrison 9 Bennett 60 Hannah 90 (pen)	5	36
28	Nat Lg	H	Forest Green Rovers	1422	L	2 - 3	Bennett 33 Hannah 87	6	37
Feb 4	FAT3	H	Kidderminster Harriers	1173	W	1 - 0	Bennett 54		38
11	Nat Lg	A	Aldershot Town	1858	D	2 - 2	Tuton 73 Hannah 90	7	39
15	Nat Lg	A	Macclesfield Town	1246	W	1 - 0	Bennett 66 (pen)	5	40
18	Nat Lg	H	Torquay United	1391	D	0 - 0		6	41
25	FATQF	A	Tranmere Rovers	3487	L	1 - 5	Williams 11		42
28	Nat Lg	H	Guiseley	642	L	0 - 1		8	43
Mar 4	Nat Lg	H	Sutton United	1145	D	0 - 0		8	44
7	Nat Lg	H	Tranmere Rovers	1251	W	2 - 1	Effiong 64 Williams 71	8	45
11	Nat Lg	A	Eastleigh	2039	L	0 - 2		8	46
18	Nat Lg	H	Dagenham & Redbridge	1102	W	2 - 1	Hughes 39 (pen) Diarra 56	8	47
21	Nat Lg	H	Wrexham	1009	D	1 - 1	Diarra 90	8	48
25	Nat Lg	A	Solihull Moors	1820	W	4 - 2	Diarra 25 Williams 27 Hughes 29 Bennett 55 (pen)	8	49
28	Nat Lg	A	Chester	1501	W	2 - 1	Bennett 2 Williams 36	6	50
Apr 1	Nat Lg	A	Maidstone Uniited	2803	L	1 - 2	Turnbull 9	7	51
8	Nat Lg	H	Woking	1326	D	2 - 2	Williams 51 Bennett 83	7	52
14	Nat Lg	A	Bromley	1049	L	1 - 4	Bennett 18 (pen)	7	53
17	Nat Lg	H	North Ferriby United	1017	W	3 - 1	Bennett 11 Beely 40 Williams 43	7	54
22	Nat Lg	A	Braintree Town	778	W	2 - 0	Harrison 64 Wright 70	7	55
29	Nat Lg	A	Dover Athletic	1212	L	2 - 3	Williams 20 Diarra	7	56

GOALSCORERS	SG	CSG	Pens	Hat tricks	Total		SG	CSG	Pens	Hat tricks	Total
2015-16 Cook					23	Yates	2				2
Bennett	20	3	3		22	Anderton	1				1
Harrison	15	4,4,4	5+1c	1	20	Beely	1				1
Williams	13				14	Effiong	1				1
Hannah	7	3	2		7	Meikle	1				1
Hughes	6	3	1		6	Opponents	1				1
Diarra	5				5	Tuton	1				1
Livesey	5				5						
Turnbull	3				3						
Wright	2				3						

BOREHAM WOOD

Club Contact Details
Meadow Park, Broughinge Road, Boreham Wood WD6 5AL
0208 953 5097

Ground Capacity: 4,502 **Seats:** 1,700 **Covered:** 2,800 **Clubhouse:** Yes **Shop:** Yes

Record Attendance
4,030 v Arsenal - Friendly 13/07/2001
Previous Grounds
Eldon Avenue 1948-63

10 YEAR RECORD

07-08		08-09		09-10		10-11		11-12		12-13		13-14		14-15		15-16		16-17	
Isth P	19	Isth P	18	Isth P	4	Conf S	14	Conf S	8	Conf S	9	Conf S	13	Conf S	2	Nat	19	Nat	11
FAC	3Q	FAC	3Q	FAC	2Q	FAC	4Q	FAC	2Q	FAC	1P	FAC	1Pr	FAC	4Q	FAC	1Pr	FAC	1Pr
FAT	1Q	FAT	2Q	FAT	1P	FAT	1P	FAT	1P	FAT	1Pr	FAT	3Q	FAT	3Q	FAT	1P	FAT	QF

Club Factfile

Founded: 1948 **Nickname:** The Wood **Manager:** Luke Garrard

Previous Names: Boreham Wood Rovers and Royal Retournez amalgamated in 1948 to form today's club

Previous Leagues: Mid Herts 1948-52, Parthenon 1952-57, Spartan 1956-66, Athenian 1966-74, Isthmian 1974-2004, Southern 2004-10

Club Colours (change): White & black (Sky blue)

RECORDS

Goalscorer: Mickey Jackson
Appearances: Dave Hatchett - 714
Additional: Received £5,000 from Dagenham & Redbridge for Steve Heffer

HONOURS

FA Comps: N/A

League: Athenian League Div. Two 1968-69, Div.One 73-74. Isthmian League Division Two 1976-77, Division One 1994-95, 2000-01, Premier Division Play-off 2009-10. Southern Div. One East 2005-06, Conference South Play-off 2014-15.

County FA: Herts Senior cup 1971-72, 98-99, 2001-02, 07-08, 13-14. Herts Charity Cup 1980-81, 83-84, 85-86, 88-89, 89-90. London Challenge Cup 1997-98.

BEST PERFORMANCES	**FA Cup:** Second Round Proper - 1996-97 and 1997-98.
	FA Trophy: Semi-Finals - 2005-06.
	FA Vase: N/A

BOREHAM WOOD MATCH RESULTS 2016-17

Date	Comp	H/A	Opponents	Att:	Result	Goalscorers	Pos	No.
Aug 6	Nat Lg	H	Forest Green Rovers	504	W 1 - 0	Shakes 30	9	1
9	Nat Lg	A	Dover Athletic	1024	W 4 - 1	Davis 59 Andrade 66 77 Balanta 78	3	2
13	Nat Lg	A	York City	2169	D 1 - 1	Shakes 89	2	3
16	Nat Lg	H	Tranmere Rovers	801	L 0 - 1		5	4
20	Nat Lg	H	Chester	335	D 1 - 1	Ferrier 5	10	5
27	Nat Lg	A	Gateshead	732	D 1 - 1	Balanta 6	11	6
29	Nat Lg	H	Maidstone United	537	L 0 - 1		16	7
Sept 3	Nat Lg	A	Dagenham & Redbridge	1312	W 2 - 0	Ferrier 49 Davis 90	12	8
10	Nat Lg	A	Barrow	1041	D 1 - 1	Ferrier 90	13	9
13	Nat Lg	H	Aldershot Town	544	D 1 - 1	Ferrier 64	12	10
17	Nat Lg	H	Torquay United	605	W 2 - 0	Jeffrey 10 Ferrier 12	8	11
24	Nat Lg	A	Solihull Moors	618	D 1 - 1	Balanta 54	10	12
Oct 1	Nat Lg	A	Wrexham	458	L 0 - 1		14	13
4	Nat Lg	H	Braintree Town	553	W 2 - 1	Ferrier 26 73	12	14
8	Nat Lg	H	Macclesfield Town	1386	W 2 - 0	Davis 70 (pen) Ferrier 82	12	15
15	FAC4Q	H	Hendon	457	W 3 - 0	Ferrier 10 Andrade 66 Balanta 90		16
22	Nat Lg	A	North Ferriby United	313	W 1 - 0	Jeffrey 47	11	17
25	Nat Lg	A	Lincoln City	3014	L 0 - 2		11	18
29	Nat Lg	H	Woking	405	W 2 - 1	Balanta 55 Andrade 60	9	19
Nov 5	FAC1	H	Notts County	1201	D 2 - 2	Ferrier 41 Balanta 50		20
12	Nat Lg	A	Bromley	818	L 0 - 1		10	21
15	FAC1r	A	Notts County	1762	L 0 - 1			22
19	Nat Lg	H	Southport	314	W 2 - 0	Davis 30 Lucas 77	8	23
22	Nat Lg	H	Sutton United	371	W 1 - 0	Jeffrey 21	7	24
26	Nat Lg	A	Guiseley	749	L 1 - 3	Davis 69	7	25
Dec 3	Nat Lg	A	Aldershot Town	1390	L 0 - 2		7	26
10	FAT1	H	Maidstone United	201	D 0 - 0			27
13	FAT1r	A	Maidstone	538	W 3 - 2	Jeffrey 47 79 Andrade 56		28
17	Nat Lg	H	Barrow	401	D 1 - 1	Balanta 53 (pen)	9	29
20	Nat Lg	H	Braintree Town	313	L 0 - 1		9	30
26	Nat Lg	A	Eastleigh	2213	D 2 - 2	Ferrier 51 Woodards 90	9	31
Jan 1	Nat Lg	H	Eastleigh	445	L 0 - 1		10	32
7	Nat Lg	A	Torquay United	1789	W 1 - 0	Andrade 72	10	33
14	FAT2	H	Alfreton Town	213	W 2 - 1	Balanta 35 Davis 90		34
21	Nat Lg	A	Solihull Moors	322	D 0 - 0		11	35
28	Nat Lg	A	Wrexham	3664	L 1 - 2	Ferrier 76 (pen)	11	36
Feb 4	FAT3	A	Sutton United	879	D 0 - 0			37
7	FAT3r	H	Sutton United	269	W 5 - 0	Balanta 5 Davis 43 75 Ferrier 48 Jeffrrey 79	10	38
11	Nat Lg	A	Forest Green Rovers	1575	L 0 - 2		14	39
18	Nat Lg	H	York City	656	D 1 - 1	Ferrier 27	13	40
21	Nat Lg	A	Tranmere Rovers	4107	L 1 - 2	Andrade 89	13	41
25	FATQF	H	Lincoln City	901	L 0 - 2			42
28	Nat Lg	A	Sutton United	1441	L 0 - 1		13	43
Mar 4	Nat Lg	H	Bromley	401	D 0 - 0		14	44
11	Nat Lg	A	Woking	1157	D 0 - 0		14	45
15	Nat Lg	H	Dover Athletic	314	W 5 - 0	Andrade 56 73 SHAKES 3 (67 83 85)	12	46
18	Nat Lg	H	Guiseley	375	D 0 - 0		12	47
21	Nat Lg	H	Lincoln City	1002	W 2 - 0	Shakes 65 Ferrier 80	11	48
25	Nat Lg	A	Southport	1010	L 0 - 1		11	49
Apr 1	Nat Lg	H	Macclesfield Town	340	L 2 - 4	Stephens 14 Andrade 74	12	50
8	Nat Lg	A	North Ferriby United	357	W 4 - 2	Ferrier 19 Gray 28 (og) Androde 6 Emerton 81 (og)	10	51
14	Nat Lg	H	Dagenham & Redbridge	801	L 1 - 3	Shakes 17	11	52
17	Nat Lg	A	Maidstone United	2880	L 0 - 1		14	53
22	Nat Lg	H	Gateshead	314	L 0 - 4		15	54
29	Nat Lg	A	Chester	2013	W 2 0	Davis 45 Balanta 61	11	55

GOALSCORERS	SG	CSG	Pens	Hat tricks	Total		SG	CSG	Pens	Hat tricks	Total
2015-16 Lucas					7	Woodards	1				1
Ferrier	14	4	1		16						
Andrade	9				11						
Balanta	10		1		10						
Davis	8		1		9						
Shakes	5				7						
Jeffery	4				6						
Opponents	2				2						
Lucas	1				1						
Stephens	1				1						

BROMLEY

Club Contact Details
The Stadium, Hayes Lane, Bromley, Kent BR2 9EF
020 8460 5291
info@bromleyfc.net

Ground Capacity: 5,000 **Seats:** 1,300 **Covered:** 2,500 **Clubhouse:** Yes **Shop:** Yes

Record Attendance
10,798 v Nigeria - 1950
Previous Grounds
White Hart Field. Widmore Road. Plaistow Cricket Ground.

10 YEAR RECORD

07-08	08-09	09-10	10-11	11-12	12-13	13-14	14-15	15-16	16-17
Conf S 11	Conf S 13	Conf S 12	Conf S 11	Conf S 17	Conf S 15	Conf S 3	Conf S 1	Nat 14	Nat 10
FAC 4Q	FAC 2Q	FAC 1P	FAC 3Qr	FAC 1P	FAC 1P	FAC 3Q	FAC 3Q	FAC 4Q	FAC 4Q
FAT 1P	FAT 3Q	FAT 3Q	FAT 3Q	FAT 3Q	FAT 3P	FAT 3Q	FAT 2P	FAT 1P	FAT 2P

Club Factfile

Founded: 1892   **Nickname:** The Lillywhites   **Manager:** Neil Smith

Previous Names: None

Previous Leagues: South London, Southern, London, West Kent, South Surburban, Kent, Spartan 1907-08,
Isthmian 1908-11, 52-2007, Athenian 1919-1952

Club Colours (change): White with black trim/black/black (All red)

RECORDS

Victory: 13-1 v Redhill - Athenian League 1945-46

Defeat: 1-11 v Barking - Athenian League 1933-34

Goalscorer: George Brown - 570 (1938-61)

Appearances: George Brown

Additional: Received £50,000 from Millwall for John Goodman

HONOURS

FA Comps: Amateur Cup 1910-11, 37-38, 48-49.

League: Spartan 1907-08. Isthmian League 1908-09, 09-10, 53-54, 60-61. Athenian League 1922-23, 48-49, 50-51.
Conference South 2014-15.

County FA: Kent Senior Cup 1949/50, 76-77, 91-92, 96-97, 2005-06, 06-07.
Kent Amateur Cup x12. London Senior Cup 1909-10, 45-46, 50-51, 2002-03, 12-13.

BEST PERFORMANCES	**FA Cup:** Second Round Proper 1937-38, 45-46.
	FA Trophy: Third Round Proper 1999-00, 2012-13.
	FA Vase: N/A

BROMLEY MATCH RESULTS 2016-17

Date	Comp	H/A	Opponents	Att:	Result	Goalscorers	Pos	No.
Aug 6	Nat Lg	H	Tranmere Rovers	1539	L 0 - 2		21	1
9	Nat Lg	A	Torquay United	2279	L 0 - 1		23	2
13	Nat Lg	A	Solihull Moors	756	L 0 - 1		24	3
16	Nat Lg	H	Aldershot Town	906	D 2 - 2	Sho-Silva 44 Dennis 74	23	4
20	Nat Lg	H	Gateshead	604	W 3 - 2	Sho-Silva 6 11 Anderson 36	20	5
27	Nat Lg	A	Guiseley	565	W 4 - 1	Turgott 51 Dennis 53 (Pen) Porter 71 Goldberg 88	16	6
29	Nat Lg	H	Eastleigh	1100	L 0 - 5		19	7
Sept 3	Nat Lg	A	Barrow	1096	D 1 - 1	Turgott 85	18	8
10	Nat Lg	H	Macclesfield Town	1011	L 0 - 1		19	9
13	Nat Lg	A	Maidstone United	2358	W 2 - 0	Porter 24 Sho-Silva 56	18	10
17	Nat Lg	A	Forest Green Rovers	1371	L 0 - 1		20	11
24	Nat Lg	H	Dagenham & Redbridge	1558	L 1 - 3	Swaine 53	20	12
Oct 1	Nat Lg	A	Southport	744	W 2 - 1	Cunnington 11 Higgs 24	18	13
4	Nat Lg	H	Woking	808	W 2 - 1	Turgott 35 MInshull 90	18	14
8	Nat Lg	H	Lincoln City	1511	D 1 - 1	Turgott 65	16	15
15	**FAC4Q**	**A**	**Braintree Town**	**343**	**L 2 - 4**	**Turgott 45 Elakobi 50 (og)**		16
22	Nat Lg	A	Wrexham	3531	L 1 - 2	Turgott 56	17	17
25	Nat Lg	H	Dover Athletic	1052	L 0 - 2		17	18
29	Nat Lg	H	North Ferriby United	354	W 2 - 1	Porter 57 Turgott 89	17	19
12	Nat Lg	H	Boreham Wood	818	W 1 - 0	Martin 41	15	20
19	Nat Lg	A	Chester	1827	D 1 1	Turgott 15	15	21
22	Nat Lg	A	Braintree Town	521	D 2 - 2	Sho-Silva 7 Minshul 52	14	22
26	Nat Lg	H	York City	1203	W 3 - 0	Holland 5 Porter 25 Cunnington 78	14	23
29	Nat Lg	A	Woking	1057	L 1 - 2	Turgott 32 (pen)	13	24
Dec 3	Nat Lg	H	Maidstone United	1676	W 2 - 0	Cunnington 1 Porter 65		25
10	**FAT1**	**H**	**Leiston**	**411**	**D 1 - 1**	**Porter 42**		26
13	**FAT1r**	**A**	**Leiston**	**306**	**W 5 - 3**	**CUNNINGTON 3 (23 50 66) Sho-Silva 50 Turgott 86**	**13**	27
17	Nat Lg	A	Macclesfield Town	1216	W 2 - 1	Sho-Silva 35 Turgott 85	13	28
26	Nat Lg	H	Sutton United	2036	W 1 - 0	Dennis 90	12	29
Jan 1	Nat Lg	A	Sutton United	1766	L 0 - 2		13	30
7	Nat Lg	H	Forest Green Rovers	1247	L 1 - 5	Swaine 50	13	31
14	**FAT2**	**H**	**Welling United**	**519**	**L 1 - 2**	**Holland 6**		32
28	Nat Lg	H	Southport	953	W 3 - 1	Hanlan 24 54 Dennis 49	14	33
Feb 4	Nat Lg	H	Torquay United	889	W 1 - 0	Turgott 13 (pen)	11	34
11	Nat Lg	A	Tranmere Rovers	4425	D 2 - 2	Hanlan 66 Holland 87	11	35
18	Nat Lg	H	Solihull Moors	1109	L 0 - 1		11	36
21	Nat Lg	A	Dagenham & Redbridge	1202	L 1 - 2	Hanlan 7	11	37
25	Nat Lg	A	Aldershot Town	2014	L 0 - 4		12	38
28	Nat Lg	H	Braintree Town	437	L 0 - 5		12	39
Mar 4	Nat Lg	A	Boreham Wood	401	D 0 - 0		12	40
11	Nat Lg	H	North Ferriby United	905	W 3 - 0	Goldberg 34 Porter 78 Wynter 90	11	41
21	Nat Lg	A	Dover Athletic	988	L 0 - 1		13	42
25	Nat Lg	H	Chester	1237	L 0 - 1		13	43
Apr 1	Nat Lg	A	Lincoln City	6843	L 0 - 1		16	44
4	Nat Lg	A	York City	3000	W 2 - 0	Dennis 2 Sho-Silva 57	13	45
8	Nat Lg	H	Wrexham	1006	W 4 - 3	Sho-Silva 9 48 Higgs 21 Turgott 83	11	46
14	Nat Lg	H	Barrow	1049	W 4 - 1	Porter 9 Turgott 22 (pen) Sho-Silva 35 85	10	47
17	Nat Lg	A	Eastleigh	1830	L 1 - 2	Higgs 83	10	48
22	Nat Lg	H	Guiseley	936	D 1 - 1	Goldberg 4	10	49
29	Nat Lg	A	Gateshead	701	W 2 0	Dennis 78 85	10	50

GOALSCORERS	SG	CSG	Pens	Hat tricks	Total		SG	CSG	Pens	Hat tricks	Total
2015-16 Ademola					17	Minshull	2				2
Turgott	13	4	3		14	Swaine	2				2
Sho-Silver	8	2			12	Anderson	1				1
Porter	8	2			8	Martin	1				1
Dennis	6		1		7	Opponents	1				1
Cunnington	4			1	6	Wynter	1				1
Hanlan	4				4						
Goldberg	3				3						
Higgs	3				3						
Holland	3				3						

CHESTER

Club Contact Details
Lookers Vauxhall Stadium, Bumpers Lane, Chester CH1 4LT
01244 371 376
info@chesterfc.com

Ground Capacity: 6,012   **Seats:** 4,170   **Covered:** Yes   **Clubhouse:** Yes   **Shop:** Yes

Record Attendance
20,378 v Chelsea - FA Cup 3rd Round replay 16/01/1952
Previous Grounds
Faulkner Street 1885-98, The Old Showground 98-99, Whipcord Lane 1901-06, Sealand Road 06-90, Macclesfield FC 90-92

10 YEAR RECORD

07-08		08-09		09-10		10-11		11-12		12-13		13-14		14-15		15-16		16-17	
FL 2	22	FL 2	23	Conf	dnf	NP1N	1	NP P	1	Conf N	1	Conf	21	Conf	12	Nat	17	Nat	19
FAC	1P	FAC	1P	FAC	4Qr					FAC	3Qr	FAC	4Q	FAC	2Pr	FAC	4Q	FAC	4Q
FLC	1P	FLC	1P	FAT	1P	FAT	N/A	FAT	2P	FAT	3Qr	FAT	1P	FAT	1Pr	FAT	3P	FAT	2P

Club Factfile

Founded: 1885   **Nickname:** Blues   **Manager:** Jon McCarthy - April 2016

Previous Names: Chester > 1983, Chester City 1983-2010

Previous Leagues: Cheshire 1919-31, Football League 1931-2000, 2004-09, Conference 2000-04, 09-10 (Did not finish the season). Northern Premier League 2010-12.

Club Colours (change): Blue/blue/white (All yellow)

RECORDS
Victory: 12-0 v York City - 01/02/1936
Goalscorer: Stuart Rimmer - 135
Appearances: Ray Gill - 406 (1951-62)
Additional: Paid £100,000 to Rotherham for Gregg Blundell.
                Received £300,000 from Liverpool for Ian Rush

HONOURS
FA Comps: Welsh Cup 1907-08, 32-33, 46-47.

League: Conference 2003-04, Conference North 2012-13.
Northern Premier League Division One North 2010-11, Premier Division 2011-12.

County FA: Cheshire Senior Cup 1894-95, 96-97, 1903-04, 07-08, 08-09, 30-31, 31-32, 2012-13.
Herefordshire Senior Cup 1991-92 (shared).

BEST PERFORMANCES	**FA Cup:** Fifth Round Proper 1976-77, 79-80.
	FA Trophy: Semi-finals 2000-01.
	FA Vase: N/A

CHESTER MATCH RESULTS 2016-17

Date	Comp	H/A	Opponents	Att:	Result	Goalscorers	Pos	No.
Aug 6	Nat Lg	A	Gateshead	991	L 0 - 3		23	1
9	Nat Lg	H	Dagenham & Redbridge	1841	W 3 - 0	Durrell 12 Shaw 24 Alabi 59	10	2
13	Nat Lg	H	Maidstone United	1912	L 1 - 3	Alabi 31	18	3
16	Nat Lg	A	Barrow	1351	L 2 - 3	Akintundi 68 Vassell 69	19	4
20	Nat Lg	A	Boreham Wood	335	D 1 - 1	Durrell	19	5
27	Nat Lg	H	Sutton United	1625	W 4 - 0	Durrell 4 Lloyd 10 Shaw 85 (pen) Richards 90	16	6
29	Nay Lg	A	Woking	1271	L 1 - 3	Lloyd 26	18	7
Sept 3	Nat Lg	H	Forest Green Rovers	1820	L 1 - 2	Durrell 79	19	8
10	Nat Lg	A	Aldershot Town	2445	D 0 - 0		18	9
13	Nat Lg	H	Guiseley	1578	W 2 - 0	Richards 50 Shaw 58 (pen)	17	10
17	Nat Lg	H	Braintree Town	1590	W 1 - 0	Hughes 16	15	11
24	Nat Lg	A	Wrexham	5058	D 0 - 0		15	12
Oct 1	Nat Lg	H	Dover Athletic	1686	W 5 - 0	Hunt 51 Alabi 52 Durrell 79 (pen) Craig 85 Akintunde 90	12	13
4	Nat Lg	A	North Ferriby United	476	W 1 - 0	Akintunde 75	10	14
8	Nat Lg	H	Torquay United	2201	W 1 - 0	Lloyd 26	11	15
15	FAC4Q	A	Southport	1674	L 0 - 1			16
22	Nat Lg	A	York City	2639	D 1 - 1	Richards 90	12	17
25	Nat Lg	A	Macclesfield Town	1922	D 0 - 0		12	18
29	Nat Lg	H	Lincoln City	2586	L 2 - 5	Asties 33 Shaw 44 (pen)	12	19
Nov 12	Nat Lg	A	Tranmere Rovers	7790	D 2 - 2	Shaw 50 Astles 90	12	20
19	Nat Lg	H	Bromley	1827	D 1 - 1	Shaw 69 (pen)	12	21
22	Nat Lg	H	Southport	1752	D 2 - 2	Richards 13 Alabi 30		22
26	Nat Lg	A	Eastleigh	1932	W 3 - 0	Richards 20 Durrell 72 Chapell 90	12	23
29	Nat Lg	A	North Ferriby United	1392	W 3 - 0	Richards 52 Alabi 54 (pen) 88		24
Dec 3	Nat Lg	A	Guiseley	957	D 1 - 1	Alabi 29	7	25
10	FAT1	A	Witton Albion	883	D 1 - 1	Chapell 36		26
13	FAT1r	H	Witton Albion	921	W 2 - 1	Alabi 86 (pen) Durrell 90		27
17	Nat Lg	H	Aldershot Town	1937	W 2 - 0	Chapell 44 Alabi 53	7	28
26	Nat Lg	A	Solihull Moors	1475	L 2 - 3	Durrell 18 Richards 90	8	29
Jan 1	Nat Lg	H	Solihull Moors	2244	L 0 - 3		10	30
7	Nat Lg	A	Braintree Town	707	W 2 - 1	Alabi 61 84		31
14	FAT2	H	Forest Green Rovers	1250	L 0 - 2			32
21	Nat Lg	H	Wrexham	3961	D 1 - 1	Alabi 60 (pen)	9	33
28	Nat Lg	A	Dover Athletic	1183	L 1 - 3	Alabi 31	10	34
Feb 4	Nat Lg	A	Dagenham & Redbridge	1250	L 2 - 3	Gregory 50 Shaw 58	12	35
11	Nat Lg	H	Gateshead	2098	L 1 - 2	Hudson 31	12	36
18	Nat Lg	A	Maidstone United	2120	L 2 - 4	Alabi 52 (pen) Hughes 67	12	37
25	Nat Lg	A	Southport	1496	W 1 - 0	Harwood 67	11	38
Mar 4	Nat Lg	H	Tranmere Rovers	3696	L 2 - 3	Alabi 5 (pen) Astles 68	11	39
18	Nat Lg	H	Eastleigh	1643	L 0 - 1		15	40
21	Nat Lg	H	Macclesfield Town	1802	L 2 - 3	Alabi 6 Richards 75	15	41
25	Nat Lg	A	Bromley	1237	W 1 - 0	Durrell 88	15	42
28	Nat Lg	A	Barrow	1501	L 1 - 2	Shaw 88	13	43
Apr 1	Nat Lg	A	Torquay United	1881	W 1 - 0	Hughes 80	13	44
8	Nat Lg	H	York City	2235	L 0 - 2		14	45
11	Nat Lg	A	Lincoln City	7401	L 0 - 1		14	46
14	Nat Lg	A	Forest Green Rovers	1936	L 0 - 3		16	47
17	Nat Lg	H	Woking	1770	L 2 - 3	Davies 55 Durrell 42	16	48
22	Nat Lg	A	Sutton United	2082	L 2 - 5	Alabai 79 82	17	49
29	Nat Lg	H	Boreham Wood	2013	L 0 - 2		19	50

GOALSCORERS	SG	CSG	Pens	Hat tricks	Total		SG	CSG	Pens	Hat tricks	Total
2015-16 Hannah					25	Craig	1				1
Alabi	15	2	5		18	Davies	1				1
Durrell	9	2	1		10	Gregory	1				1
Richards	8	3			8	Harwood	1				1
Shaw	7	3	4		8	Hudson	1				1
Akintundi	3	2			3	Hunt	1				1
Astles	3	2			3	Vassell	1				1
Chapell	3	2			3						
Hughes	3				3						
Lloyd	3				3						

DAGENHAM & REDBRIDGE

Club Contact Details

Chigwell Construction Stadium, Victoria Road, Dagenham, Essex RM10 7XL

020 8592 1549

info@daggers.co.uk

Ground Capacity: 6,078   **Seats:** 2,200   **Covered:** Yes   **Clubhouse:** Yes   **Shop:** Yes

Record Attendance

5,949 v Ipswich Town (05/01/2002) FA Cup Third Round Proper

Previous Grounds

None

10 YEAR RECORD

07-08		08-09		09-10		10-11		11-12		12-13		13-14		14-15		15-16		16-17	
FL 2	20	FL 2	8	FL 2	7	FL 1	21	FL 2	19	FL 2	22	FL 2	9	FL 2	14	FL 2	23	Nat	4
FAC	3P	FAC	2P	FAC	1P	FAC	1Pr	FAC	3Pr	FAC	1P	FAC	1P	FAC	1Pr	FAC	3P	FAC	1Pr
FLC	1P	FLC	1P	FLC	1P	FLC	1P	FLC	1P	FLC	1P	FLC	1P	FLC	1P	FLC	1P	FAT	1P

Club Factfile

Founded: 1992   **Nickname:** The Daggers   **Manager:** John Still

Previous Names: Formed by the merger of Dagenham and Redbridge Forest

Previous Leagues: Football Conference 1992-96, 2000-2007. Isthmian 1996-2000. Football League 2007-16.

Club Colours (change): Red & blue halves (All white)

RECORDS

Victory: 8-1 v Woking, Football Conference, 19.04.94

Defeat: 0-9 v Hereford United, Football Conference, 27.02.04.

Goalscorer: Danny Shipp - 105

Appearances: Tony Roberts - 507

Additional: Transfer fee received: £470,000 Dwight Gayle to Peterborough United

HONOURS

FA Comps: N/A

League: Isthmian League Premier Division 1999-2000. Football Conference 2006-07.
Football League Two Play-offs 2009-10.

County FA: Essex Senior Cup 1997-98, 2000-01.

BEST PERFORMANCES	**FA Cup:** 4th Round 2002-03.
	FA Trophy: Final 1996-97.
	FA Vase: N/A

DAGENHAM & REDBRIDGE MATCH RESULTS 2016-17

Date	Comp	H/A	Opponents	Att:	Result	Goalscorers	Pos	No.
Aug 6	Nat Lg	H	Southpoort	1296	W 3 - 0	Okenabithie 16 Guttridge 23 Maguire-Drew 67	1	1
9	Nat Lg	A	Chester	1841	L 0 - 3		11	2
13	Nat Lg	A	Guiseley	680	W 2 - 0	Assombalonga 6 Hawkins 76	7	3
16	Nat Lg	H	Lincoln City	1399	W 1 - 0	Guttridge 27	4	4
20	Nat Lg	A	Woking	1153	W 3 - 1	Robson 11 (og) Maguire -Drew 16 Okenabirhie 18	2	5
27	Nat Lg	H	Wrexham	1256	W 3 - 0	HAWKINS 3 (10 22 45 pen)	2	6
29	Nat Lg	A	Sutton United	1951	L 0 - 1		4	7
Sept 3	Nat Lg	H	Boreham Wood	1312	L 0 - 2		6	8
10	Nat Lg	A	Solihull Moors	716	W 5 - 2	HAWKINS 3 (21 64 90pen) Okenabirhie 39 Maguire-Drew 55	3	9
13	Nat Lg	H	Dover Athletic	1269	W 2 - 0	Maguire-Drew 2 Hawkins 39 (pen)	2	10
17	Nat Lg	H	North Ferriby United	1119	W 2 - 0	Hawkins 36 Howell 86	1	11
24	Nat Lg	A	Bromley	1558	W 3 - 1	Whitely 15 Maguire-Drew 53 Hawkins 56 (pen)	1	12
Oct 1	Nat Lg	H	Tranmere Rovers	1554	D 0 - 0		1	13
4	Nat Lg	A	Torquay United	1638	L 0 - 1		3	14
8	Nat Lg	A	Eastleigh	2209	W 1 - 0	Whitely 73	3	15
15	FAC4Q	H	Waldstone	1224	W 3 - 1	Okenabithie 31 Hawkins 50 Maguire-Drew 78		16
22	Nat Lg	H	Macclesfield Town	1214	D 1 - 1	Okenabithie 18	2	17
25	Nat Lg	H	Aldershot Town	1371	W 1 - 0	Whitely 81	2	18
29	Nat Lg	A	Forest Green Rovers	2268	D 1 - 1	Hawkins 74	2	19
Nov 5	FAC1	H	FC Halifax Town	1387	D 0 - 0			20
12	Nat Lg	H	Gateshead	1354	L 0 - 5		4	21
15	FAC1r	A	FC Halifax Town	1465	L 1 - 2	Whitely 73		22
19	Nat Lg	A	York City	2410	W 2 - 0	Hawkins 29 Guttridge 45	4	23
22	Nat Lg	A	Maidstone United	1970	W 1 - 0	Gutridge 26		24
26	Nat Lg	H	Barrow	1228	L 1 - 4	Whitely 65	5	25
29	Nat Lg	H	Torquay United	1072	L 0 - 1		6	26
Dec 3	Nat Lg	A	Dover Athletic	1234	W 2 - 1	Maguire-Drew 11 Benson 41		27
10	FAT1	H	Worthing	597	L 1 - 2	Benson 40		28
17	Nat Lg	H	Solihull Moors	1112	D 4 - 4	Doe 34 Hyde 41 Hawkins 83 Whitely 85	4	29
26	Nat Lg	A	Braintree Town	1353	L 2 - 3	Hawkins 32 Maguire-Drew 47		30
Jan 1	Nat Lg	H	Braintree Town	1261	W 3 - 0	Maguire-Drew 11 Guttridge 42 Whitely 80	4	31
7	Nat Lg	A	North Ferriby United	453	W 4 - 0	Okenabirhie 14 Hawkins 17 64 Guttridge 34	4	32
28	Nat Lg	A	Tranmere Rovers	5293	W 2 - 0	Whitely 24 Hawkins 47	3	33
Feb 4	Nat Lg	H	Chester	1250	W 3 - 2	Sheppard 45 Whitely 86 (pen) Maguire-Drew 90	2	34
11	Nat Lg	A	Southport	845	W 4 - 1	Maguire-Drew 34 Okenabirhie 42 Whitely 77 (p) Cundy 7 (og)	2	35
18	Nat Lg	H	Guiseley	2055	L 1 - 2	Hawkins 90	2	36
21	Nat Lg	H	Bromley	1212	W 2 - 1	Okenabithie 49 Sheppard 88	2	37
28	Nat Lg	H	Maidstone United	1456	L 0 - 2		2	38
Mar 4	Nat Lg	A	Gateshead	1030	L 0 - 1		4	39
11	Nat Lg	H	Forest Green Rovers	1459	W 2 - 1	Maguire-Drew 53 Doe 89	2	40
18	Nat Lg	A	Barrow	1102	L 1 - 2	Whitely 11	4	41
21	Nat Lg	A	Aldershot Town	2113	L 1 - 3	Doe 57	4	42
25	Nat Lg	H	York City	1659	W 1 - 0	Raymond 82	4	43
Apr 1	Nat Lg	H	Eastleigh	1332	W 4 - 0	WHITELY 3 (25 30 61 pen) Benson 28	4	44
3	Nat Lg	A	Lincoln City	7173	L 0 - 2		4	45
8	Nat Lg	A	Macclesfield Town	1251	W 4 - 1	Guttridge 41 Whitely 65 (pen) Maguire-Drew 78 89	4	46
14	Nat Lg	A	Boreham Wood	801	W 3 - 1	Benson 20 51 Whitely 75	4	47
17	Nat Lg	H	Sutton United	1634	D 2 - 2	Guttridge 27 Maguire-Drew 38	4	48
22	Nat Lg	A	Wrexham	3653	W 1 - 0	Benson 21	4	49
29	Nat Lg	H	Woking	1860	D 1 - 1	Heard 84	4	50
May 4	PO S-F1	H	Forest Green Rovers	2208	D 1 - 1	Maguire-Drew 45		51
7	PO S-F2	A	Forest Green Rovers	3237	L 0 - 2			52

GOALSCORERS	SG	CSG	Pens	Hat tricks	Total	GOALSCORERS	SG	CSG	Pens	Hat tricks	Total
Hawkins	14	4	4	2	19	Heard	1				1
Maguire-Drew	15	2			16	Howell	1				1
Whitely	13	3	1	1	16	Hyde	1				1
Guttridge	8	2			8	Raymond	1				1
Okenabithie	7	2			8						
Benson	5	2			6						
Doe	3				3						
Sheppard	2				2						
Opponents					2						
Assombalonga	1				1						

DOVER ATHLETIC

Club Contact Details
Crabble Athletic Ground, Lewisham Road, Dover, Kent CT17 0JB
01304 822 373
enquiries@doverathletic.com

Ground Capacity: 6,500 **Seats:** 1,010 **Covered:** 4,900 **Clubhouse:** Yes **Shop:** Yes

Record Attendance
4,186 v Oxford United - FA Cup 1st Round Proper November 2002
Previous Grounds
None

10 YEAR RECORD

	07-08	08-09	09-10	10-11	11-12	12-13	13-14	14-15	15-16	16-17
	Isth1S 1	Isth P 1	Conf S 2	Conf S 7	Conf S 7	Conf S 3	Conf S 5	Conf 8	Nat 5	Nat 6
FAC	2Q	3Qr	3Qr	4Q	3P	3Qr	2P	3P	1P	1Pr
FAT	3Qr	2Q	3P	3Q	3Q	3Qr	3P	QFr	QF	1Pr

Club Factfile

Founded: 1983 **Nickname:** The Whites **Manager:** Chris Kinnear

Previous Names: Dover F.C. until club folded in 1983

Previous Leagues: Southern 1983-93, 2002-04, Conference 1993-2002, Isthmian 2004-2009

Club Colours (change): White/black/black (Blue/white/white)

RECORDS
Victory: 7-0 v Weymouth - 03/04/1990
Defeat: 1-7 v Poole Town
Goalscorer: Lennie Lee - 160
Appearances: Jason Bartlett - 520+
Additional: Paid £50,000 to Farnborough Town for David Lewworthy August 1993
Received £50,000 from Brentford for Ricky Reina 1997

HONOURS

FA Comps: None

League: Southern League Southern Division 1987-88, Premier Division 1989-90, 92-93.
Isthmian League Division 1 South 2007-08, Premier Division 2008-09. Conference South Play-offs 2013-14.

County FA: Kent Senior Cup 1990-91, 2016-17.

BEST PERFORMANCES	**FA Cup:** Third Round Proper 2010-11, 14-15.
	FA Trophy: Semi-Finals 1997-98.
	FA Vase: N/A

DOVER ATHLETIC MATCH RESULTS 2016-17

Date	Comp	H/A	Opponents	Att:	Result	Goalscorers	Pos	No.
Aug 6	Nat Lg	A	Wrexham	5603	D 0 - 0		13	1
9	Nat Lg	H	Boreham Wood	1024	L 1 - 4	Miller 21 (pen)	20	2
13	Nat Lg	H	North Ferriby United	726	W 2 - 0	Emmanuel 34 Lafayette 77	14	3
16	Nat Lg	A	Eastleigh	1854	W 4 - 2	Kinnear 52 Lafayette 60 Stevenson 87 Miller 89	10	4
20	Nat Lg	H	Barrow	826	W 3 - 1	Emmanuel 30 Lafayette 56 Magri 82	4	5
27	Nat Lg	A	Torquay United	1793	L 1 - 2	Miller 75	7	6
29	Nat Lg	H	Aldershot Town	1093	L 1 - 2	Lafayette 45	12	7
Sept 3	Nat Lg	A	Southport	760	W 1 - 0	Modeste 2	10	8
10	Nat Lg	H	Forest Green Rovers	785	W 4 - 3	MILLER 3 (13 47 pen 88) Lafayette 69	7	9
13	Nat Lg	A	Dagenham & Redbridge	1269	L 0 - 2		10	10
17	Nat Lg	A	York City	2137	W 1 - 0	Miller 20	8	11
24	Nat Lg	H	Lincoln City	1509	W 2 - 0	Grimes 4 Emmanuel 53	8	12
Oct 1	Nat Lg	A	Chester	1686	L 0 - 5		9	13
4	Nat Lg	H	Sutton United	825	W 3 - 1	Miller 3 57 Stevenson 85	8	14
8	Nat Lg	A	Gateshead	688	L 2 - 4	Parkinson 36 Miller 57	9	15
15	FAC4Q	A	**Burgess Hill Town**	629	W 5 - 0	Pinnock 31 Modeste 43 51 Miller 9 58		16
22	Nat Lg	H	Braintree Town	1073	W 6 - 1	Thomas 18 MILLER 4 (22 26 33 46) Parkinson 40	8	17
25	Nat Lg	A	Bromley	1052	W 2 - 0	Miller 25 Lafayette 28	6	18
29	Nat Lg	H	Tranmere Rovers	1534	L 1 - 4	Thomas 22	7	19
Nov 5	FAC1	A	**Cambridge United**	2620	D 1 - 1	Miller 82		20
12	Nat Lg	A	Solihull Moors	837	W 3 - 2	MILLER 3 (53 60 73)	6	21
17	FAC1r	H	**Cambridge United**	1158	L 2 - 4	Miller 70 Thomas 101 (aet)		22
19	Nat Lg	H	Guiseley	3018	W 2 - 0	Miller 46 Emmanuel 49	6	23
22	Nat Lg	H	Woking	823	W 3 - 1	Lafayette 21 47 Emmanuel 42	6	24
29	Nat Lg	A	Sutton United	1091	W 6 - 0	EMMANUEL 3 (33 45 50) Lafayette 35 Miller 7 70	5	25
Dec 3	Nat Lg	H	Dagenham & Redbridge	1234	L 1 - 2	Miller 82	5	26
10	FAT1	A	**Dartford**	813	D 1 - 1	Miller 35		27
13	FAT1r	H	**Dartford**	389	L 1 - 2	Ademola 70		28
17	Nat Lg	A	Forest Green Rovers	1818	D 1 - 1	Emmanuel 70	6	29
26	Nat Lg	H	Maidstone United	2369	D 1 - 1	Miller 16 (pen)	6	30
Jan 1	Nat Lg	A	Maidstone United	2257	W 4 - 1	Emmanuel 29 55 Lafayette 74 Miller 90	4	31
7	Nat Lg	H	York City	1308	D 2 - 2	Miller 6 72 (pen)	5	32
10	Nat Lg	A	Macclesfield Town	1020	L 1 - 2	Grimes 9	5	33
20	Nat Lg	A	Lincoln City	6491	L 0 - 2		5	34
28	Nat Lg	H	Chester	1183	W 3 - 1	Miller 26 (pen) 49 Healy 58	5	35
Feb11	Nat Lg	H	Wrexham	1057	D 1 - 1	Healy 65	5	36
18	Nat Lg	A	North Ferriby United	465	W 2 - 1	Healy 55 Thomas 71	5	37
25	Nat Lg	A	Eastleigh	1164	W 3 - 0	MILLER 3 (3 71 80)	5	38
28	Nat Lg	A	Woking	1092	L 0 - 1		6	39
Mar 4	Nat Lg	H	Solihull Moors	1104	D 0 - 0		6	40
15	Nat Lg	A	Boreham Wood	314	L 0 - 5		7	41
21	Nat Lg	H	Bromley	988	W 1 - 0	Healy 59	7	42
25	Nat Lg	A	Guiseley	1261	W 4 - 0	Miller 15 80 (pen) Modeste 66 Lafayette 90 (pen)	7	43
28	Nat Lg	A	Tranmere Rovers	4281	L 0 - 1		8	44
Apr 1	Nat Lg	H	Gateshead	2507	W 2 - 0	Miller 34 78	6	45
8	Nat Lg	A	Braintree Town	704	W 2 - 1	Essam 64 Miller 89	6	46
14	Nat Lg	A	Southport	1563	W 3 - 0	Modeste 28 73 Miller 71	5	47
17	Nat Lg	H	Aldershot Town	3857	L 0 - 1		6	48
22	Nat Lg	H	Torquay United	1432	L 1 - 2	Thomas 71	6	49
26	Nat Lg	H	Macclesfield Town	932	D 2 - 2	Miller 37 (pen) Lafayette 87	6	50
29	Nat Lg	A	Barrow	1212	W 3 - 2	MILLER 3 (21 48 pen 90)	6	51

GOALSCORERS	SG	CSG	Pens	Hat tricks	Total		SG	CSG	Pens	Hat tricks	Total
2015-16 Payne					17	Essam	1				1
Miller	28	5	8	5	46	Kinnear	1				1
Lafayette	11	3	1		12	Magri	1				1
Emmanuel	7	3		1	11	Opponents	1				1
Modeste	4				6	Parkinson	1				1
Thomas	5				5	Pinnock	1				1
Healy	4	3			4						
Grimes	2				2						
Stevenson	2				2						
Ademola	1				1						

EASTLEIGH

Club Contact Details
The Silverlake Stadium 'Ten Acres', Stoneham Lane, Eastleigh SO50 9HT
02380 613 361
rmurphy@eastleighfc.com

Ground Capacity: 3,000 **Seats:** 2,700 **Covered:** Yes **Clubhouse:** Yes **Shop:** Yes

Record Attendance
5,250 v Bolton Wanderers, FA Cup Third Round 09/01/2016
Previous Grounds
Southampton Common. Walnut Avenue >1957.

10 YEAR RECORD

07-08		08-09		09-10		10-11		11-12		12-13		13-14		14-15		15-16		16-17	
Conf S	6	Conf S	3	Conf S	11	Conf S	8	Conf S	12	Conf S	4	Conf S	1	Conf	4	Nat	7	Nat	15
FAC	4Q	FAC	3Q	FAC	1P	FAC	4Q	FAC	3Q	FAC	3Q	FAC	3Q	FAC	2P	FAC	3Pr	FAC	3P
FAT	2P	FAT	3Q	FAT	3Q	FAT	3P	FAT	3Q	FAT	3Q	FAT	QF	FAT	1P	FAT	2P	FAT	1P

Club Factfile

Founded: 1946   **Nickname:** The Spitfires   **Manager:** Richard Hill

Previous Names: Swaythling Athletic 1946-59, Swaything 1973-80

Previous Leagues: Southampton Junior & Senior 1946-59, Hampshire 1950-86, Wessex 1986-2003, Southern 2003-04, Isthmian 2004-05

Club Colours (change): Blue & white

RECORDS
Victory: 12-1 v Hythe & Dibden (H) - 11/12/1948
Defeat: 0-11 v Austin Sports (A) - 01.01.1947
Goalscorer: Johnnie Williams - 177
Appearances: Ian Knight - 611
Additional: Paid £10,000 to Newport (I.O.W.) for Colin Matthews

HONOURS
FA Comps: None

League: Southampton Senior League (West) 1949-50. Hampshire League Division Three 1950-51, 53-54, Division Two 1967-68. Wessex League Division One 2002-03. Conference South 2013-14.

County FA: Hampshire Intermediate Cup 1950-51, Senior Cup 2011-12.

BEST PERFORMANCES
FA Cup: Third Round Proper 2015-16 (r), 16-17.
FA Trophy: Quarter Finals 2013-14.
FA Vase: Fourth Round 1982-83, 90-91, 94-95.

EASTLEIGH MATCH RESULTS 2016-17

Date	Comp	H/A	Opponents	Att:	Result	Goalscorers	Pos	No.
Aug 6	Nat Lg	H	Guiseley	2047	W 2 - 1	Drury 10 Partington 43	7	1
9	Nat Lg	A	Braintree Town	766	D 1 - 1	Constable 55	6	2
13	Nat Lg	A	Tranmere Rovers	4619	L 1 - 2	Dugdale 31	12	3
16	Nat Lg	H	Dover Athletic	1854	L 2 - 4	Bird 81 Guttridge 86	16	4
20	Nat Lg	A	Wrexham	4034	D 0 - 0		17	5
27	Nat Lg	H	Solihull Moors	1632	W 2 - 0	Creswell 58 Johnson 65	13	6
29	Nat Lg	A	Bromley	1100	W 5 - 0	MANDRON 3 (5 25 63) Howells 57 Dawson 71	9	7
Sept 3	Nat Lg	H	North Ferriby United	1883	W 2 - 0	Drury 3 Johnson 51	7	8
10	Nat Lg	H	Southport	1878	D 1 - 1	Mandron 49	8	9
13	Nat Lg	A	Forest Green Rovers	1444	D 1 - 1	Mandron 50	9	10
17	Nat Lg	A	Macclesfield Town	1287	W 1 - 0	Coulson 51	6	11
24	Nat Lg	H	Sutton United	2853	W 2 - 1	Coulson 48 50	6	12
Oct 1	Nat Lg	A	Woking	1403	D 3 - 3	Coulson 7 Dugdale 29 Partington 44	7	13
4	Nat Lg	H	Maidstone United	4114	W 3 - 0	Coulson 30 85 Bird 39	5	14
8	Nat Lg	H	Dagenham & Redbridge	2209	L 0 - 1		8	15
15	FAC4Q	H	North Leigh	689	W 6 - 0	BIRD 4 (9 31 53 67) Drury 45 Constable 74		16
22	Nat Lg	A	Lincoln City	3180	D 0 - 0		10	17
25	Nat Lg	H	Torquay United	2116	W 3 - 0	Cureton 47 Drury 89 Bird 90	7	18
29	Nat Lg	A	Barrow	1795	L 0 - 4		8	19
Nov 4	FAC1	H	Swindon Town	3312	D 1 - 1	Mandron 64		20
12	Nat Lg	H	York City	2341	D 1 - 1	Mandron 52	9	21
15	FAC1r	A	Swindon Town	4321	W 3 - 1	Reason 16 Drury 35 Mandron 74 (pen)		22
19	Nat Lg	A	Gateshead	703	D 2 - 2	Wilson 25 Mandron 45 (pen)	11	23
22	Nat Lg	A	Aldershot Town	1609	W 1 - 0	Mandron 45	8	24
26	Nat Lg	H	Chester	1932	L 0 - 3		8	25
29	Nat Lg	A	Maidstone United	1714	L 1 - 2	Mandron 48 (pen)	10	26
Dec 3	FAC2	H	FC Halifax Town	2098	D 2 - 2	Mandron 18 90		27
10	FAT1	A	Harlow Town	482	L 0 - 2			28
13	FAC2r	H	FC Halifax Town	1538	W 2 - 0	Wilson 44 Mandron 45 (pen)		29
17	Nat Lg	A	Southport	769	L 3 - 4	Johnson 32 Constable 58 86	12	30
26	Nat Lg	H	Boreham Wood	2213	D 2 - 2	Constable 8 Mandron 80 (pen)	12	31
Jan 1	Nat Lg	A	Boreham Wood	445	W 1 - 0	Wilson 48	9	32
7	FAC3	H	Brentford	7537	L 1 - 5	Obileye 29		33
10	Nat Lg	H	Forest Green Rovers	1917	D 1 - 1	Obileye 33	12	34
21	Nat Lg	A	Sutton United	2179	D 1 - 1	Garrett 6	12	35
28	Nat Lg	H	Woking	2036	L 0 - 1		13	36
Feb 11	Nat Lg	A	Guiseley	609	D 1 - 1	Constable 45	13	37
14	Nat Lg	H	Braintree Town	1702	L 0 - 2		13	38
18	Nat Lg	H	Tranmere Rovers	2475	L 0 - 2		15	39
21	Nat Lg	H	Macclesfield Town	2345	L 0 - 1		15	40
25	Nat Lg	A	Dover Athletic	1164	L 0 - 3		15	41
28	Nat Lg	H	Aldershot Town	2522	D 1 - 1	McAllister 80	14	42
Mar 4	Nat Lg	A	York City	2406	L 1 - 3	Stearn 16	15	43
11	Nat Lg	H	Barrow	2039	W 2 - 0	Togwell 19 Tubbs 46	13	44
18	Nat Lg	A	Chester	1643	W 1 - 0	Wilson 90	13	45
21	Nat Lg	A	Torquay United	1528	W 3 - 2	Matthews 17 65 Obileye 55	12	46
25	Nat Lg	H	Gateshead	2393	D 1 - 1	Obileye 58	12	47
Apr 1	Nat Lg	A	Dagenham & Redbridge	12332	L 0 - 4		12	48
8	Nat Lg	H	Lincoln City	2738	L 0 - 1		13	49
14	Nat Lg	A	North Ferriby United	364	L 1 - 2	Stearn 77	14	50
17	Nat Lg	H	Bromley	1830	W 2 - 1	Wilson 9 Matthews 82	12	51
22	Nat Lg	A	Solihull Moors	893	L 0 - 2		14	52
29	Nat Lg	H	Wrexham	2588	D 1 - 1	Tubbs 74	15	53

GOALSCORERS	SG	CSG	Pens	Hat tricks	Total		SG	CSG	Pens	Hat tricks	Total
2015-16 Constable					19	Partington	2				2
Mandron	12	5	5	1	15	Stearn	2				2
Bird	4			1	7	Tubbs	2				2
Coulson	4	4			6	Creswell	1				1
Constable	5	2			6	Cureton	1				1
Drury	5				5	Dawson	1				1
Wilson	5				5	Garrett	1				1
Obileye	4	2			4	Gutteridge	1				1
Johnson	3				3	Howells	1				1
Matthews	2				3	McAllister	1				1
Dugdale	2				2	Reason	1				1
						Togwell	1				1

EBBSFLEET UNITED

Club Contact Details
Stonebridge Road, Northfleet, Kent DA11 9GN
01474 533 796
info@eufc.co.uk

Ground Capacity: 4,184   **Seats:** 2,300   **Covered:** 3,000   **Clubhouse:** Yes   **Shop:** Yes

Record Attendance
12,036 v Sunderland - FA Cup 4th Round 12/02/1963
Previous Grounds
Gravesend United: Central Avenue

10 YEAR RECORD

07-08		08-09		09-10		10-11		11-12		12-13		13-14		14-15		15-16		16-17	
Conf	11	Conf	14	Conf	22	Conf S	3	Conf	14	Conf	23	Conf S	4	Conf S	8	Nat S	2	Nat S	2
FAC	4Q	FAC	1P	FAC	4Q	FAC	1Pr	FAC	4Q	FAC	1P	FAC	4Qr	FAC	3Q	FAC	2Qr	FAC	4Q
FAT	F	FAT	SF	FAT	1P	FAT	2P	FAT	3P	FAT	1P	FAT	3P	FAT	QF	FAT	1P	FAT	2P

Club Factfile

Founded: 1946   **Nickname:** The Fleet   **Manager:** Daryl McMahon

Previous Names: Gravesend United and Northfleet United merged in 1946 to form Gravesend and Northfleet > 2007

Previous Leagues: Southern 1946-79, 82-97. Alliance (FM) 1979-82. Isthmian 1997-2002.

Club Colours (change): Red & white (Yellow and blue)

RECORDS

Victory: 8-1 v Clacton Town - Southern League 1962-63
Defeat: 0-9 v Trowbridge Town - Southern League Premier Division 1991-92
Goalscorer: Steve Portway - 152 (1992-94, 97-2001)
Appearances: Ken Burrett - 537
Additional: Paid £8,000 to Wokingham Town for Richard Newbery 1996 and to Tonbridge for Craig Williams 1997
Received £35,000 from West Ham United for Jimmy Bullard 1998

HONOURS

FA Comps: FA Trophy 2007-08.

League: Southern League 1957-58, Division One South 1974-75, Southern Division 1993-94.
Isthmian League Premier 2001-02. Southern Premier Play-offs 2016-17.

County FA: Kent Senior Cup 1948-49, 52-53, 80-81, 99-00, 00-01, 01-02, 07-08, 13-14.

BEST PERFORMANCES
FA Cup: Fourth Round Proper 1962-63.
FA Trophy: Final 2007-08.
FA Vase: N/A

EBBSFLEET UNITED MATCH RESULTS 2016-17

Date	Comp	H/A	Opponents	Att:	Result	Goalscorers	Pos	No.
Aug 6	Nat S	H	Poole Town	1031	W 4 - 0	Kedwell 65 67 Rance 9 Powell 74	1	1
9	Nat S	A	Concord Rangers	452	W 1 - 0	Winfield 31	1	2
13	Nat S	A	Hungerford Town	417	D 1 - 1	Sheringham 43	2	3
16	Nat S	H	Whitehawk	933	D 1 - 1	Cook 20	5	4
20	Nat S	H	Hemel Hempstead Town	912	D 2 - 2	Rose (og) 6 Shields 80	7	5
27	Nat S	A	Eastbourne Borough	764	D 0 - 0		5	6
29	Nat S	H	Margate		W 4 - 0	McLean 14 Powell 36 Deering 61 McQueen 88	5	7
Sept 3	Nat S	A	Gosport Borough	566	L 0 - 1		9	8
5	Nat S	A	Chelmsford City	901	L 1 - 2	Powell 42	9	9
10	Nat S	H	Wealdstone	965	W 4 - 1	Powell 17 Kedwell 22 Phillips 35 Cook 82	6	10
13	Nat S	A	Bishops Stortford	375	W 3 - 0	Rance 22 McLean 52 McQueen 89	5	11
17	FAC2Q	H	AFC Sudbury	855	W 5 - 0	McQueen 53 64 Powell 80 Lewis 84 87		12
24	Nat S	H	St Albans City	1039	W 3 - 1	Deering 1 21 McQueen 15	4	13
Oct 1	FAC3Q	H	Havant & Waterlooville	742	W 7 - 0	Cook 19 McQueen 38 68 Kedwell 43 (pen) Phillips 52 Bubb 87 Powell 90		14
8	Nat S	A	Weston-s-Mare	423	W 2 - 0	Kedwell 3 McQueen 50	4	15
15	FAC4Q	H	Merstham	646	L 1 - 2	McQueen 11		16
22	Nat S	A	East Thurrock United	806	D 1 - 1	Lewis 6	6	17
29	Nat S	H	Bath City	1101	W 1 - 0	Deering 16	5	18
Nov 5	Nat S	H	Truro City	298	W 4 - 2	Powell 25 75 Shields 81 Clark 84	2	19
12	Nat S	A	Welling United	1014	W 2 - 1	McQueen 11 Powell 88	3	20
19	Nat S	H	Maidenhead United	1318	L 2 - 3	Shields 23 Bubb 77	4	21
22	Nat S	H	Hampton & Richmond B	828	D 1 - 1	Bubb 4	4	22
26	FAT3Q	H	Harrow Borough	613	W 4 - 2	Powell 1 Bubb 17 Sheringham 20 Cook 64		23
Dec 3	Nat S	A	Oxford City	752	W 3 - 1	Sheringham 39 Shields 72 Bubb 76	3	24
10	FAT 1	H	Woking	825	D 1 - 1	Winfield 87		25
13	FAT1r	A	Woking	613	W 1 - 0	Clark 52		26
!7	Nat S	H	Gosport Borough	852	W 2 - 0	McQueen 32 35	3	27
26	Nat S	A	Dartford	2404	L 1 - 2	Cook 80	6	28
Jan 1	Nat S	H	Dartford	2564	W 1 - 0	Bubb 40	2	29
7	Nat S	A	Wealdstone	785	W 4 - 2	Winfield 14 Kedwell 47 Hunt 49 (og) Deering 90	2	30
14	FAT2	A	Kidderminster Harriewrs	1078	L 0 - 3			31
21	Nat S	H	Chelmsford City	1434	W 2 - 0	Clark 42 Bubb 86	2	32
28	Nat S	A	Poole Town	681	W 2 - 0	Deering 31 Drury 55	2	33
Feb 4	Nat S	H	Concord Rangers	1028	W 4 - 0	Clark 6 Bubb 43 85 Shields 63	2	34
11 28	Nat S	A	Whitehawk	349	W 3 - 0	Kedwell 34 90 Shields 70	1	35
18	Nat S	H	Hungerford Town	1321	W 1 - 0	Drury 19	1	36
21	Nat S	A	Hemel Hempstead Town	530	D 1 - 1	Bubb 12	2	37
25	Nat S	A	Bath City	695	W 1 - 0	Bubb 50	1	38
Mar 4	Nat S	H	East Thurrock United	1267	W 6 - 1	Cook 22 42 Drury 35 65 Powell 81 McQueen 90	1	39
11	Nat S	A	St Albans City	864	W 3 - 0	Deering 28 Powell 35 Kedwell 36	1	40
18	Nat S	H	Weston-s-Mare	1325	W 2 - 1	Kedwell 80 McQueen 84	2	41
21	Nat S	H	Bishops Stortford	1229	W 8 - 0	McQUEEN 3 (27 52 60) COOK 3 (7 40 70) Bubb 82 Kedwell 89	2	42
25	Nat S	A	Hampton & Richmond B	1089	D 1 - 1	Bubb 90	2	43
April 1	Nat S	H	Welling United	1767	W 5 - 1	Powell 29 Clark 40 Kedwell 42 (pen) 73 McQueen 69	2	44
8	Nat S	A	Truro City	501	D 1 - 1	Deering 55	2	45
15	Nat S	H	Eastbourne Borough	2477	W 4 - 1	Bubb 56 87 Cook 67 McLean 90 (pen)	2	46
17	Nat S	A	Margate	896	W 1 - 0	Bubb 3	2	47
22	Nat S	A	Maidenhead United	3377	W 2 - 1	Drury 64 Winfield 74	2	48
29	Nat S	H	Oxford City	2116	W 1 - 0	Cook 5	2	49
May 3	PO SF1	H	Hampton & Richmond B	1669	W 2 1	Rance 6 McLean 43 (pen)		50
7	PO SF2	A	Hampton & Richmond B	2102	W 2 - 1	Clark 34 McQueen 89		51
13	PO Final	H	Chelmsford City	3134	W 2 - 1	Winfield 73 McQueen 76		52

GOALSCORERS	SG	CSG	Pens	Hat tricks	Total		SG	CSG	Pens	Hat tricks	Total
2015-16 Godden					30	Winfield	5				5
McQueen	15	6		1	20	Mc Lean	4	2			4
Bubb	13	4			16	Lewis	3				3
Kedwell	11		2		13	Rance	3				3
Powell	12	2			13	Sheringham	3				3
Cook	8			1	12	Opponents	2				2
Deering	8				8	Phillips	2				2
Clark	6				6						
Shields	6				6						
Drury	4				5						

FC HALIFAX TOWN

Club Contact Details
The Shay Stadium, Shay Syke, Halifax HX1 2YS
01422 341 222
mikesharman@fchalifaxtown.com

Ground Capacity: 10,401 **Seats:** 5,830 **Covered:** Yes **Clubhouse:** Yes **Shop:** Yes

Record Attendance
36,885 v Tottenham Hotspur - FA Cup 5th Round 14/02/1953
Previous Grounds
Sandhall Lane 1911-15, Exley 1919-21.

10 YEAR RECORD

07-08		08-09		09-10		10-11		11-12		12-13		13-14		14-15		15-16		16-17	
Conf	20	NP1N	8	NP1N	1	NP P	1	Conf N	3	Conf N	5	Conf	5	Conf	9	Nat	21	Nat N	3
FAC	1P	FAC	2Q	FAC	4Q	FAC	4Q	FAC	1P	FAC	4Qr	FAC	1P	FAC	1P	FAC	1P	FAC	2Pr
FAT	3P	FAT	P	FAT	3Q	FAT	2Q	FAT	3Qr	FAT	QFr	FAT	1P	FAT	QF	FAT	F	FAT	3Qr

Club Factfile

Founded: 1911 **Nickname:** Shaymen **Manager:** Billy Heath

Previous Names: Halifax Town 1911-2008 then reformed as F.C. Halifax Town

Previous Leagues: Yorkshire Combination 1911-12, Midland 1912-21, Football League (FM Division Three North)1921-93, 98-2002, Conference 1993-98, 2002-08

Club Colours (change): Blue and white

RECORDS
Victory: 12-0 v West Vale Ramblers - FA Cup 1st Qualifying Road 1913-14
Defeat: 0-13 v Stockport County - Division 3 North 1933-34
Goalscorer: Ernie Dixon - 132 (1922-30)
Appearances: John Pickering - 402 (1965-74)
Additional: Recorded a 30 game unbeaten run at The Shay between 18/04/2009 - 20/11/2010 (W 24 D 6 F 79 A 20).
Fee paid - £150,000 for Chris Tate, July 1999. Fee Received - £350,000 for Geoff Horsfield, October 1998.

HONOURS
FA Comps: FA Trophy 2015-16.

League: Conference 1997-98, Conference North Play-offs 2012-13, 16-17. Northern Premier League Division One North 2009-10, Premier Division 2010-11.

County FA: West Riding County Cup 2012-13.

BEST PERFORMANCES	**FA Cup:** Fifth Round Proper 1932-33, 52-53.
	FA Trophy: Final 2015-16.
	FA Vase: N/A

FC HALIFAX MATCH RESULTS 2016-17

Date	Comp	H/A	Opponents	Att:	Result	Goalscorers	Pos	No.
Aug 6	Nat N	A	Nuneaton Town	993	W 3 - 2	DENTON 3 (2 53 59)	3	1
9	Nat N	H	Altrincham	1836	D 2 - 2	Denton 32 Sinnott 82	3	2
13	Nat N	H	Worcester City	1576	W 3 - 1	Roberts 16 Wilde 55 Denton 83	1	3
16	Nat N	A	Stockport County	3086	D 1 - 1	Denton 33	8	4
20	Nat N	H	Tamworth	1597	W 4 - 0	Hone 25 Peniket 36 56 Sinnott 40	1	5
27	Nat N	A	AFC Fylde	1905	L 2 - 3	Denton 30 Hone 72	5	6
29	Nat N	H	Harrogate Town	1965	L 0 - 1		10	7
Sept 3	Nat N	A	AFC Telford United	1324	W 2 - 1	Peniket 20 Hotte 49	8	8
6	Nat N	A	Salford City	2049	D 2 - 2	Garner 35 Roberts 90	9	9
10	Nat N	H	Stalybridge Celtic	1552	W 1 - 0	King 36 (pen)	9	10
13	Nat N	A	Gainsborough Trinity	692	L 2 - 3	Simmons 13 King 32	10	11
17	FAC2Q	A	Ashton Athletic	479	W 5 - 0	Denton 2 Hone 32 Sinnott 36 Simmons 56 Peniket 57		12
24	Nat N	H	Bradford PA	1761	W 4 - 0	Simmons 9 18 Denton 13 Sinnott 55	8	13
Oct 1	FAC3Q	H	Stalybridge Celtic	964	W 2 - 1	Wilde 23 Hone 76		14
8	Nat N	A	Gloucester City	545	W 2 - 0	Simmons 29 King 61 (pen)	6	15
15	FAC4Q	A	Harrogate Town	1791	W 2 - 0	Sinnott 69 Hibbs 90		16
22	Nat N	A	Boston United	1236	W 4 - 1	Denton 18 87 Simmons 46 79	4	17
24	Nat N	H	FC Utd of Manchester	1938	W 3 - 1	Denton 10 19 Sinnott 44	3	18
29	Nat N	H	Brackley Town	1581	L 1 - 3	Sinnott 31	5	19
Nov 5	FAC1	A	Dagenham & Redbridge	1387	D 0 - 0			20
12	Nat N	H	Kidderminster Harriers	1704	W 2 - 0	Kosylo 50 Peniket 90	4	21
15	FAC1r	H	Dagenham & Redbridge	1465	W 2 - 1	Denton 35 Kosylo 90		22
19	Nat N	A	Curzon Ashton	654	L 2 - 4	Moyo 46 Hampson 75 (og)	6	23
26	FAT3Q	A	Matlock Town	483	D 1 - 1	Simmons 80		24
29	FAT3Qr	H	Matlock Town	479	L 2 - 3	Hibbs 57 Kosylo 68		25
Dec 4	FAC 2	A	Eastleigh	2098	D 3 - 3	Sinnott 62 Garner 66 Peniket 71		26
13	FAC2r	H	Eastleigh	1539	L 0 - 2			27
17	Nat N	H	AFC Telford United	1406	D 1 - 1	Wilde 90	8	28
26	Nat N	A	Darlington 1883	3000	L 2 - 3	Morgan 39 90	9	29
Jan 1	Nat N	H	Darlington 1883	2511	D 2 - 2	Morgan 14 65	9	30
7	Nat N	A	Stalybridge Celtic	851	L 0 - 1		9	31
10	Nat N	H	Chorley	1389	W 2 - 1	Kosylo 16 (pen) Peniket 56	9	32
14	Nat N	A	Tamworth	793	W 6 - 2	Peniket 20 40 Kosylo 24 84 Morgan 25 73	8	33
21	Nat N	H	Salford City	2153	W 4 - 2	Nti 565 King 57 Kosylo 71 (pen) Morgan 74	5	34
28	Nat N	H	Stockport County	2029	D 0 - 0		7	35
Feb 4	Nat N	A	Altrincham	1344	W 1 - 0	King 81	6	36
11	Nat N	H	Nuneaton Town	1573	W 2 - 0	Morgan 16 Kosylo 48 (pen)	5	37
18	Nat N	H	Worcester City	572	W 2 - 1	Kosylo 50 Denton 55	5	38
Mar 4	Nat N	H	Boston United	1752	D 0 - 0		5	39
7	Nat N	A	Alfreton Town	499	L 0 1		5	40
11	Nat N	A	Bradford PA	1132	W 3 - 1	Peniket 70 Denton 86 Kosylo 90	5	41
18	Nat N	H	Gloucester City	1752	L 0 - 1		7	42
21	Nat N	H	Gainsborough Trinity	1403	W 2 - 1	Salt 53 (og) Morgan 81	5	43
25	Nat N	A	FC Utd of Manchester	3149	W 3 - 0	Charles 10 Sinnott 42 King 44	3	44
April 1	Nat N	A	Kidderminster H	2025	W 2 - 1	Denton 30 Sinnott 83	3	45
4	Nat N	A	Brackley Town	447	D 0 - 0		3	46
8	Nat N	H	Alfreton Town	1634	W 1 - 0	Denton 61	3	47
15	Nat N	H	AFC Fylde	2368	L 0 - 1		3	48
17	Nat N	A	Harrogate Town	1335	W 3 - 0	Charles 10 Kosylo 28 78	3	49
22	Nat N	H	Curzon Ashton	1818	W 3 - 0	Peneket 21 Charles 36 Hone 63	3	50
29	Nat N	A	Chorley	2462	W 2 - 0	Denton 40 King 90 (pen))	3	51
May 3	PO SF1	A	Salford City	2175	D 1 - 1	Peniket 37		52
7	PO SF2	H	Salford City	3655	D 1 - 1	Peniket 96 (won 3-0 on penalties)		53
13	PO Final	H	Chorley	7920	W 2 - 1	Roberts 47 Garner 101 (aet)		54

GOALSCORERS	SG	CSG	Pens	Hat tricks	Total		SG	CSG	Pens	Hat tricks	Total
2015-16 Burrow					18	Garner	3				3
Denton	15	4		1	19	Roberts	3				3
Peniket	11				13	Wilde	3				3
Kosylo	10	3	3		12	Hibbs	2				2
Sinnott	10	2			10	Opponents	2				2
Morgan	8	2			9	Hotte	1				1
Simmons	7	3			8	Moyo	1				1
King	7	2	3		7	Nti	1				1
Hone	5	2			5						
Chartles	3				3						

GATESHEAD

Club Contact Details
The International Stadium, Neilson Road, Gateshead NE10 0EF
01914 783 883
info@gateshead-fc.com

Ground Capacity: 11,795 **Seats:** 11,795 **Covered:** 7,271 **Clubhouse:** Yes **Shop:** Yes

Record Attendance
11,750 v Newcastle United - Friendly 07/08/95
Previous Grounds
Redheugh Park 1930-71

---

10 YEAR RECORD

07-08		08-09		09-10		10-11		11-12		12-13		13-14		14-15		15-16		16-17	
NP P	3	Conf N	2	Conf	20	Conf	15	Conf	8	Conf	17	Conf	3	Conf	10	Nat	9	Nat	8
FAC	2Q	FAC	3Q	FAC	1Pr	FAC	1P	FAC	2P	FAC	4Q	FAC	1Pr	FAC	3P	FAC	4Q	FAC	4Qr
FAT	1Pr	FAT	3Q	FAT	3Pr	FAT	SF	FAT	QF	FAT	3P	FAT	2P	FAT	3Pr	FAT	QFr	FAT	2P

Club Factfile

Founded: 1930   **Nickname:** Tynesiders, The Heed   **Manager:** Neil Aspin

Previous Names: Gateshead AFC (formerly South Shields)1930-73. Gateshead Town 1973-74. Gateshead Utd (formerly South Shields) 1974-77.

Previous Leagues: Football League 1930-60, Northern Counties East 1960-62, North Regional 1962-68, Northern Premier 1968-70, 73-83, 85-86, 87-90, Wearside 1970-71, Midland 1971-72, Northern Combination 1973-74. Alliance/Conf 1983-85, 86-87, 90-98.

Club Colours (change): White & black (Blue & white)

RECORDS
Victory: 8-0 v Netherfield - Northern Premier League
Defeat: 0-9 v Sutton United - Conference 22/09/90
Goalscorer: Paul Thompson - 130
Appearances: James Curtis - 506 (2003-present)
Additional: Record transfer fee paid; £9,000 - Paul Cavell, Dagenham & Redbridge 1994
                     Record transfer fee received; £150,000 Lee Novak, Huddersfield Town 2009

HONOURS
FA Comps: N/A

League: Northern Regional 1963-64. Northern Premier League 1982-83, 85-86, NPL Premier Division play-offs 2007-08,
          Conference North play-offs 2008-09.

County FA: Durham Senior Professional Cup 1930-31, 48-49, 501-51, 54-55, 58-59.
            Durham Challenge Cup 2010-11 (Reserve Team)

BEST PERFORMANCES	**FA Cup:** Quarter Finals 1952-53.
	FA Trophy: Semi-Finals 2010-11.
	FA Vase: N/A

GATESHEAD MATCH RESULTS 2016-17

Date	Comp	H/A	Opponents	Att:	Result	Goalscorers	Pos	No.
Aug 6	Nat Lg	H	Chester	992	W 3 - 0	York 62 82 Smith 88	2	1
9	Nat Lg	A	Southport	926	W 3 - 0	Johnson 45 York 86 Brundle 90	2	2
13	Nat Lg	A	Forest Green Rovers	1143	L 0 - 1		5	3
16	Nat Lg	H	York City	1331	W 6 - 1	Bowman 17 56 Johnson 47 Ajala 74 Fyfield 80 Jones 82	2	4
20	Nat Lg	A	Bromley	604	L 2 - 3	Bolton 5 Johnson 81 (pen)	7	5
27	Nat Lg	H	Boreham Wood	732	D 1 - 1	Bowman 8	5	6
29	Nat Lg	A	Lincoln City	3687	L 0 - 3		11	7
Sept 3	Nat Lg	H	Sutton United	890	W 1 - 0	Oates 65	9	8
10	Nat Lg	A	Braintree Town	519	W 4 - 1	Styche 23 52 McLaughlin 70 York 83	6	9
13	Nat Lg	H	North Feriby United	613	L 0 - 1		8	10
17	Nat Lg	H	Solihull Moors	541	D 0 - 0		10	11
24	Nat Lg	A	Aldershot Town	1647	L 0 - 3		12	12
Oct 1	Nat Lg	A	Torquay United	693	D 0 - 0		13	13
4	Nat Lg	A	Tranmere Rovers	3048	W 1 - 0	Jones 51	13	14
8	Nat Lg	H	Dover Athletic	688	W 4 - 2	York 36 S.Jones 44 59 McLoughlin 48	10	15
15	FAC4Q	A	Alfreton Town	457	D 2 - 2	Jones 78 81		16
19	FAC4Qr	H	Alfreton Town	465	L 2 - 3	Monkhouse (og) 36 Brundle 40		17
22	Nat Lg	A	Maidstone United	2208	W 2 - 0	Johnson 45 70	9	18
25	Nat Lg	A	Guiseley	762	D 1 - 1	Johnson 86	11	19
29	Nat Lg	H	Wrexham	832	D 2 - 2	Jones 36 Johnson 49	11	20
Nov 12	Nat Lg	A	Dagenham & Redbridge	1354	W 5 - 0	Jones 20 60 Brundle 47 Johnson 62 Smith 64 (pen)	7	21
19	Nat Lg	H	Eastleigh	703	D 2 2	Jones 71 Johnson 79 (pen)	7	22
22	Nat Lg	H	Macclesfield Town	491	D 1 - 1	Johnson 12	9	23
26	Nat Lg	A	Woking	1062	L 0 - 3		9	24
29	Nat Lg	A	Tranmere Rovers	723	L 0 - 1		10	25
Dec 3	Nat Lg	A	North Ferriby United	498	L 0 - 1		11	26
10	FAT1	H	Kings Lynn Town	277	W 2 - 0	Burrow 36 Smith 88		27
17	Nat Lg	H	Braintree Town	501	D 1 - 1	McLaughlin 85 (pen)	11	28
26	Nat Lg	A	Barrow	2123	D 0 - 0		12	29
Jan 1	Nat Lg	H	Barrow	871	W 4 - 1	Hannant 25 Bell 39 Burrow 49 York 70	7	30
7	Nat Lg	A	Solihull Moors	750	W 2 - 0	Bell 22 Jones 90	8	31
14	FAT2	H	Lincoln City	578	L 1 - 3	Burrow 4		32
21	Nat Lg	H	Aldershot Town	653	D 1 - 1	Burrow 35	8	33
28	Nat Lg	A	Torquay United	1555	L 1 - 3	McLaughlin 55 (pen)	9	34
Feb 4	Nat Lg	H	Southport	620	W 3 - 0	Burrow 23 Smith 43 Johnson 62	8	35
11	Nat Lg	A	Chester	2095	W 2 - 1	Johnson 36 Burrow 63	8	36
18	Nat Lg	H	Forest Green Rovers	916	W 3 - 1	Johnson 21 30 York 56	8	37
21	Nat Lg	A	York City	2320	W 3 - 1	Johnson 1 McLaughlin (44 pen) York 76	6	38
Mar 4	Nat Lg	H	Dagenham & Redbridge	1030	W 1 - 0	Johnson 46	7	39
11	Nat Lg	A	Wrexham	3986	W 2 - 0	Burrow 52 Johnson 90	5	40
14	Nat Lg	A	Macclesfield Town	993	D 1 - 1	Smith 76	5	41
18	Nat Lg	A	Woking	832	W 2 - 1	Johnson 52 York 90	5	42
21	Nat Lg	H	Guiseley	833	D 1 - 1	York 62	5	43
25	Nat Lg	A	Eastleigh	2393	D 1 - 1	Mafuta 57	5	44
Apr 1	Nat Lg	A	Dover Athletic	2507	L 0 - 2		6	45
8	Nat Lg	H	Maidstone United	967	L 1 - 2	Mills 26 (og)	8	46
14	Nat Lg	A	Sutton United	1889	L 0 - 3		8	47
17	Nat Lg	H	Lincoln City	3770	L 1 - 2	McLaughlin 29 (pen)	8	48
22	Nat Lg	A	Boreham Wood	314	W 4 - 0	York 13 Hannant 16 Smith 86 Fyfield 90	8	49
29	Nat Lg	H	Bromley	701	L 0 - 2		8	50

GOALSCORERS	SG	CSG	Pens	Hat tricks	Total		SG	CSG	Pens	Hat tricks	Total
2015-16 Bowman					21	Fyfield	2				2
Johnson	16	6,6	2		18	Hannant	2				2
S.Jones	8	3			11	Opponents	2				2
York	10	2			11	Styche	1				2
Burrow	7	2			7	Ajala	1				1
McLaughlin	6		2		6	Bolton	1				1
Smith	6		1		6	Mafuta	1				1
Bowman	3				3	Oates	1				1
Brundle	3				3						
Bell	2	2			2						

GUISELEY

Club Contact Details
Nethermoor Park, Otley Road, Guiseley, Leeds LS20 8BT
01943 873 223 (Office) 872 872 (Club)
Admin@guiseleyafc.co.uk

Ground Capacity: 3,000 **Seats:** 510 **Covered:** 1,040 **Clubhouse:** Yes **Shop:** Yes

Record Attendance
2,486 v Bridlington Town - FA Vase Semi-final 1st Leg 1989-90
Previous Grounds
None

10 YEAR RECORD

07-08	08-09	09-10	10-11	11-12	12-13	13-14	14-15	15-16	16-17
NPP 6	NPP 3	NPP 1	Conf N 5	Conf N 2	Conf N 2	Conf N 5	Conf N 5	Nat 20	Nat 20
FAC 3Q	FAC 3Qr	FAC 3Qr	FAC 1P	FAC 3Q	FAC 1Pr	FAC 2Q	FAC 4Q	FAC 4Qr	FAC 4Qr
FAT 1P	FAT 1Q	FAT 3P	FAT QF	FAT 3P	FAT 2P	FAT 3P	FAT 1P	FAT 3Pr	FAT 2P

Club Factfile

Founded: 1909   **Nickname:** The Lions   **Manager:** Adam Lockwood - Aug 2016

Previous Names: None

Previous Leagues: Wharfedale, Leeds, West Riding Counties, West Yorkshire, Yorkshire 1968-82,
Northern Counties East 1982-91, Northern Premier 1991-2010

Club Colours (change): White/navy/navy (Yellow/black/black)

RECORDS

HONOURS

FA Comps: FA Vase 1990-91.

League: Wharfedale 1912-13. Yorkshire Division Two 1975-76. Northern Counties East 1990-91.
NPL Division One 1993-94, Premier Division 2009-10. Conference North Play-off 2014-15.

County FA: West Riding County Cup 1978-79, 79-80, 80-81, 93-94, 95-96, 2004-05, 10-11, 11-12.

BEST PERFORMANCES	**FA Cup:** First Round Proper 1991-92, 94-95, 99-00, 02-03, 10-11, 12-13(r)
	FA Trophy: Semi-Finals 1993-94.
	FA Vase: Final 1990-91(r), 91-92.

GUISELEY MATCH RESULTS 2016-17

Date	Comp	H/A	Opponents	Att:	Result	Goalscorers	Pos	No.
Aug 6	Nat Lg	A	Eastleigh	2047	L 1 - 2	Rankine 56	16	1
9	Nat Lg	H	Wrexham	1120	L 2 - 3	Rankine 11 Lawlor 84	22	2
13	Nat Lg	H	Dagenham & Redbridge	680	L 0 - 2		23	3
16	Nat Lg	A	North Ferriby United	487	L 2 - 3	Johnson 29 83	24	4
20	Nat Lg	A	Solihull Moors	554	L 2 - 3	Hatfield 44 Boyes 77	24	5
27	Nat Lg	H	Bromley	565	L 1 - 4	Smith 87	24	6
29	Nat Lg	A	Tranmere Rovers	4798	L 0 - 1		24	7
Sept 3	Nat Lg	H	Braintree Town	704	D 0 - 0		24	8
10	Nat Lg	H	Woking	549	D 1 - 1	Boyes 47	24	9
13	Nat Lg	A	Chester	1578	L 0 - 2		24	10
17	Nat Lg	A	Maidstone United	2106	D 1 - 1	Webb-Foster 65	24	11
24	Nat Lg	H	Macclesfield Town	891	L 1 - 2	Preston 36	24	12
Oct 1	Nat Lg	A	Sutton United	1282	L 0 - 1		24	13
4	Nat Lg	H	York City	1626	W 6 - 1	Cassidy 19 Purver 22 Hatfield 24 Preston 31 Hylton 55 Atkinson 82	24	14
8	Nat Lg	H	Southport	1046	W 2 - 1	Cassidy 49 Rankine 82	23	15
15	**FAC4Q**	**A**	**Lincoln City**	**2629**	**D 0 - 0**			16
18	**FAC4Qr**	**H**	**Lincoln City**	**765**	**L 1 - 2**	**Boyes 58**		17
22	Nat Lg	A	Forest Green Rovers	1723	L 0 - 3		24	18
25	Nat Lg	H	Gateshead	762	D 1 - 1	Walton 68 (pen)	24	19
29	Nat Lg	A	Aldershot Town	1731	L 0 - 1		24	20
Nov 12	Nat Lg	H	Torquay United	924	W 2 - 0	Preston 14 Cassidy 19	22	21
19	Nat Lg	A	Dover Athletic	3018	L 0 2		23	22
22	Nat Lg	A	Barrow	1070	L 0 - 3		23	23
26	Nat Lg	H	Boreham Wood	749	W 3 - 1	Atkinson 47 Hatfield 50 Cassidy 80	21	24
29	Nat Lg	A	York City	1907	D 1 - 1	Cassidy 85	22	25
Dec 3	Nat Lg	H	Chester	957	D 1 - 1	Walton 53 (pen)	22	26
10	**FAT1**	**A**	**Chorley**	**612**	**W 1 - 0**	**Rankine 17**		27
17	Nat Lg	A	Woking	969	D 0 - 0		23	28
26	Nat Lg	H	Lincoln City	2446	W 2 - 1	Hatfield 13 90	23	29
Jan 1	Nat Lg	A	Lincoln City	5148	L 1 - 3	Habergham 12 (og)	23	30
7	Nat Lg	H	Maidstone United	1040	W 2 - 0	Walton 32 (pen) Rankine 83	21	31
14	**FAT2**	**A**	**Nuneaton Town**	**554**	**L 1 - 6**	**Rankine 47**		32
21	Nat Lg	A	Macclesfield Town	1349	W 2 - 1	Rankine 21 (pen) 48 (pen)	21	33
Feb 4	Nat Lg	A	Wrexham	3730	L 1 - 3	Cassidy 12	22	34
11	Nat Lg	H	Eastleigh	697	D 1 - 1	Lawlor 90	22	35
14	Nat Lg	H	Sutton United	224	W 2 - 1	Cassidy 7 Rooney 90	20	36
18	Nat Lg	A	Dagenham & Redbridge	2055	W 2 - 1	Preston 11 52	19	37
25	Nat Lg	H	North Ferriby United	951	L 1 - 2	Hatfield 13	19	38
28	Nat Lg	H	Barrow	642	W 1 - 0	Hurst 13	18	39
Mar 4	Nat Lg	A	Torquay United	1446	W 2 - 1	Cassidy 64 Hatfield 72	17	40
11	Nat Lg	H	Aldershot Town	1009	W 1 - 0	Preston 54	17	41
18	Nat Lg	A	Boreham Wood	375	D 0 - 0		16	42
21	Nat Lg	A	Gateshead	833	D 1 - 1	Lawler 15	16	43
25	Nat Lg	H	Dover Athletic	1261	L 0 - 4		17	44
Apr 1	Nat Lg	A	Southport	981	W 1 - 0	Hurst 71	17	45
8	Nat Lg	H	Forest Green Rovers	760	L 0 - 1		17	46
14	Nat Lg	A	Braintree Town	624	L 0 - 2		17	47
17	Nat Lg	H	Tranmere Rovers	2148	L 1 - 2	Asamoah	19	48
22	Nat Lg	A	Bromley	936	D 1 - 1	Preston 50	20	49
29	Nat Lg	H	Solihull Moors	1519	D 1 - 1	Lowe 90	20	50

GOALSCORERS	SG	CSG	Pens	Hat tricks	Total		SG	CSG	Pens	Hat tricks	Total
2015-16 Boyes					*9*	Johnson	1				2
Cassidy	8	2			8	Asamoah	1				1
Rankine	6	3	2		8	Hylton	1				1
Hatfield	6				7	Lowe	1				1
Preston	6				7	Opponents	1				1
Boyes	3				3	Purver	1				1
Lawlor	3				3	Rooney	1				1
Walton	3		3		3	Smith	1				1
Atkinson	2				2	Webb-Foster	1				1
Hurst	2				2						

HARTLEPOOL UNITED

Club Contact Details
Victoria Park, Clarence Road, Hartlepool TS24 8BZT
01429 272 584
enquiries@hartlepoolunited.co.uk

Ground Capacity: 7,865   **Seats:** 4,359   **Covered:** Yes   **Clubhouse:** Yes   **Shop:** Yes

Record Attendance
17,264 v Manchester United, FA Cup Third Round Proper, 1957
Previous Grounds
None

10 YEAR RECORD

07-08		08-09		09-10		10-11		11-12		12-13		13-14		14-15		15-16		16-17	
FL 1	15	FL 1	19	FL 1	20	FL 1	16	FL 1	13	FL 1	23	FL 2	19	FL 2	22	FL 2	16	FL 2	23
FAC	2P	FAC	4P	FAC	1P	FAC	3P	FAC	1P	FAC	1P	FAC	2Pr	FAC	2P	FAC	3P	FAC	2P
FLC	2P	FLC	3P	FLC	2P	FLC	2P	FLC	1P	FLC	1P	FLC	1P	FLC	1P	FLC	2P	FLC	1P

Club Factfile

Founded: 1908   **Nickname:** Monkey Hangers   **Manager:** Craig Harrison

Previous Names: Hartlepools United 1908-68. Hartlepool 1968-77.

Previous Leagues: North Eastern 1908-21. Football League 1921-2017.

Club Colours (change): White & blue

RECORDS
Goalscorer: Joshie Fletcher - 111

Appearances: Ritchie Humphreys - 543 (Includes a run of 234 consecutive appearances)

HONOURS
FA Comps: None

League: None

County FA: None

BEST PERFORMANCES	**FA Cup:** Fourth Round Proper 1954-55(r), 77-78, 88-89(r), 92-93, 2004-05(r), 08-09.
	FA Trophy: N/A
	FA Vase: N/A

LEYTON ORIENT

Club Contact Details
Matchroom Stadium, Brisbane Road, Leyton, London E10 5NF
0871 310 1883
info@leytonorient.net

Ground Capacity: **Seats:** 9,271 **Covered:** Yes **Clubhouse:** Yes **Shop:** Yes

Record Attendance
37,615 v Tottenham Hotspur, Division Two, 16/03/1929
Previous Grounds
Whittles Athletic Ground 1896-1900. Millfields Road 1900-46 (name changed to Brisbane Road).

10 YEAR RECORD

07-08		08-09		09-10		10-11		11-12		12-13		13-14		14-15		15-16		16-17	
FL 1	14	FL 1	14	FL 1	17	FL 1	7	FL 1	20	FL 1	7	FL 1	3	FL 1	23	FL 2	8	FL 2	24
FAC	1Pr	FAC	3P	FAC	1Pr	FAC	5Pr	FAC	2P	FAC	3Pr	FAC	3P	FAC	1P	FAC	2Pr	FAC	1P
FLC	2P	FLC	1P	FLC	2P	FLC	2P	FLC	3P	FLC	2P	FLC	2P	FLC	3P	FLC	1P	FLC	1P

Club Factfile

Founded: 1881 **Nickname:** O's **Manager:** Steve Davis

Previous Names: Glyn Cricket Club 1881-86. Eagle C.C. 1886-88. Orient 1888-98. Clapton Orient 1898-46.

Previous Leagues: Clapton & District 1893-96. London 1896-05. Football League 1905-2017. London Combination 1915-19.

Club Colours (change): All red

RECORDS
Victory: 8-0 v Crystal Palace, D3S, 12/11/55. v Rochdale, D4, 14/10/87. v Colchester Utd, D4, 15/10/88. v Doncaster Rov, D3, 28/12/97.
Defeat: 0-8 v Aston Villa, FA Cup Fourth Round Proper, January 1929.
Goalscorer: Tommy Johnston - 121, 1956-58, 59-61, also holds the record for most in a season having scored 35 during 57-58.
Additional: Paid £200,000 to Oldham Athletic for Liam Kelly, July 2016.
Received £1,000,000 from Fulham for Gabriel Zakuani, July 2006 and from Brentford for Moses Odubajo, June 14.

HONOURS
FA Comps: None

League: Clapton & District 1895-96. League Division Three South 1955-56, Division Three 69-70.

County FA: Middlesex County Cup 1901-02.

BEST PERFORMANCES	**FA Cup:** Semi-finals 1977-78.
	FA Trophy: N/A
	FA Vase: N/A

MACCLESFIELD TOWN

Club Contact Details
Moss Rose Ground, London Road, Macclesfield SK11 7SP
01625 264 686
reception@mtfc.co.uk

Ground Capacity: 6,335 **Seats:** 2,599 **Covered:** Yes **Clubhouse:** Yes **Shop:** Yes

Record Attendance
9,008 v Winsford United - Cheshire Senior Cup 04.02.1948.
Previous Grounds
Rostron Field 1874-1891.

10 YEAR RECORD

	07-08		08-09		09-10		10-11		11-12		12-13		13-14		14-15		15-16		16-17	
FL 2	19	FL 2	20	FL 2	19	FL 2	15	FL 2	24	Conf	11	Conf	15	Conf	6	Nat	10	Nat	9
FAC	1P	FAC	3P	FAC	1P	FAC	2P	FAC	3Pr	FAC	4P	FAC	3Pr	FAC	4Qr	FAC	1P	FAC	2Pr
FLC	1P	FLC	2P	FLC	1P	FLC	1P	FLC	2P	FAT	1P	FAT	1P	FAT	1P	FAT	3Pr	FAT	F

Club Factfile

Founded: 1874   **Nickname:** The Silkmen   **Manager:** John Askey

Previous Names: Macclesfield Football & Athletic Club, Hallifield FC, Macclesfield FC - Current name since 1946.

Previous Leagues: Manchester. Cheshire County 1946-68. Northern Premier 1968-87. Conference 1987-97. Football League 1997-2012.

Club Colours (change): Blue & white

RECORDS
Victory:　15-0 v Chester St Marys - Cheshire Senior Cup Second Round 16.02.1886.
Defeat:　1-13 v Tranmere Rovers Reserves - 03.05.1929.
Goalscorer:　Albert Valentine scored the most goals in a season when he recorded 83 during 1933-34.
Appearances:　John Askey - 700+ (1984-2003).
Additional:　Paid: £40,000 for Danny Swailes from Bury, 2004-05.
　　　　　　　Received: £300,000 for Rickie Lambert from Stockport County, 2002-03.

HONOURS
FA Comps: FA Trophy 1969-70, 95-96.

League: Manchester 1908-09, 10-11. Cheshire County 1931-32, 32-33, 53-54, 60-61, 63-64, 67-68.
　　　　Northern Premier League 1968-69, 69-70, 86-87. Conference 1994-95, 96-97.

County FA: Cheshire Senior 1889-90, 90-91, 93-94, 95-96, 1910-11, 29-30, 34-35, 50-51, 51-52, 53-54, 59-60, 63-64, 68-69,
　　　　　　70-71, 72-73, 82-83, 90-91, 91-92, 97-98, 1999-00, 14-15. Staffordshire Senior Cup 1992-93, 95-96.

BEST PERFORMANCES
FA Cup: Fourth Round Proper 2012-13.
FA Trophy: Final 1969-70, 88-89, 95-96, 2016-17.
FA Vase: N/A

MACCLESFIELD TOWN MATCH RESULTS 2016-17

Date	Comp	H/A	Opponents	Att:	Result	Goalscorers	Pos	No.
Aug 6	Nat Lg	H	Torquay United	1501	W 2 - 0	Norburn 24 Holroyd 70	5	1
9	Nat Lg	A	York City	2468	L 0 - 1		9	2
13	Nat Lg	A	Braintree Town	703	W 3 - 1	Rowe 12 Holroyd 33 Sampson 73	6	3
16	Nat Lg	H	Southport	1329	W 3 - 1	Whitaker 5 Lewis 9 James 26	3	4
20	Nat Lg	A	Sutton United	1255	L 0 - 2		9	5
27	Nat Lg	H	Lincoln City	1615	L 1 - 2	James 43	12	6
29	Nat Lg	A	Solihull Moors	970	W 3 - 2	James 41 48 (pen) Norburn 90	8	7
3 Sept	Nat Lg	A	Woking	1221	W 3 - 1	Whitaker 28 Rowe 37 Holroyd 90	5	8
10	Nat Lg	H	Bromley	1011	W 1 - 0	Rowe 21	4	9
17	Nat Lg	A	Eastleigh	1287	L 0 - 1		9	10
24	Nat Lg	H	Guiseley	891	W 2 - 1	Holroyd 15 Norburn 26	9	11
27	Nat Lg	H	Wrexham	1579	W 3 - 0	Whitaker 35 50 Lewis 48	3	12
Oct 1	Nat Lg	H	North Ferriby United	1467	W 1 - 0	Whittaker 22 (pen)	2	13
4	Nat Lg	A	Barrow	1442	D 1 - 1	Byrne 82	4	14
8	Nat Lg	A	Boreham Wood	1386	L 0 - 2		5	15
15	FAC4Q	A	North Ferriby United	395	W 4 - 1	Whitaker 43 75 (pen) Holroyd 55 Mackreth 68		16
22	Nat Lg	A	Dagenham & Redbridge	1214	D 1 - 1	Holroyd 90	6	17
25	Nat Lg	H	Chester	1922	D 0 - 0		8	18
29	Nat Lg	A	Maidstone United	2114	L 1 - 2	Holroyd 8	10	19
Nov 5	FAC 1	A	Walsall	2334	W 1 - 0	McCombe 23		20
12	Nat Lg	H	Forest Green Rovers	1749	L 0 - 1		11	21
19	Nat Lg	A	Aldershot Town	1636	W 2 - 1	Holroyd 27 48	9	22
22	Nat Lg	A	Gateshead	491	D 1 - 1	Rowe 25	10	23
Dec 2	FAC 2	H	Oxford United	2566	D 0 - 0			24
6	Nat Lg	A	Wrexham	3204	W 3 - 0	Rowe 52 Hancox 65 Whitaker 90	7	25
13	FAC 2r	A	Oxford United	3642	L 0 - 3			26
17	Nat Lg	H	Bromley	1216	L 1 - 2	Lewis 85	8	27
20	FAT1	A	Altrincham	717	D 1 - 1	James 60		28
26	Nat Lg	A	Tranmere Rovers	7274	L 0 - 1		10	29
Jan 1	Nat Lg	H	Tranmere Rovers	3317	W 4 - 2	LEWIS 3 (12 50 83 pen) Rowe 71	8	30
4	FAT1r	H	Altrincham	548	W 2 - 1	Whittaker 49 Rowe 83		31
10	Nat Lg	H	Dover Athletic	1020	W 2 - 1	Holroyd 67 74	8	32
17	FAT2	A	AFC Sudbury United	505	W 3 - 1	Browne 23 Dudley 32 Sampson 84		33
21	Nat Lg	A	Guiseley	1349	L 1 - 2	Holroyd 30	10	34
28	Nat Lg	A	North Ferriby United	429	W 2 - 0	Pilkington 16 Whitehead 27	8	35
Feb 4	FAT3	H	Forest Green Rovers	967	W 1 - 0	Whitehead 11		36
11	Nat Lg	A	Torquay United	1400	D 1 - 1		9	37
15	Nat Lg	H	Barrow	1246	L 0 1		9	38
18	Nat Lg	H	Braintree Town	1267	W 2 - 0	Connor 71 Holroyd 73	9	39
21	Nat Lg	A	Eastleigh	2345	W 1 - 0	Browne 5	9	40
25	FATQF	A	Dulwich Hamlet	2834	D 2 - 2	Summerfield 8 18		41
Mar 4	Nat Lg	A	Forest Green Rovers	1569	L 0 - 3		9	42
7	FATQFr	H	Dulwich Hamlet	1017	W 2 - 0	Browne 19 27		43
11	FATSF1	H	Tranmere Rovers	2358	D 1 - 1	Norburn 58		44
14	Nat Lg	A	Gateshead	993	D 1 - 1	McCombe 82	9	45
18	FATSF2	H	Tranmere Rovers	6100	W 1 - 0	Norburn 68		46
21	Nat Lg	A	Chester	1802	W 3 - 2	Halis 23 Dudley 43 Norburn 85	9	47
25	Nat Lg	A	Aldershot Town	1586	L 0 - 2		9	48
28	Nat Lg	H	York City	1318	L 1 - 3	Whitaker 65 (pen)	9	49
Apr 1	Nat Lg	A	Boreham Wood	340	W 4 - 2	HANCOX 3 (26 44 45) Dudley 6	9	50
4	Nat Lg	A	Southport	792	W 2 - 1	Byrne 14 Dudley 16	9	51
8	Nat Lg	A	Dagenham & Redbridge	1281	L 1 - 4	Hancox 14	9	52
11	Nat Lg	H	Maidstone United	988	W 2 - 0	Browne 2 Whitaker 87 (pen)	9	53
14	Nat Lg	H	Woking	2068	L 0 - 1		9	54
17	Nat Lg	A	Solihull Moors	1166	L 1 - 4	Holroyd 47	9	55
22	Nat Lg	A	LIncoln City	10031	L 1 - 2	Hancox 23	9	56
25	Nat Lg	A	Dover Athletic	932	D 2 - 2	Norburn 31 Dudley 73	9	57
29	Nat Lg	H	Sutton United	1660	D 0 - 0		9	58
May 21	FAT Final	N	York City	38,224	L 2 - 3	Browne 13 Norburn 45		59

GOALSCORERS	SG	CSG	Pens	Hat tricks	Total		SG	CSG	Pens	Hat tricks	Total
2015-16 Dennis					30	Byrne	2				2
Holroyd	12	2			14	Sampson	2				2
Whitaker	10	2	4		11	McCombe	2				2
Norburn	8	2			8	Summerfield	1				2
Rowe	7	2			7	Whitehead	2	2			2
Browne	5				6	Connor	1				1
Hancox	4				6	Halis	1				1
James	6	2	1		6	Mackreth	1				1
Lewis	4	1	1	1	6	Pilkington	1				1
Dudley	5				5						

MAIDENHEAD UNITED

Club Contact Details
York Road, Maidenhead, Berkshire SL6 1SF
01628 636 314
kenneth.chandler@btinternet.com

Ground Capacity: 4,500   **Seats:** 550   **Covered:** 2,000   **Clubhouse:** Yes   **Shop:** Yes

Record Attendance
7,989 v Southall - FA Amateur Cup Quarter final 07/03/1936
Previous Grounds
Kidwells Park (Norfolkians)

10 YEAR RECORD

07-08		08-09		09-10		10-11		11-12		12-13		13-14		14-15		15-16		16-17	
Conf S	17	Conf S	6	Conf S	16	Conf S	19	Conf S	20	Conf S	19	Conf S	18	Conf S	18	Nat S	7	Nat S	1
FAC	1P	FAC	2Q	FAC	2Q	FAC	4Q	FAC	1Pr	FAC	3Q	FAC	2Q	FAC	3Qr	FAC	1Pr	FAC	2Q
FAT	1P	FAT	3Q	FAT	2P	FAT	3Q	FAT	1Pr	FAT	1P	FAT	3P	FAT	2Pr	FAT	2P	FAT	3Q

Club Factfile

Founded: 1870   **Nickname:** Magpies   **Manager:** Alan Devonshire - May 2015

Previous Names: After WWI Maidenhead F.C and Maidenhead Norfolkians merged to form Maidenhead Town >1920.

Previous Leagues: Southern (FM) 1894-1902, 2006-07, West Berkshire 1902-04, Gr. West Suburban 1904-22, Spartan 1922-39, Gr. West Comb. 1939-45, Corinthian 1945-63, Athenian 1963-73, Isthmian 1973-2004, Conference 2004-06.

Club Colours (change): Black & white stripes/black/white (Yellow/blue/yellow)

RECORDS
Victory: 14-1 v Buckingham Town - FA Amateur Cup 06/09/1952
Defeat: 0-14 v Chesham United (A) - Spartan League 31/03/1923
Goalscorer: George Copas - 270 (1924-35). Most goals in a season: Jack Palethorpe - 65 in 39 apps (1929-30).
Appearances: Bert Randall - 532 (1950-64)
Additional: Received £5,000 from Norwich City for Alan Cordice 1979

HONOURS
FA Comps: None

League: West Berkshire 1902-03. Spartan 1926-27, 31-32, 33-34. Corinthian 1957-58, 60-61, 61-62.
National South 2016-17.

County FA: Berks & Bucks Senior Cup 1894-95, 95-96, 1911-12, 27-28, 29-30, 30-31, 31-32, 38-39, 45-46, 55-56, 56-57, 60-61, 62-63, 65-66, 69-70, 97-98, 98-99, 2001-02, 02-03, 09-10, 14-15, 16-17. Wycombe Senior Cup 1999-2000.

BEST PERFORMANCES	**FA Cup:** As United - First Round Proper 1960-61, 62-63, 63-64, 71-72, 2006-07, 07-08, 11-12 (r), 15-16 (r).
	FA Trophy: Quarter-finals 2003-04.
	FA Vase: Second Round Proper 1989-90.

MAIDENHEAD UNITED MATCH RESULTS 2016-17

Date	Comp	H/A	Opponents	Att:	Result	Goalscorers	Pos	No.
Aug 6	Nat S	H	Gosport Borough	454	W 3 - 0	Pritchard 31 Marks 67 Tarpey 80	3	1
8	Nat S	A	Poole Town	502	L 0 - 1		7	2
13	Nat S	A	Whitehawk	293	W 2 - 1	Tarpey 29 54	4	3
16	Nat S	A	Hemel Hempstead Town	483	W 5 - 0	TARPEY 4 (37 39 68 74) Smith 84	3	4
20	Nat S	A	Chelmsford City	626	W 1 - 0	Tarpey 51	1	5
27	Nat S	H	Concord Rangers	241	W 1 - 0	Pritchard 63	1	6
29	Nat S	H	Truro City	751	W 2 0	Tarpey 27 52	1	7
Sept 3	Nat S	A	Dartford	1083	D 0 - 0		1	8
6	Nat S	A	Eastbourne Borough	542	W 2 - 1	Tarpey 22 57 (pen)	1	9
10	Nat S	H	St Albans City	719	D 1 - 1	Pritchard 62	1	10
13	Nat S	A	Oxford City	346	W 3 - 1	Mulley 19 Marks 44 Tarpey 90	1	11
17	FAC2Q	A	Staines Town	414	L 0 - 1			12
24	Nat S	A	Weston-s-Mare	632	W 3 - 0	Tarpey 38 69 Forbes 57	1	13
Oct 8	Nat S	H	Welling United	600	W 2 - 1	Marks 71 Tarpey 83	1	14
15	Nat S	A	Bishop Stortford	866	W 6 - 0	Marks 16 54 Mulley 40 TARPEY 3 (51 pen 82 87)	1	15
22	Nat S	A	Hampton & Richmond B	1146	W 3 - 2	Pritchard 8 Inman 16 Upward 60	1	16
29	Nat S	H	Hungerford Town	1004	D 2 - 2	Marks 59 Tarpey 70 (pen)	1	17
Nov 5	Nat S	A	East Thurrock United	298	D 0 - 0		1	18
12	Nat S	H	Bath City	1031	W 2 - 1	Pritchard 27 Tarpey 81	1	19
19	Nat S	A	Ebbsfleet United	1318	W 3 - 2	MARKS 3 (6 27 88)	1	20
26	FAT3Q	H	Wealdstone	555	D 2 - 2	Barrett 36 Pritchard 81		21
29	FAT3Q	A	Wealdstone	254	L 1 - 2	Tarpey 82		22
Dec 3	Nat S	H	Margate	821	W 2 - 0	Marks 29 Tarpey 38	1	23
17	Nat S	H	Dartford	945	W 5 - 0	TARPEY 4 (22 30 45 88 pen) Cox 59	1	24
26	Nat S	A	Wealdstone	1100	L 1 - 2	Tarpey 68 (pen)	1	25
Jan 1	Nat S	H	Wealdstone	1282	W 2 - 0	Tarpey 49 Marks 71	1	26
7	Nat S	A	St Albans City	1111	D 2 - 2	Barrett 18 50	1	27
28	Nat S	A	Gosport Borough	327	W 2 - 0	Tarpey 20 45	1	28
Feb 4	Nat S	H	Poole Town	1020	D 1 - 1	Smith 90	1	29
11	Nat S	A	Hemel Hempstead Town	545	L 1 - 2	Tarpey 89	2	30
18	Nat S	H	Whitehawk	969	W 2 - 1	Tarpey 33 Inman 87	2	31
21	Nat S	H	Eastbourne Borough	803	W 2 - 1	Cox 79 Wiltshire 88	2	32
25	Nat S	A	Hungerford Town	724	D 1 - 1	Pritchard 3	2	33
Mar 4	Nat S	H	Hampton & Richmond B	946	D 0 - 0		2	34
6	Nat S	A	Chelmsford City	847	W 1 - 0	Tarpey 45 (pen)	2	35
11	Nat S	A	Weston-s-Mare	452	W 3 - 1	Tarpey 42 73 Marks 68	1	36
18	Nat S	H	Welling United	956	W 3 - 0	Inman 24 Tarpey 28 Mulley 45	1	37
21	Nat S	H	Oxford City	1017	W 6 - 1	Parkinson 6 Tarpey 33 36 Pritchard 57 Cox 76 89 (pen)	1	38
25	Nat S	A	Bishops Stortford	431	W 2 - 0	Parkinson 11 Pritchard 59	1	39
Apr 1	Nat S	A	Bath City	708	W 5 - 1	TARPEY 3 (10 pen 39 51 pen) Marks 41 Cox 87	1	40
8	Nat S	H	East Thurrock United	1134	W 2 - 1	Tarpey 36 Parkinson 67	1	41
14	Nat S	H	Concord Rangers	1404	W 2 - 0	Marks 10 Tarpey 43 (pen)	1	42
17	Nat S	A	Truro City	721	W 3 - 0	Marks 4 24 Cox 72	1	43
22	Nat S	H	Ebbsfleet United	3377	L 1 - 2	Inman 21	1	44
29	Nat S	A	Margate	1186	W 3 - 0	Pritchard 14 59 Parkinson 52	1	45

GOALSCORERS	SG	CSG	Pens	Hat tricks	Total		SG	CSG	Pens	Hat tricks	Total
2015-16 Tarpey					21	Forbes	1				1
Tarpey	27	5,3,3,4	9	4	44	Upward	1				1
Marks	12			1	16	Wiltshire	1				1
Pritchard	10				11						
Cox	5		1		6						
Inman	4				4						
Parkinson	4				4						
Barrett	3				3						
Mulley	3				3						
Smith	2				2						

MAIDSTONE UNITED

Club Contact Details
The Gallagher Stadium, James Whatman Way, Maidstone, Kent ME14 1LQ
01622 753 817
info@maidstoneunited.co.uk

Ground Capacity: 3,030   **Seats:** 792   **Covered:** 1,850   **Clubhouse:** Yes   **Shop:** Yes

Record Attendance
3,030 v Sutton United, National League South, 05/04/2016.
Previous Grounds
London Rd 1993-2001, Central Pk 2001-02 & Bourne Pk 2002-09 (S'bourne), 11-12, The Homelands (Ashford) 2009-11.

10 YEAR RECORD

07-08	08-09	09-10	10-11	11-12	12-13	13-14	14-15	15-16	16-17
Isth P 17	Isth P 15	Isth P 18	Isth P 20	Isth1S 6	Isth1S 2	Isth P 7	Isth P 1	Nat S 3	Nat 14
FAC 2Q	FAC 4Q	FAC 3Q	FAC 1Q	FAC 2Q	FAC 3Q	FAC 3Q	FAC 2P	FAC 1P	FAC 1Pr
FAT 3Q	FAT 2Q	FAT 2P	FAT 3Q	FAT P	FAT 2P	FAT 3Q	FAT 2Q	FAT 1P	FAT 1P

Club Factfile

Founded: 1992   **Nickname:** The Stones   **Manager:** Jay Saunders

Previous Names: Maidstone Invicta > 1997

Previous Leagues: Kent County 1993-2001, Kent 2001-06. Isthmian 2006-15.

Club Colours (change): Amber/black/black & amber (All white)

RECORDS
Victory:	12-1 v Aylesford - Kent League 1993-94
Defeat:	2-8 v Scott Sports - 1995-96
Goalscorer:	Richard Sinden - 98
Appearances:	Tom Mills
Additional:	Paid £2,000 for Steve Jones - 2000

HONOURS
FA Comps: None

League: Kent County Division Four 1993-94, Div. Two 1994-95, Div. One 1998-99, Premier 2001-02. Kent 2000-02, 05-06. Isthmian Division One South 2006-07, Premier 2014-15. National League South Play-offs 2015-16.

County FA: Kent Junior Cup 1994-95, Weald of Kent Charity Cup 1999-00, 00-01, Kent Senior Trophy 2002-03.

BEST PERFORMANCES
FA Cup: Second Round Proper 2014-15.
FA Trophy: Second Round Proper 2009-10, 12-13.
FA Vase: Third Round Proper 2005-06 (r)

MAIDSTONE UNITED MATCH RESULTS 2016-17

Date	Comp	H/A	Opponents	Att:	Result	Goalscorers	Pos	No.
Aug 6	Nat Lg	H	York City	2495	D 1 - 1	Taylor 22	10	1
9	Nat Lg	A	Aldershot Town	2355	L 0 - 1		17	2
13	Nat Lg	A	Chester	1912	W 3 - 1	Acheampong 20 Greenhalgh 57 Flisher 64	10	3
16	Nat Lg	H	Braintree Town	2242	W 2 - 1	Taylor 4 30	7	4
20	Nat Lg	A	Tranmere Rovers	4797	L 1 - 2	Flisher 61	12	5
27	Nat Lg	H	Forest Green Rovers	2274	L 1 - 4	Evans 12	17	6
29	Nat Lg	A	Boreham Wood	637	W 1 - 0	Lokko 90	14	7
3 Sept	Nat Lg	H	Wrexham	2550	D 2 - 2	Greenhal;gh 21 Enver-Marum 77	16	8
10	Nat Lg	A	North Ferriby United	479	W 2 - 0	Enver-Marum 11 Flisher 47	12	9
13	Nat Lg	H	Bromley	2358	L 0 - 2		13	10
17	Nat Lg	H	Guiseley	2106	D 1 - 1	Flisher 14	13	11
24	Nat Lg	A	Torquay United	2026	W 3 - 2	Odubade 16 48 Enver-Marunm 19	11	12
Oct 1	Nat Lg	H	Solihull Noors	2119	L 2 - 4	Enver-Marum 20 Sweeney 40	15	13
4	Nat Lg	A	Eastleigh	4114	L 0 - 3		16	14
8	Nat Lg	H	Barrow	1402	L 0 - 3		17	15
15	FAC4Q	H	Billericay Town	1426	W 3 - 1	Flisher 39 54 Murphy 56		16
22	Nat Lg	H	Gateshead	2206	L 0 - 2		18	17
25	Nat Lg	A	Sutton United	1609	D 2 - 2	Taylor 25 (pen) Loza 45	16	18
29	Nat Lg	H	Macclesfield Town	2114	W 2 - 1	Enver-Marum 16 Odubade 89	16	19
Nov 5	FAC 1	H	Rochdale	2237	D 1 - 1	Taylor 21 (pen)		20
12	Nat Lg	A	Southport	932	L 2 - 3	Odubade 59 Taylor 90	17	21
15	FAC1r	A	Rochdale	1350	L 0 - 2			22
19	Nat Lg	H	Woking	2147	L 0 - 3		17	23
22	Nat Lg	H	Dagenham & Redbridge	1970	L 0 - 1		17	24
26	Nat Lg	A	Lincoln City	3917	L 0 - 2		18	25
29	Nat Lg	H	Eastleigh	1714	W 2 - 1	Sweeney 5 Taylor 59 (pen)	18	26
Dec 3	Nat Lg	A	Bromley	1676	L 0 - 2		18	27
10	FAT1	A	Boreham Wood	201	D 0 - 0			28
13	FAT1r	H	Boreham Wood	538	L 2 - 3	Greenhalgh 20 Loza 90		29
17	Nat Lg	H	North Feriby United	2006	L 1 - 2	Paxman 60	18	30
26	Nat Lg	A	Dover Athletic	2369	D 1 - 1	Loza 60	19	31
Jan 1	Nat Lg	H	Dover Athletic	2257	L 1 - 4	Kargiannis 61	20	32
7	Nat Lg	A	Guiseley	1040	L 1 - 2	Taylor 64	20	33
21	Nat Lg	A	Torquay United	2455	W 2 - 1	Sam -Yorke 53 Paxman 59	20	34
28	Nat Lg	A	Solihull Moors	1003	L 0 - 2		21	35
Feb 4	Nat Lg	H	Aldershot Town	2293	L 0 - 2		21	36
11	Nat Lg	A	York City	2816	D 1 - 1	Prestedge 47	20	37
18	Nat Lg	H	Chester	2120	W 4 - 2	Locko 2 44 Sam-Yorke 5 Pigott 13	21	38
25	Nat Lg	A	Braintree Town	1002	D 0 - 0		21	39
28	Nat Lg	H	Dagenham & Redbridge	1456	W 2 - 0	Pigott 6 Sam-Yorke 85	20	40
Mar 4	Nat Lg	H	Southport	2404	W 4 - 2	Loza 38 45 (pen) Pigott 60 Lokko 70	19	41
21	Nat Lg	H	Sutton United	2929	D 1 - 1	Loza 68 (pen)	20	42
25	Nat Lg	A	Woking	2088	W 4 - 2	LOZA 3 (29 68 76) Odubade 83		43
Apr 1	Nat Lg	H	Barrow	2803	W 2 - 1	Pigott 45 Lewis 62	18	44
8	Nat Lg	A	Gateshead	967	W 2 - 1	Hogan 73 (og) Taylor 76	16	45
11	Nat Lg	A	Macclesfield Town	988	L 0 2		16	46
14	Nat Lg	A	Wrexham	3379	W 3 - 1	Pigott 31 Loza 52 Flisher 82	15	47
17	Nat Lg	H	Boreham Wood	2880	W 1 - 0	Odubade 90	13	48
22	Nat Lg	A	Forest Green Rovers	2030	D 2 - 2	Phipps 61 Pigott 81	13	49
25	Nat Lg	H	Lincoln City	3014	D 0 - 0		13	50
29	Nat Lg	H	Tranmere Rovers	3409	L 0 1		14	51

GOALSCORERS	SG	CSG	Pens	Hat tricks	Total		SG	CSG	Pens	Hat tricks	Total
2015-16 May					13	Sweeney	2				2
Loza	7	2			10	Acheampong	1				1
Taylor	8		3		9	Evans	1				1
Flisher	5				6	Kiagiannis	1				1
Odubade	6				6	Lewis	1				1
Pigott	6	2			6	Loza	1				1
Enver-Marum	5	2			5	Murphy	1				1
Locko	3				4	Opponents	1				1
Greenhalgh	3				3	Phipps	1				1
Sam-Yorke	3				3	Prestedge	1				1
Paxman	2				2						

SOLIHULL MOORS

Club Contact Details
The Automated Technology Group Stadium, Damson Park, Damson Parkway, Solihull B91 2PP
0121 705 6770
info@solihullmoorsfc.co.uk

Ground Capacity: 3,050   **Seats:** 770   **Covered:** 1,000   **Clubhouse:** Yes   **Shop:** Yes

Record Attendance
1,995 v Tranmere Rovers, National League, 22/10/2016
Previous Grounds
None

10 YEAR RECORD

07-08	08-09	09-10	10-11	11-12	12-13	13-14	14-15	15-16	16-17
Conf N 17	Conf N 16	Conf N 17	Conf N 7	Conf N 19	Conf N 9	Conf N 8	Conf N 12	Nat N 1	Nat 16
FAC 4Q	FAC 2Q	FAC 3Q	FAC 3Q	FAC 4Q	FAC 3Q	FAC 4Q	FAC 2Q	FAC 3Q	FAC 2P
FAT 3Q	FAT 3Q	FAT 3Q	FAT 3Q	FAT 1P	FAT 2P	FAT 3Q	FAT 1P	FAT 1P	FAT 1P

Club Factfile

Founded: 2007   **Nickname:** Moors   **Manager:** Liam McDonald

Previous Names: Today's club was formed after the amalgamation of Solihull Borough and Moor Green in 2007.

Previous Leagues: None

Club Colours (change): Blue with yellow trim (Red & grey stripes/grey/grey all with yellow trim)

RECORDS
Victory: 7-2 v Corby Town, Conference North, 12/02/2011.
Defeat: 0-6 v Harrogate Town, Conference North, 23/01/2016.
Appearances: Carl Motteram - 71 (2007-08)

HONOURS
FA Comps: None

League: National North 2015-16.

County FA: Birmingham Senior Cup 2015-16.

BEST PERFORMANCES	**FA Cup:** Second Round 2016-17.
	FA Trophy: Second Round 2012-13.
	FA Vase: N/A

SOLIHULL MOORS MATCH RESULTS 2016-17

Date	Comp	H/A	Opponents	Att:	Result	Goalscorers	Pos	No.
Aug 6	Nat Lg	A	Sutton United	1305	W 3 - 1	Beswick 38 Sterling-James 53 Brown 76	4	1
9	Nat Lg	H	Woking	699	D 2 - 2	White 72 Fagbola79	5	2
13	Nat Lg	H	Bromley	756	W 1 - 0	Daly 4	3	3
16	Nat Lg	A	Wrexham	4017	L 0 - 1		8	4
20	Nat Lg	H	Guiseley	554	W 3 - 2	Brown 14 80 White 84	5	5
27	Nat Lg	A	Eastleigh	1632	L 0 - 2		9	6
29	Nat Lg	H	Macclesfield Town	970	L 2 - 3	Murombedzi 21 Asante 45 (pen)	13	7
3 Sept	Nat Lg	A	York City	2105	L 0 - 4		17	8
10	Nat Lg	H	Dagenham & Redbridge	716	L 2 - 5	Brown 78 Osborne 81	17	9
13	Nat Lg	A	LIncoln City	4029	D 0 - 0		19	10
17	Nat Lg	A	Gateshead	541	D 0 - 0		18	11
24	Nat Lg	H	Boreham Wood	618	D 1 - 1	Osborne 48	17	12
Oct 1	Nat Lg	A	Maidstone United	2119	W 4 - 2	Sterling-James 26 ASANTE 3 (34 (pen) 38 64)	16	13
4	Nat Lg	H	Southport	772	W 4 - 0	ASANTE 3 (50 73 82) Sterling-James 70	13	14
8	Nat Lg	A	Aldershot Town	1712	L 0 - 2		14	15
15	FAC4Q	H	Kettering Town	768	W 3 - 1	Beswick 18 Brown 24 65		16
22	Nat Lg	H	Tranmere Rovers	1995	L 0 - 3		15	17
25	Nat Lg	H	Forest Green Rovers	919	D 0 - 0		15	18
29	Nat Lg	A	Braintree Town	625	W 1 - 0	White 86 (pen)	15	19
Nov 5	FAC 1	A	Yeovil Town	2118	D 2 - 2	Byrne 57 63		20
12	Nat Lg	H	Dover Aththletic	837	L 2 - 3	Brown 43 Asante 90	16	21
15	FAC1r	H	Yeovil Town	1460	W 1 - 1	Asante 90 (pen) Won 4-2 on penalties		22
19	Nat Lg	A	Barrow	1184	L 1 - 2	Asante 52	16	23
22	Nat Lg	A	Torquay United	1272	L 0 - 3		16	24
26	Nat Lg	H	North Ferriby United	526	W 2 - 0	Asante 31 76	16	25
29	Nat Lg	A	Southport	703	D 0 - 0		16	26
Dec 3	FAC2	A	Luton Town	3512	L 2 - 6	Osborne 5 35		27
10	FAT1	H	Matlock Town	336	L 1 - 2	White 90		28
17	Nat Lg	A	Dagenham & Redbridge	1112	D 4 - 4	White 3 Sterling-James 19 49 Byrne 25	16	29
26	Nat Lg	H	Chester	1475	W 3 - 2	Sterling-James 45 68 White 56	16	30
Jan 1	Nat Lg	A	Chester	2244	W 3 - 0	Osborne 17 Daly 55 White 77 (pen)	15	31
7	Nat Lg	H/A	Gateshead	750	L 0 - 2		16	32
21	Nat Lg	A	Boreham Wood	322	D 0 - 0		16	33
28	Nat Lg	H	Maidstone United	1003	W 2 - 0	Kettle 7 Carline 31	15	34
31	Nat Lg	H	LIncoln City	1650	L 0 - 1		15	35
Feb 11	Nat Lg	H	Sutton United	671	W 3 - 0	Charles-Cook 2 45 Afolayan 70	15	36
14	Nat Lg	A	Woking	1000	L 1 - 2	Charles-Cook 59	15	37
18	Nat Lg	A	Bromley	1109	W 1 - 0	White 9	14	38
25	Nat Lg	H	Wrexham	1349	L 0 - 1		14	39
Mar 4	Nat Lg	A	Dover Athletic	1104	D 0 - 0		14	40
11	Nat Lg	H	Braintree Town	556	D 3 - 3	Maye 26 Afolayan 78 Carline 85	14	41
18	Nat Lg	A	North Ferriby United	363	W 4 - 1	Maye 40 Sterling-James 63 Carline 76 Nortey 90	15	42
21	Nat Lg	A	Forest Green Rovers	1445	L 1 - 2	Afolayan 59	14	43
25	Nat Lg	H	Barrow	1820	L 2 - 4	Green 66 Afolayan 73	14	44
28	Nat Lg	H	Torquay United	857	L 0 - 1		16	45
Apr 1	Nat Lg	H	Aldershot Town	1248	L 0 - 2		17	46
8	Nat Lg	A	Tranmere Rovers	5001	L 0 - 9		18	47
14	Nat Lg	A	York City	1570	L 1 - 2	White 45	20	48
17	Nat Lg	H	Macclesfield Town	1166	W 3 - 1	Carline 78 Byrne 85 Charles-Cook 90	18	49
22	Nat Lg	H	Eastleigh	893	W 2 - 0	Charles-Cook 11 Maye 22	16	50
29	Nat Lg	A	Guiseley	1519	D 1 - 1	Sterling-James 26	16	51

GOALSCORERS	SG	CSG	Pens	Hat tricks	Total		SG	CSG	Pens	Hat tricks	Total
2015-16 Asante					20	Maye	3				3
Asante	7	3	3	2	12	Beswick	2				2
Sterling-James	6	2			9	Daly	2				2
White	9	4	2		9	Fagbola	1				1
Brown	5				7	Green	1				1
Charles-Cook	4	2			5	Kettle	1				1
Osborne	6				5	Murombedzi	1				1
Afolayan	4				4	Nortey	1				1
Byrne	3				4						
Carline	4				4						

SUTTON UNITED

Club Contact Details
Borough Sports Ground, Gander Green Lane, Sutton, Surrey SM1 2EY
0208 644 4440
info@suttonunited.net

Ground Capacity: 7,032   Seats: 765   Covered: 1,250   Clubhouse: Yes   Shop: Yes

Record Attendance
14,000 v Leeds United - FA Cup 4th Round 24/01/1970
Previous Grounds
Western Road, Manor Lane, London Road, The Find

10 YEAR RECORD

07-08		08-09		09-10		10-11		11-12		12-13		13-14		14-15		15-16		16-17	
Conf S	22	Isth P	5	Isth P	2	Isth P	1	Conf S	4	Conf S	6	Conf S	2	Conf S	15	Nat S	1	Nat	12
FAC	3Q	FAC	1P	FAC	1P	FAC	1Q	FAC	2P	FAC	2Q	FAC	1P	FAC	3Q	FAC	4Q	FAC	5P
FAT	1P	FAT	3Qr	FAT	1Q	FAT	1Pr	FAT	3Q	FAT	3P	FAT	3Q	FAT	1P	FAT	3Pr	FAT	3Pr

Club Factfile

Founded: 1898   **Nickname:** The U's   **Manager:** Paul Doswell - 2008

Previous Names: Club formed after the merger of Sutton Guild Rovers and Sutton Association (formerley Sutton St Barnabas FC).

Previous Leagues: Sutton Junior, Southern Suburban, Athenian 1921-63, Isthmian 1963-86, 91-99, 2000-04, 2008-11, Conference 1999-2000, 04-08

Club Colours (change): All amber (All white with gold trim)

RECORDS
Victory: 11-1 v Clapton - 1966 and v Leatherhead - 1982-83 both Isthmian League
Defeat: 0-13 v Barking - Athenian League 1925-26
Goalscorer: Paul McKinnon - 279
Appearances: Larry Pritchard - 781 (1965-84)
Additional: Received £100,000 from AFC Bournemouth for Efan Ekoku 1990

HONOURS

FA Comps: None

League: Athenian League 1927-28, 45-46, 57-58. Isthmian League 1966-67, 84-85, 85-86, 98-99, 2010-11. National League South 2015-16.

County FA: London Senior Cup 1957-58, 82-83. Surrey Senior Cup 1945-46, 64-65, 67-68, 69-70, 79-80, 82-83, 83-84, 84-85, 85-86, 86-87, 87-88, 92-93, 94-95, 98-99, 2002-03.

BEST PERFORMANCES	**FA Cup:** Fifth Round Proper 2016-17.
	FA Trophy: Final 1980-81.
	FA Vase: N/A

SUTTON UNITED MATCH RESULTS 2016-17

Date	Comp	H/A	Opponents	Att:	Result	Goalscorers	Pos	No.
Aug 6	Nat Lg	H	Solihull Moors	1305	L 1 - 3	Beckwith 43	19	1
9	Nat Lg	A	Forest Green Rovers	1369	D 1 - 1	Bailey 55 (pen)	19	2
13	Nat Lg	A	Lincoln City	3195	W 3 - 1	Wishart 23 Collins 83 Deacon 90	11	3
16	Nat Lg	H	Torquay United	1625	W 2 - 0	Biamou 4 Bailey 55 (pen)	6	4
20	Nat Lg	H	Macclesfield Town	1255	W 2 - 1	Stearn 25 Gomis 37	3	5
27	Nat Lg	A	Chester	1625	L 0 - 4		6	6
29	Nat Lg	H	Dagenham & Redbridge	1951	W 1 - 0	Hudson-Odie 11	6	7
3 Sept	Nat Lg	A	Gateshead	890	L 0 - 1		11	8
10	Nat Lg	A	Wrexham	3890	L 0 - 1		15	9
13	Nat Lg	H	Braintree Town	922	L 1 - 2	Bailey 35 (pen)	14	10
17	Nat Lg	H	Tranmere Rovers	1680	W 1 - 0	Fitchett 47	12	11
24	Nat Lg	A	Eastleigh	2853	L 1 - 2	Stearn 81	13	12
Oct 1	Nat Lg	H	Guiseley	744	W 1 - 0	Brown 35 (og)	10	13
4	Nat Lg	A	Dover Athletic	825	L 1 - 4	Amankwaah 74	14	14
8	Nat Lg	H	Woking	1714	W 4 - 1	Deacon 22 Stearn 42 Bailey 47 McAllister 52	13	15
15	FAC4Q	H	Forest Green Rovers	751	W 2 - 1	Stearn 35 Deacon 90		16
22	Nat Lg	A	Southport	864	D 1 - 1	Collins 57 (pen)	13	17
25	Nat Lg	H	Maidstone United	1609	D 2 - 2	Fitchett 17 Bailey 23	13	18
29	Nat Lg	A	York City	2037	D 2 - 2	Collins 16 (pen) 88 (pen)	13	19
Nov 5	FAC 1	A	Dartford	1689	W 6 - 3	Biamou 1 22 Deacon 14 70 Stearn 57 90		20
12	Nat Lg	H	Barrow	1588	D 0 - 0		13	21
19	Nat Lg	A	North Ferriby United	372	L 1 - 2	Biamou 75	13	22
22	Nat Lg	A	Boreham Wood	371	L 0 - 1		13	23
26	Nat Lg	H	Aldershot Town	1847	W 2 - 2	Collins 58 80	13	24
29	Nat Lg	H	Dover Athletic	1091	L 0 - 6		14	25
Dec 3	FAC 2	H	Cheltenham Town	2224	W 2 - 1	Tubbs 46 Deacon 90		26
10	FAT1	H	Bath City	524	W 1 - 0	Jefford 38		27
17	Nat Lg	H	Wrexham	1613	W 1 - 0	Riley (og) 4	14	28
26	Nat Lg	A	Bromley	2036	L 0 - 1		14	29
Jan 1	Nat Lg	H	Bromley	1766	W 2 - 0	Biamou 45 Hudson-Odi 61	14	30
7	FAC3	H	AFC Wimbledon	5013	D 0 - 0			31
10	Nat Lg	A	Braintree Town	568	L 0 - 1		14	32
14	FAT2	A	Worthing	1398	D 2 - 2	Deacon 52 May 78		33
17	FAC3r	H	AFC Wimbledon	4768	W 3 - 1	Deacon 75 Biamou 90 Fitchett 90		34
21	Nat Lg	H	Eastleigh	2179	D 1 - 1	Tubbs 73	15	35
24	FAT2r	A	Worthing	496	W 3 - 2	McAllister 32 Beckwith 55 May 101 (aet)		36
29	FAC4	H	Leeds United	4997	W 1 - 0	Collins 53 (pen)	16	37
Feb 4	FAT3	H	Boreham Wood	879	D 0 - 0			38
7	FAT3r	A	Boreham Wood	269	L 0 - 5			39
11	Nat Lg	A	Solihull Moors	671	L 0 - 3		15	40
14	Nat Lg	A	Guiseley	664	L 1 - 2	Tubbs 36 (pen)	16	41
20	FAC5	H	Arsenal	5013	L 0 - 2			42
25	Nat Lg	A	Torquay United	1646	W 3 - 2	Deacon 30 Biamou 47 Beckwith 79	16	43
28	Nat Lg	H	Boreham Wood	1441	W 1 - 0	Biamou 30	16	44
Mar 4	Nat Lg	A	Barrow	1145	D 0 - 0		16	45
11	Nat Lg	H	York City	2171	D 2 - 2	Bailey 74 Newton 87 (og)	16	46
14	Nat Lg	H	Forest Green Rovers	1446	L 1 - 2	Cadogan 90	16	47
18	Nat Lg	A	Aldershot Town	2197	L 0 - 2		18	48
21	Nat Lg	A	Maidstone United	2929	D 1 - 1	Coyle 51 (og)	17	49
25	Nat Lg	H	North Ferriby United	1664	W 5 - 1	Deacon 13 Collins 23 Biamou 34 Cadogan 63 83	16	50
28	Nat Lg	H	Lincoln City	2246	D 1 - 1	Deacon 90	14	51
Apr 1	Nat Lg	A	Woking	1437	L 1 - 2	Cadogan 62	14	52
4	Nat Lg	A	Tranmere Rovers	4684	L 2 - 3	Jebb 77 Gueye 80	14	53
8	Nat Lg	H	Southport	1807	D 2 - 2	Cadogan 25 Deacon 90	15	54
14	Nat Lg	H	Gateshead	1889	W 3 - 0	Deacon 42 (Pen) Biamou 60 83	13	55
17	Nat Lg	A	Dagenham & Redbridge	1634	D 2 - 2	Biamou 51 53	15	56
22	Nat Lg	H	Chester	2082	W 5 - 2	Coombes 5 46 May 8 Collins 43 Bailey 71	11	57
29	Nat Lg	A	Macclesfield Town	1660	D 0 - 0		12	58

GOALSCORERS	SG	CSG	Pens	Hat tricks	Total		SG	CSG	Pens	Hat tricks	Total
2015-16 Fitchett					22	Tubbs	3				3
Biamou	10	2			13	Coombes	1				2
Deacon	12	2			13	Hudson-Odie	2				2
Collins	7		3		9	McAllister	2				2
Bailey	6		3		7	Amankwaah	1				1
Stearn	6	2			6	Gornis	1				1
Cadogan	5				5	Gueye	1				1
Opponents	4				4	Jebb	1				1
Beckwith	3				3	Jefford	1				1
Fitchett	3				3	Wishart	1				1
May	3				3						

TORQUAY UNITED

Club Contact Details
Plainmoor, Torquay, Devon TQ1 3PS
01803 328 666
reception@torquayunited.com

Ground Capacity: 6,500   **Seats:** 2,950   **Covered:** Yes   **Clubhouse:** Yes   **Shop:** Yes

Record Attendance
21,908 v Huddersfield Town, FA Cup 4th Rnd, 29/01/1955.
Previous Grounds
Recreation Ground. Cricketfield Road > 1910.

10 YEAR RECORD

07-08		08-09		09-10		10-11		11-12		12-13		13-14		14-15		15-16		16-17	
Conf	3	Conf	4	FL 2	17	FL 2	7	FL 2	5	FL 2	19	FL 2	24	Conf	13	Nat	18	Nat	17
FAC	2P	FAC	4P	FAC	3P	FAC	4P	FAC	2P	FAC	1P	FAC	1P	FAC	4Q	FAC	4Q	FAC	4Qr
FAT	F	FAT	3P	FLC	1P	FLC	1P	FLC	1P	FLC	1P	FLC	1P	FAT	SF	FAT	QF	FAT	1P

Club Factfile

Founded: 1899   **Nickname:** The Gulls   **Manager:** Kevin Nicholson - 28.09.15

Previous Names: Torquay United & Ellacombe merged to form Torquay Town 1910, then merged with Babbacombe to form Torquay Utd in 1921

Previous Leagues: Western 1921-27. Football League 1927-2007, 09-14. Conference 2007-09.

Club Colours (change): Yellow/blue/white

RECORDS
Victory: 9-0 v Swindon Town, Division Three South, 08/03/1952
Defeat: 2-10 v Fulham, Division Three South, 07/09/1931
Goalscorer: Sammy Collins - 219 in 379 games (1948-58) Scored 40 during the 1955-56 season.
Appearances: Dennis Lewis - 443 (1947-59)
Additional: Paid £75,000 for Leon Constantine from Peterborough United, December 2004.
Received £650,000 from Crewe for Rodney Jack, July 1998.

HONOURS
FA Comps: None

League: Torquay & District 1909-09. Plymouth & District 1911-12. Southern Western Section 1926-27.
Football League Fourth Division Play-offs 1990-91. Conference Play-offs 2008-09.

County FA: Devon Senior Cup 1910-11, 21-22. Devon Bowl/Devon St Luke's Bowl 1933-34, 34-35, 36-37, 45-46, 47-48, 48-49,
54-55 (shared), 57-58, 60-61, 69-70, 70-71, 71-72, 95-96 (shared), 97-98, 2006-07.

BEST PERFORMANCES	**FA Cup:** Fourth Round Proper 1948-49, 54-55, 70-71, 82-83, 89-90, 2008-09, 10-11.
	FA Trophy: Final 2007-08.
	FA Vase: N/A

TORQUAY UNITED MATCH RESULTS 2016-17

Date	Comp	H/A	Opponents	Att:	Result	Goalscorers	Pos	No.
Aug 6	Nat Lg	A	Macclesfield Town	1501	L 0 - 2		22	1
9	Nat Lg	H	Bromley	2279	W 1 - 0	Gerring 42	14	2
13	Nat Lg	H	Barrow	2207	D 1 - 1	Williams	17	3
16	Nat Lg	A	Sutton United	1625	L 0 - 2		17	4
20	Nat Lg	A	North Ferriby United	5505	L 0 - 1		21	5
27	Nat Lg	H	Dover Athletic	1798	W 2 - 1	Reid 46 Sparkes 76	18	6
29	Nat Lg	A	Braintree Town	892	W 3 - 1	Reid 22 Gallifuoco 35 Young 75	15	7
3 Sept	Nat Lg	H	Lincoln City	2061	L 1 - 2	Gallifuoco 21	16	8
10	Nat Lg	H	York City	1989	W 2 - 0	Blissett 6 29	14	9
13	Nat Lg	A	Woking	1115	L 1 - 3	Gallifuoco 28	15	10
17	Nat Lg	A	Boreham Wood	605	L 0 - 2		16	11
24	Nat Lg	H	Maidstone United	2026	L 2 - 3	Blissett 38 Sparkes 55	16	12
Oct 1	Nat Lg	A	Gateshead	693	D 0 - 0		17	13
4	Nat Lg	H	Dagenham & Redbridge	1638	W 1 - 0	Reid 23	17	14
8	Nat Lg	A	Chester	2201	L 0 - 1		18	15
15	FAC4Q	H	Woking	1348	D 1 - 1	Young 5		16
17	FAC4Qr	A	Woking	791	L 1 - 2	Cheney 22		17
22	Nat Lg	H	Aldershot Town	1788	D 0 - 0		16	18
25	Nat Lg	A	Eastleigh	2116	L 0 - 3		18	19
29	Nat Lg	H	Southport	1490	L 1 - 2	Williams 25		20
12	Nat Lg	A	Guiseley	924	L 0 - 2		19	21
19	Nat Lg	H	Wrexham	1484	D 1 - 1	Moore 88	18	22
22	Nat Lg	H	Solihull Moors	1272	W 3 - 0	MOORE 3 (28 60 71)	15	23
26	Nat Lg	A	Tranmere Rovers	4449	L 1 - 2	Sparkes 65	17	24
29	Nat Lg	A	Dagenham & Redbridge	1072	W 1 - 0	Moore 76	17	25
10	FAT1	A	Braintree Town	301	L 0 - 2			26
17	Nat Lg	A	York City	2272	D 0 0		17	27
26	Nat Lg	H	Forest Green Rovers	2540	W 4 - 3	Blissett 55 Fitzpatrick 65 McGinty 69 Gerring 82	17	28
Jan 1	Nat Lg	A	Forest Green Rovers	2383	D 5 - 5	Sparkes 15 21 Verma 40 Pinnock 50 (og) Fitzpatrick 67	17	29
7	Nat Lg	H	Boreham Wood	1789	L 0 - 1		17	30
14	Nat Lg	H	Woking	1593	L 1 - 2	Williams 86	17	31
21	Nat Lg	A	Maidstone United	2455	L 1 - 2	Williams 63	18	32
28	Nat Lg	H	Gateshead	1555	W 3 - 1	Fitzpatrick 34 Rooney 59 Williams 90	17	33
Feb 4	Nat Lg	A	Bromley	889	L 0 - 1		17	34
11	Nat Lg	H	Macclesfield United	1400	D 1 - 1	McGinty 50	17	35
18	Nat Lg	A	Barrow	1391	D 0 - 0		18	36
25	Nat Lg	H	Sutton United	1646	L 2 - 3	Young 14 Williams 46	18	37
Mar 4	Nat Lg	H	Guiseley	1446	L 1 - 2	Verma 25	21	38
11	Nat Lg	A	Southport	1159	W 2 - 1	Young 35 Keating 90	20	39
14	Nat Lg	H	Tranmere Rovers	1418	D 0 - 0		20	40
21	Nat Lg	H	Eastleigh	1528	L 2 - 3	Young 49 Harrad 62	21	41
25	Nat Lg	A	Wrexham	3328	D 1 - 1	Reid 77 (pen)	21	42
28	Nat Lg	A	Solihull Moors	857	W 1 - 0	Sparkes 88	20	43
Apr 1	Nat Lg	A	Chester	1881	L 0 - 1		21	44
8	Nat Lg	H	Aldershot Town	3007	D 1 - 1	Keating 33	22	45
14	Nat Lg	H	Lincoln City	9011	L 1 - 2	Keating 78	22	46
17	Nat Lg	A	Braintree Town	2580	W 3 - 1	Williams 41 52 Lee 90	22	47
22	Nat Lg	A	Dover Athletic	1432	W 2 - 1	Williams 43 68	19	48
29	Nat Lg	H	North Ferriby United	4026	W 2 - 0	Verma 57 Anderson 86	17	49

GOALSCORERS	SG	CSG	Pens	Hat tricks	Total		SG	CSG	Pens	Hat tricks	Total
2015-16 Blissett					8	Verma	3				3
Williams	8	2			10	Gerring	2				2
Sparkes	5				6	McGinty	2				2
Moore	3	2		1	5	Anderson	1				1
Young	4				5	Cheney	1				1
Blissett	4				4	Harrad	1				1
Reid	4	2	1		4	Lee	1				1
Fitzpatrick	3	2			3	Opponents	1				1
Gallifuoco	3	2			3	Rooney	1				1
Keating	3				3						

TRANMERE ROVERS

Club Contact Details
Prenton Park, Prenton Road West, Birkenhead, Merseyside, CH42 9PY
03330 144 452
timr@tranmererovers.co.uk

Ground Capacity: 16,567 **Seats:** 16,567 **Covered:** Yes   **Clubhouse:** Yes   **Shop:** Yes

Record Attendance
24,424, for an FA Cup tie against Stoke City on 5 February 1972
Previous Grounds
Steeles Field 1884-87. Ravenshaws Field 1887-1912.

10 YEAR RECORD

07-08		08-09		09-10		10-11		11-12		12-13		13-14		14-15		15-16		16-17	
FL 1	11	FL 1	7	FL 1	19	FL 1	17	FL 1	12	FL 1	11	FL 1	21	FL 2	24	Nat	6	Nat	2
FAC	3Pr	FAC	2Pr	FAC	3P	FAC	1P	FAC	1P	FAC	3P	FAC	2P	FAC	3P	FAC	4Qr	FAC	4Q
FLC	1P	FLC	1P	FLC	2P	FLC	2P	FLC	1P	FLC	2P	FLC	3P	FLC	1P	FAT	1P	FAT	SF

Club Factfile

Founded: 1884   **Nickname:** Superwhite Army / Rovers   **Manager:** Micky Mellon

Previous Names: Belmont FC 1884-85.

Previous Leagues: West Lancashire 1889-97. The Combination 1897-1910. Lancashire Combination 1910-19. Central 1919-21.
Football League 1921-2015.

Club Colours (change): White with blue trim

RECORDS

Victory: 13-4 v Oldham Athletic, Football League Division Three North, 26 December 1935

Goalscorer: Ian Muir - 180 (In 351+42 appearances). Bunny Bell scored 57 goals during the 1933-34 season.

Appearances: Ray Mathias - 637

HONOURS

FA Comps: Welsh FA Cup 1934-35.

League: The Combination 1907-08. Lancashire Combination 1913-14, 18-19. League Division Three North 1937-38.

County FA: Liverpool Senior Cup 1948-49, 49-50, 54-55, 69-70, 73-73, 73-74, 91-92, 94-95, 2011-12, 13-14.

BEST PERFORMANCES	**FA Cup:** Quarter-finals 1999-00, 00-01, 03-04.
	FA Trophy: Semi-Finals 2016-17.
	FA Vase: N/A

TRANMERE ROVERS MATCH RESULTS 2016-17

Date	Comp	H/A	Opponents	Att:	Result		Goalscorers	Pos	No.
Aug 6	Nat Lg	A	Bromley	1539	W	2 - 0	Norwood 8 44	6	1
9	Nat Lg	H	Barrow	4977	W	2 - 0	Cook 40 Norwood 86 (pen)	4	2
13	Nat Lg	H	Eastleigh	4619	W	2 - 1	Jennings 24 Norwood 90	1	3
16	Nat Lg	A	Boreham Wood	801	W	1 - 0	Jennings 33	1	4
20	Nat Lg	H	Maidstone United	4797	W	2 - 1	Cook 42 McNulty	1	5
27	Nat Lg	A	Southport	3046	D	1 - 1	Cook 47	1	6
29	Nat Lg	H	Guiseley	4798	W	1 - 0	Norwood 41	1	7
3 Sept	Nat Lg	A	Aldershot Town	2585	L	1 - 3	Cook 37	2	8
10	Nat Lg	H	Lincoln City	5274	L	0 - 1		3	9
13	Nat Lg	A	York City	2379	D	0 - 0		4	10
17	Nat Lg	A	Sutton United	1680	L	0 - 1		5	11
24	Nat Lg	H	Woking	4214	W	3 - 1	Cook 34 49 Norwood 69	4	12
Oct 1	Nat Lg	A	Dagenham & Redbridge	1554	D	0 - 0		7	13
4	Nat Lg	H	Gateshead	4048	L	0 - 1		9	14
8	Nat Lg	A	Wrexham	5644	W	2 - 0	Jalal 64 (og) Cook 90	7	15
15	**FAC4Q**	**A**	**Barrow**	**2133**	**L**	**1 - 2**	**Diarra 25 (og)**		16
22	Nat Lg	A	Solihull Moors	1995	W	3 - 0	Kelly 17 81 Norwood 90	4	17
25	Nat Lg	H	North Ferriby United	4326	W	1 - 0	Cook 90	4	18
29	Nat Lg	A	Dover Athletic	1534	W	4 - 1	Cook 31 60 Walker 65 (og) Tollitt 79	4	19
Nov 12	Nat Lg	H	Chester	7790	D	2 - 2	Cook 30 Tollitt 35	2	20
19	Nat Lg	A	Braintree Town	964	W	1 0	Cook 76	3	21
22	Nat Lg	A	Forest Green Rovers	2040	D	2 - 2	Maynard 4 Norwood 65	4	22
26	Nat Lg	H	Torquay United	4449	W	2 - 1	Mangan 12 46	4	23
29	Nat Lg	A	Gateshead	723	W	1 - 0	Tollitt 3	3	24
Dec 3	Nat Lg	H	York City	5076	W	1 - 0	Norwood 90	1	25
10	**FAT1**	**A**	**Wrexham**	**2159**	**W**	**1 - 0**	**Sutton 24**		26
17	Nat Lg	A	Lincoln City	6335	L	1 - 2	Hughes 29 (pen)	2	27
26	Nat Lg	H	Macclesfield Town	7274	W	1 - 0	Hughes 84	2	28
Jan 1	Nat Lg	A	Macclesfield Town	3317	L	2 - 4	McNulty 10 Sutton 37	3	29
14	**FAT2**	**H**	**South Park**	**2801**	**W**	**4 - 1**	**Sutton 14 Hughes 20 (pen) Kirby 44 Stockton 90**		30
28	Nat Lg	H	Dagenham & Redbridge	5293	L	0 - 2		4	31
31	Nat Lg	A	Woking	860	W	3 - 0	Cook 51 Tollitt 53 77	3	32
Feb 4	**FAT3**	**H**	**Chelmsford City**	**2473**	**D**	**1 - 1**	**Stockton 70**		33
8	**FAT3r**	**A**	**Chelmsford City**	**923**	**W**	**4 - 1**	**KIrby 30 70 Sutton 43 Haines (og) 34**		34
11	Nat Lg	H	Bromley	4425	D	2 - 2	Cook 8 15	4	35
18	Nat Lg	A	Eastleigh	2475	W	2 - 0	Tollitt 60 85	4	36
21	Nat Lg	A	Boreham Wood	4107	W	2 - 1	Cook 1 13	3	37
25	**FATQF**	**H**	**Barrow**	**3487**	**W**	**5 - 1**	**Ihiekwe 32 STOCKTON 3 (60 72 83 pen) Mangan 81**		38
Mar 4	Nat Lg	A	Chester	3696	W	3 - 2	Harris 54 Norwood 81 Cook 89	3	39
7	Nat Lg	A	Barrow	1251	L	1 - 2	Cook 33	3	40
11	**FATSF1**	**A**	**Macclesfield Town**	**2358**	**D**	**1 - 1**	**Hughes 2 (pen)**		41
14	Nat Lg	A	Torquay United	1418	D	0 - 0		4	42
16	**FATSF2**	**H**	**Macclesfield Town**	**6100**	**L**	**0 - 1**			43
21	Nat Lg	A	North Ferriby United	638	W	4 - 1	HARRIS 3 (23 45 90) Cook 60	3	44
25	Nat Lg	H	Braintree Town	4514	W	1 - 0	Cook 55	3	45
28	Nat Lg	H	Dover Athletic	4281	W	1 - 0	Stockton 68	2	46
Apr 1	Nat Lg	A	Wrexham	4630	W	1 - 0	Marx 10 (og)	2	47
4	Nat Lg	H	Sutton United	4684	W	3 - 2	Ihiekwe 29 90 Eastmond 60 (og)	2	48
8	Nat Lg	H	Solihull Moors	5001	W	9 - 0	STOCKTON 3(20 25 45) JENNINGS 3(48 50 90) Cook 68	2	49
							Ridehalgth 84 Collins 90		50
11	Nat Lg	H	Forest Green Rovers	6907	L	0 - 1		2	
14	Nat Lg	H	Aldershot Town	6324	D	2 - 2	Stockton 12 Jennings 23	2	51
17	Nat Lg	A	Guiseley	2148	W	2 - 1	Norwood 49 Cook 90	2	52
22	Nat Lg	H	Southport	6159	W	4 - 1	Norwood 25 46 Jennings 51 71	2	53
29	Nat Lg	A	Maidstone United	3409	W	1 - 0	Ilesanmi 56	2	54
May 3	**PO SF1**	**A**	**Aldershot Town**	**5614**	**W**	**3 - 0**	**Stockton 3 75 Norwood 47**		55
6	**PO SF2**	**H**	**Aldershot Town**	**10,241**	**D**	**2 - 2**	**Stockton 31 Norwood 90**		56
13	**PO Final**	**N**	**Forest Green Rovers**	**18,801**	**L**	**1 - 3**	**Jennings 22**		57

GOALSCORERS	SG	CSG	Pens	Hat tricks	Total		SG	CSG	Pens	Hat tricks	Total
2015-16 Norwood					22	Ihiekwe	2				3
Cook	19	4			23	Kirby	2				3
Norwood	13	3	1		15	Mangan	2				3
Stockton	7		1	2	13	Kelly	1				2
Jennings	6	2		1	9	McNulty	2				2
Tollitt	5	2			7	Collins	1				1
Opponents	6				6	Ilesanmi	1				1
Harris	2				4	Maynard	1				1
Hughes	4	2	3		4	Ridehalgh	1				1
Sutton	4	2			4						

WOKING

Club Contact Details
The Laithwaite Community Stadium, Kingfield Road, Woking, Surrey GU22 9AA
01483 772 470
admin@wokingfc.co.uk

Ground Capacity: 6,000 **Seats:** 2,500 **Covered:** 3,900 **Clubhouse:** Yes **Shop:** Yes

Record Attendance
6,000 v Swansea City - FA Cup 1978-79 and v Coventry City - FA Cup 1996-97
Previous Grounds
Wheatsheaf, Ive Lane (pre 1923)

10 YEAR RECORD

07-08		08-09		09-10		10-11		11-12		12-13		13-14		14-15		15-16		16-17	
Conf	17	Conf	21	Conf S	5	Conf S	5	Conf S	1	Conf	12	Conf	9	Conf	7	Nat	12	Nat	18
FAC	4Q	FAC	4Qr	FAC	1P	FAC	P	FAC	3Q	FAC	4Q	FAC	4Q	FAC	1P	FAC	4Q	FAC	2P
FAT	2P	FAT	1P	FAT	2P	FAT	3P	FAT	3Q	FAT	2P	FAT	2P	FAT	3Pr	FAT	QF	FAT	1Pr

Club Factfile

Founded: 1889 **Nickname:** The Cards **Manager:** Anthony Limbrick - May 2017

Previous Names: None

Previous Leagues: West Surrey 1895-1911. Isthmian 1911-92.

Club Colours (change): Red and white

RECORDS
Victory: 17-4 v Farnham - 1912-13
Defeat: 0-16 v New Crusaders - 1905-06
Goalscorer: Charlie Mortimore - 331 (1953-65)
Appearances: Brian Finn - 564 (1962-74)
Additional: Paid £60,000 to Crystal Palace for Chris Sharpling
Received £150,000 from Bristol Rovers for Steve Foster

HONOURS
FA Comps: FA Amateur Cup 1957-58. FA Trophy 1993-94, 94-95, 96-97 (Joint record number of victories).

League: West Surrey 1895-96. Isthmian League Division Two South 1986-87, Premier Division 1991-92.
Conference South 2011-12.

County FA: Surrey Senior Cup 1912-13, 26-27, 55-56, 56-57, 71-72, 90-91, 93-94, 95-96, 99-00, 03-04, 2011-12, 13-14, 16-17.

BEST PERFORMANCES	**FA Cup:** Fourth Round Proper 1990-91.
	FA Trophy: Final 1993-94, 94-95, 96-97, 2005-06.
	FA Vase: N/A

WOKING MATCH RESULTS 2016-17

Date	Comp	H/A	Opponents	Att:	Result	Goalscorers	Pos	No.
Aug 6	Nat Lg	H	Lincoln City	1592	L 1 - 2	Yakubu	20	1
9	Nat Lg	A	Solihull Moors	69	D 2 - 2	Ralph 31 Ansah 49	18	2
13	Nat Lg	A	Southport	702	L 1 - 2	Lewis 13	21	3
16	Nat Lg	H	Forest Green Rovers	864	L 0 - 1		22	4
20	Nat Lg	H	Dagenham Redbridge	1153	L 1 - 3	Edgar 48	23	5
27	Nat Lg	A	York City	1972	L 0 - 1		23	6
29	Nat Lg	H	Chester	1271	W 3 - 1	Murtagh 17 Jones 28 Ugwu 75	22	7
3 Sept	Nat Lg	A	Macclesfield Town	1221	L 1 - 3	Lewis 59	22	8
10	Nat Lg	A	Guiseley	649	D 1 - 1	Lewis 82	22	9
13	Nat Lg	H	Torquay United	1115	W 3 - 1	Sam-Yorke 50 59 Lewis 86	22	10
17	Nat Lg	H	Wrexham	1213	W 2 - 0	Saraiva 81 Kandi 89	19	11
24	Nat Lg	A	Tranmere Rovers	4214	L 1 - 3	Saraiva 68	19	12
Oct 1	Nat Lg	H	Eastleigh	1403	D 3 - 3	Tubbs 23 Sam-York 60 Kandi 79	19	13
4	Nat Lg	A	Bromley	808	L 1 - 2	Saraiva 3	19	14
8	Nat Lg	A	Sutton United	1714	L 1 - 4	Tubbs 75	20	15
15	FAC4Q	A	Torquay United	1348	D 1 - 1	Edgar 79		16
17	FAC4Qr	H	Torquay United	791	W 2 - 1	Ugwu 56 62		17
22	Nat Lg	H	Barrow	1351	D 1 - 1	Tubbs 51 (pen)	20	18
25	Nat Lg	H	Braintree Town	1362	L 2 3	Jones 24 Saraiva 29	20	19
29	Nat Lg	A	Boreham Wood	405	L 1 - 2	Jones 21	21	20
Nov 5	FAC1	A	Stockport County	4025	W 4 - 2	Jones 18 Ugwu 32 59 Saraiva 89		21
12	Nat Lg	H	North Ferriby United	1367	D 1 - 1	Kandi 90	22	22
19	Nat Lg	A	Maidstone United	2147	W 3 - 0	Saraiva 30 Ugwu 34 72	20	23
22	Nat Lg	A	Dover Athletic	823	L 1 - 3	Ugwu 56	19	24
26	Nat Lg	H	Gateshead	1062	W 3 - 0	UGWU 3 (9 56 72)	19	25
29	Nat Lg	H	Bromley	1057	W 2 - 1	Ugwu 30 Saraiva 80	19	26
Dec 3	FAC2	H	Accrington Stanley	3718	L 0 - 3			27
10	FAT1	H	Ebbsfleet United	825	D 1 - 1	Kandi 48		28
13	FAT1r	H	Ebbsfleet United	613	L 0 - 1			29
17	Nat Lg	H	Guiseley	989	D 0 - 0		19	30
26	Nat Lg	A	Aldershot Town	3436	L 0 - 4		20	31
Jan 1	Nat Lg	H	Aldershot Town	3224	L 1 - 2	Kretzschmar 65	21	32
7	Nat Lg	A	Wrexham	3575	L 1 - 2	Saraiva 55	22	33
14	Nat Lg	A	Torquay United	1593	W 2 - 1	Saraiva 6 (pen) Saah 36	20	34
28	Nat Lg	A	Eastleigh	2036	W 1 - 0	Ugwu 16	19	35
31	Nat Lg	H	Tranmere Rovers	860	L 0 - 3		19	36
11	Nat Lg	A	Lincoln City	5553	L 2 - 3	Ugwu 11 Saraiva 75 (pen)	19	37
14	Nat Lg	H	Solihull Moors	1000	W 2 1	Thomas 3 Saraiva 73	19	38
18	Nat Lg	H	Southport	1386	D 0 - 0		20	39
25	Nat Lg	A	Forest Green Rovers	1566	L 3 - 4	Jones 43 Ugwu 54 Thomas 90	20	40
28	Nat Lg	H	Dover Athletic	1092	W 1 - 0	Kretzschmar 66	19	41
Mar 4	Nat Lg	A	North Ferriby United	402	L 1 - 2	Ugwu 26	20	42
11	Nat Lg	H	Boreham Wood	1157	D 0 - 0		21	43
18	Nat Lg	A	Gateshead	832	L 1 - 2	Thomas 21	21	44
21	Nat Lg	A	Braintree Town	572	W 3 - 1	Sam-Yorke 23 26 Murtagh 69	19	45
25	Nat Lg	H	Maidstone United	2088	L 2 - 4	Sam-Yorke 13 Lucas 25	19	46
Apr 1	Nat Lg	A	Surtton United	1537	W 2 - 1	Sam-Yorke 5 Ugwu 83	20	47
8	Nat Lg	A	Bromley	1326	D 2 - 2	Lucas 45 (pen) Murtagh 70	20	48
14	Nat Lg	H	Maidstone UNited	2068	W 1 - 0	Ugwu 61 (pen)	19	49
17	Nat Lg	A	Chester	1770	W 3 - 2	Saah 53 Hall 85 Ugwu 90 (pen)	17	50
22	Nat Lg	H	York City	2702	D 1 - 1	Ugwu 66 (pen)	18	51
29	Nat Lg	A	Dagenham & Redbridge	1860	D 1 - 1	Kretzschmar 12	18	52

GOALSCORERS	SG	CSG	Pens	Hat tricks	Total		SG	CSG	Pens	Hat tricks	Total
2015-16 Goddard					17	Tubbs	3		1		3
Ugwu	14	4	1	1	20	Edgar	2				2
Saraiva	11	2	1		11	Lucas	2				2
Sam-Yorke	6	3			7	Saah	2				2
Jones	5	3			5	Ansah	1				1
Kandi	4				4	Hall	1				1
Lewis	4	3			4	Ralph	1				1
Kretzschmar	3				3	Yakubu	1				1
Murtagh	3				3						
Thomas	3				3						

WREXHAM

Club Contact Details
Racecourse Ground, Mold road, Wrexham LL11 2AH
01978 891 864
info@wrexhamfc.tv

Ground Capacity: 15,500 **Seats:** 10,771 **Covered:** 15,500 **Clubhouse:** Yes **Shop:** Yes

Record Attendance
34,445 v Manchester United - FA Cup 4th Round 26/01/57
Previous Grounds
Rhosddu Recreation Ground during the 1881-82 and 1882-83 seasons.

10 YEAR RECORD

07-08		08-09		09-10		10-11		11-12		12-13		13-14		14-15		15-16		16-17	
FL 2	24	Conf	10	Conf	11	Conf	4	Conf	2	Conf	5	Conf	17	Conf	11	Nat	8	Nat	13
FAC	2P	FAC	4Qr	FAC	2P	FAC	4Q	FAC	3Pr	FAC	1P	FAC	2P	FAC	3P	FAC	4Q	FAC	4Qr
FLC	2P	FAT	QFr	FAT	1Pr	FAT	2P	FAT	1P	FAT	F	FAT	2P	FAT	F	FAT	2P	FAT	1P

Club Factfile

Founded: 1864   **Nickname:** The Robins   **Manager:** Dean Keates

Previous Names: Wrexham Athletic for the 1882-83 season only

Previous Leagues: The Combination 1890-94, 1896-1906, Welsh League 1894-96, Birmingham & District 1906-21,
Football League 1921-2008

Club Colours (change): Red & white

RECORDS
Victory: 10-1 v Hartlepool United - Division Four 03/03/62
Defeat: 0-9 v v Brentford - Division Three
Goalscorer: Tommy Bamford - 201 (1928-34)
Appearances: Arfon Griffiths - 591 (1959-61 & 62-79)
Additional: Paid £800,000 to Birmingham City for Bryan Hughes March 1997
Received £212,000 from Liverpool for Joey Jones October 1978

HONOURS
FA Comps: Welsh FA Cup a record 23 times. FAW Premier Cup 1997-98, 99-00, 00-01, 02-03, 03-04. FA Trophy 2012-13.

League: Welsh Senior League 1894-95, 95-96. Combination 1900-01, 01-02, 02-03, 04-05.
Football League Division Three 1977-78.

County FA: Denbighshire & Flintshire (Soames) Charity Cup 1894-95, 98-99, 1902-03, 04-05, 05-06, 08-09.

BEST PERFORMANCES	**FA Cup:** Quarter-Finals 1973-74, 77-78, 96-97.
	FA Trophy: Final 2012-13, 14-15.
	FA Vase: N/A

WREXHAM MATCH RESULTS 2016-17

Date	Comp	H/A	Opponents	Att:	Result	Goalscorers	Pos	No.
Aug 6	Nat Lg	H	Dover Athletic	5603	D 0 - 0		15	1
9	Nat Lg	A	Guiseley	1120	W 3 - 2	Rooney 25 (pen) McDonagh 66 Rutherford 90	7	2
13	Nat Lg	A	Aldershot Town	1907	L 0 - 2		15	3
16	Nat Lg	H	Solihull Moors	4017	W 1 - 0	Carrington 90	13	4
20	Nat Lg	H	Eastleigh	4034	D 0 - 0		11	5
27	Nat Lg	A	Dagenham & Redbridge	1256	L 0 - 0		15	6
29	Nat Lg	H	York City	4005	W 2 - 1	Rooney 16 (pen) Newton 63 (pen)	10	7
3 Sept	Nat Lg	A	Maidstone United	2550	D 2 - 2	Powell 38 66	13	8
10	Nat Lg	H	Sutton United	3890	W 1 - 0	Newton 64	10	9
17	Nat Lg	A	Woking	213	D 0 - 2		14	10
24	Nat Lg	H	Chester	5058	D 0 - 0		11	11
27	Nat Lg	A	Macclesfield United	1579	L 0 - 3		12	12
Oct 1	Nat Lg	A	Boreham Wood	458	W 1 - 0	Rooney 57	11	13
4	Nat Lg	H	Lincoln City	3487	L 1 - 2	Bencherif 82	15	14
8	Nat Lg	A	Tranmere Rovers	5644	L 0 - 2		15	15
15	FAC4Q	A	Stamford	1264	D 1 - 1	Harrad 6		16
18	FAC4Qr	H	Stamford	1598	L 2 - 3	Harrad 86 Evans 90		17
22	Nat Lg	H	Bromley	3531	W 2 - 1	Harrad 44 McDonagh 80	14	18
25	Nat Lg	H	Barrow	3616	D 2 - 2	Tilt 25 Rooney 78	14	19
29	Nat Lg	A	Gateshead	832	D 2 - 2	Rooney 59 Bencherif 69	14	20
Nov 5	Nat Lg	A	North Ferriby United	528	D 0 - 0		14	21
12	Nat Lg	H	Braintree Town	3413	L 0 - 1		14	22
19	Nat Lg	A	Torquay United	1484	D 1 - 1	McDonagh 45	14	23
26	Nat Lg	H	Forest Green Rovers	3472	W 3 - 1	Harrad 15 McDonagh 30 90	15	24
29	Nat Lg	A	LIncoln City	3344	L 0 - 1		15	25
Dec 6	Nat Lg	H	Macclesfield Town	3204	L 0 - 3		15	26
10	FAT1	H	Tranmere Rovers	2159	L 0 - 1			27
17	Nat Lg	A	Sutton United	1613	L 0 - 1		15	28
26	Nat Lg	H	Southport	4317	W 1 - 0	Edwards 88	15	29
Jan 1	Nat Lg	A	Southport	2066	L 2 - 3	White 6 Rooney 67 (pen)	16	30
7	Nat Lg	H	Dover Athletic	3575	W 2 - 1	Rooney 51 Evans 60	15	31
14	Nat Lg	H	North Ferriby United	3625	W 1 - 0	McLeod 28	14	32
21	Nat Lg	A	Chester	3961	D 1 - 1	Rooney 53	13	33
28	Nat Lg	H	Boreham Wood	3664	W 2 - 1	Barry 27 (pen) Rooney 90 (pen)	12	34
Feb 4	Nat Lg	H	Guiseley	3730	W 3 - 1	Massanka 31 Rooney 62 90	10	35
11	Nat Lg	A	Dover Athletic	1057	D 1 - 1	White 80	10	36
18	Nat Lg	A	Aldershot Town	4308	L 0 - 2		10	37
25	Nat Lg	H	Solihull Moors	1349	W 1 - 0	Barry 6 (pen)	10	38
Mar 4	Nat Lg	A	Braintree Town	698	W 2 - 1	Massanka 4 Shenton 60	10	39
11	Nat Lg	H	Gateshead	3986	L 0 - 2		10	40
18	Nat Lg	A	Forest Green Rovers	2146	L 0 - 3		11	41
21	Nat Lg	A	Barrow	1009	D 1 1	Rutherford 90	10	42
25	Nat Lg	A	Torquay United	3328	D 1 - 1	Harry 47 (pen)	10	43
Apr 1	Nat Lg	H	Tranmere Rovers	4630	L 0 - 1		10	44
8	Nat Lg	A	Bromley	1006	L 3 - 4	White 52 Massanka 58 86	12	45
14	Nat Lg	H	Maidstone United	3379	L 1 - 3	White 9	12	46
17	Nat Lg	A	York City	4091	W 3 - 1	White 29 58 Smith 90	11	47
22	Nat Lg	H	Dagenham & Redbridge	3653	L 0 - 1		12	48
29	Nat Lg	A	Eastleigh	2588	D 1 - 1	White 46	13	49

GOALSCORERS	SG	CSG	Pens	Hat tricks	Total		SG	CSG	Pens	Hat tricks	Total
2015-16 Jennings					14	Powell	1				2
Rooney	9	3	4		11	Rutherford	2				2
White	6				7	Carrington	1				1
McDonagh	4				5	Edwards	1				1
Harrad	4	3			4	Harry	1		1		1
Massanka	3				4	McCleod	1				1
Barry	2		2		2	Shenton	1				1
Bencherif	2				2	Smith	1				1
Evans	2				2	Tilt	1				1
Newton	2		1		2						

We say farewell and....

LINCOLN CITY MATCH RESULTS 2016-17

Date	Comp	H/A	Opponents	Att:	Result	Goalscorers	Pos	No.
Aug 6	Nat Lg	A	Woking	1592	W 3 - 1	Marriott 28 Rhead 60 73 (pen)	3	1
9	Nat Lg	H	North Ferriby UNited	3622	W 6 - 1	Waterfall 16 Rhead 2 24 Arnold 5 Margetts 51 Wood 67	1	2
13	Nat Lg	H	Sutton United	3195	L 1 - 3	Habergham 51	4	3
16	Nat Lg	A	Dagenham & Redbridge	1399	L 0 - 1		14	4
20	Nat Lg	H	Southport	2440	W 4 - 0	MARGETTS 4 (16 30 45 79 Pen)	8	5
27	Nat Lg	A	Macclesfield Town	1615	W 2 - 1	Anderson 46 Marriott 75	4	6
29	Nat Lg	H	Gateshead	3687	W 3 - 0	Raggett 6 Arnold 50 Marriott 83	3	7
3 Sept	Nat Lg	A	Torquay United	2061	W 2 - 1	Rhead 3 (pen) 90	3	8
10	Nat Lg	A	Tranmere Rovers	5274	W 1 - 0	Bonne 68	1	9
13	Nat Lg	H	Solihull Moors	4029	D 0 - 0		1	10
17	Nat Lg	H	Barrow	3578	L 1 - 2	Arnold 33	4	11
24	Nat Lg	A	Dover Athletic	1509	L 0 - 2		5	12
Oct 1	Nat Lg	H	Braintree Town	3554	W 3 - 0	Arnold 3 Waterfall 52 Muldoon 89	4	13
4	Nat Lg	A	Wrexham	3487	W 2 - 1	Waterfall 31 Anderson 45	2	14
8	Nat Lg	H	Bromley	1511	D 1 - 1	Anderson 46	3	15
15	FAC4Q	H	Guiseley	2629	D 0 - 0			16
18	FAC4Q	A	Guiseley	765	W 2 - 1	Robinson 40 51		17
22	Nat Lg	H	Eastleigh	3180	D 0 - 0		3	18
25	Nat Lg	H	Boreham Wood	3014	W 2 - 0	Arnold 45 Rhead 73	3	19
29	Nat Lg	A	Chester	2586	W 5 - 2	Rhead 41 48 Raggett 45 Muldoon 81 Anderson 83	2	20
Nov 5	FAC 1	H	Altrincham	3529	W 2 - 1	Raggett 21 Power 60		21
12	Nat Lg	H	Aldershot Town	3461	D 3 - 3	Arnold 21 30 Rhead 90	2	22
19	Nat Lg	A	Forest Green Rovers	2164	W 3 - 2	Woodyard 69 Waterfall 89 Raggett 90	2	23
22	Nat Lg	A	York City	2889	W 4 - 1	Whitehouse 24 Arnold 29 Waterfall 61 Wood 75	2	24
26	Nat Lg	H	Maidstone United	3917	W 2 - 0	Robinson 52 Rhead 54	2	25
29	Nat Lg	A	Wrexham	3344	W 1 - 0	Whitehouse 14	1	26
Dec 5	FAC 2	H	Oldham Athletic	7012	W 3 - 2	Robinson 22 47 Hawkridge 24		27
17	Nat Lg	H	Tranmere Rovers	6335	W 2 - 1	Arnold 3 Marriott 81	1	28
20	FAT1	A	Nantwich Town	482	W 2 1	Whitehouse 5 Hawkridge 63		29
26	Nat Lg	A	Guiseley	2446	L 1 - 2	Waterfall 28	2	30
Jan 1	Nat Lg	H	Guiseley	5148	W 3 - 1	Power 57 (pen) Raggett 88 Arnold 90	1	31
7	FAC 3	A	Ipswich Town	16,027	D 2 - 2	Robinson 7 65		32
14	FAT2	A	Gateshead	578	W 3 - 1	Habergham 48 Whitehouse 70 Hawkridge 74		33
17	FAC3r	H	Ipswich Town	9069	W 1 - 0	Arnold 90		34
20	Nat Lg	H	Dover Athletic	6491	W 2 - 0	Sterling 9 (og) Hawkridge 83	1	35
24	Nat Lg	A	Barrow	1152	L 0 - 3		1	36
28	FAC4	H	Brighton & Hove Albion	9469	W 3 - 1	Power 57 (pen) Tomari 62 (og) Robinson 85		37
31	Nat Lg	A	Solihull Moors	1650	W 1 - 0	Muldoon 51	1	38
Feb 4	FAT3	A	Welling United	743	W 3 - 1	Southwell 8 Ward 49 53		39
11 30	Nat Lg	H	Woking	5553	W 3 - 2	Rhead 7 60 Thomas 51 (og)	1	40
18	FAC5	A	Burnley	19.185	W 1 - 0	Raggett 89		41
21	Nat Lg	A	North Ferriby United	2389	W 1 - 0	Waterfall 21	1	42
25	FATQF	A	Boreham Wood	901	W 2 - 0	Ward 62 Paine 73 (og)		43
28	Nat Lg	A	York City	6892	D 1 - 1	Power 76	1	44
Mar 4	Nat Lg	A	Aldershot Town	3595	D 0 - 0		1	45
7	Nat Lg	A	Braintree Town	1182	W 4 - 0	ANGOL 3 (15 25 82 pen) Arnold 85	1	46
11	FAC6	A	Arsenal	59,454	L 0 - 5			47
15	FATSF1	A	York City	3294	L 1 - 2	Angol 14 (pen)		48
18	FATSF2	H	York City	8409	D 1 - 1	Raggett 66		49
21	Nat Lg	A	Boreham Wood	1002	L 0 - 2		2	50
25	Nat Lg	H	Forest Green Rovers	6798	W 3 - 1	Angol 56 Habergham 76 Kelly 61 (og)	1	51
28	Nat Lg	A	Sutton United	2246	D 1 - 1	Whitehouse 81	1	52
Apr 1	Nat Lg	H	Bromley	6843	W 1 - 0	Knott 66	1	53
3	Nat Lg	H	Dagenham & Redbridge	7173	W 2 - 0	Whitehouse 47 Rhead 68	1	54
8	Nat Lg	A	Eastleigh	2738	W 1 - 0	Raggett 77	1	55
11	Nat Lg	H	Chester	7401	W 1 - 0	Anderson 36	1	56
15	Nat Lg	H	Torquay United	9011	W 2 - 1	Anderson 86 Habregham 88	1	57
17	Nat Lg	A	Gateshead	3770	W 2 - 1	Rhead 90 (pen) Arnold 90	1	58
22	Nat Lg	A	Macclesfield Town	10,031	W 2 - 1	Hawkridge 28 76	1C	59
25	Nat Lg	A	Maidstone United	3014	D 0 - 0		1	60
29	Nat Lg	A	Southport	3462	D 1 - 1	Angol 32	1	61

GOALSCORERS	SG	CSG	Pens	Hat tricks	Total		SG	CSG	Pens	Hat tricks	Total
2015-16 Rhead					14	Habergham	4				4
Rhead	10	2	3		15	Marriott	4	2			4
Arnold	12				13	Opponents	4				4
Raggett	7	2			8	Power	4		2		4
Robinson	5				8	Muldoon	3				3
Waterfall	7	2			7	Ward	2				3
Anderson	6	2			6	West	1				2
Angol	4		2	1	6	Wood	2				2
Hawkridge	5				6	Bonne	1				1
Whitehouse	6				6	Knott	1				1
Margetts	2		1	1	5	Southwell	1				1

FOREST GREEN ROVERS MATCH RESULTS 2016-17

Date	Comp	H/A	Opponents	Att:	Result	Goalscorers	Pos	No.
Aug 6	Nat Lg	A	Boreham Wood	504	L 0 - 1		14	1
9	Nat Lg	H	Sutton United	1369	D 1 - 1	Tubbs 7	16	2
13	Nat Lg	H	Gateshead	1143	W 1 - 0	Bennett 90	13	3
16	Nat Lg	A	Woking	864	W 1 - 0	Marsh-Brown 19	11	4
20	Nat Lg	H	York City	1396	W 2 - 1	Murphy 40 Tubbs 90 (pen)	6	5
27	Nat Lg	A	Maidstone United	2274	W 4 - 1	Carter 5 Doidge 45 Murphy 75 79	3	6
29	Nat Lg	H	Southport	1621	W 5 - 1	Moore 6 78 Chemial 10 Clough 61 Murphy 86	2	7
Sept 3	Nat Lg	A	Chester	1820	W 2 - 1	Noble 24 Carter 52	1	8
10	Nat Lg	A	Dover Athletic	785	L 3 - 4	Noble 7 Murphy 48 Doidge 86	2	9
13	Nat Lg	H	Eastleigh	1444	D 1 - 1	Murphy 57	3	10
17	Nat Lg	H	Bromley	1371	W 1 - 0	Marsh-Brown 73	2	11
24	Nat Lg	A	Braintree Town	621	W 1 - 0	Marsh-Brown 38	2	12
Oct 1	Nat Lg	H	Barrow	2236	D 0 - 0		2	13
4	Nat Lg	A	Aldershot Town	2195	W 4 - 0	Robert 5 27 Moore 8 45	1	14
8	Nat Lg	A	North Ferriby United	501	W 3 - 0	Pinnock 43 Clough 75 Doidge 90	1	15
15	**FAC4Q**	**A**	**Sutton United**	**751**	**L 1 - 2**	**Noble 25**		16
22	Nat Lg	H	Guiseley	1723	W 3 - 0	Carter 20 Doidge 47 Lawlor 58 (og)	1	17
25	Nat Lg	A	Solihull Moors	919	W 1 - 0	Daly 59 (og)	1	18
29	Nat Lg	H	Dagenham & Redbridge	2268	D 1 - 1	Murphy 48	1	19
Nov 5	Nat Lg	H	Aldershot Town	1638	W 2 - 1	Doidge 17 90	1	20
12	Nat Lg	A	Macclesfield Town	1749	W 1 - 0	Marsh-Brown 2	1	21
19	Nat Lg	H	Lincoln City	2164	L 2 - 3	Doidge 25 Marsh-Brown 65	1	22
22	Nat Lg	H	Tranmere Rovers	2040	D 2 - 2	Doidge 3 Noble 29	1	23
26	Nat Lg	A	Wrexham	3472	L 1 - 3	Carter 68	1	24
10	**FAT1**	**H**	**Truro City**	**828**	**D 1 - 1**	**Marsh-Brown 50**		25
13	**FAT1r**	**A**	**Truro City**	**336**	**W 1 - 0**	**Carter 108 (aet)**		26
17	Nat Lg	H	Dover Athletic	1818	D 1 - 1	Moore 90	3	27
26	Nat Lg	A	Torquay United	2540	L 3 - 4	Doidge 73 Clough 76 Pinnock 77	3	28
Jan 1	Nat Lg	H	Torquay United	2383	D 5 - 5	Marsh-Brown 4 29 Doidge 62 83 Moore (og) 88	3	29
7	Nat Lg	A	Bromley	1247	W 5 - 1	Frear 28 Doidge 43 90 Marsh-Brown 51 Pinnock 54	3	30
10	Nat Lg	A	Eastleigh	1917	D 1 - 1	Doidge 24	2	31
14	**FAT2**	**A**	**Chester**	**1250**	**W 2 - 0**	**Kelly 43 58**		32
21	Nat Lg	H	Braintree Town	1735	D 1 - 1	Clough 60	2	33
28	Nat Lg	A	Barrow	1422	W 3 - 2	Noble 6 Doidge 64 Monthe 90	2	34
Feb 4	**FAT3**	**A**	**Macclesfield Town**	**967**	**L 0 - 1**			35
11	Nat Lg	H	Boreham Wood	1575	W 2 - 0	Doidge 83 Bugiel 89	3	36
18	Nat Lg	A	Gateshead	916	L 1 - 3	Woolery 49	3	37
25	Nat Lg	H	Woking	1566	W 4 - 3	Marsh-Brown 37 Doidge 56 Bugiel 88 90	3	38
Mar 4	Nat Lg	A	Macclesfield Town	1569	W 3 - 0	Doidge 12 Noble 52 Ellis 61	2	39
11	Nat Lg	A	Dagenham & Redbridge	1459	L 1 - 2	Doidge 81	3	40
14	Nat Lg	A	Sutton United	1446	W 2 - 1	Ellis 32 Doidge 35	2	41
18	Nat Lg	H	Wrexham	2146	W 3 - 0	Bennett 45 Noble 47 (pen) Doidge 63	2	42
21	Nat Lg	H	Solihull Moors	1445	W 2 - 0	Robert 40 Doidge 90	1	43
25	Nat Lg	A	Lincoln City	6798	L 1 - 3	Doidge 11	2	44
Apr 1	Nat Lg	H	North Ferriby United	1709	L 0 - 1		3	45
8	Nat Lg	A	Guiseley	760	W 1 - 0	Doidge 26	3	46
11	Nat Lg	A	Tranmere Rovers	6907	W 1 - 0	Woolery 86	3	47
14	Nat Lg	H	Chester	1936	W 2 - 0	Doidge 50 Noble 74	3	48
17	Nat Lg	A	Southport	844	L 0 - 2		3	49
22	Nat Lg	H	Maidstone United	2030	D 2 - 2	Marsh-Brown 10 Locko (og) 55	3	50
29	Nat Lg	A	York City	3984	D 2 - 2	Bugiel 6 39	3	51
May 4	**PO S-F1**	**A**	**Dagenham & Redbridge**	**2208**	**D 1 - 1**	**Noble 29 (pen)**		52
7	**PO S-F2**	**H**	**Dagenham & Redbridge**	**3237**	**W 2 - 0**	**Doidge 34 Marsh-Brown 45**		53
13	**PO Final**	**N**	**Tranmere Rovers**	**18,801**	**W 3 - 1**	**Woolery 11 44 Doidge 41**		54

GOALSCORERS	SG	CSG	Pens	Hat tricks	Total		SG	CSG	Pens	Hat tricks	Total
2015-16 Parkin					30	Woolery	3				4
Doidge	24	7			27	Pinnock	3				3
Marsh-Brown	11	2			12	Robert	2				3
Noble	9		2		9	Bennett	2				2
Murphy	7	3			7	Ellis	2				2
Bugiel	3				5	Kelly	1				2
Carter	5				5	Tubbs	2		1		2
Moore	3				5	Chemial	1				1
Clough	4				4	Frear	1				1
Opponents	4				4	Monthe	1				1

Football Conference Play-off Final 2016-17

At Wembley, 13/05/17 - Att: 18,801

Forest Green Rovers 3-1 Tranmere Rovers

Photo: Peter Barnes

Right: Brilliant save from Scott Davies (Tranmere).
Below: Ellis (FGR) v Stockton (Tranmere).
Bottom: Ilam Noble (FGR) shoots wide of the
Tranmere goal.
Photos: Keith Clayton

National Division Statistics 2016-17

TOP SCORING CLUBS

Lincoln City	109
Tranmere Rovers	102
Forest Green Rovers	99
Dover Athletic	95

MOST GAMES WITHOUT SCORING

North Ferriby United	26 (5)
Boreham Wood	21 (4)
Wrexham	19 (3)

MOST SCORERS

Southport	22+1og
Lincoln City	20+4ogs
York City	20+1og

MOST CONSECUTIVE SCORING GAMES

Forest Green Rovers	21
Dover Athletic	20
Lincoln City	17

MOST CLEAN SHEETS

Lincoln City	23 (4)
Tranmere Rovers	23 (3)
Forest Green Rovers	19 (5)

	GT	GWS(1)	TNoS	MCSG	TCS(2)
Aldershot Town	73	13 (2)	14+2og	9	22 (2)
Barrow	92	11 (2)	15+1og	10	15 (2)
Boreham Wood	64	21 (4)	9	5	19 (5)
Braintree Town	73	15 (3)	17+1og	7	15 (2)
Bromley	68	15 (3)	14+1og	11	10 (2)
Chester	66	12 (3)	16	11	16 (7)
Dagenham & Redbridge	85	12 (2)	13+2og	11	18 (3)
Dover Athletic	95	9 (3)	14+1og	20	15 (2)
Eastleigh	71	14 (4)	22	9	14 (4)
Forest Green Rovers	99	5 (1)	18+3ogs	21	19 (5)
Gateshead	79	13 (4)	16+1og	13	15 (2)
Guiseley	53	15 (4)	18+1og	13	10 (2)
Lincoln City	109	8 (1)	20+4ogs	17	23 (4)
Macclesfield Town	83	14 (1)	18	10	15 (2)
Maidstone United	65	16 (4)	18+1og	10	7 (1)
North Ferriby United	33	26 (5)	14	2	7 (1)
Solihull Moors	71	18 (3)	17	5	14 (2)
Southport	59	15 (3)	22+1og	6	9 (2)
Sutton United	81	14 (3)	18+4ogs	11	15 (2)
Torquay United	56	16 (2)	17+1og	5	11 (2)
Tranmere Rovers	102	9 (3)	17+6ogs	16	23 (3)
Woking	73	9 (3)	17	10	9 (1)
Wrexham	50	19 (3)	18	8	10 (3)
York City	72	14 (5)	20+1og	11	9 (2)

(1) - Most consecutive goalless games in brackets.
(2) - Most consecutive clean sheets in brackets.
GT - Goals Total
GWS - Games Without Scoring
TNoS - Total Number of Scorers
MCSG - Most Consecutive Scoring Games
TCS - Total Clean Sheets

National League strikers with ten or more goals - 2016-17

LEAGUE, FA CUP AND FA TROPHY GOALS ONLY.

							PTG	CTG	FLP
Dover Athletic	Miller	46	Lafayette	12	Emmanuel	11	69	95	6
Barrow	Bennett	22	Harrison	20	Williams	14	56	92	7
Dagenham & Redbridge	Hawkins	19	Maguire-Drew	16	Whitely	16	51	85	4
Tranmere Rovers	Cook	23	Norwood	15	Stockton	13	52	102	2
Gateshead	Johnson	18	S.Jones	11	York	11	40	79	8
Boreham Wood	Ferrier	16	Andrade	11	Balanta	10	37	64	11
Aldershot Town	Mensah	13	Rendell	13	McClure	10	36	73	5
Forest Green Rovers	Doidge	27	Marsh-Brown	12			39	99	3
Woking	UgwU	20	Saraiva	11			31	73	18
Chester	Alabi	18	Durrell	10			28	66	19
Lincoln City	Rhead	15	Arnold	13			28	100	1
Bromley	Turgott	14	Sho-Silver	12			26	68	10
Suttion United	Biamou	13	Deacon	13			26	81	12
York City	Parkin	16	Oliver	10			26	72	23
Macclesfield Town	Holroyd	14	Whitaker	11			25	81	9
Braintree Town	Cheek	23					23	73	22
Eastleigh	Mandron	15					15	71	15
North Ferriby United	Thompson	12					12	33	24
Solihull Moors	Asante	12					12	71	16
Southport	Allen	11					11	59	23
Wrexham	Rooney	11					11	50	13
Maidstone United	Loza	10					10	65	14
Torquay United	Williams	10					10	56	17

PTG - Players Total Goals I CTG - Club's Total Goals I FLP - Final League Position

AFC TELFORD UNITED

Club Contact Details
New Bucks Head Stadium, Watling Street, Wellington, Telford TF1 2TU
01952 640 064
office@telfordutd.co.uk

Ground Capacity: 6,380 **Seats:** 2,200 **Covered:** 4,800 **Clubhouse:** Yes **Shop:** Yes

Record Attendance
5,710 vs Burscough 28/04/2007
Previous Grounds
None - Renovation of the old Bucks Head started in 2000 and was completed in 2003.

10 YEAR RECORD

07-08		08-09		09-10		10-11		11-12		12-13		13-14		14-15		15-16		16-17	
Conf N	2	Conf N	4	Conf N	11	Conf N	2	Conf	20	Conf	24	Conf N	1	Conf	22	Nat N	18	Nat N	17
FAC	2Q	FAC	1Pr	FAC	1P	FAC	3Qr	FAC	1P	FAC	4Qr	FAC	2Q	FAC	2P	FAC	2Q	FAC	2Qr
FAT	1P	FAT	SF	FAT	3Qr	FAT	3P	FAT	2P	FAT	2P	FAT	1Pr	FAT	2P	FAT	1P	FAT	1P

Club Factfile

Founded: 1892 **Nickname:** The Bucks **Manager:** Rob Edwards

Previous Names: Wellington Town 1892-1969. AFC Telford United was formed when Telford United folded in May 2004

Previous Leagues: Shropshire 1892-98. Birmingham & District 1898-1901, 02-06, 08-38, 39-45. The Combination 1901-02. Cheshire County 1938-39, 45-58. Southern 1958-79. Alliance/Conference 1979-2004. Northern Premier 2004-06.

Club Colours (change): White/navy/white (Red/black/black)

RECORDS
Victory: 7-0 v Runcorn (A) - Northern Premier League Division One, 17/04/06.
Defeat: 1-6 v Guiseley (A) - Conference North, 01/04/14.
Goalscorer: Andy Brown - 56 (2008-12)
Appearances: Ryan Young - 367 (2007-14)
Additional: Paid £5,000 to Tamworth for Lee Moore 08/12/06
Received £25,000 from Burnley for Duane Courtney 31/08/05

HONOURS
FA Comps: Welsh FA Cup 1901-02, 05-06, 39-40. FA Trophy 1970-71, 82-83.

League: Birmingham & District 1920-21, 34-35, 35-36, 39-40. Cheshire County 1945-46, 46-47, 51-52.
NPL Div. 1 Play-off 2004-05, Premier Division Play-off 2006-07. Conference North Play-off 2010-11, Champions 13-14.

County FA: Birmingham Senior Cup 1946-47. Walsall Senior Cup 1946-47. Shropshire Senior Cup 2008-09, 13-14, 16-17.

BEST PERFORMANCES	**FA Cup:** Fifth Round Proper 1984-85. As AFC Telford United - Second Round Proper 2014-15.
	FA Trophy: Final 1969-70, 70-71, 82-83, 87-88. As AFC Telford United - Semi-Finals 2008-09.
	FA Vase: N/A

AFC TELFORD UNITED MATCH RESULTS 2016-17

Date	Comp	H/A	Opponents	Att:	Result	Goalscorers	Pos	No.
Aug 6	Nat N	H	AFC Fylde	1139	L 0 1		20	1
9	Nat N	A	FC Utd of Manchester	2124	D 0 - 0		18	2
13	Nat N	A	Tamworth	839	L 1 - 2	Peers 15	19	3
16	Nat N	H	Stalybridge Celtic	1014	W 2 - 0	Peers 53 Hibbert 87	14	4
20	Nat N	A	Curzon Ashton	241	D 1 - 1	Reynolds 60	14	5
27	Nat N	H	Stockport County	1311	D 0 - 1			6
29	Nat N	A	Nuneaton Town	633	D 1 - 1	Wilson 78	14	7
Sept 3	Nat N	H	FC Halifax Town	1324	L 1 - 2	Samuels 13	15	8
6	Nat N	H	Kidderminster Harriers	1459	W 1 - 0	Evans 25	12	9
10	Nat N	A	Gainsborough Trinity	452	L 1 - 3	Wilson 65	13	10
13	Nat N	A	Gloucester City	313	L 0 - 3		16	11
17	FAC2Q	A	Worcester City	721	D 0 - 0			12
20	FAC2Qr	H	Worcester City	661	L 1 - 3	Hibbert 31		13
24	Nat N	H	Chorley	1033	D 0 - 0		17	14
Oct 8	Nat N	A	Bradford PA	318	D 1 - 1	Bailey 53	15	15
15	Nat N	H	FC United of Manchester	1706	W 1 - 0	McCarthy 62	14	16
22	Nat N	A	Altrincham	1074	W 2 - 0	McCarthy 24 Reid 58	12	17
29	Nat N	H	Salford City	1841	L 0 - 2		9	18
Nov 5	Nat N	A	Boston United	1021	L 1 - 2	Wilson 65	15	19
12	Nat N	A	Worcester City	652	L 1 - 2	Havern 77	16	20
19	Nat N	H	Darlington 1883	1136	W 2 - 0	Wilson 69 Reid 76	14	21
26	FAT 3Q	A	Ramsbottom United	319	W 2 - 0	McCarthy 62 Wilson 82		22
Dec 3	Nat N	A	Gloucester City	645	L 1 - 2	Royle 90	14	23
10	FAT 1	A	Kidderminster Harriers	1096	L 0 - 4			24
!7	Nat N	A	Harrogate Town	1406	D 1 - 1	Fitzpatrick 82	16	25
26	Nat N	H	Alfreton Town	1230	D 1 - 1	Reid 61	16	26
Jan 1	Nat N	A	Alfreton Town	601	L 2 - 3	Wilson 36 (pen) Kissock 89	18	27
7	Nat N	H	Gainsborough Trinity	1,081	D 1 - 1	Jones 33	18	28
14	Nat N	H	Curzon Ashton	1,002	W 3 - 1	Wilson 24 90 (pen) Jones 57	15	29
21	Nat N	A	Kidderminster Harriers	1,752	L 0 - 1		17	30
Feb 4	Nat N	H	Gloucester City	948	L 0 - 2		19	31
11	Nat N	A	AFC Fylde	1502	D 1 - 1	Hughes 57	18	32
18	Nat N	H	Tamworth	1178	W 1 - 0	McCone 19	16	33
25	Nat N	A	Salford City	1248	L 1 - 2	Hughes 12	16	34
Mar 4	Nat N	H	Altrincham	1105	W 1 - 0	Hibbert 87	16	35
7	Nat N	H	Brackley Town	844	L 0 - 6		16	36
11	Nat N	A	Chorley	1131	L 1 - 2	Wilson 38	16	37
18	Nat N	H	Bradford PA	1028	L 1 - 3	Hughes 70 (pen)	17	38
25	Nat N	A	Brackley Town	367	L 1 - 2	Gouhg 68 (og)	18	39
28	Nat N	A	Stalybridge Celtic	206	W 2 0	Bailey 52 Marsden 77	17	40
April 1	Nat N	H	Worcester City	1139	W 1 - 0	Marsden 82	16	41
8	Nat N	A	Boston United	1006	L 0 - 3		17	42
15	Nat N	A	Stockport County	4261	D 1 - 1	Dieina 78	16	43
17	Nat N	H	Nuneaton Town	1246	L 2 - 4	Bailey 42 Hughes 45	17	44
22	Nat N	A	Darlington 1883	1800	L 0 - 1		17	45
29	Nat N	H	Harrogate Town	1047	D 0 - 0		17	46

GOALSCORERS	SG	CSG	Pens	Hat tricks	Total		SG	CSG	Pens	Hat tricks	Total
2015-16 McCarthy					8	Dirina	1				1
Wilson	8		2		9	Evans	1				1
Hughes	4		1		4	Fitzpatrick	1				1
Bailey	3				3	Havern	1				1
Hibbert	3				3	Kissock	1				1
McCarthy	3				3	McCone	1				1
Reid	3				3	Opponents	1				1
Jones	2				2	Reynolds	1				1
Marsden	2				2	Royle	1				1
Peers	2	2			2	Samuels	1				1

ALFRETON TOWN

Club Contact Details
The Impact Arena, North Street, Alfreton, Derbyshire DE55 7FZ
01773 830 277
a.raisin@alfretontownfc.com

Ground Capacity: 3,600 **Seats:** 1,500 **Covered:** 2,600 **Clubhouse:** Yes **Shop:** Yes

Record Attendance
5,023 v Matlock Town - Central Alliance 1960
Previous Grounds
None

10 YEAR RECORD

07-08	08-09	09-10	10-11	11-12	12-13	13-14	14-15	15-16	16-17
Conf N 16	Conf N 3	Conf N 3	Conf N 1	Conf 15	Conf 13	Conf 11	Conf 21	Nat N 10	Nat N 18
FAC 2Qr	FAC 2P	FAC 3Qr	FAC 2Qr	FAC 1P	FAC 2P	FAC 1P	FAC 4Qr	FAC 4Q	FAC 1Pr
FAT 2Pr	FAT 1P	FAT 3Qr	FAT 3Pr	FAT 3P	FAT 1P	FAT 1P	FAT 2P	FAT 3Q	FAT 2P

Club Factfile

Founded: 1959   **Nickname:** The Reds   **Manager:** John McDermott - May 2017

Previous Names: Formed when Alfreton Miners Welfare and Alfreton United merged.

Previous Leagues: Central Alliance 1959-61. Midland 1961-82. Northern Counties East 1982-87, 99-02. Northern Premier 1987-99, 02-04.

Club Colours (change): All red

RECORDS
Victory: 15-0 v Loughbrough Midland League 1969-70
Defeat: 1-9 v Solihull - FAT 1997. 0-8 v Bridlington - 1992
Goalscorer: John Harrison - 303
Appearances: John Harrison - 561
Additional: Paid £2,000 to Worksop Town for Mick Goddard
Received £150,000 from Swindon Town for Aden Flint, January 2011

HONOURS
FA Comps: None

League: Midland 1969-70, 73-74, 76-77. Northern Counties East 1986-87, 2001-02
Northern Premier League Division One 2002-03. Conference North 2010-11

County FA: Derbyshire Senior Cup 1960-61, 69-70, 72-73, 73-74, 81-82, 94-95, 2001-02, 02-03, 15-16

BEST PERFORMANCES	**FA Cup:** Second Round Proper 2008-09, 12-13
	FA Trophy: Fourth Round Proper 2002-03 (r), 2004-05
	FA Vase: Fifth Round Proper 1999-00

ALFRETON TOWN MATCH RESULTS 2016-17

Date	Comp	H/A	Opponents	Att:	Result		Goalscorers	Pos	No.
Aug 6	Nat N	A	Stockport County	2632	L	3 - 4	Clayton 45 Allen 48 Bradley 55	18	1
9	Nat N	H	Gainsborough Trinity	445	W	4 - 0	Westcarr 2 Bradley 6 32 Smith 85	7	2
13	Nat N	H	Curzon Ashton	457	L	0 - 1		13	3
16	Nat N	A	Brackley Town	272	W	3 - 2	Bradley 38 Westcarr 58 Allen 62	10	4
20	Nat N	H	Stockport County	440	L	3 - 4	Wilson 14 Westcarr 21 Bradley 36 (pen)	12	5
27	Nat N	A	Darlington 1883	1349	W	4 - 3	Westcarr 22 Hearn 31 63 Monkhouse 43	11	6
29	Nat N	H	Tamworth	547	L	2 - 5	Monkhouse 51 Bradley 56	12	7
Sept 3	Nat N	A	Salford City	1503	L	1 - 4	Smith 76	13	8
6	Nat N	A	Worcester City	45	L	3 - 5	Smith 5 Allen 58 Hearn 90	14	9
10	Nat N	H	Harrogate Town	430	W	1 - 0	Bradley 32	12	10
13	Nat N	A	Boston United	926	L	2 - 3	Westcarr 37 Wilson 61	13	11
17	FAC2Q	H	Ashton United	263	W	1 - 0	Allen 9		12
24	Nat N	A	Kidderminster Harriers	568	D	3 - 3	Westcarr 1 Allen 11 Priestley 37	14	13
Oct 1	FAC3Q	A	Kings Lynn Town	847	W	2 - 0	Priestley 25 39		14
8	Nat N	A	FC United of Manchester	2528	L	3 - 4	Smith 41 54 McGowan 49	17	15
15	FAC4Q	H	Gateshead	457	D	2 - 2	Clayton 24 Westcarr 76		16
19	FAC4Qr	A	Gateshead	465	W	3 - 2	Westcarr 10 99 (pen) Smith 69		17
22	Nat N	A	Stalybridge Celtic	456	W	3 - 2	Westcarr 20 Smith 45 Hearn 90	15	18
29	Nat N	H	Chorley	506	D	2 - 2	Edmundson 87 90	16	19
Nov 5	FAC1	H	Newport County	1109	D	1 - 1	Kennedy 74		20
7	Nat N	H	Gloucester City	344	L	0 - 2		16	21
12	Nat N	A	Bradford PA	322	L	0 - 1		17	22
15	FAC1r	A	Newport County	1189	L	1 - 4	Priestley 74		23
19	Nat N	A	Altrincham	474	W	3 - 2	Monkhouse 74 86 Hearn 90	15	24
26	FAT 3Q	A	Gainsborough Trinity	308	D	0 - 0			25
29	FAT3Qr	H	Gainsborough Trinity	175	W	4 - 1	Westcarr 87 119 Clayton 102 110 (aet)		26
Dec 3	Nat N	A	Nuneaton Town	465	L	1 - 4	Smith 13	16	27
10	FAT 1	H	North Ferriby United	290	W	1 - 0	Wilson 64		28
!7	Nat N	H	Salford City	718	D	1 - 1	Clayton 24	18	29
26	Nat N	A	AFC Telford United	1230	D	1 - 1	Westcarr 12 (pen)	18	30
Jan 1	Nat N	H	AFC Telford United	601	W	3 - 2	Shelton 16 Westcarr 34 (pen) Marshall 43	16	31
7	Nat N	A	Harrogate Town	735	L	3 - 6	Shelton 8 Clayton 65 Westcarr 89 (pen)	16	32
14	FAT2	A	Boreham Wood	213	L	1 - 2	Heaton 56		33
21	Nat N	H	Worcester City	451	D	0 - 0		18	34
24	Nat N	A	AFC Fylde	1503	L	0 - 2		18	35
Feb 4	Nat N	A	Gainsborough Trinity	572	W	2 - 0	Westcarr 8 59	16	36
11	Nat N	H	Stockport County	993	D	1 - 1	Hearn 90	16	37
14	Nat N	H	Brackley Town	308	D	0 - 0		16	38
18	Nat N	A	Curzon Ashton	243	L	0 - 5		17	39
25	Nat N	A	Chorley	999	L	1 - 2	Hearn 23	17	40
Mar 7	Nat N	H	FC Halifax Town	499	W	1 - 0	Westcarr 61	17	41
11	Nat N	A	Kidderminster Harriers	1542	L	0 - 3		17	42
18	Nat N	H	FC Utd of Manchester	898	W	2 - 1	Smith 6 Atkinson 77	16	43
21	Nat N	H	Boston United	547	W	1 - 0	Hearn 41	15	44
25	Nat N	A	Gloucester City	436	L	0 - 4		16	45
April 1	Nat N	H	Bradford PA	459	L	0 - 1		17	46
4	Nat N	H	Stalybridge Celtic	347	L	0 - 2		17	47
8	Nat N	A	FC Ha;lifax Town	1634	L	0 - 1		18	48
15	Nat N	H	Darlington 1883	867	L	0 - 3		18	49
17	Nat N	A	Tamworth	711	L	1 - 4	Monkhouse 87	18	50
22	Nat N	A	Altrincham	801	D	1 - 1	Monkhouse 40		51
29	Nat N	H	Nuneaton Town	580	D	3 - 3	HEARN 3 (19 55 90)	18	52

GOALSCORERS	SG	CSG	Pens	Hat tricks	Total		SG	CSG	Pens	Hat tricks	Total
2015-16 Jones					14	Edmundson	2				2
Westcarr	15	3,3x3	4		18	Shelton	2	2			2
Hearn	8		1		11	Atkinson	1				1
Smith	7	2			9	Heaton	1				1
Bradley	6	2	1		7	Kennedy	1				1
Clayton	5				6	Marshall	1				1
Monkhouse	5	2			6	McGowan	1				1
Allen	5	2			5						
Priestley	3	2			4						
Wilson	2				3						

BLYTH SPARTANS

Club Contact Details
Croft Park, Blyth, Northumberland NE24 3JE
01670 352 373
generalmanager@blythspartans.com

Ground Capacity: 4,435 **Seats:** 563 **Covered:** 1,000 **Clubhouse:** Yes **Shop:** Yes

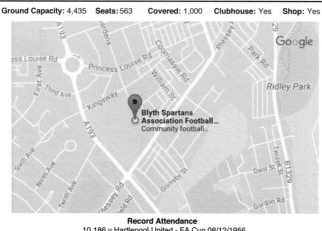

Record Attendance
10,186 v Hartlepool United - FA Cup 08/12/1956
Previous Grounds
None

10 YEAR RECORD

07-08	08-09	09-10	10-11	11-12	12-13	13-14	14-15	15-16	16-17
Conf N 18	Conf N 15	Conf N 13	Conf N 9	Conf N 21	NP P 16	NP P 8	NP P 6	NP P 2	NP P 1
FAC 3Q	FAC 3P	FAC 4Qr	FAC 2Q	FAC 1P	FAC 2Qr	FAC 1Q	FAC 3P	FAC 1Q	FAC 2Q
FAT 2P	FAT 3Q	FAT 2P	FAT QF	FAT 3Q	FAT 1Q	FAT 2Q	FAT 2Qr	FAT 3Q	FAT 3Qr

Club Factfile

Founded: 1899 **Nickname:** Spartans **Manager:** Alun Armstrong

Previous Names: None

Previous Leagues: Northumberland 1901-07, Northern All. 1907-13, 46-47, North Eastern 1913-39, Northern Com. 1945-46, Midland 1958-60, Northern Counties 1960-62, Northern 1962-94, Northern Premier 1994-2006, 13-17. Conference 2006-13.

Club Colours (change): Green & white stripes/black/black (Yellow with red sash/red/red)

RECORDS
Victory: 18-0 v Gateshead Town - Northern Alliance 28/12/1907
Defeat: 0-10 v Darlington - North Eastern League 12/12/1914
Appearances: Eddie Alder - 605 (1965-68)
Additional: Received £30,000 from Hull City for Les Mutrie

HONOURS
FA Comps: None

League: North Eastern 1935-36. Northern 1972-73, 74-75, 75-76, 79-80, 80-81, 81-82, 82-83, 83-84, 86-87, 87-88. Northern Division 1 1994-95. Northern Premier Premier Division 2005-06, 16-17.

County FA: Northumberland Senior Cup 2014-15, 16-17.

BEST PERFORMANCES	**FA Cup:** Fifth Round Proper 1977-78(r).
	FA Trophy: Quarter-finals 1979-80(r), 82-83(r), 2010-11.
	FA Vase: N/A

BLYTH SPARTANS MATCH RESULTS 2016-17

Date	Comp	H/A	Opponents	Att:	Result	Goalscorers	Pos	No.
Aug 13	NPL	H	Coalville Town	561	W 3 - 1	Maguire 6 75 Reid 35	2	1
16	NPL	A	Marine	342	L 0 - 1		7	2
20	NPL	A	Halesowen Town	376	W 5 - 0	Pattison 22 68 Maguire 61 72 Hutchinson 65	3	3
23	NPL	H	Ashton United	562	D 3 - 3	Maguire 29 Turnbull 42 Reid 70	4	4
27	NPL	H	Grantham Town	175	W 2 - 1	Richardson 64 Dale 68	3	5
29	NPL	A	Workington	652	W 2 - 0	Reid 20 Pattison 90	2	6
Sept 3	FAC1Q	H	Frickley Athletic	667	W 3 - 1	Reid 49 55 Maguire 89		7
10	NPL	H	Sutton Coldfield Town	575	W 5 - 0	Wade 45 Maguire 54 72 Reid 63 Armstrong 90	1	8
13	NPL	H	Marine	522	W 1 - 0	Pattison 65 (pen)	1	9
17	FAC2Q	H	Morpeth Town	1065	L 2 - 4	Maguire 52 Swailes 72 (og)		10
20	NPL	A	Frickley Athletic	220	L 0 - 1		2	11
24	NPL	H	Corby Town	539	L 3 - 4	Dale 22 89 Reid 87	2	12
27	NPL	A	Spennymoor Town	818	D 0 - 0		3	13
Oct 4	NPL	H	Warrington Town	507	L 0 - 3		6	14
8	NPL	H	Mickleover Sports	501	W 3 - 0	Armstrong 15 Pattison 22 Rivers 27	4	15
11	NPL	H	Matlock Town	281	D 0 - 0		6	16
15	NPL	A	Hednesford Town	465	W 2 - 1	Reid 67 Flanagan 81 (og)	4	17
18	NPL	H	Ilkeston	511	W 3 - 1	Pattison 61 Dale 64 Armstrong 90	2	18
22	NPL	H	Stourbridge	507	W 2 - 1	Buddle 28 Dale 35	2	19
29	FAT1Q	A	Goole Town	252	D 1 - 1	Wade 28		20
Nov 1	FAT1Qr	A	Goole Town	440	W 7 - 1	MAGUIRE 3 (16 28 79) ARMSTRONG 3 (37 43 85) Pell 88		21
5	NPL	A	Barwell	241	W 2 - 0	Pattison 21 62	2	22
12	FAT2Q	H	Halesowen Town	565	W 4 - 3	Buddle 29 Maguire 39 Pattison 82 90		23
19	NPL	H	Stafford Rangers	589	D 2 - 2	Armstrong 18 20	3	24
Dec 3	NPL	H	Buxton	573	D 0 - 0		4	25
10	FAT1	H	Altrincham	523	L 2 - 3	Armstrong 59 Dale 89		26
17	NPL	H	Barwell	523	W 2 - 0	Pattison 25 (pen) 68 (pen)	3	27
26	NPL	A	Whitby Town	512	L 1 - 2	Armstrong 69	5	28
Jan 2	NPL	H	Workington	673	W 3 - 2	MAGUIRE 3 (52 55 81)	4	29
7	NPL	A	Coalville Town	186	W 1 - 0	Dale 74	3	30
14	NPL	H	Nantwich Town	545	W 2 - 0	Dale 47 Turnbull 59		31
17	NPL	A	Skelmersdale United	210	W 4 - 1	Maguire 5 44 Hutchinson 54 Wrightson 90	1	32
21	NPL	A	Mickleover Sports	239	W 7 - 1	Maguire 10 REID 4 (41 60 68 88) Ladder 74 90	1	33
28	NPL	H	Matlock Town	682	W 4 - 1	Armstrong 47 Dale 79 Rivers 80 Maguire 90	1	34
Feb 4	NPL	A	Ilkeston	369	W 5 - 0	Rivers 5 55 Dale 42 Wrightson 62 Maguire 68	1	35
7	NPL	A	Warrington Town	313	W 2 - 0	Armstrong 69 Maguire 85	1	36
11	NPL	A	Hednesford Town	601	W 5 - 1	Rivers 2 16 Armstrong 56 Dale 69 Maguire 75	1	37
18	NPL	A	Stourbridge	1376	W 2 - 1	Dale 24 Maguire 45	1	38
25	NPL	H	Corby Town	644	W 4 - 2	Maguire 14 79 Reid 70 Armstrong 86	1	39
28	NPL	A	Spennymoor Town	946	L 1 - 2	Maguire 67	1	40
Mar 4	NPL	A	Sutton Coldfield Town	273	L 2 - 3	Armstrong 11 21	1	41
7	NPL	H	Frickley Athletic	587	W 5 - 1	Armstrong 1 23 Dale 58 Reid 62 Pattison 90	1	42
11	NPL	A	Buxton	445	D 2 - 2	Maguire 44 66	1	43
18	NPL	H	Skelemersdale United	667	W 4 - 0	Maguire 36 39 Watson 64 Armstrong 87	1	44
21	NPL	A	Nantwich Town	531	D 2 - 2	Armstrong 33 61	1	45
25	NPL	H	Rushall Olympic	769	W 2 - 1	McTiernan 72 Rivers 90	1	46
Apr 1	NPL	A	Stafford Rangers	809	W 1 - 0	Reid 56	1	47
4	NPL	A	Rushall Olympic	268	W 1 - 0	Maguire 7	1	48
8	NPL	H	Halesowen Town	1167	W 3 - 0	Armstrong 18 Reid 50 Wrightson 83	1	49
15	NPL	A	Ashton United	402	D 1 - 1	Buddle 27	1	50
17	NPL	H	Whitley Bay	772	W 5 - 1	Armstrong 1 42 Maguire 3 McTiernan 13 Pattison 85	1	51
22	NPL	A	Grantham Town	1041	W 5 - 1	MAGUIRE 3 (17 48 59) Dale 28 Rivers 69	1	52

GOALSCORERS	SG	CSG	Pens	Hat tricks	Total		SG	CSG	Pens	Hat tricks	Total
2015-16 Dale					25	Ladder	1				2
Maguire	23	9	3		36	McTiernan	2				2
Armstrong	18	2	1		24	Opponents	2				2
Reid	14	3	1		16	Turnbull	2				2
Dale	13	2			14	Wade	2				2
Pattison	10	2	3		12	Pell	1				1
Rivers	6				10	Richardson	1				1
Buddle	3				3	Watson	1				1
Wrightson	3				3						
Hutchinson	2				2						

BOSTON UNITED

Club Contact Details

Jakemans Stadium, York Street, Boston PE21 6JN

01205 364 406

craig.singleton@bufc.co.uk

Ground Capacity: 6,778   **Seats:** 5,711   **Covered:** 6,645   **Clubhouse:** Yes   **Shop:** Yes

Record Attendance
11,000 v Derby County, FA Cup Third Round Proper Replay, 09/01/1974
Previous Grounds
None

10 YEAR RECORD

07-08	08-09	09-10	10-11	11-12	12-13	13-14	14-15	15-16	16-17
Conf N 10	NP P 16	NP P 3	Conf N 3	Conf N 11	Conf N 16	Conf N 6	Conf N 3	Nat N 5	Nat N 15
FAC 4Q	FAC 4Q	FAC 2Q	FAC 2Q	FAC 2Qr	FAC 4Q	FAC 3Q	FAC 3Q	FAC 2Q	FAC 3Q
FAT 3Q	FAT 1P	FAT 2Qr	FAT 2P	FAT 2P	FAT 1Pr	FAT 2P	FAT 1Pr	FAT 3Q	FAT 3Q

Club Factfile

Founded: 1933   **Nickname:** The Pilgrims   **Manager:** Adam Murray

Previous Names: Reformed as Boston United when Boston Town folded in 1933

Previous Leagues: Midland 1933-58, 62-64, Southern 1958-62, 98-2000, United Counties 1965-66, West Midlands 1966-68,
Northern Premier 1968-79, 93-98, 2008-10, Alliance/Conference 1979-93, 2000-02, 07-08, Football League 2002-07.

Club Colours (change): Amber and black halves/black/black (Green/white/green with white hoops)

RECORDS

Victory: 12-0 v Spilsby Town - Grace Swan Cup 1992-93

Defeat: 2-9 v AFC Fylde - (A) National North, 19/11/2017

Goalscorer: Chris Cook - 181

Appearances: Billy Howells - 500+

Additional: Paid £30,000 to Scarborough for Paul Ellender, 08/2001
Received £50,000 from Bolton Wanderers for David Norris 2000

HONOURS

FA Comps: None

League: Central Alliance League 1961-62. United Counties League 1965-66. West Midlands League 1966-67, 67-68.
Northern Premier League 1972-73, 73-74, 76-77, 77-78. Southern League 1999-2000. Conference 2001-02.

County FA: Lincolnshire Senior Cup 1934-35, 36-37, 37-38, 45-46, 49-50, 54-55, 55-56, 56-57, 59-60, 76-77, 78-79, 85-86, 87-88,
88-89, 05-06. East Anglian Cup 1960-61.

BEST PERFORMANCES	**FA Cup:** Third Round Proper 1971-72, 73-74 (r), 2004-05 (r)
	FA Trophy: Final 1984-85
	FA Vase: N/A

BOSTON UNITED MATCH RESULTS 2016-17

Date	Comp	H/A	Opponents	Att:	Result	Goalscorers	Pos	No.
Aug 6	Nat N	H	Stalybridge Celtic	1023	L 0 - 1		21	1
9	Nat N	A	Harrogate Town	702	L 0 - 2		21	2
13	Nat N	A	Darlington 1883	1445	L 1 - 4	Rollins 90	22	3
16	Nat N	H	Tamworth	965	W 3 - 0	Fairhurst 5 Colley 68 Hilliard 72	17	4
20	Nat N	A	Chorley	1009	L 0 - 2		18	5
27	Nat N	H	Kidderminster Harriers	1047	D 1 - 1	Maguire 84	16	6
29	Nat N	A	Gloucester City	469	L 1 - 3	Smith 44	17	7
Sept 3	Nat N	H	FC United of Manchester	1424	L 2 - 3	Agnew 28 (pen) Rollins 38	18	8
6	Nat N	H	Bradford PA	905	W 1 - 0	Smith 82	16	9
10	Nat N	A	Stockport County	2466	D 1 - 1	Smith 7	18	10
13	Nat N	H	Alfreton Town	926	W 3 - 2	Rollins 56 Agnew 89 (pen) Smith 90	15	11
17	FAC2Q	A	Kirby Muxloe	330	W 2 - 1	Maguire 21 Rollins 39		12
24	Nat N	A	Altrincham	918	W 1 - 0	Agnew 70	12	13
Oct 1	FAC3Q	A	Kettering Town	628	L 0 - 2			14
8	Nat N	H	Worcester City	1138	D 0 - 0		12	15
15	Nat N	A	Salford City	1425	D 3 - 3	Allen 19 (og) Rollins 35 Smith 80	13	16
22	Nat N	H	FC Halifax Town	1236	L 1 - 4	Rollins 71	16	17
29	Nat N	A	Nuneaton Town	577	D 2 - 2	Hilliard 32 Robinson 61	17	18
Nov 5	Nat N	A	AFC Telford United	1021	W 2 - 1	St Juste 15 Smith 90	12	19
12	Nat N	H	Brackley Town	1092	L 2 - 3	Hilliard 41 Smith 65	14	20
19	Nat N	A	AFC Fylde	1503	L 2 - 9	Rollins 10 48	17	21
Dec 3	Nat N	A	Stalybridge Celtic	414	D 3 - 3	Miles 4 Smith 56 Brown 86		22
6	FAT 3Q	A	Witton Albion	194	L 2 - 4	Maguire 4 Marshall 6		23
!7	Nat N	A	FC Utd of Manchester	2393	D 1 - 1	Smith 23	17	24
20	Nat N	H	Curzon Ashton	979	W 3 - 1	Gordon 15 Hilliard 40 55	13	25
26	Nat N	H	Gainsborough Trinity	1602	D 1 - 1	Robinson 56	14	26
Jan 1	Nat N	A	Gainsborough Trinity	1005	W 2 - 1	Rollins 23 Robinson 90	13	27
7	Nat N	H	Stockport County	1360	L 0 - 2		14	28
21	Nat N	A	Bradford PA	329	W 2 - 0	Rollins 34 Thomas 74	14	29
28	Nat N	A	Tamworth	895	L 0 - 1		15	30
Feb 4	Nat N	A	Harrogate Town	1112	L 0 - 3		15	31
14	Nat N	H	Chorley	807	W 3 - 1	Chapman 55 (pen) Yeoman 62 Hilliard 74	12	32
18	Nat N	H	Darlington 1883	1243	L 1 - 2	Howley 63	13	33
25	Nat N	H	Nuneaton Town	957	L 1 - 3	Simmons 90	15	34
Mar 4	Nat N	A	FC Halifax Town	1752	D 0 - 0		15	35
11	Nat N	H	Altrincham	1026	L 0 - 1		15	36
18	Nat N	A	Worcester City	504	W 2 - 0	Chapman 2 Briscoe 43	15	37
21	Nat N	A	Alfreton Town	547	L 0 - 1		16	38
25	Nat N	H	Salford City	1242	W 2 - 0	Vince 12 Brown 73	15	39
April 1	Nat N	A	Brackley Town	333	D 0 - 0		15	40
8	Nat N	H	AFC Telford United	1006	W 3 - 0	Rollins 11 72 Dieseruvwe 61 (pen)	15	41
15	Nat N	A	Kidderminster Harriers	2056	L 0 - 1		15	42
17	Nat N	H	Gloucester City	1095	D 2 - 2	Chapman 20 (pen) Robinson 85	15	43
22	Nat N	H	AFC Fylde	1255	L 0 - 3		15	44
29	Nat N	A	Curzon Ashton	390	L 2 - 4	Shaw 45 (og) Hawley 87	15	45

GOALSCORERS	SG	CSG	Pens	Hat tricks	Total		SG	CSG	Pens	Hat tricks	Total
2015-16 Southwell					24	Briscoe	1				1
Rollins	10	2			12	Colley	1				1
Smith	9	3			9	Dieseruvwe	1		1		1
Hilliard	5				6	Fairhurst	1				1
Robinson	4	2			4	Gordon	1				1
Agnew	3		2		3	Maguire	1				1
Chapman	3		2		3	Miles	1				1
Maguire	3				3	Simmons	1				1
Brown	2				2	St Juste	1				1
Hawley	2				2	Thomas	1				1
Opponents	2				2	Vince	1				1
						Yeoman	1				1

BRACKLEY TOWN

Club Contact Details
St James Park, Churchill Way, Brackley NN13 7EJ
01280 704 077
pat.ashby55@btinternet.com

Ground Capacity: 3,500   **Seats:** 300   **Covered:** 1,500   **Clubhouse:** Yes   **Shop:** Yes

Record Attendance
2,604 v FC Halifax Town, Conference North Play-off final, 12/05/13.
Previous Grounds
Manor Road 1890-1968. Buckingham Road 1968-74.

10 YEAR RECORD

	07-08	08-09	09-10	10-11	11-12	12-13	13-14	14-15	15-16	16-17
	SthP 8	SthP 11	SthP 5	SthP 9	SthP 1	Conf N 3	Conf N 7	Conf N 18	Nat N 19	Nat N 7
FAC	1Qr	1P	2Q	2Q	1Q	3Q	2P	3Q	1Pr	2P
FAT	2Q	1P	2Qr	3Q	1P	1P	3Qr	3Q	3Q	QF

Club Factfile

Founded: 1890   **Nickname:** Saints   **Manager:** Kevin Wilkin - Sept 2015

Previous Names: N/A

Previous Leagues: Oxfordshire Senior. North Bucks & District. Banbury & District. Hellenic 1977-83, 94-97, 99-2004. United Counties 1983-84. Southern 1997-99.

Club Colours (change): Red and white stripes/white/red (All yellow)

RECORDS
Goalscorer: Paul Warrington - 320
Appearances: Terry Muckelberg - 350
Additional: Received £2,000 from Oxford City for Phil Mason 1998

HONOURS
FA Comps: N/A

League: United Counties Division One 1983-84. Hellenic Premier Division 1996-97, 2003-04. Southern Division One Midlands 2006-07, Premier Division 2011-12.

County FA: Northamptonshire Senior Cup 2010-11, 11-12, 14-15.

BEST PERFORMANCES	**FA Cup:** Second Round Proper 2013-14, 16-17.
	FA Trophy: Quarter-Finals 2016-17.
	FA Vase: Third Round Proper 1987-88.

BRACKLEY TOWN MATCH RESULTS 2016-17

Date	Comp	H/A	Opponents	Att:	Result	Goalscorers	Pos	No.
Aug 6	Nat N	H	Tamworth	360	D 0 - 0		18	1
9	Nat N	A	Kidderminster Harriers	1446	W 2 - 1	Armson 36 (pen) Gudger 74	4	2
13	Nat N	A	AFC Fylde	1365	D 1 - 1	Ndlovu 15	6	3
16	Nat N	H	Alfreton Town	272	L 2 - 3	Armson 63 (pen) 87	13	4
20	Nat N	A	Stockport County	2529	W 4 - 2	Ndlovu19 28 Dean 21 Gudger 78	7	5
27	Nat N	H	FC Utd of Manchester	565	W 1 - 0	Dean 75	8	6
29	Nat N	A	Gainsborough Trinity	473	D 1 - 1	Diggin 14	9	7
Sept 3	Nat N	H	Bradford PA	389	W 2 - 0	Armson 19 Graham 78	7	8
6	Nat N	H	Nuneaton Town	424	W 2 - 1	Walker 29 Diggin 64	4	9
10	Nat N	A	Chorley	1066	D 1 - 1	Armson 43	7	10
13	Nat N	H	Worcester City	352	L 0 - 2		8	11
17	FAC2Q	H	Rugby Town	305	W 6 - 0	Myles 1 Armson 11 67 Diggin 42 55 Pitt 69		12
24	Nat N	A	Salford City	1072	D 1 - 1	Diggin 23	9	13
Oct 1	FAC3Q	A	Worcester City	628	W 3 - 0	Diggin 24 Pitt 51 Bowen 90		14
8	Nat N	H	Darlington 1883	642	D 2 - 2	Dean 44 Byrne 74	9	15
15	FAC4Q	A	Beaconsfield SYCOB	495	W 5 - 0	Diggin 5 Armson 80 (pen) Pitt 85 Dias 90 Ndlovu 90		16
22	Nat N	H	Curzon Ashton	326	W 2 - 0	Graham 58 G.Walker 87	8	17
29	Nat N	A	FC Halifax Town	1581	W 3 - 1	Ndlovu 63 76 Diggin 65	7	18
Nov 5	FAC1	A	Gillingham	2410	D 2 - 2	Gudger 13 Armson 27		19
12	Nat N	H	Boston United	1092	W 3 - 2	DIGGIN 3 (15 22 33)	9	20
16	FAC1r	H	Gillingham	1654	W 4 - 3	ARMSON 3 (17 25 105) Nelson (og) 96 (aet)		21
19	Nat N	H	Harrogate Town	415	W 2 - 1	Moyo 50 Lowe 89	8	22
26	FAT3Q	A	Mickleover Sports	150	D 1 - 1	Gudger 90		23
29	FAT3Qr	H	Mickleover Sports	140	W 3 - 1	Moyo 25 Lowe 36 Diggin 57 (pen)		24
Dec 3	FAC2	A	Blackpool	1764	L 0 - 1			25
10	FAT1	A	AFC Fylde	641	D 1 - 1	Walker 25		26
13	FAT1r	H	AFC Fylde	164	W 4 - 0	Walker 5 Armson 12 (pen) Lowe 41 Moyo 53		27
!7	Nat N	A	Bradford P.A	276	L 1 - 2	Graham 2	9	28
20	Nat N	A	Stalybridge Celtic	211	W 1 - 0	Gudger 37	5	29
26	Nat N	H	Gloucester City	517	W 3 - 0	Walker 19 Diggin 75 Armson 84	9	30
Jan 7	Nat N	H	Chorley	525	L 0 - 1		9	31
14	FAT2	A	Stockport County	1605	D 1 - 1	Diggin 51		32
17	FAT2r	H	Stockport County	294	W 2 - 0	Armson 55 Walker 67		33
21	Nat N	A	Nuneaton Town	661	D 2 2	Ndlovu 71 Gudger 85	9	34
24	Nat N	H	Altrincham	298	D 1 - 1	Armson 25	9	35
31	Nat N	H	Stockport County	368	L 0 - 3		9	36
Feb 4	FAT3	A	Wealdstone	620	W 4 - 1	Armson 9 11 Moyo 42 Ndlovu 62		37
11	Nat N	A	Tamworth	548	L 1 - 2	Lowe 60	11	38
14	Nat N	A	Alfreton Town	308	D 0 - 0		11	39
18	Nat N	H	AFC Fylde	396	L 1 - 3	Clifton 68	11	40
21	Nat N	A	Gloucester City	262	W 3 - 1	Armson 45 (pen) 90 Walker 52	10	41
25	FATQF	A	York City	1994	L 0 - 1			42
28	Nat N	H	Kidderminster Harriers	379	W 2 0	Moyo 82 85	10	43
Mar 4	Nat N	A	Curzon Ashton	222	D 0 - 0		10	44
7	Nat N	A	AFC Telford United	844	W 6 - 0	Hempenstall 16 Byrne 40 Armson 47 Walker 50 Moyo 65 679		45
11	Nat N	H	Salford City	738	L 0 - 1		9	46
18	Nat N	A	Darlington 1883	1547	L 0 - 1		11	47
21	Nat N	H	Worcester City	321	W 2 - 1	Ndlovu 2 Barnes-Homer 67	9	48
25	Nat N	A	AFC Telford United	367	W 2 - 1	Ndlovu 41 Byrne 44	8	49
April 1	Nat N	H	Boston United	333	D 0 - 0		8	50
4	Nat N	H	FC Halifax Town	447	D 0 - 0		8	51
8	Nat N	A	Altrincham	685	W 3 - 1	Diggin 31 Hempenstall 7 Ndlovu 90	8	52
15	Nat N	A	FC Utd of Manchester	2823	W 2 - 1	Dean 35 Arnson 74	8	53
17	Nat N	H	Gainsborough Trinity	390	D 0 - 0		8	54
22	Nat N	A	Harrogate Town	660	W 2 - 1	Armson 40 Gudger 51	8	55
29	Nat N	H	Stalybridge Celtic	463	W 5 - 2	Armson 24 31 Ndlovu 49 Moyo 50 Diggin 90	7	56

GOALSCORERS	SG	CSG	Pens	Hat tricks	Total		SG	CSG	Pens	Hat tricks	Total
2015-16 Diggin					18	Graham	3				3
Armson	18	2	5	1	25	Pitt	3				3
Diggin	13	3	1	1	16	Hempenstall	2				2
Ndlovu	10				12	Barnes-Holmes	1				1
Moyo	7				9	Bowen	1				1
Walker	8	2			8	Clifton	1				1
Gudger	6				7	Dias	1				1
Dean	4	2			4	Myles	1				1
Lowe	4				4	Opponents	1				1
Byrne	3				3						

BRADFORD PARK AVENUE

Club Contact Details
Horsfall Stadium, Cemetery Road, Bradford, West Yorkshire BD6 2NG
07710 446 485
joe.mosley@bpafc.com

Ground Capacity: 5,000   **Seats:** 1,800   **Covered:** 2,000   **Clubhouse:** Yes   **Shop:** Yes

Record Attendance
2,100 v Bristol City - FA Cup 1st Round 2003
Previous Grounds
Park Ave 1907-73, 87-88, Valley Parade 73-74, Bingley Rd, Hope Ave, Avenue Rd, Bramley, M'nt Pleasant

10 YEAR RECORD

07-08		08-09		09-10		10-11		11-12		12-13		13-14		14-15		15-16		16-17	
NP1N	1	NP P	7	NP P	2	NP P	3	NP P	4	Conf N	7	Conf N	10	Conf N	13	Nat N	14	Nat N	16
FAC	4Q	FAC	2Q	FAC	3Qr	FAC	1Q	FAC	1P	FAC	1P	FAC	4Qr	FAC	2Qr	FAC	3Qr	FAC	2Q
FAT	1Q	FAT	1Q	FAT	1Q	FAT	1Q	FAT	1Qr	FAT	3Q	FAT	2P	FAT	1P	FAT	2Pr	FAT	3Q

Club Factfile

Founded: 1863   **Nickname:** Avenue   **Manager:** Mark Bower - Sept 2016

Previous Names: Bradford FC. 1863-1907. Reformed as a Sunday club in 1974, then as a Saturday club in 1988.

Previous Leagues: West York. 1895-98. Yorkshire 1898-99. Southern 1907-08. Football Lge 1908-70. NPL 1970-74, 95-04, 05-12. Bradford Am Sun. 1974-76. Bradford Sun.All. 1976-92. W. Riding Co. Am. 1988-89. Central Mids 1989-90. N.W. Co. 1990-95. Conf 2004-05

Club Colours (change): All green & white (Red, amber & black)

RECORDS

Victory: 11-0 v Derby Dale - FA Cup 1908
Defeat: 0-7 v Barnsley - 1911
Goalscorer: Len Shackleton - 171 (1940-46)
Appearances: Tommy Farr - 542 (1934-50)
Additional: Paid £24,500 to Derby County for Leon Leuty 1950
Received £34,000 from Derby County for Kevin Hector 1966

HONOURS

FA Comps: N/A

League: West Yorkshire 1895-96 (Shared). Football League Division Three North 1927-28. North West Counties Div.One 1994-95 Northern Premier Division One 2000-01, Division One North 2007-08, Premier Division Play-offs 2011-12.

County FA: West Riding Senior Cup x9. West Riding County Cup 1990-91, 2014-15, 15-16.

BEST PERFORMANCES	**FA Cup:** Quarter-finals 1912-13, 19-20, 45-46.
	FA Trophy: Fourth Round Proper 1998-99.
	FA Vase: Second Round Proper 1994-95.

BRADFORD PARK AVENUE MATCH RESULTS 2016-17

Date	Comp	H/A	Opponents	Att:	Result		Goalscorers	Pos	No.
Aug 6	Nat N	A	Gainsborough Trinity	583	D	1 - 1	Dickinson 90	12	1
10	Nat N	H	Curzon Ashton	334	D	4 - 4	McKenna 6 Dickinson 13 Sharp 76 Payne 90	10	2
13	Nat N	H	Nuneaton Town	314	D	1 - 1	Sharp 36	15	3
16	Nat N	A	Chorley	790	L	0 - 3		16	4
20	Nat N	H	Harrogate Town	301	L	2 - 3	Dean 57 66	17	5
27	Nat N	A	Tamworth	669	L	1 - 5	Monaghan 29	18	6
29	Nat N	H	AFC Fylde	347	L	1 - 4	Sharp 44	18	7
Sept 3	Nat N	A	Brackley Town	389	L	0 - 2		21	8
6	Nat N	A	Boston United	905	L	0 - 1		22	9
10	Nat N	H	Worcester City	230	L	0 - 3		22	10
14	Nat N	H	Darlington 1883	611	L	1 - 2	Sinclair 49	22	11
17	**FAC2Q**	**H**	**Salford City**	**427**	**L**	**0 - 1**			12
24	Nat N	H	FC Halifax Town	1761	L	0 - 4		22	13
Oct 8	Nat N	H	AFC Telford United	318	D	1 - 1	Sharp 52	22	14
15	Nat N	H	Chorley	390	L	0 - 3		22	15
22	Nat N	A	Gloucester City	380	L	0 - 1		22	16
25	Nat N	A	Altrincham	756	W	3 - 2	McKenna 31 Sinclare 62 Wroe 75	21	17
29	Nat N	H	Stalybridge Celtic	756	L	0 - 1		21	18
Nov 5	Nat N	A	FC Utd of Manchester	2379	W	3 - 2	McKenna 17 Dean 22 Boshell 49	22	19
12	Nat N	H	Alfreton Town	322	W	1 - 0	Wroe 20	20	20
19	Nat N	A	Stockport County	3246	W	2 - 1	Sinclair 69 Knowles 90	20	21
26	**FAT 3Q**	**A**	**Stockport County**	**1164**	**L**	**0 - 2**			22
Dec 3	Nat N	H	Kidderminster Harriers	379	L	1 - 3	Cofie 78	20	23
!7	Nat N	H	Brackley Town	276	W	2 - 1	Davis 45 Hill 90	20	24
26	Nat N	A	Salford City	1049	L	0 - 1		20	25
Jan 1	Nat N	H	Salford City	539	L	0 - 2		20	26
7	Nat N	A	Worcester City	451	W	1 - 0	Boshell 90	20	27
14	Nat N	A	Harrogate Town	995	L	0 - 1		20	28
21	Nat N	H	Boston United	329	L	0 - 2		20	29
Feb 4	Nat N	A	Curzon Ashton	227	W	2 - 1	Knowles 22 Boshell 71	20	30
11	Nat N	H	Gainsborough Trinity	272	W	5 - 1	Wroe 10 (p) 90 (p) Chippenddale 61 Johnson 71 Sharp 80	20	31
18	Nat N	A	Nuneaton Town	573	W	2 - 1	Killock 40 Johnson 71	18	32
Mar 4	Nat N	H	Gloucester City	296	L	0 - 1		18	33
11	Nat N	H	FC Halifax Town	1192	L	1 - 3	Johnson 64	18	34
14	Nat N	A	Stalybridge Celtic	300	L	3 - 4	Killock 33 Brooksby 36 Wroe 60	18	35
18	Nat N	A	AFC Telford United	1028	W	3 - 1	BROOKSBY 3 (35 79 90)	18	36
25	Nat N	H	Altrincham	516	W	2 - 1	Johnson 16 Hill 80	17	37
29	Nat N	A	Darlington 1883	1333	L	0 - 1		17	38
Apr 1	Nat N	A	Alfreton Town	459	W	1 - 0	Johnson 36	18	39
8	Nat N	H	FC Utd of Manchester	566	D	0 - 0		16	40
15	Nat N	A	Tamworth	378	D	0 - 0		16	41
17	Nat N	H	AFC Fylde	2326	D	1 - 1	Boshell 20	16	42
22	Nat N	H	Stockport County	1280	L	0 - 2		16	43
29	Nat N	A	Kidderminster Harriers	1890	L	1 - 3	Wroe 67 (pen)	16	44

GOALSCORERS	SG	CSG	Pens	Hat tricks	Total		SG	CSG	Pens	Hat tricks	Total
2015-16 Chilaka					18	Hill	2				2
Wroe	4		2		6	Killock	2				2
Johnson	5				5	Knowles	2				2
Sharp	5	2			5	Chippendale	1				1
Brooksby	2				4	Cofie	1				1
Brooksby	2				4	Davis	1				1
Dean	2				3	Monaghan	1				1
McKenna	3				3	Payne	1				1
Sinclair	3	2			3						
Dickinson	2				2						

CHORLEY
Club Contact Details
Victory Park Stadium, Duke Street, Chorley, Lancashire PR7 3DU
01257 230 007

Ground Capacity: 3,550 **Seats:** 900 **Covered:** 2,800 **Clubhouse:** Yes **Shop:** Yes

Record Attendance
9,679 v Darwen, FA Cup Fourth Qualifying Round, 15/11/1932.
Previous Grounds
Dole Lane 1883-1901, Rangletts Park 1901-05, St George's Park 1905-20.

10 YEAR RECORD

07-08		08-09		09-10		10-11		11-12		12-13		13-14		14-15		15-16		16-17	
NP1N	14	NP1N	14	NP1N	16	NP1N	3	NP P	3	NP P	8	NP P	1	Conf N	4	Nat N	8	Nat N	6
FAC	1Qr	FAC	P	FAC	3Q	FAC	P	FAC	1Qr	FAC	2Q	FAC	2Q	FAC	4Qr	FAC	4Qr	FAC	3Q
FAT	1Q	FAT	Pr	FAT	1Q	FAT	3Q	FAT	1Q	FAT	1Q	FAT	3P	FAT	2Pr	FAT	3Qr	FAT	1P

Club Factfile

Founded: 1875   **Nickname:** Magpies   **Manager:** Matt Jansen - July 2015

Previous Names: Founded as a Rugby Union side in 1875 then switched to football in 1883.

Previous Leagues: Lancashire Junior 1889-90. Lancashire Alliance 1890-94. Lancashire 1894-1903. Lancashire Combination 1903-68, 69-70. Northern Premier (founder member) 1968-69, 70-72, 82-88, 90-2014. Cheshire County 1972-82. Conference 1988-90.

Club Colours (change): Black and white stripes/black/black

RECORDS
Victory: 14-1 v Morecambe, April 1946.
Goalscorer: Peter Watson - 372 (1958-66).
Additional: Received £30,000 from Newcastle United for David Eatock 1996.

HONOURS

FA Comps: None

League: Lancs All. 1892-93. Lancashire 1896-97, 98-99. Lancs Comb. 1919-20, 22-23, 27-28, 28-29, 32-33, 33-34, 39-40, 45-46, 59-60, 60-61, 63-64. Cheshire County 1975-76, 76-77, 81-82. NPL 1987-88, 2013-14, Div. One North P-off 2010-11.

County FA: Lancashire FA Trophy (Record 17 times) 1893-94, 1908-09, 23-24, 39-40, 45-46, 57-58, 58-59, 60-61, 63-64, 64-65, 75-76, 79-80, 81-82, 82-83, 2011-12, 14-15, 15-16.

BEST PERFORMANCES	**FA Cup:** Second Round Proper 1986-87, 90-91.
	FA Trophy: Semi-finals 1995-96.
	FA Vase: N/A

CHORLEY MATCH RESULTS 2016-17

Date	Comp	H/A	Opponents	Att:	Result	Goalscorers	Pos	No.
Aug 6	Nat N	H	FC Utd of Manchester	1947	D 3 - 3	Gonzales 10 Teague 43 Leather 85	6	1
13	Nat N	A	Kidderminster Harriers	1339	D 0 - 0		17	2
16	Nat N	A	Bradford PA	790	W 3 - 0	Gonzalez 45 Whitham 68 Beesley 89	11	3
20	Nat N	H	Boston United	1009	W 2 - 0	Whitham 34 O'Keefe 39 (pen)	7	4
24	Nat N	A	Darlington 1883	1543	L 0 - 2		7	5
27	Nat N	A	Worcester City	623	W 1 - 0	Carver 69	7	6
29	Nat N	H	Stalybridge Celtic	1011	W 1 - 0	Walker 20	6	7
Sept 3	Nat N	H	Tamworth	737	W 1 - 0	Walker 21	5	8
6	Nat N	A	Altrincham	1006	D 2 - 2	Walker 25 Carver 33	5	9
10	Nat N	H	Brackley Town	1066	D 1 - 1	Cottrell 8	8	10
13	Nat N	A	Salford City	2022	W 2 - 1	Walker 47 Whitham 50	4	11
17	FAC2Q	A	**Dunston UTS**	**333**	W 2 - 0	Teague 2 Leather 46		12
24	Nat N	A	AFC Telford United	1033	D 0 - 0		5	13
Oct 1	FAC3Q	A	**Spennymoor Town**	**713**	L 0 - 1			14
8	Nat N	H	Harrogate Town	1214	W 1 - 0	Blakeman 78 (pen)	4	15
15	Nat N	A	Bradford PA	390	W 3 - 0	Cotttrell 9 Whitham 57 90	3	16
22	Nat N	H	Stockport County	2484	L 0 - 1		3	17
24	Nat N	A	Curzon Ashton	393	D 1 - 1	Walker 9 (pen)	4	18
29	Nat N	A	Alfreton Town	506	D 2 - 2	Walker 29 (pen) 41	4	19
Nov 5	Nat N	H	Nuneaton Town	969	W 1 - 0	Carver 44	3	20
12	Nat N	A	Gainsboroug Trinity	586	W 2 - 0	Whitham 72 Samizadeh 83	3	21
19	Nat N	H	Gloucester CIty	918	W 4 - 1	Cottrell 19 Carver 26 Samizadeh 82 Walker 85 (pen)	2	22
6 Dec	FAT 3Q	H	**Stafford Rangers**	**466**	W 1 - 0	Charnock 44		23
10	FAT 1	H	**Guiseley**	**612**	L 0 - 1			24
!7	Nat N	A	Tamworth	1050	D 1 - 1	Leather 49	3	25
26	Nat N	A	AFC Fylde	3858	W 2 - 0	Walker 44 47	3	26
Jan 1	Nat N	H	AFC Fylde	3128	L 1 - 3	Blakeman 46	3	27
7	Nat N	A	Brackley Town	525	W 1 0	Witham 45	3	28
10	Nat N	A	FC Halifax Town	1389	L 1 - 2	Jordan 68	3	29
21	Nat N	H	Altrincham	1127	W 2 - 0	Sampson 12 Cottrell 26	3	30
Feb 4	Nat N	H	Darlington 1883	1387	D 1 - 1	Carver 34	4	31
11	Nat N	A	FC Utd of Manchester	2404	D 3 - 3	Sampson 46 McDaid 56 Leather 90	4	32
14	Nat N	A	Boston United	807	L 1 - 3	Cottrell 24	4	33
18	Nat N	H	Kidderminster Harriers	1242	W 2 - 1	Sampson 8 Cottrell 50	4	34
25	Nat N	H	Alfreton Town	999	W 2 - 1	Sampson 87 O'Keefe 90	4	35
Mar 4	Nat N	A	Stockport County	4073	D 0 - 0		4	36
11	Nat N	H	AFC Telford United	1131	W 2 - 1	Sampson 28 Teague 50	4	37
18	Nat N	A	Harrogate Town	972	L 1 - 2	Sampson 42	4	38
21	Nat N	A	Salford City	1428	D 1 - 1	Sampson 52	4	39
25	Nat N	H	Curzon Ashton	1146	L 0 - 3		6	40
April 1	Nat N	H	Gainsborough Trinity	1030	W 4 - 0	WALKER 3 (38 51 74 pen) Carver 71	5	41
8	Nat N	A	Nuneaton Town	501	D 1 - 1	Whitham 11	6	42
15	Nat N	H	Worcester City	1393	W 1 - 0	Leather 61	4	43
17	Nat N	A	Stalybridge Celtic	761	W 1 - 0	Teague 38	4	44
22	Nat N	A	Gloucester City	526	D 2 - 2	Whitham 21 Walker 45	6	45
29	Nat N	H	FC Halifax Town	2462	L 0 - 2		6	46
May 3	PO SF1	H	**Kidderminster Harriers**	**2487**	L 0 - 1			47
7	PO SF2	A	**Kidderminster Harriers**	**3407**	W 2 - 0	Carver 18 Roscoe 90		48
13	PO Final	A	**FC Halifax Town**	**7920**	L 1 - 2	Blakeman 40		49

GOALSCORERS	SG	CSG	Pens	Hat tricks	Total		SG	CSG	Pens	Hat tricks	Total
2015-16 Stephenson					19	O'Keefe	2		1		2
Walker	10	3	4	1	14	Samizadeh	2	2			2
Whitham	7	2			9	Beesley	1				1
Sampson	7				7	Charnock	1				1
Carver	7				7	Jordan	1				1
Cottrell	6				6	McDaid	1				1
Leather	5				5	Roscoe	1				1
Teague	4				4						
Blakeman	3		1		3						
Gonzales	2				2						

CURZON ASHTON

Club Contact Details
Tameside Stadium, Richmond Street, Ashton-u-Lyme OL7 9HG
0161 330 6033
rob@curzon-ashton.co.uk

Ground Capacity: 4,000 **Seats:** 527 **Covered:** 1,100 **Clubhouse:** Yes **Shop:** Yes

Curzon Ashton defender clears as Alfreton's Paul Clayton closes in. Photo: Bill Wheatcroft.

Record Attendance
3,210 v FC United of Manchester, North West Counties Challenge Cup Final, 03/05/07.

Previous Grounds
National Park 1963-2004. Stalybridge Celtic FC 2004-05.

10 YEAR RECORD

07-08	08-09	09-10	10-11	11-12	12-13	13-14	14-15	15-16	16-17
NP1N 4	NP1N 4	NP1N 3	NP1N 4	NP1N 2	NP1N 7	NP1N 1	NP P 4	Nat N 11	Nat N 14
FAC P	FAC 2P	FAC Pr	FAC 1Qr	FAC Pr	FAC 2Q	FAC 3Q	FAC 3Q	FAC 2Q	FAC 1Pr
FAT 2Q	FAT Pr	FAT P	FAT 1P	FAT 3Q	FAT 1Q	FAT 1P	FAT 2Q	FAT 2P	FAT 2P

Club Factfile

Founded: 1963 **Nickname:** The Nash **Manager:** John Flanagan

Previous Names: Club formed when Curzon Road Methodists and Ashton Amateurs merged, and were initially known as Curzon Amateurs.

Previous Leagues: Manchester Amateur. Manchester > 1978. Cheshire (FM of Div.2) 1978-82. North West Counties (FM) 1983-87, 98-2007. Northern Premier (FM) 1987-97, 2007-15. Northern Counties East 1997-98.

Club Colours (change): All royal blue

RECORDS
Victory: 10-1 v Wakefield, 2012-13
Defeat: 0-8 v Bamber Bridge
Goalscorer: Rod Lawton - 376
Appearances: Alan Sykes

HONOURS

FA Comps: None

League: Manchester Amateur Division One 1963-64, 65-66. Manchester Premier Division 1977-78. Northern Premier Division One North 2013-14, Premier Division Play-off 2014-15.

County FA: Manchester Premier Cup 1981-82, 83-84, 85-86, 87-88, 89-90.

BEST PERFORMANCES	FA Cup: Second Round Proper 2008-09.
	FA Trophy: Second Round Proper 2015-16.
	FA Vase: Semi-finals 1979-80, 2006-07.

CURZON ASHTON MATCH RESULTS 2016-17

Date	Comp	H/A	Opponents	Att:	Result	Goalscorers	Pos	No.
Aug 6	Nat N	H	Kidderminster H	494	L 1 - 6	Guest 72		1
10	Nat N	A	Bradford PA	334	D 4 - 4	Tomsett 16 Hall 78 Howard 24 Ennis 65 (pen)		2
13	Nat N	A	Alfreton Town	457	W 1 - 0	Hampson 14		3
15	Nat N	H	Darlington 1883	482	L 1 - 2	Cummins 56		4
20	Nat N	H	AFC Telford United	261	D 1 - 1	Cummins 35		5
27	Nat N	A	Altrincham	870	W 4 - 2	Rowney 24 Brooke 17 Ennis 20 63 (pen)		6
29	Nat N	H	Salford City	888	L 0 - 2			7
Sept 3	Nat N	A	Harrogate Town	760	D 2 - 2	Flynn 36 Cummins 90 (pen)		8
6	Nat N	A	AFC Fylde	1362	L 1 - 4	Flynn 53		9
10	Nat N	H	Tamworth	212	L 1 - 5	Hunt 61		10
17	FAC2Q	H	Consett	208	D 1 - 1	Flynn 37		11
20	FAC2Qr	A	Consett	709	W 1 - 0	Wright (og) 56		12
24	Nat N	H	Stockport County	964	L 1 - 2	Cummins 70		13
27	Nat N	A	FC United of M	2166	D 0 - 0			14
Oct 1	FAC3Q	H	Bedworth United	207	W 4 - 0	Hunt 12 Ennis 15 (pen) Hall 36 91		15
8	Nat N	A	Nuneaton Town	777	W 1 - 0	Cummins 23		16
15	FAC1	A	York City	1307	D 1 - 1	Cummins 37		17
17	FAC1r	H	York City	467	W 2 - 1	Brown 41 Cummins 52 (pen)		18
22	Nat N	A	Brackley Town	326	L 0 - 2			19
24	Nat N	H	Chorley	393	D 1 - 1	Baillie 45		20
29	Nat N	H	Gainsborough Trinity	202	L 1 - 2	Howard 3		21
Nov 5	FAC1	A	Westfields	1178	D 1 - 1	Morgan 81		22
12	Nat N	A	Gloucester City	439	W 2 - 0	Tomsett 35 Morgan 90		23
14	FAC1r	H	Westfields	1075	W 3 - 1	Morgan 23 34 Cummins 70		24
19	Nat N	H	FC Halifax Town	654	W 4 - 2	Cummins 40 Morgan 46 50 Guest 74		25
28	FAT3Qr	H	Worcester City	193	L 1 - 2	Ennis 22		26
Dec 4	FAC2	H	AFC Wimbledon	1731	L 3 - 4	MORGAN 3 (1 22 63)		27
17	Nat N	H	Harrogate Town	232	W 1 - 0	Brown 62		28
20	Nat N	A	Boston United	979	L 1 - 3	Wright 13		29
26	Nat N	A	Stalybridge Celtic	558	W 2 - 1	Cummins 28 Stott 32		30
Jan 7	Nat N	A	Tamworth	568	L 2 - 3	Hall 75 Cummins 90		31
14	Nat N	A	AFC Telford United	1,002	L 1 - 3	Cummins 13		32
16	Nat N	H	Worcester City	181	D 1 - 1	Gallinagh 31(og)		33
21	Nat N	H	AFC Fylde	341	W 3 - 2	Cummins 39 Warburton 41 Hall 79		34
28	Nat N	A	Darlington 1883	1761	W 3 - 1	Hall 10 Warburton 57 67		35
30	Nat N	H	Stalybridge Celtic	422	D 0 - 0			36
Feb 4	Nat N	H	Bradford PA	227	L 1 - 2	Warburton 41		37
11	Nat N	A	Kidderminster Harriers	1560	L 2 - 2	Hall 75 Wright 82	13	38
18	Nat N	H	Alfreton Town	243	W 5 - 0	WARBURTON 3 (37 45 90) Hall 56 Cummins 69	12	39
25	Nat N	A	Gainsborough Trinity	462	W 1 - 0	Hall 15	12	40
Mar 4	Nat N	H	Brackley Town	222	D 0 - 0		12	41
11	Nat N	A	Stockport County	3495	L 1 - 2	Warburton 90 (pen)	13	42
18	Nat N	H	Nuneaton Town	206	W 2 - 1	Warburton 62 Guest 75	12	43
2	Nat N	A	Chorley	1148	W 3 - 0	Stott 8 Cummings 13 31	12	44
27	Nat N	H	FC United of M	829	L 1 - 2	Warburton 18	12	45
April 1	Nat N	H	Gloucester City	246	D 0 - 0		12	46
8	Nat N	A	Worcester City	400	D 1 - 1	Cummins 13	12	47
15	Nat N	H	Altrincham	423	L 2 - 3	Warburton 42 Hunt 76	12	48
17	Nat N	A	Salford City	1341	L 0 - 1		13	49
22	Nat N	A	FC Halifax Town	1818	L 0 - 3		14	50
29	Nat N	H	Boston United	390	W 4 - 2	Hunt 22 Warburton 50 51 Hall 58	14	51

GOALSCORERS	SG	CSG	Pens	Hat tricks	Total		SG	CSG	Pens	Hat tricks	Total
2015-16 Cummins					14	Howard	2				2
Cummins	16	3,3	1		17	Opponents	2				2
Warburton	7	2	1		13	Stott	2				2
Hall	7				10	Tomsett	2				2
Morgan	5	4			9	Wright	2				2
Ennis	4		4		5	Baillie	1				1
Hunt	4				4	Brooke	1				1
Flynn	3	2			3	Hampson	1				1
Guest	3				3	Rowney	1				1
Brown	2				2						

DARLINGTON 1883

Club Contact Details
Blackwell Meadows, Grange Road, Darlington DL1 5NR
01325 363 777
john.tempest@darlingtonfc.org

Ground Capacity: 3000   **Seats:** 280   **Covered:** Yes   **Clubhouse:** Yes   **Shop:**

Record Attendance
21,023 v Bolton Wanderers - League Cup 3rd Round 14/11/1960
Previous Grounds
Feethams 1883-2003. Darlington Arena 2003-12. Bishop Auckland 2012-16.

10 YEAR RECORD

07-08		08-09		09-10		10-11		11-12		12-13		13-14		14-15		15-16		16-17	
FL 2	6	FL 2	12	FL 2	24	Conf	7	Conf	22	NL 1	1	NP1N	2	NP1N	2	NP P	1	Nat N	5
FAC	1Pr	FAC	1Pr	FAC	1P	FAC	2P	FAC	4Qr					FAC	1Qr	FAC	1Q	FAC	2Q
						FAT	F	FAT	1P			FAT	1Qr	FAT	2Q	FAT	2Q	FAT	3Qr

Club Factfile

Founded: 1883   **Nickname:** The Quakers   **Manager:** Martin Gray

Previous Names: Darlington FC 1883-2012

Previous Leagues: Northern League 1883-1908, 2012-13, North Eastern 1908-21, Football League 1921-89, 91-2010, Conference 1989-90, 10-12.

Club Colours (change): Black & white hoops/black/black (All red)

RECORDS
Victory: 13-1 v Scarborough, FA Cup, 24/10/1891
Defeat: 0-10 v Doncaster Rovers - Division 4 25/01/1964
Goalscorer: Alan Walsh - 100, Jerry Best - 80
Appearances: Ron Greener - 490, John Peverell - 465, Brian Henderson - 463
Additional: Paid £95,000 to Motherwell for Nick Cusack January 1992.
               Received £400,000 from Dundee United for Jason Devos October 1998

HONOURS
FA Comps: FA Trophy 2010-11.

League: Northern 1895-96, 99-1900, 2012-13. North Eastern 1912-13, 20-21. Football League Division Three North 1924-25, Division Four 1990-91. Conference 1989-90. NPL Division One North Play-off 2014-15, Premier Division 2015-16.

County FA: Durham Challenge Cup 1884-85, 90-91, 92-93, 96-97, 1919-20, 99-2000.

BEST PERFORMANCES	**FA Cup:** Fifth Round Proper 1910-11, 57-58.
	FA Trophy: Final 2010-11.
	FA Vase: N/A

DARLINGTON 1883 MATCH RESULTS 2016-17

Date	Comp	H/A	Opponents	Att:	Result	Goalscorers	Pos	No.
Aug 6	Nat N	A	Altrincham	1506	D 2 - 2	Burgess 80 Galbraith 90 (pen)	9	1
13	Nat N	H	Boston United	1445	W 4 - 1	Galbraith 44 (pen) Hardy 51 Page-Ngoma 53 (og) Beck 599		2
15	Nat N	A	Curzon Ashton	482	W 2 - 1	Hardy 4 Burgess 52	1	3
21	Nat N	A	Gloucester City	665	W 2 - 1	Thompson 22 Beck 40	1	4
24	Nat N	H	Chorley	1543	W 2 - 0	Galbraith 15 (pen) 46	1	5
27	Nat N	H	Alfreteon Town	1349	L 3 - 4	Gillies 41 76 Purewal 78	4	6
29	Nat N	A	FC Utd of Manchester	2731	W 3 - 2	Hardy 4 Thompson 27 Cartman 81	4	7
Sept 2	Nat N	H	Kidderminster Harriers	1729	L 0 - 1		4	8
7	Nat N	H	Stockport County	1730	W 2 - 1	Beck 43 Mitchell 66	4	9
10	Nat N	A	Nuneaton Town	655	D 1 - 1	Beck 21	5	10
14	Nat N	A	Bradford PA	611	W 2 - 1	Hardy 80 Galbraith 82	2	11
17	FAC2Q	A	Lancaster City	580	L 1 - 2	Purewal 81		12
24	Nat N	H	Stalybridge Celtic	1231	W 4 - 1	Hardy 4 37 Gillies 44 Thompson 64	3	13
Oct 8	Nat N	A	Brackley Town	642	D 2 - 2	Thompson 26 Gillies 59	3	14
15	Nat N	H	Gainsborough Trinity	1424	W 5 - 2	Galbraith 41 (pen) 78 (pen) Brown 56 Cartman 74 Syers 812		15
22	Nat N	H	Worcester City	1479	W 5 - 1	Brown 19 BECK 3 (26 44 47) Syers 57	2	16
29	Nat N	A	Harrogate Town	2172	W 4 - 1	Gillies 4 Beck 33 Thompson 45 Syers 57	2	17
Nov 5	Nat N	A	Tamworth	914	L 1 - 2	Galbraith 2 (pen)	2	18
12	Nat N	H	AFC Fylde	2001	D 1 - 1	Gillies 44	2	19
19	Nat N	A	AFC Telford United	1136	L 0 - 2		3	20
27	FAT3Q	H	Marine	743	D 2 - 2	Galbraith 39 Thompson 65		21
Dec 3	Nat N	H	Salford City	1996	D 2 - 2	Beck 18 53	5	22
6	FAT3Qr	A	Marine	308	L 2 - 3	Hardy 13 Cartman 35		23
l7	Nat N	A	Kidderminster Harriers	1710	L 1 - 2	Syers 7	5	24
26	Nat N	H	FC Halifax Town	3000	W 3 - 2	Beck 7 52 Gillies 55	4	25
Jan 1	Nat N	A	FC Halifax Town	2511	D 2 - 2	Gillies 22 Burgess 70	4	26
7	Nat N	H	Nuneaton Town	2313	L 1 - 2	Syers 90	6	27
14	Nat N	H	Gloucester City	1837	W 2 - 0	Cartman 82 Turnbull 90	4	28
21	Nat N	A	Stockport County	3649	D 3 - 3	Gillies 33 Thompson 44 Beck 86	4	29
28	Nat N	H	Curzon Ashton	1761	L 1 - 3	Cartman 70	5	30
Feb 4	Nat N	A	Chorley	1387	D 1 - 1	Carver 34	7	31
18	Nat N	A	Boston United	1243	W 2 - 1	Cartman 14 Syers 44	7	32
25	Nat N	A	Harrogate Town	1742	L 2 - 3	Thompson 51 Hardy 87	7	33
Mar 1	Nat N	H	Altrincham	1423	W 3 - 1	Beck 3 Falkingham 29 Galbraith 80 (pen)	7	34
4	Nat N	A	Worcester City	589	D 2 - 2	Syers 70 Saunders 90	7	35
11	Nat N	A	Stalybridge Celtic	485	W 1 - 0	Beck 27 (pen)	7	36
18	Nat N	H	Brackley Town	1547	W 1 - 0	Thompson 54	5	37
25	Nat N	A	Gainsborough Trinity	744	D 3 - 3	Beck 12 Syers 76 90	7	38
29	Nat N	H	Bradford PA	1333	W 1 - 0	Saunders 80	5	39
Apr 1	Nat N	A	AFC Fylde	2365	L 1 - 4	Brown 78	6	40
8	Nat N	H	Tamworth	1694	W 3 - 2	Galbraith 5 Thompson 41 Cartman 53	5	41
15	Nat N	A	Alfreton Town	867	W 3 - 0	Cartman,34 Gillies 57 Galbraith 63 (pen)	4	42
17	Nat N	H	FC Utd of Manchester	2147	W 4 - 2	Ferguson 5 Beck 14 Galbraith 26 Brown 80	4	43
22	Nat N	H	AFC Telford United	1800	W 1 0	Beck 53 (pen)	4	44
29	Mat N	A	Salford City	2069	L 1 - 5	Beck 20	5	45

GOALSCORERS	SG	CSG	Pens	Hat tricks	Total		SG	CSG	Pens	Hat tricks	Total
2015-16 Cartman					19	Purewal	2				2
Beck	15	3	2	1	19	Saunders	2				2
Galbraith	11	2	7		12	Carver	1				1
Gillies	10				10	Falkingham	1				1
Thompson	10	2			10	Ferguson	1				1
Syers	8				9	Mitchell	1				1
Cartman	8				8	Opponents	1				1
Hardy	8				8	Page-Ngoma	1				1
Brown	4				4	Turnbull	1				1
Burgess	3				3						

FC UNITED OF MANCHESTER

Club Contact Details
Broadhurst Park, 310 Lightbowne Road, Moston, Manchester, M40 0FJ
0161 769 2005
office@fc-utd.co.uk

Ground Capacity: 4,400   **Seats:** 696   **Covered:** Yes   **Clubhouse:** Yes   **Shop:** Yes

Record Attendance
6,731 v Brighton & Hove Albion, FA Cup 2nd Round 08/12/2010 (Gigg Lane)
Previous Grounds
Gigg Lane(Bury FC) 2005-14. Bower Fold (Stalybridge Celtic FC) Aug-Dec'14. Tameside Stadium (Cuzon Ashton).

10 YEAR RECORD

	07-08		08-09		09-10		10-11		11-12		12-13		13-14		14-15		15-16		16-17	
	NP1N	2	NP P	6	NP P	13	NP P	4	NP P	6	NP P	3	NP P	2	NP P	1	Nat N	13	Nat N	13
	FAC	1Q	FAC	1Qr	FAC	4Q	FAC	2Pr	FAC	2Q	FAC	4Q	FAC	1Q	FAC	2Q	FAC	1P	FAC	3Qr
	FAT	Pr	FAT	3Q	FAT	3Q	FAT	3Q	FAT	1P	FAT	2Q	FAT	1Qr	FAT	QF	FAT	3Q	FAT	3Q

Club Factfile

Founded: 2005   **Nickname:** F.C.   **Manager:** Karl Marginson

Previous Names: N/A

Previous Leagues: North West Counties 2005-07. Northern Premier 2007-15.

Club Colours (change): Red/white/black (White/black/white)

RECORDS

Victory: 10-2 v Castleton Gabriels 10/12/2005. 8-0 v Squires Gate 14/10/06, Glossop N.E. 28/10/06 & Nelson 05/09/10
Defeat: 0-5 v Harrogate Town, 20 February 2016
Goalscorer: Rory Patterson - 99 (2005-08)
Appearances: Jerome Wright - 400
Additional: Simon Carden scored 5 goals against Castleton Gabriels 10/12/2005.
Longest unbeaten run (League): 22 games 03/12/2006 - 18/08/2007.

HONOURS

FA Comps: None

League: North West Counties League Division Two 2005-06, Division One 2006-07.
Northern Premier League Division One North Play-off 2007-08, Premier Division 2014-15.

County FA: Manchester Premier Cup 2016-17.

BEST PERFORMANCES	**FA Cup:** Second Round Proper 2010-11.
	FA Trophy: Quarter-Finals 2014-15.
	FA Vase: Third Round Proper 2006-07.

FC UNITED OF MANCHESTER MATCH RESULTS 2016-17

Date	Comp	H/A	Opponents	Att:	Result	Goalscorers	Pos	No.
Aug 6	Nat N	A	Chorley	1947	D 3 - 3	Thomson 16 63 Wright 28	7	1
9	Nat N	H	AFC Telford United	2124	D 0 - 0		11	2
13	Nat N	H	Stockport County	3030	W 2 - 0	Wolfenden 32 Lowe 86	5	3
16	Nat N	A	Salford City	1966	L 0 - 1		12	4
20	Nat N	H	Worcester City	2238	D 1 - 1	Johnson 17	13	5
27	Nat N	A	Brackley Town	565	L 0 - 1		14	6
29	Nat N	H	Darlington 1883	2731	L 2 - 3	Gilchrist 43 Thomson 68	15	7
Sept 3	Nat N	A	Boston United	1424	W 3 2	Greaves 23 33 Gilchrist 69		8
6	Nat N	A	Harrogate Town	1094	L 1 - 3	Ashworth 16	13	9
10	Nat N	H	AFC Fylde	2284	L 2 - 3	Winter 11 Thomson 77	15	10
17	FAC2Q	A	Ossett Town	694	W 7 - 1	ASHWORTH 3 (15 36 58) Sheridon 40 Thomson 52 Greaves 58 Chantler 90		11
24	Nat N	A	Tamworth	1109	D 1 - 1	Hooper 79	18	12
27	Nat N	H	Curzon Ashton	2168	D 0 - 0		17	13
Oct 1	FAC3Q	H	Harrogate Town	1541	D 3 - 3	Johnson 44 Winter 47 Thomson 63		14
4	FAC3Qr	A	Harrogate Town	1791	L 0 - 2			15
8	Nat N	H	Alfreton Town	2528	W 4 - 3	Glynn 3 Wolfendon 12 Thomson 37 Ashworth 81	14	16
15	Nat N	H	AFC Telford United	1706	L 0 - 1		16	17
22	Nat N	A	Kidderminster Harriers	2177	W 2 - 0	Lowe 22 Ashworth 62	13	18
24	Nat N	A	FC Halifax Town	1938	L 1 - 3	Thomson 72	13	19
29	Nat N	H	Gloucester City	2499	L 2 - 4	Gilchrist 1 Ashworth 87	15	20
Nov 5	Nat N	H	Bradford PA	2379	L 2 - 3	Gilchrist 45 Thomson 90	17	21
12	Nat N	A	Stalybridge Celtic	1466	W 4 - 2	Wright 15 Gilchrist 18 63 Glynn 32	15	22
19	Nat N	H	Nuneaton Town	2313	W 3 - 0	Glynn 18 Wright 24 Ashworth 56	12	23
29	FAT 3Q	H	Nuneaton Town	736	L 1 - 5	Gilchrist 48		24
Dec 3	Nat N	A	Gainsborough Trinity	1752	W 2 - 1	Wright 84 (pen) Winter 90	12	25
!7	Nat N	H	Boston United	2393	D 1 - 1	Thomson 85	12	26
26	Nat N	A	Altrincham	2490	W 3 - 0	Brown 21 Gilchrist 73 Greaves 89	11	27
Jan 1	Nat N	H	Altrincham	3030	D 1 - 1	Gilchrist 1	11	28
7	Nat N	A	AFC Fylde United	2821	L 1 - 3	Winter 79	13	29
14	Nat N	A	Worcester City	803	D 0 - 0		12	30
21	Nat N	H	Harrogate Town	2367	D 2 - 2	Gilchrist 25 Thomson 75	11	31
28	Nat N	H	Salford City	4154	L 0 - 3		12	32
Feb 11	Nat N	H	Chorley	2404	D 3 - 3	Gilchrist 7 Wolfenden 26 Lowe 45	12	33
18	Nat N	A	Stockport County	5630	L 1 - 2	Wright 74 pen)	14	34
25	Nat N	A	Gloucester City	795	W 3 - 2	Lowe 66 88 Greaves 86	13	35
Mar 4	Nat N	H	Kidderminster Harriers	2456	W 1 - 0	Thomson 24	13	36
11	Nat N	H	Tamworth	2407	W 1 - 0	Lowe 90	12	37
18	Nat N	A	Alfreton Town	898	L 1 - 2	Thomson 40	13	38
25	Nat N	H	FC Halifax Town	3149	L 0 - 3		14	39
27	Nat N	A	Curzon Ashton	829	W 2 - 1	Lowe 70 Wolfenden 88	13	40
April 1	Nat N	H	Stalybridge Celtic	2375	D 2 - 2	Wolfenden 35 Thomson 88	13	41
8	Nat N	A	Bradford PA	566	D 0 - 0		14	42
15	Nat N	H	Brackley Town	2823	L 1 - 2	Lowe 72 (pen)	14	43
17	Nat N	A	Darlington 1883	2147	L 2 - 4	Brown 34 Addaye 89	14	44
22	Nat N	A	Nuneaton Town	777	W 4 - 1	Sheridan 42 Fogbola 56 Wolfenden 60 Thomson 71	13	45
29	Nat N	H	Gainsborough Trinity	4064	W 5 - 1	Warburton 28 59 Thomson 55 84 Wright 82	13	46

GOALSCORERS	SG	CSG	Pens	Hat tricks	Total		SG	CSG	Pens	Hat tricks	Total
2015-16 Thomson					12	Johnson	2				2
Thomson	15	2			17	Brown	2				2
Gilchrist	10	3			11	Sheridon	2				2
Ashworth	6			1	8	Warburton	1				2
Lowe	7		1		7	Hooper	1				1
Wolfenden	6				6	Addaye	1				1
Wright	5		2		6	Chantler	1				1
Greaves	5				5	Fogbola	1				1
Winter	4				4						
Glynn	3				3						

GAINSBOROUGH TRINITY

Club Contact Details
The Gainsborough Martin & Co Arena, Gainsborough, Lincolnshire DN21 2QW
01427 613 295

Ground Capacity: 4,340　**Seats:** 504　**Covered:** 2,500　**Clubhouse:** Yes　**Shop:** Yes

Record Attendance
9,760 v Scunthorpe United - Midland League 1948
Previous Grounds
Played at Bowling Green Ground and Sincil Bank when Northolme was being used for cricket.

10 YEAR RECORD

07-08		08-09		09-10		10-11		11-12		12-13		13-14		14-15		15-16		16-17	
Conf N	11	Conf N	13	Conf N	14	Conf N	18	Conf N	4	Conf N	8	Conf N	16	Conf N	17	Nat N	18	Nat N	19
FAC	1P	FAC	2Q	FAC	3Q	FAC	2Q	FAC	4Q	FAC	2Qr	FAC	2Q	FAC	4Q	FAC	1P	FAC	2Q
FAT	3Qr	FAT	3Q	FAT	2Pr	FAT	3Q	FAT	3Q	FAT	SF	FAT	3Q	FAT	1P	FAT	3Qr	FAT	3Qr

Club Factfile

Founded: 1873　**Nickname:** The Blues　　　　　**Manager:** Dave Frecklington

Previous Names: Trinity Recreationists

Previous Leagues: Midland (FM) 1889-96, 1912-60, 61-68. Football League 1896-1912. Yorkshire 1960-61.
Northern Premier (FM) 1968-2004.

Club Colours (change): All blue (All lime)

RECORDS

Victory:　　7-0 v Fleetwood Town and v Great Harwood Town

Defeat:　　1-7 v Stalybridge Celtic - Northern Premier 2000-01 and v Brentford - FA Cup 03-04.

Additional:　Paid £3,000 to Buxton for Stuart Lowe

　　　　　　　Received £30,000 from Lincoln City for Tony James

HONOURS

FA Comps: None

League: Midland 1890-91, 1927-28, 48-49, 66-67.

County FA: Lincolnshire County Senior Cup 1889-90, 92-93, 94-95, 97-98, 1903-04, 04-05, 06-07, 10-11, 46-47, 47-48, 48-49,
50-51, 51-52, 57-58, 58-59, 63-64, 70-71, 2002-03, 15-16. Lincolnshire Shield 2007-08.

BEST PERFORMANCES	**FA Cup:** Third Round Proper 1886-87. (Post War) Second Round Proper 1948-49, 52-53,
	FA Trophy: Semi-Finals 2012-13.
	FA Vase: N/A

GAINSBOROUGH TRINITY MATCH RESULTS 2016-17

Date	Comp	H/A	Opponents	Att:	Result	Goalscorers	Pos	No.
Aug 6	Nat N	H	Bradford P.A.	583	D 1 - 1	Rothery 45 (pen)	13	1
9	Nat N	A	Alfreton Town	445	L 0 - 4		19	2
13	Nat N	A	Gloucester City	337	L 1 - 4	Thornhill 29	21	3
16	Nat N	H	Harrogate Town	396	L 0 - 0		22	4
20	Nat N	H	Altrincham	424	W 2 - 0	Worsfold 53 Rothery 84	16	5
27	Nat N	A	Salford City	1325	L 2 - 3	Worsfold 4 Quinn 90	17	6
29	Nat N	H	Brackley Town	473	D 1 - 1	Jarman 27	16	7
Sept 3	Nat N	A	Worcester City	535	D 2 - 2	Worsfold 26 Evans 38	18	8
6	Nat N	A	Stalybridge Celtic	321	L 2 - 3	Bailey-King 14 Reid 64	18	9
10	Nat N	H	AFC Telford United	452	W 3 - 1	Thewlis 62 (pen) Worsfold 64 90	16	10
13	Nat N	H	FC Halifax Town	692	W 3 - 2	Thewlis 28 33 Worsfold 52	14	11
17	FAC2Q	A	Altrincham	516	L 2 - 3	Reid 2 (pen) Jarman 87		12
24	Nat N	A	AFC Fylde	1385	L 1 - 3	Thewlis 44	16	13
Oct 8	Nat N	H	Tamworth	538	W 3 - 2	Thewlis 45 Jarman 63 Templeton 68	13	14
15	Nat N	A	Darlington 1883	1883	L 2 - 5	Jarman 22 Reid 54 (pen)	15	15
22	Nat N	H	Nuneaton Town	571	D 2 - 2	Quinn 22 Reid 45 (pen)	17	16
29	Nat N	A	Curzon Ashton	202	W 2 - 1	Templeton 21 Thornhill 72	13	17
Nov 12	Nat N	H	Chorley	586	L 0 - 2		15	18
15	Nat N	A	Stockport County	2112	L 0 - 1		16	19
19	Nat N	A	Kidderminster Harriers	1465	L 0 - 3		18	20
26	FAT 3Q	H	Alfreton Town	308	D 0 - 0			21
29	FAT 3Qr	A	Alfreton Town	175	L 1 - 4	Thewlis 38 (aet)		22
Dec 3	Nat N	H	FC United of Manchester	762	L 1 - 2	Jarman 23	19	23
17	Nat N	H	Worcester City	469	D 1 - 1	Worsfold 10	19	24
26	Nat N	A	Boston United	1602	D 1 - 1	Evans 68	19	25
Jan 1	Nat N	H	Boston United	1005	L 1 - 2	Reid 20 (pen)	19	26
7	Nat N	A	AFC Telford United	1081	D 1 - 1	Jarman 86	19	27
14	Nat N	A	Altrincham	996	W 3 - 2	Worsfold 6 62 Burdett 9	19	28
21	Nat N	H	Stalybridge Celtic	547	D 2 - 2	Reid 5 Worsfold 85	19	29
28	Nat N	A	Harrogate Town	892	W 3 - 1	Thornhill 25 Thewlis 62 Davie 73	17	30
Feb 4	Nat N	H	Alfreton Town	572	L 0 - 2		17	31
11	Nat N	A	Bradford P.A.	272	L 1 - 5	Rothery 51	19	32
18	Nat N	H	Gloucester City	477	D 1 - 1	Jarman 31 (pen)	19	33
25	Nat N	H	Curzon Ashton	462	L 0 - 1		19	34
Mar 4	Nat N	A	Nuneaton Town	474	L 1 - 2	Worsfold 22	19	35
11	Nat N	A	AFC Fylde	469	L 1 - 2	Thewlis 54 (pen)	20	36
18	Nat N	A	Tamworth	553	L 0 - 1		20	37
21	Nat N	H	FC Halifax Town	3149	L 1 - 2	Thewlis 21	20	38
25	Nat N	A	Darlington 1883	744	D 3 - 3	Wilson 34 Worsfold 35 Chilaka 51	20	39
April 1	Nat N	A	Chorley	1030	L 0 - 4		20	40
8	Nat N	H	Stockport County	851	L 0 - 1		20	41
15	Nat N	H	Salford City	890	W 1 - 0	Jarman 7	20	42
17	Nat N	A	Brackley Town	390	D 0 - 0		19	43
22	Nat N	H	Kidderminster Harriers	902	D 1 - 1	Jarman 19	19	44
29	Nat N	A	FC United of Manchester	4064	L 1 - 5	Salt 8	19	45

GOALSCORERS	SG	CSG	Pens	Hat tricks	Total		SG	CSG	Pens	Hat tricks	Total
2015-16 Jarman					15	Bailey-King	1				1
Worsfold	9	2			12	Burdett	1				1
Jarman	7	2	1		9	Chilaka	1				1
Thewlis	8	2	2		9	Davie	1				1
Reid, James	6	2	4		6	Salt	1				1
Rothery	3		1		3	Wilson	1				1
Thornhill	3				3						
Evans	2				2						
Quinn	2				2						
Templeton	1				2						

HARROGATE TOWN

Club Contact Details
The CNG Stadium, Wetherby Road, Harrogate HG2 7SA
01423 210 600
enquiries@harrogatetownafc.com

Ground Capacity: 3,800   **Seats:** 500   **Covered:** 1,300   **Clubhouse:** Yes   **Shop:** Yes

Record Attendance
4,280 v Railway Athletic - Whitworth Cup Final 1950
Previous Grounds
Starbeck Lane 1919-20.

10 YEAR RECORD

07-08		08-09		09-10		10-11		11-12		12-13		13-14		14-15		15-16		16-17	
Conf N	6	Conf N	9	Conf N	21	Conf N	12	Conf N	15	Conf N	6	Conf N	9	Conf N	15	Nat N	4	Nat N	11
FAC	4Q	FAC	3Qr	FAC	2Q	FAC	3Q	FAC	2Qr	FAC	2Pr	FAC	2Q	FAC	2Q	FAC	4Q	FAC	4Q
FAT	3Q	FAT	1P	FAT	1Pr	FAT	1P	FAT	1P	FAT	1P	FAT	3Qr	FAT	1P	FAT	3Q	FAT	1Pr

Club Factfile

Founded: 1914   **Nickname:** Town and Sulphurites   **Manager:** Simon Weaver

Previous Names: Harrogate AFC 1914-32. Harrogate Hotspurs 1935-48.

Previous Leagues: West Riding 1919-20, Yorkshire (FM) 1920-21, 22-31, 57-82, Midland 1921-22, Northern 1931-32, Harrogate & Dist. 1935-37, 40-46, W.Riding Co.Am. 1937-40, W.Yorks. 1946-57, N.C.E. (FM) 1982-87, N.P.L. (FM) 1987-2004

Club Colours (change): Yellow & black stripe/black/black

RECORDS
Victory: 13-0 v Micklefield
Defeat: 1-10 v Methley United - 1956
Goalscorer: Jimmy Hague - 135 (1956-58 and 1961-76)
Appearances: Paul Williamson - 428 (1980-81, 1982-85, and 1986-93)

HONOURS
FA Comps: None

League: Yorkshire 1926-27. Northern Premier League Division One 2001-02.

County FA: West Riding Challenge Cup 1924-25, 31-32, 62-63, 72-73, 85-86, 2001-02, 02-03, 07-08.

BEST PERFORMANCES	**FA Cup:** Second Round Proper 2012-13 (r)
	FA Trophy: Third Round Proper 1999-2000
	FA Vase: Fourth Round Proper 1989-90

HARROGATE TOWN MATCH RESULTS 2016-17

Date	Comp	H/A	Opponents	Att:	Result	Goalscorers	Pos	No.
Aug 6	Nat N	A	Worcester City	658	D 2 - 2	Shiels 21 Pittman 90	10	1
9	Nat N	H	Boston United	702	W 2 - 0	Knowles 43 Kerry 69	2	2
13	Nat N	H	Altrincham	635	D 2 - 2	Shiels 24 Ainge 56	4	3
16	Nat N	A	Gainsborough Trinity	396	W 2 - 0	Kerry 16 Pittman 39	2	4
20	Nat N	A	Bradford PA	301	W 3 - 2	Shiels 13 Pittman 16 Burrell 88	2	5
27	Nat N	H	Nuneaton Town	653	W 3 - 1	Pittman 7 Leesley 28 Robertson 72 (pen)	2	6
29	Nat N	A	FC Halifax Town	1965	W 1 - 0	Emmett 65	3	7
Sept 3	Nat N	H	Curzon Ashton	760	D 2 - 2	Pittman 25 31	3	8
6	Nat N	H	FC United of Manchester	1094	W 3 - 1	Platt 20 88 Pittman 58	3	9
10	Nat N	A	Alfreton Town	430	L 0 - 1		3	10
13	Nat N	A	Stalybridge Celtic	409	W 3 - 1	Thanoj 51 Pittman 55 Knowles 74	2	11
17	FAC2Q	A	Bridlington Town	294	D 1 - 1	Leesley 86		12
29	FAC2Qr	H	Bridlington Town	446	W 3 - 2	Pittman 25 Emmett 51 Chilaka 89		13
24	Nat N	H	Gloucester City	729	W 3 - 1	Ellis 25 Thanoj 45 Knowles 70	2	14
Oct 1	FAC3Q	A	FC United of Manchester	1541	D 3 - 3	Pittman 20 Gascoigne 78 Colbeck 90		15
4	FAC3Qr	H	FC United of Manchester	1791	W 2 - 0	Gascoigne 8 Leesley 75		16
8	Nat N	A	Chorley	1214	L 0 - 1		2	17
15	FAC4Q	H	FC Halifax Town	1791	L 0 - 2			18
22	Nat N	A	AFC Fylde	1935	L 1 - 2	Platt 45	5	19
25	Nat N	H	Kidderminster Harriers	728	L 0 - 2		6	20
29	Nat N	H	Darlington 1883	2172	L 1 - 4	Webb-Foster 32	8	21
Nov 5	Nat N	A	Salford City	1173	D 0 - 0		7	22
12	Nat N	H	Tamworth	975	L 3 - 4	Chilaka 36 Ainge 45 Burrell 56	10	23
19	Nat N	A	Brackley Town	415	L 1 - 2	Ainge 45	10	24
26	FAT 3Q	H	Salford City	571	D 2 - 2	Kerry 2 Shiels 45		25
Dec 3	Nat N	A	AFC Telford United	645	W 2 - 1	Pittman 58 85	10	26
6	FAT3Qr	A	Salford City	290	W 3 - 0	Leesley 44 Colbeck 57 Thanoj 62		27
10	FAT 1	H	Barrow	441	D 3 - 3	Ainge 29 Leesley 41 Pittman 61 (pen)		28
13	FAT1r	A	Barrow	816	L 2 - 4	Chilaka 32 Pittman 54 (aet)		29
!7	Nat N	A	Curzon Ashton	232	L 0 - 1		10	30
26	Nat N	H	Stockport County	1055	L 0 - 1		10	31
Jan 1	Nat N	A	Stockport County	3725	D 1 - 1	Hinchcliffe 89 (og)	10	32
7	Nat N	H	Alfreton Town	735	W 6 - 3	Burrell 17 AINGE 4 (19 22 55 82) Leesley 31	10	33
14	Nat N	H	Bradford PA	995	W 1 - 0	Ainge 10	10	34
21	Nat N	A	FC United of Manchester	2367	D 2 - 2	Platt 2 Muskwe 47	10	35
28	Nat N	H	Gainsborough Trinity	692	L 1 - 3	Kerry 22	10	36
Feb 4	Nat N	A	Boston United	1112	W 3 - 0	Ainge 31 Swain 56 Leesley 81 (pen)	9	37
11	Nat N	H	Worcester City	716	W 3 - 1	Ainge 10 Ellis 67 Swain 72	9	38
18	Nat N	A	Altrincham	782	D 0 - 0		9	39
25	Nat N	A	Darlington 1883	1742	W 3 - 2	Ainge 40 83 Kerry 76	9	40
Mar 4	Nat N	H	AFC Fylde	1018	D 3 - 3	AINGE 3 (12 65 70)	9	41
11	Nat N	A	Gloucester City	374	D 1 - 1	Ainge 58	10	42
18	Nat N	H	Chorley	972	W 2 - 1	Leesley 13 (pen) Ainge 38	9	43
25	Nat N	A	Kidderminster Harriers	2012	L 0 - 1		11	44
April 1	Nat N	A	Tamworth	1096	L 2 - 3	Burrell 58 Ainge 82	11	45
8	Nat N	H	Salford City	948	D 3 - 3	AINGE 3 (84 pen 87 pen 90 pen)	11	46
15	Nat N	H	Nuneaton Town	543	L 1 - 2	Burrell 90	11	47
17	Nat N	A	FC Halifax Town	1335	L 0 - 3		10	48
22	Nat N	H	Brackley Town	660	L 1 - 2	Leesley 58	11	49
25	Nat N	A	Stalybridge Celtic	188	W 4 - 2	Ellis 11 Knowles 79 86 Ainge 90	11	50
29	Nat N	A	AFC Telford United	1047	D 0 - 0		11	51

GOALSCORERS	SG	CSG	Pens	Hat tricks	Total		SG	CSG	Pens	Hat tricks	Total
2015-16 Daniels					23	Ellis	3				3
Ainge	15	4	1	3	23	Thanoj	3				3
Pittman	12	3	1		14	Colbeck	2				2
Leesley	9		2		9	Emmett	2				2
Burrell	5				5	Gascoigne	2				2
Kerry	5				5	Swain	2				2
Knowles	3				5	Muskwe	1				1
Platt	4				4	Opponents					1
Shiels	4				4	Robertson	1		1		1
Chilaka	3				3	Webb-Foster	1				1

KIDDERMINSTER HARRIERS

Club Contact Details
Aggborough Stadium, Hoo Road, Kidderminster DY10 1NB
01562 823 931
info@harriers.co.uk

Ground Capacity: 6,444 **Seats:** 3,140 **Covered:** 3,062 **Clubhouse:** Yes **Shop:** Yes

Record Attendance
9,155 v Hereford United, FA Cup First Round Proper, 27/11/48
Previous Grounds
Chester Road 1886-87.

10 YEAR RECORD

	07-08		08-09		09-10		10-11		11-12		12-13		13-14		14-15		15-16		16-17	
Conf		13	Conf	6	Conf	13	Conf	6	Conf	6	Conf	2	Conf	7	Conf	16	Nat	23	Nat N	2
FAC		2P	FAC	3P	FAC	4Qr	FAC	4Q	FAC	4Qr	FAC	1P	FAC	4P	FAC	4Q	FAC	4Q	FAC	1P
FAT		2Pr	FAT	3Pr	FAT	SF	FAT	1P	FAT	3P	FAT	2P	FAT	1P	FAT	2P	FAT	1P	FAT	3Q

Club Factfile

Founded: 1886   **Nickname:** Harriers   **Manager:** John Eustace

Previous Names: Kidderminster Harriers and Football Club 1886-90. Kidderminster FC 1890-1891.

Previous Leagues: Birmingham & District (FM) 1889-90, 91-1939, 47-48, 60-62. Midland 1890-91. Southern 1939-45, 48-60, 72-83. Birmingham Combination 1945-47. West Midlands (Regional) 1962-72. Conference 1983-2000. Football League 2000-05.

Club Colours (change): Red & white halves/white/red & white

RECORDS
Victory: 25-0 v Hereford (H), Birmingham Senior Cup First Round, 12/10/1889
Defeat: 0-13 v Darwen (A), FA Cup First Round Proper, 24/01/1891
Goalscorer: Peter Wassell - 448 (1963-74)
Appearances: Brendan Wassell - 686 (1962-74)
Additional: Paid £80,000 to Nuneaton Borough for Andy Ducros July 2000
                  Recieved £380,000 from W.B.A. for Lee Hughes July 1997

HONOURS
FA Comps: FA Trophy 1986-87.

League: Birmingham & District 1937-38. West Midlands (Regional) 1964-65, 68-69, 69-70, 70-71. Conference 1993-94, 1999-2000.

County FA: Worcestershire Senior Cup (27 times) Firstly in 1895-96 and most recently 2016-17. Birmingham Senior Cup (7x) Firstly in 1933-34 and most recently in 1966-67. Staffordshire Senior Cup (4x) Firstly in 1980-81 and most recently in 1984-85.

BEST PERFORMANCES	**FA Cup:** Fifth Round Proper 1993-94. **Welsh Cup:** Final 1985-86, 1988-89.
	FA Trophy: Final 1986-87, 90-91, 94-95, 2006-07.
	FA Vase: N/A

KIDDERMINSTER HARRIERS MATCH RESULTS 2016-17

Date	Comp	H/A	Opponents	Att:	Result	Goalscorers	Pos	No.
Aug 6	Nat N	A	Curzon Ashton	494	W 6 - 1	Gnahoua 34 41 Ngwatala 7 Dieseruvwe 15 Carter 23 Truslove 70	1	1
9	Nat N	H	Brackley Town	1446	D 1 - 1	Waite 77 (pen)	6	2
13	Nat N	H	Chorley	1339	D 0 - 0		7	3
16	Nat N	A	Nuneaton Town	667	W 2 - 0	McQuilkin 5 Dieseruvwe 39	4	4
20	Nat N	H	Stalybridge Celtic	1185	W 2 - 1	Diesenuvwe 16 Williams 36	4	5
27	Nat N	A	Boston United	1047	D 1 - 1	Robinson 3 (og)	6	6
29	Nat N	H	Altrincham	1489	W 1 - 0	Gnahoua 43	5	7
Sept 3	Nat N	A	Darlington 1883	1729	W 1 - 0	Gnahoua 14	2	8
6	Nat N	A	AFC Telford United	1459	L 0 - 1		6	9
10	Nat N	H	Salford City	2072	W 1 - 0	McQuilkin 9	4	10
13	Nat N	H	Tamworth	1333	W 6 - 0	Dieserunwe 13 Gnahoua 25 McQuilkin 41 Waite 60 Austin 83 Truslove 85	3	11
17	FAC2Q	H	Tamworth	1050	W 4 - 0	Ngwatala 5 Dieserunwe 11 18 Gnahoua 53		12
24	Nat N	A	Alfreton Town	568	D 3 - 3	Truslove 52 89 Brown 83	4	13
Oct 1	FAC3Q	A	Lancaster City	570	W 3 - 2	Brown 22 48 Austin 67		14
8	Nat N	H	AFC Fylde	1970	D 3 - 3	Gnahoua 13 Ngwatala 49 Lowe 86	5	15
15	FAC4Q	H	Weymouth	1382	W 6 - 0	Dieserunwe31 Tunnicliffe41 Truslove 45 Gnahoua 42 Waite 58 72		16
22	Nat N	H	FC United of Manchester	2177	L 0 - 2		6	17
25	Nat N	A	Harrogate Town	728	W 2 - 0	Truslove 29 Brown 90	5	18
29	Nat N	A	Stockport County	2883	W 1 - 0	Croasdale 65	3	19
Nov 5	FAC1	A	Blackpool	1963	L 0 - 2			20
12	Nat N	A	FC Halifax Town	1704	L 0 - 1		6	21
19	Nat N	H	Gainsborough Trinity	1464	W 3 - 0	Gnahoua 7 Ngwatala 45 Waite 63	5	22
22	Nat N	H	Gloucester City	1319	W 3 - 0	Avery 33 (og) Gnahoua 59 68	3	23
26	FAT3Q	H	Lincoln United	916	W 3 - 1	Truslove 33 48 Brown 56		24
Dec 3	Nat N	A	Bradford PA	379	W 3 - 1	Brown 4 Gnahoua 31 Croasdale 42	2	25
10	FAT 1	H	AFC Telford United	1096	W 4 - 0	Gnahoua 29 Lowe36 Dieseruvwe 75 Tunnicliffe 84		26
17	Nat N	H	Darlington 1883	1710	W 2 - 1	Waite 8 Lowe 77	2	27
26	Nat N	A	Worcester City	1869	D 0 - 0		2	28
Jan 1	Nat N	H	Worcester City	2762	W 2 - 1	McQuilkin 60 Oji 79 (Og)	2	29
7	Nat N	A	Salford City	1296	L 0 - 3		2	30
14	FAT2	H	Ebbsfleet United	1078	W 3 - 0	Ezewele 35 Williams 38 Brown 70		31
21	Nat N	H	AFC Telford United	1752	W 1 - 0	Knights 85	2	32
28	Nat N	H	Nuneaton Town	1764	W 4 - 0	Brown 35 Nqwatala 75 90 Croasdale 86	2	33
Feb 4	FAT3Q	A	Barrow	1173	L 0 - 1			34
11	Nat N	H	Curzon Ashton	1580	W 3 - 2	McQuilkin 2 14 Brown 5	2	35
18	Nat N	A	Chorley	1242	L 1 - 2	Brown 75	3	36
25	Nat N	H	Stockport County	2151	W 2 - 0	Gnahoua 45 Ngwatala 79	3	37
28	Nat N	A	Brackley Town	379	L 0 - 2		3	38
Mar 4	Nat N	A	FC United of Manchester	2456	L 0 - 1		3	39
11	Nat N	H	Alfreton Town	1542	W 3 - 0	McQuilkin 19 (pen) Truslove 27 Waite 32	3	40
18	Nat N	A	AFC Fylde	2359	D 2 - 2	Croasdale 26 Lowe 36	3	41
22	Nat N	A	Tamworth	860	W 4 - 3	Ironside 45 75 Williams 61 Lowe 90	2	42
25	Nat N	H	Harrogate Town	2012	W 1 - 0	Brown 87	2	43
April 1	Nat N	H	FC Halifax Town	2025	L 1 - 2	Ironside 11	2	44
8	Nat N	A	Gloucester City	948	W 2 - 1	Ironside 15 Nti 60	2	45
11	Nat N	A	Stalybridge Celtic	427	L 0 - 1		2	46
15	Nat N	H	Boston United	2056	W 1 - 0	Ngwatala 88	2	47
17	Nat N	A	Altrincham	826	W 4 - 1	McQuilkin 6 Ironside 51 Brown 76 Sonupe 86	2	48
22	Nat N	H	Gainsborough Trinity	902	D 1 - 1	Brown 50	2	49
29	Nat N	H	Bradford PA	1890	W 3 - 1	Ironside 22 Tunnicliffe 41 Truelove 79	2	50
May 3	PO SF2	A	Chorley	2487	W 1 - 0	Gnahoua 76		51
7	PO SF2	H	Chorley	3407	L 0 - 2			52

GOALSCORERS	SG	CSG	Pens	Hat tricks	Total		SG	CSG	Pens	Hat tricks	Total
2015-16 McQuilkin					7	Croasdale	4				4
Gnahoua	14	2			15	Opponents	3				3
Brown	12	2			13	Tunnicliffe	3				3
Truslove	10	2			10	Williams	3				3
Dieserunwe	6	2			8	Austin	2				2
McQuilkin	7	2	1		8	Carter	1				1
Ngwatala	7				8	Ezewele	1				1
Waite	6		1		7	Knights	1				1
Ironside	5				6	Nti	1				1
Lowe	5				5	Sonupe	1				1

LEAMINGTON

Club Contact Details
Phillips 66 Community Stadium, Harbury Lane, Whitmarsh, Leamington CV33 9QB
01926 430 406
info@leamingtonfc.co.uk

Ground Capacity: 5,000 **Seats:** 700 **Covered:** 720 **Clubhouse:** Yes **Shop:** Yes

Record Attendance
1,380 v Retford United - 17/02/2007
Previous Grounds
Old Windmill Ground

10 YEAR RECORD

07-08		08-09		09-10		10-11		11-12		12-13		13-14		14-15		15-16		16-17	
SthM	2	SthM	1	SthP	10	SthP	5	SthP	7	SthP	1	Conf N	13	Conf N	21	SthP	3	SthP	2
FAC	1Q	FAC	1Q	FAC	1Q	FAC	1Qr	FAC	2Q	FAC	2Q	FAC	2Qr	FAC	3Qr	FAC	1Qr	FAC	1Q
FAT	1P	FAT	1Q	FAT	1Q	FAT	3Q	FAT	1Q	FAT	1Qr	FAT	2P	FAT	3Q	FAT	1Pr	FAT	1Q

Club Factfile

Founded: 1892 **Nickname:** The Brakes **Manager:** Paul Holleran

Previous Names: Leamington Town 1892-1937, Lockheed Borg & Beck 1944-46 , Lockheed Leamington 1946-73, AP Leamington 1973-88

Previous Leagues: Birmingham Combination, Birmingham & District, West Midlands Regional, Midland Counties, Southern, Midland Combination, Midland Alliance 2005-07. Southern 2007-13, 15-17. Football Conference 2013-15.

Club Colours (change): Gold with black trim/black /gold (Blue with yellow trim/blue/blue)

RECORDS
Goalscorer: Josh Blake - 166
Appearances: Josh Blake - 314

HONOURS
FA Comps: None

League: Birmingham & Dist 1961-62. West Mids Regional 1962-63. Midland Co 1964-65. Southern League 1982-83, 2012-13, Division One Midlands 2008-09. Midland Comb Div Two 2000-01. Premier Div 2004-05. Midland All 2006-07. Southern Prem Play-offs 2016-17.

County FA: Birmingham Senior Cup 2016-17.

BEST PERFORMANCES	**FA Cup:** First Round Proper 2005-06.
	FA Trophy: Second Round Proper 2013-14.
	FA Vase: Quarter-finals 2006-07.

LEAMINGTON MATCH RESULTS 2016-17

Date	Comp	H/A	Opponents	Att:	Result	Goalscorers	Pos	No.
Aug 6	SPL	H	Cirencester Town	447	W 3 - 1	Rowe 5 17 Brown 53	1	1
9	SPL	A	Kettering Town	605	W 2 - 0	Obeng 24 Rowe 75 (pen)	2	2
13	SPL	A	Hayes & Yeading United	265	W 1 - 0	Edwards 6	2	3
16	SPL	H	Merthyr Town	464	W 1 - 0	Mace 90	1	4
20	SPL	A	Chippenham Town	364	L 0 - 1		2	5
27	SPL	H	Biggleswade Town	364	D 1 - 1	Obeng 42	3	6
29	SPL	A	Stratford Town	523	W 2 - 0	Rowe 23 45	3	7
Sept 3	FAC1Q	A	Highgate United	231	L 1 - 3	Edwards 70		8
10	SPL	H	Weymouth	455	D 1 - 1	Rowe 19	4	9
13	SPL	H	Redditch United	408	W 2 - 1	Rowe 63 Hood 83	4	10
24	SPL	A	St Ives Town	313	W 5 - 0	Obeng 11 16 Rowe 40 (pen) Baker-Richardson 79 90	3	11
27	SPL	A	Slough Town	687	L 0 2		3	12
Oct 1	SPL	H	Cinderford Town	402	W 6 - 0	Thompson-Brown 16 61 Pond 59 Baker-Richardson 78 88		13
						Edwards 86	2	
8	SPL	A	Dorchester Town	461	D 2 - 2	Thompson-Brown15 Taundry 79	2	14
11	SPL	H	Kings Lynn Town	345	W 3 - 0	Obeng 59 Baker-Richardson 84 Edwards 86	2	15
18	SPL	A	Redditch United	340	W 2 - 0	Rowe 34 56	2	16
22	SPL	A	St Neots Town	325	W 1 - 0	Rowe 65	1	17
25	SPL	H	Cambridge City	435	W 1 - 0	Gudger 87	1	18
29	FAT1Q	H	Mickleover Sports	352	L 0 - 1			19
Nov 5	SPL	H	Basingstoke Town	526	W 3 - 1	Obeng 11 Baker-Richardson 24 Edwards 56	1	20
19	SPL	H	Hayes & Yeading United	404	W 2 - 0	Broadbent 17 (og) Rowe 37	1	21
22	SPL	A	Merthyr Town	487	D 1 - 1	Pond 20	1	22
26	SPL	A	Cirencester Town	192	W 2 - 1	Edwards 24 Baker-Richardson 26	1	23
Dec 3	SPL	H	Hitchin Town	504	L 1 - 2	Baker-Richardson 81	1	24
6	SPL	A	Dunstable Town	101	W 2 - 0	Obeng 3 Baker-Richardson 57	1	25
10	SPL	A	Frome Town	219	D 0 - 0		1	26
17	SPL	A	Kings Langley	122	W 2 - 0	Gregory 10 19	1	27
26	SPL	H	Stratford Town	805	D 1 1	Gregory 26	1	28
Jan 2	SPL	A	Banbury United	734	L 0 - 1		1	29
7	SPL	H	Chippenham Town	498	D 1 - 1	Baker-Richardson 56	1	30
14	SPL	H	St Ives Town	525	W 2 - 0	Baker-Richardson 47 Obeng 55	1	31
28	SPL	H	Slough Town	645	L 0 - 6		2	32
Feb 4	SPL	A	Kings Lynn Town	601	D 0 - 0		4	33
11	SPL	H	Dorchester Town	405	W 5 - 0	Obeng 12 Powell 24 Baker-Richardson 56 Mace 50		34
					-	Thompson-Brown 72	4	
18 33	SPL	A	Chesham United	427	W 1 - 0	Goddard 45	3	35
25	SPL	A	Cambridge City	214	D 1 - 1	Edwards 30	5	36
28	SPL	H	Chesham United	306	W 2 - 0	Baker-Richardson 42 Gittings 86	2	37
Mar 4	SPL	H	St Neots Town	582	W 2 - 0	Edwards 52 Gregory 67	2	38
7	SPL	H	Kettering Town	478	W 3 - 0	Thompson-Brown 9 73 (pen) Baker-Richardson 19	2	39
11	SPL	A	Basingstoke Town	408	W 2 - 0	Obeng 6 Thompson-Brown 13	2	40
18	SPL	H	Dunstable Town	410	W 5 - 0	Baker-Richardson 14 Thompdson-Brown 25 (pen) Okito (og)		41
						Edwards 53 Taundry 27	2	
25	SPL	A	Hitchin Town	824	D 0 - 0		3	42
28	SPL	A	Cinderford Town	246	W 2 - 1	Baker-Richardson 11 Nelmes 55 (og)	2	43
April 1	SPL	H	Frome Town	508	L 0 - 1		2	44
8	SPL	H	Kings Langley	422	D 0 - 0		2	45
15	SPL	A	Biggleswade Town	320	L 0 - 2		2	46
17	SPL	H	Banbury United	846	W 1 - 0	Hood 19	2	47
22	SPL	A	Weymouth	585	L 0 - 4		2	48
26	PO SF	H	Slough Town	1032	W 1 - 0	Edwards 46		49
May 1	PO Final	H	Hitchin Town	2102	W 2 - 1	Thompson-Brown 90 Baker-Richardson 114 (aet)		50

GOALSCORERS	SG	CSG	Pens	Hat tricks	Total		SG	CSG	Pens	Hat tricks	Total
2015-16 *Mackey*					13	Pond	2				2
Baker-Richardson	15	3			17	Taundry	2				2
Rowe	9	3	2		12	Brown	1				1
Obeng	9				10	Edwards	1				1
Edwards	8				9	Gittings	1				1
Thompson-Brown	7	2			9	Goddard	1				1
Gregory	3	2			4	Gudger	1				1
Opponents	3				3	Powell	1				1
Hood	2				2						
Mace	2				2						

NORTH FERRIBY UNITED
Club Contact Details
Eon Visual Media Stadium, Grange Lane, Church Road, North Ferriby HU14 3AB
01482 634 601
info@northferribyunitedfc.co.uk

Ground Capacity: 3,000 **Seats:** 501 **Covered:** 1,000 **Clubhouse:** Yes **Shop:** Yes

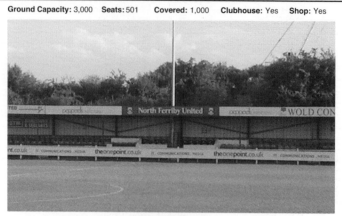

Record Attendance
1,927 v Hull City - Charity game 2005
Previous Grounds
None

10 YEAR RECORD

07-08		08-09		09-10		10-11		11-12		12-13		13-14		14-15		15-16		16-17	
NP P	15	NP P	10	NP P	4	NP P	5	NP P	9	NP P	1	Conf N	2	Conf N	10	Nat N	2	Nat	24
FAC	1Q	FAC	2Q	FAC	2Q	FAC	3Qr	FAC	2Q	FAC	2Q	FAC	4Q	FAC	4Q	FAC	4Qr	FAC	4Q
FAT	1qr	FAT	2Qr	FAT	3Qr	FAT	1Q	FAT	1P	FAT	2Q	FAT	QF	FAT	F	FAT	3Q	FAT	1P

Club Factfile

Founded: 1934   **Nickname:** United   **Manager:** Steve Housham

Previous Names: None

Previous Leagues: East Riding Church, East Riding Amateur 1946-69, Yorkshire 1969-82, Northern Counties East 1982-2000. Northern Premier 2000-13.

Club Colours (change): Green & white hoops (Blue and white)

RECORDS
Victory: 9-0 v Hatfield Main - Northern Counties East 1997-98
Defeat: 1-7 v North Shields - Northern Counties East 1991
Goalscorer: Mark Tennison - 161. Andy Flounders scored 50 during season 1998-99.
Appearances: Paul Sharp - 497 (1996-2006)
Additional: Received £60,000 from Hull City for Dean Windass

HONOURS
FA Comps: FA Trophy 2014-15.

League: East Riding Church 1937-38. Yorkshire Div. Two 1970-71. Northern Counties East Div. One 1985-86, Premier 1999-00. Northern Premier League Division One 2004-05, Premier Division 2012-13. National North Play-offs 2015-16.

County FA: East Riding Senior Cup 1970-71, 76-77, 77-78, 78-79, 90-91, 96-97, 97-98, 98-99, 99-2000, 00-01, 01-02, 02-03, 06-07, 07-08, 08-09, 09-10, 10-11, 12-13.

BEST PERFORMANCES	**FA Cup:** Fourth Qualifying Round 1997-98, 2013-14, 14-15, 15-16 (r), 16-17.
	FA Trophy: Final 2014-15.
	FA Vase: Final 1996-97.

NORTH FERRIBY UNITED MATCH RESULTS 2016-17

Date	Comp	H/A	Opponents	Att:	Result	Goalscorers	Pos	No.
Aug 6	Nat Lg	H	Braintree Town	557	D 0 - 0		14	1
9	Nat Lg	A	Lincoln City	3622	L 1 - 6	Bateson 28	21	2
13	Nat Lg	A	Dover Athletic	726	L 0 - 2		22	3
16	Nat Lg	H	Guiseley	487	W 3 - 2	Kendall 8 Emerton 23 Russell 88	18	4
20	Nat Lg	H	Torquay United	505	W 1 - 0	Clarke 69	15	5
27	Nat Lg	A	Aldershot Town	1527	L 0 - 2		19	6
29	Nat Lg	H	Barrow	581	L 0 - 1		20	7
3 Sept	Nat Lg	A	Eastleigh	1883	L 0 - 2		20	8
10	Nat Lg	H	Maidstone United	479	L 0 - 2		20	9
13	Nat Lg	A	Gateshead	614	W 1 - 0	Thompson 49	20	10
17	Nat Lg	A	Dagenham & Redbridge	1119	L 0 - 2		21	11
24	Nat Lg	H	Southport	451	L 0 - 1		21	12
Oct 1	Nat Lg	A	Macclesfield Town	1467	L 0 - 1		21	13
4	Nat Lg	H	Chester	476	L 0 - 1		21	14
8	Nat Lg	H	Forest Green Rovers	501	L 0 - 3		22	15
15	FAC4Q	H	Macclesfield Town	395	L 1 - 4	Mukendi 1		16
22	Nat Lg	A	Boreham Wood	313	L 0 - 1		22	17
25	Nat Lg	A	Tranmere Rovers	4326	L 0 - 1		24	18
29	Nat Lg	H	Bromley	354	L 1 - 2	Thompson 52	24	19
Nov 5	Nat Lg	H	Wrexham	528	D 0 - 0		23	20
12	Nat Lg	A	Woking	1367	D 1 - 1	Brogan 45	23	21
19	Nat Lg	H	Sutton United	372	W 2 - 1	Topliss 11 Thompson 46	23	22
26	Nat Lg	A	Solihull Moors	526	L 0 - 2		23	23
29	Nat Lg	A	Chester	1392	L 0 3		23	24
Dec 3	Nat Lg	H	Gateshead	498	W 1 - 0	Thompson 28	23	25
10	FAT1	A	Alfreton Town	290	L 0 - 1			26
17	Nat Lg	A	Maidstone United	2006	W 2 - 1	Wooton 16 Brogan 38 (pen)	22	27
26	Nat Lg	H	York City	1950	L 0 - 1		22	28
Jan 1	Nat Lg	A	York City	3182	W 1 - 0	Thompson 28	22	29
7	Nat Lg	H	Dagenham & Redbridge	453	L 0 - 4		23	30
14	Nat Lg	A	Wrexham	3625	L 0 - 1		23	31
21	Nat Lg	A	Southport	795	W 4 - 2	Bateson 8 Oliver 69 Kendall 85 Thompson 89	22	32
28	Nat Lg	H	Macclesfield Town	429	L 0 - 2		23	33
Feb 11	Nat Lg	A	Braintree Town	32 410	L 0 - 1		24	34
18	Nat Lg	H	Dover Athletic	465	L 1 - 2	Bateson 49	24	35
21	Nat Lg	H	Lincoln City	2389	L 0 - 1		24	36
25	Nat Lg	A	Guiseley	941	W 2 - 1	Thompson 57 Skelton 86	23	37
Mar 4	Nat Lg	H	Woking	402	W 2 - 1	Skelton 5 Thompson 69	22	38
11	Nat Lg	A	Bromley	905	L 0 - 3		22	39
18	Nat Lg	H	Solihull Moors	363	L 1 - 4	Tinkler 43	23	40
21	Nat Lg	H	Tranmere Rovers	638	L 1 - 4	Gray 13	23	41
25	Nat Lg	A	Sutton United	1664	L 1 - 5	Tinkler 48	23	42
Apr 1	Nat Lg	A	Forest Green Rovers	1709	W 1 - 0	Thompson 68	23	43
8	Nat Lg	H	Boreham Wood	357	L 2 - 4	Tinkler 67 Thompson 90	23	44
14	Nat Lg	H	Eastleigh	364	W 2 - 1	Tinkler 22 Thompson 88	23	45
17	Nat Lg	A	Barrow	1017	L 1 - 3	Thompson 4	23R	46
22	Nat Lg	H	Aldershot Town	552	L 0 - 3		23	47
29	Nat Lg	A	Torquay United	4026	L 0 - 2		24	48

GOALSCORERS	SG	CSG	Pens	Hat tricks	Total		SG	CSG	Pens	Hat tricks	Total
2015-16 Denton					23	Mukendi	1				1
Thompson	11	2			12	Oliver	1				1
Tinkler	4				4	Russell	1				1
Bateswon	3				3	Topliss	1				1
Brogan	2		1		2	Wooton	1				1
Kendall	2				2						
Skelton	2				2						
Clarke	1				1						
Emerton	1				1						
Gray	1				1						

NUNEATON TOWN

Club Contact Details
Liberty Way, Nuneaton CV11 6RR
024 7638 5738

Ground Capacity: 4,500　**Seats:** 514　**Covered:** Yes　**Clubhouse:** Yes　**Shop:** Yes

Record Attendance
22,114 v Rotherham Utd, FAC 3P 28/01/1967 (Manor Park). 3,480 v Luton Town, Conf. Prem., 22/02/14 (Liberty Way).
Previous Grounds
Higham Lane/Rose Inn/Arbury Rd/Edward St. 1889-1903. Queens Rd 03-08. Newdegate Arms 08-15. Manor Pk 19-07.

10 YEAR RECORD

07-08	08-09	09-10	10-11	11-12	12-13	13-14	14-15	15-16	16-17
Conf N 7	SthE 2	SthP 2	Conf N 6	Conf N 5	Conf 15	Conf 13	Conf 24	Nat N 6	Nat N 12
FAC 4Q	FAC 2Qr	FAC 1P	FAC 1P	FAC 4Q	FAC 1Pr	FAC 4Q	FAC 4Qr	FAC 3Q	FAC 2Q
FAT 3Qr	FAT Pr	FAT 1P	FAT 3Q	FAT 1P	FAT 1P	FAT 2Pr	FAT 1P	FAT 1P	FAT 3P

Club Factfile

Founded: 1889　　**Nickname:** The Boro / The Town　　　　**Manager:** Tommy Wright

Previous Names: Nuneaton St. Nicholas 1889-1894. Nuneaton Town 1894-37. Nuneaton Borough 1937-2008

Previous Leagues: Local 1894-1906. Birmingham Junior/Combination 1906-15, 26-33, 38-52. Birmingham 1919-24, 33-37. Central Am. 1937-38. Birmingham 1952-58. Southern 1924-25, 58-79 81-82, 87-99, 2003-04, 08-10. Conference 1979-81, 82-87, 99-03, 04-08.

Club Colours (change): Blue & white hoops/white/blue (Red & black squares/black/red)

RECORDS
Victory:　　　11-1 - 1945-46 and 1955-56

Defeat:　　　1-8 - 1955-56 and 1968-69

Goalscorer:　　Paul Culpin - 201 (55 during season 1992-93)

Appearances:　Alan Jones - 545 (1962-74)

Additional:　　Paid £35,000 to Forest green Rovers for Marc McGregor 2000
　　　　　　　　Received undisclosed from Peterborough United for Alex Penny July 2017

HONOURS
FA Comps: None

League: Coventry & Dist. 1902-03. Coventry & North Warwicks' 1904-05. Birmingham Junior 1906-07, Combination 1914-15, 28-29, 30-31. Birmingham League North 1954-55, Div.One 55-56. Southern League Midland Div. 1981-82, 92-93, 95-96, Premier Division 1988-99.

County FA: Birmingham Senior Cup 1930-31, 48-49, 54-55, 59-60, 77-78, 79-80, 92-93, 2001-02, 09-10.

BEST PERFORMANCES	FA Cup: Third Round Proper 1949-50, 66-67, 2005-06.
	FA Trophy: Quarter-Finals 1976-77, 79-80, 86-87.
	FA Vase: N/A

NUNEATON TOWN MATCH RESULTS 2016-17

Date	Comp	H/A	Opponents	Att:	Result	Goalscorers	Pos	No.
Aug 6	Nat N	H	FC Halifax Town	993	L 2 3	Williams 4 Langmead 74	19	1
13	Nat N	A	Bradford PA	314	D 1 1	Ironside 90	18	2
16	Nat N	H	Kidderminster Harriers	667	L 0 2		20	3
20	Nat N	H	Salford City	621	L 0 1		22	4
27	Nat N	A	Harrogate Town	653	L 1 3	Ironside 54	23	5
29	Nat N	H	AFC Telford United	633	D 1 - 1	Williams 21	21	6
Sept 3	Nat N	A	Stalybridge Celtic	345	W 4 - 0	Whitehouse 20 Langmead 44 46 Ironside 52	17	7
6	Nat N	A	Brackley Town	424	L 1 - 2	Ironside 67	20	8
10	Nat N	H	Darlington 1883	655	D 1 - 1	Tempest 73	19	9
13	Nat N	H	Altrincham	542	W 4 - 1	Ironside 29 Whitehouse 4 42 Williams 45	17	10
17	FAC2Q	H	Lincoln United	436	L 1 - 2	Ironside 73		11
20	Nat N	A	Gloucester City	417	D 2 - 2	McDonald 58 Williams 90		12
24	Nat N	A	Worcester City	645	W 3 - 2	Whitehouse 32 34 Williams 60	13	13
Oct 8	Nat N	H	Curzon Ashton	588	L 0 - 1		15	14
15	Nat N	A	AFC Fylde	1627	L 1 - 2	Whitehouse 43	17	15
22	Nat N	A	Gainsborough Trinity	571	D 2 - 2	Williams 14 Morgan 44 (pen)	18	16
29	Nat N	H	Boston United	577	D 2 - 2	Langmead 67 Nicholson 90	18	17
Nov 5	Nat N	A	Chorley	969	L 0 - 1		18	18
12	Nat N	H	Stockport County	806	D 1 - 1	Williams 42	19	19
19	Nat N	A	FC United of Manchester	2313	L 0 - 2		19	20
26	FAT 3Q	A	FC United of Manchester	736	W 5 - 1	Styche 3 Ironside 7 (p) Nicholson 27 Morgan 67 Williams 90		21
Dec 3	Nat N	H	Alfreton Town	465	W 4 - 1	IRONSIDE 4(24pen 63 73 84)	18	22
10	FAT 1	H	Stockbridge Park Steels	346	W 3 - 1	Morgan 45 Ironside 50 Tunnicliffe 69		23
!7	Nat N	H	Stalybridge Celtic	503	W 2 - 1	O'Brien 42 (og) Styche 44	15	24
26	Nat N	A	Tamworth	1304	W 2 - 1	Ironside 15 Nicholson 24	15	25
Jan 1	Nat N	H	Tamworth	1002	W 1 - 0	Nicholson 39	14	26
7	Nat N	A	Darlington 1883	2313	W 2 - 1	Ironside 58 (pen) Nicholson 90	12	27
14	FAT2	H	Guiseley	554	W 6 - 1	NICHOLSON 5 (33 58 63 71 82) Ironside 50		28
21	Nat N	H	Brackley Town	661	D 2 - 2	Nicholson 18 Mills 27	13	29
24	Nat N	A	Salford City	867	L 0 - 4		13	30
28	Nat N	A	Kidderminster Harriers	1764	L 0 - 4		14	31
Feb 4	FAT3	H	York City	687	L 0 - 3			32
11	Nat N	A	FC Halifax Town	1573	L 0 - 2		14	33
18	Nat N	H	Bradford PA	573	L 1 - 2	Nicholson 76	15	34
25	Nat N	A	Boston United	957	W 3 - 1	Chambers 43 Nicholson 55 Ironside 66	14	35
Mar 4	Nat N	H	Gainsborough Trinity	474	W 2 - 1	Ironside 53 Nicholson 63	14	36
11	Nat N	H	Worcester City	485	D 1 - 1	Ironside 12	14	37
18	Nat N	A	Curzon Ashton	208	L 1 - 2	Chambers 2	14	38
21	Nat N	A	Altrincham	646	W 3 - 1	Chambers 25 63 Daniels 32	14	39
25	Nat N	H	AFC Fylde	480	W 4 - 1	Daniels 27 Langmead 40 Chambers 43 Kelly-Evans 9013	14	40
April 1	Nat N	A	Stockport County	3416	D 1 - 1	Chambers 59	14	41
4	Nat N	H	Gloucester City	415	D 1 - 1	Daniels 38 (pen)	14	42
8	Nat N	H	Chorley	501	D 1 - 1	Chambers 70	13	43
15	Nat N	H	Harrogate Town	543	W 2 - 1	MIlls 45 Kelly-Evans 86	12	44
17	Nat N	A	AFC Telford United	1246	W 4 - 2	Mills 19 47 Nicholson 36 77	12	45
22	Nat N	H	FC United of Manchester	777	L 1 - 4	Nicholson 45	12	46
29	Nat N	A	Alfreton Town	580	D 3 - 3	Gascoigne 25 Chambers 36 68	12	47

GOALSCORERS	SG	CSG	Pens	Hat tricks	Total		SG	CSG	Pens	Hat tricks	Total
2015-16 Williams					14	Kelly-Evans	2				2
Ironside	15	3	3	1	18	Styche	2				2
Nicholson	12	5		1	17	Gascoigne	1				1
Chambers	7	4			9	McDonald	1				1
Williams	7	2			8	Opponents	1				1
Whitehouse	5				6	Tempest	1				1
Langmead	4				5	Tunnicliffe	1				1
Mills	3	2			4						
Daniels	3		1		3						
Morgan	3		1		3						

SALFORD CITY
Club Contact Details
Moor Lane, Kersal, Salford, Manchester M7 3OZ
0161 792 6287

Ground Capacity: 8,000   Seats: 1,300   Covered: 600   Clubhouse: Yes   Shop: Yes

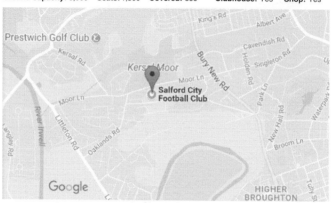

Record Attendance
3,000 v Whickham, FA Vase, 1980. 4,058 (at The Willows) v FC United, North West Counties Div.1, 03/10/06.
Previous Grounds
None

10 YEAR RECORD

07-08		08-09		09-10		10-11		11-12		12-13		13-14		14-15		15-16		16-17	
NWC1	2	NP1N	20	NP1N	11	NP1N	12	NP1N	13	NP1N	16	NP1N	12	NP1N	1	NP P	3	Nat N	4
FAC	P	FAC	2Q	FAC	3Q	FAC	1Q	FAC	Pr	FAC	2Q	FAC	P	FAC	2Q	FAC	2Pr	FAC	3Q
FAV	4P	FAT	1Q	FAT	3Q	FAT	P	FAT	2Q	FAT	P	FAT	P	FAT	P	FAT	1Q	FAT	3Qr

Club Factfile

Founded: 1940   **Nickname:** Ammies   **Manager:** Anthony Johnson & Bernard Morley

Previous Names: Salford Central 1940-63, Salford Amateurs 1963 until merger with Anson Villa, Salford F.C. > 1990

Previous Leagues: Local leagues 1940-63. Manchester 1963-80. Cheshire County 1980-82. North West Counties 1982-2008.

Club Colours (change): Red/white/white

RECORDS

HONOURS

FA Comps: None

League: Manchester League Premier Division 1974-75, 75-76, 76-77, 78-79.
Northern Premier Division One North 2014-15.

County FA: Lancashire Amateur Cup 1972-73, 74-75, 76-77. Manchester Premier Cup 1977-78, 78-79.

BEST PERFORMANCES	**FA Cup:** Second Round Proper 2015-16 (r).
	FA Trophy: Third Qualifying Round 2009-10.
	FA Vase: Fourth Round Proper 2007-08.

SALFORD CITY MATCH RESULTS 2016-17

Date	Comp	H/A	Opponents	Att:	Result	Goalscorers	Pos	No.
Aug 6	Nat N	H	Gloucester City	1074	D 1 - 1	Poole 51	15	1
13	Nat N	A	Stalybridge Celtic	752	W 4 - 0	Phenix 23 Warburton 61 Hulme 64 Walker 70 (pen)	6	2
16	Nat N	H	FC United of Manchester	1966	W 1 - 0	Phenix 30	5	3
20	Nat N	A	Nuneaton Town	621	W 1 - 0	Phenix 15	5	4
22	Nat N	A	AFC Fylde	1832	D 3 - 3	Hulme 27 Nottingham 60 Phenix 85	4	5
27	Nat N	H	Gainsborough Trinity	1325	W 3 - 2	Grand 39 Phenix 40 Priestley 86	3	6
29	Nat N	A	Curzon Ashton	888	W 2 - 0	Hulme 52 Grand 64	2	7
Sept 3	Nat N	H	Alfreton Town	1503	W 4 - 1	Phenix 12 Hulme 22 Grand 26 Warburton 68	1	8
6	Nat N	H	FC Halifax Town	2049	D 2 - 2	Walker 55 (pen) Roberts (og) 73	2	9
10	Nat N	A	Kidderminster Harriers	2072	L 0 - 1		2	10
13	Nat N	A	Chorley	2022	L 1 - 2	Nottingham 26	5	11
17	FAC2Q	A	Bradford PA	427	W 1 - 0	Poole 72		12
24	Nat N	H	Brackley Town	1072	D 1 - 1	Phenix 53	6	13
Oct 1	FAC3Q	A	Stockport County	3181	L 0 - 2			14
8	Nat N	A	Stockport County	3830	L 1 - 2	Wellens 7	7	15
15	Nat N	H	Boston United	1425	D 3 - 3	Nottingham 14 Poole 65 Johnston 70	7	16
22	Nat N	H	Tamworth	1351	L 1 - 2	Grand 65	10	17
29	Nat N	A	AFC Telford United	1841	W 2 - 0	Grand 19 Poole 35	9	18
Nov 5	Nat N	H	Harrogate Town	1173	D 0 - 0		9	19
12	Nat N	A	Altrincham	2403	W 2 - 0	Hulme 45 Allen 53	8	20
19	Nat N	H	Worcester City	1077	W 3 - 0	Haughton 11 Phenix 43 Burton 55	7	21
26	FAT3Q	A	Harrrogate Town	571	D 2 - 2	Poole 18 Nottingham 67		22
Dec 3	Nat N	A	Darlington 1883	1996	D 2 - 2	Nottingham 6 Phenix 45	6	23
6	FAT3Qr	H	Harrogate Town	290	L 0 - 3			24
!7	Nat N	A	Alfreton Town	718	D 1 - 1	Walker 76	6	25
26	Nat N	H	Bradford PA	1049	W 1 - 0	Hine 85	7	26
Jan 1	Nat N	A	Bradford PA	539	W 2 - 0	Poole 19 83	5	27
7	Nat N	H	Kidderminster Harriers	1298	W 3 - 0	Hine 65 90 Hulme 79	4	28
21	Nat N	A	F.C. Halifax Town	2157	L 2 - 4	Walker 6 (pen) Phenix 24	6	29
24	Nat N	H	Nuneaton Borough	867	W 4 - 0	Phenix 24 Longmead 56 (og) Nottingham 61 Grand 85	5	30
28	Nat N	A	FC United of Manchester	4154	W 3 - 0	Poole 16 Nottingham 65 Hulme 90	3	31
Feb 4	Nat N	H	AFC Fylde	1485	W 5 - 0	Priestley 13 HULME 3 (16 89 90pen) Phenix 76	2	32
11	Nat N	A	Gloucester City	743	L 2 - 3	Priestley 20 Phenix 70	3	33
18	Nat N	H	Stalybridge Celtic	1310	W 1 - 0	Phenix 57	3	34
25	Nat N	H	AFC Telford United	1246	W 2 - 1	Allen 49 Grand 52	2	35
Mar 4	Nat N	A	Tamworth	1301	L 0 - 2		2	36
11	Nat N	A	Brackley Town	738	W 1 - 0	Nottingham 57	2	37
18	Nat N	H	Stockport County	1735	D 1 - 1	Allen 80 (pen)	2	38
21	Nat N	H	Chorley	1428	D 1 - 1	Nottingham 89	2	39
25	Nat N	A	Boston United	1242	L 0 - 2		4	40
April 1	Nat N	H	Altrincham	1442	W 2 - 1	Walker 52 (pen) Grand 62	4	41
8	Nat N	A	Harogate Town	1049	D 3 - 3	Walker 20 (pen) Johnston 73 Haughton 85	5	42
15	Nat N	A	Gainsborough Trinity	890	L 0 - 1		5	43
17	Nat N	H	Curzon Ashton	1341	W 1 - 0	Walker 84	5	44
22	Nat N	A	Worcester City	743	W 2 1	Phenix 36 Haughton 86	5	45
29	Nat N	H	Darlington 1883	2069	W 5 - 1	Grand 10 Brown 37(og) Nottingham 40 Horsfall 52 Morris 80	4	46
May 3	PO SF1	H	FC Halifax Town	2175	D 1 - 1	Poole 86		47
	PO SF2	A	FC Halifax Town	3655	D 1 - 1	Nottingham 107 (Lost 0-3 on penalties)		48

GOALSCORERS	SG	CSG	Pens	Hat tricks	Total		SG	CSG	Pens	Hat tricks	Total
2015-16 Poole					20	Opponents	3				3
Phenix	15	5			15	Priestley	3				3
Nottingham	11	2			11	Johnston	2				2
Hulme	8	2	1	1	10	Warburton	2				2
Grand	9	2			9	Burton	1				1
Poole	8				9	Horsfall	1				1
Walker	7		4		7	Morris	1				1
Allen	2		1		3	Wellens	1				1
Haughton	3				3						
Hine	3				3						

SOUTHPORT

Club Contact Details
Merseyrail Community Stadium, Haig Avenue, Southport, Merseyside PR8 6JZ
01704 533 422
secretary@southportfc.net

Ground Capacity: 6,008   **Seats:** 1,660   **Covered:** 2,760   **Clubhouse:** Yes   **Shop:** Yes

Record Attendance
20,010 v Newcastle United - FA Cup 1932
Previous Grounds
Sussex Road Sports Ground, Scarisbrick New Road 1886-1905, Ash Lane (later named Haig Avenue)

10 YEAR RECORD

07-08		08-09		09-10		10-11		11-12		12-13		13-14		14-15		15-16		16-17	
Conf N	4	Conf N	5	Conf N	1	Conf	21	Conf	7	Conf	20	Conf	18	Conf	19	Nat	16	Nat	23
FAC	4Q	FAC	3Q	FAC	1P	FAC	1P	FAC	1P	FAC	4Q	FAC	1P	FAC	3P	FAC	4Q	FAC	1Pr
FAT	1P	FAT	QFr	FAT	1Pr	FAT	1Pr	FAT	1P	FAT	QF	FAT	1P	FAT	1Pr	FAT	2P	FAT	2P

Club Factfile

Founded: 1881   **Nickname:** The Sandgrounders   **Manager:** Alan Lewer

Previous Names: Southport Central 1888-1918, Southport Vulcan 1918-21.

Previous Leagues: Preston & District, Lancashire 1889-1903, Lancashire Combination 1903-11, Central 1911-21, Football League 1921-78, Northern Premier 1978-93, 2003-04, Conference 1993-2003.

Club Colours (change): All yellow (Green & white hoops/green/green)

RECORDS
Victory: 8-1 v Nelson - 01/01/31
Defeat: 0-11 v Oldham Athletic - 26/12/62
Goalscorer: Alan Spence - 98
Appearances: Arthur Peat - 401 (1962-72)
Additional: Paid £20,000 to Macclesfield Town for Martin McDonald

HONOURS
FA Comps: N/A

League: Football League Division Four 1972-73. Northern Premier League Premier Division 1992-93.
Conference North 2004-05, 2009-10.

County FA: Lancashire Senior Cup 1904-05. Lancashire Junior Cup 1919-20, 92-93, 96-97, 97-98, 2001-01, 05-06, 07-08, 09-10.
Liverpool Senior Cup 1930-31, 31-32, 43-44, 62-63, 74-75, 90-91, 92-93, 98-99, 2011-12.

BEST PERFORMANCES
FA Cup: Quarter-Finals 1930-31. As a Non-League side - Third Round Proper 1998-99, 2014-15.
FA Trophy: Final 1997-98.
FA Vase: N/A

SOUTHPORT MATCH RESULTS 2016-17

Date	Comp	H/A	Opponents	Att:	Result	Goalscorers	Pos	No.
Aug 6	Nat Lg	A	Dagenham & Redbridge	1296	L 0 - 3		24	1
9	Nat Lg	H	Gateshead	926	L 0 - 3		24	2
13	Nat Lg	H	Woking	702	W 2 - 1	Almond 19 88	19	3
16	Nat Lg	A	Macclesfield Town	1329	L 1 - 3	Grimes 83	19	4
20	Nat Lg	A	Lincoln City	2440	L 0 - 4		22	5
27	Nat Lg	H	Tranmere Rovers	3046	L 1 - 3	Almond 62	22	6
29	Nat Lg	A	Forest Green Rovers	1621	L 1 - 5	Bishop 50	23	7
3 Sept	Nat Lg	H	Dover Athletic	760	L 0 - 1		23	8
10	Nat Lg	A	Eastleigh	1878	D 1 - 1	Gray 71	23	9
13	Nat Lg	H	Barrow	848	L 1 - 4	Caton 85	23	10
17	Nat Lg	H	Aldershot Town	772	D 1 - 1	Gray 70	23	11
24	Nat Lg	A	North Feriby United	451	W 1 - 0	Nolan 45	23	12
Oct 1	Nat Lg	H	Bromley	744	L 1 - 2	Lussey 57	23	13
4	Nat Lg	A	Solihull Moors	772	L 0 - 4		23	14
8	Nat Lg	A	Guiseley	1046	L 1 - 2	Allen 69	24	15
15	FAC4Q	H	Chester	1674	W 1 - 0	Weeks 33		16
22	Nat Lg	H	Sutton United	864	D 1 - 1	Jones 37	23	17
25	Nat Lg	H	York City	856	W 2 - 0	Allen 48 (pen() 90	22	18
29	Nat Lg	A	Torquay United	1490	W 2 - 1	Howe 66 Caton 75	19	19
Nov 7	FAC1	H	Fleetwood	2265	D 0 - 0			20
12	Nat Lg	A	Maidstone United	932	W 3 - 2	Allen 5 52 Nolan 45	18	21
15	FAC1r	A	Fleetwood	1609	L 1 - 4	Grimes 87		22
19	Nat Lg	A	Boreham Wood	314	L 0 - 2		19	23
22	Nat Lg	A	Chester	1752	D 2 - 2	Jones 60 Allen 79	18	24
26	Nat Lg	H	Braintree Town	866	L 4 - 5	Higgins 16 Thompson 28 Jones 29 Allen 56 (pen)	21	25
29	Nat Lg	H	Solihull Moors	703	D 0 - 0		20	26
Dec 5	FAT1	A	Farsley Celtic	352	W 4 - 0	Higgins 4 Allen 33 (pen) Lussey 33 Caton 90		27
17	Nat Lg	H	Eastleigh	769	W 4 - 3	Jones 4 Nolan 30 Weeks 48 Allen 75 (pen)	20	28
26	Nat Lg	A	Wrexham	4317	L 0 - 1		20	29
Jan 1	Nat Lg	H	Wrexham	2066	W 3 - 2	Nolan 36 88 Brewster 45	19	30
7	Nat Lg	A	Aldershot Town	1772	L 1 - 2	Jones 90	19	31
10	Nat Lg	A	Barrow	956	W 1 - 0	McKenna 13	19	32
14	FAT2	H	Wealdstone	744	L 1 - 2	Wright 53		33
21	Nat Lg	H	North Ferriby United	795	L 2 - 4	McKeown 51 Weeks 90	19	34
28	Nat Lg	A	Bromley	953	L 1 - 3	Wright 22	20	35
Feb 4	Nat Lg	A	Gateshead	620	L 0 - 3		20	36
11	Nat Lg	H	Dagenham & Redbridge	845	L 1 - 4	Allen 24 (pen)	21	37
18	Nat Lg	A	Woking	1386	D 0 - 0		22	38
28	Nat Lg	A	Chester	1496	L 0 - 1		22	39
Mar 4	Nat Lg	A	Maidstone Unted	2404	L 2 - 4	McKenna 3 Allen 51	24	40
11	Nat Lg	H	Torquay United	1159	L 1 - 2	Bailey 74	24	41
18	Nat Lg	A	Braintree Town	510	L 0 - 2		24	42
21	Nat Lg	A	York City	2482	L 3 - 5	Almond 19 41 McKeown 20	24	43
25	Nat Lg	H	Boreham Wood	1010	W 1 - 0	Nolan 81	24	44
Apr 1	Nat Lg	H	Guiseley	981	L 0 - 1		24	45
4	Nat Lg	H	Macclesfield Town	792	L 1 - 2	Higgins 42	24	46
8	Nat Lg	A	Sutton United	1807	D 2 - 2	Spence 68 (og) Ashton 74	24	47
14	Nat Lg	A	Dover Athletic	1563	L 0 - 3		24	48
17	Nat Lg	H	Forest Green Rovers	844	W 2 - 0	Cundy 62 McKeown 71	24	49
22	Nat Lg	A	Tranmere Rovers	6159	L 1 - 4	Myers 61	24	50
29	Nat Lg	H	Lincoln City	3462	D 1 - 1	Ashton 88	23	51

GOALSCORERS	SG	CSG	Pens	Hat tricks	Total		SG	CSG	Pens	Hat tricks	Total
2015-16 Almond					13	McKenna	2				2
Allen	8	2	5		11	Wright	2				2
Almond	3				5	Bailey	1				1
Jones	4	2			5	Bishop	1				1
Nolan	4				5	Brewster	1				1
Caton	3				3	Cundy	1				1
Higgins	3				3	Howe	1				1
McKeown	3				3	Myers	1				1
Weeks	3				3	Nolan	1				1
Ashton	2				2	Opponnets	1				1
Gray	2				2	Thompson	1				1
Grimes	2				2						
Lussey	2				2						

SPENNYMOOR TOWN

Club Contact Details
The Brewery Field, Durham Road, Spennymoor DL16 6JN
01388 827 248
stevenlawson_16@hotmail.co.uk

Ground Capacity: 3,000   Seats: 224   Covered: 800   Clubhouse: Yes   Shop: Yes

Record Attendance
2,670 v Darlington, Northern League 2012-13.
Previous Grounds

10 YEAR RECORD

07-08		08-09		09-10		10-11		11-12		12-13		13-14		14-15		15-16		16-17	
NL 1	12	NL 1	4	NL 1	1	NL 1	1	NL 1	1	NL 1	2	NL 1	1	NP1N	5	NP1N	2	NP P	2
FAC	2Q	FAC	EP	FAC	2Q	FAC	1Q	FAC	3Q	FAC	2Q	FAC	1Q	FAC	4Qr	FAC	2Q	FAC	1P
FAV	2Q	FAV	2Q	FAV	2Pr	FAV	5P	FAV	3P	FAV	F	FAV	5P	FAT	1P	FAT	3Q	FAT	1Q

Club Factfile

Founded: 1904   **Nickname:** Moors   **Manager:** Jason Ainsley

Previous Names: Amalgamation of Evenwood Town & Spennymoor United in 2005-06.

Previous Leagues: Northern League 2005-14. Northern Premier 2014-17.

Club Colours (change): Black & white stripes/black/black

RECORDS

Victory: 10-0 v Billingham Town (H), Northern League Division One, 18/03/2014
Defeat: 2-8 v Clitheroe (A), FA Cup 2nd Qualifying Round, 29/09/2007
Goalscorer: Gavin Cpgdon - 103
Appearances: Lewis Dodds - 227
Additional: Northern League record points tally of 109 during 2012-13.

HONOURS

FA Comps: FA Vase 2012-13.

League: Northern League Division One 1948-49, 69-70, 70-71, 2009-10, 2010-11, 2011-12, 2013-14, Division Two 2006-07.

County FA: Durham Challange Cup 1969-70, 2011-12.

BEST PERFORMANCES	**FA Cup:** First Round Proper 1956-57, 2016-17. **FA Trophy:** First Round Proper 2014-14. **FA Vase:** Final 2012-13.

SPENNYMOOR TOWN MATCH RESULTS 2016-17

Date	Comp	H/A	Opponents	Att:	Result		Goalscorers	Pos	No.
Aug 13	NPL	A	Hednesford Town	459	L	1 - 1	Gott 5	22	1
16	NPL	H	Warrington Town	618	W	4 - 1	Dowson 23 Craddock 37 Armstrong 73 83	12	2
20	NPL	H	Sutton Coldfield Town	485	W	3 - 0	Anderson 55 89 Tait 64 (pen)	6	3
27	NPL	A	Barwell	177	D	1 - 1	Anderson 28	10	4
29	NPL	H	Corby Town	661	W	1 - 0	Fisher 11	7	5
Sept 3	FAC1Q	A	Radcliffe Borough	175	W	5 - 3	Lowson 22 Tait 59 Fisher 63 Curtis 69 Johnson 74		6
10	NPL	A	Rushall Olympic	189	W	5 - 1	Anderson 2 TAYLOR 3 (27 47 81) Tait 36 (pen)	5	7
17	FAC2Q	H	Whitby Town	607	W	1 - 0	Taylor 68		8
20	NPL	H	Whitby Town	576	L	0 - 1			9
24	NPL	H	Stafford Rangers	531	W	1 - 0	Taylor 6	4	10
27	NPL	A	Blyth Spartans	818	D	0 - 0		5	11
Oct 1	FAC3Q	H	Chorley	713	W	1 - 0	Taylor 63		12
8	NPL	A	Coalville Town	183	W	1 - 0	Taylor 44	7	13
11	NPL	H	Skelmersdale United	462	W	7 - 0	HENRY 3 (16 24 61) Bodie 46 (og) Armstrong 54 Dowson 76 Craddock 82	7	14
15	FAC4Q	A	Lincoln United	578	W	3 - 0	Tait 12 Dowson 27 Armstrong 76		15
18	NPL	A	Grantham Town	167	D	3 - 3	Dinanga 49 Tait 85 (Pen) Johnson 89	8	16
22	NPL	A	Buxton	501	D	2 - 2	Chandler 3 86	7	17
29	FAT1Q	H	Matlock Town	393	L	1 - 3	Anderson 29		18
Nov 1	NPL	A	Workington	570	W	4 - 1	Armstrong 12 Anderson 52 Fisher 61 Tait 64	6	19
5	FAC1	A	MK Dons	4099	L	2 - 3	Tait 19 Johnson 84		20
7	NPL	A	Ilkeston	283	W	3 - 2	Mitchell 41 Chandler 77 Armstrong 87	6	21
12	NPL	H	Stourbridge	545	D	2 - 2	Ramshaw 64 Armstrong 65	6	22
19	NPL	A	Nantwich Town	300	L	0 - 1		7	23
22	NPL	A	Workington	366	L	0 - 3		8	24
26	NPL	H	Ashton United	512	L	1 - 2	Tait 58	9	25
Dec 3	NPL	A	Ashton United	212	W	2 - 1	Curtis 20 Taylor 72	7	26
10	NPL	H	Mickleover Sports	478	W	3 - 0	Dowson 6 Taylor 42 Mitchell 82	5	27
17	NPL	A	Stourbridge	680	D	1 - 1	Anderson 59	6	28
26	NPL	H	Frickley Athletic	516	W	2 - 0	Ramshaw 2 Tait 90 (pen)	4	29
Jan 2	NPL	A	Corby Town	449	L	1 3	Taylor 50	5	30
7	NPL	H	Hednesford Town	519	W	4 - 2	Henry 6 Tait 41 (pen) Fisher 65 83	5	31
14	NPL	A	Marine	466	D	1 - 1	Armstrong 90	5	32
21	NPL	H	Coalville Town	486	W	5 - 0	Anderson 25 Taylor 33 Armstrong 72 76 Tait 90 (pen)	3	33
Feb 4	NPL	H	Grantham Town	490	L	1 - 2	Taylor 5	10	34
18	NPL	H	Buxton	538	D	1 - 1	Johnson 32	8	35
21	NPL	H	`Marine	472	W	2 - 1	Hughes 3 (og) Griffiths 87	8	36
25	NPL	A	Stafford Rangers	568	D	3 - 3	Tait 12 Taylor 23 Fisher 30	9	37
28	NPL	H	Blyth Spartans	946	W	2 - 1	Griffiths 23 Chandler 27	4	38
Mar 7	NPL	A	Whitby Town	329	L	1, - 2	Curtis 73	8	39
11	NPL	H	Halesowen Town	354	W	2 - 1	Tait 23 Chandler 75	8	40
18	NPL	H	Mickleover Sports	146	W	5 - 0	Griffiths 12 Anderson 25 Armstrong 32 Dowson 85 Ramshaw 90	7	41
21	NPL	A	Matlock Town	503	W	3 - 2	Armstrong 1 Anderson 26 Henry 35	5	42
25	NPL	H	Halesowen Town	668	D	1 - 1	Ramshaw 72	5	43
28	NPL	A	Warrington	308	W	2 - 0	Taylor 16 47	4	44
Apr 1	NPL	H	Nantwich Town	602	D	1 - 1	Henry 7	4	45
4	NPL	A	Matlock Town	331	W	4 - 0	Armstrong 16 57 Johnson 23 Taylor 26	3	46
6	NPL	H	Ilkeston	546	W	3 - 0	DOWSON 3 (55 77 90)		47
8	NPL	A	Sutton Coldfield Town	236	L	0 - 1		4	48
11	NPL	A	Skelmersdale United	212	W	2 - 0	Mason 48 Taylor 88	2	49
15	NPL	H	Rushall Olympic	578	D	1 - 1	Taylor 68	2	50
17	NPL	A	Frickley Athletic	295	W	2 - 0	Johnson 10 Fisher 82	2	51
22	NPL	H	Barwell	665	W	2 - 0	Armstrong 50 Chandler 53	2	52
25	PO SF	H	Nantwich Town	882	W	2 - 0	Griffiths 68 Johnson 80		53
29	PO Final	H	Stourbridge	1699	W	1 - 0	Ramshaw 30		54

GOALSCORERS	SG	CSG	Pens	Hat tricks	Total			SG	CSG	Pens	Hat tricks	Total
Taylor	16	2		1	18		Griffiths	4				4
Armstrong	12	2			15		Curtis	3				3
Tait	13	2	5		13		Craddock	2				2
Anderson	9	2			10		Mitchell	2				2
Dowson	6	2		1	8		Opponents	2				2
Fisher	6	2			7		Dinanga	1				1
Johnson	5				7		Gott	1				1
Chandler	5				6		Lowson	1				1
Henry	4			1	6		Mason	1				1
Ramshaw	5				5							

STOCKPORT COUNTY

Club Contact Details
Edgeley Park, Hardcastle Road, Stockport SK3 9DD
0161 286 8888
mark.lockyear@stockportcounty.com

Ground Capacity: 10,800 **Seats:** 10,800 **Covered:** Yes **Clubhouse:** Yes **Shop:** Yes

Record Attendance
27,833 v Liverpool, FA Cup 5th Round 11/02/1950. 10,273 (all seated) v Leeds United, 28/12/2008.

Previous Grounds
Heaton Norris Recreation Ground & other various locations 1883-89. Green Lane 1889-1902.

10 YEAR RECORD

07-08		08-09		09-10		10-11		11-12		12-13		13-14		14-15		15-16		16-17	
FL 2	4	FL 1	18	FL 1	24	FL 2	24	Conf	16	Conf	21	Conf N	14	Conf N	11	Nat N	9	Nat N	8
FAC	1Pr	FAC	Pr	FAC	Pr	FAC	2P	FAC	1Pr	FAC	4Q	FAC	1P	FAC	3Q	FAC	2Q	FAC	1P
FLC	2P	FLC	1P	FLC	1P	FLC	1P	FAT	1Pr	FAT	2Pr	FAT	3Qr	FAT	2Pr	FAT	3Q	FAT	2Pr

Club Factfile

Founded: 1883 **Nickname:** County or Hatters **Manager:** Jim Gannon

Previous Names: Heaton Norris Rovers 1883-88, Heaton Norris 1888-90.

Previous Leagues: Lancashire 1863-1900. Football League 1900-2011.

Club Colours (change): Blue with white & navy blue panels/blue/white (White & black)

RECORDS

Victory: 13-0 v Halifax Town, Division Three North 06/01/1934.
Defeat: 0-9 v Everton Reserves, Lancashire League, 09/12/1893.
Goalscorer: (League) Jack Connor - 132, 1951-56.
Appearances: (League) Andy Thorpe - 555, 1978-86, 88-92.
Additional: Paid, £800,000 for Ian Moore from Nottingham Forest, 07/1998.
Received, £1,600,000 for Alun Armstrong from Middlesbrough, 02/1998.

HONOURS

FA Comps: None

League: Lancashire 1899-1900.
League Division Three North 1921-22, 36-37, Division Four 1966-67.

County FA: Manchester S.C. 1897-98,98-99, 1914-15,22-23. Cheshire Medal 1922-23,24-25,28-29,29-30,30-31. Ches' Bowl 1933-34,48-49, 52-53,55-56,56-57,58-59,60-61,62-63. Ches' S.C.1905-06,46-47,48-49,65-66,2015-16. Ches' Prem. Cup 1969-70,70-71, 2010-11.

BEST PERFORMANCES	**FA Cup:** Fifth Round Proper 1934-35, 49-50, 2000-01.
	FA Trophy: Second Round Proper 2012-13 (r), 14-15 (r)
	FA Vase: N/A

STOCKPORT COUNTY MATCH RESULTS 2016-17

Date	Comp	H/A	Opponents	Att:	Result	Goalscorers	Pos	No.
Aug 6	Nat N	H	Alfreton Town	2632	W 4 - 3	Lloyd 4 Marsden 13 Odejayi 45 Stopforth 90	2	1
9	Nat N	A	Stalybridge Celtic	1601	W 3 - 1	Meppen-Walter 45 Marsden 72 Amis 80	1	2
13	Nat N	A	FC Utd of Manchester	3030	L 0 - 2		3	3
16	Nat N	H	FC Halifax Town	3086	D 1 - 1	Duxberry 54	8	4
20	Nat N	H	Brackley Town	2529	L 2 - 4	Lloyd 26 Thomas 89	10	5
27	Nat N	A	AFC Telford United	1311	D 0 - 0		12	6
29	Nat N	H	Worcester City	2514	W 1 - 0	Lloyd 41	11	7
Sept 3	Nat N	A	Altrincham	2355	W 3 - 2	Clarke 25 Spencer 74 Smalley 86	10	8
6	Nat N	A	Darlington 1883	1730	L 1 - 2	Ball 19	11	9
10	Nat N	H	Boston United	2466	D 1 - 1	Lloyd 48	14	10
17	FAC2Q	H	Hyde United	1428	W 2 - 0	Lloyd 31 Clarke 41		11
24	Nat N	A	Curzon Ashton	964	W 2 - 1	Minihan 83 Clarke 90	11	12
27	Nat N	H	AFC Fylde	2206	L 1 - 2	Spencer 90	11	13
Oct 1	FAC3Q	H	Salford City	3181	W 2 - 0	Lloyd 22 (pen) Clarke 54		14
8	Nat N	H	Salford City	3830	W 2 - 0	Stopforth 30 Cartwright 67	10	15
15	FAC4Q	H	Bishop Auckland	2770	W 2 - 0	Lloyd 32 40		16
22	Nat N	A	Chorley	2464	W 1 - 0	Lloyd 72	9	17
29	Nat N	H	Kidderminster Harriers	2883	L 0 - 1		11	18
Nov 5	FAC1	H	Woking	4025	L 2 - 4	Ball 9 44		19
12	Nat N	A	Nuneaton Town	806	D 1 - 1	Amis 36	11	20
15	Nat N	H	Gainsborough Trinity	2112	W 1 - 0	Lloyd 11		21
19	Nat N	H	Bradford PA	3246	L 1 - 2	Odejayi 26	11	22
22	Nat N	A	Tamworth	710	D 2 - 2	Lloyd 33 Amis 82	10	23
26	FAT3Q	H	Bradford PA	1164	W 2 - 0	Minihan 31 Marsden 90		24
Dec 3	Nat N	A	Gloucester City	539	W 1 - 0	Felix 74	9	25
10	FAT1	H	Marine	1411	W 3 - 2	Odejayl 42 Lloyd 85 87		26
!7	Nat N	H	Altrincham	3991	W 3 - 0	Lloyd 25 Ball 76 Minihan 90	8	27
26	Nat N	A	Harrogate Town	1055	W 1 - 0	Walters 69	8	28
Jan 1	Nat N	H	Harrogate Town	3725	D 1 - 1	Clarke 63	8	29
7	Nat N	A	Boston United	1360	W 2 - 0	Lloyd 35 90	7	30
14	FAT2	H	Brackley Town	1605	D 1 - 1	Lloyd 90		31
17	FAT2r	A	Brackley Town	294	L 0 - 2			32
21	Nat N	H	Darlington 1883	3649	D 3 - 3	Lloyd 23 37 Ball 75	7	33
28	Nat N	A	FC Halifax Town	2925	D 0 0		7	34
31	Nat N	A	Brackley Town	368	W 3 - 0	Meppen-Walter 24 36 Felix 836	6	35
Feb 4	Nat N	H	Stalybridge Celtic	3765	W 3 - 1	Lloyd 8 76 (pen) Ball 86	5	36
11	Nat N	A	Alfreton Town	993	D 1 - 1	Amis 39	6	37
18	Nat N	H	FC Utd of Manchester	5630	W 2 - 1	Osbourne 45 Duxbury 70	6	38
25	Nat N	A	Kidderminster Harriers	2151	L 0 - 2		6	39
Mar 4	Nat N	H	Chorley	4073	D 0 - 0		6	40
11	Nat N	H	Curzon Ashton	3495	W 3 - 1	Lloyd 5 40 Ball 56	6	41
18	Nat N	A	Salford City	1735	D 1 - 1	Lloyd 13	6	42
21	Nat N	A	AFC Fylde	2489	D 0 - 0		7	43
25	Nat N	H	Tamworth	3349	W 2 - 1	Rose 73 Lloyd 81	5	44
April 1	Nat N	H	Nuneaton Town	3416	D 1 - 1	Lloyd 49 (pen)	7	45
8	Nat N	A	Gainsborough Trinity	851	W 1 - 0	Lloyd 57 (pen)	7	46
14	Nat N	H	AFC Telford United	4261	D 1 - 1	Montrose 72	6	47
17	Nat N	A	Worcester City	922	D 0 - 0		7	48
22	Nat N	A	Bradford PA	1280	W 2 - 0	Amis 81 Lloyd 90	7	49
29	Nat N	H	Gloucester City	5783	D 1 - 1	Lloyd 56 (pen)	8	50

GOALSCORERS	SG	CSG	Pens	Hat tricks	Total		SG	CSG	Pens	Hat tricks	Total
2015-16 Marsden					7	Felix	2				2
Lloyd	22	3	5		29	Spencer	2				2
Ball	6	2			7	Stopforth	2				2
Amis	5				5	Cartwright	1				1
Clarke	5	2			5	Montrose	1				1
Meppen-Walter	2				3	Osbourne	1				1
Marsden	3	2			3	Ross	1				1
Minihan	3				3	Smalley	1				1
Odejayi	3				3	Thomas	1				1
Duxberry	2				2	Walters	1				1

TAMWORTH

Club Contact Details
The Lamb Ground, Kettlebrook, Tamworth, Staffordshire B77 1AA
01827 657 98
georgedelves@thelambs.co.uk

Ground Capacity: 4,100   **Seats:** 518   **Covered:** 1,191   **Clubhouse:** Yes   **Shop:** Yes

Record Attendance
5,500 v Torquay United - FA Cup 1st Round 15/11/69
Previous Grounds
Jolly Sailor Ground 1933-34

10 YEAR RECORD

	07-08	08-09	09-10	10-11	11-12	12-13	13-14	14-15	15-16	16-17
	Conf N 15	Conf N 1	Conf 16	Conf 19	Conf 18	Conf 19	Conf 23	Conf N 7	Nat N 7	Nat N 9
FAC	4Q	4Q	4Q	4Q	2P	3P	4Q	2P	4Qr	2Q	2Q
FAT	QF	3Q	QF	1P	1P	3P	QF	3Q	1P	3Qr

Club Factfile

Founded: 1933   **Nickname:** The Lambs   **Manager:** Andy Morrell

Previous Names: None

Previous Leagues: Birmingham Combination 1933-54. West Midlands (originally Birmingham & District League) 1954-72, 84-88. Southern 1972-79, 83-84, 89-2003. Northern Premier 1979-83.

Club Colours (change): All red (All yellow)

RECORDS
Victory: 14-4 v Holbrook Institue (H) - Bass Vase 1934
Defeat: 0-11 v Solihull (A) - Birmingham Combination 1940
Goalscorer: Graham Jessop - 195
Appearances: Dave Seedhouse - 869
Additional: Paid £7,500 to Ilkeston Town for David Hemmings, December 2000
Received £12,000 from Kidderminster Harriers for Scott Rickards, 2003

HONOURS
FA Comps: FA Vase 1988-89.

League: West Midlands League 1963-64, 65-66, 71-72, 87-88.
Southern League Divison One Midland 1996-97, Premier Division 2002-03. Conference North 2008-09.

County FA: Staffordshire Senior Cup 1958-59, 63-64, 65-66, 2001-02.
Birmingham Senior Cup 1960-61, 65-66, 68-69.

BEST PERFORMANCES	**FA Cup:** Third Round Proper 2005-06, 06-07, 11-12.
	FA Trophy: Final 2002-03.
	FA Vase: Final 1988-89.

TAMWORTH MATCH RESULTS 2016-17

Date	Comp	H/A	Opponents	Att:	Result	Goalscorers	Pos	No.
Aug 6	Nat N	A	Brackley Town	360	D 0 - 0		19	1
9	Nat N	H	Worcester City	770	W 1 - 0	Lane 81	5	2
13	Nat N	H	AFC Telford United	839	W 2 - 1	Newton 4 Morrell 90	2	3
16	Nat N	A	Boston United	965	L 0 - 3		9	4
20	Nat N	A	FC Halifax Town	1597	L 0 - 4		11	5
27	Nat N	H	Bradford PA	669	W 5 - 1	Taylor 19 Lane 31 Davies 50 Briscoe 86 Dyer 89	10	6
29	Nat N	A	Alfreton Town	547	W 5 - 2	Davies 38 Lane 69 Ezewele 87 Newton 90 Dyer 90		7
Sept 3	Nat N	H	Chorley	737	L 0 - 1		11	8
6	Nat N	H	Gloucester City	644	W 3 - 1	Newton 22 33 Davies 90	8	9
10	Nat N	A	Curzon Ashton	212	W 5 - 1	Tomasson 12 67 Mills 29 Newton 51 77	6	10
13	Nat N	A	Kidderminster Harriers	1333	L 0 - 6		9	11
17	FAC2Q	A	Kidderminster Harriers	1050	L 0 4			12
24	Nat N	H	FC United of Manchester	1105	D 1 - 1	Newton 45	10	13
Oct 8	Nat N	H	Gainsborough Trinity	538	L 2 3	Newton 40 Briscoe 43	11	14
22	Nat N	A	Salford City	1351	W 2 1	Dyer 13 69	11	15
29	Nat N	H	AFC Fylde	807	W 1 0	Newton 66	10	16
Nov 5	Nat N	H	Darlington 1883	914	W 2 - 1	Newton 49 57	6	17
12	Nat N	A	HarrogateTown	975	W 4 - 3	Taylor 29 Dyer 42 Newton 86 90	5	18
19	Nat N	H	Stalybridge Celtic	702	W 2 - 1	Newton 64 Mills 65	4	19
22	Nat N	H	Stockport County	710	D 2 - 2	Davies 43 Tomassen 88	5	20
26	FAT3Q	A	Farsley Celtic	227	D 2 - 2	Tomasson 70 Newton 90		21
29	FAT3Qr	H	Farsley Celtic	371	L 0 - 4			22
Dec 3	Nat N	A	Altrincham	835	W 2 - 1	Briscoe 19 38	4	23
!7	Nat N	A	Chorley	1050	D 1 - 1	Dyer 58	4	24
26	Nat N	H	Nuneaton Town	1304	L 1 - 2	Dyer 25	5	25
Jan 1	Nat N	A	Nuneaton Town	1002	L 0 - 1		6	26
7	Nat N	H	Curzon Ashton	568	W 3 - 2	Mills 14 (pen) Clarke 43 Dyer 79	5	27
14	Nat N	H	FC Halifax Town	793	L 2 - 6	Opoku 49 Burns 88	6	28
28	Nat N	H	Boston United	805	W 1 - 0	Dyer 40	6	29
31	Nat N	A	Gloucester City	256	L 0 - 2		6	30
Feb 4	Nat N	A	Worcester City	531	D 1 - 1	Newton 43	8	31
11	Nat N	H	Brackley Town	548	W 2 - 1	Green 4 Styche 74	7	32
18	Nat N	A	AFC Telford United	1178	L 0 - 1		8	33
25	Nat N	A	AFC Fylde	1572	L 1 - 3	Newton 35	8	34
Mar 4	Nat N	H	Salford City	1301	W 2 - 0	Taylor 40 Newton 44	8	35
11	Nat N	A	FC United of Manchester	2407	L 0 - 1		8	36
18	Nat N	H	Gainsborough Trinity	553	W 1 - 0	Newton 35	8	37
21	Nat N	H	Kidderminster Harriers	860	L 3 - 4	Newton 25 Styche 32 (pen) Deeney 87	8	38
25	Nat N	A	Stockport County	3349	L 1 - 2	Dyer 29	10	39
April 1	Nat N	H	Harrogate Town	1096	W 3 - 2	Newton 18 78 pen Fox 86	9	40
8	Nat N	A	Darlington 1883	1694	L 2 - 3	Newton 1 Dyer 66	9	41
15	Nat N	A	Bradford PA	378	D 0 - 0		10	42
17	Nat N	H	Alfreton Town	711	W 4 - 1	Newton 22 (pen) 37 Styche 79 Davies 90	9	43
22	Nat N	A	Stalybridge Celtic	388	W 4 - 0	NEWTON 3 (5 7 66) Fox 17	9	44
29	Nat N	H	Altrincham	902	W 2 - 1	Powell 52 Newton 74	9	45

GOALSCORERS	SG	CSG	Pens	Hat tricks	Total		SG	CSG	Pens	Hat tricks	Total
2015-16 Durrell					15	Fox	2				2
Newton	21	4	2	1	29	Burns	1				1
Dyer	10	2			11	Clarke	1				1
Davies	5	2			5	Deeney	1				1
Briscoe	3				4	Ezewele	1				1
Tomasson	3	2			4	Green	1				1
Lane	3	2			3	Morrell	1				1
Mills	3		1		3	Opoku	1				1
Styche	3		1		3	Powell	1				1
Davies	3				3						

YORK CITY

Club Contact Details
Bootham Crescent, York YO30 7AQ
01904 624 447
lisa.charlton@yorkcityfootballclub.co.uk

Ground Capacity: 9,496 **Seats:** 7,872 **Covered:** Yes **Clubhouse:** Yes **Shop:** Yes

Record Attendance
28,123 v Huddersfield Town - FA Cup Sixth Round Proper 1938
Previous Grounds
Fulfordgate 1922-32

10 YEAR RECORD

07-08		08-09		09-10		10-11		11-12		12-13		13-14		14-15		15-16		16-17	
Conf	14	Conf	17	Conf	5	Conf	8	Conf	4	FL 2	17	FL 2	7	FL 2	18	FL 2	24	Nat	21
FAC	1P	FAC	4Qr	FAC	3P	FAC	3P	FAC	4Q	FAC	1Pr	FAC	1Pr	FAC	1Pr	FAC	1P	FAC	4Qr
FAT	SF	FAT	F	FAT	QF	FAT	1P	FAT	F	FLC	1P	FLC	1P	FLC	1P	FLC	2P	FAT	F

Club Factfile

Founded: 1922 **Nickname:** Minstermen **Manager:** Gary Mills

Previous Names: None

Previous Leagues: Midland 1922-29. Football League 1929-2004, 2012-16. Conference 2004-12.

Club Colours (change): Red & blue/blue/red (White & red/white/white)

RECORDS
Victory: 9-1 v Southport - Division Three North 1957
Defeat: 0-12 v Chester City - Division Three North 1936
Goalscorer: Norman Wilkinson - 143 (1954-66)
Appearances: Barry Jackson - 539 (1958-70)
Additional: Paid £140,000 to Burnley for Adrian Randall December 1995
Received £950,000 from Sheffield Wednesday for Richard Cresswell 25/03/1999

HONOURS
FA Comps: FA Trophy 2011-12, 16-17.

League: Football League Division Four 1983-84, Third Division Play-offs 1992-93.
Conference Premier Play-offs 2011-12.

County FA: North Riding Senior Cup 1949-50, 56-57, 69-70, 79-80, 87-88. 88-89, 95-96, 98-99, 99-00, 05-06, 09-10.

BEST PERFORMANCES	**FA Cup:** Semi-Finals 1954-55.
	FA Trophy: Final 2008-09, 11-12, 16-17.
	FA Vase: N/A

YORK MATCH RESULTS 2016-17

Date	Comp	H/A	Opponents	Att:	Result	Goalscorers	Pos	No.
Aug 6	Nat Lg	A	Maidstone United	2495	D 1 - 1	Kamdjo 69	11	1
9	Nat Lg	H	Macclesfield Town	2468	W 1 - 0	Fry 51	8	2
13	Nat Lg	H	Boreham Wood	2169	D 1 - 1	Heslop 88	9	3
16	Nat Lg	A	Gateshead	1311	L 1 - 6	Brodie 45	15	4
20	Nat Lg	A	Forest Green Rovers	1396	L 1 - 2	Brodie 20	18	5
27	Nat Lg	H	Woking	1972	W 4 - 1	Brodie 9 Klukowsji 13 Wright 20 Connolly 26	14	6
29	Nat Lg	A	Wrexham	4005	L 1 - 2	Brodie 24	17	7
3 Sept	Nat Lg	H	Solihull Moors	2105	W 4 - 0	Brodie 9 Connolly 83 90 Fenwick 89	14	8
10	Nat Lg	A	Torquay United	1989	L 0 - 2		16	9
13	Nat Lg	H	Tranmere Rovers	2379	D 0 - 0		16	10
17	Nat Lg	H	Dover Athletic	2137	L 0 - 1		17	11
24	Nat Lg	A	Barrow	1628	L 0 - 2		18	12
Oct 1	Nat Lg	H	Aldershot Town	2188	L 0 - 1		19	13
4	Nat Lg	A	Guiseley	1626	L 1 - 6	Fry 1	20	14
8	Nat Lg	A	Braintree Town	728	D 1 - 1	Heslop 5	19	15
15	FAC4Q	H	Curzon Ashton	1307	D 1 - 1	Brodie 9 (pen)		16
17	FAC4Qr	A	Curzon Ashton	467	L 1 - 2	Brodie 5		17
22	Nat Lg	H	Chester	2639	D 1 - 1	Fry 70	19	18
25	Nat Lg	A	Southport	856	L 0 - 2		19	19
29	Nat Lg	H	Sutton United	2037	D 2 - 2	Nti 24 Galbraith 63	20	20
12	Nat Lg	A	Eastleigh	2341	D 1 - 1	Heslop 76	20	21
19	Nat Lg	H	Dagenham & Redbridge	2410	L 0 2		21	22
22	Nat Lg	H	Lincoln City	2889	L 1 - 4	Klukowski 68	21	23
26	Nat Lg	A	Bromley	1203	L 0 - 3		22	24
29	Nat Lg	H	Guiseley	1907	D 1 - 1	Rzonca 59	23	25
Dec 3	Nat Lg	A	Tranmerer Rovers	5075	L 0 - 1		24	26
10	FAT1	H	Worcester City	1033	W 3 - 1	Hutchison 3 (og) Parkin 14 Murphy 87 (pen)		27
17	Nat Lg	H	Torquay United	2272	D 0 - 0		24	28
26	Nat Lg	A	North Ferriby United	1950	W 1 - 0	Racine 13	23	29
Jan 1	Nat Lg	H	North Ferriby United	3182	L 0 - 1		24	30
7	Nat Lg	A	Dover Athletic	1308	D 2 - 2	Parkin 37 Rooney 77	24	31
14	FAT2	A	Harlow Town	816	W 2 - 1	Morgan-Smith 76 Heslop 78		32
21	Nat Lg	H	Barrow	2430	W 2 - 1	Morgan-Smith 21 Newton 90	24	33
28	Nat Lg	A	Aldershot Town	2230	D 0 - 0		24	34
Feb 4	FAT3	A	Nuneaton Town	687	W 3 - 0	Morgan-Smith 3 Oliver 15 Newton 19		35
11	Nat Lg	H	Maidstone United	2816	D 1 - 1	Parkin 3	23	36
18	Nat Lg	A	Boreham Wood	656	D 1 - 1	Morgan-Smith 7	23	37
21	Nat Lg	H	Gateshead	2320	L 1 - 3	Oliver 14	23	38
25	FATQF	H	Brackley Town	1994	W 1 - 0	Parkin 29		39
28	Nat Lg	A	Lincoln City	6892	D 1 - 1	Parkin 14	24	40
Mar 4	Nat Lg	H	Eastleigh	2406	W 3 - 1	Parkin 7 13 Oliver 80	23	41
11	Nat Lg	A	Sutton United	2171	D 2 - 2	Fenwick 89 Klukowski 90	22	42
14	FATSF1	H	Lincoln City	3294	W 2 - 1	Oliver 53 Connolly 69		43
18	FATSF2	A	Lincoln City	8409	D 1 - 1	Fenwick 103 (pen)		44
21	Nat Lg	H	Southport	2482	W 5 - 3	Newton 4 Oliver 45 Parkin 64 78 Morgan-Smith 72	22	45
25	Nat Lg	A	Dagenham & Redbridge	1659	L 0 - 1		22	46
28	Nat Lg	A	Macclesfield Town	1318	W 3 - 1	Heslop 6 Oliver 15 Parkin 82	22	47
Apr 1	Nat Lg	H	Braintree Town	2825	W 3 - 0	Parkin 11 Hall 44 Morgan-Smith 75	22	48
4	Nat Lg	H	Bromley	3000	L 0 - 2		22	49
8	Nat Lg	H	Chester	2235	W 2 - 0	Oliver 25 Holmes 75	19	50
14	Nat Lg	H	Solihull Moors	1570	W 2 - 1	Oliver 15 31	18	51
17	Nat Lg	A	Wrexham	4091	L 1 - 3	Parkin 1	20	52
22	Nat Lg	H	Woking	2702	D 1 - 1	Parkin 75	21	53
29	Nat Lg	A	Forest Green Rovers	3984	D 2 - 2	Parkin 34 48	21	54
May 21	FAT Final	N	Macclesfield Town	38224	W 3 - 2	Parkin 8 Oliver 22 Connolly 86		55

GOALSCORERS	SG	CSG	Pens	Hat tricks	Total		SG	CSG	Pens	Hat tricks	Total
Parkin	13	3			16	Hall	1				1
Oliver	9				10	Holmes	1				1
Brodie	7	5	1		7	Kamdjo	1				1
Morgan-Smith	5	2			6	Murphy	1		1		1
Connolly	4				5	Nti	1				1
Heslop	5				5	Opponents	1				1
Fenwick	3		1		3	Racine	1				1
Fry	3				3	Rooney	1				1
Klukowski	3				3	Rzonka	1				1
Newton	2				3	Wright	1				1
Galbraith	1				1						

BATH CITY

Club Contact Details
Twerton Park, Twerton, Bath, Somerset BA2 1DB
01225 423 087
info@bathcityfootballclub.co.uk

Ground Capacity: 8,880   **Seats:** 1,006   **Covered:** 4,800   **Clubhouse:** Yes   **Shop:** Yes

Record Attendance
18,020 v Brighton & Hove Albion - FA Cup 1960
Previous Grounds
The Belvoir Ground 1889-92 & 1902-15. Lambridge Show Ground 1919-32.

10 YEAR RECORD

	07-08	08-09	09-10	10-11	11-12	12-13	13-14	14-15	15-16	16-17
	Conf S 8	Conf S 8	Conf S 4	Conf 10	Conf 23	Conf S 11	Conf S 7	Conf S 14	Nat S 14	Nat S 9
	FAC 4Q	FAC 3Q	FAC 2P	FAC 4Qr	FAC 1Pr	FAC 3Qr	FAC 4Q	FAC 4Q	FAC 3Qr	FAC 4Q
	FAT 1P	FAT 1P	FAT 3Q	FAT 2P	FAT 3P	FAT 1P	FAT 3Q	FAT SF	FAT 3Q	FAT 1P

Club Factfile

Founded: 1889   **Nickname:** The Romans   **Manager:** Gary Owers

Previous Names: Bath AFC 1889-92. Bath Railway FC 1902-05. Bath Amateurs 1913-23 (Reserve side)

Previous Leagues: Western 1908-21. Southern 1921-79, 88-90, 97-2007. Football League Division Two North 1939-45.
Alliance/Conference 1979-88, 90-97.

Club Colours (change): Black & white stripes/black/black (All blue)

RECORDS

Victory: 8-0 v Boston United - 1998-99
Defeat: 0-9 v Yeovil Town - 1946-47
Goalscorer: Paul Randall - 106
Appearances: David Mogg - 530
Additional: Paid £15,000 to Bristol City for Micky Tanner.
Received £80,000 from Southampton for Jason Dodd.

HONOURS

FA Comps: None

League: Western Division Two 1928-29, Premier 1933-34.
Southern Premier Division 1959-60, 77-78, 2006-07.

County FA: Somerset Premier Cup 1929-30, 33-34, 35-36, 51-52, 52-53, 57-58, 59-60, 65-66, 67-68, 69-70, 77-78, 80-81, 81-82, 83-84, 84-85, 85-86, 88-89, 89-90, 93-94, 94-95, 2007-08.

BEST PERFORMANCES	**FA Cup:** Third Round Proper 1963-64 (r), 93-94 (r).
	FA Trophy: Semi-Finals 2014-15.
	FA Vase: N/A

BATH CITY MATCH RESULTS 2016-17

Date	Comp	H/A	Opponents	Att:	Result	Goalscorers	Pos	No.
Aug 6	Nat S	A	Margate	567	L 0 - 1		15	1
9	Nat S	H	Weston-s-Mare	693	L 1 - 2	Morgan 82	20	2
13	Nat S	H	St Albans City	379	W 3 - 0	Hemmings 34 Monthe 65 Fleetwood 80	14	3
16	Nat S	A	Truro City	486	W 3 - 1	Morgan 54 Murphy 81(pen) Hunter 89	10	4
20	Nat S	A	Bishop's Stortford	301	W 1 - 0	Diallo 50	9	5
27	Nat S	H	East Thurrock United	523	W 2 - 1	Diallo 3 Morgan 39	5	6
29	Nat S	A	Poole Town	797	L 0 - 1		8	7
Sept 3	Nat S	H	Whitehawk	535	W 2 - 1	Hunter 22 Monthe 88	5	8
6	Nat S	H	Oxford City	470	L 1 - 3	McCootie 28	6	9
10	Nat S	A	Hampton & Richmond B	516	L 1 - 2	McCootie 32	9	10
13	Nat S	H	Gosport Borough	331	W 4 - 0	Hunter 34 McCootie 65 Diallo 72 Hutchinson 67 (pen)	8	11
17	FAC3Q	H	Oxford City	482	D 1 - 1	Morgan 83		12
20	FAC3Qr	A	Oxford City	228	W 2 - 1	Artus 25 Poku 104 (og) (aet)		13
24	Nat S	A	Hemel Hempstead Town	417	D 3 - 3	Morgan 55 80 Marshall 62	8	14
Oct 1	FAC4Q	A	Potters Bar	465	L 1 - 1	Murphy 19 Lost 3-4 on penalties		15
8	Nat S	H	Eastbourne Borough	1008	D 1 - 1	Broom 5	9	16
22	Nat S	H	Dartford	610	L 0 - 1		11	17
29	Nat S	A	Ebbsfleet United	1101	L 0 - 1		13	18
Nov 5	Nat S	H	Concord Rangers	479	D 2 - 2	Watkins 42 Monthe 90	12	19
12	Nat S	A	Maidenhead United	1031	L 1 - 2	Monthe 65	13	20
14	Nat S	A	Wealdstone	638	W 1 - 0	Watkins 35	10	21
19	Nat S	H	Chelmsford City	540	D 2 - 2	Morgan 25 Watkins 80	10	22
26	FAT3Q	H	Basingstoke Town	366	W 2 - 0	Harvey 32 (pen) 48		23
Dec 3	Nat S	A	Welling United	466	L 1 - 3	Artus 45	12	24
10	FAT1	A	Sutton United	524	L 0 - 1			25
!7	Nat S	A	Whitehawk	290	W 2 - 0	Watkins 26 72	11	26
26	Nat S	H	Hungerford Town	798	D 1 - 1	Watkins 76	11	27
Jan 1	Nat S	A	Hungerford Town	408	D 2 - 2	McCootie 55 Hemmings 77	11	28
7	Nat S	H	Hampton & Richmond	615	D 1 - 1	Batten 33	12	29
14	Nat S	H	Bishop's Stortford	543	W 2 - 0	McCootie 41 Batten 53	9	30
28	Nat S	H	Margate	546	W 2 - 0	Watkins 2 28	9	31
Feb11	Nat S	H	Truro City	543	W 4 - 0	Andresson 33 (pen) Murphy 80 Watkins 85 90	9	32
14	Nat S	A	Oxford City	215	D 1 - 1	Watkins 90	9	33
18	Nat S	A	St Albans City	439	W 4 - 1	Morgan 2 McCootie 22 McCoulsky 60 Watkins 89	9	34
25	Nat S	H	Ebbsfleet United	695	L 0 - 1		9	35
Mar 4	Nat S	A	Dartford	944	L 0 - 2		12	36
11	Nat S	H	Hemel Hempstead Town	489	W 6 - 0	Andresson 9 20 (p) McCoulsky31 58 McCootie40 Hunter 9011		37
14	Nat S	A	Weston-s-Mare	594	W 2 - 1	Andresson 68 (pen) McCoulsky 88	10	38
18	Nat S	A	Eastbourne Borough	504	W 2 - 1	McCoulsky 47 Hobson 62 (og)	9	39
21	Nat S	A	Gosport Borough	369	L 0 - 1		9	40
25	Nat S	H	Wealdstone	1006	L 1 - 2	Hemmings 45	9	41
April 1	Nat S	H	Maidenhead United	708	L 1 - 5	Diallo 67	9	42
8	Nat S	A	Concord Rangers	202	W 5 - 0	Watkins 14 Hemmings 23 Andresson 40 McClousky 45 86 9		43
15	Nat S	A	East Thurrock United	292	L 0 - 2		9	44
17	Nat S	H	Poole Town	602	W 3 - 0	Morgan 14 McCoulsky 50 Hemmings 86	9	45
22	Nat S	A	Chelmsford City	1185	L 1 - 3	McCootie 13	9	46
29	Nat S	H	Welling United	710	W 2 - 1	McCootie 18 Watkins 24	9	47

GOALSCORERS	SG	CSG	Pens	Hat tricks	Total		SG	CSG	Pens	Hat tricks	Total
2015-16 Pratt					10	Murphy	3		1		3
Watkins	11	2			14	Artus	2				2
McCoulsky	6	2			9	Batten	2				2
Morgan	8				9	Harvey	1		1		2
McCootie	9	3			8	Opponents	2				2
Andresson	4	2	3		5	Broom	1				1
Hemmings	5				5	Fleetwood	1				1
Diallo	4	2			4	Hutchinson	1		1		1
Hunter	4				4	Marshall	1				1
Monthe	4	2			4						

BOGNOR REGIS TOWN

Club Contact Details
Nyewood Lane, Bognor Regis PO21 2TY
01243 822 325
sajcook2@aol.com

Ground Capacity: 4,100 **Seats:** 350 **Covered:** 2,600 **Clubhouse:** Yes **Shop:** Yes

Record Attendance
3,642 v Swnsea City - FA Cup 1st Round replay 1984
Previous Grounds
None

10 YEAR RECORD

07-08		08-09		09-10		10-11		11-12		12-13		13-14		14-15		15-16		16-17	
Conf S	18	Conf S	21	Isth P	22	Isth1S	2	Isth1S	2	Isth P	14	Isth P	3	Isth P	14	Isth P	2	Isth P	2
FAC	2Q	FAC	2Qr	FAC	1Q	FAC	2Q	FAC	3Q	FAC	2Q	FAC	2Qr	FAC	2Qr	FAC	1Qr	FAC	2Q
FAT	1P	FAT	1P	FAT	2Q	FAT	3Qr	FAT	P	FAT	3Q	FAT	3Q	FAT	1Qr	FAT	SF	FAT	1Q

Club Factfile

Founded: 1883   **Nickname:** The Rocks   **Manager:** Jack Pearce - July 2017

Previous Names: None

Previous Leagues: West Sussex 1896-1926, Brighton & Hove District 1926-27, Sussex County 1927-72, Southern League 1972-81, Isthmian 1982-2004, 2009-17, Conference 2004-09

Club Colours (change): White & green

RECORDS
Victory: 24-0 v Littlehampton - West Sussex League 1913-14
Defeat: 0-19 v Shoreham - West Sussex League 1906-07
Goalscorer: Kevin Clements - 206. On 16/12/14 Jason Prior scored his 100th goal for the club making it the fastest century of goals.
Appearances: Mick Pullen - 967 (20 seasons)
Additional: Paid £2,000 for Guy Rutherford 1995-96. Received £10,500 from Brighton & Hove for John Crumplin and Geoff Cooper, and from Crystal Palace for Simon Rodger.

HONOURS

FA Comps: None

League: Isthmian League Division 1 South Play-offs 2011-12. Isthmian Premier Division play-offs 2016-17.

County FA: Sussex Professional Cup 1973-74. Sussex Senior Cup x9.

BEST PERFORMANCES	**FA Cup:** Second Round Proper 1984-85, 86-86, 88-89, 95-96. **FA Trophy:** Semi-finals 2015-16. **FA Vase:** N/A

BOGNOR REGIS TOWN MATCH RESULTS 2016-17

Date	Comp	H/A	Opponents	Att:	Result	Goalscorers	Pos	No.
Aug 13	IsthP	H	Lowestoft	353	L 1 - 3	Crane 90	19	1
16	IsthP	A	Merstham	160	D 1 - 1	Pearce 43	19	2
20	IsthP	A	Grays Athletic	127	D 1 - 1	Fraser 18	18	3
23	IsthP	H	Staines Town	389	W 2 - 0	Byrne 32 Barnett 90	11	4
27	IsthP	A	Billericay Town	247	W 2 - 0	Fraser 10 32	6	5
29	IsthP	H	Worthing	1006	W 5 - 0	Byrne 15 Pearce 45 Fraser 64 79 Barnett 88	5	6
Sept 3	**FAC1Q**	**H**	**Guildford C**	**396**	**W 5 - 1**	**Fraser 2 Budd 18 Crane 31 Wild 55 Parsons 72**		7
10	IsthP	A	Harlow Town	307	L 1 - 3	Parsons 80	6	8
17	**FAC2Q**	**A**	**Billericay Town**	**336**	**L 1 - 2**	**Crane 38**		9
19	IsthP	A	Kingstonian	341	W 2 - 1	Wild 60 Parsons 65	4	10
24	IsthP	H	Tonbridge Angels	511	W 2 - 0	Pearce 54 Wild 66	4	11
27	IsthP	H	Burgess Hill Town	367	D 1 - 1	Barnett 86	4	12
Oct 8	IsthP	A	Dulwich Hamlet	2217	W 3 - 1	Fraser 18 Pearce 3 (pen) Crane 89	5	13
11	IsthP	H	Merstham	385	W 2 - 0	Pearce 55 Fraser 90	4	14
15	IsthP	H	AFC Sudbury	511	W 2 - 1	Parsons 41 Fraser 82	4	15
18	IsthP	A	Staines Town	214	W 2 - 1	El Abd 70 Crane 84	3	16
22	IsthP	A	Lowestoft	464	L 1 - 2	Crane 63	3	17
29	**FAT1Q**	**A**	**Slough Town**	**543**	**L 1 - 4**	**Pearce 32 (pen)**		18
Nov 5	IsthP	H	Wingate & Finchley	459	W 3 - 1	Pearce 13 Wild 52 Fraser 78	1	19
19	IsthP	A	Leatherhead	412	W 3 - 1	Muitt 35 Parsons 83 Pearce 88	1	20
26	IsthP	H	Hendon	451	L 0 - 2		2	21
29	IsthP	H	Kingstonian	401	W 2 - 0	Pearce 31 (pen) Budd 65	1	22
Dec 3	IsthP	A	Tonbridge Angels	447	L 1 - 4	Fraser 70	2	23
6	IsthP	H	Hallow Borough	349	W 1 - 0	Whyte 26	2	24
17	IsthP	A	Folkestone Invicta	463	W 2 - 1	Pearce 53 Fraser 86	2	25
26	IsthP	H	Havant & Waterlooville	1348	D 1 - 1	Sanders 61	2	26
31	IsthP	H	Metropolitan Police	300	W 1 - 0	Brown 90	1	27
Jan 2	IsthP	A	Worthing	1781	D 1 - 1	Wild 31	1	28
7	IsthP	H	Billericay Town	421	W 2 - 1	Field 65 Fraser 90 (pen)	1	29
14	IsthP	H	Enfield Town	447	D 1 - 1	Adebayo 57	1	30
17	IsthP	H	Needham Market	462	W 2 - 1	Muitt 59 Fraser 74	1	31
21	IsthP	A	Canvey Island	407	W 5 - 0	Fraser 3 Muitt 45 ADEBAYO 3 (54 71 83)	1	32
28	IsthP	H	Grays Athletic	452	L 1 - 2	Fraser 65	1	33
Feb 4	IsthP	A	Harrow Borough	212	W 1 - 0	Tuck 64	1	34
7	IsthP	A	Hendon	169	D 2 - 2	Field 32 Adebayo 61	1	35
11	IsthP	H	Dulwich Hamlet	447	D 1 - 1	Crane 85	1	36
18	IsthP	A	Wingate & Finchley	180	W 2 - 0	Field 59 Crane 86	1	37
25	IsthP	A	Needham Market	434	D 2 - 2	Charman 22 El-Abd 38	1	38
Mar 4	IsthP	H	Leatherhead	501	W 1 - 0	Moore 42	1	39
11	IsthP	A	Leiston	349	D 1 - 1	Wild 90	2	40
14	IsthP	A	Burgess Hill Town	405	W 3 - 1	Fraser 40 Field 45 Pearce 74	1	41
18	IsthP	H	Folkestone Invicta	531	W 7 - 1	Fraser 47 90 Devizes 58 (og) Crane 77 79 Wild 86 Pearce 88	1	42
25	IsthP	H	Canvey Island	587	W 4 - 0	FRASER 3 (14 37 (pen) 89) Muitt 65	1	43
28	IsthP	H	Leiston	667	W 1 - 0	Wild 18	1	44
Apr 1	IsthP	A	Enfield Town	687	L 0 - 1		1	45
8	IsthP	A	AFC Sudbury	362	W 4 - 0	MUITT 3 (8 31 55) Budd 70	1	46
15	IsthP	H	Harlow Town	789	W 3 - 0	Charmon 23 Fraser 45 (pen) 76 (pen)	1	47
17	IsthP	A	Havant & Waterlooville	3455	L 0 - 1		2	48
22	IsthP	H	Metropolitan Police	794	D 1 - 1	Muitt 58	2	49
27	**PO S-F**	**H**	**Wingate & Finchley**	**1001**	**W 2 - 1**	**Pearce 50 90**		50
May 1	**PO Final**	**H**	**Dulwich Hamlet**	**3119**	**W 2 - 1**	**Muitt 21 Pearce 42**		51

GOALSCORERS	SG	CSG	Pens	Hat tricks	Total		SG	CSG	Pens	Hat tricks	Total
2015-16 Prior					42	Budd	3				3
Fraser	17	3	4	1	24	Byrne	2				2
Pearce	13	3	3		15	Charman	2				2
Crane	9	2			10	El Abd	2				2
Muitt	6			1	8	Brown	1				1
Wild	8				8	Moore	1				1
Adabayo	3			1	5	Opponents	1				1
Parsons	5				5	Sanders	1				1
Bennett	4				4	Tuck	1				1
Field	4				4	Whyte	1				1

BRAINTREE TOWN

Club Contact Details
The Ironmongery Direct Stadium, off Clockhouse Way, Braintree CM7 3RD
01376 345 617
braintreeTFC@aol.com

Ground Capacity: 4,222 **Seats:** 553 **Covered:** 1,288 **Clubhouse:** Yes **Shop:** Yes

Record Attendance
4,000 v Tottenham Hotspur - Testimonial May 1952
Previous Grounds
The Fiar Field 1898-1903, Spalding Meadow 1903-23.

10 YEAR RECORD

07-08		08-09		09-10		10-11		11-12		12-13		13-14		14-15		15-16		16-17	
Conf S	5	Conf S	14	Conf S	7	Conf S	1	Conf	12	Conf	9	Conf	6	Conf	14	Nat	3	Nat	22
FAC	2Q	FAC	2Q	FAC	2Qr	FAC	3Q	FAC	4Q	FAC	1P	FAC	1Pr	FAC	1P	FAC	1Pr	FAC	2P
FAT	3P	FAT	3Qr	FAT	3Q	FAT	1P	FAT	2Pr	FAT	1Pr	FAT	2P	FAT	3Pr	FAT	2P	FAT	3Pr

Club Factfile

Founded: 1898   **Nickname:** The Iron   **Manager:** Brad Quinton

Previous Names: Manor Works 1898-1921, Crittall Athletic 1921-68, Braintree and Crittall Athletic 1968-81, Braintree 1981-83.

Previous Leagues: N.Essex 1898-1925, Essex & Suffolk Border 1925-29, 55-64, Spartan 1928-35, Eastern Co. 1935-37, 38-39, 52-55, 70-91, Essex Co. 1937-38, London 1945-52, Gt London 1964-66, Met 1966-70, Southern 1991-96, Isthmian 1996-2006

Club Colours (change): All orange (White/blue/blue)

RECORDS
Victory: 12-0 v Thetford - Eastern Counties League 1935-36
Defeat: 0-14 v Chelmsford City (A) - North Essex League 1923
Goalscorer: Chris Guy - 211 (1963-90). Gary Bennett scored 57 goals during season 1997-98
Appearances: Paul Young - 524 (1966-77)
Additional: Received £10,000 from Brentford for Matt Metcalf and from Colchester United for John Cheesewright

HONOURS

FA Comps: None

League: North Essex 1905-06, 10-11, 11-12. Eastern Counties League 1936-37, 83-84, 84-85. Essex & Suffolk Border 1959-60. Isthmian League Premier Division 2005-06. Conference South Champions 2010-11.

County FA: Essex Senior Cup 1995-96.
Essex Senior Trophy 1986-87.

BEST PERFORMANCES	**FA Cup:** Second Round Proper 2016-17
	FA Trophy: Fifth Round Proper 2001-02 (r)
	FA Vase: Fifth Round Proper 1984-85 (r)

BRAINTREE TOWN MATCH RESULTS 2016-17

Date	Comp	H/A	Opponents	Att:	Result		Goalscorers	Pos	No.
Aug 6	Nat Lg	A	North Ferriby United	557	D	0 - 0		12	1
9	Nat Lg	H	Eastleigh	766	D	1 - 1	Barnard 60	15	2
13	Nat Lg	H	Macclesfield Town	703	L	1 - 3	Barnard 81 (pen)	20	3
16	Nat Lg	A	Maidstone United	2242	L	1 - 2	Maybanks 90	21	4
20	Nat Lg	H	Aldershot Town	677	W	2 - 0	Goodman 8 Akinola 77	16	5
27	Nat Lg	A	Barrow	966	L	1 - 2	Isaac 23 (pen)	20	6
29	Nat Lg	H	Torquay United	892	L	1 - 3	Barrett 33	21	7
Sept 3	Nat Lg	A	Guiseley	704	D	0 - 0		21	8
10	Nat Lg	H	Gateshead	519	L	1 - 4	Cheek 57	21	9
13	Nat Lg	A	Sutton Unted	922	W	2 - 1	Isaac 45 (pen) 90	21	10
17	Nat Lg	H	Chester	1590	L	0 - 1		22	11
24	Nat Lg	H	Forest Green Rovers	621	L	0 - 1		22	12
Oct 1	Nat Lg	A	Lincoln City	3554	L	0 - 3		22	13
4	Nat Lg	H	Boreham Wood	553	L	1 - 2	Akinola 63	22	14
8	Nat Lg	H	York City	728	D	1 - 1	Barnard 88 (pen)	21	15
15	FAC4Q	H	**Bromley**	343	W	4 - 2	Cheek 56 71 Isaac 68 Lee 90		16
22	Nat Lg	A	Dover Athletic	1073	L	1 - 6	Matthews 17	21	17
25	Nat Lg	A	Woking	1362	W	3 - 2	Muldoon 1 Cheek 51 Allnola 83	21	18
29	Nat Lg	H	Solihull Moors	625	L	0 - 1		22	19
Nov 5	FAC 1	H	**Eastbourne Borough**	645	W	7 - 0	Patterson 6 ELOKOBI 3 (11 21 84) Barnard 64 74(p) Akinola 89		20
12	Nat Lg	A	Wrexham	3413	W	1 - 0	Cheek 26	22	21
19	Nat Lg	H	Tranmere	964	L	0 - 1		21	22
22	Nat Lg	H	Bromley	521	D	2 - 2	Hall-Johnson 3 Cheek 68	20	23
26	Nat Lg	A	Southport	866	W	5 - 4	Cheek 1 Parry 30 Muldoon 36 Higgins 45 (og) Midson 64	20	24
Dec 3	FAC2	A	**Millwall**	3345	L	2 - 5	Cheek 16 Midson 34		25
10	FAT1	H	**Torquay United**	301	W	2 - 0	Midson 73 76		26
17	Nat Lg	A	Gateshead	501	D	1 - 1	Midson 61	21	27
20	Nat Lg	A	Boreham Wood	313	W	1 - 0	Cheek 63	20	28
26	Nat Lg	H	Dagenham & Redbridge	1353	W	3 - 2	Cheek 34 Akinola 45 (pen) 64	18	29
Jan 1	Nat Lg	A	Dagenham & Redbridge	1261	L	0 - 3		18	30
7	Nat Lg	H	Chester	707	L	1 - 2	Midson 21	18	31
10	Nat Lg	H	Sutton United	568	W	1 - 0	Cheek 33	18	32
14	FAT2	A	**East Thurrock United**	313	W	5 - 2	CHEEK 3 (39 45 46) Midson 55 Barnard 80		33
21	FAT2	A	Forest Green Rovers	1735	D	1 - 1	Cheek 14	17	34
Feb 4	FAT3	H	**Dulwich Hamlet**	608	D	0 - 0			35
7	FAT3r	A	**Dulwich Hamlet**	860	L	2 - 5	Okimo 38 Parry 80		36
11	Nat Lg	H	North Ferriby United	410	W	1 - 0	Hall-Johnson 78	18	37
14	Nat Lg	A	Eastleigh	1702	W	2 - 0	Cheek 27 73	16	38
18	Nat Lg	A	Macclesfield Town	1267	L	0 - 2		16	39
25	Nat Lg	H	Maidstone United	1002	D	0 - 0		17	40
28	Nat Lg	A	Bromley	437	W	5 - 0	Cheek 5 (p) Midson 30 (p) Hall-Johnson 45 73 Patterson 70	17	41
Mar 4	Nat Lg	H	Wrexham	698	L	1 - 2	Cheek 1	18	42
7	Nat Lg	H	Lincoln City	1732	L	0 - 4		18	43
11	Nat Lg	A	Solihull Moors	556	D	3 - 3	Hall-Johnson 6 Cheek 17 23 (pen)	18	44
18	Nat Lg	H	Southport	510	W	2 - 0	Corne 43 58	17	45
21	Nat Lg	H	Woking	572	L	1 - 3	Corne 21	18	46
25	Nat Lg	A	Tranmere Rovers	4514	L	0 - 1		18	47
Apr 1	Nat Lg	A	York City	2825	L	0 - 3		19	48
8	Nat Lg	H	Dover Athletic	704	L	1 - 2	Cheek 7	21	49
14	Nat Lg	H	Guiseley	624	W	2 - 0	Okimo 57 Cheek 71	21	50
17	Nat Lg	A	Torquay United	2580	L	1 - 3	Parry 8	21	51
22	Nat Lg	H	Barrow	778	L	0 - 2		22	52
29	Nat Lg	A	Aldershot Town	3977	L	0 2		22	53

GOALSCORERS	SG	CSG	Pens	Hat tricks	Total		SG	CSG	Pens	Hat tricks	Total
2015-16 Cheek					17	Muldoon	2				2
Cheek	18	3	3	1	23	Okimo	2				2
Midson	8	4	1		8	Opponents	1				2
Akinola	5				6	Patterson	2				2
Barnard	5	2	2+1C		6	Barrett	1				1
Hall-Johnson	4				4	Goodman	1				1
Isaac	3		2		4	Lee	1				1
Corne	2				3	Matthews	1				1
Elokobi	1		1		3	Maybanks	1				1
Parry	3				3						

CHELMSFORD CITY

Club Contact Details
Melbourne Park Stadium, Salerno Way, Chelmsford CM1 2EH
01245 290 959
algbrown@blueyonder.co.uk

Ground Capacity: 3,000 **Seats:** 1,300 **Covered:** 1,300 **Clubhouse:** Yes **Shop:** Yes

Record Attendance
16,807 v Colchester United - Southern League 10/09/1949. Melbourne Park: 3,201 v AFC Wimbledon, 15/03/2008.
Previous Grounds
New Writtle Street 1938-97, Maldon Town 1997-98, Billericay Town 1998-2005

10 YEAR RECORD

07-08		08-09		09-10		10-11		11-12		12-13		13-14		14-15		15-16		16-17	
Isth P	1	Conf S	5	Conf S	3	Conf S	4	Conf S	6	Conf S	5	Conf S	17	Conf S	10	Nat S	15	Nat S	4
FAC	3Q	FAC	2Q	FAC	4Q	FAC	2P	FAC	2Pr	FAC	2P	FAC	2Q	FAC	4Qr	FAC	3Q	FAC	2Q
FAT	2Q	FAT	3Q	FAT	3P	FAT	3Q	FAT	1P	FAT	3P	FAT	3Q	FAT	3Q	FAT	1P	FAT	3Pr

Club Factfile

Founded: 1878 **Nickname:** City or Clarets **Manager:** Rod Stringer

Previous Names: Chelmsford FC 1878-1938.

Previous Leagues: North Essex (FM) 1895-1900. South Essex 1900-13. Athenian (FM) 1912-22. Middlesex County 1922-38. Essex & Suffolk Border 1923-24. London 1924-35. Eastern Counties (FM) 1935-38. Southern League 1938-2004. Isthmian 2004-08

Club Colours (change): Claret/claret/white

RECORDS

Victory: 10-1 v Bashley (H) - Southern League 26/04/2000
Defeat: 1-10 v Barking (A) - FA Trophy 11/11/1978
Goalscorer: Tony Butcher - 286 (1956-71)
Appearances: Tony Butcher - 560 (1956-71)
Additional: Paid £10,000 to Dover Athletic for Tony Rogers, 1992 and to Heybridge Swifts for Kris Lee ,2001
Received £50,000 from Peterborough United for David Morrison, 1994

HONOURS

FA Comps: None

League: Middlesex County 1923-24. London League 1930-31. Southern League 1930-40 (joint), 45-46, 67-68, 71-72, Division One South 88-89. Isthmian League Premier Division 2007-08.

County FA: Essex Senior Cup 1892-93, 1901-02, 85-86, 88-89, 92-93, 2002-03, 08-09 16-17. East Anglian Cup 1924-25, 26-27, 28-29. Essex Professional Cup 1957-58, 69-70, 70-71, 73-74, 74-75.

BEST PERFORMANCES	**FA Cup:** Fourth Round Proper 1938-39.
	FA Trophy: Semi-Finals 1969-70.
	FA Vase: N/A

CHELMSFORD CITY MATCH RESULTS 2016-17

Date	Comp	H/A	Opponents	Att:	Result	Goalscorers	Pos	No.
Aug 6	Nat S	A	Truro City	502	D 2 - 2	Bush 61 Mullings 89	10	1
8	Nat S	A	Margate	809	W 2 - 0	Jeffers 10 Mullings 38	8	2
13	Nat S	H	Dartford	780	D 1 - 1	Jeffers 65	12	3
16	Nat S	A	St Albans City	561	L 1 - 2	Mullings 79	14	4
20	Nat S	H	Maidenhead United	626	L 0 - 1		9	5
27	Nat S	H	Oxford City	613	W 2 - 0	Mullings 30 Jeffers 41	7	6
30	Nat S	A	Welling United	705	W 2 - 0	Mullings 7 Jeffers 64 (pen)	7	7
Sept 3	Nat S	H	Weston-s-Mare	747	W 1 - 0	Mullings 81	7	8
5	Nat S	H	Ebbsfleet United	901	W 2 - 1	Bricknell 30 Graham 83	3	9
10	Nat S	A	Whitehawk	289	W 1 - 0	Wilmott 42	4	10
12	Nat S	H	East Thurrock U	913	D 2 - 2	Church 44 Jeffers 90	3	11
17	FAC2Q	H	Dartford	675	L 2 - 3	Mullings 68 70		12
24	Nat S	A	Eastbourne Borough	501	W 5 - 1	Rees19 Mullings 22 Jeffers 52 62 Hare 64 (og)	3	13
Oct 8	Nat S	H	Wealdstone	1465	W 4 - 1	Mullings 4 52 Rees 7 79	2	14
15	Nat S	A	Gosport Borough	552	W 6 - 0	Bricknell 18 75 Graham 49 Rees 53 Mullings 55 72	2	15
22	Nat S	H	Hemel Hempstead Town	1068	W 4 - 4	Jeffers 63 67 (pen) Diagne 77 og Mullings 78	2	16
29	Nat S	A	Concord Rangers	894	D 2 - 2	Willmott 20 Jeffers 49 (pen)	2	17
Nov 5	Nat S	H	Poole Town	551	L 0 - 4		3	18
12	Nat S	H	Hampton & Richmond	963	D 2 - 2	Mullings 25 Bricknell 40	4	19
19	Nat S	H	Bath City	540	D 2 - 2	Jeffers 3 (pen) 49	7	20
26	FAT3Q	A	Taunton Town	505	W 1 - 0	Church 89		21
Dec 3	Nat S	H	Hungerford Town	924	D 3 - 3	Church 18 Jeffers 57 90	6	22
10	FAT1	A	Hitchin Town	469	W 1 - 0	Jeffers 2		23
17	Nat S	H	Weston-s-Mare	414	D 0 - 0		6	24
26	Nat S	H	Bishops Stortford	1014	W 4 - 0	Cornhill 12 (pen) Buchanan 35 Willmott 67 Young 75	6	25
Jan 1	Nat S	A	Bishops Stortford	717	W 3 - 1	BUCHANAN 3 (5 21 37pen)	4	26
7	Nat S	H	Whitehawk	793	W 1 - 0	Cornhill 80	3	27
14	FAT2	A	Dartford	918	W 1 - 0	Dickson 71		28
21	Nat S	H	Ebbsfleet United	1434	L 0 - 2		5	29
28	Nat S	A	Truro City	925	W 2 - 0	Buchanan 51 Jeffers 80	4	30
Feb 4	FAT3	A	Tranmere Rovers	2473	D 1 - 1	Wilmott 29		31
8	FAT3r	H	Tranmere Rovers	923	L 1 - 3	Buchanan 62		32
11	Nat S	H	St Albans City	249	D 1 - 1	Buchanan 13	7	33
18	Nat S	A	Dartford	1385	W 1 - 0	Church 71	6	34
25	Nat S	H	Concord Rangers	845	W 4 - 3	Rees 40 Jeffers 62 65 Spillane 81	5	35
28	Nat S	H	Margate	334	W 2 - 0	Jeffers 41 (pen) Hill 75	5	36
Mar 4	Nat S	A	Hemel Hempstead Town	586	D 2 - 2	Dickson 64 90	4	37
6	Nat S	A	Maidenhead United	847	L 0 - 1		4	38
11	Nat S	A	Eastbourne Borough	821	W 5 - 1	DICKSON 4 (8 38 49 77) Theophanous 90	4	39
18	Nat S	A	Wealdstone	841	D 1 - 1	Theophanous 3	4	40
21	Nat S	H	East Thurrock United	478	W 2 - 1	Hill 9 Buchanan 77	4	41
25	Nat S	A	Gosport Borough	287	W 5 - 1	Haysman 11 74 Theophanous 54 Church 64 Dickson 69	4	42
April 1	Nat S	H	Hampton & Richmond B	611	L 0 - 2	Haysman 9 Theophanous 30	3	43
8	Nat S	H	Poole Town	876	W 3 - 0	Theophanous 79 Jeffers 82 90	3	44
15	Nat S	A	Oxford City	361	L 0 - 2		3	45
17	Nat S	H	Welling United	967	W 3 - 1	Dickson 46 Spillane 49 Jeffers 88	3	46
22	Nat S	H	Bath City	1185	W 3 - 1	Spilane 42 Andersson 59 (og) Theophanous 76	3	47
29	Nat S	A	Hungerford Town	420	D 1 - 1	Rees 66	4	48
May 3	PO SF1	H	Dartford	1653	D 0 - 0			49
7	PO SF2	A	Dartford	2622	W 2 - 1	Theophanous 70 Dickson 85		50
13	PO Final	A	Ebbsfleet United	3134	L 1 - 2	Graham 56		51

GOALSCORERS	SG	CSG	Pens	Hat tricks	Total		SG	CSG	Pens	Hat tricks	Total
2015-16 Bricknell					17	Spillane	3				3
Jeffers	16	2	5		22	Cornhill	2		1		2
Mullings	12	5			15	Graham	2				2
Dickson	6			1	10	Haysman	2				2
Buchanan	5		1	1	9	Hill	2				2
Theophanous	6				7	Opponents	2				2
Rees	5	3			6	Bush	1				1
Church	5	2			5	Young	1				1
Bricknell	4				4						
Wilmott	4				4						

CHIPPENHAM TOWN

Club Contact Details

Hardenhuish Park, Bristol Road, Chippenham SN14 6LR

01249 650 400

Ground Capacity: 3,000   **Seats:** 300   **Covered:** 1,000   **Clubhouse:** Yes   **Shop:** Yes

Record Attendance

4,800 v Chippenham United - Western League 1951

Previous Grounds

Played at four different locations before moving in to Hardenhuish on 24/09/1919.

10 YEAR RECORD

07-08		08-09		09-10		10-11		11-12		12-13		13-14		14-15		15-16		16-17	
SthP	4	SthP	8	SthP	3	SthP	7	SthP	11	SthP	15	SthP	18	SthP	11	SthP	8	SthP	1
FAC	4Q	FAC	3Q	FAC	4Q	FAC	2Q	FAC	1Q	FAC	4Q	FAC	1Q	FAC	3Q	FAC	4Q	FAC	3Q
FAT	3Q	FAT	2Qr	FAT	2P	FAT	2Qr	FAT	1P	FAT	2Q	FAT	2Q	FAT	2Q	FAT	1Q	FAT	2Q

Club Factfile

Founded: 1873   **Nickname:** The Bluebirds   **Manager:** Mark Collier

Previous Names: None

Previous Leagues: Hellenic, Wiltshire Senior, Wiltshire Premier, Western. Southern >2017.

Club Colours (change): All royal blue

RECORDS

Victory: 9-0 v Dawlish Town (H) - Western League

Defeat: 0-10 v Tiverton Town (A) - Western League

Goalscorer: Dave Ferris

Appearances: Ian Monnery

HONOURS

FA Comps: None

League: Western League 1951-52. Southern League Premier Division 2016-17.

County FA: Wiltshire Senior Cup. Wiltshire Senior Shield x4.

BEST PERFORMANCES   **FA Cup:** First Round Proper 1951-52, 2005-06(r).
FA Trophy: Second Round Proper 2002-03, 09-10.
FA Vase: Final 1999-2000.

CHIPPENHAM TOWN MATCH RESULTS 2016-17

Date	Comp	H/A	Opponents	Att:	Result	Goalscorers	Pos	No.
Aug 6	SPL	H	Kings Langley	366	D 1 - 1	Sandell 1	10	1
9	SPL	A	Weymouth	740	W 4 - 1	Smith 6 54 Sandell 24 31 (pen)	7	2
13	SPL	A	Cambridge City	166	W 3 - 1	Sandell 17 Ferguson 52 56	4	3
16	SPL	H	Cinderford Town	372	W 1 - 0	Smith 32	2	4
20	SPL	H	Leamington	364	W 1 - 0	Pratt 33	1	5
27	SPL	A	St Neots Town	222	D 3 - 3	Jones 67 Griffin 68 Richards 85	1	6
29	SPL	H	Cirencester Town	468	W 4 - 1	Pratt 17 75 Jones 22 90	1	7
Sept 3	FAC1Q	H	Moneyfields	282	W 9 - 0	Sandell 6 58 PRATT 3 (25 45 66) Ferguson 75 Preece 77 Griffiths 78 80		8
10	SPL	A	St Ives Town	233	W 3 - 2	Ferguson 84 Pratt 85 Griffin 87	1	9
13	SPL	H	Banbury United	377	L 0 - 1		3	10
17	FAC2Q	H	Poole Town	436	W 4 - 1	SANDELL 3 (5 60 69) Pratt 72		11
24	SPL	H	Kings Lynn Town	536	L 0 - 4		4	12
27	SPL	A	Dorchester Town	259	W 3 - 1	Sandell 30 (pen) 69 Preece 67	4	13
Oct 1	FAC3Q	A	Billericay Town	482	L 2 - 3	Preece 30 Pratt 61		14
8	SPL	A	Kettering Town	591	W 2 - 1	Sandell 70 Griffin 89	3	15
15	SPL	H	Stratford Town	400	W 2 - 1	Richards 64 Pratt 85	3	16
18	SPL	A	Banbury United	300	L 1 - 2	Richards 65	3	17
22	SPL	A	Dunstable Town	139	W 2 - 1	Pratt 5 Sandell 21	3	18
25	SPL	H	Basingstoke Town	364	W 2 - 0	Jones 20 Sandell 83	3	19
29	FAT1	A	Salisbury	904	W 3 - 2	Pratt 7 90 Richards 41		20
Nov 1	SPL	H	Redditch United	285	D 1 - 1	Ferguson 8	3	21
5	SPL	H	Hayes & Yeading United	391	W 3 - 1	SANDELL 3 (59 80 pen 90)	2	22
12	FAT2Q	H	Leiston	306	L 0 - 1			23
19	SPL	H	Cambridge City	314	W 5 - 0	Sandell 21 60 (pen) Smith 49 Richards 83 Pratt 85	2	24
22	SPL	A	Cinderford Town	183	L 2 - 3	Sandell 27 (pen) Pratt 84	3	25
Dec 6	SPL	H	Slough	328	D 3 - 3	Sandell 12 63 (pen) Guthrie 55	3	26
10	SPL	A	Biggleswade Town	121	D 2 - 2	Pratt 71 Sandell 73	3	27
13	SPL	A	Merthyr Town	386	D 2 - 2	Sandell 47 77 (pen)	3	28
17	SPL	H	Hitchin Town	307	W 1 - 0	Pratt 74	3	29
26	SPL	A	Cirencester Town	322	D 3 - 3	Guthrie 40 Sandell 69 Pratt 74	5	30
Jan 2	SPL	H	Frome Town	553	D 2 - 2	Smith 25 Ferguson 78	4	31
7	SPL	A	Leamington	496	D 1 - 1	Pratt 28	5	32
10	SPL	H	Weymouth	382	W 2 0	Smith 76 Pratt 87	3	33
14	SPL	H	Kings Lynn Town	388	W 2 - 1	Sandell 34 Smith 58	3	34
21	SPL	A	Slough Town	753	W 1 - 0	Sandell 50	2	35
28	SPL	H	Dorchester Town	413	W 4 - 0	PRATT 4 (4 44 48 89)	1	36
Feb 4	SPL	A	Redditch United	277	W 2 - 0	McLennon 9 Richards 37	1	37
7	SPL	H	Chesham United	409	W 3 1	Sandell 19 40 (pen) Smith 55	1	38
11	SPL	H	Kettering Town	515	W 1 - 0	Richards 24	1	39
14	SPL	A	Kings Langley	101	D 1 - 1	Leon (og)	1	40
18	SPL	A	Stratford Town	236	W 1 - 0	Sandell 84 (pen)	1	41
25	SPL	H	Dorchester Town	397	W 2 - 1	Smith 2 Sandell 13	1	42
Mar 4	SPL	H	Dunstable Town	379	W 1 - 0	Pratt 63 (pen)	1	43
12	SPL	A	Hayes & Yeading United	224	W 2 - 1	Richards 83 Pratt 90	1	44
18	SPL	H	Merthyr Town	723	W 3 - 1	Pratt 48 Andrews 73 (pen) 90 (pen)	1	45
25	SPL	A	Chesham United	345	W 3 1	Pratt 2 Richards 13 Andrews 24 (pen)	1	46
April 1	SPL	H	Biggleswade Town	633	W 2 - 0	Tindle 39 Baggridge 75	1	47
8	SPL	A	Hitchin Town	812	W 3 - 1	Felix 11 Baggridge 29 Richards 57	1	48
15	SPL	H	St Neots Town	1146	L 1 - 2	Ferguson 70	1	49
17	SPL	A	Frome Town	552	W 1 - 0	Andrews 53	1	50
22	SPL	H	St Ives Town	711	W 2 - 0	Pratt 8 Smith 25	1	51

GOALSCORERS	SG	CSG	Pens	Hat tricks	Total		SG	CSG	Pens	Hat tricks	Total
2015-16 Sandell					15	Felix	2				2
Sandell	21	5	9	2	32	Griffiths	1				2
Pratt	21	4	1	2	28	Guthrie	2				2
Smith	9				10	Baggridge	1				1
Richards	8	2			9	McLennon	1				1
Ferguson	6				7	Opponents	1				1
Andrews	3		2		4	Tindle	1				1
Jones	4				4						
Griffin	3				3						
Preece	2	2			3						

CONCORD RANGERS

Club Contact Details
Aspect Arena, Thames Road, Canvey Island, Essex SS8 0HH
01268 515 750
concordrangers@btinternet.com

Ground Capacity: 3,250   **Seats:** 375   **Covered:** Yes   **Clubhouse:** Yes   **Shop:**

Record Attendance
1,537 v Mansfield Town, FA Cup First Round Replay, 25/11/2014.
Previous Grounds
Waterside 70s-85

10 YEAR RECORD

07-08		08-09		09-10		10-11		11-12		12-13		13-14		14-15		15-16		16-17	
ESen	1	Isth1N	5	Isth1N	2	Isth P	8	Isth P	14	Isth P	4	Conf S	9	Conf S	7	Nat S	10	Nat S	18
FAC	1Q	FAC	1Q	FAC	2Q	FAC	3Q	FAC	2Qr	FAC	2Qr	FAC	4Q	FAC	1Pr	FAC	2Q	FAC	3Q
FAV	QF	FAT	2Q	FAT	3Q	FAT	1Q	FAT	1Q	FAT	2Q	FAT	1P	FAT	2P	FAT	3Q	FAT	3Q

Club Factfile

Founded: 1967   **Nickname:** Beachboys   **Manager:** Adam Flanagan

Previous Names: None

Previous Leagues: Thundermite Boys League 1967-73. Vange & District 1973-79. Mid-Essex 1979-88. Essex Intermediate 1988-91. Essex Senior 1991-2008. Isthmian 2008-13.

Club Colours (change): All yellow (All blue)

RECORDS
Goalscorer: Tony Stokes - 120
Appearances: Steve King - 312 (2013-16)

HONOURS
FA Comps: None

League: Essex Intermediate League Division 2 1990-91.
Essex Senior League 1997-98, 2003-04, 07-08.

County FA: Essex Senior Cup 2013-14, 14-15, 15-16.

BEST PERFORMANCES	**FA Cup:** First Round Proper 2014-15
	FA Trophy: Second Round Proper 2014-15
	FA Vase: Quarter-Finals 2007-08

CONCORD RANGERS MATCH RESULTS 2016-17

Date	Comp	H/A	Opponents	Att:	Result		Goalscorers	Pos	No.
Aug 6	Nat S	A	St Albans City	606	L	0 - 2		19	1
9	Nat S	H	Ebbsfleet United	452	L	0 - 1		22	2
13	Nat S	H	Truro City	198	L	0 - 2		22	3
16	Nat S	A	Eastbourne Borough	383	L	1 - 2	Collins 59	22	4
20	Nat S	A	Oxford City	143	D	2 - 2	Expiteta 31 Carlos 33	22	5
27	Nat S	H	Maidenhead United	241	L	0 - 1		22	6
29	Nat S	A	Whitehawk	291	D	0 - 0		22	7
Sept 3	Nat S	H	Welling United	258	L	0 - 5		22	8
6	Nat S	H	Bishop's Stortford	234	D	0 - 0		22	9
10	Nat S	A	Weston-s-Mare	401	W	2 - 1	Carlos 4 Cawley 8	21	10
13	Nat S	H	Wealdstone	241	L	0 - 1		22	11
17	FAC3Q	H	AFC Rushden & Diamonds	192	L	1 - 3	Cawley 39 (pen)		12
24	Nat S	A	Dartford	842	L	1 - 2	Dowie 85	22	13
Oct 8	Nat S	H	Hungerford Town	170	L	2 - 4	Stokes 84 Chiedozi 90	22	14
22	Nat S	A	Margate	429	W	5 - 1	Chiedozie 13 CAWLEY 3 (34 48 67) Laucys 62	20	15
25	Nat S	A	Hemel Hempstead Town	343	L	1 - 2	Cawley 69	20	16
29	Nat S	H	Chelmsford City	894	D	2 - 2	Collins 11 75	21	17
Nov 5	Nat S	A	Bath City	479	D	2 - 2	Cawley 16 69	20	18
12	Nat S	H	Poole Town	222	W	3 - 2	Chiedozie 22 35 Stokes 90	19	19
19	Nat S	A	Gosport Borough	1005	W	5 - 2	Cawley 47 62 (pen) CHIEDOZIE 3 (49 87 90)	18	20
26	FAT3Q	H	Welling United	161	L	0 - 1			21
Dec 3	Nat S	H	Hampton & Richmond B	231	W	2 - 1	Jelley 25 (og) Chiedozie 51	18	22
!7	Nat S	A	Welling United	402	L	1 - 3	Chiedozie 8	18	23
26	Nat S	H	East Thurrock United	305	D	1 - 1	Chiedozie 78	19	24
Jan 1	Nat S	A	East Thurrock United	384	D	1 - 1	Norman 45	19	25
7	Nat S	H	Weston-s-Mare	231	L	1 - 3	Cawley 72	20	26
14	Nat S	H	Oxford City	220	D	3 - 3	Della-Verde 29 Cawley 57 (pen) 80 (pen)	19	27
21	Nat S	A	Bishops Stortford	381	L	0 - 1		19	28
28	Nat S	H	St Albans City	315	W	3 - 2	King 5 Semble-Ferris 22 90	18	29
Feb 4	Nat S	A	Ebbsfleet United	1028	L	0 - 4		18	30
11	Nat S	H	Eastbourne Borough	249	W	3 - 1	Stokes 7 31 King 80	16	31
18	Nat S	A	Truro City	419	W	2 - 1	Della-Verde 27 Cawley 39	15	32
25	Nat S	A	Chelmsford City	845	L	3 - 4	Semble-Ferris 25 Cawley 70 Delle-Verde 88	18	33
Mar 4	Nat S	H	Margate	237	D	0 - 0		17	34
11	Nat S	H	Dartford	367	D	1 - 1	Cawley 87 (pen)	17	35
18	Nat S	A	Hungerford Town	271	L	1 - 2	Nasha 31	17	36
21	Nat S	A	Wealdstone	646	D	1 - 1	Miles 66	17	37
25	Nat S	H	Hemel Hempsread Town	287	W	2 - 0	Chiedozie 29 59	18	38
April 1	Nat S	A	Poole Town	737	L	1 - 2	Cawley 72	15	39
8	Nat S	H	Bath City	202	L	0 - 5		17	40
15	Nat S	A	Maidenhead United	1404	L	0 - 2		17	41
17	Nat S	A	Whitehawk	241	W	3 - 0	Cawley 2 (pen) 32 Sembie-Ferris 69	17	42
22	Nat S	H	Gosport Rangers	237	D	2 - 2	Oastler 55 (og) White 90	17	43
28	Nat S	A	Hampton & Richmond B	701	L	0 - 1		18	44

GOALSCORERS	SG	CSG	Pens	Hat tricks	Total		SG	CSG	Pens	Hat tricks	Total
2015-16 Cawley					*19*	Dowie	1				1
Cawley	13	2	5	1	19	Expiteta	1				1
Chiedozi	8	3		1	12	Laucys	1				1
Semble-Ferris	3				4	Miles	1				1
Stokes	3				4	Nasha	1				1
Collins	2				3	Norman	1				1
Della-Verde	3				3	White	1				1
Carlos	2				2						
King	2				2						
Opponents	2				2						

DARTFORD

Club Contact Details
Princes Park Stadium, Grassbanks, Darenth Road, Dartford DA1 1RT
01322 299 991
operations@dartfordfc.com

Ground Capacity: 4,097 **Seats:** 642 **Covered:** Yes **Clubhouse:** Yes **Shop:** Yes

Record Attendance
4,097 v Horsham YMCA - Isthmian Division 1 South 11/11/2006 and v Crystal Palace - Friendly 20/07/2007
Previous Grounds
The Brent/Westgate House, Potters Meadow, Engleys Meadow, Summers Meadow, Watling Street

10 YEAR RECORD

07-08		08-09		09-10		10-11		11-12		12-13		13-14		14-15		15-16		16-17	
Isth1N	1	Isth P	8	Isth P	1	Conf S	10	Conf S	2	Conf	8	Conf	22	Conf	23	Nat S	8	Nat S	3
FAC	3Q	FAC	2Q	FAC	3Q	FAC	1Pr	FAC	4Q	FAC	4Qr	FAC	1P	FAC	2P	FAC	2Q	FAC	1P
FAT	1Qr	FAT	3Qr	FAT	3Q	FAT	3P	FAT	3Pr	FAT	SF	FAT	1Pr	FAT	3Pr	FAT	3Q	FAT	2P

Club Factfile

Founded: 1888 **Nickname:** The Darts **Manager:** Tony Burman

Previous Names: None

Previous Leagues: Kent League (FM) 1894-96, 97-98, 99-1902, 09-14, 21-26, 93-96, Southern (FM) 1896-97, 1926-81, 82-84, 86-92, 96-2006. West Kent 1902-09. Alliance 1981-82, 84-86.

Club Colours (change): White/black/black

RECORDS
Appearances: Steve Robinson - 692
Additional: Paid £6,000 to Chelmsford City for John Bartley
Received £25,000 from Redbridge Forest for Andy Hessenthaler

HONOURS
FA Comps: None

League: Southern League Division 2 1896-97, Eastern Section 1930-31, 31-32, Southern Championship 30-31, 31-32, 73-74, 83-84, Southern Division 1980-81. West Kent 1908-09. Isthmian League Div.1 North 2007-08, Premier Division 2009-10.

County FA: Kent Senior Cup 1930-31, 31-32, 32-33, 34-35, 46-47, 69-70, 72-73, 86-87, 87-88, 2010-11, 15-16. Kent Senior Trophy 1995-96.

BEST PERFORMANCES	**FA Cup:** Third Round Proper 1935-36, 36-37.
	FA Trophy: Final 1973-74.
	FA Vase: First Round Proper 1994-95.

DARTFORD MATCH RESULTS 2016-17

Date	Comp	H/A	Opponents	Att:	Result	Goalscorers	Pos	No.
Aug 6	Nat S	H	Wealdstone	1002	D 2 - 2	Bradbrook 45 Hayes 82 (pen)	11	1
10	Nat S	A	Whitehawk	322	L 0 - 1		16	2
13	Nat S	A	Chelmsford City	780	D 1 - 1	Wanadio 54	20	3
16	Nat S	H	Gosport Borough	706	D 0 - 0		17	4
20	Nat S	A	Weston-s-Mare	410	W 2 - 1	Wanadio 52 Hayes 84	13	5
27	Nat S	H	Hungerford Town	831	W 2 - 0	Ibraham 79 Brown 87	11	6
29	Nat S	A	Hampton & Richmond B	676	L 1 - 4	Harris 14	14	7
Sept 3	Nat S	H	Maidenhead United	1083	D 0 - 0		13	8
6	Nat S	H	Welling United	1210	W 2 - 1	Brown 30, (pen) Bradbrook 80	13	9
10	Nat S	A	East Thurrock United	373	D 1 - 1	Hayes 73	12	10
13	Nat S	A	Margate	574	W 2 - 0	Pugh 73 Bradbrook 87 (pen)	10	11
17	FAC2Q	A	Chelmsford City	675	W 3 - 2	Fitzimmons 9 (og) Bradbrook 32 (pen) 37		12
24	Nat S	H	Concord Rangers	842	W 2 - 1	Ofori-Acheampong 45 Harris 59	7	13
Oct 1	FAC3Q	A	Slough Town	733	W 3 - 2	Bradbrook 50 83 (pen) Pugh 90		14
8	Nat S	A	Truro City	464	W 5 - 0	Wood 3 Pugh 24 Oforie-Acheampong 43 65 Brown 72	7	15
15	FAC4Q	A	Tonbridge Angels	1391	W 3 - 0	Brown 34 Pugh 48 Bradbrook 51		16
22	Nat S	A	Bath City	610	W 1 - 0	Wanadio 82	7	17
29	Nat S	H	Oxford City	1005	W 1 - 0	Pugh 44	6	18
Nov 5	FAC1	H	Sutton United	1689	L 3 - 6	Bradbrook 4 17 Ofori-Acheampong 51		19
8	Nat S	H	St Albans City	652	L 0 - 2		8	20
12	Nat S	H	Hemel Hempstead Town	881	W 2 - 0	Harris 40 Wanadio 79	6	21
19	Nat S	A	Bishops Stortford	388	W 3 - 0	Mambo 42 (og) Pugh 57 Bradbrook 77	5	22
26	FAT3Q	A	Weston-s-Mare	240	W 4 - 2	Pugh 43 BRADBROOK 3 (47 65 76)		23
Dec 3	Nat S	H	Poole Town	886	W 2 - 1	Ofori-Acheampong 20 Wanadio 22	4	24
10	FAT1	H	Dover Athletic	813	D 1 - 1	Vint 58		25
13	FAT1r	A	Dover Athletic	389	W 2 - 1	Vint 14 Wanadio 43		26
17	Nat S	A	Maidenhead United	945	L 0 - 5		5	27
26	Nat S	H	Ebbsfleet United	2404	W 2 - 1	Bonner 47 Ofori-Acheampong 61	4	28
Jan 1	Nat S	A	Ebbsfleet United	2564	L 0 - 1		6	29
7	Nat S	H	East Thurrock United	920	W 6 - 1	Bonner 2 Brown 14 Murphy 23 Pugh 37 Hayes 54 Bradbrook 90 (pen)	5	30
14	FAT2	H	Chelmsford City	918	L 0 - 1			31
17	Nat S	H	Weston-s-Mare	538	W 3 - 2	Wynter 58 Harris 66 Brown 82	4	32
24	Nat S	A	Eastbourne Borough	472	W 3 - 2	Wanadio 10 Pugh 34 Dembele 84	3	33
28	Nat S	A	Wealdstone	611	W 4 - 0	Wanadio 20 Hayes 32 Bradbrook 41 Pugh 60	3	34
Feb 4	Nat S	H	Whitehawk	875	W 3 - 1	Hayes 20 Murphy 32 Pugh 71	3	35
11	Nat S	A	Gosport Borough	363	W 4 - 0	Pugh 7 Wanadio 63 Wood 66 Dembele 83	3	36
18	Nat S	H	Chelmsford City	1365	L 0 - 1		3	37
25	Nat S	A	Oxford City	353	D 1 - 1	Hayes 86	3	38
28	Nat S	A	Welling United	909	D 0 - 0		3	39
Mar 4	Nat S	H	Bath City	944	W 2 - 0	Bradbrook 22 (pen) Ofori-Acheampong 76	3	40
11	Nat S	A	Concord Rangers	367	D 1 - 1	Hayes 21	3	41
18	Nat S	H	Truro City	936	W 5 3	Pugh 30 86 Bradbrook 41 Wanadio 67 Murphy 90	3	42
21	Nat S	H	Margate	872	W 4 - 0	Bradbrook 24 57 Wanadio 49 Pavey 84	3	43
25	Nat S	A	St Albans City	753	L 0 - 1		3	44
April 1	Nat S	A	Hemel Hempstead Town	555	D 2 - 2	Bradbrook 30 (pen) Wanadio 61	4	45
8	Nat S	H	Eastbourne Borough	958	W 4 - 3	Pugh 11 Wanadio 43 Hayes 52 Bradbrook 55	4	46
15	Nat S	A	Hungerford Town	522	L 0 - 2		4	47
17	Nat S	A	Hampton & Richmond B	1101	W 3 - 1	Bradbrook 7 Brown 29 Vint 76	4	48
22	Nat S	H	Bishops Stortford	1025	W 4 - 0	Pugh 13 Bradbrook 25 Ofori-Acheampong 60 Pavey 85	4	49
28	Nat S	A	Poole Town	754	W 3 - 2	Pugh 9 Murphy 90 Noble 90	3	50
May 3	PO SF1	A	Chelmsford City	1653	D 0 - 0			51
7	PO SF2	H	Chelmsford City	2622	L 1 - 2	Ofori-Acheampong 90		52

GOALSCORERS	SG	CSG	Pens	Hat tricks	Total		SG	CSG	Pens	Hat tricks	Total
2015-16 E.Bradbrook					17	Bonner	2				2
E.Bradbrook	18	2	5	1	24	Dembele	2				2
Pugh	16	4			17	Opponents	2				2
Wanadio	13				13	Pavey	2				2
Ofori-Acheampong	8				9	Wood	2				2
Hayes	8		1		8	Ibraham	1				1
Brown	7	3	1		7	Noble	1				1
Harris	4				4	Wood	1				1
Murphy	4				4	Wynter	1				1
Vint	3				3						

EAST THURROCK UNITED

Club Contact Details
FutureFuel Stadium, Rookery Hill, Corringham, Essex SS17 9LB
01375 644 166
speight.n@sky.com

Ground Capacity: 3,500 **Seats:** 160 **Covered:** 1,000 **Clubhouse:** Yes **Shop:** Yes

Google map showing East Thurrock United Football Club, Pegasus Country Club, The Springhouse Sports Club & Function Suites.

Record Attendance
1,661 vs Dulwich Hamlet, Isthmian League Premier Division Play-off final, 2016

Previous Grounds
Billet, Stanford-le-Hope 1970-73, 74-76, Grays Athletic 1973-74, Tilbury FC 1977-82, New Thames Club 1982-84.

10 YEAR RECORD

07-08		08-09		09-10		10-11		11-12		12-13		13-14		14-15		15-16		16-17	
Isth P	20	Isth1N	2	Isth1N	5	Isth1N	1	Isth P	10	Isth P	5	Isth P	20	Isth P	13	Isth P	3	Nat S	13
FAC	1Q	FAC	3Q	FAC	2Q	FAC	2Qr	FAC	1P	FAC	4Qr	FAC	1Qr	FAC	1Qr	FAC	3Q	FAC	2Q
FAT	2Q	FAT	3Q	FAT	P	FAT	P	FAT	2Pr	FAT	2Qr	FAT	1Pr	FAT	3Q	FAT	1P	FAT	2P

Club Factfile

Founded: 1969   **Nickname:** Rocks   **Manager:** John Coventry

Previous Names: Corringham Social > 1969 (Sunday side)

Previous Leagues: South Essex Combination 1969-70. Greater London 1970-72. Metropolitan London 1972-75. London Spartan 1975-79. Essex Senior 1979-92. Isthmian 1992-2004, 05-16. Southern 2004-05.

Club Colours (change): Amber & black

RECORDS
Victory: 7-0 v Coggeshall (H) - Essex Senior League 1984
Defeat: 0-9 v Eton Manor (A) - Essex Senior League 1982
Goalscorer: Graham Stewart - 102
Appearances: Glen Case - 600+
Additional: £22,000 from Leyton Orient for Greg Berry 1990

HONOURS
FA Comps: None

League: Metropolitan London Division Two 1972-73.
Isthmian League Division Three 1999-2000, Division One North 2010-11.

County FA: East Anglian Cup 2002-03.

BEST PERFORMANCES	**FA Cup:** First Round Proper 2011-12, 14-15.
	FA Trophy: Second Round Proper 2004-05, 11-12 (r), 16-17.
	FA Vase: Fifth Round Proper 1988-89.

EAST THURROCK UNITED MATCH RESULTS 2016-17

Date	Comp	H/A	Opponents	Att:	Result	Goalscorers	Pos	No.
Aug 6	Nat S	H	Hungerford Town	244	L 0 - 1		17	1
9	Nat S	A	Hemel Hempstead Town	383	D 1 - 1	Marlow 39	16	2
13	Nat S	A	Hampton & Richmond B	422	W 2 - 1	Marlow 47 (pen) Ellul 79	11	3
16	Nat S	H	Welling United	286	D 1 - 1	Marlow 82 (pen)	11	4
20	Nat S	H	Gosport Borough	203	W 5 - 1	Gardner 8 Honesty 53 65 Ellul 57 Freiter 74	13	5
27	Nat S	A	Bath City	523	L 1 - 2	Harris 90	12	6
29	Nat S	H	Eastbourne Borough	304	D 1 - 1	Wraight 15	13	7
Sept 3	Nat S	A	Truro City	261	W 6 - 0	WRAIGHT 4 (9 34 41 42) Freiter 75 Harris 81	12	8
6	Nat S	A	Margate	369	L 1 - 2	Clark 62	13	9
10	Nat S	H	Dartford	373	D 1 - 1	Marlow 57 (pen)	13	10
12	Nat S	A	Chelmsford City	913	D 2 - 2	Harris 23 Gardner 57	12	11
17	FAC2Q	H	Whitehawk	223	L 2 - 3	Walker 15 Honesty 49		12
24	Nat S	H	Bishops Stortford	242	D 2 - 2	Ellui 45 Ferdinand 87	12	13
Oct 8	Nat S	A	Oxford City	267	W 1 - 0	Walker 80	11	14
15	Nat S	H	Weston-s-Mare	242	W 5 1	Ferdinand 22 Wraight 48 Harris 55 Walker 72 Ellul 80	8	15
22	Nat S	H	Ebbsfleet United	606	D 1 - 1	Ferdinand 21	8	16
29	Nat S	A	Poole Town	497	D 1 - 1	Higgins 87	8	17
Nov 5	Nat S	H	Maidenhead United	298	D 0 - 0		9	18
12	Nat S	H	Whitehawk	298	W 3 - 2	Higgins 4 Gardner 15 Wraight 25	8	19
19	Nat S	H	St Albans City	315	D 1 - 1	Higgins 68	8	20
26	FAT3Q	A	Margate	185	D 1 - 1	Higgins 5 (pen)		21
29	FAT3Qr	H	Margate	174	W 2 - 0	Wraight 57 Higgins 84		22
Dec 3	Nat S	A	Wealdstone	602	L 0 - 1		9	23
10	FAT1	H	Aldershot Town	321	D 1 - 1	Higgins 22		24
12	FAT1r	A	Aldershot Town	566	W 4 - 3	Higgins 31 Beesley 36 Southworth 49 Jarvis 73 (aet)	6	25
!7	Nat S	H	Truro City	242	W 5 - 1	WRAIGHT 3 (36 44 65) Ferdinand 63 Marlow 66	9	26
26	Nat S	A	Concord Rangers	305	D 1 - 1	Wraight 90	9	27
Jan 1	Nat S	H	Concord Rangers	384	D 1 - 1	Marlow 58	9	28
7	Nat S	A	Dartford	940	L 1 - 6	Wraight 32	11	29
14	FAT2	H	Braintree Town	313	L 2 - 5	Higgins 50 (pen) 90		30
24	Nat S	A	Gosport Borough	364	W 5 - 1	Harris 3 31 Higgins 12 19 (pen) Wraight 86	10	31
28	Nat S	A	Hungerford Town	215	L 0 - 3		10	32
Feb 4	Nat S	H	Hemel Hempstead Town	255	L 2 - 3	Clark 63 Wraight 69		33
11	Nat S	A	Welling United	424	L 0 - 2		11	34
18	Nat S	H	Hampton & Richmond B	243	W 2 - 1	Harris 11 Wraight 88	11	35
21	Nat S	H	Margate	206	W 1 0	Burns 88	10	36
25	Nat S	H	Poole Town	279	L 1 - 2	Walker 77	11	37
Mar 4	Nat S	A	Ebbsfleet United	1267	L 1 - 6	Harris 10 (pen)	13	38
11	Nat S	A	Bishops Stortford	283	W 4 - 0	Marlow 6 34 Wraight 24 Akinwande 57	12	39
18	Nat S	H	Oxford City	218	W 2 - 1	Akinwande 54 Heard 81	12	40
21	Nat S	H	Chelmsford City	478	L 1 - 2	Honesty 47	12	41
25	Nat S	A	Weston-s-Mare	433	W 3 - 1	Akinwande 72 Harris 85 90	11	42
Apr 1	Nat S	H	Whitehawk	225	L 2 - 3	Wraight 14 67	13	43
8	Nat S	A	Maidenhead United	1134	L 1 - 2	Wood 54	13	44
15	Nat S	H	Bath City	292	W 2 - 0	Higgins 27 Harris 32	11	45
17	Nat S	A	Eastbourne Borough	618	L 0 - 4		13	46
22	Nat S	A	St Albans City	641	D 2 - 2	Wraight 16 Harris 87	13	47
29	Nat S	H	Wealdstone	497	D 1 - 1	Ruel 34	13	48

GOALSCORERS	SG	CSG	Pens	Hat tricks	Total		SG	CSG	Pens	Hat tricks	Total
2015-16 Higgins					45	Gardner	3				3
Wraight	13	2		1	20	Clark	2				2
Harris	10		1		12	Freiter	2				2
Higgins	10	4	2		12	Beesley	1				1
Marlow	7	3	3		8	Burns	1				1
Ellui	4				4	Heard	1				1
Ferdinand	4				4	Jarvis	1				1
Honesty	4	2			4	Ruel	1				1
Walker	4				4	Southworth	1				1
Akinwande	3				3	Wood	1				1

EASTBOURNE BOROUGH

Club Contact Details
Langney Sports Club, Priory Lane, Eastbourne BN23 7QH
01323 766 265
janfield38@sky.com

Ground Capacity: 4,151 **Seats:** 542 **Covered:** 2,500 **Clubhouse:** Yes **Shop:** Yes

Record Attendance
3,770 v Oxford United - FA Cup 1st Round 05/11/05
Previous Grounds
Local Recreation Grounds. Princes Park >1983.

10 YEAR RECORD

07-08	08-09	09-10	10-11	11-12	12-13	13-14	14-15	15-16	16-17
Conf S 2	Conf 13	Conf 19	Conf 23	Conf S 18	Conf S 12	Conf S 10	Conf S 11	Nat S 17	Nat S 11
FAC 1P	FAC 1Pr	FAC 4Qr	FAC 4Q	FAC 4Q	FAC 3Qr	FAC 3Q	FAC 4Qr	FAC 4Q	FAC 1P
FAT 3Q	FAT 1P	FAT 2Pr	FAT 3Pr	FAT 3Qr	FAT 3Q	FAT 3Q	FAT 3Q	FAT 2P	FAT 3Qr

Club Factfile

Founded: 1964 **Nickname:** Borough **Manager:** Jamie Howell

Previous Names: Langney FC 1964-68. Langney Sports 1968-2001.

Previous Leagues: Eastbourne & District 1964-73. Eastbourne & Hastings 1973-83. Sussex County 1983-2000. Southern 2000-2004.

Club Colours (change): All red (All blue)

RECORDS
Victory: 11-1 v Crowborough, Sussex Senior Cup Quarter-final, 13/01/2009
Defeat: 0-8 v Sheppey United (A) - FA Vase 09/10/93 and v Peachaven & Tels (A) - Sussex Co. Div.1 09/11/93
Goalscorer: Nigel Hole - 146
Appearances: Darren Baker - 952 (1992-2013)
Additional: Paid £1,800 to Yeovil Town for Yemi Odoubade.
Received £25,000 from Oxford United for Yemi Odoubade.

HONOURS
FA Comps: None

League: Eastbourne & Hastings Premier Division 1981-82.
Sussex County League Division Three 1986-87, Division Two 1987-88, Division One 1999-2000, 02-03.
County FA: Sussex Senior Challenge Cup 2001-02, 08-09, 15-16.

BEST PERFORMANCES	**FA Cup:** First Round Proper 2005-06, 07-08, 08-09(r), 16-17.
	FA Trophy: Third Round Proper 2001-02, 02-03, 04-05, 10-11.
	FA Vase: Second Round Proper 1990-91, 91-92, 97-98.

EASTBOURNE BOROUGH MATCH RESULTS 2016-17

Date	Comp	H/A	Opponents	Att:	Result	Goalscorers	Pos	No.
Aug 6	Nat S	H	Hemel Hempstead Town	595	W 3 - 0	ROMAIN 3 (11 16 89)	2	1
9	Nat S	A	Hampton & Richmond B	525	L 1 - 3	Pinney 45 (pen)	8	2
13	Nat S	A	Gosport Borough	509	L 1 - 3	Romain 20	15	3
16	Nat S	H	Concord Rangers	383	W 2 - 1	Dutton 37 Pinney 90	11	4
20	Nat S	A	Hungerford Town	212	W 2 - 0	Romain 55 73	10	5
27	Nat S	H	Ebbsfleet UNited	764	D 0 - 0		7	6
29	Nat S	A	East Thurrock United	304	D 1 - 1	Romain 65	10	7
Sept 3	Nat S	H	Oxford City	541	W 4 - 0	McCallum 12 Hare 15 Hughes 30 56	6	8
6	Nat S	H	Maidenhead United	542	L 1 - 2	Baptista 49	8	9
10	Nat S	H	Poole Town	395	D 1 - 1	Romain 40	8	10
13	Nat S	A	Welling United	406	L 1 - 3	McAllister 40	11	11
17	FAC2Q	H	Metropolitan Police	441	W 2 - 1	Pinney 74 McCallum 88		12
24	Nat S	H	Chelmsford City	501	L 1 - 5	Hughes 90	13	13
Oct 1	FAC3Q	H	Hadley	418	D 0 - 0			14
5	FAC3Qr	A	Hadley	302	W 4 - 0	Pinney 31 (pen) 43 McCallum 75 Romain 83		15
8	Nat S	A	Bath City	1008	D 1 - 1	Romain 7	13	16
15	FAC4Q	H	Aldershot Town	1443	W 2 - 1	Taylor 52 Pinney 90		17
22	Nat S	A	Truro City	323	D 2 - 2	Hughes 12 Khinda-John 84	14	18
29	Nat S	H	Bishops Stortford	453	W 1 - 0	Romain 41	14	19
Nov 5	FAC1	A	Braintree Town	645	L 0 - 7			20
12	Nat S	A	Wealdstone	651	W 4 - 1	Smith 52 Hughes 76 Taylor 79 85	10	21
19	Nat S	H	Weston-s-Mare	415	L 3 - 4	Dutton 11 Romain 37 Taylor 40	13	22
22	Nat S	H	Margate	357	W 2 - 1	Smith 1 Romain 12	10	23
26	FAT 3Q	A	Leiston	212	D 1 - 1	Pinney 87 (pen)		24
Dec 3	Nat S	A	St Albans City	678	L 0 - 1		11	25
6	FAT3Qr	H	Leiston	262	L 2 - 2	Taylor 73 Simpemba 102 (aet lost 3-5 on pens)		26
!7	Nat S	A	Oxford City	234	L 0 - 1		12	27
26	Nat S	H	Whitehawk	708	W 4 - 2	Worrall 37 Hughes 51 Pinney 65 Taylor 90	12	28
Jan 7	Nat S	H	Poole Town	568	D 0 - 0		13	29
14	Nat S	H	Hungerford Town	554	D 2 - 2	Pinney 51 (pen) 81	13	30
24	Nat S	H	Dartford	472	L 2 - 3			31
28	Nat S	A	Hemel Hempstead Town	427	W 4 - 0	Hughes 14 Case 16 Pinney 19 Stone 90	11	32
Feb 4	Nat S	H	Hampton & Richmond B	541	D 2 - 2	Hughes 44 Pinney 69	12	33
7	Nat S	A	Whitehawk	324	D 1 - 1	Hughes 89	12	34
11	Nat S	A	Concord Rangers	249	L 1 - 3	Romain 35	12	35
18	Nat S	H	Gosport Borough	554	W 2 - 0	Romain 50 Pinney 80 (pen)	12	36
21	Nat S	A	Maidenhead United	803	L 1 - 2	Baptista 68 (pen)	12	37
25	Nat S	A	Bishops Stortford	282	W 4 - 1	ROMAIN 4 (47 50 85 90)	12	38
Mar 4	Nat S	H	Truro City	539	W 2 - 0	Round 12 Romain 27	11	39
11	Nat S	A	Chelmsford City	821	L 1 - 5	McCallum 62	13	40
18	Nat S	H	Bath City	504	L 1 - 2	Baptista 83	13	41
21	Nat S	H	Welling United	402	W 7 - 3	McCallum 39 TAYLOR 3 (48 86 90 p) Pinney 5 90 Hare 8013	42	
25	Nat S	A	Margate	483	D 1 - 1	Hare 79	13	43
April 1	Nat S	H	Wealdstone	691	W 5 - 1	Oxlade-Chamberlain 5 26 Taylor 31 55 Khinda-John 60	11	44
8	Nat S	A	Dartford	958	L 3 - 4	Hughes 33 McCallum 59 Worrall 61 (pen)	12	45
15	Nat S	A	Ebbsfleet United	2477	L 1 - 4	Worrall 38 (pen)	13	46
17	Nat S	H	East Thurrock United	618	W 4 - 0	Hobson 35 Taylor 38 Hughes 59 McCallum 85	12	47
22	Nat S	A	Weston-s-Mare	431	L 0 - 2		12	48
29	Nat S	H	St Albans City	621	W 3 - 2	Pinney 49 56 Oxlade-Chamberlain 90	11	49

GOALSCORERS	SG	CSG	Pens	Hat tricks	Total		SG	CSG	Pens	Hat tricks	Total
2015-16 Pinney					23	Dutton	2				2
Romain	14	2		2	20	Khinda-John	2				2
Pinney	13	3	5		17	Oxlade-Chamberlsin	2				2
Taylor	8		1	1	12	Smith	2				2
Hughes	8	3			11	Case	1				1
McCallum	7				7	Hobson	1				1
Baptista	3		1		3	McAllister	1				1
Hare	3				3	Round	1				1
Hughes	3				3	Simpemba	1				1
Worrall	3		2		3	Stoner	1				1

GLOUCESTER CITY

Club Contact Details
Cheltenham Town FC, The Abbey Business Stadium, Whaddon Road GL52 5NA
01242 573 558 (Cheltenham Town No.)

Ground Capacity: 7,289 **Seats:** 3,912 **Covered:** Yes **Clubhouse:** Yes **Shop:** Yes

Record Attendance
Longlevens: 10,500 v Tottenham - Friendly 1952. Meadow Park: 4,500 v Dagenham & Red. - FAT 3rd Q Rnd 12/04/97
Previous Grounds
Longlevens 1934-64. Horton Road 1964-86. Meadow Park 1986-2007. F.G.Rovers 07-08. Cirencester T. 08-10.

10 YEAR RECORD

07-08		08-09		09-10		10-11		11-12		12-13		13-14		14-15		15-16		16-17	
SthP	6	SthP	3	Conf N	18	Conf N	14	Conf N	14	Conf N	11	Conf N	17	Conf N	14	Nat N	15	Nat N	10
FAC	2Q	FAC	1Q	FAC	4Qr	FAC	2Q	FAC	4Qr	FAC	1P	FAC	1P	FAC	4Q	FAC	4Q	FAC	3Qr
FAT	1P	FAT	2Q	FAT	3Q	FAT	3P	FAT	3Qr	FAT	3Q	FAT	1P	FAT	3Qr	FAT	3Qr	FAT	3Q

Club Factfile

Founded: 1883 **Nickname:** The Tigers **Manager:** Tim Harris

Previous Names: Gloucester 1883-86,1889-1901, Gloucester Nomads 1888-89, Gloucester YMCA 1910-25, Gloucester City 1902-10,1925to date

Previous Leagues: Bristol & District (now Western) 1893-96, Gloucester & Dist. 1897-1907, North Gloucestershire 1907-10, Gloucestershire Northern Senior (FM) 1920-34, Birmingham Combination 1934-39, Southern 1939-2000

Club Colours (change): Yellow & black

RECORDS

Victory: 12-1 v Bristol Saint George, April 1934
Defeat: 0-14 v Brimscombe FC, January 1923
Goalscorer: Jerry Causon - 206 (1930-36)
Appearances: Tom Webb - 673 (2001 to date)
Additional: Paid £25,000 to Worcester City for Steve Ferguson 1990-91
Received £25,000 from AFC Bournemouth for Ian Hedges 1990

HONOURS

FA Comps: None

League: Gloucester & District Division One 1897-98, 99-1900, 03-04. North Gloucestershire Division One 1907-08, 08-09.
Gloucestershire Northern Senior 1933-34. Southern League Midland Division 1988-89, Premier Division Play-off 2008-09.

County FA: Glos Junior Cup 1902-03. Glos Senior Amateur Cup 1931-32. Glos Senior Cup 1937-38, 49-50, 50-51, 52-53, 54-55, 55-56, 57-58, 65-66, 68-69, 70-71, 74-75, 78-79, 79-80, 81-82, 82-83, 83-84, 90-91, 92-93.

BEST PERFORMANCES	**FA Cup:** Second Round Proper 1989-90 (r). **Welsh Cup:** Quarter-finals 1958-59 (r).
	FA Trophy: Semi-finals 1996-97 (r)
	FA Vase: N/A

GLOUCESTER CITY MATCH RESULTS 2016-17

Date	Comp	H/A	Opponents	Att:	Result	Goalscorers	Pos	No.
Aug 6	Nat N	A	Salford City	1074	D 1 - 1	Parker 67	14	1
13	Nat N	H	Gainsborough Trinity	337	W 4 - 1	Parker 26 Williams 41 90 Hooper 66	10	2
16	Nat N	A	Worcester City	527	W 3 - 2	HOOPER 3 (47 58 83)	7	3
21	Nat N	H	Darlington 1883	665	L 1 - 2	Galbraith 13 (og)	9	4
27	Nat N	A	Stalybridge Celtic	306	W 3 - 1	Dinsley 20 Hopper 33 Kotwica 75	8	5
29	Nat N	H	Boston United	469	W 3 - 1	Williams 41 Kotwica 47 Hopper 72	7	6
Sept 3	Nat N	A	AFC Fylde	1425	D 2 - 2	Reid 67 Parker 88	9	7
6	Nat N	A	Tamworth	644	L 1 - 2	Deaman 74	10	8
10	Nat N	H	Altrincham	406	W 5 - 0	Knowles 27 Parker 44 HOPPER 3 (64 67 74)	10	9
13	Nat N	H	AFC Telford United	313	W 3 - 0	Knowles 10 Hanks 63 68	6	10
17	FAC2Q	A	**Salisbury**	**945**	**W 2 - 1**	**Knowles 4 Hopper 81**		11
20	Nat N	H	Nuneaton Town	417	D 2 - 2	Kotwica 45 Avery 48	6	12
24	Nat N	A	Harrogate Town	729	L 1 - 3	Williams 66	7	13
Oct 2	FAC3Q	H	**Hemel Hempstead Town**	**489**	**D 2 - 2**	**Hanks 70 75**		14
4	FAC3Qr	A	**Hemel Hempstead Town**	**388**	**L 0 - 2**			15
8	Nat N	H	FC Halifax Town	545	L 0 - 2		8	16
22	Nat N	H	Bradford PA	380	W 1 - 0	Hanks 7	7	17
29	Nat N	A	FC United of Manchester	2499	W 4 - 2	Parker 7 Kotwica 44 66 Owen-Evans 46	6	18
Nov 7	Nat N	A	Alfreton mTown	344	W 2 - 0	Kotwica 39 Parker 45	5	19
12	Nat N	H	Curzon Ashton	439	L 0 - 2		7	20
19	Nat N	A	Chorley	918	L 1 - 4	Hopper 68	9	21
22	Nat N	A	Kidderminster Harriers	1319	L 0 - 3		9	22
								23
26	FAT 3Q	H	**AFC Fylde**	**240**	**L 2 - 3**	**Hall 2 Parker 58**		24
Dec 3	Nat N	H	Stockport County	539	L 0 - 1		11	25
!7	Nat N	H	AFC Fylde	342	L 1 - 5	Avery 2	11	26
26	Nat N	A	Brackley Town	517	L 0 - 3		11	27
Jan 7	Nat N	A	Altrincham	915	W 1 - 0	Parker 31	11	28
14	Nat N	A	Darlington 1883	1837	L 0 - 2		11	29
28	Nat N	H	Worcester City	575	W 3 - 0	Hopper 19 Finnie 37 Hanks 85	11	30
31	Nat N	H	Tamworth	256	W 2 - 0	Finnie 18 Avery 25	11	31
Feb 4	Nat N	A	AFC Telford United	948	W 2 - 0	Kotwica 19 Hopper 90	10	32
11	Nat N	H	Salford City	743	W 3 - 2	Hopper 14 74 Hanks 31 (pen)	10	33
18	Nat N	A	Gainsborough Trinity	477	D 1 - 1	Avery 67	10	34
21	Nat N	H	Brackley Town	262	L 1 - 3	Mullings 49	10	35
25	Nat N	H	FC United of Manchester	795	L 2 - 3	Avery 16 Thomas 21	10	36
Mar 4	Nat N	A	Bradford PA	296	W 1 - 0	Kotwica 55	11	37
11	Nat N	H	Harrogate Town	374	D 1 - 1	Hopper 59	11	38
18	Nat N	A	FC Halifax Town	1152	W 1 - 0	Hanks 75 (pen)	10	39
25	Nat N	H	Alfreton Town	435	W 4 - 0	KOTWICA 3 (6 73 79) Hopper 87	9	40
April 1	Nat N	A	Curzon Ashton	246	D 1 - 1	Avery 90	10	41
8	Nat N	H	Kidderminster Harriers	948	L 1 - 2	Williams 25	10	42
15	Nat N	H	Stalybridge Celtic	379	W 2 - 1	Hopper 73 84	9	43
17	Nat N	A	Boston United	1094	D 2 - 2	Kotwica 10 Hanks 35	10	44
22	Nat N	H	Chorley	526	D 2 - 2	Hopper 9 Hanks 25 (pen)	10	45
29	Nat N	A	Stockport County	5783	D 1 - 1	Kotwica 72	10	46

GOALSCORERS	SG	CSG	Pens	Hat tricks	Total		SG	CSG	Pens	Hat tricks	Total
2015-16 Hall					6	Dinsley	1				1
Hopper	12	2		2	20	Hall	1				1
Kotwica	9	2		1	13	Mullings	1				1
Hanks	7		3		10	Opponents	1				1
Parker	8	2			8	Owen-Evans	1				1
Avery	5				6	Reid	1				1
Williams	5				5	Thomas	1				1
Knowles	3	3			3						
Finnie	2				2						
Deaman	1				1						

HAMPTON & RICHMOND BOROUGH

Club Contact Details
Beveree Stadium, Beaver Close, Station Road, Hampton TW12 2BX
0208 979 2456
secretary@hamptonfc.net

HRBFC

Ground Capacity: 3,500   **Seats:** 750   **Covered:** 800   **Clubhouse:** Yes   **Shop:** Yes

Record Attendance
3,500 v Hayes & Yeading United, Conference South Play-off Final, 2008-09
Previous Grounds
Moved to the Beveree Stadium in 1959

---

10 YEAR RECORD

07-08		08-09		09-10		10-11		11-12		12-13		13-14		14-15		15-16		16-17	
Conf S	3	Conf S	2	Conf S	14	Conf S	18	Conf S	21	Isth P	13	Isth P	12	Isth P	15	Isth P	1	Nat S	7
FAC	1P	FAC	4Q	FAC	4Q	FAC	3Q	FAC	3Q	FAC	3Q	FAC	4Q	FAC	1Q	FAC	1Q	FAC	3Q
FAT	3Q	FAT	3Q	FAT	1Pr	FAT	2P	FAT	3P	FAT	1Pr	FAT	3Q	FAT	1Q	FAT	3Q	FAT	3Qr

---

Club Factfile

Founded: 1921   **Nickname:** Beavers or Borough   **Manager:** Alan Dowson - 15/09/14

Previous Names: Hampton 1921-99

Previous Leagues: Kingston & District 1921-33. South West Middlesex 1933-59. Surrey Senior 1959-64. Spartan 1964-71. Athenian 1971-73. Isthmian 1973-2007, 12-16. Conference 2007-12.

Club Colours (change): Red & blue/red/blue (Sky blue/white/sky blue)

RECORDS
Victory: 11-1 v Eastbourne United - Isthmian League Division 2 South 1990-91
Defeat: 0-13 v Hounslow Town - Middlesex Senior Cup 1962-63
Goalscorer: Peter Allen - 176 (1964-73)
Appearances: Tim Hollands - 750 (1977-95)
Additional: Paid £3,000 to Chesham United for Matt Flitter June 2000
                   Received £40,000 from Queens Park Rangers for Leroy Phillips

HONOURS
FA Comps: None

League: Surrey Senior 1963-64. Spartan 1964-65, 65-66, 66-67, 69-70.
Isthmian Premier Division 2006-07, 2015-16.

County FA: Middlesex Charity Cup 1969-70, 95-96, 97-98, 98-99. Middlesex Super Cup 1999-00, 06-07.
Middlesex Senior Cup 2005-06, 07-08, 11-12, 13-14, 16-17.

BEST PERFORMANCES	**FA Cup:** First Round Proper 2000-01, 07-08.
	FA Trophy: Third Round Proper 2011-12.
	FA Vase: N/A

HAMPTON & RICHMOND BOROUGH MATCH RESULTS 2016-17

Date	Comp	H/A	Opponents	Att:	Result	Goalscorers	Pos	No.
Aug 6	Nat S	A	Bishops Stortford	333	W 1 - 0	Jelley 89 (pen)	7	1
8	Nat S	H	Eastbourne Borough	625	W 3 - 1	Jelley 45 (pen) Lowe 45 81	3	2
13	Nat S	H	East Thurrock United	422	L 1 - 2	Lowe 56	5	3
16	Nat S	A	Margate	468	W 4 - 2	Lowe 63 Kiernan 71 Jolley 79 Kabamba 90	4	4
20	Nat S	H	Truro City	419	D 2 - 2	Lowe 69 Kiernan 77	2	5
27	Nat S	A	Wealdstone	667	W 4 - 2	Kiernan 8 Gasson 22 Lowe 40 Kabamba 90	2	6
29	Nat S	H	Dartford	676	W 4 - 1	Jolley 8 Kamara 26 Bonnor (og) 35 Kabamba 54	2	7
Sept 3	Nat S	H	St Albans City	1008	W 4 - 2	KABAMBA 3 (18 37 62) Lowe 43	2	8
6	Nat S	A	Gosport Borough	467	D 1 - 1	Lowe 66	2	9
10	Nat S	H	Bath City	516	W 2 - 1	Kamara 25 (pen) Kabamba 54	2	10
13	Nat S	H	Whitehawk	404	L 0 - 2		2	11
17	FAC2Q	A	AFC Dunstable	173	W 7 - 1	Collier 9 Lowe 11 38 Kabamba 33 56 Williams 48 Jelley 52		12
24	Nat S	A	Hungerford Town	340	W 3 - 1	Kiernan 7 Gasson 23 Kabamba 31	2	13
Oct 1	FAC3Q	A	Taunton Town	630	L 1 - 2	Kabamba 45		14
8	Nat S	H	Poole Town	934	L 0 - 2		3	15
15	Nat S	A	Ebbsfleet United	246	W 3 - 0	Kabamba 26 Lowe 45 Kiernan 54	3	16
22	Nat S	H	Maidenhead United	1146	L 2 - 3	Lowe 14 79	3	17
29	Nat S	A	Weston--s-Mare	312	W 3 - 1	Lowe 45 Kabamba 82 Hippolyte-Patrick 90	3	18
Nov 5	Nat S	H	Oxford City	606	L 0 - 1		4	19
12	Nat S	A	Chelmsford City	963	D 2 - 2	Kabamba 10 Kiernan 90	5	20
19	Nat S	H	Welling United	587	W 3 - 1	Kabamba 56 64 Lowe 76	3	21
22	Nat S	A	Ebbsfleet United	828	D 1 - 1	Lowe 88	3	22
26	FAT3Q	H	Royston Town	272	D 0 - 0			23
Dec 3	Nat S	A	Concord Rangers	231	L 1 - 2	Lowe 59	5	24
6	FAT3Qr	A	Royston Town	198	L 1 - 2	Lowe 32		25
!7	Nat S	A	St Albans City	701	W 4 - 0	Kabamba 29 51Jelley 75 Kiernan 80	4	26
26	Nat S	A	Hemel Hempstead Town	539	L 0 - 1		5	27
Jan 1	Nat S	H	Hemel Hempstead Town	808	D 3 - 3	Kiernan 13 29 Collier 80	5	28
7	Nat S	A	Bath City	615	D 1 - 1	Kabamba 79	7	29
28	Nat S	H	Bishops Stortford	561	W 4 - 1	Kiernan 14 Pavey 16 Collier 25 Murphy 56	7	30
Feb 4	Nat S	A	Eastbourne Borough	581	D 2 - 2	Jelley 34 (pen) Culley 89	8	31
7	Nat S	H	Gosport Borough	369	D 2 - 2	Culley 60 Pavey 63 (pen)	8	32
11	Nat S	H	Margate	421	W 1 - 0	Kiernan 20	6	33
18	Nat S	A	East Thurrock United	243	L 1 - 2	Culley 55	7	34
25	Nat S	H	Weston-s-Mare	505	L 0 - 2		7	35
Mar 4	Nat S	A	Maidenhead United	946	D 0 - 0		7	36
11	Nat S	H	Hungerford Town	557	W 2 - 0	Jolley 44 Odameley 88	6	37
18	Nat S	A	Poole Town	568	D 3 - 3	Kiernan 66 78 Culley 74	7	38
22	Nat S	A	Whitehawk	212	W 3 - 1	Kamara 44 45 Mullings 64	7	39
25	Nat S	H	Ebbsfleet United	1089	D 1 - 1	Odameley 60	7	40
April 1	Nat S	H	Chelmsford City	611	L 0 - 2		7	41
8	Nat S	A	Oxford City	294	W 5 - 0	Culley 8 27 KIERNAN 3 (14 45 63)	7	42
15	Nat S	H	Wealdstone	834	D 1 - 1	Jolley 25	7	43
17	Nat S	A	Dartford	1101	L 1 - 3	Collier 54	8	44
22	Nat S	A	Welling United	500	W 2 - 1	Rivic 77 90	8	45
29	Nat S	H	Conford Rangers	701	W 1 - 0	Collier 29	7	46
May 3	PO SF1	H	Ebbsfleet United	1689	L 1 - 2	Culley 45		47
7	PO SF2	A	Ebbsfleet United	2102	L 1 2	Federico 61		48

GOALSCORERS	SG	CSG	Pens	Hat tricks	Total		SG	CSG	Pens	Hat tricks	Total
2015-16 Kabamba					30	Odameley	2				2
Kabamba	14	3,3	1		19	Pavey	2		1		2
Lowe	15	5,3			18	Rivic	1				2
Kiernan	12	3		1	16	Federico	1				1
Culley	6				7	H.Patrick	1				1
Collier	5				5	Mullings	1				1
T.Jelley	5	2	3		5	Murphy	1				1
C.Jolley	3				4	Opponents	1				1
Kamara	4		1		4	Williams	1				1
Gasson	2				2						

HAVANT AND WATERLOOVILLE

Club Contact Details
Westleigh Park, Martin Road, West Leigh, Havant PO9 5TH
02392 787 822
trevor.brock52@yahoo.com

Ground Capacity: 4,800   **Seats:** 562   **Covered:** 3,500   **Clubhouse:** Yes   **Shop:** Yes

Record Attendance
4,400 v Swansea City - FA Cup 3rd Round 05/01/2008
Previous Grounds
None

10 YEAR RECORD

	07-08	08-09	09-10	10-11	11-12	12-13	13-14	14-15	15-16	16-17
	Conf S 7	Conf S 15	Conf S 6	Conf S 9	Conf S 19	Conf S 10	Conf S 6	Conf S 5	Nat S 20	Isth P 1
	FAC 4P	FAC 1P	FAC 3Q	FAC 1P	FAC 3Q	FAC 2Q	FAC 2Qr	FAC 1P	FAC 4Qr	FAC 3Q
	FAT 3Q	FAT QF	FAT 1P	FAT 3Qr	FAT 3Qr	FAT 2P	FAT SF	FAT 2P	FAT 3P	FAT 3Q

Club Factfile

Founded: 1998   **Nickname:** Hawks   **Manager:** Lee Bradbury

Previous Names: Havant Town and Waterlooville merged in 1998

Previous Leagues: Southern 1998-2004. Conference/National 2004-16. Isthmian 2016-17.

Club Colours (change): All white (Yellow)

RECORDS
Victory: 9-0 v Moneyfields - Hampshire Senior Cup 23/10/2001
Defeat: 0-5 v Worcester City - Southern Premier 20/03/2004
Goalscorer: James Taylor - 138
Appearances: James Taylor - 297
Additional: Paid £5,000 to Bashley for John Wilson
               Received £15,000 from Peterborough United for Gary McDonald

HONOURS
FA Comps: None

League: Southern League Southern Division 1998-99.
           Isthmian League Premier Division 2016-17.

County FA: Hampshire Senior Cup 2015-16.

BEST PERFORMANCES	**FA Cup:** Fourth Round Proper 2007-08 (Eventually going out to Liverpool at Anfield 2-5)
	FA Trophy: Semi-finals 2013-14.
	FA Vase: N/A

HAVANT & WATERLOOVILLE MATCH RESULTS 2016-17

Date	Comp	H/A	Opponents	Att:	Result	Goalscorers	Pos	No.
Aug 13	IsthP	A	Leiston	242	L 1 - 1	Lewis 31	20	1
15	IsthP	H	Leatherhead	572	W 3 - 1	Lewis 6 Prior 60 Fogden 72	10	2
20	IsthP	H	Folkeston Invicta	520	W 1 - 0	Rutherford 13	7	3
23	IsthP	A	Metropolitan Police	166	W 2 - 1	Rutherford 4 Patterson 84	4	4
27	IsthP	H	Lowestoft Town	575	W 1 - 0	Prior 63	3	5
29	IsthP	A	Wingate & Finchley	165	W 2 - 0	Swallow 6 Patterson 50	3	6
Sept 3	FAC1Q	A	Sholing	301	W 2 - 0	Prior 13 76		7
10	IsthP	A	Canvey Island	478	W 4 - 0	Hayter 9 Lewis 38 Barker 62 Rutherford 90	3	8
17	FAC2Q	H	Highworth Town	320	W 5 - 1	PATTERSON 3 (3 88 90) Woodford 12 Hayter 60 (pen)		9
24	IsthP	H	Staines Town	567	D 1 - 1	Prior 53	3	10
27	IsthP	H	Worthing	606	W 3 - 2	Prior 47 Barker 60 Molyneux 90	3	11
Oct 1	FAC3Q	A	Ebbsfleet United	742	L 0 - 7			12
4	IsthP	A	Burgess Hill Town	285	D 3 - 3	Lewis 7 87 Patterson 72	2	13
8	IsthP	H	Harlow Town	682	W 5 - 2	PRIOR 4 (4 40 59 66 pen) Patterson 26	2	14
12	IsthP	A	Leatherhead	337	W 1 - 0	Barker 68	2	15
18	IsthP	H	Metropolitan Police	502	L 1 - 2	Woodford 51	2	16
22	IsthP	H	Leiston	643	D 0 - 0		3	17
29	FAT1Q	A	Cirencester Town	141	W 2 - 1	Rutherford 22 Prior 90		18
Nov 5	IsthP	A	Hendon	239	D 1 - 1	Patterson 4	4	19
12	FAT2Q	H	Billericay Town	256	W 5 - 0	Swallow 36 PRIOR 3 (57 71 pen 75 pen) Ridge 81		20
15	IsthP	A	Billericay Town	216	W 2 - 0	Prior 3 (pen) 36 (pen)	2	21
19	IsthP	H	Enfield Town	626	L 0 - 2		2	22
22	IsthP	A	Worthing	519	W 2 - 1	Barker 61 Rutherford 67	2	23
26	FAT3Q	H	Harlow Town	187	L 1 - 3	Rutherford 60		24
Dec 3	IsthP	A	Staines Town	234	W 4 - 1	Rutherford 3 52 Lewis 68 Barker 78	1	25
10	IsthP	A	Merstham	156	L 1 - 2	Rutherford 49	2	26
17	IsthP	H	Grays Athletic	560	W 5 - 0	RUTHERFORD 3 (5 26 65) Williams 39 Woodford 85	3	27
26	IsthP	A	Bognor Regis Town	1348	D 1 - 1	Woodford 42	3	28
31	IsthP	H	Kingstonian	790	D 1 - 1	Patterson 90	3	29
Jan 2	IsthP	H	Wingate & Finchley	568	D 1 - 1	Patterson 34	3	30
7	IsthP	A	Lowestoft	431	W 2 - 0	Lewis 27 Rutherford 63	3	31
14	IsthP	A	Dulwich Hamlet	562	W 1 - 0	Richmond 83 (og)	3	32
17	IsthP	H	AFC Sudbury	154	W 2 - 0	Williams 72 Tarbuck 74	2	33
21	IsthP	H	Needham Market	850	L 1 - 3	Patterson 87	3	34
28	IsthP	A	Folkestone Invicta	415	W 3 - 1	Lewis 6 Rutherford 31 Patterson 62	3	35
Feb 4	IsthP	H	Billericay Town	625	L 1 - 2	Prior 85	3	36
11 31	IsthP	A	Harlow Town	216	W 2 - 0	Lewis 53 Fogden 88	3	37
19	IsthP	H	Hendon	179	W 3 - 1	Tarbuck 17 Williams 20 Rutherford 27	2	38
25	IsthP	A	Merstham	721	W 3 - 0	Lewis 56 Prior 68 (pen) 81	2	39
28	IsthP	A	Tonbridge Angels	408	D 1 - 1	Prior 82	2	40
Mar 4	IsthP	H	Enfield Town	519	W 4 - 1	Rutherford 5 Prior 49 Fogden 52 Tarbuck 80	2	41
11	IsthP	H	AFC Sudbury	695	W 6 - 0	Woodford 42 TARBUCK 3 (50 71 76p) Lewis 59 Rutherford 88	1	42
14	IsthP	A	Harrow Borough	159	L 1 - 2	Tarbuck 20	2	43
18	IsthP	A	Grays Athletic	181	W 2 - 0	Williams 9 Prior 28 (pen)	2	44
25	IsthP	A	Needham Market	4342	D 0 - 0		2	45
28	IsthP	H	Harrow Borough	628	W 3 - 1	Fogden 52 Harris 65 Hayter 76	2	46
Apr 1	IsthP	H	Dulwich Hamlet	859	W 2 - 1	Lewis 48 Prior 85 (pen)	2	47
8	IsthP	H	Tonbridge Angels	769	W 2 - 0	Lewis 29 Fogden 83	2	48
14	IsthP	A	Canvey Island	409	W 2 - 1	Lewis 42 69	1	49
17	IsthP	H	Bognor Regis Town	3455	W 1 - 0	Fogden 55	1	50
22	IsthP	A	Kingstonian	1205	D 0 - 0		1	51

GOALSCORERS	SG	CSG	Pens	Hat tricks	Total		SG	CSG	Pens	Hat tricks	Total
2015-16 Donnelly					14	Hayter	3		1		3
Prior	15	3	8	2	23	Swallow	2				2
Rutherford	14	5		1	17	Harris	1				1
Lewis	13	2			15	Molyneux	1				1
Patterson	11	2		1	12	Opponents	1				1
Tarbuck	5		1	1	7	Ridge	1				1
Fogdon	6				6						
Barker	5				5						
Woodford	5				5						
Williams	4				4						

HEMEL HEMPSTEAD TOWN

Club Contact Details
Vauxhall Road, Adeyfield Road, Hemel Hempstead HP2 4HW
01442 264 300
dean.chance@ntlworld.com

Ground Capacity: 3,152   **Seats:** 300   **Covered:** 900   **Clubhouse:** Yes   **Shop:** Yes

Record Attendance
3,500 v Tooting & Mitcham - Amateur Cup 1962 (Crabtree Lane)
Previous Grounds
Salmon Meadow 1885-1928. Gees Meadow 1928-29. Crabtree Lane (Wood Lane Ground) 1929-72.

10 YEAR RECORD

07-08		08-09		09-10		10-11		11-12		12-13		13-14		14-15		15-16		16-17	
SthP	7	SthP	5	SthP	20	SthP	15	SthP	19	SthP	4	SthP	1	Conf S	9	Nat S	6	Nat S	12
FAC	2Q	FAC	2Q	FAC	1Qr	FAC	1Q	FAC	2Q	FAC	1Q	FAC	4Qr	FAC	1P	FAC	3Qr	FAC	4Qr
FAT	1P	FAT	1P	FAT	1Q	FAT	1Q	FAT	2Q	FAT	1Qr	FAT	3Q	FAT	3P	FAT	1P	FAT	3Qr

Club Factfile

Founded: 1885   **Nickname:** The Tudors   **Manager:** Dean Brennan

Previous Names: Apsley End 1885-99. Hemel Hempstead 1899-1955, 72-99. Hemel H'stead Town 1955-72. Merged with Hemel H'stead Utd '72.

Previous Leagues: West Herts 1885-99. Herts County 1899-1922. Spartan 1922-52. Delphian 1952-63. Athenian 1963-77. Isthmian 1977-2004. Southern 2004-14.

Club Colours (change): All red

RECORDS
Victory: 13-0 v RAF Uxbridge (A), Spartan Division One, 1933-34. and v Chipperfield Corinthians (H), St Mary's Cup QF, 2014-15.
Defeat: 1-13 v Luton Town, FA Cup First Qualifying Round, 05/10/1901.
Goalscorer: Dai Price
Appearances: John Wallace - 1012

HONOURS
FA Comps: None

League: West Herts 1894-95, 97-98, 1904-05. Herts County 1899-1900. Spartan Division One 1933-34. Isthmian League Division Three 1997-98, Division Two 1999-2000. Southern Premier Division 2013-14.

County FA: Herts Senior Cup 1905-06, 07-08, 08-09, 25-26, 2012-13, 14-15. Herts Charity Shield 1925-26, 34-35, 51-52,63-64, 76-77, 83-84. Herts Charity Cup 2004-05, 08-09, 09-10.

BEST PERFORMANCES
FA Cup: First Round Proper 2014-15
FA Trophy: First Round Proper 2007-08, 08-09.
FA Vase: Third Round Proper 1999-00, 00-01.

HEMEL HEMPSTEAD MATCH RESULTS 2016-17

Date	Comp	H/A	Opponents	Att:	Result	Goalscorers	Pos	No.
Aug 6	Nat S	A	Eastbourne Borough	595	L 0 - 3		21	1
9	Nat S	H	East Thurrock United	383	D 1 - 1	Marlow 3	18	2
13	Nat S	H	Oxford City	465	W 2 - 0	Robinson 72 Poku 32 (og)	13	3
16	Nat S	A	Maidenhead United	483	L 0 - 5		16	4
20	Nat S	A	Ebbsfleet United	912	D 2 - 2	Neilson 41 Robinson 81	17	5
27	Nat S	H	Poole Town	347	L 2 - 4	Corcoran 87 Robinson 89	19	6
Aug 6	Nat S	A	Hungerford Town	265	L 0 - 3		19	7
Sept 3	Nat S	H	Bishops Stortford	438	W 3 - 2	Robinson 20 (pen) 24 Potton 48	15	8
10	Nat S	A	Welling United	401	W 3 - 2	Kelly 65 Robinson 67 Potton 85	15	9
13	Nat S	A	St Albans City	903	D 2 - 2	Weiss 69 Thorne 90	15	10
17	FAC2Q	H	Herne Bay	320	D 1 - 1	Montgomery 70		11
20	FAC2Qr	A	Herne Bay	262	W 5 - 1	Williams (og) Potton Weiss 2 Corcoran		12
24	Nat S	A	Bath City	417	D 3 - 3	Montgomery 1 Watts 30 Kaloczi 75	16	13
27	Nat S	H	Whitehawk	326	W 2 - 0	Potton 24 Taaffe 75	16	14
Oct 2	FAC3Q	A	Gloucester City	489	D 2 - 2	Robinson 29 Kalozci 64		15
4	FAC3Qr	H	Gloucester City	388	W 2 - 0	Robinson 28 Taaffe 66		16
8	Nat S	A	Margate	454	L 1 - 2	Potton 49	15	17
15	FAC4Q	A	Taunton Town	1282	D 0 - 0			18
18	FAC4Qr	H	Taunton Town	631	L 0 - 1			19
22	Nat S	A	Chelmsford City	1068	D 4 - 4	Saunders 3 20 Potton 50 Parkes 90	15	20
24	Nat S	H	Concord Rangers	343	W 2 - 1	Hayden 32 Parkes 61	12	21
29	Nat S	H	Gosport Borough	354	L 1 - 2	Parkes 66	15	22
Nov 5	Nat S	H	Wealdstone	665	L 1 - 3	Parkes 49	15	23
12	Nat S	A	Dartford	881	L 0 - 2		16	24
19	Nat S	H	Truro City	345	L 0 - 1		17	25
26	FAT3Q	A	Worthing	505	D 1 - 1	Parkes 40		26
29	FAT3Qr	H	Worthing	157	L 0 - 1			27
Dec 3	Nat S	A	Weston-s-Mare	356	W 5 - 3	ROBINSON 3 (13 52 63) Parkes 37 Gordan 81	15	28
17	Nat S	A	Bishops Stortford	393	W 4 - 0	Parkes 43 (pen) 86 (pen) Robinson 57 Saunders 72	13	29
26	Nat S	H	Hampton & Richmond B	539	W 1 - 0	Robinson 65	13	30
Jan 1	Nat S	A	Hampton & Richmond B	808	D 3 - 3	ROBINSON 3 (11 75 90)	12	31
7	Nat S	A	Welling United	463	W 2 - 0	Parkes 7 Robinson 76	10	32
14	Nat S	H	St Albans City	856	D 2 - 2	Robinson 56 77	10	33
28	Nat S	H	Eastbourne Borough	427	L 0 - 4		12	34
Feb 4	Nat S	A	East Thurrock United	255	W 3 - 2	Robinson 18 Sheringham 77 Parkes 90	10	35
11	Nat S	H	Maidenhead United	545	W 2 - 1	Sheringham 32 Robinson 57	10	36
18	Nat S	A	Oxford City	323	L 0 - 1		10	37
21	Nat S	H	Ebbsfleet United	530	D 1 - 1	Robinson 59	11	38
25	Nat S	A	Gosport Borough	307	W 6 - 0	SHERINGHAM 3 (32 35 56) Parkes 39 Robinson 48 Daniel 62	10	39
Mar 1	Nat S	A	Whitehawk	154	W 4 - 4	Sheringham 4 Driver 66 Robinson 78 83	10	40
4	Nat S	H	Chelmsford City	586	D 2 - 2	Parkes 63 (pen) 82	9	41
11	Nat S	A	Bath City	489	L 0 - 6		10	42
18	Nat S	H	Margate	490	W 3 - 2	Robinson 2 Sheringham 13 82	10	43
25	Nat S	A	Concord Rangers	287	L 0 - 2		12	44
April 1	Nat S	H	Dartford	555	D 2 - 2	Sheringham 38 Diagne 73	12	45
8	Nat S	A	Wealdstone	781	D 1 - 1	Connolly 18	11	46
15	Nat S	A	Poole Town	833	D 1 - 1	Greenhalgh	13	47
17	Nat S	H	Hungerford Town	549	W 2 - 0	Diagne 51 Greenhalgh 85	11	48
22	Nat S	A	Truro City	437	L 1 - 2	Gordon 27 (pen)	11	49
29	Nat S	H	Weston-s Mare	578	L 0 - 5		12	50

GOALSCORERS	SG	CSG	Pens	Hat tricks	Total		SG	CSG	Pens	Hat tricks	Total
2015-16 Slabba					13	Montgomery	2				2
Robinson	19	6	1	2	26	Opponents	2				2
Parkes	11	4	3		13	Taaffe	2				2
Sheringham	6			1	9	Connolly	1				1
Potton	6				6	Daniel	1				1
Saunders	3				3	Driver	1				1
Weiss	3				3	Hayden	1				1
Corcoran	2				2	Kelly	1				1
Diagne	2				2	Marlow	1				1
Gordan	2		1		2	Neilson	1				1
Greenhalgh	2				2	Thorne	1				1
Kaloczi	2				2	Watts	1				1

HUNGERFORD TOWN
Club Contact Details
Bulpitt Lane, Hungerford RG17 0AY
01488 682 939

Ground Capacity: 2,500   **Seats:** 400   **Covered:** 400   **Clubhouse:** Yes   **Shop:** Yes

Record Attendance
1,684 v Sudbury Town - FA Vase Semi-final 1988-89
Previous Grounds
Hungerford Marsh Field.

10 YEAR RECORD

07-08		08-09		09-10		10-11		11-12		12-13		13-14		14-15		15-16		16-17	
Hel P	3	Hel P	1	Sthsw	17	Sthsw	7	Sthsw	5	Sthsw	2	SthP	6	SthP	4	SthP	5	Nat S	6
FAC	Pr	FAC	EPr	FAC	2Q	FAC	3Q	FAC	2Qr	FAC	2Qr	FAC	3Q	FAC	1Q	FAC	1Qr	FAC	3Q
FAV	QF	FAV	5P	FAT	3Q	FAT	1Qr	FAT	P	FAT	P	FAT	3P	FAT	1Qr	FAT	2P	FAT	3Q

Club Factfile

Founded: 1886   **Nickname:** The Crusaders   **Manager:** Bobby Wilkinson

Previous Names: N/A

Previous Leagues: Hungerford League. Newbury League (FM) 1909-39. Newbury & District. Swindon & District. Hellenic 1958-78, 2003-09. Isthmian 1978-2003. Southern 2009-16.

Club Colours (change): White/black/black (All red)

RECORDS
Goalscorer: Ian Farr - 268
Appearances: Dean Bailey and Tim North - 400+
Additional: Paid £4,000 to Yeovil Town for Joe Scott. Received £3,800 from Barnstaple Town for Joe Scott. Isthmian representatives in Anglo Italian Cup 1981.

HONOURS
FA Comps: None

League: Newbury League 1912-13, 13-14, 19-20, 21-22.
Hellenic Division One 1970-71, Premier Division 2008-09.

County FA: Berks & Bucks Senior Cup 1981-82. Basingstoke Senior Cup 2012-13, 14-15.

BEST PERFORMANCES	**FA Cup:** First Round Proper 1979-80.
	FA Trophy: Third Round Proper 2014-15.
	FA Vase: Semi-Finals 1977-78, 79-80, 88-89.

HUNGERFORD TOWN MATCH RESULTS 2016-17

Date	Comp	H/A	Opponents	Att:	Result	Goalscorers	Pos	No.
Aug 6	Nat S	A	East Thurrock United	244	W 1 - 0	Jarvis 39	8	1
8	Nat S	H	Oxford City	285	W 2 - 0	Jones 42 Brown 64	1	2
13	Nat S	H	Ebbsfleet United	417	D 1 - 1	Bignall 48	3	3
16	Nat S	A	Bishop's Stortford	266	W 2 - 1	Jones 57 Williams 76	2	4
20	Nat S	H	Eastbourne Borough	212	L 0 - 2		4	5
27	Nat S	A	Dartford	831	L 0 - 2		9	6
29	Nat S	H	Hemel Hempstead Town	265	W 3 - 0	Preen 17 Clark 83 Jarvis 90	6	7
Sept 3	Nat S	A	Margate	642	D 1 - 1	Brown 17	6	8
6	Nat S	A	Truro City	408	L 0 - 2		9	9
10	Nat S	H	Gosport Borough	189	D 3 - 3	Jarvis 54 57 Herring 90	10	10
13	Nat S	A	Weston-s-Mare	336	W 1 - 0	Jarvis 81	9	11
17	**FAC2Q**	**A**	**Basingstoke Town**	**347**	**W 1 - 0**	**Brown 39 (pen)**		12
24	Nat S	H	Hampton & Richmond B	340	L 1 - 3	Jones 45	10	13
Oct 1	**FAC3Q**	**H**	**Leiston**	**245**	**L 1 - 4**	**Tyler 62**		14
8	Nat S	A	Concord Rangers	170	W 4 - 2	Soares 31 Tyler 45 Clark 61 Brown 83 (pen)	8	15
22	Nat S	H	Poole Town	325	L 0 - 1		10	16
29	Nat S	A	Maidenhead United	1004	D 2 - 2	Soares 3 51	10	17
Nov 12	Nat S	A	St Albans City	792	L 0 - 5		12	18
14	Nat S	H	Welling United	238	W 1 0	Herring 81	10	19
19	Nat S	H	Wealdstone	344	W 2 - 0	Jarvis 58 (pen) Goodger 89	9	20
26	**FAT3Q**	**H**	**Gosport Borough**	**144**	**L 0 - 1**			21
Dec 3	Nat S	A	Chelmsford City	924	D 3 - 3	Herring 22 Jarvis 45 Bignall 55	8	22
10	Nat S	A	Oxford City	156	W 6 - 0	Bignall 12 Williams 63 Soares 68 85 Goodger 72 83	8	23
17	Nat S	H	Margate	229	W 1 - 0	O'Brien 71	8	24
26	Nat S	A	Bath City	798	D 1 - 1	Boardman 68	8	25
Jan 1	Nat S	H	Bath City	408	D 2 - 2	Clark 30 Jarvis 75	8	26
7	Nat S	A	Gosport Borough	411	W 4 - 1	Williams 20 Boardman 22 Jarvis 56 Brown 72	8	27
14	Nat S	A	Eastbourne Borough	554	D 2 - 2	Herring 8 Williams 87	8	28
23	Nat S	H	Whitehawk	172	W 3 - 1	Jarvis 5 (pen) Hamilton (og) 65 Bentley 88	7	29
28	Nat S	H	East Thurrock United	218	W 3 - 0	Soares 27 Brown 79 Tyler 90	5	30
Feb 7	Nat S	H	Truro City	266	W 5 - 0	Williams 7 Bentley 33 BROWN 3 (45 54 (pen) 89)	4	31
11	Nat S	H	Bishop's Stortford	218	W 2 - 0	Bentley 29 Williams 70	4	32
18	Nat S	A	Ebbsfleet United	1321	L 0 - 1		5	33
25	Nat S	H	Maidenhead United	724	D 1 - 1	Jarvis 61	6	34
Mar 11	Nat S	A	Hampton & Richmond B	557	L 0 - 2		7	35
16	Nat S	H	Concord Rangers	271	W 2 - 1	Boardman 53 Brown 83	6	36
20	Nat S	H	Weston-s-Mare	296	W 2 - 1	Day 67 Brown 73 (pen)	5	37
25	Nat S	A	Welling United	517	D 0 - 0		6	38
Apr 1	Nat S	H	St Albans City	295	D 0 - 0		6	39
4	Nat S	A	Poole Town	659	D 1 - 1	Day 34	6	40
8	Nat S	A	Whitehawk	282	W 2 - 1	Bentley 72 Williams 90	6	41
15	Nat S	H	Dartford	522	W 2 - 0	Soares 46 Brown 72	6	42
17	Nat S	A	Hemel Hempstead Town	549	L 0 - 2		6	43
22	Nat S	A	Wealdstone	765	L 0 - 3		6	44
29	Nat S	H	Chelmsford City	420	D 1 - 1	Soares 81	6	45
								46
								47
								48
								49
								50

GOALSCORERS	SG	CSG	Pens	Hat tricks	Total		SG	CSG	Pens	Hat tricks	Total
2015-16 Jarvis					18	Goodger	2				3
Brown	8		4	1	12	Jones	3				3
Jarvis	10	2	2		11	Tyler	3	2			3
Soares	8				8	Day	2				2
Williams	7	2			7	O'Brien	1				1
Bentley	4				4	Opponents	1				1
Herring	4				4	Preen	1				1
Bignall	3	2			3						
Boardman	3				3						
Clark	3				3						

OXFORD CITY
Club Contact Details
Court Place Farm, Marsh Lane, Marston, Oxford OX3 0NQ

01865 744 493

Ground Capacity: 3,000   **Seats:** 520   **Covered:** 400   **Clubhouse:** Yes   **Shop:** Yes

Record Attendance
White House - 9,756 v Leytonstone, FA Amateur Cup, 05/02/1949

Previous Grounds
Grandpont 1884-1900, The White House 1900-1988, Cuttleslowe Park 1990-91, Pressed Steel 1991-93

10 YEAR RECORD

07-08		08-09		09-10		10-11		11-12		12-13		13-14		14-15		15-16		16-17	
SthW	4	SthP	6	SthP	13	SthP	14	SthP	2	Conf N	10	Conf N	20	Conf N	6	Nat S	12	Nat S	14
FAC	2Q	FAC	4Q	FAC	1P	FAC	1Q	FAC	1Pr	FAC	2Q	FAC	4Q	FAC	2Q	FAC	3Q	FAC	2Qr
FAT	1Q	FAT	2Qr	FAT	2Q	FAT	1Q	FAT	1Q	FAT	2P	FAT	3Q	FAT	2Pr	FAT	3P	FAT	3Q

Club Factfile

Founded: 1882   **Nickname:** City   **Manager:** Mark Jones

Previous Names: The original club folded in 1988 when they were evicted from their White House Ground and did not reform until 1990.

Previous Leagues: Isthmian 1907-88, 94-2005, South Midlands 1990-93, Spartan South Midlands 2005-06

Club Colours (change): Blue & white

RECORDS
Victory: 15-0 v Woodstock Town, Oxford Senior Cup, 29/01/1966
Defeat: 0-14 v Newbury, 21/12/1895
Goalscorer: John Woodley - 414. In the 1964-65 season Woodley scored 62 goals.
Appearances: John Woodley - 917 (1959-79)
Additional: Paid £3,000 to Woking for S Adams
Received £15,000 from Yeovil Town for Howard Forinton

HONOURS
FA Comps: FA Amateur Cup 1905-06.

League: Spartan South Midlands Premier Division 1992-93, 2005-06.
Isthmian Division One 1995-96.

County FA: Oxford Senior Cup 1899-00, 00-01, 11-12, 28-29 (Res), 30-31 (Res), 41-42, 43-44, 44-45, 45-46, 48-49, 50-51, 53-54, 56-57,59-60, 60-61, 61-62, 62-63, 64-65, 66-67, 67-68, 68-69, 69-70, 70-71 (Sh), 71-72, 73-74, 82-83, 83-84, 85-86, 96-97, 98-99, 99-00, 02-03.

BEST PERFORMANCES
FA Cup: Second Round Proper 1969-70.
FA Trophy: Third Round Proper 2002-03, 15-16.
FA Vase: Final 1994-95.

OXFORD CITY MATCH RESULTS 2016-17

Date	Comp	H/A	Opponents	Att:	Result	Goalscorers	Pos	No.
Aug 6	Nat S	H	Welling United	243	W 2 - 1	Enver-Marum 11 57 (pen)	6	1
8	Nat S	A	Hungerford Town	285	L 0 - 2		9	2
13	Nat S	A	Hemel Hempstead Town	465	L 0 - 2		19	3
16	Nat S	H	Wealdstone	303	L 0 - 3		20	4
20	Nat S	H	Concord Rangers	143	D 2 - 2	Soares 90 (pen) Fleet 90	18	5
27	Nat S	A	Chelmsford City	613	L 0 - 2		20	6
29	Nat S	H	Gosport Borough	201	L 1 - 2	Davies 36	21	7
Sept 3	Nat S	A	Eastbourne Borough	541	L 0 - 1		21	8
6	Nat S	A	Bath City	470	W 3 - 1	Giles 50 Fondop 79 89	19	9
10	Nat S	H	Truro City	214	D 1 - 1	Davies 65 (pen)	18	10
13	Nat S	H	Maidenhead United	346	L 1 - 3	Davies 69	20	11
17	FAC2Q	A	Bath City	482	D 1 - 1	Fondop 45		12
20	FAC2Qr	H	Bath City	228	L 1 - 2	Fondop 21 after extra time		13
24	Nat S	A	Whitehawk	318	L 0 - 3		21	14
Oct 8	Nat S	H	East Thurrock United	267	L 0 - 1		21	15
15	Nat S	A	Poole Town	498	W 3 - 1	Fondop 24 Davies 45 (pen) Louis 90	18	16
22	Nat S	H	Weston-s-Mare	272	D 0 - 0		18	17
29	Nat S	A	Dartford	1005	L 0 - 1		18	18
Nov 5	Nat S	A	Hampton & Richmond B	606	W 1 - 0	Winters 51	17	19
12	Nat S	H	Bishops Stortford	279	W 3 - 1	Fleet 22 Louis 28 Giles 63	17	20
19	Nat S	A	Margate	495	W 5 - 0	Poku 40 Henderson 45 Winters 47 Fondop 64 87	16	21
26	FAT 3Q	H	South Park	157	L 1 - 2	Winters 51		22
Dec 3	Nat S	H	Ebbsfleet United	752	L 1 - 3	Roberts 8	17	23
10	Nat S	H	Hungerford Town	156	L 0 - 6		17	24
!7	Nat S	H	Eastbourne Borough	234	W 1 - 0	Louis 81	14	25
26	Nat S	A	St Albans City	1049	W 4 - 2	Roberts 7 Louis 15 68 Fleet 25	14	26
Jan 1	Nat S	H	St Albans City	381	W 2 - 1	Fleet 6 Ngamvoulou 58	13	27
7	Nat S	A	Truro City	330	L 2 - 3	Macauley 65 Fondop 90	14	28
14	Nat S	A	Concord Rangers	220	D 3 - 3	Fondop 25 Peake-Pijnen 50 Ngamvoulou 64	14	29
28	Nat S	A	Welling United	641	L 0 - 4		16	30
Feb 11	Nat S	A	Wealdstone	511	D 1 - 1	Anderson 51	14	31
14	Nat S	H	Bath City	215	D 1 - 1	Fleet 63	14	32
18	Nat S	H	Hemel Hempstead Town	323	W 1 - 0	Henderson 38	14	33
25	Nat S	H	Dartford	353	D 1 - 1	Forde 90	14	34
Mar 4	Nat S	A	Weston-s-Mare	436	L 0 - 2		14	35
11	Nat S	A	Whitehawk	452	W 1 - 0	Louis 90	14	36
18	Nat S	H	East Thurrock United	218	L 1 - 2	Kawaja 82	14	37
21	Nat S	A	Maidenhead United	1017	L 1 - 6	Louis 86	14	38
25	Nat S	H	Poole Town	310	L 0 - 1		14	39
April 1	Nat S	A	Bishops Stortford	265	W 2 - 0	Forde 44 Davies 65 (pen)	14	40
8	Nat S	H	Hanpton & Richmond B	294	L 0 - 5		14	41
15	Nat S	H	Chelmsford City	361	W 2 - 0	Forde 9 Poku 90	14	42
17	Nat S	A	Gosport Borough	364	W 1 - 0	Anderson 10	14	43
22	Nat S	H	Margate	251	W 1 - 0	Louis 43	14	44
28	Nat S	A	Ebbsfleet United	2116	L 0 - 1		14	45

GOALSCORERS	SG	CSG	Pens	Hat tricks	Total		SG	CSG	Pens	Hat tricks	Total
2015-16 Bubb					24	Henderson	2				2
Fondop	7	2			9	Ngamvoulou	2				2
Louis	7				8	Poku	2				2
Davies	5	2	2		5	Roberts	2				2
Fleet	5				5	Kawaja	1				1
Forde	3				3	Macauley	1				1
Winters	3				3	Peake-Pijnen	1				1
Enver-Marum	1		1		2	Soares	1		1		1
Anderson	2				2						
Giles	2				2						

POOLE TOWN

Club Contact Details
Tatnam Ground, Oakdale School, School Lane, Poole BH15 3JR
01794 517 991
secretary@pooletownfc.co.uk

Ground Capacity: 2,000 **Seats:** 268 **Covered:** Yes **Clubhouse:** Yes **Shop:** Yes

Record Attendance
6,575 v Watford, FAC 1Pr, 1962-63 (at Poole Stadium). 2,203 v Corby, Southern Premier, 2014-15 (at Tatnam).

Previous Grounds
Ye Old Farm Ground. Wimborne Road Rec > 1933. Poole Stadium 1933-94. Hamworthy Utd 1994-96. Holt Utd 1996.

10 YEAR RECORD

07-08		08-09		09-10		10-11		11-12		12-13		13-14		14-15		15-16		16-17	
WexP	4	WexP	1	WexP	1	WexP	1	Sthsw	2	Sthsw	1	SthP	7	SthP	2	SthP	1	Nat S	5
FAC	EP	FAC	2Q	FAC	1Q	FAC	4Q	FAC	3Q	FAC	P	FAC	4Qr	FAC	2Qr	FAC	4Q	FAC	2Q
FAV	4Pr	FAV	2P	FAV	4P	FAV	SF	FAT	1Qr	FAT	2Qr	FAT	2Q	FAT	1P	FAT	1Q	FAT	3Qr

Club Factfile

Founded: 1890 **Nickname:** The Dolphins **Manager:** Tom Killick

Previous Names: Poole Rovers and Poole Hornets merged in 1890 to form Poole FC > 1934 (Known as Poole & St. Mary's 1919-20).

Previous Leagues: Dorset 1896-1903, 04-05, 10-11. Hampshire 1903-04, 05-10, 11-23, 34-35, 96-2004. Western 1923-26, 30-34, 35-57. Southern 1926-30, 57-96, 2011-16. Wessex 2004-11.

Club Colours (change): Red & white halves/red/white (Sky blue & navy)

RECORDS
Victory: 12-0 v Welton Rovers (H) Western League 26/04/1939.
Defeat: 1-12 v Boscombe (A) Hampshire League (West) 20/12/1913.
Additional: Transfer fee paid £5,000 for Nicky Dent 1990.
Transfer fee received reported as £180,000 for Charlie Austin from Swindon Town 2009.

HONOURS
FA Comps: None

League: Western 1956-57. Hampshire Division One 1999-00. Wessex Premier Division 2008-09, 09-10, 10-11. Southern Division One South & West 2012-13, Premier 2015-16.

County FA: Dorset Senior Cup 1894-95, 96-97, 98-99, 1901-02, 03-04, 06-07, 25-26, 26-27, 37-38, 46-47, 74-75, 88-89, 97-98, 2008-09, 12-13, 13-14.

BEST PERFORMANCES	**FA Cup:** Third Round Proper 1925-26.
	FA Trophy: First Round Proper 1969-70 (r), 70-71, 74-75, 87-88, 2014-15.
	FA Vase: Semi-final 2010-11.

POOLE TOWN MATCH RESULTS 2016-17

Date	Comp	H/A	Opponents	Att:	Result	Goalscorers	Pos	No.
Aug 6	Nat S	A	Ebbsfleet United	1031	L 0 - 4		22	1
9	Nat S	H	Maidenhead United	502	W 1 - 0	Gillespie 14	13	2
13	Nat S	H	Bishops Stortford	424	W 1 - 0	Gillespie 12	7	3
16	Nat S	A	Weston-s-Mare	510	D 0 - 0		9	4
20	Nat S	H	Margate	433	W 1 - 0	Granger 82	6	5
27	Nat S	A	Hemel Hempstead Town	347	W 4 - 2	Granger 36 Burbidge 44 Roberts 64 Case 83	4	6
29	Nat S	H	Bath City	797	W 1 - 0	Walker 90	4	7
Sept 3	Nat S	A	Wealdstone	1003	D 2 - 2	Devlin 42 (pen) Burbidge 90	3	8
6	Nat S	A	St Albans City	485	L 0 - 4		4	9
10	Nat S	H	Eastbourne Borough	395	D 1 - 1	Roberts 32	5	10
13	Nat S	A	Truro City	302	D 0 - 0		7	11
17	FAC2Q	A	**Chippenham Town**	436	L 1 - 4	**Wort 75**		12
24	Nat S	H	Welling United	418	W 2 - 1	Whisken 54 Surridge 90	5	13
Oct 8	Nat S	A	Hampton & Richmond Boro	934	W 2 - 0	Devlin 58 (pen) Surridge 76	5	14
15	Nat S	H	Oxford City	498	L 1 - 3	Surridge 67	5	15
22	Nat S	A	Hungerford Town	325	W 1 - 0	Brooks 90	4	16
29	Nat S	H	East Thurrock United	497	D 1 - 1	Roberts 43	7	17
Nov 5	Nat S	H	Chelmsford City	551	W 4 - 0	SURRIDGE 3 (24 45 66 pen) Brooks 55	5	18
12	Nat S	A	Concord Rangers	222	L 2 - 3	Spetch 52 Surridge 79	7	19
19	Nat S	H	Whitehawk	386	W 3 - 1	Burbidge 44 Brooks 47 Devlin 62	6	20
26	FAT3Q	H	**Weymouth**	755	D 1 - 1	**Lindsey 90**		21
29	FAT3Qr	A	**Weymouth**	441	L 0 - 2			22
Dec 3	Nat S	A	Dartford	886	L 1 - 2	Roberts 41	7	23
!7	Nat S	H	Wealdstone	663	D 1 - 1	Gillespie 47	7	24
26	Nat S	A	Gosport Borough	631	W 2 - 0	Devlin 16 Gillespie 71	7	25
Jan 1	Nat S	H	Gosport Borough	675	W 7 - 0	Brooks 40 80 Burbidge15 Gillespie 56 Roberts 63 Devlin 77 90	6	26
7	Nat S	A	Eastbourne Borough	598	D 0 - 0		6	27
14	Nat S	A	Margate	3534	W 2 - 0	Devlin 33 90 (pen)	3	28
28	Nat S	H	Ebbsfleet United	681	L 0 - 2		6	29
Feb 4	Nat S	A	Maidenhead United	1020	D 1 - 1	Brooks 78	7	30
7	Nat S	H	St Albans City	162	W 1 - 0	Brooks 68	5	31
11	Nat S	H	Weston-s-Mare	503	W 2 - 0	Brooks 46 Burbidge 90	5	32
18	Nat S	A	Bishops Stortford	363	W 4 - 1	Devlin 36 (pen) 47 (pen) Roberts 49 Brooks 89	4	33
25	Nat S	A	East Thurrock United	279	W 2 - 1	Devlin 39 (pen) Brooks 80	4	34
Mar 11	Nat S	A	Welling UNited	465	L 1 - 2	Devlin 84 (pen)	5	35
18	Nat S	H	Hampton & Richmond Boro	568	D 3 - 3	Baggie 1 Roberts 36 Brooks 82	5	36
21	Nat S	H	Truro City	528	W 2 - 0	Roberts 25 38	5	37
25	Nat S	A	Oxford City	310	W 1 - 0	Roberts 77	5	38
April 1	Nat S	H	Concord Rangers	737	W 2 - 1	Baggie 22 Spetch 53	5	39
4	Nat S	H	Hungerford Town	659	D 1 - 1	Devlin 25 (pen)	5	40
8	Nat S	A	Chelmsford City	876	L 0 - 3		5	41
15	Nat S	H	Hemel Hempstead Town	833	D 1 - 1	Burbidge 21	5	42
17	Nat S	A	Bath City	602	L 0 - 2		5	43
22	Nat S	A	Whitehawk	503	L 0 - 2		5	44
29	Nat S	H	Dartford	754	L 2 - 3	Brooks 25 Devlin 39	5	45

GOALSCORERS	SG	CSG	Pens	Hat tricks	Total		SG	CSG	Pens	Hat tricks	Total
2015-16 Brooks					17	Case	1				1
Devlin	10	3	7		14	Lindsey	1				1
Brooks	11	5			12	Walker	1				1
Roberts	9				10	Whisken	1				1
Surridge	5	3	1	1	7	Wort	1				1
Burbidge	6				6						
Gillespie	5	3			5						
Baggie	2				2						
Granger	2	2			2						
Spetch	2				2						

ST ALBANS CITY

Club Contact Details
Clarence Park, York Road, St. Albans, Herts AL1 4PL

01727 848 914

Ground Capacity: 5,007   **Seats:** 667   **Covered:** 1,900   **Clubhouse:** Yes   **Shop:** Yes

Record Attendance
9,757 v Ferryhill Athletic - FA Amateur Cup 1926

Previous Grounds
N/A

10 YEAR RECORD

07-08		08-09		09-10		10-11		11-12		12-13		13-14		14-15		15-16		16-17	
Conf S	19	Conf S	12	Conf S	13	Conf S	22	SthP	8	SthP	11	SthP	4	Conf S	13	Nat S	18	Nat S	10
FAC	2Q	FAC	2Qr	FAC	2Q	FAC	4Q	FAC	2Qr	FAC	3Q	FAC	1P	FAC	4Q	FAC	1P	FAC	1P
FAT	3Q	FAT	1P	FAT	3Q	FAT	1P	FAT	1Q	FAT	1Q	FAT	2P	FAT	3Qr	FAT	3Q	FAT	3Qr

Club Factfile

Founded: 1908   **Nickname:** The Saints   **Manager:** Ian Allinson

Previous Names: N/A

Previous Leagues: Herts County 1908-10. Spartan 1908-20. Athenian 1920-23. Isthmian 1923-2004. Conference 2004-11. Southern 2011-14.

Club Colours (change): Yellow/blue/white

RECORDS

Victory:	14-0 v Aylesbury United (H) - Spartan League 19/10/1912
Defeat:	0-11 v Wimbledon (H) - Isthmian League 1946
Goalscorer:	Wilfred Minter - 356 in 362 apps. (Top scorer for 12 consecutive seasons from 1920-32)
Appearances:	Phil Wood - 900 (1962-85)
Additional:	Wilfred Minter scored seven goals in an 8-7 defeat by Dulwich Hamlet, the highest tally by a player on the losing side of an FAC tie. Paid £6,000 to Yeovil Town for Paul Turner 1957. Received £92,759 from Southend United for Dean Austin 1990.

HONOURS

FA Comps: None

League: Herts County Western Division 1909-09, Western & Championship 09-10. Spartan B Division 1909-10, Spartan 11-12. Athenian League 1920-21, 21-22. Isthmian League 1923-24, 26-27, 27-28, Division One 1985-86.

County FA: London Senior Cup 1970-71.

BEST PERFORMANCES	**FA Cup:** Second Round Proper 1968-69 (r), 80-81 (r), 96-97.
	FA Trophy: Semi-final 1998-99.
	FA Vase: N/A

ST ALBANS CITY MATCH RESULTS 2016-17

Date	Comp	H/A	Opponents	Att:	Result	Goalscorers	Pos	No.
Aug 6	Nat S	H	Concord Rangers	606	W 2 - 0	Akinyemi 33 Morais 90	5	1
8	Nat S	A	Wealdstone	824	D 2 - 2	Morais 11 Theophanous 50	3	2
13	Nat S	A	Bath City	379	L 0 - 3		12	3
16	Nat S	H	Chelmsford City	561	W 2 - 1	Johnson 29 Martin 63	8	4
20	Nat S	A	Welling United	483	W 1 - 0	Morais 43 (pen)	5	5
27	Nat S	H	Whitehawk	503	W 3 - 1	Thepphanous 26 48 Meraon 87	3	6
29	Nat S	A	Weston-s-Mare	447	W 3 - 0	Ball 32 35 Theophanous 39	3	7
Sept 3	Nat S	H	Hampton & Richmond B	1008	L 2 - 4	Lucien 32 Theophanous 64	4	8
6	Nat S	H	Poole Town	485	W 4 - 0	Hill 3 THEOPHANOUS 3 (35 78 90)	3	9
10	Nat S	A	Maidenhead United	719	D 1 - 1	Lucien 80	3	10
13	Nat S	H	Hemel Hempstead Town	903	D 2 - 2	Theophanous 7 Morais 34	3	11
17	FAC2Q	A	**Dereham Town**	243	W 2 - 1	**Theophanous 65 Akinyemi 82**		12
24	Nat S	A	Ebbsfleet United	1039	L 1 - 3	Akinyemi 57	6	13
Oct 1	FAC3Q	H	**Worthing**	678	W 6 - 0	**Merson 6 32 LUCIEN 3 (48 51 88 pen) Theophanous 71**		14
8	Nat S	A	Gosport Borough	787	W 2 - 1	Merson 24 90	6	15
15	FAC4Q	A	**Egham Town**	327	W 1 - 0	**Merson 28**		16
22	Nat S	A	Bishops Stortford	424	W 5 - 1	Bender 61 Merson 62 Theophanous 65 82 Morais 90	5	17
29	Nat S	H	Truro City	720	W 5 - 0	Martin 11 Theophanous 49 69 Morais 80 90	4	18
Nov 5	FAC1	H	**Carlisle United**	3473	L 3 - 5	**Morias 4 65 Theophanus 86**		19
8	Nat S	A	Dartford	652	W 2 - 0	Merson 33 Bender 45	2	20
12	Nat S	H	Hungerford Town	702	W 5 - 0	Chappell 6 Morais 46 Theophanous 59 Akinyemi 62 Lucien 86	2	21
19	Nat S	A	East Thurrock United	315	D 1 - 1	Merson 75	2	22
26	FAT3Q	A	**Whitehawk**	326	D 1 - 1	**Theophanous 79**		23
29	FAT3Qr	H	**Whitehawk**	219	L 0 - 1			24
Dec 3	Nat S	H	Eastbourne Borough	678	W 1 - 0	Bender 43	2	25
10	Nat S	A	Margate	364	W 2 - 0	Johnson 53 Morais 89	2	26
!7	Nat S	A	Hampton & Richmond B	701	L 0 - 4		2	27
26	Nat S	H	Oxford City	1049	L 2 - 4	Cureton 27 34	2	28
Jan 1	Nat S	A	Oxford City	381	L 1 - 2	Cureton 52	3	29
7	Nat S	H	Maidenhead United	1111	D 2 - 2	Bender 72 Merson 90	4	30
14	Nat S	H	Hemel Hempstead Town	856	D 2 - 2	Cureton 70 Merson 90	5	31
28	Nat S	A	Concord Rangers	315	L 2 - 3	Lucien 68 Herd 90	8	32
31	Nat S	H	Welling United	397	W 3 - 2	Walker 17 20 Fish (og) 68	4	33
Feb 7	Nat S	A	Poole Town	462	L 0 - 1		7	34
11	Nat S	A	Chelmsford City	765	D 1 - 1	Theophanous 85	8	35
18	Nat S	H	Bath City	439	L 1 - 4	Walker 63	8	36
25	Nat S	A	Truro City	323	L 2 - 3	Bender 49 Walker 54	8	37
28	NatS	H	Wealdstone	563	L 0 3		8	38
Mar 4	Nat S	H	Bishops Stortford	602	L 0 - 1		8	39
11	Nat S	H	Ebbsfleet United	864	L 0 - 3		9	40
18	Nat S	A	Gosport Borough	315	L 0 - 4		11	41
25	Nat S	H	Dartford	753	W 1 - 0	Walker 58	10	42
April 1	Nat S	A	Hungerford Town	295	D 0 - 0		10	43
8	Nat S	H	Margate	611	D 1 - 1	Walker 90	10	44
15	Nat S	A	Whitehawk	301	D 1 - 1	Banton 28	10	45
17	Nat S	H	Weston-s-Mare	547	W 3 - 0	Walker 14 Lucien 18 Banton 31 (pen)	10	46
22	Nat S	H	East Thurrock United	641	D 2 - 2	Noble 20 90	10	47
28	Nat S	A	Eastbourne Borough	621	L 2 - 3	Merson 74 Lucien 76	10	48

GOALSCORERS	SG	CSG	Pens	Hat tricks	Total		SG	CSG	Pens	Hat tricks	Total
2015-16 Theophanous					19	Banton	2				2
Theophanous	14	4,3		1	19	Johnson	2				2
Merson	10	4,3			12	Martin	2				2
Morais	9	3	1		11	Noble	1				2
Lucien	7		1	1	9	Chappell	1				1
Walker	6				7	Herd	1				1
Bender	5				5	Hill	1				1
Akinyemi	4	2			4	Opponents	1				1
Cureton	3				4						
Ball	1				2						

TRURO CITY

Club Contact Details
Treyew Road, Truro, Cornwall TR1 2TH
01872 225 400
ianrennie@trurocityfc.net

Ground Capacity: 3,500 **Seats:** 1,675 **Covered:** Yes **Clubhouse:** Yes **Shop:** No

Record Attendance
1,400 v Aldershot - FA Vase
Previous Grounds
Truro School. Tolgarrick > mid-1900s

10 YEAR RECORD

07-08		08-09		09-10		10-11		11-12		12-13		13-14		14-15		15-16		16-17	
WestP	1	Sthsw	1	SthP	11	SthP	1	Conf S	14	Conf S	22	SthP	17	SthP	3	Nat S	4	Nat S	19
FAC	2Q	FAC	2Qr	FAC	3Qr	FAC	2Q	FAC	3Q	FAC	2Q	FAC	2Q	FAC	1Q	FAC	3Q	FAC	2Q
FAV	5P	FAT	1Qr	FAT	1Pr	FAT	3Q	FAT	1P	FAT	3Q	FAT	1Q	FAT	3Q	FAT	2Pr	FAT	1Pr

Club Factfile

Founded: 1889   **Nickname:** City, White Tigers, The Tinmen   **Manager:** Lee Hodges

Previous Names: N/A

Previous Leagues: Cornwall County. Plymouth & District >1951. South Western (FM) 1951-2006. Western 2006-08. Southern 2008-11, 13-15. Conference 2011-13.

Club Colours (change): All white (All orange)

RECORDS

Misc: 115 points & 185 goals, Western League Division One (42 games) 2006-07.
Became first British club to achieve five promotions in six seasons.

HONOURS

FA Comps: FA Vase 2006-07.

League: Plymouth & District 1936-37. South Western League 1960-61, 69-70, 92-93, 95-96, 97-98. Western Div. One 2006-07, Premier Division 07-08. Southern Division One South & West 2008-09, Premier Division 2010-11.

County FA: Cornwall Senior Cup 1894-95, 1901-02, 02-03, 10-11, 23-24, 26-27, 27-28, 37-38, 58-59, 66-67, 69-70, 94-95, 97-98, 2005-06, 06-07, 07-08.

BEST PERFORMANCES	**FA Cup:** Third Round Qualifying 2009-10 (r), 11-12.
	FA Trophy: Second Round Proper 2015-16 (r).
	FA Vase: Final 2006-07.

TRURO MATCH RESULTS 2016-17

Date	Comp	H/A	Opponents	Att:	Result	Goalscorers	Pos	No.
Aug 6	Nat S	H	Chelmsford City	502	D 2 - 2	Cooke 5 White 22	12	1
9	Nat S	A	Gosport Borough	482	L 1 - 3	Thompson 50 (pen)	17	2
13	Nat S	A	Concord Rangers	198	W 2 - 0	Neal 33 Pugh 38	10	3
16	Nat S	H	Bath City	486	L 1 - 3	Brett 87	14	4
20	Nat S	A	Hampton & Richmond B	419	D 2 - 2	Neal 7 Thompson 45	15	5
27	Nat S	H	Welling United	401	D 1 - 1	Cooke 53	15	6
29	Nat S	A	Maidenhead United	751	L 0 - 2		15	7
Sept 3	Nat S	H	East Thurrock United	261	L 0 - 6		19	8
6	Nat S	H	Hungerford Town	406	W 2 - 0	Cooke 12 Thompson 43	16	9
10	Nat S	A	Oxford City	214	D 1 - 1	Bentley 56	17	10
13	Nat S	H	Poole Town	302	D 0 - 0		16	11
17	FAC2Q	A	**Winchester City**	210	L 0 - 4			12
24	Nat S	A	Wealdstone	703	W 2 - 1	Thompson 72 Neal 85	14	13
Oct 8	Nat S	H	Dartford	464	L 0 - 5		17	14
15	Nat S	A	Whitehawk	246	L 0 - 3		17	15
22	Nat S	H	Eastbourne Borough	323	D 2 - 2	Rooney 58 Thompson 65	17	16
29	Nat S	A	St Albans City	720	L 0 - 5		17	17
Nov 5	Nat S	A	Ebbsfleet United	1020	L 2 - 4	Thompson 42 Neal 90	18	18
8	Nat S	A	Whitehawk	195	W 4 - 2	THOMPSON 3 (11 44 79) Afful 66	16	19
12	Nat S	H	Margate	369	W 2 - 0	Richards 50 Allen 57	15	20
19	Nat S	A	Hemel Hempstead Town	345	W 1 - 0	Sole 14	12	21
26	FAT3Q	H	**Frome Town**	269	W 6 - 1	Thompson 25 (pen) Bentley 27 84 Neal 49 (pen) Allen 52 57		22
Dec 3	Nat S	H	Bishops Stortford	246	L 1 - 2	Neal 31	14	23
10	FAT1	A	**Forest Green Rovers**	626	D 1 - 1	Neal 73		24
13	FAT1r	H	**Forest Green Rovers**	336	L 0 - 1	aet		25
!7	Nat S	A	East Thurrock United	242	L 1 - 5	Neal 26	16	26
26	Nat S	H	Weston-s-Mare	506	L 1 - 2	Neal 35	16	27
Jan 1	Nat S	A	Weston-s-Mare	549	D 2 - 4	Neal 4 Todd 83	16	28
7	Nat S	H	Oxford City	330	W 3 - 2	Brett 3 Neal 15 Smith 52	15	29
28	Nat S	A	Chelmsford City	925	L 0 - 2		17	30
Feb 4	Nat S	H	Gosport Borough	266	L 0 - 5		17	31
11 - 28	Nat S	A	Bath City	543	L 0 - 4		18	32
18	Nat S	H	Concord Rangers	419	L 1 - 2	Harvey 15	18	33
21	Nat S	H	Gosport Borough	319	W 2 - 0	Harvey 13 (pen) 37	17	34
25	Nat S	H	St Albans City	323	W 3 - 2	Yetton 28 Pugh 50 Harvey 78	15	35
Mar 4	Nat S	A	Eastbourne Borough	539	L 0 - 2		18	36
11	Nat S	H	Wealdstone	411	L 1 - 2	Richards 45	18	37
18	Nat S	A	Dartford	936	L 3 - 5	Neal 13 65 Richards 77	19	38
21	Nat S	A	Poole Town	528	L 0 - 2		19	39
25	Nat S	H	Whitehawk	483	W 4 - 2	Neal 27 52 Harvey 42 Cooke 66	17	40
April 1	Nat S	A	Margate	412	L 1 - 2	Neal 41	19	41
8	Nat S	H	Ebbsfleet United	501	D 1 - 1	Adelsbury 44	18	42
15	Nat S	A	Welling United	526	L 2 - 3	Martin 42 (og) Neal 48	19	43
17	Nat S	A	Maidenhead United	721	L 0 - 3		19	44
22	Nat S	H	Hemel Hempstead Town	431	W 2 1	Thompson 34 Neal 44	19	45
28	Nat S	A	Bishops Stortford	302	L 0 4		19	46

GOALSCORERS	SG	CSG	Pens	Hat tricks	Total		SG	CSG	Pens	Hat tricks	Total
2015-16 Vassell					*13*	Adelsbury	1				1
Neal	13	4			18	Afful	1				1
Thompson	9				11	Opponents	1				1
Harvey	4				5	Rooney	1				1
Cooke	4				4	Smith	1				1
Allen	2				3	Sole	1				1
Bentley	2				3	Todd	1				1
Richards	3				3	White	1				1
Brett	2				2	Yetton	1				1
Pugh	2				2						

WEALDSTONE

Club Contact Details
Grosvenor Vale, Ruislip, Middlesex HA4 6JQ
07790 038 095 / 01895 637 487 (Ground)
wealdstonefc@btconnect.com

Ground Capacity: 3,607 **Seats:** 329 **Covered:** 1,166 **Clubhouse:** Yes **Shop:** No

Record Attendance
13,504 v Leytonstone - FA Amateur Cup 4th Round replay 05/03/1949 (at Lower Mead Stadium)
Previous Grounds
Locket Road, Belmont Road, Lower Mead Stadium 1922-91, Watford FC, Yeading FC, Edgware Town, Northwood FC

10 YEAR RECORD

07-08		08-09		09-10		10-11		11-12		12-13		13-14		14-15		15-16		16-17	
Isth P	13	Isth P	7	Isth P	6	Isth P	12	Isth P	4	Isth P	3	Isth P	1	Conf S	12	Nat S	13	Nat S	8
FAC	4Q	FAC	1Qr	FAC	1P	FAC	3Qr	FAC	1Q	FAC	2Q	FAC	3Q	FAC	2Qr	FAC	1P	FAC	4Q
FAT	1P	FAT	2Q	FAT	3Q	FAT	1Pr	FAT	SF	FAT	3Qr	FAT	2Qr	FAT	2P	FAT	1P	FAT	3P

Club Factfile

Founded: 1899 **Nickname:** The Stones **Manager:** Gordon Bartlett

Previous Names: N/A

Previous Leagues: Willesden & District 1899-1906, 08-13, London 1911-22, Middlesex 1913-22, Spartan 1922-28, Athenian 1928-64, Isthmian 1964-71, 95-2006, 2007-14. Southern 1971-79, 81-82, 88-95. Conference 1979-81, 82-88

Club Colours (change): Blue/white/blue (White/blue/white)

RECORDS

Victory: 22-0 v The 12th London Regiment (The Rangers) - FA Amateur Cup 13/10/1923
Defeat: 0-14 v Edgware Town (A) - London Senior Cup 09/12/1944
Goalscorer: George Duck - 251
Appearances: Charlie Townsend - 514
Additional: Paid £15,000 to Barnet for David Gipp
Received £70,000 from Leeds United for Jermaine Beckford

HONOURS

FA Comps: FA Amateur Cup 1965-66. FA Trophy 1984-85.

League: Athenian 1951-52. Southern Division One South 1973-74, Southern Division 1981-82. Conference 1984-85. Isthmian Division Three 1996-97, Premier 2013-14.

County FA: Middlesex Junior Cup 1912-13. Senior 1929-30, 37-38, 40-41, 41-42, 42-43, 45-46, 58-59, 62-63, 63-64, 67-68, 84-85. Charity Cup 1929-30, 30-31, 37-38, 38-39, 49-50, 63-64, 68-68, 03-04, 10-11 Prem Cup 2003-04, 07-08, 08-09, 10-11. London Senior 1961-62.

BEST PERFORMANCES	**FA Cup:** Third Round Proper 1977-78.
	FA Trophy: Final 1984-85 (First club to achieve the Non-League double).
	FA Vase: Third Round Proper 1997-98.

WEALDSTONE MATCH RESULTS 2016-17

Date	Comp	H/A	Opponents	Att:	Result	Goalscorers	Pos	No.
Aug 6	Nat S	A	Dartford	1002	D 2 - 2	Benyon 53 Oshodi 90	13	1
8	Nat S	H	St Albans City	824	D 2 - 2	Benyon 13 Wellard 63	11	2
13	Nat S	H	Margate	689	W 2 - 1	Benyon 8 Koroma 30	9	3
16	Nat S	A	Oxford City	303	W 3 - 0	Green 47 Koroma 66 Benyon 71	6	4
20	Nat S	A	Whitehawk	354	D 0 - 0		8	5
27	Nat S	H	Hampton & Richmond Boro	667	L 2 - 4	Oshodi 23 Whichelow 83	10	6
29	Nat S	A	Bishop Stortford	465	W 3 - 0	Koroma 45 Green 60 Oshodi 84	7	7
Sept 3	Nat S	H	Poole Town	1003	D 2 - 2	Benyon 24 72	10	8
5	Nat S	H	Weston-s-Mare	626	W 1 - 0	Benyon 65	5	9
10	Nat S	A	Ebbsfleet United	965	L 1 - 4	Benyon 53	7	10
13	Nat S	A	Concord Rangers	241	W 1 - 0	Hamblin 56	6	11
17	FAC2Q	H	Histon	327	W 4 - 0	Benyon 16 65 Wellard 55 Hutchinson 90		12
24	Nat S	H	Truro City	703	L 1 - 2	Benyon 17	9	13
Oct 1	FAC3Q	H	Banbury United	457	W 2 - 1	Hamblin 11 Kabba 86		14
8	Nat S	A	Chelmsford City	1465	L 1 - 4	Wright 45	10	15
15	FAC4Q	A	Dagenham & Redbridge	1224	L 1 - 3	Whichelow 44		16
22	Nat S	A	Gosport Borough	487	W 3 - 1	Whichelow 14 Benyon 46 88	9	17
29	Nat S	H	Welling United	820	L 0 - 1		9	18
Nov 5	Nat S	A	Hemel Hempstead Town	665	W 3 - 1	BENYON 3 (56 89 90)	8	19
12	Nat S	H	Eastbourne Borough	651	L 1 - 4	Wright 38	9	20
15	Nat S	H	Bath City	638	L 0 - 1		9	21
19	Nat S	A	Hungerford Town	344	L 0 - 2		11	22
26	FAT3Q	A	Maidenhead United	555	D 2 - 2	Oshodi 31 Wright 68		23
29	FAT3Qr	H	Maidenhead United	254	W 2 - 1	Whichelow 59 Goulding 76		24
Dec 3	Nat S	H	East Thurrock United	602	W 1 - 0	Goulding 75	16	25
10	FAT1	H	Wingate & Finchley	364	D 2 - 2	Benyon 47(pen) Oshodi 81		26
13	FAT1r	A	Wingate & Finchlety	280	W 2 - 1	Benyon 83 Green 120 (aet)		27
!7	Nat S	A	Poole Town	663	D 1 - 1	Koroma 90	10	28
26	Nat S	H	Maidenhead United	1100	W 2 - 1	Benyon 41 Godfrey 79	10	29
Jan 1	Nat S	A	Maidenhead United	1282	L 0 - 2		10	30
7	Nat S	H	Ebbsfleet United	785	L 2 - 4	Powell 41 (og) Wright 48	11	31
14	FAT2	A	Southport	744	W 2 - 1	Graham 41 Wellard 71		32
28	Nat S	H	Dartford	611	L 0 - 4		13	33
Feb 4	FAT3	H	Brackley Town	620	L 1 - 4	Green 61		34
11	Nat S	H	Oxford City	511	D 1 - 1	Walker 4	13	35
13 -27	Nat S	H	Whitehawk	651	D 0 - 0		13	36
18	Nat S	A	Margate	547	W 1 - 0	Tajbakhsh 45	13	37
25	Nat S	A	Welling United	506	W 1 - 0	Wellard 62	13	38
28	Nat S	A	St Albans City	563	W 3 - 0	White 21 Hamblin 81 Green 88	13	39
Mar 4	Nat S	H	Gosport Borough	670	W 2 - 1	Wellard 31 Tajbakhsh 670	10	40
7	NatS	A	Weston-s-Mare	389	W 2 - 1	White 48 Godfrey 80	8	41
11	Nat S	A	Truro City	411	W 2 - 1	White 26 Hamblin 80	8	42
18	Nat S	H	Chelmsford City	841	D 1 - 1	White 69 (pen)	9	43
20	Nat S	H	Concord Rangers	646	D 1 - 1	Whichelow 83	8	44
25	Nat S	A	Bath City	1006	W 2 - 1	Green 34 White 71 (pen)	8	45
April 1	Nat S	A	Eastbourne Borough	691	L 1 - 5	Fitchett 39	8	46
8	Nat S	H	Hemel Hempstead Town	781	D 1 - 1	Green 89	8	47
15	Nat S	H	Hampton & Richmond Boro	834	D 1 - 1	Brown 50	8	48
17	Nat S	A	Bishops Stortford	620	W 5 - 0	Oshodi 2 Fitchett 5 Wright 56 Green 88 Benyon 89	8	49
22	Nat S	H	Hungerford Town	765	W 3 - 0	Fitchett 10 Day 15 (og) White 54	8	50
28	Nat S	A	East Thurrock United	497	D 1 - 1	White 43	8	51

GOALSCORERS	SG	CSG	Pens	Hat tricks	Total		SG	CSG	Pens	Hat tricks	Total
2015-16 Hudson-Odie					16	Fitchett	3				3
Benyon	15	4,3	1	1	20	Godfrey	2				2
Green	7				8	Goulding	2				2
White	7				7	Opponents	2				2
Oshodi	6	2			6	Tajbakhsh	2				2
Wellard	5	2			5	Brown	1				1
Whitchelow	5				5	Graham	1				1
Wright	5				5	Hutchinson	1				1
Hamblin	4				4	Kabba	1				1
Koroma	4	2			4	Walker	1				1

WELLING UNITED

Club Contact Details
Park View Road Ground, Welling, Kent DA16 1SY
0208 301 1196
info@wellingunited.com

Ground Capacity: 4,000 **Seats:** 1,070 **Covered:** 1,500 **Clubhouse:** Yes **Shop:** Yes

Record Attendance
4,100 v Gillingham - FA Cup First Round Proper, 22nd November 1989
Previous Grounds
Butterfly Lane, Eltham 1963-77.

10 YEAR RECORD

07-08		08-09		09-10		10-11		11-12		12-13		13-14		14-15		15-16		16-17	
Conf S	16	Conf S	7	Conf S	9	Conf S	6	Conf S	3	Conf S	1	Conf	16	Conf	20	Nat	24	Nat S	16
FAC	3Q	FAC	2Qr	FAC	3Q	FAC	2Q	FAC	2Q	FAC	4Q	FAC	2P	FAC	4Q	FAC	2P	FAC	4Q
FAT	3Q	FAT	2P	FAT	1P	FAT	1Pr	FAT	1P	FAT	3P	FAT	1P	FAT	1Pr	FAT	2P	FAT	3P

Club Factfile

Founded: 1963   **Nickname:** The Wings   **Manager:** Jamie Coyle

Previous Names: None

Previous Leagues: Eltham & District Sunday 1963-71, Metropolitan 1971-75, London Spartan 1975-78, Athenian 1978-81, Southern 1981-86, 2000-04, Conference 1986-2000

Club Colours (change): Red/red/white

RECORDS
Victory: 7-1 v Dorking - 1985-86
Defeat: 0-7 v Welwyn Garden City - 1972-73
Additional: Paid £30,000 to Enfield for Gary Abbott
Received £95,000 from Birmingham City for Steve Finnan 1995

HONOURS
FA Comps: None

League: Southern League Premier Division 1985-86. Conference South 2012-13.

County FA: Kent Senior Cup 1985-86, 98-99, 2008-09.
London Senior Cup 1989-90. London Challenge Cup 1991-92.

BEST PERFORMANCES
FA Cup: Third Round Proper 1988-89.
FA Trophy: Quarter-finals 1988-89, 2006-07.
FA Vase: Third Round Proper 1979-80.

WELLING UNITED MATCH RESULTS 2016-17

Date	Comp	H/A	Opponents	Att:	Result	Goalscorers	Pos	No.
Aug 6	Nat S	A	Oxford City	243	L 1 - 2	Waldren 22	14	1
8	Nat S	H	Bishops Stortford	502	L 1 - 2	Slabber 44	19	2
13	Nat S	H	Weston-s-Mare	458	L 0 - 2		21	3
16	Nat S	A	East Thurrock United	286	D 1 - 1	Joseph-Dubois	21	4
20	Nat S	H	St Albans City	483	L 0 - 1		21	5
27	Nat S	A	Truro City	401	D 1 - 1	Crawford 69	21	6
29	Nat S	H	Chelmsford City	705	L 0 - 2		21	7
Sept 3	Nat S	A	Concord Rangers	258	W 5 - 0	Delle-Verde 26 Joseph-Dubois 52 COOMBES 3 (61p 63 90)	20	8
6	Nat S	A	Dartford	1210	L 1 - 2	Coombes 35	21	9
10	Nat S	H	Hemel Hempstead United	401	L 2 - 3	Morgan 12 Coombes 26	22	10
13	Nat S	H	Eastbourne Borough	406	W 3 - 1	Joseph-Dubois 23 47 Walker 90	19	11
17	FAC2Q	A	Whyteleafe	231	W 2 - 0	Coombes 68 Hayles 90		12
24	Nat S	A	Poole Town	418	L 1 - 2	Morgan 16 (pen)	19	13
Oct 1	FAC3Q	H	Swindon Supermarine	325	W 7 - 1	COOMBES 6 (23 36 65 83pen 89 90) Joseph-Dubois 37		14
8	Nat S	H	Maidenhead United	600	L 1 - 2	Morgan 61	19	15
15	FAC4Q	H	Whitehawk	515	L 0 - 1			16
22	Nat S	H	Whitehawk	437	L 1 - 2	Coombes 22	21	17
29	Nat S	A	Wealdstone	820	W 1 - 0	Godrey (og) 90		18
Nov 5	Nat S	A	Gosport Borough	447	D 1 - 1	Coombes 11	19	19
12	Nat S	H	Ebbsfleet United	1014	L 1 - 2	Waldren 70	20	20
14	Nat S	A	Hungerford Town	238	L 0 - 1		20	21
19	Nat S	A	Hampton & Richmond Boro	587	L 1 - 3	Coombes 79 (pen)	21	22
26	FAT3Q	A	Concord Rangers	161	W 1 - 0	Oakley 83		23
Dec 3	Nat S	H	Bath City	466	W 3 - 1	Coombes 8 67 (pen) Crawford 77	20	24
10	FAT1	H	Hythe Town	355	W 8 - 1	Coombes 18 (pen) 42 Johnson 35 Waldren 38 52		25
						Fish 82 Williams 87 Oakley 90		
!7	Nat S	H	Concord Rangers	402	W 3 - 1	COOMBES 3 (23 pen 49 71)	19	26
26	Nat S	A	Margate	588	W 3 - 0	Coombes 43 (pen) 86 Nanetti 59	18	27
Jan 1	Nat S	H	Margate	626	W 5 - 1	Crawford 17 Francis 25 55 Oakley 31 Coombes 65	15	28
7	Nat S	A	Hemel Hempstead Town	463	L 0 - 2		17	29
14	FAT2	A	Bromley	519	W 2 - 1	Waldren 31 Coombes 83		30
28	Nat S	H	Oxford City	541	W 4 - 0	Joseph-Dubois 55 Waildren 58 Crawford 75 Coombes 8116		31
31	Nat S	A	St Albans City	397	L 2 - 3	Nanetti 41 Coombes 90	16	32
Feb 4	FAT3	H	Lincoln City	743	L 1 - 3	Waldren 60		33
11-27	Nat S	H	East Thurrock United	424	W 2 - 0	Coombes 66 Walker 67	15	34
18	Nat S	H	Weston-s-Mare	502	D 2 - 2	Coombes 45 Crawford 59	16	35
21	Nat S	A	Bishops Stortford	266	D 2 - 2	Karagiannis 13 Hatton 88	15	36
25	Nat S	H	Wealdstone	506	L 0 - 1		16	37
28	Nat S	H	Dartford	909	D 0 - 0		16	38
Mar 4	Nat S	A	Whitehawk	370	L 0 - 1		16	39
11	Nat S	H	Poole Town	485	W 2 - 1	Hastings 6 (og) Crawford 24 (pen)	15	40
18	Nat S	A	Maidenhead United	968	L 0 - 3		15	41
21	Nat S	A	Eastbourne Borough	402	L 3 - 7	Walker 20 Waldren 41 Joseph-Dubois 62	15	42
25	Nat S	H	Hungerford Town	517	D 0 - 0		16	43
April 1	Nat S	A	Ebbsfleet United	1767	L 1 - 5	Walker 7	16	44
8	Nat S	H	Gosport Borough	450	W 4 - 0	Joseph-Dubois 46 53 Cathline 60 68	15	45
15	Nat S	H	Truro City	526	W 3 - 2	Martin 32 Murrell-Williamson 71 Marsh 76	15	46
17	Nat S	A	Chelmsford City	967	L 1 - 3	Hayles 26	15	47
22	Nat S	H	Hampton & Richmond Boro	500	L 1 - 2	Murrell-Williamson 88	15	48
28	Nat S	A	Bath City	710	L 1 - 2	Hatton 78	16	49

GOALSCORERS	SG	CSG	Pens	Hat tricks	Total		SG	CSG	Pens	Hat tricks	Total
2015-16 Vidal					8	Hayles	2				2
Coombes	18	5	7	4	30	Murrell-Williamson	2				2
Joseph-Dubois	7				9	Nanetti	2				2
Waldren	6				8	Opponents	2				2
Crawford	6		1		6	Delle-Verde	1				1
Walker	4				4	Fish	1				1
Morgan	3		1		3	Johnson	1				1
Oakley	3				3	Kariagannis	1				1
Cathline	1				2	Marsh	1				1
Francis	2				2	Martin	1				1
Hatton	2				2	Slabber	1				1
						Williams	1				1

WESTON-SUPER-MARE

Club Contact Details
Woodspring Stadium, Winterstoke Road, Weston-super-Mare BS24 9AA
01934 621 618
enquiries@wsmafc.co.uk

Ground Capacity: 3,500   **Seats:** 350   **Covered:** 2,000   **Clubhouse:** Yes   **Shop:** Yes

Record Attendance
2,949 v Doncaster Rovers, FA Cup First Round Proper, 18th November 2014.

Previous Grounds
'Great Ground' Locking Road >1955. Langford Road 1955-83. Woodspring Park 1983-2004.

10 YEAR RECORD

07-08	08-09	09-10	10-11	11-12	12-13	13-14	14-15	15-16	16-17
Conf S 20	Conf S 17	Conf S 21	Conf S 12	Conf S 13	Conf S 7	Conf S 11	Conf S 17	Nat S 16	Nat S 15
FAC 3Q	FAC 2Q	FAC 2Q	FAC 3Q	FAC 4Q	FAC 3Qr	FAC 3Q	FAC 1P	FAC 4Q	FAC 2Q
FAT 3Q	FAT 3Q	FAT 3Qr	FAT 3Q	FAT 3Q	FAT 3Q	FAT 1Pr	FAT 1P	FAT 2P	FAT 3Q

Club Factfile

Founded: 1887   **Nickname:** Seagulls   **Manager:** Marc McGregor - July 2017

Previous Names: Borough or Weston-super-Mare

Previous Leagues: Western League 1900-02, 10-18, 48-92. Bristol & District and Somerset County 1921-45. Southern 1992-04.

Club Colours (change): White with black trim

RECORDS
Victory: 11-0 v Paulton Rovers
Defeat: 1-12 v Yeovil Town Reserves
Goalscorer: Matt Lazenby - 180
Appearances: Harry Thomas - 740
Additional: Received £20,000 from Sheffield Wednesday for Stuart Jones

HONOURS
FA Comps: None

League: Western League 1991-92.

County FA: Somerset Senior Cup 1926-67.
Somerset Premier Cup 2010-11, 11-12.

BEST PERFORMANCES
FA Cup: Second Round Proper 2003-04.
FA Trophy: Fourth Round Proper 1998-99, 2003-04.
FA Vase: N/A

WESTON-SUPER-MARE MATCH RESULTS 2016-17

Date	Comp	H/A	Opponents	Att:	Result	Goalscorers	Pos	No.
Aug 6	Nat S	H	Whitehawk	236	W 3 - 1	Mawford 45 Hamilton 47 (og) McCousky 66	4	1
9	Nat S	A	Bath City	693	W 2 - 1	McCoulsky 12 31	2	2
13	Nat S	A	Welling United	458	W 2 - 0	Grubb 15 McCoulsky 44	1	3
16	Nat S	H	Poole Town	510	D 0 - 0		1	4
20	Nat S	H	Dartford	410	L 1 - 2	McCoulsky 78 (pen)	3	5
27	Nat S	A	Margate	403	L 1 - 3	McCoulsky 73	8	6
29	Nat S	H	St Albans City	447	D 0 - 3		11	7
Sept 3	Nat S	A	Chelmsford City	747	L 0 - 1		14	8
5	Nat S	A	Wealdstone	626	L 0 - 1		14	9
10	Nat S	A	Concord Rangers	340	L 1 - 3	McCoulsky 47	16	10
13	Nat S	H	Hungerford Town	336	L 0 - 1		17	11
17	FAC2Q	A	North Leigh	175	L 1 - 2	Richards 66		12
24	Nat S	A	Maidenhead United	632	L 0 - 3		18	13
Oct 8	Nat S	H	Ebbsfleet United	423	L 0 - 2		18	14
15	Nat S	A	East Thurrock United	242	L 1 - 5	Grubb 45	19	15
22	Nat S	A	Oxford City	272	D 0 - 0		19	16
29	Nat S	H	Hampton & Richmond Boro	312	L 1 - 3	Ash 43 (pen)	20	17
Nov 5	Nat S	A	Bishops Stortford	288	L 1 - 2	Ash 77	21	18
12	Nat S	H	Gosport Borough	425	D 1 - 1	Cane 65	21	19
19	Nat S	A	Eastbourne Borough	315	W 4 - 3	Baldwin 23 Grubb 39 74 Moran 52		20
26	FAT3Q	H	Dartford	240	L 2 - 4	Ash 12 (pen) 26		21
Dec 3	Nat S	H	Hemel Hempstead Town	356	L 3 - 5	Ash 75 90 Saunders 90 (og)	21	22
!7	Nat S	H	Chelmsford City	414	D 0 - 0		20	23
26	Nat S	A	Truro City	506	W 2 - 1	Ash 45 Hill 56	20	24
Jan 1	Nat S	H	Truro City	549	W 4 - 2	GRUBB 3 (21 50 88) Chamberlain 58	20	25
7	Nat S	A	Concord Rangers	231	W 3 - 1	Ash 9 Chamberlain 26 Hill 43	16	26
17	Nat S	A	Dartford	538	L 2 - 3	Hill 11 Humphries 71	16	27
28	Nat S	A	Whitehawk	298	W 2 - 0	Ash 70 Grubb 81	15	28
11-27	Nat S	A	Poole Town	503	L 0 - 2		17	29
18	Nat S	H	Welling United	502	D 2 - 2	Grubb 55 72	17	30
25	Nat S	A	Hampton & Richmond Boro	505	W 2 - 0	Lee 10 Ash 86	17	31
Mar 4	Nat S	H	Oxford City	436	W 3 - 0	Grubb 20 Ash 32 76	15	32
7	Nat S	H	Wealdstone	389	L 1 - 2	Grubb 32	15	33
11	Nat S	H	Maidenhead United	452	L 1 - 3	Cane 62	16	34
14	Nat S	H	Bath City	594	L 1 - 2	Baldwin 7	16	35
18	Nat S	H	Ebbsfleet United	1325	L 1 - 2	Grubb 53	16	36
20	Nat S	A	Hungerford Town	296	L 1 - 2	Ash 8	16	37
25	Nat S	H	East Thurrock United	433	L 1 - 3	Ash 90	18	38
April 1	Nat S	A	Gosport Borough	384	D 1 - 1	Grubb 32	17	39
8	Nat S	H	Bishops Stortford	382	W 5 - 0	GRUBB 4 (8 12 30 48) Reid 78	16	40
15	Nat S	H	Margate	740	W 3 - 1	Grubb 3 Ash 25 35	15	41
17	Nat S	A	St Albans City	547	L 0 - 3		15	42
22	Nat S	H	Eastbourne Borough	431	W 2 - 0	Reid 16 Grubb 48	15	43
28	Nat S	A	Hemel Hempstead Town	578	W 5 - 0	Greenslade 42 Kington 62 Ash 64 67 Cane 78	15	44

GOALSCORERS	SG	CSG	Pens	Hat tricks	Total		SG	CSG	Pens	Hat tricks	Total
2015-16 Wilson					23	Humphries	1				1
Grubb	13	3		2	20	Kington	1				1
Ash	13	2	2		18	Lee	1				1
McCoulsky	6	3	1		7	Mawford	1				1
Cane	3				3	Moran	1				1
Hill	3				3	Oponents	1				1
Baldwin	2				2	Richards	1				1
Chamberlain	2				2						
Reid	2				2						
Greenslade	1				1						

WHITEHAWK

Club Contact Details
The Enclosed Ground, East Brighton Park, Wilson Avenue, Brighton BN2 5TS
01273 609 736

Ground Capacity: 3,000   **Seats:** 800   **Covered:** Yes   **Clubhouse:** Yes   **Shop:** No

Record Attendance
2,174 v Dagenham & Redbridge, FA Cup Second Round Proper replay, 6th December 2015.
Previous Grounds
N/A

10 YEAR RECORD

07-08		08-09		09-10		10-11		11-12		12-13		13-14		14-15		15-16		16-17	
SxC1	2	SxC1	13	SxC1	1	Isth1S	3	Isth1S	1	Isth P	1	Conf S	19	Conf S	4	Nat S	5	Nat S	17
FAC	EP	FAC	EPr	FAC	EP	FAC	3Q	FAC	2Qr	FAC	2Qr	FAC	2Q	FAC	3Qr	FAC	2Pr	FAC	1Pr
FAV	2P	FAV	2P	FAV	SF	FAT	1Q	FAT	1Q	FAT	3Q	FAT	2Pr	FAT	3Q	FAT	1P	FAT	2P

Club Factfile

Founded: 1945   **Nickname:** Hawks   **Manager:** Jimmy Dack

Previous Names: Whitehawk & Manor Farm Old Boys untill 1960.

Previous Leagues: Brighton & Hove District >1952. Sussex County 1952-2010. Isthmian 2010-13.

Club Colours (change): All red (All blue)

RECORDS
Goalscorer: Billy Ford
Appearances: Ken Powell - 1,103

HONOURS

FA Comps: None

League: Sussex County League Division One 1961-62, 63-64, 83-84, 2009-10, Division Two 1967-68, 80-81.
Isthmian League Division One South 2011-12, Premier Division 2012-13.

County FA: Sussex Senior Cup 1950-51, 61-62, 2011-12, 14-15. Sussex RUR Charity Cup 1954-55, 58-59, 90-91.

BEST PERFORMANCES	**FA Cup:** Second Round Proper 2015-169(r)
	FA Trophy: Second Round Proper 2013-14(r)
	FA Vase: Semi-finals 2009-10.

WHITEHAWK MATCH RESULTS 2016-17

Date	Comp	H/A	Opponents	Att:	Result	Goalscorers	Pos	No.
Aug 6	Nat S	A	Weston-s-Mare	236	L 1 - 3	Pope 16 (og)	18	1
10	Nat S	H	Dartford	322	W 1 - 0	Abdulla 4 (pen)	12	2
13	Nat S	H	Maidenhead United	293	L 1 - 2	Mills 7	17	3
16	Nat S	A	Ebbsfleet United	933	D 1 - 1	West 84	15	4
20	Nat S	H	Wealdstone	354	D 0 - 0		16	5
27	Nat S	A	St Albans City	503	L 1 - 3	Torres 76	18	6
29	Nat S	H	Concord Rangers	291	D 0 - 0		16	7
Sept 3	Nat S	A	Bath City	535	L 1 - 2	Lienga 53	17	8
10	Nat S	H	Chelmsford City	289	L 0 - 1		20	9
13	Nat S	A	Hampton & Richmond Boro	404	W 2 - 0	Mills 26 West 87	18	10
17	FAC2Q	H	East Thurrock United	223	W 3 - 2	Connolly 25 67 Masterton 69		11
24	Nat S	H	Oxford City	315	W 3 - 0	Mills 41 55 Connolly 53	17	12
27	NatS	A	Hemel Hempstead Town	326	L 0 - 2		17	13
Oct 1	FAC3Q	H	Merthyr Town	292	W 2 - 0	Connolly 57 Torres 90		14
8	Nat S	A	Bishops Stortford	300	W 3 - 0	MILLS 3 (3 38 40)	16	15
15	FAC4Q	A	Welling United	515	W 1 - 0	Connolly 4		16
22	Nat S	A	Welling United	437	W 2 - 1	Abdulla 20 (pen) Mills 84	12	17
29	Nat S	H	Margate	319	W 2 - 0	Assombalonga 11 Sessegnon (og) 20	11	18
Nov 5	FAC1	H	Stourbridge	727	D 1 - 1	Southam 12		19
8	Nat S	H	Truro City	195	L 2 - 4	Reid 76 Connolly 86	13	20
12	Nat S	H	East Thurrock United	298	L 2 - 3	Abdulla 45 Mills 79	14	21
14	FAC1r	A	Stourbridge	1993	L 0 - 3			22
19	Nat S	A	Poole Town	386	L 1 - 3	Hamilton 78	15	23
26	FAT3Q	H	St Albans City	326	D 1 - 1	Tagbom 90		24
29	FAT3Qr	A	St Albans City	219	W 1 - 0	Mills 49		25
Dec 3	Nat S	H	Gosport Borough	254	D 4 - 4	West 32 Abdulla 48 Southam 60 Reid 69	16	26
10	FAT1	H	Weymouth	253	D 2 - 2	West 12 Mills 82		27
13	FAT1r	H	Weymouth	401	W 2 - 1	Marimon 49 Harding 80		28
!7	Nat S	H	Bath City	290	L 0 - 2		17	29
26	Nat S	A	Eastbourne Borough	708	L 2 - 4	Hamilton 32 Harding 49	17	30
Jan 7	Nat S	A	Chelmsford City	793	L 0 - 1		19	31
14	FAT2	H	Dulwich Hamlet	530	L 1 - 1	West 40		32
24	Nat S	A	Hungerford Town	192	L 1 - 3	Mills 68	20	33
28	Nat S	H	Weston-s-Mare	298	L 0 - 2		20	34
Feb 4	Nat S	A	Dartford	875	L 1 - 3	Southam 58 (pen)	20	35
7	Nat S	H	Eastbourne Borough	324	D 1 - 1	Akanbi 84	20	36
11	Nat S	H	Ebbsfleet United	349	L 0 - 3		20	37
13	Nat S	A	Wealdstone	651	D 0 - 0		20	38
18	Nat S	A	Maidenhead United	969	L 1 - 2	Mills 77	20	39
25	Nat S	A	Margate	504	W 2 - 0	Passley 56 Southam 57	19	40
Mar 1	Nat S	H	Hemel Hempstead Town	154	L 1 - 4	Passley 73	19	41
4	Nat S	H	Welling United	370	W 1 - 0	Sutherland 84	19	42
11	Nat S	A	Oxford City	452	L 0 - 1		19	43
18	Nat S	H	Bishop's Stortford Town	226	W 1 - 0	Southam 68 (pen)	18	44
22	Nat S	H	Hampton & Richmond Boro	212	L 1 - 3	Mills 76	18	45
25	Nat S	A	Truro City	483	L 2 - 4	Gerring 28 (og) Mills 90	19	46
April 1	Nat S	A	East Thurrock United	225	W 3 - 2	Woods-Garness 33 Osborn 51 Mills 82	18	47
8	Nat S	H	Hungerford Town	282	L 1 2	Mills 66	19	48
15	Nat S	H	St Albans City	301	D 1 - 1	Southam 90	18	49
17	Nat S	A	Concord Rangers	241	L 0 - 3		18	50
22	Nat S	H	Poole Town	503	W 2 - 0	Sutherland 14 Osborn 67	18	51
29	Nat S	A	Gosport Borough	395	W 3 - 2	Mills 50 West 62 Sutherland 90 (pen)	17	52

GOALSCORERS	SG	CSG	Pens	Hat tricks	Total		SG	CSG	Pens	Hat tricks	Total
2015-16 Mills					*33*	Passley	2				2
Mills	15	4		1	18	Reid	2				2
Connolly	6	3			6	Torres	2				2
Southam	6		2		6	Akanbi	1				1
West	6				6	Assombalonga	1				1
Abdulla	4		2		4	Llenga	1				1
Opponents	3				3	Marimon	1				1
Sutherland	3		1		3	Masterton	1				1
Hamilton	2				2	Tagbom	1				1
Harding	2				2	Woods-Garness	1				1
Osborn	2				2						

National North Statistics 2016-17

TOP SCORING CLUBS

AFC Fyde	113
Brackley Town	101
FC Halifax Town	100
Kidderminster Harriers	100

MOST GAMES WITHOUT SCORING

Bradford Park Avenue	19 (3)
Worcester City	19 (2)
Stalybridge Celtic	17 (3)

MOST SCORERS

Stalybridge Celtic	24+1og
Boston United	21+2ogs
Kidderminster Harriers	18+3ogs

MOST CONSECUTIVE SCORING GAMES

Darlington 1883	25
Alfreton Town	17
Gloucester City	17

MOST CLEAN SHEETS

Kidderminster Harriers	22 (3)
Chorley	21 (3)
Stockport County	20 (4)

	GT	GWS(1)	TNoS	MCSG	TCS(2)
AFC Fylde	113	6 (1)	14+2og	10	7 (1)
AFC Telford Utd	41	14 (2)	18+1og	5	14 (2)
Alfreton Town	78	14 (5)	16	17	11 (1)
Altrincham	56	16 (2)	17+1 og	8	5 (2)
Boston United	58	14 (2)	21+2og	12	10 (3)
Brackley Town	101	11 (2)	17+1og	13	18 (3)
Bradford PA	46	19 (3)	17	4	5 (3)
Chorley	65	10 (2)	15	11	21 (3)
Curzon Ashton	80	8 (2)	17+2ogs	16	12 (3)
Darlington 1883	94	2 (1)	17+1og	25	7 (2)
FC Halifax Town	100	10 (2)	16+2og	12	18 (3)
FC Utd of Manchester	80	10 (2)	17+1og	12	10 (2)
Gainsborough T	54	12 (4)	14+1og	15	5 (2)
Gloucester City	75	7 (2)	15+1og	17	11 (3)
Harrogate Town	90	11 (2)	18+1og	9	11 (3)
Kidderminster H.	100	12 (2)	18+3og	7	22 (3)
Nuneaton Town	82	9 (4)	15+1og	14	2 (1)
Salford City	83	7 (1)	16+3ogs	11	18 (4)
Stalybridge Celtic	48	17 (3)	24 +1 og	6	7 (1)
Stockport County	73	9 (2)	19	13	20 (4)
Tamworth	75	12 (2)	18	9	8 (2)
Worcester City	50	19 (2)	12	4	11(3)

(1) - Most consecutive goalless games in brackets.

(2) - Most consecutive clean sheets in brackets.

GT - Goals Total

GWS - Games Without Scoring

TNoS - Total Number of Scorers

MCSG - Most Consecutive Scoring Games

TCS - Total Clean Sheets

Strikers with ten or more goals - 2016-17

LEAGUE, FA CUP AND FA TROPHY GOALS ONLY.

					PTG	CTG	FLP
Darlington 1993	Beck	19	Galbraith	12	51	94	5
	Thompson	10	Gillies	10			
FC Halifax Town	Denton	19	Peniket	13	54	100	3
	Kosyte	12	Sinnott	10			
Brackley Town	Armson	25	Diggin	16	53	102	7
	Ndlovu	12					
Curzon Ashton	Cummins	17	Warburton	13	40	80	14
	Hall	10					
Gloucester City	Hopper	20	Kotewica	13	43	75	10
	Hanks	10					
Kidderminster Harriers	Gnahoua	15	Brown	13	38	100	2
	Truslove	10					
Salford City	Phenix	15	Hulme	10	35	83	4
	Nottingham	10					
AFC Fylde	Rowe	50	Bradley	11	61	113	1
Alfreton Town	Westcarr	18	Hearn	11	29	78	18
FC Utd of Manchester	Thomson	17	Gilchrist	11	28	80	13
Harrogate Town	Ainge	23	Pitman	14	37	90	11
Nuneaton Town	Ironside	18	Nicholson	17	35	82	12
Tamworth	Newton	29	Dyer	11	40	75	9
Altrincham	Miller	10			10	56	22
Boston United	Rollins	12			12	58	15
Chorley	Walker	14			14	65	6
Gainsborough Trinity	Worsfold	12			12	54	19
Stockport County	Lloyd	29			29	73	8
Worcester City	L.Hughes	13			13	50	20

PTG - Players Total Goals I CTG - Club's Total Goals I FLP - Final League Position

National South Statistics 2016-17

TOP SCORING CLUBS

Club	
Ebbsfleet United	119
Dartford	103
Chelmsford City	96
Maidenhead United	96

MOST GAMES WITHOUT SCORING

Club	
Margate	26 (9)
Bishop's Stortford	24 (9)
Gosport Borough	16 (4)

MOST SCORERS

Club	
Hemel Hempstead Town	22+2ogs
Welling United	21+2ogs
Whitehawk	19+3ogs

MOST CONSECUTIVE SCORING GAMES

Club	
Ebbsfleet United	22
St Albans City	20
East Thurrock United & Eastbourne Borough	16

MOST CLEAN SHEETS

Club	
Ebbsfleet United	22 (5)
Maidenhead United	20 (5)
Chelmsford City / Dartford	17 (3) / 17 (4)

	GT	GWS(1)	TNoS	MCSG	TCS(2)
Bath City	77	9 (2)	17+2ogs	9	12 (3)
Bishop's Stortford	32	24 (9)	20+1og	4	6 (1)
Chelmsford City	96	8 (1)	17+2ogs	8	17 (3)
Concord Rangers	58	15 (4)	15+2ogs	9	5 (1)
Dartford	103	12 (1)	17+2ogs	11	17 (4)
East Thurrock United	85	6 (1)	19	16	7 (1)
Eastbourne Borough	86	8 (1)	19	16	12 (2)
Ebbsfleet United	119	3 (1)	15+2ogs	22	22 (5)
Gosport Borough	49	16 (4)	14	8	6 (1)
Hampton & Richmond B	91	8 (2)	16+1og	10	9 (1)
Hemel Hempstead T	85	13 (2)	22+2ogs	10	9 (2)
Hungerford Town	69	12 (2)	15+1og	11	15 (3)
Maidenhead United	96	5 (1)	12	15	20 (5)
Margate	34	26 (9)	16+1og	5	5 (2)
Oxford City	51	15 (3)	17	5	10 (3)
Poole Town	65	10 (2)	14	11	17 (4)
St Albans City	85	9 (4)	16+1og	20	14 (2)
Truro City	60	15 (3)	17+1og	7	6 (2)
Wealdstone	80	7 (2)	18+2ogs	15	13 (4)
Welling United	85	11(3)	21+2ogs	8	10 (1)
Weston-s-Mare	66	11(3)	15+2ogs	12	10 (2)
Whitehawk	65	12 (2)	19+3ogs	8	15 (3)

(1) - Most consecutive goalless games in brackets.
(2) - Most consecutive clean sheets in brackets.
GT - Goals Total
GWS - Games Without Scoring
TNoS - Total Number of Scorers
MCSG - Most Consecutive Scoring Games
TCS - Total Clean Sheets

Strikers with ten or more goals - 2016-17

LEAGUE, FA CUP AND FA TROPHY GOALS ONLY.

Club	Player		Player		PTG	CTG	FLP
Ebbsfleet United	McQueen	18	Bubb	16	72	117	2
	Kedwell	13	Powell	13			
	Cook	12					
Eastbourne Borough	Romain	20	Pinney	17	60	86	11
	Taylor	12	Hughes	11			
Dartford	Bradbrook, E	24	Pugh	17	54	102	3
	Wanadio	13					
East Thurrock United	Wraight	20	Harris	12	4	85	13
	Higgins	12					
Hampton & Richmond	Kabamba	19	Lowe	18	55	91	7
	Kiernan	18					
Maidenhead United	Tarpey	44	Marks	16	71	96	1
	Pritcharad	11					
Poole Town	Devlin	14	Brooks	12	36	65	5
	Roberts	10					
St Albans City	Theophanous	19	Merson	12	42	85	10
	Morais	11					
Bath City	Watkins	11			11	77	9
Chelmsford City	Jeffers	22	Mullings	15	37	94	4
Concorde Rangers	Cawley	19	Chiedozi	12	27	58	18
Hemel Hempstead T	Robinson	26	Parkes	13	29	85	12
Hungerford Town	Brown	12	Jarvis	11	23	69	6
Truro City	Neal	16	Thompson	11	27	60	18
Weston-s-Mare	Grubb	20	Ash	18	38	66	15
Gosport Borough	Wright	10			10	49	20
Wealdstone	Benyon	20			20	80	8
Welling United	Coombes	30			30	85	16
Whitehawk	Mills	18			18	65	17

PTG - Players Total Goals | CTG - Club's Total Goals | FLP - Final League Position

	Best unbeaten Run				Worst Consecutive run without a victory		
	Won	Drawn	Total		Lost	Drawn	Total
AFC Sudbury	4	3	7		6	3	9
Billericay Town	7	1	8		6	3	9
Bognor Regis Town	7	4	11		1	2	3
Burgess Hill Town	5	5	10		5	2	7
Canvey Island	5	0	5		4	3	7
Dulwich Hamlet	6	4	10		1	2	3
Enfield Town	7	1	8		2	3	5
Folkestone Invicta	3	1	4		3	2	5
Grays Atheltic	3	0	3		9	2	11
Harlow Town	8	2	10		2	2	4
Harrow Borough	4	2	6		6	3	9
Havant & Waterlooville	9	1	10		0	3	3
Hendon	4	3	7		7	2	9
Kingstonian	5	1	6		9	2	11
Leatherhead	3	0	3		5	4	9
Leiston	12	3	15		6	1	7
Lowestoft Town	5	1	6		4	1	5
Merstham	6	1	7		3	3	6
Metropolitan Police	4	2	6		5	1	6
Needham Market	6	2	8		4	2	6
Staines Town	5	6	11		4	3	7
Tonbridge Angels	8	3	11		4	5	9
Wingate & Finchley	6	4	10		3	5	8
Worthing	8	4	12		7	1	8

	Best Attendance	Opponents	Competition
AFC Sudbury	505	Macclesfield Town	FAT2Q
Billericay Town	1,970	Canvey Island	League
Bognor Regis Town	3,119	Dulwich Hamlet	League
Burgess Hill Town	629	Dover Athletic	League
Canvey Island	571	Billericay Town	League
Dulwich Hamlet	2,834	Macclesfield Town	FAT Q-F
Enfield Town	687	Bognor Regis Town	League
Folkestone Invicta	593	Tonbridge Angels	League
Grays Atheltic	380	Harrow Borough	League
Harlow Town	816	York City	FAT2
Harrow Borough	711	Dulwich Hamlet	League
Havant & Waterlooville	**3,455**	Bognor Regis Town	League
Hendon	420	Stsines Town	League
Kingstonian	1,205	Havant & Water'ville	League
Leatherhead	505	Billericay Town	League
Leiston	513	Lowestoft Town	League
Lowestoft Town	580	AFC Sudbury	League
Merstham	1,920	Oxford United	FACup1
Metropolitan Police	300	Bognor Regis Town	League
Needham Market	573	Leiston	League
Staines Town	414	Maidenhead United	FAC2Q
Tonbridge Angels	1,391	Dartford	FAC4Q
Wingate & Finchley	440	Dulwich Hamlet	League
Worthing	1,781	Bognor Regis Town	League
Average	909		

ISTHMIAN PREMIER LEAGUE TABLE 2016-17

		P	W	D	L	F	A	GD	Pts
1	Havant & Waterlooville	46	28	10	8	88	43	45	94
2	Bognor Regis Town	46	27	11	8	87	41	46	92
3	Dulwich Hamlet	46	22	14	10	89	55	34	80
4	Enfield Town	46	21	13	12	86	57	29	76
5	Wingate & Finchley	46	23	6	17	63	61	2	75
6	Tonbridge Angels	46	21	11	14	66	55	11	74
7	Leiston	46	21	10	15	98	66	32	73
8	Billericay Town	46	21	9	16	77	56	21	72
9	Needham Market	46	20	12	14	76	80	-4	72
10	Harlow Town	46	20	7	19	76	72	4	67
11	Lowestoft Town	46	18	10	18	63	73	-10	64
12	Staines Town	46	16	13	17	78	68	10	61
13	Leatherhead	46	16	12	18	72	72	0	57
14	Worthing	46	16	8	22	73	85	-12	56
15	Folkestone Invicta	46	15	10	21	75	82	-7	55
16	Kingstonian	46	16	7	23	65	73	-8	55
17	Metropolitan Police	46	15	9	22	54	72	-18	54
18	Hendon	46	14	12	20	68	88	-20	54
19	Burgess Hill Town	46	14	12	20	59	80	-21	54
20	Merstham	46	15	11	20	70	72	-2	53
21	Harrow Borough	46	14	11	21	60	80	-20	53
22	Canvey Island	46	13	13	20	63	92	-29	52
23	AFC Sudbury	46	12	10	24	57	85	-28	46
24	Grays Athletic	46	11	5	30	46	101	-55	38

Play-Off Semi Finals: Bognor Regis Town 2-1 Wingate & Finchley | Dulwich Hamlet 4-2 Enfield Town
Final: Bognor Regis Town 2-1 Dulwich Hamlet

PREMIER DIVISION	1	2	3	4	5	6	7	8	9	10	11	12	13	14	15	16	17	18	19	20	21	22	23	24
1 AFC Sudbury		2-3	0-4	3-0	1-1	2-2	2-0	3-1	5-1	1-2	1-3	0-2	0-4	1-1	1-2	1-3	1-1	0-4	3-0	1-1	3-1	0-1	2-2	1-0
2 Billericay Town	2-3		0-2	4-0	3-1	0-2	2-4	1-0	2-0	1-1	2-1	0-2	4-1	0-2	4-2	2-0	0-1	1-1	1-1	6-0	1-0	2-1	3-0	3-0
3 Bognor Regis Town	2-1	2-1		1-1	4-0	1-1	1-1	7-1	1-2	3-0	1-0	1-1	0-2	2-0	1-0	1-0	1-3	2-0	1-1	2-1	2-0	2-0	3-1	5-0
4 Burgess Hill Town	2-0	2-1	1-3		1-1	0-3	1-0	4-2	2-1	0-1	5-1	3-3	1-0	2-1	3-2	0-6	1-3	2-1	1-4	0-3	3-3	1-2	2-3	0-1
5 Canvey Island	2-2	1-2	0-5	2-1		1-0	1-5	1-3	3-1	1-1	3-0	1-2	3-1	1-2	3-0	2-3	3-0	2-2	1-2	2-2	0-6	0-1	1-4	2-0
6 Dulwich Hamlet	2-0	0-3	1-3	2-2	1-2		2-1	6-1	0-1	3-1	1-4	3-0	2-1	4-2	1-1	2-4	3-1	5-0	3-3	2-0	3-1	1-2	1-1	4-1
7 Enfield Town	1-0	2-2	1-0	0-1	1-1	2-2		3-1	2-0	3-0	0-0	1-4	6-0	3-0	2-1	1-1	2-2	2-3	1-0	3-3	2-1	1-1	0-1	2-1
8 Folkestone Invicta	4-2	1-0	1-2	3-1	6-0	1-1	2-0		0-1	1-4	3-0	1-3	1-2	3-1	1-1	2-0	4-1	0-0	2-0	0-1	1-1	1-0	1-0	2-4
9 Grays Athletic	1-3	1-0	1-1	1-1	2-0	0-2	1-3	0-3		3-1	2-5	0-2	1-2	2-1	1-2	1-1	0-3	1-0	0-2	1-2	2-2	0-2	1-2	1-4
10 Harlow Town	1-3	0-2	3-1	2-2	2-2	1-2	0-3	2-2	5-0		2-0	0-2	2-0	1-0	2-1	1-2	1-2	2-1	3-1	5-1	1-0	1-0	3-0	6-2
11 Harrow Borough	1-1	0-0	0-1	0-2	1-1	0-2	1-5	4-1	1-3	2-0		2-1	0-2	0-4	3-1	3-1	4-2	1-0	0-0	0-3	0-0	1-0	0-1	2-2
12 Havant & Waterlooville	6-0	1-2	1-0	1-0	4-0	2-1	0-2	1-0	5-0	5-2	3-1		3-2	1-1	3-1	0-0	1-0	3-0	1-2	1-3	1-1	2-0	1-1	3-2
13 Hendon	1-2	1-0	2-2	1-1	0-0	1-1	1-1	3-3	0-4	2-2	4-5	1-1		1-4	1-3	2-1	0-0	2-1	2-0	2-1	1-1	1-2	0-1	0-3
14 Kingstonian	3-0	0-3	1-2	2-0	3-1	0-1	0-2	2-2	2-1	0-1	2-3	0-0	1-1		1-2	4-2	2-5	2-1	2-1	1-2	3-2	0-3	1-2	1-3
15 Leatherhead	2-0	3-2	1-3	1-2	1-1	2-2	2-1	2-0	1-1	3-2	2-2	0-1	3-2	2-3		3-3	3-1	3-0	2-1	1-1	0-1	0-0	1-0	1-1
16 Leiston	2-1	4-1	1-1	2-0	4-0	2-2	1-1	2-1	4-1	5-2	2-2	3-1	4-4	1-0			1-2	1-2	4-0	5-1	0-1	2-0	1-2	2-0
17 Lowestoft Town	2-2	1-1	2-1	1-0	0-3	0-3	2-1	2-2	1-0	4-0	2-0	0-2	3-3	1-0	3-2			1-5	0-1	1-1	1-3	0-1	2-1	0-4
18 Merstham	0-1	1-1	1-1	2-2	0-3	1-4	2-2	3-1	6-1	1-0	5-0	2-1	3-4	0-1	0-0	2-1	1-0		2-1	4-1	0-0	5-3	0-2	1-2
19 Metropolitan Police	1-0	1-1	0-1	2-1	0-4	1-1	3-0	1-0	3-1	0-2	1-1	1-2	1-2	1-0	0-1	2-1	2-2	0-2		2-1	1-6	1-1	2-0	1-2
20 Needham Market	2-1	1-2	2-2	1-1	3-3	1-1	1-3	2-1	5-1	2-1	2-1	0-0	5-2	2-1	2-1	0-4	2-0	1-1	1-0		1-1	0-2	1-0	2-1
21 Staines Town	4-0	3-2	0-2	1-2	1-1	2-0	2-2	0-2	3-0	0-2	0-0	1-4	3-2	0-2	2-5	2-3	2-1	0-0	3-2	3-4		1-2	1-1	4-0
22 Tonbridge Angels	1-0	1-0	4-1	0-0	3-0	0-0	3-2	4-1	0-3	1-0	1-1	3-1	0-1	4-4	2-2	1-0	4-4	2-2	2-1	3-4	1-2		3-0	2-1
23 Wingate & Finchley	4-1	1-2	0-2	2-1	1-2	0-3	1-5	3-2	1-0	0-0	3-1	0-2	1-0	2-1	2-1	1-0	1-1	3-2	2-3	0-1	1-1	4-0		1-0
24 Worthing	0-0	2-2	1-1	1-1	5-0	0-1	1-3	3-3	0-1	3-2	0-4	1-2	1-2	0-0	3-2	1-3	0-1	1-0	3-1	4-3	5-3	3-0	1-4	

ISTHMIAN DIVISION ONE NORTH LEAGUE TABLE 2016-17

		P	W	D	L	F	A	GD	Pts
1	Brightlingsea Regent	46	32	7	7	114	57	57	103
2	Maldon & Tiptree	46	29	4	13	107	51	56	91
3	Thurrock	46	27	8	11	84	39	45	89
4	AFC Hornchurch	46	24	13	9	78	42	36	85
5	Haringey Borough	46	25	6	15	108	74	34	81
6	Bowers & Pitsea	46	23	9	14	102	66	36	78
7	Aveley	46	21	13	12	75	64	11	76
8	Phoenix Sports	46	22	9	15	71	72	-1	75
9	Norwich United	46	24	5	17	70	61	9	74
10	Cheshunt	46	20	11	15	85	72	13	71
11	Bury Town	46	20	9	17	74	66	8	69
12	Tilbury	46	17	13	16	67	73	-6	64
13	Witham Town	46	16	11	19	77	80	-3	59
14	Brentwood Town	46	17	5	24	63	77	-14	56
15	VCD Athletic	46	15	11	20	53	76	-23	56
16	Romford	46	15	11	20	59	90	-31	56
17	Thamesmead Town	46	16	6	24	70	78	-8	54
18	Dereham Town	46	15	9	22	70	89	-19	54
19	Soham Town Rangers	46	14	11	21	62	78	-16	53
20	Waltham Abbey	46	14	9	23	57	73	-16	51
21	Heybridge Swifts	46	13	12	21	64	81	-17	51
22	Ware	46	15	6	25	66	84	-18	51
23	Wroxham	46	6	7	33	42	103	-61	25
24	Great Wakering Rovers	46	6	7	33	49	121	-72	25

Play-Off Semi Finals: Maldon & Tiptree 5-4 Haringey Borough | Thurrock 1-0 AFC Hornchurch
Final: Maldon & Tiptree 0-1 Thurrock

DIVISION ONE NORTH	1	2	3	4	5	6	7	8	9	10	11	12	13	14	15	16	17	18	19	20	21	22	23	24
1 AFC Hornchurch		3-1	1-4	2-2	2-2	3-2	1-2	0-1	3-0	3-2	0-0	1-1	2-0	4-1	1-0	3-1	2-0	1-1	0-0	3-0	4-0	1-1	1-1	
2 Aveley	1-0		1-1	3-1	1-4	0-1	1-2	2-0	3-2	2-1	3-0	3-0	2-1	1-1	3-0	2-0	0-2	0-1	2-1	2-2	3-2	5-2	2-2	2-1
3 Bowers & Pitsea	3-2	0-1		2-0	3-4	4-1	2-3	4-0	5-2	2-1	2-0	0-1	5-0	3-1	5-0	2-2	0-0	2-0	4-0	0-1	1-1	5-0	1-5	1-1
4 Brentwood Town	0-1	1-2	4-2		1-4	0-1	1-3	3-0	1-2	3-1	1-2	1-2	3-0	0-3	2-1	0-1	2-0	2-1	0-3	2-1	3-2	0-1	1-0	2-0
5 Brightlingsea Regent	2-1	3-1	1-1	2-2		1-0	2-2	3-1	2-1	1-0	2-1	1-0	3-1	3-4	4-1	3-1	4-3	0-1	2-3	2-0	2-1	5-0	4-1	3-0
6 Bury Town	0-2	1-0	3-0	3-1	4-1		2-1	2-1	1-1	2-1	1-2	3-2	2-3	1-2	1-2	1-1	2-0	2-0	2-1	1-2	2-1	2-2	1-3	6-1
7 Cheshunt	2-2	1-2	0-1	1-0	2-2	3-1		2-3	3-1	1-1	3-1	3-1	2-3	1-2	2-1	0-4	1-3	0-1	0-0	0-0	0-2	2-0	2-0	3-1
8 Dereham Town	0-0	2-2	1-3	1-3	3-2	0-1	3-3		3-0	1-2	3-0	0-5	1-1	3-4	2-3	2-0	2-3	1-3	2-3	0-0	2-1	1-0	0-2	2-1
9 Great Wakering Rovers	2-5	2-4	1-5	1-3	1-2	1-4	1-4	0-5		1-4	0-5	0-3	1-3	1-2	1-1	2-2	2-1	0-5	2-1	0-1	3-3	0-5	1-3	2-3
10 Haringey Borough	0-2	4-5	5-4	3-2	2-3	3-0	3-5	3-0	5-2		3-2	3-1	2-1	4-0	7-1	6-0	3-2	1-2	3-2	0-2	3-1	4-1	2-2	1-0
11 Heybridge Swifts	0-3	1-1	2-2	1-1	2-2	3-1	1-3	2-1	1-4		1-0	0-1	3-2	0-1	1-4	3-0	0-5	0-1	1-2	2-2	2-1	3-1	2-1	
12 Maldon & Tiptree	3-0	3-1	2-3	0-1	2-1	3-0	4-1	2-2	2-0	2-0	2-1		3-0	6-1	5-1	1-0	2-1	4-0	3-0	3-0	2-1	4-1	4-2	3-0
13 Norwich United	0-1	1-0	1-1	4-0	4-1	3-0	2-2	2-0	1-1	2-1	2-2	2-0		0-1	4-1	2-1	2-1	0-2	1-2	4-1	0-1	2-1	2-0	2-0
14 Phoenix Sports	1-1	6-2	1-0	0-3	0-3	0-3	1-1	4-1	3-2	0-3	3-0	1-0	0-1		1-3	1-2	0-2	1-1	2-2	4-0	2-1	1-1	1-1	2-0
15 Romford	0-0	0-0	1-2	2-2	1-4	1-0	0-3	2-2	2-1	1-1	3-3	2-6	3-0	1-1		1-4	1-1	2-3	1-0	1-0	1-0	2-2	2-1	4-1
16 Soham Town Rangers	1-0	0-1	2-0	3-1	2-2	1-4	0-4	1-3	1-2	1-3	0-2	4-3	4-0	0-1	1-1		1-3	2-1	1-1	5-2	1-1	1-3	0-0	1-1
17 Thamesmead Town	0-3	3-3	2-1	1-2	0-1	1-1	0-5	5-2	1-0	1-1	2-1	0-1	1-2	0-1	1-2	1-2		0-1	0-1	2-2	0-1	2-1	4-2	4-1
18 Thurrock	2-0	2-2	3-1	5-1	0-1	4-0	0-1	3-1	3-0	1-1	0-0	0-0	0-1	4-0	2-0	3-1	1-2		6-1	4-0	1-0	2-1	2-0	1-0
19 Tilbury	0-0	0-0	1-1	2-0	1-2	1-1	2-0	2-1	1-1	1-1	1-1	3-2	1-2	0-2	2-1	4-1	1-5	1-1		5-2	2-1	1-3	2-1	1-1
20 VCD Athletic	0-2	0-0	0-2	1-1	0-5	0-0	3-0	1-2	0-0	5-2	1-0	3-1	0-3	0-2	2-3	2-0	2-3	2-1	3-1		4-1	2-0	0-3	4-3
21 Waltham Abbey	0-1	1-0	1-4	0-0	1-0	1-0	3-3	3-3	3-1	0-2	1-0	1-4	1-0	1-2	1-0	0-0	0-1	1-1	2-4	0-0		2-1	1-3	3-1
22 Ware	0-2	2-0	2-3	2-0	0-3	2-2	4-1	0-1	1-0	2-3	0-3	1-2	2-2	3-0	3-0	3-1	0-1	2-0	0-2			2-1	3-1	
23 Witham Town	1-5	2-2	5-2	4-1	0-5	2-3	2-2	1-2	0-1	1-2	5-3	1-1	2-1	0-1	2-0	1-1	3-2	2-2	2-1	1-0	2-1	2-1		1-2
24 Wroxham	2-3	0-1	0-3	0-3	0-2	0-3	0-2	1-1	1-3	0-1	2-2	0-6	1-0	1-0	1-2	0-2	3-2	0-2	2-3	4-0	0-4	2-3	1-1	

ISTHMIAN DIVISION ONE SOUTH LEAGUE TABLE 2016-17

		P	W	D	L	F	A	GD	Pts
1	Tooting & Mitcham United	46	33	6	7	120	54	66	105
2	Dorking Wanderers	46	33	6	7	103	44	59	105
3	Greenwich Borough	46	30	5	11	102	52	50	95
4	Corinthian-Casuals	46	29	6	11	99	59	40	93
5	Hastings United	46	23	13	10	128	64	64	82
6	Carshalton Athletic	46	24	9	13	106	69	37	78
7	Hythe Town	46	23	9	14	87	65	22	78
8	South Park	46	24	4	18	95	80	15	76
9	Lewes	46	23	7	16	88	75	13	76
10	Faversham Town	46	22	8	16	89	58	31	74
11	Cray Wanderers	46	19	11	16	88	86	2	68
12	Ramsgate	46	18	11	17	79	75	4	65
13	Walton Casuals	46	19	8	19	98	99	-1	65
14	Whyteleafe	46	19	7	20	81	75	6	64
15	Sittingbourne	46	17	11	18	71	86	-15	62
16	Horsham	46	17	10	19	79	80	-1	61
17	Herne Bay	46	13	12	21	74	98	-24	51
18	East Grinstead Town	46	14	5	27	82	121	-39	47
19	Molesey	46	11	10	25	61	116	-55	43
20	Chipstead	46	11	8	27	68	99	-31	41
21	Guernsey	46	9	11	26	66	112	-46	38
22	Chatham Town	46	7	10	29	57	120	-63	31
23	Three Bridges	46	7	8	31	59	114	-55	29
24	Godalming Town	46	8	3	35	49	128	-79	24

Play-Off Semi Finals: Dorking Wanderers 1-1 Hastings Town (Dorking won 4-3p) | Greenwich Borough 3-4 Corinthian-Casuals
Final: Dorking Wanderers 0-0 Corinthian Casuals (Dorking Wanderers won 5-4 on penalties)

DIVISION ONE SOUTH	1	2	3	4	5	6	7	8	9	10	11	12	13	14	15	16	17	18	19	20	21	22	23	24
1 Carshalton Athletic		6-1	2-3	1-3	2-1	3-3	3-1	2-1	10-0	1-3	2-1	4-4	4-1	5-1	0-3	4-3	3-0	1-1	2-2	1-0	5-1	1-1	5-0	2-0
2 Chatham Town	1-2		4-4	1-4	1-3	0-3	2-3	0-1	0-1	0-1	1-4	0-7	3-2	1-4	1-3	0-0	0-2	5-2	2-3	0-1	1-1	2-3	1-4	2-3
3 Chipstead	3-1	0-1		1-4	2-2	1-3	1-3	0-1	2-0	1-2	1-3	3-3	2-2	2-1	1-2	1-2	0-1	1-2	2-2	1-3	3-0	0-7	4-1	1-2
4 Corinthian-Casuals	0-2	2-2	1-0		1-1	2-0	2-0	0-0	5-1	2-0	5-2	0-1	2-1	2-1	3-6	0-2	5-1	1-0	4-0	0-1	2-0	3-3	0-0	2-1
5 Cray Wanderers	4-1	3-0	3-2	3-4		0-2	2-4	1-0	5-1	0-0	1-0	1-4	2-1	2-2	0-1	1-3	3-0	2-2	3-3	0-3	3-2	1-4	3-4	2-2
6 Dorking Wanderers	2-1	1-2	4-1	1-0	2-1		1-2	1-2	2-0	1-0	5-2	2-1	3-4	7-1	1-0	2-1	6-0	3-0	3-0	0-1	1-0	1-0	2-2	
7 East Grinstead Town	0-3	2-2	4-3	2-2	4-2	2-3		2-1	3-4	0-5	0-1	4-4	2-3	0-3	2-3	1-3	3-0	1-4	2-0	5-3	1-2	1-4	1-1	2-7
8 Faversham Town	2-0	7-1	4-1	3-0	2-2	1-2	3-0		3-2	2-5	1-0	1-1	6-3	1-1	1-2	5-0	1-0	2-0	1-1	2-2	4-1	0-3	5-1	2-1
9 Godalming Town	0-3	2-4	1-4	1-2	0-1	0-5	2-3	0-2		1-4	3-0	1-0	3-2	1-2	0-1	1-0	1-2	2-1	1-2	1-4	1-3	0-3	1-6	3-4
10 Greenwich Borough	0-2	3-0	1-2	0-3	3-1	1-1	3-0	3-2	2-0		4-0	3-2	2-0	4-1	1-0	1-0	2-1	3-1	1-3	1-3	4-2	3-2	2-1	0-1
11 Guernsey	2-2	2-2	2-0	1-4	0-0	2-4	2-1	2-4	1-1	1-1		0-1	5-1	2-3	2-2	2-0	0-3	2-1	1-3	1-1	0-6	4-1	1-2	
12 Hastings United	5-0	2-2	3-3	3-4	1-2	2-4	2-0	1-0	3-0	3-0	6-1		7-0	3-0	2-1	3-0	5-1	1-2	1-1	4-1	3-2	0-1	1-1	4-0
13 Herne Bay	2-3	2-1	3-0	1-0	0-1	0-0	6-0	1-2	3-2	0-5	1-1	1-1		0-1	0-2	1-4	2-0	2-2	3-0	1-1	1-1	1-4	1-1	2-1
14 Horsham	1-3	4-0	3-2	2-0	2-3	2-0	1-1	4-3	8-1	1-2	0-0	1-1	0-2		0-1	3-0	1-3	1-2	0-1	0-2	2-0	2-0	1-1	1-1
15 Hythe Town	2-2	6-1	1-1	0-5	2-3	0-1	3-1	1-1	2-0	2-2	8-1	1-1	3-1	3-3		4-0	1-0	1-0	2-1	1-2	1-1	0-4	6-1	1-1
16 Lewes	1-2	2-0	2-1	2-3	5-2	1-2	4-0	3-0	2-4	1-0	4-4	3-1	1-2	1-0		2-3	3-2	2-2	1-3	4-2	1-5	0-2	2-1	
17 Molesey	1-1	1-1	1-0	0-1	2-2	1-3	2-0	1-4	2-2	1-2	3-1	5-4	3-3	3-3	3-1	0-4		2-3	1-1	1-3	2-2	2-1	2-2	2-1
18 Ramsgate	1-2	2-1	0-1	3-4	2-2	2-2	4-2	1-0	1-0	1-3	2-1	1-1	0-2	1-1	3-0	1-1	5-1		1-2	1-1	2-0	1-1	0-2	5-2
19 Sittingbourne	1-0	2-2	0-1	2-1	0-4	0-1	1-0	2-1	2-1	1-5	3-3	2-4	2-2	3-2	4-0	1-3	2-0	4-0		2-0	4-4	1-3	3-2	0-3
20 South Park	3-2	3-0	1-1	2-3	1-4	0-2	2-4	3-1	6-2	0-4	3-0	1-5	3-1	1-3	0-1	0-3	6-2	1-3	2-0		1-0	3-4	5-1	1-2
21 Three Bridges	1-2	2-0	2-3	0-4	0-3	2-4	1-3	1-1	1-4	4-3	0-4	2-3	1-4	3-5	2-1	0-2	0-1	0-4		3-5	2-4	4-0	
22 Tooting & Mitcham United	1-0	4-3	3-1	3-1	4-0	2-1	5-2	1-0	1-0	1-0	2-2	0-4	1-1	2-1	0-2	0-0	8-2	3-2	2-0	2-0	1-0		2-0	2-1
23 Walton Casuals	1-0	1-2	4-1	0-3	5-1	1-2	3-7	0-2	2-3	1-0	4-2	3-2	4-4	3-0	3-1	1-2	7-0	3-3	3-2	3-5	1-0	4-3		1-3
24 Whyteleafe	1-1	0-1	3-0	0-1	0-1	2-2	2-0	2-1	3-1	1-1	5-1	0-4	3-0	3-1	3-0	0-1	4-1	1-2	4-1	1-2	0-2	1-3	1-4	

THE ALAN TURVEY TROPHY 2016-17

HOLDERS: KINGSTONIAN

FIRST ROUND

AFC Hornchurch	v	Haringey Borough	4-1	71
AFC Sudbury	v	Lowestoft Town	2-1	125
Aveley	v	Greenwich Borough	1-2	44
Billericay Town	v	Heybridge Swifts	3-0	117
Bowers & Pitsea	v	Witham Town	3-0	75
Brentwood Town	v	Ware	1-2 aet	45
Brightlingsea Regent	v	Leiston	6-3	62
Burgess Hill Town	v	Horsham	2-0	133
Canvey Island	v	Great Wakering Rovers	6-1	90
Carshalton Athletic	v	Molesey	4-1	99
Chatham Town	v	VCD Athletic	1-0	61
Cheshunt	v	Enfield Town	2-4	231
Chipstead	v	South Park	1-2	53
Corinthian-Casuals	v	Whyteleafe	2-0	74
Dulwich Hamlet	v	Grays Athletic	4-0	374
East Grinstead Town	v	Godalming Town	2-2, 5-6p	62
Faversham Town	v	Hythe Town	3-0	128
Folkestone Invicta	v	Tonbridge Angels	0-1	224
Harrow Borough	v	Wingate & Finchley	4-4, 7-8p	85
Hendon	v	Metropolitan Police	2-2, 3-4p	76
Herne Bay	v	Hastings United	1-1, 3-4p	145
Kingstonian	v	Merstham	2-2, 4-5p	124
Leatherhead	v	Walton Casuals	2-1	65
Sittingbourne	v	Ramsgate	2-1	88
Soham Town Rangers	v	Needham Market	3-4	103
Thamesmead Town	v	Romford	4-3	47
Tilbury	v	Maldon & Tiptree	0-0	51
Tooting & Mitcham United	v	Staines Town	0-3	111
Waltham Abbey	v	Harlow Town	3-1	91
Worthing	v	Three Bridges	5-0	227

SECOND ROUND

Brightlingsea Regent	v	Bowers & Pitsea	2-1	54
Burgess Hill Town	v	Godalming Town	2-3	148
Bury Town	v	Needham Market	0-2	230
Canvey Island	v	Ware	0-0, 1-3p	151
Enfield Town	v	AFC Hornchurch	1-4	120
Faversham Town	v	Hastings United	1-1, 6-5p	101
Greenwich Borough	v	Dulwich Hamlet	1-2	213
Merstham	v	Leatherhead	4-3	154
Metropolitan Police	v	Corinthian-Casuals	0-1	103
Romford	v	Chatham Town	1-0	65
South Park	v	Carshalton Athletic	2-1	72
Staines Town	v	Harrow Borough	3-4	123
Tilbury	v	Billericay Town	1-1, 2-4p	112
Tonbridge Angels	v	Sittingbourne	2-0	260
Waltham Abbey	v	AFC Sudbury	2-5	62
Worthing	v	Dorking Wanderers	2-1	280

THIRD ROUND

AFC Hornchurch	v	AFC Sudbury	1-0	76
Billericay Town	v	Brightlingsea Regent	2-1	126
Corinthian-Casuals	v	Merstham	2-5	81
Dulwich Hamlet	v	Faversham Town	2-1	321
Harrow Borough	v	South Park	0-4	53
Tonbridge Angels	v	Romford	2-2, 4-2p	133
Ware	v	Needham Market	1-2	60
Worthing	v	Burgess Hill Town	2-1	444

QUARTER-FINALS

AFC Hornchurch	v	Dulwich Hamlet	2-3	146
Merstham	v	South Park	1-1, 3-4p	110
Worthing	v	Billericay Town	0-7	318
Needham Market	v	Tonbridge Angels	1-3	148

SEMI-FINALS

Billericay Town	v	South Park	4-3	275

Billy Bricknell 3 — *D Merchant-Simmonds 40,55*
M Johnson 22 — *J Jackson 64*
L Taaffe 28
Adam Cunnington 41

Tonbridge Angels	v	Dulwich Hamlet	3-1	305

Alexander Akrofi 9,74 — *Kenny Beaney 27*
Nathan Elder 51

FINAL

Billericay Town	v	Tonbridge Angels	8-3	653

Jake Robinson 12 — *Andre McCollins 5,89*
Billy Bricknell 29,36,44 — *Paul Konchesky 49 (og)*
Adam Cunnington 48,61
Byron Lawrence 55
Kreshnic Krasniqi 83

Isthmian Premier Statistics 2016-17

TOP SCORING CLUBS

Leiston	123
Dulwich Hamlet	117
Havant & Waterlooville	103
Bognor Regis Town	96

MOST GAMES WITHOUT SCORING

Harrow Borough	20 (2)
Merstham	18 (2)
AFC Sudbury	16 (4)

MOST SCORERS

Billericay Town	29+1og
Dulwich Hamlet	21+3ogs
Hendon	20+3ogs

MOST CONSECUTIVE SCORING GAMES

Worthing	30
Bognor Regis Town	23
Havant & Waterlooville	22

MOST CLEAN SHEETS

Havant & Waterlooville	20 (4)
Tonbridge Angels	19 (3)
Dulwich Hamlet	18 (2)

	GT	GWS(1)	TNoS	MCSG	TCS(2)
AFC Sudbury	77	16 (4)	15	14	9 (1)
Billericay Town	87	13 (3)	29+1og	9	13 (2)
Bognor Regis Town	96	3 (1)	18+1og	23	16 (3)
Burgess Hill Town	78	13 (2)	20+1og	10	6 (1)
Canvey Island	70	11 (2)	20+2og	8	9 (2)
Dulwich Hamlet	117	8 (1)	21+3ogs	15	18 (2)
Enfield Town	91	10 (4)	17+1og	13	12 (3)
Folkestone Invicta	87	7 (3)	18+2ogs	16	11 (2)
Grays Atheltic	48	13 (2)	17	11	7 (2)
Harlow Town	87	10 (2)	20+1og	17	15 (3)
Harrow Borough	82	20 (2)	16	11	10 (2)
Havant & Waterlooville	103	4 (1)	14+1og	22	20 (4)
Hendon	78	11 (2)	20+3ogs	12	9 (1)
Kingstonian	71	13 (2)	15	10	9 (2)
Leatherhead	73	9 (2)	25	12	7 (2)
Leiston	123	7 (2)	15+3ogs	16	11 (2)
Lowestoft Town	64	13 (3)	17+1og	6	9 (2)
Merstham	87	18 (2)	20	5	10 (1)
Metropolitan Police	60	12 (3)	20+1og	13	8 (2)
Needham Market	79	6 (2)	18	15	9 (3)
Staines Town	83	12 (2)	19+1og	19	12 (4)
Tonbridge Angels	91	14 (2)	18+1og	11	19 (3)
Wingate & Finchley	77	13 (2)	19	10	15 (4)
Worthing	97	13 (4)	20+1og	30	10 (2)

(1) - Most consecutive goalless games in brackets.
(2) - Most consecutive clean sheets in brackets.
GT - Goals Total
GWS - Games Without Scoring
TNoS - Total Number of Scorers
MCSG - Most Consecutive Scoring Games
TCS - Total Clean Sheets

Strikers with ten or more goals - 2016-17

LEAGUE, FA CUP AND FA TROPHY GOALS ONLY.

					PTG	CTG	FLP
Leiston	Blake	38	Heath	14	85	123	7
	Francis	12	Muir-Merchant	11			
	Lawrence	10					
Dulwich Hamlet	Tomlin	16	Sekajiia	14	66	118	3
	Clunis	13	Carew	12			
	Dumaka	11					
Havant & Waterlooville	Prior	23	Rutherford	17	67	103	1
	Lewis	15	Patterson	12			
Tonbridge Angels	Elder	21	Akrofi	11	52	91	6
	Allen	10	Blewden	10			
Worthing	Dawes	24	Bugiel	23	57	97	15
	Sparks	10					
Folkestone Invicta	Draycott	22	Taylor	20	52	87	16
	Cornwall	10					
Bognor Regis Town	Fraser	24	Pearce	15	49	98	2
	Crane	10					
Needham Market	Ingram	16	Sands	14	43	79	9
	Dobson	13					
Harrow Borough	Driver	12	Meite	10	32	82	21
	Charles-Smith	10					
Enfield	Crook	17	Ottaway	15	32	91	4
Wingate & Finchley	Beccles-Richards	17	Pattie	11	28	77	5
Staines Town	Bettamer	16	Worsfold	11	27	83	12
Metropolitan Police	Collins	11	Percil	10	21	60	18
AFC Sudbury	Bantick	10	Wales	10	20	77	23
Harlow Town	Read	27			27	87	10
Kingstonian	Moss	26			26	71	17
Lowestoft Town	Reed	21			21	64	11
Canvey Island	Sykes	19			19	70	22
Merstham	Bennett	19			19	87	14
Billericay Town	Bricknell	18			18	87	8
Burgess Hill Town	Richardson-Brown	13			13	78	20
Grays Athletic	Bishop	12			12	48	24

PTG - Players Total Goals | CTG - Club's Total Goals | FLP - Final League Position

BILLERICAY TOWN

Club Contact Details
New Lodge, Blunts Wall Road, Billericay CM12 9SA
01277 652 188
info@billericaytownfc.co.uk

Ground Capacity: 3,500   **Seats:** 424   **Covered:** 2,000   **Clubhouse:** Yes   **Shop:** Yes

Record Attendance
3,841 v West Ham United - Opening of Floodlights 1977
Previous Grounds
None

10 YEAR RECORD

07-08		08-09		09-10		10-11		11-12		12-13		13-14		14-15		15-16		16-17	
Isth P	10	Isth P	11	Isth P	13	Isth P	11	Isth P	1	Conf S	21	Isth P	10	Isth P	8	Isth P	9	Isth P	8
FAC	1P	FAC	2Q	FAC	2Q	FAC	2Qr	FAC	3Q	FAC	3Qr	FAC	2Q	FAC	3Q	FAC	1Qr	FAC	4Q
FAT	2Qr	FAT	1Q	FAT	1P	FAT	3Q	FAT	3Q	FAT	1P	FAT	2Qr	FAT	1Q	FAT	1Q	FAT	2Q

Club Factfile

Founded: 1880   **Nickname:** Town or Blues   **Manager:** Harry Wheeler

Previous Names: Billericay FC.

Previous Leagues: Romford & District 1890-1914, Mid Essex 1918-47, South Essex Combination 1947-66, Essex Olympian 1966-71, Essex Senior 1971-77, Athenian 1977-79. Isthmian 1979-2012. Conference 2012-13.

Club Colours (change): Blue & white

RECORDS
Victory: 11-0 v Stansted (A) - Essex Senior League 05/05/1976
Defeat: 3-10 v Chelmsford City (A) - Essex Senior Cup 04/01/1993
Goalscorer: Freddie Claydon - 273
Appearances: J Pullen - 418
Additional: Leon Gutzmore scored 51 goals during the 1997-98 season.
                  Received £22,500+ from West Ham United for Steve Jones November 1992

HONOURS
FA Comps: FA Vase 1975-76, 76-77, 78-79.

League: Chelmsford & District Division Three 1932-33. Essex Olympian 1969-70, 70-71. Essex Senior 1972-73, 74-75, 75-76. Athenian 1977-78, 78-79. Isthmian Division Two 1979-80, Premier Division 2011-12.

County FA: Essex Senior Cup 1975-76, 2010-11. Essex Senior Trophy 1977-78, 79-80.

BEST PERFORMANCES	**FA Cup:** First Round Proper 1997-98, 2004-05, 07-08.
	FA Trophy: Fifth Round Proper 2000-01.
	FA Vase: Final 1975-76, 76-77, 78-79.

BILLERICAY MATCH RESULTS 2016-17

Date	Comp	H/A	Opponents	Att:	Result	Goalscorers	Pos	No.
Aug 13	IsthP	H	Merstham	272	D 1 - 1	Oynison 59	10	1
17	IsthP	A	Wingate & Finchley	109	W 2 - 1	Monville 23 Hubble 83	8	2
20	IsthP	A	Staines Town	205	L 2 - 3	Luke 11 Hubble 56	11	3
23	IsthP	H	Lowestoft	286	L 0 - 1		15	4
27	IsthP	H	Bognor Regis Town	247	L 0 - 2		19	5
29	IsthP	A	Tonbridge Angels	628	L 0 - 1		21	6
Sept 3	FAC1Q	A	Brightlingsea R	146	W 2 - 1	Monville 31 79		7
10	IsthP	H	Leatherhead	221	W 4 - 2	Sappleton 44 (pen) 73 Capela 69 90	18	8
17	FAC2Q	H	Bognor Regis Town	446	W 2 - 1	Stephenson 66 Gaurilovas 80		9
20	IsthP	A	AFC Sudbury	226	W 3 - 2	Luke 17 30 Krasaniqi 71	11	10
24	IsthP	H	Worthing	374	W 3 - 0	Krasaniqi 22 Cundle 36 Hubble 49	8	11
27	IsthP	H	Folkestone Invicta	211	W 1 - 0	Cundle 18	5	12
Oct 1	FAC3Q	H	Chippenham Town	482	W 3 - 2	Cundle 10 80 Capela 90		13
8	IsthP	A	Harrow Borough	236	D 0 - 0		6	14
15	FAC4Q	A	Maidstone United	1428	L 1 - 3	Sappleton 61 (pen)		15
22	IsthP	H	Merstham	183	D 1 - 1	Sappleton 68	12	16
25	IsthP	H	Wingate & Finchley	218	W 3 - 0	Hubble 56 Diau 64 Guthny 68	11	17
29	FAT1Q	H	Malden & Tiptree Ath	337	W 2 - 0	Sappleton 9 23		18
Nov 1	IsthP	A	Lowestoft Town	317	D 1 - 1	Glover (og) 11	10	19
5	IsthP	H	Grays Athletic	421	W 2 - 0	Capela 58 90	5	20
12	FAT2Q	A	Havant & Waterlooville	256	L 0 - 5			21
15	IsthP	H	Havant & Waterlooville	216	L 0 - 2		7	22
19	IsthP	H	Harlow Town	430	D 1 - 1	Sappleton 36	9	23
22	IsthP	A	Folkestone Invicta	283	L 0 - 1		11	24
26	IsthP	H	Metropolitan Police	374	D 1 - 1	Bakare 41 (pen)	10	25
29	IsthP	H	AFC Sudbury	273	L 2 - 3	Johnson 10 Bricknell 90	10	26
Dec 3	IsthP	A	Worthing	537	D 2 - 2	Sobers 2 Bricknell 61		27
10	IsthP	A	Burgess Hill Town	306	L 1 - 2	Bricknell 54 (pen)		28
17	IsthP	H	Kingstonian	364	L 0 - 2		15	29
26	IsthP	A	Canvey Island	571	W 2 - 1	Bakare 17 Akinyemi 31		30
Jan 2	IsthP	H	Tonbridge Angels	507	W 2 - 1	Capela 88 Bricknell 90	14	31
7	IsthP	A	Burgess Hill Town	421	L 1 - 2	Taafe 83	14	32
14	IsthP	H	Leiston	272	L 1 - 4	Assombalonga 5	15	33
17	IsthP	A	Metropolitan Police	108	D 1 - 1	Seymour 1	15	34
28	IsthP	A	Staines Tiown	387	W 1 - 0	Bricknell 37	14	35
Feb 4	IsthP	A	Havant & Warterlooville	625	W 2 - 1	Assombalonga 45 Taafe 72	12	36
11	IsthP	H	Harrow Borough	429	W 2 - 1	Bricknell 4 38	11	37
15	IsthP	H	Needham Market	401	W 6 - 0	Seymour 4 Swaine 34 Cunnington 39 72 Bricknell 24 Layne 87	15	38
18	IsthP	A	Grays Athletic	277	L 0 - 1		11	39
25	IsthP	H	Hendon	561	W 4 - 1	Swaine 12 Bricknell 21 28 Cunnington 66	10	40
28	IsthP	A	Enfield Town	278	D 2 - 2	Cunnington 3 Leacock-Mcleod 17	10	41
Mar 4	IsthP	A	Harlow Town	450	W 2 - 0	Cunnington 42 Bricknell 54	9	42
7	IsthP	A	Hendon	183	L 0 - 1		9	43
11	IsthP	H	Burgess Hill Town	629	W 4 - 0	Swaine 54 62 Bricknell 60 68	9	44
18	IsthP	A	Kingstonian	412	W 3 - 0	Bricknell 35 (pen) 45 McLeod 90	8	45
25	IsthP	A	Dulwich Hamlet	2805	W 3 0	Cunnington 9 Ellul 19 Robinson 30	9	46
28	IsthP	H	Dulwich Hamlet	1302	L 0 - 2		9	47
Apr 1	IsthP	H	Leiston	1453	W 2 0	Robinson 14 Sprague 42	8	48
8	IsthP	H	Enfield Town	1251	L 2 4	Ellul 13 O'Hara 73	9	49
15	IsthP	A	Leatherhead	505	L 2 - 3	Ellul 19 Bricknell 85	10	50
17	IsthP	H	Canvey Island	1970	W 3 1	Bricknell 26 (pen) 69 Robinson 90	9	51
22	IsthP	A	Needham Market	432	W 2 - 1	Robinson 54 83	8	52

GOALSCORERS	SG	CSG	Pens	Hat tricks	Total		SG	CSG	Pens	Hat tricks	Total
2015-16 Derry					14	Seymour	2				2
Bricknell	13	3	3		18	Taafe	2				2
Sappleton	5	2	2		7	Akinyemi	1				1
Capela	5				6	Diau	1				1
Cunnington	6	3			6	Gaurilovas	1				1
Robinson	4				5	Guthny	1				1
Cundle	4	3			4	Johnson	1				1
Hubble	3				4	Layne	1				1
Swaine	3				4	Leacock-McLeod	1				1
Ellul	3				3	McLeod	1				1
Luke	2				3	O'Hara	1				1
Monville	2				3	Opponents	1				1
Assombalonga	2				2	Oynison	1				1
Bakare	2		1		2	Sobers	1				1
Krasaniqi	2	2			2	Sprague	1				1
						Stephenson	1				1

BRIGHTLINGSEA REGENT

Club Contact Details
North Road, Brightlingsea, Essex CO7 0PL
01206 304 199
gridders43@pobox.com

Ground Capacity: 1,000   **Seats:** Yes   **Covered:** Yes   **Clubhouse:** Yes   **Shop:**

Record Attendance
1,200 v Colchester United, friendly, 1988.
Previous Grounds
Bell Green (Bellfield Close). Recreation Ground (Regent Road) > 1920.

10 YEAR RECORD

07-08	08-09	09-10	10-11	11-12	12-13	13-14	14-15	15-16	16-17
	EsSuP 9	EsSuP 4	EsSuP 1	EC1 5	EC1 3	ECP 2	Isth1N 6	Isth1N 8	Isth1N 1
							FAC EPr	FAC 1Q	FAC Pr	FAC 1Q
				FAV 1Q	FAV 3P	FAV 5P	FAT 1Q	FAT Pr	FAT 2Qr

Club Factfile

Founded: 1928   **Nickname:** The Rs   **Manager:** James Webster

Previous Names: Brightlingsea Athletic & Brightlingsea Town merged to form Brightlingsea United 1928-2005. Merged with Regent Park Rangers.

Previous Leagues: Essex Senior 1972-91. Eastern Counties 1990-02, 2011-14. Essex & Suffolk Border 2002-2011.

Club Colours (change): Red & black/black/red (All blue)

RECORDS

HONOURS

FA Comps: None

League: Essex & Suffolk Border Division One 1946-47, 60-61, Premier 2010-11. Essex Senior 1988-89, 89-90. Isthmian Division One North 2016-17.

County FA: None

BEST PERFORMANCES	**FA Cup:** First Qualifying Round 2014-15, 16-17.
	FA Trophy: Second Qualifying Round 2016-17(r).
	FA Vase: Fifth Round Proper 2013-14.

LEADING GOALSCORERS 2016-2017

		LGE	FAC	FAT	Pens	H-T	SG	CSG	Total
Matt Blake	Leiston	29	3	6	1	1	27	5	38
Alex Read	Harlow Town	19	2	6	1	1	21	2	27
Ryan Moss	Kingstonian	24		2	4	2	18	2	26
James Fraser	Bognor Regis Town	23	1		2	1	17	3	24
Lloyd Dawes	Worthing	20		4	8	2	17	5	24
Jason Prior	Havant & Waterlooville	17	2	4	5	2	15	3	23
Omar Bugiel	Worthing	16	6	1	4	2	16	4	23
Ian Draycott	Folkestone Invicta	17	3	2	2		19	5	22
Jake Reed	Lowestoft Town	21				1	14	2	21
Joe Taylor	Folkestone Invicta	19		1	1		16	4	20
Nathan Elder	Tonbridge Angels	16	3	2			20	6	20
Dan Bennett	Merstham	17	1	1	2	1	15	2	19
George Sykes	Canvey Island	17		2	1		17	2	19
Alfie Rutherford	Havant & Waterlooville	15		2		1	14	5	17
Billy Crook	Enfield Town	16		1	5		17	3	17
Gavin Tomlin	Dulwich Hamlet	12	2	3			13	4	17
Reece Beccles-Richards	Wingate & Finchley	12	2	3		1	13	5	17
Luke Ingram	Needham Market	16				1	13	3	16
Theo Lewis	Havant & Waterlooville	13					13	2	15
Gareth Heath	Leiston	11	1	2			13	2	14
John Sands	Needham Market	13		1	2		14	6	14
Nyren Clunis	Dulwich Hamlet	10		3			12	3	13
Reece Dobson	Needham Market	12		1			11	2	13
Ashley Carew	Dulwich Hamlet	10		2	3		11	2	12
Joe Francis	Leiston	9	2	0			8	2	12
Joe Francis	Leiston	9	2				7	2	11
Matt Patterson	Havant & Waterlooville	7	3			1	9	2	10
Ollie Pearce	Bognor Regis Town	9		1	3		10	3	10

PENALTIES

Scored		Conceded	
Worthing	8+3c+1t	Grays Athletic	9+3c
Havant & Waterlooville	7+1c+2t	Billericay Town	8
Metropolitan Police	8+1c	Dulwich Hamlet	8
Kingstonian	8	Kingstonian	8
Needham Market	6	Harrow Borough	6
Bognor Regis Town	5+1t	Folkestone Invicta	5
Dulwich Hamlet	5+1t	Hendon	5
Merstham	4+2c	Lowestoft Town	5
Enfield	5	Metropolitan Police	5
Harrow Borough	5	AFC Sudbury	4
Hendon	5	Harlow Town	4
Leatherhead	5	Needham Market	4
Burgess Hill Town	4+1c	Merstham	3+1c
Staines Town	4	Staines Town	3+1c
Billericay Town	4	Wingate & Finchley	3+1c
Tonbridge Angles	3+1c	Bognor Regis Town	3
Leiston	2+1c+1t	Leatherhead	3
Folkestone Invicta	3	Tonbridge Angels	3
Canvey Island	2+1c	Burgess Hill Town	2+1c
Harlow Town	2	Canvey Island	2
AFC Sudbury	1+1c	Leiston	3
Wingate & Finchley	1+1t	Worthing	2
Grays Athletic	1	Enfield Town	1
Lowestoft Town	1	Havant & Waterlooville	0
TOTAL	**99+12c+7t**		**99+7c**

BURGESS HILL TOWN

Club Contact Details
Leylands Park, Maple Drive, Burgess Hill, West Sussex RH15 8DL
01444 254 832
timspencer57@hotmail.com

Ground Capacity: 2,500   **Seats:** 408   **Covered:** Yes   **Clubhouse:** Yes   **Shop:** Yes

Record Attendance
2,005 v AFC Wimbledon - Isthmian League Division One 2004-05
Previous Grounds
Moved to Leylands Park in 1969.

10 YEAR RECORD

	07-08		08-09		09-10		10-11		11-12		12-13		13-14		14-15		15-16		16-17	
Isth1S	12	Isth1S	19	Isth1S	7	Isth1S	7	Isth1S	20	Isth1S	8	Isth1S	6	Isth1S	1	Isth P	21	Isth P	20
FAC	1Q	FAC	4Q	FAC	P	FAC	2Q	FAC	P	FAC	P	FAC	2Q	FAC	4Q	FAC	1Q	FAC	4Qr
FAT	P	FAT	1Q	FAT	2Q	FAT	1Q	FAT	1Q	FAT	Pr	FAT	Pr	FAT	2P	FAT	1Q	FAT	3Q

Club Factfile

Founded: 1882   **Nickname:** Hillians   **Manager:** Ian Chapman

Previous Names: Burgess Hill 1882-1969.

Previous Leagues: Mid Sussex >1958, Sussex County 1958-2003, Southern 2003-04

Club Colours (change): Green/black/green (Red/white/green)

RECORDS
Goalscorer: Ashley Carr - 208
Appearances: Paul Williams - 499

HONOURS
FA Comps: None

League: Mid-Sussex 1900-01, 03-04, 39-40, 56-57. Sussex County Division Two 1974-75, Division One 75-76, 96-97, 98-99, 2001-02, 02-03. Isthmian Division One South 2014-15.

County FA: Sussex Senior Cup 1883-84, 84-85, 85-86.

BEST PERFORMANCES	**FA Cup:** Fourth Qualifying Round 1999-2000, 08-09, 14-15, 16-17.
	FA Trophy: Second Round Proper 2003-04, 04-05, 14-15.
	FA Vase: Quarter-Finals 2001-02.

BURGESS HILL MATCH RESULTS 2016-17

Date	Comp	H/A	Opponents	Att:	Result	Goalscorers	Pos	No.
Aug 13	IsthP	A	Needham Market	228	D 1 - 1	Richardson-Brown 84	11	1
15	IsthP	H	Tonbridge Angels	387	L 1 - 2	L.Harding 90	16	2
20	IsthP	H	Enfield Town	309	W 1 - 0	Thompson 90	12	3
23	IsthP	A	Hendon	164	D 1 - 1	Thompson 70	12	4
27	IsthP	A	Leiston	203	L 0 - 2		15	5
29	IsthP	H	Folkestone Invicta	354	W 4 - 2	Richardson-Brown 12 Redwood 66 Pearse 81 Blanks 90(og)	9	6
Sept 3	FAC1Q	H	Ashford United	365	W 2 - 1	Richardson-Brown 76 Thompson 80		7
10	IsthP	A	Dulwich Hamlet	1069	D 2 - 2	Pearse 59 Richmond 90	11	8
17	FAC2Q	H	Kempston Rovers	167	D 1 - 1	Smith 65		9
20	FAC2Qr	H	Kempston Rovers	258	W 3 - 1	Fisk 41 47 Richardson-Brown 75		10
24	IsthP	A	Grays Athletic	147	D 1 - 1	Izuchukwu 45	14	11
27	IsthP	A	Bognor Regis Town	367	D 1 - 1	L.Harding 2	15	12
Oct 1	FAC3Q	H	Cadbury Heath	333	W 6 - 1	P.HARDING 3 (4 49 77) Thompson 28 (pen)		13
						Richardson-Brown 64 Pearse 84		
4	IsthP	H	Havant & Waterlooville	186	D 3 - 3	Pearse 19 P.Harding 35 90	18	14
8	IsthP	H	Leatherhead	482	W 3 - 2	Pearse 58 (pen) Fisk 64 Brivio 76	11	15
15	FAC4Q	H	Dover Athletic	629	L 0 - 5			16
22	IsthP	H	Needham Market	366	L 0 - 3		17	17
25	IsthP	H	Hendon	256	W 1 - 0	Cox 53	15	18
29	FAT1Q	H	Beaconsfield	226	W 5 - 1	Smith 5 Cox 37 90 Fisk 44 Ayunga 72		19
Nov 5	IsthP	A	Metropolitan Police	102	L 1 - 2	McDonald 86	17	20
15	FAT2Q	H	Chalfont St Peter	185	D 2 - 2	Izuchukwu 52 Richardson-Brown 78		21
19	IsthP	A	Lowestoft	404	L 0 - 1		17	22
22	FAT2Qr	H	Chalfont St Peter	54	D 1 - 1	Pearse 57 won 8-7 on penalties aet		23
26	FAT3Q	H	Hitchin Town	243	L 0 - 3			24
Dec 3	IsthP	H	Grays Athletic	305	W 2 - 1	L.Harding 90 Thompson 63	19	25
10	IsthP	H	Billericay Town	306	W 2 - 1	Pearse 19 (pen) Blake 43	17	26
13	IsthP	A	AFC Sudbury	121	L 0 - 3		18	27
17	IsthP	A	Staines Town	238	W 2 - 1	Brivio 42 L. Harding 50	17	28
26	IsthP	H	Worthing	521	L 0 - 1		18	29
31	IsthP	A	Merstham	189	D 2 - 2	Richmond 90 Medlock 90	18	30
Jan 2	IsthP	A	Folkestone Invicta	359	L 1 - 3	Medlock 57	18	31
7	IsthP	H	Leiston	303	L 0 - 6		19	32
10	IsthP	A	Wingate & Finchley	102	L 1 - 2	Pearse 8	19	33
14	IsthP	A	Havant & Waterlooville	582	L 0 - 1		20	34
17	IsthP	A	Tonbridge Angels	256	D 0 - 0		20	35
28	IsthP	A	Enfield Town	376	W 1 - 0	Richardson-Brown 84	18	36
Feb 4	IsthP	H	AFC Sudbury	302	W 2 - 0	Brivio 35 Smith-Joseph 90	17	37
11	IsthP	A	Leatherhead	240	W 2 - 1	Brivio 51 Medlock 67	16	38
14	IsthP	H	Canvey Island	201	D 1 - 1	Richardson-Brown 84	16	39
18	IsthP	H	Metropolitan Police	287	L 1 - 4	Medlock 48 (pen)	17	40
21	IsthP	H	Wingate & Finchley	263	L 2 - 3	P.Harding 36 Brivio 46	18	41
25	IsthP	A	Canvey Island	278	L 1 - 2	Richardson-Brown 33	18	42
Mar 4	IsthP	H	Lowestoft	443	L 1 - 3	Richardson-Brown 16	20	43
7	IsthP	H	Harrow Borough	241	W 5 - 1	Richmond 28 Redrigues 42 SMITH-JOSEPH 3 (45 65 76p)	18	44
11	IsthP	A	Billericay Town	829	L 0 - 4		19	45
14	IsthP	H	Bognor Regis Town	405	L 1 - 3	Richmond 60	19	46
18	IsthP	H	Staines Town	302	D 3 - 3	Smith-Joseph 29 P.Harding 30 L.Harding 57	20	47
21	IsthP	H	Harlow Town	245	L 0 - 1		20	48
25	IsthP	H	Kingstonian	438	W 2 - 1	Rodrigues 2 Fisk 65	20	49
Apr 1	IsthP	A	Harlow Town	240	D 2 - 2	Richardson-Brown 2 Hazel 85	20	50
4	IsthP	A	Kingstonian	349	L 0 - 2		20	51
8	IsthP	A	Harrow Borough	156	W 2 - 0	Richardson-Brown 29 45	18	52
15	IsthP	H	Dulwich Hamlet	243	L 0 - 3		21	53
17	IsthP	A	Worthing	565	D 1 - 1	Richardson-Brown 61	21	54
22	IsthP	H	Merstham	466	W 2 - 1	Miles 19 Fisk 90	20	55

GOALSCORERS	SG	CSG	Pens	Hat tricks	Total		SG	CSG	Pens	Hat tricks	Total
2015-16 Smith					12	Cox	2				3
Richardson-Brown	13				13	Izuchukwu	2				2
Pearse	7	3	2		8	Rodrigues	2				2
P.Harding	4	2		1	7	Smith	2				2
Fisk	6				6	Ayunga	1				1
Brivio	5				5	Blake	1				1
L.Harding	5				5	Hazel	1				1
Smith-Joseph	3	1	1		5	McDonald	1				1
Thompson	5		1		5	Miles	1				1
Medlock	4		1		4	Opponents					1
Richmond	3				4	Redwood	1				1

DORKING WANDERERS

Club Contact Details
West Humble Playing Fields, London Road, Dorking, Surrey RH5 6AD
07500 006 240
m-clarke@blueyonder.co.uk

Ground Capacity: **Seats:** Yes   **Covered:** Yes   **Clubhouse:** Yes   **Shop:** Yes

Record Attendance
Not known - If you know please email tw.publications@btinternet.com
Previous Grounds
Big Field Brockham >2007.

10 YEAR RECORD

07-08	08-09	09-10	10-11	11-12	12-13	13-14	14-15	15-16	16-17
			SxC3 1	SxC2 3	SxC1 20	SxC1 8	SxC1 2	Isth1S 2	Isth1S 2
						FAC Pr	FAC 2Qr	FAC 1Q	FAC 1Q
					FAV 2Q	FAV 2Qr	FAV 2Q	FAT 1Qr	FAT P

Club Factfile

Founded: 1999   **Nickname:** Wanderers   **Manager:** Marc White

Previous Names: None

Previous Leagues: Crawley & District 1999-2000. West Sussex 2000-2007. Sussex County 2007-2015.

Club Colours (change): Red & white stripes (Green)

RECORDS

HONOURS

FA Comps: None

League: West Sussex Division Four North 2000-01, Division Two North 2003-04, Premier Division 2006-07.
Sussex County Division Three 2010-11.

County FA: None

BEST PERFORMANCES	**FA Cup:** Second Qualifying Round 2014-15(r).
	FA Trophy: First Qualifying Round 2015-16(r).
	FA Vase: Second Qualifying Round 2012-13, 13-14(r), 14-15.

Burgess Hill Town 2016-17 and their 'magic ball' - 19th in the Premier Division. Photo: Alan Coomes.

DULWICH HAMLET

Club Contact Details
Champion Hill Stadium, Dog Kennell Hill, Edgar Kail Way SE22 8BD
020 7274 8707

Ground Capacity: 3,000   **Seats:** 500   **Covered:** 1,000   **Clubhouse:** Yes   **Shop:** Yes

Record Attendance
3,000 v Maidstone United, 18/04/2015.
Previous Grounds
Woodwarde Rd 1893-95,College Farm 95-96,Sunray Ave 1896-02,Freeman's Gd,Champ Hill 02-12,Champ Hill (old grd)12-92

10 YEAR RECORD

07-08	08-09	09-10	10-11	11-12	12-13	13-14	14-15	15-16	16-17
Isth1S 6	Isth1S 12	Isth1S 12	Isth1S 5	Isth1S 3	Isth1S 1	Isth P 6	Isth P 4	Isth P 5	Isth P 3
FAC 3Q	FAC 2Qr	FAC 1Q	FAC Pr	FAC 2Q	FAC 2Q	FAC 3Q	FAC 1Q	FAC 2Q	FAC 2Q
FAT P	FAT 2Q	FAT P	FAT 2Q	FAT 1Q	FAT P	FAT 3Qr	FAT 2Q	FAT 2P	FAT QFr

Club Factfile

Founded: 1893   **Nickname:** Hamlet   **Manager:** Gavin Rose

Previous Names: None

Previous Leagues: Camberwell 1894-97. Southern Suburban 1897-1900, 01-07. Dulwich 1900-01. Spartan 1907-08

Club Colours (change): Navy blue and pink/navy blue/navy blue (Red, white & black hoops/red/red)

RECORDS
Victory:	13-0 v Walton-on-Thames, Surrey Senior Cup, 1936-37
Defeat:	1-10 v Hendon, Isthmian league, 1963-64
Goalscorer:	Edgar Kail - 427 (1919-33)
Appearances:	Reg Merritt - 576 (1950-66)
Additional:	Received £35,000 from Charlton Athletic for Chris Dickson 2007

HONOURS
FA Comps: FA Amateur Cup 1919-20, 31-32, 33-34, 36-37.

League: Isthmian League Premier Division x4, Division One 1977-78, Division One South 2012-13.

County FA: London Senior Cup x5. Surrey Senior Cup x16.
London Challenge Cup 1998-99.

BEST PERFORMANCES	**FA Cup:** 1RP 1925-26, 26-27, 27-28, 28-29, 29-30, 30-31(r), 32-33, 33-34(r), 34-35, 35-36, 36-37, 37-38, 48-49, 98-99.
	FA Trophy: Quarter-Finals 1979-80(r), 2016-17(r).
	FA Vase: N/A

DULWICH HAMLET MATCH RESULTS 2016-17

Date	Comp	H/A	Opponents	Att:	Result	Goalscorers	Pos	No.
Aug 13	IsthP	A	AFC Sudbury	401	D 2 - 2	Beaney 37 Daniel 40	9	1
16	IsthP	H	Enfield Town	843	W 2 - 1	Clunis 45 Carr 61	7	2
20	IsthP	H	Leiston	845	L 2 - 4	Tomlin 48 Chambers 61	13	3
23	IsthP	A	Harlow Town	328	W 2 - 1	Carew 48 Carr 73	8	4
27	IsthP	H	Canvey Island	768	L 1 - 2	Tomlin 23	12	5
29	IsthP	A	Hendon	335	D 1 - 1	Tomlin 62	11	6
Sept 3	FAC1Q	A	Pagham	230	W 3 - 0	Tomlin 26 75 Weatherstone 30		7
10	IsthP	H	Burgess Hill Town	1069	D 2 - 2	Tomlin 43 Toure 74 (og)	13	8
17	FAC2Q	H	Hendon	822	L 0 - 2			9
20	IsthP	A	Metropolitan Police	188	D 1 - 1	Green 19	10	10
24	IsthP	H	Folkestone Invicta	1278	W 6 - 1	Ming 27 Tomlin 29 Clunis 37 Carr 49 (pen) Teniola 71 84	7	11
27	IsthP	H	Harrow Borough	711	L 1 - 4	Clunis 41	9	12
Oct 1	IsthP	A	Enfield Town	467	D 2 - 2	Carr 32 Carew 61	10	13
4	IsthP	A	Lowestoft Town	413	W 3 - 0	Clunis 12 90 Carr 52	6	14
8	IsthP	H	Bognor Regis Town	2217	L 1 - 3	Sekajja 21	7	15
15	IsthP	A	Leatherhead	426	D 2 - 2	Sekajja 33 Carr 85	7	16
18	IsthP	H	Harlow Town	750	W 3 1	Sekaija 35 Carew 73 (pen) Clunis76	5	17
22	IsthP	H	AFC Sudbury	1663	W 2 - 0	Dumaka 47 Tomlin 82	5	18
29	FAT1Q	A	Lowestoft Town	428	W 2 - 1	Karagiannis 21 Carr 78		19
Nov 1	IsthP	A	Staines Town	228	L 0 - 2		5	20
5	IsthP	A	Needham Market	334	D 1 - 1	Dumaka 62	6	21
12 Nov	FAT2Q	H	Chesham United	716	W 4 - 0	Green 24 Dumaka 47 Karagiannis 69 Clunis 90		22
19	IsthP	A	Worthing	2032	W 4 - 1	Dumaka 30 Karagiannis 45 Weatherstone 53 Carew 78	6	23
22	IsthP	A	Harrow Borough	205	W 2 - 0	Sekajja 23 Karagiannis 47	5	24
26	FAT3Q	A	Winchester City	319	W 1 - 0	Green 26		25
29	IsthP	A	Metropolitan Police	725	D 3 - 3	Dumaka 23 Green 25 Karagiannis	5	26
Dec 3	IsthP	A	Folkestone Invicta	434	D 1 - 1	Dumaka 80	5	27
6	IsthP	H	Staines Town	598	W 3 - 1	Dumaka 21 Karagiannis 54 (pen) Clunis 82		28
10	FAT1	H	Royston Town	701	D 2 - 2	Clunis 65 Carr 88		29
13	FAT1r	A	Royston Town	310	W 1 - 0	Clunis 85		30
17	IsthP	H	Tonbridge Angels	1541	L 1 - 2	Nelson 49 (og)	6	31
19	IsthP	A	Kingstonian	382	W 1 - 0	Clunis 5	4	32
26	IsthP	A	Grays Athletic	317	W 2 - 0	Dumaka 51 Clunis 90	4	33
31	IsthP	H	Wingate & Finchley	1910	D 1 - 1	Dumaka 21	4	34
Jan 2	IsthP	H	Hendon	1146	W 2 - 1	Carew 25 Beaney 62	4	35
7	IsthP	A	Canvey Island	314	L 0 - 1		4	36
14	FAT2	A	Whitehawk	530	W 4 - 1	Tomlin 72 76 Carew 80 90		37
28	IsthP	A	Leiston	390	D 2 - 2	Weatherstone 10 Carew 72 (pen)	7	38
Feb 4	FAT3	A	Braintree Town	608	D 0 - 0			39
7	FAT3r	H	Braintree Town	860	W 5 2	Carew 28 (pen) Parry 50 (og) Tomlin 61 Ming 78 Erskine 90		40
11	IsthP	A	Bognor Regis Town	447	D 1 - 1	Drage 18	9	41
18	IsthP	H	Needham Market	1960	W 2 - 0	Akinyemi 14 Erskine 49	8	42
25	FATQF	H	Macclesfield Town	2834	D 2 - 2	Taylor 25 Carew 87		43
Mar 4	IsthP	H	Worthing	763	W 1 - 0	Akinyemi 46	8	44
7	FATQFr	A	Macclesfield Town	1017	L 0 - 2			45
11	IsthP	H	Merstham	1564	W 5 - 0	Green 10 Tomlin 24 35 Akinyemi 59 Rutherford 88	7	46
18	IsthP	A	Tonbridge Angels	656	D 0 - 0		9	47
20	IsthP	H	Kingstonian	595	W 4 - 2	Carew 9 (pen) Sekajja 49 90 Akinyemi 53	7	48
22	IsthP	H	Havant & Waterlooville	651	W 3 - 0	Akinyami 21 Dumaka 74 Clunis 90	7	49
25	IsthP	H	Billericay Town	2805	L 0 - 3		7	50
28	IsthP	A	Billericay Town	1302	W 2 - 0	Sekajja 21 Carew 33	6	51
Apr 1	IsthP	A	Havant & Waterlooville	859	L 1 - 2	Sekaija 37	6	52
4	IsthP	H	Leatherhead	912	D 1 - 1	Kargbo 86	5	53
8	IsthP	H	Lowestoft Town	1806	W 3 - 1	Sekajja 23 Dumaka 55 Camara 75	4	54
11	IsthP	A	Merstham	336	W 4 - 1	Tomlin 11 60 Weatherstone 64 Chambers 80	3	55
15	IsthP	H	Burgess Hill Town	549	W 3 - 0	Tomlin 21 Beaney 21 Camara 86	3	56
17	IsthP	H	Grays Athletic	1874	L 0 - 1		3	57
22	IsthP	A	Wingate & Finchley	440	W 3 - 0	Sekajiia 48 60 Camara 76	3	58
27	PO SF	H	Enfield Town	2517	W 4 - 2	SEKAJJA 3 (1 31 32) Tomlin 65		59
May 1	PO F	A	Bognor Regis Town	3119	L 1 - 2	Kargbo		60

GOALSCORERS	SG	CSG	Pens	Hat tricks	Total		SG	CSG	Pens	Hat tricks	Total
2015-16 Carew					17	Opponents	3				3
Tomlin	13	4			17	Chambers	2				2
Sekajja	10	3		1	14	Erskine	2				2
Clunis	12	3			13	Kargbo	2				2
Carew	11	2	4		12	Ming	2				2
Dumaka	10	3			11	Teniola	2				2
Carr	8	2	1		8	Drage	1				1
Karagiannis	6	3	1		6	Daniel	1				1
Akinyemi	5				5	Rutherford	1				1
Green	5	2			5	Taylor	1				1
Weatherstone	4				4						
Beaney	3				3						
Camara	3				3						

ENFIELD TOWN

Club Contact Details
Queen Elizabeth Stadium, Donkey Lane, Enfield EN1 3PL
07787 875 650
nigel.howard71@gmail.com

Ground Capacity: 2,500 **Seats:** Yes **Covered:** Yes **Clubhouse:** Yes **Shop:** No

Record Attendance
969 v Tottenham Hotspur, friendly, November 2011.
Previous Grounds
Brimsdown Rovers FC 2001-2010

10 YEAR RECORD

07-08		08-09		09-10		10-11		11-12		12-13		13-14		14-15		15-16		16-17	
Isth1N	12	Isth1N	12	Isth1N	4	Isth1N	6	Isth1N	2	Isth P	16	Isth P	19	Isth P	7	Isth P	6	Isth P	4
FAC	2Qr	FAC	P	FAC	2Q	FAC	3Q	FAC	P	FAC	2Q	FAC	2Qr	FAC	2Qr	FAC	4Q	FAC	1Q
FAT	P	FAT	1Q	FAT	2Q	FAT	2Q	FAT	1Q	FAT	3Q	FAT	2Q	FAT	1Q	FAT	2Q	FAV	2Q

Club Factfile

Founded: 2001 **Nickname:** ET's or Towers   **Manager:** Andy Leese

Previous Names: Broke away from Enfield F.C. in 2001

Previous Leagues: Essex Senior 2001-2005. Southern 2005-2006.

Club Colours (change): White/blue/blue (Pink/grey/pink)

RECORDS
Victory: 7-0 v Ilford (A) - 29/04/2003
Goalscorer: Liam Hope - 108 (2009-15)
Appearances: Rudi Hall

HONOURS
FA Comps: None

League: Essex Senior 2002-03, 04-05.

County FA: Middlesex Charity Cup 2001-02, 07-08.

BEST PERFORMANCES	**FA Cup:** Fourth Qualifying Round 2015-16.
	FA Trophy: Third Qualifying Round 2012-13
	FA Vase: Third Round Proper 2003-04, 04-05.

ENFIELD TOWN MATCH RESULTS 2016-17

Date	Comp	H/A	Opponents	Att:	Result	Goalscorers	Pos	No.
Aug 13	IsthP	H	Canvey Island	404	D 1 - 1	Campbell 90	13	1
17	IsthP	A	Dulwich Hamlet	843	L 1 - 1	Crook 27 (pen)	17	2
20	IsthP	A	Burgess Hill Town	309	L 0 - 0		20	3
23	IsthP	H	Staines Town	302	W 3 - 3	Collins 6 Neita 24 Ottaway 26	14	4
27	IsthP	A	AFC Sudbury	362	D 0 - 0		18	5
29	IsthP	H	Harrow Borough	405	D 0 - 0		19	6
Sept 3	FAC1Q	A	Hanwell Town	212	L 0 - 1			7
10	IsthP	A	Folkestone Invicta	387	L 0 - 2		22	8
20	IsthP	A	Staines Town	191	D 2 - 2	Ottaway 37 Bihmoutine 90	23	9
24	IsthP	H	Hendon	313	W 6 - 0	Kiangebeni 23 Dickson 42 76 Wynter 56 Ottaway 58 Gabriel 64	18	10
27	IsthP	H	Metropolitan Police	254	W 1 - 0	Bihmoutine 76	12	11
Oct 1	IsthP	H	Dulwich Hamlet	467	D 2 - 2	Ottaway 2 Crook 82 (pen)	13	12
8	IsthP	A	Merstham	188	D 2 - 2	Devyne 84 Gabriel 90	Y	13
15	IsthP	H	Wingate & Finchley	380	L 0 - 1		17	14
17	IsthP	A	Kingstonian	271	W 2 - 0	Neita 80 Wynter 90	10	15
22	IsthP	A	Canvey Island	325	W 5 - 1	Bihmoutine 42 Neita 53 Crook 67 (pen) Wynter 82 82	7	16
29	FAT1Q	A	Canvey Island	273	W 3 - 2	Crook Devyne (2)		17
Nov 5	IsthP	A	Worthing	424	W 2 - 1	Shulton 12 Crook 72	7	18
12	FAT2Q	A	Kings Langley	222	L 0 - 1			19
19	IsthP	A	Havant & Waterlooville	626	W 2 - 0	Ottaway 2 Collins 61	8	20
26	IsthP	H	Tonbridge Angels	415	D 1 - 1	Kirby 90	9	21
29	IsthP	H	Staines Town	274	W 2 - 1	Collins 57 Purcell 64	6	22
Dec 3	IsthP	A	Hendon	256	D 1 - 1	Crook 76 (pen)	6	23
10	IsthP	H	Needham Market	354	D 3 - 3	Crook 3 Ottaway 30 Purcell 37	7	24
13	IsthP	H	Lowestoft Town	232	D 2 - 2	Campbell 32 90	7	25
17	IsthP	A	Leatherhead	375	L 1 - 2	Wynter 69	8	26
26	IsthP	H	Harlow Town	550	W 3 - 0	Kirby 49 Wynter 57 Crook 90	8	27
31	IsthP	A	Leiston	363	D 1 - 1	Shulton 63	7	28
Jan 2	IsthP	A	Harrow Borough	268	W 5 - 1	Shulton 12 Crook 13 Wynter 42 Gabriel 55 Ottaway 70	6	29
7	IsthP	H	AFC Sudbury	407	W 1 - 0	Campbell 15	6	30
14	IsthP	A	Bognor Regis Town	447	D 1 - 1	Gabriel	6	31
21	IsthP	H	Grays Athletic	575	W 2 - 0	Devyne 58 Crook 71	6	32
28	IsthP	H	Burgess Hill Town	376	L 0 - 1		6	33
31	IsthP	A	Metropolitan Police	107	L 0 - 3		6	34
Feb 4	IsthP	A	Wingate & Finchley	365	W 5 - 1	Devyne 7 Ottaway 12 81 Oliyide 31 Crook 66	6	35
11	IsthP	H	Merstham	329	L 2 - 3	Crook 23 Oliyidi 59	6	36
14	IsthP	A	Tonbridge Angels	304	L 0 - 3		6	37
18	IsthP	A	Worthing	881	W 3 - 1	Shulton 31 Crook 47 Oliyidi 58	6	38
25	IsthP	A	Lowestoft	433	L 1 - 2	Crook 32 (pen)	8	39
28	IsthP	H	Billericay Town	278	D 2 - 2	Joseph 21 Oliyide 32	7	40
Mar 4	IsthP	H	Havant & Waterlooville	519	L 1 - 4	Crook 32	8	41
11	IsthP	A	Needham Market	326	W 3 - 1	Morphew 1 (og) Joseph 12 Bihmoutine 29	8	42
18	IsthP	H	Leatherhead	515	W 2 - 1	Gabriel 60 Compton 76	7	43
25	IsthP	H	Grays Athletic	292	W 3 - 1	Shulton 15 17 Ottaway 80	7	44
Apr 1	IsthP	H	Bognor Regis Town	687	W 1 - 0	Oliyidi 30	7	45
8	IsthP	A	Billericay Town	1251	W 4 - 2	Kiangebeni 2 Ottaway 57 Wynter 75 Crook 90	5	46
15	IsthP	H	Folkestone Invicta	623	W 3 - 1	Kirby 4 Ottaway 24 Wynter 47	5	47
17	IsthP	A	Harlow Town	607	W 3 - 0	Ottaway 53 76 Oliyide 90	4	48
22	IsthP	H	Leiston	812	D 1 - 1	Devyne 86	4	49
27	PO SF	A	Dulwich Hamlet	2517	L 2 - 4	Crook 38 Ottaway 85		50

GOALSCORERS	SG	CSG	Pens	Hat tricks	Total		SG	CSG	Pens	Hat tricks	Total
2015-16 Whiteley					23	Collins	3				3
Crook	17	3	5		17	Kirby	3				3
Ottaway	13	3			15	Neita	3				3
Wynter	8				9	Dickson	1				2
Devyne	6				6	Joseph	2				2
Oliyidi	5				6	Kiangebeni	2				2
Shulton	6				6	Purcell	2				2
Gabriel	5				5	Compton	1				1
Bihmoutine	3				4	Opponents	1				1
Campbell	4				4						

FOLKESTONE INVICTA

Club Contact Details
The Fullicks Stadium, Cheriton Road CT19 5JU
01303 257 461
richardmurrill@gmail.com

Ground Capacity: 4,000   **Seats:** 900   **Covered:** Yes   **Clubhouse:** Yes   **Shop:** Yes

The Fullicks Stadium

Record Attendance
2,332 v West Ham United, benefit match, 1996-97.

Previous Grounds
South Road Hythe > 1991, County League matches on council pitches

10 YEAR RECORD

07-08		08-09		09-10		10-11		11-12		12-13		13-14		14-15		15-16		16-17	
Isth P	21	Isth1S	11	Isth1S	2	Isth P	22	Isth1S	4	Isth1S	5	Isth1S	2	Isth1S	2	Isth1S	1	Isth P	16
FAC	4Q	FAC	2Q	FAC	1Q	FAC	2Qr	FAC	1Q	FAC	1Q	FAC	2Q	FAC	1Qr	FAC	1Qr	FAC	3Q
FAT	1Q	FAT	Pr	FAT	P	FAT	3Q	FAT	3Q	FAT	Pr	FAT	2Qr	FAT	2Qr	FAT	Pr	FAT	2Q

Club Factfile

Founded: 1936   **Nickname:** The Seasiders   **Manager:** Neil Cugley

Previous Names: None

Previous Leagues: East Kent Amateur. Kent County Eastern Section. Kent 1990-98, Southern 1998-2004

Club Colours (change): Black & amber

RECORDS
Victory: 13-0 v Faversham Town - Kent League Division One, May 1995.
Defeat: 1-7 v Crockenhill - Kent League Division One, February 1993 & v Welling United, Kent Senior Cup, February 2009.
Goalscorer: James Dryden - 141
Appearances: Michael Everitt - 631

HONOURS
FA Comps: None

League: Kent County Eastern Division One 1969-70, Premier 78-79. Kent Division Two 1991-92.
Isthmian Division One South 2015-16.

County FA: Kent Intermediate Shield 1991-92.

BEST PERFORMANCES	**FA Cup:** First Round Proper 2005-06.
	FA Trophy: Third Round Proper 1998-99, 2000-01, 03-04.
	FA Vase: Fourth Round Proper 1997-98.

FOLKESTONE INVICTA MATCH RESULTS 2016-17

Date	Comp	H/A	Opponents	Att:	Result	Goalscorers	Pos	No.
Aug 13	IsthP	H	Harrow Borough	361	W 3 - 0	Pattie 60 Heard 67 Draycott 86	2	1
17	IsthP	A	Staines Town	215	W 2 - 0	Pattie 2 Vincent 75	2	2
20	IsthP	A	Havant & Waterlooville	520	L 0 - 1		6	3
23	IsthP	H	Merstham	324	D 0 - 0		6	4
27	IsthP	H	Needham Market	338	L 0 - 1		9	5
29	IsthP	A	Burgess Hill Town	354	L 2 - 4	Dolan 8 Draycott 75	13	6
Sept 3	FAC1Q	H	North Greenford United	337	W 3 - 1	Draycott 47 86 Rook 72		7
10	IsthP	H	Enfield Town	387	W 2 - 0	Muleba 44 (og) Draycott 71	7	8
17	FAC2Q	H	Waltham Forest	280	W 3 - 1	Heard 16 Draycott 62 Sahadow 90		9
20	IsthP	H	Leatherhead	447	D 1 - 1	Draycott 90	7	10
24	IsthP	A	Dulwich Hamlet	1278	L 1 - 6	Taylor 6	12	11
27	IsthP	A	Billericay Town	211	L 0 - 1		17	12
Oct 1	FAC3Q	A	North Leigh	202	L 1 - 3	Rook 86		13
8	IsthP	A	Worthing	712	D 3 - 3	Taylor 20 O'Connor 50 Chappell 90		14
15	IsthP	H	Kingstonian	441	W 3 - 1	Cornwall 18 Dolan 34 Taylor 73	16	15
18	IsthP	A	Merstham	125	L 1 - 3	Draycott 39 (pen)	19	16
22	IsthP	A	Harrow Borough	203	L 1 - 4	O'Connor 10	19	17
25	IsthP	H	Staines Town	315	D 1 - 1	Draycott 90	18	18
29	FAT1Q	A	Cheshunt	144	W 3 - 1	Taylor 1 Miller 18 Draycott 54		19
Nov 5	IsthP	H	Canvey Island	308	W 6 - 0	Chappell 37 Taylor 53 Draycott 64 Cornwell 70 89 Rook 86	16	20
8	IsthP	H	Leiston	357	W 2 - 0	Hasler 42 Wright 45	11	21
12	FAT2Q	H	North Leigh	291	L 2 - 3	Woodley 2 (og) Draycott 4		22
19	IsthP	H	AFC Sudbury	331	W 4 - 2	Taylor 21 Chappell 50 Cornwall 59 78	13	23
22	IsthP	H	Billericay Town	283	W 1 - 0	Hasler 55	7	24
Dec 3	IsthP	H	Dulwich Hamlet	436	D 1 - 1	Taylor 42 (pen)	10	25
10	IsthP	A	Hendon	147	D 3 - 3	Taylor 33 55 Wright 42		26
17	IsthP	H	Bognor Regis Town	463	L 1 - 2	Taylor 22	11	27
26	IsthP	A	Tonbridge Angels	586	D 2 - 2	Taylor 35 Dolan 83	13	28
31	IsthP	H	Grays Athletic	524	L 0 - 1		13	29
Jan 2	IsthP	H	Burgess Hill Town	359	W 3 - 1	Chappell 15 Taylor 65 86	13	30
7	IsthP	A	Needham Market	257	L 1 - 2	Cornwall 73	13	31
14	IsthP	A	Metropolitan Police	112	L 0 - 1		14	32
21	IsthP	H	Lowestoft	437	W 4 - 1	Taylor 48 Draycott 56 (pen) Wright 61 Cornwall 86	14	33
28	IsthP	H	Havant & Waterlooville	419	L 1 - 3	Hasler 43	15	34
Feb 4	IsthP	A	Kingstonian	262	D 2 - 2	Starkey 39 Draycott 79	15	35
11	IsthP	H	Worthing	309	L 2 - 4	Wright 30 Draycoct 47	15	36
14	IsthP	A	Wingate & Finchley	84	L 2 - 3	Draycoctt 69 79	15	37
18	IsthP	A	Canvey Island	361	W 3 - 1	Draycott 26 Cornwall 33 90	15	38
21	IsthP	A	Harlow Town	177	D 2 - 2	Sahadow 88 Cornwall 90	15	39
25	IsthP	H	Harlow Town	328	L 1 - 4	Taylor 72	16	40
Mar 4	IsthP	A	AFC Sudbury	300	L 1 - 3	Hasller 25	16	41
11	IsthP	A	Wingate & Finchley	347	W 1 - 0	Taylor 12	15	42
15	IsthP	A	Leatherhead	328	L 0 - 2		16	43
18	IsthP	A	Bognor Regis Town	531	L 1 - 7	Draycott 3	17	44
21	IsthP	A	Leiston	244	L 1 - 2	Taylor 51	17	45
25	IsthP	A	Lowestoft	545	D 2 - 2	Draycott 28 Chappell 69	17	46
Apr 1	IsthP	H	Metropolitan Police	419	W 2 - 0	Taylor 15 Everitt 36	16	47
8	IsthP	H	Hendon	455	L 1 - 2	Ferguson 37	19	48
15	IsthP	A	Enfield Town	623	L 1 - 3	Taylor 67	22	49
17	IsthP	H	Tonbridge Angels	593	W 1 - 0	Blanks 40	19	50
22	IsthP	A	Grays Athletic	292	W 3 - 0	Taylor 60 Draycott 79 84 (pen)	16	51

GOALSCORERS	SG	CSG	Pens	Hat tricks	Total		SG	CSG	Pens	Hat tricks	Total
Draycott	19	5	2		22	Opponents	2				2
Taylor	17	4	1		20	Pattie	2				2
Cornwall	7				10	Sahadow	2				2
Chappell	5				5	Blanks	1				1
Hasler	4				4	Everitt	1				1
Wright	4				4	Ferguson	1				1
Dolan	3				3	Miller	1				1
Rook	3				3	Starkey	1				1
Heard	2				2	Vincent	1				1
O'Connor	2				2						

HARLOW TOWN

Club Contact Details
The Harlow Arena, off Elizabeth Way, The Pinnacles, Harlow CM19 5BE
01279 443 196
harlowtownfc@aol.com

Ground Capacity: 3,500   **Seats:** 500   **Covered:** 500   **Clubhouse:** Yes   **Shop:** Yes

Record Attendance
9,723 v Leicester City - FA Cup 3rd Round replay 08/01/1980
Previous Grounds
Green Man Field 1879-60. Harlow Sportcentre 1960-2006.

10 YEAR RECORD

07-08		08-09		09-10		10-11		11-12		12-13		13-14		14-15		15-16		16-17	
Isth P	15	Isth P	20	Isth1N	22	Isth1N	4	Isth1N	7	Isth1N	21	Isth1N	4	Isth1N	2	Isth1N	3	Isth P	10
FAC	2Q	FAC	1P	FAC	Pr	FAC	2Q	FAC	P	FAC	P	FAC	2Q	FAC	1Qr	FAC	4Q	FAC	2Q
FAT	1Qr	FAT	1Q	FAT	P	FAT	1P	FAT	3Q	FAT	Pr	FAT	P	FAT	1Q	FAT	2Q	FAT	2P

Club Factfile

Founded: 1879   **Nickname:** Hawks   **Manager:** Danny Chapman

Previous Names: Harlow & Burnt Mill 1898-1902.

Previous Leagues: East Hertfordshire > 1932, Spartan 1932-39, 46-54, London 1954-61, Delphian 1961-63, Athenian 1963-73, Isthmian 1973-92, Inactive 1992-93, Southern 2004-06

Club Colours (change): All red with yellow trim (All yellow)

RECORDS
Victory: 14-0 v Bishop's Stortford - 11/04/1925
Defeat: 0-11 v Ware (A) - Spartan Division 1 East 06/03/1948
Goalscorer: Dick Marshall scored 64 during 1928-29, Alex Read scored 52 during 2013-14.
Appearances: Norman Gladwin - 639 (1951-70)

HONOURS
FA Comps: None

League: East Herts Division One 1911-12, 22-23, 28-29, 29-30. Athenian Division One 1971-72. Isthmian Division One 1978-79, Division Two North 1988-89.

County FA: Essex Senior cup 1978-79

BEST PERFORMANCES	**FA Cup:** Fourth Round Proper 1979-80.
	FA Trophy: Second Round Proper 1980-81, 81-82, 99-00, 00-01(r), 01-02(r), 02-03, 16-17.
	FA Vase: Fourth Round Proper 1998-99.

HARLOW TOWN MATCH RESULTS 2016-17

Date	Comp	H/A	Opponents	Att:	Result	Goalscorers	Pos	No.
Aug 13	IsthP	H	Kingstonian	315	W 1 - 0	Read 90	7	1
16	IsthP	A	Harrow Borough	196	L 0 - 2		12	2
20	IsthP	A	Worthing	571	L 2 - 3	Perkins 46 Noto 79 (pen)	15	3
23	IsthP	H	Dulwich Hamlet	328	L 1 - 2	Read 8	19	4
27	IsthP	H	Wingate & Finchley	227	W 3 - 0	Small 23 Eadie 28 Read 33	14	5
29	IsthP	A	Canvey Island	337	D 1 - 1	Simms 22	15	6
Sept 3	FAC1Q	H	**Romford**	313	W 3 1	Read 62 66 Wixon 90		7
10	IsthP	H	Bognor Regis Town	307	W 3 - 1	Small 26 Read 73 76	6	8
17	FAC2Q	A	**Kings Lynn Town**	674	L 0 - 1			9
20	IsthP	A	Hendon	202	D 2 - 2	Blshop 38 Antione 87	8	10
24	IsthP	H	AFC Sudbury	317	L 1 - 3	Ngamb 76	10	11
27	IsthP	H	Needham Market	204	W 5 - 1	Simms 13 Noto 33 Benjamin 43 Eadie 54 Read 54	8	12
Oct 1	IsthP	A	Lowestoft	515	L 0 - 4		11	13
5	IsthP	A	Grays Athletic	163	L 1 - 3	Sonko 41	11	14
8	IsthP	A	Havant & Waterlooville	682	L 2 - 5	Gordon 39 Bishop 90	15	15
15	IsthP	H	Staines Town	303	W 1 - 0	Ngamb 86	12	16
18	IsthP	A	Dulwich Hamlet	750	L 1 3	Read 90 (pen)	11	17
22	IsthP	A	Kingstonian	261	W 1 - 0	Small 64	10	18
25	IsthP	H	Harrow Borough	194	W 2 - 0	Da Costa 60 Antoine 89	7	19
29	FAT1Q	A	**Uxbridge**	115	W 1 - 0	Da Costa 10		20
Nov 15	FAT2Q	H	**Brightlingsea Regent**	234	D 1 - 1	Read 2		21
19	IsthP	A	Billericay Town	430	D 1 - 1	Da Costa 10	9	22
22	FAT2Qr	A	**Brightlingsea Regent**	228	W 2 - 1	Read 61 75		23
26	FAT3Q	A	**Havant & Waterlooville**	197	W 3 - 1	Eadie 40 Antione 53 Read 89		24
29	IsthP	H	Hendon	206	W 2 - 0	Small 45 Antoine 85	11	25
Dec 3	IsthP	A	AFC Sudbury	272	W 2 - 1	Pope 69 Austin 79 (og)	8	26
10	FAT1	H	**Eastleigh**	482	W 2 - 0	Read 22 Benjamin 34		27
13	IsthP	A	Needham Market	224	L 1 - 2	Read 25	11	28
17	IsthP	A	Leiston	224	L 2 - 5	Small 11 Melough 90	13	29
20	IsthP	H	Merstham	208	W 2 - 1	Yiga 40 Noto 81	12	30
26	IsthP	A	Enfield Town	550	L 0 - 3		15	31
31	IsthP	H	Leatherhead	362	W 2 - 1	Muguo 60 Da Costa 79	11	32
Jan 2	IsthP	H	Canvey Island	307	D 2 - 2	Read 38 Da Costa 45	11	33
7	IsthP	A	Wingate & Finchley	145	D 0 - 0		11	34
14	FAT2	H	**York City**	816	L 1 - 2	Read 89		35
17	IsthP	H	Lowestoft Town	155	L 1 - 2	Simms 86	11	36
21	IsthP	H	Tonbridge Angels	286	W 1 0	Dadson 32	10	37
24	IsthP	H	Metropolitan Police	144	W 3 - 1	Read 5 51 Dadson 78	8	38
28	IsthP	H	Worthing	234	W 6 - 2	Read 31 Dadson 52 70 Small 63 Eadie 78 Ngamb 90	8	39
Feb 4	IsthP	A	Staines Town	239	W 2 - 0	Noto 36 62	7	40
11	IsthP	H	Havant & Waterlooville	216	L 0 - 2		7	41
18	IsthP	A	Merstham	152	L 0 - 1		9	42
21	IsthP	H	Folkestone Invicta	177	D 2 - 2	Dadson 17 Read 67	9	43
25	IsthP	A	Folkestone Invicta	328	W 4 - 1	Noto 11 Dadson 17 58 Pope 44	7	44
Mar 4	IsthP	H	Billericay Town	450	L 0 - 2		10	45
11	IsthP	A	Metropolitan Police	91	W 2 - 0	Noto 71 Read 76	10	46
18	IsthP	H	Leiston	234	L 1 - 2	Read 71	10	47
21	IsthP	A	Burgess Hill Town	245	W 1 - 0	Sonko 90	9	48
25	IsthP	A	Tonbridge Angels	529	W 3 - 0	Sonko 3 79 Simms 84	10	49
Apr 1	IsthP	H	Burgess Hill Town	240	D 2 - 2	Small 43 Pope 76	10	50
8	IsthP	H	Grays Athletic	271	W 5 - 0	READ 3 (12 50 64) Dadson 70 85	9	51
15	IsthP	A	Bognor Regis Town	789	L 0 - 3		9	52
17	IsthP	H	Enfield Town	607	L 0 - 3		10	53
22	IsthP	A	Leatherhead	485	L 2 - 3	Read 16 Sonk 72	10	54

GOALSCORERS	SG	CSG	Pens	Hat tricks	Total		SG	CSG	Pens	Hat tricks	Total
2015-16 Whiteley					23	Pope	3				3
Read	21	2	1	1	27	Benjamin	2				2
Dadson	5				7	Bishop	2				2
Noto	6		1		7	Gordon	1				1
Small	6				7	Melough	1				1
Da Costa	5	2			5	Mukuo	1				1
Antione	4	2			4	Opponents	1				1
Eadie	4				4	Perkins	1				1
Simms	4				4	Sonk	1				1
Sonko	3				4	Wixon	1				1
Ngamb	3				3	Yiga	1				1

HARROW BOROUGH

Club Contact Details

Earlsmead, Carlyon Avenue, South Harrow HA2 8SS

0844 561 1347

peter@harrowboro.co.uk

Ground Capacity: 3,070   **Seats:** 350   **Covered:** 1,000   **Clubhouse:** Yes   **Shop:** Yes

Record Attendance

3,000 v Wealdstone - FA Cup 1st Qualifying Road 1946

Previous Grounds

Northcult Road 1933-34.

10 YEAR RECORD

07-08		08-09		09-10		10-11		11-12		12-13		13-14		14-15		15-16		16-17	
Isth P	16	Isth P	14	Isth P	14	Isth P	5	Isth P	17	Isth P	15	Isth P	18	Isth P	16	Isth P	17	Isth P	21
FAC	1Q	FAC	1Qr	FAC	1Qr	FAC	1P	FAC	2Q	FAC	1Q	FAC	1Qr	FAC	4Qr	FAC	1Qr	FAC	1P
FAT	1Q	FAT	2Q	FAT	2Qr	FAT	1Q	FAT	2Qr	FAT	1Q	FAT	1Q	FAT	1Q	FAT	1Q	FAV	3Q

Club Factfile

Founded: 1933   **Nickname:** Boro   **Manager:** Steve Baker - 25/01/15

Previous Names: Roxonian 1933-38, Harrow Town 1938-66

Previous Leagues: Harrow & District 1933-34, Spartan 1934-40, 45-58, West Middlesex Combination 1940-41, Middlesex Senior 1941-45, Delphian 1956-63, Athenian 1963-75

Club Colours (change): All red (All blue)

RECORDS

Victory: 13-0 v Handley Page (A) - 18/10/1941

Defeat: 0-8 on five occasions

Goalscorer: Dave Pearce - 153

Appearances: Les Currell - 582, Colin Payne - 557, Steve Emmanuel - 522

HONOURS

FA Comps: None

League: Isthmian League 1983-84.

County FA: Middlesex Senior Cup 1982-83, 92-93, 2014-15. Middlesex Premier Cup 1981-82. Middlesex Senior Charity Cup 1979-80, 92-93, 2005-06, 06-07, 14-15.

BEST PERFORMANCES	**FA Cup:** Second Round Proper 1983-84.
	FA Trophy: Semi-Finals 1982-83.
	FA Vase: N/A

HARROW BOROUGH MATCH RESULTS 2016-17

Date	Comp	H/A	Opponents	Att:	Result	Goalscorers	Pos	No.
Aug 13	IsthP	A	Folkestone Invicta	361	L 0 - 3		21	1
16	IsthP	H	Harlow Town	196	W 2 - 0	Hope 33 Charles-Smith 35 (pen)	11	2
20	IsthP	H	Metropolitan Police	520	D 0 - 0		14	3
23	IsthP	A	Tonbridge Angels	476	L 0 - 1		16	4
27	IsthP	H	Leatherhead	138	W 3 - 1	MEITE 3 (46 58 78)	11	5
29	IsthP	A	Enfield Town	405	D 0 - 0		10	6
Sept 3	FAC1Q	H	Sawbridgeworth Town	118	W 4 - 1	Charles-Smith 26 Babalola 40 Meite 81 Bryan 89		7
10	IsthP	H	Needham Market	156	L 0 - 3		17	8
17	FAC2Q	A	Uxbridge	178	W 2 - 1	Nicholas 18 Meite 73		9
20	IsthP	H	Wingate & Finchley	152	L 0 - 1		18	10
24	IsthP	A	Merstham	454	L 0 - 5		21	11
27	IsthP	H	Dulwich Hamlet	711	W 4 - 1	Taylor 8 Driver 16 Meite 59 62	18	12
Oct 1	FAC3Q	H	Winchester City	177	W 2 - 1	Preddie 82 Meite 90		13
8	IsthP	H	Billericay Town	236	D 0 - 0		20	14
15	FAC4Q	H	Margate	309	D 2 - 2	Newman 35 Driver 79		15
18	FAC4Qr	A	Margate	574	W 3 - 1	Babalola 39 Driver 68 Meite 81		16
22	IsthP	H	Folkestone Unvicta	203	W 4 - 1	Driver 28 32 Nichols 30 Meite 74	18	17
25	IsthP	A	Harlow Town	194	L 0 - 2		18	18
29	FAT1Q	A	Herne Bay	195	D 2 - 2	Nicholas 20 Charles-Smith 90		19
Nov 1	FAT1Qr	H	Herne Bay	96	W 3 - 0	Charles-Smith 14 15 Driver 62		20
5	FAC1	A	Northampton Town	3306	L 0 - 6			21
12	FAT2Q	A	Needham Market	203	W 2 - 1	Lomas 35 Preddie 58		22
19	IsthP	H	Kingstonian	185	L 0 - 4		23	23
22	IsthP	H	Dulwich Hamlet	205	L 0 - 2		23	24
26	FAT3Q	A	Ebbsfleet United	613	L 2 - 4	Webb 53 Charles-Smith 81		25
Dec 3	IsthP	H	Merstham	141	W 1 - 0	Charles-Smith 51	23	26
6	IsthP	A	Bognor Regis Town	349	L 0 1		23	27
17	IsthP	H	AFC Sudbury	157	D 1 - 1	Driver 40	24	28
20	IsthP	H	Tpnbridge Angels	164	W 1 0	Taylor 70	22	29
26	IsthP	A	Hendon	259	W 5 - 4	Webb 2 50 (pen) Newman 11 Babalola 31 Kabba 73	20	30
31	IsthP	H	Lowestoft	223	W 4 - 2	Webb 3 Brown 34 Kabba 38 76	19	31
Jan 2	IsthP	H	Enfield Town	268	L 1 - 5	Kabba 72	19	32
7	IsthP	A	Leatherhead	310	D 2 - 2	Kabba 19 Newman 87	18	33
14	IsthP	H	Canvey Island	158	D 1 - 1	Brown 19	18	34
28	IsthP	A	Metropolitan Police	93	D 1 - 1	Bryan 39	20	35
Feb 4	IsthP	A	Bognor Regis Town	212	L 0 - 1		20	36
8	IsthP	A	Grays Athletic	128	W 5 - 2	Nicholas 17 Cumberbatch 51 Driver 71 (pen) 83 Preddie 75	19	37
11	IsthP	A	Billericay Town	429	L 1 - 2	Webb 88 (pen)	19	38
19	IsthP	H	Leiston	179	W 3 - 1	Brown 14 Kabba 84 Newman 89	19	39
21	IsthP	A	Worthing	452	W 4 - 0	Nicholas 45 Bryan 77 Cumberbatch 80 Kabba 83	17	40
25	IsthP	H	Grays Athletic	198	L 1 - 3	Cumberbatch 21 (pen)	17	41
28	IsthP	A	Wingate & Finchley	135	L 1 - 3	Bryan 33	17	42
Mar 4	IsthP	A	Kingstonian	242	W 3 - 2	Cumberbatch 45 (pen) Babalola 62 Driver 87	16	43
7	IsthP	A	Burgess Hill Town	241	L 1 - 5	Kabba 11	16	44
11	IsthP	H	Worthing	194	D 2 - 2	Babalola 4 Charles-Smith 42	17	45
14	IsthP	H	Havant & Waterlooville	159	W 2 - 1	Driver 65 Newman 84	14	46
18	IsthP	A	AFC Sudbury	263	W 3 - 1	Charles-Smith 29 Driver 45 Cumberbatch 56	13	47
21	IsthP	A	Staines Town	192	D 0 - 0		13	48
25	IsthP	H	Staines Town	242	D 0 - 0		13	49
28	IsthP	A	Havant & Waterlooville	628	L 1 - 3	Menga 5	14	50
Apr 1	IsthP	A	Canvey Island	308	L 0 - 3		14	51
8	IsthP	H	Burgess Hill Town	156	L 0 - 2		16	52
11	IsthP	A	Leiston	267	D 2 - 2	Charles-Smith 7 Lomas 79	16	53
15	IsthP	A	Nedham Market	317	L 1 - 2	Webb 59	15	54
17	IsthP	H	Hendon	328	L 0 - 2		17	55
22	IsthP	A	Lowestoft	575	L 0 - 2		21	56

GOALSCORERS	SG	CSG	Pens	Hat tricks	Total		SG	CSG	Pens	Hat tricks	Total
2015-16 Charles-Smith					19	Bryan	4				4
Driver	9	3	1		12	Brown	3				3
Meite	7	2		1	10	Preddie	3				3
Charles-Smith	10	2	1		10	Lomas	2				2
Kabba	7				8	Taylor	2				2
Webb	5		2		6	Hope	1				1
Nicholas	5				5	Menga	1				1
Babalola	5				5						
Cumberbatch	5		2		5						
Newman	5				5						

HENDON

Club Contact Details
Silver Jubilee Park, Townsend Lane, Kingsbury, London NW9 7NE
020 8205 1645
hendonfc@freenetname.co.uk

Ground Capacity: 3,070   **Seats:** 350   **Covered:** 1,000   **Clubhouse:** Yes   **Shop:**

Record Attendance
9,000 v Northampton Town - FA Cup 1st Round 1952
Previous Grounds
Claremont Road. Vale Farm (Wembley FC). Earlsmead (Harrow Borough FC).

10 YEAR RECORD

07-08	08-09	09-10	10-11	11-12	12-13	13-14	14-15	15-16	16-17
Isth P 7	Isth P 16	Isth P 10	Isth P 15	Isth P 7	Isth P 10	Isth P 8	Isth P 2	Isth P 19	Isth P 19
FAC 2Qr	FAC 3Q	FAC 4Q	FAC 1P	FAC 4Q	FAC 1P	FAC 2P	FAC 3Q	FAC 1Q	FAC 4Q
FAT 1Q	FAT 2Q	FAT 2Q	FAT 2Q	FAT 1Q	FAT 1Q	FAT 1P	FAT 3Q	FAT 1Q	FAT 1Q

Club Factfile

Founded: 1908   **Nickname:** Dons or Greens   **Manager:** Gary McCann

Previous Names: Christ Church Hampstead > 1908, Hampstead Town > 1933, Golders Green > 1946

Previous Leagues: Finchley & District 1908-11, Middlesex 1910-11, London 1911-14, Athenian 1914-63

Club Colours (change): All green (All blue)

RECORDS
Victory: 13-1 v Wingate - Middlesex County Cup 02/02/1957
Defeat: 2-11 v Walthamstowe Avenue, Athenian League 09/11/1935
Goalscorer: Freddie Evans - 176 (1929-35)
Appearances: Bill Fisher - 787 - (1940-64)
Additional: Received £30,000 from Luton Town for Iain Dowie

HONOURS

FA Comps: FA Amateur Cup 1959-60, 64-65, 71-72. European Amateur Champions 1972-73.

League: Finchley & District Division Three 1908-09, DivisioN Two 09-10, Division One 10-11. Middlesex 1912-13, 13-14. Athenian 1952-53, 55-56, 60-61. Isthmian 1964-65, 72-73.

County FA: London Senior Cup 1963-64, 68-69, 2008-09, 11-12 14-15. Middlesex Senior Cup x15 - Firstly in 1933-34 / Most recently 2003-04. Middlesex Intermediate Cup 1964-65, 66-67, 72-73. London Intermediate Cup 1962-63, 64-65, 72-73, 75-76, 79-80.

BEST PERFORMANCES	**FA Cup:** Third Round Proper 1973-74(r).
	FA Trophy: Fifth Round Proper 1998-99.
	FA Vase: N/A

HENDON MATCH RESULTS 2016-17

Date	Comp	H/A	Opponents	Att:	Result	Goalscorers	Pos	No.
Aug 13	IsthP	H	Worthing	321	L 0 - 3		22	1
15	IsthP	A	Kingstonian	271	D 1 - 1	Robins 76	22	2
20	IsthP	A	Wingate & Finchley	170	L 0 - 1		22	3
23	IsthP	H	Burgess Hill Town	164	D 1 - 1	Oliyidi 88	20	4
27	IsthP	A	Merstham	144	W 4 - 3	Okoye 30 (og) Seeby 25 55 Lee 30	16	5
29	IsthP	A	Dulwich Hamlet	335	D 1 - 1	McCall 9 (pen)	17	6
Sept 3	FAC1Q	H	Cheshunt	257	W 5 - 2	Oliyidi 2 35 Balogun 10 Ibe 62 Muir 69		7
10	IsthP	A	Metropolitan Police	284	W 2 - 1	Robins 5 (pen) Muir 58	14	8
17	FAC2Q	A	Dulwich Hamlet	822	W 2 - 0	Muir 45 Tingey 48		9
20	IsthP	H	Harlow Town	202	D 2 - 2	Oliyidi 47 Seeby 71	12	10
24	IsthP	A	Enfield Town	313	L 0 - 6		16	11
27	IsthP	A	Canvey Island	196	L 1 - 3	Maclaren 44	20	12
Oct 1	FAC3Q	H	AFC Rushden & Diamonds	417	W 3 - 0	Olliyidi 36 McCall 57 Muir 79		13
8	IsthP	A	Lowestoft	522	D 3 - 3	Muir 22 59 Maclaren 49	22	14
15	FAC4Q	A	Boreham Wood	457	L 0 - 3			15
22	IsthP	A	Worthing	660	W 2 - 1	Cole 67 Murphy 82	21	16
25	IsthP	A	Burgess Hill Town	256	L 0 - 1		21	17
29	FAT1Q	A	Leiston	173	L 0 - 5			18
Nov 1	IsthP	H	Kingstonian	185	L 1 - 4	Muir 85	21	19
5	IsthP	H	Havant & Waterlooville	239	D 1 - 1	Lee 79	21	20
19	IsthP	A	Leiston	206	W 3 - 2	Sprague 14 Muir 56 88	19	21
22	IsthP	H	Canvey Island	131	D 0 - 0		18	22
26	IsthP	A	Bognor Regis Town	451	W 2 - 0	Cole 38 Tingey 90	16	23
29	IsthP	A	Harlow Town	206	L 0 - 2		17	24
Dec 3	IsthP	H	Enfield Town	256	D 1 - 1	Murphy 55 (pen)	17	25
7	IsthP	H	Folkestone Invicta	147	D 3 3	McLaren 51 Murphy 70 (pen) Ibe 82	17	26
10	IsthP	H	Leatherhead	173	L 1 - 3	Stanislaus 80	20	27
13	IsthP	H	Grays Athletic	126	L 0 - 4		20	28
17	IsthP	A	Needham Market	259	L 2 - 5	Olliyidi 30 Stanislaus 39	21	29
26	IsthP	H	Harrow Borough	308	L 4 - 5	Diedhiou 7 Murphy 17 (pen) Maclaren 32 Stanislaus 41	22	30
31	IsthP	A	Staines Town	251	L 2 - 3	McLaren 6 Diedhiou 904	22	31
Jan 2	IsthP	A	Dulwich Hamlet	1146	L 1 - 2	Stanislaus 71	22	32
7	IsthP	H	Merstham	187	W 2 - 1	McLaren 60 Olliyidi 85	22	33
14	IsthP	A	Tonbridge Angels	428	L 1 - 3	Olliyidi 9	22	34
21	IsthP	H	AFC Sudbury	208	L 1 - 2	Charles 64		35
28	IsthP	H	Wingate & Finchley	204	L 0 - 1		23	36
Feb 4	IsthP	A	Grays Athletic	186	W 2 - 1	Ibe 45 Ball 78	22	37
7	IsthP	H	Bognor Regis Town	169	D 2 - 2	Barrington 12 Cole 85	21	38
11	IsthP	H	Lowestoft	187	D 0 - 0		21	39
8	IsthP	A	Havant & Waterlooville	702	L 2 - 3	Ball 15 Cole 45	21	40
25	IsthP	A	Billericay Town	561	L 1 - 4	Barrington 68	23	41
Mar 4	IsthP	H	Leiston	145	W 2 - 1	Cole 41 Stanislous 48	23	42
7	IsthP	H	Billericay Town	183	W 1 - 0	Da Costa 90	21	43
11	IsthP	A	Leatherhead	283	L 2 - 3	Semaluka 10 (og) Ball 42	23	44
18	IsthP	H	Needham Market	139	W 2 - 1	Ball 8 Cole 37	22	45
25	IsthP	A	AFC Sudbury	331	W 4 - 0	Ibe 19 61 Ball 31 Cole 49	22	46
Apr 1	IsthP	H	Tonbridge Angels	284	L 1 - 2	Ball 14 (pen)	23	47
8	IsthP	A	Folkestone Invicta	455	W 2 - 1	Ibe 74 Barrington 82	22	48
15	IsthP	A	Metropolitan Police	243	W 2 - 0	Sutherland 84 (og) Barrington 88	20	49
17	IsthP	A	Harrow Borough	328	W 2 - 0	Ball 26 Da Costa 47	18	50
22	IsthP	H	Staines Town	420	D 1 - 1	Maclaren 46	19	51

GOALSCORERS	SG	CSG	Pens	Hat tricks	Total		SG	CSG	Pens	Hat tricks	Total
2015-16 Ibe					8	Seeby	3				3
Muir	7	3			9	Da Costa	2				2
Oliyidi	7				8	Diadhiou	2				2
Ball	7		1		7	Lee	2				2
Cole	7				7	McCall	2		1		2
Maclaren	6				7	Robins	2		1		2
Ibe	5				6	Tingey	2				2
Stanislaus	4				5	Balogun	1				1
Murphy	4		3		4	Barrington	1				1
Barrington	2				3	Charles	1				1
Opponents	3				3	Sprague	1				1

KINGSTONIAN

Club Contact Details
Leatherhead FC, Fetcham Grove, Guildford Road, Leatherhead, Surrey KT22 9AS
020 8330 6869
secretary@kingstonian.com

Ground Capacity: 3,400 **Seats:** 125 **Covered:** Yes **Clubhouse:** Yes **Shop:** Yes

Record Attendance
8,760 v Dulwich Hamlet at Richmond Road 1933.
Previous Grounds
Several > 1921, Richmond Road 1921-89. Kingsmeadow 1989-2017.

10 YEAR RECORD

07-08		08-09		09-10		10-11		11-12		12-13		13-14		14-15		15-16		16-17	
Isth1S	7	Isth1S	1	Isth P	5	Isth P	7	Isth P	11	Isth P	11	Isth P	2	Isth P	11	Isth P	7	Isth P	17
FAC	P	FAC	3Q	FAC	2Q	FAC	3Qr	FAC	1Q	FAC	2Q	FAC	1Q	FAC	3Q	FAC	2Q	FAC	1Q
FAT	P	FAT	P	FAT	3Q	FAT	2Q	FAT	1Q	FAT	1P	FAT	1Q	FAT	1Q	FAT	3Q	FAT	3Q

Club Factfile

Founded: 1885 **Nickname:** The K's **Manager:** Craig Edwards

Previous Names: Kingston & Suburban YMCA 1885-87, Saxons 1887-90, Kingston Wanderers 1893-1904, Old Kingstonians 1908-19

Previous Leagues: Kingston & District, West Surrey, Southern Suburban, Athenian 1919-29, Isthmian 1929-98, Conference 1998-2001

Club Colours (change): Red and white hoops/black/red & black (Sky blue/blue/blue)

RECORDS
Victory: 15-1 v Delft - 1951
Defeat: 0-11 v Ilford - Isthmian League 13/02/1937
Goalscorer: Johnnie Wing - 295 (1948-62)
Appearances: Micky Preston - 555 (1967-85)
Additional: Paid £18,000 to Rushden & Diamonds for David Leworthy 1997
Received £150,000 from West Ham United for Gavin Holligan 1999

HONOURS
FA Comps: FA Amateur Cup 1932-33. FA Trophy 1998-99, 99-2000.

League: Isthmian 1933-34, 36-37, 97-98, Division One South 2008-09.
Athenian League x2.

County FA: Surrey Senior Cup 1910-11, 13-14, 25-26, 30-31, 31-32, 34-35, 38-39, 51-52, 62-63, 63-64, 66-67, 97-98, 2005-06..
London Senior Cup 1962-63, 64-65, 86-87.

BEST PERFORMANCES	**FA Cup:** Fourth Round Proper 2000-01(r).
	FA Trophy: Final 1998-99, 99-00.
	FA Vase: N/A

KINGSTONIAN MATCH RESULTS 2016-17

Date	Comp	H/A	Opponents	Att:	Result	Goalscorers	Pos	No.
Aug 13	IsthP	A	Harlow Town	315	L 0 - 1		18	1
15	IsthP	H	Hendon	271	D 1 - 1	Moss 80	18	2
20	IsthP	H	Needham Market	234	L 1 - 2	Page 40	21	3
23	IsthP	A	Enfield Town	302	L 0 - 3		22	4
27	IsthP	A	Staines town	274	W 2 - 0	Moss 23 67	20	5
29	IsthP	H	Metropolitan Police	259	W 2 - 1	Moss 89 Pico-Gomez 90	10	6
Sept 3	FAC1Q	A	VCD Athletic	98	L 1 - 4	Lamont 49		7
10	IsthP	A	Leiston	268	D 4 - 4	Onouwigun 25 35 Moss 49 Page 55	16	8
19	IsthP	H	Bognor Regis Town	341	L 1 - 2	Pico-Gomez 80 (pen)	16	9
24	IsthP	A	Canvey Island	246	W 2 - 1	Lamont 29 Pico-Gomez 88	11	10
27	IsthP	A	Wingate & Finchley	124	L 1 - 2	Moss 7	16	11
Oct 2	IsthP	H	Grays Athletic	285	W 2 - 1	Page 16 Pico-Gomez 70 (pen)	12	12
8	IsthP	H	AFC Sudbury	276	W 3 - 0	Pico-Gomez 80 (pen) Inns 76 Turner 82	8	13
15	IsthP	A	Folkestone Invicta	441	L 1 - 3	Moss 50	10	14
17	IsthP	H	Enfield Town	271	L 0 2		10	15
22	IsthP	H	Harlow Town	261	L 0 - 1		16	16
24	IsthP	H	Worthing	303	L 1 - 3	Moss 54	16	17
29	FAT1Q	H	Lewes	245	W 2 - 1	Moss 53 57		18
Nov 1	IsthP	A	Hendon	185	W 4 - 1	Turner 30 Lamont 35 O'Leary 38 Bamba 60	13	19
Nov 5	IsthP	A	Tonbridge Angels	481	W 1 - 0	Inns 7	9	20
12	FAT2Q	H	Tonbridge Angels	318	D 1 - 1	Turner 62		21
15	FAT2Qr	A	Tonbridge Angels	286	W 2 - 1	Pico-Gomez 65 Turner 70		22
19	IsthP	A	Harrow Borough	185	W 4 - 0	MOSS 3 (51 60 80 pen) Derry 90 (pen)	11	23
26	FAT3Q	A	North Leigh	203	L 0 - 1			24
29	IsthP	A	Bognor Regis Town	401	L 0 - 2		13	25
Dec 3	IsthP	H	Canvey Island	212	W 3 - 1	MOSS 3 (65 86 90)	11	26
7	IsthP	A	Grays Athletic	126	L 1 - 2	Hogg 40	12	27
10	IsthP	H	Lowestoft	265	L 2 - 5	Moss 57 (pen) Turner 90	12	28
17	IsthP	A	Billericay Town	364	W 2 - 0	Page 20 Moss 90	9	29
19	IsthP	A	Dulwich Hamlet	382	L 0 - 1		9	30
26	IsthP	H	Merstham	268	W 2 - 1	Lamont 8 Gondoh 14	9	31
31	IsthP	H	Havant & Waterlooville	790	D 1 - 1	Turner 23	10	32
Jan 2	IsthP	A	Metropolitan Police	248	L 0 - 1		12	33
7	IsthP	H	Staines Town	324	W 3 - 2	Barnett-Johnson 5 Derry 27 Inns 37	9	34
14	IsthP	A	Leatherhead	456	W 3 - 2	Taylor 12 Bamba 69 Derry 72	9	35
28	IsthP	A	Needham Market	283	L 1 - 2	Bamba 37	10	36
30	IsthP	H	Wingate & Finchley	252	L 1 - 2	Hogg 35	10	37
Feb 4	IsthP	H	Folkestone Invicta	262	D 2 - 2	Inns 8 Moss 90 (pen)	11	38
11	IsthP	A	AFC Sudbury	215	D 1 - 1	Barnett-Johnson 38	12	39
18	IsthP	H	Tonbridge Angels	401	L 0 - 1		14	40
Mar 4	IsthP	H	Harrow Borough	242	L 2 - 3	Moss 10 13	14	41
11	IsthP	A	Lowestoft	502	L 0 - 1		16	42
18	IsthP	H	Billericay Town	412	L 0 - 3		19	43
20	IsthP	A	Dulwich Hamlet	595	L 2 - 4	Pico-Gomez 69 Turner 90	19	44
25	IsthP	A	Burgess Hill Town	438	L 1 - 2	Inns 61	19	45
Apr 1	IsthP	H	Leatherhead	481	L 1 - 2	Moss 87	21	46
3	IsthP	H	Burgess Hill Town	349	W 2 - 0	Moss 62 Turner 82	20	47
8	IsthP	A	Worthing	712	D 0 - 0		21	48
15	IsthP	H	Leiston	318	W 4 - 2	Moss 4 72 (pen) Derry 58 McAuley 85	18	49
17	IsthP	A	Merstham	264	W 1 - 0	Moss 17	16	50
22	IsthP	H	Havant & Waterlooville	1205	D 0 - 0		17	51

GOALSCORERS	SG	CSG	Pens	Hat tricks	Total		SG	CSG	Pens	Hat tricks	Total
2015-16 Gomez					16	Hogg	2				2
Moss	18	2	4	2	26	Onouwigun	1				2
Turner	9	2			8	McAuley	1				1
Pico-Gomez	6	2	3		7	O'Leary	1				1
Inns	5				5	Gondoh	1				1
Derry	4		1		4	Taylor	1				1
Lamont	4				4						
Page	4				4						
Bamba	3				3						
Barnet-Johnson	2				2						

LEATHERHEAD

Club Contact Details
Fetcham Grove, Guildford Road, Leatherhead, Surrey KT22 9AS
01372 360 151
jeangrant65@hotmail.com

Ground Capacity: 3,400 **Seats:** 125 **Covered:** Yes **Clubhouse:** Yes **Shop:** Yes

Record Attendance
5,500 v Wimbledon - 1976
Previous Grounds
None

10 YEAR RECORD

07-08		08-09		09-10		10-11		11-12		12-13		13-14		14-15		15-16		16-17	
Isth1S	17	Isth1S	15	Isth1S	5	Isth1S	4	Isth P	19	Isth1S	6	Isth1S	3	Isth P	10	Isth P	11	Isth P	13
FAC	P	FAC	P	FAC	2Qr	FAC	P	FAC	4Qr	FAC	2Q	FAC	3Q	FAC	1Q	FAC	1Qr	FAC	1Q
FAT	3Q	FAT	P	FAT	1Q	FAT	P	FAT	1Q	FAT	3Qr	FAT	2Q	FAT	3Q	FAT	1Q	FAT	1Q

Club Factfile

Founded: 1946   **Nickname:** The Tanners   **Manager:** Jimmy Bullard

Previous Names: Club was formed when Leatherhead Rose and Leatherhead United merged in 1946.

Previous Leagues: Surrey Senior 1946-50, Metropolitan 1950-51, Delphian 1951-58, Corinthian 1958-63, Athenian 1963-72

Club Colours (change): Green/white/green (All red)

RECORDS
Victory: 13-1 v Leyland Motors - Surrey Senior League 1946-47
Defeat: 1-11 v Sutton United
Goalscorer: Steve Lunn scored 46 goals during 1996-97
Appearances: P Caswell - 200
Additional: Paid £1,500 to Croydon for B Salkeld
Received £1,500 from Croydon for B Salkeld

HONOURS
FA Comps: None

League: Surrey Senior 1946-47, 47-48, 48-49, 49-50. Corinthian 1962-63. Athenian 1963-64.

County FA: Surrey Senior Cup 1968-69. Surrey Senior Shield 1968-69. Surrey Intermediate Cup 1968-69.

BEST PERFORMANCES	**FA Cup:** Fourth Round Proper 1974-75.
	FA Trophy: Final 1977-78.
	FA Vase: Second Round Proper 1994-95.

LEATHERHEAD MATCH RESULTS 2016-17

Date	Comp	H/A	Opponents	Att:	Result	Goalscorers	Pos	No.
Aug 13	IsthP	H	Grays Athletic	207	D 1 - 1	Adeloye 48	15	1
16	IsthP	A	Havant & Waterlooville	572	L 1 - 3	Davies 90	21	2
20	IsthP	A	Canvey Island	222	L 0 - 3		23	3
24	IsthP	H	Worthing	286	D 1 - 1	Harrington 57	21	4
27	IsthP	A	Harrow Borough	138	L 1 - 3	Adeloye 20	23	5
29	IsthP	H	Merstham	274	W 3 - 0	Sole 4 43 (pen) Nnamani 14	20	6
Sept 3	FAC1Q	A	Hythe Town	255	L 0 - 1			7
10	IsthP	A	Billericay Town	221	L 2 - 4	Hughes-Mason 33 Sole 79	23	8
20	IsthP	A	Folkestone Invicta	447	D 1 - 1	Francis 58	22	9
24	IsthP	H	Needham Market	308	D 1 - 1	Sole 18 (pen)	22	10
28	IsthP	H	Staines Town	301	L 0 - 1		22	11
Oct 1	IsthP	A	AFC Sudbury	258	W 2 - 1	Lopes 21 Davies 77	20	12
5	IsthP	H	Leiston	225	D 3 - 3	Seixas 56 Sole 90 (pen) Hughes-Mason 90	20	13
8	IsthP	A	Burgess Hill Town	482	L 2 - 3	Nnamani 11 Davies 65	21	14
11	IsthP	H	Havant & Waterlooville	337	L 0 - 1		21	15
15	IsthP	H	Dulwich Hamlet	438	D 2 - 2	Harris 15 Adeloye 23	21	16
18	IsthP	A	Worthing	532	L 2 - 3	Bradbrook 21 Sole 62	21	17
22	IsthP	A	Grays Athletic	169	W 2 - 1	Smith 20 Kamara 49	20	18
29	FAT1Q	H	Chesham United	255	L 1 - 2	Smith 23		19
Nov 5	IsthP	H	Lowestoft	293	W 3 - 1	Akindoyinde 10 Ricketts 89 (pen) Smith 77	18	20
15	IsthP	H	Bognor Regis Town	412	L 1 - 3	Kamara 71	18	21
22	IsthP	A	Staines Town	203	W 5 - 2	Akindayinde 23 39 Daniel 31 87 Theobalds 27	17	22
Dec 3	IsthP	A	Needham Market	258	L 1 - 2	Akindoyinde 19	18	23
10	IsthP	A	Hendon	173	W 3 - 1	Mendes 6 75 Sagaf 29	18	24
17	IsthP	H	Enfield Town	375	W 2 - 1	Sagaf 5 Mendy 52	16	25
26	IsthP	H	Metropolitan Police	372	W 2 - 1	Sagaf 49 Bray 87	15	26
31	IsthP	A	Harlow Town	362	L 1 - 2	Cash 30	15	27
Jan 2	IsthP	A	Merstham	278	D 0 - 0		15	28
7	IsthP	H	Harrow Borough	310	D 2 - 2	Cash 7 Theobalds 46	15	29
14	IsthP	H	Kingstonian	456	L 2 - 3	Daniel 70 Carr 77	17	30
21	IsthP	A	Wingate & Finchley	99	L 1 - 2	Carr 81	17	31
28	IsthP	H	Canvey Island	168	L 1 - 2	Carr 61	17	32
31	IsthP	A	Tonbridge Angels	280	D 4 - 4	Homans 12 Daniel 34 Smith 44 79	17	33
Feb 11	IsthP	H	Burgess Hill Town	240	L 1 - 2	Carr 60	22	34
18	IsthP	A	Lowestoft	520	L 0 - 1		23	35
22	IsthP	H	AFC Sudbury	236	W 2 - 0	Boakye-Yiadom 29 Daniel 84	22	36
25	IsthP	H	Tonbridge Angels	400	D 0 - 0		21	37
Mar 4	IsthP	A	Bognor Regis Town	501	L 0 - 1		22	38
11	IsthP	H	Hendon	283	W 3 - 2	Theobalds 51 Carr 68 &0 (pen)	22	39
15	IsthP	H	Folkestone Invicta	328	W 2 - 0	Federico 25 Carr 69 (pen	21	40
18	IsthP	A	Enfield Town	515	L 1 - 2	Federico 19	21	41
25	IsthP	H	Wingate & Finchley	299	W 1 - 0	Theobalds 30	21	42
Apr 1	IsthP	A	Kingstonian	461	W 2 - 1	Nnamani 66 Bookye-Yiadom 86	19	43
4	IsthP	A	Dulwich Hamlet	912	D 1 - 1	Boakye-Yiadom 70	19	44
8	IsthP	A	Leiston	308	L 0 - 1		20	45
15	IsthP	H	Billericay Town	505	W 3 - 2	Daniel 8 Moore 53 Bookye -Yiodom 82	17	46
17	IsthP	A	Metropolitan Police	248	W 1 - 0	Moore 29	13	47
22	IsthP	H	Harlow Town	485	W 3 - 2	Daniel 45 Bookye-Yiodom 82 Nnamani 90	13	48

GOALSCORERS	SG	CSG	Pens	Hat tricks	Total		SG	CSG	Pens	Hat tricks	Total
2015-16 Karagiannis					16	Cash	2				2
Carr	6		2		7	Federico	2				2
Daniel	7				7	Hughes-Mason	2				2
Sole	5		3		6	Kamara	2				2
Boakye-Yiadom	5				5	Moore	2				2
Smith	4				5	Bradbrook	1				1
Akindoyinde	3	2			4	Bray	1				1
Nnamani	4				4	Francis	1				1
Sagaf	4				4	Harrington	1				1
Theobalds	4				4	Harris	1				1
Adeloye	3				3	Homan	1				1
Davies	3				3	Lopes	1				1
Mendy	3				3	Rickets	1		1		1

LEISTON

Club Contact Details
LTAA, Victory Road, Leiston IP16 4DQ
01728 830 308
trevorelmy@btinternet.com

Ground Capacity: 2,250 **Seats:** 250 **Covered:** 500 **Clubhouse:** Yes **Shop:**

Record Attendance
1,250 v Fleetwood Town, FA Cup First round Proper, 2008-09.
Previous Grounds
Leiston Recreation Ground 1880-1921.

10 YEAR RECORD

07-08		08-09		09-10		10-11		11-12		12-13		13-14		14-15		15-16		16-17	
ECP	9	ECP	7	ECP	3	ECP	1	Isth1N	1	Isth P	12	Isth P	9	Isth P	9	Isth P	8	Isth P	7
FAC	EP	FAC	1Pr	FAC	EP	FAC	4Qr	FAC	1Q	FAC	2Q	FAC	1Q	FAC	2Q	FAC	3Q	FAC	4Q
FAV	2P	FAV	4P	FAV	3P	FAV	QF	FAT	P	FAT	3Qr	FAT	1Q	FAT	1P	FAT	2Q	FAT	1Pr

Club Factfile

Founded: 1880 **Nickname:** The Blues **Manager:** Glenn Driver

Previous Names: Leiston Works Athletic 1919-35.

Previous Leagues: North Suffolk. Suffolk & Ipswich. South East Anglian/East Anglian. Essex & Suffolk Border. Norfolk & Suffolk. Ipswich & District 1953-2001. Eastern Counties 2001-2011.

Club Colours (change): All blue (All red)

RECORDS
Goalscorer: Lee McGlone - 60 (League).
Appearances: Gareth Heath - 201 (League).

HONOURS
FA Comps: None

League: Suffolk & Ipswich/Ipswich & District 1900-01, 01-02, 02-03, Division 2B 1937-38 / Division One 83-84. Eastern Counties Premier Division 2010-11. Isthmian Division One North 2011-12.

County FA: Suffolk Junior Cup 1894-95, 82-83, 83-84. East Anglian Cup 2007-08.

BEST PERFORMANCES	**FA Cup:** First Round Proper 2008-09(r).
	FA Trophy: First Round Proper 2014-15, 16-17(r).
	FA Vase: Quarter-finals 2010-11.

LEISTON MATCH RESULTS 2016-17

Date	Comp	H/A	Opponents	Att:	Result	Goalscorers	Pos	No.
Aug 13	IsthP	H	Havant & Waterlooville	242	W 3 - 1	Ainsley 21 Heath 51 Blake 52	5	1
16	IsthP	A	Canvey Isalnd	221	W 3 - 2	Lawrence 81 90 Bullard 90	4	2
20	IsthP	A	Dulwich Hamlet	845	W 4 - 2	Francis 23 72 Heath 55 77	2	3
23	IsthP	H	Grays Athletic	412	W 4 - 1	Blake 12 49 Francis 34 Winter 90	1	4
27	IsthP	H	Burgess Hill Town	203	W 2 - 0	Blake 80 Ainsley 86 (pen)	1	5
29	IsthP	A	Needham Market	573	W 4 - 0	Francis 10 17 Blake 24 Heath 79	1	6
Sept 3	FAC1Q	H	Grays Athletic	253	W 4 - 1	Ainsley 38 Lawrence 46 Blake 52 Heath 79		7
10	IsthP	H	Kingstonian	268	D 4 - 4	Jefford 18 Lawrence 36 79 (pen) Blake 45	1	8
17	FAC2Q	A	South Park	124	W 4 - 1	Finch 41 67 Francis 82 85		9
20	IsthP	A	Tonbridge Angels	497	D 2 - 2	Heath 48 Blake 67	1	10
24	IsthP	H	Metropolitan Police	247	W 4 - 0	Finch 33 44 Blake 45 67	1	11
27	IsthP	H	AFC Sudbury	311	W 2 - 1	Brothers 52 Finch 61	1	12
Oct 1	FAC3Q	A	Hungerford Town	245	W 4 - 1	Blake 76 80 Winter 77 Lawrence 89		13
5	IsthP	A	Leatherhead	225	D 3 - 3	Jefford 5 Francis 20 Ainsley 67	1	14
8	IsthP	A	Staines Town	212	W 3 - 2	Bullard 42 Francis 73 77	1	15
15	FAC4Q	A	Westfields	741	L 0 - 1			16
22	IsthP	H	Havant & Waterlooville	643	D 0 - 0		1	17
26	IsthP	H	Grays Athletic	139	D 1 - 1	Heath 18	1	18
29	FAT1Q	H	Hendon	173	W 5 - 0	Blake 19 35 Finch 40 68 Heath 87		19
Nov 8	IsthP	A	Folkestone Invicta	357	L 0 - 2		3	20
12	FAT2Q	A	Chippenham Town	306	W 1 - 0	Ainsley 77		21
19	IsthP	H	Hendon	206	L 2 - 3	Blake 43 Ainsley 50	4	22
22	IsthP	H	AFC Sudbury	286	W 3 - 1	Blake 11 Heath 46 Baker 78 (og)	3	23
26	FAT3Q	H	Eastbourne Borough	212	D 1 - 1	Ainsley 90 (pen)		24
Dec 3	IsthP	A	Metropolitan Police	100	L 1 - 2	Brothers 17	4	25
6	FAT3Qr	A	Eastbourne Borough	262	W 2 - 2	Blake 49 Heath 119 won 5-3 on pens aet		26
10	FAT1	A	Bromley	411	D 1 - 1	Blake 65		27
13	FAT1r	H	Bromley	306	L 3 - 5	Brothers 28 Blake 30 (pen) 58		28
17	IsthP	H	Harlow Town	224	W 5 - 2	Brothers 37 Brown 41 Jones 48 (og) Muir -Merchant 64 Marsden 79	4	29
26	IsthP	A	Lowestoft	725	L 2 - 5	Muir-Merchant 30 Blake 54	5	30
31	IsthP	H	Enfield Town	363	D 1 - 1	Blake 90	5	31
Jan 2	IsthP	H	Needham Market	414	W 5 - 1	Heath 20 Lawrence 31 45 Brothers 52 Muir-Merchant 55	5	32
7	IsthP	A	Burgess Hill Town	303	W 6 - 0	Muir-Merchant 22 BLAKE 4 (24 39 45 47) Heath 70	4	33
14	IsthP	H	Billericay Town	272	W 4 - 1	Blake 17 68 Muir-Marchant 74 Brown 88	4	34
17	IsthP	H	Canvey Island	214	W 4 - 0	Ainsley 15 Muir-Marchant 38 Blake 45 Lawrence 61	4	35
21	IsthP	A	Worthing	823	W 3 - 1	Lawrence 10 Bullard 24 Blake 90	4	36
24	IsthP	A	Wingate & Finchley	129	L 0 - 1		4	37
28	IsthP	H	Dulwich Hamlet	309	D 2 - 2	Blake 19 79	4	38
Feb 11	IsthP	H	Staines Town	204	L 0 - 1		4	39
18	IsthP	A	Harrow Borough	179	L 1 - 3	Francis 66	5	40
25	IsthP	A	Wingate & Finchley	224	L 1 - 2	Francis 90	6	41
28	IsthP	H	Merstham	192	L 1 - 2	Douglas 18 (og)	6	42
Mar 4	IsthP	A	Hendon	145	L 1 - 2	Blake 22	6	43
7	IsthP	H	Tonbridge Angels	183	W 2 - 0	Muir-Merchant 63 66	6	44
11	IsthP	H	Bognor Regis Town	349	D 1 - 1	Bullard 84	6	45
18	IsthP	A	Harlow Town	234	W 2 - 1	Blake 42 90	6	46
21	IsthP	H	Folkestone Invicta	244	W 2 - 1	Muir-Merchant 31 Blake 43	4	47
25	IsthP	H	Worthing	330	W 2 - 0	Hubble 12 70	4	48
28	IsthP	A	Bognor Regis Town	667	L 0 1		4	49
Apr 1	IsthP	A	Billericay Town	1453	L 0 - 2		3	50
4	IsthP	A	Merstham Town	163	L 1 - 2	Dunbar 53	3	51
8	IsthP	H	Leatherhead	308	W 1 0	Blake 73	3	52
11	IsthP	H	Harrow Borough	267	D 2 - 2	Muir-Merchant 47 Heath 57	3	53
15	IsthP	A	Kingstonian	318	L 2 - 4	Blake 81 Muir-Merchant 90	4	54
17	IsthP	H	Lowestoft	513	L 1 - 2	Hubble 90	4	55
22	IsthP	A	Enfield Town	812	D 1 - 1	Heath 45	7	56

GOALSCORERS	SG	CSG	Pens	Hat tricks	Total		SG	CSG	Pens	Hat tricks	Total
2015-16 Finch					16	Hubble	2				3
Blake	27	5,4	1	1	38	Opponents					3
Heath	13	2			14	Brown	2				2
Francis	8	2			12	Jefford	2				2
Muir-Merchant	10	4			11	Winter	2				2
Lawrence	7	2	1		10	Dunbar	1				1
Ainsley	8	2	2		8	Marsden	1				1
Finch	5	2			7						
Brothers	5				5						
Bullard	4				4						

LOWESTOFT TOWN

Club Contact Details
Crown Meadow, Love Road, Lowestoft NR32 2PA
01502 567 280
terrylynes@yahoo.com

Ground Capacity: 3,000 **Seats:** 466 **Covered:** 500 **Clubhouse:** Yes **Shop:** Yes

Record Attendance
5,000 v Watford - FA Cup 1st Round 1967
Previous Grounds
Crown Meadow Athletic Ground 1880-1889. North Denes 1889-94.

10 YEAR RECORD

07-08		08-09		09-10		10-11		11-12		12-13		13-14		14-15		15-16		16-17	
ECP	11	ECP	1	Isth1N	1	Isth P	4	Isth P	3	Isth P	2	Isth P	4	Conf N	16	Nat N	20	Isth P	11
FAC	EP	FAC	1Q	FAC	1P	FAC	2Q	FAC	3Q	FAC	4Q	FAC	1Q	FAC	3Q	FAC	2Q	FAC	1Q
FAV	F	FAV	SF	FAT	1Q	FAT	1P	FAT	1P	FAT	1Q	FAT	1Q	FAT	1P	FAT	1P	FAT	1Q

Club Factfile

Founded: 1880   **Nickname:** The Trawler Boys or Blues   **Manager:** Ady Gallagher

Previous Names: Original club merged with Kirkley in 1887 to form Lowestoft and became Lowestoft Town in 1890

Previous Leagues: North Suffolk 1897-35, Eastern Counties 1935-2009. Isthmian 2009-2014. Conference 2014-16.

Club Colours (change): All blue

RECORDS

HONOURS

FA Comps: None

League: Eastern Counties League 1935-36 (shared), 37-38, 62-63, 64-65, 65-66, 66-67, 67-68, 69-70, 70-71, 77-78, 2005-06, 08-09. Isthmian League Division One North 2009-10.

County FA: Suffolk Senior Cup 1902-03, 22-23, 25-26, 31-32, 35-36, 46-47, 47-48, 48-49, 55-56, Premier Cup 1966-67, 71-72, 74 -75, 78-79, 79-80, 99-00, 00-01, 04-05, 05-06, 08-09, 11-12, 14-15, 15-16. East Anglian Cup 1929-30, 70-71, 77-78.

BEST PERFORMANCES	**FA Cup:** First Round Proper 1926-27, 38-39, 66-67, 67-68, 77-78, 2009-10.
	FA Trophy: Second Round Proper 1971-72(r).
	FA Vase: Final 2007-08.

LOWESTOFT MATCH RESULTS 2016-17

Date	Comp	H/A	Opponents	Att:	Result	Goalscorers	Pos	No.
Aug 13	IsthP	A	Bognor Regis Town	353	W 3 - 1	Henderson 40 65 Beck 53 (og)	6	1
16	IsthP	H	Needham Market	471	D 1 - 1	Forshaw 45	6	2
20	IsthP	H	Tonbridge Angels	520	L 0 - 1		10	3
23	IsthP	A	Billericay Town	286	W 1 - 0	Reed 47	7	4
27	IsthP	A	Havant & Waterlooville	575	L 0 - 1		10	5
29	IsthP	H	AFC Sudbury	580	D 2 - 2	Henderson 8 Marsden 84	8	6
Sept 3	FAC1Q	H	Histon	407	L 0 - 2			7
10	IsthP	A	Staines Town	190	L 1 - 2	Reed 18	15	8
24	IsthP	A	Wingate & Finchley	166	D 1 - 1	Spillane 41	18	9
28	IsthP	A	Grays Athletic	170	W 3 - 0	Marsden 41 44 Reed 83	14	10
Oct 1	IsthP	H	Harlow Town	515	W 4 - 0	Ryan Jarvis 81 REED 3 (56 72 80)	7	11
4	IsthP	H	Dulwich Hamlet	413	L 0 - 3		8	12
8	IsthP	H	Hendon	522	D 3 - 3	Spillane 60 73 Henderson 90	9	13
12	IsthP	A	Needham Market	319	L 0 - 2		11	14
15	IsthP	A	Metropolitan Police	106	D 2 - 2	Fisk 34 Glover 71	9	15
22	IsthP	H	Bognor Regis Town	464	W 2 - 1	Ryan Jarvis 16 Ross Jarvis 90	8	16
29	FAT1Q	H	Dulwich Hamlet	428	L 1 - 2	Smith 66		17
Nov 1	IsthP	H	Billericay Town	317	L 1 1	Henderson 47	7	18
5	IsthP	A	Leatherhead	293	L 1 - 3	Reed 5	14	19
8	IsthP	H	Canvey Island	249	L 0 - 3		15	20
12	IsthP	H	Grays Athletic	380	W 2 - 1	Reed 17 86	8	21
19	IsthP	H	Burgess Hill Town	404	W 1 - 0	McAuley 15	7	22
29	IsthP	A	Canvey Island	212	L 0 - 3		11	23
Dec 3	IsthP	H	Wingate & Finchley	347	W 2 - 1	Ryan Jarvis 38 (pen) Henderson 65	9	24
10	IsthP	A	Kingstonian	265	W 5 - 2	Reed 4 16 Blake-Tracy 21 Ryan Jarvis 23 Bammont 80		25
13	IsthP	A	Enfield Town	232	D 2 - 2	Reed 30 39	7	26
17	IsthP	H	Worthing	476	L 0 - 4		7	27
26	IsthP	H	Leiston	725	W 3 - 2	Cole 23 Ross Jarvis 35 Bammant 80	7	28
31	IsthP	A	Harrow Borough	223	L 2 - 4	Ross Jarvis 5 Hodd 71	8	29
Jan 2	IsthP	A	AFC Sudbury	392	D 1 - 1	Reed 89	9	30
7	IsthP	H	Havant & Waterlooville	431	L 0 - 2		12	31
17	IsthP	A	Harlow Town	155	W 2 - 1	Reed 4 67	11	32
21	IsthP	A	Folkestone Invicta	437	L 1 - 4	Reed 35	11	33
28	IsthP	A	Tonbridge Angels	421	L 0 - 1		12	34
Feb 4	IsthP	H	Metropolitan Police	443	L 0 - 1		13	35
11	IsthP	A	Hendon	167	D 0 - 0		14	36
18	IsthP	H	Leatherhead	520	W 1 - 0	Bammont 56	13	37
25	IsthP	H	Enfield Town	433	W 2 - 1	Cotton 62 87	13	38
Mar 4	IsthP	A	Burgess Hill Town	443	W 3 - 1	Bammont 7 Reed 33 Hodd 86	12	39
11	IsthP	H	Kingstonian	502	W 1 - 0	Reed 9	11	40
18	IsthP	A	Worthing	612	W 1 - 0	Bammont 87	11	41
25	IsthP	H	Folkestone Invicta	545	D 2 - 2	Bammont 47 89	11	42
Apr 1	IsthP	A	Merstham	204	L 0 - 1		11	43
8	IsthP	A	Dulwich Hamlet	1806	L 1 - 3	Cole 48	11	44
12	IsthP	H	Merstham	404	L 1 - 5	Reed 25	11	45
15	IsthP	H	Staines Town	439	L 1 - 3	Cotton 45	12	46
5	IsthP	A	Leatherhead	513	W 2 - 1	Reed 86 Cotton 89 (pen)	11	47
22	IsthP	H	Harrow Borough	575	W 2 - 0	Docherty 30 Forshaw 56	11	48

GOALSCORERS	SG	CSG	Pens	Hat tricks	Total		SG	CSG	Pens	Hat tricks	Total
2015-16 Reed					16	Forshaw	2				2
Reed	13	2		1	21	Hodd	2				2
Bammont	6				7	Blake-Tracy	1				1
Henderson	5				6	Docherty	1				1
Cotton	4		1		4	Fisk	1				1
Ryan Jarvis	2		1		4	Glover	1				1
Ross Jarvis	2				3	McCauley	1				1
Marsden	2				3	Opponents	1				1
Spillane	2				3	Smith	1				1
Cole	2				2						

MARGATE

Club Contact Details
Hartsdown Park, Hartsdown Road, Margate, Kent CT9 5QZ
01843 221 769
ryan.day@margate-fc.com

Ground Capacity: 3,000 **Seats:** 400 **Covered:** 1,750 **Clubhouse:** Yes **Shop:** Yes

Record Attendance
14,169 v Tottenham Hotspur - FA Cup 3rd Round 1973
Previous Grounds
At least six before moving to Hartsdown in 1929. Shared with Dover Ath. 2002-03 and Ashford Town 04-05.

10 YEAR RECORD

	07-08	08-09	09-10	10-11	11-12	12-13	13-14	14-15	15-16	16-17
	Isth P 9	Isth P 19	Isth P 19	Isth P 16	Isth P 15	Isth P 9	Isth P 11	Isth P 2	Nat S 19	Nat S 22
	FAC 3Q	FAC 1Q	FAC 1Q	FAC 2Qr	FAC 3Q	FAC 3Q	FAC 2Q	FAC 2Q	FAC 4Q	FAC 4Qr
	FAT 2Qr	FAT 1Q	FAT 1Q	FAT 2Q	FAT 2Qr	FAT 1Q	FAT 3Q	FAT 1Q	FAT 3Q	FAT 3Qr

Club Factfile

Founded: 1896 **Nickname:** The Gate **Manager:** Steve Watt

Previous Names: Margate Town 1896-1929.

Previous Leagues: Kent 1911-23, 24-28, 29-33, 37-38, 46-59. Southern 1933-37, 59-2001, Conference 2001-05, 15-17. Isthmian 2005-15.

Club Colours (change): Blue/blue/white (White/black/white)

RECORDS
Victory: 12-1 v Deal Cinque Ports, FA Cup 1Q, 1919-20 and v Erith & Belvedere, Kent League, 1927-28.
Defeat: 0-11 v AFC Bournemouth (A), FA Cup, 20/11/1971.
Goalscorer: Martin Buglione - 158
Appearances: Bob Harrop - 564
Additional: Paid £5,000 to Dover Athletic for Steve Cuggy

HONOURS
FA Comps: None

League: Kent 1932-33, 37-38, 46-47, 47-48. Southern League Eastern Section & Championship 1935-36, Division One 1962-63, Division One South 1977-78, Premier Division 2000-01.

County FA: Kent Senior Cup 1935-36, 36-37, 73-74, 93-94, 97-98, 2002-03, 03-04, 04-05.

BEST PERFORMANCES	**FA Cup:** Third Round Proper 1935-36, 72-73.
	FA Trophy: Quarter-final 2001-02.
	FA Vase: N/A

MARGATE MATCH RESULTS 2016-17

Date	Comp	H/A	Opponents	Att:	Result		Goalscorers	Pos	No.
Aug 6	Nat S	H	Bath City	567	W	1 - 0	Osborn 87	9	1
8	Nat S	A	Chelmsford City	809	L	0 - 2		10	2
13	Nat S	A	Wealdstone	689	L	1 - 2	Akindayini 90	18	3
16	Nat S	H	Hampton & Richmond Boro	468	W	2 - 4	Buchanan 21 Thalassitis 81	19	4
20	Nat S	A	Poole Town	433	L	0 - 1		20	5
27	Nat S	H	Weston-s-Mare	403	W	3 - 1	Buchanan 13 40 Mambo 55	17	6
29	Nat S	A	Ebbsleet United	1071	L	0 - 4		18	7
Sept 3	Nat S	H	Hungerford Town	642	D	1 - 1	Buchanan 53	16	8
6	Nat S	H	East Thurrock United	369	W	2 - 1	Sammons 35 (og) Akindayini 73	15	9
10	Nat S	A	Bishops Stortford	362	W	2 - 0	Thalassites 47 Karagianis 84 (pen)	14	10
13	Nat S	H	Dartford	574	L	0 - 2		14	11
17	FAC 2Q	H	**Biggleswade Town**	466	W	2 - 0	**Donnelly Thailasitis**		12
24	Nat S	A	Gosport Borough	447	L	0 - 1		15	13
Oct 4	FAC3Q	H	**Hastings United**	385	D	2 - 2	**Johnson 79 Parry 86**		14
8	Nat S	H	Hemel Hempstead Town	454	W	2 - 1	Buchanan 66 Akindayini 75	14	15
15	FAC4Q	A	**Harrow Borough**	309	D	2 - 2	**Cash 16 Buchanan 44 (pen)**		16
18	FAC4Qr	H	**Harrow Borough**	574	L	1 - 3	**Buchanan 57**		17
22	Nat S	H	Concord Rangers	429	L	1 - 5	Phipps 75	16	18
29	Nat S	A	Whitehawk	319	L	0 - 2		16	19
12	Nat S	A	Truro City	369	L	0 - 2		18	20
19	Nat S	H	Oxford City	495	L	0 - 5		19	21
22	Nat S	A	Eastbourne Borough	357	L	1 - 2	Williams 62	19	22
26	FAT3Q	H	**East Thurrock United**	185	D	1 - 1	**Adeboyejo 70 (pen)**		23
29	FAT3Qr	A	**East Thurrock United**	174	L	0 - 2			24
Dec 3	Nat S	A	Maidenhead United	821	L	0 - 2		19	25
10	Nat S	H	St Albans City	364	L	0 - 2		19	26
!7	Nat S	A	Hungerford Town	229	L	0 - 1		21	27
26	Nat S	H	Welling United	588	L	0 - 3		21	28
Jan 1	Nat S	A	Welling United	626	L	1 - 5	Jackson 45	21	29
7	Nat S	H	Bishops Stortford	469	L	0 - 3		22	30
14	Nat S	H	Poole Town	353	L	0 - 2		22	31
28	Nat S	A	Bath City	548	L	0 - 2		22	32
11 27	Nat S	A	Hampton & Richmond Boro	421	L	0 - 1		22	33
18	Nat S	H	Wealdstone	547	L	0 - 1		22	34
21	Nat S	A	East Thurrock United	206	L	0 1		22	35
25	Nat S	H	Whitehawk	504	L	0 - 2		22	36
28	Nat S	H	Chelmsford City	334	L	0 - 2		22	37
Mar 4	Nat S	A	Concord Rangers	237	D	0 - 0		22	38
11	Nat S	H	Gosport Borough	434	W	2 - 0	Jackson 88 (pen) 90	22	39
18	Nat S	A	Hemel Hempstead Town	490	L	2 - 3	Moore-Azill 37 Famino 74	22	40
21	Nat S	A	Dartford	872	L	0 - 4		22	41
25	Nat S	H	Eastbourne Borough	483	D	1 - 1	Jackson 52	22	42
April 1	Nat S	H	Truro City	412	W	2 - 1	Akindayini 20 47	22	43
8	Nat S	A	St Albans City	611	D	1 - 1	Thalassitis 2	21	44
15	Nat S	A	Weston-s-Mare	740	L	1 - 3	Thalassitis 18	21R	45
17	Nat S	H	Ebbsfleet United	896	L	0 - 1		21	46
22	Nat S	A	Oxford City	251	L	0 - 1		21	47
29	Nat S	H	Maidenhead United	1186	L	0 - 3		22	48

GOALSCORERS	SG	CSG	Pens	Hat tricks	Total		SG	CSG	Pens	Hat tricks	Total
2015-16 Ladapo					13	Karagiannis	1		1		1
Buchanan	6	1			7	Mambo	1				1
Akindayini	5	1			6	Moore-Azil	1				1
Jackson	3				4	Opponents	1				1
Thalassitis	4				4	Osborn	1				1
Adeboyejo	1				1	Perry	1				1
Cash	1				1	Phipps	1				1
Donnelly	1				1	Williams	1				1
Famino	1				1						
Johnson	1				1						

MERSTHAM

Club Contact Details
Moatside Stadium, Weldon Way, Merstham, Surrey RH1 3QB
01737 644 046
richardbaxter01@hotmail.com

Ground Capacity: 2,500   **Seats:** 174   **Covered:** 100   **Clubhouse:** Yes   **Shop:** No

Record Attendance
1,920 v Oxford United, FAC First Round Proper, 05/11/2016
Previous Grounds
None

10 YEAR RECORD

07-08		08-09		09-10		10-11		11-12		12-13		13-14		14-15		15-16		16-17	
CCP	1	Isth1S	8	Isth1S	16	Isth1S	19	Isth1S	9	Isth1S	12	Isth1S	7	Isth1S	4	Isth P	10	Isth P	20
FAC	EP	FAC	3Q	FAC	Pr	FAC	P	FAC	2Q	FAC	P	FAC	2Q	FAC	2Q	FAC	1Q	FAC	1P
FAV	QF	FAT	1Q	FAT	2Q	FAT	P	FAT	1Q	FAT	2Q	FAT	Pr	FAT	2Q	FAT	1Qr	FAT	2Q

Club Factfile

Founded: 1892   **Nickname:** The Moatsiders   **Manager:** Hayden Bird

Previous Names: None

Previous Leagues: Redhill & District. Surrey Intermediate. Surrey Senior 1964-78. London Spartan 1978-84. Combined Counties 1984-2008.

Club Colours (change): Yellow & black

RECORDS

HONOURS

FA Comps: None

League: Redhill & District 1934-35, 35-36, 49-50, 50-51. Surrey Intermediate 1952-53. Surrey Senior 1971-72. Combined Counties Premier Division 2007-08.

County FA: Surrey Senior Charity Cup 1976-77. East Surrey Charities Senior Cup 1979-80, 80-81. East Surrey Charity Cup 1998-99, 2004-05, 06-07. Surrey Senior Cup 2007-08, 15-16.

BEST PERFORMANCES	**FA Cup:** First Round Proper 2016-17.
	FA Trophy: Second Qualifying Round 2009-10, 12-13, 14-15, 16-17.
	FA Vase: Quarter-final 2007-08.

MERSTHAM MATCH RESULTS 2016-17

Date	Comp	H/A	Opponents	Att:	Result	Goalscorers	Pos	No.
Aug 13	IsthP	A	Billericay Town	272	D 1 - 1	Cox 82 (pen)	16	1
16	IsthP	H	Bognor Regis Town	160	D 1 - 1	Bennett 56	15	2
20	IsthP	H	AFC Sudbury	134	L 0 - 1		17	3
23	IsthP	A	Folkestone Invicta	324	D 0 - 0		18	4
27	IsthP	H	Hendon	144	L 3 - 4	Bennett 9 Willock 34 Hopkinson 85	17	5
29	IsthP	A	Leatherhead	274	L 0 - 3		20	6
Sept 3	FAC1Q	A	East Preston	158	W 4 - 1	Hector 41 Willock 55 Addai 57 Bennett 89 (pen)		7
10	IsthP	H	Grays Athletic	143	W 6 - 1	Okoye 12 Hector 18 Bennett 56 (p) Vidal 65 67 (p) Addai 78	20	8
17	FAC2Q	A	Colliers Wood United	148	D 0 - 0			9
20	FAC2Qr	H	Colliers Wood United	146	W 2 - 1	Okoye 74 Kavanagh 102 after extra time		10
24	IsthP	H	Harrow Borough	454	W 5 - 0	Addai 15 Penny 53 90 Vidal 56 (pen) Bennett 59	17	11
27	IsthP	H	Tonbridge Angels	223	W 5 - 3	Henriques 30 Penny 32 63 Bennett 48 Folkes 88	11	12
Oct 1	FAC3Q	H	Thamesmead Town	188	W 5 - 1	Henriques 5 82 Vidal 22 (pen) Hector 27 Campbell 44		13
4	IsthP	A	Worthing	404	L 0 - 1		16	14
8	IsthP	H	Enfield Town	188	D 2 - 2	Hector 34 Addai 80	17	15
11	IsthP	A	Bognor Regis Town	385	L 0 - 2		17	16
15	FAC4Q	A	Ebbsfleet United	646	W 2 - 1	Kavanagh 26 Penny 43		17
18	IsthP	H	Folkestne Invicta	125	W 3 - 1	Okoye 10 Kavanagh 19 Folkes 52	15	18
22	IsthP	H	Billericay Town	183	D 1 - 1	Bennett 23	15	19
29	FAT1Q	A	Waltham Abbey	72	W 5 - 0	Campbell 2 40 Folkes 4 42 Bennett 65		20
Nov 5	FAC1	H	Oxford United	1,920	L 0 - 5			21
8	IsthP	A	Wingate & Finchley	101	L 2 - 3	Vidal 64 74	19	22
15	FAT2Q	H	Hythe Town	105	L 0 - 3			23
19	IsthP	A	Staines Town	310	L 0 - 3			24
22	IsthP	A	Tonbridge Angels	303	D 2 - 2	Hector 54 Azeez 90	19	25
26	IsthP	H	Needham Market	116	W 4 - 1	Hector 24 BENNETT 3 (36 62 70)	17	26
Dec 3	IsthP	A	Harrow Borough	141	L 0 - 1		18	27
10	IsthP	H	Havant & Waterlooville	156	W 2 - 1	Bennett 33 Willock 83	15	28
17	IsthP	A	Canvey Island	194	D 2 - 2	Willock 45 Cooper 74	19	29
20	IsthP	A	Harlow Town	208	L 1 - 2	Henriques 90	19	30
26	IsthP	A	Kingstonian	268	L 1 - 2	Kavanagh 31	19	31
31	IsthP	H	Burgess Hill Town	189	D 2 - 2	Bennett 61 Hector 66	20	32
Jan 2	IsthP	H	Leatherhead	278	D 0 - 0		20	33
7	IsthP	A	Hendon	187	L 1 - 2	Bailey-Allen 90	20	34
28	IsthP	A	AFC Sudbury	229	W 4 - 0	McDonald 46 Okoye 73 Bennett 86 90	21	35
11	IsthP	A	Enfield Town	329	W 3 - 2	Bennett 26 McDonald 56 Vidal 87	20	36
18	IsthP	H	Harlow Town	152	W 1 - 0	Addai 62	20	37
25	IsthP	H	Havant & Waterlooville	721	L 0 - 3		20	38
28	IsthP	A	Leiston	192	W 2 - 1	McDonald 31 Cooper 52	19	39
Mar 4	IsthP	H	Staines Town	180	D 0 - 0		18	40
7	IsthP	A	Needham Market	199	D 1 - 1	Folkes 6	19	41
11	IsthP	A	Dulwich Hamlet	1564	L 0 - 5		20	42
14	IsthP	H	Metropolitan Police	110	W 2 - 0	Bennett 52 77	18	43
18	IsthP	A	Canvey Island	150	L 0 - 3		18	44
25	IsthP	A	Metropolitan Police	78	W 2 - 0	Kavanagh 9 Folkes 53	18	45
28	IsthP	H	Worthing	180	L 1 - 2	Addai 7	18	46
Apr 1	IsthP	H	Lowestoft	204	W 1 - 0	Folkes 51	15	47
4	IsthP	H	Leiston	163	W 2 - 1	Addai 50 Howard 55	14	48
8	IsthP	H	Wingate & Finchley	148	L 0 - 1		14	49
11	IsthP	H	Dulwich Hamlet	336	L 1 - 4	Hall	14	50
13	IsthP	A	Lowestoft Town	404	W 5 - 1	Cooper 16 Folkes 22 Bennett 35 Addai 45 Fufana 88	13	51
15	IsthP	A	Grays Athletic	144	L 0 - 1		13	52
17	IsthP	H	Kingstonian	264	L 0 - 1		13	53
22	IsthP	A	Burgess Hill Town	466	L 1 - 2	Kavanagh 88	20	54

GOALSCORERS	SG	CSG	Pens	Hat tricks	Total		SG	CSG	Pens	Hat tricks	Total
2015-16 Penny					20	Campbell	2				3
Bennett	15	2	2	1	19	Cooper	3				3
Addai	8	2			8	McDonald	3				3
Folkes	7				8	Azeez	1				1
Hector	7	2			7	Bailey-Allen	1				1
Vidal	5		3		7	Cox	1		1		1
Kavanagh	6				6	Fufana	1				1
Penny	5				5	Hall	1				1
Henriques	3	2			4	Hopkinson	1				1
Okoye	4				4	Howard	1				1
Willock	4				4						

METROPOLITAN POLICE

Club Contact Details
Imber Court, Ember Lane, East Molesey, Surrey KT8 0BT
020 8398 7358
ph.allen@btinternet.com

Ground Capacity: 3,000   Seats: 297   Covered: 1,800   Clubhouse: Yes   Shop: No

Record Attendance
4,500 v Kingstonian - FA Cup 1934
Previous Grounds
None

10 YEAR RECORD

07-08		08-09		09-10		10-11		11-12		12-13		13-14		14-15		15-16		16-17	
Isth1S	4	Isth1S	4	Isth1S	10	Isth1S	1	Isth P	12	Isth P	6	Isth P	17	Isth P	5	Isth P	12	Isth P	18
FAC	P	FAC	1Q	FAC	1Q	FAC	4Qr	FAC	1Q	FAC	1P	FAC	1Qr	FAC	2Q	FAC	1Qr	FAC	2Q
FAT	2Q	FAT	1Q	FAT	1Q	FAT	Pr	FAT	1Q	FAT	2Qr	FAT	2Q	FAT	3Q	FAT	3Q	FAV	1Q

Club Factfile

Founded: 1919   **Nickname:** The Met   **Manager:** Jim Cooper

Previous Names: None .

Previous Leagues: Spartan 1928-60, Metropolitan 1960-71, Southern 1971-78

Club Colours (change): All blue

RECORDS
Victory: 10-1 v Tilbury - 1995
Defeat: 1-11 v Wimbledon - 1956
Goalscorer: Mario Russo
Appearances: Pat Robert

HONOURS

FA Comps: None

League: Spartan League x7.
Isthmian League Division One South 2010-11.

County FA: Middlesex Senior Cup 1927-28, Surrey Senior Cup 1932-33, 2014-15. London Senior Cup 2009-10.

BEST PERFORMANCES	**FA Cup:** First Round Proper 1931-32, 84-85, 93-94, 2012-13.
	FA Trophy: Second Round Proper 1989-90.
	FA Vase: Quarter-finals 1994-95.

METROPOLITAN POLICE MATCH RESULTS 2016-17

Date	Comp	H/A	Opponents	Att:	Result	Goalscorers	Pos	No.
Aug 13	IsthP	H	Staines Town	139	L 1 - 6	Smith 67 (og)	24	1
16	IsthP	A	Worthing	505	L 1 - 3	Pacquette 90	24	2
20	IsthP	A	Harrow Borough	155	D 0 - 0		24	3
23	IsthP	H	Havant & Waterlooville	166	L 1 - 2	Collins 3	24	4
27	IsthP	H	Tonbridge Angels	144	D 1 - 1	Smart 90	24	5
29	IsthP	A	Kingstonian	259	L 1 - 2	Collins 60 (pen)	24	6
Sept 3	FAC1Q	A	CB Hounslow United	91	W 3 - 1	Collins 34 (pen) 78 Smith 49		7
10	IsthP	H	Hendon	284	L 1 - 2	Bartley 50	24	8
17	FAC2Q	A	Eastbourne Borough	441	L 1 - 2	Robinson 8		9
20	IsthP	H	Dulwich Hamlet	188	D 1 - 1	Collins 65	24	10
24	IsthP	A	Leiston	247	L 0 - 4		24	11
27	IsthP	A	Enfield Town	254	L 0 - 1		24	12
Oct 1	IsthP	H	Needham Market	160	L 0 - 1		24	13
8	IsthP	A	Canvey Island	240	W 2 - 1	Lodge 45 Hickey 81	24	14
11	IsthP	H	Worthing	131	L 1 - 2	Smith 28	24	15
15	IsthP	H	Lowestoft	108	D 2 - 2	Smth 8 Charles 79	24	16
18	IsthP	A	Havant & Waterlooville	501	W 2 - 1	Lane 25 Nurse 90	23	17
22	IsthP	A	Staines Town	229	L 2 - 3	Hamici 54 (pen) 62	23	18
29	FAT1Q	H	Brightlingsea	124	L 2 - 6	Collins 30 Summers 45		19
Nov 5	IsthP	H	Burgess Hill Town	102	W 2 - 1	Reid 13 Sogbanmu 46	23	20
19	IsthP	A	Grays Athletic	98	W 3 - 1	Macklin 41 Sogbanmu 84 Collina 90	21	21
26	IsthP	A	Billericay Town	374	D 1 - 1	Williams 84	22	22
29	IsthP	A	Dulwich Hamlet	725	D 3 3	Reid 39 59 Percil 90 (pen)	22	23
Dec 3	IsthP	H	Leiston	100	W 2 - 1	Robinson 12 Percil 80	21	24
17	IsthP	H	Wingate & Finchley	68	W 2 - 0	Robinson 54 Percil 67	20	25
26	IsthP	A	Leatherhead	372	L 1 - 2	Summers 81 (pen)	21	26
31	IsthP	H	Bognor Regis Town	300	L 0 - 1		21	27
Jan 2	IsthP	H	Kingstonian	248	W 1 - 0	Collins 59 (pen)	21	28
7	IsthP	A	Tonbridge Angels	420	L 1 - 2	Macklin 39	21	29
10	IsthP	A	AFC Sudbury	162	L 0 - 3		21	30
14	IsthP	H	Folkestone Invicta	112	W 1 - 0	Collins 9	19	31
17	IsthP	H	Billericay Town	108	D 1 - 1	Percil 42	18	32
24	IsthP	A	Harlow Town	144	L 1 - 3	Percil 65	19	33
28	IsthP	H	Harrow Borough	92	D 1 - 1	Percil 68 (pen)	19	34
31	IsthP	H	Enfield Town	107	W 3 - 0	MACKLIN 3 (22 30 86)	17	35
Feb 4	IsthP	A	Lowestoft	443	W 1 - 0	Bartley 31	16	36
11	IsthP	H	Canvey Island	89	L 0 - 4		17	37
18	IsthP	H	Burgess Hill Town	287	W 4 - 1	Macklin 5 Percil 12 Smith 18 Robinson 68	15	38
25	IsthP	H	AFC Sudbury	78	W 1 - 0	Bartley 51	15	39
Mar 4	IsthP	A	Grays Athletic	153	W 2 - 0	Sutherland 21 Percil 49	14	40
11	IsthP	H	Harlow Town	91	L 0 - 2		14	41
14	IsthP	A	Merstham	110	L 1 - 2	Robinson 48	14	42
18	IsthP	A	Wingate & Finchley	117	W 3 - 2	Collins 54 (pen) Robinson 69 Percil	15	43
25	IsthP	H	Merstham	78	L 0 - 2		15	44
Apr 1	IsthP	A	Folkestone Invicta	419	L 0 - 2		15	45
8	IsthP	H	Needham Market	101	W 2 - 1	Collins 75 (pen) Percil 90	15	46
15	IsthP	A	Hendon	243	L 0 - 2		16	47
17	IsthP	H	Leatherhead	248	L 0 - 1		18	48
22	IsthP	A	Bognor Regis Town	794	D 1 - 1	Salmon 71	18	49

GOALSCORERS	SG	CSG	Pens	Hat tricks	Total		SG	CSG	Pens	Hat tricks	Total
2015-16 Collins					13	Charles	1				1
Collins	10	2	5		11	Hickey	1				1
Percil	10	3	2		10	Lane	1				1
Macklin	4			1	6	Lodge	1				1
Robinson	6				6	Nurse	1				1
Smith	4	2			4	Opponents	1				1
Bartley	3				3	Pacquette	1				1
Reid	2				3	Salmon	1				1
Hamici	1		1		2	Smart	1				1
Sogbanmu	2	2			2	Sutherland	1				1
Summers	2		1		2	Williams	1				1

NEEDHAM MARKET

Club Contact Details
Bloomfields, Quinton Road, Needham Market IP6 8DA
01449 721 000
m.easlea@sky.com

Ground Capacity: 4,000   **Seats:** 250   **Covered:** 250   **Clubhouse:** Yes   **Shop:** Yes

Record Attendance
1,784 v Cambridge United, FAC Fourth Qualifying Round, 26/10/2013.
Previous Grounds
Young's Meadow 1919. Crowley Park >1996.

10 YEAR RECORD

	07-08		08-09		09-10		10-11		11-12		12-13		13-14		14-15		15-16		16-17	
ECP	2	ECP	3	ECP	1	Isth1N	2	Isth1N	4	Isth1N	16	Isth1N	5	Isth1N	1	Isth P	20	Isth P	9
FAC	1Qr	FAC	2Q	FAC	2Q	FAC	3Q	FAC	2Q	FAC	1Q	FAC	4Q	FAC	3Q	FAC	1Qr	FAC	1Q
FAV	SF	FAV	QF	FAV	QF	FAT	1Qr	FAT	1Q	FAT	P	FAT	P	FAT	P	FAT	1Q	FAT	2Q

Club Factfile

Founded: 1919   **Nickname:** The Marketmen   **Manager:** Richard Wilkins

Previous Names: None

Previous Leagues: Suffolk & Ipswich Senior, Eastern Counties

Club Colours (change): All red with white trim (Blue with white trim)

RECORDS
Victory: 10-1 v I[swich Wanderers (A) , FA Cup Preliminary Round, 01/09/2007
Defeat: 2-6 v Lowestoft Town (A), FA Trophy First round Qualifier, 19/10/2010
Goalscorer: Craig Parker - 111 (2007-2011) Most goals in a season - Craig Parker 40 (2011-11).
Appearances: Rhys Barber - 334 (2006-2012)
Additional: Most goals scored in a season - 196 in 70 games (2007-08)

HONOURS
FA Comps: None

League: Eastern Counties Premier Division 2009-10. Isthmian Division One North 2014-15.

County FA: Suffolk Senior Cup 1989-90, 2004-05. Suffolk & Ipswich Senior League 1995-96. East Anglian Cup 2006-07. Suffolk Premier Cup 2016-17.

BEST PERFORMANCES	**FA Cup:** Fourth Qualifying Round 2013-14.
	FA Trophy: Second Qualifying Round 2016-17.
	FA Vase: Semi-finals 2007-08.

NEEDHAM MARKET MATCH RESULTS 2016-17

Date	Comp	H/A	Opponents	Att:	Result	Goalscorers	Pos	No.
Aug 13	IsthP	H	Burgess Hill Town	228	D 1 - 1	Curtis 10	17	1
17	IsthP	A	Lowestoft	471	D 1 - 1	Ingram 1	14	2
20	IsthP	A	Kingstonian	234	W 2 - 2	Curtis 56 Dobson 80	8	3
27	IsthP	A	Folkestone Invicta	338	W 1 - 0	Dobson 53	7	4
29	IsthP	H	Leiston	573	L 0 - 4		12	5
Sept 3	FAC1Q	A	Uxbridge	109	L 0 - 2			6
6	IsthP	H	Canvey Island	229	D 3 - 3	Brothers 26 Morphew 39 Curtis 53	7	7
10	IsthP	A	Harrow Borough	156	W 3 - 0	Curtis 10 Brothers 38 45	5	8
20	IsthP	H	Grays Athletic	222	W 5 - 1	Booth 10 Curtis 53 Osei 73 Dobson 79 85	4	9
24	IsthP	A	Leatherhead	308	D 1 - 1	Sands 77	5	10
27	IsthP	A	Harlow Town	204	L 1 - 5	Coakley 44	6	11
Oct 1	IsthP	H	Metropolitan Police	180	W 1 - 0	Ingram 51	4	12
8	IsthP	A	Wingate & Finchley	110	W 1 - 0	Sands 52	4	13
11	IsthP	H	Lowestoft	319	W 2 - 0	Sands 65 Izzet 85 (pen)	4	14
15	IsthP	H	Worthing	230	W 2 - 1	Sands 5 Holland 83	3	15
22	IsthP	A	Burgess Hill Town	368	W 3 - 0	Dobson 17 70 Sands 34	2	16
25	IsthP	A	Canvey Island	207	D 2 - 2	Sands 7 Gay 90	1	17
29	FAT1Q	H	Wroxham	205	W 2 0	Sands 50 Snaith 75		18
Nov 5	IsthP	A	Dulwich Hamlet	334	D 1 - 1	Curtis 69	2	19
12	FAT2Q	H	Harrow Borough	203	L 1 - 2	Dobson 48		20
19	IsthP	H	Tonbridge Angels	258	L 0 - 2		3	21
26	IsthP	A	Merstham	116	L 1 - 4	Holland 56	4	22
30	IsthP	A	Grays Athletic	128	W 2 1	Harrison 25 Ingram 59	3	23
Dec 3	IsthP	H	Leatherhead	258	W 2 - 1	Ingram 22 Whight 27	3	24
10	IsthP	A	Enfield Town	354	D 3 - 3	Harrison 9 Dobson 12 Sands 87	3	25
13	IsthP	H	Harlow Town	224	W 2 - 1	Dobson 15 62	1	26
17	IsthP	H	Hendon	259	W 5 - 2	Whight 7 INGRAM 3 (12 31 37) Izzet 34 (pen)	1	27
26	IsthP	H	AFC Sudbury	419	W 2 - 1	Izzet 46 (pen) Holland 50	1	28
Jan 2	IsthP	A	Leiston	414	L 1 - 4	Ingram 64	2	29
7	IsthP	H	Folkestone INvicta	257	W 2 - 1	Holland 1 77	2	30
14	IsthP	H	Staines Town	212	D 1 - 1	Nunn 37	2	31
17	IsthP	A	Bognor Regis Town	462	L 1 - 2	Izzett 18 (pen)	3	32
21	IsthP	A	Havant & Waterlooville	850	W 3 - 2	Dobson 5 Ingram 18 Harrison 40	2	33
28	IsthP	H	Kingstonian	283	W 2 - 1	Ingram 77 Sands 90 (pen)	2	34
Feb 4	IsthP	A	Worthing	726	L 3 - 4	Ingram 18 Dobson 61 Sands 89 (pen)	2	35
11	IsthP	H	Wingate & Finchley	227	W 1 - 0	Clark 78	2	36
15-- 34	IsthP	A	Billericay Town	401	L 0 - 6		2	37
18	IsthP	H	Dulwich Hamlet	1960	L 0 - 2		3	38
25	IsthP	H	Bognor Regis Town	434	D 2 - 2	Ingram 36 Izzet 44	3	39
Mar 4	IsthP	A	Tonbridge Angels	555	W 4 - 3	Sands 49 Ingram 63 Dobson 77 Nunn 85	3	40
7	IsthP	H	Merstham	199	D 1 - 1	Ingram 80	3	41
11	IsthP	H	Enfield Town	326	L 1 - 3	Miller 63	3	42
18	IsthP	A	Hendon	139	L 1 - 2	Ingram 79	3	43
25	IsthP	H	Havant & Waterlooville	434	D 0 - 0		3	44
Apr 1	IsthP	A	Staines Town	177	L 1 - 4	Miller 5	5	45
8	IsthP	H	Metropolitan Police	101	L 1 - 2	Sands 55	8	46
15	IsthP	H	Harrow Borough	317	W 2 - 1	Sands 8 Coakley 78	8	47
17	IsthP	A	AFC Sudbury	353	D 1 - 1	Ingram 43	7	48
22	IsthP	H	Billericay Town	432	L 1 - 2	Sands 74	9	49

GOALSCORERS	SG	CSG	Pens	Hat tricks	Total		SG	CSG	Pens	Hat tricks	Total
2015-16 Brothers					10	Miller	2				2
Ingram	13	3		1	16	Nunn	2				2
Sands	14	6	2		14	Whight	2				2
Dobson	11	2			13	Booth	1				1
Holland	4	3			6	Clark	1				1
Curtis	5				5	Gay	1				1
Izzet	5		4		5	Morphew	1				1
Brothers	2				3	Osei	1				1
Harrison	3				3	Snaith	1				1
Coakley	2				2						

STAINES TOWN

Club Contact Details
Wheatsheaf Park, Wheatsheaf Lane, Staines TW18 2PD
01784 469 240
steve@stainestownfootballclub.co.uk

Ground Capacity: 3,000   **Seats:** 300   **Covered:** 850   **Clubhouse:** Yes   **Shop:** Yes

Record Attendance
2,860 v Stockport County, FAC, 2007

Previous Grounds
Groundshared with Walton & Hersham and Egham Town whilst new Wheatsheaf stadium was built 2001-03.

10 YEAR RECORD

	07-08	08-09	09-10	10-11	11-12	12-13	13-14	14-15	15-16	16-17
	Isth P 2	Isth P 2	Conf S 8	Conf S 15	Conf S 15	Conf S 18	Conf S 8	Conf S 21	Isth P 16	Isth P 12
	FAC 2P	FAC 2Qr	FAC 2Pr	FAC 4Q	FAC 4Q	FAC 2Q	FAC 1P	FAC 3Qr	FAC 1P	FAC 3Q
	FAT 1Qr	FAT 1Q	FAT 3Q	FAT 3Q	FAT 2P	FAT 3Qr	FAT 1Pr	FAT 3Qr	FAT 1Q	FAT 1Q

Club Factfile

Founded: 1892   **Nickname:** The Swans   **Manager:** Johnson Hippolyte

Previous Names: Staines Albany & St Peters Institute merged in 1895. Staines 1905-18, Staines Lagonda 1918-25, Staines Vale (WWII)

Previous Leagues: Great Western Suburban, Hounslow & District 1919-20, Spartan 1924-35, 58-71, Middlesex Senior 1943-52, Parthenon 1952-53, Hellenic 1953-58, Athenian 1971-73, Isthmian 1973-2009, Conference 2009-15.

Club Colours (change): Yellow/blue/white

RECORDS

Victory: 14-0 v Croydon (A) - Isthmian Division 1 19/03/1994
Defeat: 1-18 - Wycombe Wanderers (A) - Great Western Suburban League 27/12/1909
Goalscorer: Alan Gregory - 122
Appearances: Dickie Watmore - 840

HONOURS

FA Comps: None

League: Spartan League 1959-60. Athenian League Division Two 1971-72, Division One 1974-75, 88-89.

County FA: Middlesex Senior cup 1975-76, 76-77, 77-78, 88-89, 90-91, 94-95, 97-98, 2009-10, 12-13. Barassi Cup 1975-76.

BEST PERFORMANCES	**FA Cup:** Second Round Proper 2007-08, 09-10(r).
	FA Trophy: Fourth Round Proper 2003-04(r).
	FA Vase: N/A

STAINES TOWN MATCH RESULTS 2016-17

Date	Comp	H/A	Opponents	Att:	Result	Goalscorers	Pos	No.
Aug 13	IsthP	A	Metropolitan Police	139	W 6 - 1	Vanderhyde 5 Brown 8 Worsfold 18 Miller-Rodney 24		1
						Tison-Lascaris 82 Hippolyte 90	1	
15	IsthP	H	Folkestone Invicts	215	L 0 - 2		9	2
20	IsthP	H	Billericay Town	205	W 3 - 2	Haysman 36 Miller-Rodney 39 Louis 60 (pen)	5	3
23	IsthP	A	Bognor Regis Town	389	L 0 - 2		9	4
27	IsthP	H	Kingstonian	274	L 0 - 2		13	5
29	IsthP	H	Grays Athletic	174	D 2 - 2	Miller-Rodney 23 Brown 88	14	6
Sept 3	FAC1Q	A	**Godalming Town**	241	W 4 - 0	**Bettamer (2) Louis Haysman**		7
10	IsthP	H	Lowestoft	190	W 2 - 1	Louis 59 Worsfold 70	9	8
17	FAC2Q	H	**Maidenhead United**	414	W 1 - 0	**Worsfold 66**		9
20	IsthP	H	Enfield Town	191	D 2 - 2	Haysman 1 Louis 57	9	10
24	IsthP	A	Havant & Waterlooville	567	D 1 - 1	Clifton 49	9	11
28	IsthP	A	Leatherhead	301	D 1 - 1	Clifton 47	8	12
Oct 1	FAC3Q	A	**Chesham Utd**	354	L 0 - 2			13
8	IsthP	H	Leiston	212	L 2 - 3	Hypolyte 29 Worsfold 64	10	14
15	IsthP	A	Harlow Town	303	L 0 - 1		15	15
18	IsthP	H	Bognor Regis Town	214	L 0 2		15	16
22	IsthP	H	Metropolitan Police	229	W 3 - 2	Bettamer 24 61 Adams 58 (pen)	14	17
25	IsthP	A	Folkestone Invicta	315	D 1 - 1	Bettamer 42	14	18
29	FAT1Q	H	**Basingstoke Town**	291	L 1 - 4	**Bettamer 84**	15	19
Nov 1	IsthP	H	Dulwich Hamlet	228	W 2 - 0	Adams 18 47	10	20
5	IsthP	A	AFC Sudbury	261	L 1 - 3	Adams 58	12	21
12	IsthP	A	Canvey Island	214	W 6 - 0	O'Raw 19 (og) Clifton 2 Bettamer 28 Adams 63 Worsfield 78 Brewer 82		22
19	IsthP	H	Merstham	310	W 3 - 0	McKain 20 Wiltshire 54 Bettamer 90	5	23
22	IsthP	H	Leatherhead	203	L 2 - 5	Adams 43 56	6	24
29	IsthP	A	Enfield Town	274	L 1 - 2	Brewer 31	6	25
Dec 3	IsthP	H	Havant & Waterlooville	234	L 1 4	Dalling 87	7	26
6	IsthP	A	Dulwich Hamlet	598	L 1 3	Bettamer 24	7	27
10	IsthP	A	Tonbridge Angels	481	W 2 - 1	Worsfold 22 64	7	28
13	IsthP	A	Worthing	403	L 3 - 5	Clifton 30 Worsfold 53 Adams 59	9	29
17	IsthP	H	Burgess Hill Town	238	L 1 - 2	Coker 20	10	30
26	IsthP	A	Wingate & Finchley	170	D 1 - 1	Clifton 11	12	31
31	IsthP	H	Hendon	251	W 3 - 2	Coker 60 Clifton 62 70	12	32
Jan 2	IsthP	H	Grays Athletic	226	W 3 - 0	Ahmidi 21 Bettamer 58 (pen) Coker 80	8	33
7	IsthP	A	Kingstonian	324	L 2 - 3	Bettamer 30 Brown 87	10	34
14	IsthP	A	Needham Market	212	D 1 - 1	Brewer 75	10	35
28	IsthP	A	Billericay Town	387	L 0 - 1		13	36
Feb 4	IsthP	H	Harlow Town	239	L 0 - 2		14	37
11	IsthP	A	Leiston	208	W 1 - 0	Hippolyte 59	13	38
18	IsthP	H	AFC Sudbury	251	W 4 - 0	Worsfold 40 Hippolyte 41 Bettamer 44 Halle 90 (pen)	12	39
25	IsthP	H	Worthing	210	W 4 - 0	Worsfold 4 Coker 9 Bettamer 68 Collins 74	12	40
Mar 4	IsthP	A	Merstham	180	D 0 - 0		12	41
11	IsthP	H	Tonbridge Angels	251	D 1 - 1	Hippolyte 30	12	42
18	IsthP	A	Burges Hill Twn	302	D 3 - 3	Collins 21 47 Bettamer 57	12	43
21	IsthP	H	Harrow Borough	192	D 0 - 0		12	44
25	IsthP	A	Harrow Borough	242	D 0 - 0		12	45
Apr 1	IsthP	H	Needham Market	177	W 4 - 1	Ahmidi 40 Brown 56 Clifton 67 Hippolyte 90	12	46
8	IsthP	H	Canvey Island	234	D 1 - 1	Bettamer 8	12	47
15	IsthP	A	Lowestoft Town	439	W 3 - 1	Collins 21 Worsfold 28 Hippolyte 47	11	48
17	IsthP	H	Wingate & Finchley	386	L 0 - 1		12	49
22	IsthP	A	Hendon	420	D 1 - 1	Bettamer 5	12	50

GOALSCORERS	SG	CSG	Pens	Hat tricks	Total		SG	CSG	Pens	Hat tricks	Total
2015-16 Cox					26	Haysman	3				3
Bettamer	14	3	1		16	Miller-Rodney	3				3
Worsfold	10	2			11	Ahmidi	2				2
Adams	7	3	1		8	Dalling	1				1
Clifton	7	2			8	Halle	1		1		1
Hippolyte	7				7	McKain	1				1
Brown	4				4	Opponents	1				1
Coker	4				4	Tison-Lascaris	1				1
Collins	3				4	Vanderhyde	1				1
Louis	4		1		4	Wiltshire	1				1
Brewer	3				3						

THURROCK

Club Contact Details
South Way, Ship Lane, Grays, Essex RM19 1YN
01708 865 492
normpos@aol.com

Ground Capacity: 3,500 **Seats:** 524 **Covered:** 1,000 **Clubhouse:** Yes **Shop:** Yes

Record Attendance
2,572 v West Ham United - Friendly 1998
Previous Grounds
None

10 YEAR RECORD

07-08	08-09	09-10	10-11	11-12	12-13	13-14	14-15	15-16	16-17
Conf S 12	Conf S 20	Conf S 10	Conf S 20	Conf S 22	Isth P 21	Isth1N 6	Isth1N 5	Isth1N 2	Isth1N 3
FAC 2Q	FAC 2Q	FAC 4Q	FAC 3Q	FAC 3Qr	FAC 3Qr	FAC 2Q	FAC 2Q	FAC 1Q	FAC P
FAT 3Q	FAT 3Q	FAT 3Q	FAT 3Q	FAT 3Q	FAT 3Q	FAT 1Q	FAT 1Q	FAT 3Q	FAT P

Club Factfile

Founded: 1985 **Nickname:** The Fleet **Manager:** Mark Stimson

Previous Names: Purfleet > 2003

Previous Leagues: Essex Senior 1985-89, Isthmian 1989-2004. Conference 2004-12.

Club Colours (change): Yellow/green/green (All purple)

RECORDS
Victory: 10-0 v Stansted (H) - Essex Senior Lge 1986-87 and v East Ham United (A) - Essex Senior Lge 1987-88
Defeat: 0-6 v St Leonards Stamco (A) - FA Trophy 1996-97 and v Sutton United (H) - Isthmian League 1997-98
Goalscorer: George Georgiou - 106
Appearances: Jimmy McFarlane - 632

HONOURS
FA Comps: None

League: Essex Senior 1987-88. Isthmian Division Two 1991-92.

County FA: Essex Senior Cup 2003-04, 05-06.

BEST PERFORMANCES	**FA Cup:** First Round Proper 2003-04, 04-05.
	FA Trophy: Fourth Round Proper 2004-05.
	FA Vase: Fourth Round Proper 1990-91.

Greenwich Borough 2016-17 - 3rd in Division One South. Photo: Alan Coomes.

TONBRIDGE ANGELS

Club Contact Details
Longmead Stadium, Darenth Avenue, Tonbridge, Kent TN10 3JF
01732 352 417
chcole1063@aol.com

Ground Capacity: 3,000 **Seats:** 760+ **Covered:** 1,500 **Clubhouse:** Yes **Shop:** Yes

Record Attendance
8,236 v Aldershot - FA Cup 1951 at The Angel.
Previous Grounds
The Angel 1948-80

10 YEAR RECORD

07-08		08-09		09-10		10-11		11-12		12-13		13-14		14-15		15-16		16-17	
Isth P	8	Isth P	3	Isth P	8	Isth P	2	Conf S	9	Conf S	16	Conf S	21	Isth P	20	Isth P	4	Isth P	6
FAC	4Q	FAC	1Q	FAC	3Q	FAC	1Q	FAC	2Q	FAC	2Q	FAC	3Q	FAC	2Q	FAC	2Q	FAC	4Q
FAT	2P	FAT	1Q	FAT	3Q	FAT	3Q	FAT	3Qr	FAT	2P	FAT	1Pr	FAT	3Qr	FAT	2Q	FAT	2Qr

Club Factfile

Founded: 1947 **Nickname:** Angels **Manager:** Steve McKimm

Previous Names: Tonbridge FC 1947-94.

Previous Leagues: Southern 1948-80, 93-2004, Kent 1989-93, Isthmian 2004-11.

Club Colours (change): Blue with white trim/white (All red with white trim)

RECORDS
Victory: 11-1 v Worthing - FA Cup 1951
Defeat: 2-11 v Folkstone - Kent Senior Cup 1949
Goalscorer: Jon Main scored 44 goals in one season including seven hat-tricks
Appearances: Mark Giham

HONOURS
FA Comps: None

League: Kent 1992-93.

County FA: Kent Senior Cup 1964-65, 74-75. Kent Senior Shield 1951-52, 55-56, 57-58, 58-59, 63-64.

BEST PERFORMANCES	**FA Cup:** First Round Proper 1967-68, 72-73.
	FA Trophy: Third Round Proper 2004-05(r).
	FA Vase: Third Round Proper 1993-94.

TONBRIDGE ANGELS MATCH RESULTS 2016-17

Date	Comp	H/A	Opponents	Att:	Result	Goalscorers	Pos	No.
Aug 13	IsthP	H	Wingate & Finchley	492	W 3 - 0	McCollin 25 Scannell 35 Elder 45	3	1
17	IsthP	A	Burgess Hill Town	387	W 2 - 1	Wheeler 23 Fortnam-Tomlinson 88	3	2
20	IsthP	A	Lowestoft	520	W 1 - 0	Elder 81	3	3
23	IsthP	H	Harrow Borough	476	W 1 - 0	Elder 8	2	4
27	IsthP	A	Metropolitan Police	14	D 1 - 1	Elder 2	2	5
29	IsthP	H	Billericay Town	628	W 1 - 0	Elder 78	2	6
Sept 3	FAC1Q	A	Ascot United	430	D 2 - 2	Elder 28 Allen 61 (pen)		7
7	FAC1Qr	H	Ascot United	376	W 7 - 0	Elder 22 Scannell 39 84 Allen 53 Fortnam-Tomlinson 66 Phipp 90 Wilson 37 (og)		8
10	IsthP	A	AFC Sudbury	351	W 1 - 0	Allen 24	2	9
17	FAC2Q	H	Wingate & Finchley	167	W 3 - 0	Dundas 15 16 Elder 79		10
20	IsthP	H	Leiston	497	D 2 - 2	Folkes 25 Allen 38	2	11
24	IsthP	A	Bognor Regis Town	511	L 0 - 2		2	12
27	IsthP	A	Merstham	223	L 3 - 5	Scannell 11 Allen 48 Fortnam-Tomlinson 90	3	13
Oct 1	FAC3Q	H	Hereford	1112	W 4 - 2	Allen 2 Wheeler 9 Dundas 64 Blewden 70		14
8	IsthP	A	Grays Athletic	210	W 2 - 0	Elder 47 Blewden 90	3	15
15	FAC4Q	H	Dartford	1391	L 0 - 3			16
22	IsthP	A	Wingate & Finchley	151	L 0 - 4		6	17
27	FAT1Q	H	Ashford Town	381	D 3 - 3	Wheeler 55 68 Elder 82		18
Nov 1	FAT1Qr	A	Ashford Town	227	W 4 - 1	Allen 2 Blewden 32 90 Sobers 84		19
5	IsthP	H	Kingstonian	481	L 0 - 1		8	20
12	FAT2Q	A	Kingstonian	318	D 1 - 1	Whitnell 38		21
15	FAT2Qr	H	Kingstonian	286	L 1 - 2	Elder 54		22
19	IsthP	A	Needham Market	258	W 2 - 0	Blewden 2 Elder 24	10	23
22	IsthP	H	Merstham	303	W 2 - 0	Akrofi 21 Phipp 38	7	24
26	IsthP	A	Enfield Town	415	D 1 - 1	Blewden 11	8	25
Dec 3	IsthP	H	Bognor Regis Town	447	W 4 - 1	Elder 13 80 Akrofi 33 Nelson 39	7	26
10	IsthP	H	Staines Town	481	L 1 - 2	Allen 73	8	27
13	IsthP	H	Canvey Island	235	W 3 - 0	Blewden 62 Akrofi 88 Scannell 90	7	28
17	IsthP	A	Dulwich Hamlet	1541	W 2 - 1	Parkinson 25 Akrofi 87	5	29
20	IsthP	A	Harrow Borough	164	L 0 - 1		5	30
26	IsthP	H	Folkestone Invicta	586	D 2 - 2	Agrofi 40 61	6	31
31	IsthP	A	Worthing	752	L 0 - 3		6	32
Jan 2	IsthP	A	Billericay Town	507	L 1 - 2	Blewden 10	7	33
7	IsthP	H	Metropolitan Police	420	W 2 - 1	Akrofi 52 Blewden 66	7	34
14	IsthP	H	Hendon	428	W 3 - 1	Nelson 14 Akrofi 38 (pen) Beavan 49	7	35
17	IsthP	H	Burgess Hill Town	256	D 0 - 0		6	36
21	IsthP	A	Harlow Town	286	L 0 - 1		7	37
28	IsthP	H	Lowestoft	421	W 1 - 0	Elder 8	5	38
31	IsthP	H	Leatherhead	280	D 4 - 4	Wheeler 4 Phipp 48 Parter 70 Elder 76	5	39
Feb 4	IsthP	A	Canvey Island	325	W 1 - 0	Akrofi 4	5	40
11	IsthP	H	Grays Athletic	312	W 4 - 1	Phipp 17 Akrofi 30 (pen) 33 McCollin 90 (pen)	5	41
14	IsthP	H	Enfield Town	304	W 3 - 0	Elder 19 Allen 52 Parter 76	5	42
18	IsthP	A	Kingstonian	401	W 3 - 0	Allen 46 Parter 60 Elder 90	4	43
25	IsthP	A	Leatherhead	400	D 0 - 0		4	44
28	IsthP	H	Havant & Waterlooville	408	D 1 - 1	Acrofi 18	3	45
Mar 4	IsthP	H	Needham Market	555	L 3 - 4	Udogi 18 Elder 37 Nelson 52	4	46
7	IsthP	A	Leiston	183	L 0 - 2		4	47
11	IsthP	A	Staines Town	251	D 1 - 1	Wheeler 53	4	48
18	IsthP	H	Dulwich Hamlet	656	D 0 - 0		4	49
25	IsthP	H	Harlow Town	529	L 0 - 3		5	50
Apr 1	IsthP	A	Hendon	264	D 2 - 2	Elder 68 McCollin 86	4	51
8	IsthP	A	Havant & Waterlooville	769	L 0 - 2		7	52
15	IsthP	H	AFC Sudbury	554	W 1 - 0	Elder 78	7	53
17	IsthP	A	Folkestone Invicta	593	L 0 - 1		8	54
22	IsthP	H	Worthing	569	W 2 - 1	Wheeler 13 Blewden 23	6	55

GOALSCORERS	SG	CSG	Pens	Hat tricks	Total		SG	CSG	Pens	Hat tricks	Total
2015-16 Elder					27	McCollin	3		1		3
Elder	20	6			21	Nelson	3				3
Akrofi	10		2		11	Parter	3				3
Allen	10	3	1		10	Beavan	2				2
Blewden	9	2			10	Folkes	1				1
Wheeler	6				7	Opponents	1				1
Scannell	4				5	Parkinson	1				1
Phipp	4				4	Sobers	1				1
Dundas	3				3	Udogi	1				1
Fortnam-Tomlinson	3				3	Whitnell	1				1

TOOTING & MITCHAM UNITED

Club Contact Details
KNK Stadium, Imperial Fields, Bishopsford Road, Morden, Surrey SM4 6BF
020 8685 6193
jackie@tmunited.org

Ground Capacity: 3,500 **Seats:** 612 **Covered:** 1,200 **Clubhouse:** Yes **Shop:** Yes

Record Attendance
17,500 v Queens Park Rangers - FA Cup 2nd Round 1956-57 (At Sandy Lane)
Previous Grounds
Sandy Lane, Mitcham

10 YEAR RECORD

	07-08	08-09	09-10	10-11	11-12	12-13	13-14	14-15	15-16	16-17
	Isth1S 2	Isth P 9	Isth P 12	Isth P 14	Isth P 21	Isth1S 16	Isth1S 11	Isth1S 11	Isth1S 17	Isth1S 1
FAC	P	1Q	1P	2Q	1Q	1Q	P	3Q	2Q	P
FAT	Pr	1Q	2Q	1Q	1Q	1Q	P	P	1Q	1Q

Club Factfile

Founded: 1932 **Nickname:** The Terrors **Manager:** Frank Wilson

Previous Names: Tooting Town (Founded in 1887) and Mitcham Wanderers (1912) merged in 1932 to form Tooting & Mitcham FC.

Previous Leagues: London 1932-37, Athenian 1937-56

Club Colours (change): Black and white stripes/black/black (blue/white/blue)

RECORDS
Victory: 11-0 v Welton Rovers - FA Amateur Cup 1962-63
Defeat: 1-8 v Kingstonian - Surrey Senior Cup 1966-67
Goalscorer: Alan Ives - 92
Appearances: Danny Godwin - 470
Additional: Paid £9,000 to Enfield for David Flint
Received £10,000 from Luton Town for Herbie Smith

HONOURS

FA Comps: None

League: Athenian 1949-50, 54-55. Isthmian 1975-76, 59-60, Division Two 2000-01, Division One South 2016-17.

County FA: London Senior Cup 1942-43, 48-49, 58-59, 59-60, 2006-07, 07-08, 15-16. Surrey Senior cup 1937-38, 43-44, 44-45, 52-53, 59-60, 75-76, 76-77, 77-78, 2007-07. Surrey Senior Shield 1951-52, 60-61, 61-62, 65-66.

BEST PERFORMANCES	**FA Cup:** Fourth Round Proper 1975-76. **FA Trophy:** Quarter-finals 1975-76. **FA Vase:** Quarter-finals 2000-01

NATIONAL STRIKE FORCE 2016-2017
(Part One - See page 257 for P2)

			LGE	FAC	FAT	Pens	H-T	SG	CSG	Total
Danny Rowe	AFC Fylde	NN	47		3	4	6	29	5	50
Ricky Miller	Dover Athletic	NL	41	4	1	8	5	28	5	46
Dave Tarpey	Maidenhead United	NS	43		1	9	4	27	5	44
Matt Blake	Leiston	IsthP	29	3	6	1	1	27	5	38
Dan Maguire	Blyth Spartans	NPLP	30	2	4		3	23	9	36
Luke Benbow	Stourbridge	NPLP	33	3		7		29	5	36
Andy Sandell	Chippenham Town	SP	27	5		9	2	21	5	32
Adam Coombes	Welling United	NS	20	7	3	7	3	18	5	30
Marcus Dinanga	Matlock Town	NPLP	22	1	6	2	1	23	3	29
Danny Lloyd	Stockport County	NN	22	4	3	5		22	3	29
Danny Newton	Tamworth	NN	28		1	2	1	21	4	29
David Pratt	Chppenham Town	SP	21	5	2	1	2	21	4	28
Omar Bugiel	Worthing + Forest Green	IsthP+NL	16+5	6	1	4	2	16+3	4	28
Chris Doidge	Forest Green Rovers	NL	25+2PO					24	7	27
Alex Read	Harlow Town	IsthP	19	2	6	1	1	21	2	27
Jake Robinson	Hemel Hempstead Town	NS	24	2		1	2	19	6	26
Ryan Moss	Kingstonian	IsthP	24		2	4	2	18	2	26
Dayle Hopson	Whitby Town	NPLP	26			7	3	21	4	26
James Armson	Brackley Town	NN	14	7	4	5	1	18	2	25
Dan Mitchley	Marine	NPLP	17	2	6	5		20	3	25
Ian Traylor	Merthyr Town	SP	19	4	2	1		19	5	25
Kayne McLaggon	Merthyr Town	SP	17	2	3		1	17	2	25
Inih Effiong	Biggleswade T & Barrow	SP+NL	23+1			5	2	16+1	5	24
Luke Armstrong	Blyth Spartans	NPLP	20		4		1	18	2	24
James Fraser	Bognor Regis Town	IsthP	23	1		2	1	17	3	24
Ellis Bradbrook	Dartford	NS	14	7	3	5	1	18	2	24
Joe Ironside	Nuneaton T & Kidd'ster H	NN	15+6	1	2	3	1	15+5	3	24
Lloyd Dawes	Worthing	IsthP	20		4	8	2	17	5	24
Michael Cheek	Braintree Town	NL	17	3	3	3	1	18	3	23
Lee Shaw	Grantham Town	NPLP	20	1	2	2		21	6	23
Simon Ainge	Harrogate Town	NN	22		1	3	3	15	4	23
Jason Prior	Havant & Waterlooville	IsthP	17	2	4	5	2	15	3	23
Andy Cook	Tranmere Rovers	NL	23					19	4	23
Richie Bennett	Barrow	NL	15	2	5	3		20	3	22
Shaun Jeffers	Chelmsford City	NS	21		1	5		16	2	22
Ian Draycott	Folkestone Invicta	IsthP	17	3	2	2		19	5	22
Jake Jackson	Frome Town	SP	22			1	3	17	4	22
Brady Hickey	Barwell	NPLP	19	2		3	2	17	3	21
Jake Reed	Lowestoft Town	IsthP	21				1	14	2	21
Byron Harrison	Barrow	NL	17	3		6	1	15	4	20
Brad Grayson	Buxton	NPLP	17			4		17	3	20
Elliott Romain	Eastbourne Borough	NS	19	1			2	14	2	20
Joe Taylor	Folkestone Invicta	IsthP	19		1	1		16	4	20
Robbie Burns	Hitchin Town	SP	17		1	2		17	2	20
Sean Cooke	Nantwich Town	NPLP	17	2	1	2	1	14	2	20
Nathan Elder	Tonbridge Angels	IsthP	16	3	2			20	6	20
Elliot Benyon	Wealdstone	NS	16	2	2	1	1	15	4	20
Dayle Grubb	Weston-s-Mare	NS	20				1	13	3	20
Gozie Ugwu	Woking	NL	19	1		3	1	15	4	20
Tony Burnett	Biggleswade Town	SP	19				1	11	3	19
George Sykes	Canvey Island	IsthP	17		2	1		17	2	19
Steve Cawley	Concord Rangers	NS	18		1	6	1	13	2	19
Oliver Hawkins	Dagenham & Redbridge	NL	18	1		4	2	13	4	19
Mark Beck	Darlington 1883	NN	19			2	1	15	3	19
Tom Denton	FC Halifax Town	NN	15	2			1	15	4	19

WINGATE & FINCHLEY

Club Contact Details
Maurice Rebak Stadium, Summers Lane, Finchley N12 0PD
020 8446 2217
tony@wingatefinchley.com

Ground Capacity: 1,500   **Seats:** 500   **Covered:** 500   **Clubhouse:** Yes   **Shop:** No

Record Attendance
528 v Brentwood Town (Division One North Play-Off) 2010/11
Previous Grounds
None

10 YEAR RECORD

	07-08		08-09		09-10		10-11		11-12		12-13		13-14		14-15		15-16		16-17	
Isth	Isth1N	18	Isth1N	7	Isth1N	3	Isth1N	3	Isth P	13	Isth P	18	Isth P	21	Isth P	12	Isth P	13	Isth P	5
FAC	FAC	P	FAC	2Q	FAC	2Qr	FAC	Pr	FAC	1Q	FAC	2Q	FAC	1Qr	FAC	3Q	FAC	3Q	FAC	2Q
FAT	FAT	P	FAT	1P	FAT	Pr	FAT	1Q	FAT	2Qr	FAT	2Qr	FAT	2Qr	FAT	1Q	FAT	1Q	FAT	1Pr

Club Factfile

Founded: 1991   **Nickname:** Blues   **Manager:** Keith Rowland

Previous Names: Wingate (founded 1946) and Finchley (founded late 1800s) merged in 1991

Previous Leagues: South Midlands 1991-95, Isthmian 1995-2004, Southern 2004-2006

Club Colours (change): Blue & white

RECORDS
Victory: 9-1 v Winslow, South Midlands League, 23/11/1991
Defeat: 0-9 v Edgware, Isthmian Division Two, 15/01/2000
Goalscorer: Marc Morris 650 (including with Wingate FC)
Appearances: Marc Morris 720 (including with Wingate FC)

HONOURS
FA Comps: None

League: None

County FA: London Senior Cup 2010-11.

BEST PERFORMANCES	**FA Cup:** Third Qualifying Round 1999-00, 2014-15, 15-16.
	FA Trophy: First Round Proper 2003-04, 08-09, 16-17(r).
	FA Vase: Third Round Proper 1994-95.

WINGATE & FINCHLEY MATCH RESULTS 2016-17

Date	Comp	H/A	Opponents	Att:	Result	Goalscorers	Pos	No.
Aug 13	IsthP	A	Tonbridge Angels	492	L 0 - 3		23	1
15	IsthP	H	Billericay Town	109	L 1 - 2	Smith 41	23	2
20	IsthP	H	Hendon	170	W 1 - 0	Wales 33	16	3
23	IsthP	A	AFC Sudbury	245	D 2 - 2	Beckles-Richards 12 Laney 72	17	4
27	IsthP	A	Harlow Town	227	L 0 - 3		21	5
29	IsthP	H	Havant & Waterlooville	165	L 0 - 2		22	6
Sept 3	FAC1Q	A	Waltham Abbey	130	W 5 - 0	Cronin 15 Beckles-Richards 52 53 Ogleby 75 Healey 81		7
10	IsthP	A	Worthing	497	W 4 - 1	Williams 6 Mbamarah 58 Moncur 83 90	19	8
17	FAC2Q	H	Tonbridge Angels	167	L 0 - 3			9
20	IsthP	A	Harrow Borough	152	W 1 - 0	Healey 65	14	10
24	IsthP	H	Lowestoft	166	D 1 - 1	Cronin 89	13	11
27	IsthP	H	Kingstonian	124	W 2 - 1	Moncur 34 Ogleby 79	9	12
Oct 8	IsthP	H	Needham Market	110	L 0 - 1		14	13
15	IsthP	A	Enfield Town	380	W 1 - 0	Wales 68	11	14
22	IsthP	A	Tonbridge Angels	151	W 4 - 0	Ifil 36 Wales 40 90 (pen) Beckles-Richards 78	9	15
25	IsthP	A	Billericay Town	218	L 0 - 3		11	16
30	FAT1Q	A	Grays Athletic	146	D 1 - 1	Wales 26		17
Nov 1	FAT1Qr	H	Grays Athletic	96	W 2 0	Healey Vilco		18
Nov 5	IsthP	A	Bognor Regis Town	459	L 1 - 3	Beckles-Richards 90	15	19
8	IsthP	H	Merstham	101	W 3 - 2	Beckles-Richards 25 85 Pattie 52	11	20
12	FAT2Q	A	Ware	93	W 2 - 0	Beckles-Richards Laney		21
19	IsthP	A	Canvey Island	219	W 4 - 1	Pattie 22 BECCLES-RICHARDS 3 (41 65 76)	12	22
26	FAT3Q	A	Slough Town	353	W 4 - 2	Laney 4 Beckles-Richards 21 Pattie 58 Rifat 89		23
Dec 3	IsthP	A	Lowestoft	347	L 1 - 2	Kyle 82	14	24
10	FAT1Q	A	Wealdstone	364	D 2 - 2	Laney 39 Wales 86 (pen)		25
13	FAT1Qr	H	Wealdstone	280	L 1 - 2	Beckles-Richards 4 (aet)		26
17	IsthP	A	Metropolitan Police	68	L 0 - 2		18	27
26	IsthP	H	Staines Town	170	D 1 - 1	Abrahams 4	17	28
31	IsthP	A	Dulwich Hamlet	1910	D 1 - 1	Beckles-Richards 3	17	29
Jan 2	IsthP	A	Havant & Waterlooville	568	D 1 - 1	Tejan-Sie 87	17	30
7	IsthP	H	Harlow Town	145	D 0 - 0		17	31
10	IsthP	H	Burgess Hill Town	102	W 2 - 0	Wales 32 Pattie 53	16	32
14	IsthP	A	Grays Athletic	124	W 2 - 1	Laney 37 Rifat 89	13	33
21	IsthP	H	Leatherhead	99	W 2 - 1	Beckles-Richards 19 Rifat 59	13	34
24	IsthP	H	Leiston	129	W 1 - 0	Wales 77	11	35
28	IsthP	A	Hendon	204	W 1 - 0	Abrahams 42	9	36
30	IsthP	A	Kingstonian	252	W 2 - 1	Laney 23 Pattie 90	9	37
Feb 4	IsthP	H	Enfield Town	365	L 1 - 5	Pattie 55	8	38
11	IsthP	A	Needham Market	227	L 0 - 1		10	39
14	IsthP	H	Folkestone Invicta	84	W 3 - 2	Wales 53 Beckles-Richards 85 Laney 88		40
18	IsthP	H	Bognor Regis Town	180	L 0 - 2		8	41
21	IsthP	H	Burgess Hill Town	263	W 3 - 2	Rifat 69 Figueira 87 Cronin 90	6	42
25	IsthP	A	Leiston	224	W 2 - 1	Pattie 70 Tejan-Sie 84	5	43
28	IsthP	H	Harrow Borough	135	W 3 - 1	Rifat 367 47 Pattie 90	5	44
Msr 4	IsthP	H	Canvey Island	116	L 1 - 2	Pattie 62	5	45
7	IsthP	H	AFC Sudbury	101	W 4 - 1	Rifat 18 Beckles-Richards 34 Pattie 40 Tejan-Sie 61	5	46
11	IsthP	A	Folkestone Invicta	347	L 0 - 1		5	47
18	IsthP	H	Metropolitan Police	117	L 2 - 3	Pattie 52 Beckles-Richards 65	5	48
25	IsthP	A	Leatherhead	299	L 0 - 1		8	49
Apr 1	IsthP	H	Grays Athletic	103	W 1 - 0	Rifat 37	9	50
8	IsthP	A	Merstham	146	W 2 - 0	Vicu 8 Ifil 69	6	51
15	IsthP	H	Worthing	135	W 1 - 0	Obafemi 81	6	52
17	IsthP	A	Staines Town	386	W 1 - 0	Cronin 64	5	53
22	IsthP	H	Dulwich Hamlet	440	L 0 - 3		5	54
27	PO SF	A	Bognor Regis Town	1001	L 1 - 2	Cronin 86		55

GOALSCORERS	SG	CSG	Pens	Hat tricks	Total		SG	CSG	Pens	Hat tricks	Total
2015-16 Healey					22	Abrahams	2				2
Beckles-Richards	14	5		1	18	Ifil	2				2
Pattie	11	2			11	Ogleby	2				2
Wales	7	2	2		9	Vilcu	2				2
Rifat	7				8	Obafemi	1				1
Laney	7				7	Figueira	1				1
Cronin	5				5	Kyle	1				1
Healey	2				3	Mbamarah	1				1
Moncur	2				3	Smith	1				1
Tejan-Sie	3				3	Williams	1				1

WORTHING

Club Contact Details
Woodside Road, Worthing, West Sussex BN14 7HQ
01903 233 444
secretary@worthingfc.com

Ground Capacity: 3,650 **Seats:** 500 **Covered:** 1,500 **Clubhouse:** Yes **Shop:** No

Record Attendance
3,600 v Wimbledon - FA Cup 14/11/1936
Previous Grounds
None

10 YEAR RECORD

07-08		08-09		09-10		10-11		11-12		12-13		13-14		14-15		15-16		16-17	
Isth1S	5	Isth1S	5	Isth1S	3	Isth1S	14	Isth1S	7	Isth1S	10	Isth1S	15	Isth1S	6	Isth1S	3	Isth P	15
FAC	3Q	FAC	3Q	FAC	2Q	FAC	2Q	FAC	3Q	FAC	1Q	FAC	P	FAC	2Q	FAC	3Q	FAC	3Q
FAT	3Qr	FAT	2Q	FAT	Pr	FAT	1Q	FAT	2Q	FAT	P	FAT	P	FAT	2Q	FAT	1Q	FAT	2Pr

Club Factfile

Founded: 1886   **Nickname:** Rebels   **Manager:** Gary Elphick

Previous Names: None

Previous Leagues: West Sussex 1896-1904, 1905-14, 19-20, Brighton Hove & District 1919-20, Sussex County 1920-40, Corinthian 1948-63, Athenian 1963-77

Club Colours (change): All red (Sky blue & grey/grey/sky blue)

RECORDS

Victory: 25-0 v Littlehampton (H) - Sussex League 1911-12

Defeat: 0-14 v Southwick (A) - Sussex County League 1946-47

Goalscorer: Mick Edmonds - 276

Appearances: Mark Knee - 414

Additional: Received £7,500 from Woking for Tim Read 1990

HONOURS

FA Comps: None

League: Sussex League 1920-21, 21-22, 26-27, 28-29, 30-31, 33-34, 38-39. Sussex League West 1945-46.
Isthmian League Division Two 1981-82, 92-93, Division One 1982-83.

County FA: Sussex Senior Cup x21.

BEST PERFORMANCES	**FA Cup:** Second Round Proper 1982-83.
	FA Trophy: Fourth Round Proper 2003-04(r).
	FA Vase: Fifth Round Proper 1978-79.

WORTHING MATCH RESULTS 2016-17

Date	Comp	H/A	Opponents	Att:	Result	Goalscorers	Pos	No.
Aug 13	IsthP	A	Hendon	321	W 3 - 0	Stanislaus 61 73 Sparks 66	4	1
16	IsthP	H	Metropolitan Police	505	W 3 - 1	Stanislaus 36 Sparks 39 Newton 69	1	2
20	IsthP	H	Harlow Town	571	W 3 - 2	Bugiel 45 82 Sparks 65	1	3
24	IsthP	A	Leatherhead	286	D 1 - 1	Bugiel 81	1	4
27	IsthP	H	Grays Athletic	621	L 0 - 1		5	5
29	IsthP	A	Bognor Regis Town	1006	L 0 - 5		6	6
Sept 3	FAC1Q	H	Carshalton Athletic	497	D 3 - 3	BUGIEL 3 (21 78 90 pen)	10	7
6	FAC1Qr	A	Carshalton Athletic	286	W 6 - 2	Hendon 44 O'Neill 50 Sparks 52 Bugiel 73 83 Metcalf 81		8
10	IsthP	H	Wingate & Finchley	497	L 1 - 4	Bugiel 23	10	9
17	FAC2Q	A	Hayes & Yeading	175	W 2 - 0	Bugiel 47 Sparks 73		10
24	IsthP	A	Billericay Town	374	L 0 - 3		15	11
27	IsthP	A	Havant & Waterlooville	606	L 2 - 3	Bugiel 8 Dawes 32	19	12
Oct 1	FAC3Q	A	St Albans City	678	L 0 - 6			13
4	IsthP	H	Merstham	404	W 1 - 0	Wills 26	15	14
8	IsthP	H	Folkestone Invicta	712	D 3 - 3	Sparks 12 Dawes 56 64 (pen)	16	15
11	IsthP	A	Metropolitan Police	131	W 2 - 1	Dawes 57 (pen) Brodie 86		16
15	IsthP	A	Needham Market	230	L 1 - 2	Dawes 66	13	17
18	IsthP	H	Leatherhead	532	W 3 - 2	O'Neill 4 Rents 14 Dawes 52	11	18
22	IsthP	H	Hendon	660	L 1 - 2	Hendon 74	11	19
24	IsthP	A	Kingstonian	303	W 3 - 1	Stanislaus 6 Newton 69 Sparks 73	9	20
29	FAT1Q	H	Kempston Rovers	418	W 3 - 1	Sparks 12 Bugiel 80 (pen) Wills 89		21
Nov 5	IsthP	A	Enfield Town	424	L 1 - 2	Cook 35	11	22
13	FAT2Q	A	Cray Wanderers	164	W 2 - 1	Dawes 12 Newton 46		23
19	IsthP	A	Dulwich Hamlet	2032	L 1 - 4	Bugiel 69	13	24
22	IsthP	H	Havant & Waterlooville	519	L 1 - 2	Bugiel 69	15	25
26	FAT3Q	H	Hemel Hempstead Town	504	D 1 - 1	Dawes 73 (pen)		26
29	FAT3Qr	A	Hemel Hempstead Town	157	W 1 - 0	O'Neill		27
Dec 3	IsthP	H	Billericay Town	537	D 2 - 2	Dawes 35 (pen) Newton 83	16	28
10	FAT1	A	Dagenham & Redbridge	597	W 2 - 1	Dawes 71 Staunton 62 (og)		29
13	IsthP	H	Staines Town	403	W 5 - 3	BUGIEL 3 (12 20 66) Hopkinson 14 Dawes 87 (pen)	15	30
17	IsthP	A	Lowestoft	476	W 4 - 0	Dawes 26 Cook 56 Wills 65 Newton 85	12	31
26	IsthP	A	Burgess Hill Town	521	W 1 - 0	Edwards 67	10	32
31	IsthP	H	Tonbridge Angels	752	W 3 - 0	Bugiel 28 (pen) 71 (pen) Newton 81	9	33
Jan 2	IsthP	A	Bognor Regis Town	1781	D 1 - 1	Bugiel 51	10	34
7	IsthP	A	Grays Athletic	202	W 4 - 1	DAWES 3 (26 pen 50 90) Wills 67	8	35
10	IsthP	H	Canvey Island	506	W 5 - 0	DAWES 3 (8 12 45) Bugiel 12 Hopkinson 29	7	36
14	FAT2	H	Sutton United	1308	D 2 - 2	Bugiel 43 Lemon 85		37
21	IsthP	H	Leiston	823	L 1 - 3	Rents 78	8	38
24	FAT2r	A	Sutton United	496	L 2 - 3	Rents 73 Dawes 90 (Pen)		39
28	IsthP	A	Harlow Town	254	L 2 - 6	Dawes 66 Sparks 74	10	40
Feb 4	IsthP	H	Needham Market	726	W 4 - 3	Dawes 28 (pen) Hopkinson 52 Sparks 80 Bugiel 82	10	41
11	IsthP	A	Folkestone Invicta	309	W 4 - 2	Dawes 25 60 Clark 33 50	8	42
14	IsthP	A	AFC Sudbury	153	L 0 - 1			43
18	IsthP	H	Enfield Town	881	L 1 - 3	Dawes 69	10	44
21	IsthP	H	Harrow Borough	452	L 0 - 4		10	45
25	IsthP	A	Staines Town	210	L 0 - 4		11	46
Mar 4	IsthP	H	Dulwich Hamlet	763	L 0 - 1		13	47
7	IsthP	A	Canvey Island	226	L 0 - 2		13	48
11	IsthP	A	Harrow Borough	194	D 2 - 2	Williamson 39 Summers 50	13	49
18	IsthP	H	Lowestoft	612	L 0 - 1		14	50
25	IsthP	A	Leiston	330	L 0 - 2		14	51
28	IsthP	A	Merstham	180	W 2 - 1	Hendon 39 Wills 61	12	52
Apr 1	IsthP	H	AFC Sudbury	643	D 0 - 0		13	53
8	IsthP	H	Kingstonian	712	D 0 - 0		13	54
15	IsthP	A	Wingate & Finchley	135	L 0 - 1		14	55
17	IsthP	H	Burgess Hill Town	565	D 1 - 1	Newhouse 90	14	57
22	IsthP	A	Tonbridge Angels	589	L 1 - 2	Pope 27	15	58

GOALSCORERS	SG	CSG	Pens	Hat tricks	Total		SG	CSG	Pens	Hat tricks	Total
Dawes	17	5	8	2	24	Cook	2				2
Bugiel	16	4	4	2	23	Brodie	1				1
Sparks	10	3			10	Edwards	1				1
Newton	6				6	Lemon	1				1
Wills	5				5	Metcalf	1				1
Stanislaus	4				4	Newhouse	1				1
Hendon	3				3	Opponents	1				1
Hopkinson	3				3	Pope	1				1
O'Neill	2				3	Summers	1				1
Rents	3				3	Williamson	1				1
Clark	1				2						

AFC HORNCHURCH

Club Contact Details
The Stadium, Bridge Avenue, Upminster, Essex RM14 2LX
01708 220 080
peter.butcher5@btinternet.com

Founded: 2005   **Nickname:** The Urchins   **Manager:** Jim McFarlane
Previous Names: Formed in 2005 after Hornchurch F.C. folded
Previous Leagues: Essex Senior 2005-06. Isthmian 2006-12. Conference 2012-13.

Club Colours (change): Red and white

Ground Capacity: 3,500   **Seats:** 800   **Covered:** 1,400   **Clubhouse:** Yes   **Shop:** Yes
Previous Grounds: None
Record Attendance: 3,500 v Tranmere Rovers - FA Cup 2nd Round 2003-04

RECORDS
Misc: Won the Essex League with a record 64 points in 2005-06

HONOURS
FA Comps: None

League: Essex Senior 2005-06. Isthmian League Division One North 2006-07, Premier Division Play-offs 2011-12.

County FA: Essex Senior Cup 2012-13.

07-08		08-09		09-10		10-11		11-12		12-13		13-14		14-15		15-16		16-17	
Isth P	4	Isth P	6	Isth P	9	Isth P	10	Isth P	2	Conf S	20	Isth P	5	Isth P	23	Isth1N	5	Isth1N	4
FAC	4Q	FAC	1P	FAC	1Q	FAC	2Qr	FAC	1Q	FAC	2Q	FAC	4Q	FAC	1Qr	FAC	4Q	FAC	1Q
FAT	2Qr	FAT	1Qr	FAT	3Qr	FAT	1P	FAT	2P	FAT	3Q	FAT	1Q	FAT	3Q	FAT	1Q	FAT	P

AFC SUDBURY

Club Contact Details
Wardale Williams Stadium, Brundon Lane, Sudbury CO10 7HN
01787 376 213
dave-afc@supanet.com

Founded: 1999   **Nickname:** Yellows or The Suds   **Manager:** Jamie Godbold - 12/01/15
Previous Names: Sudbury Town (1874) and Sudbury Wanderers (1958) merged in 1999
Previous Leagues: Eastern Counties 1999-2006, Isthmian 2006-08, Southern 2008-10.

Club Colours (change): Yellow & blue

Ground Capacity: 2,500   **Seats:** 200   **Covered:** 1,500   **Clubhouse:** Yes   **Shop:** Yes
Previous Grounds: The Priory Stadium
Record Attendance: 1,800

RECORDS
Goalscorer: Gary Bennett - 172
Appearances: Paul Betson - 376

HONOURS
FA Comps: None

League: Eastern Counties League 2000-01, 01-02, 02-03, 03-04, 04-05. Isthmian League Division One North 2015-16.

County FA: Suffolk Premier Cup 2001-02, 02-03, 03-04.

07-08		08-09		09-10		10-11		11-12		12-13		13-14		14-15		15-16		16-17	
Isth1N	2	SthM		SthM	14	Isth1N	7	Isth1N	8	Isth1N	17	Isth1N	10	Isth1N	3	Isth1N	1	Isth P	23
FAC	P	FAC	Pr	FAC	1Q	FAC	Pr	FAC	3Q	FAC	1Q	FAC	3Q	FAC	1Q	FAC	2Q	FAC	2Q
FAT	1Qr	FAT	1P	FAT	1Qr	FAT	1P	FAT	1Q	FAT	P	FAT	3Qr	FAT	1P	FAT	2Q	FAT	2P

AVELEY

Club Contact Details
Mill Field, Mill Road, Aveley, Essex RM15 4SJ
01708 865 940
craigjohnson.aveleyfc@gmail.com

Founded: 1927   **Nickname:** The Millers   **Manager:** Terry Spillane

Previous Names: Lodge Meadow 1927-51.

Previous Leagues: Thurrock Combination 1946-49, London 1949-57, Delphian 1957-63, Athenian 1963-73,
Isthmian 1973-2004, Southern 2004-06

Club Colours (change): All blue

Ground Capacity: 4,000   **Seats:** 400   **Covered:** 400   **Clubhouse:** Yes   **Shop:** No

Previous Grounds: None

Record Attendance: 3,741 v Slough Town - FA Amateur Cup 27/02/1971

RECORDS

Victory:	11-1 v Histon - 24/08/1963
Defeat:	0-8 v Orient, Essex Thameside Trophy
Goalscorer:	Jotty Wilks - 214
Appearances:	Ken Riley - 422

HONOURS

FA Comps: None

League: London Division One 1950-51, Premier Division 54-55. Athenian 1970-71. Isthmian Division One North 2008-09.

County FA: Essex Thameside Trophy 1979-80, 2004-05, 06-07.

07-08		08-09		09-10		10-11		11-12		12-13		13-14		14-15		15-16		16-17	
Isth1N	11	Isth1N	1	Isth P	3	Isth P	19	Isth P	20	Isth P	5	Isth1N	13	Isth1N	9	Isth1N	12	Isth1N	7
FAC	1Qr	FAC	1Q	FAC	3Qr	FAC	1Q	FAC	2Q	FAC	2Q	FAC	1Q	FAC	3Q	FAC	3Q	FAC	P
FAT	Pr	FAT	1Q	FAT	1Q	FAT	1Q	FAT	1Q	FAT	P	FAT	P	FAT	P	FAT	P	FAT	P

BARKING

Club Contact Details
Mayesbrook Park, Lodge Avenue, Dagenham RM8 2JR
02032 440 069
secretary@barking-fc.co.uk

Founded: 1880   **Nickname:** The Blues   **Manager:** Glen Golby & Steve Willis

Previous Names: Barking Rov. Barking Woodville. Barking Working Lads Institute, Barking Institute. Barking T. Barking & East Ham United.

Previous Leagues: South Essex, London, Athenian. Isthmian. Southern. Essex Senior >2017.

Club Colours (change): All blue

Ground Capacity: 2,500   **Seats:** 200   **Covered:** 600   **Clubhouse:** Yes   **Shop:** Yes

Previous Grounds: Barking Park Recreation Ground. Vicarage Field 1884-1973.

Record Attendance: Att: 1,972 v Aldershot, FA Cup Second Round Proper, 1978.

RECORDS

Goalscorer:	Neville Fox - 241 (1965-73).
Appearances:	Bob Makin - 566.

HONOURS

FA Comps: None

League: South Essex Division One 1898-99, 1911-12, Division Two 1900-01. Division Two 1901-02. London Division One A 1909-10, Premier 1920-21. Athenian 1934-35. Isthmian Premier 1978-79. Essex Senior 2016-17.

County FA: Essex Senior Cup 1893-94, 95-96, 1919-20, 45-46, 62-63, 69-70, 89-90.
London Senior Cup 1911-12, 20-21, 26-27, 78-79.

07-08		08-09		09-10		10-11		11-12		12-13		13-14		14-15		15-16		16-17	
ESen	9	ESen	12	ESen	8	ESen	6	ESen	7	ESen	6	ESen	12	ESen	3	ESen	4	ESen	1
FAC	Pr	FAC	EP	FAC	EP	FAC	P	FAC	EPr	FAC	EPr	FAC	Pr	FAC	EP	FAC	Pr	FAC	Pr
FAV	2P	FAV	1Qr	FAV	2Qr	FAV	1P	FAV	1P	FAV	1P	FAV	2P	FAV	1Q	FAV	2P	FAV	1P

BOWERS & PITSEA

Club Contact Details
Len Salmon Stadium, Crown Avenue, Pitsea, Basildon SS13 2BE

01268 045 268

lee-stevens@sky.com

Founded: 1946   **Nickname:**   **Manager:** Rob Small
Previous Names: Bowers United > 2004.
Previous Leagues: Thurrock & Thameside Combination. Olympian. Essex Senior >2016.

Club Colours (change): Red & white

Ground Capacity: 2,000   **Seats:** 200   **Covered:** 1,000   **Clubhouse:** Yes   **Shop:** Yes
Previous Grounds: Pitsea Market. Gun Meadow.
Record Attendance: Att: 1,800 v Billericay Town, FA Vase.

RECORDS
Victory: 14-1 v Stansted, 2006-07
Defeat: 0-8 v Ford United, 1996-97
Goalscorer: David Hope scored 50 during the 1998-99 season.

HONOURS
FA Comps: None
League: Thurrock & Thameside Combination 1958-59. Essex Senior 1980-81, 98-99, 2015-16.

County FA: None

07-08		08-09		09-10		10-11		11-12		12-13		13-14		14-15		15-16		16-17	
ESen	7	ESen	11	ESen	17	ESen	14	ESen	15	ESen	19	ESen	14	ESen	2	ESen	1	Isth1N	6
FAC	EP	FAC	EP	FAC	P	FAC	P	FAC	EP	FAC	EP	FAC	EP	FAC	1Q	FAC	EP	FAC	Pr
FAV	1P	FAV	1Pr	FAV	1Q	FAV	2Q	FAV	2Q	FAV	1Q	FAV	1P	FAV	1P	FAV	SF	FAT	1Q

BRENTWOOD TOWN

Club Contact Details
The Arena, Brentwood Centre, Doddinghurst Road, Brentwood CM15 9NN

07768 006 370

r.w.stevens@btinternet.com

Founded: 1954   **Nickname:** Blues   **Manager:** Craig Shipman
Previous Names: Manor Athletic, Brentwood Athletic, Brentwood F.C.
Previous Leagues: Romford & District, South Essex Combination, London & Essex Border, Olympian, Essex Senior

Club Colours (change): Blue & white

Ground Capacity: 1,000   **Seats:** 150   **Covered:** 250   **Clubhouse:** Yes   **Shop:** No
Previous Grounds: King George's Playing Fields (Hartswood), Larkins Playing Fields 1957-93
Record Attendance: 763 v Cheshunt, Isthmian Division One North, 23/04/2011.

RECORDS

HONOURS
FA Comps: None
League: Essex Senior 2000-01, 2006-07.

County FA: None

07-08		08-09		09-10		10-11		11-12		12-13		13-14		14-15		15-16		16-17	
Isth1N	6	Isth1N	3	Isth1N	12	Isth1N	5	Isth1N	9	Isth1N	9	Isth1N	19	Isth1N	4	Isth P	22	Isth1N	14
FAC	3Q	FAC	1Qr	FAC	P	FAC	3Qr	FAC	1Qr	FAC	3Q	FAC	1Qr	FAC	2Q	FAC	4Q	FAC	P
FAV	2Q	FAV	1Q	FAV	1Q	FAV	1Q	FAV	1Q	FAV	3Qr	FAV	P	FAV	1Qr	FAV	2Q	FAV	P

BURY TOWN

Club Contact Details
Ram Meadow, Cotton Lane, Bury St Edmunds IP33 1XP
01284 754 721
wendy@burytownfc.co.uk

Founded: 1872   **Nickname:** The Blues   **Manager:** Ben Chenery
Previous Names: Bury St Edmunds 1872-1885, 1895-1908. Bury Town 1885-95. Bury United 1908-23.
Previous Leagues: Norfolk & Suffolk Border, Essex & Suffolk Border, Eastern Counties 1935-64, 76-87, 97-2006, Metropolitan 1964-71, Southern 1971-76, 87-97

Club Colours (change): Blue & white

Ground Capacity: 3,500   **Seats:** 300   **Covered:** 1,500   **Clubhouse:** Yes   **Shop:** Yes
Previous Grounds: Kings Road 1888-1978
Record Attendance: 2,500 v Enfield - FA Cup 1986

RECORDS
Goalscorer: Doug Tooley - 251 in nine seasons
Appearances: Dick Rayner - 610 over 12 seasons
Additional: Paid £1,500 to Chelmsford City for Mel Springett
              Received £5,500 from Ipswich Town for Simon Milton

HONOURS
FA Comps: None
League: Metropolitan 1965-66, 68-69. Eastern Counties 1963-64. Southern Division One Central 2009-10

County FA: Suffolk Senior Cup 1936-37, 37-38, 38-39, 44-45, 84-85.
               Suffolk Premier Cup x12 - Firstly in 1958-59 and most recently in 2013-14.

	07-08	08-09	09-10	10-11	11-12	12-13	13-14	14-15	15-16	16-17
	Isth1N 7	SthC 7	SthC 1	Isth P 3	Isth P 5	Isth P 7	Isth P 15	Isth P 24	Isth1N 13	Isth1N 11
FAC	2Q	1P	4Q	3Qr	2Q	4Q	1Q	1Q	2Q	P
FAT	1Qr	1P	P	2Q	3Qr	1Qr	1P	1Q	1P	1Q

CANVEY ISLAND

Club Contact Details
The Frost Financial Stadium, Park Lane, Canvey Island, Essex SS8 7PX
01268 682 991
g.sutton@sky.com

Founded: 1926   **Nickname:** The Gulls   **Manager:** Danny Heale
Previous Names: None
Previous Leagues: Southend & District, Thurrock & Thames Combination, Parthenon, Metropolitan, Greater London 1964-71, Essex Senior 1971-95, Isthmian 1995-2004, Conference 2004-06

Club Colours (change): Yellow & blue

Ground Capacity: 4,100   **Seats:** 500   **Covered:** 827   **Clubhouse:** Yes   **Shop:** Yes
Previous Grounds: None
Record Attendance: 3,553 v Aldershot Town - Isthmian League 2002-03

RECORDS
Goalscorer: Andy Jones
Appearances: Steve Ward
Additional: Paid £5,000 to Northwich Victoria for Chris Duffy
              Received £4,500 from Farnborough Town for Brian Horne

HONOURS
FA Comps: FA Trophy 2000-01.
League: Thurrock Combination 1955-56. Greater London Division One 1967-68, 68-69. Essex Senior 1986-87, 92-93. Isthmian Division Two 1995-96, 97-98, Division One 1998-99, Premier Division 2003-04.
County FA: Essex Senior Cup 1998-99, 99-00, 01-02, 11-12.

	07-08	08-09	09-10	10-11	11-12	12-13	13-14	14-15	15-16	16-17
	Isth1N 5	Isth P 12	Isth P 16	Isth P 6	Isth P 8	Isth P 8	Isth P 13	Isth P 17	Isth P 14	Isth P 22
FAC	P	1Q	2Q	3Qr	2Q	1Q	4Q	4Qr	1Q	2Qr
FAT	1P	1Qr	1Q	1Q	3Q	3Qr	2Q	1Qr	2Q	1Q

CHESHUNT

Club Contact Details
Cheshunt Stadium, Theobalds Lane, Cheshunt, Herts EN8 8RU

01992 625 793

clubsecretary@cheshuntfc.com

Founded: 1946   **Nickname:** Ambers   **Manager:** Paul Wickenden
Previous Names: None
Previous Leagues: London 1947-51, 56-59, Delphian 1952-55, Aetolian 1960-62, Spartan 1963-64, 88-93, Athenian 1965-76, Isthmian 1977-87, 94-2005, Southern 2006-08.

Club Colours (change): Amber & black

Ground Capacity: 3,500   **Seats:** 424   **Covered:** 600   **Clubhouse:** Yes   **Shop:** No
Previous Grounds: Gothic Sports Ground 1946-47. College Road 1947-50. Brookfield Lane 1950-52, 53-58.
Record Attendance: 5,000 v Bromley - FA Amateur Cup 2nd Round 28/01/1950

RECORDS
Defeat: 0-10 v Etonn Manor - London League 17/04/1956
Goalscorer: Eddie Sedgwick - 148 (1967-72, 1980)
Appearances: John Poole - 526 (1970-76, 79-83)
Additional: Received £10,000 from Peterborough United for Lloyd Opara

HONOURS
FA Comps: None
League: London Division One 1947-48, 48-49, Premier 49-50, Division One 1948, 49. Spartan 1962-63. Athenian 1967-68, 75-76. Isthmian Division Two 2002-03.
County FA: London Charity Cup 1974. East Anglian Cup 1975. Herts Charity Cup 2006, 2008.

07-08		08-09		09-10		10-11		11-12		12-13		13-14		14-15		15-16		16-17	
SthP	22	Isth1N	14	Isth1N	15	Isth1N	18	Isth1N	18	Isth1N	11	Isth1N	15	Isth1N	18	Isth1N	6	Isth1N	10
FAC	1Q	FAC	1Q	FAC	P	FAC	1Q	FAC	Pr	FAC	Pr	FAC	P	FAC	P	FAC	P	FAC	1Q
FAT	1Q	FAT	1Q	FAT	P	FAT	P	FAT	P	FAT	P	FAT	1Q	FAT	P	FAT	2Q	FAT	1Q

DEREHAM TOWN

Club Contact Details
Aldiss Park, Norwich Road, Dereham, Norfolk NR20 3PX

01362 690 460

cheshiredodders@hotmail.com

Founded: 1884   **Nickname:** Magpies   **Manager:** Neal Simmons
Previous Names: Dereham and Dereham Hobbies.
Previous Leagues: Norwich District. Dereham & District. Norfolk & Suffolk. Anglian Comb. Eastern Counties > 2013.

Club Colours (change): Black & white

Ground Capacity: 3,000   **Seats:** 150   **Covered:** 500   **Clubhouse:** Yes   **Shop:** Yes
Previous Grounds: Bayfields Meadow. Recreation Ground >1996.
Record Attendance: 3000 v Norwich City, Friendly, 07/2001.

RECORDS

HONOURS
FA Comps: None
League: Anglian Combination Division One 1989-90, Premier Division 97-98. Eastern Counties Premier Division 2012-13.

County FA: Norfolk Senior Cup 2005-06, 06-07, 15-16.

07-08		08-09		09-10		10-11		11-12		12-13		13-14		14-15		15-16		16-17	
ECP	4	ECP	4	ECP	10	ECP	2	ECP	10	ECP	1	Isth1N	7	Isth1N	7	Isth1N	9	Isth1N	18
FAC	Pr	FAC	Pr	FAC	1Q	FAC	EP	FAC	EP	FAC	3Qr	FAC	1Q	FAC	2Q	FAC	P	FAC	2Q
FAV	1P	FAV	5P	FAV	2P	FAV	1Q	FAV	1P	FAV	2P	FAT	1Q	FAT	2Q	FAT	P	FAT	P

GRAYS ATHLETIC

Club Contact Details
Aveley FC, Mill Field, Mill Field Road, Aveley RM15 4SJ
07738 355 619
graysathleticfc@hotmail.co.uk

Founded: 1890   **Nickname:** The Blues   **Manager:** Jamie Stuart
Previous Names: Grays Juniors 1890.
Previous Leagues: Grays & District. South Essex. Athenian 1912-14, 58-83. London 1914-24, 26-39,.Kent 1924-26. Corinthian 1945-58. Isthmian 1958-2004. Conference 2004-10

Club Colours (change): All royal blue (All white)

Ground Capacity: 4,000 **Seats:** 400 **Covered:** 400 **Clubhouse:** Yes **Shop:** No
Previous Grounds: Recreation Ground Bridge Road. Rookery Hill (East Thurrock Utd). Rush Green Road.
Record Attendance: 9,500 v Chelmsford City - FA Cup 4th Qualifying Round 1959

RECORDS
Victory: 12-0 v Tooting & Mitcham United - London League 24/02/1923
Defeat: 0-12 v Enfield (A) - Athenian League 20/04/1963
Goalscorer: Harry Brand - 269 (1944-52)
Appearances: Phil Sammons - 673 (1982-97)
Additional: Paid £12,000 to Welling United for Danny Kedwell.
Received £150,000 from Peterborough United for Aaron McLean.

HONOURS
FA Comps: FA Trophy 2004-05, 05-06.
League: South Essex Division Two B 1908-09. Corinthian 1945-46. London Prmier (Amateur) 1914-15, Premier 1921-22, 26-27, 29-30. Isthmian Division Two South 1984-85, Division One North 2012-13. Conference South 2004-05.
County FA: Essex Senior Cup 1914-15, 20-21, 22-23, 44-45, 56-57, 87-88, 93-94, 94-95. East Anglian Cup 1944-45.

07-08		08-09		09-10		10-11		11-12		12-13		13-14		14-15		15-16		16-17	
Conf	10	Conf	19	Conf	23	Isth1N	10	Isth1N	5	Isth1N	1	Isth P	14	Isth P	6	Isth P	15	Isth P	24
FAC	4Qr	FAC	1Pr	FAC	4Q	FAC	2Qr	FAC	1Q	FAC	2Q	FAC	3Q	FAC	3Qr	FAC	4Qr	FAC	1Q
FAT	2Pr	FAT	1P	FAT	1P	FAT	3Qr	FAT	2Q	FAT	2Qr	FAT	3Q	FAT	2Q	FAT	3Qr	FAT	1Qr

HARINGEY BOROUGH

Club Contact Details
Coles Park, White Hart Lane, Tottenham, London N17 7JP
0208 889 1415 (Matchday)
baconjw@hotmail.com

Founded: 1973   **Nickname:** Borough   **Manager:** Tom Loizou
Previous Names: Edmonton & Haringey 1973-76. Haringey Borough 1976-95. Tufnell Park 1995-96.
Previous Leagues: Athenian 1973-84. Isthmian 1984-89. Spartan South Midlands 1989-2013. Essex Senior 2013-15.

Club Colours (change): Yellow/blue/yellow (All green)

Ground Capacity: 2,500 **Seats:** 280 **Covered:** yes **Clubhouse:** Yes **Shop:** No
Previous Grounds: None
Record Attendance: 400

RECORDS

HONOURS
FA Comps: None
League: Essex Senior 2014-15.

County FA: London Senior Cup 1990-91

07-08		08-09		09-10		10-11		11-12		12-13		13-14		14-15		15-16		16-17	
SSM1	2	SSM P	18	SSM P	15	SSM P	8	SSM P	5	SSM P	9	ESen	2	ESen	1	Isth1N	15	Isth1N	5
FAC	EPr	FAC	EP	FAC	EPr	FAC	P	FAC	P	FAC	EP	FAC	2Q	FAC	EP	FAC	1Q	FAC	1Q
FAV	1Q	FAV	1Q	FAV	1Qr	FAV	1P	FAV	3P	FAV	2Q	FAV	3P	FAV	1Pr	FAT	2Qr	FAT	P

HERTFORD TOWN

Club Contact Details
Hertingfordbury Park, West Street, Hertford, SG13 8EZ
01992 583 716
dave-thomas@ntlworld.com

Founded: 1901   **Nickname:** The Blues   **Manager:** Gavin Kelsey
Previous Names: Port Vale Rovers 1901.
Previous Leagues: Herts Senior County 1908-20. Middlsex 1920-21. Spartan 1921-59. Delphian 1959-63. Athenian 1963-72. Eastern Counties 1972-73. Spartan South Midlands 1973-2017.

Club Colours (change): All blue (All yellow or all red)

Ground Capacity: 6,500   **Seats:** 200   **Covered:** 1,500   **Clubhouse:** Yes   **Shop:** Yes
Previous Grounds: Hartham Park 1901-08.
Record Attendance: 5,000 v Kingstonian FA Am Cup 2nd Round 1955-56.

RECORDS
Appearances: Robbie Burns

HONOURS
FA Comps: None
League: Spartan Division One Eastern Section 1949-50. Delphian 1960-61, 61-62.
County FA: Herts Senior Cup 1966-67. East Anglian Cup 1962-63, 69-70.

07-08		08-09		09-10		10-11		11-12		12-13		13-14		14-15		15-16		16-17	
SSM P	4	SSM P	10	SSM P	16	SSM P	9	SSM P	16	SSM P	17	SSM P	16	SSM P	11	SSM P	8	SSM P	2
FAC	1Qr	FAC	EP	FAC	EP	FAC	P	FAC	1Q	FAC	EP	FAC	1Q	FAC	1Q	FAC	EPr	FAC	P
FAV	1P	FAV	1P	FAV	2Q	FAV	1P	FAV	1Q	FAV	3P	FAV	1Q	FAV	1P	FAV	3P	FAV	1P

HEYBRIDGE SWIFTS

Club Contact Details
The Texo Stadium, Scraley Road, Heybridge, Maldon, Essex CM9 8JA
01621 852 978
hsfcdaines@aol.com

Founded: 1880   **Nickname:** Swifts   **Manager:** Jody Brown
Previous Names: Heybridge FC.
Previous Leagues: Essex & Suffolk Border, North Essex, South Essex, Essex Senior 1971-84

Club Colours (change): Black & white

Ground Capacity: 3,000   **Seats:** 550   **Covered:** 1,200   **Clubhouse:** Yes   **Shop:** Yes
Previous Grounds: Bentall's Sports Ground 1890-1964. Sadd's Athletic ground share 1964-66.
Record Attendance: 2,477 v Woking - FA Trophy Quarter-finals 1997.

RECORDS
Goalscorer: Julian Lamb - 115 (post War)
Appearances: Hec Askew - 500+. John Pollard - 496
Additional: Paid £1,000 for Dave Rainford and for Lee Kersey
Received £35,000 from Southend United for Simon Royce

HONOURS
FA Comps: None
League: Essex & Suffolk Border Division Two (West) 1920-21, Division One 30-31. Essex Senior 1981-82, 82-83, 83-84. Isthmian Division Two North 1989-90.
County FA: Essex Junior Cup 1931-32. East Anglian Cup 1993-94, 94-95.

07-08		08-09		09-10		10-11		11-12		12-13		13-14		14-15		15-16		16-17	
Isth P	12	Isth P	21	Isth1N	6	Isth1N	9	Isth1N	16	Isth1N	6	Isth1N	3	Isth1N	12	Isth1N	20	Isth1N	21
FAC	3Qr	FAC	2Q	FAC	3Qr	FAC	P	FAC	1Q	FAC	2Q	FAC	4Q	FAC	P	FAC	1Q	FAC	1Qr
FAT	2Q	FAT	3Q	FAT	P	FAT	Pr	FAT	P	FAT	P	FAT	1Q	FAT	1Q	FAT	2Qr	FAT	1Q

MALDON & TIPTREE

Club Contact Details
Wallace Binder Ground, Park Drive, Maldon CM9 5JQ
07817 499 540
club.secretary@maldontiptreefc.co.uk

Founded: 1946 **Nickname:** The Jammers **Manager:** Kevin Horlock
Previous Names: Maldon Town were rebranded in 2010.
Previous Leagues: Chelmsford & Mid-Essex. North Essex. Essex & Suffolk Border. Eastern Counties 1966-72. Essex Senior 1972-2004. Southern 2004-05.

Club Colours (change): Blue & red

Ground Capacity: 2,800 **Seats:** 155 **Covered:** 300 **Clubhouse:** Yes **Shop:**
Previous Grounds: Sadd's Ground 1946-47. Promenade 1947-50. Farmbridge Road 1950-1994.
Record Attendance: 1,163 v AFC Sudbury, FA Vase semi-final 2003.

RECORDS

HONOURS
FA Comps: None
League: Mid-Essex Premier Division 1949-50, 50-51. Essex & Suffolk Border Premier Division 1965-66. Essex Senior 1984-85.

County FA: Essex Intermediate Cup 1951-52.

07-08		08-09		09-10		10-11		11-12		12-13		13-14		14-15		15-16		16-17	
Isth1N	9	Isth1N	16	Isth1N	17	Isth1N	8	Isth1N	11	Isth1N	2	Isth1N	9	Isth1N	19	Isth1N	7	Isth1N	2
FAC	2Qr	FAC	Pr	FAC	1Q	FAC	2Q	FAC	3Q	FAC	2Qr	FAC	1Q	FAC	P	FAC	P	FAC	1Q
FAT	1Q	FAT	P	FAT	P	FAT	P	FAT	3Q	FAT	P	FAT	1Q	FAT	P	FAT	P	FAT	1Q

MILDENHALL TOWN

Club Contact Details
Recreation Way, Mildenhall, Suffolk IP28 7HG
01638 713 449
bhensby@talktalk.net

Founded: 1898 **Nickname:** The Hall **Manager:** Dean Greygoose - Dec 2014
Previous Names: None
Previous Leagues: Bury & District. Cambridgeshire. Cambridgeshire Premier. Eastern Counties >2017.

Club Colours (change): Amber/black/black. (Red & white/white/red).

Ground Capacity: 2,000 **Seats:** 100 **Covered:** 200 **Clubhouse:** Yes **Shop:** Yes
Previous Grounds: None
Record Attendance: 450 v Derby County, Friendly, July 2001.

RECORDS

HONOURS
FA Comps: None
League: Eastern Counties Premier Division 2016-17.

County FA: Suffolk Junior Cup 1899-1900. Cambridgeshire Junior Cup 1992-93. Cambridgeshire Invitation Cup 1995-96, 2009-10, 10-11.

07-08		08-09		09-10		10-11		11-12		12-13		13-14		14-15		15-16		16-17	
ECP	5	ECP	11	ECP	6	ECP	5	ECP	7	ECP	7	ECP	10	ECP	10	ECP	6	ECP	1
FAC	1Qr	FAC	1Q	FAC	2Q	FAC	EP	FAC	EP	FAC	EP	FAC	1Qr	FAC	1Q	FAC	2Q	FAC	EP
FAV	3P	FAV	2P	FAV	1Q	FAV	1Q	FAV	2Q	FAV	1Q	FAT	1Pr	FAT	2Q	FAT	2P	FAT	2Q

NORWICH UNITED

Club Contact Details
Plantation Park, Blofield, Norwich NR13 4PL
01603 716 963
secretary.nufc@hotmail.co.uk

Founded: 1903   **Nickname:** Planters   **Manager:** Steve Eastaugh
Previous Names: Poringland & District > 1987
Previous Leagues: Norwich & District. Anglian Combination. Eastern Counties >2016.

Club Colours (change): Yellow & blue

Ground Capacity: 3,000   **Seats:** 100   **Covered:** 1,000   **Clubhouse:** Yes   **Shop:** Yes
Previous Grounds: Gothic Social Club 1985-90.
Record Attendance: Att: 401 v Wroxham, Eastern Co. Lge, 1991-92.

RECORDS
Goalscorer: M. Money
Appearances: Tim Sayer

HONOURS
FA Comps: None
League: Anglian Combination Premier Division 1988-99.
        Eastern Counties Division One 1990-91, 01-02, Premier Division 2014-15, 15-16.
County FA: Norfolk Junior Cup 1978-79, 1980-81.

07-08		08-09		09-10		10-11		11-12		12-13		13-14		14-15		15-16		16-17	
ECP	15	ECP	19	ECP	15	ECP	6	ECP	9	ECP	13	ECP	6	ECP	1	ECP	1	Isth1N	9
FAC	P	FAC	EPr	FAC	P	FAC	Pr	FAC	EP	FAC	1Q	FAC	EP	FAC	2Qr	FAC	Pr	FAC	P
FAV	2Qr	FAV	2Q	FAV	2Q	FAV	1P	FAV	2Q	FAV	2Q	FAV	4P	FAV	5P	FAV	2P	FAT	P

POTTERS BAR TOWN

Club Contact Details
Pakex Stadium, Parkfield, Watkins Rise, Potters Bar EN6 1QB
01707 654 833
jeff@jeffbarnes.co.uk

Founded: 1960   **Nickname:** Grace or Scholars   **Manager:** Steve Ringrose - 21/02/15
Previous Names: Mount Grace Old Scholars 1960-84. Mount Grace 1984-91.
Previous Leagues: Barnet & District 1960-65, North London Combination 1965-68, Herts Senior County 1968-91,
        Spartan South Midlands 1991-2005, Southern 2005-06, 13-17. Isthmian 2006-13.

Club Colours (change): Maroon/white/maroon (Yellow/yellow/black)

Ground Capacity: 2,000   **Seats:** 150   **Covered:** 250   **Clubhouse:** Yes   **Shop:** Yes
Previous Grounds: None
Record Attendance: 268 v Wealdstone - FA Cup 1998 (4,000 watched a charity match in 1997)

RECORDS
Goalscorer: Micky Gray scored 51 during a single season. Richard Howard has come closest to that record having scored 49
        goals during seasons 2004-05 and 2006-07 respectively.

HONOURS
FA Comps: None
League: North London Combination Premier Division 1967-68. Herst Senior county Premier Division 1990-91.
        Spartan South Midlands Premier Division 1996-97, 2004-05.
County FA: None

07-08		08-09		09-10		10-11		11-12		12-13		13-14		14-15		15-16		16-17	
Isth1N	17	Isth1N	19	Isth1N	14	Isth1N	13	Isth1N	12	Isth1N	10	SthC	15	SthC	14	SthC	12	SthC	9
FAC	1Q	FAC	Pr	FAC	3Q	FAC	P	FAC	P	FAC	1Qr	FAC	P	FAC	P	FAC	2Q	FAC	4Q
FAT	P	FAT	P	FAT	Pr	FAT	1Qr	FAT	2Q	FAT	1Q	FAT	1Qr	FAT	P	FAT	Pr	FAT	P

ROMFORD

Club Contact Details
Thurrock FC, South Way, Ship Lane, Aveley RM19 1YN
01708 865 492
ewenson@aol.com

Founded: 1876   **Nickname:** Boro   **Manager:** Paul Martin
Previous Names: Original club founded in 1876 folded during WW1, Reformed in 1929 folded again in 1978 and reformed in 1992
Previous Leagues: Essex Senior 1992-96, 2002-09. Isthmian 1997-2002.

Club Colours (change): Yellow & blue

Ground Capacity: 4,500   **Seats:** 300   **Covered:** 1,000   **Clubhouse:** Yes   **Shop:**
Previous Grounds: Hornchurch Stadium 1992-95. Rush Green 1995-96. Sungate 1996-2001. The Mill Field (Aveley FC).
Record Attendance: 820 v Leatherhead - Isthmian Division Two

RECORDS
Goalscorer: Danny Benstock. Vinny John scored 45 goals during season 1997-98.
Appearances: Paul Clayton - 396 (2006-15)
Victory: 9-0 v Hullbridge Sports, Essex Senior, 21/10/1995.
Misc: Mark Lord became the oldest player to player for the club aged 48yrs 90 days on 03/03/2015.

HONOURS
FA Comps: None
League: Essex Senior 1995-96, 2008-09. Isthmian Division Two 1996-97.

County FA: East Anglian Cup 1997-98.

07-08		08-09		09-10		10-11		11-12		12-13		13-14		14-15		15-16		16-17	
ESen	5	ESen	1	Isth1N	13	Isth1N	12	Isth1N	13	Isth1N	8	Isth1N	11	Isth1N	20	Isth1N	16	Isth1N	16
FAC	EP	FAC	P	FAC	1Qr	FAC	2Q	FAC	1Q	FAC	P	FAC	1Q	FAC	2Qr	FAC	Pr	FAC	1Q
FAV	3Pr	FAV	2P	FAT	P	FAT	3Q	FAT	P	FAT	1Q	FAT	P	FAT	Pr	FAT	1Q	FAT	2Q

SOHAM TOWN RANGERS

Club Contact Details
Julius Martin Lane, Soham, Ely, Cambridgeshire CB7 5EQ
01353 720 732
strfc@live.co.uk

Founded: 1947   **Nickname:** Greens, Town or Rangers   **Manager:** Rob Mason
Previous Names: Soham Town and Soham Rangers merged in 1947
Previous Leagues: Peterborough & District, Eastern Counties 1963-2008, Southern 2008-11.

Club Colours (change): Green & white stripes/green/green (All yellow)

Ground Capacity: 2,000   **Seats:** 250   **Covered:** 1,000   **Clubhouse:** Yes   **Shop:** Yes
Previous Grounds: None
Record Attendance: 3,000 v Pegasus - FA Amateur Cup 1963

RECORDS

HONOURS
FA Comps: None
League: Peterborough & District 1959-60, 61-62. Eastern Counties Premier Division 2007-08.

County FA: Cambridgeshire Challenge Cup 1957-58. Cambridgeshire Invitation Cup 1990-91, 97-98, 98-99, 2005-06.

07-08		08-09		09-10		10-11		11-12		12-13		13-14		14-15		15-16		16-17	
ECP	1	SthC	15	SthC	11	SthC	17	Isth1N	19	Isth1N	7	Isth1N	8	Isth1N	11	Isth1N	17	Isth1N	19
FAC	2Q	FAC	P	FAC	Pr	FAC	P	FAC	P	FAC	1Q	FAC	P	FAC	P	FAC	P	FAC	1Qr
FAV	2P	FAT	2Q	FAT	1Qr	FAT	1Q	FAT	P	FAT	2Q	FAT	2Q	FAT	P	FAT	P	FAT	1Q

TILBURY

Club Contact Details
Chadfields, St Chads Road, Tilbury, Essex RM18 8NL
01375 843 093
amercer67@googlemail.com

Founded: 1895   **Nickname:** The Dockers   **Manager:** Gary Henty - 10/14
Previous Names: None
Previous Leagues: Grays & District/South Essex, Kent 1927-31, London, South Essex Combination (Wartime), Corinthian 1950-57, Delphian 1962-63, Athenian 1963-73, Isthmian 1973-2004, Essex Senior 2004-05

Club Colours (change): Black & white/black/black (All purple)

Ground Capacity: 4,000   **Seats:** 350   **Covered:** 1,000   **Clubhouse:** Yes   **Shop:** No
Previous Grounds: Orient Field 1895-46.
Record Attendance: 5,500 v Gorleston - FA Cup 1949

RECORDS
Goalscorer: Ross Livermore - 282 in 305 games
Appearances: Nicky Smith - 424 (1975-85)
Additional: Received £2,000 from Grays Athletic for Tony Macklin 1990 and from Dartford for Steve Connor 1985

HONOURS
FA Comps: None
League: Athenian 1968-69. Isthmian Division Two 1975-76.
County FA: Essex Senior Cup x4. East Anglian Cup 2008-09.

07-08		08-09		09-10		10-11		11-12		12-13		13-14		14-15		15-16		16-17	
Isth1N	20	Isth1N	11	Isth1N	11	Isth1N	19	Isth1N	3	Isth1N	16	Isth1N	16	Isth1N	14	Isth1N	11	Isth1N	12
FAC	P	FAC	P	FAC	P	FAC	1Q	FAC	1Q	FAC	1Q	FAC	2Q	FAC	1Q	FAC	1Q	FAC	1Q
FAT	P	FAT	1Qr	FAT	P	FAT	P	FAT	P	FAT	P	FAT	1Q	FAT	Pr	FAT	1P	FAT	Pr

WALTHAM ABBEY

Club Contact Details
Capershotts, Sewardstone Road, Waltham Abbey, Essex EN9 1NX
01992 711 287
secretary@wafc.info

Founded: 1944   **Nickname:** Abbotts   **Manager:** Paul Joynes
Previous Names: Abbey Sports amalgamated with Beechfield Sports in 1974 to form Beechfields. Club then renamed to Waltham Abbey in 1976
Previous Leagues: London Spartan/Spartan. Essex & Herts Border. Essex Senior.

Club Colours (change): Green and white hoops/green/green & white (Blue & white hoops/blue/blue & white)

Ground Capacity: 3,500   **Seats:** 200   **Covered:** 500   **Clubhouse:** Yes   **Shop:** No
Previous Grounds: None
Record Attendance:

RECORDS

HONOURS
FA Comps: None
League: London Spartan Division One 1977-78, Senior Division 1978-79.
County FA: London Senior Cup 1998-99. Essex Senior Cup 2004-05.

07-08		08-09		09-10		10-11		11-12		12-13		13-14		14-15		15-16		16-17	
Isth1N	14	Isth1N	4	Isth1N	21	Isth1N	11	Isth1N	14	Isth1N	12	Isth1N	18	Isth1N	10	Isth1N	21	Isth1N	20
FAC	1Q	FAC	1Q	FAC	1Q	FAC	P	FAC	1Q	FAC	2Q	FAC	1Q	FAC	3Q	FAC	P	FAC	1Q
FAT	P	FAT	Pr	FAT	1Q	FAT	P	FAT	Pr	FAT	1Q	FAT	1Q	FAT	P	FAT	2Q	FAT	1Q

WARE

Club Contact Details
Wodson Park, Wadesmill Road, Ware, Herts SG12 0UQ

01920 462 064

spink405@btinternet.com

Founded: 1892   **Nickname:** Blues   **Manager:** Kem Kemal

Previous Names: Ware Town.

Previous Leagues: East Herts, North Middlesex 1907-08, Herts County 1908-25, Spartan 1925-55, Delphian 1955-63, Athenian 1963-75, Isthmian 1975-2015. Southern 2015-16.

Club Colours (change): Blue & white

Ground Capacity: 3,300   **Seats:** 500   **Covered:** 312   **Clubhouse:** Yes   **Shop:** Yes

Previous Grounds: Highfields, Canons Park, London Road, Presdales Lower Park 1921-26

Record Attendance: 3,800 v Hendon - FA Amateur Cup, January 1957.

RECORDS
Victory:	10-1 v Wood Green Town
Defeat:	0-11 v Barnet
Goalscorer:	George Dearman scored 98 goals during 1926-27
Appearances:	Gary Riddle - 654

HONOURS
FA Comps: None

League: East Herts 1897-88, 98-99, 99-1900, 02-03, 03-04, 05-06 (shared), 06-07. Herts County 1908-09, 21-22. Spartan Division Two B 1926-27, Division One 51-52, Premier 52-53. Isthmian Division Two 2005-06.

County FA: Herts Senior Cup 1898-99, 1903-04, 06-07, 21-22, 53-54. Herts Charity Shield 1926-27, 52-53, 56-57, 58-59, 62-63, 85-86. East Anglian Cup 1973-74.

07-08		08-09		09-10		10-11		11-12		12-13		13-14		14-15		15-16		16-17	
Isth1N	4	Isth1N	9	Isth1N	19	Isth1N	14	Isth1N	21	Isth1N	19	Isth1N	21	Isth1N	10	SthC	11	Isth1N	22
FAC	1P	FAC	3Q	FAC	1Q	FAC	P	FAC	P	FAC	1Q	FAC	P	FAC	P	FAC	P	FAC	P
FAT	P	FAT	1Q	FAT	P	FAT	P	FAT	P	FAT	P	FAT	Pr	FAT	1Q	FAT	P	FAT	2Q

WITHAM TOWN

Club Contact Details
Village Glass Stadium, Spa Road, Witham CM8 1UN

01376 511 198

withamtownfc@gmail.com

Founded: 1947   **Nickname:** Town   **Manager:** Adam Flint

Previous Names: Witham Town Football Clubs did exist before both World Wars with both folding due to the conflicts.

Previous Leagues: Mid-Essex 1947-52. South Essex 1952-58. Essex & Suffolk Border 1958-71. Essex Senior 1971-87, 2009-12. Isthmian 1987-2009.

Club Colours (change): White/blue/green (All yellow).

Ground Capacity: 2,500   **Seats:** 157   **Covered:** 780   **Clubhouse:** Yes   **Shop:** No

Previous Grounds: Crittall Windows works ground 1949-75.

Record Attendance: Att: 800 v Billericay Town, Essex Senior Lge, May 1976.

RECORDS
Goalscorer:	Colin Mitchell.
Appearances:	Keith Dent.

HONOURS
FA Comps: None

League: Mid-Essex Division Three 1947-48, Division Two 48-49. South Essex 1955-56. Essex & Suffolk Border 1964-65, 70-71. Essex Senior 1970-71, 85-86, 2011-12.

County FA: Essex Senior trophy 1985-86.

07-08		08-09		09-10		10-11		11-12		12-13		13-14		14-15		15-16		16-17	
Isth1N	20	Isth1N	21	ESen	2	ESen	3	ESen	1	Isth1N	4	Isth1N	2	Isth P	22	Isth1N	19	Isth1N	13
FAC	P	FAC	1Q	FAC	P	FAC	Pr	FAC	P	FAC	1Q	FAC	2Qr	FAC	4Q	FAC	2Q	FAC	2Q
FAT	3Q	FAT	1Q	FAV	1P	FAV	3P	FAV	3P	FAT	P	FAT	1Q	FAT	2Q	FAT	P	FAT	1Q

ASHFORD UNITED

Club Contact Details
The Homelands, Ashford Road TN26 1NJ
01233 611 838
aufootballclub@yahoo.com

Founded: 1930   **Nickname:** The Nuts & Bolts   **Manager:** Danny Lye

Previous Names: Ashford Town 1930-2010.

Previous Leagues: Kent 1930-59. Southern 1959-2004. Isthmian 2004-10. Kent Invicta 2011-2013. Southern Counties East 2013-17.

Club Colours (change): Green & white

Ground Capacity: 3,200   **Seats:** 500   **Covered:** Yes   **Clubhouse:** Yes   **Shop:**

Previous Grounds: Essella Park 1931-1987.

Record Attendance: At Essella Park - 6,525 v Crystal Palace, FAC 1st Rnd, 1959-60. At Homelands - 3,363 v Fulham, FAC 1st , 1994-95.

RECORDS
Victory: 15-0 v Erith & Belvedere, Kent League, 28/04/1937.

Defeat: 3-14 v Folkestone Reserves, Kent League, 1933-34.

Goalscorer: Dave Arter - 197. Shaun Welford scored 48 goals during the 2016-17 season.
Stuart Zanone scored 7 v Lingfield (A), Southern Counties East, 24/03/2015.

Appearances: Peter McRobert - 765

HONOURS
FA Comps: None

League: Kent 1948-49. Southern Counties East 2016-17.

County FA: Kent Senior Cup 1958-59, 62-63, 92-93, 95-96. Kent Senior Trophy 2016-17.

07-08		08-09		09-10		10-11	11-12		12-13		13-14		14-15		15-16		16-17	
Isth1S	8	Isth1S	7	Isth1S	20		K_Iv	5	K_Iv	3	SCEP	2	SCEP	2	SCEP	3	SCEP	1
FAC	P	FAC	1Q	FAC	1Q				FAC	P	FAC	P	FAC	P	FAC	EP	FAC	1Q
FAT	1Q	FAT	P	FAT	1Q		FAV	1Qr	FAV	2Q	FAV	4P	FAV	4P	FAV	QF	FAV	2P

CARSHALTON ATHLETIC

Club Contact Details
War Memorial Sports Ground, Colston Avenue, Carshalton SM5 2PN
020 8642 2551
chrisblanchard@carshaltonathletic.co.uk

Founded: 1905   **Nickname:** Robins   **Manager:** Peter Adeniyi

Previous Names: Mill Lane Mission 1905-07.

Previous Leagues: Croydon & District 1905-10. Southern Suburban 1910-22. Surrey Senior (Founding Members) 1922-23. London 1923-46. Corinthian 1946-56. Athenian 1956-73. Isthmian 1973-2004. Conference 2004-06.

Club Colours (change): All red (All white)

Ground Capacity: 8,000   **Seats:** 240   **Covered:** 4,500   **Clubhouse:** Yes   **Shop:** Yes

Previous Grounds: Various before moving to Colston Avenue during the 1920-21 season.

Record Attendance: 7,800 v Wimbledon - London Senior Cup, Jan 1959.

RECORDS
Victory: 13-0 v Worthing - Isthmian League Cup 28/01/1991.

Defeat: 0-11 v Southall - Athenian League March 1963

Goalscorer: Jimmy Bolton - 242 during seven seasons

Appearances: Jon Warden - 504

Additional: Paid £15,000 to Enfield for Curtis Warmington
Received £30,000 from Crystal Palace for Ian Cox 1994

HONOURS
FA Comps: None

League: Corinthian 1952-53, 53-54. Isthmian Division One South 2002-03.

County FA: Surrey Intermediate Cup 1921-22, 31-32. Surrey Senior Shield 1975-76. Surrey Senior Cup 1988-89, 89-90, 91-92. London Challenge Cup 1991-92.

07-08		08-09		09-10		10-11		11-12		12-13		13-14		14-15		15-16		16-17	
Isth P	18	Isth P	4	Isth P	17	Isth P	13	Isth P	16	Isth P	20	Isth P	23	Isth1S	20	Isth1S	10	Isth1S	6
FAC	2Q	FAC	2Q	FAC	1Q	FAC	4Qr	FAC	2Q	FAC	2Q	FAC	1Q	FAC	1Q	FAC	2Q	FAC	1Qr
FAT	1P	FAT	1Q	FAT	2Pr	FAT	2Q	FAT	3P	FAT	2Q	FAT	3Q	FAT	P	FAT	P	FAT	Pr

CHIPSTEAD

Club Contact Details
High Road, Chipstead, Surrey CR5 3SF
01737 553 250
secretarycfc@virginmedia.com

Founded: 1906   **Nickname:** Chips   **Manager:** Anthony Williams
Previous Names: None
Previous Leagues: Surrey Intermediate 1962-82, Surrey Premier 1982-86, Combined Counties 1986-2007

Club Colours (change): Green & white

Ground Capacity: 2,000   **Seats:** 150   **Covered:** 200   **Clubhouse:** Yes   **Shop:** Yes
Previous Grounds: None
Record Attendance: 1,170

RECORDS
Goalscorer: Mick Nolan - 124

HONOURS
FA Comps: None
League: Combined Counties Premier 1989-90, 2006-07.
County FA: East Surrey Charity Cup 1960-61.

07-08		08-09		09-10		10-11		11-12		12-13		13-14		14-15		15-16		16-17	
Isth1S	15	Isth1S	21	Isth1S	19	Isth1S	10	Isth1S	12	Isth1S	20	Isth1S	13	Isth1S	15	Isth1S	21	Isth1S	20
FAC	P	FAC	4Q	FAC	1Q	FAC	2Qr	FAC	2Q	FAC	1Q	FAC	3Q	FAC	1Qr	FAC	P	FAC	1Q
FAT	1Q	FAT	P	FAT	2Q	FAT	P	FAT	1Q	FAT	P	FAT	P	FAT	P	FAT	1Q	FAT	Pr

CORINTHIAN-CASUALS

Club Contact Details
King George's Field, Queen Mary Close, Hook Rise South, KT6 7NA
020 8397 3368
hanna.newton@icloud.com

Founded: 1939   **Nickname:** Casuals   **Manager:** James Bracken
Previous Names: Casuals and Corinthians merged in 1939
Previous Leagues: Isthmian 1939-84, Spartan 1984-96, Combined Counties 1996-97

Club Colours (change): Chocolate and pink halves/chocolate/chocolate (All blue)

Ground Capacity: 2,000   **Seats:** 161   **Covered:** 700   **Clubhouse:** Yes   **Shop:** Yes
Previous Grounds: Kingstonian's Richmond Road 1939-46. Polytechnic Ground in Chiswick 46-50. Oval 50-63. Dulwich Hamlet's Champion Hill 63-68,
Record Attendance: Tooting & Mitcham United's Sandy Lane 68-83, Molesey's Walton Road 83-84, 86-88. Wimbledon Park Athletics Stadium 84-86.

RECORDS
Goalscorer: Cliff West - 215
Appearances: Simon Shergold - 526

HONOURS
FA Comps: None
League: London Spartan Senior Division 1985-86.
County FA: Surrey Senior Cup 1953-54, 2010-11.

07-08		08-09		09-10		10-11		11-12		12-13		13-14		14-15		15-16		16-17	
Isth1S	20	Isth1S	20	Isth1S	13	Isth1S	20	Isth1S	13	Isth1S	14	Isth1S	17	Isth1S	13	Isth1S	6	Isth1S	4
FAC	P	FAC	P	FAC	P	FAC	1Q	FAC	P	FAC	P	FAC	F	FAC	F	FAC	F	FAC	1Q
FAT	1Q	FAT	P	FAT	1Q	FAT	P	FAT	P	FAT	P	FAT	P	FAT	Pr	FAT	1P	FAT	1Q

CRAY WANDERERS

Club Contact Details
Bromley FC, Hayes Lane, Bromley, Kent BR2 9EF
020 8460 5291
marksimpson937@btinternet.com

Founded: 1860   **Nickname:** Wanderers or Wands   **Manager:** Tony Russell - 04/05/2015
Previous Names: Cray Old Boys (immediately after WW1); Sidcup & Footscray (start of WW2).
Previous Leagues: Kent 1894-1903, 1906-07, 1909-1914, 1934-38, 1978-2004; West Kent & South Suburban Leagues (before WW1); London 1920-1934, 1951-1959; Kent Amateur 1938-1939, 1946-1951; South London Alliance 1943-1946; Aetolian 1959-1964; Greater London 1964-1966; Metropolitan 1966-1971; Met. London 1971-1975: London Spartan 1975-1978.
Club Colours (change): Amber & black

Ground Capacity: 5,000   **Seats:** 1,300   **Covered:** 2,500   **Clubhouse:** Yes   **Shop:** Yes
Previous Grounds: Northfield Farm (1950-51), Tothills (aka Fordcroft, 1951-1955), Grassmeade (1955-1973), Oxford Road (1973-1998).
Record Attendance: (Grassmeade) 2,160vLeytonstone,FAAm.R3, 68-69; (Oxford R) 1,523vStamford,FAVQF 79-80; (Hayes L)1,082vAFC Wim, 04-05

RECORDS
Victory: 15-0 v Sevenoaks - 1894-95.
Defeat: 2-15 (H) and 0-14 (A) v Callenders Athletic - Kent Amateur League, 1947-48.
Goalscorer: Ken Collishaw 274 (1954-1965)
Appearances: John Dorey - 454 (1961-72).
Additional: Unbeaten for 28 Ryman League games in 2007-2008.

HONOURS
FA Comps: None
League: Kent 1901-02, 80-81, 2002-03, 03-04. London 1956-57, 57-58. Aetolian 1962-63. Greater London 1965-66. Metropolitan London 1974-75; London Spartan 1976-77, 77-78.
County FA: Kent Amateur Cup 1930-31, 62-63, 63-64, 64-65. Kent Senior Trophy 1992-93, 2003-04.

07-08		08-09		09-10		10-11		11-12		12-13		13-14		14-15		15-16		16-17	
Isth1S	3	Isth1S	2	Isth P	15	Isth P	9	Isth P	9	Isth P	17	Isth P	24	Isth1N	16	Isth1N	4	Isth1S	11
FAC	1Q	FAC	1Q	FAC	1Q	FAC	2Qr	FAC	3Q	FAC	3Q	FAC	1Q	FAC	1Q	FAC	1Q	FAC	1Q
FAT	1Qr	FAT	3Q	FAT	1Q	FAT	2Q	FAT	1Q	FAT	3Q	FAT	1Q	FAT	3Q	FAT	P	FAT	2Q

EAST GRINSTEAD TOWN

Club Contact Details
The GAC Stadium, East Court, College Lane, East Grinstead RH19 3LS
01342 325 885
brian.mcc@egtfc.co.uk

Founded: 1890   **Nickname:** The Wasps   **Manager:** Mat Longhurst
Previous Names: East Grinstead 1890-1997.
Previous Leagues: Mid Sussex, Sussex County, Souhern Amateur. Sussex County >2014.

Club Colours (change): Amber & black stripes (Blue & yellow)

Ground Capacity: 3,000   **Seats:** Yes   **Covered:** Yes   **Clubhouse:** Yes   **Shop:** No
Previous Grounds: West Ground 1890-1962. King George's Field 1962-67.
Record Attendance: 2,006 v Lancing F A Am Cup, November 1947

RECORDS
Appearances: Guy Hill

HONOURS
FA Comps: None
League: Mid-Sussex 1901-02, 36-37. Southern Amateur DivisioN Three 1931-32. Sussex County Division Two 2007-08.
County FA: Sussex RUR Cup 2003-04.

07-08		08-09		09-10		10-11		11-12		12-13		13-14		14-15		15-16		16-17	
SxC2	1	SxC1	17	SxC1	15	SxC1	7	SxC1	9	SxC1	8	SxC1	2	Isth1S	22	Isth1S	20	Isth1S	18
FAC	EPr	FAC	P	FAC	1Q	FAC	1Q					FAC	EP	FAC	Pr	FAC	P	FAC	P
FAV	2Q	FAV	2P	FAV	1P	FAV	2Q			FAV	1Qr	FAV	2P	FAT	Pr	FAT	1Q	FAT	1Q

FAVERSHAM TOWN

Club Contact Details
Shepherd Neame Stadium, Salters Lane, Faversham Kent ME13 8ND
01795 591 900
wendy-walker@hotmail.co.uk

Founded: 1884   **Nickname:** Lillywhites   **Manager:** Ray Turner
Previous Names: Faversham Invicta, Faversham Services, Faversham Railway and Faversham Rangers pre War.
Previous Leagues: Kent 1884-1900, 1904-12, 24-34, 37-59, 66-71, 76-2003. Kent County 1934-37. Aetolian/Greater London 1959-66. Metropolitan 1971-73. Athenian 1973-76. Kent County 2005-10.

Club Colours (change): White & black

Ground Capacity: 2,000   **Seats:** 200   **Covered:** 1,800   **Clubhouse:** Yes   **Shop:** No
Previous Grounds: Moved in to Salters Lane in 1948.
Record Attendance:

RECORDS

HONOURS
FA Comps: None
League: Kent 1969-70, 70-71, 77-78, 89-90, Division Two 1895-96. Kent County 2009-10.

County FA: Kent Amateur Cup 1956-57, 58-59, 71-72, 72-73, 73-74. Kent Senior Trophy 1976-77, 77-78.

07-08	08-09	09-10	10-11	11-12	12-13	13-14	14-15	15-16	16-17
Kent P 13	Kent P 4	Kent P 1	Isth1S 8	Isth1S 17	Isth1S 3	Isth1S 10	Isth1S 3	Isth1S 5	Isth1S 10
FAC P	FAC EP	FAC 1Q	FAC 1Q	FAC 1Q	FAC 1Qr	FAC 2Q	FAC 2Q	FAC 1Qr	FAC 3Qr
FAV 2Q	FAV 2Q	FAV 2P	FAT 1Q	FAT 2Q	FAT 1Q	FAT P	FAT 1Q	FAT P	FAT 1Q

GREENWICH BOROUGH

Club Contact Details
DGS Marine Stadium, Middle Park Avenue, Eltham SE9 5HP
07946 721 878
geoffgrant@ntlworld.com

Founded: 1928   **Nickname:** Boro   **Manager:** Gary Alexander
Previous Names: Woolwich Borough Council Athletic 1928-65. London Borough of Greenwich 1965-84.
Previous Leagues: Woolwich & District 1928-29. Kent Amateur 1929-39, 46-48. South London Alliance 1948-76. London Spartan 1976-84. Kent/Southern Counties East 1984-2016.

Club Colours (change): Red & black

Ground Capacity: 1,000   **Seats:** 100   **Covered:** Yes   **Clubhouse:** Yes   **Shop:**
Previous Grounds: Danson Park 1928-37. Harrow Meadow 1937-2009. Holmesdale FC 2009-13. Dartford FC 2013-16.
Record Attendance: 2,000 v Charlton Athletic, turning on of floodlights, 1978.

RECORDS

HONOURS
FA Comps:
League: Woolwich & District 1928-29. South London Alliance Division Two 1954-55, Division One 1955-56, Premier Division 1960-61, 61-62, 62-63, 63-64, 64-65, 65-66, 73-74. London Spartan 1979-80. Kent 1986-87, 87-88. Southern Counties East 2015-16.
County FA: Kent Senior Trophy 1984-85.

07-08	08-09	09-10	10-11	11-12	12-13	13-14	14-15	15-16	16-17
Kent P 8	Kent P 3	Kent P 5	Kent P 4	Kent P 16	Kent P 15	SCE 9	SCE 4	SCE 1	Isth1S 3
			FAC EP	FAC EP	FAC 1Q	FAC P	FAC 4Q	FAC 1Q	FAC 1Q
FAV 5Pr		FAV 1P	FAV 1P	FAV 1P	FAV 1Q	FAV 1P	FAV 4P	FAV 2P	FAT Pr

GUERNSEY

Club Contact Details
Footes Lane Stadium, St Peter Port, Guernsey GY1 2UL
01481 747 279
mark.letissier@guernseyfc.com

Founded: 2011 **Nickname:** Green Lions **Manager:** Tony Vance
Previous Names: None
Previous Leagues: Combined Counties 2011-13.

Club Colours (change): Green & white

Ground Capacity: 5,000 **Seats:** 720 **Covered:** Yes **Clubhouse:** Yes **Shop:** No
Previous Grounds: None
Record Attendance: 4,290 v. Spennymoor Town, FA Vase semi-final first leg, 23/03/2013

RECORDS
Victory: 11-0 v Crawley Down Gatwick, Isthmian Division One South, 01/01/2014
Defeat: 2-6 v Horsham, Isthmian Division One South, 14/12/2013
Goalscorer: Ross Allen - 163 (Scored 57 in all comps during 2011-12)
Appearances: Dom Heaume - 136

HONOURS
FA Comps: None
League: Combined Counties Division One 2011-12.

County FA: None

07-08	08-09	09-10	10-11	11-12	12-13	13-14	14-15	15-16	16-17
				CC1 1	CCP 2	Isth1S 4	Isth1S 10	Isth1S 13	Isth1S 21
						FAC 2Q	FAC P	FAC Pr	FAC Pr
					FAV SF	FAT 1Q	FAT 1Q	FAT P	FAT P

HASTINGS UNITED

Club Contact Details
The Pilot Field, Elphinstone Road, Hastings TN34 2AX
01424 444 635
richardcosens@btinternet.com

Founded: 1894 **Nickname:** The U's or The Arrows **Manager:** Adam Hinshelwood
Previous Names: Rock-a-Nore 1894-1921. Hastings and St Leonards Amateurs 1921-79. Hastings Town 1979-2002.
Previous Leagues: South Eastern 1904-05, Southern 1905-10, Sussex County 1921-27, 52-85, Southern Amateur 1927-46, Corinthian 1946-48

Club Colours (change): All white (All claret)

Ground Capacity: 4,050 **Seats:** 800 **Covered:** 1,750 **Clubhouse:** Yes **Shop:** Yes
Previous Grounds: Bulverhythe Recreation > 1976
Record Attendance: 4,888 v Nottingham Forest - Friendly 23/06/1996

RECORDS
Goalscorer: Terry White scored 33 during 1999-2000
Additional: Paid £8,000 to Ashford Town for Nicky Dent
Received £50,000 from Nottingham Forest for Paul Smith

HONOURS
FA Comps: None
League: Southern Division Two B 1909-10, Southern Division 1991-92, Eastern Division 2001-01.
Sussex County Division Two 1979-80.
County FA: Sussex Senior Cup 1935-36, 37-38, 95-96, 97-98.

07-08	08-09	09-10	10-11	11-12	12-13	13-14	14-15	15-16	16-17
Isth P 14	Isth P 17	Isth P 7	Isth P 18	Isth P 18	Isth P 22	Isth1S 5	Isth1S 19	Isth1S 7	Isth1S 5
FAC 1Q	FAC 1Q	FAC 1Q	FAC 1Q	FAC 1Q	FAC 3P	FAC 1Q	FAC 2Q	FAC 3Q	FAC 3Qr
FAT 2Q	FAT 3Q	FAT 1Q	FAT 1Qr	FAT 1Qr	FAT 1Q	FAT 2Q	FAT P	FAT 2Q	FAT 2Qr

HERNE BAY

Club Contact Details
Winch's Field, Stanley Gardens, Herne Bay CT6 5SG
01227 374 156
johnbhbfc@aol.com

Founded: 1886   **Nickname:** The Bay   **Manager:** John Embery & Jermaine Darlington
Previous Names: None.
Previous Leagues: East Kent. Faversham & Dist. Cantebury & Dist. Kent Am. Athenian.

Club Colours (change): Blue with white sleeves/blue/blue (Yellow with black sleeves/yellow/yellow)

Ground Capacity: 3,000 **Seats:** 200 **Covered:** 1,500 **Clubhouse:** Yes **Shop:** Yes
Previous Grounds: Mitchell's Athletic Ground. Herne Bay Memorial Park.
Record Attendance: 2,303 v Margate, FA Cup 4th Qual. 1970-71.

RECORDS
Victory: 19-3 v Hythe Wanderers - Feb 1900.
Defeat: 0-11 v 7th Dragon Guards - Oct 1907.
Misc: Most League Victories in a Season: 34 - 1996-97.

HONOURS
FA Comps: None
League: East Kent 1902-03, 03-04, 04-05, 05-06. Athenian Division Two 1970-71. Kent 1991-92, 93-94, 96-97, 97-98, 2011-12, Division Two 1954-55.
County FA: Kent Amateur Cup 1957-58. Kent Senior Trophy 1978-79, 1996-97.

07-08	08-09	09-10	10-11	11-12	12-13	13-14	14-15	15-16	16-17
Kent P 6	Kent P 6	Kent P 2	Kent P 2	Kent P 1	Isth1S 19	Isth1S 18	Isth1S 9	Isth1S 8	Isth1S 17
FAC 2Qr	FAC Pr	FAC EP	FAC EP	FAC 1Q	FAC P	FAC Pr	FAC 1Q	FAC 2Qr	FAC 2Qr
FAV 2Q	FAV 1Q	FAV 2P	FAV 4P	FAV SF	FAT P	FAT 1Qr	FAT P	FAT 2Qr	FAT 1Qr

HORSHAM

Club Contact Details
Sussex FA Headquaters, Culver Road, Lancing West Sussex BN15 9AX
01403 252 689 / 07952 351 712 (MD)
jeff.barrett@btinternet.com

Founded: 1881   **Nickname:** Hornets   **Manager:** Dominic Di Paola
Previous Names: None
Previous Leagues: West Sussex Senior, Sussex Co 1926-51, Metropolitan 1951-57, Corinthian 1957-63, Athenian 1963-73, Isthmian 1973-2015. Southern Combination 2015-16,

Club Colours (change): Orange/green/orange (All white)

Ground Capacity: **Seats:** Yes **Covered:** Yes **Clubhouse:** Yes **Shop:** Yes
Previous Grounds: Horsham Park, Hurst Park, Springfield Park, Gorings Mead
Record Attendance: 7,134 v Swindon - FA Cup First Round Proper, November 1966

RECORDS
Victory: 16-1 v Southwick - Sussex County League 1945-46
Defeat: 1-11 v Worthing - Sussex Senior Cup 1913-14
Goalscorer: Mick Browning
Appearances: Mark Stepney
Additional: Paid £2,500 to Lewes for Lee Farrell, July 2007.
           Received £10,000 from Tonbridge Angels for Carl Rook, December 2008.

HONOURS
FA Comps: None
League: West Sussex Senior 1899-00, 1900-01, 01-02, 25-26. Sussex County 1931-32, 32-33, 34-35, 36-37, 37-38, 46-47. Metropolitan 1951-52. Athenian Division Two 1969-70, Division One 72-73. Isthmian Division Three 1995-96. Southern Combination 2015-16.
County FA: Sussex Senior Cup 1933-34, 38-39, 49-50, 53-54, 71-72, 73-74, 75-76.

07-08	08-09	09-10	10-11	11-12	12-13	13-14	14-15	15-16	16-17
Isth P 11	Isth P 13	Isth P 11	Isth P 17	Isth P 22	Isth1S 15	Isth1S 16	Isth1S 24	SCom 1	Isth1S 16
FAC 2Pr	FAC 4Qr	FAC 1Q	FAC 1Q	FAC 2Qr	FAC 2Q	FAC 3Q	FAC 1Q	FAC Pr	FAC P
FAT 2Q	FAT 2Q	FAT 1Qr	FAT 2Q	FAT 1Q	FAT P	FAT 1Q	FAT 3Q	FAV 1P	FAT 1Q

HYTHE TOWN

Club Contact Details
Reachfields Stadium, Fort Road, Hythe CT21 6JS
01303 264 932 / 238 256
martinandsuegiles@gmail.com

Founded: 1910   **Nickname:** The Cannons   **Manager:** Clive Cook
Previous Names: Hythe Town 1910-1992, Hythe United 1992-2001
Previous Leagues: Kent Amateur League, Kent League, Southern League, Kent County League, Kent League.

Club Colours (change): All red (All blue)

Ground Capacity: 3,000   **Seats:** 350   **Covered:** 2,400   **Clubhouse:** Yes   **Shop:** Yes
Previous Grounds: South Road 1910-77.
Record Attendance: 2,147 v Yeading, FA Vase Semi-Final, 1990.

RECORDS
Victory: 10-1 v Sporting Bengal, 2008-09
Defeat: 1-10 v Swanley Furness, 1997-98
Goalscorer: Dave Cook - 130
Appearances: John Walker - 354, Jason Brazier - 349, Dave Cook - 346, Lee Winfield - 344

HONOURS
FA Comps: None
League: Kent County Eastern Division Two 1936-37, Division One 71-72, Premier Division 73-74, 74-75, 75-76.
    Kent League 1988-89, 2010-11.
County FA: Kent Senior Cup 2011-12.
    Kent Senior Trophy 1990-91.

07-08		08-09		09-10		10-11		11-12		12-13		13-14		14-15		15-16		16-17	
Kent P	4	Kent P	2	Kent P	3	Kent P	1	Isth1S	8	Isth1S	4	Isth1S	8	Isth1S	16	Isth1S	4	Isth1S	7
FAC	3Q	FAC	1Qr	FAC	2Qr	FAC	1P	FAC	2Q	FAC	P	FAC	P	FAC	2Q	FAC	P	FAC	2Q
FAV	1P	FAV	1P	FAV	1P	FAV	3P	FAT	2Q	FAT	1Qr	FAT	2Qr	FAT	1Q	FAT	P	FAT	1P

LEWES

Club Contact Details
The Dripping Pan, Mountfield Road, Lewes, East Sussex BN7 2XD
01273 470 820
barry@lewesfc.com

Founded: 1885   **Nickname:** Rooks   **Manager:** Darren Freeman
Previous Names: None
Previous Leagues: Mid Sussex 1886-1920, Sussex County 1920-65, Athenian 1965-77, Isthmian 1977-2004, Conference 2004-11.

Club Colours (change): Red and black/black/black (All light blue)

Ground Capacity: 3,000   **Seats:** 600   **Covered:** 1,400   **Clubhouse:** Yes   **Shop:** Yes
Previous Grounds: Played at Convent Field for two seasons before WWI
Record Attendance: 2,500 v Newhaven - Sussex County League 26/12/1947

RECORDS
Goalscorer: 'Pip' Parris - 350
Appearances: Terry Parris - 662
Additional: Paid £2,000 for Matt Allen
    Received £2,500 from Brighton & Hove Albion for Grant Horscroft

HONOURS
FA Comps:
League: Mid Sussex 1910-11, 13-14. Sussex County 1964-65. Athenian Division Two 1967-68, Division One 1969-70.
    Isthmian Division Two 2001-02, Division One South 2003-04. Conference South 2007-08.
County FA: Sussex Senior Cup 1964-65, 70-71, 84-85, 2000-01, 05-06.

07-08		08-09		09-10		10-11		11-12		12-13		13-14		14-15		15-16		16-17	
Conf S	1	Conf	24	Conf S	19	Conf S	21	Isth P	6	Isth P	19	Isth P	16	Isth P	19	Isth P	23	Isth1S	9
FAC	1P	FAC	4Qr	FAC	3Q	FAC	4Q	FAC	1Q	FAC	2Q	FAC	3Q	FAC	2Q	FAC	1Q	FAC	1Qr
FAT	1P	FAT	2Pr	FAT	2P	FAT	3Q	FAT	2Q	FAT	2Qr	FAT	1Q	FAT	3Q	FAT	1Qr	FAT	1Q

MOLESEY

Club Contact Details
412 Walton Road, West Molesey KT8 2JG
020 8979 4823
teaguetracy90@gmail.com

Founded: 1953   **Nickname:** The Moles   **Manager:** Peter Leilliott
Previous Names: None.
Previous Leagues: Surrey Senior. Spartan. Athethian. Isthmian. Combined Counties 2008-15.

Club Colours (change): White/black/black.

Ground Capacity: 4,000   **Seats:** 160   **Covered:** Yes   **Clubhouse:** Yes   **Shop:** Yes
Previous Grounds: None
Record Attendance: 1,255 v Sutton United, Surrey Senior Cup sem-final 1966.

RECORDS
Goalscorer: Michael Rose (139).
Appearances: Frank Hanley (453).

HONOURS
FA Comps: None
League: Surrey Senior 1957-58. Combined Counties Premier Division 2014-15.
County FA: Surrey Junior Cup 1920-21.

07-08	08-09	09-10	10-11	11-12	12-13	13-14	14-15	15-16	16-17
Isth1S 22	CCP 11	CCP 8	CCP 3	CCP 5	CCP 10	CCP 11	CCP 1	Isth1S 9	Isth1S 19
FAC Pr	FAC P	FAC 1Q	FAC EP	FAC EP	FAC EP	FAC Pr	FAC P	FAC 1Q	FAC P
FAT P	FAV 3P	FAV 1P	FAV 1P	FAV 1P	FAV 1Q	FAV 1Q	FAV 2Q	FAT 3Q	FAT P

PHOENIX SPORTS

Club Contact Details
Phoenix Sports Ground, Mayplace Road East, Barnehurst, Kent DA7 6JT
01322 526 159
alf_levy@sky.com

Founded: 1935   **Nickname:** None   **Manager:** Steve O'Boyle
Previous Names: St Johns Welling. Lakeside. Phoenix.
Previous Leagues: Spartan League. Kent County > 2011. Kent Invicta 2011-13.

Club Colours (change): Green & black

Ground Capacity: 2,000   **Seats:** 108   **Covered:** Yes   **Clubhouse:** Yes   **Shop:** No
Previous Grounds: Danson Park >1950.
Record Attendance:

RECORDS

HONOURS
FA Comps: None
League: Kent County Division One West 1999-2000, 2007-08, Division Two West 2004-05. Kent Invicta 2012-13.
Southern Counties East 2014-15.
County FA: None

07-08	08-09	09-10	10-11	11-12	12-13	13-14	14-15	15-16	16-17
KC1W 1	KC P 8	KC P 4	KC P 5	K_Iv 2	K_Iv 1	SCE 6	SCE 1	Isth1N 14	Isth1N 8
							FAC EPr	FAC 2Q	FAC P
						FAV 1P	FAV 5P	FAT 1Qr	FAT 2Q

RAMSGATE

Club Contact Details
Southwood Stadium, Prices Avenue, Ramsgate, Kent CT11 0AN
01843 591 662
secretary@ramsgate-fc.co.uk

Founded: 1945   **Nickname:** The Rams   **Manager:** Lloyd Blackman
Previous Names: Ramsgate Athletic > 1972
Previous Leagues: Kent 1949-59, 1976-2005, Southern 1959-76

Club Colours (change): All red

Ground Capacity: 2,500   **Seats:** 400   **Covered:** 600   **Clubhouse:** Yes   **Shop:** Yes
Previous Grounds: None
Record Attendance: 5,038 v Margate - 1956-57

RECORDS
Victory: 11-0 & 12-1 v Canterbury City - Kent League 2000-01
Goalscorer: Mick Willimson

HONOURS
FA Comps: None
League: Kent Division One 1949-50, 55-56, 56-57, Premier 1998-99, 2004-05. Isthmian Division One 2005-06.
County FA: Kent Senior Shield 1960-61, 67-68, 68-69. Kent Senior Cup 1963-64. Kent Senior Trophy 1987-88, 88-89, 98-99.

07-08	08-09	09-10	10-11	11-12	12-13	13-14	14-15	15-16	16-17
Isth P 5	Isth P 22	Isth1S 14	Isth1S 9	Isth1S 10	Isth1S 7	Isth1S 12	Isth1S 21	Isth1S 12	Isth1S 12
FAC 2Q	FAC 1Q	FAC P	FAC Pr	FAC Pr	FAC P	FAC P	FAC P	FAC P	FAC 1Q
FAT 1Q	FAT 3Q	FAT 3Q	FAT 1Qr	FAT P	FAT 3Q	FAT 3Q	FAT P	FAT 1Q	FAT P

SHOREHAM

Club Contact Details
Middle Road, Shoreham-by-Sea, West Sussex, BN43 6GA
01273 454 261
spencerdial@googlemail.com

Founded: 1892   **Nickname:** Musselmen   **Manager:** Brian Donelly
Previous Names: None.
Previous Leagues: West Sussex. Sussex County/Southern Combination >2017.

Club Colours (change): All blue (All red).

Ground Capacity: 2,000   **Seats:** 150   **Covered:** 700   **Clubhouse:** Yes   **Shop:** No
Previous Grounds: None
Record Attendance: 1,342 v Wimbledon

RECORDS

HONOURS
FA Comps: None
League: West Sussex Junior Division 1897-98, Senior Division 1902-03, 04-05, 05-06. Sussex County Division One 1951-52, 52-53, 77-78, Division Two 1961-62, 76-77, 84-85, 93-94. Southern Combination Premier Division 2016-17.
County FA: Sussex Senior Cup 1901-02, 05-06. Sussex RUR Cup 1902-03, 05-06.

07-08	08-09	09-10	10-11	11-12	12-13	13-14	14-15	15-16	16-17
SxC1 12	SxC1 6	SxC1 9	SxC1 18	SxC1 18	SxC1 17	SxC1 14	SxC1 16	SCP 17	SCP 1
FAC EP	FAC P	FAC P	FAC EP	FAC 1Q	FAC EPr	FAC P	FAC P	FAC 1Q	FAC P
FAV 2Q	FAV 3P	FAV 3P	FAV 1P	FAV 2Q	FAV 1Q	FAV 2Q	FAV 2Q	FAV 1Q	FAV 1P

SITTINGBOURNE

Club Contact Details
Woodstock Park, Broadoak Road, Sittingbourne ME9 8AG

01795 410 777

john@sittingbournefc.com

Founded: 1886   **Nickname:** Brickies   **Manager:** Nick Davis - 05/11/14
Previous Names: Sittingbourne United 1881-86
Previous Leagues: Kent 1894-1905, 1909-27, 30-39, 45-59, 68-91, South Eastern 1905-09, Southern 1927-30, 59-67

Club Colours (change): Red & black (Yellow & blue)

Ground Capacity: 3,000   **Seats:** 300   **Covered:** 600   **Clubhouse:** Yes   **Shop:** Yes
Previous Grounds: Sittingbourne Rec. 1881-90, Gore Court 1890-92, The Bull Ground 1892-1990. Central Park 1990-2001
Record Attendance: 5,951 v Tottenham Hotspur - Friendly 26/01/1993

RECORDS
Victory: 15-0 v Orpington, Kent League 1922-23)
Defeat: 0-10 v Wimbledon, SL Cup 1965-66)
Additional: Paid £20,000 to Ashford Town for Lee McRobert 1993
                  Received £210,000 from Millwall for Neil Emblem and Michael Harle 1993

HONOURS
FA Comps: None
League: Kent 1902-03, 57-58, 58-59, 75-76, 83-84, 90-91. Southern Southern Division 1992-93, 95-96.

County FA: Kent Senior Cup 1901-02, 28-29, 29-30, 57-58.

07-08		08-09		09-10		10-11		11-12		12-13		13-14		14-15		15-16		16-17	
Isth1S	9	Isth1S	6	Isth1S	9	Isth1S	11	Isth1S	19	Isth1S	9	Isth1S	14	Isth1S	12	Isth1S	18	Isth1S	15
FAC	1Qr	FAC	1Q	FAC	2Q	FAC	P	FAC	1Q	FAC	1Q	FAC	3Q	FAC	P	FAC	2Q	FAC	Pr
FAT	1Q	FAT	1Q	FAT	1Q	FAT	P	FAT	1Q	FAT	1Q	FAT	P	FAT	P	FAT	P	FAT	P

SOUTH PARK

Club Contact Details
King George's Field, Whitehall Lane, South Park RH2 8LG

01737 245 963

spfc1897@hotmail.com

Founded: 1897   **Nickname:** The Sparks   **Manager:** Malcolm Porter
Previous Names: South Park & Reigate Town 2001-03.
Previous Leagues: Redhill & District. Crawley & District > 2006. Combined Counties 2006-14.

Club Colours (change): All red (All blue with yellow trim)

Ground Capacity: 2,000   **Seats:** 113   **Covered:** Yes   **Clubhouse:** Yes   **Shop:** Yes
Previous Grounds: Crescent Road. Church Road.
Record Attendance: 643 v Metropolitan Police, 20/10/2012

RECORDS

HONOURS
FA Comps: None
League: Combined Counties Premier Division 2013-14.

County FA: Surrey Premier Cup 2010-11.

07-08		08-09		09-10		10-11		11-12		12-13		13-14		14-15		15-16		16-17	
CC1	12	CC1	14	CC1	6	CC1	3	CCP	8	CCP	4	CCP	1	Isth1S	14	Isth1S	11	Isth1S	8
						FAC	1Q	FAC	P	FAC	4Q	FAC	1Qr	FAC	1Qr	FAC	2Q	FAC	2Q
		FAV	2Q	FAV	2Qr	FAV	2Q	FAV	4P	FAV	3P	FAV	3P	FAT	1Q	FAT	1Q	FAT	2P

THAMESMEAD TOWN

Club Contact Details
Dartford FC, Princes Park, Grassbanks, Darenth Road, Dartford DA1 1RT
01322 299 991
secretaryttfc@hotmail.com

Founded: 1969   **Nickname:** The Mead   **Manager:** Tommy Warrilow
Previous Names: Thamesmead FC 1969-85.
Previous Leagues: London Spartan 1980-91. Kent 1991-2008.

Club Colours (change): All green (All light blue)

Ground Capacity: 4,097   **Seats:** 640   **Covered:** Yes   **Clubhouse:** Yes   **Shop:** Yes
Previous Grounds: Crossways. Meridian Sports Ground > 1985. Bayliss Avenue 1985-2017.
Record Attendance: 400 v Wimbledon - Ground opening 1988

RECORDS
Victory: 9-0 v Kent Police - Kent League 19/04/1994
Goalscorer: Delroy D'Oyley

HONOURS
FA Comps: None
League: Kent Premier 2007-08

County FA: Kent Senior Trophy 2004-05.

	07-08	08-09	09-10	10-11	11-12	12-13	13-14	14-15	15-16	16-17
	Kent P 1	Isth1N 18	Isth1N 7	Isth1N 17	Isth1N 10	Isth1N 3	Isth P 22	Isth1N 13	Isth1N 10	Isth1N 17
	FAC 1Q	FAC 2Qr	FAC 1Q	FAC P	FAC 2Qr	FAC 2Q	FAC 2Q	FAC P	FAC 1Q	FAC 3Q
	FAV 2P	FAT P	FAT Pr	FAT 2Qr	FAT 3Qr	FAT 1Q	FAT 1Q	FAT 2Q	FAT 3Q	FAT P

VCD ATHLETIC

Club Contact Details
Oakwood, Old Road, Crayford DA1 4DN
01322 524 262
davejoyo@yahoo.co.uk

Founded: 1916   **Nickname:** The Vickers   **Manager:** Keith McMahon
Previous Names: Vickers (Erith). Vickers (Crayford) Now Vickers Crayford Dartford Athletic.
Previous Leagues: Dartford & District. Kent County. Isthmian

Club Colours (change): Green & white/white (Blue/black/black)

Ground Capacity: 1,180   **Seats:** Yes   **Covered:** Yes   **Clubhouse:** Yes   **Shop:** No
Previous Grounds: Groundshared with Thamesmead (5 seasons), Lordswood (2) and Greenwich Boro' (1) whilst waiting for planning at Oakwood.
Record Attendance: 13,500 Away v Maidstone, 1919.

RECORDS

HONOURS
FA Comps: None
League: Kent County 1952-53, 63-64, 96-97. Kent 2008-09. Isthmian Division One North 2013-14.

County FA: Kent Junior Cup 1926-27. Kent Amateur Cup 1961-62, 63-64. Kent Intermediate Cup 1995-96.
     Kent Senior Trophy 2005-06, 08-09.

	07-08	08-09	09-10	10-11	11-12	12-13	13-14	14-15	15-16	16-17
	Kent P 2	Kent P 1	Isth1N 8	Kent P 3	Kent P 3	Kent P 2	Isth1N 1	Isth P 18	Isth P 24	Isth1N 15
	FAC P	FAC 2Q	FAC 1Q	FAC Pr	FAC 2Qr	FAC 1Q	FAC P	FAC 2Q	FAC 1Qr	FAC 2Q
	FAV 4P	FAV 4P	FAT 1Q	FAV 2P	FAV 3Pr	FAV 1Pr	FAT Pr	FAT 1Q	FAT 2Q	FAT 1Q

WALTON CASUALS

Club Contact Details
Elmbridge Sports Hub, Waterside Drive, Walton-on-Thames, Surrey KT12 2JP
07927 222 010
g.schofield1@ntlworld.com

Founded: 1948   **Nickname:** The Stags   **Manager:** Anthony Gale
Previous Names: None
Previous Leagues: Surrey Intermediate 1948-69. Surrey Senior 1969-71. Suburban 1971-92. Surrey County 1992-95.
Combined Counties 1995-2005.

Club Colours (change): Orange/black/orange (All blue)

Ground Capacity: 2,000   **Seats:** 153   **Covered:** 403   **Clubhouse:** Yes   **Shop:** Yes
Previous Grounds: Elm Grove Rec. 1948-69. Franklyn Road 69-71. Stompond Lane 71-72. Liberty Lane 72-80. Waterside Stadium 80-2015.
Record Attendance: 1,748 v AFC Wimbledon - Combined Counties League 12/04/2004   Moatside 2015-16. Church Road 2016-17.

RECORDS
Goalscorer: Paul Mills - 111 in 123 appearances (1993-99).
Appearances: Lawrence Ennis - 288
Victory: 10-0 v Chessington United, Combined Counties Premier, 28/12/2004.
Defeat: 0-7 v Redhill, Surrey Senior Cup 1st Rnd, 08/12/98. v Chipstead, Combined Counties Premier, 09/11/2002.
v Faversham Town, Isthmian Division One, 08/12/2012. v Faversham Town, Isthmian Division One, 09/04/2016.

HONOURS
FA Comps: None
League: Surban Southern Section 1982-83, Premier B 2012-13. Combined Counties Premier Division 2004-05.

County FA: None

07-08		08-09		09-10		10-11		11-12		12-13		13-14		14-15		15-16		16-17	
Isth1S	16	Isth1S	17	Isth1S	21	Isth1S	12	Isth1S	15	Isth1S	22	Isth1S	9	Isth1S	18	Isth1S	16	Isth1S	13
FAC	P	FAC	1Q	FAC	3Q	FAC	1Q	FAC	P	FAC	P	FAC	P	FAC	Pr	FAC	P	FAC	3Q
FAT	P	FAT	1Qr	FAT	Pr	FAT	1Q	FAT	Pr	FAT	P	FAT	Pr	FAT	1Q	FAT	1Qr	FAT	1P

WHYTELEAFE

Club Contact Details
15 Church Road, Whyteleafe, Surrey CR3 0AR
0208 660 5491
chris@theleafe.co.uk

Founded: 1946   **Nickname:** The Leafe   **Manager:** Leigh Dynan
Previous Names: None
Previous Leagues: Caterham & Ed, Croydon. Thornton Heath & District. Surrey Interm. (East) 1954-58. Surrey Senior 1958-75. Spartan 1975-81.
Athenian 1981-84. Isthmian 1984-2012.

Club Colours (change): White with green slash (Red with black slash)

Ground Capacity: 2,000   **Seats:** 400   **Covered:** 600   **Clubhouse:** Yes   **Shop:** Yes
Previous Grounds: None
Record Attendance: 2,210 v Chester City - FA Cup 1999-2000

RECORDS
Misc: Paid £1,000 to Carshalton Athletic for Gary Bowyer
Received £25,000 for Steve Milton

HONOURS
FA Comps: None
League: Surrey Senior Premier Division 1968-69. Southern Counties East 2013-14.

County FA: Surrey Senior Cup 1968-69.

07-08		08-09		09-10		10-11		11-12		12-13		13-14		14-15		15-16		16-17	
Isth1S	11	Isth1S	18	Isth1S	15	Isth1S	16	Isth1S	21	Kent P	6	SCE	1	Isth1S	5	Isth1S	15	Isth1S	14
FAC	P	FAC	3Q	FAC	P	FAC	P	FAC	P	FAC	Pr	FAC	EP	FAC	2Q	FAC	1Q	FAC	2Q
FAT	P	FAT	P	FAT	2Qr	FAT	Pr	FAT	1Q	FAV	1P	FAV	2P	FAT	2Q	FAT	P	FAT	P

	Best unbeaten Run				Worst Consecutive run without a victory		
	Won	Drawn	Total		Lost	Drawn	Total
Ashton United	3	3	6		3	1	4
Barwell	3	4	7		4	1	5
Blyth Spartans	11	0	11		4	1	5
Buxton	4	1	5		1	3	4
Coalville Town	3	2	5		4	4	8
Corby Town	4	1	5		9	2	11
Frickley Athletic	3	1	4		11	0	11
Grantham Town	10	4	14		3	3	6
HalesowenTown	4	3	7		5	3	8
Hednesford Town	4	1	5		3	1	4
Ilkeston	3	0	3		15	3	18
Marine	2	2	4		7	2	9
Matlock Town	4	2	6		4	0	4
MIckleover Sports	3	0	3		5	2	7
Nantwich Town	9	5	14		5	2	7
Rushall Olympic	4	3	7		6	3	9
Skelmersdale Utd	0	3	3		7	3	10
Spennymoor Town	5	3	8		3	1	4
Stafford Rangers	7	3	10		6	5	11
Stourbridge	8	4	12		3	0	3
Sutton Coldfield T	1	3	4		8	1	9
Warrington Town	5	0	5		3	2	5
Whitby Town	5	5	10		4	1	5
Workington	6	0	6		3	1	4

	Best Attendance	Opponents	Competition
Ashton United	402	Blyth Spartans	League
Barwell	327	Corby Town	League
Blyth Spartans	1167	Halesowen Town	League
Buxton	602	Whitby Town	League
Coalville Town	467	Corby Town	League
Corby Town	785	Grantham Town	League
Frickley Athletic	373	Buxton	League
Grantham Town	1040	Blyth Spartans	League
HalesowenTown	2127	Stourbridge	League
Hednesford Town	910	Stafford Rangers	FAC2Q
Ilkeston	474	Matlock Town	League
Marine	565	Skelmersdale United	League
Matlock Town	1071	Altrincham	FAC4Q
MIckleover Sports	509	Ilkeston	League
Nantwich Town	780	Stafford Rangers	FAC4Q
Rushall Olympic	804	Hednesford Town	League
Skelmersdale Utd	536	Corby Town	League
Spennymoor Town	1699	Stourbridge	PO Final
Stafford Rangers	1826	Hednesford Town	League
Stourbridge	**2520**	Northampton Town	FAC1Q
Sutton Coldfield T	623	Hereford United	FAC2Q
Warrington Town	561	Matlock Town	League
Whitby Town	612	Blyth Spartans	League
Workington	652	Blyth Spartans	League
Average	**895**		

NORTHERN PREMIER LEAGUE PREMIER DIVISION LEAGUE TABLE 2016-17

		P	W	D	L	F	A	GD	Pts
1	Blyth Spartans	46	31	8	7	114	44	70	101
2	Spennymoor Town	46	25	12	9	96	48	48	87
3	Stourbridge	46	25	10	11	84	51	33	85
4	Workington	46	26	5	15	73	56	17	83
5	Nantwich Town	46	23	12	11	86	59	27	81
6	Whitby Town	46	23	10	13	64	56	8	79
7	Buxton	46	22	12	12	81	54	27	78
8	Grantham Town	46	22	10	14	74	57	17	76
9	Matlock Town	46	22	9	15	68	58	10	75
10	Warrington Town	46	22	8	16	65	57	8	74
11	Ashton United	46	19	11	16	85	78	7	68
12	Rushall Olympic	46	18	10	18	60	60	0	64
13	Stafford Rangers	46	16	15	15	63	60	3	63
14	Barwell	46	16	14	16	58	53	5	62
15	Hednesford Town	46	18	7	21	68	65	3	61
16	Mickleover Sports	46	19	3	24	68	71	-3	60
17	Coalville Town	46	15	10	21	71	79	-8	55
18	Marine	46	14	13	19	62	74	-12	55
19	Halesowen Town	46	13	12	21	46	70	-24	51
20	Sutton Coldfield Town	46	12	11	23	49	79	-30	47
21	Corby Town	46	12	10	24	49	72	-23	46
22	Frickley Athletic	46	12	3	31	47	97	-50	39
23	Ilkeston	46	7	6	33	31	86	-55	27
24	Skelmersdale United	46	5	9	32	40	118	-78	24

Play-Off Semi Finals: Stourbridge 3-2 Workington | Spennymoor Town 2-0 Nantwich Town
Final: Spennymoor Town 1-0 Stourbridge

PREMIER DIVISION	1	2	3	4	5	6	7	8	9	10	11	12	13	14	15	16	17	18	19	20	21	22	23	24
1 Ashton United		0-0	1-1	1-3	3-0	3-1	1-3	4-3	2-1	2-0	1-0	1-4	1-0	3-2	1-1	1-2	1-1	1-2	2-1	0-2	3-1	2-1	3-1	1-2
2 Barwell	4-1		0-2	0-1	1-0	3-0	1-2	1-1	0-0	2-0	2-1	1-1	1-1	4-0	1-1	2-1	0-1	1-1	0-0	2-2	1-2	0-2		
3 Blyth Spartans	3-3	2-0		0-0	3-1	4-2	5-1	5-1	3-0	5-1	3-1	1-0	4-1	3-0	2-0	2-1	4-0	0-0	2-2	2-1	5-0	0-3	5-1	3-2
4 Buxton	1-2	0-0	2-2		2-1	1-0	2-0	0-1	2-0	2-0	2-0	3-0	2-1	1-0	4-1	3-0	0-0	2-2	1-3	1-1	2-1	3-3	3-0	2-1
5 Coalville Town	1-3	1-2	0-1	2-1		4-1	3-1	1-2	3-1	2-2	2-3	0-0	1-4	3-2	3-1	3-3	3-3	0-1	0-0	1-1	1-1	1-2	2-3	2-1
6 Corby Town	3-3	0-2	4-3	1-1	1-2		2-0	3-0	0-0	3-2	1-2	0-0	0-0	1-0	0-2	1-4	3-0	3-1	0-0	1-2	5-1	0-0	0-2	1-3
7 Frickley Athletic	1-3	2-3	1-0	4-4	0-4	0-2		0-2	0-1	0-1	4-0	2-0	1-0	0-4	1-4	1-0	3-2	2-1	0-2	2-0	0-3	0-1	2-2	
8 Grantham Town	2-1	2-2	1-2	0-1	5-1	4-0	3-0		2-3	4-1	1-1	3-0	0-0	1-0	0-4	2-1	1-1	3-3	2-1	2-1	1-2	2-0	2-2	
9 Halesowen Town	2-2	1-1	0-5	2-4	1-0	1-1	1-2	1-1		1-3	2-1	0-1	0-3	4-2	0-0	1-2	1-0	1-2	2-2	0-1	0-0	1-0	2-0	3-2
10 Hednesford Town	2-2	1-1	1-2	1-2	1-2	3-0	4-0	1-0	1-2		3-1	1-1	0-2	1-0	1-2	2-1	5-0	3-1	0-1	1-1	4-1	1-0	1-1	0-2
11 Ilkeston	0-2	1-0	0-5	1-0	0-0	0-1	1-0	0-3	0-0	0-2		1-2	0-1	0-1	2-3	0-2	3-0	2-3	1-2	1-2	1-0	0-2		0-1
12 Marine	3-1	0-0	1-0	5-5	4-2	3-2	3-3	1-0	4-0	3-0	2-2		0-1	1-3	1-3	1-1	1-0	1-1	1-0	1-1	1-4	0-1	1-4	0-1
13 Matlock Town	3-0	2-1	0-0	3-1	0-0	1-2	1-0	2-1	2-1	2-0	0-0	2-1		2-2	0-4	2-1	1-1	0-4	3-0	3-1	3-1	1-1	2-1	1-2
14 Mickleover Sports	4-1	4-1	1-7	0-3	1-2	2-0	3-0	2-1	0-1	0-1	7-0	2-1	2-0		0-1	0-2	3-1	0-5	1-3	0-4	3-1	1-0	0-1	4-0
15 Nantwich Town	3-2	2-2	2-2	1-0	3-0	1-1	3-2	1-1	1-2	1-1	3-0	4-1	0-0	1-3		1-0	4-0	1-0	0-1	2-3	1-0	4-1	0-2	0-1
16 Rushall Olympic	1-1	3-1	0-1	1-0	2-5	0-0	0-1	3-1	1-0	1-1	1-1	2-3	1-2	1-3	1-0		1-5	1-0	0-2	3-1	2-2	1-0	1-2	
17 Skelmersdale United	1-10	0-5	1-4	0-6	1-2	1-0	3-1	1-1	1-2	1-3	2-1	0-3	0-2	1-3	2-3	1-2		0-2	1-1	0-4	1-3	4-0	0-1	1-2
18 Spennymoor Town	1-2	2-0	2-1	1-1	5-0	1-0	2-0	1-2	1-1	4-2	3-0	2-1	3-2	3-0	1-1	1-1	7-0		1-0	2-2	3-0	4-1	0-1	4-1
19 Stafford Rangers	1-3	1-1	0-1	1-2	2-1	0-1	3-2	0-1	3-1	2-1	2-1	3-0	2-0	1-0	3-3	0-2	4-4	3-3		0-0	0-0	2-2	0-0	3-2
20 Stourbridge	4-1	2-1	1-2	3-2	2-0	1-0	4-1	1-2	2-2	1-2	3-1	2-0	5-3	0-0	4-2	0-0	2-1	1-1	2-0		0-1	0-1	2-1	5-0
21 Sutton Coldfield Town	2-2	2-1	3-2	1-1	0-3	5-1	3-1	0-2	1-0	0-5	1-0	3-2	2-3	0-1	1-1	0-4	2-0	1-0	1-1	4-1		0-1	1-1	1-1
22 Warrington Town	1-1	1-2	0-2	1-0	2-1	2-1	2-1	0-1	1-0	1-0	4-1	1-0	5-3	1-0	2-3	2-0	2-0	0-2	1-2	2-0	2-1		0-1	1-2
23 Whitby Town	2-1	1-2	2-1	4-2	1-1	1-0	4-0	0-2	4-1	1-0	2-1	3-1	1-0	1-1	1-3	1-1	1-0	2-1	2-2	1-3	2-0	2-2		1-1
24 Workington	1-0	0-1	0-2	2-0	0-4	1-0	2-0	1-0	1-0	0-2	2-0	4-0	1-3	4-1	3-1	2-0	0-1	3-0	1-2	3-1	0-0	3-1	4-0	

NORTHERN PREMIER LEAGUE DIVISION ONE NORTH LEAGUE TABLE 2016-17

		P	W	D	L	F	A	GD	Pts
1	Lancaster City	42	27	4	11	73	41	32	85
2	Farsley Celtic	42	26	6	10	100	50	50	84
3	Scarborough Athletic	42	22	7	13	70	47	23	73
4	Ossett Town	42	22	7	13	69	49	20	73
5	Colne	42	22	7	13	74	50	24	72
6	Trafford	42	18	16	8	80	46	34	70
7	Clitheroe	42	20	10	12	74	54	20	70
8	Glossop North End	42	21	6	15	72	70	2	69
9	Brighouse Town	42	17	17	8	66	48	18	68
10	Hyde United	42	16	14	12	78	58	20	61
11	Bamber Bridge	42	16	7	19	59	58	1	54
12	Kendal Town	42	14	12	16	61	62	-1	54
13	Droylsden	42	14	12	16	71	77	-6	54
14	Ramsbottom United	42	16	9	17	64	81	-17	53
15	Colwyn Bay	42	13	11	18	61	57	4	50
16	Prescot Cables	42	13	11	18	71	81	-10	47
17	Mossley	42	14	4	24	67	87	-20	46
18	Ossett Albion	42	13	6	23	47	78	-31	45
19	Tadcaster Albion	42	11	11	20	57	70	-13	44
20	Radcliffe Borough	42	12	8	22	59	82	-23	44
21	Goole AFC	42	9	9	24	39	83	-44	36
22	Burscough	42	6	6	30	26	109	-83	24

Play-Off Semi Finals: Farsley Celtic 4-0 Colne | Scarborough Athletic 1-3 Ossett Town
Final: Farsley Celtic 4-2 Ossett Town

DIVISION ONE NORTH	1	2	3	4	5	6	7	8	9	10	11	12	13	14	15	16	17	18	19	20	21	22
1 Bamber Bridge		1-1	3-0	1-4	1-2	0-2	0-1	2-0	2-0	4-0	2-1	2-1	1-0	4-1	3-1	4-0	1-5	2-0	0-1	0-3	0-0	0-4
2 Brighouse Town	2-0		1-1	2-1	2-2	2-1	2-3	2-1	2-2	2-1	2-0	1-1	0-1	1-1	1-1	1-1	2-1	2-0	2-2	1-1	3-3	0-0
3 Burscough	1-3	2-1		0-1	1-2	0-3	1-1	0-5	0-4	2-0	0-2	1-3	0-0	1-2	0-1	0-1	0-5	1-2	0-2	1-0	2-1	0-3
4 Clitheroe	3-1	3-1	0-0		2-2	1-0	3-2	1-3	2-3	2-0	2-1	0-0	1-2	2-1	2-0	0-3	1-2	1-1	4-0	3-0	3-1	1-1
5 Colne	1-0	0-0	8-0	2-1		2-1		0-3	0-2	4-0	1-2	3-2	0-2	2-1	1-2	2-1	5-1	2-2	0-1	1-0	4-1	1-3
6 Colwyn Bay	1-1	1-2	6-0	3-2	1-1		4-0	2-2	1-2	2-2	3-1	1-2	2-0	0-4	1-1	0-2	2-1	1-2	1-2	0-1	0-0	1-1
7 Droylsden	0-1	1-2	4-1	1-2	2-1	2-4		1-1	1-3	3-1	1-3	2-2	1-0	1-3	2-1	6-1	2-2	3-3	1-1	2-2	4-3	0-3
8 Farsley Celtic	5-3	3-2	3-1	2-4	2-1	1-0	1-1		4-1	1-2	2-1	1-0	2-4	3-1	2-1	0-2	2-1	4-0	0-0	2-1	5-1	0-1
9 Glossop North End	1-1	2-0	2-3	1-0	1-0	2-1	2-2	0-2		2-0	1-0	3-2	2-5	3-2	2-1	3-1	2-4	2-1	2-1	2-1	3-1	2-2
10 Goole AFC	0-3	0-3	4-1	0-1	1-3	3-1	2-0	0-3	2-1		0-0	1-2	1-1	1-1	1-1	0-3	1-2	0-1	4-2	1-1	0-0	1-3
11 Hyde United	2-2	0-0	3-2	4-4	2-2	2-2	2-0	4-5	2-1	4-0		3-0	1-2	1-2	0-0	2-2	1-1	1-1	5-0	3-2	2-0	2-2
12 Kendal Town	2-0	1-2	4-0	0-3	0-1	1-2	5-0	0-5	2-2	1-1	1-1		1-0	3-0	1-2	1-0	3-1	1-1	2-1	2-1	2-2	1-1
13 Lancaster City	3-2	2-3	3-1	0-0	1-2	1-1	3-2	3-0	1-0	1-0	3-0		4-3	2-0	0-2	2-0	3-1	3-1	2-0	1-0	0-1	
14 Mossley	2-0	0-4	2-1	0-1	0-1	0-3	3-4	0-2	2-1	0-1	1-4	2-2	0-1		1-3	0-2	7-2	2-1	1-1	0-2	0-1	1-4
15 Ossett Albion	1-4	0-4	4-0	2-2	0-1	3-1	0-4	0-0	2-1	1-2	0-3	2-4	0-1	2-1		1-0	3-0	2-0	0-4	0-1	2-5	0-6
16 Ossett Town	2-0	4-2	3-0	1-2	1-2	1-0	1-3	3-2	1-0	0-2	1-1	2-0	1-3	1-0	0-2		3-1	1-1	1-1	4-2	3-1	1-1
17 Prescot Cables	1-1	0-0	4-0	2-2	3-2	0-1	0-0	0-3	7-2	2-2	0-4	1-1	2-0	0-5	5-0	2-0		1-1	2-4	0-2	1-0	2-0
18 Radcliffe Borough	1-0	0-3	0-1	0-1	1-3	3-0	1-2	0-5	1-2	5-1	4-0	3-1	0-3	3-4	2-1	0-4	1-5		2-1	2-3	2-3	2-0
19 Ramsbottom United	1-0	2-0	2-2	3-4	0-3	1-3	3-2	0-7	2-2	3-1	1-3	1-0	1-0	4-2	2-1	0-5	1-1	4-0		0-4	3-3	0-2
20 Scarborough Athletic	0-0	0-1	5-0	1-0	1-0	3-1	1-4	1-0	2-0	3-2	1-0	1-3	8-0	2-1	0-0	4-1	1-3	3-2		1-0	1-1	
21 Tadcaster Albion	2-1	1-1	0-0	1-0	1-2	0-0	2-1	0-0	2-1	3-0	1-2	1-2	1-2	2-3	3-0	0-1	2-2	2-1	0-1	2-3		4-3
22 Trafford	0-3	1-1	4-0	2-2	2-0	2-1	1-1	1-0	0-1	6-0	1-1	2-2	1-4	1-1	0-1	2-3	5-1	2-1	2-2	0-0	3-1	

NORTHERN PREMIER LEAGUE DIVISION ONE SOUTH LEAGUE TABLE 2016-17

		P	W	D	L	F	A	GD	Pts
1	Shaw Lane AFC	42	32	6	4	104	36	68	102
2	Witton Albion	42	31	6	5	100	41	59	96
3	Spalding United	42	24	7	11	74	42	32	79
4	Stocksbridge Park Steels	42	22	7	13	67	50	17	73
5	AFC Rushden & Diamonds	42	20	11	11	73	52	21	71
6	Basford United	42	20	13	9	78	53	25	70
7	Newcastle Town	42	21	4	17	59	59	0	67
8	Lincoln United	42	19	8	15	67	61	6	65
9	Leek Town	42	18	10	14	63	63	0	64
10	Belper Town	42	15	13	14	55	55	0	58
11	Bedworth United	42	15	12	15	73	72	1	57
12	Kidsgrove Athletic	42	16	7	19	72	66	6	55
13	Romulus	42	14	9	19	65	75	-10	51
14	Market Drayton Town	42	16	2	24	60	93	-33	50
15	Sheffield	42	13	9	20	62	60	2	48
16	Stamford	42	13	9	20	62	80	-18	48
17	Chasetown	42	13	8	21	64	75	-11	47
18	Gresley	42	12	9	21	56	83	-27	45
19	Carlton Town	42	10	12	20	48	68	-20	42
20	Loughborough Dynamo	42	10	4	28	45	94	-49	34
21	Rugby Town	42	8	6	28	44	77	-33	30
22	Northwich Victoria	42	8	12	22	53	89	-36	26

Play-Off Semi Finals: Spalding United 3-2 aet Stocksbridge Park Steels | Witton Albion 1-0 AFC Rushden & Dia.
Final: Witton Albion 2-1 Spalding United

DIVISION ONE SOUTH	1	2	3	4	5	6	7	8	9	10	11	12	13	14	15	16	17	18	19	20	21	22
1 AFC Rushden & Diamonds		2-2	2-0	0-0	5-1	1-3	3-3	2-5	2-1	1-1	4-0	1-1	1-0	6-1	0-0	3-0	1-1	2-1	1-2	1-1	0-2	0-2
2 Basford United	3-0		3-3	7-1	2-1	1-2	1-0	2-0	4-2	1-1	2-1	1-0	6-0	2-2	1-0	4-0	1-0	1-1	1-0	3-2	3-2	1-2
3 Bedworth United	1-2	2-2		0-2	1-0	1-3	1-0	3-0	2-1	1-4	5-1	2-0	1-5	2-2	4-2	1-1	0-1	4-0	2-2	2-3	2-2	0-4
4 Belper Town	1-4	1-1	2-3		1-1	3-3	1-2	3-1	0-0	0-0	4-1	2-1	1-3	0-0	4-2	3-0	3-1	1-1	1-2	0-2	0-0	3-1
5 Carlton Town	1-3	0-0	0-0	0-1		3-1	2-3	0-2	0-1	1-1	3-3	1-0	2-2	2-2	1-1	1-0	1-5	1-3	4-3	4-4	1-0	3-2
6 Chasetown	2-1	4-2	2-3	0-0	1-0		5-2	1-1	0-3	1-3	5-0	5-1	1-2	1-1	0-3	1-0	1-3	0-0	1-1	1-2	1-2	1-4
7 Gresley	1-2	3-0	1-2	1-1	2-1	1-0		2-1	1-1	1-3	0-1	3-2	0-1	0-2	2-1	2-2	0-3	1-1	0-2	2-3	1-0	0-2
8 Kidsgrove Athletic	0-1	2-1	3-4	1-3	0-2	5-0	5-1		2-2	7-2	2-1	1-2	1-0	2-1	0-2	0-1	0-2	2-1	0-1	3-0	1-2	2-2
9 Leek Town	0-1	0-5	1-1	0-1	4-1	3-2	5-1	2-2		2-2	2-1	3-2	2-0	1-0	2-2	2-0	1-2	1-0	0-4	3-1	1-1	1-2
10 Lincoln United	0-1	0-0	2-1	3-1	2-0	2-0	4-1	2-3	1-1		3-0	2-0	2-1	2-3	1-2	1-0	0-6	2-1	0-2	1-0	0-2	1-2
11 Loughborough Dynamo	0-3	1-2	0-3	0-2	0-0	2-0	1-1	1-4	0-2	1-0		4-1	1-2	3-2	1-1	3-2	0-3	1-0	0-3	0-1	2-3	0-4
12 Market Drayton Town	2-1	0-1	3-2	1-0	0-3	0-3	2-1	1-3	1-2	2-1	0-3		3-2	4-2	3-1	2-3	1-1	0-5	2-3	4-2	3-1	3-2
13 Newcastle Town	1-0	3-1	2-2	1-1	2-1	3-1	3-0	2-1	1-0	0-2	1-0	2-0		2-1	2-1	1-0	2-3	0-1	2-1	2-1	1-3	0-2
14 Northwich Victoria	1-4	2-2	2-0	1-1	1-0	2-3	2-2	3-1	0-0	1-3	1-5	0-1	1-2		1-2	1-3	0-4	2-5	1-3	0-0	3-0	0-5
15 Romulus	3-2	2-2	1-4	2-1	1-1	0-1	2-2	3-1	1-2	4-1	5-1	2-4	2-1	3-0		0-3	2-3	1-1	1-2	4-2	0-1	1-1
16 Rugby Town	1-1	1-1	3-1	0-1	0-1	2-2	1-2	1-3	1-0	1-2	0-1	0-3	2-0	0-2	1-2		1-2	2-3	1-2	1-2	0-1	1-2
17 Shaw Lane AFC	1-1	2-0	2-2	4-1	2-1	2-0	5-3	2-1	6-0	5-2	4-0	3-1	2-1	2-2	2-0	5-0		2-0	3-1	3-1	1-0	1-0
18 Sheffield	1-2	3-0	2-2	0-1	0-1	2-1	3-2	1-1	2-1	3-2	2-1	9-0	1-2	1-2	0-1	4-2	0-1		0-4	1-1	1-2	0-1
19 Spalding United	1-2	0-0	0-1	1-0	2-0	2-1	2-2	0-0	0-1	1-0	2-1	3-0	1-1	3-1	4-0	3-1	0-1	3-0		2-1	2-3	0-1
20 Stamford	1-1	2-3	2-1	0-1	1-1	2-1	0-1	1-1	2-3	1-3	2-0	0-2	3-1	4-0	4-2	3-2	1-1	1-1	1-2		0-5	1-3
21 Stocksbridge Park Steels	2-3	1-2	1-1	2-1	2-1	1-1	1-2	0-2	1-2	0-3	4-2	4-1	1-0	2-1	1-0	0-0	1-0	2-1	2-0	4-0		3-4
22 Witton Albion	2-0	2-1	1-0	2-1	2-0	3-2	3-1	3-0	5-2	0-0	4-1	3-1	3-0	1-1	5-0	3-4	3-2	1-0	2-2	4-1	0-0	

THE DOODSON SPORT LEAGUE CUP 2016-17

HOLDERS: MARINE

PRELIMINARY ROUND

Brighouse Town	v	Shaw Lane AFC	A-A, AW	
Hyde United	v	Glossop North End	0-0, 4-5p	180
Market Drayton Town	v	Romulus	3-3, 2-3p	
Prescot Cables	v	Kendal Town	1-2	120

ROUND ONE

AFC Rushden & Dia.	v	Corby Town	2-1	184
Ashton United	v	Warrington Town	2-0	83
Bamber Bridge	v	Marine	4-1	150
Barwell	v	Coalville Town	2-1	109
Bedworth United	v	Matlock Town	3-4	62
Belper Town	v	Mickleover Sports	1-1, 5-3p	183
Burscough	v	Lancaster City	2-1	53
Buxton	v	Radcliffe Borough	6-2	108
Carlton Town	v	Spalding United	2-5	54
Droylsden	v	Trafford	3-5	75
Frickley Athletic	v	Tadcaster Albion	0-2	149
Glossop North End	v	Witton Albion	6-0	221
Grantham Town	v	Gresley FC	3-2	91
Halesowen Town	v	Rushall Olympic	1-1, 2-3p	145
Kendal Town	v	Clitheroe	0-2	81
Kidsgrove Athletic	v	Chasetown	1-5	94
Leek Town	v	Hednesford Town	1-0	115
Lincoln United	v	Stamford	1-0	91
Loughborough Dynamo	v	Basford United	2-4	58
Mossley	v	Nantwich Town	1-2	72
Newcastle Town	v	Stafford Rangers	3-1	111
Northwich Victoria	v	Colwyn Bay	2-2, 5-3p	73
Ossett Albion	v	Farsley Celtic	2-4	70
Ossett Town	v	Scarborough Athletic	0-1	100
Romulus	v	Sheffield FC	0-2	94
Rugby Town	v	Ilkeston FC	0-0, 4-3p	74
Skelmersdale United	v	Colne	1-3	120
Stocksbridge Park Steels	v	Spennymoor Town	0-2	74
Sutton Coldfield Town	v	Stourbridge	3-3, 2-4p	84
Whitby Town	v	Goole AFC	2-3	165
Workington	v	Ramsbottom United	2-2, 4-2p	181

ROUND TWO

Ashton United	v	Northwich Victoria	1-0	85
Barwell	v	Stourbridge	0-2	97
Belper Town	v	Chasetown	2-4	112
Burscough	v	Bamber Bridge	0-2	70
Buxton	v	Nantwich Town	4-3	91
Colne	v	Trafford	1-1, 3-4p	102
Farsley Celtic	v	Goole AFC	5-2	61
Leek Town	v	Glossop North End	2-2, 2-4p	131
Lincoln United	v	Grantham Town	2-3	199
Matlock Town	v	Basford United	2-2, 8-9p	185
Newcastle Town	v	Sheffield FC	2-1	51
Rugby Town	v	AFC Rushden & Dia.	1-3	147
Rushall Olympic	v	Spalding United	0-2	71
Scarborough Athletic	v	Spennymoor Town	3-1	141
Tadcaster Albion	v	Shaw Lane AFC	2-1	195
Workington	v	Clitheroe	0-2	172

ROUND THREE

AFC Rushden & Dia.	v	Spalding United	0-0, 5-4p	183
Ashton United	v	Farsley Celtic	3-2	67
Bamber Bridge	v	Glossop North End	1-0	141
Basford United	v	Chasetown	4-1	116
Buxton	v	Newcastle Town	1-0	92
Clitheroe	v	Trafford	3-2	203
Scarborough Athletic	v	Tadcaster Albion	2-1	214
Stourbridge	v	Grantham Town	1-4	291

QUARTER-FINALS

AFC Rushden & Dia.	v	Buxton	2-3	247
Bamber Bridge	v	Ashton United	2-1	188
Clitheroe	v	Scarborough Athletic	3-2	201
Grantham Town	v	Basford United	1-1, 5-3p	164

SEMI-FINALS

Bamber Bridge	v	Buxton	0-0, 4-2p	291
Grantham Town	v	Clitheroe	2-1	234
Lee Shaw 34, 47		*Kurt Willoughby 54*		

FINAL

Grantham Town	v	Bamber Bridge	1-2	474
Danny Meadows 63		*Jamie Milligan 45*		
		Regan Linney 57		

Northern Premier Premier Division Statistics 2016-17

TOP SCORING CLUBS	
Spennymoor Town	106
Nantwich Town	102
Stourbridge	101
Matlock Town	90

MOST GAMES WITHOUT SCORING	
Ilkeston	22 (4)
Corby Town	21 (5)
Skelmersdale United	21 (3)

MOST SCORERS	
Sutton Coldfield Town	26+2 ogs
Ashton United	25+2 ogs
Warrington Town	23+2 ogs

MOST CONSECUTIVE SCORING GAMES	
Nantwich Town	31
Blyth Spartans	27
Spennymoor Town	22

MOST CLEAN SHEETS	
Spennymoor Town	20 (6)
Workington	18 (5)
Blyth Spartans	18 (3)

	GT	GWS(1)	TNoS	MCSG	TCS(2)
Ashton United	85	6 (2)	25 +2ogs	14	6 (1)
Barwell	66	13 (2)	17+1og	8	14 (3)
Blyth Spartans	133	6 (2)	16+2ogs	27	18 (3)
Buxton	84	10 (2)	17+1og	13	17 (3)
Coalville Town	73	14 (3)	20+2ogs	7	7 (2)
Corby Town	49	21 (5)	17+1og	8	13 (2)
Frickley Athletic	50	20 (4)	22	5	7 (2)
Grantham Town	83	8 (5)	15+2ogs	13	13 (2)
Halesowen Town	59	16 (5)	21	7	13 (2)
Hednesford Town	75	9 (3)	23	13	11 (2)
Ilkeston	39	22 (4)	9+1og	7	11 (2)
Marine	76	14 (2)	21	6	11 (2)
Matlock Town	91	14 (1)	14	10	16 (2)
Mickleover Sports	76	17 (4)	17 +2ogs	7	12 (2)
Nantwich Town	102	6 (2)	16+4ogs	31	16 (3)
Rushall Olympic	65	10 (2)	25	15	14 ((2)
Skelmersdale United	43	21 (3)	22+2ogs	9	4 (1)
Spennymoor Town	109	5 (2)	18+2ogs	22	20 (6)
Stafford Rangers	69	15 (3)	20+2ogs	11	11 (2)
Stourbridge	101	9 (2)	22+2ogs	14	17(3)
Sutton Coldfield Town	55	16 (3)	26+2ogs	5	8 (2)
Warrington Town	65	11 (2)	23+2ogs	10	15 (2)
Whitby Town	72	10 (3)	11+1og	9	14 (2)
Workington	84	7 (3)	16+1og	19	18 (5)

(1) - Most consecutive goalless games in brackets.
(2) - Most consecutive clean sheets in brackets.
GT - Goals Total
GWS - Games Without Scoring
TNoS - Total Number of Scorers
MCSG - Most Consecutive Scoring Games
TCS - Total Clean Sheets

Strikers with ten or more goals - 2016-17

LEAGUE, FA CUP AND FA TROPHY GOALS ONLY.

					PTG	CTG	FLP
Blyth Spartans	Maguire	36	Armstrong	24	112	133	1
	Reid	16	Dale	14			
	Pattison	12	Rivers	10			
Spennymoor Town	Taylor	18	Armstrong	15	56	109	2
	Tait	13	Anderson	10			
Matlock Town	Dinanga	29	Newsham	14	54	91	9
	Williams	11					
Mickleover Sports	Baskerville	18	Hall	11	39	76	16
	Blake 10						
Nantwich Town	Cooke	20	Jones	12	42	102	5
	Brooke	10					
Ashton United	Chadwick	19	Crowther	10	29	85	11
Barwell	Hickey	21	Ball	14	35	66	14
Buxton	Grayson	20	Hardy	10	30	84	7
Coalville Town	Watson	15	McDonald	11	26	73	17
Grantham Town	Shaw,Lee	23	Barcelos	13	36	83	8
Hednesford Town	Glover	13	Carline	10	26	75	15
Marine	Mitchley	25	Sherlock	11	26	81	18
Stourbridge	Benbow	36	Archer	11	47	104	3
Whitby Town	Hopson	26	Tymon	17	43	72	6
Workington	Symington	14	Allison	13	27	84	4
Halesowen Town	Anderson	18			18	59	19
Rushall Olympic	Reid	15			15	65	12
Stafford Rangers	Perry	12			12	69	13

PTG - Players Total Goals I CTG - Club's Total Goals I FLP - Final League Position

ALTRINCHAM

Club Contact Details

The J Davidson Stadium, Moss Lane, Altrincham, Cheshire WA15 8AP

0161 928 1045

dwilshaw@altrinchamfootballclub.co.uk

Ground Capacity: 6,085 **Seats:** 1,154 **Covered:** Yes **Clubhouse:** Yes **Shop:** Yes

Record Attendance

10,275 - Altrincham Boys v Sunderland Boys English Schools Shield 28/02/1925.

Previous Grounds

Pollitts Field 1903-10.

---

10 YEAR RECORD

	07-08		08-09		09-10		10-11		11-12		12-13		13-14		14-15		15-16		16-17	
Conf		21	Conf	15	Conf	14	Conf	22	Conf N	8	Conf N	4	Conf N	3	Conf	17	Nat	22	Nat N	22
FAC		1P	FAC	1Pr	FAC	4Q	FAC	4Q	FAC	2Q	FAC	1Pr	FAC	2Q	FAC	1P	FAC	2P	FAC	1P
FAT		1P	FAT	1P	FAT	2P	FAT	2P	FAT	3Q	FAT	1P	FAT	1P	FAT	3P	FAT	2P	FAT	1Pr

---

Club Factfile

Founded: 1891 **Nickname:** The Robins **Manager:** Phil Parkinson

Previous Names: Rigby Memorial Club 1891-93. Merged with the 'Grapplers' to form Broadheath FC 1893-1903.

Previous Leagues: Manchester (Founder members) 1893-1911. Lancashire Combination 1911-19. Cheshire County (Founder members) 1919-68. Northern Premier (Founder members) 1968-79, 97-99, 00-04. Alliance/Conference (Founder members) 1979-97, 99-00, 04-15.

Club Colours (change): Red & white stripes/black/white.

RECORDS

Victory: 14-2 v Sale Holmfield, Cheshire Amateur Cup, 05/12/1903

Defeat: 1-13 v Stretford (H) - 04.11.1893

Goalscorer: Jack Swindells - 252 (1965-71)

Appearances: John Davison - 677 (1971-86)

Additional: Transfer fee paid - £15k to Blackpool for Keith Russell. Received - £50k from Leicester for Kevin Ellison

HONOURS

FA Comps: FA Trophy 1977-78, 85-86

League: Manchester 1904-05, 06-07. Cheshire 1965-66, 66-67. Football Alliance Champions 1979-80, 80-81. N.P.L. Premier Division 1998-99. Conference North & South Play-off Winners 2004-05.

County FA: Cheshire Amateur Cup 1903-04. Cheshire Senior Cup Winners 1904-05, 33-34, 66-67, 81-82, 98-99, 04-05, 08-09.

BEST PERFORMANCES	**FA Cup:** Fourth Round Proper 1985-86
	FA Trophy: Final 1977-78, 81-82, 85-86
	FA Vase: N/A

ALTRINCHAM MATCH RESULTS 2016-17

Date	Comp	H/A	Opponents	Att:	Result	Goalscorers	Pos	No.
Aug 6	Nat N	H	Darlington 1883	1506	D 2 - 2	Lawrie 14 Moult 89 (pen)	8	1
9	Nat N	A	FC HalifaxTown	1836	D 2 - 2	Lawrie 28 Hobson 51	10	2
13	Nat N	A	Harrogate Town	635	D 2 - 2	Lawrie 10 Reeves 90	14	3
16	Nat N	H	AFC Fylde	850	L 0 - 6		18	4
20	Nat N	A	Gainsboorough Trinity	424	L 0 - 2		19	5
27	Nat N	H	Curzon Ashton	870	L 2 - 4	Sinclair 1 Reeves 86	19	6
29	Nat N	A	Kidderminster Harriers	1489	L 0 - 1		19	7
Sept 3	Nat N	H	Stockport County	2355	L 2 - 3	Lawrie 13 Miller 35	20	8
6	Nat N	H	Chorley	1006	D 2 - 2	Reeves 13 Mlller 39	21	9
10	Nat N	A	Gloucester City	406	L 0 - 5		21	10
13	Nat N	A	Nuneaton Town	541	L 1 - 4	Miller 17	21	11
17	FAC2Q	H	Gainsborough Trinity	516	W 3 - 2	Cyrus 43 Reeves 45 90		12
24	Nat N	H	Boston United	918	L 0 - 1		21	13
Oct 1	FAC3Q	H	Morpeth Town	658	W 3 - 0	Reeves 41 Miller 76 Richman 90		14
8	Nat N	A	Stalybridge Celtic	777	D 2 - 2	Patterson 87 Wilkinson 90		15
15	FAC4Q	H	Matlock T	1071	W 3 - 1	Reeves 37 Miller 47 52		16
22	Nat N	A	AFC Telford United	1074	L 0 - 2		20	17
25	Nat N	H	Bradford PA	756	L 2 - 3	Lawrie 8 Miller 84	20	18
29	Nat N	A	Worcester City	527	L 0 - 3		21	19
Nov 5	FAC1	A	Lincoln City	3529	L 1 - 2	Cyrus 75		20
12	Nat N	H	Salford City	2403	L 0 - 2		22	21
19	Nat N	A	Alfreton Town	474	L 2 - 3	Wilkinson 32 Moult 83	22	22
Dec 3	Nat N	H	Tamworth	835	L 1 - 2	Lawrie 32	22	23
6	FAT3Q	H	Blyth Spartans	276	D 2 - 2	Moult 6 39 (pen)		24
10	FAT3Qr	A	Blyth Spartans	523	W 3 - 2	Miller 6 41 Hobson 43		25
!7	Nat N	A	Stockport County	3991	L 0 - 3		22	26
20	FAT1	H	Macclesfield Town	717	D 1 - 1	Miller 39	20	27
26	Nat N	H	FC Utd of Manchester	2490	L 0 - 3		22	28
Jan 1	Nat N	A	FC Utd of Manchester	3030	D 1 - 1	Owens 20	22	29
4	FAT1r	A	Macclesfield Town	548	L 1 - 3	Cain 25		30
7	Nat N	H	Gloucester City	915	L 0 - 1		22	31
14	Nat N	H	Gainsborough Trinity	996	L 2 - 3	Owens 80 Cyrus 81	22	32
21	Nat N	A	Chorley	1127	L 0 - 2		22	33
24	Nat N	A	Brackley Town	298	D 1 - 1	Clee 6	22	34
28	Nat N	A	AFC Fylde	1739	L 1 - 4	Lawrie 45	22	35
Feb 4	Nat N	H	FC Halifax Town	1344	L 0 - 1		22	36
18	Nat N	H	Harrogate Town	782	D 0 - 0		22	37
25	Nat N	H	Worcester City	854	W 2 - 0	Newby 1 Lynch 13	22	38
Mar 1	Nat N	A	Darlington 1883	1423	L 1 - 3	Newby 33	22	39
4	Nat N	A	AFC Telford United	1105	L 0 - 1		22	40
11	Nat N	A	Boston United	1026	W 1 - 0	Newby 32	21	41
18	Nat N	H	Stalybridge Celtic	1236	D 0 - 0		22	42
21	Nat N	H	Nuneaton Town	646	L 1 - 3	Richman 44	22	43
25	Nat N	A	Bradford PA	516	L 1 - 2	Newby 26	22	44
April 1	Nat N	A	Salford City	1442	L 1 - 2	Jones 37	22	45
8	Nat N	H	Brackley Town	685	L 1 - 3	Evans 90	22R	46
14	Nat N	A	Curzon Ashton	423	W 3 - 2	Moult 45 (pen) 62 (pen) Richman 90	22	47
16	Nat N	H	Kidderminster Harriers	826	L 1 - 4	Reeves 38	22	48
22	Nat N	H	Alfreton Town	801	D 1 - 1	Spiess 56 (og)	22	49
29	Nat N	A	Tamworth	902	L 1 - 2	Lawrie 33	22	50

GOALSCORERS	SG	CSG	Pens	Hat tricks	Total		SG	CSG	Pens	Hat tricks	Total
2015-16 Rankine					15	Wilkinson	2				2
Miller	8	2			10	Cain	1				1
Lawrie	7	3			8	Clee	1				1
Reeves	8				8	Evans	1				1
Moult	4	2	3		6	Jones	1				1
Newby	4				4	Lynch	1				1
Cyrus	3				3	Opponents	1				1
Richman	3				3	Patterson	1				1
Hobson	2				2	Sinclair	1				1
Owens	2				2						

ASHTON UNITED

Club Contact Details
Hurst Cross, Surrey Street, Ashton-u-Lyne OL6 8DY
0161 339 4158
ashtonunitedfc@gmail.com

Ground Capacity: 4,500   **Seats:** 250   **Covered:** 750   **Clubhouse:** Yes   **Shop:** Yes

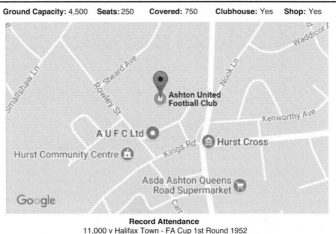

Record Attendance
11,000 v Halifax Town - FA Cup 1st Round 1952
Previous Grounds
Rose HIll 1878-1912

10 YEAR RECORD

	07-08		08-09		09-10		10-11		11-12		12-13		13-14		14-15		15-16		16-17	
NP P		10	NP P	9	NP P	12	NP P	14	NP P	12	NP P	10	NP P	5	NP P	3	NP P	3	NP P	11
FAC		1Q	FAC	1Q	FAC	2Q	FAC	2Q	FAC	2Q	FAC	2Q	FAC	3Q	FAC	3Q	FAC	3Q	FAC	1Q
FAT		1Q	FAT	2Q	FAT	1Q	FAT	1Qr	FAT	1Q	FAT	1Q	FAT	1Q	FAT	1Q	FAV	1P	FAT	1Q

Club Factfile

Founded: 1878   **Nickname:** Robins   **Manager:** Jody Banim

Previous Names: Hurst 1878-1947

Previous Leagues: Manchester, Lancashire Combination 1912-33, 48-64, 66-68, Midland 1964-66,
Cheshire County 1923-48, 68-82, North West Counties 1982-92

Club Colours (change): Red and white halves/red/red (Blue & black halves/blue/blue)

RECORDS

Victory: 11-3 v Stalybridge Celtic - Manchester Intermediate Cup 1955
Defeat: 1-11 v Wellington Town - Cheshire League 1946-47
Appearances: Micky Boyle - 462
Additional: Paid £9,000 to Netherfield for Andy Whittaker 1994
Received £15,000 from Rotherham United for Karl Marginson 1993

HONOURS

FA Comps: None

League: Manchester League 1911-12. Lancashire Combination 1916-17.
North West Counties Division Two 1987-88, Division One 1991-92.

County FA: Manchester Senior Cup 1894-95, 1913-14, 75-76, 77-78. Manchester Premier Cup 1979-80, 82-83, 91092, 2000-01,
01-02, 02-03. Manchester Challenge Shield 1992-93.

BEST PERFORMANCES	**FA Cup:** Second Round Proper 1883-84, 85-86.
	FA Trophy: Quarter-finals 1996-97.
	FA Vase: Fourth Round Proper 1992-93.

ASHTON UNITED MATCH RESULTS 2016-17

Date	Comp	H/A	Opponents	Att:	Result	Goalscorers	Pos	No.
Aug 13	NPL	A	Frickley Athletic	198	W 3 - 1	Gaskell 30 50 Wilkins 35	1	1
16	NPL	H	Nantwich Town	160	D 1 - 1	Gaskell 48	5	2
20	NPL	H	Hednesford Town	174	W 2 - 0	Moss 13 Baguley 80	1	3
23	NPL	A	Blyth Spartans	562	D 3 - 3	Gee 10 Dorney 40 Gaskell 82	2	4
27	NPL	A	Ilkeston	372	W 2 - 0	Lees 45 Gorton 64	2	5
29	NPL	H	Skelmersdale United	216	D 1 - 1	Chadwick 70	3	6
Sept 3	FAC1Q	H	Nantwich Town	213	L 0 - 3			7
10	NPL	A	Stafford Rangers	577	W 3 - 1	Dorney 48 Crowther 78 Nevins 82	3	8
17	NPL	A	Hednesford Town	375	D 2 - 2	Baguley 7 Chadwick 64	3	9
20	NPL	H	Buxton	242	L 1 - 3	Dorney 19	4	10
24	NPL	H	Rushall Olympic	143	L 1 - 2	Dyche 15	6	11
27	NPL	A	Whitby Town	287	L 1 - 2	Banim 52	7	12
Oct 1	NPL	H	Coalville Town	152	W 3 - 0	Dyche 14 51 Gaskell 22	5	13
8	NPL	A	Halesowen Town	423	D 2 - 2	Knight 74 Gaskell 90	8	14
11	NPL	H	Grantham Town	125	W 4 - 3	Smith 24 90 Chadwick 64 Knight 75	8	15
15	NPL	H	Barwell	178	D 0 - 0		7	16
18	NPL	A	Workington	374	W 0 - 1		9	17
22	NPL	A	Sutton Coldfield Town	148	D 2 - 2	Chadwick 34 Steenson 61	8	18
29	FAT1Q	H	Marine	124	L 0 - 4			19
1 Nov	NPL	H	Marine	135	L 1 - 4	Knight 83	8	20
5	NPL	H	Mickleover Sports	144	W 3 - 2	Smith 63 80 Lansdowne 66 (og)	9	21
12	NPL	H	Frickley Athletic	146	L 1 - 3	Connor 24	10	22
19	NPL	A	Corby Town	415	D 3 - 3	Frost 14 51 Gaskell 33	11	23
26	NPL	A	Spennymoor Town	512	W 2 - 1	Dorney 63 Gaskell 75	11	24
Dec 3	NPL	H	Spennymoor Town	212	L 1 - 2	Chadwick 86	11	25
10	NPL	H	Stourbridge	165	L 0 - 2		14	26
17	NPL	A	Mickleover Sports	201	L 1 - 4	Gaskell 13	15	27
26	NPL	H	Warrington Town	205	W 2 - 1	Chadwick 27 (pen) Crowther 54	15	28
Jan 7	NPL	H	Whitby Town	137	W 3 - 1	Chadwick 31 85 Crowther 49	13	29
21	NPL	H	Halesowen Town	157	W 2 - 1	Crowther 12 Smalley 28	13	30
28	NPL	A	Grantham Town	243	L 1 - 2	Dyche 31	14	31
Feb 4	NPL	H	Sutton Coldfield Town	162	W 3 - 1	Dyche 6 Chadwick 31 90	14	32
6	NPL	A	Stourbridge	504	L 1 - 4	Haining 52	14	33
11	NPL	A	Barwell	127	L 1 - 4	Knight 77	14	34
18	NPL	A	Coalville Town	119	W 3 - 1	Maiese 14 Crowther 31 Lowe 89	14	35
25	NPL	A	Rushall Olympic	238	D 1 - 1	Dyche 43	14	36
Mar 7	NPL	A	Buxton	248	W 2 - 1	Crowthorne 13 Dyche 50	14	37
11	NPL	A	Marine	331	L 1 - 3	Dyche 90	14	38
18	NPL	H	Matlock Town	201	W 1 - 0	Chadwick 51	14	39
21	NPL	A	Skelmersdale United	167	W 10- 1	Stachini 5 CHADWICK 4 (16 29 56 88) Duke 19 Mason 38	13	40
					-	Dyche 58 Banim 70 79	13	
25	NPL	A	Matlock Town	453	L 0 - 3		13	41
Apr 1	NPL	H	Corby Town	143	W 3 - 1	Crowther 36 85 Chadwick 90	12	42
4	NPL	H	Workington	169	L 1 - 2	Chadwick 6	12	43
8	NPL	A	Nantwich Town	301	L 2 - 3	Crowther 58 Hancock 90 (og)	12	44
13	NPL	H	Stafford Rangers	178	W 2 - 1	Lees 38 Chadwick 55	11	45
15	NPL	H	Blyth Spartans	402	D 1 - 1	Crowther 61	11	46
17	NPL	A	Workington Town	267	D 1 - 1	Chadwick 12	11	47
22	NPL	A	Ilkeston	182	W 1 - 0	Smith 52	11	48

GOALSCORERS	SG	CSG	Pens	Hat tricks	Total		SG	CSG	Pens	Hat tricks	Total
2015-16 Pilkington					29	Connor	1				1
Chadwick	16	2	1	1	19	Duke	1				1
Crowther	9	3			10	Gee	1				1
Dyche	8	3			9	Gorton	1				1
Gaskell	8	2			9	Haining	1				1
Smith	5				5	Lowe	1				1
Dorney	4				4	Maiese	1				1
Knight	3				4	Mason	1				1
Banim	2				3	Moss	1				1
Baguley	2				2	Nevins	1				1
Frost	2				2	Smalley	1				1
Lees	2				2	Stachini	1				1
Opponents	2				2	Steenson	1				1
						Wilkins	1				1

BARWELL

Club Contact Details
Kirkby Road Sports Ground, Kirkby Road, Barwell LE9 8FQ
07961 905 141
shirley.brown16@ntlworld.com

Ground Capacity: 2,500   **Seats:** 256   **Covered:** 750   **Clubhouse:** Yes   **Shop:** Yes

Record Attendance
1,279 v Whitley Bay, FA Vase Semi-Final 2009-10.
Previous Grounds
None

10 YEAR RECORD

07-08		08-09		09-10		10-11		11-12		12-13		13-14		14-15		15-16		16-17	
MidAl	10	MidAl	2	MidAl	1	NP1S	1	SthP	9	SthP	7	NP P	14	NP P	8	NP P	9	NP P	14
FAC	P	FAC	1Q	FAC	EP	FAC	4Q	FAC	2Q	FAC	3Qr	FAC	1Q	FAC	4Q	FAC	1P	FAC	2Q
FAV	2P	FAV	3P	FAV	SF	FAT	P	FAT	2Q	FAT	1Q	FAT	1Q	FAT	3Qr	FAT	1Q	FAT	2Q

Club Factfile

Founded: 1992   **Nickname:** Canaries   **Manager:** Jimmy Ginnelly

Previous Names: Barwell Athletic FC and Hinckley FC amalgamated in 1992.

Previous Leagues: Midland Alliance 1992-2010, Northern Premier League 2010-11. Southern 2011-13.

Club Colours (change): Yellow with green yolk/green/yellow (Green/black/green)

RECORDS
Goalscorer: Andy Lucas
Appearances: Adrian Baker

HONOURS
FA Comps: None

League: Midland Alliance 2009-10.
          Northern Premier Division One South 2010-11.
County FA: Leicestershire Challenge Cup 2014-15, 16-17.

BEST PERFORMANCES	**FA Cup:** First Round Proper 2015-16.
	FA Trophy: Third Qualifying 2014-15(r).
	FA Vase: Semi-finals 2009-10.

BARWELL MATCH RESULTS 2016-17

Date	Comp	H/A	Opponents	Att:	Result	Goalscorers	Pos	No.
Aug 13	NPL	H	Marine	152	L 1 - 2	Hickey 21	17	1
16	NPL	A	Stafford Rangers	620	D 1 - 1	Ballenger 90	17	2
20	NPL	A	Workington	422	W 1 - 0	Shannon-Lewis 53	13	3
23	NPL	H	Mickleover Sports	159	W 2 - 1	Shannon-Lewis 3 Anderson 38	8	4
27	NPL	H	Spennymoor United	177	D 1 - 1	Rowe 76	8	5
29	NPL	A	Stourbridge	695	L 1 - 2	Hickey 82 (pen)	12	6
Sept 3	FAC1Q	A	Evesham United	237	D 2 - 2	Hickey 23 (pen) Story 40		7
6	FAC1Qr	H	Evesham United	204	W 2 - 0	Hickey 32 (pen) Mitchell 79		8
10	NPL	A	Buxton	277	D 0 - 0		11	9
17	FAC2Q	H	Ilkeston	214	L 0 - 1			10
20	NPL	H	Grantham Town	154	D 1 - 1	Kay 75	12	11
24	NPL	H	Halesowen Town	174	D 0 - 0		13	12
27	NPL	A	Rushall Olympic	166	L 1 - 3	Towers 72	16	13
Oct 1	NPL	A	Frickley Athletic	242	W 3 - 2	HICKEY 3 (21 41 44)	14	14
8	NPL	H	Nantwich Town	153	D 1 - 1	Hickey 38	14	15
11	NPL	A	Ilkeston	242	L 0 - 1		17	16
15	NPL	A	Ashton United	178	D 0 - 0		17	17
19	NPL	H	Hednesford Town	237	W 2 - 0	Julien 82 Hickey 90	14	18
22	NPL	H	Whitby Town	224	L 1 - 2	Julien 84	16	19
29	FAT1Q	A	Ilkeston	262	W 2 - 0	Story 34 Balllinger 59		20
Nov 1	NPL	A	Matlock Town	268	L 1 - 2	Gibson 88	17	21
5	NPL	H	Blyth Spartans	241	L 0 - 2		18	22
12	FAT2Q	H	Farsley Celtic	159	L 2 - 3	Story 17 32		23
19	NPL	A	Warrington Town	292	W 2 - 1	Ball 66 Towers 84	16	24
22	NPL	H	Matlock Town	142	W 1 - 0	Story 30	15	25
26	NPL	A	Corby Town	437	W 2 - 0	Ball 16 Hickey 50	15	26
Dec 3	NPL	H	Skelmersdale United	138	W 4 - 0	Ball 13 (pen) Barlone 40 (pen) Tomkinson 43 Hickey 60	13	27
10	NPL	H	Sutton Coldfield Town	136	D 1 - 1	Nisevic 90	12	28
17	NPL	A	Blyth Spartans	523	L 0 - 2		14	29
21	NPL	H	Stafford Rangers	309	W 2 - 1	Ball 8 Hickey 26	13	30
26	NPL	A	Coalville Town	240	W 2 - 1	Hickey 54 Story 79	10	31
Jan 2	NPL	H	Stourbridge	302	L 0 - 1		11	32
7	NPL	A	Marine	301	D 0 - 0		12	33
14	NPL	A	Grantham Town	229	D 2 - 2	Ball 2 Kay 70	12	34
21	NPL	A	Nantwich Town	265	D 2 - 2	Ball 21 Hickey 50	12	35
28	NPL	H	Ilkeston	217	W 2 - 1	Ball 31 Hickey 81	10	36
Feb 4	NPL	A	Hednesford Town	377	D 1 - 1	Barlone 68	11	37
11	NPL	H	Ashton United	127	W 4 - 1	Barlone 6 Hickey 23 Ball 35 (pen) Towers 71	11	38
18	NPL	A	Whitby Town	285	W 2 - 1	Ball 40 74	9	39
21	NPL	H	Frickley Athletic	154	L 1 - 2	Ball 51	9	40
25	NPL	A	Halesowen Town	378	D 1 - 1	Mwanyongo 76	12	41
Mar 4	NPL	H	Buxton	172	L 0 - 1		13	42
11	NPL	A	Skelmersdale United	108	W 5 - 0	HICKEY 3 (8 14 53) Barlone 63 Ball 68	11	43
18	NPL	H	Corby Town	327	W 3 - 0	Hickey 32 Smith 80 (og) Baldwin 89	11	44
25	NPL	A	Sutton Coldfield Town	283	L 1 - 2	Ball 45	11	45
28	NPL	H	Rushall Olympic	146	D 1 - 1	Towers 50	11	46
Apr 1	NPL	H	Warrington Town	157	L 0 - 2		13	47
8	NPL	H	Workington	187	L 0 - 2		13	48
15	NPL	A	Mickleover Sports	201	L 1 - 4	Ball 9 (pen)	14	49
17	NPL	H	Coalville Town	258	W 1 - 0	Hickey 78	12	50
22	NPL	A	Spennymoor Town	665	L 0 2		14	51

GOALSCORERS	SG	CSG	Pens	Hat tricks	Total		SG	CSG	Pens	Hat tricks	Total
2015-16 Hickey					29	Anderson	1				1
Hickey	17	3	3	2	21	Baldwin	1				1
Ball	11	3	3		14	Gibson	1				1
Story	6	2			6	Mitchell	1				1
Barlone	4		1		4	Mwanyongo	1				1
Towers	4				4	Nisevic	1				1
Ballenger	2				2	Opponents	1				1
Julien	2				2	Rowe	1				1
Kay	2				2	Tomkinson	1				1
Shannon-Lewis	1				2						

BUXTON

Club Contact Details
The Silverlands, Buxton, Derbyshire SK17 6QH
01298 23197
don@buxtonfc.co.uk

Ground Capacity: 5,200   **Seats:** 490   **Covered:** 2,500   **Clubhouse:** Yes   **Shop:** Yes

Record Attendance
6,000 v Barrow - FA Cup 1st Round 1962-63

Previous Grounds
The Park (Cricket Club) 1877-78. Fields at Cote Heath and Green Lane 1878-84.

10 YEAR RECORD

	07-08	08-09	09-10	10-11	11-12	12-13	13-14	14-15	15-16	16-17
NP P	5	14	8	6	13	7	13	10	11	7
FAC	2Q	3Q	4Q	4Q	2Q	4Q	2Q	2Q	3Qr	1Q
FAT	3Q	2Q	2Q	1Q	2Q	1Pr	2Q	2Q	3Q	2Q

Club Factfile

Founded: 1877   **Nickname:** The Bucks   **Manager:** Martin McIntosh

Previous Names: None

Previous Leagues: Combination 1891-99. Manchester 1899-1932. Cheshire County 1932-40, 46-73.
Northern Premier 1973-98, 2006- Northern Counties East 1998-2006.

Club Colours (change): All royal blue with yellow trim (All red with black trim)

RECORDS
Goalscorer: Mark Reed - 251 (469 appearances)

Appearances: David Bainbridge - 642

Additional: Paid £5,000 to Hyde United for Gary Walker 1989
Received £16,500 from Rotherham for Ally Pickering 1989

HONOURS
FA Comps: None

League: Manchester 1931-32. Cheshire County 1972-73.
Northern Counties East 2005-06. Northern Premier Division One 2006-07.

County FA: Derbyshire Senior Cup 1938-39, 45-46, 56-57, 59-60, 71-72, 80-81, 85-86, 86-87, 2008-09, 11-12.

BEST PERFORMANCES	**FA Cup:** Third Round Proper 1951-52.
	FA Trophy: Quarter-finals 1970-71, 71-72.
	FA Vase: Fifth Round Proper 2005-06.

BUXTON MATCH RESULTS 2016-17

Date	Comp	H/A	Opponents	Att:	Result	Goalscorers	Pos	No.
Aug 13	NPL	H	Halesowen Town	321	W 2 - 0	Walker 30 Abbott 66	5	1
16	NPL	A	Grantham Town	229	W 1 - 0	Walker 45	1	2
20	NPL	A	Coalville Town	149	L 1 - 2	Burns 60	6	3
23	NPL	H	Workington	265	W 2 - 1	May 13 (og) Grayson 41 (pen)	1	4
27	NPL	H	Marine	328	W 3 - 0	Jackson 63 Grayson 73 Bembo-Leta 83	1	5
29	NPL	A	Mickleover Sports	361	W 3 - 0	Grayson 34 Doran 72 Abbott 80	1	6
Sept 3	FAC1Q	A	Witton Abion	324	L 0 - 3			7
10	NPL	H	Barwell	277	D 0 - 0		2	8
17	NPL	A	Corby Town	469	D 1 - 1	Grayson 83	2	9
20	NPL	A	Ashton United	242	W 3 - 1	Burns 71 Grayson 90 Abbott 90	1	10
23	NPL	A	Ilkeston	421	L 0 - 1		1	11
27	NPL	H	CorbyTown	289	W 1 - 0	Jackson 64	1	12
Oct 1	NPL	A	Hednesford Town	409	W 2 - 1	Jackson 34 Garnett 84	1	13
8	NPL	H	Whitby Town	602	W 3 - 0	Taylor 8 Abbott 44 Doran 72	1	14
11	NPL	A	Warrington Town	307	L 0 - 1		1	15
15	NPL	A	Frickley Athletic	373	D 4 - 4	Doran 16 Bembo-Leta 57 90 Bennett 85	1	16
22	NPL	H	Spennymoor United	501	D 2 - 2	Bembo-Leta 40 Walker 74	3	17
27	FAT1Q	H	Glossop North End	518	W 2 - 0	Jackson 49 Young 90		18
Nov 1	NPL	A	Nantwich Town	255	L 0 - 1		5	19
5	NPL	H	Sutton Coldfield Town	353	W 2 - 1	Ravenhill 83 Bembo-Leta 89	5	20
12	FAT2Q	H	Kings Lynn Town	302	L 1 - 3	Abbott 19 (pen)		21
19	NPL	A	Stourbridge	760	L 2 - 3	Grayson 83 90	5	22
22	NPL	H	Nantwich `Town	268	W 4 - 1	Bembo-Leta 54 73 Abbott 84 Grayson 87 (pen)	4	23
26	NPL	H	Rushall Olympic	313	W 3 - 0	Grayson 1 78 Walker 60	2	24
Dec 3	NPL	A	Blyth Spartans	573	D 0 - 0		2	25
10	NPL	H	Skelmersdale United	321	D 0 - 0		2	26
17	NPL	A	Sutton Coldfield Town	174	D 1 - 1	Grayson 52	2	27
26	NPL	A	Matlock Town	1051	L 1 - 3	Grayson 30	3	28
Jan 2	NPL	H	MIckleover Sport	364	W 1 - 0	Grayson 90 (pen)	3	29
7	NPL	A	Halesowen Town	355	W 4 - 2	Jackson 39 45 Young 51 Walker 90	1	30
17	NPL	H	Stafford Rangers	312	L 1 - 3	Hardy 45	2	31
21	NPL	A	Whitby Town	282	L 2 - 4	Abbott 12 Hardy 79	5	32
28	NPL	H	Warrington Town	335	D 3 - 3	Hardy 45 Bembo-Letts 49 McGee 66	3	33
Feb 4	NPL	A	Stafford Rangers	674	W 2 - 1	Hardy 69 78	2	34
14	NPL	H	Hednesford Town	231	W 2 - 0	Grayson 35 Taylor 55	2	35
18	NPL	A	Spennymoor Town	538	D 1 - 1	Abbott 10	2	36
Mar 4	NPL	A	Barwell	172	W 1 - 0	Grayson 85	4	37
7	NPL	H	Ashton United	248	L 1 - 2	Hardy 67	5	38
11	NPL	H	Blyth Spartans	445	D 2 - 2	Hardy 18 Green 26	5	39
18	NPL	A	Rushall Olympic	212	L 0 - 1		9	40
25	NPL	A	Skelmersdale United	208	W 6 - 0	Green 41 Young 51 Grayson 54 McGee 62 Hardy 65 77 7	7	41
28	NPL	H	Frickley Athletic	308	W 2 0	Young 17 Hardy 48 (pen)	7	42
Apr 1	NPL	H	Stourbridge	504	D 1 - 1	Doran 4	7	43
4	NPL	H	Ilkeston	209	W 2 - 0	Grayson 63 Doran 90	6	44
8	NPL	H	Coalville Town	374	W 2 - 1	McGhee 26 Grayson 71 (pen)	5	45
11	NPL	A	Workington	506	L 0 - 2		6	46
15	NPL	H	Grantham Town	439	L 0 - 1		8	47
17	NPL	H	Matlock Town	547	W 2 - 1	Grayson 15 29	6	48
22	NPL	A	Marine	439	D 5 - 5	Hinsley 17 McGee 29 Williams 47 Young 59 Walker 79	7	49

GOALSCORERS	SG	CSG	Pens	Hat tricks	Total		SG	CSG	Pens	Hat tricks	Total
2015-16 Hardy					25	Burns	2				2
Grayson	17	3x3	4		20	Green	2				2
Hardy	8		1		10	Taylor	2				2
Abbott	6	2	2		8	Bennett	1				1
Bembo-Letts	8	2			8	Garnett	1				1
Jackson	5	2			6	Hinsley	1				1
Walker	6	2			6	Opponents	1				1
Doran	5				5	Ravenhill	1				1
Young	5				5	Williams	1				1
McGee	4				4						

COALVILLE TOWN

Club Contact Details
Owen Street Sports Ground, Owen St, Coalville LE67 3DA
01530 833 365
coalville.secretary@gmail.com

The Ravens

Ground Capacity: 2,000 **Seats:** 240 **Covered:** 240 **Clubhouse:** Yes **Shop:** Yes

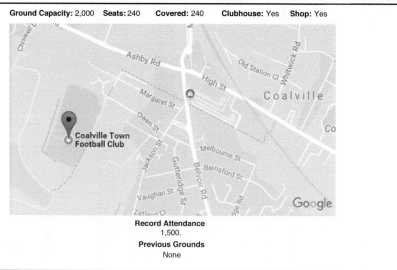

Record Attendance
1,500.

Previous Grounds
None

10 YEAR RECORD

07-08		08-09		09-10		10-11		11-12		12-13		13-14		14-15		15-16		16-17	
MidAl	8	MidAl	3	MidAl	2	MidAl	1	NP1S	14	NP1S	2	NP1S	2	NP1S	10	NP1S	3	NP P	17
FAC	EP	FAC	3Q	FAC	P	FAC	2Q	FAC	P	FAC	1Q	FAC	2Q	FAC	2Qr	FAC	2Q	FAC	2Q
FAV	2Q	FAV	4Pr	FAV	3P	FAV	F	FAT	P	FAT	2Q	FAT	1Pr	FAT	P	FAT	1Q	FAT	1Q

Club Factfile

Founded: 1926 **Nickname:** The Ravens **Manager:** Tommy Brookbanks

Previous Names: Ravenstoke Miners Ath. 1926-58. Ravenstoke FC 1958-95. Coalville 1995-98.

Previous Leagues: Coalville & Dist. Amateur. North Leicester. Leicestershire Senior. Midland Alliance > 2011.

Club Colours (change): Black & white stripes/black/white (Red & yellow stripes/red/red)

RECORDS
Appearances: Nigel Simms.
Additional: 153 goals scored during 2010-11 season.

HONOURS
FA Comps: None

League: Coalville & District Amateur 1952-53. North Leicestershire 1988-89, 89-90. Leicestershire Senior 2001-02, 02-03. Midland Football Alliance 2010-11.

County FA: Leicestershire Senior Cup 1999-00. Leicestershire Challenge Cup 2012-13.

BEST PERFORMANCES	**FA Cup:** First Round Proper 2004-05.
	FA Trophy: First Round Proper 2013-14.
	FA Vase: Final 2010-11.

COALVILLE TOWN MATCH RESULTS 2016-17

Date	Comp	H/A	Opponents	Att:	Result		Goalscorers	Pos	No.
Aug 13	NPL	A	Blyth Spartans	561	L	1 - 3	McDonald 10	19	1
16	NPL	H	Sutton Coldfield Town	136	D	1 - 1	McDonald 28	19	2
20	NPL	H	Buxton	149	W	2 - 1	Munn 67 Watson 88	16	3
23	NPL	A	Skelmersdale United	184	W	2 - 1	Watson 38 50	9	4
29	NPL	H	Rushall Olympic	198	D	3 - 3	Woodward 38 McDonald 41 Watson 54	11	5
Sept 3	FAC1Q	H	Redditch United	161	W	2 - 1	Woodward 58 Munn 83		6
10	NPL	A	Marine	304	L	2 - 4	Walshe 53 Watson 90 (pen)	15	7
17	FAC2Q	H	AFC Mansfield	139	L	0 - 1			8
20	NPL	H	Matlock Town	134	L	1 - 4	Watson 76	17	9
24	NPL	H	Warrington Town	130	L	1 - 2	McDonald 90	19	10
27	NPL	A	Grantham Town	151	L	1 - 5	McDonald 85	20	11
Oct 1	NPL	A	Ashton United	152	L	0 - 3		20	12
4	NPL	H	Mickleover Sports	147	W	3 - 2	Towers 29 Demidh 34 90	18	13
8	NPL	H	Spennymoor United	183	L	0 - 1		18	14
11	NPL	A	Frickley Athletic	240	W	4 - 0	Demidh 48 62 Woodward 82 Trokes 89	18	15
15	NPL	A	Stafford Rangers	567	L	1 - 2	Towers 65	19	16
19	NPL	H	Stourbridge	110	D	1 - 1	Woodward 33	19	17
22	NPL	H	Ilkeston	213	L	2 - 3	Trokes 25 Watson 37	20	18
27	FAT1Q	A	AFC Rushden & Diamonds	448	L	0 - 1			19
Nov 1	NPL	A	Mickleover Sports	183	W	2 - 1	Matthews 1Towers 7	19	20
5	NPL	A	Halesowen Town	402	L	0 - 1		19	21
12	NPL	A	Sutton Coldfield Tpwn	190	W	3 - 0	Robbins 41 Woodward 87 Wilson 90 (pen)	18	22
19	NPL	H	WhitbyTown	137	L	2 - 3	Watson 29 Rojewski 90	19	23
26	NPL	A	Hednesford Town	340	W	2 - 1	McDonald 67 Torr 90	17	24
Dec 3	NPL	H	Nantwich Town	166	W	3 - 1	McMillan 5 Robbins 53 McDonald 81	16	25
10	NPL	A	Workington	335	W	4 - 0	McMillan 22 Walshe 42 Rojewski 62 McDonald 72	15	26
17	NPL	H	Halesowen Town	170	W	3 - 1	McDonald 26 Robbins 76 Dean 79	13	27
26	NPL	H	Barwell	240	L	1 - 2	Coleman 78	16	28
Jan 7	NPL	H	Blyth Spartans	186	L	0 - 1		17	29
18	NPL	A	Corby Town	454	W	2 - 1	Coleman 9 42 (pen)	17	30
21	NPL	A	Spennymoor Town	486	L	0 - 5		17	31
28	NPL	H	Frickley Athletic	326	W	3 - 1	Watson 25 (pen) McDonald 58 Antonio 79	15	32
Feb 4	NPL	A	Stourbridge	733	L	0 - 2		16	33
11	NPL	H	Stafford Rangers	171	D	0 - 0		17	34
14	NPL`	A	Ilkeston	253	D	0 - 0		16	35
	NPL	H	Ashton United	119	L	1 - 3	Smalley 40 (og)	17	36
25	NPL	H	Warrington Town	229	L	1 - 3	Coleman 10	17	37
Mar 4	NPL	H	Marine	125	D	0 - 0		17	38
7	NPL	A	Matlock Town	293	D	0 - 0		17	39
11	NPL	A	Nantwich Town	374	L	0 - 3		17	40
18	NPL	H	Hednesford Town	165	D	2 - 2	Watson 71 (pen) Jenno 81	17	41
21	NPL	A	Rushall Olympic	151	W	5 - 2	Watson 26 (p)Brown 32 McDonald 60Freeman 68 Hull 79(og)	16	42
25	NPL	H	Workington	191	W	2 - 1	Watson 18 Dean 74	16	43
Apr 1	NPL	A	Whitby Town	367	D	1 - 1	Coleman 80 (pen)	16	44
8	NPL	A	Buxton	374	L	1 - 2	Freeman 47	16	45
11	NPL	H	Grantham Town	227	L	1 - 2	Jenno 57	16	46
15	NPL	H	Skelmersdale United	194	D	3 - 3	Doble 5 (og) Lovelle-Moore 25 Watson79	17	47
17	NPL	A	Barwell	258	L	0 - 1		18	48
22	NPL	H	Corby Town	467	W	4 - 1	Watson 15 22 Marshall 52 Coleman 90	17	49

GOALSCORERS	SG	CSG	Pens	Hat tricks	Total		SG	CSG	Pens	Hat tricks	Total
Watson	12	3	2		15	McMillan	2	2			2
McDonald	10	4			11	Munn	2	1			2
Coleman	5				6	Rojewski	2				2
Woodward	5	2			5	Trokes	2				2
Demidh	3				4	Walshe	2				2
Opponents					3	Antonio	1				1
Robbins	3				3	Brown	1				1
Towers	3				3	Lovell-Moore	1				1
Dean	2				2	Marshall	1				1
Freeman	2				2	Matthews	1				1
Jenno	2				2	Torr	1				1
						Wilson	1		1		1

FARSLEY CELTIC

Club Contact Details
Throstle Nest, Newlands, Pudsey, Leeds, LS28 5BE
0113 255 7292
jgreaves@farsleyceltic.com

Ground Capacity: 4,000 **Seats:** 300 **Covered:** 1,500 **Clubhouse:** Yes **Shop:** Yes

Record Attendance

Previous Grounds
None

10 YEAR RECORD

07-08	08-09	09-10	10-11	11-12	12-13	13-14	14-15	15-16	16-17
			NCEP 1	NP1N 4	NP1N 14	NP1N 7	NP1N 12	NP1N 9	NP1N 2
					FAC 1Qr	FAC P	FAC 2Q	FAC 1Q	FAC 3Q
				FAT 1Qr	FAT Pr	FAT P	FAT 1Q	FAT 1Q	FAT 1P

Club Factfile

Founded: 2010 **Nickname:** The Villagers **Manager:** Adam Lakeland

Previous Names: Farsley AFC 2010-15.

Previous Leagues: Northern Counties East 2010-11.

Club Colours (change): All blue (All orange)

RECORDS
Victory: 8-0 v Arnold Town (H) Northern Counties East Premier 2010-11.
Defeat: 5-1 v Tadcaster Albion, President's Cup Final 27/04/11.

HONOURS
FA Comps: None

League: Northern Counties East Premier Division 2010-11.

County FA: West Riding County Cup 2016-17.

BEST PERFORMANCES	**FA Cup:** Third Qualifying Round 2016-17.
	FA Trophy: First Round Proper 2016-17.
	FA Vase: N/A

LEADING GOALSCORERS 2016-2017

		LGE	FAC	FAT	Pens	H-T	SG	CSG	Total
Dan Maguire	Blyth Spartans	30	2	4		3	23	9	36
Luke Benbow	Stourbridge	33	3		7		29	5	36
Marcus Dinanga	Matlock Town	22	1	6	2	1	23	3	29
Dayle Hopson	Whitby Town	26			7	3	21	4	26
Dan Mitchley	Marine	17	2	6	5		20	3	25
Luke Armstrong	Blyth Spartans	20		4		1	18	2	24
Lee Shaw	Grantham Town	20	1	2	2		21	6	23
Brady Hickey	Barwell	19	2		3	2	17	3	21
Brad Grayson	Buxton	17			4		17	3	20
Sean Cooke	Nantwich Town	17	2	1	2	1	14	2	20
Adam Baskerville	Mickleover Sports	12	1	3	3		18	2	18
Kaiman Anderson	Halesowen Town	14	4		2		15	6	18
Sean Reid	Blyth Spartans	16	2			1	12	2	18
Matt Tyman	Whitby Town	13	3	1	8		14	4	17
Glen Taylor	Spennymoor Town	14	2			1	16	2	16
Sean Reid	Blyth Spartans	14	2			1	12	2	16
Alex Reid	Rushall Olympic	14	1				13	6	15
Callum Ball	Barwell	14			3		11	3	14
Matt Newsham	Matlock Town	10	4		1		11	2	14
Robbie Dale	Blyth Spartans	13		1			13	2	14
Felipe Barcelos	Grantham Town	10		3	2		12	6	13
Matty Pattison	Blyth Spartans	11		2	1		9	2	13
Scott Allison	Workington	11	2				12	4	13
Kurt Sherlock	Marine	8	1	2		5	10	2	11
Matt Newsham	Matlock Town	7	4		1		8	2	11
George Carline	Hednesford Town	9		1			9	3	10

PENALTIES

	Scored			Conceded
Marine	8+2t		Frickley Athletic	8+1c
Workington	9		Barwell	7
Mickleover Sports	8		Corby Town	7
Whitby Town	8		Skelmersdale U	7
Stourbridge	7+1t		Stafford Rangers	7
Coalville Town	7		Stourbridge	7
Nantwich Town	7		Coalville Town	6
Barwell	5+2c		Marine	6
Matlock Town	4+2c+1t		Mickleover Sports	5+1c
Hednesford Town	6		Nantwich Town	5+1c
Buxton	5+1t		Warrington Town	5+1c
Warrington Town	5		Workington	4+1c
Spennymoor Town	5		Ashton United	4
Grantham Town	4+1c		Buxton	4
Sutton Coldfield T	4		Halesowen Town	4
Rushall Olympic	4		Rushalll Olympic	4
Blyth Spartans.	3		Sutton Coldfield	4
Stafford Rangers	2+1t		Spennymoor Town	2+1c
Skelmersdale U	2+1c		Grantham Town	3
Corby Town	2		Ilkeston Town	3
Halesowen Town	1+1c		Whitby Town	2
Ashton United	1		Blyth Spartans	1
Frickley Athletic	1		Matlock Town	2
Ilkeston	0		Hednesford Town	1+1c
TOTAL	**108+7c+6t**			**108+7c**

GRANTHAM TOWN

Club Contact Details
South Kesteven Sports Stadium, Trent Road, Gratham NG31 7XQ
01476 402 224
psnixon@hotmail.com

Ground Capacity: 7,500 **Seats:** 750 **Covered:** 1,950 **Clubhouse:** Yes **Shop:** Yes

Record Attendance
6,578 v Middlesbrough, FA Cup Third Round Proper, 1973-74.
Previous Grounds
London Road >1990-91. Spalding United FC 1990-91.

10 YEAR RECORD

	07-08	08-09	09-10	10-11	11-12	12-13	13-14	14-15	15-16	16-17
	NP 1 6	NP1S 13	NP1S 11	NP1S 5	NP1S 1	NP P 19	NP P 15	NP P 12	NP P 18	NP P 8
	FAC 2Q	FAC 1Q	FAC Pr	FAC Pr	FAC 3Q	FAC 2Q	FAC 1Qr	FAC 3Q	FAC 1Q	FAC 1Qr
	FAT 1Q	FAT P	FAT Pr	FAT P	FAT 1Q	FAT 1Q	FAT 1Qr	FAT 1Q	FAT 1Q	FAT 2Q

Club Factfile

Founded: 1874   **Nickname:** Gingerbreads   **Manager:** Adam Stevens

Previous Names: Grantham FC 1874-1987.

Previous Leagues: Midland Amateur Alliance, Central Alliance 1911-25, 59-61, Midland Counties 1925-59, 61-72, Southern 1972-79, 85-2006, Northern Premier 1979-85

Club Colours (change): Black & white stripes/black/black (Orange & black/orange/orange)

RECORDS
Victory: 13-0 v Rufford Colliery (H) - FA Cup 15/09/1934
Defeat: 0-16 v Notts County Rovers (A) - Midland Amateur Alliance 22/10/1892
Goalscorer: Jack McCartney - 416
Appearances: Chris Gardner - 664
Additional: Received £20,000 from Nottingham Forest for Gary Crosby

HONOURS

FA Comps: None

League: Midland Amateur 1910-11. Central Alliance 1924-25. Midland 1963-64, 70-71, 71-72.
Southern Division One North 1972-73, 78-79, Midland Division 97-98. Northern Premier Division One South 2011-12.

County FA: Lincolnshire Senior Cup 1884-85, 1971-72, 82-83, County Senior Cup 1936-37, Senior Cup 'A' 1953-54, 60-61, 61-62, County Shield 2003-04, 04-05.

BEST PERFORMANCES
FA Cup: Third Round Proper 1883-84, 86-87, 73-74.
FA Trophy: Quarter-finals 1971-72, 97-98.
FA Vase: N/A

GRANTHAM TOWN MATCH RESULTS 2016-17

Date	Comp	H/A	Opponents	Att:	Result	Goalscorers	Pos	No.
Aug 13	NPL	A	Skelmersale United	203	D 1 - 1	Burrows 74	9	1
16	NPL	H	Buxton	229	L 0 - 1		18	2
20	NPL	A	Warrington	236	W 1 - 0	Saunders 40	14	3
23	NPL	A	Rushall Olympic	202	L 1 - 3	Saunders 71	16	4
27	NPL	A	Blyth Spartans	175	L 1 - 2	Meadows 70 (pen)	18	5
29	NPL	H	Sutton Coldfield Town	186	W 2 - 1	Ryan 18 39	16	6
Sept 3	FAC1Q	A	Chasetown	233	D 1 - 1	Meadows 16		7
6	FAC1Qr	H	Chasetown	261	D 2 - 2	Lee Shaw 40 Ryan 74 won 6-5 on penalties.	19	8
10	NPL	H	Nantwich Town	170	L 0 - 4			9
17	NPL	H	Warrington Town	163	L 1 - 2	Lee Shaw 44	19	10
20	NPL	A	Barwell	154	D 1 - 1	Ryan 60	18	11
24	NPL	A	Workington	419	L 0 - 1		20	12
27	NPL	H	Coalville Town	151	W 5 - 1	Clifton 44 79 Meadows 46 Freeman 72 (og) Barcelos 89	17	13
Oct 1	NPL	A	Marine	311	L 0 - 1		17	14
4	NPL	H	Whitby Town	189	W 2 - 0	Saunders 54 Lee Shaw 86	15	15
8	NPL	A	Stafford Rangers	263	W 2 - 1	Burrowa 4 Hollingsworth 22	13	16
11	NPL	H	Grantham Town	125	L 3 - 4	Lewis 16 Barcelos 47 Burrows 90	13	17
15	NPL	A	Stourbridge	193	L 2 - 3	Luke Shaw 9 Barcelos 55 (pen)	15	18
18	NPL	H	Spennymoor Town	167	D 3 - 3	Wilden 38 Barcelos 49 Lee Shaw 64	17	19
22	NPL	H	Mickleover Sports	213	W 1 - 0	Barcelos 49	14	20
29	FAT1Q	A	Stratford Town	204	D 2 - 2	Barcelos 6 (pen) Lee Shaw 35		21
Nov 1	FAT1Qr	H	Stratford Town	142	W 4 - 0	Lee Shaw 19 Barcelos 48 87 Clifton 80		22
5	NPL	A	Halesowen Town	420	L 0 - 1		19	23
8	NPL	A	Matlock Town	234	L 1 - 2	Lee Shaw 40	19	24
12	FAT2Q	H	Matlock Town	259	L 0 - 2			25
19	NPL	H	Frickley Athletic	216	W 3 - 0	Lee Shaw 7 Luke Shaw 33 Barcelos 77	15	26
22	NPL	A	Whitby Town	209	W 2 - 0	Lee Shaw 26 74	14	27
26	NPL	H	Skelmersdale United	213	D 1 - 1	Batchelor 82	14	28
Dec 3	NPL	A	Ilkeston	373	W 3 - 0	Meadows 7 Barcelos 9 Walters 58 (og)	14	29
10	NPL	A	Halesowen Town	316	D 1 - 1	Barcelos 48	13	30
17	NPL	H	Hednesford Town	223	W 4 - 1	Meadows 36 Lee Shaw 38 77 Dasaolu 74	12	31
26	NPL	H	Corby Town	334	W 4 - 0	Luke Shaw 28 (pen) 60 Dasaolu 33 Lewis 63	9	32
Jan 2	NPL	A	Sutton Coldfield Town	262	W 2 - 0	Lee Shaw 40 Clifton 74	7	33
14	NPL	H	Barwell	229	D 2 - 2	Lee Shaw 56 Barcelos 63	9	34
21	NPL	A	Stafford Rangers	710	W 1 - 0	Lee Shaw 73	8	35
28	NPL	H	Ashton United	243	W 2 - 1	Barcelaos 22 Lee Shaw 55	8	36
Feb 4	NPL	A	Spennymoor Town	490	W 2 - 1	Luke Shaw 59 (pen) Lee Shaw 61	5	37
11	NPL	H	Stourbridge	408	W 2 - 1	Lee Shaw 47 Clifton 55	5	38
14	NPL	H	Matlock Town	309	D 0 - 0		4	39
18	NPL	A	Mickleover Sports	311	L 1 - 2	Lee Shaw 60	6	40
25	NPL	H	Workington	283	D 2 - 2	Luke Shaw 37 Lewis 90	6	41
Mar 4	NPL	A	Nantwich Town	465	D 1 - 1	Lee Shaw 8	6	42
11	NPL	H	Ilkeston	314	D 1 - 1	Luke Shaw 21	10	43
18	NPL	A	Marine	225	W 3 - 0	Burrows 42 Galinski 82 Dasaolu 85	8	44
25	NPL	A	Stourbridge	965	W 2 - 1	Luke Shaw 3 Lee Shaw 47	8	45
Apr 1	NPL	A	Frickley Athletic	275	W 2 - 1	Meadows 17 Luke Shaw 23	8	46
8	NPL	H	Rushall Olympic	241	W 2 - 1	Lee Shaw 58 Galinski 70	8	47
11	NPL	A	Coalville Town	227	D 2 - 2	Wildin 25 Dasaolu 65	9	48
15	NPL	A	Buxton	439	W 1 - 0	Lee Shaw 76	5	49
17	NPL	A	Corby Town	785	L 0 - 3		7	50
22	NPL	H	Blyth Spartans	1041	L 1 - 5	Clifton 71	8	51

GOALSCORERS	SG	CSG	Pens	Hat tricks	Total		SG	CSG	Pens	Hat tricks	Total
2015-16 Lewis					11	Saunders	3				3
Lee Shaw	21	6			23	Galinski	2				2
Barcelos	12	6	2		13	Opponents	2				2
Luke Shaw	8	2	2		9	Wildin	2				2
Clifton	6				6	Batchelor	1				1
Meadows	6		1		6	Dasaolu	1				1
Burrows	4				4	Hollingsworth	1				1
Ryan	3				4						
Dassalu	3				3						
Lewis	3				3						

HALESOWEN TOWN

Club Contact Details
The Grove, Old Hawne Lane, Halesowen B63 3TB
0121 629 0727
secretary@halesowentown.com

Ground Capacity: 5,000 **Seats:** 525 **Covered:** 930 **Clubhouse:** Yes **Shop:** Yes

Record Attendance
5,000 v Hendon - FA Cup 1st Round Proper 1954
Previous Grounds
None

10 YEAR RECORD

07-08		08-09		09-10		10-11		11-12		12-13		13-14		14-15		15-16		16-17	
SthP	3	SthP	10	SthP	8	SthP	21	Sthsw	12	NP1S	7	NP1S	1	NP P	11	NP P	13	NP P	19
FAC	3Q	FAC	3Q					FAC	P	FAC	P	FAC	3Q	FAC	3Q	FAC	2Q	FAC	3Qr
FAT	1Q	FAT	1Qr			FAT	1Q	FAT	P	FAT	2Q	FAT	1Q	FAT	1P	FAT	1Q	FAT	2Q

Club Factfile

Founded: 1873   **Nickname:** Yeltz   **Manager:** John Hill

Previous Names: None

Previous Leagues: Birmingham & District/West Midlands 1892-1905, 06-11, 46-86, Birmingham Combination 1911-39.

Club Colours (change): All blue (Yellow/black/yellow)

RECORDS
Victory:	13-1 v Coventry Amateurs - Birmingham Senior cup 1956
Defeat:	0-8 v Bilston - West Midlands League 07/04/1962
Goalscorer:	Paul Joinson - 369
Appearances:	Paul Joinson - 608
Additional:	Paid £7,250 to Gresley Rovers for Stuart Evans
	Received £40,000 from Rushden & Diamonds for Jim Rodwell

HONOURS

FA Comps: FA Vase 1984-85, 85-86

League: West Midlands (Reg) 1946-47, 82-83, 83-84, 84-85, 85-86. Southern League Midland Division 1989-90, Western Division 2001-02. Northern Premier Division One South 2013-14.

County FA: Worcestershire Senior Cup 1951-52, 61-62, 2002-03, 04-05. Birmingham Senior Cup 1983-84, 97-98. Staffordshire Senior Cup 1988-89.

BEST PERFORMANCES	**FA Cup:** First Round Proper 1955-56, 85-86(r), 86-87, 87-88(r), 88-89, 89-90, 9-91, 91-92(r), 2004-05.
	FA Trophy: Third Round Proper 1994-95, 99-00(r), 02-03.
	FA Vase: Final 1982-83, 84-85, 85-86.

HALESOWEN TOWN MATCH RESULTS 2016-17

Date	Comp	H/A	Opponents	Att:	Result	Goalscorers	Pos	No.
Aug 13	NPL	A	Buxton	321	L 0 - 2		23	1
16	NPL	H	Corby Town	371	D 1 - 1	Delaney 45	21	2
20	NPL	H	Blyth Spartans	376	L 0 - 5		21	3
23	NPL	A	Nantwich Town	265	W 2 - 1	Melvin 58 Anderson 75	17	4
27	NPL	A	Rushall Olympic	227	L 0 - 1		19	5
29	NPL	H	Hednesford Town	567	L 1 - 3	Anderson 87	20	6
Sept 3	FAC1Q	H	Coleshill Town	376	W 3 - 0	Delaney 1 Anderson70 (pen) 79		7
10	NPL	H	Workington	421	W 3 - 2	Anderson 15 77 Chilton 24	20	8
17	FAC2Q	H	Belper Town	318	W 1 - 0	Colley 79		9
19	NPL	A	Stourbridge	1575	D 2 - 2	Chilton 1 Morrison 6	17	10
24	NPL	A	Barwell	174	D 0 - 0		17	11
27	NPL	H	Ilkeston	346	W 2 - 1	Anderson 33 70	15	12
Oct 1	FAC3Q	H	Nantwich Town	532	D 1 - 1	Anderson 62		13
4	FAC3Qr	A	Nantwich Town	362	L 1 - 2	Anderson 72		14
8	NPL	H	Ashton United	423	D 2 - 2	Goddard 45 Anderson 51	17	15
11	NPL	A	Mickleover Sports	168	W 1 - 0	Anderson 1	11	16
15	NPL	A	Grantham	193	W 3 - 2	Melvin 1 Anderson 25 Hancocks 90	11	17
18	NPL	H	Matlock Town	353	L 0 - 3		16	18
22	NPL	H	Warrington	430	W 1 - 0	Anderson 34	12	19
29	FAT1Q	A	Rushall Olympic	189	W 2 - 1	Delaney 39 Goddard 68		20
Nov 1	NPL	A	Stafford Rangers	423	L 1 - 3	Charlton 40	13	21
5	NPL	H	Coalville Town	402	W 1 - 0	Anderson 9 (pen)	12	22
12	FAT2Q	A	Blyth Spartans	565	L 3 - 4	Denny 54 Delaney 64 66		23
26	NPL	H	Frickley Athletic	352	L 1 - 2	Anderson 52	16	24
Dec 3	NPL	A	Marine	313	L 0 4		19	25
10	NPL	H	Grantham Town	316	D 1 - 1	Digie 20	19	26
17	NPL	A	Coalville Toqn	170	L 1 3	Anderson 20	19	27
26	NPL	H	Sutton Coldfield Town	607	D 0 - 0		19	28
30	NPL	A	Corby Town	413	D 0 - 0		19	29
7	NPL	H	Buxton	355	L 2 - 4	Anderson 30 Charlton 72	19	30
14	NPL	H	Whitby Town	364	W 2 - 0	Dunkley 37 Bowerman 90	19	31
21	NPL	A	Ashton United	239	L 1 - 2	Bragoli 17	19	32
28	NPL	H	Mickleover Sports	379	W 4 - 2	Chilton 1 Dunkley 52 76 Delaney 88	19	33
Feb 4	NPL	A	Matlock Town	382	L 1 - 2	Bennett-Tindale 70	19	34
7	NPL	H	Stafford Rangers	517	D 2 - 2	Clarke 57 O'Neill-Martin 90	19	35
11	NPL	H	Skelmersdale United	202	W 2 - 1	Slade 57 Delaney 73	18	36
18	NPL	A	Warrington Town	278	L 0 - 1		18	37
25	NPL	H	Barwell	378	D 1 - 1	Bragoli 57	18	38
Mar 7	NPL	H	Stourbridge	2,127	L 0 - 1		20	39
11	NPL	H	Spennymoor Town	354	L 1 - 2	Clarke 16	20	40
14	NPL	A	Whitby Town	237	L 1 - 4	Slade 3	20	41
18	NPL	A	Frickley Athletic	250	W 1 - 0	Bragoli 66	18	42
25	NPL	A	Spennymoor Town	668	D 1 - 1	Steele 26	19	43
28	NPL	H	Marine	316	L 0 - 1		22	44
Apr 1	NPL	H	Skelmersdale United	403	W 1 - 0	Lewis 55	18	45
5	NPL	A	Hednesford Town	353	W 2 - 1	Bragoli 33 Charlton 80	17	46
8	NPL	A	Blyth Spartans	1167	L 0 3		18	47
11	NPL	A	Ilkeston Town	211	D 0 - 0		18	48
15	NPL	A	Workington	542	L 0 1		19	49
17	NPL	A	Sutton Coldfield Town	338	L 0 - 1		19	50
19	NPL	H	Nnatwich Town	365	D 0 - 0		19	51
22	NPL	H	Rushall Olympic	487	L 1 - 2	Johnson 45	19	52

GOALSCORERS	SG	CSG	Pens	Hat tricks	Total		SG	CSG	Pens	Hat tricks	Total
2015-16 *Anderson*					8	Bennett-Tindale	1				1
Anderson	15	6	2		18	Bowerman	1				1
Delaney	6				7	Colley	1				1
Bragoli	4				4	Denny	1				1
Charlton	2				3	Digie	1				1
Chilton	3				3	Hancocks	1				1
Dunkley	3				3	Johnson	1				1
Clarke	2				2	Lewis	1				1
Goddard	2				2	Morrison	1				1
Melvin	2				2	O'Neill-Martin	1				1
Slade	2				2	Steele	1				1

HEDNESFORD TOWN

Club Contact Details
Keys Park, Park Road, Hednesford, Cannock WS12 2DZ
01543 422 870
carlcooper@hednesfordtownfc.com

Ground Capacity: 6,500 **Seats:** 1,011 **Covered:** 5,335 **Clubhouse:** Yes **Shop:** Yes

Record Attendance
4,412 v FC United of Manchester, Northern Premier League Premier Division play-off final, 11/05/13.

Previous Grounds
The Tins 1880-1903. The Cross Keys 1903-95.

10 YEAR RECORD

07-08		08-09		09-10		10-11		11-12		12-13		13-14		14-15		15-16		16-17	
NP P	8	NP P	8	SthP	4	SthP	2	NP P	5	NP P	2	Conf N	4	Conf N	8	Nat N	21	NP P	15
FAC	3Q	FAC	1Q	FAC	1Q	FAC	1Q	FAC	3Q	FAC	3Qr	FAC	1P	FAC	2Q	FAC	3Q	FAC	1Q
FAT	2Q	FAT	3P	FAT	1Q	FAT	1Q	FAT	2Qr	FAT	1P	FAT	1P	FAT	3Q	FAT	3Q	FAT	2Qr

Club Factfile

Founded: 1880 **Nickname:** The Pitmen **Manager:** Neil Tooth

Previous Names: Hednesford 1938-74

Previous Leagues: Walsall & District, Birmingham Comb. 1906-15, 45-53, West Mids 1919-39, 53-72, 74-84, Midland Counties 1972-74, Southern 1984-95, 2001-2005, 2009-11, Conference 1995-2001, 05-06, 13-16. Northern Premier 2006-09, 11-13.

Club Colours (change): White/black/black with white hoops (Red/red//red with white hoops)

RECORDS

Victory: 12-1 v Redditch United - Birmingham Combination 1952-53
Defeat: 0-15 v Burton - Birmingham Combination 1952-53
Goalscorer: Joe O'Connor - 220 in 430 games
Appearances: Kevin Foster - 470
Additional: Paid £12,000 to Macclesfield Town for Steve Burr
Received £40,000 from Blackpool for Kevin Russell

HONOURS

FA Comps: FA Trophy 2003-04.

League: Birmingham Combination 1909-10, 50-51. West Midlands (Reg) 1940-41, 77-78.
Southern League Premier Division 1994-95.

County FA: Staffordshire Senior Cup 1897-98, 1969-70, 73-74, 2012-13.
Birmingham Senior Cup 1935-36, 2008-09, 12-13.

BEST PERFORMANCES	**FA Cup:** Fourth Round Proper 1996-97. **Welsh Cup:** Final 1991-92.
	FA Trophy: Final 2003-04.
	FA Vase: N/A

HEDNESFORD TOWN MATCH RESULTS 2016-17

Date	Comp	H/A	Opponents	Att:	Result	Goalscorers	Pos	No.
Aug 13	NPL	H	Spennymoor Town	459	W 3 - 1	Sammons 61 Dunkley 79 Singh 87	3	1
15	NPL	A	Stourbridge	772	W 2 - 1	Dunkley 33 Carline 90	1	2
20	NPL	A	Ashton United	174	L 0 - 2		8	3
22	NPL	H	Marine	424	D 1 - 1	Thorley 73	3	4
27	NPL	H	Whitby Town	387	D 1 - 1	Logan 82	6	5
29	NPL	A	Halesowen Town	567	W 3 - 1	Carline 8 Sammons 74 Glover 76	6	6
Sept 3	FAC1Q	H	Belper Town	391	L 1 - 2	Bramall 77		7
10	NPL	H	Frickley Athletic	401	W 4 - 0	Glover 25 (pen) 34 (pen) Carline 57 Singh 90	4	8
17	NPL	H	Ashton United	378	D 2 - 2	Singh 56 67	4	9
24	NPL	A	Nantwich Town	249	D 1 - 1	Singh 47		10
26	NPL	H	Mickleover Sports	356	W 1 - 0	Glover 59	3	11
Oct 1	NPL	H	Buxton	409	L 1 - 2	Carline 4	6	12
4	NPL	A	Sutton Coldfield Town	284	W 5 - 0	Mayo 18 Glover 19 43 (pen) Carline 52 Singh 74 (pen)	4	13
8	NPL	A	Rushall Olympic	804	L 1 - 2	Carline 19	5	14
10	NPL	H	Corby Town	324	W 3 - 0	Sammons 20 Carline 71 Mutton 78	5	15
15	NPL	H	Blyth Spartans	465	L 1 - 2	Singh 78	6	16
18	NPL	A	Barwell	237	L 0 - 2		6	17
22	NPL	A	Skelmersdale United	212	W 3 - 1	Mayo 9 Sammons 53 Logan 90	5	18
29	FAT1Q	A	Stamford	345	W 4 - 1	Glover 21 53 Carline 68 Singh 71		19
31	NPL	H	Sutton Coldfield Town	362	W 4 - 1	Mayo 43 Matthews 47 56 Carline 60	3	20
Nov 5	NPL	H	Grantham Town	420	W 1 0	Carline 40	4	21
12	FAT2Q	H	Stafford Rangers	910	D 1 - 1	Maye 84		22
15	FAT2Qr	A	Stafford Rangers	1005	L 1 - 2	Dunckley 90 (aet)		23
19	NPL	A	Matlock Town	426	L 0 - 2		4	24
26	NPL	A	Coalville Town	340	L 1 - 2	Sammons 84 (pen)		25
Dec 3	NPL	A	Workington	366	W 2 - 0	Sheldon 2 McDermott 7	5	26
10	NPL	H	Warrington Town	351	W 1 - 0	Sammons 42 (pen)_	4	27
17	NPL	A	Grantham Town	223	L 1 - 4	Brenan 22	5	28
26	NPL	A	Stafford Rangers	1826	L 1 - 2	Glover 36	6	29
Jan 7	NPL	A	Spennymoor Town	519	L 2 - 4	Mukendi 53 90		30
21	NPL	H	Rushall Olympic	415	W 2 - 1	Mukendl 35 Weir-Daley 37	10	31
28	NPL	A	Corby Town	431	L 2 - 3	Mukendi 27 Thorley 48	11	32
Feb 4	NPL	H	Barwell	377	D 1 - 1	Thorley 31	12	33
11	NPL	A	Blyth Spartans	601	L 1 - 5	Mukendi 24	12	34
14	NPL	A	Buxton	231	L 0 2		12	35
18	NPL	H	Skelmersdale United	318	W 5 - 0	Washourne 6 McNaught 17 Brennan 43 Glover 59 McDermott 73	12	36
21	NPL	A	Ilkeston Town	257	W 2 - 0	Thorley 47 90	11	37
25	NPL	H	Nantwich Town	419	L 1 - 2	Glover 3	13	38
Mar 4	NPL	A	Frickley Athletic	286	W 1 - 0	Glover 87	11	39
11	NPL	H	Workington	358	L 0 - 2		13	40
18	NPL	A	Coalville Town	165	D 2 - 2	Clarke 68 Martin 90	13	41
25	NPL	A	Warrington Town	478	L 0 - 1		15	42
28	NPL	H	Ilkeston Town	275	W 3 1	Nadat 42 McNaught 45 Thorley 78	13	43
Apr 1	NPL	H	Matlock Town	235	W 1 - 0	Ballinger 54	11	44
4	NPL	H	Stourbridge	486	D 1 - 1	Glover 38	11	45
5	NPL	H	Halesowen Town	353	L 1 - 2	Clarke 41	12	46
8	NPL	H	Matlock Town	355	L 0 - 2		12	47
15	NPL	A	Marine	383	L 0 - 3		12	48
17	NPL	H	Stafford Rangers	772	L 0 - 2		14	49
22	NPL	A	Whitby Town	342	L 0 - 1		15	50

GOALSCORERS	SG	CSG	Pens	Hat tricks	Total		SG	CSG	Pens	Hat tricks	Total
2015-16 *Perry*					8	McDermott	2				2
Glover	10		2		13	McNaught	2				2
Carline	10	3			10	Ballinger	1				1
Singh	7		1		8	Bramall	1				1
Sammons	6		2		6	Martin	1				1
Mukendi	4				5	Mayo	1				1
Thorley	5				6	Mutton	1				1
Dunckley	3				3	Nadat	1				1
Mayo	3				3	Sheldon	1				1
Brennan	2				2	Washbourne	1				1
Clarke	2				2	Weir-Daley	1				1
Logan	2				2						
Matthews	1				2						

LANCASTER CITY

Club Contact Details
Giant Axe, West Road, Lancaster LA1 5PE
01524 382 238
secretary@lancastercityfc.com

Ground Capacity: 3,500 **Seats:** 513 **Covered:** 900 **Clubhouse:** Yes **Shop:** Yes

Record Attendance
7,506 v Carlisle United - FA Cup Fourth Qualifying Round, 17/11/1927
Previous Grounds
None

10 YEAR RECORD

07-08		08-09		09-10		10-11		11-12		12-13		13-14		14-15		15-16		16-17	
NP1N	11	NP1N	7	NP1N	2	NP1N	8	NP1N	6	NP1N	13	NP1N	6	NP1N	11	NP1N	6	NP1N	1
FAC	P	FAC	P	FAC	1Q	FAC	P	FAC	3Q	FAC	P	FAC	1Q	FAC	2Qr	FAC	2Q	FAC	3Q
FAT	1Qr	FAT	1Qr	FAT	2Qr	FAT	2Q	FAT	P	FAT	P	FAT	1Q	FAT	Pr	FAT	Pr	FAT	1Q

Club Factfile

Founded: 1911 **Nickname:** Dolly Blues **Manager:** Phil Brown

Previous Names: Lancaster Town 1911-37

Previous Leagues: Lancashire Combination 1911-70, Northern Premier League 1970-82, 87-2004, North West Counties 1982-87, Conference 2004-07

Club Colours (change): Blue & white hoops/blue/blue (Yellow with blue trim/blue/yellow)

RECORDS

Victory: 17-2 v Appleby, FA Cup, 1915.
Defeat: 0-10 v Matlock Town - Northern Premier League Division 1 1973-74
Goalscorer: David Barnes - 130, 1979-84, 88-91. Jordan Connerton scored 38 during the 2009-10 season.
Appearances: Edgar J Parkinson - 591, 1949-64.
Additional: Paid £6,000 to Droylsden for Jamie Tandy
Received £25,000 from Birmingham City for Chris Ward

HONOURS

FA Comps: None

League: Northern Premier Division One 1995-96, Division One North 2016-17.

County FA: Lancashire Junior Cup (ATS Challenge Trophy) 1927-28, 28-29, 30-31, 33-34, 51-52, 74-75.

| BEST PERFORMANCES | **FA Cup:** Second Round Proper 1972-73.
FA Trophy: Fourth Round 2004-05.
FA Vase: Second Round Proper 1986-87, 90-91. |
|---|---|

NATIONAL STRIKE FORCE 2016-2017
(Part Two - See pages 203 for P1 & 269 for P3)

			LGE	FAC	FAT	Pens	H-T	SG	CSG	Total
Nicke Kabamba	Hampton & Richmond	NS	16	3			1	14	3	19
Dan Bennett	Merstham	IsthP	17	1	1	2	1	15	2	19
Jevani Brown	St Neots Town	SP	19				3	12	4	19
Craig Westcarr	Alfreton Town	NN	13	3	2	4		15	3	18
Sean Reid	Blyth Spartans	NPLP	16	2			1	12	2	18
James Alabi	Chester	NL	17		1		4	15	2	18
Darren McQueen	Ebbsfleet United	NS	13	5			1	15	6	18
Danny Johnson	Gateshead	NL	18			2		16	6	18
Kaiman Anderson	Halesowen Town	NPLP	14	4		2		15	6	18
Jamal Lowe	Hampton & Richmond	NS	15	2	1			15	5	18
Adam Baskerville	Mickleover Sports	NPLP	12	1	3	3		18	2	18
Joe Ironside	Nuneaton Town	NN	15	1	2	3	1	15	3	18
Danny Mills	Whitehawk	NS	16		2		1	15	4	18
Niall Cummins	Curzon Ashton	NN	13	3	1	1		16	3	17
Andy Pugh	Dartford	NS	14	2	1			16	4	17
Gavin Tomlin	Dulwich Hamlet	IsthP	12	2	3			13	4	17
Billy Crook	Enfield Town	IsthP	16		1	5		17	3	17
George Thomson	FC Utd of Manchester	NN	15	2				15	2	17
Alfie Rutherford	Havant & Waterlooville	IsthP	15		2		1	14	5	17
Courtny Baker-Richardson	Leamington	SP	17					15	3	17
Jordan Nicholson	Nuneaton Town	NN	11		6		1	12	5	17
James Dobson	Slough Town	SP	11	4	2	2		15	2	17
Andrew Neal	Truro City	NS	15		2	1		12	4	17
Matt Tyman	Whitby Town	NPLP	13	3	1	8		14	4	17
Reece Beccles-Richards	Wingate & Finchley	IsthP	12	2	3		1	13	5	17
Sean Reid	Blyth Spartans	NPLP	14	2			1	12	2	16
Morgan Ferrier	Boreham Wood	NL	13	2	1	1		14	4	16
Dave Pearce	Chesham United	SP	13	1	2	2		13	2	16
Maguire-Drew	Dagenham & Redbridge	NL	15	1				15	2	16
Luke Ingram	Needham Market	IsthP	16				1	13	3	16
Glen Taylor	Spennymoor Town	NPLP	14	2			1	16	2	16
Ricky Johnson	Banbury United	SP	12	3		2		13	2	15
Shamir Mullins	Chelmsford City	NS	13	2				12	5	15
Nat Pinney	Eastbourne Borough	NS	12	3	1			12	3	15
Michael Mandron	Eastleigh	NL	10	4	1	5	1	12	5	15
Theo Lewis	Havant & Waterlooville	IsthP	13					13	2	15
Brett Donnelly	Hitchin Town	SP	12	3				13	2	15
Arthur Gnahoua	Kidderminster Harriers	NN	12	2	1			14	2	15
Matt Rhead	Lincoln City	NL	15			2		10	2	15
Alex Reid	Rushall Olympic	NPLP	14	1				13	6	15
Mike Phenix	Salford City	NN	15					15	5	15
James Hall	St Neots Town	SP	13		2	5	1	10	2	15
James Norwood	Tranmere Rovers	NL	15			1		13	3	15
Jon Parkin	York City	NL	13		2			12	3	15
Jordan Williams	Barrow	NL	12	1	1			13	2	14
Callum Ball	Barwell	NPLP	14			3		11	3	14
Robbie Dale	Blyth Spartans	NPLP	13		1			13	2	14
Blair Turgott	Bromley	NL	12	1	1	3		11	4	14
JP Pittman	Harrogate Town	NN	10	2	2	1		12	3	14
Gareth Heath	Leiston	IsthP	11	1	2			13	2	14
Chris Holroyd	Macclesfield Town	NL	13	1				10	2	14
Matt Newsham	Matlock Town	NPLP	10	4			1	11	2	14
John Sands	Needham Market	IsthP	13		1	2		14	6	14

MARINE

Club Contact Details

The Marine Travel Arena, College Road, Crosby, Liverpool L23 3AS

0151 924 1743

richard@marinefc.com

Ground Capacity: 3,185   Seats: 400   Covered: 1,400   Clubhouse: Yes   Shop: Yes

Record Attendance
4,000 v Nigeria - Friendly 1949
Previous Grounds
Waterloo Park 1894-1903

10 YEAR RECORD

	07-08	08-09	09-10	10-11	11-12	12-13	13-14	14-15	15-16	16-17
NP P	7	13	9	9	7	11	20	21	15	18
FAC	1Q	1Q	1Q	1Qr	1Q	4Q	1Q	3Q	3Q	2Qr
FAT	2Qr	2Q	1Q	2Q	3Q	1Q	2Q	2Q	3Q	1P

Club Factfile

Founded: 1894   **Nickname:** Mariners   **Manager:** Tommy Lawson

Previous Names: None

Previous Leagues: Liverpool Zingari, Liverpool County Combination, Lancashire Combination 1935-39, 46-69, Cheshire County 1969-79

Club Colours (change): White/black/black (Amber/black/amber & black hoops)

RECORDS

Victory: 14-0 v Sandhurst - FA Cup 1st Qualifying Round 01/10/1938

Defeat: 2-11 v Shrewsbury Town - FA Cup 1st Round 1995

Goalscorer: Paul Meachin - 200

Appearances: Peter Smith 952

Additional: Paid £6,000 to Southport for Jon Penman October 1985
Received £20,000 from Crewe Alexandra for Richard Norris 1996

HONOURS

FA Comps: None

League: I Zingari Division Two 1901-02, Division One 02-03, 03-04, 09-10, 19-20, 20-21, 22-23. Liverpool Combination Division One 1927-28, 30-31, 33-34, 34-35, 43-44. Cheshire County 1973-74, 75-76, 76-77. Northern Premier Premier Division 1993-94, 84-95.

County FA: Lancashire Amateur Cup 1921-22, 25-26, 30-31, Junior Cup /Trophy 78-79, 87-88, 90-91, 99-00. Liverpool Challenge Cup 42-43, 44-45, 71-72, Non-League Cup 1968-69, 75-76, 76-77, Senior Cup 78-79, 84-85, 87-88, 89-90, 93-94, 99-00, 07-08.

BEST PERFORMANCES	**FA Cup:** Third Round Proper 1992-93.
	FA Trophy: Semi-finals 1983-84, 91-92.
	FA Vase: N/A

MARINE MATCH RESULTS 2016-17

Date	Comp	H/A	Opponents	Att:	Result	Goalscorers	Pos	No.
Aug 13	NPL	A	Barwell	152	W 2 - 1	Mitchley 22 (pen) 85	7	1
16	NPL	H	Blyth Spartans	342	W 1 - 0	Mitchley 82	4	2
20	NPL	H	Rushall Olympic	282	D 1 - 1	Smart 47	2	3
22	NPL	A	Hednesford Town	424	D 1 - 1	Mwasile 48	1	4
27	NPL	A	Buxton	328	L 0 - 3		9	5
29	NPL	H	Warrington Town	432	D 1 - 1	Goulding 89	10	6
Sept 3	FAC1Q	A	Marske United	264	W 2 - 0	Mwasile 39 Davies 64		7
10	NPL	H	Coalville Town	304	W 4 - 2	Bellew 11 18 Mswasile 15 Lindfield 25	7	8
13	NPL	A	Blyth Spartans	522	L 0 - 1		7	9
17	FAC2Q	A	Nantwich Town	403	D 2 - 2	Sherlock 45 Threlfall 86		10
20	FAC2Qr	H	Nantwich Town	279	L 2 - 3	Mitchley 10 14		11
24	NPL	A	Frickley Athletic	271	L 0 - 2		12	12
27	NPL	H	Sutton Coldfield Town	293	W 1 - 0	Mitchley 43	11	13
Oct 1	NPL	A	Grantham Town	311	W 1 - 0	Sherlock 36 (pen)	9	14
8	NPL	H	Stourbridge	462	D 1 - 1	Sherlock 4 (pen)	10	15
11	NPL	A	Stafford Rangers	386	L 0 - 3		11	16
15	NPL	A	Whitby Town	293	L 1 - 2	Mwasile 84	12	17
18	NPL	H	Nantwich Town	260	L 1 - 3	Sherlock 29 (pen)	15	18
22	NPL	H	Matlock Town	293	L 0 - 1		17	19
29	FAT1Q	A	Ashton United	124	W 4 - 0	Smart 13 Mitchley 15 Sherlock 78 90		20
Nov 1	NPL	A	Ashton United	135	W 4 - 1	Hughes 6 Sherlock 29 Smart 42 Bellew 86	14	21
5	NPL	H	Ilkeston	346	D 2 - 2	Mitchley 27 Sherlock 35 (pen)	13	22
8	NPL	A	Workington	285	L 0 - 4		15	23
12	FAT2Q	H	St Neots Town	288	D 1 - 1	Mitchley 62		24
15	FAT2Qr	A	St Neots Town	178	W 4 - 2	Hughes 19 Threlfall 77 Monaghan 120 Mitchley 120 (aet)		25
19	NPL	A	Mickleover Sports	205	L 0 - 2		17	26
27	FAT3Q	A	Darlington 1883	743	D 2 - 2	Monaghan 29, Hughes 31		27
Dec 3	NPL	H	Halesowen Town	313	W 4 - 0	Sherlock 6 83 (pen) Mitchley 40 Monoghan 44	18	28
6	FAT3Qr	H	Darlington 1883	308	W 3 - 2	Anoruo 38 Mitchley 81 90 (pen)		29
10	FAT1	A	Stockport County	1411	L 2 - 3	Mitchley 7 (pen) Mitchell 45		30
17	NPL	A	Ilkeston	249	W 2 - 1	Sherlock 34 Bellew 68	17	31
26	NPL	H	Skelmersdale United	565	D 3 - 3	Monaghan 16 Mitchley 35 (pen) Bellew 67	17	32
Jan 7	NPL	H	Barwell	301	D 0 - 0		18	33
14	NPL	H	Spennymoor Town	466	D 1 - 1	Foley 4	18	34
21	NPL	A	Stourbridge	857	L 0 - 2		18	35
28	NPL	H	Stafford Rangers	460	W 1 - 0	Hamilton 5	18	36
31	NPL	A	Warrington Town	212	L 0 1		18	37
Feb 4	NPL	A	Nantwich Town	337	L 1 - 4	Thompson 52	18	38
11	NPL	H	Whitley Bay	292	L 1 - 4	Lindfield 67	19	39
18	NPL	A	Matlock Town	441	L 1 - 2	Hamilton 32	19	40
21	NPL	A	Spennymoor Town	472	L 1 - 2	Strickland 35	19	41
25	NPL	H	Frickley Athletic	338	D 3 - 3	Foley 75 Mahoney 80 Mitchley 83	19	42
28	NPL	A	Sutton Coldfield Town	112	L 2 - 3	Wylie 48 Strickland 52	19	43
Mar 4	NPL	A	Coalville Town	125	D 0 - 0		20	44
7	NPL	H	Workington	300	L 0 - 1		20	45
11	NPL	A	Ashton United	331	W 3 - 1	Strickland 33 Mitchley 44 68	18	46
18	NPL	H	Grantham Town	225	L 0 - 3		19	47
21	NPL	A	Corby Town	318	W 3 - 2	Mitchley 54 55 (pen) Fosu-Mensah 88	18	48
25	NPL	H	Corby Town	538	D 0 - 0		18	49
28	NPL	A	Halesowen Town	316	W 1 - 0	Fosu-Mensah 55	17	50
Apr 8	NPL	H	Mickleover Sports	289	L 1 - 3	Davies 57	19	51
11	NPL	A	Rushall Olympic	167	D 1 - 1	Mitchley 18	19	52
15	NPL	H	Hednesford Town	383	W 3 - 0	Mitchley 7 Wall 81 Hamilton 90	18	53
17	NPL	A	Skelmersdale United	403	W 3 - 0	Mitchley 3 64 Hamilton 37	17	54
22	NPL	H	Buxton	439	D 5 - 5	Hamilton 45 Menagh 49 Foley 51 Shacklock 74 Mitchley 9018		55

GOALSCORERS	SG	CSG	Pens	Hat tricks	Total		SG	CSG	Pens	Hat tricks	Total
2015-16 *Mitchley*					8	Lindfield	2				2
Mitchley	20	3	4		25	Thelfall	2				2
Sherlock	9	3	5		11	Anoruo	1				1
Bellew	4	2			5	Goulding	1				1
Hamilton	5				5	Mahoney	1				1
Monaghan	3				4	Menagh	1				1
Mwasile	3				4	Mitchell	1				1
Foley	3				3	Shacklock	1				1
Hughes	2				3	Thompson	1				1
Smart	3	2			3	Wall	1				1
Strickland	3				3	Wylie	1				1
Davies	2				2						
Fosu-Mensah	2				2						

MATLOCK TOWN

Club Contact Details
DCJ Group Insurance Arena, Causeway Lane, Matlock, Derbyshire DE4 3AR
01629 583 866
keith61brown@yahoo.co.uk

Ground Capacity: 2,257 **Seats:** 560 **Covered:** 1,200 **Clubhouse:** Yes **Shop:** Yes

Record Attendance
5,123 v Burton Albion - FA Trophy Semi-final, 1975
Previous Grounds
None

10 YEAR RECORD

07-08	08-09	09-10	10-11	11-12	12-13	13-14	14-15	15-16	16-17
NP P 16	NP P 15	NP P 7	NP P 11	NP P 14	NP P 17	NP P 12	NP P 14	NP P 17	NP P 9
FAC 3Q	FAC 1Q	FAC 2Qr	FAC 3Q	FAC 2Q	FAC 1Qr	FAC 2Q	FAC 2Q	FAC 1Qr	FAC 4Q
FAT 2Q	FAT 1Q	FAT 1P	FAT 2Qr	FAT 3Q	FAT 2P	FAT 3Q	FAT 1Q	FAT 1P	FAT 2P

Club Factfile

Founded: 1885 **Nickname:** The Gladiators   **Manager:** Craig Hopkins & Glen Kirkwood

Previous Names: None

Previous Leagues: Midland Combination 1894-96, Matlock and District, Derbyshire Senior, Central Alliance 1924-25, 47-61, Central Combination 1934-35, Chesterfield & District 1946-47, Midland Counties 1961-69

Club Colours (change): Blue/white/blue with white trim (Yellow with blue trim/yellow/yellow)

RECORDS
Victory: 10-0 v Lancaster City (A) - 1974
Defeat: 0-8 v Chorley (A) - 1971
Goalscorer: Peter Scott
Appearances: Mick Fenoughty
Additional: Paid £2,000 for Kenny Clark 1996
Received £10,000 from York City for Ian Helliwell

HONOURS
FA Comps: FA Trophy 1974-75. Anglo Italian Non-League Cup 1979.

League: Central Alliance North Division 1959-60, 60-61. Midland Counties 1961-62, 68-69.

County FA: Derbyshire Senior Cup 1974-75, 76-77, 77-78, 83-84, 84-85, 91-92, 2003-04, 09-10, 14-15, 16-17.

BEST PERFORMANCES	**FA Cup:** Third Round Proper 1976-77. **FA Trophy:** Final 1974-75. **FA Vase:** N/A

MATLOCK TOWN MATCH RESULTS 2016-17

Date	Comp	H/A	Opponents	Att:	Result	Goalscorers	Pos	No.
Aug 13	NPL	A	Corby Town	525	D 0 - 0		14	1
16	NPL	H	Skelmersdale United	244	D 1 - 1	Wilson 59	14	2
20	NPL	H	Nantwich Town	297	L 0 - 4		20	3
23	NPL	A	Sutton Coldfield Town	277	W 3 - 1	Newsham 66 Williams 70 Dinanga 77	13	4'
27	NPL	A	Warrington Town	161	L 3 - 5	Newsham 15 57 Dinanga 18	16	5
29	NPL	H	Ilkeston Town	419	D 0 - 0		17	6
Sept 3	FAC1Q	H	**Heanor Town**	421	W 4 - 2	**DeGirolamo 5 Newsham 15 52 Dinanga 24**		7
10	NPL	H	Stourbridge	278	W 3 - 1	DINANGA 3 (47 67 74 pen)	13	8
17	FAC2Q	A	**Kidsgrove Athletic**	257	W 2 - 1	**Cribley 73 Newsham 90 (pen)**		9
20	NPL	A	Coalville Town	134	W 4 - 1	Newsham 8 33 Williams 50 74	9	10
24	NPL	H	Mickleover Sorts	291	L 0 - 2		11	11
27	NPL	H	Frickley Athletic	250	W 1 - 0	Wiley 60	14	12
Oct 1	FAC3Q	H	**Workington**	489	D 1 - 1	**Newsham 43**		13
4	FAC3Qr	A	**Workington**	562	W 3 - 1	**Cribley 42 Wiley 53 Williams 82 (pen)**		14
8	NPL	A	Workington	435	W 3 - 1	Dinanga 20 Newsham 65 Cribley 90 (pen)	11	15
11	NPL	H	Blyth Spartans	281	D 0 - 0		9	16
15	FAC4Q	H	**Altrincham**	1071	L 1 - 3	**McManus 32**		17
18	NPL	A	Halesowen Town	353	W 3 - 0	Dinanga 49 69 Newsham 84	10	18
22	NPL	A	Marine	293	W 1 - 0	Williams 31	9	19
29	FAT1Q	A	**Spennymoor Town**	393	W 2 1	**McManus 12 Morrison 85**		20
Nov 1	NPL	H	Barwell	268	W 2 - 1	Dinanga 28 McManus 80	7	21
5	NPL	A	Whitby Town	306	L 0 - 1		8	22
7	NPL	H	Grantham Town	234	W 2 - 1	Williams 37 Cribley 82	7	23
12	FAT2Q	A	**Grantham Town**	250	W 2 - 0	**Williams 23 Dinanga 39**		24
19	NPL	H	Hednesford Town	426	W 2 - 0	Dinanga 7 McManus 65	6	25
22	NPL	A	Barwell	142	L 0 - 1		6	26
26	FAT3Q	H	**FC Halifax Town**	483	D 1 - 1	**Morrison 44**		27
29	FAT3Qr	A	**FC Halifax Town**	479	W 3 - 2	**Dinanga 22 34 Cribley 72**		28
Dec 3	NPL	A	Stafford Rangers	563	L 0 - 2		8	29
10	FAT1	A	**Solihull Moors**	336	W 2 - 1	**DeGirolamo 19 Dinanga 60**		30
17	NPL	H	Whitby Town	395	W 2 - 1	Pursehouse 76 Dinanga 89	8	31
26	NPL	H	Buxton	1051	W 3 - 1	DeGirolamo 27 Pursehouse 29 McManus 76	7	32
Jan 2	NPL	A	Ilkeston	474	W 1 - 0	Dinanga 64	5	33
7	NPL	H	Corby Town	542	L 1 - 2	Pursehouse 89	6	34
14	FAT2	A	**Barrow**	978	L 2 - 3	**Dinanga 48 (pen) 56**		35
21	NPL	H	Workington	400	L 1 - 2	Cribley 8	11	36
28	NPL	A	Blyth Spartans	682	L 1 - 4	Newsham 49	12	37
Feb 4	NPL	H	Halesowen Town	382	W 2 - 1	Williams 37 DeGirolamo 90	11	38
11	NPL	A	Rushalll Olympic	204	W 3 - 2	Yates 44 Cribley 70 Dinanga 89	10	39
14	NPL	A	Grantham Town	309	D 0 - 0		10	40
18	NPL	H	Matrine	441	W 2 - 1	Dinanga 28 Morrison 85		41
21	NPL	A	Skelmersdale United	191	W 2 - 0	Dinanga 54 Ennis 60	8	42
25	NPL	H	Mickleover Sports	524	D 2 - 2	Dinanga 45 (pen) Williams 64	5	43
28	NPL	A	Frickley Town	235	L 0 - 1		5	44
Mar 4	NPL	A	Stourbridge	819	L 3 - 5	Newsham 7 Dinanga 22 37 (pen)	7	45
7	NPL	H	Coalville Town	293	D 0 - 0		7	46
11	NPL	H	Stafford Rangers	485	W 3 - 0	Williams 1 Sharpe 7 Wiley 20	6	47
18	NPL	A	Ashton United	201	L 0 - 1		10	48
21	NPL	H	Spennymoor Town	503	L 2 - 3	Taylor 53 McManus 65	10	49
25	NPL	A	Ashton United	453	W 3 - 0	Williams 51 Dinanga 71 Yates 77	9	50
28	NPL	A	Nantwich Town	315	D 0 - 0		8	51
Apr 1	NPL	A	Rushall Olympic	383	W 2 - 1	McManus 65 Wiley 86	8	52
4	NPL	H	Spennymoor Town	331	L 0 - 4		8	53
8	NPL	A	Nantwich Town	353	W 2 - 0	McManus 62 Dinanga 88	7	54
15	NPL	H	Sutton Coldfield Town	305	W 3 - 2	Dinanga 10 Wiley 45 Newsham 69	9	55
17	NPL	A	Buxton	547	L 1 - 2	Dinanga 58	9	56
22	NPL	H	Warrington Town	392	D 1 - 1	Wiley 65	9	57

GOALSCORERS	SG	CSG	Pens	Hat tricks	Total		SG	CSG	Pens	Hat tricks	Total
2015-16 *Purkiss*					8	Yates	2				2
Dinanga	23	3	4	1	29	Ennis	1				1
Newsham	11	2	1		14	Sharpe	1				1
Williams	10	2	1		11	Taylor	1				1
Cribley	7	2	1		7	Wilson	1				1
McManus	8	2			8						
Wiley	6				6						
DeGirolamo	4				4						
Morrison	3				3						
Pursehouse	3				3						

MICKLEOVER SPORTS

Club Contact Details
Don Arnott Arena, Mickleover Sports Club, Station Rd, Mickleover Derby DE3 9JG
01332 512 826
tonyshawmickleoversports@gmail.com

Ground Capacity: 1,500   **Seats:** 280   **Covered:** 500   **Clubhouse:** Yes   **Shop:** Yes

Record Attendance
1,074 v FC United of Manchester, Northern Premier League Premier Division, 02/10/10.
Previous Grounds
None

10 YEAR RECORD

07-08		08-09		09-10		10-11		11-12		12-13		13-14		14-15		15-16		16-17	
NCEP	14	NCEP	1	NP1S	1	NP P	15	NP P	21	NP1S	21	NP1S	5	NP1S	1	NP P	20	NP P	16
FAC	F	FAC	F	FAC	F	FAC	F	FAC	F	FAC	F	FAC	2Qr	FAC	3Q	FAC	1Q	FAC	2Q
				FAT	P	FAT	2Q	FAT	QF	FAT	P	FAT	2Q	FAT	3Q	FAT	1Q	FAT	3Qr

Club Factfile

Founded: 1948   **Nickname:** Sports   **Manager:** John McGrath

Previous Names: Mickleover Old Boys 1948-93

Previous Leagues: Derby & District Senior 1948-93. Central Midlands 1993-99, Northern Counties East 1999-2009

Club Colours (change): Red and black stripes/black/red (All blue)

RECORDS
Misc: Won 16 consecutive League matches in 2009-10 - a Northern Premier League record

HONOURS

FA Comps: None

League: Central Midlands Supreme Division 1998-99. Northern Counties East Division One 2002-03, Premier Division 2008-09. Northern Premier League Division One South 2009-10, 14-15.

County FA: None

BEST PERFORMANCES	**FA Cup:** Third Qualifying Round 2010-11, 14-15.
	FA Trophy: Third Qualifying Round 2014-15, 16-17(r).
	FA Vase: Fourth Round Proper 2000-01.

MICKLEOVER SPORTS MATCH RESULTS 2016-17

Date	Comp	H/A	Opponents	Att:	Result	Goalscorers	Pos	No.
Aug 13	NPL	A	Nantwich Town	258	W 3 - 1	Baskerville 31 Broadhead 70 Dales 87	4	1
16	NPL	H	Rushall Olympic	189	L 0 - 2		9	2
20	NPL	H	Skelmersdale United	147	W 3 - 1	Litchfield 18 73 Baskerville 44	5	3
23	NPL	A	Barwell	159	L 1 - 2	Litchfield 45 (pen)	11	4
27	NPL	A	Frickley Athletic	184	W 4 - 0	Baskerville 34 Dales 36 37 Norcross 84	5	5
29	NPL	H	Buxton	361	L 0 - 3		8	6
Sept 3	FAC1Q	H	Spalding United	172	W 3 - 2	Baskerville 40 Bennett 60 Stainfield 81		7
10	NPL	A	Whitby Town	219	D 1 - 1	Baskerville 56 (pen)	10	8
17	FAC2Q	H	Stourbridge	258	L 1 - 2	Morrison 52		9
20	NPL	H	Warrington Town	105	W 1 - 0	Dales 55	7	10
24	NPL	H	Matlock Town	291	W 2 - 0	Marsden 14 (og) Dales 44	7	11
26	NPL	A	Hednesford Town	356	L 0 - 1		7	12
Oct 1	NPL	A	Skelmersdale United	187	W 3 - 1	Baskerville 45 (pen) Litchfield 51 53 (pen)	7	13
4	NPL	A	Coalville Town	147	L 2 - 3	Baskerville 45 (pen) Litchfield 86 (pen)	11	14
8	NPL	A	Blyth Spartans	501	L 0 - 3		9	15
11	NPL	H	Halesowen Town	168	L 0 - 1		10	16
15	NPL	H	Corby Town	184	W 2 - 0	McGrath 17 Baskerville 52	9	17
18	NPL	A	Sutton Coldfield Town	130	W 1 - 0	Baskerville 50	7	18
22	NPL	A	Grantham Town	213	L 0 - 1		10	19
29	FAT1Q	A	Leamington	352	W 1 - 0	Thomas 20		20
Nov 1	NPL	H	Coalville Town	183	L 1 - 2	Thomas 72		21
5	NPL	A	Ashton United	144	L 2 - 3	Thomas 22 65	11	22
12	FAT2Q	A	Trafford	206	W 1 - 0	Baskerville 6		23
19	NPL	H	Marine	205	W 2 - 1	Thomas 13 18	13	24
26	FAT3Q	H	Brackley Town	150	D 1 - 1	Baskerville 90		25
29	FAT3Qr	A	Brackley Town	140	L 1 - 3	Baskerville 90		26
10	NPL	A	Spennymoor Town	478	L 0 - 3		16	27
17	NPL	H	Ashton United	201	W 4 - 1	HALL 3 (39 40 67) Baskerville 83	16	28
20	NPL	A	Rushall Olympic	282	W 2 - 1	Hall 13 (pen) MIlls 43	13	29
26	NPL	H	Ilkeston	509	W 7 - 0	HALL 5 (6 23 26 45 47) Baskerville 16 Bennett 54	12	30
Jan 2	NPL	A	Buxton	364	L 0 - 1		13	31
7	NPL	H	Nantwich Town	242	L 0 - 1		14	32
14	NPL	A	Workington	448	L 1 - 4	Bergin 20	14	33
17	NPL	H	Stourbridge	202	L 0 - 4		15	34
21	NPL	H	Blyth Spartans	239	L 1 - 7	Lansdowne 26	16	35
28	NPL	A	Halesowen Town	379	L 2 - 3	Blake 59 90	17	36
Feb 4	NPL	H	Workington	209	W 4 - 0	BLAKE 3 (48 76 85) Dales 52	15	37
11	NPL	A	Corby Town	408	L 0 - 1		16	38
18	NPL	H	Grantham Town	311	W 2 - 1	Mills 20 Morrison 45	16	39
25	NPL	A	Matlock Town	524	D 2 - 2	Morrison 32 Blake 61	16	40
Mar 7	NPL	A	Warrington Town	160	L 0 - 1		16	41
11	NPL	A	Stourbridge	753	D 0 - 0		16	42
18	NPL	H	Spennymoor Town	146	L 0 - 5		16	43
21	NPL	H	Stafford Rangers	367	L 0 - 1		16	44
25	NPL	H	Stafford Rangers	336	L 1 3	Blake 6	17	45
Apr 1	NPL	H	Hednesford Town	235	L 0 - 1		19	46
4	NPL	H	Sutton Coldfield Town	145	W 3 - 1	Hall 9 Belgrave 3 Blake 83	17	47
8	NPL	A	Marine	289	W 3 - 1	Belgrave 65 Blake 86 (pen) Baskerville 87	17	48
11	NPL	H	Whitby Town	185	L 0 - 1		17	49
15	NPL	H	Barwell	201	W 4 - 1	Abalimba 16 Baskerville 20 44 Hall 41	16	50
17	NPL	A	Ilkeston	251	W 1 - 0	Thornberry 25 (og)	16	51
22	NPL	H	Frickley Athletic	218	W 3 - 0	Mills 57 Dales 59 Baskerville 88	16	52

GOALSCORERS	SG	CSG	Pens	Hat tricks	Total		SG	CSG	Pens	Hat tricks	Total
2015-16 Dales					8	Bennett	2				2
Baskerville	18	2	3		18	Opponents	2				2
Hall	5	3	1	2	11	Abalimba	1				1
Blake	6		1	1	10	Bergin	1				1
Dales	5	2			6	Broadhead	1				1
Litchfield	3	2	3		6	Lansdowne	1				1
Thomas	4	3			6	McGrath	1				1
Mills	3				3	Norcross	1				1
Morrison	3				3	Stainfield	1				1
Belgrave	2				2						

NANTWICH TOWN

Club Contact Details
Weaver Stadium, Waterlode, Kingsley Fields, Nantwich, CW5 5BS
01270 621 771
secretary@nantwichtownfc.com

Ground Capacity: 3,500 **Seats:** 350 **Covered:** 495 **Clubhouse:** Yes **Shop:** Yes

Record Attendance
5,121 v Winsford United - Cheshire Senior Cup 2nd Round 1920-21
Previous Grounds
London Road/Jackson Avenue (1884-2007)

10 YEAR RECORD

07-08		08-09		09-10		10-11		11-12		12-13		13-14		14-15		15-16		16-17	
NP1S	3	NP P	3	NP P	10	NP P	17	NP P	10	NP P	14	NP P	19	NP P	15	NP P	8	NP P	5
FAC	2Qr	FAC	4Q	FAC	1Q	FAC	2Q	FAC	1P	FAC	1Q	FAC	1Q	FAC	1Q	FAC	1Q	FAC	4Q
FAT	1Qr	FAT	1P	FAT	1P	FAT	1P	FAT	1Q	FAT	2Qr	FAT	3Q	FAT	2Q	FAT	SF	FAT	1P

Club Factfile

Founded: 1884 **Nickname:** The Dabbers **Manager:** Phil Parkinson - 04/02/15

Previous Names: Nantwich

Previous Leagues: Shropshire & Dist. 1891-92, Combination 1892-94, 1901-10, Cheshire Junior 1894-95, Crewe & Dist. 1895-97, North Staffs & Dist. 1897-1900, Cheshire 1900-01, Manchester 1910-12, 65-68, Lancs. Com. 1912-14, Cheshire Co. 1919-38, 68-82, Crewe & Dist. 1938-39, 47-48, Crewe Am. Comb. 1946-47, Mid-Cheshire 1948-65, North West Co. 1982-2007

Club Colours (change): All green (Yellow/dark navy blue/yellow)

RECORDS
Victory: 20-0 v Whitchurch Alexandra (home) 1900/01 Cheshire League Division 1, 5 April 1901

Defeat: 2-16 v Stalybridge Celtic (away) 1932/33 Cheshire County League, 22 Oct 1932

Goalscorer: John Scarlett 161 goals (1992/3 to 2005/6).

Additional: Bobby Jones scored 60 goals during season 1946-47, Gerry Duffy scored 42 during season 1961-62
Received £20,000 from Crewe Alexandra for Kelvin Mellor - Feb 2008

HONOURS
FA Comps: FA Vase 2005-06.

League: Mid-Cheshire 1963-64. Cheshire County 1980-81.

County FA: Crew Amateur Combination 1946-47. Cheshire Amateur Cup 1895-96, 1963-64.
Cheshire Senior Cup 1932-33, 75-76, 2007-08, 11-12.

BEST PERFORMANCES	**FA Cup:** First Round Proper 2011-12.
	FA Trophy: Semi-finals 2015-16.
	FA Vase: Final 2005-06.

NANTWICH TOWN MATCH RESULTS 2016-17

Date	Comp	H/A	Opponents	Att:	Result	Goalscorers	Pos	No.
Aug 13	NPL	H	Mickleover Sports	258	L 1 - 3	Stair 33	21	1
16	NPL	A	Ashton United	160	D 1 - 1	Jones 57	20	2
20	NPL	A	Matlock Town	297	W 4 - 0	Cooke 21 Jones 42 54 Gordon 79	9	3
23	NPL	H	Halesowen Town	265	L 1 - 2	Cooke 65 (pen)	14	4
27	NPL	H	Stourbridge	289	L 2 - 3	Stair 41 Harrison 44	17	5
29	NPL	A	Stafford Rangers	702	D 3 - 3	Brooke 1 Cooke 85 Stair 90	18	6
Sept 3	FAC1Q	A	Ashton United	213	W 3 - 0	White 15 Abadaki 78 Gordon 82		7
10	NPL	A	Grantham Town	170	W 4 - 0	COOKE 3 (4 38 44) Stair 90	14	8
17	FAC2Q	H	Marine	403	D 2 - 2	Abadaki 20 Jones 90		9
20	FAC2Qr	A	Marine	279	W 3 - 2	Goulding 5 (og) Cooke 41 Stair 62		10
24	NPL	H	Hednesford Town	249	D 1 - 1	Bell 5	16	11
27	NPL	A	Warrington Town	303	W 3 - 2	Cooke 83 90 Jones 88	14	12
Oct 1	FAC3Q	A	Halesowen Town	532	D 1 - 1	Hancock 78		13
4	FAC3Qr	H	Halesowen Town	362	W 2 - 1	Cooke 39 Hall 45		14
8	NPL	A	Barwell	153	D 1 - 1	Hancock 90 (pen)	16	15
11	NPL	H	Rushall Olympic	221	W 1 - 0	Brooke 66	14	16
15	FAC4Q	H	Stourbridge	755	L 1 - 3	Hancock 39 (pen)		17
18	NPL	A	Marine	353	W 3 - 1	HANCOCK 3 (21 pen 54 69)	12	18
22	NPL	A	Corby Town	478	W 2 - 0	Abadaki 9 Walker 70	11	19
29	FAT1Q	A	Warrington Town	274	W 2 - 0	Abadaki 35 Jones 64		20
Nov 1	NPL	H	Buxton	255	W 1 - 0	Brooke 73	10	21
5	NPL	A	Frickley Town	243	W 4 - 1	Brooke 40 45 Cooke 72 Sanders 90	7	22
12	FAT2Q	H	Kendal Town	281	W 2 - 0	Hancock 81 Grundy 83 (og)		23
19	NPL	H	Spennymoor United	300	W 1 - 0	Cooke 35	8	24
22	NPL	A	Buxton	268	L 1 - 4	Brooke 7	9	25
26	FAT3Q	A	Shaw Lane AFC	215	L 1 - 3	Cooke 50 Shaw Lane AFC removed from competition		26
Dec 3	NPL	A	Coalville Town	168	L 1 - 3	Mwasile 18	12	27
10	NPL	A	Whitby Town	261	W 3 - 1	ABADAKI 3 (56 61 80)	9	28
13	NPL	H	Skelmersdale United	229	W 4 - 0	Bell 10 90 Mwasile 27 White 80	7	29
20	FAT1	H	Lincoln City	482	L 1 - 2	Walker 90		30
26	NPL	A	Workington	461	L 1 - 3	Brooke 74	11	31
Jan 2	NPL	H	Stafford Rangers	780	L 0 - 1		12	32
7	NPL	A	Mickleover Sports	242	W 1 - 0	Hall 79	9	33
14	NPL	A	Blyth Spartans	545	L 0 - 2		10	34
17	NPL	H	Sutton Coldfield Town	225	W 1 0	Harrison 31	8	35
21	NPL	H	Barwell	265	D 2 - 2	White 45 Bell 85	9	36
28	NPL	A	Rushall Olympic	256	W 3 - 1	Cooke 50 79 Bell 90	9	37
Feb 4	NPL	H	Marine	337	W 4 - 1	Jones 1 Cooke 3 (19 30 74)	7	38
7	NPL	A	Stafford Rangers	305	W 3 - 2	Jones 39 Peers 43 Mwasile 45	3	39
11	NPL	A	Sutton Coldfield Town	208	D 1 - 1	Stair 8	4	40
18	NPL	H	Corby Town	360	D 1 - 1	Bell 43	5	41
25	NPL	A	Hednesford Town	419	W 2 - 1	Peers 14 Haynes 55 (og)	3	42
28	NPL	A	Warrington Town	248	W 4 - 1	Bell 6 28 White 29 Brooke 90 (pen)	3	43
Mar 4	NPL	H	Grantham Town	465	D 1 - 1	Johnston 28	3	44
7	NPL	A	Skelmersdale United	213	W 3 - 2	Brooke 27 Jones 48 Cooke 74 (pen)	2	45
11	NPL	H	Coalville Town	374	W 3 - 0	Johnston 32 Cooke 41 Peers 51	2	46
18	NPL	A	Ilkeston	229	W 3 - 2	Bell 8 Peers 22 Hall 33	2	47
21	NPL	H	Blyth Sparrtans	531	D 2 - 2	Hancock 38 Johnston 48	2	48
25	NPL	H	Whitby Town	481	L 0 - 2		2	49
28	NPL	H	Matlock Town	315	D 0 - 0		2	50
Apr 1	NPL	A	Spennymoor Town	602	D 1 - 1	Jones 64	2	51
8	NPL	H	Ashton United	301	W 3 - 1	Mwasile 17 Smalley 38 (og) Jones 89	2	52
15	NPL	A	Ilkeston	402	W 3 0	Jones 41 Brooke 51 (pen) Abadaki 58	3	53
17	NPL	H	Workington	512	L 0 - 1		4	54
20	NPL	A	Halesowen Town	365	D 0 - 0			55
22	NPL	A	Stourbridge	1312	L 2 - 4	Mukendi 18 Hancocck 55	5	56
25	PO SF	A	Spennymoor Town	882	L 0 - 2			57

GOALSCORERS	SG	CSG	Pens	Hat tricks	Total		SG	CSG	Pens	Hat tricks	Total
2015-16 *Shotton*					8	Peers	4				4
Cooke	17	2	2	1	20	White	3				4
Jones	10				12	Hall	3				3
Brooke	8	2	2		10	Johnston	3				3
Bell	5				9	Gordon	2				2
Abadaki	6	2		1	8	Harrison	2				2
Hancock	6	2	3	1	8	Walker	2				2
Stair	5	2			6	Sanders	1				1
Mwasile	4				4						
Opponents	4				4						

RUSHALL OLYMPIC

Club Contact Details
Dales Lane off Daw End Lane, Rushall, Nr Walsall WS4 1LJ
01922 641 021
rushallolympic@yahoo.co.uk

Ground Capacity: 1,400 **Seats:** 200 **Covered:** 200 **Clubhouse:** Yes **Shop:** Yes

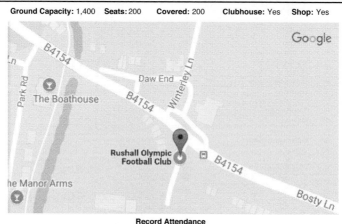

Record Attendance
2,000 v Leeds United Ex players
Previous Grounds
Rowley Place 1951-75, Aston University 1976-79

10 YEAR RECORD

07-08		08-09		09-10		10-11		11-12		12-13		13-14		14-15		15-16		16-17	
SthM	5	NP1S	5	NP1S	12	NP1S	3	NP P	8	NP P	6	NP P	7	NP P	9	NP P	10	NP P	12
FAC	4Q	FAC	P	FAC	1Q	FAC	Pr	FAC	4Q	FAC	1Q	FAC	4Q	FAC	2Q	FAC	3Q	FAC	2Q
FAT	3Qr	FAT	1Qr	FAT	1Q	FAT	2Q	FAT	1Q	FAT	1P	FAT	2Q	FAT	3Qr	FAT	2Qr	FAT	1Q

Club Factfile

Founded: 1951   **Nickname:** The Pics   **Manager:** Wayne Thomas

Previous Names: None

Previous Leagues: Walsall Amateur 1952-55, Staffordshire County (South) 1956-78, West Midlands 1978-94, Midland Alliance 1994-2005, Southern 2005-08

Club Colours (change): Gold and black/black/black (Red with white trim/red/red)

RECORDS
Goalscorer: Graham Wiggin
Appearances: Alan Dawson - 400+

HONOURS
FA Comps: None

League: West Midlands (Reg) Division One 1979-80. Midland Alliance 2004-05.

County FA: Staffordshire Senior Cup 2015-16. Walsall Senior Cup 2015-16.

BEST PERFORMANCES	**FA Cup:** Fourth Qualifying Round 2007-08, 11-12, 13-14.
	FA Trophy: First Round Proper 2012-13.
	FA Vase: Fifth Round Proper 2000-01.

RUSHALL OLYMPIC MATCH RESULTS 2016-17

Date	Comp	H/A	Opponents	Att:	Result	Goalscorers	Pos	No.
Aug 13	NPL	H	Workington	248	L 1 - 2	Reid 77	18	1
16	NPL	A	Mickleover Sports	189	W 2 - 0	Reid 43 75	8	2
20	NPL	A	Marine	282	D 1 - 1	Walters 51	10	3
23	NPL	H	Grantham Town	202	W 3 - 1	Martin 40 64 Reid 58	5	4
27	NPL	H	Halesowen Town	227	W 1 - 0	Forde 34	4	5
29	NPL	A	Coalville Town	198	D 3 - 3	Reid 64 83 Keates 80	5	6
Sept 3	FAC1Q	H	Soham Town Rangers	161	D 2 - 2	Fitzpatrick 52 Mugisha 89		7
6	FAC1Qr	A	Soham Town Rangers	169	W 1 - 0	McKenzie 6		8
10	NPL	H	Spennymoor Town	189	L 1 - 5	Eze 17	8	9
17	FAC2Q	H	Kettering Town	241	L 1 - 2	Reid 58		10
24	NPL	A	Ashton United	143	W 2 - 1	Kettle 27 Reid 35	9	11
27	NPL	H	Barwell	166	W 3 1	Reid 9 Whittall 31 Mugisha 63	6	12
Oct 1	NPL	A	Stafford Rangers	492	W 2 - 0	Diop 7 Reid 45	4	13
4	NPL	H	Ilkeston	189	W 1 - 0	Reid 19	3	14
8	NPL	H	Hednesford Town	804	W 2 - 1	Reid 48 Mugisha 87	2	15
11	NPL	A	Nantwich Town	221	L 0 - 1		2	16
15	NPL	A	Matlock Town	196	W 4 - 0	Luckie 1 Reid 42 Forde 45 (pen) Martin 64	2	17
18	NPL	H	Warrington Town	220	D 2 - 2	Reid 9 Fitzpatrick 43	4	18
22	NPL	H	Frickley Athletic	264	L 0 - 1		4	19
29	FAT1Q	H	Halesowen Town	189	L 1 - 2	Hull 49		20
Nov 1	NPL	A	Ilkeston	283	W 2 - 0	Diop 77 Cooper 90	3	21
5	NPL	H	Skelmersdale United	217	W 1 - 0	Luckie 69	3	22
12	NPL	A	Warrington Town	294	L 0 - 2		3	23
19	NPL	A	Sutton Coldfield Town	269	W 3 - 0	Eze 2 Christophorou 42 Whittall 54	2	24
26	NPL	A	Buxton	313	L 0 - 3		3	25
Dec 3	NPL	H	Whitby Town	261	W 1 - 0	Mugisha 89	1	26
10	NPL	H	Corby	316	W 4 - 1	Reid 6 Hawley 29 (pen) Hull 55 Mugisha 84	1	27
17	NPL	A	Skelmersdale United	304	W 2 - 1	Luckie 34 Hull 90	1	28
20	NPL	H	Mickleover Sports	282	L 1 - 2	Hull 83	1	29
26	NPL	A	Stourbridge	1431	D 0 - 0		1	30
Jan 7	NPL	A	Workington	447	L 0 - 2		2	31
21	NPL	A	Hednesford Town	415	L 1 - 2	Forde 72	6	32
28	NPL	H	Nantwich Town	258	L 1 - 3	Forde 36	7	33
Feb 11	NPL	H	Matlock Town	204	L 2 - 3	Forde 37 (pen) Bottomer 66	9	34
18	NPL	A	Frickley Athletic	223	L 0 - 1		11	35
21	NPL	H	Stafford Rangers	242	W 1 - 0	Forde 4 (pen)	9	36
25	NPL	H	Nantwich Town	238	D 1 - 1	Singh 68	10	37
Mar 7	NPL	H	Corby Town	174	D 0 - 0		11	38
11	NPL	A	Whitby Town	308	D 1 - 1	Bannister 71	12	39
18	NPL	H	Buxton	212	W 1 - 0	Bowerman 4	12	40
21	NPL	H	Coalville Town	151	L 2 - 5	Singh 16 Forde 87	12	41
25	NPL	A	Blyth Spartans	769	L 1 - 2	Mugisha 90	12	42
28	NPL	A	Barwell	146	D 1 - 1	Towers 50	12	43
Apr 1	NPL	A	Matlock Town	383	L 1 - 2	Johnson 24	14	44
4	NPL	H	Blyth Spartans	268	L 0 - 1		14	45
8	NPL	A	Grantham Town	241	L 1 - 2	Freeman 47	15	46
11	NPL	H	Marine	167	D 1 - 1	Hull 79	13	47
15	NPL	H	Spennymoor Town	578	D 1 - 1	Probert 70	13	48
17	NPL	A	Stourbridge	536	L 0 - 2		15	49
22	NPL	A	Halesowen Town	467	W 2 - 1	Mugisha 15 Bannister 69	12	50

GOALSCORERS	SG	CSG	Pens	Hat tricks	Total		SG	CSG	Pens	Hat tricks	Total
2015-16 *Benbow*					8	Bottomer	1				1
Reid, Alex	13	6			15	Bowerman	1				1
Forde	7	3	3		7	Cooper	1				1
Mugisha	7	2			7	Christophorou	1				1
Hull	5	3			5	Freeman	1				1
Luckie	3				3	Hawley	1	1			1
Martin	3				3	Johnson	1				1
Bannister	2				2	Keates	1				1
Diop	2				2	Kettle	1				1
Eze	2				2	McKenzie	1				1
Fitzpatrick	2				2	Probert	1				1
Singh	2				2	Towers	1				1
Whittall	2				2	Walters	1				1

SHAW LANE AFC
Club Contact Details
Athersley Rec. FC, Sheerien Park, Ollerton Road, Athersley North, Barnsley, S71 3DP

01226 203 509

dave.exley50@hotmail.co.uk

Ground Capacity: 2,000   **Seats:** 150   **Covered:** Yes   **Clubhouse:** Yes   **Shop:**

Record Attendance
904 v Athersley Rec NECL Prem League
Previous Grounds
Shaw Lane Sports Club (pictured above) >2017.

10 YEAR RECORD

07-08	08-09	09-10	10-11	11-12	12-13	13-14	14-15	15-16	16-17
SHS1 7	SHS1 4	SHS1 8	SHS1 9	SHS1 2	SHSP 1	NCE1 2	NCEP 1	NP1S 2	NP1S 1
								FAC P	FAC P
							FAV QF	FAT 2Q	FAT 3Qr

Club Factfile

Founded: 1991   **Nickname:** The Ducks   **Manager:** Craig Elliot

Previous Names: Shaw Lane 1991-2004. Merged with Worsbrough Common to form Aquaforce Barnsley. 04-07. Merged with Barugh FC to form Shaw Lane Aquaforce.

Previous Leagues: Sheffield & Hallamshire County 2011-13. Northern Counties East 2013-15.

Club Colours (change): Blue & white stripes/black/black (Cherry/midnight blue/cherry)

RECORDS
Victory: 13-0 v Grimsby Borough 1/4/2013 NECL Div 1
Defeat: 3-6 v Athersley Rec Sheffield Senior Cup 2014/15

HONOURS
FA Comps: None

League: Sheffield & Hallamshire County Senior League 2012-13. Northern Counties East Premier Division 2014-15. Northern Premier Division One South 2016-17.

County FA: Sheffield & Hallamshire Senior Challenge Cup 2016-17.

BEST PERFORMANCES	**FA Cup:** Preliminary Round 2015-16.
	FA Trophy: Third Round Qualifying 2016-17.
	FA Vase: Quarter-finals 2014-15.

NATIONAL STRIKE FORCE 2016-2017
(Part Three - See page 203 for P1)

			LGE	FAC	FAT	Pens	H-T	SG	CSG	Total
Bernard Mensah	Aldershot Town	NL	11		2			12	2	13
Scott Rendell	Aldershot Town	NL	13				1	10	2	13
Matty Pattison	Blyth Spartans	NPLP	11		2	1		9	2	13
Nyren Clunis	Dulwich Hamlet	IsthP	10		3			12	3	13
Felipe Barcelos	Grantham Town	NPLP	10		3	2		12	6	13
Nathan Arnold	Lincoln City	NL	12		1			11		13
Reece Dobson	Needham Market	IsthP	12		1			11	2	13
Max Biamou	Sutton United	NL	10	3				10	2	13
Rory Deacon	Sutton United	NL	7	5	1	1		12	2	13
Cole Stockton	Tranmere Rovers	NL	8		5		2	8	2	13
Lee Hughes	Worcester City	NN	12	1		1		11	3	13
Scott Allison	Workington	NPLP	11	2				12	4	13
Ross Lafayette	Dover Athletic	NL	12			1		11	3	12
Ashley Carew	Dulwich Hamlet	IsthP	10		2	3		11	2	12
Ryan Rowe	Leamington	SP	12			2		9	3	12
Joe Francis	Leiston	IsthP	9	2	0			8	2	12
Charlie Moone	Slough Town	SP	8	2	2			10	3	12
Akwasi Asante	Solihull Moors	NL	11	1		3	2	7	3	12
Ricky Johnson	Banbury United	SP	8	3		2		11	2	11
Tony Burnett	Biggleswade Town	SP	11				1	6	3	11
Niall Cummins	Curzon Ashton	NN	7	3	1	1		11	3	11
Moses Emannuel	Dover Athletic	NL	11				1	7	3	11
Ross Lafayette	Dover Athletic	NL	11					11	3	11
Sam Jones	Gateshead	NL	8					8	3	11
Wes York	Gateshead	NL	10					10	2	11
Joe Francis	Leiston	IsthP	9	2				7	2	11
Kurt Sherlock	Marine	NPLP	8	1	2		5	10	2	11
Matt Newsham	Matlock Town	NPLP	7	4		1		8	2	11
Jamie Allen	Southport	NL	10		1	5		8	2	11
Junior Morais	St Albans City	NS	8	2	1	1		9	2	11
Sam Rooney	Wrexham	NL	11			4		9	3	11
Matt McClure	Aldershot Town	NL	9		1	2		10	2	10
Ollie Pearce	Bognor Regis Town	IsthP	9		1	3		10	3	10
Shaun Jeffers	Chelmsford City	NS	10			3		7	2	10
Steve Cawley	Concord Rangers	NS	9	1		1	1	6	2	10
George Thomson	FC United	NN	8	2				9	2	10
Matt Patterson	Havant & Waterlooville	IsthP	7	3			1	9	2	10
George Carline	Hednesford Town	NPLP	9		1			9	3	10
George Carline	Hednesford Town	NPLP	9		1			9	3	10
Lewis Toomey	Kings Langley	SP	6	3	1	2	1	7	3	10
Akwasi Asante	Solihull Moors	NN	9	1		1	2	6	3	10
Akwasi Asante	Solihull Moors	NN	9	1		1	2	6	3	10
James Hall	St Neots	SP	8		2	2	1	7	2	10
Brett Williams	Torquay United	NL	10					8	2	10
Niall Thompson	Truro City	NS	9		1	1	1	7	2	10
Danny Mills	Whitehawk	NS	9		1		1	7		10

STAFFORD RANGERS

Club Contact Details
Marston Road, Stafford ST16 3BX
01785 602 430
secretary@staffordrangersfc.co.uk

Ground Capacity: 4,000   **Seats:** 530   **Covered:** Yes   **Clubhouse:** Yes   **Shop:** Yes

Record Attendance
8,536 v Rotherham United - FA Cup 3rd Round 1975
Previous Grounds
None

10 YEAR RECORD

07-08		08-09		09-10		10-11		11-12		12-13		13-14		14-15		15-16		16-17	
Conf	23	Conf N	18	Conf N	16	Conf N	20	NP P	16	NP P	15	NP P	22	NP1S	6	NP1S	1	NP P	13
FAC	4Qr	FAC	2Q	FAC	2Qr	FAC	2Qr	FAC	2Q	FAC	2Q	FAC	2Q	FAC	1Qr	FAC	P	FAC	1Q
FAT	3Pr	FAT	3Q	FAT	3Q	FAT	3Q	FAT	2Q	FAT	1P	FAT	1Q	FAT	1Q	FAT	1Qr	FAV	3Q

Club Factfile

Founded: 1876   **Nickname:** Rangers   **Manager:** Neil Kitching

Previous Names: None

Previous Leagues: Shropshire 1891-93, Birmingham 1893-96, N. Staffs. 1896-1900, Cheshire 1900-01, Birmingham Combination 1900-12, 46-52, Cheshire County 1952-69, N.P.L. 1969-79, 83-85, Alliance 1979-83, Conf. 1985-95, 2005-11. Southern >2005.

Club Colours (change): Black & white stripes/black/black (All red)

RECORDS
Victory: 15-0 v Kidsgrove Athletic - Staffordshire Senior Cup 2003
Defeat: 0-12 v Burton Town - Birmingham League 1930
Goalscorer: M. Cullerton - 176.   Les Box scored seven against Dudley Town, FA Cup, 06/09/1958.
Appearances: Jim Sargent
Additional: Paid £13,000 to VS rugby for S. Butterworth
                  Received £100,000 from Crystal Palace for Stan Collymore

HONOURS
FA Comps: FA Trophy 1971-72.

League: Birmingham Combination 1912-13. Cheshire County 1968-69. Northern Premier 1971-72, 84-85, Division One South 2015-16. Southern Premeir Division 2002-03. Coference North 2005-06.

County FA: Staffordshire Senior Cup 1954-55, 56-57, 62-63, 71-72, 77-78, 86-87, 91-92, 2002-03, 04-05, 14-15.

BEST PERFORMANCES	**FA Cup:** Fourth Round Proper 1974-75.
	FA Trophy: Final 1971-72.
	FA Vase: N/A

STAFFORD RANGERS MATCH RESULTS 2016-17

Date	Comp	H/A	Opponents	Att:	Result	Goalscorers	Pos	No.
Aug 16	NPL	H	Barwell	620	D 1 - 1	1 Reid 35	15	1
20	NPL	H	Frickley Athletic	560	W 3 - 2	Jones 14 Bowerman 52 Pearson 80 (og)	11	2
24	NPL	A	Corby Town	494	D 0 - 0		13	3
27	NPL	A	Skelmersdale United	515	D 4 - 4	Bowerman 15 Perry 17 28 Cater 49	13	4
29	NPL	H	Nantwich Town	702	D 3 - 3	Perry 1 Bowerman 40 Sherratt 53	13	5
Sept 3	FAC1Q	H	Kidsgrove Rovers	659	L 1 - 2	Stevenson 66		6
10	NPL	H	Ashton United	577	L 1 - 3	Sherratt 5	16	7
17	NPL	A	Frickley Athletic	244	L 1 - 2	Bowerman 18	17	8
20	NPL	A	Sutton Coldfield Town	231	D 1 - 1	Perry 72	15	9
24	NPL	A	Spennymoor Town	531	L 0 - 1		18	10
27	NPL	H	Stourbridge	545	D 0 - 0		19	11
Oct 1	NPL	H	Rushall Olympic	492	L 0 - 2		19	12
8	NPL	A	Grantham Town	263	L 1 - 2	Townsend 40	22	13
11	NPL	H	Marine	386	W 3 - 0	Taylor 55 Geddes 70 Perry 79	20	14
15	NPL	H	Coalville Town	567	W 2 - 1	Hodge 47 Gordon 51	18	15
22	NPL	A	Workington	481	W 2 - 1	1.Reid 13 Bailey 20	18	16
29	FAT1Q	A	Corby Town	435	W 2 - 0	Hodge 69 Gordon 90		17
Nov 1	NPL	H	Halesowen Town	524	W 3 - 1	Taylor 25 Hodge 52 Tait 64	15	18
5	NPL	H	Warrington Town	653	D 2 - 2	Taylor 12 Bailey 16	14	19
12	FAT2Q	A	Hednesford Town	910	D 1 - 1	Geddes 15		20
15	FAT2Qr	H	Hednesford Town	1005	W 2 - 1	Gordon 81 L. Reid 116 (pen) (aet)		21
19	NPL	A	Blyth Spartans	589	D 2 - 2	1.Reid 13 Bailey 20	16	22
Dec 3	NPL	H	Matlock	563	W 2 - 0	Gordon 9 Batchelor 60	17	23
6	FAT3Q	A	Chorley	466	L 0 - 1			24
21	NPL	A	Barwell	309	L 1 - 2	Gordon 15 (pen)	18	25
26	NPL	H	Hednesford Town	1826	W 2 - 1	Perry 22 Morris 62	18	26
Jan 2	NPL	A	Nantwich Town	780	W 1 - 0	1.Reid 34	17	27
7	NPL	H	Ilkeston	763	W 2 - 1	Hannis 47 (og) Gordon 70	16	28
17	NPL	A	Buxton	312	W 3 - 1	Gordon 38 L. Reid 61 Perry 81	13	29
21	NPL	H	Grantham Town	710	L 0 - 1		15	30
28	NPL	A	Marine	460	L 0 - 1		16	31
Feb 4	NPL	H	Buxton	674	L 1 - 2	Batchelor 21	17	32
7	NPL	A	Halesowen Town	517	D 2 2	L.Reid 7 12 (pen)	16	33
11	NPL	A	Coalville Town	171	D 0 - 0		15	34
18	NPL	H	Workington	653	W 3 - 2	Perry 4 L.Reid 25 Gordon 46	15	35
21	NPL	A	Rushall Olympic	242	L 0 - 1		15	36
25	NPL	H	Spennymoor Town	566	D 3 - 3	Perry 15 46 Griffiths 52	15	37
27	NPL	H	Stourbridge	744	L 0 - 2		15	38
Mar 7	NPL	H	Sutton Coldfield Town	440	D 0 - 0		15	39
11	NPL	A	Matlock Town	485	L 0 - 3		15	40
14	NPL	A	Ilkeston	212	W 2 - 1	Perry 14 1.Reid 20	15	41
18	NPL	H	Whitby Town	506	D 0 - 0		15	42
21	NPL	A	Mickleover Sports	367	W 1 - 0	Bailey 35	16	43
25	NPL	A	Mickleover Sports	336	W 3 - 1	1.Reid 11 Morris 27 L.Reid 81	14	44
28	NPL	A	Whitby Town	304	D 2 - 2	Barton 17 Morris 88	15	45
Apr 1	NPL	H	Blyth Spartans	809	L 0 - 1		15	46
8	NPL	A	Warrington Town	315	W 2 - 1	Sherratt 26 Haseley 55	15	47
13	NPL	A	Ashton United	178	L 1 - 2	Lyttle 87	16	48
15	NPL	H	Corby Town	715	L 0 - 1		15	49
17	NPL	A	Hednesford Town	772	W 2 - 0	Sherratt 40 Reid 82	13	50
22	NPL	A	Skelmersdale United	302	D 1 - 1	L.Reid 78	13	51

GOALSCORERS	SG	CSG	Pens	Hat tricks	Total		SG	CSG	Pens	Hat tricks	Total
Perry	10	2			12	Geddes	2				2
Gordon	9		1		8	Opponents	2				2
I.Reid	7				7	Barton	1				1
L.Reid	6		2		7	Cater	1				1
Bailey	4				4	Giffiths	1				1
Bowerman	4	2			4	Haseley	1				1
Sherratt	4				4	Jones	1				1
Hodge	3	2			3	Lyttle	1				1
Morris	3				3	Stevenson	1				1
Taylor	2	2			3	Tait	1				1
Batchelor	2				2						

STALYBRIDGE CELTIC

Club Contact Details
Bower Fold, Mottram Road, Stalybridge, Cheshire SK15 2RT
0161 338 2828
secretary@stalybridgeceltic.co.uk

Ground Capacity: 6,500 **Seats:** 1,500 **Covered:** 2,400 **Clubhouse:** Yes **Shop:** Yes

Record Attendance
9,753 v West Bromwich Albion - FA Cup replay 1922-23
Previous Grounds
None

10 YEAR RECORD

07-08		08-09		09-10		10-11		11-12		12-13		13-14		14-15		15-16		16-17	
Conf N	2	Conf N	6	Conf N	9	Conf N	10	Conf N	6	Conf N	13	Conf N	19	Conf N	19	Nat N	12	Nat N	21
FAC	3Q	FAC	3Q	FAC	3Qr	FAC	4Q	FAC	2Q	FAC	4Q	FAC	2Q	FAC	2Q	FAC	1P	FAC	3Q
FAT	3Q	FAT	2P	FAT	2P	FAT	2P	FAT	2P	FAT	3Q	FAT	1P	FAT	3Qr	FAT	3Q	FAT	3Qr

Club Factfile

Founded: 1909 **Nickname:** Celtic **Manager:** Steve Burr

Previous Names: None

Previous Leagues: Lancs & Cheshire Am. 1909-11. Lancashire Comb 1911-12, Central 1912-14, 15-21, Southern 1914-15, Football Lge 1921-23, Cheshire Co. 1923-82, North West Co. 1982-87, N.P.L. 1987-92, 98-2001, 02-04, Conference 1992-98, 01-02, 04-17.

Club Colours (change): Royal blue/white/blue

RECORDS
Victory: 16-2 v Manchester NE - 01/05/1926 and v Nantwich - 22/10/1932
Defeat: 1-10 v Wellington Town - 09/03/1946
Goalscorer: Harry Dennison - 215
Appearances: Kevan Keelan - 395
Additional: Cecil Smith scored 77 goals during the 1931-32 season
Paid £15,000 to Kettering Town for Ian Arnold 1995. Received £16,000 from Southport for Lee Trundle.

HONOURS
FA Comps: None

League: Lancashire Combination Division Two 1911-12. Cheshire County 1979-80. North West Counties 1983-84, 86-87.
Northern Premier League Premier Division 1991-92, 2000-01.

County FA: Manchester Senior Cup 1922-23.
Cheshire Senior Cup 1952-53, 2000-01.

BEST PERFORMANCES	**FA Cup:** Second Round Proper 1993-94, 99-2000.
	FA Trophy: Quarter-finals 2001-02.
	FA Vase: N/A

STALYBRIDGE CELTIC MATCH RESULTS 2016-17

Date	Comp	H/A	Opponents	Att:	Result	Goalscorers	Pos	No.
Aug 6	Nat N	A	Boston United	1023	W 1 - 0	Owens 16	5	1
9	Nat N	H	Stockport County	1601	L 1 - 3	Ball 65	9	2
13	Nat N	H	Salford City	752	L 0 - 4		16	3
16	Nat N	A	AFC Telford United	1014	L 0 - 2		19	4
20	Nat N	A	Kidderminster Harriers	1185	L 1 - 2	Ryan 52	20	5
27	Nat N	H	Gloucester City	306	L 1 - 3	Tames 52	20	6
29	Nat N	A	Chorley	1011	L 0 - 1		21	7
Sept 3	Nat N	H	Nuneaton Town	345	L 0 - 4		22	8
6	Nat N	H	Gainsborough Trinity	321	W 3 - 2	Chippendale 38 Owens 60 (pen) 90 (pen)	19	9
10	Nat N	A	FC Halifax Town	1552	L 0 - 1		20	10
13	Nat N	H	Harrogate Town	409	L 1 - 3	Owens 23	20	11
17	FAC2Q	A	Witton Albion	316	D 1 - 1	Chalmers 60		12
20	FAC2Qr	H	Witton Albion	241	W 2 - 1	Hughes 51 Owens 62		13
23	Nat N	A	Darlington 1883	1231	L 1 - 4	Owens 17	20	14
Oct 1	FAC3Q	A	FC Halifax Town	964	L 1 - 2	O'Brien 30		15
8	Nat N	H	Altrincham	777	L 0 - 2		21	16
15	Nat N	A	Worcester City	464	L 0 - 4		21	17
22	Nat N	H	Alfreton Town	456	L 2 - 3	Spencer 53 Chippendale 65	21	18
29	Nat N	A	Bradford PA	342	W 1 - 0	Gee 53	20	19
Nov 5	Nat N	A	AFC Fylde	1647	L 0 - 5		21	20
12	Nat N	H	FC United of Manchester	1466	L 2 - 4	Chippendale 13 Summerskill 52	21	21
19	Nat N	A	Tamworth	702	L 1 - 2	Spencer 49	21	22
26	FAT3Q	A	Stocksbridge Park Steels	142	D 2 - 2	Chippendale 20 Wilkins 52		23
Dec 3	Nat N	H	Boston United	414	D 3 - 3	Cockerline 28 59 Wilkins 49	21	24
10	FAT3Qr	H	Stocksbridge Park Steels	140	L 2 - 3	McNight 30 Owens 51		25
!7	Nat N	A	Nuneaton Town	503	L 1 - 2	Syers 7	21	26
20	Nat N	H	Brackley Town	211	L 0 - 1		21	27
26	Nat N	H	Curzon Ashton	558	L 1 - 2	Chippendale 57	21	28
Jan 7	Nat N	H	FC Halifax Town	851	W 1 - 0	Baguley	21	29
21	Nat N	A	Gainsborough Trinity	547	D 2 - 2	Dunbar 8 Horsfall 75	21	30
30	Nat N	H	Stalybridge Celtic	422	D 0 - 0		21	31
Feb 4	Nat N	A	Stockport County	3765	L 1 - 3	Dunbar 46	21	32
18	Nat N	A	Salford City	1310	L 0 - 1		21	33
Mar 11	Nat N	H	Darlington 1883	712	L 0 - 1		22	34
14	Nat N	H	Bradford PA	300	W 4 - 3	Pilkington 13 Roberts 39 Chalmers 57 Ahmadi 74	21	35
18	Nat N	A	Altrincham	1236	D 0 - 0		21	36
25	Nat N	H	Worcester City	268	L 0 - 1		21	37
28	Nat N	H	AFC Telford United	296	L 0 - 2		21	38
April 1	Nat N	H	FC United of Manchester	2375	D 2 - 2	Hughes 28 Sinnott 83	21	39
4	Nat N	A	Alfreton Town	347	W 2 - 0	Wisdom 37 Bishop 52	21	40
8	Nat N	H	AFC Fylde	551	W 2 - 1	Wisdom 23 Pllkington 52	21	41
11	Nat N	H	Kidderminster Harriers	427	W 1 - 0	Pilkington 62	21	42
15	Nat N	A	Gloucester City	379	L 1 - 2	Dunbar 81	21	43
17	Nat N	H	Chorley	761	L 0 1		21	44
22	Nat N	H	Tamworth	388	L 0 - 4		21R	45
25	Nat N	H	Harrogate Town	188	L 2 - 4	Gee 70 (og) 31	21	46
29	Nat N	A	Brackley Town	463	L 2 5	Ahmandi 55 Gee 82 (pen)	21	47

GOALSCORERS	SG	CSG	Pens	Hat tricks	Total		SG	CSG	Pens	Hat tricks	Total
2015-16 Higgins					12	Baguley	1				1
Owens	7	2	2		7	Ball	1				1
Chippendale	5				5	Bishop	1				1
Dunbar	3				3	Horsfall	1				1
Gee	3		1		3	McNight	1				1
Pilkington	3				3	O'Brien	1				1
Ahmadi	2				2	Opponent	1				1
Chalmers	2				2	Roberts	1				1
Cockerline	1				2	Ryan	1				1
Hughes	2				2	Sinnott	1				1
Spencer	2				2	Summerskill	1				1
Wilkins	2	2			2	Syers	1				1
Wisdom	2				2	Tames	1				1

STOURBRIDGE

Club Contact Details
War Memorial Athletic Ground, High Street, Amblecote DY8 4HN
01384 394 040
clive1974eades@gmail.com

Ground Capacity: 2,089   **Seats:** 250   **Covered:** 750   **Clubhouse:** Yes   **Shop:** Yes

Record Attendance
5,726 v Cardiff City - Welsh Cup Final 1st Leg 1974

Previous Grounds
None

10 YEAR RECORD

	07-08		08-09		09-10		10-11		11-12		12-13		13-14		14-15		15-16		16-17	
	SthM	3	SthP	16	SthP	9	SthP	8	SthP	6	SthP	2	SthP	5	NP P	16	NP P	6	NP P	3
	FAC	2Q	FAC	2Qr	FAC	1P	FAC	2Q	FAC	2P	FAC	1Qr	FAC	2P	FAC	3Qr	FAC	2P	FAC	3P
	FAT	1Qr	FAT	1P	FAT	3Qr	FAT	3Q	FAT	3Q	FAT	1Q	FAT	3Qr	FAT	2Q	FAT	3P	FAT	1Q

Club Factfile

Founded: 1876   **Nickname:** The Glassboys   **Manager:** Gary Hackett

Previous Names: Stourbridge Standard 1876-87

Previous Leagues: West Midlands (Birmingham League) 1892-1939, 54-71, Birmingham Combination 1945-53, Southern 1971-2000. Midland Alliance 2000-06. Southern 2006-14.

Club Colours (change): Red and white stripes/red/red (Yellow/green/yellow)

RECORDS
Goalscorer: Ron Page - 269
Appearances: Ron Page - 427
Additional: Received £20,000 from Lincoln City for Tony Cunningham 1979

HONOURS
FA Comps: None

League: Birmingham 1923-24. Birmingham Combination 1951-52. Southern Division One North 1973-74, Midland Division 1990-91. Midland Alliance 2001-02, 02-03.

County FA: Worcestershire Junior Cup 1927-28. Hereford Senior Cup 1954-55. Birmingham Senior Cup 1949-50, 58-59, 67-68. Worcestershire Senior Cup x11 - Firstly in 1904-05 and most recently in 2012-13.

BEST PERFORMANCES   **FA Cup:** Third Round Proper 2016-17.   **Welsh Cup:** Final 1973-74.
FA Trophy: Quarter-finals 1970-71.
FA Vase: Quarter-finals 2004-05.

STOURBRIDGE MATCH RESULTS 2016-17

Date	Comp	H/A	Opponents	Att	Result	Goalscorers	Pos	No.
Aug 13	NPL	A	Warrington Town	321	L 0 - 2		24	1
15	NPL	H	Hednesford Town	772	L 1 - 2	Brown 17	24	2
23	NPL	A	Frickley Athletic	224	W 2 - 0	Benbow 10 21	18	3
27	NPL	A	Nantwich Town	289	W 3 - 2	Jones 9 (og) Benbow 12 Hague 90	14	4
29	NPL	H	Barwell	695	W 2 - 1	Brown 19 Benbow 78	9	5
Sept 3	FAC1Q	A	**Peterborough Sports**	**206**	W 3 - 1	**Scarr 39 Benbow 55 Tonks 60**		6
10	NPL	A	Matlock Town	278	L 1 - 3	Hague 87	12	7
17	FAC2Q	A	**Mickleover Sports**	**258**	W 2 - 1	**Lait 45 Canavan 83**		8
19	NPL	H	Halesowen Town	1575	D 2 - 2	Benbow 39 (pen) 56	11	9
24	NPL	H	Whitby Town	1006	W 2 - 1	Benbow 28 Broadhurst 74	10	10
27	NPL	A	Stafford Rangers	545	D 0 - 0		12	11
Oct 1	FAC3Q	H	**Ilkeston**	**413**	W 2 - 1	**Broadhurst 36 Benbow 50**		12
5	NPL	A	Corby Town	462	W 2 - 1	Benbow 66 (pen) 69	11	13
8	NPL	A	Marine	462	D 1 - 1	Hague 90	12	14
10	NPL	H	Sutton Coldfield Town	529	L 0 - 1		13	15
15	FAC4Q	A	**Nantwich Town**	**755**	W 3 - 1	**Broadhurst 8 36 Benbow 32**		16
18	NPL	A	Coalville Town	110	D 1 - 1	Benbow 65	13	17
22	NPL	A	Blyth Spartans	507	L 1 - 2	Benbow 52	15	18
29	FAT1Q	H	**Kings Lynn Town**	**465**	L 1 - 2	**Smith 75 (pen)**		19
31	NPL	H	Corby Town	486	W 1 - 0	Duggan 86	12	20
Nov 5	FAC 1	A	**Whitehawk**	**767**	D 1 - 1	**Scarr 52**		21
7	NPL	H	Skelmersdale United	532	W 2 - 1	Canavan 35 Hague 68	12	22
12	NPL	A	Spennymoor Town	545	D 2 - 2	Pierpoint 30 Birch 70	12	23
14	FAC1r	H	**Whitehawk**	**1993**	W 3 - 0	**Lait 51 Lewis 60 76**		24
19	NPL	H	Buxton	760	W 3 - 2	Benbow 14 59 Brown 73	12	25
26	NPL	H	Workington	644	W 5 - 0	Benbow 5 (pen) 27 Archer 16 Duggan 20 Brown 23	8	26
10	NPL	A	Ashton United	165	W 2 - 0	Benbow 39 Brown 68	8	27
13	FAC2	H	**Northampton Town**	**2520**	W 1 0	**Duggan 86**		28
17	NPL	H	Spennymoor Town	680	D 1 - 1	Canavan 90	9	29
26	NPL	H	Rushall Olympic	1431	D 0 - 0		13	30
Jan 2	NPL	A	Barwell	302	W 1 0	Duggan 51	9	31
7	FAC3	A	**Wycombe Wanderers**	**6312**	L 1 - 2	**Scott 70**		32
14	NPL	A	Skelmersdale United	305	W 4 - 0	Green 22 Benbow 28 Smith 34 (og) Lait 37	7	33
17	NPL	A	Mickleover Sports	202	W 4 - 0	Benbow 14 52 Archer 26 48	6	34
21	NPL	H	Marine	857	W 2 - 0	Archer 32 37	4	35
28	NPL	A	Sutton Coldfield Town	534	L 1 - 4	Archer 85	6	36
Feb 4	NPL	H	Coalville Town	733	W 2 - 0	Benbow 30 90	4	37
6	NPL	H	Ashton United	504	W 4 - 1	Brown 3 71 Tonks 31 Archer 41	2	38
11	NPL	A	Grantham Town	331	L 1 - 3	Heath 90	3	39
18	NPL	H	Blyth Spartans	1376	L 1 - 2	Tonks 90	4	40
20	NPL	H	Warrington Town	640	L 0 - 1		4	41
25	NPL	A	Whitby Town	278	W 3 - 1	Benbow 56 Tonks 74 Jones 79	2	42
27	NPL	H	Stafford Rangers	744	W 2 - 0	Archer 12 Preston 83	2	43
Mar 4	NPL	H	Matlock Town	819	W 5 - 3	Westlake 3 Benbow 10 Archer 17 Jones 26 Tonks 72	2	44
7	NPL	A	Halesowen Town	2127	W 1 - 0	Benbow 6	2	45
11	NPL	H	Mickleover Sports	753	D 0 - 0		3	46
18	NPL	A	Workington	403	L 1 - 3	Benbow 73 (pen)	3	47
20	NPL	H	Ilkeston	632	W 3 - 1	Benbow 75 (pen) Rodgers 78 Preston 83	3	48
25	NPL	H	Grantham Town	965	L 1 - 2	Benbow 15	3	49
Apr 1	NPL	A	Buxton	504	D 1 - 1	Benbow 44	3	50
4	NPL	A	Hednesford Town	486	D 1 - 1	Benbow 83	4	51
8	NPL	A	Ilkeston	326	W 2 - 1	Jones 6 Digie 59	4	52
15	NPL	H	Frickley Athletic	844	W 4 - 1	Benbow 27 Brown 56 Tonks 57 Jones 74	4	53
17	NPL	H	Rushall Olympic	536	W 2 - 0	Benbow 29 (pen) Jones 47	3	54
22	NPL	H	Nantwich Town	1312	W 4 - 2	Benbow 50 (pen) Pierpoint 58 Brown 61 Archer 70	3	55
24	PO SF	H	**Workington**	**1628**	W 3 - 2	**Pierpoint 33 Benbow 76 Archer 97 (aet)**		56
29	PO F	A	**Spennymoor Town**	**1699**	L 0 - 1			57

GOALSCORERS	SG	CSG	Pens	Hat tricks	Total		SG	CSG	Pens	Hat tricks	Total
2015-16 Hawley					**8**	Opponents					2
Benbow	29	5	7		36	Preston	2				2
Archer	9	3			11	Scarr	2				2
Brown	8	3			9	Birch	1				1
Tonks	6				6	Digie	1				1
Jones	5				5	Green	1				1
Broadhurst	3				4	Heath	1				1
Duggan	4				4	Rodgers	1				1
Hague	4				4	Scott	1				1
Canavan	3				3	Smith	1		1		1
Lait	3				3	Westlake	1				1
Pierpoint	3				3						
Lewis	2				2						

SUTTON COLDFIELD TOWN

Club Contact Details
Central Ground, Coles Lane, Sutton Coldfield B72 1NL
0121 354 2997
murralln@gmail.com

Ground Capacity: 4,500   **Seats:** 200   **Covered:** 500   **Clubhouse:** Yes   **Shop:** Yes

Record Attendance
2,029 v Doncaster Rovers - FA Cup 1980-81
Previous Grounds
Meadow Plat 1879-89, Coles Lane 1890-1919

10 YEAR RECORD

07-08		08-09		09-10		10-11		11-12		12-13		13-14		14-15		15-16		16-17	
SthM	4	SthM	6	SthM	6	NP1S	6	NP1S	12	NP1S	6	NP1S	6	NP1S	4	NP P	12	NP P	20
FAC	2Q	FAC	P	FAC	P	FAC	3Qr	FAC	1Q	FAC	P	FAC	1Q	FAC	2Q	FAC	1Q	FAC	2Q
FAT	P	FAT	2Q	FAT	1Qr	FAT	P	FAT	1Q	FAT	P	FAT	P	FAT	P	FAT	1P	FAT	1Q

Club Factfile

Founded: 1879   **Nickname:** Royals   **Manager:** Richard Sneekes

Previous Names: Sutton Coldfield F.C. 1879-1921

Previous Leagues: Central Birmingham, Walsall Senior, Staffordshire County, Birmingham Combination 1950-54,
West Midlands (Regional) 1954-65, 79-82, Midlands Combination 1965-79

Club Colours (change): All blue with white trim (Yellow/black/black)

RECORDS
Goalscorer: Eddie Hewitt - 288
Appearances: Andy Ling - 550
Additional: Paid £1,500 to Gloucester for Lance Morrison, to Burton Albion for Micky Clarke and to Atherstone United for Steve Farmer 1991. Received £25,000 from West Bromwich Albion for Barry Cowdrill 1979

HONOURS
FA Comps: None

League: West Midlands League 1979-80. Midland Combination x2.
NPL Division One South Play-off 2014-15.

County FA: Birmingham Senior Cup 2010-11.

BEST PERFORMANCES	**FA Cup:** First Round Proper 1980-81, 92-93.
	FA Trophy: Third Round Proper 2004-05.
	FA Vase: N/A

SUTTON COLDFIELD TOWN MATCH RESULTS 2016-17

Date	Comp	H/A	Opponents	Att:	Result	Goalscorers	Pos	No.
Aug 13	NPL	H	Whitby Town	78	D 1 - 1	O'Callaghan 90	11	1
16	NPL	A	Coalville Town	136	D 1 - 1	Lyng 43	12	2
20	NPL	A	Spennymoor Town	485	L 0 - 3		19	3
23	NPL	A	Matlock Town	277	L 1 - 3	Rodgers 10	22	4
27	NPL	H	Workington	171	D 1 - 1	Rodgers 25	22	5
29	NPL	A	Grantham Town	186	L 1 - 2	Rodgers 27	22	6
Sept 3	FAC1Q	A	Eynsbury Rovers	195	W 3 - 1	Woodend 34 (og) Rodgers 35 Washbourne 79		7
10	NPL	A	Blyth Spartans	575	L 0 - 5		22	8
17	FAC2Q	H	Hereford United	623	L 2 - 3	Edmunds 39 Trainer 86		9
20	NPL	H	Stafford Rangers	231	D 1 - 1	Edmunds 13	23	10
24	NPL	H	Skelmersdale United	135	W 2 - 0	Bailey-Nicholls 37 Blake 79	23	11
27	NPL	A	Marine	293	L 0 - 1		23	12
Oct 1	NPL	A	Whitby Town	249	L 0 - 2		23	13
4	NPL	H	Hednesford Town	284	L 0 - 5		23	14
8	NPL	H	Frickley Athletic	220	W 3 - 1	Ricketts 39 Keen 59 Francis 87	20	15
10	NPL	A	Stourbridge	529	W 1 - 0	O'Callaghan 45	19	16
15	NPL	H	Rushall Olympic	196	L 0 - 4		21	17
18	NPL	H	Mickleover Town	130	L 0 - 1		21	18
22	NPL	H	Ashton United	148	D 2 - 2	Campion 9 Keen 42	21	19
29	FAT1Q	A	Leek Town	315	L 1 - 2	Liam 90		20
31	NPL	A	Hednesford Town	362	L 1 - 4	Williams 17 (og)	21	21
Nov 5	NPL	A	Buxton	353	L 1 - 2	Blake 38	21	22
12	NPL	H	Coalville Town	190	L 0 - 3		22	23
19	NPL	H	Rushall Olympic	269	L 1 - 3	Hildreth 44	22	24
26	NPL	A	Warrington Town	236	L 1 - 2	O'Callaghan 80	23	25
Dec 3	NPL	H	Corby Town	184	W 5 - 1	Washbourne 8 38 RODGERS 3 (29 66 75pen)	22	26
10	NPL	A	Barwell	136	D 1 - 1	Washbourne 55	22	27
17	NPL	H	Buxton	174	D 1 - 1	O'Callaghan 2 (pen)	21	28
26	NPL	A	Halesowen Town	607	D 0 - 0		21	29
Jan 2	NPL	H	Grantham Town	262	L 0 - 2		21	30
7	NPL	H	Ilkeston	283	W 1 - 0	Wright 45	21	31
17	NPL	A	Nantwich Town	225	L 0 - 1		21	32
21	NPL	A	Frickley Athletic	257	L 0 - 2		21	33
28	NPL	H	Stourbridge	534	W 4 - 1	Geddes 53 (pen) HOWARTH 3 (59 65 76)	21	34
Feb 4	NPL	A	Ashton United	162	L 1 - 3	Sho-Silva 90	22	35
11	NPL	H	Nantwich Town	208	D 1 - 1	Geddes 6 (pen)	22	36
18	NPL	A	Ilkeston	312	L 0 - 1		22	37
28	NPL	H	Marine	112	W 3 - 2	Robins 25 Townsend 40 Birch 57	22	38
Mar 4	NPL	H	Blyth Spartans	273	W 3 - 2	Curley 37 Robins 56 Townsend 72	22	39
7	NPL	A	Stafford Rangers	440	D 0 - 0		22	40
11	NPL	A	Corby Town	452	L 1 - 5	Curley	22	41
14	NPL	A	Skelmersdale United	160	W 3 - 1	Venney 5 Howarth 69 Birch 87	22	42
18	NPL	H	Warrington Town	187	L 0 - 1		22	43
25	NPL	H	Barwell	263	W 2 - 1	Townsend 52 Wright 88	21	44
Apr 4	NPL	A	Mickleover Sports	145	L 1 - 3	Kelly 74	21	45
8	NPL	A	Spennymoor Town	236	W 1 - 0	Cartwright 62	20	46
15	NPL	A	Matlock Town	305	L 2 - 3	Robins 30 Njie90	21	47
17	NPL	H	Halesowen Town	338	W 1 - 0	Kelly 83	21	48
22	NPL	A	Workington	676	D 0 - 0		20	49

GOALSCORERS	SG	CSG	Pens	Hat tricks	Total		SG	CSG	Pens	Hat tricks	Total
2015-16 Forde					10	Wright	2				2
Rodgers	5	4	1	1	7	Bailey-Nicholls	1				1
Howarth	2		1		4	Campion	1				1
O'Callaghan	4		1		4	Cartwright	1				1
Washbourne	3				4	Francis	1				1
Robins	3				3	Hildreth	1				1
Townsend	3				3	Liam	1				1
Birch	2				2	Lyng	1				1
Blake	2				2	Njie	1				1
Curley	2				2	Ricketts	1				1
Edmunds	2				2	Sho-Silova	1				1
Geddes	2		2		2	Trainer	1				1
Keen	2				2	Venney	1				1
Kelly	2				2						
Opponents	2				2						

WARRINGTON TOWN

Club Contact Details
Cantilever Park, Common Lane, Latchford, Warrington WA4 2RS
01925 653 044
info@warringtontownfc.co.uk

Ground Capacity: 2,500 **Seats:** 350 **Covered:** 650 **Clubhouse:** Yes **Shop:** Yes

Record Attendance
2,600 v Halesowen Town - FA Vase Semi-final 1st leg 1985-86
Previous Grounds
Stockton Lane 1949-50, 55-56. London Road 1950-53. Loushers Lane 1953-55.

10 YEAR RECORD

07-08		08-09		09-10		10-11		11-12		12-13		13-14		14-15		15-16		16-17	
NP1S	13	NP1N	19	NP1N	9	NP1N	9	NP1N	11	NP1N	10	NP1N	3	NP1N	9	NP1N	1	NP P	10
FAC	P	FAC	1Q	FAC	2Qr	FAC	3Q	FAC	2Q	FAC	2Q	FAC	2Qr	FAC	2P	FAC	P	FAC	1Q
FAT	2Q	FAT	3Q	FAT	1Q	FAT	P	FAT	Pr	FAT	P	FAT	P	FAT	P	FAT	3Q	FAT	1Q

Club Factfile

Founded: 1949   **Nickname:** The Wire   **Manager:** Paul Carden

Previous Names: Stockton Heath Albion 1949-61

Previous Leagues: Warrington & District 1949-52, Mid Cheshire 1952-78, Cheshire County 1978-82, North West Counties 1982-90 Northern Premier 1990-97

Club Colours (change): Yellow/blue/yellow (Blue/white/blue)

RECORDS
Goalscorer: Steve Hughes - 167
Appearances: Neil Whalley
Additional: Paid £50,000 to Preston North End for Liam Watson Received £60,000 from P.N.E. for Liam Watson
Players to progress - Roger Hunt, Liverpool legend and 1966 World Cup winner.

HONOURS
FA Comps: None
League: Mid-Cheshire 1960-61. North West Counties 1989-90, Division Two 2000-01. Northern Premier Division One North 2015-16.
County FA: None

BEST PERFORMANCES	**FA Cup:** Second Round Proper 2014-15.
	FA Trophy: Quarter-finals 1992-93.
	FA Vase: Final 1986-87.

WARRINGTON TOWN MATCH RESULTS 2016-17

Date	Comp	H/A	Opponents	Att:	Result	Goalscorers	Pos	No.
Aug 13	NPL	H	Stourbridge	321	W 2 - 0	Ventre 18 36	6	1
16	NPL	A	Spennymoor Town	618	L 1 - 4	Kinsella 76	12	2
20	NPL	H	Grantham Town	238	L 0 - 1		16	3
23	NPL	H	Whitby Town	231	L 0 - 1		19	4
27	NPL	H	Matlock Town	561	W 5 - 3	Kilheeney 40 Deegan 47 62 McCarten 64 Grogan 83	15	5
29	NPL	A	Marine	432	D 1 - 1	Grogan 57	14	6
Sept 3	FAC1Q	A	Workington AFC	448	L 0 - 3			7
10	NPL	H	Ilkeston	333	W 4 - 1	Kinsella 12 Shaw 25 Deegan 43 Kilheeney 75	9	8
17	NPL	A	Grantham Town	163	W 2 - 1	Kilheeney 69 89	7	9
20	NPL	A	Mickleover Sports	105	L 0 - 1		8	10
24	NPL	A	Coalville Town	130	W 2 - 1	Gillespie 15 Kilheeney 75	8	11
27	NPL	H	Nantwich Town	303	L 2 - 3	Codling 20 McCarten 39	9	12
Oct 1	NPL	H	Corby Town	301	W 2 - 1	Kilheeney 39 Peers 54	8	13
4	NPL	A	Blyth Spartans	507	W 3 - 0	Peers 11 Metcalfe 18 Kilheeney 65	5	14
8	NPL	A	Skelmersdale United	231	L 0 - 4		6	15
11	NPL	H	Buxton	407	W 1 - 0	Grogan 45	5	16
15	NPL	H	Workington	346	L 1 - 2	Grogan 78	6	17
18	NPL	A	Rushall Olympic	220	D 2 - 2	Speed 81 Grogan 88	5	18
22	NPL	A	Halesowen Town	430	L 0 - 1		6	19
29	FAT1Q	H	Nantwich Town	274	L 0 - 2			20
Nov 5	NPL	A	Stafford Rangers	653	D 2 - 2	Kilheeney 31 (pen) 89 (pen)	10	21
12	NPL	H	Rushall Olympic	294	W 2 0	Kilheeney 45 Eze 85 (og)	8	22
19	NPL	H	Barwell	292	L 1 - 2	McCarten 30	10	23
26	NPL	H	Sutton Coldfield Town	236	W 2 - 1	Codling 9 57	7	24
Dec 3	NPL	A	Frickley Athletic	197	W 3 - 0	Harries 37 Ilesanmi 63 Hattersley 71	6	25
10	NPL	A	Hednesford Town	351	L 0 - 1		7	26
26	NPL	A	Ashton United	205	L 1 - 2	Vassallo 81	14	27
Jan 14	NPL	A	Corby Town	468	D 0 - 0		15	28
21	NPL	H	Skelmersdale United	319	W 2 - 0	Ilesanmi 22 Codling 62	14	29
28	NPL	A	Buxton	338	D 3 - 3	Monaghan 1, 90 Vassalo 89 (pen)	13	30
31	NPL	H	Marine	212	W 1 0	Monaghan 59	10	31
Feb 7	NPL	H	Blyth Spartans	313	L 0 - 2		13	32
11	NPL	A	Workington	371	L 1 - 3	Vassallo 88	13	33
18	NPL	H	Halesowen Town	273	W 1 - 0	Hattersley 45	13	34
20	NPL	A	Stourbridge	640	W 1 - 0	Jerome 73	13	35
25	NPL	H	Coalville Town	229	W 2 - 1	Jerome 82 87	11	36
28	NPL	A	Nantwich Town	248	L 1 - 4	Monaghan 51 (pen)	11	37
Mar 4	NPL	A	Ilkeston	293	W 2 - 0	Jerome 68 McCarthy 88	8	38
7	NPL	H	Mickleover Sports	160	W 1 - 0	Jerome 64	6	39
11	NPL	H	Frickley Athletic	247	W 2 - 1	McCarten 45 Hattersley 89	4	40
18	NPL	A	Sutton Coldfield Town	187	W 1 - 0	Hattersley 57	4	41
25	NPL	H	Hednesford Town	478	W 1 - 0	Duggan 32	4	42
28	NPL	H	Spennymoor United	308	L 0 - 2		6	43
Apr 1	NPL	A	Barwell	157	W 2 0	Stanley 25 (og) Bakkor 83	5	44
8	NPL	H	Stafford Rsngers	315	L 1 - 2	Bakkor 78 (pen)	8	45
15	NPL	A	Whitby Town	491	D 2 - 2	Hattersley 10 53	10	46
17	NPL	H	Ashton United	267	D 1 - 1	Bakare 88	10	47
22	NPL	A	Matlock Town	392	D 1 - 1	Bakare 23	10	48

GOALSCORERS	SG	CSG	Pens	Hat tricks	Total		SG	CSG	Pens	Hat tricks	Total
Kilheeney	6		1		7	Ilesanmi	2				2
Hattersley	5				6	Kinsella	2				2
Grogan	5	2			5	Opponents	2				2
Jerome	4				5	Peers	2				2
Kilheeney	4				4	Ventre	1				2
McCarten	4				4	Duggan	1				1
Monaghan	3		1		4	Gillespie	1				1
Codling	2				3	Harries	1				1
Deegan	3				3	McCarthy	1				1
Vassallo	3		1		3	Metcalfe	1				1
Bakare	2				2	Shaw	1				1
Bakkor	2		1		2	Speed	1				1

WHITBY TOWN

Club Contact Details
Turnbull Ground, Upgang Lane, Whitby, North Yorks YO21 3HZ
Office: 01947 604847   CH: 01947 605 153
peterjohnt17@hotmail.com

Ground Capacity: 3,500   **Seats:** 622   **Covered:** 1,372   **Clubhouse:** Yes   **Shop:** Yes

Record Attendance
4,000 v Scarborough - North Riding Cup 18/04/1965
Previous Grounds
None

10 YEAR RECORD

	07-08	08-09	09-10	10-11	11-12	12-13	13-14	14-15	15-16	16-17
NP P	12	19	14	16	17	13	9	13	19	6
FAC	2Q	2Qr	2Q	1Q	3Q	3Q	1Qr	1Qr	1Qr	2Q
FAT	1Q	3Q	2Q	3Qr	1Q	3Q	1Q	1Q	2Q	2Q

Club Factfile

Founded: 1926   **Nickname:** Seasiders   **Manager:** Chris Hardy

Previous Names: Whitby United was formed after Whitby Whitehall Swifts and Whitby Town merged 1926-49.

Previous Leagues: Northern 1926-97

Club Colours (change): All royal blue (All white)

RECORDS
Victory: 11-2 v Cargo Fleet Works - 1950
Defeat: 3-13 v Willington - 24/03/1928
Goalscorer: Paul Pitman - 382
Appearances: Paul Pitman - 468
Additional: Paid £2,500 to Newcastle Blue Star for John Grady 1990
Received £5,000 from Gateshead for Graham Robinson 1997

HONOURS
FA Comps: FA Vase 1996-97.

League: Northern 1992-93, 96-97.
Northern Premier Division One 1997-98.

County FA: North Riding Senior Cup 1964-65, 67-68, 82-83, 89-90, 2004-05, 16-17.

BEST PERFORMANCES	**FA Cup:** Second Round Proper 1983-84, 85-86.
	FA Trophy: Quarter-finals 1983-84, 98-99.
	FA Vase: Final 1996-97.

WHITBY TOWN MATCH RESULTS 2016-17

Date	Comp	H/A	Opponents	Att:	Result	Goalscorers	Pos	No.
Aug 13	NPL	A	Sutton Coldfield Town	78	D 1 - 1	Hopson 8	12	1
20	NPL	H	Corby Town	216	W 1 - 0	Hopson 72 (pen)	12	2
23	NPL	A	Warrington Town	231	W 1 - 0	Hopson 63	6	3
27	NPL	A	Hednesford Town	387	D 1 - 1	Bythway 90	6	4
29	NPL	H	Frickley Athletic	302	W 4 - 0	Hopson 61 (pen) 70 (pen) Roberts 86 Round 90	4	5
Sept 3	FAC1Q	H	Winsford United	239	D 3 - 3	Tymon 33 60 Snaith 42		6
5	FAC1Qr	A	Winsford United	270	W 2 - 1	Tymon 32 Snaith 67		7
10	NPL	H	Mickleover Sports	219	D 1 - 1	Tymon 49	6	8
13	NPL	H	Ilkeston	242	W 2 - 1	Hopson 30 Tymon 45	4	9
17	FAC2Q	A	Spennymoor Town	607	L 0 - 1			10
20	NPL	A	Spennymoor Town	576	W 1 - 0	Hopson 90	3	11
24	NPL	A	Stourbridge	1005	L 1 - 2	Gell 76	3	12
27	NPL	H	Ashton United	287	W 2 - 1	McTiernan 20 Tymon 39	3	13
Oct 1	NPL	H	Sutton Coldfield Town	249	W 2 - 0	Hopson 6 10	2	14
4	NPL	A	Grantham Town	189	L 0 - 2		3	15
8	NPL	A	Buxton	602	L 0 - 3		3	16
11	NPL	H	Workington	260	D 1 - 1	Bythway 31	4	17
15	NPL	H	Marine	293	W 3 - 1	Roberts 45 Tymon 50 65	3	18
18	NPL	A	Skelmersdale United	142	W 1 - 0	Hopson 72 (pen)	1	19
22	NPL	A	Barwell	224	W 2 - 1	Roberts 37 Towers 51 (og)	1	20
29	FAT1Q	H	Workington	321	W 4 - 3	Roberts 19 50 Tymon 44 Weledji 81		21
Nov 5	NPL	A	Matlock Town	306	W 1 - 0	Hopson 63	1	22
12	FAT2Q	A	Shaw Lane AFC	320	L 0 3			23
19	NPL	A	Coalville Town	137	W 3 - 2	Hopson 29 Tymon 55 Blackford 88	1	24
22	NPL	H	Grantham Town	209	L 0 - 2		1	25
26	NPL	A	Ilkeston	270	D 0 - 0		1	26
Dec 3	NPL	A	Rushall Olympic	261	L 0 - 1		3	27
10	NPL	H	Nantwich Town	261	L 1 - 3	Hopson 55	3	28
17	NPL	A	Matlock Town	395	L 1 - 2	Gell 27	4	29
26	NPL	H	Blyth Spartans	612	W 2 - 1	Tymon 15 Gell 64	2	30
Jan 2	NPL	A	Frickley Athletic	243	W 1 - 0	Tymon 51	2	31
7	NPL	A	Ashton United	137	L 1 - 3	Hopson 53	4	32
14	NPL	A	Halesowen Town	364	L 0 - 2		4	33
21	NPL	H	Buxton	282	W 4 - 2	Hopson 25 (pen) Snaith 39 Weledji 83 Tymon 89	2	34
28	NPL	A	Workington	453	L 0 - 4		4	35
Feb 4	NPL	H	Skelmersdale United	219	W 1 - 0	Carson 54	3	36
11	NPL	A	Marine	292	W 4 - 1	Carson 2 69 Tymon 53 84	2	37
18	NPL	H	Barwell	285	L 1 - 2	Bythway 44	3	38
25	NPL	H	Stourbridge	276	L 1 - 3	Hopson 3	7	39
Mar 7	NPL	H	Spennymoor Town	329	W 2 - 1	Hopson 61 (pen) Roberts 90	9	40
11	NPL	H	Rushall Olympic	308	D 1 - 1	Hopson 66	9	41
14	NPL	H	Halesowen Town	237	W 4 - 1	Roberts 44 Tymon 58 Hopson 68 Carson 75	8	42
18	NPL	A	Stafford Rangers	506	D 0 - 0		6	43
25	NPL	H	Nantwich Town	481	W 2 - 0	Carson 1 Hopson 64	6	44
28	NPL	H	Stafford Rangers	304	D 2 - 2	Hopson 11 (pen) 89 (pen)	5	45
Apr 1	NPL	H	Coalville Town	367	D 1 - 1	Weledji 90	6	46
8	NPL	A	Corby Town	496	W 2 - 0	Hopson 14 Bythway 64	6	47
11	NPL	A	Mickleover Sports	185	W 1 - 0	Hopson 90	5	48
15	NPL	A	Warrington Town	491	D 2 - 2	Hopson 50 Tymon 78	7	49
15	NPL	A	Blyth Spartans	772	L 1 - 5	Hopson 81	8	50
22	NPL	H	Hednesford Town	342	W 1 - 0	Hopson 66	6	51

GOALSCORERS	SG	CSG	Pens	Hat tricks	Total		SG	CSG	Pens	Hat tricks	Total
2015-16 Roberts					10	McTiernan	1				1
Hopson	22	5	7		27	Opponents	1				1
Tymon	14	4			17	Round	1				1
Roberts	4				7						
Carson	4				5						
Bythway	4				4						
Gell	3				3						
Snaith	3				3						
Weledji	3				3						
Blackford	1				1						

WITTON ALBION

Club Contact Details
Wincham Park, Chapel Street, Wincham, CW9 6DA
01606 430 08
mike.harper@sky.com

Ground Capacity: 4,813 **Seats:** 650 **Covered:** 2,300 **Clubhouse:** Yes **Shop:** Yes

Record Attendance
3,940 v Kidderminster Harries - FA Trophy Semi-final 13/04/1991
Previous Grounds
Central Ground (1910-1989)

10 YEAR RECORD

07-08		08-09		09-10		10-11		11-12		12-13		13-14		14-15		15-16		16-17	
NP P	2	NP P	20	NP1S	7	NP1N	10	NP1N	3	NP P	4	NP P	16	NP P	22	NP1N	11	NP1S	2
FAC	1Q	FAC	2Qr	FAC	P	FAC	P	FAC	4Q	FAC	2Q	FAC	1Q	FAC	1Q	FAC	2Q	FAC	2Qr
FAT	3Qr	FAT	1Q	FAT	3Qr	FAT	3Qr	FAT	3Q	FAT	2Q	FAT	2Q	FAT	2Qr	FAT	1Q	FAT	1Pr

Club Factfile

Founded: 1887 **Nickname:** The Albion **Manager:** Carl Macauley - 19/10/15

Previous Names: None

Previous Leagues: Lancashire Combination, Cheshire County > 1979, Northern Premier 1979-91, Conference 1991-94

Club Colours (change): Red & white stripes/navy/red (All orange)

RECORDS
Victory: 13-0 v Middlewich (H)
Defeat: 0-9 v Macclesfield Town (A) - 18/09/1965
Goalscorer: Frank Fidler - 175 (1947-50)
Appearances: Brian Pritchard - 729
Additional: Paid £12,500 to Hyde United for Jim McCluskie 1991
Received £11,500 from Chester City for Peter Henderson

HONOURS
FA Comps: None

League: Cheshire County 1948-49, 49-50, 53-54. Northern Premier Premier Division 1990-91.

County FA: Cheshire Senior Cup x7.

BEST PERFORMANCES
FA Cup: Second Round Proper 1951-52(r), 53-54(r), 91-92.
FA Trophy: Final 1991-92.
FA Vase: N/A

Tolani Omotola (Witton) scores the third (Market Drayton).

Incredible goal from Steve Tames (Witton) beating Stewart (Shaw Lane).

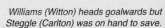

Tames (Witton) skins Jackson and Miller (Spalding).

Williams (Witton) heads goalwards but Steggle (Carlton) was on hand to save.

Photos by Keith Clayton.

WORKINGTON

Club Contact Details
Borough Park, Workington, Cumbria CA14 2DT
01900 602 871
olenacum@gmail.com

Ground Capacity: 3,101 **Seats:** 500 **Covered:** 1,000 **Clubhouse:** Yes **Shop:** Yes

Record Attendance
21,000 v Manchester United - FA Cup 3rd round 04/01/1958
Previous Grounds
Lonsdale Park 1921-37.

10 YEAR RECORD

	07-08	08-09	09-10	10-11	11-12	12-13	13-14	14-15	15-16	16-17
	Conf N 14	Conf N 12	Conf N 4	Conf N 11	Conf N 13	Conf N 14	Conf N 22	NP P 2	NP P 5	NP P 4
FAC	1P	2Qr	4Q	4Qr	2Q	4Q	4Q	2Q	2Q	3Qr
FAT	2Pr	3P	QF	3Qr	3Q	3Q	3Q	3Q	1Q	1Q

Club Factfile

Founded: 1921 **Nickname:** Reds **Manager:** Lee Andrews & David Hewson

Previous Names: Workington AFC 1921-

Previous Leagues: North Eastern 1921-51, Football League 1951-77, Northern Premier 1977-2005. Conference 2005-14.

Club Colours (change): Red with two white diagonal bands/white/red (Yellow with two red diagonal bands/yellow/yellow)

RECORDS

Victory: 17-1 v Cockermouth Crusaders - Cumberland Senior League 19/01/1901
Defeat: 0-9 v Chorley (A) - Northern Premier League 10/11/1987
Goalscorer: Billy Charlton - 193
Appearances: Bobby Brown - 469
Additional: Paid £6,000 to Sunderland for Ken Chisolm 1956
Received £33,000 from Liverpool for Ian McDonald 1974

HONOURS

FA Comps: None

League: North West Counties 1998-99

County FA: Cumberland County Cup x25 (Most recently 2016-17).

BEST PERFORMANCES	**FA Cup:** Fourth Round Proper 1933-34.
	FA Trophy: Quarter-finals 2009-10.
	FA Vase: Quarter-finals 1998-99.

WORKINGTON MATCH RESULTS 2016-17

Date	Comp	H/A	Opponents	Att:	Result	Goalscorers	Pos	No.
Aug 13	NPL	A	Rushall Olympic	248	W 2 - 1	Earl 5 Allison 71	8	1
16	NPL	H	Frickley Athletic	576	W 2 - 0	Calvert 71 Wilson 90	5	2
20	NPL	H	Barwell	422	L 0 - 1		7	3
23	NPL	A	Buxton	265	L 1 - 2	Allison 81	12	4
27	NPL	A	Sutton Coldfield Town	171	D 1 - 1	Kilifin 15	14	5
29	NPL	H	Blyth Spartans	652	L 0 - 2		15	6
Sept 3	FAC1Q	H	Warrington Town	448	W 3 - 0	Calvert 37 Simpson 44 Allison 71		7
10	NPL	H	Halesowen Town	421	L 2 - 3	Douglas 63 Calvert 80	18	8
13	NPL	A	Frickley Athletic	238	D 2 - 2	McGee 61 Symington 81	16	9
17	FAC2Q	H	Shildon	563	W 3 - 1	Allison 26 Tinnion 50 McGee 60		10
24	NPL	H	Grantham Town	419	W 1 - 0	Symington 24 (pen)	14	11
27	NPL	A	Skelmersdale United	210	W 1 - 0	Symington 22	9	12
Oct 1	FAC3Q	A	Matlock Town	489	D 1 - 1	May64		13
4	FAC3Qr	H	Matlock Town	562	L 1 - 3	Symington 88		14
8	NPL	H	Matlock Town	435	L 1 - 3	Newby 49	15	15
11	NPL	A	Whitby Town	260	D 1 - 1	Waterston 69	15	16
15	NPL	A	Warrington Town	346	W 2 - 1	Newby 30 Symington 68 (pen)	14	17
18	NPL	H	Ashton United	370	W 1 - 0	Wilson 13	11	18
22	NPL	H	Stafford Rangers	481	L 1 - 2	Earl 31	13	19
29	FAT1Q	A	Whitby Town	321	L 3 - 4	Waterston 2 Earl 11 56		20
Nov 1	NPL	A	Spennymoor town	570	L 1 - 4	Newby 40	15	21
7	NPL	H	Marine	485	W 4 0	Allison 9 Newby 29 (pen) Tinnion 50 Ryan 72 (pen)	14	22
12	NPL	H	Corby Town	362	W 1 - 0	Allison 17	11	23
19	NPL	H	Barwell	277	W 2 - 0	Wilson 7 Allison 48	9	24
22	NPL	H	Spennymoor Town	366	W 3 0	Tinnion 54 Allison 59 68	7	25
26	NPL	A	Stourbridge	644	L 0 - 5		8	26
Dec 3	NPL	H	Hednesford Town	366	L 0 - 2		9	27
10	NPL	H	Coalville Town	335	L 0 - 4		11	28
17	NPL	A	Corby Town	377	W 3 - 1	McGee 14 Newby 82 Allison 90	11	29
26	NPL	H	Nantwich Town	461	W 3 - 1	Simpson 13 Symington 75 Wilson 85	8	30
Jan 2	NPL	A	Blyth Spartans	673	L 2 - 3	Wilson 35 Allison 68	10	31
7	NPL	H	Rushall Olympic	447	W 2 - 0	May 35 Tinnion 37	7	32
14	NPL	H	Mickleover Sports	448	W 4 - 1	SYMINGTON 3 (40 pen 50 57 pen) Wilson 54	6	33
21	NPL	A	Matlock Town	400	W 2 - 1	Tinnion 41 Ryan 88	8	34
28	NPL	H	Whitby Town	463	W 4 - 0	Wilson 5 Allison 37 77 Joel 90	2	35
Feb 4	NPL	A	Mickleover Sports	209	L 0 - 4		6	36
11	NPL	H	Warrington Town	371	W 3 - 1	Symington 53 (pen) Tinnion 66 79	6	37
18	NPL	A	Stafford Rangers	653	L 2 - 3	Calvert 38 Symington 43 (pen)	7	38
25	NPL	A	Grantham Town	283	D 2 - 2	Calvert 24 47	8	39
28	NPL	H	Skelmersdale United	329	L 0 - 1		9	40
7	NPL	A	Marine	300	W 1 - 0	Joel 55	8	41
Mar 11	NPL	A	Hednesford Town	358	W 2 - 0	May 59 Waterston 75	7	42
18	NPL	H	Stourbridge	403	W 3 - 1	Symington 43 Joel 45 55	5	43
25	NPL	A	Coalville Town	191	L 1 - 2	Jerino 90 (og)	10	44
Apr 4	NPL	A	Ashton United	169	W 2 - 1	Calvert 3 Smith 74	10	45
8	NPL	A	Barwell	187	W 2 - 0	Wilson 14 (pen) Ryan 19	10	46
11	NPL	H	Buxton	206	W 2 - 0	Symington 65 Calvert 79	8	47
15	NPL	H	Halesowen Town	542	W 1 - 0	Tinnion 40	6	48
17	NPL	A	Nantwich Town	512	W 1 - 0	Ryan 40	5	49
19	NPL	H	Ilkeston	634	W 2 - 0	Joel 65 Smith 77	5	50
24	PO SF	A	Stourbridge	1628	L 2 - 3	Symington 68 Wordsworth 90		51

GOALSCORERS	SG	CSG	Pens	Hat tricks	Total		SG	CSG	Pens	Hat tricks	Total
2015-16 Allison					10	May	3				3
Symington	12	2	6		14	McGee	3	2			3
Allison	12	4			13	Waterston	3				3
Calvert	6	2			8	Simpson	2				2
Tinnion	7				8	Smith	2				2
Wilson	8		1		8	Douglas	1				1
Joel	4				5	Kilifin	1				1
Newby	5		1		5	Opponents	1				1
Earl	3	2			4	Wordsworth	1				1
Ryan	4		1		4						

ATHERTON COLLIERIES

Club Contact Details
The Kensite Stadium, Alder Street, Atherton, Greater Manchester M46 9EY
07968 548 056
emilanderson@yahoo.com

Founded: 1916   **Nickname:** The Colts   **Manager:** Michael Clegg
Previous Names: None
Previous Leagues: Bolton Combination 1918-21, 52-71. Lancashire Alliance 1921. Manchester 1945-48. West Lancashire 1948-50. Lancashire Combination 1950-52, 71-78. Cheshire County 1978-82.

Club Colours (change): Black & white

Ground Capacity: 2,500   **Seats:** Yes   **Covered:** Yes   **Clubhouse:** Yes   **Shop:** No
Previous Grounds: None
Record Attendance: 3,300 in the Bolton Combination 1920's.

RECORDS

HONOURS
FA Comps: None
League: Bolton Combination 1919-20, 36-37, 37-38, 38-39, 40-41, 44-45, 56-57, 58-59, 60-61, 64-65.
North West Counties Division Three 1986-87, Division One 2014-15, Premier 2016-17.
County FA: Lancashire County FA Shield 1919-20, 22-23, 41-42, 45-46, 56-57, 64-65.

07-08		08-09		09-10		10-11		11-12		12-13		13-14		14-15		15-16		16-17	
NWC1	15	NWCP	22	NWC1	6	NWC1	5	NWC1	4	NWC1	4	NWC1	5	NWC1	1	NWCP	3	NWCP	1
FAC	1Q	FAC	EP	FAC	P	FAC	Pr	FAC	P	FAC	1Q	FAC	Pr	FAC	Pr	FAC	Pr	FAC	P
FAV	2Q	FAV	2Q	FAV	2Q	FAV	2Q	FAV	EP	FAT	EP	FAT	EP	FAT	EP	FAT	EP	FAT	EP

BAMBER BRIDGE

Club Contact Details
Sir Tom Finney Stadium, Brownedge Road, Bamber Bridge PR5 6UX
01772 909 690
admin@bamberbridgefc.com

Founded: 1952   **Nickname:** Brig   **Manager:** Neil Reynolds
Previous Names: None
Previous Leagues: Preston & District 1952-90, North West Counties 1990-93

Club Colours (change): White & black/black/black (Red & black/red/red)

Ground Capacity: 3,000   **Seats:** 554   **Covered:** 800   **Clubhouse:** Yes   **Shop:** Yes
Previous Grounds: King George V, Higher Wallton 1952-86
Record Attendance: 2,300 v Czech Republic - Pre Euro '96 friendly

RECORDS
Victory: 8-0 v Curzon Ashton - North West Counties 1994-95
Additional: Paid £10,000 to Horwich RMI for Mark Edwards
Received £15,000 from Wigan Athletic for Tony Black 1995

HONOURS
FA Comps: None
League: Preston & District Premier Division 1980-81, 85-86, 86-87, 89-90. North West Counties Division Two 1991-92.
Northern Premier Division 1995-96.
County FA: Lancashire FA Amateur Shield 1981-82, Trophy 1994-95.

07-08		08-09		09-10		10-11		11-12		12-13		13-14		14-15		15-16		16-17	
NP1N	5	NP1N	11	NP1N	14	NP1N	7	NP1N	10	NP1N	9	NP1N	4	NP1N	3	NP1N	12	NP1N	11
FAC	4Q	FAC	1Q	FAC	2Q	FAC	2Qr	FAC	1Q	FAC	2Q	FAC	1Qr	FAC	3Q	FAC	4Q	FAC	P
FAT	1P	FAT	P	FAT	1Q	FAT	2Q	FAT	1Q	FAT	P	FAT	P	FAT	1Q	FAT	P	FAT	1Q

BRIGHOUSE TOWN

Club Contact Details
Yorkshire Payments Stadium, St Giles Road, Hove Edge, Brighouse, HD6 2PN
01484 380 088
dave.parker2000@btinternet.com

Founded: 1963   **Nickname:** Town   **Manager:** Vill Powell
Previous Names: Blakeborough
Previous Leagues: Huddersfield Works 1963-75. West Riding County Amateur 1975-08.

Club Colours (change): Orange/black/orange (All green with white trim)

Ground Capacity: 1,000   **Seats:** 100   **Covered:** 200   **Clubhouse:** Yes   **Shop:** No
Previous Grounds: Woodhouse Recreation Ground. Green Lane.
Record Attendance: 1,059 v Scarborough Athletic, Northern Counties East Premier Division, 13/04/2013.

RECORDS

HONOURS
FA Comps: None
League: Hudersfield Works 1966-67, 68-69, 73-74, 74-75. West Riding County Amateur Premier Division 1990-91, 94-95, 95-96, 2000-01, 01-02, Division One 88-89. Northern Counties East Premier 2013-14.
County FA: West Riding county Cup 1991-92.

07-08		08-09		09-10		10-11		11-12		12-13		13-14		14-15		15-16		16-17	
WRCP	8	NCE1	15	NCE1	2	NCEP	16	NCEP	4	NCEP	2	NCEP	1	NP1N	14	NP1N	14	NP1N	9
						FAC	EP	FAC	EP	FAC	P	FAC	2Q	FAC	1Q	FAC	1Q	FAC	1Q
				FAV	2Q	FAV	1Pr	FAV	1Q	FAV	4P	FAV	3Pr	FAT	P	FAT	1Q	FAT	P

CLITHEROE

Club Contact Details
Shawbridge, off Pendle Road, Clitheroe, Lancashire BB7 1LZ
01200 423 344
secretary@clitheroefc.co.uk

Founded: 1877   **Nickname:** The Blues   **Manager:** Simon Haworth
Previous Names: Clitheroe Central 1877-1903.
Previous Leagues: Blackburn & District, Lancashire Combination 1903-04, 05-10, 25-82, North West Counties 1982-85

Club Colours (change): All blue (Red/black/red)

Ground Capacity: 2,000   **Seats:** 250   **Covered:** 1,400   **Clubhouse:** Yes   **Shop:** No
Previous Grounds: None
Record Attendance: 2,050 v Mangotsfield - FA Vase Semi-final 1995-96

RECORDS
Goalscorer: Don Francis
Appearances: Lindsey Wallace - 670
Additional: Received £45,000 from Crystal Palace for Carlo Nash.

HONOURS
FA Comps: None
League: Lancashire Combination Division Two 1959-60, Division One 1979-80.
          North West Counties Division Three 1983-84, Division Two 1984-85, Division One 1985-86, 2003-04.
County FA: Lancashire Challenge Trophy 1892-93, 1984-85.

07-08		08-09		09-10		10-11		11-12		12-13		13-14		14-15		15-16		16-17	
NP1N	13	NP1N	12	NP1N	8	NP1N	6	NP1N	19	NP1N	8	NP1N	17	NP1N	13	NP1N	7	NP1N	7
FAC	3Q	FAC	2Q	FAC	1Q	FAC	P	FAC	2Q	FAC	1Q	FAC	P	FAC	1Q	FAC	1Q	FAC	P
FAT	2Q	FAT	2Q	FAT	2Q	FAT	2Q	FAT	Pr	FAT	Pr	FAT	Pr	FAT	1Q	FAT	P	FAT	P

COLNE

Club Contact Details
The XLCR Stadium, Harrison Drive, Colne, Lancashire BB8 9SL
01282 862 545
secretary@colnefootballclub.com

Founded: 1996   **Nickname:** The Reds   **Manager:** Steve Cunningham
Previous Names: None
Previous Leagues: North West Counties 1996-2016.

Club Colours (change): Red/black/black (White/red/red).

Ground Capacity: 1,800   **Seats:** 160   **Covered:** 1,000   **Clubhouse:** Yes   **Shop:** Yes
Previous Grounds: None
Record Attendance: 1,742 v AFC Sudbury F.A. Vase SF 2004. 2,762 (at Accrington Stanley) v FC United, NWC Challenge Cup,

RECORDS
Goalscorer: Geoff Payton
Appearances: Richard Walton

HONOURS
FA Comps: None
League: North West Counties League Division Two 2003-04, Premier Division 2015-16.

County FA: None

07-08		08-09		09-10		10-11		11-12		12-13		13-14		14-15		15-16		16-17	
NWC1	5	NWCP	18	NWCP	8	NWCP	5	NWCP	8	NWCP	8	NWCP	9	NWCP	4	NWCP	1	NP1N	5
FAC	P	FAC	1Q	FAC	EP	FAC	P	FAC	EP	FAC	EPr	FAC	EPr	FAC	EP	FAC	1Q	FAC	1Q
FAV	1P	FAV	1P	FAV	1P	FAV	1P	FAV	1P	FAV	2Q	FAV	2Q	FAV	1P	FAV	2P	FAT	P

COLWYN BAY

Club Contact Details
Llanelian Road, Old Colwyn, North Wales LL29 8UN
01492 514 680
pauledwardscbfc@gmail.com

Founded: 1881   **Nickname:** The Bay / Seagulls   **Manager:** Phil Hadland
Previous Names: Colwyn Bay United 1907
Previous Leagues: North Wales Coast 1898-1900. 1901-21, 33-35, Welsh National 1921-30, North Wales Combination 1930-31,
Welsh League (North) 1945-84, North West Counties 1984-91. Northern Premier 1991-2011. Football Conference 2011-15.

Club Colours (change): Sky blue and claret/sky blue/claret (Yellow/mid blue/yellow)

Ground Capacity: 2,500   **Seats:** 500   **Covered:** 700   **Clubhouse:** Yes   **Shop:** Yes
Previous Grounds: Eirias Park >1984.
Record Attendance: 5,000 v Borough United at Eirias Park 1964

RECORDS
Goalscorer: Peter Donnelly
Appearances: Bryn A Jones

HONOURS
FA Comps: None
League: North Wales Football Combination 1930-31. Welsh League (North) 1964-65, 80-81, 82-83, 83-84.
Northern Division One 1991-92.
County FA: None

07-08		08-09		09-10		10-11		11-12		12-13		13-14		14-15		15-16		16-17	
NP1S	7	NP1N	4	NP1N	4	NP P	2	Conf N	12	Conf N	18	Conf N	12	Conf N	20	NP P	23	NP1N	15
FAC	2Q	FAC	P	FAC	P	FAC	2Qr	FAC	2Q	FAC	3Qr	FAC	4Q	FAC	3Qr	FAC	1Q	FAC	1Q
FAT	1P	FAT	1Qr	FAT	P	FAT	2Q	FAT	1P	FAT	3Q	FAT	3Q	FAT	3Q	FAT	1Q	FAT	1Qr

DROYLSDEN

Club Contact Details
The Butchers Arms Ground, Market Street, Droylsden, M43 7AY

0161 370 1426

windowsindenton@gmail.com

Founded: 1892   **Nickname:** The Bloods   **Manager:** David Pace

Previous Names: None

Previous Leagues: Manchester, Lancashire Combination 1936-39, 50-68, Cheshire County 1939-50, 68-82, North West Counties 1982-87, Northern Premier 1986-2004

Club Colours (change): All red with black trim (Yellow with blue trim/blue/blue)

Ground Capacity: 3,000   **Seats:** 500   **Covered:** 2,000   **Clubhouse:** Yes   **Shop:** Yes

Previous Grounds: None

Record Attendance: 15,000 v Hyde United, Manchester League, 1921.

RECORDS

Victory: 13-2 v Lucas Sports Club

Goalscorer: E. Gillibrand - 275 (1931-35)

Appearances: Paul Phillips - 326

Additional: Received £11,000 from Crewe Alexandra for Tony Naylor 1990

Defeat: 1-13 v Chorley, Northern Prmeier Premier Division, 05/04/2014.

HONOURS

FA Comps: None

League: Manchester 1930-31, 32-33. North West Counties Division Two 1986-87. Northern Premier Division One 1998-99. Conference North 2006-07.

County FA: Manchester Junior Cup 1922-23, Manchester Premier Cup x12 - Firstly in 1946-47 and most recently in 2009-10, Manchester Senior Cup 1972-73, 75-76, 78-79.

	07-08		08-09		09-10		10-11		11-12		12-13		13-14		14-15		15-16		16-17	
	Conf	24	Conf N	7	Conf N	5	Conf N	8	Conf N	9	Conf N	21	NP P	24	NP1N	10	NP1N	19	NP1N	13
	FAC	1P	FAC	2Pr	FAC	2Q	FAC	2Pr	FAC	4Qr	FAC	2Q	FAC	1Q	FAC	2Q	FAC	3Q	FAC	Pr
	FAT	3P	FAT	3Q	FAT	3Q	FAT	3Pr	FAT	2P	FAT	3Q	FAT	1Q	FAT	P	FAT	P	FAT	Pr

GLOSSOP NORTH END

Club Contact Details
Surrey Street, Glossop, Derbys SK13 7AJ

01457 855 469

lesleyodonnell1971@sky.com

Founded: 1886   **Nickname:** Peakites / The Hillmen   **Manager:** Steve Halford & Paul Phillips

Previous Names: Glossop North End 1886-1896 and Glossop FC 1898-1992. Reformed in 1992.

Previous Leagues: North Cheshire 1890-94. Combination 1894-96. Midland 1896-98. The Football League 1898-1918. Lancashire Comb. 1919 -20, 57-66. Manchester 1920-57, 66-78. Cheshire County (Founder member) 1978-82. North West Counties (FM)1982-2015.

Club Colours (change): All royal blue with white stripe and trim (Orange/black/orange).

Ground Capacity: 2,374   **Seats:** 209   **Covered:** 509   **Clubhouse:** Yes   **Shop:** Yes

Previous Grounds: Pyegrove. Silk Street. Water Lane. Cemetery Road. North Road 1890-1955.

Record Attendance: 10,736 v Preston North End F.A. Cup 1913-1914

RECORDS

HONOURS

FA Comps: None

League: Manchester 1927-28. North West Counties Premier Division 2014-15.

County FA: Manchester FA Premier Cup 1996-97, 97-98. Derbyshire Senior Cup 2000-01.

	07-08		08-09		09-10		10-11		11-12		12-13		13-14		14-15		15-16		16-17	
	NWC1	7	NWCP	5	NWCP	7	NWCP	14	NWCP	6	NWCP	13	NWCP	3	NWCP	1	NP1N	4	NP1N	8
	FAC	P	FAC	P	FAC	1Q	FAC	1Q	FAC	EP	FAC	P	FAC	1Q	FAC	2Q	FAC	1Qr	FAC	Pr
	FAV	1P	FAV	F	FAV	3P	FAV	1P	FAV	3P	FAV	2Qr	FAV	2P	FAV	F	FAT	Pr	FAT	1Q

GOOLE AFC

Club Contact Details
Victoria Pleasure Gardens, Marcus Road, Goole DN14 6TN
01405 762 794 (Match days)
andym236566609@aol.com

Founded: 1997   **Nickname:** The Vikings   **Manager:** Karl Rose
Previous Names: Goole Town > 1996.
Previous Leagues: Central Midlands 1997-98.
         Northern Counties East 2000-04.

Club Colours (change): Red & black stripes/red/red (Dark & light blue/dark blue/dark blue)

Ground Capacity: 3,000   **Seats:** 300   **Covered:** 800   **Clubhouse:** Yes   **Shop:** Yes
Previous Grounds: None
Record Attendance: 976 v Leeds United - 1999

RECORDS
Goalscorer: Kevin Severn (1997-2001)
Appearances: Phil Dobson - 187 (1999-2001)

HONOURS
FA Comps: None
League: Central Midlands 1997-98.
         Northern Counties East Division One 1999-2000, Premier Division 2003-04.
County FA: West Riding County Cup 2006-07.

07-08		08-09		09-10		10-11		11-12		12-13		13-14		14-15		15-16		16-17	
NP 1	9	NP1S	18	NP1S	18	NP1S	13	NP1S	10	NP1N	21	NP1S	13	NP1S	16	NP1S	19	NP1N	21
FAC	P	FAC	P	FAC	P	FAC	P	FAC	Pr	FAC	P	FAC	P	FAC	Pr	FAC	1Qr	FAC	P
FAT	P	FAT	1Q	FAT	1Q	FAT	1Q	FAT	Pr	FAT	Pr	FAT	P	FAT	2Q	FAT	1Q	FAT	1Qr

HYDE UNITED

Club Contact Details
Ewen Fields, Walker Lane, Hyde SK14 5PL
0161 367 7273
gmbranchpcs@gmail.com

Founded: 1919   **Nickname:** The Tigers   **Manager:** Darren Kelly
Previous Names: Hyde United 1919-2010, Hyde F.C. 2010-15.
Previous Leagues: Lancashire & Cheshire 1919-21, Manchester 1921-30, Cheshire County 1930-68, 1970-82,
         Northern Premier 1968-70, 1983-2004. Football Conference 2004-15.

Club Colours (change): Red/white/red (Yellow & black stripes/black/black)

Ground Capacity: 4,250   **Seats:** 530   **Covered:** 4,073   **Clubhouse:** Yes   **Shop:** Yes
Previous Grounds: None
Record Attendance: 7,600 v Nelson - FA Cup 1952

RECORDS
Victory: 13-1 v Eccles United, 1921-22.
Goalscorer: Pete O'Brien - 247. Ernest Gillibrand 86 goals during the 1929-30 season, including 7 against New Mills.
Appearances: Steve Johnson - 623 (1975-1988)
Additional: Paid £8,000 to Mossley for Jim McCluskie 1989
             Received £50,000 from Crewe Alexandra for Colin Little 1995

HONOURS
FA Comps: None
League: Manchester 1920-21, 21-22, 22-23, 28-29, 29-30. Cheshire 1954-55, 55-56, 81-82.
         Northern Premier Division One North 2003-04, Premier Division 2004-05. Conference North 2011-12.
County FA: Cheshire Senior Cup 1945-46, 62-63, 69-70, 80-81, 89-90, 96-97. Manchester Senior Cup 1974-75, Premier Cup 1993-94,
         94-95, 95-96, 98-99.

07-08		08-09		09-10		10-11		11-12		12-13		13-14		14-15		15-16		16-17	
Conf N	9	Conf N	20	Conf N	15	Conf N	19	Conf N	1	Conf	18	Conf	24	Conf N	22	NP P	22	NP1N	10
FAC	2Q	FAC	2Q	FAC	2Qr	FAC	2Qr	FAC	3Q	FAC	4Qr	FAC	4Q	FAC	2Q	FAC	2Qr	FAC	2Q
FAT	3Q	FAT	3Qr	FAT	3Qr	FAT	1P	FAT	1P	FAT	1Pr	FAT	1P	FAT	2P	FAT	1Qr	FAT	P

KENDAL TOWN

Club Contact Details
Pye Motors Stadium, Parkside Road, Kendal, Cumbria LA9 7BL
01539 727 472
gudge1@talk21.com

Founded: 1919   **Nickname:** The Mintcakes / The Field / The Town   **Manager:** David Foster

Previous Names: Netherfield AFC 1919-2000

Previous Leagues: Westmorland, North Lancashire Combination 1945-68, Northern Premier 1968-83, North West Counties 1983-87

Club Colours (change): Black and white stripes/black/red (Light blue/navy/navy)

Ground Capacity: 2,490   **Seats:** 450   **Covered:** 1000   **Clubhouse:** Yes   **Shop:** Yes

Previous Grounds: None

Record Attendance: 5,184 v Grimsby Town - FA Cup 1st Round 1955

RECORDS
Victory: 11-0 v Great Harwood - 22/03/1947

Defeat: 0-10 v Stalybridge Celtic - 01/09/1984

Goalscorer: Tom Brownlee

Additional: Received £10,250 from Manchester City for Andy Milner 1995

HONOURS
FA Comps: None

League: Lancashire Combination 1948-49, 64-65.

County FA: Westmorlands Senior Cup x12. Lancashire Senior Cup 2002-03.

07-08	08-09	09-10	10-11	11-12	12-13	13-14	14-15	15-16	16-17
NP P 11	NP P 5	NP P 5	NP P 8	NP P 11	NP P 21	NP1N 10	NP1N 16	NP1N 15	NP1N 12
FAC 4Q	FAC 2Q	FAC 4Q	FAC 1Q	FAC 3Q	FAC 3Q	FAC P	FAC Pr	FAC 2Q	FAC P
FAT 2Q	FAT 1Q	FAT 1Q	FAT 3Q	FAT 2Qr	FAT 1Qr	FAT 1Qr	FAT P	FAT 1Q	FAT 2Q

MOSSLEY

Club Contact Details
Seel Park, Market Street, Mossley, Lancashire OL5 0ES
01457 832 369
john.wharmby@mossleyfc.com

Founded: 1903   **Nickname:** Lilywhites   **Manager:** Peter Band & Lloyd Morrison

Previous Names: Park Villa 1903-04, Mossley Juniors

Previous Leagues: Ashton, South East Lancashire, Lancashire Combination 1918-19, Cheshire County 1919-72, Northern Premier 1972-95, North West Counties 1995-2004

Club Colours (change): White/black/black (Orange/black/black)

Ground Capacity: 4,000   **Seats:** 220   **Covered:** 1,500   **Clubhouse:** Yes   **Shop:** Yes

Previous Grounds: Moved to Seel Park in 1911.

Record Attendance: 7,000 v Stalybridge Celtic 1950

RECORDS
Victory: 9-0 v Urmston, Manchester Shield, 1947

Defeat: 2-13 v Witton Albion, Cheshire League, 1926

Goalscorer: David Moore - 235 (1974-84). Jackie Roscoe scored 58 during the 1930-31 season.

Appearances: Jimmy O'Connor - 613 (1972-87)

Additional: Paid £2,300 to Altrincham for Phil Wilson
Received £25,000 from Everton for Eamonn O'Keefe

HONOURS
FA Comps: None

League: Ashton & District 1911-12, 14-15. Northern Premier 1978-79, 79-80, Division One 2005-06.

County FA: Manchester Premier Cup 1937-38, 48-49, 60-61, 66-67, 67-68, 88-89, 90-91, 2011-12, 12-13, 14-15, 15-16. Manchester Challenge Trophy 2011-12.

07-08	08-09	09-10	10-11	11-12	12-13	13-14	14-15	15-16	16-17
NP1N 15	NP1N 10	NP1N 7	NP1N 15	NP1N 14	NP1N 5	NP1N 15	NP1N 7	NP1N 13	NP1N 17
FAC Pr	FAC 3Q	FAC P	FAC 4Q	FAC Pr	FAC Pr	FAC Pr	FAC Pr	FAC Pr	FAC 1Q
FAT 1Q	FAT P	FAT 3Qr	FAT 2Q	FAT P	FAT 1Qr	FAT 2Q	FAT 1Q	FAT 1Q	FAT 1Q

OSSETT ALBION

Club Contact Details
Queens Terrace, Dimple Wells, Ossett, Yorkshire WF5 8JU
01924 273 746
simonturfrey@aol.com

Founded: 1944   **Nickname:** Albion   **Manager:** Richard Tracey
Previous Names: None
Previous Leagues: Heavy Woollen Area 1944-49, West Riding County Amateur 1949-50, West Yorkshire 1950-57,
Yorkshire 1957-82, Northern Counties East 1982-2004

Club Colours (change): Gold/black/black (All white)

Ground Capacity: 3,000   **Seats:** Yes   **Covered:** 750   **Clubhouse:** Yes   **Shop:** Yes
Previous Grounds: Fearn House
Record Attendance: 1,200 v Leeds United - Opening of floodlights 1986

RECORDS
Victory: 12-0 v British Ropes (H) - Yorkshire League Division 2 06/05/1959
Defeat: 2-11 v Swillington (A) - West Yorkshire League Division 1 25/04/1956
Goalscorer: John Balmer
Appearances: Peter Eaton - 800+ (22 years)

HONOURS
FA Comps: None
League: Yorkshire Division One 1974-75, Division Two 78-79, 80-81. Northern Counties East Division One 1986-87, Premier Division
1998-99, 2003-04.
County FA: West Riding County Cup 1964-65, 65-66, 67-68, 98-99.

07-08		08-09		09-10		10-11		11-12		12-13		13-14		14-15		15-16		16-17	
NP1N	6	NP1N	6	NP1N	21	NP1N	22	NP1N	18	NP1N	20	NP1N	21	NP1N	17	NP1N	10	NP1N	18
FAC	P	FAC	P	FAC	2Q	FAC	1Q	FAC	P	FAC	4Q	FAC	P	FAC	1Q	FAC	1Q	FAC	1Q
FAT	P	FAT	P	FAT	P	FAT	1Q	FAT	P	FAT	P	FAT	P	FAT	P	FAT	Pr	FAT	Pr

OSSETT TOWN

Club Contact Details
The 4G Voice & Data Stadium, Ingfield, Prospect Road, Ossett, Wakefield WF5 9HA
01924 272 960
ossetttownfc@gmail.com

Founded: 1936   **Nickname:** Town   **Manager:** Grant Black
Previous Names: None
Previous Leagues: Leeds 1936-39, Yorkshire 1945-82, Northern Counties East 1983-99

Club Colours (change): All red with white trim (All blue with white trim)

Ground Capacity: 1,950   **Seats:** 360   **Covered:** 1,000   **Clubhouse:** Yes   **Shop:** Yes
Previous Grounds: Wakefield Road 1936-39. Back Lane 1939-57.
Record Attendance: 2,600 v Manchester United - Friendly 1989

RECORDS
Victory: 10-1 v Harrogate RA (H) - Northern Counties East 27/04/1993
Defeat: 0-7 v Easington Colliery - FA Vase 08/10/1983
Goalscorer: Dave Leadbitter
Appearances: Steve Worsfold
Additional: Received £1,350 from Swansea Town for Dereck Blackburn

HONOURS
FA Comps: None
League: Northern Counties East Division Two 1988-89.
County FA: West Riding Senior Cup 1949-50, County Cup 1958-59, 81-82.

07-08		08-09		09-10		10-11		11-12		12-13		13-14		14-15		15-16		16-17	
NP P	18	NP P	12	NP P	19	NP P	21	NP1N	17	NP1N	12	NP1N	8	NP1N	18	NP1N	17	NP1N	4
FAC	1Q	FAC	1Q	FAC	2Q	FAC	1Q	FAC	1Q	FAC	1Qr	FAC	3Q	FAC	1Q	FAC	P	FAC	2Q
FAT	1P	FAT	1P	FAT	1Q	FAT	1Q	FAT	3Qr	FAT	1P	FAT	P	FAT	1Qr	FAT	P	FAT	P

PRESCOT CABLES

Club Contact Details
Valerie Park, Eaton Street, Prescot L34 6HD

0151 430 0507

howard.nulty@sthelenslaw.co.uk

Founded: 1884   **Nickname:** Tigers   **Manager:** Brian Richardson

Previous Names: Prescot > 1995

Previous Leagues: Liverpool County Combination, Lancashire Combination 1897-98, 1918-20, 27-33, 36-76, Mid Cheshire 1976-78, Cheshire County 1978-82, North West Counties 1982-2003

Club Colours (change): Amber & black/black/black (All red)

Ground Capacity: 3,200   **Seats:** 500   **Covered:** 600   **Clubhouse:** Yes   **Shop:** Yes

Previous Grounds: None

Record Attendance: 8,122 v Ashton National - 1932

RECORDS

Victory:	18-3 v Great Harwood - 1954-55
Defeat:	1-12 v Morecambe - 1936-37
Goalscorer:	Freddie Crampton
Appearances:	Harry Grisedale

HONOURS

FA Comps: None

League: Lancashire Combination Division Two 1951-52, Premier 1956-57. Mid-Cheshire 1976-77. Cheshire County Division Two 1979-80. North West Counties 2002-03.

County FA: Liverpool Challenge Cup 1927-28, 28-29, 29-30, 48-49, 61-62, 77-78. Liverpool Non-League Cup 1952-53, 58-59, 60-61. Liverpool Senior Cup 2016-17.

07-08	08-09	09-10	10-11	11-12	12-13	13-14	14-15	15-16	16-17
NP P 13	NP P 22	NP1N 15	NP1N 21	NP1N 16	NP1N 17	NP1N 20	NP1N 20	NP1N 16	NP1N 16
FAC 2Qr	FAC 3Q	FAC P	FAC 1Qr	FAC P	FAC 1Q	FAC 1Q	FAC 1Q	FAC P	FAC P
FAT 1Q	FAT 1Q	FAT P	FAT 1Q	FAT P	FAT 1Q	FAT P	FAT 1Q	FAT P	FAT 1Q

RADCLIFFE BOROUGH

Club Contact Details
Stainton Park, Pilkington Road, Radcliffe, Lancashire M26 3PE

0161 724 8346

ric.fielding@radcliffeboro.com

Founded: 1949   **Nickname:** Boro   **Manager:** Joe Gibbons

Previous Names: None

Previous Leagues: South East Lancashire, Manchester 1953-63, Lancashire Combination 1963-71, Cheshire County 1971-82, North West Counties 1982-97

Club Colours (change): Royal blue & white hoops/royal blue/white (Black & red hoops/black/black)

Ground Capacity: 4,000   **Seats:** 350   **Covered:** 1,000   **Clubhouse:** Yes   **Shop:** Yes

Previous Grounds: Ashworth Street. Bright Street > 1970.

Record Attendance: 2,495 v York City - FA Cup 1st Round 2000-01

RECORDS

Goalscorer:	Ian Lunt - 147. Jody Banim scored 46 during a single season.
Appearances:	Simon Kelly - 502
Additional:	Paid £5,000 to Buxton for Gary Walker 1991 Received £20,000 from Shrewsbury Town for Jody Banim 2003

HONOURS

FA Comps: None

League: South Lancashire Division Two 1950-51, Division One 51-52, Premier 80-81. North West Counties Division Two 1982-83, Division One 84-85. Northern Premier Division One 1996-97.

County FA: Manchester Premier Cup 2007-08.

07-08	08-09	09-10	10-11	11-12	12-13	13-14	14-15	15-16	16-17
NP1N 16	NP1N 16	NP1N 10	NP1N 18	NP1N 15	NP1N 15	NP1N 18	NP1N 19	NP1N 18	NP1N 20
FAC 2Q	FAC P	FAC 3Q	FAC 1Q	FAC 3Q	FAC Pr	FAC 1Q	FAC 1Q	FAC P	FAC 1Q
FAT 3Q	FAT 1Q	FAT 1Qr	FAT 2Qr	FAT 2Qr	FAT 1Q	FAT 1Q	FAT P	FAT 2Q	FAT P

RAMSBOTTOM UNITED

Club Contact Details
The Harry Williams Stadium, Acrebottom (off Bridge Street) BL0 0BS.
01706 822 799
secretary@rammyunited.co.uk

Founded: 1966   **Nickname:** The Rams   **Manager:** Mark fell
Previous Names: None
Previous Leagues: Bury Amateur 1966-69. Bolton Combination 1969-89. Manchester 1989-95. North West Counties 1995-2012.

Club Colours (change): Blue/blue/white (Red/black/red).

Ground Capacity: 2,000   **Seats:** Yes   **Covered:** Yes   **Clubhouse:** Yes   **Shop:** No
Previous Grounds: None
Record Attendance: 2,104 v FC United of Manchester, Northern Premier League Premier Division, 04/04/15.

RECORDS
Victory: 9-0 v Stantondale (H), NWCFL Division Two, 9th November 1996.
Defeat: 0-7 v Salford City (A), NWCFL Division One, 16th November 2002.
Goalscorer: Russell Brierley - 176 (1996-2003). Russell Brierley scored 38 during the 1999-2000 season.

HONOURS
FA Comps: None
League: Bolton Combination Division One 1972-73, Premier Division 76-77. Manchester Division One 1990-91.
North West Counties Division Two 1996-97, Premier Division 2011-12.
County FA: None

07-08		08-09		09-10		10-11		11-12		12-13		13-14		14-15		15-16		16-17	
NWC1	16	NWCP	14	NWCP	4	NWCP	2	NWCP	1	NP1N	6	NP1N	5	NP P	17	NP P	24	NP1N	14
FAC	EP	FAC	P	FAC	P	FAC	1Q	FAC	1Q	FAC	1Q	FAC	2Q	FAC	1Q	FAC	1Q	FAC	P
FAV	2Q	FAV	1P	FAV	1P	FAV	1P	FAV	2P	FAT	2Q	FAT	3Q	FAT	1P	FAT	1Qr	FAT	3Q

SCARBOROUGH ATHLETIC

Club Contact Details
Flamingo Land Stadium, Scarborough Leisure Village, Ashburn Rd YO11 2JW
01723 379 113
club.secretary@seadogtrust.com

Founded: 2007   **Nickname:** The Seadogs   **Manager:** Steve Kittrick - Jan 2016
Previous Names: Formed after Scarborough F.C. folded in 2007.
Previous Leagues: Northern Counties East 2007-13.

Club Colours (change): Red & white hoops/red/red (Sky blue & white stripes/white/white).

Ground Capacity: 2,000   **Seats:** 250   **Covered:** Yes   **Clubhouse:** Yes   **Shop:** No
Previous Grounds: Queensgate - Bridlington FC >2017.
Record Attendance: 2,038 v Sheffield United, Opening of the new ground friendly, 15/07/2017.

RECORDS
Victory: 13-0 v Brodsworth, Northern Counties East, 2009-10.
Defeat: 0-6 v Thackley 16/04/2013 and AFC Telford United 16/11/2013.
Goalscorer: Ryan Blott - 231, including 42 scored during the 2008-09 season and 5 each against Yorkshire Amateur's (08/11/08)
and Armthorpe Welfare (14/04/12).
Appearances: Ryan Blott - 376 (20/10/07 - 29/04/16).

HONOURS
FA Comps: None
League: Northern Counties East Division One 2008-09, Premier 2012-13.

County FA: None

07-08		08-09		09-10		10-11		11-12		12-13		13-14		14-15		15-16		16-17	
NCE1	5	NCE1	1	NCEP	5	NCEP	10	NCEP	3	NCEP	1	NP1S	7	NP1N	6	NP1N	20	NP1N	3
				FAC	EP	FAC	P	FAC	1Q	FAC	EP	FAC	2Q	FAC	2Q	FAC	P	FAC	P
		FAV	4P	FAV	2P	FAV	3P	FAV	1P	FAV	1P	FAT	3Q	FAT	1Q	FAT	P	FAT	P

SKELMERSDALE UNITED

Club Contact Details
Prescot Cables FC, Valerie Park, Eaton Street, Prescot L34 6HD
01695 722 123
alangreenhalgh@live.co.uk

Founded: 1882   **Nickname:** Skem / Blueboys   **Manager:** Alan Rogers
Previous Names: Skelmsdale Young Rovers. Skelmersdale Wesleyans.
Previous Leagues: Liverpool County Combination, Lancashire Combination 1891-93, 1903-07, 21-24, 55-56, 76-78,
       Cheshire County 1968-71, 78-82, Northern Premier 1971-76, North West Counties 1983-2006

Club Colours (change): All blue (Yellow/black/black)

Ground Capacity: 3,200   **Seats:** 500   **Covered:** 600   **Clubhouse:** Yes   **Shop:** Yes
Previous Grounds: White Moss Park >2002. Westgate Interactive Stadium 2002-04. West Lancashire College Stadium 2004-17.
Record Attendance: 7,000 v Slough Town - FA Amateur Cup Semi-final 1967

RECORDS
Goalscorer: Stuart Rudd - 230
Appearances: Robbie Holcroft - 422 including 398 consecutively
Additional: Paid £2,000 for Stuart Rudd
       Received £4,000 for Stuart Rudd

HONOURS
FA Comps: FA Amateur Cup 1970-71. Barassi Anglo-Italian Cup 1970-71.
League: Northern Premier Division One North 2013-14.
County FA: Lancashire Junior Cup x2. Lancashire Non-League Cup x2. Liverpool Senior Cup 2014-15.

07-08		08-09		09-10		10-11		11-12		12-13		13-14		14-15		15-16		16-17	
NP1N	3	NP1N	2	NP1N	5	NP1N	2	NP1N	7	NP1N	1	NP P	6	NP P	7	NP P	16	NP P	24
FAC	2Q	FAC	1Q	FAC	P	FAC	2Q	FAC	P	FAC	2Q	FAC	2Q	FAC	2Q	FAC	2Q	FAC	1Qr
FAT	1Q	FAT	1P	FAT	2Q	FAT	1Q	FAT	P	FAT	3P	FAT	1Q	FAT	1Q	FAT	1Pr	FAT	1Q

SOUTH SHIELDS

Club Contact Details
Mariners Park, Shaftesbury Avenue, Jarrow, Tyne & Wear NE32 3UP
0191 4547800
philip.reay@southshieldsfc.co.uk

Founded: 1974   **Nickname:** Mariners   **Manager:** Graham Fenton & Lee Picton
Previous Names: South Shields Mariners.
Previous Leagues: Northern Alliance 1974-76, Wearside 1976-95.

Club Colours (change): Claret & blue/white/white

Ground Capacity: 3,500   **Seats:** Yes   **Covered:** Yes   **Clubhouse:** Yes   **Shop:** No
Previous Grounds: Filtrona Park (renamed Mariners Park in 2015) 1992-2013. Eden Lane 2013-15.
Record Attendance: 3,464 v Coleshill Town, FA Vase semi-final, 2016-17.

RECORDS

HONOURS
FA Comps: FA Vase 2016-17.
League: Northern Alliance 1975-76. Wearside 1976-77, 92-93, 94-95. Northern Division Two 2015-16, Division One 2016-17.
County FA: Monkwearmouth Charity Cup 1986-87. Durham Senior Challenge Cup 2016-17.

07-08		08-09		09-10		10-11		11-12		12-13		13-14		14-15		15-16		16-17	
NL 2	2	NL 1	19	NL 1	11	NL 1	11	NL 1	13	NL 1	23	NL 2	17	NL 2	15	NL 2	1	NL 1	1
FAC	P	FAC	P	FAC	EP	FAC	Pr	FAC	Pr	FAC	1Q	FAC	Pr					FAC	EP
FAV	1Qr	FAV	1Q	FAV	1P	FAV	1P	FAV	1P	FAV	1P	FAV	1P	FAV	2Q	FAV	3P	FAV	F

TADCASTER ALBION

Club Contact Details
i2i Stadium, Ings Lane, Tadcaster LS24 9AY
01904 606 000
ian.nottingham@enteri2i.com

Founded: 1892   **Nickname:** The Brewers / Taddy   **Manager:** Michael Morton
Previous Names: John Smith's FC > 1923.
Previous Leagues: York, Harrogate, Yorkshire 1973-82. Northern Counties East 1982-2016.

Club Colours (change): White & blue

Ground Capacity: 2,000   **Seats:** 159   **Covered:** 259   **Clubhouse:** Yes   **Shop:** No
Previous Grounds: None
Record Attendance: 1,307 v Highworth Town, FA Vase, 2014-15.

RECORDS
Victory: 13-0 v Blidworth Welfare, NCEL Division One, 1997-98
Defeat: 10-2 v Thackley, 1984-85

HONOURS
FA Comps: None
League: York Division One 1909-10, 23-24, 32-33, Premier 47-48.
       Northern Counties East Division One 2009-10, Premier Division 2015-16.
County FA: None

07-08	08-09	09-10	10-11	11-12	12-13	13-14	14-15	15-16	16-17
NCE1 12	NCE1 17	NCE1 1	NCEP 4	NCEP 8	NCEP 6	NCEP 2	NCEP 3	NCEP 1	NP1N 19
FAC EP	FAC EP		FAC 1Qr	FAC 2Q	FAC 3Q	FAC EPr	FAC P	FAC P	FAC 2Q
FAV 2Q	FAV 1P	FAV 1P	FAV 4P	FAV 2P	FAV 1Q	FAV 1Q	FAV QFr	FAV 3P	FAT P

TRAFFORD

Club Contact Details
First Point, Shawe View, Pennybridge Lane, Flixton Urmston M41 5AQ
0161 747 1727
foxxytfc18@gmail.com

Founded: 1990   **Nickname:** The North   **Manager:** Tom Baker
Previous Names: North Trafford 1990-94
Previous Leagues: Mid Cheshire 1990-92, North West Counties 1992-97, 2003-08, Northern Premier 1997-2003

Club Colours (change): All white (All yellow)

Ground Capacity: 2,500   **Seats:** 292   **Covered:** 740   **Clubhouse:** Yes   **Shop:** Yes
Previous Grounds: None
Record Attendance: 803 v Flixton - Northern Premier League Division 1 1997-98. 2,238 (at Altrincham FC) FAC P v FC United

RECORDS
Victory: 10-0 v Haslingden St.Mary's (Lancs Amt Shield 1991)
Goalscorer: Scott Barlow - 100
Appearances: Lee Southwood - 311
Additional: NWC League Record: 18 consecutive league wins in 2007-08
              Most Points In One Season: 95 points from 38 games 2007-08

HONOURS
FA Comps: None
League: North West Counties Division One 1996-97, 2007-08.

County FA: Manchester Challenge Trophy 2004-05.

07-08	08-09	09-10	10-11	11-12	12-13	13-14	14-15	15-16	16-17
NWC1 1	NP1N 15	NP1N 12	NP1N 14	NP1N 12	NP1N 4	NP P 10	NP P 23	NP1N 8	NP1N 6
FAC P	FAC P	FAC Pr	FAC 1Q	FAC 1Q	FAC 3Q	FAC 3Q	FAC 1Q	FAC P	FAC 2Q
FAV 3P	FAT 1Q	FAT P	FAT P	FAT P	FAT 2Q	FAT 2Q	FAT 2Q	FAT P	FAT 2Q

Northern Premier League
Division One South.
Photos: Keith Clayton.

Steve Tames (Witton) sets off
on a run despite the Newcastle
Town player looking to halt him.

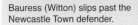

Steve Tames (Witton) crashes home the first goal against Rushden.

Bauress (Witton) slips past the
Newcastle Town defender.

The hand of Steggles (Carlton)
denies Hopley and Tames
(Witton).

ALVECHURCH

Club Contact Details
Lye Meadow, Redditch Road, Alvechurch B48 7RS
0121 445 2929
alvechurchfc@btinternet.com

Founded: 1929　　**Nickname:** The Church　　　　　　　**Manager:** Ian Long
Previous Names: Alvechurch FC >1993. Re-formed in 1994 as Alvechurch Villa > 1996.
Previous Leagues: Worcestershire Combination/Midland Combination 1961-73, 94-2003. West Midlands (Reg) 1973-78. Southern 1978-93. Midland Alliance 2003-14. Midland Football League 2014-17.

Club Colours (change): Amber & black.

Ground Capacity: 3,000　**Seats:** 100　　**Covered:** 300　　**Clubhouse:** Yes　**Shop:**
Previous Grounds: Played in the local park until moving to Lye Meadow.
Record Attendance: 13,500 v Enfield, FA Amateur Cup Quarter-final, 1964-65.

RECORDS
Victory:　　　13-0 v (A) Alcester Town.
Defeat:　　　0-9 v (H) Coalville Town.
Goalscorer:　Graham Allner. Keith Rostill scored 53 goals during the 2002-03 season.
Appearances: Kevin Palmer.
Additional:　Paid £3,000 to Worcester City for Peter Gocan, 1989. Received £34,000 from Aston Villa for Andy Comyn, 1989. In 1971, the club played out the longest FA Cup tie in history when it took six games to beat Oxford City in the 4Q Round.

HONOURS
FA Comps: None
League: Worcestershire Combination Division 1962-63, 64-65, 66-67. Midland Combination Division One 1971-72, Premier 2002-03.
　　　West Midlands (Reg) Premier 1973-74, 74-75, 75-76, 76-77. Southern Midland Division 1980-81. Midland Football Premier 2016-17.
County FA: Worcestershire Senior Cup 1972-73, 73-74, 76-77, Senior Urn 2003-04, 04-05, 07-08, 12-13.

07-08		08-09		09-10		10-11		11-12		12-13		13-14		14-15		15-16		16-17	
MidAl	14	MidAl	10	MidAl	7	MidAl	20	MidAl	13	MidAl	11	MidAl	13	MFLP	15	MFLP	2	MFLP	1
FAC	1Q	FAC	P	FAC	P	FAC	EP	FAC	1Q	FAC	EPr	FAC	EP	FAC	EP	FAC	P	FAC	P
FAV	2Pr	FAV	1P	FAV	2Q	FAV	2Q	FAV	2Q	FAV	2Q	FAV	3P	FAV	1Q	FAV	4P	FAV	2P

BASFORD UNITED

Club Contact Details
Greenwich Avenue, off Bagnall Road, Basford, Nottingham NG6 0LD
0115 924 4491
traciewitton@basfordunitedfc.co.uk

Founded: 1900　　**Nickname:** Community　　　　　　　**Manager:** Martin Carruthers
Previous Names: None
Previous Leagues: Notts Alliance 1905-39, 1946-2004. Notts Amateur League 1939-46. Notts Amateur Alliance 2004-06. Notts Senior 2006-11. Central Midlands 2011-12. East Midlands Counties 2012-13. Northern Counties East 2013-14. Midland League 2014-15.

Club Colours (change): All amber (All white)

Ground Capacity:　　**Seats:**　　**Covered:** Yes　　**Clubhouse:** Yes　**Shop:**
Previous Grounds: Old Peer Tree Inn, Dolly Tub > 1903, Catchems Corner 1903-30, Vernon Avenue 1930-34, Mill Street 1934-91.
Record Attendance: 3,500 v Grantham United, FACup 1937.

RECORDS
Misc:　　　Former club secretary, Wallace Brownlow, who took up the post when 19 in 1907, remained in the position until his death in 1970 - a world record of 63 years.

HONOURS
FA Comps: None
League: Notts Alliance 1905-06, 07-08, 19-20, Division One 1997-98. Central Midlands Southern 2011-12.
　　　East Midland Counties 2012-13. Midland Football Premier Division 2014-15.
County FA: Notts Senior Cup 1946-47, 87-88, 2014-15, 15-16, Intermediate Cup 2005-06.

07-08		08-09		09-10		10-11		11-12		12-13		13-14		14-15		15-16		16-17	
NottS	5	NottS	3	NottS	2	NottS	2	CMSth	1	EMC	1	NCEP	5	MFLP	1	NP1S	4	NP1S	6
												FAC	1Q	FAC	Pr	FAC	2Q	FAC	P
										FAV	2P	FAV	2Q	FAV	2Q	FAT	2Q	FAT	P

BEDWORTH UNITED

Club Contact Details
The Oval, Coventry Road, Bedworth CV12 8NN
02476 314 752
andrew.stickley@live.co.uk

Founded: 1895   **Nickname:** Greenbacks   **Manager:** Stuart Storer
Previous Names: Bedworth Town 1947-68
Previous Leagues: Birmingham Combination 1947-54, Birmingham/West Midlands 1954-72. Southern 1972-2013, 14-16.
Northern Premier 2013-14.

Club Colours (change): All green (Yellow/blue/yellow)

Ground Capacity: 3,000   **Seats:** 300   **Covered:** 300   **Clubhouse:** Yes   **Shop:** Yes
Previous Grounds: British Queen Ground 1911-39
Record Attendance: 5,172 v Nuneaton Borough - Southern League Midland Division 23/02/1982

RECORDS
Goalscorer: Peter Spacey - 1949-69
Appearances: Peter Spacey - 1949-69
Additional: Paid £1,750 to Hinckley Town for Colin Taylor 1991-92
Received £30,000 from Plymouth Argyle for Richard Landon

HONOURS
FA Comps: None
League: Birmingham Combination 1948-49, 49-50.

County FA: Birmingham Senior Cup 1978-79, 80-81, 81-82.

07-08		08-09		09-10		10-11		11-12		12-13		13-14		14-15		15-16		16-17	
SthM	15	SthM	14	SthM	16	SthC	15	SthC	3	SthP	21	NP1S	20	SthC	4	SthP	21	NP1S	11
FAC	2Q	FAC	Pr	FAC	4Q	FAC	2Q	FAC	1Q	FAC	2Q	FAC	P	FAC	2Qr	FAC	2Q	FAC	3Q
FAT	1Qr	FAT	2Q	FAT	P	FAT	1Q	FAT	1Q	FAT	1Q	FAT	P	FAT	P	FAT	1Q	FAT	1Q

BELPER TOWN

Club Contact Details
The Marstons Stadium, Christchurch Meadow, Bridge Street, Belper DE56 1BA
01773 825 549
wright.ian24@gmail.com

Founded: 1883   **Nickname:** The Nailers   **Manager:** Antony Danylyk & Paul Donnelly
Previous Names: None
Previous Leagues: Derbyshire Senior (Founder members) 1890-1911. Notts & Derbyshire (FM) 1911-12. Central Alliance 1957-61,
Midland Counties 1961-82, Northern Counties East 1982-97

Club Colours (change): Yellow/black/black (All white)

Ground Capacity: 2,650   **Seats:** 500   **Covered:** 850   **Clubhouse:** Yes   **Shop:** Yes
Previous Grounds: Acorn Ground > 1951
Record Attendance: 3,200 v Ilkeston Town - 1955

RECORDS
Victory: 15-2 v Nottingham Forest 'A' - 1956
Defeat: 0-12 v Goole Town - 1965
Goalscorer: Mick Lakin - 231
Appearances: Craig Smithurst - 678
Additional: Paid £2,000 to Ilkeston Town for Jamie Eaton 2001
Received £2,000 from Hinckley United for Craig Smith

HONOURS
FA Comps: None
League: Central Alliance 1958-59. Midland Counties 1979-80. Northern Counties East 1984-85.

County FA: Derbyshire Senior Cup 1958-59, 61-62, 63-64, 79-80, 2007-08.

07-08		08-09		09-10		10-11		11-12		12-13		13-14		14-15		15-16		16-17	
NP 1	8	NP1S	2	NP1S	6	NP1S	14	NP1S	6	NP1S	3	NP1S	4	NP P	24	NP1S	13	NP1S	10
FAC	3Q	FAC	4Qr	FAC	Pr	FAC	P	FAC	P	FAC	2Qr	FAC	2Q	FAC	1Qr	FAC	1Q	FAC	2Q
FAT	Pr	FAT	P	FAT	Pr	FAT	P	FAT	2Q	FAT	2Q	FAT	1Q	FAT	1Q	FAT	1Qr	FAT	P

CARLTON TOWN

Club Contact Details
Bill Stokeld Stadium, Stoke Lane, Gedling NG4 2QS
0115 940 3192
secretary.carltontownfc@gmail.com

Founded: 1904   **Nickname:** The Millers   **Manager:** Wayne Scott
Previous Names: Sneinton FC
Previous Leagues: Notts Alliance, Central Midlands, Northern Counties East

Club Colours (change): Yellow with royal blue trim/royal blue with white trim/royal blue (Red with white trim/red with white trim/red)

Ground Capacity: 1,500   **Seats:** 164   **Covered:** 100   **Clubhouse:** Yes   **Shop:** No
Previous Grounds: Club played at several grounds before moving to Stoke Lane (Bill Stokeld Stadium) in the 1990s.
Record Attendance: 1,000 - Radio Trent Charity Match

RECORDS

HONOURS
FA Comps: None
League: Notts Alliance 1905-06, 07-08, 08-09, 09-10, Division Two 1984-85, Division One 1992-93.
     Central Midlands Supreme Division 2002-03. Northern Counties East Division One 2005-06.
County FA: Notts Senior Cup 2012-13, 16-17.

07-08		08-09		09-10		10-11		11-12		12-13		13-14		14-15		15-16		16-17	
NP 1	10	NP1S	4	NP1S	9	NP1S	8	NP1S	2	NP1S	12	NP1S	10	NP1S	18	NP1S	18	NP1S	19
FAC	1Q	FAC	P	FAC	2Qr	FAC	2Q	FAC	2Q	FAC	3Q	FAC	3Q	FAC	1Q	FAC	P	FAC	P
FAT	P	FAT	1Q	FAT	2Q	FAT	1Qr	FAT	P	FAT	P	FAT	Pr	FAT	1Qr	FAT	2Q	FAT	1Q

CHASETOWN

Club Contact Details
The Scholars, Church Street, Chasetown, Walsall WS7 3QL
01543 682 222
chasetownfc@gmail.com

Founded: 1954   **Nickname:** The Scholars   **Manager:** Scott Dundas
Previous Names: Chase Terrace Old Scholars 1954-72
Previous Leagues: Cannock Youth 1954-58, Lichfield & District 1958-61, Staffordshire County 1961-72,
     West Midlands 1972-94, Midland Alliance 1994-2006, Southern 2006-09

Club Colours (change): Royal blue/royal blue/white & red (All red with white trim)

Ground Capacity: 2,000   **Seats:** 151   **Covered:** 220   **Clubhouse:** Yes   **Shop:** Yes
Previous Grounds: Burntwood Recreation
Record Attendance: 2,420 v Cardiff City - FA Cup 3rd Round January 2008

RECORDS
Victory: 14-1 v Hanford - Walsall Senior Cup 1991-92
Defeat: 1-8 v Telford United Reserves - West Midlands League
Goalscorer: Tony Dixon - 197. Mick Ward scored 39 goals during the 1987-88 season, whilst a player by the name of Keith Birch
     scored 11 in a 21-1 win over Lichfield Laundry.
Misc: The club became the first from the eighth tier of English football to reach the Third Round Proper of the FA Cup during
     the 2007-08 season.

HONOURS
FA Comps: None
League: West Midlands 1978. Midland Alliance 2004-05.

County FA: Walsall Senior Cup 1990-91, 92-93, 2004-05.

07-08		08-09		09-10		10-11		11-12		12-13		13-14		14-15		15-16		16-17	
SthM	7	SthM	4	NP1S	2	NP P	10	NP P	20	NP1S	5	NP1S	12	NP1S	13	NP1S	7	NP1S	17
FAC	3P	FAC	3Q	FAC	Pr	FAC	1Q	FAC	2Q	FAC	2Q	FAC	1Qr	FAC	1Qr	FAC	3Qr	FAC	2Q
FAT	2Qr	FAT	3Q	FAT	1Qr	FAT	QF	FAT	2Q	FAT	2Q	FAT	1Q	FAT	3Q	FAT	Pr	FAT	P

CLEETHORPES TOWN

Club Contact Details
The Bradley Football Development Centre Bradley Road, Grimsby, DN37 0AG
01472 325 300
andrew.aisthorpe@cleethorpestownfc.com

Founded: 1998   **Nickname:** The Owls   **Manager:** Marcus Newell
Previous Names: Lincolnshire Soccer School Lucarlys 1998-2008.
Previous Leagues: Lincolnshire 2003-05, 10-12. Central Midlands 2005-06. Humber Premier 2006-09. Northern Counties East 2012-17.

Club Colours (change): Blue & black stripes (Red & black stripes)

Ground Capacity: 1,000   **Seats:** 180   **Covered:** 200   **Clubhouse:** Yes   **Shop:**
Previous Grounds: None
Record Attendance: 1,154 v Bromsgrove Sporting, FA Vase Semi-Final second leg, 18/03/2017.

RECORDS

HONOURS
FA Comps: None
League: Lincolnshire 2011-12. Northern Counties East Division One 2013-14, Premier 2016-17.

County FA: Lincolnshire Senior Trophy 2016-17.

07-08		08-09		09-10		10-11		11-12		12-13		13-14		14-15		15-16		16-17	
Humb	10	Humb	9	Humb	Exp	Lincs	3	Lincs	1	NCE1	4	NCE1	1	NCEP	4	NCEP	3	NCEP	1
														FAC	2Q	FAC	P	FAC	P
												FAV	2P	FAV	2P	FAV	5P	FAV	F

CORBY TOWN

Club Contact Details
Steel Park, Jimmy Kane Way, Rockingham Road, Corby NN17 2AE
01536 406 640
gerry21@gmail.com

Founded: 1948   **Nickname:** The Steelmen   **Manager:** David Bell
Previous Names: Stewart & Lloyds (Corby) > 1947
Previous Leagues: United Counties 1935-52. Midland 1952-58. Southern 1958-2009, 13-15. Football Conference 2009-13, 15-16.

Club Colours (change): White/black/black (All blue)

Ground Capacity: 3,893   **Seats:** 577   **Covered:** 1,575   **Clubhouse:** Yes   **Shop:** Yes
Previous Grounds: Occupation Road 1948-85.
Record Attendance: 2,240 v Watford - Friendly 1986-87

RECORDS
Goalscorer: David Holbauer - 159 (1984-95)
Appearances: Derek Walker - 601
Additional: Paid £2,700 to Barnet for Elwun Edwards 1981
Received £20,000 from Oxford United for Matt Murphy 1993

HONOURS
FA Comps: None
League: United Counties League 1950-51, 51-52. Southern League Premier Division 2008-09, 2014-15.

County FA: Northants Senior Cup 1950-51, 62-63, 75-76, 82-83, 2009-10, 12-13.

07-08		08-09		09-10		10-11		11-12		12-13		13-14		14-15		15-16		16-17	
SthP	16	SthP	1	Conf N	6	Conf N	13	Conf N	17	Conf N	20	SthP	11	SthP	1	Nat N	22	NP P	21
FAC	4Q	FAC	2Q	FAC	2Q	FAC	1Pr	FAC	1P	FAC	4Q	FAC	1P	FAC	1Qr	FAC	2Qr	FAC	1Q
FAT	2Qr	FAT	2Q	FAT	3P	FAT	3Q	FAT	3Qr	FAT	2Pr	FAT	1Q	FAT	1Q	FAT	3Q	FAV	1Q

FRICKLEY ATHLETIC

Club Contact Details
Westfield Lane, South Elmsall, Pontefract WF9 2EQ
01977 642 460

Founded: 1910   **Nickname:** The Blues   **Manager:** Karl Rose
Previous Names: Frickley Colliery
Previous Leagues: Sheffield, Yorkshire 1922-24, Midland Counties 1924-33, 34-60, 70-76, Cheshire County 1960-70, Northern Premier 1976-80, Conference 1980-87

Club Colours (change): All royal blue (All yellow)

Ground Capacity: 2,087   **Seats:** 490   **Covered:** 700   **Clubhouse:** Yes   **Shop:** Yes
Previous Grounds: None
Record Attendance: 5,800 v Rotherham United - FA Cup 1st Round 1971

RECORDS
Goalscorer: K Whiteley
Additional: Received £12,500 from Boston United for Paul Shirtliff and from Northampton Town for Russ Wilcox

HONOURS
FA Comps: None
League: None

County FA: Sheffield & Hallamshire Senior Cup x14 - Firstly in 1927-28 and most recently in 2015-16.

07-08		08-09		09-10		10-11		11-12		12-13		13-14		14-15		15-16		16-17	
NP P	14	NP P	11	NP P	15	NP P	18	NP P	19	NP P	18	NP P	21	NP P	19	NP P	7	NP P	22
FAC	1Q	FAC	3Q	FAC	3Qr	FAC	3Qr	FAC	3Q	FAC	3Q	FAC	2Q	FAC	1Q	FAC	2Q	FAC	1Q
FAT	2Q	FAT	1Q	FAT	2Q	FAT	1Q	FAT	1Q	FAT	1Q	FAT	1Q	FAT	1Q	FAT	1Q	FAT	1Q

GRESLEY

Club Contact Details
The Moat Ground, Moat Street, Church Gresley, Derbyshire DE11 9RE
01283 215 316
ian.collins@gresleyfc.com

Founded: 2009   **Nickname:** The Moatmen   **Manager:** Damion Beckford-Quailey
Previous Names: Gresley Rovers
Previous Leagues: East Midlands 2009-11. Midland Football Alliance 2011-12.

Club Colours (change): All red (All blue)

Ground Capacity: 2,400   **Seats:** Yes   **Covered:** Yes   **Clubhouse:** Yes   **Shop:** Yes
Previous Grounds: None
Record Attendance: 861 v Whitehawk (FA Vase Quarter Final 27th Feb 2010)

RECORDS
Victory: 9-0 v Anstey Nomads 30th August 2010 (EMCL)
Defeat: 1-5 v Westfields (MFA)
Goalscorer: Royce Turville - 61
Appearances: Jamie Barrett - 142

HONOURS
FA Comps: None
League: East Midlands Counties 2010-11. Midland Alliance 2011-12.

County FA: None

07-08		08-09		09-10		10-11		11-12		12-13		13-14		14-15		15-16		16-17	
				EMC	2	EMC	1	MidAl	1	NP1S	11	NP1S	9	NP1S	5	NP1S	16	NP1S	18
				FAC	EPr	FAC	1Qr	FAC	1Q	FAC	3Q	FAC	2Qr	FAC	Pr	FAC	Pr	FAC	2Qr
				FAV	QF	FAV	4P	FAV	5P	FAT	1Q	FAT	1P	FAT	3Q	FAT	1Q	FAT	1Q

KIDSGROVE ATHLETIC

Club Contact Details
The Novus Stadium, Hollinwood Road, Kidsgrove, Staffs ST7 1DH
01782 782 412

Founded: 1952   **Nickname:** The Grove   **Manager:** Peter Ward & Ant Buckle
Previous Names: None
Previous Leagues: Buslem and Tunstall 1953-63, Staffordshire County 1963-66, Mid Cheshire 1966-90, North West Counties 1990-2002

Club Colours (change): All blue (All red)

Ground Capacity: 2,000   **Seats:** 1,000   **Covered:** 800   **Clubhouse:** Yes   **Shop:** Yes
Previous Grounds: Vickers and Goodwin 1953-60
Record Attendance: 1,903 v Tiverton Town - FA Vase Semi-final 1998

RECORDS
Victory:	23-0 v Cross Heath W.M.C. - Staffordshire Cup 1965
Defeat:	0-15 v Stafford Rangers - Staffordshire Senior Cup 20/11/2001
Goalscorer:	Scott Dundas - 53 (1997-98)
Additional:	Paid £10,000 to Stevenage Borough for Steve Walters
	Received £3,000 for Ryan Baker 2003-04

HONOURS
FA Comps: None
League: Staffordshire County Division Two 1963-64, Premier 65-66. Mid-Cheshire 1970-71, 77-78, 86-87, 87-88. North West Counties Premier Division 1997-98, 2001-02.
County FA: Staffordshire Senior Cup 2003-04, 06-07, 08-09, 10-11, 11-12.

	07-08		08-09		09-10		10-11		11-12		12-13		13-14		14-15		15-16		16-17	
NP	1	17	NP1S	15	NP1S	4	NP1S	7	NP1S	13	NP1S	18	NP1S	21	NP1S	20	NP1S	15	NP1S	12
FAC		2Q	FAC	1Q	FAC	1Q	FAC	2Q	FAC	4Q	FAC	P	FAC	1Q	FAC	P	FAC	Pr	FAC	2Q
FAT		P	FAT	1Q	FAT	P	FAT	Pr	FAT	1Q	FAT	1Q	FAT	2Q	FAT	P	FAT	2Qr	FAT	2Q

LEEK TOWN

Club Contact Details
Harrison Park, Macclesfield Road, Leek, Cheshire ST13 8LD
01538 399 278

Founded: 1946   **Nickname:** The Blues   **Manager:** Anthony Danylyk
Previous Names: None
Previous Leagues: Staffordshire Co., Manchester 1951-54, 57-73, West Midlands (B'ham) 1954-56, Cheshire Co. 1973-82, North West Counties 1982-87, Northern Premier 1987-94, 95-97, Southern 1994-95, Conference 1997-99

Club Colours (change): All blue (Amber & black/black/amber)

Ground Capacity: 3,600   **Seats:** 650   **Covered:** 3,000   **Clubhouse:** Yes   **Shop:** Yes
Previous Grounds: None
Record Attendance: 3,512 v Macclesfield Town - FA Cup 1973-74

RECORDS
Goalscorer:	Dave Sutton - 144
Appearances:	Gary Pearce - 447
Additional:	Paid £2,000 to Sutton Town for Simon Snow
	Received £30,000 from Barnsley for Tony Bullock

HONOURS
FA Comps: None
League: Staffordshire County 1949-50, 50-51. Manchester 1951-52, 71-72, 72-73. Cheshire County 1974-75. Northern Premier Division One 1989-90, Premier Division 1996-97.
County FA: Staffordshire Senior Cup 1995-96.

	07-08		08-09		09-10		10-11		11-12		12-13		13-14		14-15		15-16		16-17	
NP	P	19	NP1S	9	NP1S	8	NP1S	16	NP1S	5	NP1S	10	NP1S	3	NP1S	2	NP1S	8	NP1S	9
FAC		1Q	FAC	1Qr	FAC	P	FAC	P	FAC	3Qr	FAC	3Q	FAC	Pr	FAC	4Q	FAC	1Qr	FAC	1Q
FAT		1Q	FAT	P	FAT	2Q	FAT	P	FAT	2Qr	FAT	2Qr	FAT	2P	FAT	2Qr	FAT	P	FAT	2Q

LINCOLN UNITED

Club Contact Details
Sun Hat Stadium, Ashby Avenue, Hartsholme, Lincoln LN6 0DY
01522 690 674
andylav2u@yahoo.com

Founded: 1938   **Nickname:** United   **Manager:** Sam Wilkinson
Previous Names: Lincoln Amateurs > 1954
Previous Leagues: Lincolnshire 1945-46, 60-67, Lincoln 1946-60, Yorkshire 1967-82,
     Northern Counties East 1982-86, 92-95, Central Midlands 1982-92

Club Colours (change): All white with black trim (Claret & light blue/light blue/light blue)

Ground Capacity: 2,200   **Seats:** 400   **Covered:** 1,084   **Clubhouse:** Yes   **Shop:** Yes
Previous Grounds: Skew Bridge 1940s, Co-op Sports Ground > 1960s, Hartsholme Cricket Club > 1982
Record Attendance: 2,000 v Crook Town - FA Amateur Cup 1st Round 1968

RECORDS
Victory:	12-0 v Pontefract Colliery - 1995
Defeat:	0-7 v Huddersfield Town - FA Cup 1st Round 16/11/1991
Goalscorer:	Tony Simmons - 215
Appearances:	Steve Carter - 447
Additional:	Paid £1,000 to Hucknall Town for Paul Tomlinson December 2000
	Received £3,000 from Charlton Athletic for Dean Dye July 1991

HONOURS
FA Comps: None
League: Yorkshire Division Two 1967-68, Division One 70-71, 73-74. Central Midlands Supreme Division 1991-92.
     Northern Counties East Division One (South) 82-83, Division Two 1985-86, Division One 92-93, Premier Division 1994-95.
County FA: Lincolnshire Senior Cup 2016-17.

07-08		08-09		09-10		10-11		11-12		12-13		13-14		14-15		15-16		16-17	
NP P	20	NP1S	10	NP1S	19	NP1S	12	NP1S	18	NP1S	20	NP1S	17	NP1S	9	NP1S	5	NP1S	8
FAC	1Q	FAC	2Q	FAC	4Q	FAC	2Q	FAC	P	FAC	P	FAC	P	FAC	1Q	FAC	2Q	FAC	4Q
FAT	1Q	FAT	1Q	FAT	P	FAT	1Qr	FAT	1Q	FAT	1Q	FAT	P	FAT	P	FAT	2Q	FAT	3Q

LOUGHBOROUGH DYNAMO

Club Contact Details
Nanpantan Sports Ground, Nanpantan Road, Loughborough LE11 3YE
01509 237 148
brian.pugh1@btinternet.com

Founded: 1955   **Nickname:** The Moes   **Manager:** Peter Ward
Previous Names: None
Previous Leagues: Loughborough Alliance 1957-66, Leicestershire & District 1966-71, East Midlands 1971-72,
     Central Alliance 1972-89, Leicestershire Senior 1989-2004, Midland Alliance 2004-08

Club Colours (change): Gold/black/gold (Blue with red shoulder flash/blue/red)

Ground Capacity: 1,500   **Seats:** 250   **Covered:** Yes   **Clubhouse:** Yes   **Shop:** No
Previous Grounds: None
Record Attendance: Not known

RECORDS

HONOURS
FA Comps: None
League: Loughborough Alliance Division Three 1959-60, Division One 64-65. Leicester & District Division One 1969-70.
     Leicestershire Senior Division One 2001-02, Premier Division 2003-04.
County FA: Leicestershire Charity Cup 1987-88, 2003-04, 11-12, Senior Cup 2002-03, 03-04.

07-08		08-09		09-10		10-11		11-12		12-13		13-14		14-15		15-16		16-17	
MidAl	2	NP1S	14	NP1S	14	NP1S	17	NP1S	8	NP1S	16	NP1S	14	NP1S	14	NP1S	20	NP1S	20
FAC	EP	FAC	P	FAC	1Q	FAC	2Q	FAC	2Q	FAC	1Qr	FAC	P	FAC	P	FAC	P	FAC	P
FAV	2Q	FAT	P	FAT	1Q	FAT	P	FAT	P	FAT	P	FAT	P	FAT	2Q	FAT	P	FAT	P

MARKET DRAYTON TOWN

Club Contact Details
Greenfields Sports Ground, Greenfields Lane, Market Drayton TF9 3SL
01630 661 780
rpope2nt@gmail.com

Founded: 1969   **Nickname:** None   **Manager:** Martyn Davies
Previous Names: Little Drayton Rangers > 2003
Previous Leagues: West Midlands (Regional) 1969-2006, Midland Alliance 2006-09

Club Colours (change): All red (All blue)

Ground Capacity: 1,000   **Seats:** Yes   **Covered:** Yes   **Clubhouse:** Yes   **Shop:** No
Previous Grounds: Not known
Record Attendance: 440 vs. AFC Telford, Friendly 11/07/09. 229 vs. Witton Albion, Unibond South 25/08/09

RECORDS
Victory: (League) 9-0 Home vs. Racing Club Warwick 10/03/09

HONOURS
FA Comps: None
League: West Midlands (Regional) 2005-06. Midland Alliance 2008-09.

County FA: None

07-08		08-09		09-10		10-11		11-12		12-13		13-14		14-15		15-16		16-17	
MidAl	3	MidAl	1	NP1S	13	NP1S	18	NP1S	16	NP1S	15	NP1S	19	NP1S	19	NP1S	11	NP1S	14
FAC	2Qr	FAC	P	FAC	2Q	FAC	2Q	FAC	P	FAC	1Qr	FAC	P	FAC	1Q	FAC	1Q	FAC	P
FAV	2P	FAV	5P	FAT	Pr	FAT	1Qr	FAT	P	FAT	P	FAT	P	FAT	1Qr	FAT	P	FAT	1Q

NEWCASTLE TOWN

Club Contact Details
Lyme Valley Stadium, Buckmaster Avenue, Clayton, ST5 3BX
01782 662 350
rftatton@tiscali.co.uk

Founded: 1964   **Nickname:** The Castle   **Manager:** Robert Askey
Previous Names: Parkway Hanley, Clayton Park & Parkway Clayton. Merged as NTFC in 1986.
Previous Leagues: Newcatle & District, Staffs Co & Mid Cheshire, North West Counties

Club Colours (change): Blue/white/red (White/navy/navy)

Ground Capacity: 4,000   **Seats:** 300   **Covered:** 1,000   **Clubhouse:** Yes   **Shop:** Yes
Previous Grounds: None
Record Attendance: 3,948 v Notts County - FA Cup 1996

RECORDS
Goalscorer: Andy Bott - 149
Appearances: Dean Gillick - 632

HONOURS
FA Comps: None
League: Mid Cheshire Division Two 1982-83, 90-91, Division One 85-86. North West Counties Premier Division 2009-10.

County FA: Walsall Senior Cup 1993-94, 94-95. Staffordshire Senior Cup 2009-10.

07-08		08-09		09-10		10-11		11-12		12-13		13-14		14-15		15-16		16-17	
NWC1	3	NWCP	3	NWCP	1	NP1S	2	NP1S	15	NP1S	17	NP1S	8	NP1S	3	NP1S	14	NP1S	7
FAC	EPr	FAC	P	FAC	P	FAC	4Q	FAC	1Qr	FAC	P	FAC	1Qr	FAC	Pr	FAC	1Q	FAC	P
FAV	1P	FAV	2P	FAV	2P	FAT	1Q	FAT	1Qr	FAT	1Q	FAT	P	FAT	1Q	FAT	1Qr	FAT	P

PETERBOROUGH SPORTS

Club Contact Details
Lincoln Road, Peterborough PE1 3HA
01733 308 993
jrobo1510@gmail.com

Founded: 1919   **Nickname:** The Turbines   **Manager:** James Dean

Previous Names: Brotherhoods Engineering Works 1919-99. Bearings Direct during 1999-2001.

Previous Leagues: Northants League (former UCL) 1919-23. Peterborough & District 1923-2013.

Club Colours (change): All blue

Ground Capacity: **Seats:** Yes   **Covered:** Yes   **Clubhouse:** Yes   **Shop:** No

Previous Grounds: None

Record Attendance: Not known

RECORDS

HONOURS

FA Comps: None

League: Northants 1919-20, United Counties 1919-20, Division One 2015-16, Premier 2016-17.
Peterborough & District Division Three 1925-26, Division Three South 1980-81, Premier 2006-07.

County FA: Northants Junior Cup 2006-07, 15-16,

07-08	08-09	09-10	10-11	11-12	12-13	13-14	14-15	15-16	16-17
				P&D P 3	P&D P 3	UCL 1 16	UCL 1 5	UCL 1 1	UCL P 1
								FAC 1Qr	FAC 1Q
							FAV 2P	FAV 1Q	FAV 4P

ROMULUS

Club Contact Details
Sutton Coldfield FC, Central Ground, Coles Lane B72 1NL
0121 354 2997
moz-football@hotmail.co.uk

Founded: 1979   **Nickname:** The Roms   **Manager:** Richard Evans & Andy Turner

Previous Names: None

Previous Leagues: Midland Combination 1999-2004, Midland Alliance 2004-07, Southern 2007-2010

Club Colours (change): Red and white stripes/red/red (Yellow & black stripes/black/black)

Ground Capacity: 2,000   **Seats:** 200   **Covered:** 500   **Clubhouse:** Yes   **Shop:** Yes

Previous Grounds: Vale Stadium.

Record Attendance: Not known

RECORDS

Misc: Players who have progressed: Dean Sturridge, Stuart Bowen, Luke Rogers, Darius Vassell and Zat Knight.

HONOURS

FA Comps: None

League: Midland Combination Division One 1999-00, Premier Division 2003-04.

County FA: None

07-08		08-09		09-10		10-11		11-12		12-13		13-14		14-15		15-16		16-17	
SthM	10	SthM	11	SthM	8	NP1S	10	NP1S	20	NP1S	19	NP1S	11	NP1S	12	NP1S	10	NP1S	13
FAC	Pr	FAC	2Q	FAC	2Q	FAC	1Q	FAC	1Q	FAC	P	FAC	P	FAC	1Q	FAC	P	FAC	1Qr
FAT	1Q	FAT	2Qr	FAT	1Q	FAT	2Q	FAT	2Q	FAT	3Q	FAT	Pr	FAT	1Q	FAT	Pr	FAT	Pr

SHEFFIELD

Club Contact Details
Home of Football Stadium, Sheffield Road, Dronfield S18 2GD
0114 362 7016
bill@sheffieldfc.com

Founded: 1857   **Nickname:** The Club   **Manager:** Mark Hume
Previous Names: None
Previous Leagues: Yorkshire 1949-82

Club Colours (change): Red/black/black (All blue)

Ground Capacity: 2,089   **Seats:** 250   **Covered:** 500   **Clubhouse:** Yes   **Shop:** Yes
Previous Grounds: Abbeydale Park, Dore 1956-89, Sheffield Amateur Sports Stadium, Hillsborough Park 1989-91, Don Valley Stadium 1991-97
Record Attendance: 2,000 v Barton Rovers - FA Vase Semi-final 1976-77

RECORDS
Misc: Oldest Football Club in the World.
Paid £1,000 to Arnold Town for David Wilkins. Received £1,000 from Alfreton for Mick Godber 2002.

HONOURS
FA Comps: FA Amateur Cup 1902-03.
League: Northern Counties East Division One 1988-89, 90-91.
County FA: Sheffield and Hallamshire Senior Cup 1993-94, 2004-05, 05-06, 07-08, 09-10.

07-08		08-09		09-10		10-11		11-12		12-13		13-14		14-15		15-16		16-17	
NP 1	4	NP1S	11	NP1S	5	NP1S	11	NP1S	4	NP1S	9	NP1S	16	NP1S	15	NP1S	17	NP1S	15
FAC	P	FAC	4Q	FAC	1Q	FAC	4Qr	FAC	P	FAC	P	FAC	1Q	FAC	2Qr	FAC	Pr	FAC	1Q
FAT	3Qr	FAT	1Q	FAT	P	FAT	1Qr	FAT	3Q	FAT	P	FAT	3Q	FAT	1Q	FAT	1Q	FAT	P

SPALDING UNITED

Club Contact Details
Sir Halley Stewart Playing Fields, Winfrey Avenue, Spalding PE11 1DA
01775 712 047
tulips@uk2.net

Founded: 1921   **Nickname:** Tulips   **Manager:** Chris Rawlinson
Previous Names: None
Previous Leagues: Peterborough, United Counties 1931-55,68-78,86-88,91-99,03-04, 11-14 Eastern Counties 1955-60, Central Alliance 1960-61, Midland Co. 1961-68, Northern Counties East 1982-86, Southern 1988-91, 99-03. NPL 2003-11.

Club Colours (change): All royal blue (Orange/black/black)

Ground Capacity: 3,500   **Seats:** 1,000   **Covered:** 1,000   **Clubhouse:** Yes   **Shop:** Yes
Previous Grounds: Stadium known as the Black Swan Ground before being renamed after Halley Stewart MP in 1954.
Record Attendance: 6,972 v Peterborough - FA Cup 1982

RECORDS

HONOURS
FA Comps: None
League: Peterborough & District 1930-31. United Counties 1954-55, 75-75, 87-88, 98-99, 2003-04, 13-14.
Northern Counties East 1983-84.
County FA: Lincolnshire Senior Cup 1952-53.

07-08		08-09		09-10		10-11		11-12		12-13		13-14		14-15		15-16		16-17	
NP 1	18	NP1S	17	NP1S	21	NP1S	22	UCL P	13	UCL P	3	UCL P	1	NP1S	7	NP1S	12	NP1S	3
FAC	1Q	FAC	P	FAC	P	FAC	1Qr	FAC	EP	FAC	EP	FAC	2Q	FAC	2Q	FAC	3Qr	FAC	1Q
FAT	P	FAT	1Qr	FAT	1Q	FAT	P	FAV	2P	FAV	5P	FAV	3P	FAT	1Qr	FAT	P	FAT	P

STAMFORD

Club Contact Details
Zeeco Stadium, Ryhall Road, Stamford. PE9 1US
01780 751 471
phil.bee1947@hotmail.co.uk

Founded: 1896   **Nickname:** The Daniels   **Manager:** Graham Drury
Previous Names: Stamford Town and Rutland Ironworks amalgamated in 1894 to form Rutland Ironworks > 1896
Previous Leagues: Peterborough, Northants (UCL) 1908-55, Central Alliance 1955-61, Midland counties 1961-72, United Counties 1972-98,
         Southern 1998-2007

Club Colours (change): Red with white trim/red/red (Yellow/black/yellow)

Ground Capacity: 2,000   **Seats:** 300   **Covered:** 1,250   **Clubhouse:** Yes   **Shop:** Yes
Previous Grounds: Hanson's Field 1894-2014.
Record Attendance: 1,264 v Wrexham, FA Cup Fourth Qualifying, 15/10/2016.

RECORDS
Victory: 13-0 v Peterborough Reserves - Northants League 1929-30
Defeat: 0-17 v Rothwell - FA Cup 1927-28
Goalscorer: Bert Knighton - 248
Appearances: Dick Kwiatkowski - 462

HONOURS
FA Comps: FA Vase 1979-80.
League: United Counties 1911-12, 75-76, 77-78, 79-80, 80-81, 81-82, 96-97, 97-98.

County FA: Lincolnshire Senior Cup 2000-01, Senior Shield 2006-07, 08-09, 10-11, 13-14, 14-15.

07-08	08-09	09-10	10-11	11-12	12-13	13-14	14-15	15-16	16-17
NP P 20	NP1S 7	NP1S 10	NP1S 19	NP1S 7	NP1S 4	NP P 18	NP P 20	NP P 21	NP1S 16
FAC 3Q	FAC 2Q	FAC P	FAC 2Q	FAC P	FAC 2Q	FAC 4Q	FAC 2Q	FAC 2Q	FAC 1P
FAT 1Qr	FAT 2Q	FAT P	FAT 1Q	FAT 1Q	FAT 3Q	FAT 1Q	FAT 1Q	FAT 1Q	FAT 1Q

STOCKSBRIDGE PARK STEELS

Club Contact Details
Look Local Stadium, Bracken Moor Lane, Stocksbridge, Sheffield S36 2AN
0114 288 8305 (Match days)
mickgrimmer@gmail.com

Founded: 1986   **Nickname:** Steels   **Manager:** Chris Hilton
Previous Names: Stocksbridge Works and Oxley Park merged in 1986
Previous Leagues: Northern Counties East 1986-96

Club Colours (change): Yellow/royal blue/yellow (All red with white trim)

Ground Capacity: 3,500   **Seats:** 450   **Covered:** 1,500   **Clubhouse:** Yes   **Shop:** Yes
Previous Grounds: Stonemoor 1949-51, 52-53
Record Attendance: 2,050 v Sheffield Wednesday - opening of floodlights October 1991

RECORDS
Victory: 17-1 v Oldham Town - FA Cup 2002-03
Defeat: 0-6 v Shildon
Goalscorer: Trevor Jones - 145
Appearances: Paul Jackson scored 10 v Oldham Town in the 2002-03 FA Cup - a FA Cup record
               Received £15,000 from Wolverhampton Wanderers for Lee Mills

HONOURS
FA Comps: None
League: Northern Counties East Division One 1991-92, Premier Division 1993-94.

County FA: Sheffield Senior Cup 1951-52, 92-93, 95-96, 98-99, 2006-07, 08-09.

07-08	08-09	09-10	10-11	11-12	12-13	13-14	14-15	15-16	16-17
NP1S 5	NP1S 3	NP P 11	NP P 13	NP P 18	NP P 20	NP P 23	NP1S 17	NP1S 6	NP1S 4
FAC 2Q	FAC 2Q	FAC 2Q	FAC 2Q	FAC 3Q	FAC 1Q	FAC 1Q	FAC P	FAC P	FAC P
FAT 2Q	FAT 2Q	FAT 1Q	FAT 3Q	FAT 1Qr	FAT 1P	FAT 1Q	FAT P	FAT 1P	FAT 1P

SOUTHERN LEAGUE PREMIER DIVISION LEAGUE TABLE 2016-17

		P	W	D	L	F	A	GD	Pts
1	Chippenham Town	46	31	10	5	94	47	+47	103
2	Leamington	46	27	11	8	74	32	+42	92
3	Merthyr Town	46	25	14	7	92	42	+50	89
4	Hitchin Town	46	24	14	8	79	45	+34	86
5	Slough Town	46	26	7	13	84	56	+28	85
6	Banbury United	46	24	8	14	67	40	+27	80
7	Biggleswade Town	46	21	11	14	85	59	+26	74
8	Frome Town	46	20	14	12	80	67	+13	74
9	Kettering Town	46	21	10	15	84	66	+18	73
10	Weymouth	46	16	18	12	79	58	+21	66
11	Chesham United	46	18	10	18	67	62	+5	64
12	Basingstoke Town	46	18	8	20	65	72	-7	62
13	King's Lynn Town	46	14	18	14	60	69	-9	60
14	Stratford Town	46	13	17	16	64	66	-2	56
15	St Ives Town	46	15	11	20	49	70	-21	56
16	Dunstable Town	46	16	6	24	46	65	-19	54
17	Redditch United	46	13	11	22	54	75	-21	50
18	Dorchester Town	46	12	12	22	52	80	-28	48
19	St Neots Town	46	14	6	26	66	101	-35	48
20	Kings Langley	46	11	14	21	57	72	-15	47
21	Cambridge City	46	12	11	23	46	72	-26	47
22	Cirencester Town	46	11	9	26	54	92	-38	42
23	Hayes & Yeading United	46	10	11	25	48	81	-33	41
24	Cinderford Town	46	8	3	35	49	106	-57	27

Play-Off Semi Finals: Leamington 1-0 Slough Town | Merthyr Town 1-1, 1-4p Hitchin Town
Final: Leamington 2-1 Hitchin Town

PREMIER DIVISION	1	2	3	4	5	6	7	8	9	10	11	12	13	14	15	16	17	18	19	20	21	22	23	24
1 Banbury United		0-1	1-1	2-0	1-0	2-1	4-0	2-1	1-2	0-1	1-2	5-0	1-1	1-2	4-0	3-0	1-0	1-1	0-1	1-0	1-0	2-1	2-1	1-1
2 Basingstoke Town	0-1		2-1	2-1	3-2	1-2	3-0	0-1	1-1	5-1	1-1	1-1	3-0	1-2	3-0	0-2	3-2	0-1	4-1	0-2	1-0	2-1	1-6
3 Biggleswade Town	2-1	0-0		2-1	2-2	2-2	5-0	6-0	3-0	2-2	4-1	6-0	1-3	2-2	2-0	0-4	2-0	2-5	2-0	3-0	3-1	2-0	1-2	1-3
4 Cambridge City	1-2	0-2	1-1		3-1	1-3	1-0	2-1	1-0	0-2	0-3	2-2	0-4	2-3	0-0	1-1	1-1	1-0	1-4	3-4	1-2	3-0	0-0	2-1
5 Chesham United	0-4	4-0	1-2	3-1		1-3	1-0	3-0	3-0	1-0	1-1	6-0	2-0	1-0	1-2	5-2	0-1	1-1	1-1	2-0	3-2	1-1	1-1
6 Chippenham Town	0-1	2-0	2-0	5-0	3-1		1-0	4-1	4-0	1-0	2-2	3-0	1-0	1-0	2-1	1-1	1-0	3-1	1-1	3-3	2-0	1-2	2-1	2-0
7 Cinderford Town	1-2	2-3	1-2	0-1	0-1	3-2		0-2	4-0	1-3	4-2	1-2	0-1	1-3	1-2	0-4	1-2	3-2	1-1	2-1	0-1	5-2	2-2
8 Cirencester Town	1-4	2-3	1-0	0-3	1-2	3-3	3-2		4-1	2-0	1-4	1-2	0-0	1-6	1-1	0-1	1-2	0-2	2-1	1-3	1-2	2-1	1-2	3-0
9 Dorchester Town	0-1	1-1	2-1	0-2	3-2	1-3	2-0	2-2		2-0	3-0	2-1	2-2	0-2	1-1	1-0	2-2	1-2	0-0	0-4	1-1	1-0	2-2	1-1
10 Dunstable Town	1-0	1-3	0-2	2-1	0-0	1-2	2-0	1-1	2-1		0-2	0-2	2-1	2-3	0-0	1-2	0-2	0-1	1-0	0-1	4-1	1-0	2-0	1-1
11 Frome Town	1-2	1-1	2-0	2-0	2-0	0-1	3-2	3-2	0-4	1-0		2-1	1-1	3-3	1-3	0-0	0-0	2-2	8-1	1-0	2-2	1-1	3-1	2-0
12 Hayes & Yeading Utd	0-1	2-3	0-0	0-0	1-0	1-2	5-0	1-1	1-2	0-1	1-3		2-0	1-2	0-1	0-2	1-6	2-1	2-3	1-0	2-2	1-2	0-0
13 Hitchin Town	3-1	1-0	1-1	1-0	1-1	1-3	4-3	2-1	0-1	2-0	2-2	3-0		0-0	5-0	2-0	0-0	1-1	4-2	2-3	4-1	4-1	1-0	1-1
14 Kettering Town	2-2	2-1	3-1	0-0	1-2	1-2	2-0	3-1	1-0	1-3	4-1	1-1	0-0		1-1	1-0	0-2	1-3	1-2	3-0	1-1	2-2	0-3	3-1
15 King's Lynn Town	1-0	2-1	1-2	1-1	3-1	4-0	3-0	1-1	3-3	0-1	1-1	2-2	1-2	1-2		1-1	0-0	1-1	2-1	5-2	2-1	1-2	2-0	1-6
16 Kings Langley	0-1	2-0	4-5	2-0	1-2	1-1	0-1	1-0	2-0	0-1	2-2	1-0	1-2	1-2	2-2		0-2	2-2	1-2	2-3	2-3	1-3	1-1
17 Leamington	1-0	3-1	1-1	1-0	1-1	6-0	3-1	5-0	5-0	0-1	2-0	1-2	3-0	3-0	0-0		1-0	2-1	0-6	2-0	2-0	1-1	1-1
18 Merthyr Town	1-0	4-0	1-0	5-0	1-0	2-2	2-0	3-0	2-0	4-3	1-2	4-0	2-2	2-0	1-1	5-0	1-1		2-0	1-1	2-0	3-0	1-1	2-2
19 Redditch United	0-0	2-2	0-2	1-2	3-1	0-2	2-2	4-1	4-2	1-0	2-1	2-1	1-3	1-1	0-0	0-2	0-1		0-4	0-2	1-4	1-1	2-1
20 Slough Town	2-0	3-2	3-0	1-0	1-2	0-1	4-1	0-2	2-1	1-0	1-2	2-1	0-1	3-2	3-0	2-2	2-0	1-0	1-1		3-0	2-0	0-0	3-0
21 St Ives Town	1-1	0-1	0-1	0-0	0-2	2-3	1-0	1-1	1-0	3-1	1-1	1-1	0-3	0-7	2-0	2-1	0-5	0-0	2-1	2-0		2-1	1-1	1-2
22 St Neots Town	1-4	2-1	0-5	0-3	4-1	3-3	3-1	1-1	3-2	2-0	3-3	1-5	1-2	1-5	5-2	5-2	0-1	2-3	1-0	1-1	0-4		1-1	0-4
23 Stratford Town	2-0	1-1	1-0	3-3	1-1	0-1	4-2	0-1	1-1	2-0	3-0	0-0	3-2	4-1	1-1	2-2	0-2	0-1	3-4	1-2	2-3	5-2		0-5
24 Weymouth	2-2	3-0	2-2	2-0	2-0	1-4	3-0	4-0	2-1	3-3	2-1	2-2	0-2	3-2	0-0	1-1	4-0	0-1	1-0	0-1	1-1	0-2	1-1	

SOUTHERN LEAGUE DIVISION ONE CENTRAL LEAGUE TABLE 2016-17

		P	W	D	L	F	A	GD	Pts
1	Royston Town	42	32	6	4	121	48	73	102
2	Farnborough	42	28	6	8	96	51	45	90
3	Barton Rovers	42	23	8	11	91	66	25	77
4	Marlow	42	23	8	11	65	43	22	77
5	Egham Town	42	20	14	8	79	51	28	74
6	Kempston Rovers	42	21	10	11	82	61	21	73
7	AFC Dunstable	42	21	8	13	85	53	32	71
8	Bedford Town	42	18	13	11	76	58	18	67
9	Potters Bar Town	42	16	14	12	71	61	10	62
10	Ashford Town (Mx)	42	17	8	17	73	71	2	59
11	Hanwell Town	42	16	10	16	64	67	-3	57*
12	Kidlington	42	18	5	19	70	79	-9	56*
13	Aylesbury United	42	16	7	19	58	68	-10	55
14	Fleet Town	42	13	11	18	72	81	-9	50
15	Arlesey Town	42	14	8	20	55	69	-14	50
16	Beaconsfield SYCOB	42	13	9	20	81	85	-4	48
17	Uxbridge	42	13	8	21	67	80	-13	47
18	Chalfont St Peter	42	14	5	23	49	77	-28	47
19	Aylesbury	42	12	8	22	54	75	-21	44
20	Northwood	42	9	12	21	57	88	-31	39
21	Histon	42	9	7	26	54	93	-39	34
22	Petersfield Town	42	2	3	37	32	127	-95	9

Play-Off Semi Finals: Barton Rovers 2-0 Marlow I Farnborough 4-0 Egham Town
Final: Farnborough 2-0 Barton Rovers

DIVISION ONE CENTRAL	1	2	3	4	5	6	7	8	9	10	11	12	13	14	15	16	17	18	19	20	21	22
1 AFC Dunstable		1-2	4-1	2-0	2-0	3-3	1-0	2-2	4-0	1-2	1-3	2-0	1-0	4-0	1-2	2-2	2-2	3-1	3-1	3-1	0-1	1-2
2 Arlesey Town	1-0		0-3	0-2	3-3	1-2	2-0	0-2	0-1	1-1	0-1	1-0	1-2	2-1	1-2	0-1	0-4	3-0	6-1	1-1	5-4	0-3
3 Ashford Town (Mx)	2-3	2-1		1-0	1-1	6-3	1-2	1-1	2-3	1-1	1-0	3-4	1-3	1-2	3-1	5-1	3-1	0-2	1-0	0-3	1-4	2-0
4 Aylesbury	2-2	2-3	2-2		0-1	1-4	3-2	0-1	1-3	1-0	3-2	5-0	0-1	2-1	0-3	0-1	1-0	1-1	1-2	0-0	0-6	2-2
5 Aylesbury United	0-5	0-0	1-2	3-0		0-1	1-3	2-1	2-3	1-0	0-2	3-1	0-3	1-0	0-2	2-1	0-2	2-1	1-1	1-3	0-1	3-1
6 Barton Rovers	1-1	1-0	1-1	3-3	3-2		3-1	1-1	2-1	1-1	0-1	1-2	4-0	2-6	3-2	4-2	2-1	5-1	8-0	1-1	0-4	4-0
7 Beaconsfield SYCOB	0-1	3-0	1-2	1-4	1-2	2-1		1-5	5-1	1-2	0-4	4-4	3-0	2-2	1-1	6-0	2-2	0-0	3-2	3-4	4-6	1-2
8 Bedford Town	2-1	1-1	2-2	3-2	3-2	1-1	4-1		3-2	1-1	2-1	1-1	2-2	5-2	0-1	0-2	3-0	0-1	4-1	1-1	0-1	3-3
9 Chalfont St Peter	1-1	2-3	0-0	2-2	3-2	0-2	1-0	2-3		0-0	0-2	1-0	0-2	2-0	0-3	0-2	1-3	0-2	4-1	0-4	2-0	2-0
10 Egham Town	3-4	2-1	3-1	3-1	0-5	2-0	4-1	1-0	2-0		1-1	2-0	2-0	6-3	3-0	1-1	3-0	1-1	3-0	1-1	1-1	6-4
11 Farnborough	2-1	3-3	2-1	1-0	1-0	4-0	6-1	3-2	3-1	4-0		4-3	2-3	2-1	3-2	3-0	0-3	2-1	2-0	2-0	3-3	2-2
12 Fleet Town	1-4	1-1	3-0	2-3	2-1	0-1	2-1	1-1	3-2	2-2	1-2		1-0	1-1	0-3	6-1	0-2	7-0	2-0	4-4	1-1	0-3
13 Hanwell Town	2-4	3-0	2-2	2-1	0-2	3-5	1-1	3-2	3-5	0-0	1-4	3-2		1-1	1-1	2-1	1-3	2-0	4-1	1-1	4-1	1-2
14 Histon	2-1	0-2	1-4	1-1	1-2	1-2	2-3	1-2	0-0	0-2	0-5	4-5	0-0		1-2	1-4	1-2	2-2	2-1	1-2	1-2	3-2
15 Kempston Rovers	2-1	1-1	2-0	2-1	2-3	0-2	0-2	1-2	1-0	2-1	0-0	3-1	3-2	4-1		2-1	1-2	2-2	4-0	1-1	1-2	2-1
16 Kidlington	3-0	2-0	1-2	2-3	3-4	3-1	0-5	1-1	1-2	2-2	0-3	3-1	0-3	1-2	1-0		3-0	2-1	3-1	1-2	2-1	4-2
17 Marlow	0-1	3-0	1-0	1-0	3-2	1-2	0-0	3-1	1-0	1-2	5-0	1-0	0-2	1-1	2-1		2-1	2-2	0-0	0-2	1-1	
18 Northwood	1-1	0-3	1-3	0-2	1-1	2-0	3-3	3-2	0-1	2-2	2-4	1-1	1-1	6-0	4-4	2-4	0-2		4-0	3-2	0-4	1-2
19 Petersfield Town	0-7	2-3	0-2	0-1	0-1	0-3	0-6	2-3	0-2	0-5	3-2	2-2	0-1	3-4	0-3	2-4	0-2	1-2		1-2	0-1	0-1
20 Potters Bar Town	1-2	3-1	3-2	3-1	0-0	2-0	1-1	0-2	2-1	0-3	2-2	1-2	1-1	2-0	2-3	0-3	1-4	4-0	3-1		1-3	2-3
21 Royston Town	1-0	3-0	5-3	5-0	5-2	3-6	4-1	1-0	4-0	3-2	5-0	2-0	2-0	2-0	4-4	1-1	4-2	2-1	6-0	0-0		5-2
22 Uxbridge	1-2	0-2	0-2	1-0	1-1	0-2	1-3	0-1	2-0	1-1	1-3	2-3	3-0	2-3	3-3	0-0	1-2	5-0	4-1	1-4	0-2	

SOUTHERN LEAGUE DIVISION ONE SOUTH & WEST LEAGUE TABLE 2016-17

		P	W	D	L	F	A	GD	Pts
1	Hereford	42	33	8	1	108	32	76	107
2	Salisbury	42	29	2	11	118	52	66	89
3	Tiverton Town	42	27	7	8	92	50	42	88
4	Taunton Town	42	27	7	8	114	42	72	85
5	Evesham United	42	24	8	10	88	50	38	80
6	North Leigh	42	22	9	11	84	65	19	75
7	Swindon Supermarine	42	21	9	12	85	57	28	72
8	Mangotsfield United	42	21	7	14	73	69	4	70
9	Shortwood United	42	19	5	18	65	77	-12	62
10	Bideford	42	15	12	15	61	58	3	57
11	Wimborne Town	42	17	6	19	67	68	-1	57
12	Didcot Town	42	14	12	16	70	71	-1	54
13	Larkhall Athletic	42	13	14	15	69	69	0	53
14	Winchester City	42	16	5	21	62	70	-8	53
15	Paulton Rovers	42	15	6	21	62	69	-7	51
16	Bishops Cleeve	42	14	8	20	66	86	-20	50
17	Barnstaple Town	42	13	6	23	52	68	-16	45
18	Yate Town	42	12	8	22	49	77	-28	44
19	AFC Totton	42	10	9	23	49	86	-37	39
20	Slimbridge	42	10	7	25	47	90	-43	37
21	Wantage Town	42	4	9	29	29	110	-81	21
22	Bridgwater Town	42	2	4	36	23	117	-94	10

Play-Off Semi Finals: Salisbury 2-1 Evesham United I Tiverton Town 3-1 Taunton Town
Final: Salisbury 0-2 Tiverton Town

DIVISION ONE SOUTH & WEST	1	2	3	4	5	6	7	8	9	10	11	12	13	14	15	16	17	18	19	20	21	22
1 AFC Totton		1-1	3-3	4-0	2-1	2-1	2-4	1-2	1-6	0-1	0-3	1-0	0-4	2-0	3-1	1-2	1-3	1-3	2-2	1-6	1-3	1-1
2 Barnstaple Town	2-1		0-1	0-2	5-0	2-1	1-2	0-2	4-3	1-1	3-1	1-0	1-4	0-1	3-1	0-1	0-1	0-4	1-1	1-0	1-3	1-1
3 Bideford	0-0	2-1		2-1	2-0	2-2	1-1	0-0	1-1	0-1	0-2	1-1	0-1	1-3	1-0	4-0	2-4	0-3	3-1	2-0	1-2	2-0
4 Bishops Cleeve	3-2	1-1	3-3		3-0	1-1	0-2	0-4	0-1	2-2	1-2	1-4	0-5	4-1	0-0	1-4	1-5	1-1	2-1	4-0	1-0	1-2
5 Bridgwater Town	0-2	0-3	1-4	1-3		1-2	0-5	0-4	0-4	1-3	0-1	0-5	1-3	1-2	0-0	0-5	1-5	1-0	2-3	2-2	0-1	2-1
6 Didcot Town	3-2	1-0	4-2	2-2	4-0		1-2	1-2	0-0	0-2	1-1	1-0	0-1	1-2	1-0	1-5	2-3	3-3	3-1	2-0	4-0	1-2
7 Evesham United	0-0	1-0	2-0	4-2	1-0	2-2		0-2	5-1	1-0	1-1	2-2	3-2	1-2	1-2	1-1	2-0	1-4	5-1	2-0	3-1	3-1
8 Hereford	5-0	2-2	2-1	4-0	6-0	2-2	2-1		2-1	3-2	4-1	2-1	3-1	2-0	3-0	2-0	1-2	2-1	3-2	2-2	4-0	4-1
9 Larkhall Athletic	0-0	0-1	0-1	0-4	2-2	0-1	1-2	2-2		3-0	3-1	3-2	1-5	0-2	2-0	3-1	3-0	0-1	1-1	1-0	1-2	1-1
10 Mangotsfield United	3-0	3-2	2-1	3-3	6-0	2-3	1-5	0-1	1-1		1-0	2-1	1-3	1-5	3-0	1-1	0-4	1-2	0-0	2-1	3-3	3-1
11 North Leigh	2-3	4-2	2-1	1-0	1-0	2-2	1-4	3-3	2-2	2-3		1-0	3-2	2-2	3-1	2-1	1-0	2-3	4-1	1-1	2-0	2-1
12 Paulton Rovers	2-2	4-3	2-1	2-0	1-0	2-0	0-3	1-3	2-2	0-3	0-3		3-1	1-3	0-0	2-1	2-5	5-1	0-1	2-0	1-1	0-1
13 Salisbury	2-0	5-0	4-4	4-1	7-0	3-2	1-0	0-4	5-0	2-1	1-2	3-1		1-0	3-0	2-2	5-2	1-2	7-0	5-2	3-1	4-0
14 Shortwood United	2-1	1-0	1-2	1-3	1-1	3-3	2-0	0-3	0-5	0-1	2-5	1-3	0-3		4-4	1-0	0-3	1-0	7-1	1-3	2-1	2-2
15 Slimbridge	2-0	0-1	2-0	0-1	1-2	2-3	1-5	0-3	1-5	0-3	0-2	2-0	2-1	1-2		1-1	0-7	5-2	2-2	1-1	5-3	3-1
16 Swindon Supermarine	1-0	4-2	4-1	2-4	3-1	1-3	1-3	0-3	0-0	5-0	3-3	0-1	1-6	4-0	2-0		2-1	2-2	5-0	1-0	0-2	3-1
17 Taunton Town	5-0	0-1	0-0	4-2	1-0	3-0	2-1	1-1	10-2	6-1	2-2	4-1	3-1	3-0	0-0	0-0		2-0	3-0	2-1	3-1	2-0
18 Tiverton Town	3-2	2-1	1-1	4-2	2-0	3-1	2-1	1-1	1-1	3-2	4-1	3-1	2-0	1-2	2-1	2-3	1-1		2-0	4-3	1-0	4-0
19 Wantage Town	0-0	2-1	0-2	0-2	1-0	1-1	1-1	0-1	1-4	1-2	0-4	0-3	0-1	0-2	2-0	0-5	0-9	0-3		0-1	0-1	1-2
20 Wimborne Town	3-0	3-0	0-4	4-1	2-0	1-1	1-3	2-3	2-1	1-2	3-2	3-1	1-5	2-1	1-0	4-1		1-0	4-1		2-2	0-3
21 Winchester City	0-1	0-3	0-0	1-2	4-1	3-1	4-1	0-2	0-0	0-2	1-2	3-2	4-2	4-3	7-0	0-2	1-1	0-4	3-0	0-1		1-0
22 Yate Town	1-3	1-0	1-2	2-1	3-2	3-2	1-1	0-2	2-2	1-3	3-2	0-1	3-1	0-1	1-2	1-2	1-5	0-1	1-1	0-3	1-0	

LEAGUE CHALLENGE CUP 2016-17

HOLDERS: MERTHYR TOWN

ROUND ONE

AFC Dunstable	v	Aylesbury	0-1	59
AFC Totton	v	Winchester City	2-3	157
Aylesbury United	v	Wantage Town	0-0, 5-3p	51
Banbury United	v	Cirencester Town	1-1, 4-1p	177
Barnstaple Town	v	Tiverton Town	1-1, 4-1p	187
Barton Rovers	v	Dunstable Town	4-0	76
Bedford Town	v	Kempston Rovers	2-0	167
Bideford	v	Taunton Town	4-0	134
Biggleswade Town	v	Arlesey Town	3-2	82
Bishops Cleeve	v	Slimbridge	1-0	62
Bridgwater Town	v	Paulton Rovers	1-3	119
Cambrideg City	v	Histon	1-1, 1-4p	145
Fleet Town	v	Farnborough	3-0	99
Hayes & Yeading United	v	Hanwell Town	1-1, 4-3p	49
Kidlington	v	Swindon Supermarine	3-1	78
Kings Langley	v	Chalfont St Peter	1-2	40
Larkhall Athletic	v	Frome Town	0-0, 6-5p	61
Leamington	v	Evesham United	4-1	218
Merthyr Town	v	Cinderford Town	0-0, 3-4p	210
North Leigh	v	Didcot Town	3-3, 4-2p	58
Northwood	v	Beaconsfield SYCOB	2-2, 4-2p	68
Petersfield Town	v	Basingstoke Town	2-3	107
Potters Bar Town	v	Chesham United	2-3	71
Redditch United	v	Stratford Town	3-4	159
Royston Town	v	Hitchin Town	1-0	141
Salisbury	v	Dorchester Town	10-0	437
Shortwood United	v	Yate Town	3-1	71
Slough Town	v	Ashford Town (Mx)	9-2	314
St Ives Town	v	King's Lynn Town	0-0, 6-5p	137
St Neots Town	v	Kettering Town	6-0	123
Uxbridge	v	Egham Town	0-2	49
Weymouth	v	Wimborne Town	4-0	141

ROUND TWO

Aylesbury	v	St Neots Town	3-2	50
Barton Rovers	v	Chesham United	2-2, 7-6p	61
Basingstoke Town	v	Fleet Town	4-1	127
Bideford	v	Barnstaple Town	1-4	320
Biggleswade Town	v	Histon	3-2	80
Bishops Cleeve	v	Cinderford Town	4-1	72
Hayes & Yeading United	v	Egham Town	3-0	46
Kidlington	v	Aylesbury United	1-2	55
North Leigh	v	Banbury United	0-2	65
Northwood	v	Slough Town	1-0	76
Paulton Rovers	v	Weymouth	1-1, 4-3p	102
Royston Town	v	Chalfont St Peter	1-2	79
Salisbury	v	Winchester City	2-0	348
Shortwood United	v	Larkhall Athletic	2-2, 4-3p	45
St Ives Town	v	Bedford Town	3-0	102
Stratford Town	v	Leamington	4-0	232

ROUND THREE

Aylesbury	v	Barton Rovers	2-3	59
Aylesbury United	v	Banbury United	3-2	112
Barnstaple Town	v	Paulton Rovers	2-1	108
Bishops Cleeve	v	Stratford Town	1-1, 4-3p	72
Hayes & Yeading United	v	Basingstoke Town	3-0	62
Northwood	v	Chalfont St Peter	0-1	59
Salisbury	v	Shortwood United	4-3	331
St Ives Town	v	Biggleswade Town	3-0	105

QUARTER-FINALS

Barnstaple Town	v	Salisbury	1-2	159
Barton Rovers	v	St Ives Town	2-3	80
Bishops Cleeve	v	Aylesbury United	0-2	57
Hayes & Yeading United	v	Chalfont St Peter	4-2	69

SEMI-FINALS

Hayes & Yeading United	v	Salisbury	4-0	139

Anthony Edgar 23
Soloman Sambou 52
Graeme Montgomery 55
Adam Flint 90 (og)

St Ives Town	v	Aylesbury United	2-0	117

Joshua Dawkin 20,39

FINAL

St Ives Town	v	Hayes & Yeading Utd	1-1,2-4p	385

Charlie Death 15   *Anthony Edgar 25 (pen)*

Southern Premier Statistics 2016-17

TOP SCORING CLUBS

Chippenham Town	110
Merthyr Town	106
Slough Town	105
Weymouth	104

MOST GAMES WITHOUT SCORING

Cinderford Town	22 (3)
Hayes & Yeading	19 (4)
Cambridge City and Dunstable Town	18 (4)

MOST SCORERS

Cambridge City	27+1og
Redditch United	25+1og
Frome Town	21+2ogs

MOST CONSECUTIVE SCORING GAMES

Chippenham Town	27
Biggleswade Town	18
Slough Town	16

MOST CLEAN SHEETS

Leamington	27 (6)
Merthyr Town	21 (4)
Hitchin Town	20 (2)

	GT	GWS(1)	TNoS	MCSG	TCS(2)
Banbury United	77	11 (3)	19+4ogs	12	17(6)
Basingstoke Town	71	14 (3)	14	12	10(2)
Biggleswade Town	90	10 (2)	17+2ogs	18	17
Cambridge City	51	18 (4)	27+1og	9	13(6)
Chesham United	81	9 (2)	15+1og	14	14(3)
Chippenham Town	110	3 (1)	15+1og	27	16(3)
Cinderford Town	50	22 (3)	20	5	2(1)
Cirencester Town	57	9 (2)	24	11	9 (2)
Dorchester Town	52	17 (3)	17+3ogs	6	8 (2)
Dunstable Town	50	18 (4)	22	8	13 (3)
Frome Town	84	7 (2)	21+2ogs	15	13 (4)
Hayes & Yeading	50	19 (4)	27	7	12 (2)
Hitchin Town	94	10 (2)	17+2ogs	10	20 (2)
Kettering Town	96	9 (2)	16+1og	13	10 (2)
Kings Langley	67	13 (2)	22	10	14 (4)
Kings Lynn Town	72	13 (2)	20+2ogs	9	10 (3)
Leamington	75	12 (3)	16+3 ogs	8	27 (6)
Merthyr Town	107	6 (1)	18+3ogs	12	21 (4)
Redditch Town	59	14 (4)	25+1og	13	6 (2)
Slough Town	105	10 (2)	19+1og	16	17 (2)
Sy Ives Town	56	16 (3)	13+1og	6	10 (2)
St Neots Town	74	14 (5)	20+2ogs	10	3 (1)
Stratford Town	67	12 (2)	19	7	8 (2)
Weymouth	104	11 (2)	19+1og	7	13 (2)

(1) - Most consecutive goalless games in brackets.
(2) - Most consecutive clean sheets in brackets.
GT - Goals Total
GWS - Games Without Scoring
TNoS - Total Number of Scorers
MCSG - Most Consecutive Scoring Games
TCS - Total Clean Sheets

Strikers with ten or more goals - 2016-17

LEAGUE, FA CUP AND FA TROPHY GOALS ONLY.

Club							PTG	CTG	FLP
Slough Town	Dobson	17	James	14	Moone	12	74	105	5
	Harris	11	Dunn	10	Flood	10			
Chesham United	Pearce	16	Roberts	15			55	81	11
	Youngs	13	Blake	11					
Weymouth	Fleetwood	18	Davis	13			54	104	10
	Yetton	13	Shepherd	10					
Chippenham Town	Sandell	32	Pratt	28	Smith	10	70	110	1
Merthyr Town	McLaggon	25	Traynor	25	Prosser	14	64	107	3
Biggleswade Town	Effiong	23	Burnett	19	Hoenes	14	56	90	7
Hitchin Town	Burns	20	B.Donnelly	15	Lench	13	48	94	4
St Neots Town	Brown	19	Hall	15	Rogers	11	45	74	19
Kettering Town	O'Connor	18	Weir-Daley	15	Howe	12	45	96	9
Leamington	Baker-Richardson	17	Rowe	12	Obeng	10	39	75	2
Frome Town	Jackson	22	Davies	12			34	84	8
Banbury United	Johnson	15	McDonagh	13			28	77	6
St Ives Town	Seymore-Shove	13	Dawkin	11			24	56	19
Basingstoke Town	Jarvis	13	Owusu	10			23	71	12
Stratford Town	Ahenkorah	13	Taylor	10			23	67	14
Cinderford Town	Hill	11	Chambers	10			21	50	24
Kings Lynn	Clunan	11					11	72	13
Kings Langley	L.Toomey	11					11	67	20
Dorchester Town	Walker	11					11	52	18

PTG - Players Total Goals I CTG - Club's Total Goals I FLP - Final League Position

BANBURY UNITED

Club Contact Details
The Banbury Plant Hire Community Stadium, off Station Road, Banbury OX16 5AD
01295 263 354
bworsley@btinternet.com

Ground Capacity: 6,500 **Seats:** 250 **Covered:** 250 **Clubhouse:** Yes **Shop:** Yes

Record Attendance
7,160 v Oxford City - FA Cup 3rd Qualifying Round 30/10/1948
Previous Grounds
Middleton Road 1931-34.

10 YEAR RECORD

	07-08		08-09		09-10		10-11		11-12		12-13		13-14		14-15		15-16		16-17	
SthP		9	SthP	19	SthP	12	SthP	16	SthP	16	SthP	16	SthP	19	SthP	21	Sthsw	2	SthP	6
FAC		1Q	FAC	1Q	FAC	1Qr	FAC	1Q	FAC	1Q	FAC	1Qr	FAC	1Q	FAC	2Q	FAC	P	FAC	3Q
FAT		1Q	FAT	1Q	FAT	2Qr	FAT	2Q	FAT	3Qr	FAT	1Qr	FAT	1Q	FAT	3Q	FAT	1Qr	FAT	1Q

Club Factfile

Founded: 1931   **Nickname:** Puritans   **Manager:** Mike Ford

Previous Names: Spencer Villa 1931-34. Banbury Spencer. Club reformed in 1965 as Banbury United

Previous Leagues: Banbury Junior 1933-34, Oxon Senior 1934-35, Birmingham Combination 1935-54, West Midlands 1954-66, Southern 1966-90, Hellenic 1991-2000

Club Colours (change): Red & gold

RECORDS
Victory: 12-0 v RNAS Culham - Oxon Senior Cup 1945-46
Defeat: 2-11 v West Bromwich Albion 'A' - Birmingham Combination 1938-39
Goalscorer: Dick Pike and Tony Jacques - 222 (1935-48 and 1965-76 respectively). Jacues also scored 62 in a single season, 1967-68.
Appearances: Jody McKay - 576
Additional: Paid £2,000 to Oxford United for Phil Emsden
                    Received £20,000 from Derby County for Kevin Wilson 1979

HONOURS

FA Comps: None

League: Oxfordshire Junior Banbury Division 1933-34. Oxfordshire Senior 1934-35. Hellenic Premier 1999-2000.

County FA: Oxford Senior Cup 1978-79, 87-88, 2003-04, 05-06, 06-07, 14-15.

BEST PERFORMANCES	**FA Cup:** First Round Proper 1947-48, 61-62, 72-73, 73-74.
	FA Trophy: Third Round Proper 1970-71(r), 73-74(2r).
	FA Vase: Second Round Proper 1999-2000.

BANBURY UNITED MATCH RESULTS 2016-17

Date	Comp	H/A	Opponents	Att:	Result	Goalscorers	Pos	No.
Aug 6	SPL	A	Basingstoke Town	482	W 1 - 0	Johnson 63	9	1
9	SPL	H	Slough Town	423	W 1 - 0	McEachran 88	5	2
13	SPL	H	Kings Lynn Town	335	W 4 - 0	Bell 3 Barcelos 11 44 Martin 17	1	3
16	SPL	A	Dunstable Town	203	L 0 - 1		4	4
20	SPL	H	Dorchester Town	324	L 1 - 2	Jones 90	7	5
27	SPL	A	Hitchin Town	350	L 1 - 3	Howards 90	10	6
29	SPL	H	Redditch Town	403	L 0 - 1		13	7
Sept 3	FAC1Q	A	**Dorchester Town**	249	**W 3 - 0**	**Johnson 30 (pen) Barcelos 55 60**		8
10	SPL	A	Kettering Town	480	D 2 - 2	Johnson 25 (pen) Jeacock 45	13	9
13	SPL	A	Chippenham Town	377	W 1 - 0	Nash 19	9	10
17	FAC2Q	A	**Cirencester Town**	155	**W 6 - 1**	**Barcelos 16 65 McEachran 31 McDonagh 56 Johnson 72 Browne 89**		11
24	SPL	H	Kings Langley	352	W 3 - 0	Jeacock 24 McDonagh 28 Johnson 30	5	12
27	SPL	A	Merthyr Town	306	D 1 - 1	Self 90	8	13
Oct 1	FAC3Q	A	**Wealdstone**	457	**L 1 - 2**	**Johnson 57**		14
8	SPL	H	Biggleswade Town	346	D 1 - 1	Johnson 56	9	15
10	SPL	A	Cambridge City	145	W 2 - 1	McDonagh 45 Uttridge 90 (og)	4	16
18	SPL	H	Chippenham Town	300	W 2 - 1	McDonagh 17 Tindle 38 (og)	7	17
22	SPL	H	Frome Town	344	L 1 - 2	Johnson 21	8	18
25	SPL	A	St Ives Town	204	D 1 - 1	McDonagh 12	9	19
29	FAT1Q	H	**Bishops Cleeve**	220	**L 0 - 1**		8	20
Nov 1	SPL	A	St Neots Town	196	W 4 - 1	Oduamo 36 Self 45 Jeacock 75 85	6	21
5	SPL	A	Cirencester Town	154	W 4 - 1	Browne 9 33 Brown 12 (og) McDonough 17	6	22
19	SPL	A	Kings Lynn Town	587	L 0 - 1		7	23
22	SPL	H	Dunstable Town	222	L 0 - 1		9	24
29	SPL	A	Slough Town	463	L 0 - 2		9	25
Dec 3	SPL	H	Stratford Town	378	W 2 - 1	Clark 78 (og) White 90	9	26
10	SPL	A	Hayes & Yaeding United	238	W 5 - 0	Westbrook 1 White 4 Johnson 25 McDonagh 71 Browne 897		27
17	SPL	H	Cinderford Town	444	W 4 - 0	McDonough 1 Johnson 25 90 Gunn 27	8	28
26	SPL	A	Redditch United	402	D 0 - 0		8	29
Jan 2	SPL	H	Leamington	734	W 1 - 0	Bell 90	7	30
7	SPL	A	Dorchester Town	491	W 1 - 0	Bell 86 (pen)	7	31
14	SPL	A	Kings Langley	152	W 1 - 0	McDonagh 70	7	32
17	SPL	A	Weymouth	325	D 2 - 2	Humphreys 25 Self 37	6	33
21	SPL	H	St Neots Town	427	W 2 - 1	McDonough 41 47	5	34
28	SPL	A	Merthyr Town	529	L 0 - 1		6	35
31	SPL	H	Basingstoke Town	242	L 0 - 1		6	36
Feb 4	SPL	H	Cambridge City	425	W 2 - 0	Self 30 Carnell 73	6	37
11	SPL	A	Biggleswade Town	154	L 1 - 2	Self 41	6	38
18--35	SPL	H	Weymouth	411	D 1 - 1	Nash 22	6	39
25	SPL	H	St Ives Town	334	W 1 - 0	Johnson 90	6	40
Mar 4	SPL	A	Frome Town	270	W 2 - 1	Johnson 2 McEachran 48	6	41
11	SPL	H	Cirencester Town	374	W 2 - 1	Carnell 18 McDonagh 58	6	42
14	SPL	H	Chesham United	347	W 1 - 0	White 68	6	43
18	SPL	A	Chesham United	386	W 4 - 0	Johnson 25 75 Carnell 29 Humphreys 90	6	44
25	SPL	A	Stratford Town	417	L 0 - 2		6	45
April 1	SPL	H	Hayes & Yeading United	201	W 1 - 0	McDonagh 38	6	46
8	SPL	A	Cinderford Town	175	W 2 - 1	Carnell 15 Duku 79	6	47
15	SPL	H	Hitchin Town	740	D 1 - 1	McEachran 44	6	48
17	SPL	A	Leamington	846	L 0 - 1		6	49
22	SPL	H	Kettering Town	477	L 1 - 2	Duku 71 (pen)	6	50

GOALSCORERS	SG	CSG	Pens	Hat tricks	Total		SG	CSG	Pens	Hat tricks	Total
Johnson	13	2	2		15	White	3	2			3
McDonagh	12	2			13	Duku	2		1		2
Barcelos	3				6	Humphreys	2				2
Self	5				5	Nash	2				2
Browne	3				4	Gunn	1				1
Carnell	4				4	Howards	1				1
Jeacock	3				4	Jones	1				1
McEachran	4				4	Martin	1				1
Opponents	4				4	Oduamo	1				1
Bell	3		1		3	Westbrook	1				1

BASINGSTOKE TOWN

Club Contact Details
The Ark Cancer Charity Stadium, Western Way, Basingstoke RG22 6EZ
01256 327 575
richard.trodd@ntlworld.com

Ground Capacity: 6,000 **Seats:** 651 **Covered:** 2,000 **Clubhouse:** Yes **Shop:** Yes

Record Attendance
5,085 v Wycombe Wanderers - FA Cup 1st Round replay 1997-98
Previous Grounds
Castle Field 1896-1947

10 YEAR RECORD

	07-08	08-09	09-10	10-11	11-12	12-13	13-14	14-15	15-16	16-17
	Conf S 15	Conf S 18	Conf S 15	Conf S 13	Conf S 5	Conf S 14	Conf S 14	Conf S 3	Nat S 22	SthP 12
	FAC 2Q	FAC 4Q	FAC 3Q	FAC 4Q	FAC 1P	FAC 3Q	FAC 2Q	FAC 1Pr	FAC 1P	FAC 2Q
	FAT 3Q	FAT 2P	FAT 3Q	FAT 1P	FAT 2P	FAT 3Q	FAT 1Pr	FAT 1Pr	FAT 3Q	FAT 3Q

Club Factfile

Founded: 1896   **Nickname:** Dragons   **Manager:** Terry Brown

Previous Names: The club was formed by the merger of Aldworth United and Basingstoke Albion in 1896.

Previous Leagues: Hampshire 1900-40, 45-71, Southern 1971-87, Isthmian 1987-2004. Conference 2004-16.

Club Colours (change): All blue (All white)

RECORDS
Victory: 10-1 v Chichester City (H) - FA Cup 1st Qualifying Round 1976
Defeat: 0-8 v Aylesbury United - Southern League April 1979
Goalscorer: Paul Coombs - 159 (1991-99)
Appearances: Billy Coomb
Additional: Paid £4,750 to Gosport Borough for Steve Ingham

HONOURS
FA Comps: None

League: Hampshire North Division 1911-12, 19-20, Division One 1967-68, 69-70, 70-71.
Southern Southern Division 1984-85.

County FA: Hampshire Senior Cup 1970-71, 89-90, 95-96, 96-97, 2007-08, 13-14, 16-17.

BEST PERFORMANCES	**FA Cup:** Second Round Proper 1989-90, 97-98, 2006-07.
	FA Trophy: Third Round Proper 1998-99, 2003-04.
	FA Vase: N/A

BASINGSTOKE TOWN MATCH RESULTS 2016-17

Date	Comp	H/A	Opponents	Att:	Result	Goalscorers	Pos	No.
Aug 6	SPL	H	Banbury United	462	L 0 - 1		19	1
9	SPL	A	Merthyr Town	508	L 0 - 4		23	2
13	SPL	A	Stratford Town	219	D 1 - 1	Hallahan 55	22	3
16	SPL	H	Hayes & Yeading United	411	D 1 - 1	Jarvis 23	21	4
20	SPL	H	Kettering Town	474	W 3 - 0	Hallahan 19 34 Deadfield 47	18	5
27	SPL	A	Cinderford Town	162	W 3 - 2	Atkinson 35 Collier 57 Deadfield 83	13	6
29	SPL	A	Frome Town	447	L 1 - 3	Deadfield 76	17	7
Sept 3	FAC1Q	H	Bemerton Heath Harlequins	237	W 4 - 0	Partridge 5 HALLAHAN 3 (16 37 76)		8
10	SPL	A	Hitchin Town	303	L 0 - 1		20	9
13	SPL	A	Kings Langley	112	L 0 - 2		20	10
17	FAC2Q	H	Hungerford Town	347	L 0 - 1			11
24	SPL	H	Cambridge City	383	W 2 - 1	Rose 48 Johnson-Schuster 65	17	12
27	SPL	H	Cirencester Town	331	L 0 - 1		18	13
Oct 1	SPL	A	Dunstable Town	181	W 3 - 1	Rose 16 Owusu 70 Whittingham 77	17	14
8	SPL	H	St Neots town	396	W 1 - 0	Rose 35	14	15
11	SPL	A	Weymouth	464	L 0 - 3		15	16
15	SPL	A	Biggleswade Town	158	D 0 - 0		15	17
18	SPL	H	Kings Langley	294	W 3 - 0	Whittingham 64 (pen) Hallahan 85 90	10	18
22	SPL	H	Slough Town	596	W 4 - 1	Jarvis 48 65 Owusu 62 Redford 90	9	19
25	SPL	A	Chippenham Town	364	L 0 - 2		10	20
29	FAT1Q	A	Staines Town	291	W 4 - 1	Whittingham 16 Ray 38 Redford 54 Jarvis 64		21
Nov 5	SPL	A	Leamington	526	L 1 - 3	Redford 76	11	22
12	FAT2Q	A	Dorchester Town	306	W 3 - 0	Owusu 42 Redford (pen) Deadfield 90		23
19	SPL	H	Stratford Town	362	W 2 - 1	Atkinson 28 Owusu 83	11	24
26	FAT3Q	A	Bath City	366	L 0 - 2			25
29	SPL	H	Merthyr Town	318	W 3 - 2	Owusu 3 Rose 45 Partridge 51	12	26
Dec 3	SPL	H	St IvesTown	377	L 0 - 2		12	27
10	SPL	A	Chesham United	317	L 0 - 4		13	28
13	SPL	H	Kings Lynn Town	294	L 1 - 2	Jarvis 69	13	29
17	SPL	H	Redditch United	366	L 0 - 1		16	30
26	SPL	A	Frome Town	366	D 1 - 1	Jarvis 16	16	31
Jan 2	SPL	H	Dorchester Town	436	D 1 - 1	Deadfield 57	17	32
7	SPL	A	Kettering Town	658	L 1 - 2	Redford 71	18	33
14	SPL	A	Cambridge City	209	W 2 - 0	Ray 15 41	15	34
28	SPL	A	Cirencester Town	161	W 3 - 2	Owusu 54 90 Jarvis 64	15	35
31	SPL	A	Banbury United	242	W 1 - 0	Owusu 53		36
Feb 4	SPL	H	Weymouth	426	L 1 - 6	Redford 47	16	37
11	SPL	A	St Neots Town	209	L 1 - 2	Deadfield 6	16	38
14	SPL	A	Hayes & Yeading United	152	W 3 2	Johnson-Schuster 14 Jarvis 15 Gater 63	12	39
18	SPL	H	Biggleswade Town	348	W 2 - 1	Jarvis 39 Artwell 75	11	40
25	SPL	H	Chippenham Town	397	L 1 - 2	Artwell 7	12	41
Mar 4	SPL	A	Slough Town	728	L 2 - 3	Redford 55 80	12	42
11	SPL	H	Leamington	408	L 0 - 2		13	43
18	SPL	A	Kings Lynn Town	506	L 1 - 2	Jarvis 65	13	44
25	SPL	A	St Ives Town	248	W 1 - 0	Partridge 65	13	45
April 1	SPL	H	Chesham United	376	W 3 - 2	Artwell 35 52 Redford 49	12	46
8	SPL	A	Redditch United	216	D 2 - 2	Jarvis 9 Partridge 35	12	47
15	SPL	H	Cinderford Town	395	W 3 - 0	Owusu 8 (pen) Partridge 70 Jarvis 77	12	48
17	SPL	A	Dorchester Town	477	D 1 - 1	Owusu 29 (pen)	12	50
22	SPL	H	Hitchin Town	617	D 1 - 1	Jarvis 40	12	51

GOALSCORERS	SG	CSG	Pens	Hat tricks	Total		SG	CSG	Pens	Hat tricks	Total
2015-16 Flood					10	Whittingham	3		1		3
Jarvis	13				13	Atkinson	2				2
Owusu	9	3	2		10	Johnson-Schuster	2				2
Redford	8		1		9	Collier	1				1
Hallahan	4			1	8	Gater	1				1
Deadfield	6				6						
Partridge	5				5						
Artwell	3				4						
Rose	4	2			4						
Ray	2				3						

BIGGLESWADE TOWN

Club Contact Details
The Carlsberg Stadium, Langford Road, Biggleswade SG18 9JT
01767 318 202 (Matchdays)
michaeldraxler@hotmail.com

Ground Capacity: 3,000 **Seats:** 300   **Covered:** 400   **Clubhouse:** Yes   **Shop:**

Record Attendance
2,000
Previous Grounds
Fairfield

10 YEAR RECORD

	07-08		08-09		09-10		10-11		11-12		12-13		13-14		14-15		15-16		16-17	
	SSM P	3	SSM P	1	SthM	12	SthC	4	SthC	8	SthC	4	SthP	9	SthP	19	SthP	14	SthP	7
	FAC	EP	FAC	EP	FAC	P	FAC	1Q	FAC	2Qr	FAC	1Q	FAC	1P	FAC	3Q	FAC	2Q	FAC	2Q
	FAV	2Q	FAV	QF	FAT	1Q	FAT	1Q	FAT	1Q	FAT	P	FAT	1Q	FAT	2Q	FAT	1Q	FAT	2Qr

Club Factfile

Founded: 1874   **Nickname:** The Waders   **Manager:** Chris Nunn

Previous Names: Biggleswade FC. Biggleswade & District.

Previous Leagues: Biggleswade & District 1902-20. Bedford & District. Northamptonsonshire/United Counties 1920-39 / 1951-55, 1963-80. Spartan 1945-51. Eastern Counties 1955-63. South Midlands/SSM 1980-2009.

Club Colours (change): White with green trim/green/green (Blue & black stripes/black/blue & black)

RECORDS
Victory: 12-0 v Newmarket Town (A), Eastern Counties.

HONOURS

FA Comps: None

League: Biggleswade & District 1902-03. Spartan South Midlands Premier Division 2008-09.

County FA: Bedfordshire Senior Cup 1902-03, 07-08, 46-47, 50-51, 61-62, 62-63, 66-67, 73-74.
Bedfordshire Premier Cup 2009. Bedfordshire Senior Challenge Cup 2012-13.

BEST PERFORMANCES	**FA Cup:** First Round Proper 2013-14.
	FA Trophy: Second Qualifying Round 1974-75(r), 2014-15, 16-17(r).
	FA Vase: Quarter-finals 2008-09.

BIGGLESWADE TOWN MATCH RESULTS 2016-17

Date	Comp	H/A	Opponents	Att:	Result	Goalscorers	Pos	No.
Aug 6	SPL	H	Weymouth	202	L	1 - 3	Effiong 8	20	1
8	SPL	A	Cambridge City	177	D	1 - 1	Effiong 31	18	2
13	SPL	A	Cirencester Town	75	L	0 - 0		21	3
16	SPL	H	Kings Langley	131	L	0 - 0		21	4
20	SPL	H	Cinderford Town	126	W	5 - 5	EFFIONG 3 (10 pen 71 76) Burnett 25 61	20	5
27	SPL	A	Leamington	364	D	1 - 1	Effiong 15	21	6
29	SPL	H	St Neots Town	345	W	2 - 2	Hall 51 Effiong 68	18	7
Sept 3	FAC1Q	A	Maldon & Tiptree	115	W	1 - 0	Anderson 73		8
10	SPL	A	Frome Town	215	L	0 - 2		19	9
14	SPL	A	Kings Lynn Town	175	W	2 - 0	Daniel 63 Bailey 90	13	10
17	FAC2Q	A	Margate	466	L	0 - 2			11
24	SPL	A	Slough Town	575	L	0 - 3		16	12
27	SPL	A	St Ives Town	259	W	1 - 0	Effiong 8	14	13
Oct 1	SPL	H	Redditch United	135	W	2 - 0	Daniel 15 30	9	14
8	SPL	A	Banbury United	346	D	1 - 1	Effiong 4	10	15
11	SPL	H	Kettering Town	222	D	2 - 2	Effiong 29 Burnett 90		16
15	SPL	H	Basingstoke Town	158	D	0 - 0		11	17
22	SPL	A	Merthyr Town	468	L	0 - 1		14	18
29	FAT1Q	H	Witham Town	111	W	1 - 0	Ahern 16 (og)		19
Nov 5	SPL	H	Dunatable Town	152	D	2 - 2	Burnett 26 49	14	20
12	FAT2Q	H	Hitchin Town	325	D	1 - 1	Hall 88		21
14	FAT2Qr	A	Hitchin Town	201	L	2 - 3	Hall 65 (pen) Burnett 84		22
19	SPL	H	Cirencester Town	132	W	6 - 0	BURNETT 4 (20 34 78 85) Effiong 67 Hall 80	13	23
22	SPL	A	Kings Langley	86	W	5 - 4	Lucan 5 Effiong 61 81 Burnett 62 Hoenes 75	11	24
29	SPL	H	Cambridge City	111	D	2 - 1	Burnett 8 Hall 31	10	25
Dec 3	SPL	A	Dorchester Town	314	L	1 2	Hall 48	11	26
10	SPL	H	Chippenham Town	121	D	2 - 2	Effiong 3 (pen) Lewis 89	12	27
17	SPL	H	Chesham United	151	D	2 - 2	Short 20 Effiong 90 (pen)	12	28
26	SPL	A	St Neots Town	323	W	5 - 0	EFFIONG 3 (44 58 83) Hall 67 Daniel 90	12	29
29	SPL	A	Weymouth	573	D	2 - 2	Effiong 7 85	11	30
Jan 2	SPL	H	Hitchin Town	551	L	1 - 3	Effiong 37 (pen)	12	31
7	SPL	A	Cinderford Town	125	W	2 - 1	Short 4 Hoenes 33	11	32
17	SPL	A	Kings Lynn Town	345	W	2 - 1	Effiong 25 (pen) 90 (pen)	11	33
21	SPL	A	Redditch Uited	255	W	2 - 0	Patrick 11 Hoenes 24	9	34
28	SPL	H	St Ives Town	228	W	3 - 1	Daniel 48 Hoenes 60 Hall 68 (pen)	9	35
Feb 4	SPL	A	Kettering Town	511	L	1 - 3	Parker 90	10	36
7	SPL	A	Hayes & Yeading	159	D	0 - 0		10	37
11	SPL	H	Banbury Town	154	W	2 - 1	Hoyle 31 Parker 90	10	38
14	SPL	H	Stratford Town	80	L	1 - 2	Kalenda 21 (og)	10	39
18	SPL	A	Basingstoke Town	348	L	1 - 2	Bignall 5	10	40
25	SPL	A	Stratford Town	144	L	0 - 1		10	41
Mar 4	SPL	H	Merthyr Town	224	L	2 - 5	Hoenes 8 35	10	42
8	SPL	H	Slough Town	190	W	3 - 0	HOENES 3 (13 80 87) Burnett 63 82 Daniel 74	10	43
11	SPL	A	Dunstable Town	127	W	2 - 0	Daniel 49 Emery 77	10	44
18	SPL	A	Hayes & Yeading United	165	W	6 - 0	HOENES 3 (16(p) 66 (p) 69 (p))	9	45
25	SPL	H	Dorchester Town	203	W	3 - 0	Burnett 52 77 Hoenes 67 (pen)	8	46
April 1	SPL	A	Chippenham Town	633	L	0 - 2		9	47
8	SPL	A	Chesham United	283	W	2 - 1	Hoenes 22 Richens 81	9	48
15	SPL	H	Leamington	320	W	2 - 0	Hall 35 Burnett 49	8	49
17	SPL	A	Hitchin Town	766	D	1 - 1	Vincent 45	8	50
22	SPL	H	Frome Town	165	W	4 - 1	Burnett 3 81 Emery 84 Daniel 90	7	51

GOALSCORERS	SG	CSG	Pens	Hat tricks	Total		SG	CSG	Pens	Hat tricks	Total
2015-16 *Effiong*					*15*	Anderson	1				1
Effiong	16	5	6	2	23	Bailey	1				1
Burnett	11	4		1	19	Bignall	1				1
Hoenes	9		3	2	14	Hoyle	1				1
Hall	9	3	2		9	Lewis	1				1
Daniel	6				8	Lucan	1				1
Emery	2				2	Patrick	1				1
Opponents	1				2	Richens	1				1
Parker	2				2	Vincent	1				1
Short	2				2						

BISHOP'S STORTFORD

Club Contact Details

ProKit Uk Stadium, Woodside Park, Dunmow Road, Bishop's Stortford CM23 5RG

01279 306 456

fredplume@hotmail.co.uk

Ground Capacity: 4,000 **Seats:** 525 **Covered:** 700 **Clubhouse:** Yes **Shop:** Yes

Record Attendance

6,000 v Peterborough Town - FA Cup 2nd Round 1972-73 and v Middlesbrough - FA Cup 3rd Round replay 1982-83

Previous Grounds

Silver Leys 1874-97. Hadham Rd 97-1900. Havers Lane 00-03. Laundry Field 03-19. Brazier's Field 1919-97.Shared>99

10 YEAR RECORD

07-08		08-09		09-10		10-11		11-12		12-13		13-14		14-15		15-16		16-17	
Conf S	10	Conf S	9	Conf S	18	Conf S	16	Conf N	10	Conf N	17	Conf S	15	Conf S	16	Nat S	11	Nat S	21
FAC	3Q	FAC	4Q	FAC	2Q	FAC	2Qr	FAC	4Q	FAC	1P	FAC	1P	FAC	2Qr	FAC	2Q	FAC	3Q
FAT	2Pr	FAT	3Qr	FAT	1P	FAT	3Q	FAT	1P	FAT	1P	FAT	3Q	FAT	1P	FAT	3Q	FAT	3Q

Club Factfile

Founded: 1874 **Nickname:** Blues or Bishops **Manager:** Kevin Watson

Previous Names: None

Previous Leagues: East Herts 1896-97, 1902-06, 19-21, Stansted & Dist. 1906-19, Herts Co. 1921-25, 26-29, Herts & Essex Border 1925-26, Spartan 1929-51, Delphian (FM) 1951-63, Athenian 1963-71, Isthmian 1971-2004, Conference 2004-17.

Club Colours (change): Blue & white stripes/blue/blue (Red & black stripes/black/black)

RECORDS

Victory: 11-0 v Nettleswell & Buntwill - Herts Junior Cup 1911

Defeat: 0-13 v Cheshunt (H) - Herts Senior Cup 1926

Goalscorer: Post 1929 Jimmy Badcock - 123

Appearances: Phil Hopkins - 543

HONOURS

FA Comps: FA Amateur Cup 1973-74. FA Trophy 1980-81.

League: Stansted & District 1910-11, 12-13, 19-20. Spartan Division Two East 1931-32. Delphian 1954-55. Athenian Division One 1965-66, Premier 69-70. Isthmian Division One 1980-81, 93-94.

County FA: Herts Senior Cup 1932-33, 58-59, 59-60, 63-64, 70-71, 72-73, 73-74, 75-76, 86-87, 2005-06, 09-10, 11-12. London Senior Cup 1973-74.

BEST PERFORMANCES	**FA Cup:** Third Round Proper 1982-83.
	FA Trophy: Final 1980-81.
	FA Vase: N/A

BISHOP'S STORTFORD MATCH RESULTS 2016-17

Date	Comp	H/A	Opponents	Att:	Result	Goalscorers	Pos	No.
Aug 6	Nat S	H	Hampton & Richmond B	333	L 0 - 1		16	1
9	Nat S	A	Welling United	532	W 2 - 1	Eyong 61 Woods-Garness 90	9	2
13	Nat S	A	Poole Town	424	L 0 - 1		16	3
16	Nat S	H	Hungerford Town	266	L 1 - 2	O'Neill 24	18	4
20	Nat S	H	Bath City	301	L 0 - 1		19	5
27	Nat S	A	Gosport Borough	487	W 1 - 0	Smith 90	16	6
29	Nat S	H	Wealdstone	465	L 0 - 3		17	7
Sept 3	Nat S	A	Hemel Hempstead Town	438	L 2 - 3	Smith 4 Varouxakis 86	18	8
6	Nat S	A	Concord Rangers	234	D 0 - 0		16	9
10	Nat S	H	Margate	362	L 0 - 2		19	10
13	Nat S	H	Ebbsfleet United	375	L 0 - 3		21	11
17	FAC 3Q	A	Felixstowe & Walton Utd	416	L 1 - 2	Kouassi 58		12
24	Nat S	A	East Thurrock United	242	D 2 - 2	Osei 20 78	20	13
Oct 8	Nat S	H	Whitehawk	300	L 0 - 3		20	14
15	Nat S	A	Maidenhead United	866	L 0 - 6		21	15
21	Nat S	H	St Albans City	424	L 1 - 5	Akinwande 89	22	16
28	Nat S	A	Eastbourne United	453	L 0 - 1		22	17
Nov 5	Nat S	H	Weston-s-Mare	268	W 2 - 1	Riches 14 Akinwande 15	22	18
12	Nat S	A	Oxford City	279	L 1 - 3	Merritt 90	22	19
19	Nat S	H	Dartford	388	L 0 - 3		22	20
26	FAT3Q	A	Hythe Town	234	L 2 - 4	Akinwande 6 Moncur 53 (pen)		21
Dec 3	Nat S	A	Truro City	246	W 2 - 1	Morgan 38 (pen) Bentley 56 (og)	22	22
17	Nat S	H	Hemel Hempstead Town	393	L 0 - 4		22	23
26	Nat S	A	Chelmsford City	1014	L 0 - 4		22	24
Jan 1	Nat S	H	Chelmsford City	717	L 1 - 3	Greene 7	22	25
7	Nat S	A	Margate	469	W 3 - 0	Cundle 20 Walsh 50 Adebowale 72	21	26
14	Nat S	A	Bath City	543	L 0 - 2		21	27
21	Nat S	H	Concord Rangers	381	W 1 - 0	Cundle 87	21	28
28	Nat S	A	Hampton & Richmond	561	L 1 - 4	Barnwell 61 (pen)	21	29
Feb 11	Nat S	A	Hungerford Town	216	L 0 - 2		21	30
18	Nat S	H	Poole Town	363	L 1 - 4	Greene 85	21	31
21	Nat S	H	Welling United	266	D 2 - 2	Callander 34 57	21	32
25	Nat S	H	Eastbourne Borough	282	L 1 - 4	Callander 17	21	33
Mar 4	Nat S	A	St Albans City	602	W 1 - 0	Ford 46	21	34
11	Nat S	H	East Thurrock United	283	L 0 - 4		21	35
18	Nat S	A	Whitehawk	226	L 0 - 1		21	36
21	Nat S	A	Ebbsfleet United	1229	L 0 - 8		21	37
25	Nat S	H	Maidenhead United	431	L 0 - 2		21	38
April 1	Nat S	H	Oxford City	265	L 0 - 2		22	39
8	Nat S	A	Weston-s-Mare	382	L 0 - 5		22	40
14	Nat S	H	Gosport Borough	268	L 0 - 2		22R	41
17	Nat S	A	Wealdstone	620	L 0 - 5		22	42
22	Nat S	A	Dartford	1025	L 0 - 4		22	43
29	Nat S	H	Truro City	302	W 4 - 0	Ford 9 Ronto 24 Kouassi 38 (pen) Greene 39	21	44

GOALSCORERS	SG	CSG	Pens	Hat tricks	Total		SG	CSG	Pens	Hat tricks	Total
2015-16 Buchanan					28	Eyong	1				1
Akinwande	4				3	Merritt	1				1
Callander	2	2			3	Moncur	1		1		1
Greene	3				3	Morgan	1		1		1
Cundle	2				2	O'Neill	1				1
Ford	2				2	Opponents	1				1
Kouassi	2		1		2	Richens	1				1
Osei	1				2	Ronto	1				1
Smith	2				2	Varouxakis	1				1
Adebowale	1				1	Walsh	1				1
Barnwell	1		1		1	Woods-Garness	1				1

CHESHAM UNITED

Club Contact Details
The Meadow, Amy Lane, Amersham Road, Chesham HP5 1NE
01494 783 964
a.lagden@sky.com

Ground Capacity: 5,000 **Seats:** 284 **Covered:** 2,500 **Clubhouse:** Yes **Shop:** Yes

Record Attendance
5,000 v Cambridge United - FA Cup 3rd Round 05/12/1979
Previous Grounds
None

10 YEAR RECORD

	07-08		08-09		09-10		10-11		11-12		12-13		13-14		14-15		15-16		16-17	
SthM	6	SthM	5	SthM	4	SthP	6	SthP	4	SthP	3	SthP	2	SthP	12	SthP	13	SthP	11
FAC	2Qr	FAC	3Q	FAC	3Q	FAC	2Qr	FAC	2Q	FAC	1Q	FAC	1Q	FAC	1Qr	FAC	2P	FAC	1P
FAT	2Q	FAT	1P	FAT	1Qr	FAT	1Qr	FAT	2Qr	FAT	2P	FAT	1P	FAT	1Q	FAT	1Pr	FAT	2Q

Club Factfile

Founded: 1917 **Nickname:** The Generals **Manager:** Danny Talbot & Jon Meakes

Previous Names: Chesham Town and Chesham Generals merged in 1917 to form Chesham United.

Previous Leagues: Spartan 1917-47, Corinthian 1947-63, Athenian 1963-73, Isthmian 1973-2004

Club Colours (change): Claret & blue/claret/claret (Yellow & black/black/yellow)

RECORDS
Goalscorer: John Willis
Appearances: Martin Baguley - 600+
Additional: Received £22,000 from Oldham Athletic for Fitz Hall

HONOURS
FA Comps: None

League: Spartan 1921-22, 22-23, 24-25, 32-33. Isthmian Division Two North 1986-87, Division One 1986-87, 97-97, Premier Division 1992-93.

County FA: Berks & Bucks Senior Cup x12.

BEST PERFORMANCES
FA Cup: Third Round Proper 1979-80.
FA Trophy: Fourth Round Proper 1998-99.
FA Vase: N/A

CHESHAM UNITED MATCH RESULTS 2016-17

Date	Comp	H/A	Opponents	Att:	Result	Goalscorers	Pos	No.
Aug 6	SPL	A	Redditch United	144	L 1 - 3	Pearce 65	21	1
9	SPL	H	St Ives Town	302	W 2 - 0	Youngs 8 49	12	2
13	SPL	H	Dorchester Town	289	W 3 - 0	Roberts 21 48 Youngs 39	7	3
15	SPL	A	Hitchin Town	362	D 1 - 1	Roberts 79	5	4
20	SPL	A	Dunstable Town	305	D 0 - 0		9	5
27	SPL	H	Weymouth	288	D 1 - 1	Pearce 16	8	6
29	SPL	H	Kings Langley	310	W 2 - 1	Martin 19 Wadkins 22	6	7
Sept 3	FAC1Q	H	Saffron Walden Town	325	W 5 - 0	Pearce 40 72 Wadkins 55 60 Blake 86		8
10	SPL	H	Kings Lynn Town	257	L 1 - 2	Pearce 16	7	9
13	SPL	A	Hayes & Yeading United	216	L 0 - 1		10	10
17	FAC2Q	A	Sevenoaks Town	426	D 2 - 2	Watson 4 Hayles 90		11
20	FAC2Qr	H	Sevenoaks Town	273	W 2 - 1	Pearce 21 Roberts 50		12
24	SPL	H	Cirencester Town	292	W 3 - 0	Bennett 12 (og) Hayles 33 59	8	13
27	SPL	H	Cambridge City	238	W 3 - 1	Blake 7 Wadkins 20 Pearce 88	6	14
Oct 1	FAC3Q	H	Staines Town	354	W 2 - 0	Roberts 48 71 (pen)		15
8	SPL	H	Merthyr Town	367	D 1 - 1	Blake 83	7	16
15	FAC4Q	H	Potters Bar Town	777	W 1 - 0	Roberts 14 (pen)		17
22	SPL	A	Cinderford Town	151	W 1 - 0	Roberts 42 (pen)	11	18
25	SPL	H	Kettering Town	360	W 1 - 0	Wadkins 14	7	19
29	FAT1Q	A	Leatherhead	255	W 3 - 2	Pearce 10 30 Blake 53		20
Nov 5	FAC1	A	Peterborough United	4328	L 1 - 2	Blake 80		21
12	FAT2Q	A	Dulwich Hamlet	716	L 0 - 4			22
16	SPL	A	Frome Town	169	L 0 - 2		10	23
19	SPL	A	Dorchester Town	315	L 2 - 3	Purse 8 Roberts 64 (pen)	12	24
22	SPL	H	Hitchin Town	252	W 2 - 0	Youngs 22 Blake 49	10	25
26	SPL	H	Redditch United	307	D 1 - 1	Youngs 77	11	26
Dec 6	SPL	H	Hayes & Yeading United	250	W 6 - 0	Blake 5 Youngs 31 Pearce 42 52 Roberts 75 Wadkins 83	11	27
10	SPL	H	Basingstoke Town	317	W 4 - 0	Wadkins 32 Roberts 53 71 Youngs 83	11	28
17	SPL	A	Biggleswade Town	151	D 2 - 2	Roberts 26 (pen) Blake 53	9	29
26	SPL	H	Kings Langley	542	W 5 - 2	Hayles 45 69 Mitchell-King 48 Pearce 88 (pen) Youngs 90	9	30
Jan 2	SPL	A	Slough Town	918	W 2 - 1	Hayles 55 Pearce 56	8	31
7	SPL	H	Dunstable Town	369	W 1 - 0	Blake 8	8	32
14	SPL	A	Cirencester Town	1267	W 2 - 1	Little 26 Wadkins 90	8	33
17	SPL	H	Stratford Town	222	D 1 - 1	Youngs 45	8	34
28	SPL	A	Cambridge City	194	L 1 - 3	Youngs 16	8	35
Feb 4	SPL	H	St Neots Town	331	W 3 - 2	Hayles 3 Hutton 10 Pearce 90	8	36
7	SPL	A	Chippenham Town	409	L 1 - 3	Martin 72	8	37
11	SPL	A	Merthyr Town	405	L 0 - 1		8	38
14	SPL	A	St Neots Town	148	L 1 - 4	Roberts 28	8	39
18	SPL	H	Leamington	427	L 0 - 1		9	40
21	SPL	A	St Ives Town	152	W 2 - 0	Blake 64, Youngs 79		41
25	SPL	A	Kettering Town	517	W 2 - 1	Roberts 12 Youngs 14	8	42
28	SPL	A	Leamington	306	L 0 - 2			43
Mar 4	SPL	H	Cinderford Town	310	W 1 - 0	Purse 45 (pen)	7	44
7	SPL	H	Frome Town	215	D 1 - 1	Youngs 82	7	45
11	SPL	A	Stratford Town	196	D 1 - 1	Blake 79	7	46
14	SPL	A	Banbury United	347	L 0 - 1		7	47
18	SPL	H	Banbury United	386	L 0 - 4		8	48
25	SPL	H	Chippenham Town	345	L 1 - 3	Blake 15	10	49
April 1	SPL	A	Basingstoke Town	376	L 2 - 3	Youngs 76 Ujah 85	10	50
8	SPL	H	Biggleswade Town	283	L 1 - 2	Pearce 44 (pen)	10	51
14	SPL	A	Weymouth	561	L 0 - 2		11	52
17	SPL	H	Slough Town	508	D 1 - 1	Pearce 1	10	53
22	SPL	A	Kings Lynn Town	554	L 1 - 3	Devanney 9	11	54

GOALSCORERS	SG	CSG	Pens	Hat tricks	Total		SG	CSG	Pens	Hat tricks	Total
2015-16 Pearce					15	Little	1				1
Pearce	13	2	2		16	Mitchell-King	1				1
Roberts	11	3	5		15	Opponents	1				1
Youngs	13	4			14	Pearcew	1				1
Blake	12	2			12	Purse	1		1		1
Wadkins	7	2			8	Ujah	1				1
Hayles	5				7	Watson	1				1
Martin	2				2						
Devanney	1				1						
Hutton	1				1						

DORCHESTER TOWN

Club Contact Details
The Avenue Stadium, Weymouth Avenue, Dorchester DT1 2RY
01305 262 451
david.ring@dorchestertownfc.com

Ground Capacity: 5,229   **Seats:** 710   **Covered:** 2,846   **Clubhouse:** Yes   **Shop:** Yes

Record Attendance
4,159 v Weymouth - Southern Premier 1999
Previous Grounds
Council Recreation Ground, Weymouth Avenue 1908-1929, 1929-90, The Avenue Ground 1929

10 YEAR RECORD

	07-08	08-09	09-10	10-11	11-12	12-13	13-14	14-15	15-16	16-17
	Conf S 21	Conf S 19	Conf S 17	Conf S 17	Conf S 11	Conf S 8	Conf S 22	SthP 17	SthP 12	SthP 18
	FAC 2Qr	FAC 1Pr	FAC 3Q	FAC 3Q	FAC 2Q	FAC 2P	FAC 2Q	FAC 4Q	FAC 1Qr	FAC 1Q
	FAT 2P	FAT 3Q	FAT 3Q	FAT 2Pr	FAT 3Q	FAT 1Pr	FAT 3Q	FAT 1Q	FAT 2Qr	FAT 2Q

Club Factfile

Founded: 1880   **Nickname:** The Magpies   **Manager:** Craig Laird

Previous Names: None

Previous Leagues: Dorset, Western 1947-72

Club Colours (change): Black & white/black/black

RECORDS
Victory: 7-0 v Canterbury (A) - Southern League Southern Division 1986-87

Defeat: 0-13 v Welton Rovers (A) - Western League 1966

Appearances: Mark Jermyn - 600+ over 14 seasons

Additional: Denis Cheney scored 61 goals in one season. Paid £12,000 to Gloucester City for Chris Townsend 1990. Received £35,000 from Portsmouth for Trevor Sinclair.

HONOURS
FA Comps: None

League: Western Division One 1954-55. Southern Southern Division 1979-80, 86-87, Division One East 2002-03.

County FA: Dorset Senior Cup x12 - Firstly in 1950-51 and most recently in 2011-12.

BEST PERFORMANCES	FA Cup: Second Round Proper 1954-55, 57-58, 81-82(r), 2012-13.
	FA Trophy: Third Round Proper 1971-72(r), 96-97.
	FA Vase: N/A

DORCHESTER TOWN MATCH RESULTS 2016-17

Date	Comp	H/A	Opponents	Att:	Result	Goalscorers	Pos	No.
Aug 6	SPL	H	Kettering Town	421	L 0 - 2		23	1
9	SPL	A	Cinderford Town	210	L 0 - 4		24	2
13	SPL	A	Chesham United	289	L 0 - 3		24	3
16	SPL	H	Cirencester Town	301	D 2 - 2	Griffin 12 (pen) Walker 30	24	4
20	SPL	A	Banbury United	324	W 2 - 1	Westbrook 27 (og) Dillon 75	22	5
27	SPL	H	Cambridge City	301	L 0 - 2		23	6
29	SPL	A	Weymouth	1231	L 1 - 2	Oldring 76	23	7
Sept 3	FAC1Q	H	Banbury United	249	L 0 - 3			8
10	SPL	H	Stratford Town	294	D 2 - 2	Jermyn 15 Dillon 47	23	9
14	SPL	A	Frome Town	235	W 4 - 0	WALKER 3 (43 78 89) Mateus 43	22	10
24	SPL	H	St Neots Town	318	W 1 - 0	Walker 48	19	11
27	SPL	H	Chippenham Town	259	L 1 - 3	Smeeton 52	19	12
Oct 2	SPL	A	Hayes & Yeading United	169	W 1 - 2	Morgan 4 Jerrard 85		13
8	SPL	H	Leamington	461	D 2 - 2	Smeeton 69 (pen) Wood 86	18	14
11	SPL	A	Merthyr Town	603	L 0 - 2		19	15
15	SPL	A	Dunstable Town	169	L 1 - 2	Walker 88	19	16
18	SPL	H	Frome Town	249	W 3 - 0	Smeeton 25 37 (pen) Jerrard 87	16	17
22	SPL	H	Redditch United	353	D 0 - 0		17	18
25	SPL	A	Slough Town	589	L 1 - 2	Walker 10	17	19
29	FAT1Q	H	Barnstaple Town	344	W 3 - 1	Blair 29 Walker 35 Bassett 90		20
Nov 5	SPL	A	Kings Langley	115	L 0 - 2		19	21
12	FAT2Q	H	Basingstole Town	306	L 0 - 3			22
19	SPL	H	Chesham United	315	W 3 - 2	Smeeton 47 (pen) Clarke 51 Bassett 90	17	23
22	SPL	A	Cirencester Town	88	L 1 - 4	Bassett 75	18	24
26	SPL	A	Kettering Town	470	L 0 - 1		18	25
29	SPL	H	Cinderford Town	149	W 2 - 0	Walker 63 Oldring 83	14	26
Dec 3	SPL	H	Biggleswade Town	314	W 2 - 1	Smeeton 16 Jerrard 19	14	27
13	SPL	H	St Ives Town	168	D 1 - 1	McDevitt 55 (og)	14	28
17	SPL	A	Kings Lynn Town	568	D 3 - 3	Blair 3 Smeeton 75 Jerrard 80	14	29
26	SPL	H	Weymouth	2033	D 1 - 1	Walker 45 (pen)	15	30
Jan 2	SPL	A	Basingstoke Town	436	D 1 - 1	Blair 2	16	31
7	SPL	H	Banbury United	491	L 0 - 1		17	32
14	SPL	A	St Neots Town	198	L 2 - 3	Wood 68 Oldring 90	19	33
28	SPL	A	Chippenham Town	473	L 0 - 4		19	34
Feb 4	SPL	H	Merthyr Town	469	L 1 - 2	Wood 1	19	35
11	SPL	A	Leamington	405	L 0 - 5		19	36
18	SPL	H	Dunstable Town	412	W 2 - 0	Bassett 45 Mehew	18	37
25	SPL	H	Slough Town	446	L 0 - 4		18	38
27	SPL	A	Hltchin Town	318	W 1 - 0	Blair 5	18	39
Mar 4	SPL	A	Redditch United	256	L 2 - 4	Mehew 29 31	18	40
7	SPL	H	Hayes & Yeading United	264	W 2 - 1	Mawford 2 Ormrod 85	18	41
11	SPL	H	Kings Langley	393	W 1 - 0	Vance 56	17	42
18	SPL	A	St Ives Town	203	L 0 - 1		18	43
25	SPL	A	Biggleswade Town	203	L 0 - 3		19	44
April 1	SPL	H	Hitchin Town	407	D 2 - 2	Walster 54 (og) Martin 81	18	45
8	SPL	A	Kings Lynn Town	356	D 1 - 1	Mawford 78	18	46
15	SPL	A	Cambridge City	264	L 0 - 1		18	47
17	SPL	H	Basingstoke Town	477	D 1 - 1	Walker 65 (pen)	18	48
22	SPL	A	Stratford Town	279	D 1 - 1	Jerrard 80	18	49

GOALSCORERS	SG	CSG	Pens	Hat tricks	Total		SG	CSG	Pens	Hat tricks	Total
2015-16 *Davis*					15	Dillon	2				2
Walker	9	2	2	1	11	Mawford	2				2
Smeeton	5	2	3		7	Clarke	1				1
Jerrard	5				5	Griffin	1		1		1
Bassett	4				4	Jermyn	1				1
Blair	4				4	Martin	1				1
Mehew	2				3	Mateus	1				1
Oldring	3				3	Morgan	1				1
Opponents	3				3	Ormrod	1				1
Wood	3				3	Vance	1				1

DUNSTABLE TOWN
Club Contact Details
Creasey Park Stadium, Brewers Hill Rd, Dunstable LU6 1BB
01582 891 433
hpauljharris@aol.com

Ground Capacity: 3,500 **Seats:** 350 **Covered:** 1000 **Clubhouse:** Yes **Shop:** Yes

Record Attendance
10,000 (approx) v Manchester United, friendly, July 1974
Previous Grounds
Kingsway 1950-58.

10 YEAR RECORD

	07-08		08-09		09-10		10-11		11-12		12-13		13-14		14-15		15-16		16-17	
	SthM	13	SthM	21	SSM P	7	SSM P	7	SSM P	2	SSM P	1	SthC	1	SthP	14	SthP	11	SthP	16
	FAC	2Q	FAC	2Q	FAC	P	FAC	EP	FAC	3Q	FAC	1Qr	FAC	2Q	FAC	2Q	FAC	3Q	FAC	1Q
	FAT	1Qr	FAT	P	FAV	1P	FAV	5P	FAV	2P	FAV	3P	FAT	2Q	FAT	1Q	FAT	1Q	FAT	2Q

Club Factfile

Founded: 1883   **Nickname:** The Duns / The Blues   **Manager:** Tony McCool - June 2017

Previous Names: Dunstable Town 1883-1976. Dunstable FC 1976-98.

Previous Leagues: Metropolitan & District 1950-61, 64-65. United Counties 1961-63. Southern 1965-76, 2004-09.
Spartan South Midlands 1998-2003, 09-13. Isthmian 2003-04.

Club Colours (change): Blue & white (Red & white)

RECORDS
Victory: 12-0 v Welwyn Garden City, Spartan South Midlands League 2009-10.
Defeat: 0-13 v Arsenal 'A', Metropolitan League
Additional: Received £25,000 from Reading for Kerry Dixon 1980.

HONOURS

FA Comps: None

League: Spartan South Midlands Division One 1999-00, Premier 2002-03, 12-13. Southern Division One Central 2013-14.

County FA: Bedfordshire Senior Cup x12 - Firstly in 1895–96 and most recently in 2008–09. Bedforshire Premier Cup 1980–81, 82–83, 90–91, 2006–07, 11-12. Bedfordshire Intermediate Cup 1999-2000, 08-09.

BEST PERFORMANCES	**FA Cup:** First Round Proper 1956-57.
	FA Trophy: First Round Proper 2004-05.
	FA Vase: Fifth Round Proper 2010-11.

DUNSTABLE TOWN MATCH RESULTS 2016-17

Date	Comp	H/A	Opponents	Att:	Result	Goalscorers	Pos	No.
Aug 6	SPL	H	Cambridge City	157	W 2 - 1	Cathline 47 Talbot 68	7	1
9	SPL	A	Kings Lynn Town	122	W 1 - 0	Hutchinson 22 (pen)	4	2
13	SPL	A	Merthyr Town	513	L 3 - 4	Bush 29 Talbot 38 Cathline 73	10	3
16	SPL	H	Banbury United	203	W 1 - 0	Cathline 21	5	4
20	SPL	H	Chesham United	305	D 0 - 0		6	5
27	SPL	A	Hayes & Yeading United	225	W 1 - 0	Cathline 38	4	6
29	SPL	H	Hitchin Town	234	W 2 - 1	Cathline 23 Bola 74	4	7
Sept 3	FAC1Q	A	Canvey Island	238	L 1 - 2	Keenleyside 32		8
10	SPL	A	Cinderford Town	131	W 3 - 1	Sonuga 13 Bush 55 Talbot 59	3	9
13	SPL	H	St Ives Town	171	W 4 - 1	Cathline 35 Talbot 40 Bush 53 Green 78	2	10
24	SPL	A	Kettering Town	562	W 3 - 1	Bossman 55 Hutchinson 68 Cathline 94 (pen)	2	11
27	SPL	A	Redditch United	210	W 1 - 0	Smeeton 52	2	12
Oct 1	SPL	H	Basingstoke Town	181	L 1 - 3	Hutchinson 43	3	13
8	SPL	A	Stratford Town	183	L 0 - 2		4	14
11	SPL	H	Slough Town	208	L 0 - 1		4	15
15	SPL	H	Dorchester Town	169	W 2 - 1	Sonuga 60 Cathline 72	4	16
22	SPL	H	Chippenham Town	139	L 1 - 2	Green 30	5	17
25	SPL	A	Cirencester Town	362	L 0 2		5	18
29	FAT1Q	A	Tooting & Mitcham	185	W 4 - 2	Talbot 20 Reynolds 50 Bossman 62 Williams 90		19
Nov 5	SPL	A	Biggleswade Town	152	D 2 - 2	Bola 20 Moussi 45	6	20
12	FAT2Q	H	Weymouth	106	L 1 - 4	Moussi 60		21
15	SPL	A	St Ives Town	145	L 1 - 3	Cathline 15	7	22
19	SPL	H	Merthyr Tydfil	102	L 0 - 1		8	23
22	SPL	A	Banbury United	222	W 1 - 0	Doolan 76	7	24
26	SPL	A	Cambridge City	135	W 2 - 0	Talbot 4 Bola 21	6	25
Dec 3	SPL	H	Kings Lynn Town	151	D 0 - 0		7	26
6	SPL	A	Leamington	101	L 0 - 2		9	27
17	SPL	H	Frome Town	88	L 0 - 2		11	28
26	SPL	A	Hitchin Town	613	L 0 - 2		11	29
Jan 2	SPL	H	St Neots Town	133	W 1 - 0	Bola 48	11	30
7	SPL	A	Chesham United	369	L 0 - 1		12	31
10	SPL	H	Kings Langley	125	L 1 - 2	Longe-King 30	12	32
28	SPL	H	Redditch United	109	W 1 - 0	Pepers 17	13	33
Feb 4	SPL	A	Slough Town	503	L 0 - 1		14	34
14	SPL	A	Weymouth	328	D 3 - 3	Hewitt 6 Bola 37 38	13	35
18	SPL	A	Dorchester Town	412	L 0 - 2		15	36
21	SPL	H	Kettering Town	181	L 2 - 3	Longe-King 32 Bola 44		37
25	SPL	H	Cirencester Town	94	D 1 - 1	Olukanmi 31	15	38
28	SPL	A	Basingstoke Town	292	L 1 - 5	Oyinsan 4		39
Mar 4	SPL	A	Chippenham Town	379	L 0 - 1		16	40
11	SPL	H	Biggleswade Town	127	L 0 - 2		16	41
14	SPL	H	Stratford Town	74	W 2 - 0	Talbot 35 51	14	42
18	SPL	A	Leamington	410	L 0 - 5		16	43
25	SPL	A	Kings Lynn Town	567	W 1 - 0	Esso 85	14	44
April 1	SPL	H	Weymouth	174	D 1 - 1	Esso 20	15	45
8	SPL	A	Frome Town	221	L 0 - 1		16	46
15	SPL	H	Hayes & Yeading United	155	L 0 - 2		16	47
17	SPL	A	St Neots Town	307	L 0 - 2		16	48
22	SPL	H	Cinderford Town	103	W 2 - 0	Diaz 28 Oyinsan 60	16	49

GOALSCORERS	SG	CSG	Pens	Hat tricks	Total		SG	CSG	Pens	Hat tricks	Total
2015-16 *Talbot*					15	Oyinsan	2				2
Cathline	9	2	1		9	Sonuga	2				2
Talbot	7	2			8	Diaz	1				1
Bola	6				7	Doolan	1				1
Bush	3				3	Hewitt	1				1
Hutchinson	3		1		3	Keenleyside	1				1
Bossman	2				2	Olukanmi	1				1
Esso	2				2	Pepers	1				1
Green	2				2	Reynolds	1				1
Longe-King	2				2	Smeeton	1				1
Moussi	2				2	Williams	1				1

FARNBOROUGH

Club Contact Details

Rushmoor Community Stadium, Cherrywood Road, Farnborough, Hants GU14 8DU

07957 936 436

clubsecretary@farnboroughfc.co.uk

Ground Capacity: 7,000   **Seats:** 627   **Covered:** 1,350   **Clubhouse:** Yes   **Shop:** Yes

Record Attendance

2,230 v Corby Town - Southern Premier 21/03/2009

Previous Grounds

Queens Road Recreation ground.

10 YEAR RECORD

	07-08		08-09		09-10		10-11		11-12		12-13		13-14		14-15		15-16		16-17	
	SthW	1	SthP	2	SthP	1	Conf S	2	Conf S	16	Conf S	13	Conf S	16	Conf S	20	Isth P	18	SthC	2
	FAC	P	FAC	2Q	FAC	4Qr	FAC	4Qr	FAC	2Qr	FAC	2Q	FAC	2Qr	FAC	2Qr	FAC	2Qr	FAC	2Q
	FAT	2Q	FAT	2P	FAT	1P	FAT	3Q	FAT	1Pr	FAT	1P	FAT	3Qr	FAT	3P	FAT	1Qr	FAT	P

Club Factfile

Founded: 1967   **Nickname:** Boro   **Manager:** Spencer Day

Previous Names: Farnborough Town 1967-2007

Previous Leagues: Surrey Senior 1968-72, Spartan 1972-76, Athenian 1976-77, Isthmian 1977-89, 99-2001, 15-16.
Alliance/Conference 1989-90, 91-93, 94-99, 2010-15. Southern 1990-91, 93-94, 2007-10.

Club Colours (change): Yellow with blue hoops/white/white (White with blue hoops)

RECORDS

Victory: 7-0 v Newport (I.O.W.) (A) - Southern League Division 1 South & West 01/12/2007

Defeat: 0-4 v Hednesford Town (A) - Southern League Premier Division 04/03/2010

Goalscorer: Dean McDonald - 35 (in 53+3 Appearances 2009-10)

Appearances: Nic Ciardini - 147 (2007-10)

HONOURS

FA Comps: None

League: Spartan 1972-73, 73-74, 74-75. London Spartan 1975-76. Athenian Division Two 1976-77. Isthmian Division Two 1978-79, Division One 84-85, Premier 2000-01. Southern Premier 1990-91, 93-94, 2009-10, Division One South & West 2007-08.

County FA: Hampshire Senior Cup 1974-75, 81-82, 83-84, 85-86, 90-91, 2003-04, 05-06.

BEST PERFORMANCES	**FA Cup:** Fourth Round Proper 2002-03.
	FA Trophy: Quarter-finals 1992-93, 2002-03.
	FA Vase: Semi-finals 1975-76, 76-77.

	Best unbeaten Run				Worst Consecutive run without a victory		
	Won	Drawn	Total		Lost	Drawn	Total
Banbury United	7	2	9		4	0	4
Basingstoke Town	3	3	6		5	2	7
Biggleswade Town	2	3	5		4	0	4
Cambridge City	5	1	6		14	3	17
Chesham United	7	3	10		7	1	8
Chippenham Town	15	7	22		1	3	4
Cinderford Town	2	0	2		13	1	14
Cirencester Town	1	3	4		9	2	11
Dorchester Town	2	4	6		5	4	9
Dunstable Town	4	0	4		4	2	6
Frome Town	5	4	9		3	1	4
Hayes & Yeading	2	2	4		6	4	10
Hitchin Town	8	6	14		1	5	6
Kettering Town	4	1	5		3	2	5
Kings Langley	2	3	5		7	2	9
Kings Lynn Town	2	5	7		5	5	10
Leamington	7	3	10		2	1	3
Merthyr Town	9	2	11		4	1	5
Redditch Town	3	2	5		6	3	9
Slough Town	10	1	11		3	0	3
St Ives Town	3	3	6		6	2	8
St Neots Town	2	0	2		8	3	11
Stratford Town	4	1	5		6	5	11
Weymouth	3	7	10		1	6	7

	Best Attendance	Opponents	Competition
Banbury United	734	Leamington	League
Basingstoke Town	596	Slough Town	League
Biggleswade Town	551	Hitchin Town	League
Cambridge City	433	Kettering Town	League
Chesham United	777	Potters Bar Town	FA Cup
Chippenham Town	553	Frome Town	League
Cinderford Town	784	Merthyr Town	League
Cirencester Town	362	Dunstable Town	League
Dorchester Town	**2,033**	Weymouth	League
Dunstable Town	305	Chesham United	League
Frome Town	412	Weymouth	League
Hayes & Yeading	476	St Ives Town	League
Hitchin Town	708	Biggleswade Town	FACup
Kettering Town	656	Kings Lynn Town	League
Kings Langley	310	Chesham United	League
Kings Lynn Town	821	St Ives Town	League
Leamington	805	Stratford Town	League
Merthyr Town	784	Cinderford Town	League
Redditch Town	410	Slough Town	League
Slough Town	1,401	Hayes & Yeading	League
Sy Ives Town	539	Cambridge City	League
St Neots Town	357	St Ives Town	FACup
Stratford Town	523	Leamington	League
Weymouth	1,231	Dorchester Town	League
Average	**687**		

FROME TOWN

Club Contact Details
The Special Effect Stadium, Badgers Hill, Berkley Road, Frome BA11 2EH
01373 464 087
gary@frometownfc.co.uk

Ground Capacity: 2,200 **Seats:** 250 **Covered:** Yes **Clubhouse:** Yes **Shop:** Yes

Record Attendance
8,000 v Leyton Orient - FA Cup 1st Round 1958
Previous Grounds
None

10 YEAR RECORD

07-08		08-09		09-10		10-11		11-12		12-13		13-14		14-15		15-16		16-17	
WestP	4	WestP	2	Sthsw	6	Sthsw	4	SthP	12	SthP	18	SthP	14	SthP	20	SthP	16	SthP	8
FAC	P	FAC	3Qr	FAC	P	FAC	2Q	FAC	2Qr	FAC	2Q	FAC	1Qr	FAC	3Qr	FAC	1Qr	FAC	1Q
FAV	1P	FAV	3P	FAT	1Q	FAT	1Q	FAT	1Q	FAT	1Q	FAT	1Qr	FAT	1Q	FAT	3Qr	FAT	3Q

Club Factfile

Founded: 1904 **Nickname:** The Robins **Manager:** Josh Jefferies

Previous Names: None

Previous Leagues: Wiltshire Premier 1904, Somerset Senior 1906-19, Western 1919, 63-2009

Club Colours (change): Red and white

RECORDS

HONOURS

FA Comps: None

League: Somerset County 1906-07, 08-09, 10-11.
Western Division Two 1919-20, Division One 2001-02, Premier Division 1978-79.

County FA: Somerset Senior Cup 1932-33, 33-34, 50-51 Somerset Premier Cup 1966-67, 68-69 (shared), 82-83, 2008-09.

BEST PERFORMANCES	**FA Cup:** First Round Proper 1954-55.
	FA Trophy: Second Round Proper 1984-85.
	FA Vase: Quarter-finals 2004-05.

FROME TOWN MATCH RESULTS 2016-17

Date	Comp	H/A	Opponents	Att:	Result	Goalscorers	Pos	No.
Aug 6	SPL	H	Hayes & Yeading United	229	W 2 - 1	Page 9 Cleverley 39	8	1
9	SPL	A	Cirencester Town	123	W 4 - 1	Davies 13 (pen) Page 38 Cleverley 70 Jackson 87	2	2
13	SPL	A	St Neots Town	251	L 2 - 3	Davies 30 (pen) Jackson 90	5	3
17	SPL	H	Weymouth	412	W 2 - 0	Davies 22 Jackson 88	3	4
20	SPL	A	KIngs Langley	560	D 2 - 2	Cleverley 27 Jackson 70	4	5
27	SPL	H	Kings Lynn Town	237	L 1 - 3	Jefferies 5	7	6
29	SPL	A	Basingstoke Town	447	W 3 - 1	Miller 4 Kirby 50 Teale 63	8	7
Sept 3	FAC1Q	A	Salisbury	832	L 0 - 2			8
10	SPL	H	Biggleswade Town	215	W 2 - 0	Jefferies 26 Davies 90	5	9
14	SPL	H	Dorchester Town	235	L 0 - 4		5	10
17	SPL	A	Stratford Town	210	L 0 - 3		5	11
24	SPL	A	Redditch United	260	L 1 - 2	Jackson 73	6	12
Oct 8	SPL	A	St Ives Town	275	D 1 - 1	Roberts 37	13	13
12	SPL	H	Cinderford Town	171	W 3 - 2	Miller 42 Kirby 76 Cleverley 85	10	14
15	SPL	H	Hitchin Town	201	D 1 - 1	Summers 26	9	15
18	SPL	A	Dorchester Town	249	L 0 - 3		10	16
22	SPL	A	Banbury United	344	W 2 - 1	Cleverley 55 Moore 69	10	17
26	SPL	H	Merthyr Town	290	D 2 - 2	Davies 45 Jefferies 47	8	18
29	FAT1Q	A	Evesham United	235	D 1 - 1	Davies 4		19
Nov 2	FAT1Qr	H	Evesham United	152	W 1 - 0	Davies		20
5	SPL	A	Cambridge City	189	W 2 - 0	Cleverley 62 Jefferies 87	8	21
12	FAT2Q	A	Hanwell Town	104	W 1 - 0	Mapstone 38		22
16	SPL	H	Chesham United	169	W 2 - 0	Roberts 36 Davies 43	7	23
19	SPL	H	St Neots Town	181	D 1 - 1	Davies 85	6	24
22	SPL	A	Weymouth	367	L 1 - 2	Summers 75	6	25
26	FAT3Q	A	Truro City	269	L 1 - 6	Bryant 80		26
Dec 3	SPL	A	Slough Town	460	W 2 - 1	Hollis 4 (og) Knight 67	8	27
10	SPL	H	Leamington	219	D 0 - 0		9	28
13	SPL	A	Hayes & Yeading	142	W 3 - 1	Jackson 12 69 Green 19	6	29
17	SPL	A	Dunstable Town	88	W 2 - 0	Jackson 42 Knight 50	6	30
21	SPL	H	Cirencester Town	218	W 3 - 2	Bryant 8 21 Griffiths 48	6	31
26	SPL	H	Basingstoke Town	366	D 1 - 1	Knight 65	6	32
Jan 2	SPL	A	Chippenham Town	553	D 2 - 2	Jackson 16 Bryant 33	6	33
7	SPL	H	Kings Langley	264	D 0 - 0		6	34
14	SPL	H	Redditch United	210	W 8 - 1	JACKSON 3 (25 77 90) Knight 30 Bryant 41 80 Teale 54 Davies 77 (pen)	6	35
24	SPL	A	Kettering Town	352	L 1 - 4	Jackson 62	7	36
28	SPL	H	Stratford Town	231	W 3 - 1	Kalenda 3 (og) Davies 33 (pen) 84	7	37
Feb 11	SPL	H	St Ives Town	235	D 2 - 2	Teale 9 Jackson 28	7	38
18 34	SPL	A	Hitchin Town	570	D 2 - 2	Jefferies 45 Jackson 66	7	39
25	SPL	A	Merthyr Town	340	W 2 - 1	Roberts 24 Teale 67	7	40
Mar 4	SPL	H	Bsnbury United	270	L 1 - 2	Green 78	8	41
7	SPL	A	Chesham United	215	D 1 - 1	Kirby 84	8	42
11	SPL	A	Cambridge City	253	W 3 - 0	JACKSON 3 (9 52 90)	8	43
18	SPL	H	Kettering Town	222	D 3 - 3	Fitzgibbon 1 34 Knight 68	7	44
21	SPL	A	Cinderford Town	142	L 2 - 4	Teale 35 Jackson 61 (pen)	7	45
25	SPL	H	Slough Town	307	W 1 - 0	Bath 45	7	46
April 1	SPL	A	Leamington	508	W 1 - 0	Jackson 64	7	47
8	SPL	H	Dunstable Town	221	W 1 - 0	Mapstone 37	7	48
15	SPL	A	Kings Lynn Town	505	D 1 - 1	Jackson 81	7	49
17	SPL	H	Chippenham Town	552	L 0 - 1		7	50
22	SPL	A	Biggleswade Town	165	L 1 - 4	Jackson 74	8	51

GOALSCORERS	SG	CSG	Pens	Hat tricks	Total		SG	CSG	Pens	Hat tricks	Total
2015-16 *Miller*					15	Summers	2				2
Jackson	17	4	1	2	22	Opponents	1				2
Davies	11	3	4		12	Bath	1				1
Cleverley	6	2			6	Green	1				1
Bryant	5				6	Jarrard	1				1
Jefferies	5	2			5	Jones	1				1
Knight	5				5	Knight	1				1
Teale	5				5	Mapstone	1				1
Kirby	3				3	Milhench	1				1
Roberts	3				3	Mortimer-Jones	1				1
Fitzgibbon	1				2	Spalding	1				1
Page	2				2						

GOSPORT BOROUGH

Club Contact Details

Aerial Direct Stadium, Privett Park, Privett Road, Gosport, Hampshire PO12 0SX

023 9250 1042 (Match days only)

bucko60@hotmail.co.uk

Ground Capacity: 4,500 **Seats:** 1,000 **Covered:** Yes **Clubhouse:** Yes **Shop:** Yes

Record Attendance

4,770 v Pegasus - FA Amateur Cup 1953

Previous Grounds

None

10 YEAR RECORD

07-08		08-09		09-10		10-11		11-12		12-13		13-14		14-15		15-16		16-17	
Sthsw	11	Sthsw	12	Sthsw	8	Sthsw	13	Sthsw	3	SthP	5	Conf S	12	Conf S	6	Nat S	9	Nat S	20
FAC	1Qr	FAC	3Q	FAC	P	FAC	Pr	FAC	P	FAC	4Qr	FAC	2Q	FAC	1P	FAC	3Qr	FAC	2Q
FAT	3Q	FAT	1Q	FAT	2Q	FAT	P	FAT	1P	FAT	2Q	FAT	F	FAT	2P	FAT	3Q	FAT	1P

Club Factfile

Founded: 1944 **Nickname:** The 'Boro' **Manager:** Alex Pike

Previous Names: Gosport Borough Athletic

Previous Leagues: Portsmouth & District 1944-45. Hampshire 1945-78. Southern 1978-92, 2007-13. Wessex 1992-2007. Conference 2013-17.

Club Colours (change): Yellow & blue

RECORDS

Victory: 19-1 v Widbrook United, Portsmouth Senior Cup, 2016-17.

Defeat: 0-9 v Gloucester City - Southern Premier Division 1989-90 and v Lymington & N.M. - Wessex Lge 99-2000

Goalscorer: Justin Bennett- 257

Appearances: Tony Mahoney - 765

HONOURS

FA Comps: None

League: Portsmouth & District 1944-45. Hampshire 1945-46, 76-77, 77-78. Wessex 2006-07.

County FA: Hampshire Senior Cup 1987-88, 2014-15.

BEST PERFORMANCES	FA Cup: First Round Proper 2014-15.
	FA Trophy: Final 2013-14.
	FA Vase: Quarter-finals 1976-77(r), 2003-04.

GOSPORT BOROUGH MATCH RESULTS 2016-17

Date	Comp	H/A	Opponents	Att:	Result	Goalscorers	Pos	No.
Aug 6	Nat S	A	Maidenhead United	454	L 0 - 3		20	1
8	Nat S	H	Truro City	482	W 3 - 1	Flood 25 Bentley 72 86	10	2
13	Nat S	H	Eastbourne Borough	509	W 3 - 1	BENTLEY 3 (35 56 89)	6	3
16	Nat S	A	Dartford	706	D 0 - 0		7	4
20	Nat S	A	East Thurrock United	203	L 1 - 5	Bird 36	12	5
27	Nat S	H	Bishop Stortford	487	L 0 - 1		14	6
29	Nat S	A	Oxford City	201	W 2 - 1	Carmichael 40 Wooden 77	12	7
Sept 3	Nat S	H	Ebbsfleet United	566	W 1 - 0	Bentley 22	11	8
6	Nat S	H	Hampton & Richmond B	467	D 1 - 1	Wooden 71	10	9
10	Nat S	A	Hungerford Town	189	D 3 - 3	Legg 4 (og) Wright 22 Bentley 73 (pen)	11	10
13	Nat S	A	Bath City	331	L 0 - 4		12	11
17	FAC2Q	A	Weymouth	527	L 2 - 3	Carmichael 11 Wooden 90		12
24	Nat S	H	Margate	447	W 1 - 0	Wright 77	11	13
Oct 8	Nat S	A	St Albans City	787	L 1 - 2	Poate 29	12	14
15	Nat S	H	Chelmsford City	552	L 0 - 6		12	15
22	Nat S	H	Wealdstone	487	L 1 - 3	Poate 45	13	16
29	Nat S	A	Hemel Hempstead Town	354	W 2 - 1	Bentley 40 Ostler 90		17
Nov 5	Nat S	H	Welling United	447	D 1 - 1	Wright 90	11	18
12	Nat S	A	Weston-s-Mare	425	D 1 - 1	Flood 75	11	19
19	Nat S	H	Concord Rangers	1005	L 2 - 5	Dawson 50 Wright 90	14	20
26	FAT 3Q	A	Hungerford Town	144	W 1 - 0	Flood 37		21
Dec 3	Nat S	A	Whitehawk	254	D 4 - 4	Wright 8 78 Bentley 54 Flood 90	13	22
10	FAT 1	A	AFC Sudbury	198	L 1 - 2	Flood 51		23
l7	Nat S	A	Ebbsfleet United	852	L 0 - 2		16	24
26	Nat S	H	Poole Town	631	L 0 - 2		15	25
Jan 1	Nat S	A	Poole Town	675	L 0 - 7		17	26
7	Nat S	H	Hungerford Town	411	L 1 - 4	Wright 49 (pen)	18	27
24	Nat S	H	East Thurrock United	364	L 1 - 5	Wright 8	19	28
28	Nat S	H	Maidenhead United	327	L 0 - 2		19	29
Feb 7	Nat S	A	Hampton & Richmond B	369	D 2 - 2	Lee 21 73	19	30
11	Nat S	H	Dartford	363	L 0 - 4		19	31
18	Nat S	A	Eastbourne Borough	554	L 0 - 2		19	32
21	Nat S	A	Truro City	319	L 0 - 2		19	33
25	Nat S	H	Hemel Hempstead Town	307	L 0 - 6		20	34
Mar 4	Nat S	A	Wealdstone	670	L 1 - 2	Dawson 7	20	35
11	Nat S	A	Margate	434	L 0 - 2		20	36
18	Nat S	H	St Albans City	315	W 4 - 0	Lee 3 37 Lea 34 Bailey 86	20	37
21	Nat S	H	Bath City	369	W 1 - 0	Lanahan 5	20	38
25	Nat S	A	Chelmsford City	952	L 1 - 5	Wright 5	20	39
April 1	Nat S	H	Weston-s-Mare	384	D 1 - 1	Lanahan 11	20	40
8	Nat S	A	Welling United	450	L 0 - 4		20	41
15	Nat S	A	Bishops Stortford	268	W 2 - 0	Lea 60 Lee 86	20	42
17	Nat S	H	Oxford City	364	L 0 - 1		20	43
22	Nat S	A	Concord Rangers	237	D 2 - 2	Lee 60 70	20R	44
29	Nat S	H	Whitehawk	395	L 2 - 3	Wright 44 Suraci 58	20	45

GOALSCORERS	SG	CSG	Pens	Hat tricks	Total		SG	CSG	Pens	Hat tricks	Total
2015-16 Bennett					30	Poate	2				2
Wright	9		1		10	Bailey	1				1
Bentley	6	2	1	1	9	Bird	1				1
Lee	3				7	Opponents	1				1
Flood	5				5	Otter	1				1
Wooden	3				3	Suraci	1				1
Carmichael	2				2						
Dawson	2				2						
Lanahan	2				2						
Lea	2				2						

HEREFORD

Club Contact Details
Edgar Street, Hereford HR4 9JU
01432 268 257
fd@herefordfc.co.uk

Ground Capacity: 8,843 **Seats:** 2,761 **Covered:** 6,082 **Clubhouse:** Yes **Shop:**

Record Attendance
4,406 v Evesham United, 02/01/2017
Previous Grounds
None

10 YEAR RECORD

07-08	08-09	09-10	10-11	11-12	12-13	13-14	14-15	15-16	16-17
								MidL 1	Sthsw 1
									FAC 3Q
								FAV F	FAT P

Club Factfile

Founded: 2014   **Nickname:** The Bulls   **Manager:** Pete Beadle

Previous Names: Formed in 2014 after the demise of Hereford United who folded during the 2014-15 season.

Previous Leagues: Midland 2015-16.

Club Colours (change): White/black/white

RECORDS
Victory: 8-0 v Heanor Town - Midland League 23/04/16.
Defeat: 4-5 v Coleshill Town - Midland League 2015-16.
Goalscorer: John Mills - 52 - 2015-16.

HONOURS
FA Comps: None

League: Midland League 2015-16. Southern Division One South & West 2016-17.

County FA: Herefordshire County Cup 2015-16.

BEST PERFORMANCES	**FA Cup:** Third Qualifying Round 2016-17.
	FA Trophy: Preliminary Round 2016-17.
	FA Vase: Final 2015-16.

LEADING GOALSCORERS 2016-2017

		LGE	FAC	FAT	Pens	H-T	SG	CSG	Total
Andy Sandell	Chippenham Town	27	5		9	2	21	5	32
David Pratt	Chippenham Town	21	5	2	1	2	21	4	28
Ian Traylor	Merthyr Town	19	4	2	1		19	5	25
Kayne McLaggon	Merthyr Town	17	2	3		1	17	2	25
Inih Effiong	Biggleswade Town	23			5	2	16	5	23
Jake Jackson	Frome Town	22			1	3	17	4	22
Robbie Burns	Hitchin Town	17		1	2		17	2	20
Jevani Brown	St Neots Town	19				3	12	4	19
Tony Burnett	Biggleswade Town	19				1	11	3	19
Courtny Baker-Richardson	Leamington	17					15	3	17
James Dobson	Slough Town	11	4	2	2		15	2	17
Dave Pearce	Chesham United	13	1	2	2		13	2	16
Brett Donnelly	Hitchin Town	12	3				13	2	15
James Hall	St Neots Town	13		2	5	1	10	2	15
Ricky Johnson	Banbury United	12	3		2		13	2	15
Charlie Moone	Slough Town	8	2	2			10	3	12
Ryan Rowe	Leamington	12			2		9	3	12
Ricky Johnson	Banbury United	8	3		2		11	2	11
Tony Burnett	Biggleswade Town	11				1	6	3	11
James Hall	St Neots	8		2	2	1	7	2	10
Lewis Toomey	Kings Langley	6	3	1	2	1	7	3	10

PENALTIES

	Scored			Conceded
Chippenham Town	13		Cinderford Town	10+1t
Biggleswade Town	12		Dorchester Town	8+1c+1t
St Neots Town	9+1t		Hayes & Yeading	9
Chesham United	6+2c		Kings Lynn Town	8
Weymouth	5 +2t		Kings Langley	6+2c
Hitchin Town	5+1t		Chesham United	6+2c
Dorchester Town	6		Weymouth	5+1c+1t
Frome Town	5		Kettering Town	6
Merthyr Town	4+1c		Dunstable Town	4+2c
Slough Town	4+1c		Hitchin Town	4+2c
Kings Langley	2+2c+1t		Slough Town	5
Hayes & Yeading Utd	4		Cambridge City	5
Stratford Town	4		Cirencester Town	5
Banbury United	3+1c		Frome Town	3+2c
Basingstoke Town	3+1t		Redditch United	4
Kings Lynn Town	3+1t		St Ives Town	4
Cinderford Town	3		Chippenham Town	3
Cambridge City	3		Stratford Town	3
Cirencester Town	3		Biggleswade Town	2
St Ives Town	3		Leamington	2
Dunstable Town	2		Merthyr Town	2
Kettering Town	2		St Neots Town	2
Leamington	2		Basingstoke Town	1+1c
Redditch United	2		Banbury United	1
TOTAL	**108+10c+4t**			**108+11c+3t**

HITCHIN TOWN

Club Contact Details
Top Field, Fishponds Road, Hitchin SG5 1NU
01462 459 028 (match days only)
roy.izzard@outlook.com

Ground Capacity: 5,000   **Seats:** 500   **Covered:** 1,250   **Clubhouse:** Yes   **Shop:** Yes

Record Attendance
7,878 v Wycombe Wanderers - FA Amateur Cup 3rd Round 08/02/1956
Previous Grounds
None

10 YEAR RECORD

	07-08		08-09		09-10		10-11		11-12		12-13		13-14		14-15		15-16		16-17	
SthP	18		SthP	20		SthC	2		SthC	2		SthP	14		SthP	13		SthP	13		SthP	9		SthP	3		SthP	4
FAC	4Qr		FAC	3Q		FAC	1Qr		FAC	2Qr		FAC	1Q		FAC	3Qr		FAC	1Qr		FAC	2Q		FAC	3Qr		FAC	2Qr
FAT	3Qr		FAT	2Q		FAT	3Qr		FAT	P		FAT	2Q		FAT	3Q		FAT	1Qr		FAT	1Qr		FAT	3Q		FAT	1P

Club Factfile

Founded: 1865   **Nickname:** Canaries   **Manager:** Mark Burke

Previous Names: Hitchin FC 1865-1911. Re-formed in 1928

Previous Leagues: Spartan 1928-39, Herts & Middlesex 1939-45, Athenian 1945-63, Isthmian 1964-2004

Club Colours (change): Yellow & green

RECORDS
Victory: 13-0 v Cowley and v RAF Uxbridge - both Spartan League 1929-30
Defeat: 0-10 v Kingstonian (A) and v Slough Town (A) - 1965-66 and 1979-80 respectively
Goalscorer: Paul Giggle - 214 (1968-86)
Appearances: Paul Giggle - 769 (1968-86)
Additional: Paid £2,000 to Potton United for Ray Seeking
Received £30,000 from Cambridge United for Zema Abbey, January 2000

HONOURS
FA Comps: None

League: Spartan 1934-35. Isthmian League Division One 1992-93.

County FA: AFA Senior Cup 1931-32. London Senior Cup 1969-70. East Anglian Cup 1972-73.
Herts Senior Cup x14 Most recently 2016-17.

BEST PERFORMANCES
FA Cup: Second Round Proper 1973-74, 76-77(r), 94-95, 95-96.
FA Trophy: Fifth Round Proper 1998-99.
FA Vase: N/A

HITCHIN TOWN MATCH RESULTS 2016-17

Date	Comp	H/A	Opponents	Att:	Result	Goalscorers	Pos	No.
Aug 6	SPL	H	Cinderford Town	334	W 4 - 3	Spencer 76 C.Donnelly 82 Kirkpatrick 88 Wright 90 (pen)	6	1
9	SPL	A	Hayes & Yeading United	341	L 0 - 2		14	2
13	SPL	A	Kettering Town	506	D 0 - 0		13	3
15	SPL	H	Chesham United	362	D 1 - 1	Brooks 61	12	4
20	SPL	A	Stratford Town	176	L 2 - 3	Brooks 14 Pearson 21	17	5
27	SPL	H	Banbury United	350	W 3 - 1	B.Donnelly 13 Lench 25 Burns 87	12	6
29	SPL	A	Dunstable Town	254	L 1 - 2	Burns 90	16	7
Sept 3	FAC1Q	H	Biggleswade United	708	W 4 - 2	Lench 3 B.Donnelly 65 Kirkpatrick 8 90		8
10	SPL	H	Basingstoke Town	303	W 1 - 0	B.Donnelly 89	9	9
12	SPL	A	Canbridge City	231	W 4 - 0	C.Donnelly 18 Walster 35 (pen) Burns 77 Barnes 88	6	10
17	FAC2Q	H	Faversham Town	195	D 2 - 2	B.Donnelly 23 38		11
20	FAC2Qr	H	Faversham Town	251	L 0 - 1			12
24	SPL	H	Merthyr Town	514	D 1 - 1	Burns 15	9	13
26	SPL	H	St Neots Town	305	W 4 - 1	Lench 13 Wright 42 Burns 60 74	5	14
Oct 1	SPL	A	Cirencester Town	98	D 0 - 0		5	15
8	SPL	H	Weymouth	384	D 1 - 1	Walster 42	6	16
11	SPL	A	Kings Langley	161	W 2 - 1	Burns 26 B.Donnelly 48	5	17
15	SPL	A	Frome Town	201	D 1 - 1	Smith 89	5	18
17	SPL	H	Cambridge City	294	W 1 - 0	B.Donnelly 90	5	19
22	SPL	H	St Ives Town	413	W 4 - 1	Webb 20 Wright 43 Burns 70 81	4	20
25	SPL	A	Kings Lynn Town	463	W 2 - 1	Walster 7 Lench 59	4	21
29	FAT1Q	A	Hayes & Yeading United	127	W 1 - 0	Wright 83		22
Nov 5	SPL	A	Slough Town	646	W 1 - 0	Walster 49	4	23
12	FAT2Q	A	Biggleswade Town	325	D 1 - 1	Bickerstaff 39		24
14	FAT2Qr	A	Biggleswade Town	201	W 3 - 2	Kirkpatrick 43 Burns 48 70		25
19	SPL	H	Kettering Town	451	D 0 - 0		5	26
22	SPL	A	Chesham United	252	L 0 - 2		5	27
26	FAT3Q	H	Burgess Hill Town	243	W 3 - 0	Walster 22 (pen) Burns 14 C.Donnelly 86		28
28	SPL	H	Hayes & Yeading United	285	W 3 - 0	Brooks 18 Burns 67 Bickerstaff 74	4	29
Dec 3	SPL	A	Leamington	504	W 2 - 1	B.Donnelly 30 66	3	30
10	FAT1	A	Chelmsford City	469	L 0 - 1			31
12	SPL	H	Redditch United	233	W 4 - 2	Webb 4 Lench 10 Walster 56 Rolfe 68	3	32
17	SPL	A	Chippenham Town	307	L 0 - 1		5	33
20	SPL	A	Cinderford Town	171	W 1 - 0	Lench 13	3	34
26	SPL	H	Dunstable Town	613	W 2 - 0	Barnes 83 Walster 87	3	35
Jan 2	SPL	A	Biggleswade town	551	W 3 - 1	Smith 30 Lench 35 67	2	36
7	SPL	H	Stratford Town	455	W 1 - 0	Burns 4	2	37
28	SPL	A	St Neots Town	347	W 2 - 1	Burns 31 B.Donnelly 67	3	38
Feb 4	SPL	H	Kings Langley	690	W 2 - 0	Wright 52 (pen) 86 (pen)	3	39
11	SPL	A	Weymouth	400	W 2 - 0	B.Donnelly 58 Burns 60	3	40
18	SPL	H	Frome Town	570	D 2 - 2	B.Donnelly 50 Webb 70	2	41
25	SPL	H	Kings Lynn Town	517	W 5 - 0	C.Donnelly 2 Burns 13 47 Lench 24 Kirkpatrick 43	2	42
27	SPL	H	Dorchester Town	318	L 0 - 1		2	43
Mar 5	SPL	H	Cirencester Town	340	W 2 - 0	Spring 70 Wright 84 (pen)	3	44
11	SPL	A	Weymouth	400	W 2 - 0	B.Donnelly 58 Burns 60	3	45
11	SPL	H	Slough Town	828	L 2 - 3	B.Donnelly 38 Smith 79	4	46
18	SPL	A	Redditch United	258	W 2 - 1	B.Donnelly 40 Webb 78	4	47
21	SPL	A	St Ives Town	274	W 3 - 0	McDevitt 8 (og) Lench 11 McNamara 45	3	48
25	SPL	H	Leamington	824	D 0 - 0		3	49
April 1	SPL	A	Dorchester Town	407	D 2 - 2	Lench 12 Down 36 (og)	3	50
8	SPL	H	Chippenham Town	812	L 1 - 3	Wright 42	3	51
15	SPL	A	Banbury United	740	D 1 - 1	McNamara 81	3	52
17	SPL	H	Biggleswade Town	766	D 1 - 1	Lench 2	3	53
22	SPL	A	Basingstoke Town	617	D 1 - 1	Lench 58	4	54
26	PO SF	A	Merthyr Town	1453	D 1 - 1	Burns 20 (won 4-1 on penalties)		55
May 1	PO Final	A	Leamington	2102	L 1 - 2	Lench 11		56

GOALSCORERS	SG	CSG	Pens	Hat tricks	Total		SG	CSG	Pens	Hat tricks	Total
2015-16 *McNamara*					15	Smith	3				3
Burns	17	2			20	Barnes	2				2
B.Donnelly	14	2			15	Bickerstaff	2				2
Lench	13				14	McNamara	2				2
Wright	7		3		8	Opponents	2				2
Walster	7		2		7	Pearson	1				1
Kirkpatrick	4				5	Rolfe	1				1
C.Donnelly	4				4	Spencer	1				1
Webb	4				4	Spring	1				1
Brooks	3				3						

KETTERING TOWN

Club Contact Details
Latimer Park, Burton Latimer, Kettering NN15 5PS
01536 217 006
neil.griffin@ketteringtownfc.com

Ground Capacity: **Seats:** Yes **Covered:** Yes **Clubhouse:** Yes **Shop:**

Record Attendance
11,536 v Peterborough - FA Cup 1st Round replay 1958-59
Previous Grounds
North Park, Green Lane, Rockingham Road > 2011. Nene Park 2011-13.

10 YEAR RECORD

07-08		08-09		09-10		10-11		11-12		12-13		13-14		14-15		15-16		16-17	
Conf N	1	Conf	8	Conf	6	Conf	14	Conf	24	SthP	22	SthC	3	SthC	1	SthP	6	SthP	9
FAC	3Q	FAC	4P	FAC	2Pr	FAC	4Q	FAC	1P	FAC	2Q	FAC	P	FAC	2Q	FAC	3Qr	FAC	4Q
FAT	1P	FAT	3P	FAT	1P	FAT	1Pr	FAT	1P	FAT	1Q	FAT	1Q	FAT	1Q	FAT	2Q	FAT	2Q

Club Factfile

Founded: 1872 **Nickname:** The Poppies **Manager:** Marcus Law

Previous Names: Kettering > 1924

Previous Leagues: Midland 1892-1900, also had a team in United Counties 1896-99, Southern 1900-30, 1950-79, 2001-02, Birmingham 1930-50, Alliance/Conference 1979-2001, 02-03, Isthmian 2003-04

Club Colours (change): Red & black/black/red (Blue & white/blue/blue)

RECORDS
Victory: 16-0 v Higham YMCI - FA Cup 1909
Defeat: 0-13 v Mardy - Southern League Division Two 1911-12
Goalscorer: Roy Clayton - 171 (1972-81)
Appearances: Roger Ashby
Additional: Paid £25,000 to Macclesfield for Carl Alford 1994.
Recieved £150,000 from Newcastle United for Andy Hunt

HONOURS

FA Comps: None

League: Midland 1895-96, 99-1900. United Counties 1904-05, 38-39. Southern 1927-28, 56-57, 72-73, 2001-02, Division One Central 2014-15. Conference North 2007-08.

County FA: Northamptonshire Senior Cup 2016-17.

BEST PERFORMANCES
FA Cup: Fourth Round Proper 1988-89, 2008-09.
FA Trophy: Final 1978-79, 1999-2000.
FA Vase: N/A

KETTERING TOWN MATCH RESULTS 2016-17

Date	Comp	H/A	Opponents	Att:	Result	Goalscorers	Pos	No.
Aug 6	SPL	A	Dorchester Town	421	W 2 - 0	Canavan 51 Westwood 78	4	1
9	SPL	H	Leamington	605	L 0 - 2		13	2
13	SPL	H	Hitchin Town	506	D 0 - 0		12	3
16	SPL	A	Redditch United	212	W 3 - 1	Westwood 66 Weir-Daley 73 85	8	4
20	SPL	A	Basingstokre Town	474	L 0 - 3		10	5
27	SPL	H	Stratford Town	430	L 0 - 3		17	6
29	SPL	A	KIngs Lynn Town	724	W 2 - 1	Solkhon 67 Carvalho 78	12	7
Sept 3	FAC1Q	A	Leek Town	416	W 3 - 2	Howe 22 Hicks 63 O'Connor 90		8
10	SPL	H	Banbury United	480	D 2 - 2	Howe 38 Haran 61	10	9
13	SPL	A	St Neots Town	339	W 5 - 1	WEIR-DALEY 3 (15 66 89) Hicks 38 Carvalho 89	7	10
17	FAC2Q	A	Rushall Olympic	241	W 2 - 1	Carvalho 8 Weir-Daley 40		11
24	SPL	H	Dunstable Town	562	L 1 - 3	Carvalho 5	12	12
27	SPL	H	Hayes & Yeading United	409	D 1 - 1	Canavan 59	12	13
Oct 1	FAC3Q	H	Boston United	628	W 2 - 0	Canavan 43 Carvalho 90		14
8	SPL	A	Chippenham Town	591	L 1 - 2	Weir-Daley 48	17	15
11	SPL	A	Biggleswade Town	222	D 2 - 2	Brighton 9 Hicks 23	16	16
15	FAC4Q	A	Solihull Moors	768	L 1 - 3	Haran 65	17	17
18	SPL	H	St Neots Town	374	D 2 - 2	O'Connor 57 Carvalho 73	16	18
22	SPL	H	Weymouth	542	W 3 - 1	O'Connor 66 Solkhon 85 Canavan 90	13	19
25	SPL	A	Chesham United	360	L 0 - 1		12	20
29	FAT1Q	H	Market Drayton Town	357	W 5 - 1	WEIR-DALEY 4 (17 60 67 69) Hicks 90		21
Nov 1	SPL	A	Merthyr Town	408	L 0 - 2		13	22
5	SPL	A	St Ives Town	495	W 7 - 0	Brighton 7 WEIR-DALEY 4 (34 55 57pen 62) Howe 80 Carvalho 89	12	23
12	FAT2Q	A	Witton Albion	339	L 1 - 2	Canavan 9		24
15	SPL	A	Kings Langley	128	W 2 - 1	Canavan 58 Malone 88	10	25
19	SPL	A	Hitchin Town	451	D 0 - 0		10	26
22	SPL	H	Redditch United	343	L 1 - 2	Brighton 1		27
26	SPL	H	Dorchester Town	475	W 1 - 0	Howe 73	10	28
Dec 3	SPL	H	Cinderford Town	433	W 2 - 0	O'Connor 8 Solkhon 10		29
10	SPL	A	Cirencester Town	135	W 6 - 1	Howe1 O'Connor 3 Haran10 52 Brighton 22 Barnes-Homer 64	8	30
17	SPL	A	Slough Town	586	L 2 - 3	O'Connor 89 Howe 90	10	31
26	SPL	H	Kings Lynn Town	656	D 1 - 1	O'Connor 63	10	32
Jan 2	SPL	A	Cambridge CIty	433	W 3 - 2	Canavan 26 O'Connor 87 Carvalho 33	10	33
7	SPL	H	Basingstoke Town	658	W 2 - 1	Malone 27 Howe 43	9	34
21	SPL	H	Merthyr Town	493	L 1 - 3	Edge 79	10	35
24	SPL	H	Frome Town	352	W 4 - 1	Howe 29 Hall 35 79 Solkhon 45	9	36
29	SPL	A	Hayes & Yeading United	223	W 2 - 1	Langdon 67 Howe 85	8	37
Feb 4	SPL	H	Biggleswade Town	511	W 3 - 1	Canavan 10 Howe 42 O'Connor 65	9	38
11	SPL	A	Chippenham Town	515	L 0 - 1		9	39
18	SPL	H	Kings Langley	560	W 1 - 0	Hall 27	9	40
21	SPL	A	Dunstable Town	181	W 3 - 2	O'Connor 23 42 Howe 778	9	41
25	SPL	H	Chesham United	517	L 1 - 2	Howe 66	9	42
Mar 4	SPL	A	Weymouth	457	L 2 - 3	Solkhon 21 O'Connor 26	9	43
7	SPL	A	Leamington	478	L 0 - 3		9	44
11	SPL	H	St Ives Town	493	D 1 - 1	O'Connor 84	9	45
18	SPL	A	Frome Town	222	D 3 - 3	O'Connor 18 Brighton 40 Walker 58 (og)	10	46
25	SPL	A	Cinderford Town	231	W 3 - 1	Brighton 75 O'Connor 62 Baker 85	9	47
April 1	SPL	H	Cirencester Town	507	W 3 - 1	Hicks 37 O'Connor 85 Hall 90 (pen)	8	48
8	SPL	H	Slough Town	521	W 3 - 0	Brighton 52 Canavan 60 Howe 90	8	49
15	SPL	A	Stratford Town	309	L 1 - 4	Baker 90	9	50
17	SPL	H	Cambridge City	548	D 0 - 0		9	51
22	SPL	A	Banbury United	477	W 2 - 1	Baker 12 O'Connor 82	9	52

GOALSCORERS	SG	CSG	Pens	Hat tricks	Total		SG	CSG	Pens	Hat tricks	Total
2015-16 *Carvalho*					12	Hall	3				4
O'Connor	17	5			19	Haran	3				4
Weir-Daley	6	2	1	3	15	Westwood	2				2
Howe	12	3			12	Barnes-Homer	1				1
Canavan	9				9	Edge	1				1
Brighton	7				7	Langdon	1				1
Carvalho	6	3			7	Malone	1				1
Hicks	5				5	Opponents	1				1
Solkhon	5				5						
Baker	4				4						

KING'S LYNN TOWN

Club Contact Details

The Walks Stadium, Tennyson Road, King's Lynn PE30 5PB

01553 760 060

ncesar1947@yahoo.co.uk

Ground Capacity: 8,200 **Seats:** 1,400 **Covered:** 5,000 **Clubhouse:** Yes **Shop:** Yes

Record Attendance
12,937 v Exeter City FAC 1st Rnd 1950-51.
Previous Grounds
None

10 YEAR RECORD

07-08	08-09	09-10	10-11	11-12	12-13	13-14	14-15	15-16	16-17
			UCL P 2	UCL P 2	NP1S 1	NP P 11	NP P 18	SthP 9	SthP 13
				FAC 4Q	FAC 1Qr	FAC 1Q	FAC 4Q	FAC 3Q	FAC 3Q
			FAV SF	FAV 2P	FAT 3P	FAT 1Q	FAT 3Q	FAT 2Q	FAV 1P

Club Factfile

Founded: 1879 **Nickname:** Linnets **Manager:** Ian Culverhouse

Previous Names: King's Lynn Town formed in 2010 after King's Lynn FC folded.

Previous Leagues: United Counties 2010-12. Northern Premier 2012-15.

Club Colours (change): Yellow & blue

RECORDS

HONOURS

FA Comps: None

League: Northern Premier Division One South 2012-13.

County FA: Norfolk Senior Cup 2016-17.

BEST PERFORMANCES	**FA Cup:** Fourth Qualifying Round 2011-12, 14-15.
	FA Trophy: Third Round Proper 2012-13.
	FA Vase: Semi-finals 2010-11.

KING'S LYNN MATCH RESULTS 2016-17

Date	Comp	H/A	Opponents	Att:	Result	Goalscorers	Pos	No.
Aug 6	SPL	H	Merthyr Town	720	D 1 - 1	Stevenson 85	11	1
9	SPL	A	St Neots Town	327	L 2 - 5	Hilliard 69 80	21	2
13	SPL	A	Banbury United	335	L 0 - 4		23	3
16	SPL	H	Cambridge City	562	D 1 - 1	Mettam 74	15	4
20	SPL	H	Redditch United	560	W 2 - 1	McWilliams 1 Castellon 67	19	5
27	SPL	A	Frome Town	237	W 3 - 1	Clunan 59 Stevenson 77 Hilliard 85	14	6
29	SPL	H	Kettering Town	724	L 1 - 2	Edge 1	18	7
Sept 3	FAC1Q	H	Brigg Town	511	W 6 - 1	Mettam 38 Clunan 38 42 Stevenson 50 Edge 80 Barford(og)		8
10	SPL	A	Cirencester Town	257	W 2 - 1	Zielonka 24 Clunan 53	12	9
13	SPL	A	Biggleswade town	175	L 0 - 2		15	10
17	FAC2Q	H	Harlow Town	674	W 1 - 0	Mills 77		11
24	SPL	H	Chippenham Town	536	W 4 - 0	Revan 28 Gaughran 58 Zielonka 61 Edge 66	13	12
27	SPL	H	Kings Langley	409	D 1 - 1	Revan 65		13
Oct 1	FAC3Q	H	Alfreton Town	647	L 0 - 2			14
8	SPL	H	Hitchin Town	575	D 1 - 1	Mettam 90	16	15
11	SPL	A	Leamington	345	L 0 - 3		17	16
15	SPL	A	Hayes & Yeading United	476	D 2 - 2	Mettam 16 89	16	17
22	SPL	A	Stratford Town	226	D 1 - 1	Stevenson 68	22	18
25	SPL	H	Hitchin Town	463	L 1 2	Clunan 72 (pen)	18	19
29	FAT1Q	A	Stourbridge	465	W 2 - 1	Hilliard 11 Clunan 41 (pen)		20
Nov 5	SPL	H	Cinderford Town	485	W 3 - 1	Mettam 41 (pen) Edge 78 Shipp 89	13	21
12	FAT2Q	A	Buxton	302	W 3 - 1	Hilliard 33 Stevenson 69 Mettam 86		22
19	SPL	H	Banbury United	587	W 1 - 0	Hilliard 75	14	23
26	FAT3Q	A	St Ives Town	684	W 1 - 0	Clunan		24
Dec 3	SPL	A	Dunstable Town	151	D 0 - 0		15	25
10	FAT1	A	Gateshead	277	L 0 - 2			26
13	SPL	A	Basingstoke Town	294	W 2 - 1	Quigley 23 Stevenson 41	14	27
17	SPL	H	Dorchester Town	568	D 3 - 3	Fryatt 42 6 Clunan 60	13	28
20	SPL	H	Leamington	122	L 0 - 2		14	29
26	SPL	A	Kettering Town	656	D 1 - 1	T.Ward 69	14	30
Jan 2	SPL	H	St Ives Town	821	L 1 - 2	Ogbonna 22	13	31
7	SPL	A	Redditch United	274	D 1 - 1	Hilliard 76	14	32
14	SPL	A	Chippenham Town	388	L 1 - 2	Stevenson 78	14	33
17	SPL	H	Biggleswade Town	345	L 1 - 2	Clunan 53	14	34
21	SPL	H	Weymouth	566	L 1 - 6	Edge 79	16	35
24	SPL	A	Merthyr Town	409	D 1 - 1	Stevenson 37	15	36
28	SPL	A	Kings Langley	170	D 2 - 2	Balogun 3 (og) McWilliams 77	16	37
31	SPL	H	Slough Town	278	W 5 - 2	WARBURTON 3 (7 14 32) McWilliams 11 38	15	38
Feb 4	SPL	H	Leamington	601	D 0 - 0		15	39
11	SPL	A	Cirencester Town	110	D 1 - 1	McWilliams 25	15	40
18	SPL	H	Hayes & Yeading United	167	W 1 - 0	Stevenson 86	14	41
20	SPL	A	Cambridge City	213	D 0 - 0		14	42
25	SPL	A	Hitchin Town	517	L 0 - 5		13	43
Mar 4	SPL	H	Stratford Town	645	W 2 - 0	McWilliams 3 T.Ward 64	13	44
11	SPL	A	Cinderford Town	140	W 2 - 0	Fryatt 35 90	11	45
18	SPL	H	Basingstoke Town	506	W 2 - 1	C.Ward 51 T.Ward 66	12	46
21	SPL	H	St Neots Town	429	L 1 - 2	Zielonka 84	12	47
25	SPL	H	Dunstable Town	567	L 0 - 1		12	48
April 1	SPL	A	Slough Town	607	L 0 - 3		13	49
8	SPL	A	Dorchester Town	356	D 1 - 1	Clunan 82 (pen)	13	50
15	SPL	H	Frome Town	505	D 1 - 1	Harnwell 29	13	51
17	SPL	A	St Ives Town	265	L 0 2		13	52
22	SPL	H	Chesham United	554	W 3 1	Hilliard 61 Clunan 71 Hawkins 75	13	53

GOALSCORERS	SG	CSG	Pens	Hat tricks	Total		SG	CSG	Pens	Hat tricks	Total
2015-16 *Stevenson*					13	Opponents	2				2
Clunan	10	2	3		11	Rivan	2				2
Stevenson	9				9	C.Ward	1				1
Hilliard	7				8	Castellon	1				1
Mettam	6	2	1		7	Gaughran	1				1
McWilliams	5				6	Harnwell	1				1
Edge	5				5	Hawkins	1				1
Fryatt	4				4	Mills	1				1
T.Ward	3				3	Ogbonna	1				1
Warburton	1		1		3	Quigley	1				1
Zielonka	3				3	Shipp	1				1

KINGS LANGLEY

Club Contact Details
Gaywood Park, Hempstead Road, Kings Langley Herts WD4 8BS
07730 410 330
derry_edgar@hotmail.com

Ground Capacity: 1,963 **Seats:** Yes **Covered:** Yes **Clubhouse:** Yes **Shop:**

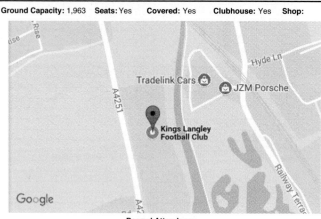

Record Attendance
Not known

Previous Grounds
Groomes Meadow. Blackwell Meadow. Kings Langley Common. Home Park 1913-80.
Oxhey, Rolls Royce & Buncefield Lane and Leavesden Hospital Ground between 1980-97.

10 YEAR RECORD

07-08		08-09		09-10		10-11		11-12		12-13		13-14		14-15		15-16		16-17	
SSM2	1	SSM1	2	SSM1	7	SSM1	3	SSM1	4	SSM1	6	SSM1	2	SSM P	1	SthC	1	SthP	20
								FAC	EP	FAC	EPr	FAC	1Q	FAC	Pr	FAC	P	FAC	2Q
						FAV	1Q	FAV	2Q	FAV	1Q	FAV	1Q	FAV	2P	FAT	1Q	FAT	3Q

Club Factfile

Founded: 1886   **Nickname:** Kings   **Manager:** Paul Hobbs

Previous Names: None

Previous Leagues: West Herts (Founder Member) 1891-1920, 22-34. Southern Olympian 1934-39.
Hertfordshire County 1920-22, 46-52, 55-2001. Parthenon 1952-55. Spartan South Midlands 1955-2015.

Club Colours (change): White & black/white/white

RECORDS
Misc: 47 consecutive matches unbeaten in all competitions between 15-09-07 and 15-10-08.

HONOURS
FA Comps: None

League: West Herts Div.3 1911-12, Div.2 1919-20, 30-31, 34-35. Southern Olympian Div.1 1936-37. Herts County 1949-50, 51-52, 65-66, 66
-67, Div.1 1975-76. Spartan South Midlands Div.2 2007-08, Premier 2014-15. Southern Div.1 Central 2015-16.

County FA: Herts Charity Shield 1966-67. Herts Intermediate Cup 2006-07, 07-08. Herts Senior Centenary Trophy 2011-12.

BEST PERFORMANCES	FA Cup: Second Qualifying Round 2016-17.
	FA Trophy: Third Qualifying Round 2016-17.
	FA Vase: Second Round Proper 2014-15.

KINGS LANGLEY MATCH RESULTS 2016-17

Date	Comp	H/A	Opponents	Att:	Result	Goalscorers	Pos	No.
Aug 6	SPL	A	Chippenham Town	366	D 1 - 1	Chamberlain 45	12	1
9	SPL	H	Dunstable Town	122	L 0 - 1		17	2
13	SPL	H	Slough Town	180	L 2 - 3	L.Toomey 14 27	19	3
16	SPL	A	Biggleswade Town	131	W 4 - 0	Duku 17 9 Waldren 60 Coughlan 84	15	4
20	SPL	H	Frome Town	74	D 2 - 2	Waldren 21 L.Toomey 27 (pen)	15	5
27	SPL	H	Redditch United	71	L 1 - 2	Coughlan 89	19	6
29	SPL	H	Chesham United	310	L 1 - 2	L.Toomey 84	21	7
Sept 3	FAC1Q	H	Sporting Bengal United	101	W 6 - 1	L.Toomey 3 (5 pen 40 84) Hutton 8 58 Plowright 56		8
10	SPL	A	Cirencester Town	87	W 1 - 0	L.Toomey 45	16	9
13	SPL	H	Basingstoke Town	112	W 2 - 0	Ward 2 Coughlan 50	12	10
17	FAC2Q	A	Hadley	125	L 1 - 2	Duku 18 (pen)		11
24	SPL	A	Banbury United	352	L 0 - 3		15	12
27	SPL	A	Kings Lynn Town	446	D 1 - 1	Chamberlain 37	16	13
Oct 1	SPL	H	St Ives Town	61	W 2 - 1	C.Toomey 49 Gallagher 90	12	14
8	SPL	A	Cinderford Town	134	W 4 - 0	Hutchinson 30 Ward 39 Duku 64 75	8	15
11	SPL	H	Hitchin Town	161	L 1 - 2	Hutchinson 87	13	16
18	SPL	A	Basingstoke Town	294	L 0 - 3		15	17
22	SPL	A	Cambridge City	144	D 1 - 1	Pope 30	16	18
25	SPL	H	St Neots Town	88	L 2 - 3	Hutton 30 Chamberlain 87	16	19
29	FAT1Q	H	Heybridge Swifts	61	W 1 - 0	L.Toomey 63 (pen)		20
Nov 5	SPL	H	Dorchester Town	118	W 2 - 0	Waldren 18 L.Toomey 43	13	21
12	FAT2Q	H	Enfield Town	222	W 1 - 0	Amoo 90		22
15	SPL	H	Kettering Town	128	L 1 - 2	Johnson 54	16	23
19	SPL	A	Slough Town	513	D 2 - 2	Amoo 65 Hutton 81	15	24
22	SPL	H	Biggleswade Town	86	L 4 - 5	Ward 27 Calvin 33 Duku 48 Hitchcock 78	15	25
26	FAT3Q	H	AFC Sudbury	151	L 1 - 3	Calvin 48		26
Dec 3	SPL	H	Weymouth	128	D 1 - 1	Hitchcock 72	17	27
10	SPL	A	Merthyr Town	478	L 0 - 5		19	28
17	SPL	H	Leamington	122	L 0 - 2		19	29
20	SPL	A	Stratford Town	136	D 2 - 2	Plowright 12 Amoo 22	19	30
26	SPL	A	Chesham United	542	L 2 - 5	Ward 34 Plowright 74	19	31
Jan 2	SPL	H	Hayes & Yeading United	268	W 1 - 0	Hutton 45	19	32
7	SPL	A	Frome Town	264	D 0 - 0		19	33
10	SPL	A	Dunstable Town	125	W 2 - 1	Ward 42 Johnson 65	17	34
14	SPL	H	Banbury United	152	L 0 - 1		18	35
21	SPL	A	St Ives Town	291	L 1 - 2	Waldren 80	18	36
28	SPL	H	Kings Lynn Town	170	D 2 - 2	West 12 L.Toomey 62 (pen)	18	37
Feb 4	SPL	A	Hitchin Town	690	L 0 - 2		18	38
11	SPL	H	Cinderford Town	115	L 0 - 1		14	39
14	SPL	H	Chippenham Town	101	D 1 - 1	Johnson 48	18	40
18	SPL	A	Kettering Town	560	L 0 - 1		19	41
25	SPL	A	St Neots Town	235	L 2 - 5	KIng 47 90	19	42
Mar 11	SPL	A	Dorchester Town	393	L 0 - 1		20	43
14	SPL	H	Cambridge City	191	W 2 - 0	Turner 49 Ward 90	20	44
18	SPL	H	Stratford Town	168	L 1 - 3	Hitchcock 60	20	45
25	SPL	A	Weymouth	496	D 1 - 1	Cox 48	20	46
April 1	SPL	H	Merthyr Town	205	D 2 - 2	Stobbs 85 Pattison 90	20	47
8	SPL	A	Leamington	422	D 0 - 0		20	48
15	SPL	H	Redditch United	168	D 0 - 0		21	49
17	SPL	A	Hayes & Yeading United	354	W 2 - 0	Plowright 45 Amoo 55	20	50
22	SPL	H	Cirencester Town	120	W 1 - 0	Ward 28	20	51

GOALSCORERS	SG	CSG	Pens	Hat tricks	Total		SG	CSG	Pens	Hat tricks	Total
2015-16 *Stevenson*					13	Hutchinson	2				2
L.Toomey	8	3	4		11	Johnson	2				2
Ward	8				8	King	2				2
Duku	5		1		6	Cox	1				1
Amoo	4				4	Gallagher	1				1
Hutton	4				4	Pattison	1				1
Waldren	4				4	Pope	1				1
Chamberlain	3				3	Stobbs	1				1
Hitchcock	3				3	C.Toomey	1				1
Hutton	3				3	Turner	1				1
Plowright	3				3	West	1				1
Calvin	2				2						
Coughlan	2				2						

MERTHYR TOWN

Club Contact Details
Loadlok Community Stadium, Penydarren Park, Park Terrance CF47 8RF
0772 567 302
footballsecretary@merthyrtownfc.co.uk

Ground Capacity: **Seats:** Yes   **Covered:** Yes   **Clubhouse:** Yes   **Shop:**

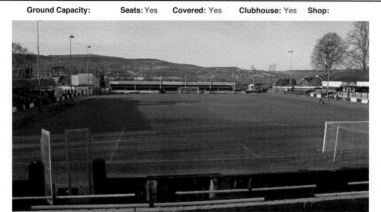

Record Attendance
Not known
Previous Grounds
Rhiw Dda'r (Taff's Well AFC) 2010-11.

10 YEAR RECORD

07-08	08-09	09-10	10-11	11-12	12-13	13-14	14-15	15-16	16-17
			West1 1	WestP 1	Sthsw 3	Sthsw 2	Sthsw 1	SthP 10	SthP 3
			FAC EP	FAC 1Qr	FAC 3Q	FAC 1Q	FAC P	FAC 2Q	FAC 3Q
			FAV 2Q	FAV 2Q	FAT 1P	FAT 3Q	FAT 3Qr	FAT 3Qr	FAT 2Qr

Club Factfile

Founded: 2010   **Nickname:** Martyrs   **Manager:** Gavin Williams

Previous Names: None

Previous Leagues: Western League 2010-12.

Club Colours (change): White/black/black

RECORDS
Victory: 9-0 v Bishops Cleeve, Southern Division One South & West, 06/04/2015.

HONOURS
FA Comps: None

League: Western League Division One 2010-11, Premier Division 2011-12.
       Southern Division One South & West 2014-15.

County FA: None

BEST PERFORMANCES	**FA Cup:** Third Qualifying Round 2012-13, 16-17.
	FA Trophy: First Round Proper 2012-13.
	FA Vase: Second Qualifying Round 2010-11, 11-12.

MERTHYR TOWN MATCH RESULTS 2016-17

Date	Comp	H/A	Opponents	Att:	Result	Goalscorers	Pos	No.
Aug 6	SPL	A	Kings Lynn Town	720	D 1 - 1	Prosser 90 (pen)	13	1
9	SPL	H	Basingstoke Town	508	W 4 - 0	Barrow 40 Traylor 76 90 Gater 80 (og)	6	2
13	SPL	H	Dunstable Town	513	W 4 - 3	McLaggon 12 Prosser 69 Wright 90 Barrow 90	3	3
16	SPL	A	Leamington	464	L 0 - 1		6	4
20	SPL	H	Cirencester Town	403	W 3 - 0	Traylor 15 Baggridge 42 Brown 73	3	5
29	SPL	H	Cinderford Town	303	L 2 - 3	Traylor 30 Prosser 39	8	6
Sept 3	FAC1Q	A	Barnstaple Town	210	W 4 - 0	McLaggon 9 82 Traylor 30 75		7
10	SPL	A	Hayes & Yeading United	143	W 6 - 1	Everitt 9 (og) Baggridge 16 McLAGGON 3 (16 24 28) Traylor 61	6	8
17	FAC2Q	A	AFC Portchester	215	W 2 - 0	Traylor 44 80	6	9
20	SPL	A	St Ives Town	210	D 0 - 0			10
24	SPL	A	Hitchin Town	514	D 1 - 1	McDonald 7	7	11
27	SPL	A	Banbury United	306	D 1 - 1	Wright 28	9	12
Oct 1	FAC3Q	A	Whitehawk	292	L 0 - 2			13
8	SPL	A	Chesham United	367	D 1 - 1	McLaggon 50		14
11	SPL	H	Dorchester Town	345	W 2 - 0	McLaggon 25 77	8	15
15	SPL	H	Slough Town	628	D 1 - 1	Yorworth 31	7	16
18	SPL	A	Stratford Town	191	W 3 - 0	Prosser 36 Reffell 51 87	6	17
22	SPL	H	Biggleswade Town	468	L 1 - 2	McLaggon 22	6	18
26	SPL	A	Frome Town	290	D 2 - 2	Wright 65 Traylor 82	5	19
29	FAT1Q	H	Cinderford Town	283	W 6 - 1	Trayler 12 (pen) 35 McLaggon 18 60 Richards 31 Williams 38		20
Nov 1	SPL	H	Kettering Town	408	W 2 - 0	Traylor 22 Yorworth 91	4	21
5	SPL	A	Weymouth	537	W 1 - 0	McLaggon 43	5	22
12	FAT2Q	H	Slough Town	370	D 2 - 2	Yorworth 13 McLaggon 43		23
15	FAT2Qr	A	Slough Town	429	L 0 - 2			24
19	SPL	A	Dunstable Town	102	W 1 - 0	Traylor 45	4	25
22	SPL	H	Leamington	487	D 1 - 1	Prosser 5	4	26
26	SPL	H	Kings Lynn Town	215	D 1 - 1	Traylor 63	4	27
28	SPL	A	Basingstoke Town	318	L 2 - 3	Prosser 24 McLaggon 69	5	28
Dec 3	SPL	A	Cambridge City	215	L 0 - 1		5	29
10	SPL	H	Kings Langley	478	W 5 - 0	Prosser 12 McLaggon 29 41 Traylor 90 Watkins 90	5	30
13	SPL	A	Chippenham Town	386	D 2 - 2	Prosser 7 30	6	31
17	SPL	H	St Neots Town	484	W 3 - 0	Traylor 37 McLaggon 48 Richards 81	4	32
26	SPL	A	Cinderford Town	784	W 2 - 0	Traylor 24 30	4	33
31	SPL	H	Redditch United	401	W 2 - 0	McDonald 28 Barrow 44	3	34
Jan 7	SPL	A	Cirencester Town	170	W 2 - 0	Prosser 39 McLaggon 45	3	35
21	SPL	A	Kettering Town	493	W 3 - 1	McDonald 8 Richards 16 Jenkins 76	4	36
24	SPL	H	Kings Lynn Town	409	D 1 - 1	Traylor 38	4	37
28	SPL	H	Banbury United	529	W 1 - 0	McLaggon 73	4	38
Feb 4	SPL	A	Dorchester Town	489	W 2 - 1	Prosser 7 Richards 18	2	39
11	SPL	H	Weymouth	405	W 1 - 0	Wright 75	2	40
18	SPL	A	Slough Town	757	L 0 - 1		2	41
21	SPL	H	Hitchin Town	535	D 2 - 2	Compton 13 Jenkins 85	3	42
25	SPL	H	Frome Town	340	L 1 - 2	Compton 63	4	43
Mar 4	SPL	A	Biggleswade Town	224	W 5 - 2	McLaggon 40 76 Wright 70 Traylor 87 Jenkins 90	4	44
11	SPL	H	Weymouth	611	D 2 - 2	Evans 16 Copp 77 (pen)	5	45
18	SPL	A	Chippenham Town	723	L 1 - 3	Compton 84	5	46
25	SPL	H	Cambridge City	441	W 5 - 0	Barrow 42 Prosser 64 Bull 68 Traylor 74 90 (pen)	5	47
April 1	SPL	A	Kings Langley	205	D 2 - 2	Barrow 54 Traylor 78	5	48
8	SPL	A	St Neots Town	187	W 3 - 2	Parr 2 (og) Wright 83 Traylor 88	5	49
15	SPL	H	St Ives Town	608	W 2 - 0	Prosser 56 (pen) 70	4	50
17	SPL	A	Redditch United	291	W 1 - 0	Evans 65	3	51
22	SPL	H	Hayes & Yeading United	685	W 4 - 0	Jenkins 40 Richards 54 McLaggon 62 64	3	52
26	PO SF	H	Hitchin Town	1453	D 1 - 1	McLaggon 8 (lost 1-4 on penalties)		53

GOALSCORERS	SG	CSG	Pens	Hat tricks	Total		SG	CSG	Pens	Hat tricks	Total
2015-16 *Traylor*					13	Yorworth	2				3
Traylor	19	5	1		25	Opponents	3				3
McLaggon	17	2		1	25	Baggridge	2				2
Prosser	13	2	2		14	Evans	2				2
Wright	6	2			6	McDonald	3				2
Barrow	5				5	Brown	1				1
Richards	5				5	Bull	1				1
Jenkins	4				4	Copp	1		1		1
Compton	3				3	Watkins	1				1
Reffell	2				3	Yorworth	1				1

REDDITCH UNITED

Club Contact Details
Valley Stadium, Bromsgrove Road, Redditch B97 4RN
01527 67450
rbfc.jw@gmail.com

Ground Capacity: 5,000 **Seats:** 400 **Covered:** 2,000 **Clubhouse:** Yes **Shop:** Yes

Record Attendance
5,500 v Bromsgrove Rovers - Wets Midlands League 1954-55
Previous Grounds
HDA Sports Ground, Millsborough Road

10 YEAR RECORD

	07-08	08-09	09-10	10-11	11-12	12-13	13-14	14-15	15-16	16-17
	Conf N 13	Conf N 14	Conf N 19	Conf N 21	SthP 15	SthP 19	SthP 10	SthP 6	SthP 2	SthP 17
FAC	2Q	2Q	4Qr	4Q	1Q	1Q	1Qr	1Qr	1Q	1Q
FAT	1P	2P	1P	1P	1Q	1Q	3Q	3Q	1Q	FAV 2Q

Club Factfile

Founded: 1891   **Nickname:** The Reds   **Manager:** Julian Workman

Previous Names: Redditch Town

Previous Leagues: Birmingham Combination 1905-21, 29-39, 46-53, West Midlands 1921-29, 53-72, Southern 1972-79, 81-2004, Alliance 1979-80. Conference 2004-11.

Club Colours (change): All royal blue (Red/navy/navy)

RECORDS
Misc: Paid £3,000 to Halesowen Town for Paul Joinson. Received £40,000 from Aston Villa for David Farrell. Played nine games in nine days at the end of the 1997-98 season.

HONOURS

FA Comps: None

League: Birmingham Combination 1913-14, 32-33, 52-53. Birmingham & District Southern Division 1954-55. Southern Division One North 1975-76, Western Division 2003-04.

County FA: Worcestershire Senior Cup 1893-94, 29-30, 74-75, 76-76, 2007-08, 13-14. Birmingham Senior Cup 1924-25, 31-32, 38-39, 76-77, 2004-05. Staffordshire Senior Cup 1990-91.

BEST PERFORMANCES	**FA Cup:** First Round Proper 1971-72(r), 89-90.
	FA Trophy: Fourth Round Proper 1998-99.
	FA Vase: N/A

REDDITCH UNITED MATCH RESULTS 2016-17

Date	Comp	H/A	Opponents	Att:	Result	Goalscorers	Pos	No.
Aug 6	SPL	H	Chesham United	144	W 3 - 1	Roberts 32 Morrison 44 Luckie 90	2	1
9	SPL	A	Stratford Town	327	W 4 - 2	Johnson 2 Hewitt 3 Roberts 44 Spink 89	1	2
13	SPL	A	Weymouth	509	L 0 - 1		6	3
16	SPL	H	Kettering Town	212	L 1 - 3	Jones 15	12	4
20	SPL	A	Kings Lynn	560	L 1 - 2	Johnson 78	12	5
27	SPL	H	Kings Langley	71	W 2 - 1	Bako 62 Hales 76	11	6
29	SPL	A	Banbury United	403	W 1 - 0	Luckie 62	7	7
Sept 3	FAC1Q	A	**Coalville Town**	161	L 1 - 2	**McDonald 82**		8
10	SPL	H	Slough Town	410	L 0 - 4		8	9
13	SPL	A	Leamington	408	L 1 - 2	Johnson 1	11	10
24	SPL	H	Frome Town	260	W 2 - 1	Johnson 43 Courtney 76	10	11
27	SPL	H	Dunstable Town	210	W 1 - 0	Johnson 73	7	12
Oct 1	SPL	A	Biggleswade Town	135	L 0 2		7	13
8	SPL	H	Hayes & Yeading United	402	W 2 - 1	McDermott 1 Hewitt 53	5	14
15	SPL	A	Cambridge City	145	W 4 - 1	Shearer 5 Johnson 45 (p) Apostopopoulos 85 Loveridge 94	6	15
18	SPL	H	Leamington	40	L 0 - 2		8	16
22	SPL	A	Dorchester Town	353	D 0 - 0		7	17
29	FAT1Q	H	**Cambridge City**	242	W 3 - 1	**Bako 7 Hales 25 35**		18
Nov 1	SPL	A	Chippenham Town	285	D 1 - 1	Hales 61 (pen)	7	19
5	SPL	H	St Neots Town	285	L 1 - 4	Johnson 1	9	20
15	FAT2Q	A	**Ramsbottom United**	139	L 1 - 4	**Shearer 90**		21
19	SPL	H	Weymouth	236	W 2 - 1	Cobourne 79 Johnson 81	9	22
22	SPL	A	Kettering Town	343	W 2 - 1	Apostopopoulos 58 Loveridge 87	8	23
26	SPL	A	Chesham United	307	D 1 - 1	Mitchell-King 63 (og)	7	24
29	SPL	H	Stratford Town	232	D 1 - 1	Keen 10	7	25
Dec 3	SPL	H	Cirencester Town	218	W 4 - 1	Keen 6 Cobourne 24 Singh 43 53	6	26
6	SPL	H	Cinderford Town	194	D 2 - 2	Keen 9 (pen) Culimane -Liburd	6	27
10	SPL	A	St Ives Town	224	L 1 - 2	Keen 64	6	28
13	SPL	A	Hitchin Town	233	L 2 - 4	Dillon 22 65	7	29
17	SPL	A	Basingstoke Town	366	W 1 - 0	Hales 25	7	30
26	SPL	H	Banbury United	402	D 0 - 0		7	31
Jan 7	SPL	H	Kings Lynn Town	274	D 1 - 1	Singh 90	10	32
14	SPL	A	Frome Town	210	L 1 - 8	Johnson 58	10	33
21	SPL	H	Biggleswade Town	255	L 0 - 2		11	34
28	SPL	A	Dunstable Town	109	L 0 - 1		11	35
31 Jan	SPL	A	Merthyr Town	401	L 0 - 2		11	36
Feb 4	SPL	H	Chippenham Town	277	L 0 - 2		13	37
11	SPL	A	Hayes & Yeading United	157	L 1 - 2	Keen 57	13	38
18	SPL	H	Cambridge City	208	L 1 - 2	Morris 32	16	39
25	SPL	A	Cinderford Town	162	D 1 - 1	Rodgers 90	16	40
Mar 4	SPL	H	Dorchester Town	258	W 4 - 2	KEEN 3 (2 21 25) Cullinane-Liburd 45	14	41
11	SPL	A	St Neots Town	228	L 0 - 1		14	42
18	SPL	H	Hitchin Town	258	L 1 - 2	Angus 64	15	43
25	SPL	A	Cirencester Town	138	L 1 - 2	Angus 77	17	44
April 1	SPL	H	St Ives Town	234	L 0 - 2		17	45
8	SPL	H	Basingstoke Town	216	D 2 - 2	Hussain 8 Keen 75	17	46
15	SPL	A	Kings Langley	168	D 0 - 0		17	47
17	SPL	H	Merthyr Town	291	L 0 - 1		17	48
22	SPL	A	Slough Town	613	D 1 - 1	Coates 63	17	49

GOALSCORERS	SG	CSG	Pens	Hat tricks	Total		SG	CSG	Pens	Hat tricks	Total
2015-16 *Sammons*					12	Luckie	2				2
Johnson	9	3	1		9	Roberts	2	2			2
Keen	6	3	1	1	9	Shearer	2				2
Hales	4		1		5	Coates	1				1
Singh	2				3	Courtney	1				1
Angus	2				2	Hussain	1				1
Apostocopulos	2				2	Jones	1				1
Bako	2				2	McDermott	1				1
Cobourne	2				2	McDonald	1				1
Cullirnane-Liburd	2				2	Morris	1				1
Dillon	1				2	Morrison	1				1
Hewitt	2				2	Opponents	1				1
Loveridge	2				2	Rodgers	1				1
						Spink	1				1

ROYSTON TOWN

Club Contact Details
Garden Walk, Royston, Herts, SG8 7HP
01763 241 204
terry.mckinnell@talktalk.net

Ground Capacity: 5,000 Seats: 300 Covered: Yes Clubhouse: Yes Shop: No

Record Attendance
876 v Aldershot Town, 1993-94.
Previous Grounds
Newmarket Road, Baldock Road and Mackerell Hall before acquiring Garden Walk in 1932.

10 YEAR RECORD

07-08		08-09		09-10		10-11		11-12		12-13		13-14		14-15		15-16		16-17	
SSM1	5	SSM1	1	SSM P	4	SSM P	3	SSM P	1	SthC	7	SthC	7	SthC	2	SthC	2	SthC	1
FAC	EP	FAC	1Q	FAC	1Q	FAC	EP	FAC	P	FAC	1Qr	FAC	2Q	FAC	P	FAC	Pr	FAC	P
FAV	2P	FAV	1P	FAV	5P	FAV	2Pr	FAV	4P	FAT	1Qr	FAT	P	FAT	1Q	FAT	2Q	FAT	1Pr

Club Factfile

Founded: 1872 **Nickname:** The Crows **Manager:** Steve Castle

Previous Names: None

Previous Leagues: Buntingford & District 1919-29. Cambridgeshire 1929-48. Herts County 1948-60, 63-77. South Midlands 1960-63, 77-84. Isthmian 1984-94. Spartan South Midlands 1994-2012.

Club Colours (change): White/black/black (All red)

RECORDS

HONOURS

FA Comps: None

League: Cambridgeshire Division Two 1929-30. Herts County Division One 1969-70, 72-73, Premier 1976-77. South Midlands Division One 1977-78, 2008-09, Premier Division 2011-12.

County FA: Herts Charity Shield 1981-82, 96-97. Herts Intermediate Cup 1988-89.

BEST PERFORMANCES	**FA Cup:** Third Qualifying Round 1998-99.
	FA Trophy: First Round Proper 2016-17(r)
	FA Vase: Fifth Round Proper 2009-10.

Orlando-Young (Royston) tries to get between Quainton and Castle (Kidlington).

Murray's (Royston) header goes over Conway (Kempston) to win the game. Photos: Keith Clayton.

SLOUGH TOWN

Club Contact Details
Arbour Park, Stoke Road, SLough SL2 5AY

07792 126 124

kay.lathey@gmail.com

Ground Capacity: 2,000 **Seats:** 250 **Covered:** Yes **Clubhouse:** Yes **Shop:** Yes

Record Attendance
1,401 v Hayes & Yeading United, Southern Premier, 29/08/2016 - first fixture at the all new Arbour Park.

Previous Grounds
Dolphin Stadium 1890-1936. Maidenhead United FC. Wrexham Park Stadium >2003. Stag Meadow Windsor & Eton FC 2003-07. Holloways Park Beaconsfield SYCOB FC 2007-16.

10 YEAR RECORD

07-08		08-09		09-10		10-11		11-12		12-13		13-14		14-15		15-16		16-17	
Sthsw	21	Sthsw	16	SthM	5	SthC	5	SthC	2	SthC	6	SthC	5	SthP	16	SthP	17	SthP	5
FAC	P	FAC	1Q	FAC	3Q	FAC	1Q	FAC	3Qr	FAC	1Pr	FAC	Pr	FAC	1Q	FAC	2Q	FAC	3Q
FAT	Pr	FAT	1Q	FAT	2Q	FAT	1Qr	FAT	P	FAT	1Qr	FAT	1Q	FAT	2Qr	FAT	2Q	FAT	3Q

Club Factfile

Founded: 1890 **Nickname:** The Rebels **Manager:** Neil Baker & Jon Underwood

Previous Names: Slough FC. Slough United.

Previous Leagues: Southern Alliance 1892-93, Berks & Bucks 1901-05, Gt Western Suburban 1909-19, Spartan 1920-39, Herts & Middx 1940-45, Corinthian 1946-63, Athenian 1963-73, Isthmian 1973-90, 94-95, Conference 1990-94.

Club Colours (change): Amber/navy blue/amber (All purple)

RECORDS

Victory: 17-0 v Railway Clearing House - 1921-22

Defeat: 1-11 v Chesham Town - 1909-10

Goalscorer: Ted Norris - 343 in 226 appearances. Scored 84 during the 1925-26 season.

Appearances: Terry Reardon - 475 (1964-81)

Additional: Paid £18,000 to Farnborough Town for Colin Fielder
Received £22,000 from Wycombe Wanderers for Steve Thompson

HONOURS

FA Comps: None

League: Isthmian League 1980-81, 89-90. Athenian League x3.

County FA: Berks & Bucks Senior Cup x10.

BEST PERFORMANCES	**FA Cup:** Second Round Proper 1970-71, 79-80, 82-83, 85-86(r), 86-87, 2004-05.
	FA Trophy: Semi-finals 1976-77, 97-98.
	FA Vase: N/A

SLOUGH TOWN MATCH RESULTS 2016-17

Date	Comp	H/A	Opponents	Att:	Result	Goalscorers	Pos	No.
Aug 6	SPL	H	St Neots Town	345	W 2 - 0	Moone 15 Harris 53	5	1
9	SPL	A	Banbury United	423	L 0 - 1		12	2
13	SPL	A	Kings Langley	180	W 3 - 2	Dunn 32 Dobson 35 Moone 83	9	3
16	SPL	H	Stratford Town	336	D 0 - 0		9	4
20	SPL	H	St Ives Town	349	W 3 - 0	Hollis 35 Moone 47 Barney 64	6	5
27	SPL	A	Cirencester Town	125	W 3 -- 1	James 4 80 Putman 69	2	6
29	SPL	H	Hayes & Yeading United	1401	W 2 - 1	Barney 20 Dobson 75	2	7
Sept 3	FAC1Q	H	Chipstead	472	W 6 - 2	Moone 5 30 Harris 33 Dobson 66 Barney 80 88		8
10	SPL	A	Redditch United	410	W 4 - 0	Harris 7 89 Barney 33 James 92	2	9
13	SPL	A	Weymouth	516	W 1 - 0	Harris 81	1	10
17	FAC2Q	A	Canbridge City	208	W 3 - 1	Dobson 27 87 James 36		11
24	SPL	H	Biggleswade Town	575	W 3 - 0	Harris 8 Barney 33 James 90	1	12
27	SPL	H	Leamington	687	W 2 - 0	James 36 Dobson 66	1	13
Oct 1	FAC3Q	H	Dartford	733	L 2 - 3	Brabrook 5 (og) Dobson 58 (pen)		14
8	SPL	H	Cambridge City	656	W 1 - 0	Nisbet 74	1	15
11	SPL	A	Dunstable Town	208	W 1 - 0	Dunn 47	1	16
15	SPL	A	Merthyr Town	628	D 1 - 1	Dobson 21	1	17
22	SPL	A	Basingstoke Town	596	L 1 - 4	Putman 27	2	18
25	SPL	H	Dorchester Town	589	W 2 - 1	Moone 24 Hollis 88	2	19
29	FAT1Q	H	Bognor Regis Town	543	W 4 - 1	ADEBAYO 3 (1 45 90) Dobson 22		20
Nov 5	SPL	H	Hitchin Town	646	L 0 - 1		3	21
12	FAT2Q	A	Merthyr Town	370	D 2 - 2	Moone 70 Dobson 75		22
15	FAT2Qr	H	Merthyr Town	429	W 2 - 0	Moone 17 Dunn 45		23
19	SPL	H	Kings Langley	513	D 2 - 2	Harris 89 Moone 90	3	24
22	SPL	A	Stratford Town	202	W 2 - 1	Harris 74 Adebayo 77	3	25
26	FAT3Q	H	Wingate & Finchley	353	L 2 - 4	Togwell 29 Gokmen 88		26
29	SPL	H	Banbury United	463	W 2 - 0	Hollis 64 Dobson 87		27
Dec 3	SPL	H	Frome Town	460	L 1 - 2	Dobson 70 (pen)	2	28
6	SPL	A	Chippenham Town	328	D 3 - 3	Hollis 50 Dunn 73 Moone 89	2	29
17	SPL	H	Kettering Town	548	W 3 - 2	Moone 2 29 Dobson 57	2	30
26	SPL	A	Hayes & Yeading United	474	W 3 - 2	Nisbet 46 Fraser 51 James 72	2	31
Jan 2	SPL	H	Chesham United	918	L 1 - 2	James 21	3	32
7	SPL	A	St Ives Town	305	L 0 - 2		4	33
21	SPL	H	Chippenham Town	753	L 0 - 1		6	34
28	SPL	A	Leamington	646	W 6 - 0	FLOOD 3 (13 348 67) James 17 Holgate 75 Dunn 86	5	35
31	SPL	A	Kings Lynn Town	278	L 2 - 5	Williams 58 Flood 73	5	36
Feb 4	SPL	H	Dunstable Town	503	W 1 - 0	Dunn 52	5	37
7	SPL	H	Weymouth	612	W 3 - 0	James 4 (pen) 86 Flood 53	5	38
11	SPL	A	Cambridge City	208	W 4 - 3	Dunn 11 James 31 Flood 51 Harris 84	5	39
18	SPL	H	Merthyr Town	757	W 1 - 0	Flood 70	5	40
21	SPL	A	Cinderford Town	167	L 1 - 2	Smart 53	5	41
25	SPL	A	Dorchester Town	446	W 4 - 0	Williams 6 Dobson 37 75 Rose 90	3	42
Mar 4	SPL	H	Basingstoke Town	728	W 3 - 2	Flood 8 29 Dobson 75	3	43
8	SPL	A	Biggleswade Town	190	L 0 3		3	44
11	SPL	A	Hitchin Town	828	W 3 - 2	Harris 2 Hollis 7 Dobson 69 (pen)	3	45
14	SPL	A	St Neots Town	210	D 1 - 1	Dunn 19	3	46
18	SPL	H	Cinderford Town	626	W 4 - 1	Harris 23 James 45 71 Flood 51	3	47
25	SPL	A	Frome Town	307	L 0 - 1		4	48
April 1	SPL	H	Kings Lynn Town	607	W 3 - 0	Flood 7 Dunn 25 Enver-Marum 50	4	49
8	SPL	A	Kettering Town	521	L 0 - 3		4	50
15	SPL	H	Cirencester Town	780	L 0 - 2		5	51
17	SPL	A	Chesham United	508	D 1 - 1	Enver-Marum 10	5	52
22	SPL	H	Redditch United	613	D 1 - 1	Enver-Marum 90 (pen)	5	53
26	PO SF	A	Leamington	1032	L 0 - 1			54

GOALSCORERS	SG	CSG	Pens	Hat tricks	Total		SG	CSG	Pens	Hat tricks	Total
2015-16 *Mpi*					14	Nisbet	2				2
Dobson	15	2	3		17	Putman	2				2
James	12	3	1		14	Williams	2				2
Moone	10	3			12	Fraser	1				1
Harris	10	3			11	Gokmen	1				1
Dunn	9				10	Holgate	1				1
Flood	7		1		10	Opponents	1				1
Barney	5	3			6	Rose	1				1
Hollis	5				5	Smart	1				1
Adebayo	2		1		4	Togwell	1				1
Enver-Marum	3				3						

ST. IVES TOWN

Club Contact Details
Pro-Edge Stadium, Westwood Road, St. Ives PE27 6DT
01480 463 207
sitfcsecretary@aol.com

Ground Capacity: 2,000   **Seats:** Yes   **Covered:** Yes   **Clubhouse:** Yes   **Shop:** No

Record Attendance
1,523 v AFC Rushden & Diamonds, Southern Division One Central Play-off Final, 02/05/2016.
Previous Grounds
Meadow Lane.

10 YEAR RECORD

	07-08		08-09		09-10		10-11		11-12		12-13		13-14		14-15		15-16		16-17	
UCL P	5	UCL P	6	UCL P	10	UCL P	11	UCL P	3	UCL P	2	SthC	13	SthC	9	SthC	4	SthP	15
FAC	P	FAC	EP	FAC	1Q	FAC	EP	FAC	Pr	FAC	P	FAC	2Q	FAC	Pr	FAC	2Q	FAC	1Q
FAV	5Pr	FAV	5P	FAV	5P	FAV	4P	FAV	QF	FAV	2Pr	FAT	2Q	FAT	P	FAT	1Q	FAV	3Q

Club Factfile

Founded: 1887   **Nickname:** Saints   **Manager:** Ricky Marheineke

Previous Names: None

Previous Leagues: Cambridgeshire, Central Amateur, Hunts, Peterborough & District. United Counties > 2013.

Club Colours (change): Black & white

RECORDS

HONOURS

FA Comps: None

League: Southern Division One Central Play-offs 2015-16.

County FA: Hunts Senior Cup 1900/01, 11-12, 22-23, 25-26, 29-30, 81-82, 86-87, 87-88, 2006-07, 08-09, 11-12, 15-16.
Hunts Premier Cup 2006-07, 08-09.

BEST PERFORMANCES	**FA Cup:** Second Qualifying Round 2013-14, 15-16.
	FA Trophy: Third Qualifying Round 2016-17.
	FA Vase: Quarter-finals 2011-12.

ST. IVES TOWN MATCH RESULTS 2016-17

Date	Comp	H/A	Opponents	Att:	Result		Goalscorers	Pos	No.
Aug 6	SPL	H	Stratford Town	342	D	1 - 1	Higgs 45	14	1
9	SPL	A	Chesham United	302	L	0 - 2		20	2
13	SPL	A	Cinderford Town	163	W	1 - 0	Seymore-Shove	14	3
16	SPL	H	St Neots Town	528	W	2 - 1	Wood 73 (og) Dawkin 88	10	4
20	SPL	A	Slough Town	349	L	0 - 3		11	5
29	SPL	A	Cambridge City	429	W	2 - 1	Sinclair 25 Higgs 33 (pen)	10	6
Sept 3	FAC1Q	A	Westfields	190	L	0 - 4			7
10	SPL	H	Chippenham Town	122	L	2 - 3	McGowan 15 O'Malley 34	16	8
13	SPL	A	Dunstable Town	171	L	1 - 4	Kelly 15	18	9
20	SPL	H	Merthyr Tydfil	210	D	0 - 0		17	10
24	SPL	H	Leamington	313	L	0 - 5		20	11
27	SPL	H	Biggleswade Town	259	L	0 - 1		20	12
Oct 1	SPL	A	Kings Langley	61	L	1 - 2	Seymore-Shove 64	20	13
8	SPL	H	Frome Town	275	D	1 - 1	Death 90	20	14
11	SPL	A	Hayes & Yeading United	130	L	0 - 1		20	15
15	SPL	A	Cirencester Town	118	W	2 - 1	Death 38 Seymore-Shove 71	20	16
22	SPL	A	Hitchin Town	413	L	1 - 4	Ogbornna 64	21	17
25	SPL	H	Banbury United	204	D	1 - 1	Dawkin 33	21	18
29	FAT1Q	A	Carlton Town	93	W	4 - 1	Seymour-Shove 8 89 Harradine 18 Dawkin 48		19
Nov 5	SPL	H	Kettering Town	495	L	0 - 7		22	20
12	FAT2Q	H	Leek Town	160	W	2 - 1	O'Malley Seymore -Shove		21
15	SPL	H	Dunstable Town	145	W	3 - 1	Kelly 10 52 Dawkin 41	20	22
19	SPL	H	Cinderford Town	202	W	1 - 0	Kelly 18	18	23
26	FAT3Q	A	Kings Lynn Town	684	L	0 - 1			24
Dec 3	SPL	A	Basingstoke Town	377	W	2 - 0	Ogbonna 3 Kelly 35	16	25
10	SPL	H	Redditch United	224	W	2 - 1	Dawkin 5 Kelly 57	15	26
13	SPL	A	Dorchester Town	168	D	1 - 1	Dawkin 85	15	27
17	SPL	A	Weymouth	457	D	1 - 1	Dawkin 55	16	28
20	SPL	A	St Neo0ts Town	357	W	4 - 0	McDevitt 19 Kelly 29 Seymour-Shove 41 Dawkin 51	14	29
26	SPL	H	Cambridge City	539	D	0 - 0		13	30
2 Jan	SPL	A	KIngs Lynn Town	821	L	1 - 2	Ogbonna 22	13	31
7	SPL	H	Slough Town	308	W	2 - 0	Ogbonna 16 Higgs 82 (pen)	13	32
14	SPL	A	Leamington	525	L	0 - 2		13	33
21	SPL	H	Kings Langley	291	W	2 - 1	Seymour-Shove 1 Dawkin 78	12	34
24	SPL	A	Stratford Town	136	W	3 - 2	Bradshaw 7 89 Seymour-Shove 90	12	35
28	SPL	A	Biggleswade Town	228	L	1 - 3	Ogbonna 40	12	36
Feb 4	SPL	H	Hayes & Yeading United	220	D	1 - 1	Higgs 76 (pen)	12	37
11	SPL	A	Frome Town	235	D	2 - 2	Death 70 Dawkin 90	11	38
18	SPL	H	Cirencester Town	217	D	1 - 1	Higgs 26	13	39
21	SPL	H	Chesham United	152	L	0 - 2			40
25	SPL	A	Banbury Town	334	L	0 - 1		14	41
Mar 11	SPL	A	Kettering Town	483	D	1 - 1	Seymour-Shove 54	15	42
18	SPL	H	Dorchester Town	203	W	1 - 0	Seymore-Shove 8	14	43
21	SPL	H	Hitchin Town	274	L	1 - 2	Zielonka	14	44
25	SPL	H	Basingstoke Town	248	L	0 - 1		15	45
April 1	SPL	A	Redditch United	234	W	2 - 0	Seymore-Shove 67 Dawkin 80	14	46
8	SPL	H	Weymouth	224	L	1 - 2	Seymore-Shove 12	14	47
15	SPL	A	Merthyr Town	608	L	0 - 2		15	48
17	SPL	H	Kings Lynn Town	265	W	2 - 0	McDevitt 67 Kelly 80	14	49
22	SPL	A	Chippenham Town	711	L	0 - 2		15	50

GOALSCORERS	SG	CSG	Pens	Hat tricks	Total		SG	CSG	Pens	Hat tricks	Total
Seymore-Shove	13	2			13	McGowan	1				1
Dawkin	11	4			11	Opponents	1				1
Kelly	6	2			8	Sinclair	1				1
Higgs	5		3		5	Zielonka	1				1
Ogbonna	5				5						
Death	3				3						
Bradshaw	1				2						
McDevitt	2				2						
O'Malley	2				2						
Harradine	1				1						

ST. NEOTS TOWN

Club Contact Details
Rowley Park, Kester Way, Cambridge Road, St Neots, PE19 6SN
01480 470 012
garygwilson@sky.com

Ground Capacity: 3,000 **Seats:** 250 **Covered:** 850 **Clubhouse:** Yes **Shop:** No

Record Attendance
2,000 v Wisbech 1966
Previous Grounds
Town Common 1879-1899. Shortsands 1899-1988. Priory Park 1990-93. Old Rowley Park 1993-2008.

10 YEAR RECORD

07-08		08-09		09-10		10-11		11-12		12-13		13-14		14-15		15-16		16-17	
UCL P	8	UCL P	17	UCL P	2	UCL P	1	SthC	1	SthP	12	SthP	16	SthP	5	SthP	20	SthP	19
FAC	EP	FAC	P	FAC	P	FAC	1Q	FAC	P	FAC	2Q	FAC	2Qr	FAC	1Qr	FAC	2Qr	FAC	1Qr
FAV	2Q	FAV	3P	FAV	2Q	FAV	5P	FAT	2Q	FAT	1Q	FAT	2Q	FAT	3Qr	FAT	2Q	FAT	2Qr

Club Factfile

Founded: 1879 **Nickname:** Saints **Manager:** Matt Clements

Previous Names: St Neots 1879-1924. St. Neots & District 1924-1957.

Previous Leagues: Biggleswade & Dist. Bedfordshire & Dist/South Midlands 1927-36, 46-49. United Co. 1936-39, 51-56, 66-69, 73-88, 94-2011. Metropolitan (Founder Members) 1949-51, 60-66. Central Alliance 1956-60. Eastern Co. 1969-73. Hunts Junior 1990-94.

Club Colours (change): All dark blue

RECORDS

Misc: 105 points obtained in the 2010-11 season - a United Counties record.

In 1968-69 the club won the Huntingdonshire Senior Cup for the 12th consecutive time - an English record for Senior cups.

HONOURS

FA Comps: None

League: South Midlands 1932-33. Metropolitan 1949-50. United Counties 1967-68, 2010-11, Division One 1994-95. Huntingdonshire 1990-91, 91-92, 92-93, 93-94. Southern Division One Central 2011-12.

County FA: Huntingdonshire Senior Cup x37 - Firstly in 1888-89 and most recently in 2013-14. Huntingdonshire Premier Cup 2001-02.

BEST PERFORMANCES	**FA Cup:** First Round Proper 1966-67.
	FA Trophy: Third Qualifying Round 2014-15(r).
	FA Vase: Fifth Round Proper 2010-11.

ST. NEOTS TOWN MATCH RESULTS 2016-17

Date	Comp	H/A	Opponents	Att:	Result	Goalscorers	Pos	No.
Aug 6	SPL	A	Slough Town	345	L 0 - 2		24	1
9	SPL	H	Kings Lynn Town	327	W 5 - 2	HALL 3 (22 pen 36 63 pen) Rogers 43 Ogbonna 75	9	2
13	SPL	H	Frome Town	251	W 3 - 2	Rogers 1 90 Clark 62	8	3
16	SPL	A	St Ives Town	528	L 1 - 2	Clark 28	11	4
20	SPL	A	Weymouth	512	W 2 - 0	Matthews 29 (og) Patrick 69	8	5
27	SPL	H	Chippenham Town	222	D 3 - 3	Hall 37 Rogers 46 Parr 90	6	6
29	SPL	A	Biggleswade Town	345	L 0 - 2		9	7
Sept 3	FAC1Q	H	Stamford	351	D 1 - 1	Rogers 53		8
6	FAC1Qr	A	Stamford	273	L 1 - 4	Clark 49		9
10	SPL	H	Cambridge City	343	L 0 - 3		15	10
13	SPL	H	Kettering Town	339	L 1 - 5	Hawkins 53	17	11
24	SPL	A	Dorchester Town	318	L 0 - 1		21	12
26	SPL	A	Hitchin Town	306	L 1 - 4	Ward 17	21	13
Oct 8	SPL	A	Basingstoke Town	396	L 0 - 1			14
15	SPL	H	Cinderford Town	334	W 3 - 1	Mulready 22 34 Clark 90	21	15
18	SPL	A	Kettering Town	374	D 2 - 2	Hall 22 Mulready 44	22	16
22	SPL	H	Leamington	325	L 0 - 1		22	17
25	SPL	A	Kings Langley	88	W 3 - 2	Hall 11 70 Mulready 76	20	18
29	FAT1Q	A	Bedworth United	122	W 3 - 2	Hall 14 45 (pen) Parr 83		19
Nov 1	SPL	H	Banbury United	196	L 1 - 4	McGeorge 12	21	20
5	SPL	A	Redditch United	285	W 4 - 1	Hall 39 57 Rogers 51 72	17	21
12	FAT2Q	A	Marine	288	D 1 - 1	Wood 89		22
15	FAT2Qr	H	Marine	178	L 2 - 4	Rogers 14 Mulready 51		23
19	SPL	A	Frome Town	181	D 1 - 1	Rogers 53	19	24
Dec 3	SPL	H	Hayes & Yeading United	265	L 1 - 5	Hall 72 (pen)	21	25
6	SPL	H	Cirencester Town	97	D 1 - 1	Hall 10	21	26
10	SPL	A	Stratford Town	144	L 2 - 5	Rogers 74 L'Gout 90	21	27
17	SPL	A	Merthyr Town	484	L 0 - 3		21	28
20	SPL	H	St Ives Town	357	L 0 - 4		21	29
26	SPL	H	Biggleswade Town	323	L 0 - 5		21	30
Jan 2	SPL	A	Dunstable Town	133	L 0 - 1		21	31
7	SPL	H	Weymouth	296	L 0 - 4		21	32
14	SPL	H	Dorchester Town	198	W 3 - 2	Hall 33 (pen) 62 Brown 90	20	33
21	SPL	A	Banbury United	427	L 1 - 2	Brown 21	20	34
28	SPL	H	Hitchin Town	347	L 1 - 2	Brown 27	20	35
Feb 4	SPL	A	Chesham United	331	L 2 - 3	Fortnam-Tomlinson 17 Herd 90	22	36
11	SPL	H	Basingstoke Town	200	W 2 - 1	Hall 30 Fortnam-Tomlinson 40	20	37
14	SPL	H	Chesham United	148	W 4 - 1	BROWN 3 (27 (pen) 32 71) Tricks 85	20	38
18	SPL	A	Cinderford Town	176	L 2 - 5	Brown 33 87	20	39
25	SPL	H	Kings Langley	235	W 5 - 2	BROWN 3 (9 18 (pen) 90) Bell-Toxtle 38 Connolly 90 (og)	20	40
Mar 4	SPL	A	Leamington	582	L 0 - 2		20	41
11	SPL	H	Redditch United	228	W 1 - 0	Brown 82	19	42
14	SPL	H	Slough Town	210	D 1 - 1	Brown 88 (pen)	19	43
18	SPL	A	Cirencester Town	91	L 1 - 2	Brown 23	19	44
21	SPL	A	Kings Lynn Town	429	W 2 - 1	Brown 7 74	19	45
25	SPL	A	Hayes & Yeading United	177	L 0 - 2		19	46
April 1	SPL	H	Stratford Town	253	D 1 - 1	Wilson 17	19	47
8	SPL	H	Merthyr Town	187	L 2 - 3	Rogers 15 Clarke 34	19	48
15	SPL	A	Chippenham Town	1146	W 2 - 1	Brown 10 43 (pen)	19	49
17	SPL	H	Dunstable Town	307	W 2 - 0	Clarke 35 Brown 85 (pen)	18	50
22	SPL	A	Cambridge City	442	L 0 - 3		19	51

GOALSCORERS	SG	CSG	Pens	Hat tricks	Total		SG	CSG	Pens	Hat tricks	Total
2015-16 *Meechan*					14	Hawkins	1				1
Brown	12	4	5	2	19	Herd	1				1
Hall	10	2	5	1	15	Hill	1				1
Rogers	8	2			11	L'Ghoul	1				1
Mulready	4	2			5	McGeorge	1				1
Clark	4	2			4	Ogbonne	1				1
Clarke	2				2	Patrick	1				1
Fortnam-Tomlinson	2				2	Tricks	1				1
Opponents	2				2	Ward	1				1
Parr	2				2	Wilson	1				1
Bell-Toxtle	1				1	Wood	1				1

STRATFORD TOWN

Club Contact Details
The DCS Stadium, Knights Lane, Tiddington, Stratford Upon Avon CV37 7BZ
01789 261 037
stratfordtownfcsecretary@outlook.com

Ground Capacity: 1,400   **Seats:** Yes   **Covered:** Yes   **Clubhouse:** Yes   **Shop:** Yes

Record Attendance
1,078 v Aston Villa, Birmingham Senior Cup, Oct. 1996.
Previous Grounds
A number of pitches before Alcester Road by the late 1940s where they stayed until 2007.

10 YEAR RECORD

07-08		08-09		09-10		10-11		11-12		12-13		13-14		14-15		15-16		16-17	
MidAl	7	MidAl	6	MidAl	3	MidAl	5	MidAl	8	MidAl	1	Sthsw	10	Sthsw	3	SthP	19	SthP	14
FAC	1Qr	FAC	1Q	FAC	2Qr	FAC	P	FAC	3Q	FAC	EP	FAC	P	FAC	P	FAC	1Q	FAC	1Q
FAV	2P	FAV	5P	FAV	2P	FAV	1P	FAV	1P	FAV	2Q	FAT	Pr	FAT	2Q	FAT	2Q	FAT	1Qr

Club Factfile

Founded: 1941   **Nickname:** The Town   **Manager:** Carl Adams

Previous Names: Straford Rangers 1941-49. Stratford Town Amateurs 1964-70.

Previous Leagues: Local leagues > 1954. Worcestershire/Midland Combination 1954-57, 70-75, 77-94. Birmingham & District/West Midlands (Reg) 1957-70. Hellenic 1975-77. Midland Alliance (Founder Members) 1994-2013.

Club Colours (change): All blue

RECORDS

HONOURS

FA Comps: None

League: Worcestershire/Midland Combination 1956-57, 86-87.
Midland Alliance 2012-13.

County FA: Birmingham Senior Cup 1962-63.

BEST PERFORMANCES
FA Cup: Third Qualifying Round 2004-05, 06-07, 11-12.
FA Trophy: Second Qualifying Round 2014-15, 15-16.
FA Vase: Fifth Round Proper 2008-09.

STRATFORD TOWN MATCH RESULTS 2016-17

Date	Comp	H/A	Opponents	Att:	Result	Goalscorers	Pos	No.
Aug 6	SPL	A	St Ives Town	342	D 1 - 1	Taylor 69	15	1
9	SPL	H	Redditch United	327	L 2 - 4	Cullinane-Liburd 25 Gregory 76	18	2
13	SPL	H	Basingstoke Town	219	D 1 - 1	Clark 15	18	3
16	SPL	A	Slough Town	336	D 0 - 0		19	4
20	SPL	H	Hitchin Town	176	W 3 - 2	Summerfield 13 Sheldon 38 54	13	5
27	SPL	A	Kettering Town	430	W 3 - 0	Gregory 30 Grocutt 69 Sheldon 75	9	6
29	SPL	H	Leamington	523	L 0 - 2		14	7
Sept 3	FAC1Q	A	AFC Mansfield	95	L 1 - 2	Clark		8
10	SPL	A	Dorchester Town	294	D 2 - 2	Ahenkorah 16 Sheldon 29	14	9
17	SPL	H	Frome Town	210	W 3 - 0	Gregory 32 Ahenkorah 62 Mbunga 87	9	10
24	SPL	H	Weymouth	242	L 0 - 5		14	11
Oct 1	SPL	A	Cambridge City	134	D 0 - 0		16	12
8	SPL	H	Dunstable Town	183	W 2 - 0	Tulloch 8 Sheldon 19 (pen)	12	13
11	SPL	A	Cirencester Town	116	W 2 - 1	Sheldon 9 Tulloch 49	12	14
15	SPL	A	Chippenham Town	400	L 1 - 2	Connolly 16	10	15
18	SPL	H	Merthyr Town	191	L 0 - 3		12	16
22	SPL	H	Kings Lynn Town	228	D 1 - 1	Gregory 58	12	17
29	FAT1Q	H	Grantham Town	204	D 2 - 2	Sheldon 82 Francis 90		18
Nov 1	FAT1Qr	A	Grantham Town	142	L 0 - 4			19
12	SPL	A	Cambridge City	201	D 3 - 3	Gregory 6 14 Ahenkorah 63	14	20
19	SPL	A	Basingstoke Town	362	L 1 - 2	Gregory 12	16	21
22	SPL	H	Slough Town	303	L 1 - 2	Gregory 26	17	22
26	SPL	A	Merthyr Town	215	D 1 - 1	Ahenkorah 33	16	23
29	SPL	A	Redditch United	232	D 1 - 1	Ahenkorah 89	16	24
Dec 3	SPL	A	Banbury United	578	L 1 - 2	Stephens 57	18	25
10	SPL	H	St Neots Town	144	W 5 - 2	Francis 5 Taylor 9 AHENKORAH 3 (13 (pen) 44 47)	16	26
17	SPL	H	Hayes & Yeading United	199	D 0 - 0		17	27
20	SPL	H	Kings Langley	136	D 2 - 2	Stephens 2 Marsden 90	17	28
26	SPL	A	Leamington	805	D 1 - 1	Westwood 83	17	29
Jan 2	SPL	H	Cinderford Town	220	W 4 - 2	TAYLOR 3 (27 54 88) Ahenkorah 70	15	30
7	SPL	A	Hitchin Town	455	L 0 - 1		16	31
14	SPL	A	Weymouth	450	D 1 - 1	Ahenkorah 6 (pen)	17	32
17	SPL	A	Chesham United	222	D 1 - 1	Clark 52	17	33
24	SPL	H	St Ives Town	136	L 2 - 3	Marsden 1 Grocutt 84	17	34
28	SPL	A	Frome Town	231	L 1 - 3	Taylor 68	17	35
Feb 4	SPL	H	Cirencester Town	193	L 0 - 1		17	36
14	SPL	A	Biggleswade Town	80	W 2 - 1	Francis 55 Taylor 82	17	37
18	SPL	H	Chippenham Town	236	L 0 - 1		17	38
25	SPL	H	Biggleswade Town	144	W 1 - 0	Spencer 12	17	39
Mar 4	SPL	A	Kings Lynn Town	645	L 0 - 2		17	40
11	SPL	H	Chesham United	196	D 1 - 1	Taylor 48	18	41
14	SPL	A	Dunstable Town	74	L 0 - 2		18	42
18	SPL	A	Kings Langley	166	W 3 - 1	Ahenkorah 17 43 Taylor 90	17	43
25	SPL	H	Banbury United	417	W 2 - 0	Grocutt 6 Taylor 41	16	44
April 1	SPL	A	St Neots Town	253	D 1 - 1	Spencer 80	16	45
8	SPL	A	Hayes & Yeading United	152	W 2 - 1	Ahenkorah 24 Spencer 71	15	46
15	SPL	H	Kettering Town	309	W 4 - 1	Forsyth 3 Thomas 58 Spencer 80 Grocutt 90 (pen)	14	47
17	SPL	A	Cinderford Town	135	L 1 - 2	Forsyth 24	15	48
22	SPL	H	Dorchester Town	279	D 1 - 1	Summerfield 89	14	49

GOALSCORERS	SG	CSG	Pens	Hat tricks	Total		SG	CSG	Pens	Hat tricks	Total
2015-16 *Gregory*					12	Summerfield	2				2
Ahenkorah	9	2	2	1	13	Tulloch	2	2			2
Taylor	10			1	10	Connolly	1				1
Gregory	7	3			8	Culinane-Liburd	1				1
Sheldon	6		1		7	Marsden	1				1
Grocutt	4				4	Mbunga	1				1
Spencer	4				4	Pope	1				1
Clark	3				3	Thomas	1				1
Francis	2				3	Westwood	1				1
Forsyth	2				2						
Stephens	2				2						

TIVERTON TOWN

Club Contact Details
Ladysmead, Bolham Road, Tiverton, Devon EX16 6SG
01884 252 397
ramsayfindlay@hotmail.co.uk

Ground Capacity: 3,500 **Seats:** 520 **Covered:** 2,300 **Clubhouse:** Yes **Shop:** Yes

Record Attendance
3,000 v Leyton Orient - FA Cup 1st Round Proper 12/11/1994.
Previous Grounds
Athletic Ground (Amory Park) 1913-21. Elm Field (The Elms) 1921-46.

10 YEAR RECORD

	07-08		08-09		09-10		10-11		11-12		12-13		13-14		14-15		15-16		16-17	
SthP	17		SthP	12		SthP	19		SthP	20		Sthsw	9		Sthsw	16		Sthsw	3		Sthsw	16		Sthsw	8		Sthsw	3
FAC	1Qr		FAC	2Q		FAC	1Q		FAC	1Qr		FAC	P		FAC	P		FAC	P		FAC	1Qr		FAC	P		FAC	Pr
FAT	1Q		FAT	2Pr		FAT	1Q		FAT	1Q		FAT	3Q		FAT	1Q		FAT	3Qr		FAT	1Q		FAT	2Q		FAT	1Q

Club Factfile

Founded: 1913 **Nickname:** Tivvy **Manager:** Martyn Rogers

Previous Names: Tiverton Athletic.

Previous Leagues: East Devon 1913-28. North Devon 1928-32. Exeter & District 1932-73. Western 1973-99.

Club Colours (change): All yellow (All white)

RECORDS
Victory: 14-1 v University College SW, 11/02/1933.
Defeat: 0-10 v Dawlish Town, 27/12/1969.
Goalscorer: Phil Everett - 378.
Appearances: Tom Gardner - 510.

HONOURS
FA Comps: FA Vase 1997-98, 98-99.

League: East Devon Senior Division 1924-25, 25-26, 26-27, 27-28. North Devon 1931-32.
Exeter & District 1933-34, 64-65, 65-66. Western 1993-94, 94-95, 96-97, 97-98.

County FA: Devon Senior Cup 1955-56, 65-66.
Devon St Luke's Cup 1990-91, 91-92, 92-93, 93-94, 94-95, 96-97, 1999-2000, 02-03, 05-06, 16-17.

BEST PERFORMANCES
FA Cup: First Round Proper 1990-91, 91-92, 94-95, 97-98, 2001-02, 02-03, 04-05.
FA Trophy: Fifth Round Proper 2000-01.
FA Vase: Final 1997-98, 98-99.

Knight (Frome) heads home against Dunstable.

John (Larkhall) beaten by a free kick from Gregory (Barnstaple) during this Southern Division One South & West league match. Photos: Keith Clayton.

WEYMOUTH

Club Contact Details
Bob Lucas Stadium, Radipole Lane, Weymouth DT4 9XJ
01305 785 558
secretary@theterras.co.uk

Ground Capacity: 6,600 **Seats:** 900 **Covered:** Yes **Clubhouse:** Yes **Shop:** Yes

Record Attendance
4,995 v Manchester United - Ground opening 21/10/97
Previous Grounds
Recreation Ground > 1987.

10 YEAR RECORD

	07-08	08-09	09-10	10-11	11-12	12-13	13-14	14-15	15-16	16-17
	Conf 18	Conf 23	Conf S 22	SthP 18	SthP 17	SthP 9	SthP 12	SthP 7	SthP 7	SthP 10
FAC	2P	4Q	2Q	2Q	3Q	2Q	4Q	4Qr	1Q	4Q
FAT	3P	1P	1P	2Q	2P	2Q	2Q	1Pr	3Q	1Pr

Club Factfile

Founded: 1890   **Nickname:** The Terras   **Manager:** Mark Molesley

Previous Names: None

Previous Leagues: Dorset, Western 1907-23, 28-49, Southern 1923-28, 49-79, 89-2005, Alliance/Conference 1979-89, 2005-10.

Club Colours (change): Claret & blue/white/claret

RECORDS
Goalscorer: W 'Farmer' Haynes - 275

Appearances: Tony Hobsons - 1,076

Additional: Paid £15,000 to Northwich Victoria for Shaun Teale
Received £100,000 from Tottenham Hotspur for Peter Guthrie 1988

Defeat: 0-9 v Rushden & Diamonds, Conference South, 21/02/2009 - this was a game which, due to an administration issue, the club had to field their U18 team.

HONOURS

FA Comps: None

League: Dorset 1897-98, 1913-14, Division One 1921-22. Western Division One 1922-23, 36-37, 37-38, Division Two 33-34. Southern 1964-65, 65-66, Southern Division 1997-98. Conference South 2005-06.

County FA: Dorset Senior Cup x12 - Firstly in 1985-86 and most recently in 2016-17.

BEST PERFORMANCES	**FA Cup:** Fourth Round Proper 1961-62.
	FA Trophy: Quarter-finals 1973-74, 76-77(r).
	FA Vase: N/A

WEYMOUTH MATCH RESULTS 2016-17

Date	Comp	H/A	Opponents	Att:	Result	Goalscorers	Pos	No.
Aug 6	SPL	A	Biggleswade Town	202	W 3 - 1	Jordan 66 90 Wannell 82	3	1
9	SPL	H	Chippenham Town	740	L 1 - 4	Shephard 81	14	2
13	SPL	H	Redditch United	509	W 1 - 0	Davis 90 (pen)	11	3
17	SPL	A	Frome Town	412	L 0 - 3		13	4
20	SPL	H	St Neots Town	512	L 0 - 2		14	5
27	SPL	A	Chesham United	288	D 1 - 1	Yetton 44	16	6
29	SPL	H	Dorchester Town	1231	W 2 - 1	Lowes 39 Davis 72	11	7
Sept 3	FAC1Q	H	Paulton Rovers	472	W 2 - 1	Rodrigues 36 Davis 52		8
10	SPL	A	Leamington	455	D 1 - 1	Davis 89 (pen)	11	9
13	SPL	H	Slough Town	516	L 0 - 1		14	10
17	FAC2Q	H	Gosport Borough	527	W 3 - 2	Yetton 33 Thomson 62 Davis 81		11
24	SPL	A	Stratford Town	242	W 5 - 0	Shephard 17 20 Smith 59 Jordan 80 85	11	12
27	SPL	A	Cinderford Town	130	D 2 - 2	Thomson 21 Zubar 76	13	13
Oct 1	FAC3Q	H	Brimscombe & Thrupp	643	W 6 - 0	Shephard 3 YETTON 3 (37 78 84) Evans 45 Jordan 90		14
8	SPL	A	Hitchin Town	384	D 1 - 1	Yetton 54	15	15
11	SPL	H	Basingstoke Town	464	W 3 - 0	Thomson 8 Yetton 25 Lowes 47	11	16
15	FAC4Q	A	Kidderminster Harriers	1382	L 0 - 6			17
22	SPL	A	Kettering Town	542	L 1 - 3	Tarbuck 13	15	18
29	FAT1Q	H	Wantage Town	402	W 4 0	Jeavon 9 60 Yetton 38 Evans 48		19
Nov 5	SPL	H	Merthyr Town	537	L 0 - 1		18	20
12	FAT2Q	A	Dunstable Town	106	W 4 - 1	Yetton 15 84 Thomson 25 90		21
19	SPL	A	Redditch United	236	L 1 - 2	Yetton 10	20	22
22	SPL	H	Frome Town	267	W 2 - 1	Davis 35 Thomson 54	16	23
26	FAT3Q	A	Poole Town	755	D 1 - 1	Evans 33		24
29	FAT3Qr	H	Poole Town	441	W 2 - 0	Shephard 22 Fleetwood 63		25
Dec 3	SPL	A	Kings Langley	128	D 1 - 1	Shephard 50 (pen)	19	26
6	SPL	A	Kings Lynn Town	403	D 0 - 0		19	27
10	FAT1	A	Whitehawk	253	D 2 - 2	Davis 81 Shephard 87 (pen)		28
13	FAT1r	H	Whitehawk	401	L 1 - 2	Davis 23 (pen)		29
17	SPL	H	St Ives Town	457	D 1 - 1	Fleetwood 54	18	30
26	SPL	A	Dorchester Town	2033	D 1 - 1	Shephard 60	18	31
29	SPL	H	Biggleswade Town	573	D 2 - 2	Thomson 17 Brooks 90	18	32
Jan 2	SPL	H	Cirencester Town	540	W 4 - 0	Copp 24 26 Yetton 82 Fleetwood 90	18	33
7	SPL	A	St Neots Town	296	W 4 - 0	Copp 17 Jeavon 47 Evans 79 Fleetwood 90	15	34
10	SPL	A	Chippenham Town	382	L 0 - 2		15	35
14	SPL	H	Stratford Town	480	D 1 - 1	Wannell 17	16	36
17	SPL	H	Banbury United	325	D 2 - 2	Fleetwood 45 Rodrigues 84	14	37
21	SPL	A	Kings Lynn Town	566	W 6 - 1	Fleetwood 5 Evans 35 Davis 45 Molesley 75 Shephard 78 Yetton 80	14	38
28	SPL	H	Cinderford Town	501	W 3 - 0	Fleetwood 29 57 Shephard 41	14	39
30	SPL	A	Cambridge City	210	L 1 - 2	Fleetwood 6	14	40
Feb 4	SPL	A	Basingstoke Town	428	W 6 - 1	FLEETWOOD 3 (26 64 81) Davis 29 39 Evans 61	11	41
7	SPL	A	Slough Town	612	L 0 - 3		11	42
11	SPL	H	Hitchin Town	400	L 0 - 2		12	43
14	SPL	H	Dunstable Town	328	D 3 - 3	Molesey 40 Talbot 82 (og) Wells 90	12	44
18--35	SPL	A	Banbury United	411	D 1 - 1	Davis 3 (pen)	12	45
25	SPL	A	Hayes & Yeading United	451	D 2 - 2	Cooper 61 Fleetwood 73	11	46
Mar 4	SPL	H	Kettering Town	457	W 3 - 2	Fleetwood 14 Copp 57 (pen) Zubar 87	11	47
11	SPL	H	Merthyr Town	611	D 2 - 2	Fleetwood 72 Evans 80	12	48
14	SPL	A	Hayes & Yeading United	151	D 0 - 0		11	49
18	SPL	H	Cambridge City	459	W 2 - 0	Rodriguez 23 Brooks 58	11	50
25	SPL	H	Kings Langley	496	D 1 - 1	Cooper 12	11	51
April 1	SPL	A	Dunstable Town	174	D 1 - 1	Davis 42	11	52
8	SPL	A	St Ives Town	224	W 2 - 1	Zubar 78 88	11	53
14	SPL	H	Chesham United	561	W 2 - 0	Thomson 63 Rodriguez 83	10	54
17	SPL	A	Cirencester Town	213	L 0 - 3		11	55
22	SPL	H	Leamington	585	W 4 - 0	FLEETWOOD 3 (37 44 55) Thomson 55	10	56

GOALSCORERS	SG	CSG	Pens	Hat tricks	Total		SG	CSG	Pens	Hat tricks	Total
2015-16 *Yetton*					12	Jeavon	2				3
Fleetwood	11	5		2	18	Brooks	2				2
Davis	12	3	4		13	Cooper	2				2
Yetton	11	3		1	13	Lowes	2				2
Shephard	9	3	2		10	Molesley	2				2
Thomson	9				9	Wannell	2				2
Evans	7				7	Opponents	1				1
Jordan	4				5	Smith	1				1
Copp	4		1		4	Tarbuck	1				1
Rodrigues	4				4	Wells	1				1
Zubar	3				4						

AFC DUNSTABLE

Club Contact Details
Creasey Park, Creasey Park Drive, Brewers Hill Road LU6 1BB
01582 891 433
afcdunstable2016@gmail.com

Founded: 1981   **Nickname:** Od's   **Manager:** Steve Heath
Previous Names: Old Dunstablians 1981- 2004.
Previous Leagues: Dunstable Alliance 1981-83. Luton District & South Bedfordshire 1983-95. South Midlands/Spartan South Midlands 1995-2016.

Club Colours (change): All royal blue

Ground Capacity: 3,200   **Seats:** 350   **Covered:** 1,000   **Clubhouse:** Yes   **Shop:** Yes
Previous Grounds: Manshead School 1981-94. Dunstable Cricket Club (Totternhoe) 1994-2009.
Record Attendance: Not known.

RECORDS

HONOURS
FA Comps: None
League: Spartan South Midlands Division Two 2003-04, 06-07, Premier Division 2015-16.

County FA: Bedfordshire Junior Cup 1989-90. Bedfordshire Senior Trophy 2006-07, 07-08. Bedfordshire Senior Cup 2016-17.

07-08	08-09	09-10	10-11	11-12	12-13	13-14	14-15	15-16	16-17
SSM2 4	SSM2 3	SSM1 5	SSM1 2	SSM P 3	SSM P 8	SSM P 9	SSM P 3	SSM P 1	SthC 7
					FAC P	FAC 2Qr	FAC EP	FAC P	FAC 1Q	FAC 2Q
			FAV 2P	FAV 2Q	FAV 1P	FAV 1Qr	FAV 3P	FAV 4P	FAT P

AFC RUSHDEN & DIAMONDS

Club Contact Details
Kempston Rovers FC, Hillgrounds Leisure, Hill Grounds Road, Kempston MK42 8SZ
01234 852 346
secretary@afcdiamonds.com

Founded: 2011   **Nickname:** The Diamonds   **Manager:** Andy Peaks
Previous Names: None
Previous Leagues: United Counties 2012-15. Southern 2015-16. Northern Premier 2016-17.

Club Colours (change): White/royal blue/white (Yellow/black/yellow and grey/luminous yellow/grey)

Ground Capacity: 2,000   **Seats:** 100   **Covered:** 250   **Clubhouse:** Yes   **Shop:** No
Previous Grounds: The Dog & Duck Wellingborough Town FC 2011-17.
Record Attendance: 1,162 v Barwell, 27/10/2015.

RECORDS
Victory: 9-0 v Buckingham Town (A) 15/12/12 and v Desborough Town (A) 21/02/15
Goalscorer: Tom Lorraine - 54 in 150 appearances, 2014- present.
Appearances: Brad Harris - 213, 2013 - present
Additional: 28 matches unbeaten, 13/01/2015 - 31/10/2015.

HONOURS
FA Comps: None
League: United Counties Premier Division 2014-15.

County FA: Northamptonshire Senior Cup 2015-16.

07-08	08-09	09-10	10-11	11-12	12-13	13-14	14-15	15-16	16-17
					UCL 1 2	UCL P 3	UCL P 1	SthC 5	NP1S 5
						FAC 3Q	FAC 1Q	FAC 4Qr	FAC 3Q
					FAV 3P	FAV 4P	FAV 2P	FAT P	FAT 2Q

ARLESEY TOWN

Club Contact Details
New Lamb Meadow, Hitchin Road, Arlesey SG15 6RS
01462 734 504
chris.sterry@ntlworld.com

Founded: 1891   **Nickname:** The Blues   **Manager:** Zema & Nathan Abbey - 11/02/15
Previous Names: None
Previous Leagues: Biggleswade & Dist., Bedfordshire Co. (South Midlands) 1922-26, 27-28, Parthenon, London 1958-60, United Co. 1933-36, 82-92, Spartan South Mid. 1992-2000, Isthmian 2000-04, 06-08, Southern 2004-07

Club Colours (change): Light & dark blue

Ground Capacity: 2,920   **Seats:** 150   **Covered:** 600   **Clubhouse:** Yes   **Shop:** Yes
Previous Grounds: The Bury. Lamb Meadow.
Record Attendance: 2,000 v Luton Town Reserves - Bedfordshire Senior Cup 1906

RECORDS
Appearances: Gary Marshall

HONOURS
FA Comps: FA Vase 1994-95.
League: South Midlands Premier Division 1951-52, 52-53, 94-95, 95-96. Spartan South Midlands Premier Division 1999-2000. United Counties Premier Division 1984-85. Isthmian Division Three 2000-01. Southern Division One Central 2010-11.
County FA: Bedfordshire Intermediate Cup 1957-58. Bedfordshire Senior Cup 1965-66, 78-79, 96-97, 2010-11. Bedfordshire Premier Cup 1983-84, 2001-02.

07-08		08-09		09-10		10-11		11-12		12-13		13-14		14-15		15-16		16-17	
Isth1N	15	SthC	18	SthC	9	SthC	1	SthP	18	SthP	6	SthP	15	SthP	22	SthC	16	SthC	15
FAC	P	FAC	2Q	FAC	1Q	FAC	1Q	FAC	1P	FAC	1P	FAC	3Q	FAC	1Q	FAC	1Q	FAC	Pr
FAT	1Q	FAT	P	FAT	1Pr	FAT	2Qr	FAT	2Q	FAT	2Qr	FAT	1P	FAT	2Qr	FAT	Pr	FAT	Pr

ASHFORD TOWN (MIDDLESEX)

Club Contact Details
Robert Parker Stadium, Stanwell, Staines TW19 7BH
01784 245 908
yellowdot1@gmail.com

Founded: 1958   **Nickname:** Ash Trees   **Manager:** Ben Murray
Previous Names: Ashford Albion 1958-64.
Previous Leagues: Hounslow & District 1964-68, Surrey Intermediate 1968-82, Surrey Premier 1982-90, Combind Counties 1990-2000, 14-16, Isthmian 20 00-04, 06-10, Southern 2004-06, 10-14.

Club Colours (change): Tangerine and white stripes/black/tangerine

Ground Capacity: 2,550   **Seats:** 250   **Covered:** 250   **Clubhouse:** Yes   **Shop:** No
Previous Grounds: Clockhouse Lane Recreation 1958-85.
Record Attendance: 992 v AFC Wimbledon - Isthmian League Premier Division 26/09/2006

RECORDS
Goalscorer: Andy Smith
Appearances: Alan Constable - 650
Additional: Received £10,000 from Wycombe Wanderers for Dannie Bulman 1997

HONOURS
FA Comps: None
League: Surrey Intermediate (Western) Prmeier Division A 1974-75. Surrey Premier 1982-90. Combined Counties 1994-95, 95-96, 96-97, 97-98, 99-00.
County FA: Middlesex Senior Charity Cup 1999-00, 11-12, 16-17. Middlesex Premier Cup 2006-07. Surrey Senior Cup 2008-09.

07-08		08-09		09-10		10-11		11-12		12-13		13-14		14-15		15-16		16-17	
Isth P	6	Isth P	10	Isth P	20	SthC	16	SthC	9	SthC	10	SthC	22	CCP	3	CCP	2	SthC	10
FAC	1Q	FAC	4Qr	FAC	3Qr	FAC	1Qr	FAC	P	FAC	2Q	FAC	1Q	FAC	Pr	FAC	1Q	FAC	1Q
FAT	1Q	FAT	1Qr	FAT	1Q	FAT	2P	FAT	2Q	FAT	1Qr	FAT	P	FAV	1P	FAV	1Pr	FAT	1Qr

AYLESBURY

Club Contact Details
SRD Stadium, Haywood Way, Aylesbury, Bucks. HP19 9WZ
01296 431 655
apriljbenson@googlemail.com

Founded: 1930   **Nickname:** The Moles   **Manager:** Davis Haule
Previous Names: Negretti & Zambra FC 1930-54, Stocklake 1954-2000, Haywood United > 2000, Haywood FC 2000-06, Aylesbury Vale 2006-09.
Previous Leagues: Aylesbury District. Wycombe & District. Chiltern, Spartan South Midlands

Club Colours (change): Red & black (Blue & yellow)

Ground Capacity: **Seats:** Yes   **Covered:** Yes   **Clubhouse:** Yes   **Shop:** No
Previous Grounds: Negretti & Zambra King's Cross 1930-49. Stocklake Industrial Estate 1949-87.
Record Attendance: Not known - if you know please email tw.publications@btinternet.com

RECORDS

HONOURS
FA Comps: None
League: Spartan South Midlands Division One 2003-04, Premier Division 2009-10.
County FA: Buckingham Charity Cup 2005-06. Berks & Bucks Senior Cup 2015-16.

07-08	08-09	09-10	10-11	11-12	12-13	13-14	14-15	15-16	16-17
SSM P 9	SSM P 15	SSM P 1	SthC 8	SthC 20	SthC 12	SthC 16	SthC 3	SthC 8	SthC 19
		FAC 4Q	FAC Pr	FAC P	FAC P	FAC 1Q	FAC 1Q	FAC 1Qr	FAC P
		FAV 1Q	FAT 1Qr	FAT 1Qr	FAT P	FAT 1Q	FAT 1Q	FAT 1Qr	FAT P

AYLESBURY UNITED

Club Contact Details
Chesham United FC, The Meadow, Amy Lane, Chesham HP5 1NE
01296 487 367 (Office)
stevepb42@hotmail.com

Founded: 1897   **Nickname:** The Ducks   **Manager:** Glyn Creaser
Previous Names: None
Previous Leagues: Post War: Spartan >1951, Delphian 51-63, Athenian 63-76, Southern 76-88, 2004-10, Conf. 88-89, Isthmian 89-2004. Spartan South Midlands 2010-13.

Club Colours (change): Green & white

Ground Capacity: 2,800   **Seats:** 155   **Covered:** 300   **Clubhouse:** Yes   **Shop:** No
Previous Grounds: Turnfurlong Lane. Buckingham Road >2006. Meadow View Park (Thame Utd) 2006-17.
Record Attendance: Turnfurlong Lane - 7,440 v Watford FAC 1st Rnd 1951-52. Buckingham Road - 6,031 v England 04/06/1988.

RECORDS
Victory: 10-0 v Hornchurch & Upminster (H), Delphain League 17/04/1954
Defeat: 0-9 v Bishop's Stortford (A), Delphain League 08/10/1955
Goalscorer: Cliff Hercules - 301 (1984-2002)
Appearances: Cliff Hercules - 651+18 (1984-2002)

HONOURS
FA Comps: None
League: Spartan Western Division 1908-09, 28-29. Delphian 1953-54. Southern 1987-88.
County FA: Berks & Bucks Senior Cup 1913-14, 85-86, 96-97, 99-00. Berks & Bucks Senior Shield 2012-13.

07-08	08-09	09-10	10-11	11-12	12-13	13-14	14-15	15-16	16-17
SthM 8	SthM 10	SthM 22	SSM P 6	SSM P 4	SSM P 2	SthC 12	SthC 13	SthC 19	SthC 13
FAC 2Qr	FAC 4Q	FAC 1Qr	FAC 1Q	FAC Pr	FAC P	FAC 2Q	FAC P	FAC P	FAC P
FAT 1Qr	FAT 1Q	FAT P	FAV 2P	FAV 2Q	FAV 1P	FAT 1Q	FAV P	FAT P	FAT 1Q

BARTON ROVERS

Club Contact Details
Luton Road, Barton-le-Clay, Bedford MK45 4SD

01582 707 772

bartonrovers@talktalk.net

Founded: 1898   **Nickname:** Rovers   **Manager:** James Gray - June 2016

Previous Names: None

Previous Leagues: Local village football leagues >1939. Luton & District 1947-54, South Midlands 1954-79, Isthmian 1979-2004

Club Colours (change): All royal blue

Ground Capacity: 4,000   **Seats:** 160   **Covered:** 1,120   **Clubhouse:** Yes   **Shop:** Yes

Previous Grounds: None

Record Attendance: 1,900 v Nuneaton Borough - FA Cup 4th Qualifying Round 1976

RECORDS
Goalscorer: Richard Camp - 152 (1989-98)

Appearances: Tony McNally - 598 (1988-2005)

Additional: Paid £1,000 to Hitchin Town for Bill Baldry 1980

                    Received £2,000 from AFC Wimbledon for Paul Barnes

HONOURS
FA Comps: None

League: South Midlands Division Two 1954-55, Division One 64-65, Premier 70-71, 71-72, 72-73, 74-75, 75-76, 76-77, 77-78, 78-79.

County FA: Bedfordshire Senior Cup 1971-72, 72-73, 80-81, 81-82, 89-90, 97-98, 98-99, 2014-15, Premier Cup 1995-96, Senior Challenge Cup 2015-16.

07-08		08-09		09-10		10-11		11-12		12-13		13-14		14-15		15-16		16-17	
SthM	11	SthM	17	SthM	21	SthC	12	SthC	11	SthC	14	SthC	6	SthC	5	SthC	18	SthC	3
FAC	1Qr	FAC	1Qr	FAC	P	FAC	P	FAC	1Qr	FAC	1Q	FAC	2Qr	FAC	3Q	FAC	1Q	FAC	2Q
FAT	1Q	FAT	P	FAT	2Qr	FAT	1Q	FAT	1Q	FAT	1Q	FAT	P	FAT	P	FAT	Pr	FAT	P

BEACONSFIELD SYCOB

Club Contact Details
Holloways Park, Windsor Road, Beaconsfield, Bucks HP9 2SE

01494 676 868

robin.woolman@btinternet.com

Founded: 1994   **Nickname:** The Rams   **Manager:** Gary Meakin - June 2017

Previous Names: Slough YCOB and Beaconsfield United merged in 1994

Previous Leagues: Spartan South Midlands 1004-2004, 07-08, Southern 2004-07

Club Colours (change): Red, white & blue

Ground Capacity: 3,500   **Seats:** Yes   **Covered:** Yes   **Clubhouse:** Yes   **Shop:** No

Previous Grounds: None

Record Attendance: Not known

RECORDS
Goalscorer: Allan Arthur

Appearances: Allan Arthur

HONOURS
FA Comps: None

League: Spartan South Midlands 2000-01, 03-04, 07-08.

County FA: Berks and Bucks Senior Trophy 2003-04, Senior Cup 2012-13.

07-08		08-09		09-10		10-11		11-12		12-13		13-14		14-15		15-16		16-17	
SSM P	1	Sthsw	4	SthM	19	SthC	22	SthC	5	SthC	5	SthC	8	SthC	20	SthC	9	SthC	16
FAC	1Qr	FAC	1Q	FAC	P	FAC	P	FAC	2Qr	FAC	P	FAC	1Q	FAC	2Q	FAC	1Q	FAC	4Q
FAV	1P	FAT	P	FAT	1Q	FAT	1Q	FAT	P	FAT	Pr	FAT	P	FAT	P	FAT	P	FAT	1Q

BEDFORD TOWN

Club Contact Details
The Eyrie, Meadow Lane, Cardington, Bedford MK44 3LW
01234 831 558
james.smiles@bedfordeagles.net

Founded: 1989   **Nickname:** The Eagles   **Manager:** Jon Taylor
Previous Names: Original Bedford Town founded in 1908 folded in 1982
Previous Leagues: South Midlands 1989-94, Isthmian 1994-2004, Southern 2004-06, Conference 2006-07

Club Colours (change): All blue (All yellow)

Ground Capacity: 3,000   **Seats:** 300   **Covered:** 1,000   **Clubhouse:** Yes   **Shop:** Yes
Previous Grounds: Allen Park, Queens Park, Bedford Park Pitch 1991-93
Record Attendance: 3,000 v Peterborough United - Ground opening 06/08/1993

RECORDS
Defeat: 0-5 v Hendon
Goalscorer: Jason Reed
Appearances: Eddie Lawley

HONOURS
FA Comps: None
League: South Midlands Division One 1992-93, Premier Division 93-94. Isthmian Division Two 1998-99.

County FA: Bedfordshire Senior Cup 1994-95.

07-08		08-09		09-10		10-11		11-12		12-13		13-14		14-15		15-16		16-17	
SthP	19	SthP	15	SthP	18	SthP	17	SthP	10	SthP	10	SthP	22	SthC	17	SthC	14	SthC	8
FAC	2Qr	FAC	2Qr	FAC	3Qr	FAC	2Q	FAC	1Q	FAC	1Q	FAC	2Q	FAC	Pr	FAC	1Q	FAC	P
FAT	1Q	FAT	1Q	FAT	1Q	FAT	1Q	FAT	1Q	FAT	2Q	FAT	1Qr	FAT	3Qr	FAT	2Q	FAT	P

CAMBRIDGE CITY

Club Contact Details
St Ives Town FC, Westwood Road, St Ives, Cambridgeshire PE27 6DT
01223 233 226
andy.dewey@btinternet.com

Founded: 1908   **Nickname:** Lilywhites   **Manager:** Robbie Nightingale
Previous Names: Cambridge Town 1908-51
Previous Leagues: Bury & District 1908-13, 19-20, Anglian 1908-10, Southern Olympian 1911-14,
                Southern Amateur 1913-35, Spartan 1935-50, Athenian 1950-58, Southern 1958-2004

Club Colours (change): White/black/black & white (Light blue/light blue/light blue & dark blue)

Ground Capacity: 2,722   **Seats:** 526   **Covered:** 220   **Clubhouse:** Yes   **Shop:** Yes
Previous Grounds: City Ground.
Record Attendance: 12,058 v Leytonstone - FA Amateur Cup 1st Round 1949-50

RECORDS
Goalscorer: Gary Grogan
Appearances: Mal Keenan
Additional: Paid £8,000 to Rushden & Diamonds for Paul Coe
            Received £100,000 from Millwall for Neil Harris 1998

HONOURS
FA Comps: None
League: Southern 1962-63, Southern Division 1985-86.

County FA: Suffolk Senior Cup 1909-10. East Anglian x9. Cambridgeshire Professional Cup 2012-13, 14-15, Invitational Cup 2014-15.

07-08		08-09		09-10		10-11		11-12		12-13		13-14		14-15		15-16		16-17	
Conf S	14	SthP	4	SthP	6	SthP	4	SthP	5	SthP	8	SthP	3	SthP	13	SthP	18	SthP	21
FAC	2Qr	FAC	2Qr	FAC	3Q	FAC	3Q	FAC	1Qr	FAC	1Pr	FAC	2Q	FAC	1Q	FAC	1Q	FAC	2Q
FAT	2P	FAT	1P	FAT	2Q	FAT	3Q	FAT	2Q	FAT	1Q	FAT	2Qr	FAT	1Q	FAT	1Q	FAT	1Q

CHALFONT ST PETER

Club Contact Details
Mill Meadow, Gravel Hill, Amersham Road, Chalfont St Peter SL9 9QX
01753 885 797
colinfinch.cspfc1962@gmail.com

Founded: 1926   **Nickname:** Saints   **Manager:** Danny Edwards
Previous Names: None
Previous Leagues: G W Comb. Parthernon. London. Spartan. L Spartan. Athenian. Isthmian, Spartan South Midlands 2006-11.

Club Colours (change): Red/green/red. (All royal blue).

Ground Capacity: 4,500   **Seats:** 220   **Covered:** 120   **Clubhouse:** Yes   **Shop:** Yes
Previous Grounds: Gold Hill Common 1926-49.
Record Attendance: 2,550 v Watford benefit match 1985

RECORDS
Victory: 10-1 v Kentish Town (away) Spartan League Premier Division 23 Dec 2008
Defeat: 0-13 v Lewes (away) Isthmian Division 3, 7 Nov 2000
Appearances: Colin Davies

HONOURS
FA Comps: None
League: Spartan Division Two 1975-76. Isthmian Division Two 1987-88. Spartan South Midlands Premier Division 2010-11.
County FA: Berks & Bucks Intermediate Cup 1952-53, 84-85.

07-08	08-09	09-10	10-11	11-12	12-13	13-14	14-15	15-16	16-17
SSM P 2	SSM P 3	SSM P 2	SSM P 1	SthC 12	SthC 16	SthC 14	SthC 16	SthC 6	SthC 18
FAC 2Q	FAC 2Q	FAC P	FAC P	FAC 1Q	FAC 3Qr	FAC 2Q	FAC 3Q	FAC P	FAC 1Q
FAV 2P	FAV SF	FAV 2P	FAV 2Pr	FAT 1Q	FAT 1Q	FAT Pr	FAT 1Q	FAT 1Q	FAV 2Qr

---

EGHAM TOWN

Club Contact Details
Runnymead Stadium, Tempest Road, Egham TW20 8XD
01784 435 226
danielbennett1974@yahoo.co.uk

Founded: 1877   **Nickname:** Sarnies   **Manager:** Chris Moore - June 2017
Previous Names: Runnymead Rovers 1877-1905. Egham F.C. 05-63.
Previous Leagues: West Surrey. Surrey Senior. Spartan. Athenian. Isthmian. Southern. Combined Counties 2006-13.

Club Colours (change): Red & white

Ground Capacity: 5500   **Seats:** 262   **Covered:** 3300   **Clubhouse:** Yes   **Shop:** No
Previous Grounds: Moved to Recreation Ground - now Runnymead Stadium - in 1963.
Record Attendance: 1400 v Wycombe Wanderers, FAC 2nd Qualifying Round 1972-73.

RECORDS
Goalscorer: Mark Butler - 153.
Appearances: Dave Jones - 850+.

HONOURS
FA Comps: None
League: West Surrey 1921-22. Surrey Senior 1922-23. Spartan 1971-72. Athenian Division Two 1974-75.
          Combined Counties 2012-13.
County FA: None

07-08	08-09	09-10	10-11	11-12	12-13	13-14	14-15	15-16	16-17
CCP 12	CCP 13	CCP 4	CCP 13	CCP 4	CCP 1	SthC 11	SthC 15	SthC 3	SthC 5
FAC EP	FAC EP	FAC EPr	FAC EP	FAC Pr	FAC P	FAC P	FAC P	FAC Pr	FAC 4Q
FAV 2Q	FAV 2P	FAV 2Q	FAV 2P	FAV 2P	FAV 1P	FAT 2Q	FAT 1Q	FAT 1Q	FAT P

FLEET TOWN

Club Contact Details
Calthorpe Park, Crookham Road, Fleet, Hants GU51 5FA

01252 623 804 Match day only

rcwhittington@virginmedia.com

Founded: 1890   **Nickname:** The Blues   **Manager:** Steve Dormer

Previous Names: Fleet FC 1890-1963

Previous Leagues: Hampshire 1961-77, Athenian, Combined Counties, Chiltonian, Wessex 1989-95, 2000-02, Southern 1995-2000, 02-04, 07-08, Isthmian 2004-07, 2008-11.

Club Colours (change): Blue & white

Ground Capacity: 2,000   **Seats:** 250   **Covered:** 250   **Clubhouse:** Yes   **Shop:** Yes

Previous Grounds: Watsons Meadow > 1923.

Record Attendance: 1,336 v AFC Wimbledon, Isthmian League 08/01/2005

RECORDS

Victory: 15-0 v Petersfield , Wessex League 26/12/1994

Defeat: 0-7 v Bashley, Southern League 12/04/2004

Goalscorer: Mark Frampton - 428

Appearances: Mark Frampton - 250

Additional: Paid £3,000 to Aldershot for Mark Russell

HONOURS

FA Comps: None

League: Wessex 1994-95.

County FA: Hampshire Senior Cup 2008-09. North Hants FA Cup 2008-09, 09-10.

07-08		08-09		09-10		10-11		11-12		12-13		13-14		14-15		15-16		16-17	
Sthsw	2	Isth1S	3	Isth1S	6	Isth1S	13	SthC	21	SthC	18	Sthsw	21	Sthsw	19	SthC	17	SthC	14
FAC	3Q	FAC	3Q	FAC	Pr	FAC	2Qr	FAC	1Q	FAC	P	FAC	P	FAC	2Q	FAC	1Qr	FAC	1Qr
FAT	1Qr	FAT	1Q	FAT	2Q	FAT	1Q	FAT	1Q	FAT	Pr	FAT	P	FAT	1Q	FAT	P	FAT	1Q

HANWELL TOWN

Club Contact Details
Reynolds Field, Preivale Lane, Perivale, Greenford, UB6 8TL

020 8998 1701

clivecooke2@sky.com

Founded: 1920   **Nickname:** Magpies   **Manager:** Ray Duffy

Previous Names: None

Previous Leagues: London. Dauntless. Wembley & District. Middlesex County 1970-83. London Spartan/Spartan 1983-97. Spartan South Midlands (Founder Member) 1997-2006, 2007-14. Southern 2006-07.

Club Colours (change): Black & white

Ground Capacity: 1,250   **Seats:** 175   **Covered:** 600   **Clubhouse:** Yes   **Shop:** No

Previous Grounds: Moved to Reynolds Field in 1981.

Record Attendance: 600 v Spurs, floodlight switch on, 1989.

RECORDS

Goalscorer: Keith Rowlands

Appearances: Phil Player 617 (20 seasons)

HONOURS

FA Comps: None

League: London Spartan Senior Division 1983-84. Spartan South Midlands Premier 2013-14.

County FA: London Senior Cup 1991-92, 92-93.

07-08		08-09		09-10		10-11		11-12		12-13		13-14		14-15		15-16		16-17	
SSM P	9	SSM P	7	SSM P	13	SSM P	15	SSM P	21	SSM P	6	SSM P	1	SthC	7	SthC	20	SthC	11
FAC	P	FAC	P	FAC	P	FAC	EP	FAC	EP	FAC	EP	FAC	EPr	FAC	P	FAC	3Q	FAC	2Qr
FAV	2P	FAV	2Q	FAV	2Q	FAV	1Q	FAV	1P	FAV	1Pr	FAV	5P	FAT	P	FAT	P	FAT	2Q

HARTLEY WINTNEY

Club Contact Details
Memorial Playing Fields, Green Lane, Hartley Wintney RG27 8DL
01252 843 586
mulley@ntlworld.com

Founded: 1897 **Nickname:** The Row **Manager:** Dan Brownlie & Anthony Millerick
Previous Names: None
Previous Leagues: Basingstoke & District. Aldershot & District >1978. Founder members of the Home Counties League (renamed Combined Counties League) 1978- 2017.

Club Colours (change): All orange

Ground Capacity: 2,000 **Seats:** 113 **Covered:** Yes **Clubhouse:** Yes **Shop:** Yes
Previous Grounds: Causeway Farm 1897-1953.
Record Attendance: 1,392 v AFC Wimbledon , Combined Counties League Premier, 25/01/03.

RECORDS

HONOURS
FA Comps: None
League: Combined Counties League 1982-83, 2015-16, 16-17.

County FA: None

07-08		08-09		09-10		10-11		11-12		12-13		13-14		14-15		15-16		16-17	
CC1	3	CCP	21	CC1	5	CC1	7	CC1	3	CCP	19	CCP	7	CCP	9	CCP	1	CCP	1
		FAC	P	FAC	EP	FAC	Pr	FAC	3Q	FAC	P	FAC	4Q	FAC	Pr	FAC	3Q	FAC	EP
FAV	2Q	FAV	1Q	FAV	2Q	FAV	1Q	FAV	1P	FAV	1Q	FAV	2P	FAV	2Q	FAV	5P	FAV	2P

HAYES & YEADING UNITED

Club Contact Details
SKYex Community Stadium, Beaconsfield Road, Hayes UB4 0SL
0208 573 2075
secretary@hyufc.com

Founded: 2007 **Nickname:** None **Manager:** Paul Hughes
Previous Names: Hayes - Botwell Mission 1909-29. Hayes and Yeading merged to form today's club in 2007
Previous Leagues: Isthmian. Conference 2007-16.

Club Colours (change): Red/black/black (All blue)

Ground Capacity: 6,000 **Seats:** 2,500 **Covered:** 3,900 **Clubhouse:** Yes **Shop:** Yes
Previous Grounds: Kingfield Stadium (Woking FC) 2012-13.
Record Attendance: 1,881 v Luton Town - Conference Premier 06/03/2010

RECORDS
Victory: 8-2 v Hillingdon Borough (A) - Middlesex Senior Cup 11/11/08
Defeat: 0-8 v Luton Town (A) - Conference Premier 27/03/10
Goalscorer: Josh Scott - 40 (2007-09)
Appearances: James Mulley - 137 (2007-10)

HONOURS
FA Comps: None
League: None

County FA: None

07-08		08-09		09-10		10-11		11-12		12-13		13-14		14-15		15-16		16-17	
Conf S	13	Conf S	4	Conf	17	Conf	16	Conf	21	Conf S	17	Conf S	20	Conf S	19	Nat S	21	SthP	23
FAC	4Q	FAC	4Q	FAC	4Q	FAC	1P	FAC	4Q	FAC	4Q	FAC	2Qr	FAC	2Q	FAC	2Q	FAC	2Q
FAT	1P	FAT	2P	FAT	1P	FAT	1P	FAT	1P	FAT	1P	FAT	1P	FAT	1P	FAT	3Qr	FAT	1Q

KEMPSTON ROVERS

Club Contact Details
Hillgrounds Leisure, Hillgrounds Road, Kempston, Bedford MK42 8SZ

01234 852 346

howlett.home@btinternet.com

Founded: 1884   **Nickname:** Walnut Boys   **Manager:** Jimmy Stoyles & Gary Flinn

Previous Names: Kempston Rovers 1884-2004. AFC Kempston Rovers 2004-16.

Previous Leagues: Bedford & District. Biggleswade & District. Bedfordshire & District County/South Midlands 1927-53. United Counties 1957-2016.

Club Colours (change): Red, white & black

Ground Capacity: 2,000   **Seats:** 100   **Covered:** 250   **Clubhouse:** Yes   **Shop:** Yes

Previous Grounds: None

Record Attendance: Not known

RECORDS

HONOURS

FA Comps: None

League: Bedford & District Division One 1907-08, 08-09, Division Two South 22-23, 33-34. Biggleswade & District 1910-11. United Counties Premier Division 1957-58, 73-74, 2015-16, Division One 85-86, 2010-11, Division Two 1955-56,

County FA: Bedfordshire Senior Cup 1908-09, 37-38, 76-77, 91-92. Huntingdonshire Premier Cup 1999-2000, 00-01.

07-08		08-09		09-10		10-11		11-12		12-13		13-14		14-15		15-16		16-17	
UCL P	12	UCL 1	5	UCL 1	5	UCL 1	1	UCL P	10	UCL P	17	UCL P	12	UCL P	8	UCL P	1	SthC	6
		FAC	EP			FAC	1Q	FAC	EP	FAC	1Q	FAC	EP	FAC	P	FAC	P	FAC	2Qr
FAV	1Q	FAV	2Q	FAV	2Q	FAV	1Q	FAV	2Q	FAV	2Q	FAV	1Q	FAV	2P	FAV	2P	FAT	1Q

MARLOW

Club Contact Details
Alfred Davies Memorial Ground, Oak tree Road, Marlow SL7 3ED

01628 483 970

terry.staines@ntlworld.com

Founded: 1870   **Nickname:** The Blues   **Manager:** Mark Bartley

Previous Names: Great Marlow

Previous Leagues: Reading & District, Spartan 1908-10, 28-65, Gt Western Suburban, Athenian 1965-84, Isthmian 1984-2004. Southern 2004-12. Hellenic 2012-13.

Club Colours (change): All royal blue

Ground Capacity: 3,000   **Seats:** 250   **Covered:** 600   **Clubhouse:** Yes   **Shop:** No

Previous Grounds: Crown ground 1870-1919, Star Meadow 1919-24

Record Attendance: 3,000 v Oxford United - FA Cup 1st Round 1994

RECORDS

Goalscorer: Kevin Stone

Appearances: Mick McKeown - 500+

Additional: Paid £5,000 to Sutton United for Richard Evans
                 Received £8,000 from Slough Town for David Lay

HONOURS

FA Comps: None

League: Spartan 1937-38, Division Two West 1929-30. Isthmian Division One 1987-88. Hellenic Premier Division 2012-13.

County FA: Berks & Bucks Senior Cup x11

07-08		08-09		09-10		10-11		11-12		12-13		13-14		14-15		15-16		16-17	
Sthsw	9	SthM	9	SthM	15	SthC	11	SthC	22	Hel P	1	SthC	17	SthC	11	Sthsw	13	SthC	4
FAC	Pr	FAC	1Q	FAC	1Q	FAC	P	FAC	1Q	FAC	1Q	FAC	P	FAC	P	FAC	Pr	FAC	Pr
FAT	P	FAT	1Q	FAT	2Q	FAT	Pr	FAT	1Qr	FAV	2P	FAT	3Q	FAT	P	FAT	3Q	FAT	1Q

MONEYFIELDS

Club Contact Details
Moneyfields Sports Ground, Moneyfield Ave, Copnor, Portsmouth PO3 6LA
02392 665 260
larks1954@hotmail.co.uk

Founded: 1987   **Nickname:** Moneys   **Manager:** David Carter
Previous Names: Portsmouth Civil Service 1987-94.
Previous Leagues: Portsmouth 1987-91. Hampshire 1991-98. Wessex 1998-2017.

Club Colours (change): Yellow/navy/navy (White/green/green).

Ground Capacity: 2,000   **Seats:** 150   **Covered:** 150   **Clubhouse:** Yes   **Shop:** Yes
Previous Grounds: Copnor Road 1987-94.
Record Attendance: 250 v Fareham, Wessex Division One 2005-06

RECORDS
Victory: 9-0v Blackfield & Langley 01-02.

Goalscorer: Lee Mould - 86

Appearances: Matt Lafferty - 229

HONOURS
FA Comps: None

League: Portsmouth Premier 1990-91.
       Hampshire Division Three 1991-92, Division Two 1992-93, Division One 1996-97.
County FA: Hampshire Intermediate 1991-92, 92-93.

07-08		08-09		09-10		10-11		11-12		12-13		13-14		14-15		15-16		16-17	
WexP	7	WexP	3	WexP	12	WexP	7	WexP	4	WexP	4	WexP	9	WexP	4	WexP	8	WexP	2
FAC	2Q	FAC	P	FAC	P	FAC	P	FAC	1Qr	FAC	P	FAC	1Q	FAC	EP	FAC	P	FAC	1Q
FAV	3P	FAV	1Q	FAV	2P	FAV	3P	FAV	2Q	FAV	2P	FAV	3P	FAV	2Q	FAV	4P	FAV	2P

NORTHWOOD

Club Contact Details
Northwood Park, Chestnut Avenue, Northwood, Middlesex HA6 1HR
01923 827 148
alan.evansnfc@btopenworld.com

Founded: 1926   **Nickname:** Woods   **Manager:** Simon Lane
Previous Names: Northwood United 1926-1945.
Previous Leagues: Harrow & Wembley 1932-69, Middlesex 1969-78, Hellenic 1979-84, London Spartan 1984-93,
       Isthmian 1993-2005, 2007-10, Southern 2005-07

Club Colours (change): All red

Ground Capacity: 3,075   **Seats:** 308   **Covered:** 932   **Clubhouse:** Yes   **Shop:** No
Previous Grounds: Northwood Recreation Ground 1926-1928. Northwood Playing Fields 1928-1971.
Record Attendance: 1,642 v Chlesea - Friendly July 1997

RECORDS
Victory: 15-0 v Dateline (H) - Middlesex Intermediate Cup 1973

Defeat: 0-8 v Bedfont - Middlesex League 1975

Goalscorer: Lawrence Yaku scored 61 goals during season 1999-2000

Appearances: Chris Gell - 493+

HONOURS
FA Comps: None

League: Harrow, Wembley & District Premier 1932-33, 33-34, 34-35, 35-36, 36-37, 47-48, 48-49. Middlesex Premier 1977-78.
       Hellenic Division One 1978-79. Spartan Premier 1991-92. Isthmian Division One North 2002-03.
County FA: Middlesex Intermediate Cup 1978-79. Middlesex Senior Cup 2006-07, 15-16.

07-08		08-09		09-10		10-11		11-12		12-13		13-14		14-15		15-16		16-17	
Isth1N	10	Isth1N	6	Isth1N	10	SthC	20	SthC	7	SthC	13	SthC	9	SthC	10	SthC	7	SthC	20
FAC	1Q	FAC	P	FAC	1Qr	FAC	1Q	FAC	P	FAC	3Q	FAC	P	FAC	1Qr	FAC	2Q	FAC	P
FAT	3Q	FAT	2Q	FAT	1Pr	FAT	Pr	FAT	Pr	FAT	P	FAT	P	FAT	2Q	FAT	1Q	FAT	1Qr

THAME UNITED

Club Contact Details

The ASM Stadium, Meadow View Park, Tythrop Way, Thame, Oxon OX9 3RN

01844 214 401

jake@jcpc.org.uk

Founded: 1883   **Nickname:** Red Kites   **Manager:** Mark West
Previous Names: Thame F.C.
Previous Leagues: Oxon Senior. Hellenic 1959-88, 2006-17. South Midlands 1988-91. Isthmian 1991-2004. Southern 2004-06.

Club Colours (change): Red & black/black/red.

Ground Capacity: 2,500   **Seats:** Yes   **Covered:** Yes   **Clubhouse:** Yes   **Shop:**
Previous Grounds: Windmill Road 1883-2005. Aylesbury United FC 2005-06. AFC Wallingford 2006-11.
Record Attendance: 1,382 v Oxford United Jan 2011.

RECORDS
Appearances: Steve Mayhew

HONOURS
FA Comps: None
League: Hellenic 1961-62, 69-70, 2016-17. Division One East 2009-10. South Midlands League 1990-91.
        Isthmian Division Two 1994-95.
County FA: None

07-08		08-09		09-10		10-11		11-12		12-13		13-14		14-15		15-16		16-17	
Hel1E	10	Hel1E	9	Hel1E	1	Hel P	10	Hel P	9	Hel P	9	Hel P	10	Hel P	5	Hel P	6	Hel P	1
FAC	EP	FAC	EPr	FAC	1Q	FAC	2Qr	FAC	2Q	FAC	P	FAC	EP	FAC	1Q	FAC	EPr	FAC	P
FAV	2Q	FAV	1Q	FAV	2Qr	FAV	2Q	FAV	2Q	FAV	2P	FAV	2Q	FAV	2P	FAV	3P	FAV	1P

UXBRIDGE

Club Contact Details

Honeycroft Road, West Drayton, Middlesex UB7 8HX

01895 443 557

sec@uxbridgefc.co.uk

Founded: 1871   **Nickname:** The Reds   **Manager:** Tony Choules
Previous Names: Uxbridge Town 1923-45
Previous Leagues: Southern 1894-99, Greatt Western Suburban 1906-19, 20-23, Athenian 1919-20, 24-37, 63-82,
        Spartan 1937-38, London 1938-46, Great Western Comb. 1939-45, Corinthian 1946-63, Isthmian

Club Colours (change): Red/white/red (Sky blue/navy/navy)

Ground Capacity: 3,770   **Seats:** 339   **Covered:** 760   **Clubhouse:** Yes   **Shop:**
Previous Grounds: RAF Stadium 1923-48, Cleveland Road 1948-78
Record Attendance: 1,000 v Arsenal - Opening of the floodlights 1981

RECORDS
Goalscorer: Phil Duff - 153
Appearances: Roger Nicholls - 1,054

HONOURS
FA Comps: None
League: Corinthian 1959-60.
County FA: Middlesex Senior Cup 1893-94, 95-96, 1950-51, 2000-01, Charity Cup 1907-08, 12-13, 35-36, 81-82, 2012-13, 13-14.
        London Challenge Cup 1993-94, 96-97, 98-99.

07-08		08-09		09-10		10-11		11-12		12-13		13-14		14-15		15-16		16-17	
Sthsw	5	Sthsw	13	Sthsw	15	SthC	13	SthC	4	SthC	11	SthC	10	SthC	12	SthC	15	SthC	17
FAC	P	FAC	1Qr	FAC	2Q	FAC	P	FAC	P	FAC	1Q	FAC	1Q	FAC	2Q	FAC	3Q	FAC	2Q
FAT	3Q	FAT	2P	FAT	1Qr	FAT	2P	FAT	1P	FAT	2Qr	FAT	P	FAT	2Q	FAT	P	FAT	1Q

AFC TOTTON

Club Contact Details
Testwood Stadium, Salisbury Road, Calmore, Totton SO40 2RW
02380 868 981
secretary.afctotton@gmail.com

Founded: 1886   **Nickname:** Stags   **Manager:** Louis Langdown - Nov 2016
Previous Names: Totton FC until merger with Totton Athletic in 1975
Previous Leagues: New Forest (Founder Members) 1904. Southampton Senior. Hampshire 1920-86, Wessex 1986-2008.

Club Colours (change): All dark blue (All yellow)

Ground Capacity: 3,000   **Seats:** 500   **Covered:** 500   **Clubhouse:** Yes   **Shop:** Yes
Previous Grounds: South Testwood Park 1886-1933.
Record Attendance: 2,315 v Bradford Park Avenue, 12/11/2011.

RECORDS
Appearances: Michael Gosney - 427

HONOURS
FA Comps: None
League: New Forest 1905-06, 10-11, 13-14, 19-20, 25-26, 26-27, 47-48, 60-61, 61-62. Hampshire West 1924-25. Hampshire Division Two 1930-31, 66-67, Division One 81-82, 84-85. Wessex Premier Division 2007-08. Southern Division South & West 2010-11.
County FA: Hampshire Senior Cup 2010-11.

07-08		08-09		09-10		10-11		11-12		12-13		13-14		14-15		15-16		16-17	
WexP	1	Sthsw	3	Sthsw	2	Sthsw	1	SthP	3	SthP	14	SthP	21	Sthsw	15	Sthsw	15	Sthsw	19
FAC	2Qr	FAC	4Q	FAC	4Q	FAC	P	FAC	2P	FAC	4Q	FAC	1Q	FAC	1Q	FAC	P	FAC	P
FAV	2P	FAT	3Qr	FAT	2Q	FAT	2Q	FAT	1Q	FAT	1P	FAT	1Q	FAT	1Q	FAT	P	FAT	Pr

BARNSTAPLE TOWN

Club Contact Details
Mill Road, Barnstaple, North Devon EX31 1JQ
01271 343 469
jane@barnstapletownfc.com

Founded: 1906   **Nickname:** Barum   **Manager:** Richard Pears
Previous Names: Pilton Yeo Vale
Previous Leagues: North Devon, Devon & Exeter, South Western. Western >2016.

Club Colours (change): All red. (All blue)

Ground Capacity: 5,000   **Seats:** 250   **Covered:** 1,000   **Clubhouse:** Yes   **Shop:** Yes
Previous Grounds: None
Record Attendance: 6,200 v Bournemouth & Boscombe Athletic, FA Cup 1st Round, 1951-52.

RECORDS
Victory: 12-1 v Tavistock, F.A. Cup 3rd Qualifying Round 1954.
Defeat: 0-11 v Odd Down, Western, 25/04/2013.
Appearances: Ian Pope
Additional: Paid £4,000 to Hungerford Town for Joe Scott.
Received £6,000 from Bristol City for Ian Doyle.

HONOURS
FA Comps: None
League: North Devon 1904-05, 08-09. Exeter & District 1946-47. Western 1952-53, 79-80, Division One 1993-94, 2014-15.
County FA: Devon Pro Cup 1952-53, 62-63, 64-65, 67-68, 69-70, 71-72, 72-73, 74-75, 76-77, 77-78, 78-79, 79-80. 80-81.
Devon St Lukes Cup 1987-88. Devon Senior Cup 1992-93.

07-08		08-09		09-10		10-11		11-12		12-13		13-14		14-15		15-16		16-17	
WestP	12	WestP	18	WestP	15	WestP	11	WestP	15	WestP	20	West1	3	West1	1	WestP	2	Sthsw	17
FAC	P	FAC	EP	FAC	P	FAC	EP	FAC	P	FAC	EP	FAC	EP	FAC	EP	FAC	1Q	FAC	1Q
FAV	1Q	FAV	1P	FAV	1P	FAV	2Q	FAV	3P	FAV	1P	FAV	2P	FAV	2Q	FAV	2P	FAT	1Q

BIDEFORD

Club Contact Details
The Sports Ground, Kingsley Road, Bideford EX39 2LH
01237 474 974
k.tyrell@talktalk.net

Founded: 1946   **Nickname:** The Robins   **Manager:** Sean Joyce
Previous Names: Bideford Town
Previous Leagues: Devon & Exeter 1947-49, Western 1949-72, 75-2010, Southern 1972-75

Club Colours (change): All red (All blue)

Ground Capacity: 6,000   **Seats:** 375   **Covered:** 1,000   **Clubhouse:** Yes   **Shop:**
Previous Grounds: None
Record Attendance: 5,975 v Gloucester City - FA Cup 4th Qualifying Round 1949

RECORDS
Victory: 16-1 v Soundwell, 1950-51
Defeat: 1-10 v Taunton Town, 1998-99
Goalscorer: Tommy Robinson - 259
Appearances: Derek May - 647

HONOURS
FA Comps: None
League: Western 1963-64, 70-71, 71-72, 81-82, 82-83, 2001-02, 03-04, 04-05, 05-06, 09-10, Division Two 1951-52, Division Three
1949-50. Southern Division One South & West 2011-12.
County FA: Devon Pro Cup 1960-61, 61-62, 63-64, 65-66, 66-67, 68-69, 70-71. Devon Senior Cup 1979-80.
Devon St Lukes Bowl 1981-82, 83-84, 85-86, 95-96, 2009-10.

07-08		08-09		09-10		10-11		11-12		12-13		13-14		14-15		15-16		16-17	
WestP	6	WestP	6	WestP	1	Sthsw	10	Sthsw	1	SthP	20	SthP	8	SthP	15	SthP	23	Sthsw	10
FAC	EP	FAC	1Qr	FAC	P	FAC	P	FAC	2Q	FAC	2Q	FAC	2Q	FAC	2Q	FAC	2Q	FAC	1Q
FAV	4P	FAV	QF	FAV	2P	FAT	3Q	FAT	1Q	FAT	1Q	FAT	2Q	FAT	1Qr	FAT	3Q	FAT	P

BISHOP'S CLEEVE

Club Contact Details
Kayte Lane, Bishop's Cleeve, Cheltenham GL52 3PD
01242 676 166
themitres@outlook.com

Founded: 1905   **Nickname:** The Mitres   **Manager:** Stephen Cleal
Previous Names: None
Previous Leagues: Cheltenham. North Gloucestershire. Hellenic 1983-2006.

Club Colours (change): Green & black

Ground Capacity: 1,500   **Seats:** 50   **Covered:** 50   **Clubhouse:** Yes   **Shop:** Yes
Previous Grounds: Stoke Road and ground shared with Moreton Town, Wollen Sports, Highworth Town and Forest Green Rovers
Record Attendance: 1,300 v Cheltenham Town - July 2006

RECORDS
Goalscorer: Kevin Slack
Appearances: John Skeen

HONOURS
FA Comps: None
League: Cheltenham Division Two 1924-25, 30-31, 58-59, Division One 31-32, 34-35, 61-62, 63-64, 65-66, 66-67.
Gloucestershire Northern Senior Division Two 1967-68, Division One 68-69, 69-70, 72-73. Hellenic Division One 1986-87.
County FA: Gloucestershire Junior Cup North. Gloucestershire Senior Amateur Cup North x3.

07-08		08-09		09-10		10-11		11-12		12-13		13-14		14-15		15-16		16-17	
SthM	12	Sthsw	18	Sthsw	11	Sthsw	15	Sthsw	11	Sthsw	21	Sthsw	20	Sthsw	21	Sthsw	12	Sthsw	16
FAC	1Qr	FAC	P	FAC	3Q	FAC	2Q	FAC	P	FAC	2Q	FAC	Pr	FAC	1Q	FAC	P	FAC	P
FAT	P	FAT	1Q	FAT	P	FAT	1Q	FAT	P	FAT	1Q	FAT	P	FAT	1Q	FAT	P	FAT	2Q

BRISTOL MANOR FARM

Club Contact Details
The Creek, Portway, Sea Mills, Bristol BS9 2HS
0117 968 3571
secretary@bristolmanorfarm.com

Founded: 1964 **Nickname:** The Farm **Manager:** Lee Lashenko
Previous Names:
Previous Leagues: Bristol Suburban 1964-69. Somerset Senior 1969-77. Western 1977-2017.

Club Colours (change): Red & black

Ground Capacity: 2,000 **Seats:** 200 **Covered:** 350 **Clubhouse:** Yes **Shop:** No
Previous Grounds: None
Record Attendance: 1,417 v Bristol City, pre-season friendly, 09/07/2017.

RECORDS
Appearances: M. Baird
Victory: 10-0 v Devizes Town, Les Phillips Cup, 19/11/2016.

HONOURS
FA Comps: None
League: Western Division One 1982-83, Premier 2016-17.

County FA: Gloucestershire Challenge Trophy 1987-88, 2015-16. Gloucestershire Amateur Cup 1989-90.

07-08		08-09		09-10		10-11		11-12		12-13		13-14		14-15		15-16		16-17	
WestP	16	WestP	5	WestP	7	WestP	7	WestP	8	WestP	18	WestP	2	WestP	4	WestP	3	WestP	1
FAC	EP	FAC	EP	FAC	1Q	FAC	2Qr	FAC	EPr	FAC	EP	FAC	2Qr	FAC	P	FAC	1Q	FAC	EPr
FAV	1Q	FAV	1Q	FAV	4P	FAV	2P	FAV	2Q	FAV	2Q	FAV	1P	FAV	2P	FAV	QF	FAV	5P

CINDERFORD TOWN

Club Contact Details
The Causeway, Hildene, Cinderford, Gloucestershire GL14 2QH
07896 887 162
maskellbilly@yahoo.co.uk

Founded: 1922 **Nickname:** The Foresters **Manager:** Paul Michael
Previous Names: None
Previous Leagues: Gloucestershire Northern Senior 1922-39, 60-62, Western 1946-59, Warwickshire Combination 1963-64,
West Midlands 1965-69, Gloucestershire Co. 1970-73, 85-89, Midland Comb. 1974-84, Hellenic 1990-95

Club Colours (change): White & black

Ground Capacity: 3,500 **Seats:** 250 **Covered:** 1,000 **Clubhouse:** Yes **Shop:** Yes
Previous Grounds: Mousel Lane, Royal Oak
Record Attendance: 4,850 v Minehead - Western League 1955-56

RECORDS
Victory: 13-0 v Cam Mills - 1938-39
Defeat: 0-10 v Sutton Coldfield - 1978-79
Appearances: Russel Bowles - 528

HONOURS
FA Comps: None
League: Western Division Two 1956-57. Warwickshire Combination Western Division 1964-65. Hellenic Premier Division 1994-95.
Southern Division One South & West 2015-16.
County FA: Gloucestershire Senior Amateur Cup North x6. Gloucestershire Junior Cup North 1980-81. Gloucestershire Senior Cup
2000-01.

07-08		08-09		09-10		10-11		11-12		12-13		13-14		14-15		15-16		16-17	
SthM	16	SthM	11	Sthsw	16	Sthsw	12	Sthsw	10	Sthsw	10	Sthsw	15	Sthsw	9	Sthsw	1	SthP	24
FAC	1Qr	FAC	P	FAC	P	FAC	3Q	FAC	2Q	FAC	1Qr	FAC	P	FAC	P	FAC	1Q	FAC	1Q
FAT	2Q	FAT	P	FAT	1Q	FAT	2Q	FAT	P	FAT	1Q	FAT	P	FAT	Pr	FAT	P	FAT	1Q

CIRENCESTER TOWN

Club Contact Details
The Corinium Stadium, Kingshill Lane, Cirencester GL7 1HS
01285 654 543
scott.griffin@cirentownfc.plus.com

Founded: 1889   **Nickname:** Centurions   **Manager:** Charlie Griffin
Previous Names: None
Previous Leagues: Cheltenham 1889-1935. Gloucestershire Northern Senior 1935-68. Gloucestershire County (Founder Members) 1968-69.
Hellenic 1969-96.

Club Colours (change): Red & black stripes/black/red

Ground Capacity: 4,500   **Seats:** 550   **Covered:** 1,250   **Clubhouse:** Yes   **Shop:** Yes
Previous Grounds: Smithfield Stadium >2002.
Record Attendance: 2,600 v Fareham Town - 1969

RECORDS
Misc: Paid £4,000 to Gloucester City for Lee Smith

HONOURS
FA Comps: None
League: Cheltenham Division One 1927-28, 29-30, 48-49, 54-55, 55-56. Gloucestershire Northern Senior 1966-67, 67-68.
Hellenic Division One 1973-74, Premier Division 95-96. Southern Division One South & West 2013-14.
County FA: Gloucestershire Senior Amateur Cup 1989-90. Gloucestershire Senior Challenge Cup 1995-96, 2015-16.

	07-08	08-09	09-10	10-11	11-12	12-13	13-14	14-15	15-16	16-17
	SthP 21	Sthsw 14	Sthsw 5	SthP 13	SthP 22	Sthsw 11	Sthsw 1	SthP 8	SthP 15	SthP 22
	FAC 2Q	FAC P	FAC 3Q	FAC 1Qr	FAC 1Q	FAC P	FAC 3Q	FAC 1Qr	FAC 2Q	FAC 2Q
	FAT 1Q	FAT P	FAT 1Q	FAT 1Pr	FAT 2Q	FAT P	FAT 1Q	FAT 1Q	FAT 1Pr	FAT 1Q

DIDCOT TOWN

Club Contact Details
Draycott Engineering Loop Meadow Stadium, Bowmont Water, Didcot OX11 7GA
01235 813 138
jaquelyn-dtc@virginmedia.com

Founded: 1907   **Nickname:** Railwaymen   **Manager:** Andy Ballard
Previous Names: Didcot Village and Northbourne Wanderers amalgamated to form Didcot Town in 1907.
Previous Leagues: Metropolitan 1957-63, Hellenic 1963-2006

Club Colours (change): Red & white

Ground Capacity: 3,000   **Seats:** 350   **Covered:** 200   **Clubhouse:** Yes   **Shop:** Yes
Previous Grounds: Fleet Meadow. Edmonds Park. Cow Lane. Haydon Road. Station Road 1923-99.
Record Attendance: 2,707 - v Exeter City, FA Cup 1st Round, 08/11/2015

RECORDS
Goalscorer: Ian Concanon

HONOURS
FA Comps: FA Vase 2004-05.
League: Hellenic Premier Division 1953-54, 2005-06, Division One 1976-77, 87-88.

County FA: Berks & Bucks Senior Trophy 2001-02, 02-03, 05-06.

	07-08	08-09	09-10	10-11	11-12	12-13	13-14	14-15	15-16	16-17
	Sthsw 3	Sthsw 5	SthP 15	SthP 19	Sthsw 16	Sthsw 17	Sthsw 12	Sthsw 7	Sthsw 10	Sthsw 12
	FAC 1Q	FAC 1Q	FAC 2Q	FAC 3Q	FAC 1Qr	FAC 4Q	FAC 3Q	FAC P	FAC 1P	FAC P
	FAT 1Q	FAT P	FAT 1Q	FAT 1Q	FAT 1P	FAT 3Q	FAT Pr	FAT 1Pr	FAT 1Q	FAT P

EVESHAM UNITED

Club Contact Details
Jubilee Stadium, Cheltenham Road, Evesham WR11 2LZ
01386 442 303
eveshamunitedsecretary@hotmail.com

Founded: 1945 **Nickname:** The Robins **Manager:** Paul Collicut
Previous Names: None
Previous Leagues: Worcester, Birmingham Combination, Midland Combination 1951-55, 65-92,
West Midlands (Regional) 1955-62

Club Colours (change): Red and white stripes/black/black

Ground Capacity: 3,000 **Seats:** Yes **Covered:** Yes **Clubhouse:** Yes **Shop:** Yes
Previous Grounds: The Crown Meadow > 1968, Common Reed 1968-2006. Ground shared with Worcester City 2006-12.
Record Attendance: 2,338 v West Bromwich Albion - Friendly 18/07/1992

RECORDS
Victory:	11-3 v West Heath United
Defeat:	1-8 v Ilkeston Town
Goalscorer:	Sid Brain
Appearances:	Rob Candy
Additional:	Paid £1,500 to Hayes for Colin Day 1992
	Received £5,000 from Cheltenham Town for Simon Brain

HONOURS
FA Comps: None

League: Midland Combination Premier Division 1991-92, Division One 1965-66, 67-68, 68-69.
Southern Division One Midlands 2007-08.
County FA: Worcestershire Senior Urn 1976-77, 77-78, Senior Cup 2008-09.

07-08		08-09		09-10		10-11		11-12		12-13		13-14		14-15		15-16		16-17	
SthM	1	SthP	9	SthP	16	SthP	12	SthP	20	Sthsw	14	Sthsw	16	Sthsw	2	Sthsw	6	Sthsw	5
FAC	4Qr	FAC	1P	FAC	2Q	FAC	1Q	FAC	3Q	FAC	P	FAC	1Q	FAC	4Q	FAC	P	FAC	1Qr
FAT	3Qr	FAT	2Q	FAT	2Qr	FAT	2Q	FAT	1Qr	FAT	P	FAT	1Q	FAT	1Qr	FAT	2Q	FAT	1Qr

KIDLINGTON

Club Contact Details
Yarnton Road, Kidlington, Oxford OX5 1AT
01865 849 777
dplatt45@hotmail.co.uk

Founded: 1909 **Nickname:** Greens **Manager:** Julian McCalmon
Previous Names: None.
Previous Leagues: Villages Leagues > 1945. Oxford City Junior 1945-51. Oxfordshire Senior 1951-54. Hellenic 1954-2016.

Club Colours (change): All green

Ground Capacity: 1,500 **Seats:** Yes **Covered:** Yes **Clubhouse:** Yes **Shop:** No
Previous Grounds: None
Record Attendance: 2,000 v Showbiz XI, 1973.

RECORDS

HONOURS
FA Comps: None

League: Oxfordshire Senior 1952-53. Hellenic Premier Division 2015-16.

County FA: Oxfordshire Intermediate Cup 1952-53, 69-70, 84-85.

07-08		08-09		09-10		10-11		11-12		12-13		13-14		14-15		15-16		16-17	
Hel P	15	Hel P	9	Hel P	11	Hel P	7	Hel P	18	Hel P	13	Hel P	6	Hel P	4	Hel P	1	SthC	12
FAC	P	FAC	P	FAC	1Q	FAC	EP	FAC	P	FAC	EPr	FAC	EPr	FAC	P	FAC	2Q	FAC	P
FAV	2Qr	FAV	1P	FAV	1P	FAV	1P	FAV	2Q	FAV	3P	FAV	3P	FAV	1Q	FAV	QFr	FAT	P

LARKHALL ATHLETIC

Club Contact Details
Plain Ham, Charlcombe Lane, Larkhall, Bath BA1 8DJ
01225 334 952
larkhallathletic@gmail.com

Founded: 1914   **Nickname:** Larks   **Manager:** Phil Bater
Previous Names: None
Previous Leagues: Somerset Senior. Western 1976-2014.

Club Colours (change): All royal blue

Ground Capacity: 1,000   **Seats:** Yes   **Covered:** 50   **Clubhouse:** Yes   **Shop:** No
Previous Grounds: None
Record Attendance: 280 v Tunbridge Wells, FA Vase, Feb 2013

RECORDS
Victory: 8-0 v Oldland Abbotonians, 2007
Defeat: 1-6 v Exmouth Town, 2001
Goalscorer: Ben Highmore scored 52 goals during the 2008-09 season.
Appearances: Luke Scott - 600+ (as at July 2014)

HONOURS
FA Comps: None
League: Western Division One 1988-89, 08-09, Premier Division 2010-11, 13-14.

County FA: Somerset Junior Cup 1962-63, Senior Cup 1975-76, 2003-04.

07-08		08-09		09-10		10-11		11-12		12-13		13-14		14-15		15-16		16-17	
West1	3	West1	1	WestP	14	WestP	1	WestP	3	WestP	5	WestP	1	Sthsw	5	Sthsw	11	Sthsw	13
		FAC	1Q	FAC	P	FAC	P	FAC	1Q	FAC	1Qr	FAC	1Q	FAC	2Qr	FAC	2Qr	FAC	P
FAV	1Q	FAV	4P	FAV	3P	FAV	1Q	FAV	5P	FAV	5P	FAV	5P	FAT	P	FAT	1Q	FAT	P

MANGOTSFIELD UNITED

Club Contact Details
Cossham Street, Mangotsfield, Bristol BS16 9EN
0117 956 0119
davidj693@hotmail.co.uk

Founded: 1950   **Nickname:** The Field   **Manager:** David Mehew
Previous Names: None
Previous Leagues: Bristol & District 1950-67. Avon Premier Combination 1967-72. Western 1972-2000.

Club Colours (change): Maroon & sky blue/sky blue/sky blue (White/black/black)

Ground Capacity: 2,500   **Seats:** 300   **Covered:** 800   **Clubhouse:** Yes   **Shop:** Yes
Previous Grounds: None
Record Attendance: 1,253 v Bath City - F.A. Cup 1974

RECORDS
Victory: 17-0 v Hanham Sports (H) - 1953 Bristol & District League
Defeat: 3-13 v Bristol City United - Bristol & District League Division 1
Goalscorer: John Hill
Appearances: John Hill - 600+
Misc: In the last 10 matches of the 2003/04 season, the club went 738 minutes (just over 8 games) without scoring and then finished the campaign with 13 goals in the last two, which included a 9-0 away win.

HONOURS
FA Comps: None
League: Bristol & District Div.7 1951-52, Div.6 52-53, Div.4 53-54, Div.3 54-55, Div.2 55-56, Premier Comb Div.1 68-69. Somerset Senior Div.3 74-75, Div.2 75-76, 97-98, Prem 2004-05. Western 1990-91. Southern Division One West 2004-05.
County FA: Gloucestershire Senior Cup 1968-69, 75-76, 2002-03, 12-13. Gloucestershire F.A. Trophy x6. Somerset Premier Cup 1987-88.

07-08		08-09		09-10		10-11		11-12		12-13		13-14		14-15		15-16		16-17	
SthP	14	SthP	22	Sthsw	9	Sthsw	3	Sthsw	14	Sthsw	13	Sthsw	11	Sthsw	10	Sthsw	14	Sthsw	8
FAC	2Q	FAC	2Q	FAC	4Q	FAC	2Q	FAC	P	FAC	1Q	FAC	2Q	FAC	1Q	FAC	1Q	FAC	P
FAT	2Qr	FAT	1Q	FAT	Pr	FAT	Pr	FAT	2Qr	FAT	Pr	FAT	2Q	FAT	2Q	FAT	2Q	FAT	P

NORTH LEIGH

Club Contact Details
Eynsham Hall Park, North Leigh, Witney, Oxon OX29 6SL

07583 399 577

huxley893@btinternet.com

Founded: 1908   **Nickname:** The Millers   **Manager:** John Brough
Previous Names: None
Previous Leagues: Witney & District, Hellenic 1990-2008

Club Colours (change): Yellow/black/yellow (All red)

Ground Capacity: 2,000   **Seats:** 175   **Covered:** 200   **Clubhouse:** Yes   **Shop:** No
Previous Grounds: None
Record Attendance: 426 v Newport County - FA Cup 3rd Qualifying Round 16/10/2004

RECORDS
Goalscorer: P Coles
Appearances: P King

HONOURS
FA Comps: None
League: Witney & District Premier 1985-86, 86-87, 87-88, 88-89, 89-90. Hellenic Premier Division 2002-03, 07-08.

County FA: Oxfordshire Senior Cup 2011-12, 16-17.

07-08		08-09		09-10		10-11		11-12		12-13		13-14		14-15		15-16		16-17	
Hel P	1	Sthsw	8	Sthsw	10	Sthsw	6	Sthsw	6	Sthsw	9	Sthsw	7	Sthsw	8	Sthsw	9	Sthsw	6
FAC	Pr	FAC	1Q	FAC	1Q	FAC	P	FAC	1Q	FAC	3Q	FAC	1Q	FAC	P	FAC	3Q	FAC	4Q
FAV	1P	FAT	1Q	FAT	P	FAT	1Qr	FAT	P	FAT	1Qr	FAT	1Q	FAT	1Q	FAT	1Q	FAT	1Pr

PAULTON ROVERS

Club Contact Details
Athletic Ground, Winterfield Road, Paulton, Bristol BS39 7RF

01761 412 907

footballsecretary.prfc@gmail.com

Founded: 1881   **Nickname:** The Robins or Rovers   **Manager:** John Rendell - June 2017
Previous Names: None
Previous Leagues: Wiltshire Premier, Somerset Senior, Western

Club Colours (change): All maroon

Ground Capacity: 2,500   **Seats:** 253   **Covered:** 2,500   **Clubhouse:** Yes   **Shop:** Yes
Previous Grounds: Chapel Field, Cricket Ground, Recreation Ground
Record Attendance: 2,000 v Crewe Alexandra - FA Cup 1906-07

RECORDS
Goalscorer: Graham Colbourne
Appearances: Steve Tovey

HONOURS
FA Comps: None
League: None

County FA: Somerset Junior Cup 1898-99, Senior Cup x12 - Firstly in 1900-01 and most recently in 1974-75, Premier Cup 2012-13.

07-08		08-09		09-10		10-11		11-12		12-13		13-14		14-15		15-16		16-17	
Sthsw	7	Sthsw	10	Sthsw	7	Sthsw	11	Sthsw	7	Sthsw	5	Sthsw	4	SthP	10	SthP	24	Sthsw	15
FAC	3Q	FAC	3Q	FAC	1P	FAC	2Q	FAC	P	FAC	Pr	FAC	P	FAC	2Qr	FAC	2Q	FAC	1Q
FAT	P	FAT	Pr	FAT	P	FAT	2Q	FAT	2Q	FAT	Pr	FAT	1Q	FAT	2Q	FAT	1Q	FAT	P

SALISBURY

Club Contact Details
Raymond McEnhill Stadium, Partridge Way, Old Sarum SP4 6PU
07803 247 874
douglasj71@virginmedia.com

Founded: 2015   **Nickname:** The Whites   **Manager:** Steve Claridge
Previous Names: None
Previous Leagues: Wessex 2015-16.

Club Colours (change): White with black trim/black/white (Royal blue with yellow trim/royal blue/royal blue)

Ground Capacity: 4,000   **Seats:** 500   **Covered:** 2,247   **Clubhouse:** Yes   **Shop:**
Previous Grounds: None
Record Attendance: 3,450 v Hereford FC, FA Vase Semi-final 2nd leg, 2015-16.

RECORDS
Victory: 9-1 v Bournemouth - Wessex Premier 25/08/15.
Defeat: 4-1 v AFC Porchester - Wessex Premier 30/04/16.
Goalscorer: Sam Wilson - 40 - 2015-16.
Appearances: Thomas Whelan - 54 - 2015-16.

HONOURS
FA Comps: None
League: Wessex Premier Division 2015-16.

County FA: None

07-08	08-09	09-10	10-11	11-12	12-13	13-14	14-15	15-16		16-17	
								WexP	1	Sthsw	2
										FAC	2Q
								FAV	SF	FAT	1Q

SHORTWOOD UNITED

Club Contact Details
Meadowbank, Shortwood, Nailsworth GL6 0SJ
01453 833 936
squish.shortwoodfc@live.co.uk

Founded: 1900   **Nickname:** The Wood   **Manager:** Paul Meredith
Previous Names: None.
Previous Leagues: Stroud & District. Gloucestershire Northern Senior. Gloucestershire County. Hellenic >2012.

Club Colours (change): Red, white & black

Ground Capacity: 2,000   **Seats:** 50   **Covered:** 150   **Clubhouse:** Yes   **Shop:** No
Previous Grounds: Played at Nailsworth Playing Field, Table Land and Wallow Green before moving to Meadowbank in 1972.
Record Attendance: 1,247 v Port Vale, FA Cup First Round, 11/11/2013.

RECORDS
Goalscorer: Peter Grant.
Appearances: Peter Grant.

HONOURS
FA Comps: None
League: Gloucestershire 1981-82. Hellenic 1984-85, 91-92.

County FA: Gloucestershire FA Trophy 1982-83.

07-08		08-09		09-10		10-11		11-12		12-13		13-14		14-15		15-16		16-17	
Hel P	5	Hel P	2	Hel P	2	Hel P	6	Hel P	2	Sthsw	8	Sthsw	6	Sthsw	11	Sthsw	7	Sthsw	9
FAC	3Q	FAC	2Qr	FAC	1Qr	FAC	Pr	FAC	Pr	FAC	P	FAC	1P	FAC	3Qr	FAC	2Q	FAC	P
FAV	1P	FAV	1P	FAV	4P	FAV	2P	FAV	QF	FAT	3Qr	FAT	1Q	FAT	1Q	FAT	P	FAT	P

SLIMBRIDGE

Club Contact Details
Thornhill Park, Cambridge, Glos GL2 7AF
07702 070 229
colin.gay@slimbridgeafc.co.uk

Founded: 1899   **Nickname:** The Swans   **Manager:** Freddy Ward
Previous Names: None
Previous Leagues: Stroud & District. Gloucester Northern. Gloucestershire County >2009. Hellenic 2009-2013. Western 2013-15.

Club Colours (change): All blue (Green/black/black)

Ground Capacity: 1,500   **Seats:** Yes   **Covered:** Yes   **Clubhouse:** Yes   **Shop:** Yes
Previous Grounds: Various venues around Slimbridge before moving to Wisloe Road (now Thornhill Park) in 1951.
Record Attendance: 525 v Shortwood United, Hellenic Premier, 24/08/2003.

RECORDS
Victory: 12-1 v Cheltenham Civil Service, Reg Davis Cup, 18.08.2007
Defeat: 1-6 v North Leigh, Hellenic Premier, 06.11.2004
Goalscorer: Julian Freeman - 79 (in 122 appearances)
Appearances: Fred Ward - 207

HONOURS
FA Comps: None
League: Stroud & District Division Three 1951-52, Division Two 1952-53, Division one 1953-54, 98-99, Division Four 1989-90.
     Hellenic Division 1 West 2009-10, Premier 06-07. Gloucester Northern 2007-08. Gloucestershire County 2008-09.
County FA: Gloucester Challenge Trophy 2003-04, 05-06, 06-07. Gloucester Northern Senior Cup 2000-01.

07-08	08-09	09-10	10-11	11-12	12-13	13-14	14-15	15-16	16-17
GlN1 1	GlCo 1	Hel1W 1	Hel P 5	Hel P 5	Hel P 6	WestP 16	WestP 3	Sthsw 18	Sthsw 20
FAC P				FAC P	FAC EP	FAC EPr	FAC P	FAC 2Q	FAC 2Q
			FAV 1Q	FAV 1P	FAV 1Q	FAV 2Q	FAV 2Pr	FAT P	FAT P

SWINDON SUPERMARINE

Club Contact Details
The Webbswood Stadium, South Marston, Swindon SN3 4BZ
01793 828 778
supermarinefc@aol.com

Founded: 1992   **Nickname:** Marine   **Manager:** Dave Webb
Previous Names: Club formed after the amalgamation of Swindon Athletic and Supermarine
Previous Leagues: Wiltshire, Hellenic 1992-2001.

Club Colours (change): All blue (All red)

Ground Capacity: 2,600   **Seats:** 325   **Covered:** Yes   **Clubhouse:** Yes   **Shop:** Yes
Previous Grounds: Supermarine: Vickers Airfield > Mid 1960s
Record Attendance: 1,550 v Aston Villa

RECORDS
Goalscorer: Damon York - 136 (1990-98)
Appearances: Damon York - 314 (1990-98)
Additional: Paid £1,000 to Hungerford Town for Lee Hartson

HONOURS
FA Comps: None
League: Hellenic League Premier Division 1997-98, 2000-01.

County FA: Wiltshire Premier Shield 1996-97, 2006-07. Senior Cup 2016-17.

07-08	08-09	09-10	10-11	11-12	12-13	13-14	14-15	15-16	16-17
SthP 12	SthP 13	SthP 14	SthP 10	SthP 21	Sthsw 4	Sthsw 5	Sthsw 14	Sthsw 4	Sthsw 7
FAC 1Q	FAC 1Q	FAC 1Q	FAC 2P	FAC 2Q	FAC 1Q	FAC P	FAC 2Q	FAC 1Q	FAC 3Q
FAT 1Qr	FAT 3P	FAT 1Q	FAT 1Q	FAT 1P	FAT 1Q	FAT 1Q	FAT P	FAT 2Q	FAT 1Q

TAUNTON TOWN

Club Contact Details
The Viridor Stadium, Wordsworth Drive, Taunton, Somerset TA1 2HG
01823 254 909
admin@tauntontown.com

Founded: 1947   **Nickname:** The Peacocks   **Manager:** Leigh Robinson
Previous Names: None
Previous Leagues: Western 1954-77, 83-2002, Southern 1977-83

Club Colours (change): Claret/sky blue/sky blue (Yellow/blue/yellow)

Ground Capacity: 2,500   **Seats:** 300   **Covered:** 1,000   **Clubhouse:** Yes   **Shop:** Yes
Previous Grounds: Mountfields. French Weir. Victoria Park. Huish Old Boys. Denman's Park > 1953.
Record Attendance: 3,284 v Tiverton Town - FA Vase Semi-final 1999

RECORDS
Victory: 12-0 v Dawlish Town (A) - FA Cup Preliminary Round 28/08/1993
Defeat: 0-8 v Cheltenham Town (A) - FA Cup 2nd Qualifying Round 28/09/1991
Goalscorer: Tony Payne. Reg Oram scored 67 in one season
Appearances: Tony Payne

HONOURS
FA Comps: FA Vase 2000-01.
League: Western League 1968-69, 89-90, 95-96, 98-99, 99-2000, 2000-01.
County FA: Somerset Senior Cup 1969-70, Premier Cup 2002-03, 05-06, 13-14, 14-15, 16-17.

07-08		08-09		09-10		10-11		11-12		12-13		13-14		14-15		15-16		16-17	
Sthsw	18	Sthsw	20	Sthsw	19	Sthsw	9	Sthsw	17	Sthsw	18	Sthsw	8	Sthsw	4	Sthsw	3	Sthsw	4
FAC	1Q	FAC	1Q	FAC	1Q	FAC	1Q	FAC	1Qr	FAC	1Qr	FAC	Pr	FAC	1Q	FAC	2Qr	FAC	1Pr
FAT	1Q	FAT	P	FAT	1Q	FAT	Pr	FAT	1Q	FAT	2Q	FAT	P	FAT	Pr	FAT	2Q	FAT	3Q

WIMBORNE TOWN

Club Contact Details
The W+S Stadium, Cowgrove Road, Wimborne, Dorset BH21 4EL
01202 884 821
barhamp@hotmail.co.uk

Founded: 1878   **Nickname:** Magpies   **Manager:** Matty Holmes
Previous Names: None
Previous Leagues: Dorset, Dorset Combination, Western 1981-86, Wessex 1986-2010

Club Colours (change): Black and white stripes/black/black

Ground Capacity: 3,250   **Seats:** 275   **Covered:** 425   **Clubhouse:** Yes   **Shop:** Yes
Previous Grounds: None
Record Attendance: 3,250 v Bamber Bridge

RECORDS
Goalscorer: Jason Lovell
Appearances: James Sturgess

HONOURS
FA Comps: FA Vase 1991-92.
League: Dorset Division One 1980-81. Wessex 1991-92, 93-94, 99-2000.
County FA: Dorset Minor Cup 1912-13, Senior Amateur Cup 1936-37, 63-64, Senior Cup 91-92, 96-97.

07-08		08-09		09-10		10-11		11-12		12-13		13-14		14-15		15-16		16-17	
WexP	3	WexP	4	WexP	2	Sthsw	19	Sthsw	19	Sthsw	12	Sthsw	13	Sthsw	13	Sthsw	17	Sthsw	11
FAC	1Q	FAC	1Q	FAC	1Q	FAC	1Q	FAC	P	FAC	P	FAC	P	FAC	1Q	FAC	2Q	FAC	Pr
FAV	3P	FAV	3P	FAV	2P	FAT	1Qr	FAT	P	FAT	2Q	FAT	P	FAT	1P	FAT	P	FAT	2Q

WINCHESTER CITY

Club Contact Details
The Simplyhealth City Ground, Hillier Way, Winchester SO23 7SR
07768 848 905
secretary.wcfc@gmail.com

Founded: 1884 **Nickname:** The Capitals **Manager:** Craig Davis - Mar 2017
Previous Names: None
Previous Leagues: Hampshire 1898-71, 73-03. Southern 1971-73, 2006-09, 2012-13. Wessex 2003-06. 2009-12, 13-15.

Club Colours (change): Red & black stripes/red/red

Ground Capacity: 4,500 **Seats:** 180 **Covered:** 275 **Clubhouse:** Yes **Shop:** Yes
Previous Grounds: None
Record Attendance: 1,818 v Bideford, FA Vase Semi-final.

RECORDS
Goalscorer: Andy Forbes.
Appearances: Ian Mancey.

HONOURS
FA Comps: FA Vase 2004.
League: Hampshire Division Two 1973-74, 91-92, Division One 2000-01, Premier Division 2002-03.
Wessex Division One 2003-04, 05-06, Premier Division 2011-12.
County FA: Hants Senior Cup 1930-31, 2004-05.

07-08		08-09		09-10		10-11		11-12		12-13		13-14		14-15		15-16		16-17	
SthW	17	SthW	22	WexP	11	WexP	3	WexP	1	SthC	22	WexP	5	WexP	2	Sthsw	5	Sthsw	14
FAC	P	FAC	1Q	FAC	EP	FAC	EP	FAC	P	FAC	1Q	FAC	1Q	FAC	3Q	FAC	2Qr	FAC	3Q
FAT	1Qr	FAV	1Q	FAV	1P	FAV	2Q	FAV	2P	FAT	P	FAV	1P	FAV	1P	FAT	1Q	FAT	3Q

YATE TOWN

Club Contact Details
Jelf Stadium, Lodge Road, Yate, Bristol BS37 7LE
01454 228 103
admin@yatetownfc.com

Founded: 1906 **Nickname:** The Bluebells **Manager:** Paul Britton
Previous Names: Yate Rovers 1906-1930s. Yate YMCA 1933-58.
Previous Leagues: Bristol Premier Combination > 1968, Gloucestershire County 1968-83, Hellenic 1983-89, 2000-03, Southern 1989-2000

Club Colours (change): White & navy blue

Ground Capacity: 2,000 **Seats:** 236 **Covered:** 400 **Clubhouse:** Yes **Shop:** Yes
Previous Grounds: Yate Aerodrome 1954-60. Sunnyside Lane 1960-84.
Record Attendance: 2,000 v Bristol Rovers v Bristol Rovers Past XI - Vaughan Jones testimonial 1990

RECORDS
Victory: 13-3 v Clevedon - Bristol Premier Combination 1967-68
Goalscorer: Kevin Thaws
Appearances: Gary Hewlett
Additional: Paid £2,000 to Chippenham Town for Matt Rawlings 2003
Received £15,000 from Bristol Rovers for Mike Davis

HONOURS
FA Comps: None
League: Hellenic 1987-88, 88-89.

County FA: Gloucestershire Senior Cup 2004-05, 05-06.

07-08		08-09		09-10		10-11		11-12		12-13		13-14		14-15		15-16		16-17	
SthP	10	SthP	21	Sthsw	13	Sthsw	14	Sthsw	13	Sthsw	6	Sthsw	9	Sthsw	6	Sthsw	16	Sthsw	18
FAC	1Q	FAC	1Q	FAC	1Qr	FAC	P	FAC	2Qr	FAC	1P	FAC	3Qr	FAC	1Q	FAC	P	FAC	P
FAT	2Q	FAT	2Q	FAT	2Qr	FAT	P	FAT	2Q	FAT	Pr	FAT	Pr	FAT	P	FAT	P	FAT	1Q

COMBINED COUNTIES LEAGUE

Sponsored by: Cherry Red Records

Founded: 1978

Recent Champions - 2014: South Park

2015: Molesey **2016:** Hartley Wintney

PREMIER DIVISION

		P	W	D	L	F	A	GD	Pts
1	Hartley Wintney	44	35	6	3	131	41	90	111
2	Westfield	44	28	9	7	106	52	54	93
3	Hanworth Villa	44	24	9	11	73	47	26	81
4	Epsom & Ewell	44	23	10	11	90	57	33	79
5	Walton & Hersham	44	21	15	8	70	42	28	78
6	Camberley Town	44	22	6	16	84	58	26	72
7	Horley Town	44	21	7	16	89	67	22	70
8	Bedfont Sports	44	17	13	14	78	80	-2	64
9	Spelthorne Sports	44	18	9	17	80	76	4	63
10	Abbey Rangers	44	17	12	15	71	73	-2	63
11	Windsor	44	17	10	17	78	71	7	61
12	Sutton Common Rovers	44	18	5	21	64	72	-8	59
13	North Greenford United	44	16	10	18	83	78	5	58
14	Knaphill	44	18	6	20	83	81	2	57*
15	Colliers Wood United	44	15	11	18	75	80	-5	56
16	Guildford City	44	15	8	21	78	86	-8	53
17	AFC Hayes	44	14	9	21	64	82	-18	51
18	Farnham Town	44	14	7	23	59	83	-24	49
19	Chertsey Town	44	14	7	23	55	91	-36	49
20	CB Hounslow United	44	14	5	25	55	85	-30	47
21	Badshot Lea	44	11	6	27	61	113	-52	39
22	Bedfont & Feltham	44	9	7	28	54	118	-64	34
23	Raynes Park Vale	44	7	9	28	43	91	-48	30

DIVISION ONE

		P	W	D	L	F	A	GD	Pts
1	Banstead Athletic	34	25	6	3	117	34	83	81
2	Redhill	34	23	4	7	106	35	71	73
3	Balham	34	20	7	7	104	52	52	67
4	Worcester Park	34	21	2	11	93	53	40	65*
5	Chessington & Hook United	34	19	7	8	72	43	29	64
6	Eversley & California	34	19	5	10	90	69	21	62
7	AC London	34	18	12	4	93	40	53	60*
8	Bagshot	34	19	3	12	91	74	17	60
9	Sheerwater	34	16	4	14	64	75	-11	52
10	Staines Lammas	34	14	7	13	56	51	5	49
11	Cobham	34	15	3	16	64	64	0	48
12	Ash United	34	13	5	16	62	78	-16	44
13	Frimley Green	34	10	9	15	57	56	1	38*
14	South Park Reserves	34	7	8	19	64	103	-39	29
15	Dorking	34	7	4	23	48	87	-39	25
16	Farleigh Rovers	34	6	5	23	65	123	-58	23
17	Cove	34	4	5	25	57	124	-67	17
18	Epsom Athletic	34	2	0	32	19	161	-142	6

PREMIER CHALLENGE CUP

HOLDERS: FARNHAM TOWN

ROUND 1

South Park Reserves	v	Balham	1-4
Westfield	v	North Greenford United	3-2
Redhill	v	Bedfont & Feltham	4-0
CB Hounslow United	v	Farnham Town	3-4
Knaphill	v	Camberley Town	0-2
Spelthorne Sports	v	Sutton Common Rovers	1-4
Worcester Park	v	Dorking	2-1
Epsom & Ewell	v	Abbey Rangers	1-0
Cobham	v	Bagshot	3-2 aet

ROUND 2

Badshot Lea	v	Guildford City	0-5
AFC Hayes	v	Balham	3-4
Raynes Park Vale	v	Colliers Wood United	2-0
Hartley Wintney	v	AC London	4-0
Frimley Green	v	Banstead Athletic	1-2
Westfield	v	Redhill	8-4
Staines Lammas	v	Farnham Town	0-1
Chertsey Town	v	Camberley Town	1-2
Sutton Common Rovers	v	Bedfont Sports	2-1 aet
Walton & Hersham	v	Eversley & California	5-1
Worcester Park	v	Cove	8-1
Hanworth Villa	v	Epsom & Ewell	2-4 aet
Ash United	v	Farleigh Rovers	2-0
Epsom Athletic	v	Windsor	1-5
Horley Town	v	Sheerwater	2-2, 5-4p
Cobham	v	Chessington & Hook United	1-3

ROUND 3

Guildford City	v	Balham	2-1
Raynes Park Vale	v	Hartley Wintney	2-1
Banstead Athletic	v	Westfield	4-4, 2-4p
Farnham Town	v	Camberley Town	0-4
Sutton Common Rovers	v	Walton & Hersham	1-3
Worcester Park	v	Epsom & Ewell	3-6
Ash United	v	Windsor	0-2
Horley Town	v	Chessington & Hook United	2-0

QUARTER FINALS

Guildford City	v	Raynes Park Vale	1-2
Westfield	v	Camberley Town	4-1
Walton & Hersham	v	Epsom & Ewell	1-3
Windsor	v	Horley Town	2-0

SEMI FINALS

Raynes Park Vale	v	Westfield	0-4
Epsom & Ewell	v	Windsor	2-0

FINAL

Westfield	v	Epsom & Ewell	4-1

DIVISION ONE CHALLENGE CUP

HOLDERS: WORCESTER PARK

ROUND 1

AC London	v	Banstead Athletic	2-0
Cobham	v	Staines Lammas	4-7 aet

ROUND 2

Redhill	v	Sheerwater	2-1
Dorking	v	Balham	1-6
Bagshot	v	Eversley & California	4-4, 4-5p
Ash United	v	Cove	4-1
AC London	v	Chessington & Hook United	2-1
Frimley Green	v	Epsom Athletic	2-2, 4-2p
Staines Lammas	v	Worcester Park	2-4 aet
South Park Reserves	v	Farleigh Rovers	5-1

QUARTER FINALS

Redhill	v	Balham	4-2
Eversley & California	v	Ash United	1-3
AC London	v	Frimley Green	2-0
Worcester Park	v	South Park Reserves	6-1

SEMI FINALS

Redhill	v	Ash United	4-1
AC London	v	Worcester Park	1-0

FINAL

Redhill	v	AC London	2-3

CLUB MOVEMENTS

Premier Division - In: Balham (P), Banstead Athletic (P), Godalming Town (R - Isthmian DivS), Redhill (P). **Out:** Badshot Lea (R), Bedfont & Feltham (R), Hartley Wintney (P - Southern Div1C). Raynes Park Vale (R). Windsor (S - Hellenic). **Division One - In:** Badshot Lea (R), Bedfont & Feltham (R), Fleet Spurs (S - Wessex), FC Deportivo Galicia (P - Middlesex County), Kensington Borough (S - Spartan South Midlands), Raynes Park Vale (R), **Out:** Balham (P), Banstead Athletic (P), Dorking (F), Epsom Athletic (R), Redhill (P).

PREMIER DIVISION	1	2	3	4	5	6	7	8	9	10	11	12	13	14	15	16	17	18	19	20	21	22	23
1 Abbey Rangers		1-1	4-0	4-1	0-2	1-2	0-3	0-1	1-4	0-1	1-0	2-4	1-1	2-2	0-2	3-3	2-2	2-0	4-3	1-0	1-1	1-0	2-0
2 AFC Hayes	1-2		0-1	1-4	3-1	1-3	1-0	0-2	1-4	1-0	0-2	4-1	1-2	2-3	2-2	0-4	3-0	2-0	2-2	1-1	2-5	2-4	1-0
3 Badshot Lea	1-2	2-2		3-1	2-2	0-2	2-4	3-1	3-4	1-4	1-2	1-1	2-5	0-9	2-1	2-1	2-1	1-1	3-2	1-3	4-3	0-3	1-3
4 Bedfont & Feltham	1-3	1-3	0-1		0-0	1-5	3-1	2-2	3-2	2-9	0-4	2-2	0-4	2-7	4-2	0-3	0-3	0-2	1-2	1-2	1-4	0-3	1-0
5 Bedfont Sports	3-3	1-2	4-3	4-1		0-2	2-2	2-2	1-1	1-3	5-0	4-2	2-2	1-4	0-4	3-3	1-0	2-1	1-0	1-2	1-4	3-3	2-2
6 Camberley Town	1-1	1-3	5-1	5-0	1-3		2-1	1-2	3-3	2-0	5-1	0-1	0-1	2-3	3-0	2-0	0-0	1-1	4-2	0-1	2-1	2-6	0-3
7 CB Hounslow United	0-2	2-2	3-1	0-3	1-2	0-3		1-2	3-1	0-2	1-0	2-3	0-1	0-2	3-2	2-4	0-3	2-1	0-2	1-0	1-5	2-1	
8 Chertsey Town	1-0	3-2	1-4	3-3	2-1	0-2	1-0		2-0	0-3	0-1	1-2	1-2	0-0	3-4	0-1	4-2	2-1	2-2	0-1	1-2	0-3	1-3
9 Colliers Wood United	1-2	0-2	2-1	3-0	0-2	0-3	3-3	2-1		5-0	3-0	1-1	1-3	1-2	2-2	1-0	1-2	0-1	0-3	2-4	0-4	1-1	0-2
10 Epsom & Ewell	7-1	2-2	4-2	4-1	5-1	0-0	1-5	2-1	0-1		2-2	1-0	2-2	0-1	3-0	4-0	3-2	1-1	3-2	2-1	1-1	2-1	2-0
11 Farnham Town	2-3	4-1	1-0	5-2	2-3	1-4	0-1	2-2	2-2	1-2		2-3	0-0	0-2	0-1	2-1	1-0	2-1	2-2	3-1	1-1	0-3	2-2
12 Guildford City	2-3	2-0	2-0	2-0	2-0	2-3	3-0	6-1	0-4	0-2	7-3		0-1	0-1	2-7	1-3	4-4	5-1	1-4	0-1	1-0	1-1	3-3
13 Hanworth Villa	1-0	1-1	4-0	2-2	0-2	2-1	0-1	3-0	1-0	1-0	1-0	2-1		0-0	1-3	2-1	3-7	0-0	0-1	2-1	1-2	0-2	1-2
14 Hartley Wintney	4-2	6-2	2-2	2-3	5-0	2-1	3-1	5-1	4-1	3-1	2-0	1-0	2-0		0-1	3-1	7-0	6-1	4-3	2-1	1-1	3-1	2-1
15 Horley Town	3-2	3-1	1-1	3-2	2-1	2-2	2-0	1-0	2-2	1-2	1-2	4-1	2-1	1-2		2-3	4-1	4-0	1-2	3-0	0-0	1-2	5-3
16 Knaphill	2-1	2-1	2-0	4-0	2-2	3-2	1-2	5-0	3-3	1-2	2-1	1-3	1-3	1-4	2-0		0-1	5-2	1-2	2-5	2-1	2-2	3-1
17 North Greenford United	1-1	0-1	3-2	1-1	1-1	0-3	3-0	8-0	1-1	2-1	0-2	2-1	1-2	0-1	2-0	1-3		5-3	2-1	6-0	1-2	3-2	1-1
18 Raynes Park Vale	0-1	1-0	0-1	0-1	1-3	0-2	1-0	4-0	2-2	1-1	2-0	2-2	1-2	0-4	0-4	2-1	1-1		0-1	0-2	2-3	1-3	2-3
19 Spelthorne Sports	1-1	1-2	3-2	2-0	2-1	4-0	4-0	2-1	4-5	2-2	2-0	3-0	0-5	1-4	0-3	2-0	2-3	2-2		0-1	2-1	0-2	3-3
20 Sutton Common Rovers	1-3	2-1	3-2	0-1	0-1	0-1	1-2	0-2	1-2	1-1	2-3	2-2	1-2	2-8	1-1	4-0	4-2	3-1	2-1		0-1	1-1	3-1
21 Walton & Hersham	1-1	1-1	2-0	2-0	0-0	2-0	1-1	1-1	3-1	1-1	1-0	1-0	0-0	3-1	4-2	2-1	2-0	0-0	1-0			2-2	1-2
22 Westfield	2-2	2-1	4-0	3-2	1-2	2-1	5-1	1-3	2-1	3-1	2-0	2-1	1-1	2-0	2-1	3-2	5-0	1-1	4-1	3-1			2-1
23 Windsor	4-2	1-2	6-0	1-1	2-4	1-0	2-2	1-2	0-1	2-1	5-0	4-2	0-5	0-2	2-1	1-1	2-2	2-0	3-0	1-0	0-0	1-3	

DIVISION ONE	1	2	3	4	5	6	7	8	9	10	11	12	13	14	15	16	17	18
1 AC London		0-1	1-1	1-2	1-1	1-0	1-1	7-1	3-2	11-0	3-3	8-0	2-1	0-0	1-1	7-2	1-1	1-2
2 Ash United	2-3		0-5	1-4	1-7	0-4	4-1	4-4	3-1	5-1	3-0	3-0	1-1	2-3	3-0	1-2	1-2	1-8
3 Bagshot	1-5	3-5		0-4	0-4	2-5	0-2	3-0	3-1	9-1	5-1	7-2	2-0	1-0	2-3	6-0	2-2	3-2
4 Balham	1-1	2-2	3-5		3-4	1-2	2-1	3-1	1-1	8-1	7-1	2-2	0-2	2-1	3-2	3-1	3-3	4-2
5 Banstead Athletic	3-3	2-0	2-0	2-1		1-1	1-2	3-2	4-0	10-1	4-1	6-1	1-1	0-0	5-0	4-1	3-2	0-0
6 Chessington & Hook United	0-2	3-1	0-3	0-0	4-1		0-0	6-1	1-0	1-0	2-2	4-1	2-0	2-1	3-2	3-1	2-1	1-3
7 Cobham	0-2	3-0	1-2	1-3	1-7	5-4		6-1	3-1	8-0	0-2	3-2	0-2	0-3	2-0	3-5	1-2	3-1
8 Cove	5-5	1-2	3-3	0-4	1-6	1-3	1-3		2-1	5-1	2-4	4-6	3-0	0-10	1-4	1-5	0-2	0-3
9 Dorking	0-5	1-5	2-4	1-7	1-2	0-5	2-0	5-2		6-0	0-2	3-2	2-1	0-2	2-2	1-1	0-3	3-2
10 Epsom Athletic	AW	0-1	1-2	0-7	0-3	0-3	0-2	2-1	1-2		2-5	0-7	0-3	0-12	1-3	1-2	0-2	0-5
11 Eversley & California	2-3	3-0	4-1	1-3	2-5	2-2	5-0	2-2	4-1	7-0		5-3	0-3	3-1	2-1	6-2	2-1	3-2
12 Farleigh Rovers	0-4	1-5	2-4	3-4	2-11	1-0	2-3	2-1	1-0	6-0	3-5		2-2	1-4	2-2	2-2	0-4	0-9
13 Frimley Green	0-0	2-2	2-3	1-1	0-2	1-1	1-3	1-3	3-2	4-0	0-6	6-1		0-2	6-0	3-0	0-2	0-2
14 Redhill	0-3	6-0	6-1	3-0	1-0	2-3	3-0	6-3	2-0	4-0	3-1	2-1	2-2		5-1	7-0	2-0	2-1
15 Sheerwater	1-3	0-0	1-4	3-2	0-4	1-0	0-4	4-1	3-1	5-1	1-2	3-2	4-3	1-0		4-3	3-0	3-2
16 South Park Reserves	2-3	0-2	9-1	0-6	0-2	1-4	1-1	3-3	2-2	1-2	0-2	5-4	1-1	4-4	1-2		2-2	4-2
17 Staines Lammas	0-0	2-1	0-3	1-4	1-2	1-1	2-0	2-1	2-1	5-2	0-0	1-0	1-4	1-3	1-2	6-1		0-2
18 Worcester Park	4-2	3-0	HW	2-4	0-5	4-0	2-1	3-0	4-3	6-1	4-0	1-1	3-1	2-4	3-2	2-0	2-1	

ABBEY RANGERS

Founded: 1976   Nickname:

Secretary: Graham Keable   **(T)** 07711 042 588   **(E)** graham.keable@ntlworld.com
Chairman: Denis Healy   **Manager:** Mike Woolgar   **Prog Ed:** Clive Robertson
Ground: Addlestone Moor, Addlestone, KT15 2QH   **(T)** 01932 422 962
Capacity: **Seats:** Yes   **Covered:** Yes   **Midweek Matchday:** Monday   **Clubhouse:** Yes

Colours(change): Black & white stripes/black/black
Previous Names: None
Previous Leagues: Surrey Elite 2011-2015

HONOURS: FA Comps: None
     League: Surrey & Hants Border League 2004-05.
10 YEAR RECORD Surrey Intermediate League (Western) Division One 2008-09.

07-08	08-09	09-10	10-11	11-12	12-13	13-14	14-15	15-16	16-17
	SuI1 1	SuIP	SuIP	SuEI 10	SuEI 7	SuEI 3	SuEI 4	CC1 3	CCP 10
									FAC EP
								FAV 2P	FAV 3P

AFC HAYES

Founded: 1976   Nickname: The Brook

Secretary: Barry Crump   **(T)** 07966 468 029   **(E)** afchayesfootballsec@hotmail.co.uk
Chairman: Barry Stone   **Manager:** Paul Palmer   **Prog Ed:** Graham White
Ground: Farm Park, Kingshill Avenue, Hayes UB4 8DD   **(T)** 020 8845 0110
Capacity: 2,000   **Seats:** 150   **Covered:** 200   **Midweek Matchday:** Tuesday   **Clubhouse:** Yes

Colours(change): Blue and white stripes/blue/blue
Previous Names: Brook House > 2007.
Previous Leagues: Spartan South Midlands 1988-2004. Isthmian 2004-06.
                Southern 2006-15.
HONOURS: FA Comps: None
     League: Spartan South Midlands Premier South 1997-98.
10 YEAR RECORD

07-08	08-09	09-10	10-11	11-12	12-13	13-14	14-15	15-16	16-17
Sthsw 14	Sthsw 9	Sthsw 21	SthC 19	SthC 10	SthC 15	SthC 18	SthC 22	CCP 16	CCP 17
FAC P	FAC P	FAC P	FAC P	FAC P	FAC 1Q	FAC P	FAC 1Q	FAC Pr	FAC P
FAT P	FAT 1Q	FAT P	FAT 1Q	FAT 1Q	FAT P	FAT 1Q	FAT Pr	FAV 2Q	FAV 1Q

BALHAM

Founded: 2011   Nickname:

Secretary: Greg Cruttwell   **(T)** 07763 581 523   **(E)** g.cruttwell@btinternet.com
Chairman: Jennie Molyneux   **Manager:** Greg Cruttwell   **Prog Ed:** Anthony Lawrence
Ground: Colliers Wood Utd, Wibandune Sports Gd, Lincoln Green, Wimbledon SW20 0AA   **(T)** 020 8942 8062
Capacity: 2000   **Seats:** 102   **Covered:**   **Midweek Matchday:**   **Clubhouse:** Yes

Colours(change): White & black/black/black (Maroon/white/maroon)
Previous Names:
Previous Leagues: Surrey South Eastern Combination 2011-15. Surrey Elite Intermediate 2015-2016

HONOURS: FA Comps: None
     League: Surrey South Eastern Combination Intermediate Division One 2013-14.
10 YEAR RECORD

07-08	08-09	09-10	10-11	11-12	12-13	13-14	14-15	15-16	16-17
				SSECJ1 4	SSECI2 3	SSECI1 1	SuEI 3	SuEI 2	CC1 3

BANSTEAD ATHLETIC

Founded: 1944   Nickname: The A's

Secretary: Terry Molloy   **(T)** 07958 436 483   **(E)** terrymolloy@leyfield.eclipse.co.uk
Chairman: Terry Molloy   **Manager:** James Cameron   **Prog Ed:** Bob Lockyar
Ground: Merland Rise, Tadworth, Surrey KT20 5JG   **(T)** 01737 350 982
Capacity: 4000   **Seats:** 250   **Covered:** 800   **Midweek Matchday:** Tuesday   **Clubhouse:** Yes   **Shop:** Yes

Colours(change): Amber & black/black/black
Previous Names: Banstead Juniors 1944-46.
Previous Leagues: Surrey Senior 1949-79. Athenian 1979-85. Isthmian 1985-2006.

HONOURS: FA Comps: None
     League: Surrey Senior League 1950-51, 51-52, 52-53, 53-54, 56-57, 64-65.
10 YEAR RECORD Combined Counties League Division One 2016-17.

07-08	08-09	09-10	10-11	11-12	12-13	13-14	14-15	15-16	16-17
CCP 17	CCP 10	CCP 20	CCP 17	CCP 22	CC1 17	CC1 12	CC1 6	CC1 6	CC1 1
FAC P	FAC EP	FAC EPr	FAC P	FAC 1Q	FAC EP			FAC EPr	FAC Pr
FAV 2Q	FAT 2P	FAV 2Q	FAV 2Q	FAV 2Q	FAV 2Q	FAV 2Q	FAV 1P	FAV 2Q	FAV 1P

BEDFONT SPORTS
Founded: 2000 **Nickname:** The Eagles

Secretary: David Sturt **(T)** 07712 824 112 **(E)** dave.sturt2@blueyonder.co.uk
Chairman: David Reader **Manager:** Mick Snowden **Prog Ed:** Terry Reader
Ground: Bedfont Sports Club, Hatton Road, Bedfont TW14 8JA **(T)** 0208 831 9067
Capacity: 3,000 **Seats:** Yes **Covered:** 200 **Midweek Matchday:** Tuesday **Clubhouse:**

Colours(change): Red & black hoops/black/red & black hoops
Previous Names: Bedfont Sunday became Bedfont Sports in 2002 - Bedfont Eagles (1978) merged with the club shortly afterwards.
Previous Leagues: Hounslow & District 2003-04. Middlesex County 2004-09.

HONOURS: FA Comps: None
League: Hounslow & District League Division One 2003-04.

10 YEAR RECORD

07-08	08-09	09-10	10-11	11-12	12-13	13-14	14-15	15-16	16-17
		CC1 9	CC1 4	CC1 2	CCP 13	CCP 17	CCP 16	CCP 13	CCP 8
				FAC Pr	FAC EP	FAC P	FAC EP	FAC P	FAC P
			FAV 1Q	FAV 1P	FAV 2Q	FAV 2Q	FAV 1P	FAV 1P	FAV 3Pr

CAMBERLEY TOWN
Founded: 1895 **Nickname:** Reds or Town

Secretary: Ben Clifford **(T)** 07876 552 210 **(E)** benjaminclifford@sky.com
Chairman: **Manager:** Dan Turkington
Ground: Krooner Park, Wilton Road, Camberley, Surrey GU15 2QW **(T)** 01276 65 392
Capacity: 1,976 **Seats:** 196 **Covered:** 300 **Midweek Matchday:** Tuesday **Clubhouse:** Yes **Shop:** Yes

Colours(change): Red and white stripes/red/red
Previous Names: St Michael's FC (St Michael's Camberley) 1895-1901. Camberley & Yorktown 1901-46. Camberley 1946-67.
Previous Leagues: East & West Surrey (West Surrey) 1898-99, 1910-22. Aldershot Comb 1902-03. Ascot & Dist 1903-10. Surrey Senior 1922-73. Spartan 1973-75. Athenian 1975-77, 82-84. Isthmian 1977-82, 84-2006.

HONOURS: FA Comps: None
League: Ascot & Dist. 1904-05, 07-08, 08-09, 09-10. Aldershot Sen. Civilian 1912-13. West Surrey 1913-14. Surrey Senior 1930-31, 31-32, 32-33.

10 YEAR RECORD

07-08	08-09	09-10	10-11	11-12	12-13	13-14	14-15	15-16	16-17
CCP 3	CCP 5	CCP 3	CCP 4	CCP 6	CCP 16	CCP 2	CCP 2	CCP 3	CCP 6
FAC 2Qr	FAC P	FAC EP	FAC P	FAC P	FAC P	FAC 1Qr	FAC EP	FAC EP	FAC 1Q
FAV 5P	FAV 3P	FAV 1P	FAV 2P	FAV 1P	FAV 2Q	FAV 2Q	FAV 1P	FAT QF	FAV 2P

CB HOUNSLOW UNITED
Founded: 1989 **Nickname:** None

Secretary: Stephen Hosmer **(T)** 07900 604 936 **(E)** stephen.hosmer@btinternet.com
Chairman: Frank James **Manager:** Barry Chapman **Prog Ed:** As Secretary
Ground: Bedfont & Feltham FC, The Orchard, Hatton Road, Bedfont TW14 9QT **(T)** 0208 890 7264
Capacity: 1200 **Seats:** 100 **Covered:** Yes **Midweek Matchday:** Tuesday **Clubhouse:** Yes

Colours(change): Green/black/green
Previous Names: CB United 1989-94.
Previous Leagues: Hounslow & District 1989-94. Middlesex County 1994-2006.

HONOURS: FA Comps: None
League: Combined Counties League Division One 2015-16.

10 YEAR RECORD

07-08	08-09	09-10	10-11	11-12	12-13	13-14	14-15	15-16	16-17
CC1 10	CC1 10	CC1 15	CC1 14	CC1 15	CC1 8	CC1 14	CC1 7	CC1 1	CCP 20
									FAC 1Q
							FAV 1Q	FAV 2Q	FAV 2Q

CHERTSEY TOWN
Founded: 1890 **Nickname:** Curfews

Secretary: Chris Gay **(T)** 07713 473 313 **(E)** chrisegay@googlemail.com
Chairman: Steve Powers **Manager:** Kim Harris **Prog Ed:** Chris Gay
Ground: Alwyns Lane, Chertsey, Surrey KT16 9DW **(T)** 01932 561 774
Capacity: 3,000 **Seats:** 240 **Covered:** 760 **Midweek Matchday:** Tuesday **Clubhouse:** Yes **Shop:** Yes

Colours(change): Royal blue & white stripes/royal blue/royal blue
Previous Names: Chertsey 1890-1950.
Previous Leagues: Metropolitan. Spartan. Athenian. Isthmian, Combined Counties 2006-11. Southern 2011-14.

HONOURS: FA Comps: None
League: None

10 YEAR RECORD

07-08	08-09	09-10	10-11	11-12	12-13	13-14	14-15	15-16	16-17
CCP 8	CCP 3	CCP 2	CCP 2	SthC 17	SthC 20	SthC 21	CCP 20	CCP 18	CCP 19
FAC P	FAC P	FAC P	FAC 2Q	FAC 2Q	FAC P	FAC 2Q	FAC EPr	FAC P	FAC 1Q
FAV 1P	FAV 1P	FAV 5Pr	FAV 2P	FAT 3Q	FAT 1Q	FAT 1Q	FAV 1P	FAV 2Q	FAV 1Q

COLLIERS WOOD UNITED
Founded: 1874   Nickname: The Woods

Secretary: Chris Clapham   **(T)** 07812 181 601   **(E)** collierswoodunited@yahoo.co.uk
Chairman: Steve Turner   **Manager:** Tony Hurrell   **Prog Ed:** Chris Clapham
Ground: Wibandune Sports Ground, Lincoln Green, Wimbledon SW20 0AA   **(T)** 0208 942 8062
Capacity: 2000   **Seats:** 102   **Covered:** 100   **Midweek Matchday:** Wednesday   **Clubhouse:** Yes   **Shop:** Yes

Colours(change): Royal blue & navy/black/black (Red & white stripes/red/red or All green)
Previous Names: Vandyke 1874-1997. Vandyke Colliers United 1997-99.
Previous Leagues: Wimbledon & Sutton. Surrey Intermediate. Surrey County Senior

HONOURS: FA Comps: None
League: Surrey County Premier League 1997-98.

10 YEAR RECORD

07-08		08-09		09-10		10-11		11-12		12-13		13-14		14-15		15-16		16-17	
CCP	7	CCP	14	CCP	19	CCP	11	CCP	19	CCP	18	CCP	16	CCP	11	CCP	8	CCP	15
FAC	1Q	FAC	1Q	FAC	P	FAC	EP	FAC	EPr	FAC	P	FAC	P	FAC	EP	FAC	EP	FAC	2Qr
FAV	1P	FAV	1Q	FAV	1Q	FAV	3P	FAV	1P	FAV	3P	FAV	1Q	FAV	4P	FAV	3P	FAV	1Q

EPSOM & EWELL
Founded: 1918   Nickname: E's or Salts

Secretary: Peter Beddoe   **(T)** 07767 078 132   **(E)** p.beddoe1@ntlworld.com
Chairman: Peter Beddoe   **Manager:** Glyn Mandeville   **Prog Ed:** Richard Lambert
Ground: Chipstead FC, High Road, Chipstead, Surrey CR5 3SF   **(T)** 01737 553 250
Capacity: 2,000   **Seats:** 150   **Covered:** 200   **Midweek Matchday:** Tuesday   **Clubhouse:** Yes

Colours(change): Royal blue & white hoops/royal blue/royal blue
Previous Names: Epsom T (previously Epsom FC) merged with Ewell & Stoneleigh in 1960
Previous Leagues: Corinthian. Athenian. Surrey Senior. Isthmian >2006.

HONOURS: FA Comps: None
League: Sutton & Dist. Prem. 1922-23. Southern Suburban 1923-24.
Surrey Senior 1925-26, 26-27, 74-75. London 1927-28. Isthmian Division Two 1977-78.

10 YEAR RECORD

07-08		08-09		09-10		10-11		11-12		12-13		13-14		14-15		15-16		16-17	
CCP	10	CCP	4	CCP	5	CCP	10	CCP	14	CCP	5	CCP	3	CCP	7	CCP	4	CCP	4
FAC	EP	FAC	1Q	FAC	P	FAC	1Q	FAC	P	FAC	1Q	FAC	EPr	FAC	Pr	FAC	EP	FAC	P
FAV	2Qr	FAV	1P	FAT	3P	FAV	2Q	FAV	2Q	FAV	1Q	FAV	2Q	FAV	1P	FAV	1Q	FAV	2P

FARNHAM TOWN
Founded: 1906   Nickname: The Town

Secretary: Jane Warner   **(T)** 07846 774 560   **(E)** janeannwarner@btinternet.com
Chairman: Ray Bridger   **Manager:** Paul Tanner   **Prog Ed:** Meghan Charlton
Ground: Memorial Ground, West Street, Farnham GU9 7DY   **(T)** 01252 715 305
Capacity: 1,500   **Seats:** 50   **Covered:**   **Midweek Matchday:** Tuesday   **Clubhouse:** Yes

Colours(change): Claret & sky blue/white, claret & sky blue/sky blue
Previous Names: Formed after the merger of Farnham Bungs and Farnham Star.
Previous Leagues: Surrey Intermediate. Surrey Senior 1947-71. Spartan 1971-75, London Spartan 1975-80, Combined Co. 1980-92, 93-2006, Isthmian 1992-93 (resigned pre-season).

HONOURS: FA Comps: None
League: Surrey Intermediate 1929-30, 30-31. Surrey Senior 1965-66, 66-67, 67-68.
Combined Counties 1990-91, 91-92, Division One 2006-07.

10 YEAR RECORD

07-08		08-09		09-10		10-11		11-12		12-13		13-14		14-15		15-16		16-17	
CC1	5	CC1	8	CC1	11	CC1	2	CCP	12	CCP	8	CCP	15	CCP	10	CCP	10	CCP	18
FAC	EP	FAC	EP	FAC	EPr	FAC	P	FAC	P	FAC	EP	FAC	P	FAC	EP	FAC	1Q	FAC	P
FAV	1P	FAV	2Q	FAV	2Q	FAV	2Q	FAV	1P	FAV	2Q	FAV	1P	FAV	1Pr	FAV	1P	FAV	1Q

GODALMING TOWN
Founded: 1950   Nickname: The G's

Secretary: Ross Mose   **(T)**   **(E)** secretary@godalmingtownfc.com
Chairman: Kevin Young   **Manager:** Simon Funnell   **Prog Ed:** Giles Pattison
Ground: Wey Court, Meadrow, Guildford, Surrey GU7 3JE   **(T)** 01483 417 520
Capacity: 3,000   **Seats:** 200   **Covered:** 400   **Midweek Matchday:**   **Clubhouse:** Yes   **Shop:** Yes

Colours(change): Yellow & green
Previous Names: Godalming United 1950-71. Godalming & Farncombe 1971-79. Godalming Town 1979-92. Godalming & Guildford 1992-2005.
Previous Leagues: Combined Counties, Southern 2006-08, 12-16. Isthmian 2008-12, 16-17.

HONOURS: FA Comps: None
League: Combined Counties Premier Division 1983-84, 2005-06.

10 YEAR RECORD

07-08		08-09		09-10		10-11		11-12		12-13		13-14		14-15		15-16		16-17	
Sthsw	12	Isth1S	9	Isth1S	4	Isth1S	17	Isth1S	5	SthC	3	Sthsw	18	SthC	8	SthC	10	Isth1S	24
FAC	Pr	FAC	3Q	FAC	P	FAC	1Q	FAC	4Q	FAC	1Qr	FAC	P	FAC	1Qr	FAC	1Q	FAC	1Q
FAT	P	FAT	P	FAT	3Q	FAT	2Qr	FAT	2Q	FAT	P	FAT	P	FAT	P	FAT	P	FAT	P

GUILDFORD CITY
Founded: 1996   **Nickname:** The Sweeney

Secretary: Barry Underwood   **(T)** 07757 730 304   **(E)** barry.underwood@guildfordcityfc.co.uk
Chairman: Mark Redhead   **Manager:** Chris Balchin   **Prog Ed:** Barry Underwood
Ground: Spectrum Leisure Centre, Parkway, Guildford GU1 1UP   **(T)** 01483 443 322
Capacity: 1100   **Seats:** 269   **Covered:** Yes   **Midweek Matchday:** Wednesday   **Clubhouse:** Yes   **Shop:** Yes

Colours(change): Red & white stripes/black/red (Yellow & blue stripes/blue/blue)
Previous Names: AFC Guildford 1996-2005. Guildford United 2005-06.
Previous Leagues: Surrey Senior. Combined Counties > 2012. Southern 2012-14.

HONOURS: FA Comps: None
League: Southern League 1937-38, 55-56, League cup 1962-63, 66-67.

10 YEAR RECORD | Combined Counties Division One 2003-04, Premier Division 2010-11, 11-12

07-08	08-09	09-10	10-11	11-12	12-13	13-14	14-15	15-16	16-17
CCP 2	CCP 20	CCP 7	CCP 1	CCP 1	SthC 9	Sthsw 22	CCP 17	CCP 14	CCP 16
FAC P	FAC EP	FAC 1Qr	FAC 2Q	FAC EP	FAC 1Q	FAC P	FAC EP	FAC P	FAC 1Q
FAV 2P	FAV 1P	FAV 2Q	FAV 4P	FAV 2P	FAT 1Q	FAT P	FAV 1P	FAV 1Q	FAV 1Q

HANWORTH VILLA
Founded: 1976   **Nickname:** The Vilans

Secretary: Dave Brown   **(T)** 07971 650 297   **(E)** david.h.brown@btconnect.com
Chairman: Gary Brunning   **Manager:** Rufus Brevett   **Prog Ed:** Gary Brunning
Ground: Rectory Meadows, Park Road, Hanworth TW13 6PN   **(T)** 020 8831 9391
Capacity: 600   **Seats:** 100   **Covered:** Yes   **Midweek Matchday:** Tuesday   **Clubhouse:** Yes

Colours(change): Red & white/black/black
Previous Names: None
Previous Leagues: Hounslow & District Lge. West Middlesex Lge. Middlesex County League.

HONOURS: FA Comps: None
League: Hounslow & District Div.1 & Prem. West Middlesex Division One & Division Two.

10 YEAR RECORD | Middlesex County 2002-03, 04-05.

07-08	08-09	09-10	10-11	11-12	12-13	13-14	14-15	15-16	16-17
CC1 2	CC1 2	CCP 17	CCP 5	CCP 3	CCP 9	CCP 8	CCP 19	CCP 7	CCP 3
				FAC 4Q	FAC P	FAC P	FAC Pr	FAC EP	FAC P
			FAV 2Q	FAV 3Pr	FAV 4P	FAV 4P	FAV 3P	FAV 1P	FAV 1Q

HORLEY TOWN
Founded: 1896   **Nickname:** The Clarets

Secretary: Spencer Mitchell   **(T)** 07802 962 499   **(E)** mitchandharri@yahoo.co.uk
Chairman: Mark Sale   **Manager:** Glynn Stephens   **Prog Ed:** Philippa Burbidge
Ground: The New Defence, Court Lodge Road, Horley RH6 8SP   **(T)** 01293 822 000
Capacity: 1800   **Seats:** 150   **Covered:** 100   **Midweek Matchday:** Tuesday   **Clubhouse:** Yes   **Shop:** Yes

Colours(change): Claret & blue/claret/sky blue (White/black/black)
Previous Names: Horley >1975
Previous Leagues: Surrey Intermediate 1925-51, 55- Surrey Senior 1951-55, 71-78, London Spartan 1978-81, Athenian 1981-84, Combined Counties 1984-96, Surrey County Senior 2002-03.

HONOURS: FA Comps: None
League: Surrey Intermediate 1926-27, Eastern Section 1950-51. Surrey Senior 1976-77.

10 YEAR RECORD

07-08	08-09	09-10	10-11	11-12	12-13	13-14	14-15	15-16	16-17
CCP 5	CCP 12	CCP 14	CCP 16	CCP 7	CCP 12	CCP 19	CCP 12	CCP 6	CCP 7
FAC 1Q	FAC EPr	FAC Pr	FAC P	FAC 1Q	FAC Pr	FAC 1Q	FAC EP	FAC Pr	FAC EP
FAV 2Q	FAV 1P	FAV 2Q	FAV 1P	FAV 2Q	FAV 1P	FAV 1Q	FAV 3P	FAV 1Q	FAV 1P

KNAPHILL
Founded: 1924   **Nickname:** The Knappers

Secretary: Mike Clement   **(T)** 07795 322 031   **(E)** knaphillfc.seniorsecretary@gmail.com
Chairman: David Freeman   **Manager:** Keith Hills   **Prog Ed:** David Freeman
Ground: Brookwood Country Park, Redding Way, Knaphill GU21 2AY   **(T)** 01483 475 150
Capacity: 750   **Seats:** 50   **Covered:** Yes   **Midweek Matchday:** Tuesday   **Clubhouse:** Yes

Colours(change): Red/black/red
Previous Names: None
Previous Leagues: Woking & District. Surrey Intermediate (Western) > 2007

HONOURS: FA Comps: None
League: Woking & District League 1978-79.

10 YEAR RECORD | Surrey Intermediate League Division Three 1980-81, Division One 2005-06, Premier 06-07.

07-08	08-09	09-10	10-11	11-12	12-13	13-14	14-15	15-16	16-17
CC1 7	CC1 5	CC1 3	CC1 9	CC1 12	CC1 12	CC1 3	CCP 13	CCP 5	CCP 14
							FAC 1Q	FAC EP	FAC EPr
				FAV 1Q	FAV 1Q	FAV 2P	FAV 2P	FAV 4P	FAV 3P

NORTH GREENFORD UNITED
Founded: 1944   Nickname: Blues

Secretary: Mrs Barbara Bivens   **(T)** 07915 661 580   **(E)** barbarabivens@talktalk.net
Chairman: John Bivens   **Manager:** Danny Vincent   **Prog Ed:** Graham White
Ground: Berkeley Fields, Berkley Avenue, Greenford UB6 0NX   **(T)** 0208 422 8923
Capacity: 2,000 **Seats:** 150   **Covered:** 100   **Midweek Matchday:** Tuesday   **Clubhouse:** Yes

Colours(change): Royal blue & white/Royal blue/royal blue
Previous Names: None
Previous Leagues: London Spartan, Combined Counties 2002-10. Southern 2010-16.

HONOURS: FA Comps: None
League: Combined Counties League Premier Division 2009-10

10 YEAR RECORD

07-08		08-09		09-10		10-11		11-12		12-13		13-14		14-15		15-16		16-17	
CCP	6	CCP	2	CCP	1	SthC	20	SthC	18	SthC	19	SthC	20	SthC	21	SthC	22	CCP	13
FAC	P	FAC	EP	FAC	EP	FAC	3Q	FAC	3Qr	FAC	P	FAC	3Q	FAC	2Q	FAC	1Qr	FAC	1Q
FAV	1P	FAV	2Q	FAV	2P	FAT	1Q	FAT	P	FAT	P	FAT	2Q	FAT	P	FAT	P	FAV	2Q

REDHILL
Founded: 1894   Nickname: Reds/Lobsters

Secretary: Kevin Sapsford   **(T)** 07941 754 689   **(E)** ksapsford@hotmail.com
Chairman: Jerry O'Leary   **Manager:** Perry Gough   **Prog Ed:** Terry Austin
Ground: Kiln Brow, Three Arch Road, Redhill, Surrey RH1 5AE   **(T)** 01737 762 129
Capacity: 2,000 **Seats:** 150   **Covered:** 150   **Midweek Matchday:** Tuesday   **Clubhouse:** Yes   **Shop:** Yes

Colours(change): Red & white stripes/red/red
Previous Names: None
Previous Leagues: E & W Surrey. Spartan. Southern Sub. London. Athenian. Sussex County > 2013. Isthmian 2013-15.

HONOURS: FA Comps: None
League: London League 1922-23. Athenian League 1924-25, 83-84.

10 YEAR RECORD

07-08		08-09		09-10		10-11		11-12		12-13		13-14		14-15		15-16		16-17	
SxC1	8	SxC1	7	SxC1	5	SxC1	8	SxC1	10	SxC1	2	Isth1S	22	Isth1S	23	CCP	20	CC1	2
FAC	P	FAC	EP	FAC	EP	FAC	EP	FAC	1Q	FAC	1Q	FAC	1Q	FAC	3Q	FAC	EP	FAC	P
FAV	2Q	FAV	1P	FAV	2P	FAV	2Q	FAV	2Q	FAV	1Q	FAT	P	FAT	Pr	FAV	2Q	FAV	1Q

SPELTHORNE SPORTS
Founded: 1922   Nickname: Spelly

Secretary: Stephen Flatman   **(T)** 07709 068 609   **(E)** flatty1@tiscali.co.uk
Chairman: Ian Croxford   **Manager:** Steve Flatman   **Prog Ed:** Yvonne Hunter
Ground: Spelthorne Sports Club, 296 Staines Rd West, Ashford Common, TW15 1RY   **(T)** 01932 961 055
Capacity: **Seats:** 50   **Covered:** Yes   **Midweek Matchday:** Tuesday   **Clubhouse:** Yes

Colours(change): Navy & sky blue/navy blue/navy blue
Previous Names: None
Previous Leagues: Surrey Intermediate (West) > 2009. Surrey Elite Intermediate 2009-11.

HONOURS: FA Comps: None
League: Surrey Elite Intermediate League 2010-11. Combined Counties Division One 2013-14.

10 YEAR RECORD

07-08		08-09		09-10		10-11		11-12		12-13		13-14		14-15		15-16		16-17	
				SuEl	5	SuEl	1	CC1	7	CC1	6	CCP	1	CCP	6	CCP	11	CCP	9
																FAC	P	FAC	P
																FAV	1P	FAV	1Q	FAV	1Qr

SUTTON COMMON ROVERS
Founded: 1978   Nickname: Commoners

Secretary: Ken Reed   **(T)** 07850 211 165   **(E)** scrfcsecretary@outlook.com
Chairman: Alan Salmon   **Manager:** Darren Salmon   **Prog Ed:** Gary Brigden
Ground: Sutton United FC, Gander Green Lane, Sutton. Surrey SM1 2EY   **(T)** 020 8644 4440
Capacity: 7,032 **Seats:** 765   **Covered:** 1,250   **Midweek Matchday:** Monday   **Clubhouse:** Yes   **Shop:** Yes

Colours(change): All yellow
Previous Names: Inrad FC. Centre 21 FC . SCR Plough, SCR Grapes, SRC Litten Tree, SCR Kingfisher, Mole Valley SCR >2015.
Previous Leagues: South Eastern Combination.

HONOURS: FA Comps: None
League: Combined Counties League Division One 2009-10.

10 YEAR RECORD

07-08		08-09		09-10		10-11		11-12		12-13		13-14		14-15		15-16		16-17	
		CC1	4	CC1	1	CCP	8	CCP	21	CC1	2	CCP	18	CCP	18	CCP	19	CCP	12
						FAC	EP	FAC	EP	FAC	EPr	FAC	EP	FAC	P	FAC	EP	FAC	EPr
				FAV	1P	FAV	1Q	FAV	2Q	FAV	2Q	FAV	2Q	FAV	1Q	FAV	4P	FAV	3P

WALTON & HERSHAM

Founded: 1945   Nickname: Swans

Secretary: Grant Langley   **(T)** 07969 068 731   **(E)** langley.grant@sky.com
Chairman: Alan Smith   **Manager:** Simon Haughney
Ground: Sports Ground, Stompond Lane, Walton-on-Thames KT12 1HF   **(T)** 01932 245 263
Capacity: 5,000   **Seats:** 400   **Covered:** 2,500   **Midweek Matchday:** Tuesday   **Clubhouse:** Yes   **Shop:** Yes

Colours(change):   Red with white trim/red/red
Previous Names: Walton FC (Founded in 1895) amalgamated with Hersham FC in 1945.
Previous Leagues: Surrey Senior, Corinthian 1945-50, Athenian 1950-71. Isthmian 1971-2016.

HONOURS: FA Comps: Amateur Cup 1972-73
League: Corinthian 1946-47, 47-48, 48-49. Athenian League 1968-69.

10 YEAR RECORD

07-08		08-09		09-10		10-11		11-12		12-13		13-14		14-15		15-16		16-17	
Isth1S	10	Isth1S	14	Isth1S	8	Isth1S	6	Isth1S	11	Isth1S	18	Isth1S	21	Isth1S	17	Isth1S	22	CCP	5
FAC	2Q	FAC	P	FAC	3Q	FAC	1Q	FAC	1Q	FAC	1Qr	FAC	P	FAC	P	FAC	P	FAC	Pr
FAT	2Qr	FAT	1Q	FAT	1Q	FAT	P	FAT	P	FAT	1Q	FAT	P	FAT	1Q	FAT	P	FAV	2P

WESTFIELD

Founded: 1953   Nickname: The Field

Secretary: Michael Lawrence   **(T)** 07780 684 416   **(E)** michaelgeorgelawrence@hotmail.com
Chairman: Stephen Perkins   **Manager:** Dan Snare
Ground: Woking Park, off Elmbridge Lane, Kingfield, Woking GU22 9BA   **(T)** 01483 771 106
Capacity: 1000   **Seats:** Yes   **Covered:** Yes   **Midweek Matchday:** Tuesday   **Clubhouse:** Yes

Colours(change):   Yellow/black/black
Previous Names: None
Previous Leagues: Surrey Senior

HONOURS: FA Comps: None
League: Surrey Senior League 1972-73, 73-74.

10 YEAR RECORD

07-08		08-09		09-10		10-11		11-12		12-13		13-14		14-15		15-16		16-17	
CC1	4	CC1	13	CC1	16	CC1	13	CC1	8	CC1	3	CCP	4	CCP	14	CCP	9	CCP	2
FAC	EP	FAC	EP	FAC	EP	FAC	N/A	FAC	EP	FAC	EP	FAC	1Qr	FAC	P	FAC	EPr	FAC	EP
FAV	2Q	FAV	2Q	FAV	1Q	FAV	1Q	FAV	2Q	FAV	1Q	FAV	1P	FAV	2P	FAV	2Q	FAV	2Q

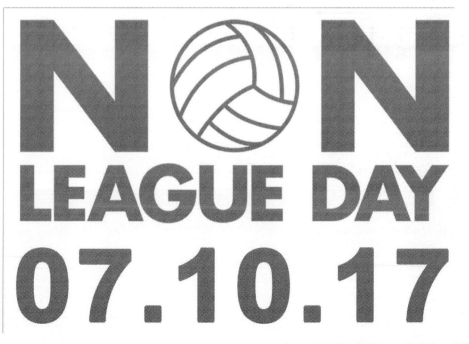

AC LONDON
Founded: 2012   Nickname:

Secretary: Prince Choudary   **(T)** 07579 599 999   **(E)** princehaseebchoudary@gmail.com
Chairman: Prince Choudary   **Manager:** Prince Choudary   Prince Choudary
Ground: Banstead Athletic FC, Merland Rise, Tadworth, Surrey KT20 5JG   **(T)** 01737 350 982   **Capacity:** 4,000
Colours(change): Red &white/black/white (All navy blue)
HONOURS: FA Comps: None   **League:** None

10 YEAR RECORD									
07-08	08-09	09-10	10-11	11-12	12-13	13-14	14-15	15-16	16-17
								K_lv 10	CC1 7
									FAV 1Pr

ASH UNITED
Founded: 1911   Nickname: Green Army

Secretary: Paul Blair   **(T)** 07795 612 664   **(E)** sec@ashunited.co.uk
Chairman: Kevin Josey   **Manager:** Daniel Bishop   **Prog Ed:** Paul Blair
Ground: Shawfields Stadium, Youngs Drive off Shawfield Road, Ash, GU12 6RE.   **(T)** 01252 320 385 / 345 757   **Capacity:** 2500
Colours(change): All green & red.
HONOURS: FA Comps: None   **League:** Combined Counties 1981-82, 86-87, 98-99.

10 YEAR RECORD									
07-08	08-09	09-10	10-11	11-12	12-13	13-14	14-15	15-16	16-17
CCP 15	CCP 9	CCP 11	CCP 18	CCP 13	CCP 20	CCP 1	CC1 10	CC1 10	CC1 12
FAC Pr	FAC EP	FAC 1Q	FAC EP	FAC EP	FAC EP	FAC EP	FAC EP		
FAV 1P	FAV 1P	FAV 1P	FAV 2Q	FAV 1Q	FAV 2P	FAV 1Q	FAV 1Q	FAV 1Q	FAV 1P

BADSHOT LEA
Founded: 1907   Nickname: Baggies

Secretary: Mrs Nicky   **(T)** 07921 466 858   **(E)** nstaszkiewicz@ashgatepublishing.com
Chairman: Mark Broad   **Manager:** Ben Dillon   **Prog Ed:** Peter Collison
Ground: Ash United, Shawfields Stadium, Youngs Drive off Shawfield Rd, Ash, GU12 6RE.   **(T)** 01252 320 385   **Capacity:** 2500
Colours(change): All claret & sky blue
HONOURS: FA Comps: None   **League:** Surrey Intermediate Division One 1936-37, 37-38, 85-86, Division Two 92-93

10 YEAR RECORD									
07-08	08-09	09-10	10-11	11-12	12-13	13-14	14-15	15-16	16-17
Hel P 11	CCP 7	CCP 10	CCP 6	CCP 17	CCP 7	CCP 15	CCP 8	CCP 17	CCP 21
		FAC 2Q	FAC EP	FAC P	FAC 3Q	FAC P	FAC P	FAC P	FAC P
	FAV 1P	FAV 3P	FAV 1Q	FAV 2Q	FAV 1Q	FAV 1Q	FAV 1Q	FAV 2Q	FAV 2Q

BAGSHOT
Founded: 1906   Nickname:

Secretary: Zane Wickens   **(T)** 07810 007 389   **(E)** jwautomotiveuk@yahoo.co.uk
Chairman: John Wickens   **Manager:** Brett Wickens
Ground: Fleet Spurs FC, Kennels Lane, Southwood, Farnborough, Hants GU14 0ST   **(T)**
Colours(change): All dark blue
HONOURS: FA Comps: None   **League:** Aldershot & District Division Two 2005-06, Division One 2008-09, Senior Division 2011-12, 12-13, 13-14, 15-16.

10 YEAR RECORD									
07-08	08-09	09-10	10-11	11-12	12-13	13-14	14-15	15-16	16-17
	A&D1 1	A&DS 2	A&DS 3	A&DS 1	A&DS 1	A&DS 1	A&DS 1	A&DS 1	CC1 8

BEDFONT & FELTHAM
Founded: 2012   Nickname: The Yellows

Secretary: Scott Savoy   **(T)** 07539 219 924   **(E)** ssavoyffc@msn.com
Chairman: Brian Barry   **Manager:** Joe Monks   **Prog Ed:** Rob Healey
Ground: The Orchard, Hatton Road, Bedfont TW14 9QT   **(T)** 020 8890 7264   **Capacity:** 1200
Colours(change): Yellow & blue/blue/blue
HONOURS: FA Comps: None   **League:** None

10 YEAR RECORD									
07-08	08-09	09-10	10-11	11-12	12-13	13-14	14-15	15-16	16-17
					CC1 13	CC1 5	CC1 5	CC1 2	CCP 22
							FAC 1Q	FAC 1Q	FAC EP
					FAV 2Q	FAV 1P	FAV 1Q	FAV 1Q	FAV 2Q

CHESSINGTON & HOOK UNITED
Founded: 1921   Nickname: Chessey

Secretary: Steve Kent   **(T)** 07774 491 009   **(E)** conquestexeccars@aol.com
Chairman: Graham Ellis   **Manager:** Darren Woods   **Prog Ed:** Eric Wicks
Ground: Chalky Lane, Chessington, Surrey KT9 2NF   **(T)** 01372 602 263   **Capacity:** 3000
Colours(change): All blue
HONOURS: FA Comps: None   **League:** Kingston & District Division Four 1922-23, Division Two 1955-56, Division One 1957-58.

10 YEAR RECORD

07-08		08-09		09-10		10-11		11-12		12-13		13-14		14-15		15-16		16-17	
CCP	11	CCP	19	CCP	6	CCP	12	CCP	20	CCP	17	CCP	22	CC1	3	CCP	21	CC1	5
FAC	P	FAC	EP	FAC	EP	FAC	EP	FAC	P	FAC	P	FAC	P	FAC	1Q	FAC	1Q	FAC	Pr
FAV	2Pr	FAV	1P	FAV	1Q	FAV	1Q	FAV	1Q	FAV	2Q	FAV	2P	FAV	2P	FAV	1Q	FAV	1Qr

COBHAM
Founded: 1892   Nickname: Hammers

Secretary: Stuart Cook   **(T)** 07780608639 (Sam Mersion)   **(E)** cobhamfootballclub@hotmail.com
Chairman: Dave Tippetts   **Manager:** Barry Wilde   **Prog Ed:** Sam Merison
Ground: Leg O'Mutton Field, Anvil Lane, Cobham KT11 1AA   **(T)** 01932 866 386   **Capacity:** 2000
Colours(change): Red/black/black
HONOURS: FA Comps: None   **League:** Kingston & District Division One 1928-29, 29-30.

10 YEAR RECORD

07-08		08-09		09-10		10-11		11-12		12-13		13-14		14-15		15-16		16-17	
CCP	21	CCP	22	CC1	7	CC1	8	CC1	11	CC1	11	CC1	16	CC1	11	CC1	7	CC1	11
FAC	EP	FAC	P	FAC	P	FAC	1Q	FAC	1Q	FAC	EPr								
FAV	2Pr	FAV	1P	FAV	1Q	FAV	1Q	FAV	1Q	FAV	2Q	FAV	2Q	FAV	2Q	FAV	2Q	FAV	2Q

COVE
Founded: 1897   Nickname: None

Secretary: Scott Cunningham   **(T)** 07961 711 001   **(E)** scottcunningham68@outlook.com
Chairman: Salvo di Prima   **Manager:** Paul Duncan   **Prog Ed:** Graham Brown
Ground: Oak Farm Fields, 7 Squirrels Lane, Farnborough GU14 8PB   **(T)** 01252 543 615   **Capacity:** 2500
Colours(change): Yellow/black/yellow
HONOURS: FA Comps: **League:** Combined Counties League 2000-01.

10 YEAR RECORD

07-08		08-09		09-10		10-11		11-12		12-13		13-14		14-15		15-16		16-17	
CCP	4	CCP	6	CCP	12	CCP	9	CCP	11	CCP	3	CCP	5	CCP	4	CCP	22	CC1	17
FAC	P	FAC	EP	FAC	P	FAC	EPr	FAC	EP	FAC	P	FAC	1Q	FAC	EP	FAC	P	FAC	EP
FAV	1Qr	FAV	1P	FAV	2Q	FAV	1P	FAV	2Q	FAV	2Q	FAV	2P	FAV	1Q	FAV	1P	FAV	1Q

EVERSLEY & CALIFORNIA
Founded: 1910   Nickname: The Boars

Secretary: Annette Borg   **(T)** 07970 066 716   **(E)** secretary@eversley-californiafc.co.uk
Chairman: Ben Sharpe   **Manager:** Phil Ruggles   **Prog Ed:** Dean Floodgate
Ground: ESA Sports Complex, Fox Lane, Eversley RG27 0NS   **(T)** 0118 973 2400   **Capacity:** 300+
Colours(change): White & royal blue hoops/royal blue/royal blue
HONOURS: FA Comps: None   **League:** Surrey Elite Intermediate 2008-09.

10 YEAR RECORD

07-08		08-09		09-10		10-11		11-12		12-13		13-14		14-15		15-16		16-17	
07-08		SuEl	1	CC1	8	CC1	11	CC1	5	CC1	4	CC1	2	CC1	9	CC1	5	CC1	6
														FAV	2Q			FAV	2Q

FARLEIGH ROVERS
Founded: 1922   Nickname: The Foxes

Secretary: Peter Collard   **(T)** 07545 444 820   **(E)** peter.collard@aquatots.com
Chairman: Mark Whittaker   **Manager:** Matt Nash   **Prog Ed:** Peter Collard
Ground: Parsonage Field, Harrow Road, Warlingham CR6 9EX   **(T)** 01883 626 483   **Capacity:** 500
Colours(change): Red & black stripes/black/black
HONOURS: FA Comps: None   **League:** Surrey County Premier 1982-83. Combined Counties Division One 2014-15.

10 YEAR RECORD

07-08		08-09		09-10		10-11		11-12		12-13		13-14		14-15		15-16		16-17	
CC1	18	CC1	12	CC1	10	CC1	6	CC1	16	CC1	16	CC1	8	CC1	1	CC1	16	CC1	16

FC DEPORTIVO GALICIA

Founded: 1968   **Nickname:**

Secretary: Roger Loureda   **(T)** 07956 300 681   **(E)** rogelioloureda@hotmail.com
Chairman:
Ground: Bedfont Sports, Hatton Road, Bedfont, Middlesex TW14 8JA   **(T)** 020 8831 9067
Colours(change):
HONOURS: FA Comps: None   **League:** Middlesex County Premier Division 2016-17.

10 YEAR RECORD

07-08		08-09		09-10		10-11		11-12		12-13		13-14		14-15		15-16		16-17	
MidxP	10	MidxP	12	MidxP	14	MidxP	7	MidxP	12	MidxP	13	MidxP	6	MidxP	12	MidxP	13	MidxP	1
																		FAV	1Q

FLEET SPURS

Founded: 1948   **Nickname:** Spurs

Secretary: Phil Blakey   **(T)** 07941 005 579   **(E)** secretary@fleetspurs.co.uk
Chairman: Kierin Gurrie   **Manager:** Sam Knowles
Ground: Kennels Lane Southwood Farnborough Hampshire, GU14 0ST   **(T)**
Colours(change): Dark blue with red trim/dark blue/red (Yellow/black/yellow)
HONOURS: FA Comps: None   **League:** Surrey Premier A Division 1968-69. Aldershot Senior 1990-91. Hampshire Division Two 1997-98.

10 YEAR RECORD

07-08		08-09		09-10		10-11		11-12		12-13		13-14		14-15		15-16		16-17	
Wex1	15	Wex1	21	Wex1	3	Wex1	10	Wex1	7	Wex1	10	Wex1	12	Wex1	9	Wex1	12	Wex1	16
								FAC	EP	FAC	EP								
						FAV	2Q	FAV	1Q	FAV	2Q	FAV	1Q	FAV	1Qr	FAV	1Q	FAV	2Q

FRIMLEY GREEN

Founded: 1919   **Nickname:** The Green

Secretary: Mark O'Grady   **(T)** 07812 026 390   **(E)** mogradyuk@yahoo.co.uk
Chairman: Matthew Flude   **Manager:** John Cook & Jamie Daltry   **Prog Ed:** Mark O'Grady
Ground: Frimley Green Rec. Ground, Frimley Green, Camberley GU16 6JY   **(T)** 01252 835 089   **Capacity:** 2000
Colours(change): All blue
HONOURS: FA Comps: None   **League:** Combined Counties Division One 2012-13.

10 YEAR RECORD

07-08		08-09		09-10		10-11		11-12		12-13		13-14		14-15		15-16		16-17	
CC1	6	CC1	16	CC1	13	CC1	15	CC1	10	CC1	1	CCP	12	CCP	21	CC1	12	CC1	13
FAC	EP	FAC	P	FAC	EP	FAC	EP					FAC	P	FAC	EP	FAC	EP		
FAV	1Q	FAV	3Pr	FAV	2Q	FAV	2Q	FAV	1Q	FAV	2P	FAV	1Q	FAV	2Q	FAV	2Q	FAV	2Q

KENSINGTON BOROUGH

Founded: 2012   **Nickname:**

Secretary: Ahmed Bhairien   **(T)** 07814 517 086   **(E)** a.bhairien_kenboro@hotmail.com
Chairman: Adrian Maloney   **Manager:** Mohammed Bakkali   **Prog Ed:** Ahmed Bhairien
Ground: Amersham Town FC, Spratleys Meadow, School Lane, Amersham HP7 0EL   **(T)** 0207 289 3395
Colours(change): All green (Yellow/black/black)
HONOURS: FA Comps: None   **League:** None

10 YEAR RECORD

07-08	08-09	09-10	10-11	11-12	12-13	13-14		14-15		15-16		16-17	
						Midx2	3	Midx1SE	6	SSM2	5	SSM1	12

RAYNES PARK VALE

Founded: 1995   **Nickname:** The Vale

Secretary: Paul Armour   **(T)** 07980 914 211   **(E)** paul.armour@bt.com
Chairman: Paul Bentley   **Manager:** Gavin Bolger
Ground: Prince George's Playing Field, Raynes Park SW20 9NB   **(T)** 0208 540 8843   **Capacity:** 1500
Colours(change): All blue (All yellow)
HONOURS: FA Comps: None   **League:** Combined Counties Division One 2002-03.

10 YEAR RECORD

07-08		08-09		09-10		10-11		11-12		12-13		13-14		14-15		15-16		16-17	
CCP	19	CCP	8	CCP	18	CCP	15	CCP	9	CCP	11	CCP	10	CCP	15	CCP	15	CCP	23
FAC	EPr	FAC	P	FAC	P	FAC	P	FAC	P	FAC	Pr	FAC	P	FAC	Pr	FAC	EP	FAC	EP
FAV	1P	FAV	2Q	FAV	1Q	FAV	1P	FAV	1P	FAV	2Q	FAV	1Q	FAV	1P	FAV	1Q	FAV	1Q

SHEERWATER
Founded: 1958   Nickname: Sheers

Secretary: Trevor Wenden   **(T)** 07791 612 008   **(E)** trevor.wenden2@ntlworld.com
Chairman: **Manager:** Peter Ruggles   **Prog Ed:** Trevor Wenden
Ground: Sheerwater Recreation Ground, Blackmore Crescent, Woking GU21 5NS   **(T)**   **Capacity:** 1,000
Colours(change): All royal blue
HONOURS: FA Comps: None   **League:** None

10 YEAR RECORD

07-08	08-09	09-10	10-11	11-12	12-13	13-14	14-15	15-16	16-17
CC1 16	CC1 9	CC1 17	CC1 17	CC1 18	CC1 15	CC1 11	CC1 14	CC1 13	CC1 9

SOUTH PARK RESERVES
Founded: 1897   Nickname:

Secretary: Nick Thatcher   **(T)** 07817 613 674   **(E)** spfc1897@hotmail.com
Chairman: Ricky Kidd   **Manager:** Jason Stephens   **Prog Ed:** Nick Thatcher
Ground: King George's Field, Whitehall Lane, South Park, Reigate, Surrey RH2 8LG   **(T)** 01737 245 963
Colours(change): All red
HONOURS: FA Comps: None   **League:** None

10 YEAR RECORD

07-08	08-09	09-10	10-11	11-12	12-13	13-14	14-15	15-16	16-17
								CC1 14	CC1 14

STAINES LAMMAS
Founded: 1926   Nickname: Lammas or The Blues

Secretary: Bob Parry   **(T)** 07771 947 757   **(E)** bobandtracey1@btopenworld.com
Chairman: Phil Ellery   **Manager:** Adam Bessent   **Prog Ed:** Bob Parry
Ground: The Lucan Pavilion, The Boradway, Laleham, Staines, Middlesex TW18 1RZ   **(T)** 01784 465 204
Colours(change): All blue
HONOURS: FA Comps: None   **League:** Combined Counties Division One 2007-08, 08-09.

10 YEAR RECORD

07-08	08-09	09-10	10-11	11-12	12-13	13-14	14-15	15-16	16-17
CC1 1	CC1 1	CC1 4	CC1 10	CC1 6	CC1 7	CC1 4	CC1 8	CC1 9	CC1 10
			FAC 1Q	FAC 1Q	FAC P	FAC EP	FAC P		
		FAV 1Q	FAV 1Q	FAV 1Q	FAV 1Q	FAV 1P	FAV 1Qr		

WORCESTER PARK
Founded: 1921   Nickname: The Skinners

Secretary: Kristina Maitre   **(T)** 07768 179 938   **(E)** kristinajayne@hotmail.co.uk
Chairman: Sam Glass   **Manager:** Gary Taylor   **Prog Ed:** Alan Pearce
Ground: Skinners Field, Green Lane, Worcester Park, Surrey KT4 8AJ   **(T)** 0208 337 4995
Colours(change): All blue
HONOURS: FA Comps: None   **League:** Surrey County Premier/Senior League 1999-2000, 2000-01.
Combined Counties Division One 2010-11.

10 YEAR RECORD

07-08	08-09	09-10	10-11	11-12	12-13	13-14	14-15	15-16	16-17
CC1 9	CC1 6	CC1 2	CC1 1	CC1 9	CC1 10	CC1 9	CC1 4	CC1 4	CC1 4

EAST MIDLANDS COUNTIES LEAGUE

Sponsored by: No sponsor
Founded: 2008

Recent Champions: 2014: Thurnby Nirvana
2015: Bardon Hill **2016:** St Andrews

		P	W	D	L	F	A	GD	Pts
1	West Bridgford	42	29	7	6	115	52	63	94
2	South Normanton Athletic	42	26	8	8	94	46	48	86
3	Birstall United	42	27	4	11	105	48	57	85
4	Aylestone Park	42	25	6	11	104	59	45	81
5	Dunkirk	42	23	7	12	106	70	36	76
6	Blaby & Whetstone Athletic	42	23	7	12	105	71	34	76
7	Radford	42	21	11	10	100	57	43	74
8	Kimberley Miners Welfare	42	23	5	14	85	62	23	74
9	Radcliffe Olympic	42	22	5	15	101	97	4	71
10	Ashby Ivanhoe	42	20	10	12	97	66	31	70
11	Stapenhill	42	20	7	15	104	88	16	67
12	Borrowash Victoria	42	16	10	16	98	87	11	58
13	Belper United	42	17	7	18	78	73	5	58
14	Barrow Town	42	15	13	14	86	82	4	58
15	Arnold Town	42	17	6	19	88	101	-13	57
16	Holwell Sports	42	17	4	21	78	86	-8	55
17	Anstey Nomads	42	12	9	21	70	97	-27	45
18	Holbrook Sports	42	9	6	27	55	110	-55	33
19	Graham Street Prims	42	9	4	29	52	120	-68	31
20	Gedling Miners Welfare	42	7	3	32	40	132	-92	24
21	Greenwood Meadows	42	10	6	26	57	79	-22	18*
22	Ellistown & Ibstock United	42	0	3	39	23	158	-135	3

LEAGUE CUP

HOLDERS: AYLESTONE PARK

ROUND 1
Blaby & Whetstone Athletic	v	Stapenhill	4-6
Barrow Town	v	Gedling Miners Welfare	5-2
West Bridgford	v	South Normanton Athletic	2-2
South Normanton Athletic	v	West Bridgford	1-1, 5-3p
Holbrook Sports	v	Ashby Ivanhoe	1-4
Greenwood Meadows	v	Borrowash Victoria	2-5
Dunkirk	v	Graham Street Prims	4-1

ROUND 2
Anstey Nomads	v	Belper United	2-3
Arnold Town	v	Birstall United	0-3
Aylestone Park	v	Ellistown & Ibstock United	4-1
Ashby Ivanhoe	v	Holwell Sports	2-1
Dunkirk	v	Barrow Town	2-2
Barrow Town	v	Dunkirk	2-4
Kimberley Miners Welfare	v	South Normanton Athletic	2-1
Stapenhill	v	Radford	0-4
Radcliffe Olympic	v	Borrowash Victoria	3-5

QUARTER FINALS
Ashby Ivanhoe	v	Borrowash Victoria	7-0
Kimberley Miners Welfare	v	Dunkirk	1-3
Belper United	v	Birstall United	2-3
Aylestone Park	v	Radford	4-3

SEMI FINALS
Ashby Ivanhoe	v	Birstall United	1-0
Aylestone Park	v	Dunkirk	0-1

FINAL
Ashby Ivanhoe	v	Dunkirk	1-2

CLUB MOVEMENTS - In: Clifton All Whites (P - Notts Senior), Selston (P - Central Midlands South), Teversal (S - Northern Counties East). **Out:** Elliston & Ibstock United (R - Leicester Senior), Greenwood Meadows (R- Central Midlands South), South Normanton Athletic (P - Midlands League Prem.)

		1	2	3	4	5	6	7	8	9	10	11	12	13	14	15	16	17	18	19	20	21	22
1	Anstey Nomads		4-0	1-4	1-3	3-2	1-1	0-0	0-3	1-2	1-3	3-2	0-2	5-1	1-1	2-1	0-3	2-0	3-3	2-3	1-4	3-7	0-3
2	Arnold Town	0-1		1-3	2-3	0-4	2-1	1-6	1-4	6-5	3-0	5-0	4-3	1-0	3-3	0-1	6-2	2-1	2-5	2-2	1-4	1-3	4-5
3	Ashby Ivanhoe	2-2	0-0		0-2	1-4	1-2	0-1	1-1	4-0	1-3	5-1	7-1	6-0	1-1	4-3	1-0	3-2	5-1	0-0	1-1	3-2	0-5
4	Aylestone Park	5-4	4-2	2-1		2-1	3-2	0-1	1-1	5-1	4-2	3-0	3-1	2-0	1-2	0-2	5-1	0-0	1-2	2-3	0-1	5-1	2-2
5	Barrow Town	4-0	2-2	0-3	1-1		3-1	3-0	2-2	2-2	2-5	4-0	6-2	3-1	2-2	4-4	0-0	2-0	4-1	0-2	0-0	0-2	1-4
6	Belper United	0-0	0-1	1-5	0-3	3-0		0-1	0-3	1-2	3-0	3-0	1-0	1-1	2-3	2-0	3-1	3-0	1-2	0-5	2-2	5-1	4-4
7	Birstall United	0-1	0-2	1-0	0-4	6-2	4-1		0-1	1-0	2-0	3-0	2-0	6-1	2-0	5-1	1-0	2-1	2-3	2-2	1-1	4-0	0-2
8	Blaby & Whetstone Athletic	2-1	1-2	1-5	3-4	2-2	1-2	2-1		4-2	0-5	5-1	7-0	3-0	4-0	3-2	3-0	2-2	5-1	1-1	1-1	6-3	2-7
9	Borrowash Victoria	3-0	1-4	4-4	0-0	0-2	4-0	4-4	8-1		1-2	5-1	8-1	3-1	1-2	1-1	5-1	1-3	2-3	3-1	2-2	3-3	1-3
10	Dunkirk	1-2	3-1	3-2	2-1	3-3	0-2	0-2	2-0	1-1		8-1	3-1	13-0	H-W	3-2	1-3	3-0	5-1	4-2	2-4	1-3	2-1
11	Ellistown & Ibstock United	1-5	4-4	1-5	0-3	1-2	1-9	0-11	0-4	1-4	1-1		1-4	1-2	0-3	0-2	0-2	1-2	1-2	0-4	0-3	0-3	0-6
12	Gedling Miners Welfare	4-3	0-3	0-1	0-3	2-2	3-3	2-8	0-1	0-1	1-2	0-0		3-2	H-W	1-0	0-4	0-1	1-2	0-5	0-6	1-2	0-6
13	Graham Street Prims	3-1	2-3	0-2	0-3	2-2	0-3	0-6	0-5	0-0	1-3	5-1	3-2		2-0	1-1	1-3	3-4	0-2	0-3	1-5	3-0	0-1
14	Greenwood Meadows	2-3	1-3	A-W	2-2	2-5	2-5	1-5	1-3	A-W	1-4	2-0	4-1	0-1		1-0	A-W	2-5	1-2	A-W	0-3	3-1	0-1
15	Holbrook Sports	4-1	1-2	3-3	2-7	1-4	2-1	1-2	0-4	0-0	3-4	1-0	1-0	1-5	1-7		1-6	0-1	0-3	0-6	0-3	5-1	0-2
16	Holwell Sports	4-2	1-2	0-0	0-1	2-1	0-2	4-0	2-5	3-4	2-2	7-1	4-0	3-0	1-3	4-3		2-1	1-4	1-1	0-1	3-1	0-3
17	Kimberley Miners Welfare	1-1	4-2	2-1	3-2	4-0	4-1	0-2	0-2	2-3	3-0	4-0	4-1	4-1	3-1	3-2	1-2		3-1	1-1	2-0	4-1	0-3
18	Radcliffe Olympic	5-1	3-3	2-2	3-5	5-1	1-2	1-2	0-3	3-4	2-4	2-0	2-3	1-0	2-1	4-0	3-1	1-2		4-1	3-3	3-3	4-2
19	Radford	3-3	5-0	2-3	3-1	3-1	2-2	3-4	2-1	4-1	1-0	2-0	4-0	2-1	0-0	5-0	3-4	5-6		0-1	0-2	2-2	
20	South Normanton Athletic	0-1	3-2	0-2	3-2	4-0	1-3	0-3	3-2	1-0	1-1	4-0	6-0	2-1	3-1	3-2	2-1	5-1	2-0		0-2	0-1	
21	Stapenhill	2-2	3-2	6-3	3-0	1-2	3-0	1-0	4-0	7-3	1-1	3-1	4-0	0-6	1-1	5-0	7-3	0-2	7-1	1-1	1-2		2-2
22	West Bridgford	3-2	3-1	4-2	1-4	1-1	0-1	4-2	2-1	2-0	4-4	3-0	2-0	4-3	4-0	2-3	1-1	0-1	0-2	3-0	3-1		

ANSTEY NOMADS
Founded: 1947   Nickname: Nomads

Secretary: Chris Hillebrandt   **(T)** 0794 685 6430   **(E)** chille1055@hotmail.com
Chairman: Carl Watson   **Manager:** Rob Harris   **Prog Ed:** Helen Preston-Hayes
Ground: Davidson Homes Park, Cropston Road, Anstey, Leicester LE7 7BP   **(T)** 07709 149 608   **Capacity:** 1000
Colours(change): Red & white/black/red & white (All blue)
HONOURS: FA Comps: None   **League:** Leicestershire Senior 1951-52, 53-54, 81-82, 82-83, 2008-09, Division Two 1973-74.

10 YEAR RECORD

07-08	08-09	09-10	10-11	11-12	12-13	13-14	14-15	15-16	16-17
LeicSP 12	LeicSP 1	EMC 20	EMC 12	EMC 9	EMC 14	EMC 17	EMC 14	EMC 4	EMC 17
				FAC EP	FAC EP				FAC EP
FAV 1Q	FAV 2Q	FAV 1Q	FAV 1P	FAV 2Q	FAV 2Q	FAV 1Q	FAV 1Q	FAV 1P	FAV 2Q

ARNOLD TOWN
Founded: 1989   Nickname: Eagles

Secretary: Steve Holland   **(T)** 01159 261 550   **(E)** sharon.holland@btinternet.com
Chairman: Graham Peck   **Prog Ed:** Mick Gretton
Ground: Eagle Valley, Oxton Road, Arnold, Nottingham NG5 8PS   **(T)** 0115 965 6000
Colours(change): All maroon (Yellow/blue/yellow)
HONOURS: FA Comps: None   **League:** Northern Counties East 1985-86. Central Midlands 1992-93. Northern Counties Division One 1993-94.

10 YEAR RECORD

07-08	08-09	09-10	10-11	11-12	12-13	13-14	14-15	15-16	16-17
NCEP 10	NCEP 6	NCEP 8	NCEP 18	NCEP 9	NCEP 19	EMC 6	EMC 10	EMC 18	EMC 15
FAC EPr	FAC EP	FAC EP	FAC EP	FAC 1Q	FAC EP	FAC Pr	FAC EP		
FAV 1Q	FAV 3Pr	FAV 1P	FAV 1Pr	FAV 1P	FAV 2Q	FAV 1Q	FAV 1Q	FAV 2Q	FAV 1Q

ASHBY IVANHOE
Founded: 1948   Nickname: The Knights

Secretary: Charlie Tissington   **(T)** 07966 293 355   **(E)** charlie.tissington@btinternet.com
Chairman: Stuart Bonser   **Prog Ed:** Matthew Lester
Ground: NFU Sports Ground, Lower Packington Road, Ashby de la Zouch LE65 1TS   **(T)** 01530 413 140
Colours(change): Blue/blue/red (Red/red/blue)
HONOURS: FA Comps: None   **League:** North Leicestershire 1994-95, 96-97, 98-99, 2002-03. Leicestershire Senior Premier Division 2010-11.

10 YEAR RECORD

07-08	08-09	09-10	10-11	11-12	12-13	13-14	14-15	15-16	16-17
LeicS1 2	LeicSP 3	LeicSP 5	LeicSP 1	LeicSP 8	LeicSP 4	LeicSP 3	EMC 6	EMC 3	EMC 10
									FAC 1Q
		FAV 1Q	FAV 2Q	FAV 2Q				FAV 1Q	FAV 1P

AYLESTONE PARK
Founded: 1968   Nickname:

Secretary: Steve Cramp   **(T)** 07884 447 076   **(E)** apsec@hotmail.co.uk
Chairman: Bob Stretton MBE   **Prog Ed:** Andy Talbott
Ground: Mary Linwood Recreation Ground, Saffron Lane, Leicester LE2 6TG   **(T)** 0116 278 5485
Colours(change): Red/white/white (All blue)
HONOURS: FA Comps: None   **League:** None

10 YEAR RECORD

07-08	08-09	09-10	10-11	11-12	12-13	13-14	14-15	15-16	16-17
LeicSP 15	LeicSP 11	LeicSP 14	LeicSP 8	LeicSP 3	EMC 7	EMC 18	EMC 19	EMC 5	EMC 4
									FAC EP
				FAV 2Q		FAV 2Q	FAV 1Q	FAV 2Q	FAV 1Q

BARROW TOWN
Founded: Late 1800s   Nickname: The Riversiders

Secretary: Chris Newton   **(T)** 07704 063 642   **(E)** newton-chris@sky.com
Chairman: Michael Bland   **Prog Ed:** Joanne Newton
Ground: Riverside Park, Bridge Street, Quorn, Leicestershire LE12 8EN   **(T)** 01509 620 650
Colours(change): Red & black/black/red (Yellow & blue/blue/blue)
HONOURS: FA Comps: None   **League:** Leicester Senior Division One 1992-93.

10 YEAR RECORD

07-08	08-09	09-10	10-11	11-12	12-13	13-14	14-15	15-16	16-17
LeicSP 2	EMC 6	EMC 12	EMC 5	EMC 5	EMC 2	EMC 19	EMC 9	EMC 13	EMC 14
	FAC P	FAC EP	FAC P	FAC 3Q	FAC EP	FAC EP	FAC EP	FAC EP	
FAV 2Q	FAV 2Q	FAV 1Q	FAV 1Q	FAV 2Q	FAV 1Q	FAV 2Q	FAV 2Q	FAV 2Q	FAV 1Q

BELPER UNITED

Founded: 1920 Nickname:

Secretary: Colin Davies **(T)** 07729 967 395 **(E)** colin@tws-ltd.co.uk
Chairman: Fraser Shaw
Ground: Borrowash Victoria FC, Anderson Electrical Arena, Spondon, Derby DE21 7PH **(T)** 01332 669 688
Colours(change): Green/black/green (Black & red/white/red)
HONOURS: FA Comps: None **League:** Midlands Regional Alliance Premier Division 1985-86, 94-95, Division One 2004-05.

10 YEAR RECORD

07-08	08-09	09-10	10-11	11-12	12-13	13-14	14-15	15-16	16-17
MidRAP 12	MidRAP 20	MidRAP 13	MidRAP 10	CMSth 9	CMSth 3	CMSth 10	CMSth 5	CMSth 2	EMC 13
						FAV 1Q	FAV 1P	FAV 1Q	FAV 1Q

BIRSTALL UNITED SOCIAL

Founded: 1961 Nickname:

Secretary: Sandra Plumb **(T)** 07510 542 035 **(E)** sandraplumb3012@hotmail.com
Chairman:
Ground: Meadow Lane, Birstall LE4 4FN **(T)** 0116 267 1230
Colours(change): White.navy/navy (Red/red/green)
HONOURS: FA Comps: None **League:** Leicester Mutual Division One 1972-73, 73-74, 75-76. Leicestershire Senior Division Two 1976-77, Premier 2015-16.

10 YEAR RECORD

07-08	08-09	09-10	10-11	11-12	12-13	13-14	14-15	15-16	16-17
LeicSP 8	LeicSP 10	LeicSP 9	LeicSP 9	LeicSP 6	LeicSP 11	LeicSP 4	LeicSP 4	LeicSP 1	EMC 3
FAV 2Q	FAV 1Q	FAV 1Q		FAV 2Q	FAV 1Q				FAV 2Qr

BLABY & WHETSTONE ATHLETIC

Founded: 1993 Nickname: Warwick Roaders

Secretary: Javeed Virk **(T)** 0782 506 7853 **(E)** blabywhetath@hotmail.com
Chairman: Mark Jenkins **Prog Ed:** Javeed Virk
Ground: Warwick Road, Whetstone, Leicester LE8 6LW **(T)** 0116 286 4852
Colours(change): All royal blue (All gold)
HONOURS: FA Comps: None **League:** None

10 YEAR RECORD

07-08	08-09	09-10	10-11	11-12	12-13	13-14	14-15	15-16	16-17
LeicSP 11	LeicSP 2	LeicSP 4	LeicSP 3	EMC 12	EMC 6	EMC 4	EMC 5	EMC 7	EMC 6
					FAC 1Qr	FAC 2Q	FAC 2Qr	FAC EP	FAC P
FAV 1Q	FAV 2Q	FAV 2P	FAV 1P	FAV 1Q	FAV 2Q	FAV 3P	FAV 2Q	FAV 1Q	FAV 2Q

BORROWASH VICTORIA

Founded: 1911 Nickname: The Vics

Secretary: Marko Markelic **(T)** 07772 301 906 **(E)** marko18@live.co.uk
Chairman: Fraser Watson
Ground: Anderson Electrical Arena, Borrowash Road, Spondon, Derby DE21 7PH **(T)** 07726 683 957
Colours(change): Red & white stripes/red/red (Yellow/blue/yellow)
HONOURS: FA Comps: None **League:** Derby & District 1952-53. East Midlands regional Premier 1977-78. Midland Division One 1980-81. Northern Counties East Div.1 South 1983-84.

10 YEAR RECORD

07-08	08-09	09-10	10-11	11-12	12-13	13-14	14-15	15-16	16-17
NCE1 13	EMC 2	EMC 11	EMC 2	EMC 2	EMC 4	EMC 5	EMC 16	EMC 9	EMC 12
FAC EP	FAC EP	FAC Pr	FAC P	FAC P	FAC P	FAC P	FAC EP		
FAV 2P	FAV 1P	FAV 1P	FAV 2Q	FAV 2Q	FAV 4P	FAV 2P	FAV 2P	FAV 1P	FAV 1Q

CLIFTON ALL WHITES

Founded: 1963 Nickname: All Whites

Secretary: David Wigley **(T)** 07775 615 237 **(E)** d.wigley@ntlworld.com
Chairman: Mark Woodford
Ground: Green Lane, Clifton, Nottingham NG11 9AZ **(T)** 07775 615 237
Colours(change): All white (All royal blue)
HONOURS: FA Comps: None **League:** Notts Alliance Division One 1998-99. Central Midlands 2013-14. Notts Senior Premier Division 2016-17.

10 YEAR RECORD

07-08	08-09	09-10	10-11	11-12	12-13	13-14	14-15	15-16	16-17
				NottS1 2	CMSth 4	CMSth 1	CMSth 8	NottSP 6	NottSP 1
								FAV 2Q	FAV 2Q

DUNKIRK
Founded: 1946   Nickname: The Boatmen

Secretary: Steve Throssell   **(T)** 07903 322 446   **(E)**
Chairman: **Prog Ed:** Philip Allen
Ground: Ron Steel Spts Ground, Lenton Lane, Clifton Bridge, Nottingham NG7 2SA   **(T)** 0115 985 0803   **Capacity:** 1,500
Colours(change): Red/black/black (All blue)
HONOURS: FA Comps: None   **League:** Notts Alliance Division Two 1981-82, Division One 1984-85.
Central Midlands Supreme Division 2004-05. East Midlands 2009-10.

10 YEAR RECORD

07-08		08-09		09-10		10-11		11-12		12-13		13-14		14-15		15-16		16-17	
CM Su	4	EMC	5	EMC	1	MidAl	8	MidAl	18	MidAl	10	MidAl	19	MFLP	19	MFLP	20	EMC	5
				FAC	EP	FAC	EP	FAC	1Q	FAC	EP	FAC	P	FAC	1Q	FAC	EP	FAC	3Q	FAC	1Q
FAV	2P	FAV	2P	FAV	3P	FAV	3P	FAV	2Q	FAV	1P	FAV	2Q	FAV	2Q	FAV	2P	FAV	2Q

GEDLING MINERS WELFARE
Founded: 1919   Nickname: Miners

Secretary: Norman Hay   **(T)** 07748 138 732   **(E)** norman.hay@virginmedia.com
Chairman: Vic Hulme   **Manager:** Graham Walker   **Prog Ed:** Ian Williams
Ground: Plains Social Club, Plains Road, Mapperley, Nottingham NG3 5RH   **(T)** 0115 926 6300
Colours(change): Yellow/royal blue/yellow (All red)
HONOURS: FA Comps: None   **League:** Notts Alliance 1945-46, 49-50, 50-51, 51–52, 53-54, 55-56, 57-58, 58-59,
59-60, 60-61, Division Two 2000-01.

10 YEAR RECORD

07-08		08-09		09-10		10-11		11-12		12-13		13-14		14-15		15-16		16-17	
CM Su	6	EMC	8	EMC	8	EMC	4	EMC	13	EMC	13	EMC	12	EMC	12	EMC	14	EMC	20
				FAC	EP	FAC	EPr	FAC	P	FAC	EPr								
FAV	1P	FAV	1Q	FAV	1Q	FAV	2Q	FAV	1Q	FAV	2Q	FAV	1Q	FAV	1P	FAV	1Q	FAV	1Q

GRAHAM STREET PRIMS
Founded: 1904   Nickname: Prims

Secretary: Peter Davis   **(T)** 07902 403 074   **(E)** j.davis16@sky.com
Chairman: Dave Tice   **Manager:** Anton Broughton & Matt McCaul   **Prog Ed:** Edward Davis
Ground: Baytree Cars Arena, Borrowash Road, Spondon DE21 7PH   **(T)** 01332 332 092
Colours(change): Red & white/black/black (All blue)
HONOURS: FA Comps: None   **League:** Central Alliance Premier Division 1970-71.
East Midlands Regional 1978-79.

10 YEAR RECORD

07-08		08-09		09-10		10-11		11-12		12-13		13-14		14-15		15-16		16-17	
CM Su	13	EMC	13	EMC	18	EMC	14	EMC	14	EMC	8	EMC	10	EMC	18	EMC	11	EMC	19
												FAC	EP	FAC	EP				
FAV	2Q	FAV	1Q	FAV	2Q	FAV	2Q	FAV	1Q	FAV	1P	FAV	3P	FAV	1P	FAV	2Q	FAV	1Q

HOLBROOK SPORTS
Founded: 1996   Nickname: The Brookies

Secretary: Paul Romney   **(T)** 07833 228 230   **(E)** paul.romney@btinternet.com
Chairman: Howard Williams   **Manager:** Paul Romney
Ground: APC Sealants Ground, Shaw Lane, Holbrook, Derbyshire DE56 0TG   **(T)** 01332 880 259
Colours(change): All blue (Burgundy/blue/blue)
HONOURS: FA Comps: None   **League:** Central Midlands Premier Division 1999-2000.

10 YEAR RECORD

07-08		08-09		09-10		10-11		11-12		12-13		13-14		14-15		15-16		16-17	
CM Su	5	EMC	3	EMC	3	EMC	6	EMC	6	EMC	9	EMC	13	EMC	11	EMC	8	EMC	18
				FAC	1Q	FAC	1Q	FAC	P	FAC	P	FAC	EP						
FAV	1P	FAV	2Qr	FAV	2Q	FAV	5P	FAV	3Pr	FAV	3P	FAV	1Q	FAV	2Q	FAV	1Q	FAV	1Q

HOLWELL SPORTS
Founded: 1902   Nickname:

Secretary: Heather Taylor   **(T)** 07910 879 919   **(E)** hataylor64@gmail.com
Chairman: Graham Lewin
Ground: Welby Road, Asfordby Hill, Melton Mowbray, Leicestershire LE14 3RD   **(T)** 01664 812 080   **Capacity:** 1000
Colours(change): Green & gold/green/green (Sky blue & white/black/sky blue)
HONOURS: FA Comps: None   **League:** Leic Senior Premier 1911-12, 87-88, 91-92, 92-93, Division One 1984-85.
Leicester & District 1907-08, 08-09. Melton Mowbray & Dist Am 1933-34.

10 YEAR RECORD

07-08		08-09		09-10		10-11		11-12		12-13		13-14		14-15		15-16		16-17	
LeicSP	6	LeicSP	4	EMC	13	EMC	13	EMC	11	EMC	5	EMC	9	EMC	8	EMC	16	EMC	16
				FAC	EPr	FAC	EPr			FAC	EP	FAC	EP	FAC	1Q	FAC	1Qr		
FAV	1Q	FAV	1Q	FAV	2Q	FAV	2P	FAV	1P	FAV	1Q	FAV	3P	FAV	2Q	FAV	2Q	FAV	1P

KIMBERLEY MINERS WELFARE

Founded: 1926   Nickname: Miners

Secretary: John Beeston   **(T)** 07803 267 825   **(E)** johnbeeston1775@sky.com
Chairman: Neil Johnson
Ground: Kimberley MWFC, The Stag Ground, Kimberley, Nottingham NG16 2NB   **(T)** 07803 267 825
Colours(change): Red & black/white/white (Sky blue/blue/blue)

HONOURS: FA Comps: None   **League:** Spartan League 1947-48, 64-65, 65-66. Notts Amateur League 1985-86. Notts Alliance Division Two 1994-95, Division One 95-96.

10 YEAR RECORD

07-08	08-09	09-10	10-11	11-12	12-13	13-14	14-15	15-16	16-17
				NottSP 13	NottSP 5	NottSP 2	EMC 13	EMC 15	EMC 8
								FAV 1Q	FAV 2Qr

RADCLIFFE OLYMPIC

Founded: 1876   Nickname: Olympic

Secretary: Scott Carlton   **(T)** 07500 804 057   **(E)** scott.carlton@live.co.uk
Chairman: Rick Bright   **Prog Ed:** Scott Carlton
Ground: The Recreation Ground, Wharfe Lane, Radcliffe on Trent, Nottingham NG12 2AN   **(T)** 07500 804 057
Colours(change): Blue & red/blue & red/blue (Red & black/red &black/red)

HONOURS: FA Comps: None   **League:** Notts Alliance 1900-01, Div.2 31-32, Div.1 90-91, Sen 2002-03. South Notts 1931-32. Notts Realm Div.1 1946-47. Central Midlands Premier 2003-04, Supreme 08-09.

10 YEAR RECORD

07-08	08-09	09-10	10-11	11-12	12-13	13-14	14-15	15-16	16-17
CM Su 3	CM Su 1	EMC 5	EMC 7	EMC 16	EMC 10	EMC 14	EMC 17	EMC 10	EMC 9
			FAC 3Qr	FAC EP					
FAV 2Q	FAV 2Q	FAV 2Q	FAV 1Q	FAV 1Q	FAV 1Q	FAV 1P	FAV 2Q	FAV 1P	FAV 2Q

RADFORD

Founded: 1964   Nickname: The Pheasants

Secretary: Jon Holt   **(T)** 07508 384 276   **(E)** vote4holt@hotmail.co.uk
Chairman: Bob Thomas   **Manager:** Glenn Russell   **Prog Ed:** Jon Holt
Ground: Selhurst Street, Off Radford Road, Nottingham NG7 5EH   **(T)** 0115 942 3250
Colours(change): All claret (Yellow/green/yellow)

HONOURS: FA Comps: None   **League:** East Midlands Regional League 1982-83.

10 YEAR RECORD

07-08	08-09	09-10	10-11	11-12	12-13	13-14	14-15	15-16	16-17
CM Su 8	EMC 14	EMC 19	EMC 19	EMC 17	EMC 19	EMC 15	EMC 3	EMC 2	EMC 7
		FAC EP						FAC P	FAC EP
FAV 1Q	FAV 2Q	FAV 2Q	FAV 1Q	FAV 2Q	FAV 2Q	FAV 1Q	FAV 1Q	FAV 1P	FAV 2P

SELSTON

Founded: 1968   Nickname: The Parishioners

Secretary: Nicola Johnson   **(T)** 07532 183 393   **(E)** nicolajohnson80@ntlworld.com
Chairman: Mark Wilson   **Prog Ed:** Tracey Purdon
Ground: Parish Hall, Mansfield Road, Selston, Nottinghamshire NG16 6EE   **(T)** 01773 812 540
Colours(change): Blue & black/black/black (All yellow)

HONOURS: FA Comps: None   **League:** Midland Regional Alliance Division Two 2007-08. Notts Senior 2013-14. Central Midlands South Division 2015-16, 16-17.

10 YEAR RECORD

07-08	08-09	09-10	10-11	11-12	12-13	13-14	14-15	15-16	16-17
MidRA2 1	MidRA1 4	MidRA1 3	MidRA1 5	NottSP 11	NottSP 11	NottSP 1	NottSP 4	CMSth 1	CMSth 1

STAPENHILL

Founded: 1947   Nickname: The Swans

Secretary: Helen Bedwell   **(T)** 01283 527 670   **(E)** helen.bedwell@drakelowsiteservices.co.uk
Chairman: Ian Gough   **Prog Ed:** Helen Bedwell
Ground: Edge Hill, Maple Grove, Stapenhill DE15 9NN.   **(T)** 01283 516 433
Colours(change): All red (Yellow/black/yellow)

HONOURS: FA Comps: None   **League:** Leicestershire Senior 1958-59, 59-60, 86-87, 88-89, 2006-07.

10 YEAR RECORD

07-08	08-09	09-10	10-11	11-12	12-13	13-14	14-15	15-16	16-17
MidAl 20		LeicSP 12	LeicSP 4	LeicSP 5	LeicS1 5	EMC 2	EMC 15	EMC 12	EMC 11
FAC EPr	FAC EP						FAC EPr		
FAV 1Q	FAV 1Q				FAV 1Q	FAV 1Q	FAV 1Q	FAV 1Q	FAV 2Q

TEVERSAL

Founded: 1918   Nickname: Tevie Boys

Secretary: Kevin Newton   **(T)** 07711 358 060   **(E)** Kev1.Newton@ntlworld.com
Chairman: Peter Cockerill   **Manager:** Dean Short   **Prog Ed:** Kevin Newton
Ground: Teversal Grange Spts and So.Centre, Carnarvon St, Teversal, NG17 3HJ   **(T)** 01623 554 924   **Capacity:** 2,000
Colours(change): Red & white/black/red (Blue & white/blue/blue)
HONOURS: FA Comps: None   **League:** Central Midlands Division Two 1987-88.

10 YEAR RECORD

07-08		08-09		09-10		10-11		11-12		12-13		13-14		14-15		15-16		16-17	
NCE1	10	NCE1	14	NCE1	11	NCE1	18	NCE1	15	NCE1	10	NCE1	15	NCE1	20	NCE1	14	NCE1	16
FAC	Pr	FAC	EP	FAC	EPr	FAC	EPr			FAC	EP	FAC	EP						
FAV	2Q	FAV	1P	FAV	1Q	FAV	1Q	FAV	2Q	FAV	2Q	FAV	2Q	FAV	1Q	FAV	2Q	FAV	1Q

WEST BRIDGFORD

Founded: 1990   Nickname:

Secretary: Adrian Clark   **(T)** 07791 633 221   **(E)** adrianmclark@btinternet.com
Chairman: Peter Stansbury   **Prog Ed:** Adrian Clark
Ground: Regatta Way, Gamston, West Bridgford, Nottingham NG2 5AT   **(T)** 07791 633 221
Colours(change): Black & red/black/black (All royal blue)
HONOURS: FA Comps: None   **League:** East Midlands Counties 2016-17.

10 YEAR RECORD

07-08	08-09	09-10	10-11	11-12		12-13		13-14		14-15		15-16		16-17	
				NottS2	2	NottS1	5	NottS1	2	NottSP	2	NottSP	3	EMC	1
														FAV	2Q

Hadleigh United 2016-17 - 18th in Eastern Counties Premier. Photo: Alan Coomes.

EASTERN COUNTIES LEAGUE

Sponsored by: Thurlow Nunn
Founded: 1935

Recent Champions: 2013: Dereham Town
2014: Hadleigh United **2015:** Norwich United

PREMIER DIVISION

		P	W	D	L	F	A	GD	Pts
1	Mildenhall Town	40	32	3	5	97	29	68	99
2	Felixstowe & Walton United	40	29	3	8	94	31	63	90
3	Newmarket Town	40	26	6	8	122	70	52	84
4	Gorleston	40	24	6	10	88	51	37	78
5	Great Yarmouth Town	40	20	8	12	61	47	14	68
6	Stanway Rovers	40	19	9	12	67	47	20	66
7	Thetford Town	40	18	11	11	75	46	29	65
8	Brantham Athletic	40	17	9	14	67	57	10	60
9	Saffron Walden Town	40	15	10	15	62	67	-5	55
10	Ipswich Wanderers	40	17	4	19	67	75	-8	55
11	Kirkley & Pakefield	40	15	9	16	73	61	12	54
12	Godmanchester Rovers	40	15	8	17	69	74	-5	53
13	Ely City	40	12	11	17	63	73	-10	47
14	Walsham le Willows	40	13	8	19	67	87	-20	47
15	Fakenham Town	40	13	7	20	60	73	-13	46
16	Haverhill Rovers	40	11	11	18	57	72	-15	44
17	Long Melford	40	11	7	22	42	74	-32	40
18	Hadleigh United	40	10	8	22	51	82	-31	38
19	Wivenhoe Town	40	7	12	21	51	99	-48	33
20	FC Clacton	40	9	4	27	52	114	-62	31
21	Swaffham Town	40	6	8	26	45	101	-56	26

DIVISION ONE

		P	W	D	L	F	A	GD	Pts
1	Stowmarket Town	40	28	10	2	108	22	86	93*
2	Coggeshall Town	40	27	9	4	127	34	93	90
3	Haverhill Borough	40	27	7	6	116	41	75	88
4	Woodbridge Town	40	26	5	9	126	46	80	83
5	Holland FC	40	23	8	9	105	48	57	77
6	Diss Town	40	21	8	11	88	60	28	71
7	Framlingham Town	40	20	10	10	82	62	20	70
8	Braintree Town Res	40	22	3	15	72	59	13	69
9	Halstead Town	40	18	11	11	72	64	8	65
10	Kings Lynn Town Res	40	19	6	15	69	55	14	63
11	Whitton United	40	17	3	20	73	90	-17	54
12	Debenham LC	40	15	8	17	58	69	-11	53
13	Wisbech St Mary	40	15	7	18	68	76	-8	52
14	Downham Town	40	13	12	15	74	70	4	51
15	Cornard United	40	13	8	19	63	72	-9	47
16	March Town United	40	9	10	21	49	91	-42	37
17	Team Bury	40	11	3	26	56	104	-48	36
18	AFC Sudbury Res	40	10	5	25	63	92	-29	35
19	Needham Market Res	40	6	4	30	54	151	-97	22
20	Dereham Town Res	40	5	4	31	36	136	-100	19
21	Leiston	40	3	3	34	37	154	-117	12

RESERVE DIVISION

		P	W	D	L	F	A	GD	Pts
1	Stanway Rovers Res	26	21	2	3	83	31	52	65
2	Woodbridge Town Res	26	18	3	5	68	44	24	57
3	Witham Town Res	26	16	4	6	79	41	38	52
4	Stowmarket Town Res	26	14	4	8	72	46	26	46
5	Halstead Town Res	25	13	7	5	60	38	22	46
6	Walsham le Willows Res	25	14	2	9	62	46	16	44
7	Wivenhoe Town Res	26	14	2	10	62	58	4	44
8	Felixstowe & Walton Utd Res	25	11	2	12	45	44	1	35
9	Whitton United Res	26	9	3	14	46	66	-20	30
10	Saffron Walden Town Res	26	8	4	14	47	56	-9	28
11	Long Melford Res	26	6	4	16	27	70	-43	22
12	Newmarket Town Res	25	6	2	17	63	72	-9	20
13	Hadleigh United Res	26	4	3	19	32	74	-42	15
14	Cornard United Res	26	3	4	19	24	84	-60	13

LEAGUE CUP

HOLDERS: MILDENHALL TOWN

ROUND 1

Framlingham Town	v	Walsham le Willows	1-2
Halstead Town	v	Saffron Walden Town	1-2
Stanway Rovers	v	Holland FC	2-1
Dereham Town Res	v	Fakenham Town	2-4
Wisbech St Mary	v	Swaffham Town	1-3
Brantham Athletic	v	Hadleigh United	7-0

ROUND 2

Stowmarket Town	v	Diss Town	0-3
Kirkley & Pakefield	v	Needham Market Res	6-2
Ely City	v	Downham Town	0-3
Mildenhall Town	v	Thetford Town	6-0
Whittton United	v	Walsham le Willows	2-3
Saffron Walden Town	v	Haverhill Rovers	1-1, 3-4p
FC Clacton	v	Stanway Rovers	0-4
Felixstowe & Walton United	v	Woodbridge Town	4-0
Fakenham Town	v	Swaffham Town	2-3
March Town United	v	King's Lynn Town Res	1-3
Team Bury	v	Godmanchester Rovers	0-0, 4-3p
Gorleston	v	Leiston Res	4-0
Wivenhoe Town	v	Ipswich Wanderers	1-2
Coggeshall Town	v	Brantham Athletic	4-2
AFC Sudbury Res	v	Long Melford	3-1
Cornard United	v	Newmarket Town	1-8

ROUND 3

Diss Town	v	Kirkley & Pakefield	0-0, 4-5p
Downham Town	v	Mildenhall Town	1-1, 3-4p
Walsham le Willows	v	Haverhill Rovers	1-2
Stanway Rovers	v	Felixstowe & Walton United	2-0
Swaffham Town	v	King's Lynn Town Res	2-1
Team Bury	v	Gorleston	0-1
Ipswich Wanderers	v	Coggeshall Town	0-2
AFC Sudbury Res	v	Newmarket Town	1-2

QUARTER-FINALS

Kirkley & Pakefield	v	Mildenhall Town	0-1
Haverhill Rovers	v	Stanway Rovers	4-0
Swaffham Town	v	Gorleston	2-6
Coggeshall Town	v	Newmarket Town	1-5

SEMI-FINALS

Mildenhall Town	v	Haverhill Rovers	5-0
Gorleston	v	Newmarket Town	0-3

FINAL

Mildenhall Town	v	Newmarket Town	2-1

DIVISION ONE LEAGUE CUP

HOLDERS: HAVERHILL BOROUGH

ROUND 1

Downham Town	v	Team Bury	0-0, 5-6p
Framlingham Town	v	Needham Market Res	4-3
Wisbech St Mary	v	Dereham Town Res	2-1
Stowmarket Town	v	Coggeshall Town	0-7
Cornard United	v	Holland FC	1-3

ROUND 2

King's Lynn Town Res	v	March Town United	4-0
AFC Sudbury Res	v	Whitton United	1-3
Haverhill Borough	v	Team Bury	1-3
Debenham LC	v	Leiston Res	2-1
Woodbridge Town	v	Framlingham Town	0-0, 5-6p
Diss Town	v	Wisbech St Mary	1-4
Coggeshall Town	v	Holland FC	7-0
Halstead Town	v	Braintree Town Res	7-0

QUARTER FINALS

King's Lynn Town Res	v	Whitton United	3-2
Team Bury	v	Debenham LC	1-0
Framlingham Town	v	Wisbech St Mary	1-2
Coggeshall Town	v	Halstead Town	2-0

SEMI FINALS

King's Lynn Town Res	v	Team Bury	2-0
Wisbech St Mary	v	Coggeshall Town	2-1

FINAL

King's Lynn Town Res	v	Wisbech St Mary	1-0

PREMIER DIVISION	1	2	3	4	5	6	7	8	9	10	11	12	13	14	15	16	17	18	19	20	21
1 Brantham Athletic		2-0	1-2	2-1	2-0	2-0	1-3	0-1	0-0	1-0	3-0	2-3	0-0	0-3	2-2	1-0	1-3	4-2	1-1	3-2	1-1
2 Ely City	2-2		0-1	1-0	1-3	2-2	2-1	2-1	1-2	2-1	2-4	3-0	2-0	0-2	2-3	2-3	1-1	2-2	1-3	5-4	3-1
3 Fakenham Town	0-1	1-3		4-0	0-4	1-1	2-2	1-2	2-0	1-2	1-1	3-4	2-0	1-5	0-2	5-2	1-2	1-2	1-3	1-1	2-1
4 FC Clacton	1-4	4-2	4-2		1-2	5-0	2-4	0-2	0-1	2-0	3-4	2-0	2-0	1-7	0-6	2-0	0-5	1-0	0-4	0-3	2-3
5 Felixstowe & Walton United	2-1	4-2	2-0	8-0		0-1	6-0	1-1	1-0	2-1	3-0	3-0	4-0	3-0	2-0	1-0	1-3	3-0	2-2	3-1	3-1
6 Godmanchester Rovers	1-1	0-1	2-1	2-1	0-3		2-1	1-3	2-2	2-0	3-1	1-3	2-0	2-3	0-1	1-2	1-1	7-1	2-1	4-1	0-4
7 Gorleston	0-3	5-0	1-1	1-0	2-1	3-1		3-0	4-1	1-1	2-1	3-1	3-0	0-2	1-1	2-0	1-1	6-0	3-0	2-0	6-0
8 Great Yarmouth Town	2-1	2-1	2-3	1-1	0-1	1-0	1-3		4-0	1-1	2-4	1-4	1-2	1-0	0-2	3-0	1-0	2-1	2-1	4-0	4-0
9 Hadleigh United	0-3	0-1	2-2	5-1	0-4	2-4	2-1	3-4		0-0	0-0	2-1	6-1	0-1	0-2	3-0	0-2	2-2	0-3	1-2	1-5
10 Haverhill Rovers	0-1	0-2	2-1	2-2	0-3	4-2	2-2	0-0	4-2		3-0	3-0	1-1	1-2	2-4	1-2	3-1	2-2	0-3	2-3	0-0
11 Ipswich Wanderers	2-4	2-1	2-0	2-2	0-3	0-2	3-0	1-2	1-2	3-2		0-1	2-1	2-1	7-3	2-3	3-0	1-0	1-4	3-6	2-1
12 Kirkley & Pakefield	4-2	3-3	3-0	10-0	1-2	1-1	0-1	1-1	1-1	1-3	1-0		2-1	1-2	0-0	2-1	1-2	3-3	2-3	4-1	4-1
13 Long Melford	1-2	1-1	1-1	4-3	0-2	0-2	1-0	0-2	2-1	2-3	1-0	1-0		1-3	2-4	3-2	0-0	2-0	0-4	1-2	2-0
14 Mildenhall Town	1-0	1-1	5-0	1-0	0-2	3-2	2-0	2-0	4-1	2-0	1-1	2-0	2-1		2-1	1-2	1-0	4-0	2-0	2-0	9-0
15 Newmarket Town	3-2	4-3	3-1	6-2	0-3	6-2	8-2	0-2	6-1	5-3	4-2	1-1	3-1	1-3		4-1	1-3	2-1	2-4	5-1	
16 Saffron Walden Town	1-1	1-1	0-3	5-0	2-0	4-1	1-2	1-0	1-0	2-0	2-3	3-1	2-2	1-1	3-4		1-4	1-1	1-1	2-2	1-1
17 Stanway Rovers	2-1	1-1	0-1	2-1	2-1	2-5	0-1	2-0	0-0	6-0	2-1	1-1	4-0	0-2	1-2	1-2		0-2	1-0	3-2	0-3
18 Swaffham Town	3-1	1-0	2-3	0-3	1-3	3-2	1-5	1-1	1-2	2-2	0-1	1-4	2-4	0-5	4-4	0-1	1-6		0-2	2-0	1-2
19 Thetford Town	5-2	2-2	1-0	4-0	3-1	1-1	0-1	1-1	5-2	1-2	0-1	1-1	2-0	0-2	1-2	2-2	1-1	3-0		1-1	3-2
20 Walsham le Willows	0-3	2-1	2-5	3-1	2-1	3-5	1-5	1-1	4-2	1-1	1-4	1-0	0-3	1-2	2-2	0-2	0-1	2-0	1-1		1-1
21 Wivenhoe Town	3-3	1-1	0-3	2-2	1-1	0-0	0-5	1-2	0-2	2-3	3-0	0-3	0-0	2-4	1-10	3-3	2-2	1-0	0-1	1-4	

CLUB MOVEMENTS

PREMIER DIVISION

In: Coggeshall Town (P), Haverhill Borough (P), Histon (R - Southern D1C), Stowmarket Town (P), Wroxham (R - Isthmian D1N).
Out: Mildenhall Town (P - Isthmian Div.1 North), Swaffham Town (R).

DIVISION ONE

In: Little Oakley (P - Essex & Suffolk Border), Norwich CMS formerly Spixworth (P - Anglian Combination), Norwich United Reserves (N).
Out: Coggeshall Town (P), Haverhill Borough (P), Stowmarket Town (P).

DIVISION ONE	1	2	3	4	5	6	7	8	9	10	11	12	13	14	15	16	17	18	19	20	21
1 AFC Sudbury Res		0-1	1-4	2-2	0-2	3-1	4-4	3-0	3-6	1-4	1-1	0-2	1-2	6-1	1-1	1-5	1-3	4-0	0-2	3-0	3-4
2 Braintree Town Res	2-0		3-5	0-1	3-1	5-0	3-1	1-5	2-2	1-0	1-0	2-3	0-3	3-2	5-0	1-0	0-2	1-0	1-0	5-3	2-1
3 Coggeshall Town	3-1	6-0		1-0	1-1	5-0	4-0	2-0	3-1	0-0	5-1	1-1	5-0	3-0	1-1	9-0	1-2	2-0	6-3	4-0	4-1
4 Cornard United	2-0	1-3	1-5		0-1	1-1	2-4	0-0	0-0	1-3	2-3	2-3	2-2	2-0	2-1	5-0	0-2	4-1	6-3	2-4	0-4
5 Debenham LC	1-3	3-2	1-3	3-0		2-3	0-0	3-2	1-4	0-1	1-5	0-2	2-1	2-0	1-2	3-0	0-3	4-0	1-3	3-3	0-2
6 Dereham Town Res	2-3	0-2	0-5	0-5	1-2		1-2	0-0	0-0	5-5	0-4	0-5	1-2	1-2	0-3	1-2	0-4	4-3	0-3	1-5	0-3
7 Diss Town	1-0	2-1	0-2	0-2	2-1	3-0		0-1	2-4	4-0	1-1	3-3	2-1	7-1	4-2	6-0	2-2	1-0	2-2	4-1	1-0
8 Downham Town	0-0	4-2	1-2	0-1	0-0	1-3	4-2		0-1	1-1	1-1	0-2	3-1	6-0	3-0	4-0	0-6	3-0	5-1	1-1	0-2
9 Framlingham Town	2-1	1-0	2-1	2-0	3-2	5-1	0-3	4-1		2-2	2-4	2-2	6-1	4-0	4-2	1-1	2-2	4-1	0-0	1-4	0-1
10 Halstead Town	3-0	2-3	0-8	3-1	0-0	3-1	1-1	3-3	1-2		0-2	2-1	0-2	5-1	1-1	2-1	0-0	4-0	2-0	2-1	0-4
11 Haverhill Borough	2-1	3-0	3-0	2-1	6-1	8-1	2-0	3-3	2-1	0-1		4-0	1-2	13-0	4-0	6-1	1-0	4-1	3-1	3-1	0-2
12 Holland FC	5-1	0-3	1-1	0-0	4-0	4-0	1-1	2-3	4-1	1-2	3-0		1-0	10-0	7-0	5-1	0-4	6-0	3-1	3-1	0-2
13 King's Lynn Town Res	4-1	1-0	0-0	1-1	2-2	0-1	0-2	2-1	3-2	0-0	2-1			7-0	3-0	8-2	0-3	2-1	2-0	1-2	2-5
14 Leiston Res	5-3	1-3	0-3	1-4	2-2	0-1	1-3	0-1	2-0	1-5	2-3	0-2	0-2		2-4	4-6	0-5	1-5	0-5	0-3	1-3
15 March Town United	2-0	1-1	0-0	3-2	1-4	4-0	1-0	1-1	3-4	1-1	2-3	1-4	0-1	3-1		2-2	1-1	1-0	0-1	0-2	1-4
16 Needham Market Res	0-5	0-3	2-12	0-3	1-1	2-1	1-6	2-2	2-4	1-3	1-3	0-5	0-3	5-1	4-1		2-4	3-6	2-3	0-1	0-6
17 Stowmarket Town	3-0	1-1	0-0	1-1	2-0	7-1	3-0	3-0	3-0	2-1	2-2	4-1	1-0	2-2	5-0	7-0		4-0	2-0	6-1	0-0
18 Team Bury	2-1	1-3	1-1	2-1	0-1	4-1	2-4	3-4	0-0	2-1	0-5	0-3	0-2	4-2	1-1	2-1	0-2		3-5	0-5	4-2
19 Whitton United	8-1	0-3	5-4	0-1	2-3	3-2	3-2	5-4	0-1	1-3	1-1	1-2	1-0	2-1	2-1	3-2	0-2	0-2		2-1	0-9
20 Wisbech St Mary	0-2	2-0	0-3	2-1	0-1	6-0	1-3	3-2	1-3	1-1	0-1	1-1	1-1	0-0	4-1	3-1	0-2	2-4	1-0		1-4
21 Woodbridge Town	0-2	1-0	1-2	9-1	0-2	10-1	2-3	4-4	1-1	5-1	1-0	2-2	3-1	6-0	5-0	5-1	2-1	5-1	6-0	1-1	

BRANTHAM ATHLETIC

Founded: 1887   Nickname: Blue Imps

Secretary: Dan Allen   **(T)** 07896 266 074   **(E)** branthamathfc@hotmail.co.uk
Chairman: Peter Crowhurst   **Manager:** Paul Skingley - Jan 2015
Ground: Brantham Leisure Centre, New Village, Brantham CO11 1RZ   **(T)** 01206 392 506
Capacity: 1,200 **Seats:** 200 **Covered:** 200   **Midweek Matchday:** Tuesday   **Clubhouse:** Yes

Colours(change): All blue. (Red & black stripes/black/black)
Previous Names: Brantham & Stutton United 1996-98.
Previous Leagues: Eastern Counties. Suffolk & Ipswich.

HONOURS: FA Comps: None
       League: Essex & Suffolk Border 1972-73, 73-74, 75-76, 76-77. Suffolk & Ipswich Senior League 2007-08.

10 YEAR RECORD

07-08		08-09		09-10		10-11		11-12		12-13		13-14		14-15		15-16		16-17	
S&I S	1	EC1	8	EC1	3	ECP	13	ECP	3	ECP	4	ECP	11	ECP	8	ECP	11	ECP	8
						FAC	P	FAC	P	FAC	P	FAC	1Q	FAC	EPr	FAC	1Q	FAC	EP
				FAV	2Q	FAV	1Q	FAV	1P	FAV	5P	FAV	4P	FAV	3P	FAV	1P	FAV	2Q

COGGESHALL TOWN

Founded: 1878   Nickname: Seedgrowers

Secretary: Peter Smith   **(T)** 07899 763 027   **(E)** secretary@coggeshalltownfc.co.uk
Chairman: Graeme Smith   **Manager:** Graeme Smith - June 2014   **Prog Ed:** Paul Hammond
Ground: The Crops, West Street, Coggeshall CO6 1NS   **(T)** 01376 562 843
Capacity: **Seats:** Yes **Covered:** Yes   **Midweek Matchday:** Tuesday   **Clubhouse:** Yes

Colours(change): Red & black/black/red (Blue & white/blue/white)
Previous Names: None
Previous Leagues: North Essex 1899-1909. Colchester & District/Essex & Suffolk Border 1909-39, 58-72, 90-96, 2000-2016. North Essex. Braintree & District. Colchester & East Essex 1950-58. Essex Senior 1972-90. Essex Intermediate 1996-98, 99-00.
HONOURS: FA Comps: None
       League: North Essex x4. Essex & Suffolk Border Division II B 1909-10, 10-11, Division One 1962-63,
10 YEAR RECORD   Premier Division 1966-67, 67-68, 69-70, 2015-16.

07-08	08-09		09-10		10-11		11-12		12-13		13-14		14-15		15-16		16-17	
	EsSuP	16	EsSu1	4	EsSu1	5	EsSu1	5	EsSu1	2	EsSuP	7	EsSuP	6	EsSuP	1	EC1	2

ELY CITY

Founded: 1885   Nickname: Robins

Secretary: Derek Oakey   **(T)** 07720 542 882   **(E)** derek.oakey@tesco.net
Chairman: Robert Button   **Manager:** Brady Stone - Feb 2014   **Prog Ed:** Barnes Print
Ground: Unwin Sports Ground, Downham Road, Ely CB6 2SH   **(T)** 01353 662 035
Capacity: 1,500 **Seats:** 200 **Covered:** 350   **Midweek Matchday:** Tuesday   **Clubhouse:** Yes **Shop:** Yes

Colours(change): All red. (All blue).
Previous Names: None.
Previous Leagues: Cambridgeshire 1901-02, 03-51. Peterborough & District 1951-58. Central Alliance 1958-60.

HONOURS: FA Comps: None
       League: Peterborough & District 1955-56.
10 YEAR RECORD   Eastern Counties Division One 1996-97.

07-08		08-09		09-10		10-11		11-12		12-13		13-14		14-15		15-16		16-17	
EC1	2	ECP	14	ECP	9	ECP	15	ECP	2	ECP	11	ECP	17	ECP	20	EC1	2	ECP	13
FAC	P	FAC	EP	FAC	EP	FAC	1Q	FAC	1Qr	FAC	Pr	FAC	EP	FAC	EP	FAC	EPr	FAC	EP
FAV	1P	FAV	1Q	FAV	3P	FAV	1Qr	FAV	1Q	FAV	4P	FAV	2Pr	FAV	1Q	FAV	2Q	FAV	5P

FAKENHAM TOWN

Founded: 1884   Nickname: Ghosts

Secretary: Paul Chivers   **(T)** 01328 862 836   **(E)** chilvers.paul@yahoo.com
Chairman: Andrew Jarvis   **Manager:** Wayne Anderson - Jan 2016   **Prog Ed:** Tony Miles
Ground: Clipbush Park, Clipbush Lane, Fakenham, Norfolk NR21 8SW   **(T)** 01328 854 617
Capacity: **Seats:** Yes **Covered:** Yes   **Midweek Matchday:** Wednesday   **Clubhouse:** Yes

Colours(change): Amber & black/black/black (White with blue trim/white/white)
Previous Names: None
Previous Leagues: Norwich & District. Norfolk & Suffolk/Anglian Combination 1935-88.

HONOURS: FA Comps: None
       League: Anglian Combination Division One 1971-72.
10 YEAR RECORD

07-08		08-09		09-10		10-11		11-12		12-13		13-14		14-15		15-16		16-17	
EC1	17	EC1	20	EC1	19	EC1	14	EC1	11	EC1	5	EC1	2	ECP	13	ECP	17	ECP	15
FAC	EP	FAC	P							FAC	EP	FAC	EP	FAC	EPr	FAC	P	FAC	EP
FAV	2Q	FAV	1Q	FAV	1Qr	FAV	1Q	FAV	2Q	FAV	2Q	FAV	2P	FAV	2Q	FAV	2Q

FC CLACTON
Founded: 1892   Nickname: The Seasiders

Secretary: Danny Coyle   **(T)** 07581 056 174   **(E)** fcclactonsecretary@gmail.com
Chairman: David Ballard   **Manager:** Kieron Shelley - September 2016   **Prog Ed:** Mark Oswick
Ground: Rush Green Bowl, Rush Green Rd, Clacton-on-Sea CO16 7BQ   **(T)** 07581 056 174
Capacity: 3,000 **Seats:** 200 **Covered:** Yes **Midweek Matchday:** Tuesday **Clubhouse:** Yes **Shop:** Yes

Colours(change): White & royal blue with red trim/royal blue/royal blue. (Red & black stripes/black/black).
Previous Names: Clacton Town > 2007
Previous Leagues: Eastern Counties 1935-37, 38-58. Essex County 1937-38. Southern League 1958-64.

HONOURS: FA Comps: None
League: North Essex D2 1898-99, 99-1900. Clacton & District 1905-06. South East Anglian D2 1907-08. Colchester & District D2 1909-10. East Anglian 1910-11. Southern D1 1959-60. Eastern Counties D1 1994-95, 98-99.

10 YEAR RECORD									
07-08	08-09	09-10	10-11	11-12	12-13	13-14	14-15	15-16	16-17
EC1 10	EC1 7	EC1 2	ECP 16	ECP 15	ECP 20	ECP 15	ECP 16	ECP 10	ECP 20
FAC P	FAC 1Q	FAC P	FAC Pr	FAC P	FAC EP	FAC 2Qr	FAC P	FAC P	FAC EP
FAV 1Q	FAV 4P	FAV 2P	FAV 1P	FAV 1P	FAV 2Q	FAV 1Q	FAV 2Q	FAV 1P	FAV 1Q

FELIXSTOWE & WALTON UNITED
Founded: 2000   Nickname: Seasiders

Secretary: Tony Barnes   **(T)** 07584 010 933   **(E)** tgbarnes@live.co.uk
Chairman: Andy Wilding   **Manager:** Kevin O'Donnell - Oct 2012   **Prog Ed:** Adam Whalley
Ground: Goldstar Ground, Dellwood Avenue, Felixstowe IP11 9HT   **(T)** 01394 282 917
Capacity: 2,000 **Seats:** 200 **Covered:** 200 **Midweek Matchday:** Tuesday **Clubhouse:** Yes **Shop:** Yes

Colours(change): Red & white stripes/red/red. (Sky blue & white/white/navy).
Previous Names: Felixstowe Port & Town and Walton United merged in July 2000.
Previous Leagues: None

HONOURS: FA Comps: None
League: None

10 YEAR RECORD									
07-08	08-09	09-10	10-11	11-12	12-13	13-14	14-15	15-16	16-17
ECP 8	ECP 12	ECP 7	ECP 18	ECP 18	ECP 14	ECP 3	ECP 5	ECP 4	ECP 2
FAC EPr	FAC EP	FAC EP	FAC 2Qr	FAC P	FAC Pr	FAC P	FAC 1Q	FAC EPr	FAC 3Q
FAV 2Q	FAV 1Pr	FAV 1Pr	FAV 1P	FAV 2P	FAV 2Q	FAV 1Q	FAV 1P	FAV 1Q	FAV 2P

GODMANCHESTER ROVERS
Founded: 1911   Nickname: Goody/Rovers

Secretary: Tracy Cosbey   **(T)** 07837 193 514   **(E)** secretary@godmanchesterroversfc.co.uk
Chairman: Karl Hurst   **Manager:** Chris Hyem - October 2016   **Prog Ed:** Steve Bengree
Ground: The David Wilson Homes Ground, Godmanchester, Huntingdon PE29 2LQ   **(T)**
Capacity: **Seats:** Yes **Covered:** Yes **Midweek Matchday:** Wednesday **Clubhouse:** Yes

Colours(change): Sky blue/navy/navy (All red)
Previous Names: None
Previous Leagues: Huntingdonshire County. Cambridgeshire >2002.

HONOURS: FA Comps: None
League: Eastern Counties League Division One 2011-12.

10 YEAR RECORD									
07-08	08-09	09-10	10-11	11-12	12-13	13-14	14-15	15-16	16-17
EC1 16	EC1 10	EC1 12	EC1 9	EC1 1	ECP 5	ECP 5	ECP 2	ECP 2	ECP 12
		FAC 1Q	FAC EPr	FAC P	FAC P	FAC P	FAC P	FAC P	FAC Pr
FAV 2Q	FAV 1Q	FAV 1Qr	FAV 2P	FAV 3P	FAV 1P	FAV 1P	FAV 1Pr	FAV 1Pr	FAV 1P

GORLESTON
Founded: 1887   Nickname: The Greens

Secretary: Colin Bray   **(T)** 07918 186 645   **(E)** colin-bray@sky.com
Chairman: Alan Gordon   **Manager:** Ricci Butler - May 2015   **Prog Ed:** Colin Bray
Ground: Emerald Park, Woodfarm Lane, Gorleston, Norfolk NR31 9AQ   **(T)** 01493 602 802
Capacity: **Seats:** Yes **Covered:** Yes **Midweek Matchday:** Tuesday **Clubhouse:** Yes

Colours(change): All green (All sky blue)
Previous Names: None
Previous Leagues: Aldred/Yarmouth & District 1900-08. Norfolk & Suffolk/Anglian Combination 1908-35, 60-69. Eastern Counties 1935-60.

HONOURS: FA Comps: None
League: Yarmouth & District 1905-06, 07-08. Norfolk & Suffolk/Anglian Comb. 1920-21, 25-26, 29-30, 31-32, 32-33, 33-34, 34-35, 68-69. Eastern Counties 1952-53, 72-73, 79-80, 80-81, Division One 1995-96, 2010-11.

10 YEAR RECORD									
07-08	08-09	09-10	10-11	11-12	12-13	13-14	14-15	15-16	16-17
EC1 8	EC1 6	EC1 4	EC1 1	ECP 12	ECP 3	ECP 4	ECP 12	ECP 16	ECP 4
FAC P	FAC EP	FAC Pr	FAC EP	FAC P	FAC 1Q	FAC P	FAC 1Q	FAC EP	FAC EP
FAV 1P	FAV 2Q	FAV 2Qr	FAV 2P	FAV 2Q	FAV 1P	FAV 1P	FAV 1P	FAV 2P	FAV 4P

GREAT YARMOUTH TOWN

Founded: 1897 **Nickname:** The Bloaters

Secretary: John Lewsley   **(T)** 07776 147 508   **(E)** jglewsley@btinternet.com
Chairman: Kevin Cruickshank   **Manager:** Martyn Sinclair & Adam Mason   **Prog Ed:** Barnes Print Ltd
Ground: The Wellesley, Sandown Road, Great Yarmouth NR30 1EY   **(T)** 07873 861 983
Capacity: 3,600 **Seats:** 500 **Covered:** 2,100 **Midweek Matchday:** Tuesday   **Clubhouse:** Yes **Shop:** Yes

Colours(change): Amber & black/black/black (White & blue/blue/blue)
Previous Names: None
Previous Leagues: Norfolk & Suffolk 1897-1935.

HONOURS: FA Comps: None
     League: Norfolk & Suffolk 1913-14, 26-27, 27-28. Eastern Counties 1968-69, Division One 2009-10.

10 YEAR RECORD

	07-08		08-09		09-10		10-11		11-12		12-13		13-14		14-15		15-16		16-17	
EC1	11	EC1	5	EC1	1	ECP	14	ECP	21	EC1	10	EC1	8	EC1	4	EC1	3	ECP	5
FAC	EP	FAC	Pr	FAC	P	FAC	EP	FAC	EP	FAC	P	FAC	EP	FAC	P	FAC	EP	FAC	EP
FAV	2Q	FAV	2Q	FAV	1Q	FAV	2Q	FAV	2Q	FAV	2Q	FAV	2P	FAV	3P	FAV	1P	FAV	1P

HADLEIGH UNITED

Founded: 1892 **Nickname:** Brettsiders

Secretary: Neil Henderson   **(T)** 07771 522 695   **(E)** waffhenderson@aol.com
Chairman: Rolf Beggerow   **Manager:** Stuart Alston - May 2016   **Prog Ed:** Barnes Print Ltd
Ground: The Millfield, Tinkers Lane, Duke St, Hadleigh IP7 5NF   **(T)** 01473 822 165
Capacity: 3,000 **Seats:** 250 **Covered:** 500 **Midweek Matchday:** Tuesday   **Clubhouse:** Yes

Colours(change): All navy blue (All red)
Previous Names: None
Previous Leagues: Ipswich & District/Suffolk & Ipswich 1929-91.

HONOURS: FA Comps: None
     League: Suffolk & Ipswich 1953-54, 56-57, 73-74, 76-77, 78-79, Division Two 1958-59.

10 YEAR RECORD   Eastern Counties 1993-94, 2013-14.

	07-08		08-09		09-10		10-11		11-12		12-13		13-14		14-15		15-16		16-17	
EC1	5	EC1	2	ECP	18	ECP	9	ECP	11	ECP	8	ECP	1	ECP	7	ECP	7	ECP	18
FAC	EP	FAC	EP	FAC	EP	FAC	EP	FAC	P	FAC	1Q	FAC	P	FAC	1Q	FAC	EP	FAC	EP
FAV	1Q	FAV	1P	FAV	2Q	FAV	1P	FAV	1Q	FAV	QF	FAV	5P	FAV	2P	FAV	2Q	FAV	2Q

HAVERHILL BOROUGH

Founded: 2011 **Nickname:** Borough

Secretary: Gary Brown   **(T)** 01799 586 560   **(E)** gabrown306@hotmail.com
Chairman: Dave Hardwick   **Manager:** Anthony Choat   **Prog Ed:** Gary Brown
Ground: The New Croft, Chalkestone Way, Haverhill, Suffolk CB9 0BW   **(T)** 01440 702 137
Capacity: 3,000 **Seats:** 200 **Covered:** **Midweek Matchday:** Wednesday   **Clubhouse:** Yes

Colours(change): All royal blue (All white)
Previous Names: Haverhill Sports Association > 2013.
Previous Leagues: Essex & Suffolk Border > 2013.

HONOURS: FA Comps: None
     League: Essex & Suffolk Border Division One 2011-12.

10 YEAR RECORD

	07-08	08-09	09-10	10-11	11-12		12-13		13-14		14-15		15-16		16-17	
					EsSu1	1	EsSuP	2	EC1	4	EC1	6	EC1	8	EC1	3
											FAC	1Q	FAC	EP		
									FAV	1Q	FAV	1P	FAV	1Q	FAV	1P

HAVERHILL ROVERS

Founded: 1886 **Nickname:** Rovers

Secretary: Barbara Jones   **(T)** 01440 702 137   **(E)** barbarajoneshrfc@outlook.com
Chairman: Steve Brown   **Manager:** Ben Cowling - May 2016   **Prog Ed:** Malcolm Loft
Ground: The New Croft, Chalkstone Way, Haverhill, Suffolk CB9 0BW   **(T)** 01440 702 137
Capacity: 3,000 **Seats:** 200 **Covered:** 200 **Midweek Matchday:** Tuesday   **Clubhouse:** Yes

Colours(change): All red (White/black/black & white).
Previous Names: None.
Previous Leagues: East Anglian. Essex & Suffolk Border.

HONOURS: FA Comps: None
     League: Essex & Suffolk Border 1947-48, 62-63, 63-64.

10 YEAR RECORD   Eastern Counties 1978-79.

	07-08		08-09		09-10		10-11		11-12		12-13		13-14		14-15		15-16		16-17	
ECP	10	ECP	21	ECP	12	ECP	8	ECP	14	ECP	10	ECP	7	ECP	17	ECP	12	ECP	16
FAC	2Qr	FAC	EPr	FAC	EPr	FAC	Pr	FAC	1Q	FAC	P	FAC	P	FAC	EPr	FAC	EP	FAC	EP
FAV	2Q	FAV	2Q	FAV	1P	FAV	1P	FAV	1P	FAV	1P	FAV	1Q	FAV	2Q	FAV	1Q	FAV	2Q

HISTON
Founded: 1904   Nickname: The Stutes

Secretary: David Simpson   **(T)** 01223 237 373   **(E)**
Chairman: John Hall   **Manager:** Lance Key
Ground: The Glassworld Stadium, Bridge Road, Impington, Cambridge CB24 9PH   **(T)** 01223 237 373
Capacity: 3,250 **Seats:** 450 **Covered:** 1,800 **Midweek Matchday:** Tuesday **Clubhouse:** Yes **Shop:** Yes

Colours(change): Red and black stripes/black/black (Blue & white stripes/blue/blue)
Previous Names: Histon Institute
Previous Leagues: Cambridgeshire 1904-48, Spartan 1948-60, Delphian 1960-63, Eastern Counties 1966-2000, Southern 2000-05, 14-17. Conference 2005-14.
HONOURS: FA Comps: None
League: Eastern Counties 1999-2000. Southern League Premier 2004-05. Conference South 2006-07.

10 YEAR RECORD	07-08		08-09		09-10		10-11		11-12		12-13		13-14		14-15		15-16		16-17	
	Conf	7	Conf	3	Conf	18	Conf	24	ConfN	16	ConfN	19	ConfN	21	SthP	18	SthP	22	SthC	21
	FAC	1P	FAC	3P	FAC	4Q	FAC	4Q	FAC	2Qr	FAC	3Qr	FAC	3Q	FAC	2Qr	FAC	1Q	FAC	2Q
	FAT	3Pr	FAT	1P	FAT	1P	FAT	1P	FAT	3Q	FAT	3Q	FAT	3Q	FAT	2Q	FAT	1Qr	FAT	Pr

IPSWICH WANDERERS
Founded: 1980   Nickname: Wanderers

Secretary: Paul Crickmore   **(T)** 07577 745 778   **(E)** iwfc@hotmail.co.uk
Chairman: Keith Lloyd   **Manager:** Shane Wardley - May 2016   **Prog Ed:** Joe Topple
Ground: SEH Sports Centre, Humber Doucy Lane, Ipswich IP4 3NR   **(T)** 01473 720 691
Capacity: **Seats:** Yes **Covered:** Yes **Midweek Matchday:** Wednesday **Clubhouse:** Yes

Colours(change): All blue (All red)
Previous Names: Under-14's boys team 1980-82. Loadwell Ipswich 1982-89.
Previous Leagues: Ipswich Sunday League 1982-88.

HONOURS: FA Comps: None
League: Eastern Counties Division One 1997-98, 04-05.

10 YEAR RECORD	07-08		08-09		09-10		10-11		11-12		12-13		13-14		14-15		15-16		16-17	
	ECP	22	EC1	17	EC1	17	EC1	10	EC1	12	EC1	4	EC1	3	ECP	9	ECP	15	ECP	10
	FAC	P	FAC	Pr					FAC	Pr	FAC	EP	FAC	P	FAC	1Qr	FAC	2Q	FAC	EPr
	FAV	EP	FAV	2Q	FAV	2Q	FAV	1P	FAV	2Q	FAV	1P	FAV	1P	FAV	2P	FAV	5Pr	FAV	2P

KIRKLEY & PAKEFIELD
Founded: 1886   Nickname: The Kirks

Secretary: David Hackney   **(T)** 01502 582 865   **(E)** davidra1945@hotmail.co.uk
Chairman: Jon Reynolds   **Manager:** Mark Willis - July 2016   **Prog Ed:** Colin Foreman
Ground: Walmer Road, Lowestoft NR33 7LE   **(T)** 01502 513 549
Capacity: 2,000 **Seats:** 150 **Covered:** 150 **Midweek Matchday:** Tuesday **Clubhouse:** Yes **Shop:** Yes

Colours(change): Royal blue & white/royal blue/royal blue (All maroon).
Previous Names: Kirkley. Kirkley & Waveney 1929-33. Merged with Pakefield in 2007.
Previous Leagues: North Suffolk. Norfolk & Suffolk. Anglian Combination.

HONOURS: FA Comps: None
League: North Suffolk 1894-95, 96-97, 1901-02, 05-06, 07-08, 08-09.
Anglian Combination Premier Division 2001-02, 02-03.

10 YEAR RECORD	07-08		08-09		09-10		10-11		11-12		12-13		13-14		14-15		15-16		16-17	
	ECP	6	ECP	6	ECP	4	ECP	12	ECP	13	ECP	12	ECP	12	ECP	4	ECP	5	ECP	11
	FAC	2Q	FAC	EP	FAC	2Q	FAC	EP	FAC	EP	FAC	P	FAC	P	FAC	P	FAC	2Q	FAC	P
	FAV	2Q	FAV	2P	FAV	4P	FAV	2P	FAV	1Q	FAV	1Q	FAV	2Q	FAV	2P	FAV	2P	FAV	1Q

LONG MELFORD
Founded: 1868   Nickname: The Villagers

Secretary: Richard Powell   **(T)** 07897 751 298   **(E)** richard.j.powell@hotmail.co.uk
Chairman: Colin Woodhouse   **Manager:** Jules Mumford - May 2012   **Prog Ed:** Andy Cussans
Ground: Stoneylands Stadium, New Road, Long Melford, Suffolk CO10 9JY   **(T)** 01787 312 187
Capacity: **Seats:** Yes **Covered:** Yes **Midweek Matchday:** Tuesday **Clubhouse:** Yes

Colours(change): Black & white stripes/black/black (Yellow/blue/blue)
Previous Names: N/A
Previous Leagues: Essex & Suffolk Border > 2003

HONOURS: FA Comps: None
League: Essex & Suffolk Border Champions x5.
Eastern Counties Division One 2014-15.

10 YEAR RECORD	07-08		08-09		09-10		10-11		11-12		12-13		13-14		14-15		15-16		16-17	
	EC1	19	EC1	19	EC1	16	EC1	12	EC1	9	EC1	13	EC1	11	EC1	1	ECP	9	ECP	17
	FAC	EP	FAC	EP					FAC	P	FAC	EP					FAC	P	FAC	P
	FAV	2Q	FAV	1P	FAV	2Qr	FAV	2Q	FAV	1Q	FAV	1P	FAV	2Q	FAV	2Q	FAV	2Q	FAV	2Q

NEWMARKET TOWN
Founded: 1877   Nickname: The Jockeys

Secretary: Graham Edwards   **(T)** 07757 635 887   **(E)** graham.edwards@ntlworld.com
Chairman: John Olive   **Manager:** Kevin Grainger - Sept 2006   **Prog Ed:** Barnes Print Ltd
Ground: Ridgeons Stadium, Cricket Field Road, Off Cheveley Rd, Newmarket CB8 8BT   **(T)** 01638 663 637
Capacity: 2,750   **Seats:** 144   **Covered:** 250   **Midweek Matchday:** Tuesday   **Clubhouse:** Yes   **Shop:** Yes

Colours(change): Yellow/blue/blue (All red)
Previous Names: None
Previous Leagues: Cambridgeshire Senior. Bury & District. Suffolk & Ipswich >1937. Eastern Counties 1937-52. Peterborough & District 1952-59.

HONOURS: FA Comps: None
    League: Cambridgeshire Senior 1919-20. Bury & District 1926-27. Suffolk & Ipswich 1931-32, 32-33, 33-34.

10 YEAR RECORD | Peterborough & District 1957-58. Eastern Counties Division One 2008-09.

	07-08		08-09		09-10		10-11		11-12		12-13		13-14		14-15		15-16		16-17	
ECP	21	EC1	1	ECP	16	ECP	19	ECP	20	EC1	2	ECP	9	ECP	6	ECP	13	ECP	3
FAC	P	FAC	EP	FAC	EP	FAC	P	FAC	EP	FAC	EP	FAC	Pr	FAC	1Q	FAC	P	FAC	EP
FAV	3P	FAV	1P	FAV	1P	FAV	2Q	FAV	2Q	FAV	2Q	FAV	2Q	FAV	2Q	FAV	1P	FAV	2Q

SAFFRON WALDEN TOWN
Founded: 1872   Nickname: The Bloods

Secretary: Brian Wilson   **(T)** 07747 500 659   **(E)** brisaff@aol.com
Chairman: Brian Wilson   **Manager:** Stuart Wardley - May 2013   **Prog Ed:** Jim Duvall
Ground: The Meadow, 1 Catons Lane, Saffron Walden, Essex CB10 2DU   **(T)** 01799 520 980
Capacity: **Seats:** Yes   **Covered:** Yes   **Midweek Matchday:** Tuesday   **Clubhouse:** Yes

Colours(change): Red & black stripes/black/red (Blue & white stripes/blue/blue)
Previous Names: Saffron Walden > 1967
Previous Leagues: Essex Senior >2003. Eastern Counties 2004-11. Folded in 2011 reformed for 2012-13 season.

HONOURS: FA Comps: None
    League: Essex Senior 1973-74, 99-00. Eastern Counties 1982-83.

10 YEAR RECORD

	07-08		08-09		09-10		10-11		11-12	12-13		13-14		14-15		15-16		16-17	
EC1	6	EC1	7	EC1	14	EC1	6		EC1	6	ECP	5	EC1	3	ECP	8	ECP	9
FAC	1Q	FAC	1Q	FAC	EP	FAC	Pr				FAC	EP	FAC	EP	FAC	1Q	FAC	1Q
FAV	2Q	FAV	2Q	FAV	1Q	FAV	2Q		FAV	2Q	FAV	2Q	FAT	4P	FAV	3P	FAV	1P

STANWAY ROVERS
Founded: 1956   Nickname: Rovers

Secretary: Michael Pulford   **(T)** 07736 045 007   **(E)** mpulford@colne.essex.sch.uk
Chairman: Roy Brett   **Manager:** Kemi Izzet   **Prog Ed:** Michael Pulford
Ground: Hawthorns, New Farm Road, Stanway, Colchester CO3 0PG   **(T)** 01206 578 187
Capacity: 1,500   **Seats:** 100   **Covered:** 250   **Midweek Matchday:** Tuesday   **Clubhouse:** Yes   **Shop:** Yes

Colours(change): Amber & black (Royal blue & light blue).
Previous Names: None.
Previous Leagues: Colchester & East Essex. Essex & Suffolk Border.

HONOURS: FA Comps: None
    League: Colchester & East Essex Premier Division 1973-74. Essex & Suffolk Border Division Two 1981-82, 85-86.

10 YEAR RECORD | Eastern Counties Division One 2005-06.

	07-08		08-09		09-10		10-11		11-12		12-13		13-14		14-15		15-16		16-17	
ECP	7	ECP	9	ECP	5	ECP	7	ECP	5	ECP	9	ECP	13	ECP	3	ECP	3	ECP	6
FAC	P	FAC	2Qr	FAC	1Qr	FAC	1Qr	FAC	EP	FAC	EP	FAC	EPr	FAC	EP	FAC	2Q	FAC	1Q
FAV	5P	FAV	4Pr	FAV	3P	FAV	3P	FAV	2Q	FAV	2Q	FAV	2Q	FAV	5P	FAV	3P	FAV	2P

STOWMARKET TOWN
Founded: 1883   Nickname: Gold and

Secretary: Neil Sharp   **(T)** 07747 774 030   **(E)** footballsecretary@stowmarkettownfc.co.uk
Chairman: Neil Sharp   **Manager:** Rick Andrews - April 2013   **Prog Ed:** Ian Moyes
Ground: Greens Meadow, Bury Road, Stowmarket, Suffolk IP14 1JQ   **(T)** 01449 612 533
Capacity: **Seats:** Yes   **Covered:** Yes   **Midweek Matchday:** Tuesday   **Clubhouse:** Yes

Colours(change): Old Gold & black/black/black (All red)
Previous Names: Stowuplands Corinthians. Stowmarket Corinthians. Stowmarket FC
Previous Leagues: Ipswich & District 1896-1925. Essex & Suffolk Border 1925-52.

HONOURS: FA Comps: None
    League: Ipswich & District/Suffolk & Ipwich 1896-97, 97-98, 99-1900, 21-22. Essex & Suffolk Border 1950-51.

10 YEAR RECORD | Eastern Counties Division One 2016-17.

	07-08		08-09		09-10		10-11		11-12		12-13		13-14		14-15		15-16		16-17	
EC1	14	EC1	12	EC1	15	EC1	7	EC1	15	EC1	17	EC1	14	EC1	11	EC1	14	EC1	1
FAC	EP	FAC	EP	FAC	EP			FAC	EP										
FAV	1Q	FAV	2Q	FAV	2Q	FAV	2Q	FAV	2Q	FAV	1Q	FAV	2Q	FAV	2Q	FAV	2Q	FAV	1Q

THETFORD TOWN
Founded: 1883 Nickname: Brecklanders

Secretary: Jackie Skipp **(T)** 07753 147 098 **(E)** jackieskipp@live.co.uk
Chairman: Nigel Armes **Manager:** Daniel White - Oct 2015 **Prog Ed:** Barnes Print
Ground: Recreation Ground, Mundford Road, Thetford, Norfolk IP24 1NB **(T)** 01842 766 120
Capacity: **Seats:** Yes **Covered:** Yes **Midweek Matchday:** Tuesday **Clubhouse:** Yes

Colours(change): Claret & blue/claret/claret (All sky blue)
Previous Names: None
Previous Leagues: Norwich & District. Norfolk & Suffolk. Founder member of Eastern Counties League

HONOURS: FA Comps: None
 League: Norfolk & Suffolk League 1954-55.

10 YEAR RECORD

07-08		08-09		09-10		10-11		11-12		12-13		13-14		14-15		15-16		16-17	
EC1	13	EC1	16	EC1	11	EC1	5	EC1	2	ECP	19	ECP	16	ECP	14	ECP	19	ECP	7
		FAC	EP			FAC	EPr	FAC	EP	FAC	EP	FAC	P	FAC	P	FAC	P	FAC	EP
FAV	2Q	FAV	2Q	FAV	2Q	FAV	2Q	FAV	2P	FAV	2Q	FAV	1P	FAV	2Q	FAV	1Q	FAV	2P

WALSHAM-LE-WILLOWS
Founded: 1888 Nickname: The Willows

Secretary: Gordon Ross **(T)** 07742 111 892 **(E)** gordonaross2@gmail.com
Chairman: Keith Mills **Manager:** Paul Smith - July 2011 **Prog Ed:** Barnes Print
Ground: The Meadow, Summer Road, Walsham-le-Willows IP31 3AH **(T)** 01359 259 298
Capacity: **Seats:** 100 **Covered:** 100 **Midweek Matchday:** Wednesday **Clubhouse:** Yes

Colours(change): Yellow/red/yellow (Red/black/red & black)
Previous Names: None
Previous Leagues: St Edmundsbury/Bury & District 1907-89. Suffolk & Ipswich 1989-2004.

HONOURS: FA Comps: None
 League: Suffolk & Ipswich Senior Division 2001-02, 02-03. Eastern Counties Division One 2006-07.

10 YEAR RECORD

07-08		08-09		09-10		10-11		11-12		12-13		13-14		14-15		15-16		16-17	
ECP	16	ECP	10	ECP	13	ECP	17	ECP	17	ECP	6	ECP	8	ECP	15	ECP	14	ECP	14
FAC	Pr	FAC	P	FAC	EPr	FAC	EP	FAC	Pr	FAC	EP	FAC	EP	FAC	EPr	FAC	EP	FAC	EPr
FAV	1P	FAV	2Q	FAV	2Q	FAV	2P	FAV	1P	FAV	1Pr	FAV	2P	FAV	2Q	FAV	2Q	FAV	1P

WIVENHOE TOWN
Founded: 1925 Nickname: The Dragons

Secretary: Lorraine Stevens **(T)** 07565 364 019 **(E)** lorraineosman1969@yahoo.com
Chairman: Mo Osman **Manager:** Mo Osman **Prog Ed:** Richard Charnock
Ground: Maple Tree Cars Stadium, Broad Lane, Elmstead Road, Wivenhoe CO7 7HA **(T)**
Capacity: 2876 **Seats:** 161 **Covered:** 1300 **Midweek Matchday:** Wednesday **Clubhouse:** Yes **Shop:** Yes

Colours(change): All blue (Red/black/black)
Previous Names: Wivenhoe Rangers.
Previous Leagues: Brightlingsea & District, Colchester & East Essex. Essex & Suffolk Border, Essex Senior, Isthmian

HONOURS: FA Comps: None
 League: Brightlingsea & Dist 1932-33, 36-37, 47-48. Colchester & East Essex Prem 1952-53, 55-56, D1 59-60, 69-70.
10 YEAR RECORD Essex & Suffolk D2 1971-72, D1 72-73, Prem 78-79. Isth D2N 1987-88, D1 1989-90. Eastern C. D1 2015-16.

07-08		08-09		09-10		10-11		11-12		12-13		13-14		14-15		15-16		16-17	
Isth1N	22	ECP	17	ECP	20	ECP	20	ECP	19	ECP	18	ECP	19	ECP	18	EC1	1	ECP	19
FAC	P	FAC	EP	FAC	EPr					FAC	EPr	FAC	EPr	FAC	P	FAC	EP	FAC	EP
FAT	P	FAV	3P	FAV	1P			FAV	1Q	FAV	2Qr	FAV	1Q	FAV	1P	FAV	2Q	FAV	1Q

WROXHAM
Founded: 1892 Nickname: Yachtsmen

Secretary: Chris Green **(T)** 07508 219 072 **(E)** secretary@wroxhamfc.com
Chairman: Lee Robson **Manager:** Tom Parke & Ross Potter Barnes Print
Ground: Trafford Park, Skinners Lane, Wroxham NR12 8SJ **(T)** 01603 783 536
Capacity: 2,500 **Seats:** 50 **Covered:** 250 **Midweek Matchday:** Tuesday **Clubhouse:** Yes

Colours(change): Blue & white/blue/blue (White with blue trim/white/blue)
Previous Names: None
Previous Leagues: East Norfolk. Norwich City. East Anglian. Norwich & Dist. Anglian Comb.

HONOURS: FA Comps: None
 League: Anglian County League 1981-82, 82-83, 83-84, 84-85, 86-87.
10 YEAR RECORD Eastern Counties Division One 1988-89, Prem 91-92, 92-93, 93-94, 96-97, 97-98, 98-99, 2006-07, 11-12.

07-08		08-09		09-10		10-11		11-12		12-13		13-14		14-15		15-16		16-17	
ECP	3	ECP	5	ECP	8	ECP	3	ECP	1	Isth1N	14	Isth1N	22	Isth1N	8	Isth1N	22	Isth1N	23
FAC	1Q	FAC	3Q	FAC	P	FAC	Pr	FAC	3Q	FAC	1Q	FAC	1Q	FAC	2Q	FAC	1Q	FAC	P
FAV	2P	FAV	1P	FAV	F	FAV	3P	FAV	1P	FAT	1Qr	FAT	1Q	FAT	P	FAT	P	FAT	1Q

DIVISION ONE

AFC SUDBURY RESERVES Founded: 1999 Nickname: AFC

Secretary: David Webb **(T)** 07885 327 510 **(E)** dave-afc@supanet.com
Chairman: Philip Turner **Manager:** Danny Laws - Jan 2015 **Prog Ed:** Danny Laws
Ground: The Wardale Williams Stadium, Brundon Lane, Sudbury CO10 7HN **(T)** 01787 376 213
Colours(change): Yellow/blue/yellow (All navy)
HONOURS: FA Comps: None **League:** None

10 YEAR RECORD

07-08	08-09	09-10	10-11	11-12	12-13	13-14	14-15	15-16	16-17
						EC1 16	EC1 14	EC1 10	EC1 18

BRAINTREE TOWN RESERVES Founded: 1898 Nickname: The Iron

Secretary: Adam Morris **(T)** 07887 931 719 **(E)** adam_morris@hotmail.co.uk
Chairman: Lee Harding **Manager:** Lee Fisher & Luke Nash
Ground: Stoneylands Stadium, New Road, Long Melford, Sudbury CO10 9JY **(T)** 01787 312 187
Colours(change): Orange/blue/orange (Sky blue & white stripes/white/sky blue)
HONOURS: FA Comps: None **League:** None

10 YEAR RECORD

07-08	08-09	09-10	10-11	11-12	12-13	13-14	14-15	15-16	16-17
					EC1 8	EC1 9	EC1 13	EC1 12	EC1 8

CORNARD UNITED Founded: 1964 Nickname: Ards

Secretary: Paul Williams **(T)** 07470 131 779 **(E)** paulw_66@outlook.com
Chairman: Harvey Doherty **Manager:** Chris Tracey - Aug 2015 **Prog Ed:** Barnes Print
Ground: Backhouse Lane, Great Cornard, Sudbury, Suffolk CO10 0NL **(T)**
Colours(change): All blue (Pink/black/black)
HONOURS: FA Comps: None **League:** Colchester & East Essex Div.6 1971-72, Div.5 72-73, Div.4 73-74, Div.3 74-75
Essex & Suffolk Border 1988-89. Eastern Counties Division One 1989-90.

10 YEAR RECORD

07-08		08-09		09-10		10-11		11-12		12-13		13-14		14-15		15-16		16-17	
EC1	18	EC1	11	EC1	13	EC1	17	EC1	16	EC1	18	EC1	18	EC1	18	EC1	15	EC1	15
FAC	EP	FAC	1Q	FAC	EP														
FAV	2Q	FAV	2P	FAV	1Q	FAV	1Q	FAV	2Q	FAV	1Q	FAV	2Q	FAV	1Q	FAV	1Q	FAV	1Q

DEBENHAM LC Founded: 1991 Nickname: The Hornets

Secretary: Dan Snell **(T)** 07840 246 837 **(E)** snelly1992@hotmail.co.uk
Chairman: Steve Sherwood **Manager:** Mark Benterman - Jan 2017 **Prog Ed:** Lauren Squirrell
Ground: Debenham Leisure Centre, Gracechurch Street, Debenham IP14 6BL **(T)** 01728 861 101 **Capacity:** 1,000
Colours(change): Yellow/black/yellow & black. (All navy blue).
HONOURS: FA Comps: None **League:** Suffolk & Ipswich Division Seven 1991-92, Four 96-97, Three 99-2000,
One 03-04.

10 YEAR RECORD

07-08		08-09		09-10		10-11		11-12		12-13		13-14		14-15		15-16		16-17	
EC1	9	EC1	3	ECP	14	ECP	22	EC1	7	EC1	15	EC1	12	EC1	7	EC1	13	EC1	12
FAC	2Q	FAC	EP					FAC	EP	FAC	EP					FAC	EP		
FAV	1P	FAV	2P			FAV	2Q	FAV	2Q	FAV	1Qr	FAV	1P	FAV	2Q	FAV	2Q	FAV	1Q

DISS TOWN Founded: 1888 Nickname: Tangerines

Secretary: Steve Flatman **(T)** 01379 641 406 **(E)** pam@dissfc.wanadoo.co.uk
Chairman: Richard Upson **Manager:** Ross Potter - Aug 2015 **Prog Ed:** Gary Enderby
Ground: Brewers Green Lane, Diss, Norfolk IP22 4QP **(T)** 01379 651 223
Colours(change): All tangerine (Sky blue/navy/sky blue)
HONOURS: FA Comps: FA Vase 1993-94. **League:** Anglian Combination Division One 1967-68, 73-74, Premier 76-77, 78-79.
Eastern Counties Division One 1991-92.

10 YEAR RECORD

07-08		08-09		09-10		10-11		11-12		12-13		13-14		14-15		15-16		16-17	
EC1	4	EC1	9	EC1	5	EC1	3	ECP	16	ECP	17	ECP	18	ECP	19	EC1	7	EC1	6
FAC	P	FAC	EP	FAC	EP	FAC	EP	FAC	EP	FAC	EP	FAC	EP	FAC	EP	FAC	EP		
FAV	1P	FAV	1P	FAV	2Qr	FAV	1Q	FAV	3P	FAV	2P	FAV	1P	FAV	1Q	FAV	1P	FAV	2Q

DOWNHAM TOWN
Founded: 1881   Nickname: Town
Secretary: George Dickson   **(T)** 07545 181 242   **(E)** george.dickson@me.com
Chairman: Sandra Calvert   **Manager:** Pawel Guziejko - Feb 2016   **Prog Ed:** Barnes Print
Ground: Memorial Field, Lynn Road, Downham Market PE38 9AU   **(T)**
Colours(change): Red/black/red (All blue)
HONOURS: FA Comps: None   **League:** Peterborough & District 1962-63, 73-74, 78-79, 86-87, 87-88.

10 YEAR RECORD

07-08	08-09	09-10	10-11	11-12	12-13	13-14	14-15	15-16	16-17
EC1 12	EC1 15	EC1 18	EC1 16	EC1 14	EC1 16	EC1 17	EC1 9	EC1 16	EC1 14
				FAV 2Q	FAV 2Q	FAV 1Q		FAV 2Q	FAV 2Q

FRAMLINGHAM TOWN
Founded: 1887   Nickname: The Castlemen
Secretary: Fiona Whatling   **(T)** 01728 723 524   **(E)** fionawhatling@tiscali.co.uk
Chairman: Dean Warner   Melvyn Aldis   Graham Botting
Ground: Framingham Sports Club, Badingham Road, Framlingham IP13 9HS   **(T)**
Colours(change): Green & white hoops/white/white (All red)
HONOURS: FA Comps: None   **League:** Suffolk & Ipswich Division Two 1980-81, Senior Division 91-92.

10 YEAR RECORD

07-08	08-09	09-10	10-11	11-12	12-13	13-14	14-15	15-16	16-17
S&I 1 3	S&I S 7	S&I S 11	S&I S 10	S&I S 16	S&I 1 10	S&I 1 5	S&I 1 2	S&I S 5	EC1 7
			FAV 1P	FAV 2Q					FAV 1Q

HALSTEAD TOWN
Founded: 1879   Nickname: Humbugs
Secretary: Steve Webber   **(T)** 0753 945 154   **(E)** halsteadtownfc@aol.com
Chairman: Darren Mitchell   **Manager:** Mark McLean - Jan 2017   **Prog Ed:** Barnes Print
Ground: Rosemary Lane, Broton Industrial Estate, Halstead, Essex CO9 1HR   **(T)** 01787 472 082
Colours(change): Black & white stripes/black/black (All red)
HONOURS: FA Comps: None   **League:** Essex & Suffolk Border Premier Division 1957-58, 68-69, 77-78. Eastern Counties 1994-95, 95-96, Division One 2002-03.

10 YEAR RECORD

07-08	08-09	09-10	10-11	11-12	12-13	13-14	14-15	15-16	16-17
EC1 6	EC1 4	EC1 6	EC1 11	EC1 6	EC1 11	EC1 6	EC1 10	EC1 4	EC1 9
FAC EPr	FAC P	FAC 1Qr	FAC P	FAC EP	FAC P	FAC EP	FAC EP	FAC EPr	FAC 1Q
FAV 2Q	FAV 1P	FAV 2Pr	FAV 2Q	FAV 1P	FAV 2Q	FAV 2Q	FAV 1Q	FAV 2Q	FAV 2Q

HOLLAND
Founded: 2006   Nickname:
Secretary: Mark Sorrell   **(T)** 07778 142 118   **(E)** mark.sorrell@btinternet.com
Chairman: Mark Sorrell   **Manager:** Rob Batten
Ground: Eastcliff Sports Ground, Dulwich Road, Holland-on-Sea CO15 5HP   **(T)** 07778 142 118
Colours(change): Orange/white/orange (All light blue)
HONOURS: FA Comps: None   **League:** Essex & Suffolk Border Division One 2008-09.

10 YEAR RECORD

07-08	08-09	09-10	10-11	11-12	12-13	13-14	14-15	15-16	16-17
	EsSu1 1	EsSuP 7	EsSuP 5	EsSuP 12	EsSuP 4	EsSuP 10	EsSuP 4	EsSuP 4	EC1 5

KING'S LYNN RESERVES
Founded: 1879   Nickname: The Linnets
Secretary: Norman Cesar   **(T)** 07887 373 956   **(E)** ncesar1947@yahoo.co.uk
Chairman: Stephen Cleeve   **Manager:** Robbie Back
Ground: The Walks Stadium, Tennyson Road, King's Lynn PE30 5PB.   **(T)** 01553 760 060   **Capacity:** 8,200
Colours(change): Yellow/blue/yellow. (Red/black/red).
HONOURS: FA Comps: None   **League:** None

10 YEAR RECORD

07-08	08-09	09-10	10-11	11-12	12-13	13-14	14-15	15-16	16-17
ECP 14	ECP 15	ECP Exp					EC1 5	EC1 5	EC1 10

LEISTON RESERVES

Founded: 1880   Nickname: Blues

Secretary: David Rees   **(T)** 07977 782 559   **(E)** gagrees@aol.com
Chairman: Andy Crisp   **Manager:** Damian Brown - August 2016   **Prog Ed:** Peter Douglas
Ground: The LTAA, Victory Road, Leiston, Suffolk IP16 4DQ   **(T)** 01728 830 308
Colours(change): All blue (All red)
HONOURS: FA Comps: None   **League:** None

10 YEAR RECORD									
07-08	08-09	09-10	10-11	11-12	12-13	13-14	14-15	15-16	16-17
							EC1 19	EC1 6	EC1 21

LITTLE OAKLEY

Founded: 1947   Nickname: The Acorns

Secretary: David Chopping   **(T)**   **(E)**
Chairman: Michael Good   **Manager:** Sean Tynan
Ground: War Memorial Club Ground, Harwich Road, Little Oakley, Harwich CO12 5ED   **(T)** 01255 880 370
Colours(change): White & blue
HONOURS: FA Comps: None   **League:** Essex & Suffolk Border Division One 1985-86,
Premier Division 1986-87, 87-88, 92-93, 2003-04, 15-16, 16-17.

10 YEAR RECORD									
07-08	08-09	09-10	10-11	11-12	12-13	13-14	14-15	15-16	16-17
	EsSuP 4	EsSuP 6	EsSuP 13	EsSuP 6	EsSuP 7	EsSuP 6	EsSuP 2	EsSuP 4	EsSuP 1

MARCH TOWN UNITED

Founded: 1885   Nickname: Hares

Secretary: Raymond Bennett   **(T)** 01354 659 901   **(E)** r.bennett639@btinternet.com
Chairman: Phil White   **Manager:** Mel Mattless - Oct 2016   **Prog Ed:** Barnes Print
Ground: GER Sports Ground, Robin Goodfellow Lane, March, Cambs PE15 8HS   **(T)** 01354 653 073
Colours(change): Amber & black/black/black (All blue)
HONOURS: FA Comps: None   **League:** United Counties Division One 1953-54. Eastern Counties 1987-88.

10 YEAR RECORD									
07-08	08-09	09-10	10-11	11-12	12-13	13-14	14-15	15-16	16-17
EC1 15	EC1 13	EC1 7	EC1 8	EC1 4	EC1 14	EC1 19	EC1 8	EC1 11	EC1 16
FAC EP	FAC P	FAC EP	FAC P	FAC Pr	FAC EP				
FAV 2Q	FAV 2Q	FAV 1P	FAV 1Q	FAV 1Q	FAV 1Q	FAV 2Q			FAV 2Q

NEEDHAM MARKET RESERVES

Founded: 1919   Nickname: The Marketmen

Secretary: Mark Easlea   **(T)** 07795 456 502   **(E)** m.easlea@sky.com
Chairman: Dr Keith Nunn   **Manager:** Steve Foley   **Prog Ed:** Martin Chambers
Ground: Bloomfields, Quinton Road, Needham Market IP6 8DA.   **(T)** 01449 721 000   **Capacity:** 1,000
Colours(change): Red/red/red & white hoops (Blue & black stripes/black/blue)
HONOURS: FA Comps: None   **League:** None

10 YEAR RECORD									
07-08	08-09	09-10	10-11	11-12	12-13	13-14	14-15	15-16	16-17
						EC1 15	EC1 16	EC1 19	EC1 19

NORWICH CBS

Founded: 1888   Nickname:

Secretary: Shaun Maxey   **(T)** 07745 036 715   **(E)**
Chairman: Clive Cook   **Manager:** Mark & Andrew Collison
Ground: Football Development Centre, Bowthorpe Park, Clover Hill Road, Norwich NR5 9ED   **(T)** 07745 036 715
Colours(change): Maroon with sky blue trim
HONOURS: FA Comps: None   **League:** Anglian Combination Premier Division 2016-17.

10 YEAR RECORD									
07-08	08-09	09-10	10-11	11-12	12-13	13-14	14-15	15-16	16-17
AnCP 4	AnCP 12	AnCP 12	AnCP 11	AnCP 4	AnCP 2	AnCP 2	AnCP 5	AnCP 2	AnCP 1

NORWICH UNITED RESERVES
Founded: 1903   Nickname: The Planters

Secretary: Keith Cutmore   (T)   (E)
Chairman: John Hilditch
Ground: Plantatio Park, Blofield, Norwich NR13 4PL   (T) 01603 716 963
Colours(change):
HONOURS: FA Comps: None   **League:** None

10 YEAR RECORD

07-08	08-09	09-10	10-11	11-12	12-13	13-14	14-15	15-16	16-17

SWAFFHAM TOWN
Founded: 1892   Nickname: Pedlars

Secretary: Ray Ewart   (T) 07990 526 744   (E) rayewart@aol.com
Chairman: Andy Farr   **Manager:** Paul Hunt - Oct 2016   **Prog Ed:** Andy Black
Ground: The Pavillion, Shoemakers Lane, Swaffham, Norfolk PE37 7NT   (T) 01760 722 700
Colours(change): Black & white stripes/black/black (All red)
HONOURS: FA Comps: None   **League:** Anglian Combination Division Two 1973-74.
Eastern Counties Division One 2000-01.

10 YEAR RECORD

07-08		08-09		09-10		10-11		11-12		12-13		13-14		14-15		15-16		16-17	
ECP	20	EC1	18	EC1	14	EC1	15	EC1	13	EC1	9	EC1	7	EC1	2	ECP	18	ECP	21
												FAC	P	FAC	EP	FAC	EP	FAC	EP
		FAV	1Q	FAV	1Q	FAV	2Q	FAV	1Q	FAV	1P	FAV	1Pr	FAV	1Q	FAV	1P	FAV	1P

TEAM BURY
Founded: 2005   Nickname: The Blues

Secretary: Daniel Connor   (T) 07931 309 282   (E) daniel.connor@wsc.ac.uk
Chairman: Sara Cox   **Manager:** Guy Hayes - June 2016   **Prog Ed:** Ross Wilding
Ground: Bury Town FC, Ram Meadow, Cotton Lane, Bury St Edmunds IP33 1XP   (T) 01284 754 721
Colours(change): All blue (All red)
HONOURS: FA Comps: None   **League:** Essex & Suffolk Border Division One 2006-07.

10 YEAR RECORD

07-08		08-09		09-10		10-11		11-12		12-13		13-14		14-15		15-16		16-17	
EsSuP	8	EsSuP	2	EC1	9	EC1	13	EC1	10	EC1	12	EC1	10	EC1	12	EC1	18	EC1	17
						FAC	P			FAC	EP			FAC	EP				
				FAV	2Q	FAV	2Q	FAV	2P	FAV	2Q	FAV	1P	FAV	2Q	FAV	1Q	FAV	1Q

WHITTON UNITED
Founded: 1926   Nickname: The Boyos

Secretary: Phil Pemberton   (T) 07429 116 538   (E) secretary@whittonunited.co.uk
Chairman: Mark Richards   **Manager:** Paul Bugg - June 2012
Ground: King George V Playing Fields, Old Norwich Road, Ipswich IP1 6LE   (T) 01473 464 030
Colours(change): Green and white stripes/green/green (All orange)
HONOURS: FA Comps: None   **League:** Suffolk & Ipswich Senior 1946-47, 47-48, 65-66, 67-68, 91-92, 92-93.
Eastern Counties Division One 2013-14.

10 YEAR RECORD

07-08		08-09		09-10		10-11		11-12		12-13		13-14		14-15		15-16		16-17	
EC1	3	ECP	dnf	EC1	10	EC1	2	EC1	3	EC1	7	EC1	1	ECP	11	ECP	20	EC1	11
		FAC	EPr	FAC	EP	FAC	P	FAC	EP	FAC	P	FAC	Pr	FAC	P	FAC	P	FAC	EPr
FAV	1P	FAV	2Q	FAV	1P	FAV	2P	FAV	2P	FAV	1P	FAV	2Q	FAV	1P	FAV	1P	FAV	1Q

WISBECH ST MARY
Founded: 1993   Nickname: The Saints

Secretary: Martin Holmes   (T) 07711 221 475   (E) martin@jsholmes.com
Chairman: Ian Rawlins   **Manager:** Arran Duke
Ground: Wisbech St Mary Playing Fields, Beechings Close, Wisbech St Mary PE13 4SS   (T) 01945 411 777
Colours(change): All purple (All yellow)
HONOURS: FA Comps: None   **League:** Cambridgeshire County Division 1B 2008-09, Senior B 10-11,

10 YEAR RECORD

07-08		08-09		09-10		10-11		11-12		12-13		13-14		14-15		15-16		16-17	
Cam1B	7	Cam1B	1	CamSB	3	CamSB	1	CamSA	3	CamP	7	CamP	8	CamP	15	CamP	5	EC1	13
																FAV	2Q	FAV	1Q

WOODBRIDGE TOWN

Founded: 1885   Nickname: The Woodpeckers

Secretary: Terry Fryatt   **(T)** 07803 073 558   **(E)** tfryatt6@btinternet.com
Chairman: John Beecroft   **Manager:** Jamie Scales - July 2014   **Prog Ed:** Terry Fryatt
Ground: Notcutts Park, Fynn Road, Woodbridge IP12 4LS   **(T)** 01394 385 308   **Capacity:** 3,000
Colours(change): Black & white stripes/black/black. (All red).
HONOURS: FA Comps: None   **League:** Ipswich & District/Suffolk & Ipswich Senior 1912-13, 88-89, Division One 1986-87, 70-71.

10 YEAR RECORD

07-08		08-09		09-10		10-11		11-12		12-13		13-14		14-15		15-16		16-17	
ECP	17	ECP	18	ECP	19	ECP	10	ECP	6	ECP	15	ECP	20	EC1	17	EC1	9	EC1	4
FAC	P	FAC	P	FAC	EP	FAC	EP	FAC	EPr	FAC	EP	FAC	EP	FAC	EP				
FAV	2Pr	FAV	2Q	FAV	2P	FAV	2Q	FAV	1Pr	FAV	2Q	FAV	2Q	FAV	1P	FAV	2Q	FAV	2Q

ESSEX SENIOR LEAGUE

Sponsored by: No sponsor

Founded: 1971

Recent Champions: 2014: Great Wakering Rovers
2015: Haringey Borough **2016:** Bowers & Pitsea

Premier Division	P	W	D	L	F	A	GD	Pts
1 Barking	42	32	4	6	125	46	79	100
2 Clapton	42	29	5	8	89	46	43	92
3 FC Romania	42	27	7	8	125	56	69	88
4 Takeley	42	25	8	9	93	51	42	83
5 Sawbridgeworth Town	42	25	8	9	98	67	31	83
6 Ilford	42	22	9	11	85	56	29	75
7 Southend Manor	42	22	5	15	76	56	20	71
8 Stansted	42	20	10	12	82	50	32	70
9 Basildon United	42	18	7	17	81	72	9	61
10 Barkingside	42	19	9	14	81	74	7	60*
11 Hullbridge Sports	42	16	12	14	72	66	6	60
12 Waltham Forest	42	17	8	17	67	67	0	59
13 West Essex	42	17	7	18	77	79	-2	58
14 Redbridge	42	16	7	19	93	87	6	55
15 Wadham Lodge	42	13	10	19	56	75	-19	49
16 Eton Manor	42	14	4	24	74	98	-24	46
17 London Bari	42	12	8	22	59	88	-29	44
18 Enfield 1893	42	12	6	24	69	114	-45	42
19 Sporting Bengal United	42	11	6	25	65	95	-30	39
20 Tower Hamlets	42	6	6	30	47	100	-53	24
21 Burnham Ramblers	42	5	6	31	45	130	-85	21
22 Haringey & Waltham	42	4	8	30	38	124	-86	20

LEAGUE CHALLENGE CUP

HOLDERS: BASILDON UNITED

ROUND 1

Redbridge	v	Barkingside	4-3
Waltham Forest	v	Sawbridgeworth Town	0-4
Barking	v	Sporting Bengal United	1-0
Ilford	v	Southend Manor	2-0
Clapton	v	Hullbridge Sports	0-1
Enfield 1893	v	West Essex	1-1, 3-1p

ROUND 2

Redbridge	v	Sawbridgeworth Town	2-6
Barking	v	Burnham Ramblers	8-1
Eton Manor	v	Ilford	1-1, 4-5p
Stansted	v	FC Romania	4-4, 4-5p
Takeley	v	Haringey & Waltham	7-0
Tower Hamlets	v	Hullbridge Sports	1-7
Basildon United	v	London Bari	1-0
Enfield 1893	v	Wadham Lodge	1-2

QUARTER FINALS

Sawbridgeworth Town	v	Barking	3-1
Ilford	v	FC Romania	1-0
Takeley	v	Hullbridge Sports	2-1
Basildon United	v	Wadham Lodge	1-1, 4-1p

SEMI FINALS

Sawbridgeworth Town	v	Ilford	0-2
Takeley	v	Basildon United	0-0, 4-3p

FINAL

Sawbridgeworth Town	v	Takeley	0-1

CLUB MOVEMENTS: In: Great Wakering Rovers (R - Isthmian D1N), Hackney Wick (Merged with London Bari), Woodford Town (NC - from Haringey & Waltham). **Out:** Barking (P - Isthmian D1N), Eton Manor (W).

GORDON BRASTED MEMORIAL CUP

HOLDERS: CLAPTON

ROUND 1

Barking	v	Clapton	4-2
FC Romania	v	Southend Manor	1-5
Stansted	v	Ilford	0-2
Wadham Lodge	v	Sawbridgeworth Town	2-2, 4-2p
Basildon United	v	Barkingside	2-3
London Bari	v	West Essex	0-0, 4-5p

ROUND 2

Barking	v	Sporting Bengal United	3-0
Southend Manor	v	Redbridge	1-3
Haringey & Waltham	v	Takeley	1-8
Ilford	v	Enfield 1893	1-0
Burnham Ramblers	v	Wadham Lodge	3-5
Waltham Forest	v	Tower Hamlets	3-0
Eton Manor	v	Barkingside	3-1
Hullbridge Sports	v	West Essex	1-2

QUARTER-FINALS

Barking	v	Redbridge	3-2
Takeley	v	Ilford	2-0
Wadham Lodge	v	Waltham Forest	4-5 aet
Eton Manor	v	West Essex	3-3, 5-3

SEM-IFINALS

Barking	v	Takeley	0-1
Waltham Forest	v	Eton Manor	2-2, 6-5p

FINAL

Takeley	v	Eton Manor	3-0 aet

PREMIER DIVISION	1	2	3	4	5	6	7	8	9	10	11	12	13	14	15	16	17	18	19	20	21	22
1 Barking		3-1	1-1	7-0	3-0	5-0	2-0	0-2	6-1	4-2	1-2	5-0	4-0	1-2	3-0	2-1	2-5	5-3	3-1	4-0	2-1	3-0
2 Barkingside	1-0		1-1	2-2	5-2	4-2	3-1	1-1	1-1	1-2	0-0	0-1	1-0	4-0	1-3	0-3	2-2	4-0	6-2	0-2	1-1	1-1
3 Basildon United	0-3	1-2		7-0	0-1	6-1	4-5	1-1	4-0	1-0	3-1	2-0	3-1	3-5	2-2	2-0	4-1	2-4	4-4	3-1	1-2	0-1
4 Burnham Ramblers	0-5	2-5	1-0		1-3	2-2	2-3	3-4	4-2	1-4	0-3	2-2	2-3	0-1	2-0	1-1	0-4	3-1	1-2	1-4	2-2
5 Clapton	4-2	0-1	4-0	7-0		6-2	5-2	0-2	4-1	4-1	2-0	3-2	0-0	0-1	2-1	4-3	1-1	2-0	1-1	1-0	1-1
6 Enfield 1893	3-4	3-4	1-2	3-0	1-2		1-1	2-4	1-0	1-2	4-1	0-2	5-3	1-2	2-6	3-1	1-1	1-1	3-2	1-2	1-4	3-4
7 Eton Manor	0-3	4-3	2-3	3-1	0-1	2-3		0-4	5-0	1-5	0-2	1-2	1-3	0-2	0-4	7-0	1-1	3-1	3-2	4-0	3-3	0-5
8 FC Romania	2-5	4-2	5-0	5-2	1-2	7-0	2-0		5-0	5-1	1-2	5-1	2-2	4-1	1-2	3-2	2-0	2-2	3-1	2-2	3-2	3-1
9 Haringey & Waltham	3-4	2-3	1-2	1-1	0-1	2-2	1-3	1-7		0-1	2-2	1-5	0-2	2-1	0-5	0-1	0-3	0-2	1-3	0-1		1-5
10 Hullbridge Sports	2-2	2-2	0-4	0-1	3-1	0-0	3-0	0-6	6-2		1-1	1-2	1-1	2-1	0-0	5-0	0-3	0-2	3-0	1-1	2-2	3-4
11 Ilford	0-0	5-1	3-0	6-0	0-2	1-3	4-2	2-2	4-0	1-1		6-2	1-3	0-2	2-1	3-0	1-0	2-0	2-0	2-2	3-1	2-0
12 London Bari	1-2	0-1	1-0	1-0	1-0	0-1	3-2	0-3	1-0	1-1	1-5		2-1	3-4	2-4	2-2	1-1	1-2	0-5	0-3	2-2	2-2
13 Redbridge	1-3	4-2	2-0	4-0	3-4	5-1	3-3	1-4	4-1	1-1	3-4	4-2		3-6	2-1	2-3	1-2	0-2	5-2	4-0	4-2	5-1
14 Sawbridgeworth Town	1-3	5-1	3-1	8-2	0-1	2-4	H-W	3-1	0-0	3-2	3-3	0-0	2-1		5-1	3-2	4-4	2-3	2-1	3-2	1-1	0-2
15 Southend Manor	0-2	2-0	1-1	2-0	0-1	2-0	3-0	0-1	2-2	2-4	3-0	4-1	4-2	1-2		1-0	1-2	3-2	1-1	4-1	3-1
16 Sporting Bengal United	3-5	2-3	1-3	2-1	3-1	4-0	1-3	2-2	1-2	1-0	2-3	2-2	2-0	1-5	0-4		1-3	0-2	1-2	2-2	5-0	3-1
17 Stansted	0-0	0-1	1-2	3-0	2-3	0-1	1-2	2-1	5-0	1-1	2-1	4-0	5-2	0-0	1-3	2-0		3-3	4-0	1-2	2-0	3-0
18 Takeley	0-1	2-2	1-0	5-1	0-1	6-1	2-3	1-0	5-2	0-1	1-0	2-1	1-1	2-1	3-2	0-1		1-1	2-1	4-1	4-1
19 Tower Hamlets	1-4	1-3	1-4	1-1	1-1	3-1	0-1	1-4	0-1	0-3	1-2	1-6	2-4	0-5	0-1	0-0	1-2	1-4		0-1	1-1	0-1
20 Wadham Lodge	2-4	2-0	0-3	1-1	0-2	4-2	4-1	1-3	3-0	2-3	0-1	2-1	0-0	0-1	0-1	1-1	2-5	1-0	0-1		2-0	0-3
21 Waltham Forest	0-2	1-3	5-0	1-0	1-2	4-0	2-1	4-3	3-0	1-0	1-1	0-1	1-2	1-0	3-2	1-0	1-3	0-3	1-1	3-1		3-0
22 West Essex	0-5	1-2	3-2	3-1	0-3	1-2	4-1	1-3	7-1	0-2	2-1	3-2	2-2	4-1	1-2	4-1	0-0	1-5	4-0	0-0	0-1	

BARKINGSIDE

Founded: 1898   Nickname: The Side / Sky

Secretary: Jimmy Flanagan   **(T)** 07956 894 194   **(E)** confclothing@aol.com
Chairman: Jimmy Flanagan
Ground: Cricketfield Stadium, 3 Cricklefield Place, Ilford IG1 1FY   **(T)** 020 8552 3995
Capacity: 3,500 **Seats:** 216   **Covered:** Yes   **Midweek Matchday:** Monday   **Clubhouse:** Yes

Colours(change): Sky blue/navy blue/sky blue. (Yellow/yellow/navy)
Previous Names: None
Previous Leagues: London. Greater London. Met London. Spartan, South Midlands. Essex Senior > 2013. Isthmian 2013-16.

HONOURS: FA Comps: None
League: Spartan Premier Division 1996-97. Spartan South Midlands 1998-99.

10 YEAR RECORD

07-08		08-09		09-10		10-11		11-12		12-13		13-14		14-15		15-16		16-17	
ESen	3	ESen	5	ESen	9	ESen	15	ESen	8	ESen	2	Isth1N	20	Isth1N	22	Isth1N	23	ESen	10
FAC	2Q	FAC	P	FAC	EP	FAC	EP	FAC	EP	FAC	EPr	FAC	P	FAC	1Q	FAC	P	FAC	P
FAV	1P	FAV	2P	FAV	2Q	FAV	2Q	FAV	2Qr	FAV	1Q	FAT	P	FAT	2Q	FAT	P	FAV	2Q

BASILDON UNITED

Founded: 1963   Nickname: The Bees

Secretary: Richard Mann   **(T)** 07527 743 535   **(E)** ritchiemann591@gmail.com
Chairman: Lee Connor   **Manager:** Aaron Bloxham   **Prog Ed:** Richard Mann
Ground: The Stuart Bingham Stadium, Gardiners Close, Basildon SS14 3AW   **(T)** 01268 520 268
Capacity: 2,000 **Seats:** 400   **Covered:** 1,000   **Midweek Matchday:** Tuesday   **Clubhouse:** Yes   **Shop:** No

Colours(change): Yellow/black/yellow (Green/white/green)
Previous Names: Armada Sports.
Previous Leagues: Grays & Thurrock. Greater London. Essex Senior. Athenian. Isthmian.

HONOURS: FA Comps: None
League: Essex Senior 1976-77, 77-78, 78-79, 79-80, 93-94.
10 YEAR RECORD Isthmian Division Two 1983-84.

07-08		08-09		09-10		10-11		11-12		12-13		13-14		14-15		15-16		16-17	
ESen	16	ESen	8	ESen	12	ESen	12	ESen	18	ESen	13	ESen	8	ESen	12	ESen	2	ESen	9
					P		EP		EP		1Q		P		P		1Q		P
FAV	1Q	FAV	2P	FAV	1P	FAV	2Q	FAV	1P	FAV	1Q	FAV	1Q	FAV	1Q	FAV	3P	FAV	3P

BURNHAM RAMBLERS

Founded: 1900   Nickname: Ramblers

Secretary: Martin Leno   **(T)** 07702 592 418   **(E)** martin.leno@btopenworld.com
Chairman: Martin Leno   **Manager:** Lee Hughes   **Prog Ed:** Martin Leno
Ground: Leslie Fields Stadium, Springfield Road CM0 8TE   **(T)** 01621 784 383
Capacity: 2,000 **Seats:** 156   **Covered:** 300   **Midweek Matchday:** Tuesday   **Clubhouse:** Yes   **Shop:** No

Colours(change): Navy & sky blue stripes/navy/sky blue (All red).
Previous Names: None
Previous Leagues: North Essex. Mid-Essex. Olympian. South East Essex. Essex Senior > 2013. Isthmian 2013-15.

HONOURS: FA Comps: None
League: Mid-Essex 1927-28, 54-55, 62-63. Essex Olympian 1966-67. Essex Senior League 2012-13.

10 YEAR RECORD

07-08		08-09		09-10		10-11		11-12		12-13		13-14		14-15		15-16		16-17	
ESen	8	ESen	7	ESen	3	ESen	7	ESen	4	ESen	1	Isth1N	17	Isth1N	24	ESen	14	ESen	21
FAC	1Q	FAC	P	FAC	EP	FAC	1Q	FAC	Pr	FAC	P	FAC	1Q	FAC	P	FAC	EP	FAC	EP
FAV	2P	FAV	2Q	FAV	1P	FAV	2P	FAV	1P	FAV	2P	FAT	1Q	FAT	P	FAV	1Qr	FAV	2Q

CLAPTON

Founded: 1878   Nickname: Tons

Secretary: Shirley Doyle   **(T)** 07983 588 883   **(E)** secretary@claptonfc.com
Chairman: John Murray-Smith   **Manager:** Jon Fowell
Ground: The Old Spotted Dog, Upton Lane, Forest Gate E7 9NP   **(T)** 07983 588 883
Capacity: 2,000 **Seats:** 100   **Covered:** 180   **Midweek Matchday:** Tuesday   **Clubhouse:** Yes   **Shop:** No

Colours(change): Red & white stripes/black/black (Blue & yellow stripes/blue & yellow/blue)
Previous Names: None
Previous Leagues: Southern (founder member). London. Isthmian (founder member).

HONOURS: FA Comps: FA Amateur Cup 1906-07, 08-09, 14-15, 23-24, 24-25.
League: Isthmian 1910-11, 22-23, Division Two 1982-83.

10 YEAR RECORD

07-08		08-09		09-10		10-11		11-12		12-13		13-14		14-15		15-16		16-17	
ESen	11	ESen	16	ESen	16	ESen	17	ESen	17	ESen	18	ESen	10	ESen	8	ESen	7	ESen	2
FAC	EP	FAC	EP	FAC	EP	FAC	EP	FAC	EP	FAC	EP	FAC	P	FAC	EPr	FAC	EP	FAC	P
FAV	2Q	FAV	1Q	FAV	1Q	FAV	1Q	FAV	2Q	FAV	1P	FAV	1P	FAV	2Q	FAV	2Q	FAV	1Q

ENFIELD 1893 FC
Founded: 1893   Nickname: The E's

Secretary: Mark Wiggs   **(T)** 07957 647 820   **(E)** enfieldfc@ntlworld.com
Chairman: Steve Whittington   **Manager:** Matt Hanning
Ground: The Harlow Arena, Elizabeth Way, Harlow, Essex CM19 5BE   **(T)** 07957 647 820
Capacity: 3,500 **Seats:** 500 **Covered:** Yes **Midweek Matchday:** Tuesday **Clubhouse:** Yes

Colours(change): White/royal blue/white (Green & black/green/green)
Previous Names: Enfield Spartans > 1900. Enfield > 2007.
Previous Leagues: Tottenham & District, North Middlesex, London, Athenian, Isthmian, Alliance, Southern

HONOURS: FA Comps: FA Amateur Cup 1966-67, 69-70. FA Trophy 1981-82, 87-88.
     League: Alliance 1982-83, 85-86. Essex Senior 2010-11.

10 YEAR RECORD

07-08	08-09	09-10	10-11	11-12	12-13	13-14	14-15	15-16	16-17
ESen 2	ESen 2	ESen 4	ESen 1	ESen 7	ESen 9	ESen 3	ESen 16	ESen 20	ESen 18
		FAC 2Q	FAC EP	FAC Pr	FAC EP	FAC EPr	FAC EP	FAC EP	FAC EP
	FAV 2Q	FAV 2P	FAV 1P	FAV 4P	FAV 4P	FAV 4P	FAV 1P	FAV 1Q	FAV 2Q

FC ROMANIA
Founded: 2006   Nickname:

Secretary: Terry Cecil   **(T)** 07956 266 969   **(E)** terrycecilfcr@gmail.com
Chairman: Ion Vintila   **Manager:** Ion Vintila
Ground: Cheshunt FC, Theobalds Lane, Cheshunt, Herts EN8 8RU   **(T)** 01992 625 793
Capacity: 3,500 **Seats:** 424 **Covered:** 600 **Midweek Matchday:** Wednesday **Clubhouse:** Yes

Colours(change): Yellow/red/blue/ (All sky blue)
Previous Names: None
Previous Leagues: Sunday London Weekend 2006-07. Essex Business Houses 2007-10. Middlesex County 2010-13.

HONOURS: FA Comps: None
     League: None

10 YEAR RECORD

07-08	08-09	09-10	10-11	11-12	12-13	13-14	14-15	15-16	16-17
	EsxBH2 6	EsxBH2 4	Midx1SE 2	MidxP 2	MidxP 2	ESen 5	ESen 6	ESen 3	ESen 3
							FAC 2Q	FAC EP	FAC EP
					FAV 2Q	FAV 1Q	FAV 2Q	FAV 4P	FAV 3Pr

GREAT WAKERING ROVERS
Founded: 1919   Nickname: Rovers

Secretary: Daniel Ellis   **(T)** 07828 048 671   **(E)** secretary@gwrovers.com
Chairman: John Galley   **Manager:** Ian O'Connell   **Prog Ed:** Andy Wilkins
Ground: Burroughs Park, Little Wakering Hall Lane, Great Wakering SS3 0HH   **(T)** 01702 217 812
Capacity: 2,500 **Seats:** 150 **Covered:** 300 **Midweek Matchday:** Tuesday **Clubhouse:** Yes

Colours(change): Green and white stripes/green/green & white (Yellow/black/yellow & black hoops)
Previous Names: None
Previous Leagues: Southend & District 1919-81, Southend Alliance 1981-89, Essex Intermediate 1989-92, Essex Senior 1992-99, 2012-14, Isthmian 1999-2004, 14-17, Southern 2004-05.
HONOURS: FA Comps: None
     League: Essex Intermediate Division Three 1990-91, Division Two 91-92. Essex Senior 1994-95, 2013-14.

10 YEAR RECORD

07-08	08-09	09-10	10-11	11-12	12-13	13-14	14-15	15-16	16-17
Isth1N 13	Isth1N 13	Isth1N 9	Isth1N 15	Isth1N 22	ESen 4	ESen 1	Isth1N 15	Isth1N 18	Isth1N 24
FAC 1Qr	FAC 1Q	FAC Pr	FAC 1Q	FAC Pr	FAC P	FAC P	FAC P	FAC P	FAC P
FAT 1Q	FAT 2Qr	FAT P	FAT P	FAT P	FAV 1P	FAV 3P	FAT P	FAT P	FAT P

HACKNEY WICK
Founded: 1995   Nickname: The Wickers

Secretary: **(T)**   **(E)**
Chairman: Tony Ray
Ground: The Old Spotted Dog, Upton Lane, Forest Gate E7 9NP   **(T)** 07960 384 338
Capacity: 2,000 **Seats:** 100 **Covered:** 180 **Midweek Matchday:** Tuesday **Clubhouse:** Yes

Colours(change): All red (All blue)
Previous Names: Bari FC 1995-12. London Bari 2012-17. Merged with Hackney Wick 2017.
Previous Leagues: South Essex 1995-98. Asian League. Essex Sunday Corinthian League > 2012.

HONOURS: FA Comps: None
     League: Essex Sunday Corinthian 2011-12.

10 YEAR RECORD

07-08	08-09	09-10	10-11	11-12	12-13	13-14	14-15	15-16	16-17
				EsxSC 1	ESen 10	ESen 20	ESen 15	ESen 8	ESen 17
								FAC EP	FAC EP
							FAV 2Q	FAV 1Q	FAV 1P

HULLBRIDGE SPORTS
Founded: 1945   Nickname:

Secretary: Mandy Addington   **(T)** 07754 733 467   **(E)** beryl@petre1942.fsnet.co.uk
Chairman: Trevor Lammas   **Manager:** Aaron Hunwicks
Ground: Lower Road, Hullbridge, Hockley Essex SS5 6BJ   **(T)** 01702 230 420
Capacity: 1,500 **Seats:** 60   **Covered:** 60   **Midweek Matchday:** Tuesday   **Clubhouse:** Yes   **Shop:** No
Colours(change): Blue & white stripes/blue/blue (Yellow & blue stripes/yellow/yellow)
Previous Names: None
Previous Leagues: Southend & District. Southend Alliance.

HONOURS: FA Comps: None
League: Southend & District Division Two 1951-52, Division Three 1956-57, Division One 1965-66.

10 YEAR RECORD

07-08	08-09	09-10	10-11	11-12	12-13	13-14	14-15	15-16	16-17
ESen 14	ESen 9	ESen 11	ESen 9	ESen 11	ESen 15	ESen 9	ESen 4	ESen 11	ESen 11
FAC EP	FAC P	FAC EPr	FAC EP	FAC EP	FAC EP	FAC P	FAC EP	FAC 2Q	FAC P
FAV 2Q	FAV 2Q	FAV 1Q	FAV 2P	FAV 1P	FAV 1P	FAV 4P	FAV 4P	FAV 4P	FAV 2P

ILFORD
Founded: 1987   Nickname: The Foxes

Secretary: Marion Chilvers   **(T)** 020 8591 5313   **(E)** rogerchilvers@aol.com
Chairman: Michael Foley   **Manager:** Allen Fenn
Ground: Cricklefield Stadium, 486 High Road, Ilford, Essex IG1 1FY   **(T)** 020 8514 8352
Capacity: 3,500 **Seats:** 216   **Covered:** Yes   **Midweek Matchday:** Wednesday   **Clubhouse:** Yes   **Shop:** No
Colours(change): Blue and white hoops/royal blue/royal blue (All red)
Previous Names: Reformed as Ilford in 1987 after the original club merged with Leytonstone in 1980.
Previous Leagues: Spartan 1987-94, Essex Senior 1996-2004, Isthmian 2004-05, 2006-13, Southern 2005-06.

HONOURS: FA Comps: FA Amateur Cup 1928-29, 29-30.
League: Isthmian 1906-07, 20-21, 21-22, Division Two 2004-05.

10 YEAR RECORD

07-08	08-09	09-10	10-11	11-12	12-13	13-14	14-15	15-16	16-17
Isth1N 21	Isth1N 17	Isth1N 20	Isth1N 20	Isth1N 20	Isth1N 22	ESen 16	ESen 10	ESen 5	ESen 6
FAC P	FAC P	FAC P	FAC 1Q	FAC Pr	FAC P	FAC EP	FAC EP	FAC P	FAC P
FAT 1Q	FAT P	FAT Pr	FAT 1Q	FAT P	FAT 1Q	FAV 1P	FAV 2Q	FAV 1P	FAV 1P

REDBRIDGE
Founded: 1958   Nickname: Motormen

Secretary: Bob Holloway   **(T)** 07890 699 907   **(E)** r.holloway338@btinternet.com
Chairman: Rick Eaton   **Manager:** Ricky Eaton
Ground: Oakside Stadium, Station Road, Barkingside, Essex IG6 1NB   **(T)**
Capacity: 3,000 **Seats:**   **Covered:**   **Midweek Matchday:** Tuesday   **Clubhouse:** Yes
Colours(change): All white (All red)
Previous Names: Ford United 1958-2004
Previous Leagues: Aetolian 1959-64, Greater London 1964-71, Metropolitan 1971-74, Essex Senior 1974-97, Isthmian 1997-2004, 05-16.

HONOURS: FA Comps: None
League: Aetolian 1959-60, 61-62. Greater London 1970-71. Essex Senior 1991-92, 96-97.

10 YEAR RECORD Isthmian Division Three 1998-99, Division One 2001-02.

07-08	08-09	09-10	10-11	11-12	12-13	13-14	14-15	15-16	16-17
Isth1N 3	Isth1N 8	Isth1N 18	Isth1N 16	Isth1N 6	Isth1N 20	Isth1N 14	Isth1N 23	Isth1N 24	ESen 14
FAC P	FAC P	FAC P	FAC 2Q	FAC 2P	FAC P	FAC P	FAC Pr	FAC P	FAC EP
FAT Pr	FAT P	FAT P	FAT 1Q	FAT 3Q	FAT 1Q	FAT P	FAT P	FAT 1Q	FAV 2Q

SAWBRIDGEWORTH TOWN
Founded: 1890   Nickname: Robins

Secretary: Keith Handley   **(T)** 07960 148 587   **(E)** keith.handley@outlook.com
Chairman: Steve Day   **Prog Ed:** Paul Wildman
Ground: Crofters End, West Road, Sawbridgeworth CM21 0DE   **(T)** 01279 722 039
Capacity: 2,500 **Seats:** 175   **Covered:** 300   **Midweek Matchday:** Tuesday   **Clubhouse:** Yes
Colours(change): Red & black/black/red (All blue)
Previous Names: Sawbridgeworth > 1976.
Previous Leagues: Stortford. Spartan. Herts County. Essex Olympian.

HONOURS: FA Comps: None
League: Essex Olympian 1971-72.

10 YEAR RECORD

07-08	08-09	09-10	10-11	11-12	12-13	13-14	14-15	15-16	16-17
ESen 12	ESen 13	ESen 10	ESen 16	ESen 6	ESen 14	ESen 6	ESen 5	ESen 10	ESen 5
FAC EPr				FAC EP	FAC EP	FAC EP	FAC EP	FAC EP	FAC 1Q
FAV 2Q			FAV 2Q	FAV 2Q	FAV 2Q	FAV 2Q	FAV 1Q	FAV 1Q	FAV 2Q

SOUTHEND MANOR
Founded: 1955   Nickname: The Manor

Secretary: Steven Robinson   **(T)** 07788 580 360   **(E)** southendmanor@btinternet.com
Chairman: Steven Robinson
Ground: The Arena, Southchurch Park, Northumberland Crescent, Southend SS1 2XB   **(T)** 07788 580 360
Capacity: 2,000 **Seats:** 500   **Covered:** 700   **Midweek Matchday:** Tuesday   **Clubhouse:** Yes   **Shop:** No

Colours(change): Yellow/black/yellow & black (White & red/red/red)
Previous Names: None
Previous Leagues: Southend Borough Combination. Southend & District Alliance.

HONOURS: FA Comps: None
League: Southend Borough Combination 1971-72, 73-74, 78-79, 79-80, 80-81, 81-82.
10 YEAR RECORD | Southend & District Alliance 1983-84, 84-85. Essex Senior 1990-91.

07-08	08-09	09-10	10-11	11-12	12-13	13-14	14-15	15-16	16-17
ESen 6	ESen 4	ESen 7	ESen 5	ESen 2	ESen 7	ESen 19	ESen 18	ESen 16	ESen 7
FAC	FAC EP	FAC EPr	FAC P	FAC 4Q	FAC 1Q	FAC EPr	FAC EP	FAC P	FAC EPr
FAV 1Q	FAV 2Q	FAV 1P	FAV 2Q	FAV 3Pr	FAV 3P	FAV 2Q	FAV 2Q	FAV 2Qr	FAV 2Q

SPORTING BENGAL UNITED
Founded: 1996   Nickname: Bengal Tigers

Secretary: Shakil Rahman   **(T)** 07957 337 313   **(E)** shax101@hotmail.com
Chairman: Aroz Miah   **Manager:** Imrul Gazi
Ground: Mile End Stadium, Rhodeswell Rd, Off Burdett Rd E14 7TW   **(T)** 020 8980 1885
Capacity: 2,000 **Seats:** Yes   **Covered:** Yes   **Midweek Matchday:** Wednesday   **Clubhouse:** Yes

Colours(change): All royal blue (Orange/black/black)
Previous Names: None.
Previous Leagues: Asian League. London Intermediate, Kent 2003-11.

HONOURS: FA Comps: None
League: None
10 YEAR RECORD

07-08	08-09	09-10	10-11	11-12	12-13	13-14	14-15	15-16	16-17
Kent P 17	Kent P 17	Kent P 15	Kent P 15	ESen 10	ESen 11	ESen 13	ESen 20	ESen 12	ESen 19
FAC EPr	FAC P	FAC EP			FAC EPr	FAC EPr	FAC EP	FAC EP	FAC 1Q
FAV 2Q	FAV 1Q	FAV 1Q		FAV 3P	FAV 1P	FAV 1P	FAV 1Q	FAV 2P	FAV 1P

STANSTED
Founded: 1902   Nickname: Blues

Secretary: Tom Williams   **(T)** 07921 403 842   **(E)** tom.williams16@btopenworld.com
Chairman: Glyn Warwick   **Manager:** Paul Pittuck
Ground: Hargrave Park, Cambridge Road, Stansted CM24 8BX   **(T)** 07921 403 842
Capacity: 2,000 **Seats:** 200   **Covered:** 400   **Midweek Matchday:** Tuesday   **Clubhouse:** Yes   **Shop:** No

Colours(change): White & blue
Previous Names: None.
Previous Leagues: East Herts. Herts Senior County 1946-71.

HONOURS: FA Comps: FA Vase 1983-84.
League: East Herts 1934-35. Essex Senior 2009-10.
10 YEAR RECORD

07-08	08-09	09-10	10-11	11-12	12-13	13-14	14-15	15-16	16-17
ESen 10	ESen 10	ESen 1	ESen 2	ESen 16	ESen 17	ESen 17	ESen 7	ESen 9	ESen 8
FAC 1Q	FAC P	FAC EP	FAC EP	FAC 1Q	FAC EP	FAC EPr	FAC EP	FAC Pr	FAC EP
FAV 2Q	FAV 1Q	FAV 2P	FAV 5P	FAV 2P	FAV 2Q	FAV 2Q	FAV 2Q	FAV 1Q	FAV 1Q

TAKELEY
Founded: 1903   Nickname:

Secretary: Mick Rabey   **(T)** 07831 845 466   **(E)** Takeleyfc@mail.com
Chairman: Pat Curran   **Manager:** Marc Das   **Prog Ed:** Dave Edwards
Ground: Station Road, Takeley, Bishop's Stortford CM22 6SQ   **(T)** 01279 870 404
Capacity: 2,000 **Seats:** Yes   **Covered:** Yes   **Midweek Matchday:** Tuesday   **Clubhouse:** Yes

Colours(change): All royal blue (All red)
Previous Names: None.
Previous Leagues: Essex Intermediate/Olympian.

HONOURS: FA Comps: None
League: Essex Olympian/Intermediate 1987-88, 2001-02, Division Two 1993-94.
10 YEAR RECORD

07-08	08-09	09-10	10-11	11-12	12-13	13-14	14-15	15-16	16-17
EssxO 2	ESen 3	ESen 6	ESen 13	ESen 3	ESen 3	ESen 7	ESen 11	ESen 18	ESen 4
			FAC EP	FAC EPr	FAC P	FAC EP	FAC EPr	FAC EP	FAC EP
		FAV 2Q	FAV 1P	FAV 2Q	FAV 2P	FAV 2P	FAV 1Q	FAV 2Qr	FAV 2Q

TOWER HAMLETS

Founded: 2000   Nickname: Green Army

Secretary: Adam Richardson   **(T)** 07535 858493   **(E)** thfcsecretary@hotmail.com
Chairman: Mohammed Nural Hoque   **Manager:** Ade Abayomi
Ground: Mile End Stadium, Rhodeswell Rd, Poplar E14 7TW   **(T)** 020 8980 1885
Capacity: 2,000 **Seats:** Yes   **Covered:** Yes   **Midweek Matchday:** Monday   **Clubhouse:** Yes

Colours(change): All green (Orange/black/black)
Previous Names: Bethnal Green United 2000-2013.
Previous Leagues: Canery Wharf Summer League. Inner London. London Intermediate. Middlesex County >2009.

HONOURS: FA Comps: None
League: Middlesex County Premier Division 2008-09.

10 YEAR RECORD

07-08	08-09	09-10	10-11	11-12	12-13	13-14	14-15	15-16	16-17
MidxP 8	MidxP 1	ESen 5	ESen 4	ESen 9	ESen 12	ESen 4	ESen 17	ESen 17	ESen 20
						FAC P	FAC EP	FAC Pr	FAC P
						FAV 1P	FAV 1P	FAV 1Q	FAV 1Q

WADHAM LODGE

Founded: 2008   Nickname: Wad Army

Secretary: Sharon Fitch   **(T)** 07903 061 692   **(E)** wadamlodge.fc@hotmail.com
Chairman: Martyn Fitch
Ground: Wadham Lodge Sports Ground, Kitchener Road, Walthamstow E17 4JP   **(T)** 07903 061 692
Capacity: 3,000 **Seats:** 216   **Covered:** Yes   **Midweek Matchday:** Wednesday   **Clubhouse:** Yes

Colours(change): All white (All red)
Previous Names: None
Previous Leagues: Essex Business House League 2008-09. Essex Olympian League 2009-15.

HONOURS: FA Comps: None
League: Essex Olympian Division Three 2009-10, Division Two 2010-11.

10 YEAR RECORD

07-08	08-09	09-10	10-11	11-12	12-13	13-14	14-15	15-16	16-17
		EsxO3 1	EsxO2 1	EsxO1 4	EsxO1 2	EsxOP 9	EsxOP 4	ESen 6	ESen 15
									FAV 2P

WALTHAM FOREST

Founded: 1964   Nickname: The Stags

Secretary: Andrew Perkins   **(T)** 07748 983 792   **(E)** andrewpeterperkins@hotmail.com
Chairman: Turgut Esendagli   **Manager:** Qayum Shakoor   **Prog Ed:** Andrzej Perkins
Ground: Wadham Lodge, Kitchener Road, Walthamstow E17 4JP   **(T)** 07715 640 171
Capacity: 3,500 **Seats:** 216   **Covered:** Yes   **Midweek Matchday:** Wednesday   **Clubhouse:** Yes

Colours(change): White/blue/blue (All yellow)
Previous Names: Pennant 1964-88. Walthamstow Pennant 1988-95. Merged with Leyton to form Leyton Pennant 1995-2003.
Previous Leagues: Isthmian 2003-04, 06-14. Southern 2004-06.

HONOURS: FA Comps: None
League: None

10 YEAR RECORD

07-08	08-09	09-10	10-11	11-12	12-13	13-14	14-15	15-16	16-17
Isth1N 19	Isth1N 20	Isth1N 16	Isth1N 21	Isth1N 17	Isth1N 18	Isth1N 23	ESen 9	ESen 19	ESen 12
FAC 1Q	FAC P	FAC 1Q	FAC P	FAC 2Q	FAC 2Q	FAC P	FAC EP	FAC EP	FAC 2Q
FAT P	FAT P	FAT 1Qr	FAT 1Q	FAT 1Q	FAT 1Q	FAT P	FAV 1P	FAV 2Q	FAV 1P

WEST ESSEX

Founded: 1989   Nickname:

Secretary: Dan Reading   **(T)** 07956 557 438   **(E)** daniel.reading@marks-and-spencers.
Chairman: Richard Kent   **Manager:** Kwame Kwateng
Ground: Barking FC, Mayesbrook Park, Lodge Avenue, Dagenham RM8 2JR   **(T)** 07956 557 438
Capacity: 2,500 **Seats:** 200   **Covered:** 600   **Midweek Matchday:** Tuesday   **Clubhouse:** Yes

Colours(change): Red & black/black/red (Yellow & black/black/yellow)
Previous Names: None
Previous Leagues: Ilford & District 1989-94. Essex Business Houses 1994-2010. Middlesex County 2010-2016.

HONOURS: FA Comps: None
League: Essex Business Houses Division One 2008-09.
Middlesex County Division One (Central & East) 2010-11, Premier Division 2015-16.

10 YEAR RECORD

07-08	08-09	09-10	10-11	11-12	12-13	13-14	14-15	15-16	16-17
EsxBH1 11	EsxBH1 1	EsxBHP 8	Midx1SE 1	MidxP 11	MidxP 10	MidxP 9	MidxP 7	MidxP 1	ESen 13
									FAV 1Q

WOODFORD TOWN 2017

Founded: 2000   Nickname:

Secretary: Tim Aleshe   **(T)** 07956 491 958   **(E)** timbukk2@msn.com
Chairman: Trevor Duberry   **Manager:** Tony Levoli
Ground: Broxbourne Borough FC, Goffs Lane, Cheshunt, Herts EN7 5QN   **(T)** 0207 5114 477
Capacity: 5,000 **Seats:** 300   **Covered:** Yes   **Midweek Matchday:** Wednesday   **Clubhouse:** Yes

Colours(change): All blue (All red)
Previous Names: Mauritius Sports merged with Walthamstow Ave & Pennant 2007. Mauritius Sports Ass. 09-11. Haringey & Waltham Dev. 11-13. Grhouse London 13-15
Previous Leagues: London Intermediate 2001-03.   **Previous Names Cont:** Greenhouse Sports 15-16. Haringey & Waltham 16-17.
Middlesex County 2003-2007.
HONOURS: FA Comps: None
League: None

10 YEAR RECORD

07-08		08-09		09-10		10-11		11-12		12-13		13-14		14-15		15-16		16-17	
ESen	13	ESen	15	ESen	18	ESen	11	ESen	12	ESen	8	ESen	18	ESen	19	ESen	15	ESen	22
						FAC	EP	FAC	Pr	FAC	P	FAC	1Q						
				FAV	1Q	FAV	1Q	FAV	2P	FAV	1Qr	FAV	2Q			FAV	2P		

	Reserve Division	P	W	D	L	F	A	GD	Pts
1	Thurrock Res	22	19	1	2	75	26	49	58
2	Heybridge Swifts Res	22	14	5	3	74	33	41	47
3	Barkingside Res	22	11	8	3	53	38	15	41
4	Sawbridgeworth Town Res	22	11	4	7	48	31	17	37
5	Takeley Res	22	10	2	10	50	53	-3	32
6	Waltham Abbey Res	22	8	4	10	46	38	8	28
7	Redbridge Res	22	8	2	12	47	54	-7	26
8	Stansted Res	22	7	4	11	31	41	-10	25
9	Barking Res	22	7	2	13	45	74	-29	23
10	Hullbridge Sports Res	22	6	3	13	43	59	-16	21
11	Bishop's Stortford Dev	22	6	2	14	40	62	-22	20
12	AFC Sudbury Res	22	6	1	15	36	79	-43	19

NON LEAGUE DAY 07.10.17

HELLENIC LEAGUE

Sponsored by: Uhlsport
Founded: 1953

Recent Champions: 2014: Wantage Town
2015: Flackwell Heath **2016:** Kidlington

PREMIER DIVISION	P	W	D	L	F	A	GD	Pts
1 Thame United	34	26	6	2	118	39	79	84
2 Bracknell Town	34	26	3	5	113	37	76	81
3 Flackwell Heath	34	23	4	7	94	41	53	73
4 Thatcham Town	34	21	5	8	90	48	42	68
5 Ardley United	34	20	4	10	75	53	22	64
6 Highworth Town	34	19	4	11	87	59	28	61
7 Brimscombe & Thrupp	34	18	4	12	80	58	22	58
8 Binfield	34	16	4	14	65	49	16	52
9 Lydney Town	34	15	6	13	65	64	1	51
10 Tuffley Rovers	34	15	5	14	61	57	4	50
11 Royal Wootton Bassett	34	15	3	16	61	64	-3	45*
12 Longlevens AFC	34	11	3	20	67	83	-16	36
13 Brackley Town Saints	34	10	4	20	48	97	-49	34
14 Highmoor-Ibis	34	8	8	18	52	82	-30	32
15 Ascot United	34	8	4	22	49	80	-31	28
16 Oxford City Nomads	34	6	6	22	45	87	-42	24
17 Burnham	34	6	1	27	42	129	-87	19
18 Henley Town	34	4	4	26	40	125	-85	16

Carterton withdrew 06/09/16.

DIVISION ONE EAST	P	W	D	L	F	A	GD	Pts
1 Penn & Tylers Green	26	20	3	3	87	22	65	63
2 Woodley United	26	20	3	3	55	17	38	63
3 Headington Amateur's	26	17	4	5	85	38	47	55
4 Finchampstead	26	14	1	11	58	38	20	43
5 Bicester Town	26	12	4	10	60	40	20	40
6 Chalfont Wasps	26	11	7	8	42	38	4	40
7 AFC Aldermaston	26	12	1	13	54	46	8	37
8 Sandhurst Town	26	10	7	9	38	41	-3	37
9 Didcot Town Res'	26	10	4	12	53	52	1	34
10 Chinnor	26	9	4	13	40	58	-18	31
11 Rayners Lane	26	9	3	14	35	52	-17	30
12 Wokingham & Emmbrook	26	7	7	12	48	53	-5	28
13 Holyport	26	6	2	18	45	66	-21	20
14 Wantage Town Res	26	0	0	26	15	154	-139	0

DIVISION ONE WEST	P	W	D	L	F	A	GD	Pts
1 Fairford Town	30	24	3	3	131	26	105	75
2 Abingdon United	30	21	1	8	83	30	53	64
3 Hook Norton	30	20	3	7	80	44	36	63
4 Easington Sports	30	17	5	8	57	37	20	56
5 Cirencester Town Dev'	30	16	4	10	76	51	25	52
6 Purton	30	15	6	9	71	52	19	51
7 Shrivenham	30	13	5	12	49	41	8	44
8 North Leigh	30	14	5	11	64	67	-3	44*
9 Shortwood United Res	30	11	9	10	51	44	7	42
10 Clanfield 85'	30	11	6	13	46	44	2	39
11 Letcombe	30	11	4	15	44	54	-10	37
12 Milton United	30	9	5	16	53	63	-10	32
13 New College Swindon	30	9	2	19	43	72	-29	29
14 Cheltenham Saracens	30	7	5	18	34	139	-105	26
15 Tytherington Rocks	30	3	5	22	25	68	-43	14
16 Woodstock Town	30	3	4	23	24	99	-75	13

LEAGUE CHALLENGE CUP

HOLDERS: FLACKWELL HEATH
ROUND 1

Chinnor	v	Shortwood United Res	0-0, 6-4p
Aston Clinton Dev	v	Didcot Town Res	1-7
Headington Amateurs	v	Finchampstead	2-1
Lynch Pin	v	AFC Aldermaston	2-1
Bourton Rovers	v	Letcombe	2-0
Brackley Town Saints	v	Woodstock Town	4-0
Holyport	v	Cheltenham Saracens	6-0
Bicester Town	v	North Leigh	1-5
Longlevens AFC	v	Stokenchurch	10-2
Hook Norton	v	Rayners Lane	2-4
Burnham	v	Bracknell Town	2-5
Woodley United	v	Shrivenham	1-1, 1-3p
Milton Keynes Academy	v	Binfield	1-3
Oxford City Dev	v	Henley Town	5-0
Cirencester Town Dev	v	Sandhurst Town	2-3
Moreton Rangers	v	Tytherington Rocks	3-1
Abingdon United	v	Ardley United	1-3
Highmoor-Ibis	v	Penn & Tylers Green	1-1, 5-4p
Fairford Town	v	Highworth Town	1-2
Oxford City Nomads	v	Purton	2-0
Tuffley Rovers	v	Carterton	HW
Clanfield	v	New College Swindon	2-3
Chalvey Sports	v	Kidlington Res	3-1 aet
Chalfont Wasps	v	Wantage Town Res	3-1 aet
Wokingham & Emmbrook	v	Lydney Town	3-4
Milton United	v	Easington Sports	0-1
Faringdon Town	v	Thame United	0-4

ROUND 2

Chinnor	v	Didcot Town Res	2-1
Headington Amateurs	v	Lynch Pin	5-2
Bourton Rovers	v	Brackley Town Saints	1-4 aet
Holyport	v	North Leigh	4-1 aet
Longlevens AFC	v	Rayners Lane	3-2
Bracknell Town	v	Shrivenham	4-3
Binfield	v	Oxford City Dev	7-3
Royal Wootton Bassett	v	Sandhurst Town	2-3
Thatcham Town	v	Moreton Rangers	3-0
Ardley United	v	Flackwell Heath	1-1, 8-9
Ascot United	v	Highmoor-Ibis	1-2
Highworth Town	v	Oxford City Nomads	2-0
Tuffley Rovers	v	Brimscombe & Thrupp	0-2
New College Swindon	v	Chalvey Sports	1-1, 2-4p
Chalfont Wasps	v	Lydney Town	1-2
Easington Sports	v	Thame United	2-0

ROUND 3

Chinnor	v	Headington Amateurs	3-4
Brackley Town Saints	v	Holyport	5-1
Longlevens AFC	v	Bracknell Town	3-5
Binfield	v	Sandhurst Town	5-2
Thatcham Town	v	Flackwell Heath	1-2
Highmoor-Ibis	v	Highworth Town	1-4
Brimscombe & Thrupp	v	Chalvey Sports	4-0
Lydney Town	v	Easington Sports	4-0

QUARTER FINALS

Headington Amateurs	v	Brackley Town Saints	2-1
Bracknell Town	v	Binfield	3-1
Flackwell Heath	v	Highworth Town	1-3
Brimscombe & Thrupp	v	Lydney Town	2-1

SEMI FINALS

Headington Amateurs	v	Bracknell Town	1-5
Highworth Town	v	Brimscombe & Thrupp	3-2

FINAL

Bracknell Town	v	Highworth Town	2-0

CLUB MOVEMENTS- Premier Division - In: Abingdon United (P), Fairford Town (P), Wantage Town (R - Southern D1S&W), Woodley United (P), Windsor (S - Combined Counties). **Out:** Henley Town (R), Thame United (P - Southern D1C).
Division One East - In: Headington Amateur's (T), Milton United (T), Wallingford Town (N).
Out: Headington Amateur's (T), Rayners Lane (T - Spartan South Midlands), Wantage Town Res (R), Woodley United (P).
Division One West - In: Headington Amateur's (T), Kidlington Res (N), Pewsey Vale (T - Wessex).
Out: Abingdon United (P), Fairford Town (P), Hook Norton (F), Milton United (T).

PREMIER DIVISION

	PREMIER DIVISION	1	2	3	4	5	6	7	8	9	10	11	12	13	14	15	16	17	18
1	Ardley United		5-0	3-1	2-0	4-1	0-1	3-1	0-5	4-1	6-3	0-4	1-4	0-1	2-0	2-1	3-4	1-0	1-0
2	Ascot United	1-3		3-2	1-3	1-3	1-5	7-2	0-1	1-2	1-2	1-5	2-2	0-2	1-1	1-3	0-4	0-3	6-3
3	Binfield	0-3	1-0		1-2	0-1	1-3	4-0	0-3	9-0	3-0	1-2	5-0	4-1	1-1	3-1	3-1	2-1	1-2
4	Brackley Town Saints	2-2	1-2	1-2		0-3	2-1	0-4	1-2	4-1	5-2	3-1	0-5	3-5	0-0	1-3	1-4	1-1	4-1
5	Bracknell Town	2-1	3-2	3-2	9-0		7-2	7-0	1-1	1-1	0-2	1-2	4-1	3-0	4-1	6-0	2-0	5-2	3-0
6	Brimscombe & Thrupp	4-2	2-3	1-1	6-1	1-2		6-1	4-0	3-0	4-0	2-4	2-0	0-2	4-3	1-1	1-5	2-3	0-0
7	Burnham	2-3	2-1	0-4	0-1	0-5	2-4		0-9	2-1	3-2	1-3	3-6	0-4	1-2	2-1	2-3	0-11	0-2
8	Flackwell Heath	3-0	2-0	0-3	10-0	3-1	3-0	4-0		7-1	2-1	1-2	2-1	3-2	6-1	5-1	1-2	1-1	3-2
9	Henley Town	2-9	2-5	1-2	1-3	0-5	3-6	4-2	2-2		0-0	1-3	1-3	2-1	2-1	1-3	0-9	0-5	3-3
10	Highmoor-Ibis	1-0	2-2	1-0	1-1	0-6	1-2	1-1	0-3	4-1		4-2	2-4	3-1	1-0	0-2	0-3	2-4	2-2
11	Highworth Town	2-2	2-3	4-0	1-0	1-2	0-4	6-1	0-1	3-0	6-6		3-0	4-0	2-1	3-3	4-4	1-3	1-2
12	Longlevens AFC	3-4	4-0	3-5	2-5	1-2	3-1	1-0	2-2	8-3	3-2	0-2		0-1	1-1	1-4	2-5	1-3	0-3
13	Lydney Town	1-1	1-0	0-0	3-2	2-3	0-1	4-1	2-4	4-1	1-1	1-2	3-1		3-0	4-3	2-2	1-3	2-1
14	Oxford City Nomads	1-2	2-0	1-2	2-1	1-4	1-2	2-4	0-3	3-2	1-1	2-3	1-2	4-4		2-3	1-3	0-4	3-2
15	Royal Wootton Bassett	1-2	0-0	0-1	3-0	0-6	2-0	5-1	0-1	4-0	3-2	0-4	3-1	1-3	4-0		0-3	0-3	2-0
16	Thame United	1-1	3-2	3-0	5-0	3-3	2-2	8-1	5-0	2-0	3-0	4-2	2-0	5-1	8-1	1-0		3-3	4-0
17	Thatcham Town	0-1	1-2	3-0	6-0	1-4	2-1	2-1	2-1	2-1	4-2	3-2	5-2	1-1	3-2	1-3	0-2		2-2
18	Tuffley Rovers	0-2	1-0	1-1	5-0	2-1	0-2	3-2	4-0	2-0	3-1	2-1	1-0	5-2	2-3	3-1	1-2	1-2	

DIVISION ONE EAST

	DIVISION ONE EAST	1	2	3	4	5	6	7	8	9	10	11	12	13	14
1	AFC Aldermaston		0-1	0-2	1-3	2-1	1-2	2-3	5-2	0-4	3-1	3-1	6-0	2-0	0-2
2	Bicester Town	3-2		2-1	6-0	6-2	1-2	2-3	3-1	0-0	3-1	1-2	5-1	1-1	1-1
3	Chalfont Wasps	1-0	3-2		0-2	1-0	2-1	1-1	2-1	1-1	2-1	2-2	4-1	1-1	1-5
4	Chinnor	1-4	3-6	1-1		0-4	2-1	1-5	4-0	0-3	0-3	1-1	3-0	1-3	1-2
5	Didcot Town Res	4-2	4-1	1-2	0-0		1-1	2-2	1-0	1-2	0-1	1-3	8-1	2-1	0-2
6	Finchampstead	1-3	1-0	2-1	0-1	6-2		1-2	6-0	1-3	3-2	4-2	10-0	2-1	0-1
7	Headington Amateur's	2-2	2-1	2-1	3-2	8-1	2-1		0-1	2-1	5-0	1-2	7-1	7-1	0-1
8	Holyport	1-4	1-2	3-0	1-2	0-4	1-2	2-7		1-4	1-2	1-1	9-1	3-1	1-3
9	Penn & Tylers Green	5-1	3-0	2-1	7-0	5-1	3-0	4-2	6-3		1-1	2-0	12-1	4-2	1-0
10	Rayners Lane	2-1	4-2	0-4	0-3	2-2	0-1	4-3	0-2	1-3		0-0	2-0	1-3	0-4
11	Sandhurst Town	1-3	0-0	0-0	3-1	1-0	2-4	1-4	2-1	1-5	1-0		3-2	1-1	1-2
12	Wantage Town Res	0-4	0-9	2-4	0-7	1-6	1-4	0-7	0-8	0-6	1-2	0-5		2-4	0-5
13	Wokingham & Emmbrook	2-3	0-2	2-2	1-1	1-2	3-2	2-4	1-1	1-0	2-4	1-2	9-0		4-3
14	Woodley United	1-0	2-0	3-2	3-0	1-3	1-0	1-1	3-0	1-0	2-1	1-0	5-0	0-0	

DIVISION ONE WEST

	DIVISION ONE WEST	1	2	3	4	5	6	7	8	9	10	11	12	13	14	15	16
1	Abingdon United		12-0	3-1	3-0	2-0	2-1	1-0	2-0	3-2	2-1	7-0	1-2	3-0	0-2	4-1	5-1
2	Cheltenham Saracens	0-6		1-1	0-5	0-7	0-17	3-3	1-6	2-10	3-5	0-5	3-2	0-8	1-1	1-0	3-1
3	Cirencester Town Dev'	1-1	10-1		1-4	1-3	3-2	2-6	2-1	4-0	3-2	4-2	1-0	1-2	3-2	3-0	4-0
4	Clanfield 85'	0-1	3-1	2-4		0-1	0-2	1-2	0-3	0-0	0-1	1-2	0-0	2-0	1-0	2-0	1-2
5	Easington Sports	0-4	3-1	1-0	2-2		0-3	0-3	2-1	2-1	3-0	2-1	2-1	1-2	1-1	2-1	9-1
6	Fairford Town	5-2	7-0	2-1	1-1	4-0		5-0	7-0	5-0	6-0	5-0	2-2	3-2	1-1	5-1	11-0
7	Hook Norton	0-3	9-0	3-1	3-4	1-0	0-3		3-2	1-2	7-1	7-2	3-2	0-0	2-1	1-0	2-1
8	Letcombe	0-3	1-2	0-1	2-2	1-4	1-0	2-2		1-1	3-1	2-3	1-2	3-2	1-3	2-1	1-1
9	Milton United	2-1	9-0	3-1	1-2	0-3	2-3	1-2	1-0		3-1	2-2	0-3	1-4	3-0	2-0	1-1
10	New College Swindon	2-1	1-3	1-8	3-0	0-2	0-2	1-3	0-2	5-1		1-2	2-0	2-3	0-4	2-0	4-1
11	North Leigh	2-4	3-1	1-3	1-1	1-0	0-2	3-2	3-1	4-1	5-1		6-9	2-2	2-3	6-0	2-0
12	Purton	1-0	2-2	2-2	3-1	2-2	3-5	1-3	3-1	4-0	0-4	4-0		5-1	1-1	2-0	3-1
13	Shortwood United Res	3-0	1-0	2-2	0-2	1-1	1-6	1-2	2-1	0-0	0-1	2-2	0-0		1-2	6-1	3-1
14	Shrivenham	1-2	0-2	4-2	1-3	0-1	2-5	0-2	1-4	0-1	1-1	0-0	0-3	2-0		3-0	4-0
15	Tytherington Rocks	1-5	1-1	0-3	3-1	1-1	1-3	1-4	0-1	1-1	0-0	1-2	5-0	0-2	0-1		4-2
16	Woodstock Town	1-0	0-2	0-3	1-6	1-2	1-8	0-4	0-2	2-0	3-1	0-1	2-7	0-0	1-4	1-1	

ABINGDON UNITED

Founded: 1946   Nickname: The Yellows

Secretary: John Blackmore   **(T)** 07747 615 691   **(E)** secretaryaufc@virginmedia.com
Chairman: Debbie Blackmore   **Manager:** Steve Alman   **Prog Ed:** Bill Fletcher
Ground: The Northcourt, Northcourt Road, Abingdon OX14 1PL   **(T)** 01235 203 203
Capacity: 2,000 **Seats:** 158   **Covered:** 258   **Midweek Matchday:** Tuesday   **Clubhouse:** Yes

Colours(change): Yellow/blue/blue
Previous Names: None
Previous Leagues: North Berkshire 1949-58, Hellenic 1958-2006. Southern 2006-13.

HONOURS: FA Comps: None
     League: North Berks 1952-53.

10 YEAR RECORD

07-08	08-09	09-10	10-11	11-12	12-13	13-14	14-15	15-16	16-17
Sthsw 16	Sthsw 15	Sthsw 14	Sthsw 16	Sthsw 18	Sthsw 20	Hel P 17	Hel P 15	Hel P 19	Hel1W 2
FAC 1Qr	FAC Pr	FAC 2Qr	FAC P	FAC 1Q	FAC P	FAC EPr	FAC 2Q	FAC EP	FAC EPr
FAT 2Qr	FAT 1Q	FAT 1Q	FAT 1Q	FAT 1Q	FAT P	FAV 1P	FAV 2Pr	FAV 1Q	FAV 1P

ASCOT UNITED

Founded: 1965   Nickname: Yellaman

Secretary: Mark Gittoes   **(T)** 07798 701 995   **(E)** secretary@ascotunited.net
Chairman: Mike Harrison   **Manager:** Neil Richards   **Prog Ed:** Neal Jeffs
Ground: Ascot Racecourse, Car Park 10, Winkfield Rd, Ascot SL5 7RA   **(T)** 01344 291 107
Capacity: 1,150 **Seats:**   **Covered:**   **Midweek Matchday:** Tuesday   **Clubhouse:** Yes   **Shop:** Yes

Colours(change): Yellow/blue/yellow
Previous Names: None.
Previous Leagues: Reading Senior.

HONOURS: FA Comps: None
     League: Reading Senior Division 2006-07.

10 YEAR RECORD

07-08	08-09	09-10	10-11	11-12	12-13	13-14	14-15	15-16	16-17
Hel1E 4	Hel1E 2	Hel P 15	Hel P 12	Hel P 14	Hel P 7	Hel P 3	Hel P 3	Hel P 4	HantP 15
				FAC EP	FAC P	FAC EP	FAC P	FAC EP	FAC 1Qr
			FAV 2Q	FAV 2Q	FAV QFr	FAV 2P	FAV QF	FAV 3Pr	FAV 2P

BINFIELD

Founded: 1892   Nickname: Moles

Secretary: Rob Challis   **(T)** 07515 336 989   **(E)** robchallis@binfieldfc.com
Chairman: Bob Bacon   **Manager:** Roger Herridge   **Prog Ed:** Colin Byers
Ground: Stubbs Lane off Hill Farm Lane, Binfield RG42 5NR   **(T)** 01344 860 822
Capacity: **Seats:** yes   **Covered:** yes   **Midweek Matchday:** Monday   **Clubhouse:** Yes

Colours(change): All red (All yellow)
Previous Names: None.
Previous Leagues: Ascot & District. Great Western Combination. Reading & Dist. Chiltonian.

HONOURS: FA Comps: None
     League: Great Western Combination 1946-47. Reading & District Division One 1975-76, 87-88, Division Two 86-87.
     Hellenic Division One East 2008-09.

10 YEAR RECORD

07-08	08-09	09-10	10-11	11-12	12-13	13-14	14-15	15-16	16-17
Hel1E 9	Hel1E 1	Hel P 8	Hel P 2	Hel P 8	Hel P 3	Hel P 5	Hel P 6	Hel P 8	Hel P 8
		FAC EP	FAC 1Q	FAC P	FAC EP	FAC 2Q	FAC EP	FAC P	FAC EP
	FAV 2P	FAV 1Q	FAV 2P	FAV 4P	FAV 3P	FAV 3P	FAV 2Q	FAV 1Qr	FAV 2Q

BRACKLEY TOWN SAINTS

Founded: 1890   Nickname: The Saints

Secretary: Matthew Wise   **(T)** 07798 836 625   **(E)** matthewwise@banburylitho.co.uk
Chairman: Matthew Wise   **Manager:** Gordon Kille   **Prog Ed:** Steve Goodman
Ground: St James Park, Churchill Way, Brackley, Northamptonshire, NN13 7EF   **(T)** 01280 704 077
Capacity: 3,500 **Seats:** 300   **Covered:** 1,500   **Midweek Matchday:** Wednesday   **Clubhouse:** Yes

Colours(change): Red & white/white/red
Previous Names: Brackley Town Development > 2015
Previous Leagues: None

HONOURS: FA Comps: None
     League: None

10 YEAR RECORD

07-08	08-09	09-10	10-11	11-12	12-13	13-14	14-15	15-16	16-17
							Hel1E 2	Hel P 16	Hel P 13
									FAV 1Qr

BRACKNELL TOWN
Founded: 1896   Nickname: The Robins

Secretary: Ian Brooks   **(T)** 07527 006 098   **(E)** ianbrooksics@gmail.com
Chairman: Kayne Steinborn-Busse   **Manager:** Mark Tallentire   **Prog Ed:** Paul Wakefield
Ground: Larges Lane Bracknell RG12 9AN   **(T)** 01344 412 305
Capacity: 2,500 **Seats:** 150   **Covered:** 500   **Midweek Matchday:** Tuesday   **Clubhouse:** Yes   **Shop:** Yes

Colours(change): All red
Previous Names: Old Bracknell Wanderers 1896-1962.
Previous Leagues: Ascot & District. Reading & District 1949-58. Great Western Comb. 1958-63, Surrey Senior 1963-70, London Spartan 1970-75, Isthmian 1984-2004, Southern 2004-10
HONOURS: FA Comps: None
   League: Ascot & District 1911-12, 32-33, Division Two 13-14. Surrey Senior 1969-70.
10 YEAR RECORD | Spartan Senior Division 1980-81, Premier 1982-83. Isthmian Division Three 1993-94.

07-08	08-09	09-10	10-11	11-12	12-13	13-14	14-15	15-16	16-17
Sthsw 20	Sthsw	Sthsw 22	Hel P 16	Hel P 21	Hel1E 5	Hel P 13	Hel P 9	Hel P 14	Hel P 2
FAC P	FAC 1Q	FAC P	FAC P	FAC EP	FAC 1Q	FAC P	FAC EP	FAC 1Q	FAC P
FAT 1Q	FAT 1Q	FAT 1Q	FAV 2P	FAV 2Q	FAV 2Q	FAV 2Q	FAV 2Q	FAV 2Qr	FAV 1P

BRIMSCOMBE & THRUPP
Founded: 1886   Nickname: Lilywhites

Secretary: Allan Boulton   **(T)** 07850 471 331   **(E)** allanboulton1@sky.com
Chairman: Clive Baker   **Manager:** Sam Prior   **Prog Ed:** Robert Hill
Ground: 'The Meadow', London Road, Brimscombe Stroud, Gloucestershire GL5 2SH   **(T)** 07833 231 464
Capacity: **Seats:** Yes   **Covered:** Yes   **Midweek Matchday:** Tuesday   **Clubhouse:** Yes

Colours(change): All white (All blue)
Previous Names: Brimscombe AFC 1886- late 1970s. Brimscombe and Thrupp merged.
Previous Leagues: Stroud & District. Gloucestershire Northern Senior. Gloucestershire County
HONOURS: FA Comps: None
   League: Stroud & Dist. 1902-03, 06-07, 07-08, 12-13. Gloucestershire Northern Senior 1922-23, 30-31, 47-48, Division
10 YEAR RECORD | Two 2004-05. Gloucestershire County 2010-11. Hellenic Division One West 2012-13.

07-08	08-09	09-10	10-11	11-12	12-13	13-14	14-15	15-16	16-17
		GlCo 5	GlCo 1	Hel1W 4	Hel1W 1	Hel P 12	Hel P 10	Hel P 5	Hel P 7
							FAC EP	FAC Pr	FAC 3Q
						FAV 2P	FAV 1P	FAV 3Pr	FAV 2Pr

BURNHAM
Founded: 1878   Nickname: The Blues

Secretary: Gary Reeves   **(T)** 07919 415 141   **(E)** burnhamfcsec@aol.com
Chairman: Gary Reeves   **Manager:** Mark Betts   **Prog Ed:** AM Print & Copy
Ground: The Gore, Wymers Wood Road, Burnham, Slough SL1 8JG   **(T)** 01628 668 654
Capacity: 2,500 **Seats:** Yes   **Covered:** Yes   **Midweek Matchday:** Tuesday   **Clubhouse:** Yes   **Shop:** Yes

Colours(change): Blue & white/white/white
Previous Names: Burnham & Hillingdon 1985-87
Previous Leagues: Hellenic 1971-77, 95-99, Athenian 1977-84, London Spartan 1984-85, Southern 1985-95, 99-16.
HONOURS: FA Comps: None
   League: Hellenic 1975-76, 98-99. London Spartan 1984-85.
10 YEAR RECORD | Southern Division One Central 2012-13.

07-08	08-09	09-10	10-11	11-12	12-13	13-14	14-15	15-16	16-17
Sthsw 10	Sthsw 17	SthM 3	SthC 14	SthC 15	SthC 1	SthP 20	SthP 23	Sthsw 21	Hel P 17
FAC Pr	FAC Pr	FAC 2Qr	FAC 2Q	FAC 3Q	FAC P	FAC 2Q	FAC 2Q	FAC Pr	FAC EP
FAT 3Q	FAT 2Q	FAT 3Q	FAT 1Qr	FAT Pr	FAT 2Q	FAT 2Q	FAT 2Qr	FAT P	FAV 2Q

FAIRFORD TOWN
Founded: 1891   Nickname: Town

Secretary: Bill Beach   **(T)** 07919 940 909   **(E)** secretary@fairfordtownfc.co.uk
Chairman: Mike Tanner   **Manager:** Gareth Davies   **Prog Ed:** Andrew Meaden
Ground: Cinder Lane, London Road, Fairford GL7 4AX   **(T)** 01285 712 071
Capacity: 2,000 **Seats:** 100   **Covered:** 250   **Midweek Matchday:** Tuesday   **Clubhouse:** Yes   **Shop:** Yes

Colours(change): All red.
Previous Names: None.
Previous Leagues: Cirencester & District. Swindon & District.
HONOURS: FA Comps: None
   League: Swindon & District Prmeier Division 1964-65, 68-69.
10 YEAR RECORD | Hellenic Division One A 1971-72, Division One West 2016-17.

07-08	08-09	09-10	10-11	11-12	12-13	13-14	14-15	15-16	16-17
Hel P 20	Hel P 14	Hel P 20	Hel P 21	Hel P 20	Hel1W 4	Hel1W 4	Hel1W 14	Hel1W 4	Hel1W 1
FAC EP	FAC 1Q	FAC EP	FAC EPr	FAC P	FAC EP	FAC EP	FAC EP		FAC EP
FAV 2Q	FAV 2Qr	FAV 2Q	FAV 1P	FAV 1P	FAV 1P	FAV 2Q	FAV 1Q	FAV 1P	FAV 1P

FLACKWELL HEATH
Founded: 1907   Nickname: Heathens

Secretary: Jo Parsons	**(T)** 07984 199 878	**(E)** joparsons19@sky.com
Chairman: Terry Glynn	**Manager:** Paul Shone	**Prog Ed:** Chris Parsons
Ground: Wilks Park, Magpie Lane, Heath End Rd, Flackwell Hth HP10 9EA		**(T)** 01628 523 892 / 07932 952
Capacity: 2,000 **Seats:** 150	**Covered:** Yes	**Midweek Matchday:** Tuesday	**Clubhouse:** Yes

Colours(change): All red.
Previous Names: None.
Previous Leagues: High Wycombe & District 1907-50. Great Western Combination 1950-76. Hellenic 1976-82. Athenian 1982-84. Isthmian 1984-2007.
HONOURS: FA Comps: None
    League: Great Western Combination Division Two 1950-51, Premier 1957-58, 62-63.

10 YEAR RECORD   Hellenic Premier Division 2014-15.

07-08	08-09	09-10	10-11	11-12	12-13	13-14	14-15	15-16	16-17
Hel P 9	Hel P 16	Hel P 4	Hel P 8	Hel P 4	Hel P 10	Hel P 8	Hel P 1	Hel P 3	Hel P 3
FAC EP	FAC P	FAC 2Q	FAC P	FAC EP	FAC EP	FAC EPr	FAC 3Q	FAC EP	FAC 1Q
FAV 3P	FAV 1P	FAV 3P	FAV 2P	FAV 3P	FAV 1P	FAV 1Q	FAV 5P	FAV 2P	FAV 1P

HIGHMOOR IBIS
Founded: 2001   Nickname: Mighty Moor

Secretary: Chris Gallimore	**(T)** 07717 154 435	**(E)** chris.gallimore@sjpp.co.uk
Chairman: Martin Law	**Manager:** Marcus Richardson	**Prog Ed:** Martin Law
Ground: Scours Lane, Tilehurst, Reading RG30 6AY		**(T)** 01189 453 999
Capacity: **Seats:**	**Covered:** Yes	**Midweek Matchday:** Monday	**Clubhouse:** Yes

Colours(change): All blue (Yellow/white/white)
Previous Names: Highmoor and Ibis merged to form today's club in 2001.
Previous Leagues: Reading 2001-2011.

HONOURS: FA Comps: None
    League: Reading Senior Division 2003-04, 10-11.

10 YEAR RECORD

07-08	08-09	09-10	10-11	11-12	12-13	13-14	14-15	15-16	16-17
ReadS 6	ReadS 2	ReadS 4	ReadS 1	Hel1E 2	Hel P 12	Hel P 4	Hel P 2	Hel P 11	Hel P 14
						FAC 1Q	FAC P	FAC EP	FAC P
					FAV 2Q	FAV 1P	FAV 1P	FAV 1P	FAV 1P

HIGHWORTH TOWN
Founded: 1893   Nickname: Worthians

Secretary: Fraser Haines	**(T)** 07939 032 451	**(E)** fraserhaines@btinternet.com
Chairman: Rohan Haines	**Manager:** Jeff Roberts	**Prog Ed:** Mike Markham
Ground: Elms Recreation Ground, Highworth SN6 7DD		**(T)** 07939 032 451
Capacity: 2,000 **Seats:** 150	**Covered:** 250	**Midweek Matchday:** Wednesday	**Clubhouse:** Yes	**Shop:** No

Colours(change): All red
Previous Names: None.
Previous Leagues: Cirencester & District. Swindon & District. Wiltshire Combination.

HONOURS: FA Comps: None
    League: Cirencester & District Division Two 1931-32. Swindon & District Division Three 1933-34, 54-55, Two 1955-56,

10 YEAR RECORD   One 1956-57, Premier 57-58, 58-59, 60-61, 61-62, 62-63, 63-64, 65-66, 66-67, 67-68. Hellenic Premier 2004-05.

07-08	08-09	09-10	10-11	11-12	12-13	13-14	14-15	15-16	16-17
Hel P 6	Hel P 6	Hel P 9	Hel P 4	Hel P 6	Hel P 16	Hel P 11	Hel P 7	Hel P 7	Hel P 6
FAC EPr	FAC EP	FAC 1Q	FAC 1Qr	FAC EP	FAC EP	FAC EP	FAC P	FAC P	FAC 2Q
FAV 2P	FAV 2Q	FAV 2Q	FAV 1Q	FAV 2Pr	FAV 1Qr	FAV 1Q	FAV SF	FAV 3P	FAV 2P

LONGLEVENS AFC
Founded: 1954   Nickname: Levens

Secretary: Bill Davis	**(T)** 07526 958 972	**(E)** bill1853@outlook.com
Chairman: Chris Bishop	**Manager:** Mark Moore	**Prog Ed:** Chris Bishop
Ground: Saw Mills End, Corinium Avenue, Gloucester GL4 3DG		**(T)** 01452 530 388 (Clubhouse)
Capacity: 500 **Seats:** Yes	**Covered:** Yes	**Midweek Matchday:** Tuesday	**Clubhouse:** Yes

Colours(change): Red & black/black/red (All sky blue)
Previous Names: None
Previous Leagues: Gloucestershire Northern Senior > 2011. Gloucestershire County 2011-14.

HONOURS: FA Comps: None
    League: Gloucestershire Northern Division One 2008-09. Gloucestershire County 2012-13, 13-14.

10 YEAR RECORD   Hellenic Division One West 2014-15.

07-08	08-09	09-10	10-11	11-12	12-13	13-14	14-15	15-16	16-17
GlN1 4	GlN1 1	GlN1 5	GlN1 4	GlCo 9	GlCo 1	GlCo 1	Hel1W 1	Hel P 10	Hel P 12
									FAC P
								FAV 1Q	FAV 2Q

LYDNEY TOWN
Founded: 1911   Nickname: The Town

Secretary: Roger Sansom   **(T)** 07887 842 125   **(E)** rogersansom@outlook.com
Chairman: Ashley Hancock   **Manager:** Mark Lee   **Prog Ed:** Richard Thomas
Ground: Lydney Recreation Ground, Swan Road, Lydney GL15 5RU   **(T)** 01594 844 523
Capacity: 1,000   **Seats:** Yes   **Covered:** Yes   **Midweek Matchday:** Tuesday   **Clubhouse:** Yes

Colours(change): Black & white/black/black
Previous Names: None
Previous Leagues: Local leagues 1911-52. Gloucestershire Northern Senior 1952-80, 84-. Hellenic 1980-84. Gloucestershire County 2005-06.

HONOURS: FA Comps: None
League: Gloucesteeshire Northern Senior 1979-80. Gloucestershire County 2005-06. Hellenic League Division One West
10 YEAR RECORD 2006-07.

07-08	08-09	09-10	10-11	11-12	12-13	13-14	14-15	15-16	16-17
Hel P 10	Hel1W 8	Hel1W 8	Hel1W 5	Hel1W 13	Hel1W 10	Hel1W 2	Hel1W 3	Hel P 12	Hel P 9
		FAC EP	FAC P	FAC EP					FAC EP
	FAV 1Q	FAV 1Q	FAV 1P	FAV 1P	FAV 2Q	FAV 2Q		FAV 2Q	FAV 1P

OXFORD CITY NOMADS
Founded: 1936   Nickname: The Nomads

Secretary: Ryan Gurton   **(T)** 07856 142 383   **(E)** ryan.gourton@oxcityfc.co.uk
Chairman: Brian Cox   **Manager:** Rob Tutton   **Prog Ed:** Frank Thompson
Ground: Court Place Farm Stadium, Marsh Lane, Marston OX3 0NQ   **(T)** 01865 744 493
Capacity: 2,000   **Seats:** 250   **Covered:** 400   **Midweek Matchday:** Tuesday   **Clubhouse:** Yes   **Shop:** Yes

Colours(change): Blue & white/blue/blue
Previous Names: Quarry Nomads 1936-2005.
Previous Leagues: Local leagues 1936-85. Folded for 2 years reformed in 1987. Oxford City FA Junior. Oxfordshire Senior. Chiltonian 1994-2001.

HONOURS: FA Comps: None
League: Oxfordshire Senior 1962-63, 93-94.
10 YEAR RECORD Hellenic Division One East 2002-03, Premier Division 2011-12.

07-08	08-09	09-10	10-11	11-12	12-13	13-14	14-15	15-16	16-17
Hel1W 9	Hel1W 3	Hel P 10	Hel P 17	Hel P 1	Hel P 4	Hel P 9	Hel P 13	Hel P 9	Hel P 16
			FAV 1Qr	FAV 1Q	FAV 2P	FAV 2P	FAV 2Q	FAV 1P	FAV 2Q

ROYAL WOOTTON BASSETT
Founded: 1882   Nickname: Bassett

Secretary: Ian Thomas   **(T)** 07714 718 122   **(E)** ian.thomas@wbtfc.co.uk
Chairman: Andy Walduck   **Manager:** Richard Hunter   **Prog Ed:** Mark Smedley
Ground: Gerrard Buxton Sports Ground Malmesbury Rd Royal Wootton Bassett SN4 8DS   **(T)** 01793 853 880
Capacity: 4,500   **Seats:** 550   **Covered:** 1,250   **Midweek Matchday:** Wednesday   **Clubhouse:** Yes   **Shop:** No

Colours(change): All blue
Previous Names: Wootton Bassett Town > 2015.
Previous Leagues: Vale of White 1898-99. Swindon & District 1899-1903. Wiltshire County 1903-08, 35-69, 76-88. Calne & District 1930. Wiltshire Combination 1969-76.
HONOURS: FA Comps: None
League: Calne & District 1931-32, 34-35, 35-36.
10 YEAR RECORD Wiltshire Division One 1958-59, Division Two 1984-85, Division One 1987-88.

07-08	08-09	09-10	10-11	11-12	12-13	13-14	14-15	15-16	16-17
Hel1W 15	Hel1W 4	Hel1W 2	Hel P 15	Hel1W 5	Hel1W 2	Hel P 14	Hel P 11	Hel P 15	Hel P 11
FAC 1Qr	FAC EPr	FAC P	FAC 1Qr	FAC EP	FAC 2Q	FAC EP	FAC P	FAC EP	FAC EP
FAV 2Q	FAV 2P	FAV 1Q	FAV 1P	FAV 1Q	FAV 1Q	FAV 2Q	FAV 2Q	FAV 2Q	FAV 2Q

THATCHAM TOWN
Founded: 1895   Nickname: Kingfishers

Secretary: Ron Renton   **(T)** 07561 149 558   **(E)** ron.renton@btinternet.com
Chairman: Eric Bailey   **Manager:** Danny Robinson   **Prog Ed:** Andy Morris
Ground: Waterside Park, Crookham Hill, Thatcham, Berks RG18 4QR   **(T)** 01635 862 016
Capacity: 1,500   **Seats:** 300   **Covered:** 300   **Midweek Matchday:** Tuesday   **Clubhouse:** Yes   **Shop:** Yes

Colours(change): Blue and white/blue/blue
Previous Names: Thatcham 1895-1974.
Previous Leagues: Reading Temperance 1896-1953. Hellenic (founder member) 1953-82, Athenian 1982-84, London Spartan 1984-86, Wessex 1986-2006. Southern 2006-14.
HONOURS: FA Comps: None
League: Reading Temperance Division Two 1905-06. Hellenic Division One 1958-59, 64-65, 72-73, Premier 1974-75.
10 YEAR RECORD Wessex 1995-96.

07-08	08-09	09-10	10-11	11-12	12-13	13-14	14-15	15-16	16-17
Sthsw 15	Sthsw 6	Sthsw 12	Sthsw 5	Sthsw 8	SthC 17	Sthsw 19	Hel P 12	Hel P 2	Hel P 4
FAC 1Q	FAC 2Q	FAC P	FAC 1Q	FAC P	FAC 2Q	FAC P	FAC EPr	FAC 1Q	FAC EP
FAT P	FAT 2Q	FAT 2Q	FAT P	FAT 2Qr	FAT P	FAT P	FAV 1P	FAV 2Q	FAV 3P

TUFFLEY ROVERS

Founded: 1929   Nickname: Rovers

Secretary: Neil Spiller   **(T)** 07545 492 261   **(E)** admin@tuffleyroversfc.co.uk
Chairman: Neil Spiller   **Manager:** Mark Prichett   **Prog Ed:** Neil Spiller
Ground: Glevum Park Lower Tuffley Lane, Tuffley, Gloucester GL2 5DT   **(T)** 07545 492 261
Capacity: 1,000 **Seats:** 100   **Covered:** yes   **Midweek Matchday:** Tuesday   **Clubhouse:** Yes

Colours(change): Claret & blue/claret/claret
Previous Names: None
Previous Leagues: Gloucestershire County 1988-91, 2007-13. Hellenic 1991-06. Gloucestershire Northern 2006-07.

HONOURS: FA Comps: None
League: Gloucester County 1990-91. Gloucestershire Northern Division One 2006-07.

10 YEAR RECORD									
07-08	08-09	09-10	10-11	11-12	12-13	13-14	14-15	15-16	16-17
GlCo 4	GlCo 11	GlCo 3	GlCo 6	GlCo 3	GlCo 2	Hel1W 6	Hel1W 2	Hel P 17	Hel P 10
								FAC 1Q	FAC EP
							FAV 1P	FAV 1Q	FAV 2P

WANTAGE TOWN

Founded: 1892   Nickname: Alfredians

Secretary: Mike Skinner   **(T)** 07890 063 396   **(E)** wantagetownfc-secretary@outlook.com
Chairman: Ian Glover   **Manager:** Ben Sadler   **Prog Ed:** Toni Cooper
Ground: Alfredian Park, Manor Road, Wantage OX12 8DW   **(T)** 01235 764 781
Capacity: 1,500 **Seats:** 50   **Covered:** 300   **Midweek Matchday:** Tuesday   **Clubhouse:** Yes

Colours(change): Green & white/white/green with white hoops
Previous Names: None.
Previous Leagues: Swindon & District. North Berkshire. Reading & District. Hellenic > 2014. Southern 2014-17.

HONOURS: FA Comps: None
League: Swindon & District 1907-08, 33-34, 52-53, 55-56. North Berks Division One 1919-20, 21-22.
Hellenic Division 1 East 1980-81, 03-04, Premier Division 2010-11, 13-14.

10 YEAR RECORD									
07-08	08-09	09-10	10-11	11-12	12-13	13-14	14-15	15-16	16-17
Hel P 12	Hel P 11	Hel P 5	Hel P 1	Hel P 12	Hel P 2	Hel P 1	Sthsw 20	Sthsw 20	Sthsw 21
FAC EP	FAC EP	FAC 1Q	FAC EP	FAC P	FAC 1Q	FAC P	FAC 1Qr	FAC P	FAC 1Qr
FAV 1Qr	FAV 2Q	FAV 1P	FAV 3P	FAV 3P	FAV 2P	FAV 2P	FAT P	FAT P	FAT 1Qr

WINDSOR

Founded: 1892   Nickname: The Royalists

Secretary: Alan King   **(T)** 07899 941 41   **(E)** windsorfcsecretary@aol.com
Chairman: Kevin Stott   **Manager:** Mick Woodham   **Prog Ed:** Matthew Stevens
Ground: Stag Meadow, St Leonards Road, Windsor, Berks SL4 3DR   **(T)** 01753 860 656
Capacity: 4,500 **Seats:** 450   **Covered:** 650   **Midweek Matchday:** Tuesday   **Clubhouse:** Yes   **Shop:** Yes

Colours(change): Red, white & green/red/white
Previous Names: Formed when Windsor Phoenix and Windsor St. Albans merged in 1892. Windsor & Eton 1892-2011.
Previous Leagues: W.Berks, Gt Western, Suburban, Athenian 22-29,63-81, Spartan 29-32, Gt W.Comb. Corinthian 45-50, Met 50-60, Delphian 60-63, Isthmian 1963-2006, Stouthern 2006-11. Combined Counties 2011-17.
HONOURS: FA Comps: None
League: Athenian League 1979-80, 80-81. Isthmian League Division 1 1983-84.
Southern League Division 1 South & West 2009-10.

10 YEAR RECORD									
07-08	08-09	09-10	10-11	11-12	12-13	13-14	14-15	15-16	16-17
Sthsw 8	Sthsw 2	Sthsw 3	SthP Exp	CCP 2	CCP 6	CCP 6	CCP 5	CCP 12	CCP 11
FAC 2Qr	FAC P	FAC 2Q	FAC 1Q		FAC 1Q	FAC P	FAC P	FAC EP	FAC EP
FAT 3Q	FAT 3Q	FAT 1Qr	FAT 2Q	FAV 2Q	FAV 1P	FAV 1P	FAV 1P	FAV 1P	FAV 1Q

WOODLEY UNITED

Founded: 1904   Nickname: Woods or United

Secretary: John Mailer   **(T)** 07883 341 628   **(E)** john.mailer@hotmail.co.uk
Chairman: Colum Moon   **Manager:** Michael Herbert   **Prog Ed:** Mark Beaven
Ground: Rivermoor Stadium, Scours Lane, Reading, Berkshire, RG30 6AY   **(T)** 0118 9453 555
Capacity: 2,000 **Seats:** Yes   **Covered:** Yes   **Midweek Matchday:** Tuesday   **Clubhouse:** Yes

Colours(change): Sky blue/grey/sky blue
Previous Names: Formed when Woodley Hammers and Woodley Town merged in 2015.
Previous Leagues: Wargrave & District. Reading & District. Reading

HONOURS: FA Comps: None
League: Wargrave & District 1909-10, 26-27. Reading & District Division Three 28-29, Division One 32-33, Division Two 50-51, Premier 57-58, 58-59, 85-86. Reading Division Four Kennet 91-92, Division Three Kennet 92-93, Senior Division 2008-09.

10 YEAR RECORD									
07-08	08-09	09-10	10-11	11-12	12-13	13-14	14-15	15-16	16-17
ReadS 5	ReadS 1	Hel1E 4	Hel1E 5	Hel1E 5	Hel1E 3	Hel1E 14	Hel1E 8	Hel1E 13	Hel1E 2
							FAV 2Q	FAV 1Q	FAV 1Q

AFC ALDERMASTON

Founded: 1952   Nickname: The Atomics

Secretary: Damion Bone   **(T)** 07768 031 842   **(E)** damionbone@hotmail.com
Chairman: Martin Desay   **Manager:** Kieron Jennings   **Prog Ed:** Matt Desay
Ground: AWE, Aldermaston, Reading RG7 8UA   **(T)** 01189 824 454
Colours(change): Red & black stripes (Blue & black stripes)
HONOURS: FA Comps: None   **League:** None

10 YEAR RECORD

07-08	08-09	09-10	10-11	11-12	12-13	13-14	14-15	15-16	16-17
Wex1 21	Wex1 14	Wex1 21	HantP 15	HantP 9	HantP 8	HantP 10	ReadP 5	ReadP 7	Hel1E 7

BICESTER TOWN

Founded: 1876   Nickname: Foxhunters

Secretary: David Powell   **(T)** 07827 306 010   **(E)** david_powell_128@msn.com
Chairman: Tim Holloway   **Manager:** John Prpa   **Prog Ed:** Steve Marriott
Ground: Ardley United FC, The Playing Fields Fritwell Road Ardley OX27 7PA   **(T)** 07711 009198
Colours(change): Red & black/black/red
HONOURS: FA Comps: None   **League:** Hellenic 1960-61, 79-80, Division One 1977-78.

10 YEAR RECORD

07-08	08-09	09-10	10-11	11-12	12-13	13-14	14-15	15-16	16-17
Hel P 16	Hel P 20	Hel P 21	Hel1W 2					Hel1E 2	Hel1E 5
		FAC EP	FAC EP						
FAV 1P	FAV 1Q	FAV 2Q	FAV 1Q						FAV 2Q

CHALFONT WASPS

Founded: 1922   Nickname: The Stingers

Secretary: Bob Cakebread   **(T)** 07895 094 579   **(E)** robert.cakebread@btinternet.com
Chairman: Steve Waddington   **Manager:** Gareth Williams   **Prog Ed:** Alan Yeomans
Ground: Crossleys, Bowsridge Lane Chalfont, St Giles HP8 4QN   **(T)** 01494 875 050
Colours(change): Yellow and black/black/black
HONOURS: FA Comps: None   **League:** Wycombe Combination Division One 1930-31, 60-61, Division Two 1948-49, Premier 1964-64. Hellenic Division One East 2007-08.

10 YEAR RECORD

07-08	08-09	09-10	10-11	11-12	12-13	13-14	14-15	15-16	16-17
Hel1E 1	Hel P 7	Hel1E 9	Hel1E 6	Hel1E 4	Hel1E 9	Hel1E 6	Hel1E 14	Hel1E 9	Hel1E 6
	FAV 2Q								

CHINNOR

Founded: 1971   Nickname: The Biz

Secretary: Andy Bennett   **(T)** 07951 215 659   **(E)** andy@fslaerospace.co.uk
Chairman: Andy Bennett   **Manager:** James Tovey   **Prog Ed:** Cathy Searl
Ground: Station Road, Chinnor, Oxon OX39 4PX   **(T)** 01844 352 579
Colours(change): Yellow/black/yellow
HONOURS: FA Comps: None   **League:** None

10 YEAR RECORD

07-08	08-09	09-10	10-11	11-12	12-13	13-14	14-15	15-16	16-17
Hel1E 15	Hel1E 8	Hel1E 10	Hel1E 13	Hel1E 10	Hel1E 6	Hel1E 8	Hel1E 5	Hel1E 6	Hel1E 10
						FAC EP		FAC EP	
					FAV 2Q	FAV 2Q	FAV 1P	FAV 1Q	

DIDCOT TOWN RESERVES

Founded: 1907   Nickname: Railwaymen

Secretary: Jacquelyn Chalk   **(T)** 07535 313 940   **(E)** jacquelyn-dtfc@virginmedia.com
Chairman: John Bailey   **Manager:** Chris Hurley   **Prog Ed:** Jacquelyn Chalk
Ground: Loop Meadow Stadium, Bowmont Water, Didcot OX11 7GA   **(T)** 01235 813 138   **Capacity:** 5,000
Colours(change): All red
HONOURS: FA Comps: None   **League:** None

10 YEAR RECORD

07-08	08-09	09-10	10-11	11-12	12-13	13-14	14-15	15-16	16-17
		Hel1E 15	Hel1E 14	Hel1E 16	Hel1E 3	Hel1E 12	Hel1E 12	Hel1E 11	Hel1E 9

HENLEY TOWN

Founded: 1871 | Nickname: Red Kites

Secretary: Lawrence Tindell | **(T)** 07706 136 798 | **(E)** Theredkites.henleytown.f.c@hotmail.com
Chairman: John Hooper | **Manager:** Jock Mowat | **Prog Ed:** Tony Kingston
Ground: The Triangle Ground, Mill Lane, Henley RG9 4HB | **(T)** 07758 376 369
Colours(change): Red & black/red/red

HONOURS: FA Comps: None | **League:** Reading Temp Div.1 1912-13. Wycombe & Dist. 78-79. Spartan Div.1 36-37. Hellenic Div.1 63-64, 67-68, Div.1 East 2000-01. Chiltonian Div.1 87-88, Prem 99-00.

10 YEAR RECORD

07-08	08-09	09-10	10-11	11-12	12-13	13-14	14-15	15-16	16-17
Hel1E 6	Hel1E 7	Hel1E 5	Hel1E 2	Hel P 7	Hel1E 15	Hel1E 7	Hel1E 6	Hel1E 3	Hel P 18
FAC 1Q	FAC EP								FAC EP
FAV 1P	FAV 2Q	FAV 1Q		FAV 1P	FAV 1Q		FAV 2Q	FAV 2Q	FAV 2Q

HOLYPORT

Founded: 1934 | Nickname: The Villagers

Secretary: Richard Tyrell (Acting) | **(T)** 07515 789 415 | **(E)** richardtyrell@googlemail.com
Chairman: Tony Andrews | **Prog Ed:** Richard Tyrell
Ground: Summerleaze Village SL6 8SP | **(T)** 07515 789 415
Colours(change): Claret/green/claret

HONOURS: FA Comps: None | **League:** Hayes & Giles Premier Division 1998-99, 99-2000, 01-02. Hellenic Division One East 2010-11.

10 YEAR RECORD

07-08	08-09	09-10	10-11	11-12	12-13	13-14	14-15	15-16	16-17
Hel1E 7	Hel1E 5	Hel1E 3	Hel1E 1	Hel P 13	Hel P 14	Hel P 18	Hel P 16	Hel1E 7	Hel1E 13
			FAC EP	FAC EP	FAC EP	FAC EP	FAC EP	FAC EP	
	FAV 2Q	FAV 2Q	FAV 2P	FAV 1Q	FAV 1P	FAV 2Q	FAV 1Q	FAV 1Qr	FAV 1Q

MILTON UNITED

Founded: 1909 | Nickname: Miltonians

Secretary: Lee Chapple | **(T)** 07845 961 276 | **(E)** milton.united.fc@hotmail.co.uk
Chairman: Andy Burchette | **Manager:** Tim Davies | **Prog Ed:** AM Print & Copy
Ground: Potash Lane, Milton Heights, OX13 6AG | **(T)** 01235 832 999
Colours(change): Claret/sky blue/claret

HONOURS: FA Comps: None | **League:** Hellenic 1990-91, Division One East 2013-14.

10 YEAR RECORD

07-08	08-09	09-10	10-11	11-12	12-13	13-14	14-15	15-16	16-17
Hel P 7	Hel P 21	Hel1E 7	Hel1E 4	Hel1E 14	Hel1E 14	Hel1E 1	Hel P 14	Hel P 18	Hel1W 12
FAC EPr	FAC EP	FAC P	FAC EP	FAC EP			FAC 1Q	FAC P	FAC EP
FAV 2Q	FAV 2Qr	FAV 2Q	FAV 1Q	FAV 2Q	FAV 2Q	FAV 1P	FAV 2Q	FAV 2Q	FAV 2Q

PENN & TYLERS GREEN

Founded: 1905 | Nickname: Penn

Secretary: Andrea Latta | **(T)** 07904 538 868 | **(E)** hsvlatta1955@yahoo.co.uk
Chairman: Tony Hurst | **Manager:** Giovanni Sepede | **Prog Ed:** James Keating
Ground: French School Meadows, Elm Road, Penn, Bucks HP10 8LF | **(T)** 01494 815 346
Colours(change): Blue & white stripes/blue/blue

HONOURS: FA Comps: None | **League:** Wycombe Comb. Div.A 1911-12, Div.2 35-36, 56,57, 60-61, North 39-40, Div.1 46-47, Div.3 55-56, Prem 62-63. Wycombe & Dist Sen 83-84. Hellenic D1E 2015-16, 16-17

10 YEAR RECORD

07-08	08-09	09-10	10-11	11-12	12-13	13-14	14-15	15-16	16-17
Hel1E 11	Hel1E 12	Hel1E 17	Hel1E 10	Hel1E 12	Hel1E 4	Hel1E 5	Hel1E 9	Hel1E 1	Hel1E 1

SANDHURST TOWN

Founded: 1910 | Nickname: Fizzers

Secretary: Anne Brummer | **(T)** 07760 881189 | **(E)** secretarystfc@hotmail.co.uk
Chairman: Tony Dean | **Manager:** Luke Turkington | **Prog Ed:** Lee Pollard
Ground: Bottom Meadow, Memorial Ground, Yorktown Rd, GU47 9BJ | **(T)** 01252 878 460 | **Capacity:** 1000
Colours(change): Red/black/black.

HONOURS: FA Comps: None | **League:** Reading & Disttrict Division One 1932-33, Premier 33-34. Aldershot & District Division One 1980-81.

10 YEAR RECORD

07-08	08-09	09-10	10-11	11-12	12-13	13-14	14-15	15-16	16-17
CCP 16	CCP 16	CCP 9	CCP 7	CCP 15	CCP 21	CC1 13	CC1 16	CC1 11	Hel1E 8
FAC 1Q	FAC EP	FAC EPr	FAC EP	FAC EP	FAC EP	FAC EPr			
FAV 1P	FAV 2P	FAV 1Q	FAV 2Q	FAV 1Q	FAV 1P	FAV 1Q			FAV 1Q

DIVISION ONE WEST

THAME RANGERS
Founded: Nickname: None
Secretary: Richard Carr   **(T)** 07786 115 089   **(E)** rjcarr5@btinternet.com
Chairman: Richard Carr   **Manager:** Craig Faulconbridge   **Prog Ed:** Jake Collinge
Ground: Meadow View Park, Tythrop Way, Thame OX9 3RN   **(T)** 01844 214 401
Colours(change): Red & black/black/red
HONOURS: FA Comps: None   **League:** Wycombe & District Senior Division 2015-16. Spartan South Midlands Division Two 2016-17.

10 YEAR RECORD

07-08	08-09	09-10	10-11	11-12	12-13	13-14	14-15	15-16	16-17
								WyDS 1	SSM2 1

VIRGINIA WATER
Founded: 1920   Nickname: The Waters
Secretary: Graham Poulter   **(T)** 07720 557 675   **(E)** gp738@hotmail.com
Chairman: Dave McBride   **Manager:** Ceri Jones   **Prog Ed:** Dave McBride
Ground: Windsor FC, Stag Meadow, St Leonards Road Windsor SL4 3DR   **(T)** 01753 860 656
Colours(change): Red/black/black
HONOURS: FA Comps: None   **League:** Surrey County Premier Division 1992-93, 96-97. Surrey Elite Intermediate 2016-17.

10 YEAR RECORD

07-08	08-09	09-10	10-11	11-12	12-13	13-14	14-15	15-16	16-17
			SuEI 6	SuEI 14	SuEI 11	SuEI 8	SuEI 7	SuEI 5	SuEI 1

WALLINGFORD TOWN
Founded: 1995   Nickname: Wally
Secretary: Steve Sherwood   **(T)** 07876 805 679   **(E)** stevesherwood@hotmail.co.uk
Chairman: Simon Cowlard   **Manager:** Duncan Mitchell   **Prog Ed:** Arthur Morris
Ground: Wallingford Sports Park, Hithercroft Road, Wallingford OX10 9RB   **(T)** 01491 835 044   **Capacity:** 1,500
Colours(change): Red & white/black/red
HONOURS: FA Comps: None   **League:** None

10 YEAR RECORD

	07-08	08-09	09-10	10-11	11-12	12-13	13-14	14-15	15-16	16-17
Hel P	22	NBk 1 10	NBk 1 5	NBk 1 4	NBk 1 11	NBk 1 9	NBk 1 9	NBk 1 4	NBk 1 6	NBk 1 3
FAC	EP									
FAV	1Q	FAV 2Q	FAV 1Q	FAV 1P	FAV 1Q					

WOKINGHAM & EMMBROOK
Founded: 2004   Nickname: Satsumas
Secretary: Bob Good   **(T)** 07970 846 868   **(E)** secretary@wokinghamandemmbrookfcyouth.com
Chairman: Steve Williams   **Manager:** Dan Bateman   **Prog Ed:** Steve Williams
Ground: Lowther Road Wokingham RG41 1JB   **(T)** 01189 780 209
Colours(change): Orange/black/black.
HONOURS: FA Comps: None   **League:** Hellenic Division One East 2014-15.

10 YEAR RECORD

07-08	08-09	09-10	10-11	11-12	12-13	13-14	14-15	15-16	16-17
Hel1E 12	Hel1E 4	Hel1E 2	Hel P 11	Hel P 10	Hel P 8	Hel1E 2	Hel1E 1	Hel P 20	Hel1E 12
				FAC 1Q	FAC EP				
			FAV 2Q	FAV 2Q	FAV 1P			FAV 1P	

ARDLEY UNITED
Founded: 1945   Nickname: None
Secretary: Norman Stacey   **(T)** 07711 009 198   **(E)** ardleyfc@gmail.com
Chairman: Ian Feaver   **Manager:** Craig Adey   **Prog Ed:** Peter Sawyer
Ground: The Playing Fields, Fritwell Road, Ardley OX27 7PA   **(T)** 07711 009 198   **Capacity:** 1,000
Colours(change): All sky blue
HONOURS: FA Comps: None   **League:** Banbury District & Lord Jersey FA Divion One 1984-85. Oxfordshire Senior Division One 1988-89, Premier 1990-91. Hellenic Division One 1996-97, 97-98.

10 YEAR RECORD

07-08	08-09	09-10	10-11	11-12	12-13	13-14	14-15	15-16	16-17
Hel P 13	Hel P 5	Hel P 7	Hel P 3	Hel P 3	Hel P 5	Hel P 2	Hel P 8	Hel P 13	Hel P 5
FAC EP	FAC EP	FAC EPr	FAC EP	FAC EP	FAC Pr	FAC P	FAC 1Qr	FAC 2Q	FAC EP	FAC P
FAV 2P	FAV 2Q	FAV 1P	FAV 2Q	FAV 1P	FAV 3P	FAV 1Q	FAV 1P	FAV 1Q	FAV 2Q

CHELTENHAM SARACENS
Founded: 1964 Nickname: Sara's

Secretary: Daniel Organ **(T)** 07443 594 983 **(E)** dannyorg@blueyonder.co.uk
Chairman: Graham Roberts **Manager:** Ryan Betteridge **Prog Ed:** Graham Roberts
Ground: Petersfield Park, Tewkesbury Road GL51 9DY **(T)** 01242 584 134
Colours(change): Yellow/blue/yellow
HONOURS: FA Comps: None **League:** Hellenic Division One 1999-2000.

10 YEAR RECORD

07-08	08-09	09-10	10-11	11-12	12-13	13-14	14-15	15-16	16-17
Hel1W 5	Hel1W 12	Hel1W 4	Hel1W 3	Hel P 15	Hel P 11	Hel P 16	Hel P 20	Hel1W 2	Hel1W 14
						FAC Pr	FAC P	FAC 1Q	
	FAV 1Q	FAV 2Q	FAV 1Q	FAV 1Q	FAV 1P	FAV 1Q	FAV 1Q	FAV 1Q	

CIRENCESTER TOWN DEV.
Founded: 2011 Nickname: Centurions

Secretary: Scott Griffin **(T)** 07968 338 106 **(E)** scott.griffin@cirentownfc.plus.com
Chairman: Steve Abbley **Manager:** Alan Lloyd **Prog Ed:** Mark O'Brien
Ground: Corinium Stadium, Kingshill Lane, Cirencester Glos GL7 1HS **(T)** 01285 654 543
Colours(change): Red & black/black/red.
HONOURS: FA Comps: None **League:** None

10 YEAR RECORD

07-08	08-09	09-10	10-11	11-12	12-13	13-14	14-15	15-16	16-17
					Hel2W 3	Hel2W 3	Hel1W 4	Hel1W 11	Hel1W 5

CLANFIELD 85
Founded: 1890 Nickname: Robins

Secretary: Mick Cross **(T)** 07758 808 597 **(E)** jolimetz@ntlworld.com
Chairman: Peter Osborne **Manager:** Peter Osborne **Prog Ed:** Trevor Cuss
Ground: Radcot Road, Clanfield OX18 2ST **(T)** 01367 810 314
Colours(change): All red
HONOURS: FA Comps: None **League:** North Berks Division Two 1924-25.
Hellenic Division One 1969-70.

10 YEAR RECORD

07-08	08-09	09-10	10-11	11-12	12-13	13-14	14-15	15-16	16-17
Hel1W 12	Hel1W 11	Hel1W 10	Hel1W 4	Hel1W 8	Hel1W 11	Hel1W 5	Hel1W 9	Hel1W 12	Hel1W 10
			FAC EP	FAC EP					
FAV 1Q	FAV 2P	FAV 1Qr	FAV 2P	FAT 1P	FAV 1Q				

EASINGTON SPORTS
Founded: 1946 Nickname: The Clan

Secretary: Jamie Hunter **(T)** 07791 681 204 **(E)** jamiehunter@hotmail.co.uk
Chairman: Richard Meadows **Manager:** Darren Beckett **Prog Ed:** Ang Clives
Ground: Addison Road, Banbury OX16 9DH **(T)** 01295 257 006
Colours(change): Red & white stripes/black/red (Yellow & black stripes/black/black)
HONOURS: FA Comps: None **League:** Oxfordshire Senior Premier Division 1957-58, 58-59, Division One 1965-66.

10 YEAR RECORD

07-08	08-09	09-10	10-11	11-12	12-13	13-14	14-15	15-16	16-17
Hel1W 6	Hel1W 13	Hel1W 6	Hel1W 11	Hel1W 6	Hel1W 8	Hel1W 9	Hel1W 4	Hel1W 5	Hel1W 4

HEADINGTON AMATEURS
Founded: 1949 Nickname: A's

Secretary: Donald Light **(T)** 07764 943 778 **(E)** donlight7@gmail.com
Chairman: Donald Light **Manager:** Stuart Bishop **Prog Ed:** Donald Light
Ground: Horspath Sports Ground, Oxford Rd, Horspath, Oxford OX4 2RR **(T)** 07764 943 778
Colours(change): All red
HONOURS: FA Comps: None **League:** Oxfordshire Senior 1972-73, 73-74, 75-76, 76-77, Division One 1968-69.
Hellenic Division One West 2010-11.

10 YEAR RECORD

07-08	08-09	09-10	10-11	11-12	12-13	13-14	14-15	15-16	16-17
Hel1E 10	Hel1W 14	Hel1W 3	Hel1W 1	Hel1W 14	Hel1E 2	Hel1E 4	Hel1E 11	Hel1E 4	Hel1E 3

KIDLINGTON RESERVES
Founded: 1909   Nickname: Greens

Secretary: Barry Hiles   **(T)** 07850 403 026   **(E)** barry.hiles@btinternet.com
Chairman: David Platt   **Manager:** Nick East   **Prog Ed:** Dave Morris
Ground: Yarnton Road, Kidlington, Oxford OX5 1AT   **(T)** 01865 849 777   **Capacity:** 1,500
Colours(change): All green
HONOURS: FA Comps: None   **League:** None

10 YEAR RECORD

07-08	08-09	09-10	10-11	11-12	12-13	13-14	14-15	15-16	16-17

LETCOMBE
Founded: 1910   Nickname: Brooksiders

Secretary: Des Williams   **(T)** 07765 144 985   **(E)** deswilliams45@btinternet.com
Chairman: Dennis Stock   **Manager:** Garry Cook   **Prog Ed:** Russell Stock
Ground: Bassett Road, Letcombe Regis OX12 9JU   **(T)** 07765 144 985
Colours(change): Purple/white/purple
HONOURS: FA Comps: None   **League:** North Berkshire Division One 1912-13 (shared), 89-90.
Chiltonian Division One 1990-91.

10 YEAR RECORD

07-08	08-09	09-10	10-11	11-12	12-13	13-14	14-15	15-16	16-17
Hel1W 3	Hel1W 5	Hel1W 7	Hel1W 9	Hel1W 13	Hel1W 16	Hel1W 15	Hel1W 13	Hel1W 9	Hel1W 11

NEW COLLEGE ACADEMY
Founded: 1984   Nickname: Blue College

Secretary: Matt Cosnett   **(T)** 07846 204 174   **(E)** newcollegeswinfcsec@yahoo.co.uk
Chairman: Ian Howell   **Manager:** Mark Teasedale   **Prog Ed:** Matt Cosnett
Ground: Supermarine S&S Club, Supermarine Drive, Swindon SN3 4BZ   **(T)** 01793 824 828
Colours(change): All royal blue
HONOURS: FA Comps: None   **League:** Wiltshire Premier Division 2008-09, 09-10.

10 YEAR RECORD

07-08	08-09	09-10	10-11	11-12	12-13	13-14	14-15	15-16	16-17
	Wilt 1	Wilt 1	Wilt 3	Hel1W 11	Hel1W 14	Hel1W 11	Hel1W 12	Hel1W 13	Hel1W 13
						FAV 2Q	FAV 2Q	FAV 1Q	FAV 2Q

NORTH LEIGH DEVELOPMENT
Founded: 1908   Nickname: The Millers

Secretary: Keith Huxley   **(T)** 07775 818 066   **(E)** huxley893@btinternet.com
Chairman: Peter King   **Manager:** Paul Lewis & Malcolm McIntosh   **Prog Ed:** Alan Blackwell
Ground: Eynsham Hall Park Sports Ground OX29 6SL.   **(T)** 01993 880 157   **Capacity:** 2,000
Colours(change): Yellow & black/black/yellow
HONOURS: FA Comps: None   **League:** None

10 YEAR RECORD

07-08	08-09	09-10	10-11	11-12	12-13	13-14	14-15	15-16	16-17
HelR1 5	HelR1 1	Hel1W 12			Hel1W 12	Hel1W 8	Hel1W 7	Hel1W 6	Hel1W 8

PEWSEY VALE
Founded: 1948   Nickname: Vale

Secretary: Julie Wootton   **(T)** 07789 198 303   **(E)** pewseyvalefc@hotmail.co.uk
Chairman: Craig Wall   **Manager:** Alistair Tuttle   **Prog Ed:** Craig Wall
Ground: Recreation Ground, Kings Corner Ball Road, Pewsey SN9 5BS   **(T)** 01672 5629 090
Colours(change): White/navy/navy
HONOURS: FA Comps: None   **League:** Wiltshire Division One 1989-90, 92-93.

10 YEAR RECORD

07-08	08-09	09-10	10-11	11-12	12-13	13-14	14-15	15-16	16-17
Hel1W 7	Hel1W 17	Wilt 3	Wex1 4	Wex1 11	Wex1 5	Wex1 8	Wex1 10	Wex1 17	Wex1 21
				FAC EP	FAC P	FAC EP	FAC EP		
FAV 2Q	FAV 1Q	FAV 2Q	FAV 1Q	FAV 2Qr	FAV 1Q	FAV 1Q	FAV 1Q	FAV 1Q	

SHORTWOOD UNITED RESERVES

Founded: 1900　　　Nickname: The Woods

Secretary: Mark Webb　　**(T)** 07792 323 784　　　**(E)** squish.shortwoodfc@live.co.uk
Chairman: William Reay　　**Manager:** Nick Ackland　　　**Prog Ed:** Paul Webb
Ground: Meadowbank, Shortwood, Nailsworth GL6 0SJ　　**(T)** 01453 833 936
Colours(change): Red & white/black/black
HONOURS: FA Comps: None　　**League:** Gloucestershire Northern Senior Division One 2011-12.
Hellenic Division Two West 2012-13.

10 YEAR RECORD

07-08		08-09		09-10		10-11		11-12		12-13		13-14		14-15		15-16		16-17	
GIN1	9	GIN1	10	GIN1	9	GIN1	3	GIN1	1	Hel2W	1	Hel1W	3	Hel1W	8	Hel1W	10	Hel1W	9

SHRIVENHAM

Founded: 1900　　　Nickname: Shrivy

Secretary: Chris Rawle　　**(T)** 07754 726 264　　　**(E)** chrisrawle11@aol.com
Chairman: Matt Hirst　　**Manager:** Michael McNally　　　**Prog Ed:** Matt Hirst
Ground: The Recreation Ground, Barrington Park, Shrivenham SN6 8BJ　　**(T)** 07775 933 076
Colours(change): Blue & white/blue/blue.
HONOURS: FA Comps: None　　**League:** North Berks Division Two 1994-95, Division One 1997-98, 2000-01.
Hellenic Division One West 2004-05.

10 YEAR RECORD

07-08		08-09		09-10		10-11		11-12		12-13		13-14		14-15		15-16		16-17	
Hel P	8	Hel P	18	Hel P	16	Hel P	20	Hel P	16	Hel P	19	Hel P	15	Hel P	19	Hel1W	8	Hel1W	7
FAC	EPr	FAC	EP	FAC	1Q	FAC	EP	FAC	EP	FAC	P	FAC	EP	FAC	P	FAC	EP		
FAV	4P	FAT	2Pr	FAT	1P	FAT	1P	FAV	2Q	FAV	2Q	FAV	2Q	FAV	1Q	FAV	2Q	FAV	1Q

TYTHERINGTON ROCKS

Founded: 1896　　　Nickname: The Rocks

Secretary: Ted Travell　　**(T)** 01454 412 606　　　**(E)** tramar1618@btinternet.com
Chairman: Ted Travell　　　**Prog Ed:** Mark Brown
Ground: Hardwicke Playing Field, Woodlands Road, Tytherington Glos GL12 8UJ　　**(T)** 07837 555 776
Colours(change): Amber & black/black/black
HONOURS: FA Comps: None　　**League:** Iron Acton & District 1944-45. Bristol & Suburban Div.3 1949-50, Prem Div.2 93-94,
Prem Div.1 96-97, Prem Div.1 97-98. Hellenic Div.1W 2011-12, 13-14.

10 YEAR RECORD

07-08		08-09		09-10		10-11		11-12		12-13		13-14		14-15		15-16		16-17	
Hel1W	8	Hel1W	9	Hel1W	11	Hel1W	8	Hel1W	1	Hel1W	3	Hel1W	1	Hel1W	15	Hel1W	14	Hel1W	15
																FAV	2Qr	FAV	1Q

WOODSTOCK TOWN

Founded: 1998　　　Nickname:

Secretary: Ian Whelan　　**(T)** 07827 894 869　　　**(E)** ian.whelan@lucyelectric.com
Chairman: James Newton　　**Manager:** Matt Pike　　　**Prog Ed:** AM Print & Copy
Ground: New Road, Woodstock OX20 1PD　　**(T)** 07748 1522 246　　**Capacity:** 1,000
Colours(change): All red
HONOURS: FA Comps: None　　**League:** Oxfordshire Senior 1998-99.

10 YEAR RECORD

07-08		08-09		09-10		10-11		11-12		12-13		13-14		14-15		15-16		16-17	
Hel1W	2	Hel P	17	Hel P	13	Hel P	9	Hel1W	2	Hel1W	6	Hel1W	14	Hel1E	3	Hel1E	12	Hel1W	16
				FAV	2Q	FAC	2Q	FAC	EP	FAC	EP								
						FAV	2Q	FAV	4P	FAV	2P								

Highworth Town 2016-17 - 6th in Hellenic Premier. Photo: Roger Turner.

DIVISION TWO EAST	P	W	D	L	F	A	GD	Pts
1 Chalvey Sports	22	19	2	1	77	13	64	59
2 Flackwell Heath Res	22	16	1	5	77	34	43	49
3 Oxford City Dev'	22	13	4	5	69	38	31	43
4 Milton Keynes Academy	22	12	4	6	69	38	31	40
5 Lynch Pin	22	12	3	7	60	54	6	39
6 Penn & Tylers Green Res	22	9	4	9	45	36	9	28*
7 Chalfont Wasps Res	22	8	4	10	37	55	-18	28
8 Sandhurst Town Res	22	8	2	12	45	57	-12	26
9 Stokenchurch	22	7	2	13	44	83	-39	23
10 Thame United Res	22	6	2	14	31	45	-14	20
11 Wokingham & Emmbrook Res	22	3	2	17	23	69	-46	11
12 Aston Clinton Dev	22	3	2	17	22	77	-55	11.

DIVISION TWO WEST	P	W	D	L	F	A	GD	Pts
1 Bourton Rovers	22	16	1	5	72	29	43	49
2 Kidlington Res	22	15	2	5	63	27	36	47
3 Highworth Town Res	22	15	1	6	48	28	20	46
4 Abingdon United Res	22	14	1	7	59	28	31	43
5 Moreton Rangers	22	13	2	7	53	28	25	41
6 Oxford City Nomads Dev'	22	10	1	11	68	61	7	31
7 Fairford Town Res'	22	9	3	10	41	39	2	30
8 Faringdon Town	22	7	3	12	34	65	-31	24
9 Brimscombe & Thrupp Res	22	5	8	9	47	47	0	23
10 Easington Sports Res	22	6	4	12	29	59	-30	22
11 Hook Norton Res	22	5	1	16	21	70	-49	16
12 Shrivenham Res	22	2	3	17	23	77	-54	9

MIDLAND FOOTBALL LEAGUE

Founded: 2014 After the merger of the Midland Football Alliance (1994) and the Midland Football Combination (1927)
Recent Champions: 2015: Basford United **2016:** Hereford

PREMIER DIVISION	P	W	D	L	F	A	GD	Pts
1 Alvechurch	42	28	8	6	91	33	58	92
2 Coleshill Town	42	27	5	10	109	59	50	86
3 Sporting Khalsa	42	24	10	8	92	50	42	82
4 Lye Town	42	22	10	10	73	45	28	76
5 Westfields	42	20	10	12	98	75	23	70
6 Heanor Town	42	20	9	13	87	65	22	69
7 Highgate United	42	18	9	15	84	71	13	63
8 Coventry United	42	18	8	16	63	57	6	62
9 St Andrews	42	18	8	16	86	88	-2	62
10 Coventry Sphinx	42	16	9	17	78	79	-1	57
11 Quorn	42	16	9	17	58	74	-16	57
12 Boldmere St Michaels	42	15	10	17	73	63	10	55
13 Stourport Swifts	42	14	11	17	73	83	-10	53
14 Long Eaton United	42	15	8	19	74	87	-13	53
15 Shepshed Dynamo	42	14	10	18	65	68	-3	52
16 Rocester	42	13	13	16	71	86	-15	52
17 AFC Wulfrunians	42	14	8	20	55	72	-17	50
18 Loughborough University	42	11	15	16	67	66	1	48
19 Shawbury United	42	14	5	23	69	91	-22	47
20 Walsall Wood	42	14	5	23	57	86	-29	47
21 Brocton	42	10	4	28	50	112	-62	34
22 Tividale	42	6	6	30	48	111	-63	24

DIVISION TWO	P	W	D	L	F	A	GD	Pts
1 Droitwich Spa	30	20	5	5	80	31	49	65
2 Paget Rangers	30	20	4	6	93	40	53	64
3 Alvis Sporting Club	30	19	6	5	59	29	30	63
4 Redditch Borough	30	20	4	6	87	30	57	61*
5 Fairfield Villa	30	17	4	9	75	51	24	55
6 Knowle	30	13	8	9	60	41	19	47
7 Coton Green	30	13	8	9	56	44	12	47
8 Sutton United	30	12	5	13	62	72	-10	40*
9 Earlswood Town	30	11	5	14	49	53	-4	38
10 Feckenham	30	9	8	13	45	64	-19	35
11 Smithswood Firs	30	8	9	13	63	70	-7	33
12 Barnt Green Spartak	30	9	3	18	45	80	-35	30
13 Bloxwich Town	30	8	6	16	32	67	-35	30
14 Hampton	30	6	5	19	33	77	-44	23
15 Leamington Hibernian	30	6	4	20	38	79	-41	22
16 Continental Star	30	3	8	19	32	81	-49	17

DIVISION THREE	P	W	D	L	F	A	GD	Pts
1 NKF Burbage	26	22	4	0	76	14	62	70
2 Montpellier	26	19	4	3	88	34	54	61
3 Moors Academy	25	17	3	5	68	38	30	54
4 Northfield Town	26	17	3	6	69	36	33	54
5 Shipston Excelsior	26	12	5	9	52	53	-1	41
6 FC Stratford	26	11	3	12	64	47	17	36
7 Alcester Town	26	10	5	11	34	32	2	35
8 Inkberrow	26	9	5	12	45	57	-12	32
9 Coventrians	26	9	3	14	50	72	-22	30
10 Barton United	25	7	7	11	43	41	2	28
11 Enville Athletic	26	8	2	16	23	50	-27	26
12 AFC Solihull	26	5	3	18	30	73	-43	18
13 Boldmere Sports & Social Falcons	26	4	5	17	23	63	-40	17
14 Castle Vale Town	26	3	4	19	34	89	-55	13

DIVISION ONE	P	W	D	L	F	A	GD	Pts
1 Bromsgrove Sporting	38	33	5	0	132	23	109	104
2 Hinckley AFC	38	27	4	7	133	47	86	85
3 Leicester Road	38	25	4	9	117	36	81	79
4 Atherstone Town	38	24	5	9	99	58	41	77
5 Cadbury Athletic	38	19	13	6	78	45	33	70
6 Racing Club Warwick	38	19	9	10	92	72	20	66
7 Lichfield City	38	17	7	14	66	61	5	58
8 Heather St Johns	38	17	4	17	67	69	-2	55
9 Littleton	38	16	4	18	64	64	0	52
10 Nuneaton Griff	38	15	6	17	71	76	-5	51
11 Uttoxeter Town	38	14	7	17	68	82	-14	49
12 Coventry Copsewood	38	14	5	19	74	90	-16	47
13 Bolehall Swifts	38	15	1	22	80	97	-17	46
14 Heath Hayes	38	12	8	18	67	69	-2	44
15 Studley	38	12	5	21	69	97	-28	41
16 Stafford Town	38	10	9	19	69	79	-10	39
17 Chelmsley Town	38	10	8	20	62	81	-19	38
18 Pershore Town	38	10	8	20	48	81	-33	38
19 Pelsall Villa	38	9	7	22	53	99	-46	34
20 Southam United	38	0	5	33	12	195	-183	5

LEAGUE CUP

HOLDERS: HEREFORD
ROUND 1

Bromsgrove Sporting	v	Sporting Khalsa	0-3
Littleton	v	Studley	9-1
Pershore Town	v	Southam United	3-2
Racing Club Warick	v	Cadbury Athletic	1-3
St Andrews	v	Coventry United	2-1
Shepshed Dynamo	v	Heather St Johns	0-2
Coventry Sphinx	v	Coleshill Town	0-5
Atherstone Town	v	Bolehall Swifts	0-1
Heanor Town	v	Stafford Town	3-2 aet
Brocton	v	Uttoxeter Town	1-0 aet

ROUND 2

Alvechurch	v	Westfields	1-0
Lye Town	v	Heath Hayes	3-1
Sporting Khalsa	v	Pelsall Villa	1-2
Chelmsley Town	v	Littleton	2-1
AFC Wulfrunians	v	Shawbury United	5-1
Tividale	v	Walsall Wood	0-3
Stourport Swifts	v	Highgate United	1-2
Pershore Town	v	Cadbury Athletic	3-3, 4-3p
Lichfield City	v	Long Eaton United	4-0
Coventry Copsewood	v	St Andrews	1-3
Heather St Johns	v	Leicester Road	1-2
Quorn	v	Loughborough University	1-2
Coleshill Town	v	Hinckley AFC	2-4 aet
Bolehall Swifts	v	Boldmere St Michaels	1-3
Rocester	v	Heanor Town	2-1
Nuneaton Griff	v	Brocton	2-5

ROUND 3

Alvechurch	v	Lye Town	1-0
Pelsall Villa	v	Chelmsley Town	2-2, 4-3p
AFC Wulfrunians	v	Walsall Wood	1-2
Highgate United	v	Pershore Town	10-0
Lichfield City	v	St Andrews	2-4
Leicester Road	v	Loughborough University	2-0
Hinckley AFC	v	Boldmere St Michaels	6-2
Rocester	v	Brocton	4-3

QUARTER FINALS

Alvechurch	v	Pelsall Villa	4-1
Walsall Wood	v	Highgate United	1-2
St Andrews	v	Leicester Road	4-1
Hinckley AFC	v	Rocester	6-1

SEMI FINALS (over 2 legs)

Alvechurch	v	Highgate United	0-1
Highgate United	v	Alvechurch	0-2
St Andrews	v	Hinckley AFC	4-3
Hinckley AFC	v	St Andrews	1-4

(St Andrews removed from the Cup having played an ineligible player in the Semi-finals)

FINAL

Alvechurch	v	Hinckley AFC	2-1

PREMIER DIVISION

#	Club	1	2	3	4	5	6	7	8	9	10	11	12	13	14	15	16	17	18	19	20	21	22
1	AFC Wulfrunians		0-2	2-0	2-3	0-0	1-4	4-1	2-0	2-2	4-3	3-2	0-1	0-2	2-2	1-0	0-1	1-3	0-4	0-3	0-0	1-0	2-1
2	Alvechurch	3-1		2-1	2-0	2-0	2-0	1-0	1-1	3-0	1-2	3-2	0-1	5-0	3-0	3-0	2-2	2-2	5-1	1-1	4-0	4-1	2-0
3	Boldmere St Michaels	1-0	3-0		5-1	4-2	1-1	4-3	0-2	0-4	1-0	2-2	2-3	1-2	1-2	3-0	0-0	2-0	8-0	1-3	3-0	1-2	1-5
4	Brocton	0-5	0-3	2-1		0-4	1-0	1-1	3-2	2-6	1-4	0-2	3-1	1-2	1-1	1-3	0-4	1-6	1-3	1-3	1-0	1-1	1-2
5	Coleshill Town	2-1	2-0	4-1	3-2		3-4	4-0	2-3	2-3	0-2	2-3	1-0	5-2	6-1	2-0	3-3	5-1	4-3	4-2	5-2	3-1	
6	Coventry Sphinx	3-0	0-2	0-0	8-0	1-1		1-2	1-0	1-1	4-1	2-1	1-1	2-3	4-4	3-1	2-1	0-5	0-5	1-3	1-1	4-0	2-3
7	Coventry United	0-1	0-1	0-2	4-1	1-3	1-0		2-1	1-3	3-1	0-0	1-2	2-0	2-0	2-0	1-0	2-2	2-4	5-0	5-1	2-0	1-1
8	Heanor Town	1-2	2-2	1-1	3-2	2-3	1-2	2-1		2-0	0-0	2-1	4-0	2-3	2-1	3-2	1-1	2-1	4-0	2-1	4-1	3-1	4-2
9	Highgate United	2-0	0-3	0-6	1-2	0-1	4-1	0-1	1-3		1-2	0-0	0-3	2-1	3-0	4-2	5-1	2-2	3-5	4-0	2-1	3-2	4-0
10	Long Eaton United	2-3	2-3	3-1	3-2	2-2	2-0	2-1	1-1	1-1		2-2	2-1	3-1	0-1	2-3	1-2	4-6	2-0	5-1	2-0	0-2	3-3
11	Loughborough University	3-3	0-2	1-1	2-4	2-4	4-1	1-3	2-4	1-0	3-1		3-3	0-1	1-1	1-1	2-1	0-1	1-3	1-0	4-2	1-1	1-1
12	Lye Town	2-0	1-2	1-1	3-1	0-1	5-0	0-0	1-1	1-2	4-0	1-0		3-0	0-0	4-0	3-0	0-1	1-0	2-0	2-1	2-0	2-1
13	Quorn	2-0	0-5	0-4	0-0	2-1	1-1	2-1	2-2	3-2	0-2	1-1	1-1		0-3	1-0	0-0	0-2	2-1	4-3	1-2	1-1	2-1
14	Rocester	0-0	0-3	3-0	5-4	0-4	1-4	1-0	3-2	1-2	2-1	1-3	1-3	3-2		2-2	1-2	2-2	4-4	0-0	4-1	3-2	2-4
15	Shawbury United	2-1	1-1	4-0	2-2	2-1	4-3	1-1	0-3	2-4	5-1	0-5	0-3	1-2	4-3		2-1	0-1	2-6	3-0	2-0	1-2	5-1
16	Shepshed Dynamo	5-1	0-1	3-1	3-0	1-3	2-3	2-2	3-2	1-1	2-2	1-2	2-2	3-3	2-1	2-1		1-0	1-1	1-2	3-0	1-0	4-5
17	Sporting Khalsa	1-0	0-1	2-2	4-0	1-1	4-2	0-1	2-1	1-1	5-0	2-1	3-0	3-2	5-3	1-0	3-2		2-0	5-1	3-0	0-2	1-1
18	St Andrews	1-2	1-1	2-2	1-0	2-1	1-0	0-2	4-3	0-0	5-1	4-3	1-1	2-1	0-0	4-1	2-0	0-2		3-6	1-4	5-2	0-4
19	Stourport Swifts	2-2	1-1	0-0	2-0	0-2	2-3	1-2	1-1	1-6	2-2	2-1	3-1	1-1	3-2	3-1	1-1	2-2			4-0	1-2	0-5
20	Tividale	3-1	1-4	0-3	1-3	1-5	1-3	0-2	1-4	2-2	2-4	1-1	0-2	3-2	2-2	2-1	1-2	2-3	2-4	1-5		0-2	2-2
21	Walsall Wood	3-5	2-1	0-2	3-1	1-2	1-3	1-1	1-3	1-4	1-0	1-1	1-3	0-3	4-0	2-5	1-0	2-1	2-1	1-0	1-3		3-4
22	Westfields	0-0	2-0	1-0	1-2	0-4	2-2	6-1	5-1	7-1	1-0	0-3	2-2	3-2	1-2	2-2	3-2	2-0	3-2	3-3	3-1	4-0	

DIVISION ONE

#	Club	1	2	3	4	5	6	7	8	9	10	11	12	13	14	15	16	17	18	19	20
1	Atherstone Town		1-0	0-4	1-3	4-1	5-0	2-1	0-1	3-0	1-1	1-1	0-5	5-0	4-1	1-0	3-1	3-2	4-1	1-2	0-3
2	Bolehall Swifts	1-2		0-8	4-3	4-2	1-2	4-0	5-2	3-7	0-8	1-2	1-2	2-4	0-4	3-1	1-2	7-0	4-2	1-2	0-3
3	Bromsgrove Sporting	2-2	3-0		3-2	3-2	5-2	2-1	5-0	1-0	5-0	2-0	4-2	10-0	5-0	3-1	1-0	1-1	1-1	2-0	2-1
4	Cadbury Athletic	1-1	3-0	1-1		2-2	2-0	2-0	2-2	0-3	0-2	2-1	3-2	1-1	1-1	3-0	2-0	6-0	3-0	2-2	4-0
5	Chelmsley Town	0-5	2-3	1-4	0-2		4-2	1-6	1-2	3-6	0-2	3-3	1-0	1-2	1-0	4-1	3-1	8-0	0-0	6-1	0-1
6	Coventry Copsewood	2-1	1-3	1-3	1-4	3-1		2-3	1-3	2-2	0-3	3-0	2-1	1-2	3-3	1-0	1-3	8-0	3-2	0-4	1-5
7	Heath Hayes	3-4	1-2	0-4	0-2	0-2	2-1		2-1	0-2	0-2	0-3	1-1	2-3	5-0	4-0	4-0	0-2	3-0	2-0	3-3
8	Heather St Johns	0-2	1-0	0-3	1-1	4-0	4-1	0-1		1-3	0-1	1-0	1-0	3-0	1-1	2-4	10-0	1-2	4-3	4-3	
9	Hinckley AFC	2-3	4-1	1-2	5-3	1-2	2-0	3-2	2-0		2-0	2-0	2-2	4-0	6-0	4-1	4-1	12-0	2-1	5-1	6-2
10	Leicester Road	2-2	4-0	0-1	0-1	4-1	4-2	1-1	5-1	2-1		4-1	7-2	3-1	5-1	1-2	1-1	11-0	3-1	3-1	5-0
11	Lichfield City	5-0	3-1	0-1	0-2	2-1	2-4	2-1	3-0	0-4	1-0		3-0	3-1	1-3	3-0	2-2	5-0	1-1	0-3	1-1
12	Littleton	1-2	3-2	0-2	2-2	2-2	1-3	0-1	4-2	2-1	1-3	2-1		1-3	2-1	1-0	2-0	1-0	3-1	1-2	
13	Nuneaton Griff	3-5	0-3	0-5	3-0	2-1	2-4	0-0	0-2	1-1	1-3	0-1	0-0		2-1	3-4	3-7	7-0	1-0	6-0	2-0
14	Pelsall Villa	1-6	4-1	1-5	1-2	0-0	2-3	2-3	2-1	1-6	2-1	0-0	1-5	4-0		1-4	2-2	4-0	3-1	2-4	0-0
15	Pershore Town	2-0	0-6	0-3	0-3	2-2	0-3	2-2	1-2	3-2	1-4	0-6	0-3	1-1	4-0		0-2	2-0	1-1	4-0	0-0
16	Racing Club Warwick	2-5	1-1	0-3	2-3	1-2	2-2	1-3	2-0	1-7	1-0	3-5	3-1	1-1	2-0	3-3		15-0	3-1	2-0	3-1
17	Southam United	0-8	0-3	0-6	0-0	1-1	1-1	0-6	1-2	0-10	0-7	2-2	0-4	0-4	2-2	0-4	1-2		0-3	1-6	1-2
18	Stafford Town	2-4	6-1	0-4	3-3	1-1	2-0	4-4	4-2	1-2	2-6	4-1	0-1	2-2	1-0	2-4	3-4	7-0		2-5	0-2
19	Studley	1-5	1-4	2-7	1-1	0-1	2-4	2-2	2-3	1-1	0-6	1-2	4-3	3-2	4-0	1-2	1-2	4-0	1-1		1-3
20	Uttoxeter Town	1-3	4-1	2-2	2-2	2-0	4-4	3-1	1-2	1-6	1-5	1-2	2-1	1-4	2-2	1-2	1-2	4-0	1-3	1-2	

DIVISION TWO

#	Club	1	2	3	4	5	6	7	8	9	10	11	12	13	14	15	16
1	Alvis Sporting Club		4-0	1-0	3-2	0-2	1-0	0-2	4-0	0-0	4-1	1-0	2-0	0-2	3-1	4-0	3-2
2	Barnt Green Spartak	1-4		4-2	0-2	0-2	0-2	3-3	1-7	6-0	2-1	2-1	5-3	0-1	1-6	0-8	5-2
3	Bloxwich Town	1-0	1-1		1-0	0-0	0-4	1-0	0-1	0-1	3-1	1-1	1-4	1-5	0-1	3-3	2-2
4	Continental Star	1-2	0-2	3-2		4-2	2-4	0-3	0-4	1-1	1-1	0-1	1-1	2-4	0-5	2-4	2-3
5	Coton Green	0-3	4-1	2-1	1-1		3-3	1-2	6-2	3-3	1-3	3-1	2-1	0-1	5-3	2-2	2-3
6	Droitwich Spa	1-1	3-2	0-1	7-0	1-1		5-0	3-2	3-3	4-1	4-3	1-0	1-1	0-2	3-1	10-1
7	Earlswood Town	1-2	2-1	0-2	2-0	3-0	0-2		0-2	2-1	1-2	2-0	3-1	0-3	2-2	2-0	0-1
8	Fairfield Villa	2-2	2-1	4-1	1-1	0-0	0-1	3-2		0-1	0-2	6-3	2-4	3-1	4-1	1-1	
9	Feckenham	1-3	0-3	6-1	3-1	3-3	2-0	2-7	4-3		0-1	2-0	3-4	1-1	1-1	0-4	3-0
10	Hampton	0-1	1-1	2-3	2-2	1-2	0-2	2-1	1-7	1-2		1-0	5-0	0-6	0-0	2-2	1-0
11	Knowle	1-1	4-0	2-1	1-1	3-3	2-0	1-1	5-2	0-1	2-0		4-1	1-2	2-0	1-1	3-1
12	Leamington Hibernian	0-3	1-0	0-0	2-1	0-4	0-3	1-2	1-3	3-2	3-1	1-6		0-2	0-2	5-3	1-1
13	Paget Rangers	2-2	7-1	0-1	7-0	2-1	2-2	3-1	6-3	4-0	7-0	3-2	6-1		2-5	2-3	1-2
14	Redditch Borough	4-2	0-1	9-0	9-0	0-1	3-1	2-4	6-2	2-0	1-1	3-4	4-0	3-0		0-2	5-0
15	Smithswood Firs	0-0	2-1	5-1	1-1	1-3	1-0	1-1	2-4	2-2	2-3	0-4	4-3	1-2	1-1		4-5
16	Sutton United	2-3	5-0	5-1	2-1	1-2	0-2	1-5	3-6	2-0	8-1	1-1	3-2	1-3	0-3	3-2	

CLUB MOVEMENTS - Premier Division - In: Haughmond (P - West Midlands), Rugby Town (R - NPL D1S), West Bridgford (P - EMCL), Worcester City (NLN). **Out:** Alvechurch (P - NPL D1S), St Andrews (T - UCL), Tividale (R - West Midlands). **Division One - In:** Coventry Alvis fomerley Alvis Sporting Club (P), Ilkeston Town (N). **Out:** Pelsall Villa (R), Southam United (R/W).

AFC WULFRUNIANS

Founded: 2005   Nickname: The Wulfs

Secretary: Ian Davies   **(T)** 07989 953 738   **(E)** iantash@icloud.com
Chairman: Clive Morris   **Manager:** Richard Forsyth   **Prog Ed:** Paul Tudor
Ground: Castlecroft Stadium, Castlecroft Road, Wolverhampton WV3 8NA   **(T)** 01902 761410
Capacity: 2,000 **Seats:** Yes   **Covered:** Yes   **Midweek Matchday:**   **Clubhouse:** Yes
Colours(change): Red/black/red (All blue)
Previous Names: None
Previous Leagues: West Midlands (Regional). Midland Alliance 2013-14.

HONOURS: FA Comps: None
League: West Midlands (Regional) League Division Two 2005-06, Premier Division 2008-09, 12-13.

10 YEAR RECORD									
07-08	08-09	09-10	10-11	11-12	12-13	13-14	14-15	15-16	16-17
WMP 6	WMP 1	WMP 3	WMP 3	WMP 5	WMP 1	MidAl 8	MFLP 7	MFLP 13	MFLP 17
	FAC EPr	FAC 2Q	FAC EP	FAC 1Q	FAC 1Q	FAC 2Q	FAC P	FAC 1Q	FAC EP
FAV 2Q	FAV 2Q	FAV 1P	FAV 2Q	FAV 2Q	FAV 3P	FAV 2P	FAV 1Pr	FAV 4P	FAV 2P

BOLDMERE ST. MICHAELS

Founded: 1883   Nickname: The Mikes

Secretary: Clive Faulkner   **(T)** 07866 122 254   **(E)** faulkner-c1@sky.com
Chairman: Rob Mallaband
Ground: Trevor Brown Memorial Ground, Church Road, Boldmere B73 5RY   **(T)** 0121 373 4435
Capacity: 2,500 **Seats:** 230   **Covered:** 400   **Midweek Matchday:** Tuesday   **Clubhouse:** Yes
Colours(change): White & black
Previous Names: None.
Previous Leagues: West Midlands (Regional). Midland Combination. Midland Alliance > 2014.

HONOURS: FA Comps: None
League: Midland Combination Premier 1985-86, 88-89, 89-90.

10 YEAR RECORD									
07-08	08-09	09-10	10-11	11-12	12-13	13-14	14-15	15-16	16-17
MidAl 4	MidAl 4	MidAl 6	MidAl 3	MidAl 12	MidAl 9	MidAl 2	MFLP 9	MFLP 11	MFLP 12
FAC P	FAC P	FAC EP	FAC EP	FAC EP	FAC 1Q	FAC EP	FAC 1Q	FAC P	FAC P
FAV 2Q	FAV 2P	FAV 3P	FAV 2P	FAV 2P	FAV 2P	FAV 2Q	FAV 2Q	FAV 1P	FAV 2Q

BROMSGROVE SPORTING

Founded: 2009   Nickname: The Rouslers

Secretary: David Stephens   **(T)** 07955 121 966   **(E)** dave@bromsgrovesporting.co.uk
Chairman:
Ground: The Victoria Ground, Birmingham Road, Bromsgrove, Worcs, B61 0DR   **(T)** 01527 876949
Capacity: 3,500 **Seats:**   **Covered:**   **Midweek Matchday:**   **Clubhouse:** Yes
Colours(change): Red & white
Previous Names: None
Previous Leagues: Midland Combination 2010-14.

HONOURS: FA Comps: None
League: Midland Football League Division One 2016-17.

10 YEAR RECORD									
07-08	08-09	09-10	10-11	11-12	12-13	13-14	14-15	15-16	16-17
			MCm2 3	MCm1 3	MCmP 6	MCmP 2	MFL1 2	MFL1 2	MFL1 1
							FAC Pr	FAC P	FAC P
						FAV 1P	FAV 3P	FAV 1P	FAV SF

COLESHILL TOWN

Founded: 1894   Nickname: The Coleman

Secretary: David Brown   **(T)** 07799 075 828   **(E)** dave.brown@skanska.co.uk
Chairman: Paul Billing   **Prog Ed:** David Brown
Ground: Pack Meadow, Packington Lane, Coleshill B46 3JQ   **(T)** 01675 463 259
Capacity: 2,070 **Seats:** 570   **Covered:**   **Midweek Matchday:** Tuesday   **Clubhouse:** Yes
Colours(change): White & red
Previous Names: None.
Previous Leagues: Midland Combination. Midland Alliance 2008-2014.

HONOURS: FA Comps: None
League: Midland Combination Division Two 1969-70, Premier 07-08.

10 YEAR RECORD									
07-08	08-09	09-10	10-11	11-12	12-13	13-14	14-15	15-16	16-17
MCmP 1	MidAl 11	MidAl 8	MidAl 12	MidAl 16	MidAl 15	MidAl 4	MFLP 2	MFLP 5	MFLP 2
FAC EPr	FAC P	FAC P	FAC 3Q	FAC Pr	FAC EPr	FAC EP	FAC 1Q	FAC 3Q	FAC 1Q
FAV 3P	FAV 1P	FAV 1P	FAV 1Q	FAV 1Q	FAV 1Q	FAV 4P	FAV 2P	FAV 4P	FAV SF

COVENTRY SPHINX
Founded: 1946   Nickname: Sphinx

Secretary: Sharon Taylor   **(T)** 07979 233 845   **(E)** sharon@coventrysphinx.co.uk
Chairman: Dannie Cahill   Stuart Dutton   Sharon Taylor
Ground: Sphinx Sports & Social Club, Sphinx Drive, Coventry CV3 1WA   **(T)** 02476 451 361
Capacity: 1,000 **Seats:** Yes   **Covered:** Yes   **Midweek Matchday:** Tuesday   **Clubhouse:** Yes
Colours(change): Sky blue & white stripes/navy/navy (Yellow & royal blue stripes/yellow/royal blue)
Previous Names: Armstrong Siddeley Motors. Sphinx > 1995.
Previous Leagues: Midland Combination. Midland Alliance 2007-14.

HONOURS: FA Comps: None
League: Midland Combination Premier 2006-07.

10 YEAR RECORD

07-08	08-09	09-10	10-11	11-12	12-13	13-14	14-15	15-16	16-17
MidAl 19	MidAl 7	MidAl 9	MidAl 16	MidAl 3	MidAl 14	MidAl 7	MFLP 18	MFLP 19	MFLP 10
FAC EPr	FAC EP	FAC 3Q	FAC 2Q	FAC P	FAC P	FAC 2Q	FAC Pr	FAC P	FAC EP
FAV QFr	FAV 2P	FAV 2Q	FAV 2P	FAV 2Q	FAV 2P	FAV 2P	FAV 2Q	FAV 2P	FAV 2Q

COVENTRY UNITED
Founded: 2013   Nickname: Cov United

Secretary: Graham Wood   **(T)** 07863 563 943   **(E)** graham.wood@coventryunited.co.uk
Chairman: Jason Kay
Ground: Coventry RFC, Butts Park Arena, The Butts, Coventry CV1 3GE   **(T)**
Capacity: 3,000 **Seats:** Yes   **Covered:** Yes   **Midweek Matchday:**   **Clubhouse:** Yes
Colours(change): Red
Previous Names: None
Previous Leagues: Midland Combination 2013-14.

HONOURS: FA Comps: None
League: Midland Football League Division Two 2014-15, Division One 2015-16.

10 YEAR RECORD

07-08	08-09	09-10	10-11	11-12	12-13	13-14	14-15	15-16	16-17
						MCm2 2	MFL2 1	MFL1 1	MFLP 8
									FAC 1Q
								FAV 2P	FAV 1P

HAUGHMOND
Founded: 1980   Nickname: Academicals

Secretary: Stuart Williams   **(T)** 07785 531 754   **(E)** stuartlwilliams@btinternet.com
Chairman: William Gough
Ground: Sundorne Sports Village, Sundorne Road, Shrewsbury. SY1 4RQ   **(T)** 07785 531 754
Capacity: **Seats:** Yes   **Covered:** Yes   **Midweek Matchday:**   **Clubhouse:** Yes
Colours(change): White/black/white & black
Previous Names: None
Previous Leagues: West Midlands >2017.

HONOURS: FA Comps: None
League: Shropshire County Premier Division 2010-11. West Midlands Division Two 2011-12, Premier Division 2016-17.

10 YEAR RECORD

07-08	08-09	09-10	10-11	11-12	12-13	13-14	14-15	15-16	16-17
ShCP 4	ShCP 2	ShCP 2	ShCP 1	WM2 1	WM1 4	WM1 2	WMP 8	WMP 5	WMP 1
									FAC EP
								FAV 2P	FAV 1P

HEANOR TOWN
Founded: 1883   Nickname: The Lions

Secretary: Amanda Jones   **(T)** 07581 015 868   **(E)** amanda.jones10@live.co.uk
Chairman: Geoff Clarence
Ground: The Town Ground, Mayfield Avenue, Heanor DE75 7EN   **(T)** 01773 713 742
Capacity: 2,700 **Seats:** 100   **Covered:** 1,000   **Midweek Matchday:** Tuesday   **Clubhouse:** Yes
Colours(change): White & black
Previous Names: None
Previous Leagues: Midland 1961-72. Central Midlands 1986-2008. East Midlands Counties 2008-12. Northern Counties East 2012-15.

HONOURS: FA Comps: None
League: Central Midlands Supreme Division 1994-95, 96-97.
East Midlands Counties 2011-12.

10 YEAR RECORD

07-08	08-09	09-10	10-11	11-12	12-13	13-14	14-15	15-16	16-17
CM Su 11	EMC 12	EMC 7	EMC 3	EMC 1	NCEP 11	NCEP 8	NCEP 6	MFLP 6	MFLP 6
		FAC EP	FAC EPr	FAC 1Q	FAC P	FAC EP	FAC P	FAC EP	FAC 1Q
FAV 1P	FAV 2P	FAV 2Qr	FAV 2P	FAV 1Q	FAT 1Pr	FAV 1P	FAV 4P	FAV 2P	FAV 1P

HIGHGATE UNITED
Founded: 1948   Nickname: Red or Gate

Secretary: Paul Davis   **(T)** 07527 941 993   **(E)** jimmymerry777@gmail.com
Chairman: Ashley Pulisciano
Ground: The Coppice, Tythe Barn Lane, Shirley Solihull B90 1PH   **(T)**
Capacity: 2,000 **Seats:**   **Covered:**   **Midweek Matchday:** Tuesday   **Clubhouse:** Yes

Colours(change): All red
Previous Names: None.
Previous Leagues: Worcestershire/Midland Combination. Midland Alliance 2008-14.

HONOURS: FA Comps: None
League: Midland Combination Premier 1972-73, 73-74, 74-75.

10 YEAR RECORD									
07-08	08-09	09-10	10-11	11-12	12-13	13-14	14-15	15-16	16-17
MCmP 2	MidAl 13	MidAl 18	MidAl 18	MidAl 20	MidAl 19	MidAl 3	MFL1 1	MFLP 9	MFLP 7
FAC	FAC P	FAC EPr	FAC EP	FAC P	FAC EPr				FAC 2Q
FAV 2Q	FAV	FAV 2Qr	FAV 2Q	FAV 1P	FAV 2Q			FAV 2P	FAV 2Q

LONG EATON UNITED
Founded: 1956   Nickname: Blues

Secretary: Jim Fairley   **(T)** 07971 416 444   **(E)** jim@longeatonutd.co.uk
Chairman: Jim Fairley
Ground: Grange Park, Station Rd, Long Eaton, Derbys NG10 2EG   **(T)** 0115 973 5700
Capacity: 1,500 **Seats:** 450 **Covered:** 500 **Midweek Matchday:** Tuesday   **Clubhouse:** Yes **Shop:** No

Colours(change): All blue
Previous Names: None
Previous Leagues: Central Alliance 1956-61, Mid Co Football Lge 1961-82, NCE 1982-89, 2002-14. Central Midlands 1989-2002

HONOURS: FA Comps: None
League: Northern Counties East Division One South 1984-85.

10 YEAR RECORD									
07-08	08-09	09-10	10-11	11-12	12-13	13-14	14-15	15-16	16-17
NCEP 12	NCEP 2	NCEP 10	NCEP 12	NCEP 15	NCEP 12	NCEP 11	MFLP 3	MFLP 18	MFLP 14
FAC Pr	FAC 2Q	FAC P	FAC EPr	FAC EP		FAC 1Q	FAC EP	FAC 1Q	FAC P
FAV 2P	FAV 3P	FAV 2P	FAV 1Q	FAV 2P	FAV 3P	FAV 2P	FAV 1P	FAV 2P	FAV 3P

LOUGHBOROUGH UNIVERSITY
Founded: 1920   Nickname: The Scholars

Secretary: Margaret Folwell   **(T)** 01509 226 127 (Office Hrs)   **(E)** footballsecretary@lboro.ac.uk
Chairman: Michael Skubala
Ground: Loughborough Uni Stadium, Holywell Sports Complex, Holywell Park LE11 3TU   **(T)** 01509 228 774
Capacity: 3,300 **Seats:** Yes **Covered:** Yes **Midweek Matchday:**   **Clubhouse:** Yes

Colours(change): Purple/purple/grey
Previous Names: Loughborough College
Previous Leagues: Leicestershire Senior. Midland Combination. Midland Alliance 2009-14.

HONOURS: FA Comps: None
League: Midland Combination 2008-09.

10 YEAR RECORD									
07-08	08-09	09-10	10-11	11-12	12-13	13-14	14-15	15-16	16-17
MCmP 4	MCmP 1	MidAl 13	MidAl 4	MidAl 5	MidAl 4	MidAl 14	MFLP 20	MFLP 14	MFLP 18
		FAC EP	FAC EP	FAC 1Q	FAC P	FAC 1Q	FAC P	FAC P	FAC P
	FAV 1P	FAV 1Pr	FAV 2Q	FAV 1P	FAV 1Q	FAV 2P	FAV 1Q	FAV 1Pr	FAV 2Q

LYE TOWN
Founded: 1930   Nickname: The Flyers

Secretary: Paul Roberts   **(T)** 07429 887 570   **(E)** dprobbo@gmail.com
Chairman: Brian Blakemore
Ground: Sports Ground, Stourbridge Road, Lye, Stourbridge, West Mids DY9 7DH   **(T)** 01384 422 672
Capacity: 1,000 **Seats:**   **Covered:**   **Midweek Matchday:**   **Clubhouse:** Yes

Colours(change): Blue & white
Previous Names: Lye & Wollescote 1930-31.
Previous Leagues: Worcestershire Combination 1931-39. Birmingham & Dist/West Midlands (Regional) 1947-62/1962-2014.

HONOURS: FA Comps: None
League: West Midlands (Regional) 2013-14.

10 YEAR RECORD									
07-08	08-09	09-10	10-11	11-12	12-13	13-14	14-15	15-16	16-17
WMP 10	WMP 11	WMP 19	WMP 11	WMP 15	WMP 2	WMP 1	MFLP 6	MFLP 8	MFLP 4
FAC EP	FAC P	FAC EP		FAC EP	FAC P	FAC P	FAC EP	FAC EPr	FAC P
FAV 1Qr	FAV 1P	FAV 1Q	FAV 2Q	FAV 1Q	FAV 1P	FAV 1Q	FAV 2Q	FAV 2Q	FAV 1Q

QUORN
Founded: 1924   Nickname: Reds

Secretary: Reg Molloy	**(T)** 07729 173 333	**(E)** k.molloy@ntlworld.com
Chairman: Stuart Turner		

Ground: Farley Way Stadium, Farley Way, Quorn, Leicestershire LE12 8RB   **(T)** 01509 620 232
Capacity: 1,550 **Seats:** 350   **Covered:** 250   **Midweek Matchday:**   **Clubhouse:** Yes

Colours(change): All red
Previous Names: Quorn Methodists
Previous Leagues: Leicestershire Senior, Midland Alliance > 2007. NPL 2007-2012. United Counties 2012-13. Midland Alliance 2013-14.

HONOURS: FA Comps: None
League: Leicestershire Senior 2000-01

10 YEAR RECORD

07-08		08-09		09-10		10-11		11-12		12-13		13-14		14-15		15-16		16-17	
NP	1	NP1S	12	NP1S	20	NP1S	15	NP1S	21	UCL P	7	MidAl	5	MFLP	11	MFLP	17	MFLP	11
FAC	2Q	FAC	P	FAC	1Q	FAC	P	FAC	2Q	FAC	1Q	FAC	Pr	FAC	P	FAC	EP	FAC	EP
FAT	Pr	FAT	1Q	FAT	3Q	FAT	1Q	FAT	P	FAV	1P	FAV	1Q	FAV	2Q	FAV	2P	FAV	3P

ROCESTER
Founded: 1876   Nickname: Romans

Secretary: Barry Smith	**(T)** 07770 762 825	**(E)** secretary@rocesterfc.net
Chairman: Michael Frost		**Prog Ed:** Barry Smith

Ground: Hillsfield, Mill Street, Rocester, Uttoxeter ST14 5JX   **(T)** 01889 591 301
Capacity: 4,000 **Seats:** 230   **Covered:** 500   **Midweek Matchday:** Tuesday   **Clubhouse:** Yes   **Shop:** Yes

Colours(change): Amber & black
Previous Names: None.
Previous Leagues: Staffs Sen. (Founder Member). West Midlands (Regional) 1987-94. Midland Alliance 1994-99, 2003-04. Southern 1999-2003. Northern Premier 2004-05. Midland Alliance 2003-04, 05-14.
HONOURS: FA Comps: None
League: Staffordshire Senior 1985-86, 86-87. West Mids (Regional) Division One 1987-88.

10 YEAR RECORD   Midland Alliance 1998-99, 2003-04.

07-08		08-09		09-10		10-11		11-12		12-13		13-14		14-15		15-16		16-17	
MidAl	5	MidAl	20	MidAl	16	MidAl	14	MidAl	6	MidAl	13	MidAl	20	MFLP	12	MFLP	12	MFLP	16
FAC	1Q	FAC	EP	FAC	P	FAC	EP	FAC	1Q	FAC	P	FAC	EPr	FAC	EPr	FAC	Pr	FAC	P
FAV	2Q	FAV	2Q	FAV	1Q	FAV	1Q	FAV	1Q	FAV	4P	FAV	2P	FAV	1P	FAV	1P	FAV	2P

RUGBY TOWN
Founded: 1956   Nickname: The Valley

Secretary: Doug Wilkins	**(T)** 07976 284 614	**(E)** rugbytown@melbros.com
Chairman: Brian Melvin	**Manager:** Dave Stringer - May 2017	**Prog Ed:** Chris Peters

Ground: Butlin Road, Rugby, Warwicks CV21 3SD   **(T)** 01788 844 806
Capacity: 6,000 **Seats:** 750   **Covered:** 1,000   **Midweek Matchday:** Tuesday   **Clubhouse:** Yes   **Shop:** Yes

Colours(change): Sky blue/white/sky blue (Red/navy blue/navy blue)
Previous Names: Valley Sports 1956-71, Valley Sport Rugby 1971-73, VS Rugby 1973-2000, Rugby United 2000-05
Previous Leagues: Rugby & District 1956-62, Coventry & Partnership, North Warwickshire 1963-69, United Counties 1969-75 West Midlands 1975-83. Southern 1983-2015.
HONOURS: FA Comps: FA Vase 1982-83.
League: Southern Midland Division 1986-87. Midland Combination Division 1 2001-02.

10 YEAR RECORD

07-08		08-09		09-10		10-11		11-12		12-13		13-14		14-15		15-16		16-17	
SthP	15	SthP	17	SthP	22	SthC	6	SthC	6	SthC	2	SthC	2	SthC	6	NP1S	9	NP1S	21
FAC	1Q	FAC	3Q	FAC	2Q	FAC	1Q	FAC	Pr	FAC	1Qr	FAC	3Qr	FAC	2Q	FAC	3Qr	FAC	2Q
FAT	1Q	FAT	2Q	FAT	1Q	FAT	2Q	FAT	Pr	FAT	1Qr	FAT	P	FAT	P	FAT	P	FAT	Pr

SHAWBURY UNITED
Founded: 1992   Nickname:

Secretary: Dia Martin	**(T)** 07739 915 089	**(E)** daibando161274@aol.com
Chairman: Chris Kirkup		

Ground: Butler Sports Ground, Bowensfield, Wem, Shrewsbury SY4 5AP   **(T)** 01939 233 287
Capacity: 1,000 **Seats:** Yes   **Covered:** Yes   **Midweek Matchday:**   **Clubhouse:** Yes

Colours(change): Black & white
Previous Names: None
Previous Leagues: Shrewsbury & Shropshire Alliance 1992-2000. West Midlands (Regional) 2000-2016.

HONOURS: FA Comps: None
League: West Midlands (Regional) Premier Division 2015-16.

10 YEAR RECORD

07-08		08-09		09-10		10-11		11-12		12-13		13-14		14-15		15-16		16-17	
WMP	2	WMP	10	WMP	21	WMP	17	WMP	10	WMP	4	WMP	4	WMP	7	WMP	1	MFLP	19
																		FAC	EPr
FAV	4P	FAV	2Pr	FAV	2Q	FAV	1Q	FAV	2Q	FAV	2P	FAV	1P	FAV	2Q	FAV	1Q	FAV	1P

SHEPSHED DYNAMO — Founded: 1994 — Nickname: Dynamo

Secretary: Danny Pole — **(T)** 07866 500 187 — **(E)** secretary@shepsheddynamo.co.uk
Chairman: Mick Sloan
Ground: The Dovecote, Butt Hole Lane, Shepshed, Leicestershire LE12 9BN — **(T)** 01509 650 992
Capacity: 2,050 **Seats:** 570 **Covered:** 400 **Midweek Matchday:** **Clubhouse:** Yes **Shop:** Yes

Colours(change): Black & white
Previous Names: Shepshed Albion/Charterhouse > 1994
Previous Leagues: Leics Sen 1907-16,19-27, 46-50, 51-81, Mid Co 81-82,N.C.E. 82-83, Sth 83-88, 96-04, N.P.L.88-93, 04-12, Mid Com 93-94, Mid All 94-95,13-14. UCL 12-13.
HONOURS: FA Comps: Leicestershire Senior Cup x7
League: Midland Counties 1981-82. Northern Counties East 1982-83.
10 YEAR RECORD Midland Alliance 1995-96.

07-08		08-09		09-10		10-11		11-12		12-13		13-14		14-15		15-16		16-17	
NP 1	15	NP1S	8	NP1S	17	NP1S	21	NP1S	22	UCL P	9	MidAl	16	MFLP	16	MFLP	4	MFLP	15
FAC	1Qr	FAC	2Q	FAC	P	FAC	Pr	FAC	Pr	FAC	EP	FAC	P	FAC	1Q	FAC	1Qr	FAC	EP
FAT	1Q	FAT	P	FAT	2Q	FAT	1Q	FAT	P	FAV	2P	FAV	2Q	FAV	2P	FAV	1Q	FAV	4P

SOUTH NORMANTON ATHLETIC — Founded: 1926 — Nickname: The Shiners

Secretary: Stephen Harris — **(T)** 07505 366 136 — **(E)** manor2@ntlworld.com
Chairman: Phil Bailey
Ground: M J Robinson Structures Arena, Lees Lane South Normanton, Derby DE55 2AD — **(T)** 07834 206 253
Capacity: **Seats:** 150 **Covered:** 300 **Midweek Matchday:** Tuesday **Clubhouse:** Yes

Colours(change): Blue & white
Previous Names: South Normanton Miners Welfare 1926-90. Folded in 2008, reformed in 2009.
Previous Leagues: Alfreton &District Sunday Lge 1980-87, Mansfield Sunday Lge 1987-90, Central Midlands League 1990-2003, East Midlands Counties 2002-17.
HONOURS: FA Comps: None
League: None
10 YEAR RECORD

07-08		08-09	09-10		10-11		11-12		12-13		13-14		14-15		15-16		16-17	
NCEP	17		CM P	11	CM P	3	CMSth	3	CMSth	9	CMSth	2	EMC	7	EMC	4	EMC	2
FAC	Pr														FAC	Pr	FAC	P
FAV	2Qr						FAV	1Q	FAV	2Q			FAV	2Q	FAV	2Q	FAV	1Q

SPORTING KHALSA — Founded: 1991 — Nickname: Sporting

Secretary: Manjit Gill — **(T)** 07976 220 444 — **(E)** manjit.gill@globeproperty.co.uk
Chairman: Rajinder Gill
Ground: Aspray Arena, Noose Lane, Willenhall WV13 3BB — **(T)** 01902 219 208
Capacity: 5,000 **Seats:** Yes **Covered:** Yes **Midweek Matchday:** **Clubhouse:** Yes

Colours(change): Yellow & blue
Previous Names: None
Previous Leagues: Walsall & District Sunday 1991-96. West Midlands (Regional) 1996-97, 2005-15.
HONOURS: FA Comps: None
League: West Midlands (Regional) Premier Division 2014-15.
10 YEAR RECORD

07-08		08-09		09-10		10-11		11-12		12-13		13-14		14-15		15-16		16-17	
WM1	15	WM1	17	WM1	17	WM1	3	WMP	14	WMP	11	WMP	6	WMP	1	MFLP	3	MFLP	3
										FAC	Pr			FAC	P	FAC	4Q	FAC	P
FAV	2Q	FAV	1Q	FAV	1Q	FAV	1Q	FAV	1Q	FAV	1Q	FAV	2Q	FAV	2Qr	FAV	1P	FAV	QF

STOURPORT SWIFTS — Founded: 1882 — Nickname: Swifts

Secretary: Graham Haighway — **(T)** 07780 997 758 — **(E)** ghaighway@hotmail.co.uk
Chairman: Chris Reynolds
Ground: Walshes Meadow, Harold Davis Drive, Stourport on Severn DY13 0AA — **(T)** 01299 825 188
Capacity: 2,000 **Seats:** 250 **Covered:** 150 **Midweek Matchday:** **Clubhouse:** Yes **Shop:** Yes

Colours(change): Gold & black
Previous Names: None
Previous Leagues: Kidderminster/Worcestershire/West Midlands (Regional) > 1998, Midland Alliance 1998-2001, 12-14, Southern 2001-12.
HONOURS: FA Comps: None
League: Midland Alliance 2000-01.
10 YEAR RECORD

07-08		08-09		09-10		10-11		11-12		12-13		13-14		14-15		15-16		16-17	
SthM	17	SthM	16	SthM	17	Sthsw	17	Sthsw	21	MidAl	5	MidAl	10	MFLP	10	MFLP	10	MFLP	13

WESTFIELDS

Founded: 1966   Nickname: The Fields

Secretary: Andrew Morris   **(T)** 07860 410 548   **(E)** andrewmorris@westfieldsfc.com
Chairman: John Morgan
Ground: Allpay Park, Widemarsh Common, Hereford HR4 9NA   **(T)** 07860 410 548
Capacity: 2,250 **Seats:** 220   **Covered:** 150   **Midweek Matchday:** Wednesday   **Clubhouse:** Yes   **Shop:** Yes

Colours(change): All Maroon & sky blue
Previous Names: None.
Previous Leagues: Herefordshire Sunday 1966-73. Worcester & Dist. 1973-78. West Midlands (Regional) 1978-04. Midland Alliance 2004-14.

HONOURS: FA Comps: None
League: West Midlands (Regional) Division One 1986-87, Premier 2002-03.

10 YEAR RECORD

	07-08	08-09	09-10	10-11	11-12	12-13	13-14	14-15	15-16	16-17
	MidAl 11	MidAl 17	MidAl 5	MidAl 6	MidAl 2	MidAl 2	MidAl 12	WMP 8	MFLP 16	MFLP 5
FAC	Pr	FAC P	FAC 1Q	FAC P	FAC EP	FAC 2Qr	FAC EP	FAC P	FAC 1Q	FAC 1P
FAV	2Q	FAV 3Pr	FAV 2P	FAV 3P	FAV 1P	FAV 1P	FAV 4P	FAV 3P	FAV 1P	FAV 3P

WORCESTER CITY

Founded: 1902   Nickname: City

Secretary: Kevin Preece   **(T)** 07811 076 933   **(E)** kevinpreece1987@gmail.com
Chairman: Anthony Hampson   **Manager:** John Snape & Lee Hughes   **Prog Ed:** Terry Brumpton
Ground: The Victoria Ground, Birmingham Road, Bromsgrove B61 0DR   **(T)** 01905 23003
Capacity: 4,893 **Seats:** 400   **Covered:** Yes   **Midweek Matchday:**   **Clubhouse:** Yes   **Shop:** Yes

Colours(change): Blue & white stripes/blue/blue (All green)
Previous Names: Formed when Berwick Rangers and Worcester Rovers amalgamated
Previous Leagues: Birmingham & District 1902-38. Southern 1938-79, 85-2004. Alliance 1979-85. Conference 2004-17.

HONOURS: FA Comps: None
League: Birmingham League 1913-14, 24-25, 28-29, 29-30.

10 YEAR RECORD   Southern League Division One North 1967-68, 76-77, Premier 1978-79.

	07-08	08-09	09-10	10-11	11-12	12-13	13-14	14-15	15-16	16-17
	Conf N 12	Conf S 16	Conf S 20	Conf N 16	Conf N 7	Conf N 15	Conf N 15	Conf N 9	Nat N 17	Nat N 20
FAC	2Q	FAC 2Q	FAC 3Qr	FAC 3Q	FAC 2Q	FAC 4Q	FAC 4Qr	FAC 2Pr	FAC 1P	FAC 3Q
FAT	3Q	FAT 3Q	FAT 3P	FAT 2Pr	FAT 3Q	FAT 3Q	FAT 2P	FAT 1P	FAT 1Pr	FAT 1P

Coleshill Town 2016-17 - 2nd in Midland League Premier. Photo: Alan Coomes.

ATHERSTONE TOWN

Founded: 2004   Nickname: The Adders

Secretary: Graham Read   **(T)** 07552 673 008   **(E)** grahamgdr777@aol.com
Chairman: Justin Palmer
Ground: Sheepy Road, Atherston, Warwickshire CV9 3AD   **(T)** 01827 717 829
Colours(change): Red & white
HONOURS: FA Comps: None   **League:** Midland Combination Division 1 2004-05, Premier Division 2005-06. Midland Alliance 2007-08.

10 YEAR RECORD

07-08		08-09		09-10		10-11		11-12		12-13		13-14		14-15		15-16		16-17	
MidAl		SthM	3	SthM	13	SthC	21	MidAl	21	MCmP	9	MCmP	9	MFL1	13	MFL1	13	MFL1	4
FAC	1Q	FAC	3Qr	FAC	P	FAC	Pr	FAC	P	FAC	EP	FAC	3Q	FAC	EPr				
FAV	2Q	FAT	P	FAT	1Q	FAT	P	FAV	1P	FAV	1Q	FAV	1P	FAV	2Q	FAV	1Q	FAV	2Q

BOLEHILL SWIFTS

Founded: 1953   Nickname:

Secretary: Mark Brooks   **(T)** 07539 957 995   **(E)** bruavt2005@aol.com
Chairman: Les Fitzpatrick
Ground: Rene Road, Bolehall, Tamworth, Staffordshire B77 3NN   **(T)** 07702 786 722
Colours(change): Yellow & green
HONOURS: FA Comps: None   **League:** Midland Combination Division Two 1984-85.

10 YEAR RECORD

07-08		08-09		09-10		10-11		11-12		12-13		13-14		14-15		15-16		16-17	
MCmP	17	MCmP	19	MCmP	18	MCmP	7	MCmP	4	MCmP	8	MCmP	4	MFL1	4	MFL1	17	MFL1	13
FAC	P	FAC	EP	FAC	EP	FAC	EP					FAC	P	FAC	EP	FAC	EPr		
FAV	2Qr	FAV	1Q	FAV	2Q	FAV	2Q			FAV	1Q	FAV	3P	FAV	3P	FAV	2Q	FAV	2Q

BROCTON

Founded: 1937   Nickname: The Badgers

Secretary: Terry Homer   **(T)** 07791 841 774   **(E)** terryhomer@yahoo.co.uk
Chairman: Brian Townsend   **Manager:** Sam Norton   **Prog Ed:** Brian Chandler
Ground: Silkmore Lane Sports Grd, Silkmore Lane, Stafford, Staffordshire ST17 4JH   **(T)**
Colours(change): Green & white/white/green (All red)
HONOURS: FA Comps: None   **League:** Midland Combination Premier 2013-14.

10 YEAR RECORD

07-08		08-09		09-10		10-11		11-12		12-13		13-14		14-15		15-16		16-17	
MCmP	9	MCmP	16	MCmP	7	MCmP	8	MCmP	6	MCmP	5	MCmP	1	MFLP	13	MFLP	15	MFLP	21
		FAC	EPr	FAC	P	FAC	EPr	FAC	EP	FAC	EPr	FAC	1Q	FAC	Pr	FAC	EP	FAC	P
FAV	2Q	FAV	1Qr	FAV	2Q	FAV	2Q	FAV	3Pr	FAV	1Q	FAV	4P	FAV	4P	FAV	3P	FAV	2Q

CADBURY ATHLETIC

Founded: 1994   Nickname:

Secretary: Kevin Wilks   **(T)** 07967 204 921   **(E)** cadburyathleticfc@hotmail.co.uk
Chairman: John Peckham   **Manager:** Matt Kirby   **Prog Ed:** Tony Florletta
Ground: TSA Sports Ground, Eckersall Road, Kings Norton, Birmingham, B38 8SR   **(T)** 0121 4584 570   **Capacity:** 1,500
Colours(change): Purple & white quarters/purple/white (Yellow with black trim/black/yellow)
HONOURS: FA Comps: None   **League:** Midland Combination Division One 2013-14.

10 YEAR RECORD

07-08		08-09		09-10		10-11		11-12		12-13		13-14		14-15		15-16		16-17	
MCmP	12	MCmP	11	MCmP	19	MCmP	6	MCmP	12	MCm1	3	MCm1	1	MFL1	6	MFL1	15	MFL1	5
FAC	EPr	FAC	EP	FAC	EP			FAC	EP							FAC	P		
FAV	1P	FAV	2Q	FAV	1Q	FAV	1Q	FAV	1Q	FAV	1Q	FAV	1Q	FAV	1Q	FAV	1Q	FAV	1P

CHELMSLEY TOWN

Founded: 1927   Nickname:

Secretary: Jason Gibbons   **(T)** 07736 296 246   **(E)** jason@chelmsleytown.co.uk
Chairman: Derek Brennan
Ground: Coleshill FC Pack Meadow, Packington Lane, Coleshill, B46 3JQ   **(T)** 07736 296 246   **Capacity:** 2,070
Colours(change): Sky blue & black
HONOURS: FA Comps: None   **League:** Midland Combination Division One 1987-88.

10 YEAR RECORD

07-08		08-09		09-10		10-11		11-12		12-13		13-14		14-15		15-16		16-17	
MCm2	6	MCm2	8	MCm2	13	MCm2	11	MCm2	3	MCm1	13	MCm1	6	MCm2	6	MCm2	2	MCm1	17

COVENTRY ALVIS

Founded: 1928 Nickname:

Secretary: David Taylor **(T)** 07719 461 536 **(E)** david.taylor166@btinternet.com
Chairman: Don Corrigan
Ground: Alvis Sports & Social Club, Green Lane, Coventry, CV3 6EA **(T)** 07904 496 954
Colours(change): Sky blue & navy
HONOURS: FA Comps: None **League:** Midland Combination Division One 2012-13.
Midland Football League Division Two 2015-16.

10 YEAR RECORD									
07-08	08-09	09-10	10-11	11-12	12-13	13-14	14-15	15-16	16-17
		CovAP 2	CovAP 2	MCm1 5	MCm1 1	MCmP 9	MFL1 20	MFL2 1	MFL2 3

COVENTRY COPSEWOOD

Founded: 1923 Nickname: The G's

Secretary: David Wilson **(T)** 07884 585 440 **(E)** davide.wilson@hotmail.co.uk
Chairman: Robert Abercrombie
Ground: Copsewood Sports & Social Club, Allard Way, Binley, Coventry CV3 1JP **(T)** 07884 585 440 **Capacity:** 2,000
Colours(change): All blue
HONOURS: FA Comps: None **League:** Midland Combination Division One 1996-97.

10 YEAR RECORD									
07-08	08-09	09-10	10-11	11-12	12-13	13-14	14-15	15-16	16-17
MCmP 21	MCmP 9	MCmP 5	MCmP 4	MCmP 3	MCmP 12	MCmP 16	MFL1 8	MFL1 11	MFL1 12
FAV 1Q	FAV 1Q	FAV 2Qr	FAV 2P	FAV 1P	FAV 1Q	FAV 1Q	FAV 1Q	FAV 1Q	FAV 1P

HEATH HAYES

Founded: 1965 Nickname: The Hayes

Secretary: Kathlyn Davies **(T)** 07969 203 063 **(E)** kathlyndavies@aol.com
Chairman: John Deans
Ground: Coppice Colliery Grd, Newlands Lane, Heath Hayes, Cannock, WS12 3HH **(T)** 07969 203 063 **Capacity:** 1,000
Colours(change): Blue & white/blue/white
HONOURS: FA Comps: None **League:** Staffordshire County Division One 1977-78. West Midlands (Regional)
Division One North 1998-99. Midland Combination Premier Division 2009-10.

10 YEAR RECORD									
07-08	08-09	09-10	10-11	11-12	12-13	13-14	14-15	15-16	16-17
MCmP 10	MCmP 10	MCmP 1	MidAl 11	MidAl 14	MidAl 18	MidAl 8	MFLP 22	MFL1 8	MFL1 14
	FAC EP	FAC P	FAC P	FAC EP	FAC P	FAC EP	FAC EP	FAC EP	FAC EP
FAV 3P	FAV 2Q	FAV 1Q	FAV 3P	FAV 1P	FAV 1Q	FAV 1Q	FAV 1Q	FAV 1Q	FAV 1Q

HEATHER ST. JOHN'S

Founded: 1949 Nickname:

Secretary: Adrian Rock **(T)** 07952 633 331 **(E)** adrianrock@hotmail.co.uk
Chairman: Michael Brookes
Ground: St John's Park, Ravenstone Rd, Heather LE67 2QJ **(T)** 01530 263 986
Colours(change): All royal blue
HONOURS: FA Comps: None **League:** Leicester & District Division One 1965-66., 69-70, 71-72.
Midland Combination Division One 2006-07, Premier 10-11.

10 YEAR RECORD									
07-08	08-09	09-10	10-11	11-12	12-13	13-14	14-15	15-16	16-17
MCmP 7	MCmP 5	MCmP 2	MCmP 1	MidAl 19	MidAl 20	MidAl 22	MFL1 16	MFL1 16	MFL1 8
	FAC EP	FAC P	FAC P			FAC EP	FAC EP		
FAV 2Q	FAV 1Q	FAV 2Q	FAV 3P		FAV 1P	FAV 2Q	FAV 2Q	FAV 1Q	FAV 1Q

HINCKLEY AFC

Founded: 2014 Nickname:

Secretary: Stephen Jelfs **(T)** 07720 299 313 **(E)** secretary@hinckleyafc.org.uk
Chairman:
Ground: St. John's Park, Ravenstone Road, Heather, Leicestershire, LE67 2QJ **(T)** 01530 263 986 **Capacity:** 1,500
Colours(change): Red & blue/blue/blue
HONOURS: FA Comps: None **League:** None

10 YEAR RECORD									
07-08	08-09	09-10	10-11	11-12	12-13	13-14	14-15	15-16	16-17
							MFL1 3	MFL1 5	MFL1 2
								FAC 2Q	FAC EPr
							FAV 1Q	FAV 1P	FAV 5P

ILKESTON TOWN
Founded: 1945   Nickname: The Robins

Secretary: (T)   **(E)** info@ilkestonfc.co.uk
Chairman: Alan Hardy   **Manager:** Steve Chettle
Ground: New Manor Ground, Awsworth Road, Ilkeston, Derbyshire DE7 8JF   **(T)** 0115 944 428   **Capacity:** 3,029
Colours(change): Red & blue/white/white (Blue & white /white/white)
HONOURS: FA Comps: None   **League:** Midland Counties 1967-68. West Midlands Division One 1991-92, Premier Division 1993-94.

10 YEAR RECORD

07-08	08-09	09-10	10-11	11-12	12-13	13-14	14-15	15-16	16-17
NP P 17	NP P 2	Conf N 8	Conf N Exp	NP1S 3	NP P 12	NP P 17	NP P 5	NP P 14	NP P 23
FAC 1Q	FAC 3Qr	FAC 1P	FAC 2Q			FAC 4Qr	FAC 1Q	FAC 1Q	FAC 3Q
FAT 3Q	FAT 2P	FAT 1P		FAT 3Qr	FAT 2Q	FAT 1Q	FAT 1Q	FAT 2Qr	FAT 1Q

LEICESTER ROAD
Founded: 2013   Nickname: The Knitters

Secretary: Stuart Millidge   **(T)** 07814 414 726   **(E)** stuart.millidge43@hotmail.com
Chairman: Ku Akeredulu   **Manager:** Neil Lyne   **Prog Ed:** Ian info@booksindesign.com
Ground: Leicester Road Stadium, Leicester Road, Hinckley, LE10 3DR   **(T)**
Colours(change): Blue & red/blue/blue (Amber/black/black)
HONOURS: FA Comps: None   **League:** None

10 YEAR RECORD

07-08	08-09	09-10	10-11	11-12	12-13	13-14	14-15	15-16	16-17
							MFL2 2	MFL1 4	MFL1 3
									FAC 1Qr
								FAV 2Q	FAV 1P

LICHFIELD CITY
Founded: 1970   Nickname:

Secretary: Michael Tyler   **(T)** 07756 521 301   **(E)** tylermick1954@hotmail.co.uk
Chairman: Darren Leaver
Ground: Brownsfield Park, Brownsfield Road, Lichfield, Staffs, WS13 6AY   **(T)** 01543 258 338   **Capacity:** 1,500
Colours(change): All blue
HONOURS: FA Comps: None   **League:** None

10 YEAR RECORD

07-08	08-09	09-10	10-11	11-12	12-13	13-14	14-15	15-16	16-17
	MCm3 5	MCm2 3	MCm2 4	MCm1 4	MCmP 10	MCmP 7	MFL1 12	MFL1 7	MFL1 7
							FAC P		FAC P
						FAV 1Q	FAV 2Q	FAV 1Q	FAV 2P

LITTLETON
Founded: 1890   Nickname: The Ton

Secretary: Marion Brighton   **(T)** 01905 909 125   **(E)** littletonfc@outlook.com
Chairman: Paul Harrison
Ground: 5 Acres, Pebworth Road, North Littleton, Evesham, Worcs, WR11 8QL   **(T)** 07765 224 290   **Capacity:** 1,000
Colours(change): Red/red/white
HONOURS: FA Comps: None   **League:** Midland Combination Division Three 2001-02.

10 YEAR RECORD

07-08	08-09	09-10	10-11	11-12	12-13	13-14	14-15	15-16	16-17
MCm1 9	MCm1 5	MCm1 8	MCm1 5	MCm1 2	MCmP 2	MCmP 11	MFL1 9	MFL1 9	MFL1 9
								FAV 2Q	FAV 2Q

NUNEATON GRIFF
Founded: 1972   Nickname: The Heartlanders

Secretary: Peter Kemp   **(T)** 07944 457 250   **(E)** nuneatongriff@sky.com
Chairman: John Gore
Ground: The Pingles Stadium, Avenue Road, Nuneaton, Warwickshire CV11 4LX   **(T)** 07944 457 250   **Capacity:** 1,500
Colours(change): Blue & white
HONOURS: FA Comps: None   **League:** Coventry Alliance Premier 1996-97, 97-98. Midland Combination Premier Division 1999-2000, 00-01.

10 YEAR RECORD

07-08	08-09	09-10	10-11	11-12	12-13	13-14	14-15	15-16	16-17
MCmP 13	MCmP 6	MCmP 12	MCmP 2	MCmP 11	MCmP 4	MCmP 3	MFL1 17	MFL1 3	MFL1 10
FAC EP	FAC P	FAC P	FAC P	FAC EP	FAC 2Q	FAC EP	FAC EP		FAC EPr
FAV 2Qr	FAV 1Q	FAV 1Q	FAV 1Q	FAV 1Q	FAV 2Q	FAV 2Q	FAV 1P	FAV 5P	FAV 3P

PAGET RANGERS

Founded: 2011   Nickname: Bears or The Wee Gers

Secretary: Rob Paterson   **(T)** 07528 177 046   **(E)** paterson_r3@sky.com
Chairman: Matthew Dainty   **Manager:** Jason Lanns   **Prog Ed:** John Bird
Ground: Trevor Brown Memorial Ground, Church Road, Boldmere, Birmingham, B73 5RY   **(T)** 07528 177 046
Colours(change): Black & gold stripes/black/black & gold hoops (All blue)
HONOURS: FA Comps: None   **League:** None

10 YEAR RECORD

07-08	08-09	09-10	10-11	11-12	12-13	13-14	14-15	15-16	16-17
						MCm2 3	MFL2 11	MFL2 4	MFL2 2
								FAV 1Q	FAV 2P

PERSHORE TOWN

Founded: 1988   Nickname: Town

Secretary: Cindy Webb   **(T)** 07590 408 205   **(E)** cindywebb1@hotmail.co.uk
Chairman: Steve BRadstock
Ground: King George V Playing Field, King George's Way, Pershore WR10 1QU   **(T)**   **Capacity:** 1,000
Colours(change): Blue & white
HONOURS: FA Comps: None   **League:** Midland Combination Division Two 1989-90, Premier 1993-94.

10 YEAR RECORD

07-08	08-09	09-10	10-11	11-12	12-13	13-14	14-15	15-16	16-17
MCmP 8	MCmP 13	MCmP 20	MCmP 13	MCmP 16	MCmP 13	MCmP 15	MFL1 11	MFL1 14	MFL1 18
	FAC EP	FAC EP							
FAV 1Q	FAV 2Q	FAV 2Q	FAV 2Q	FAV 2Q	FAV 2Q	FAV 2Q	FAV 2Q	FAV 1Q	FAV 1Q

RACING CLUB WARWICK

Founded: 1919   Nickname: Racers

Secretary: Pat Murphy   **(T)** 07926 188 553   **(E)** pja.murphy@hotmail.co.uk
Chairman:
Ground: Townsend Meadow, Hampton Road, Warwick, Warwickshire CV34 6JP   **(T)** 01926 495 786   **Capacity:** 1,300
Colours(change): Gold/black/black
HONOURS: FA Comps: None   **League:** Warwick 1933-34, 34-35, 35-36. Leamington & District 37-38, 45-46, 46-47, 47-48. Midland Combination Premier Division 1987-88.

10 YEAR RECORD

07-08	08-09	09-10	10-11	11-12	12-13	13-14	14-15	15-16	16-17
MidAl 18	MidAl 21	MCmP 22	MCmP 19	MCmP 13	MCmP 17	MCmP 12	MFL1 18	MFL1 10	MFL1 6
FAC EP	FAC P								
FAV 2Q	FAV 1P		FAV 1Q	FAV 2P	FAV 2Q	FAV 1P	FAV 1Q	FAV 2P	FAV 1Q

STAFFORD TOWN

Founded: 1976   Nickname: Reds or Town

Secretary: David Howard   **(T)** 07789 110 923   **(E)** staffordtown@hotmail.co.uk
Chairman: Gordon Evans   Dave Downing   David Howard
Ground: Evans Park, Riverway, Stafford ST16 3TH   **(T)** 07789 110 923   **Capacity:** 2,500
Colours(change): All red (All yellow)
HONOURS: FA Comps: None   **League:** Midland Combination Division Two 1978-79.
West Midlands (Regional) Division One 1993-94, Premier 1999-2000.

10 YEAR RECORD

07-08	08-09	09-10	10-11	11-12	12-13	13-14	14-15	15-16	16-17
WM1 4	WM1 4	WM1 2	WMP 15	WMP 18	MCmP 11	MCmP 8	MFL1 14	MFL1 18	MFL1 16
						FAC EP	FAC P		
			FAV 1Q	FAV 2P	FAV 2Q	FAV 2Q	FAV 1Q	FAV 2Q	FAV 1Q

STUDLEY

Founded: 1971   Nickname: Bees

Secretary: Bob Fletcher   **(T)** 07745 310 077   **(E)** bobtheat@hotmail.co.uk
Chairman: Barry Cromwell
Ground: The Beehive, Abbeyfields Drive, Studley B80 7BF   **(T)** 01527 853 817   **Capacity:** 1,500
Colours(change): Blue & white
HONOURS: FA Comps: None   **League:** Midland Combination Division One 1991-92.

10 YEAR RECORD

07-08	08-09	09-10	10-11	11-12	12-13	13-14	14-15	15-16	16-17
MidAl 13	MidAl 14	MidAl 11	MidAl 7	MidAl 17	MidAl 21	MCmP 6	MFL1 10	MFLP 12	MFLP 15
FAC EPr	FAC EP	FAC P	FAC EP	FAC P	FAC P	FAC P	FAC EP		
FAV 4P	FAV 2Pr	FAV 1P	FAV 1P	FAV 2Q	FAV 1Q	FAV 2Q	FAV 1P	FAV 2Q	FAV 1Q

UTTOXETER TOWN

Founded: 1983　　Nickname: Town

Secretary: Andy Hornsey　　**(T)** 07545 273 826　　**(E)** andy@hornseys.co.uk
Chairman: Peter Douglas
Ground: Oldfields Sports Ground, Springfield Road, Uttoxeter, ST14 7JX　　**(T)** 01889 564 347　　**Capacity:** 1,000
Colours(change): Yellow & blue
HONOURS: FA Comps: None　　　**League:** None

10 YEAR RECORD

07-08	08-09	09-10	10-11	11-12	12-13	13-14	14-15	15-16	16-17
						StfSP 2	MFL1 5	StfSP 6	MFL1 11
								FAV 3P	FAV 2P

WALSALL WOOD

Founded: 1915　　Nickname: The Wood or The Prims

Secretary: George Evangelou　　**(T)** 07775 512 373　　**(E)** gevangelou67@gmail.com
Chairman: Justin Hodgin
Ground: Oak Park, Lichfield Road, Walsall Wood, Walsall WS9 9NP　　**(T)**
Colours(change): Red & white
HONOURS: FA Comps: None　　　**League:** Worcestershire/Midland Combination 1951-52, 2012-13.

10 YEAR RECORD

07-08	08-09	09-10	10-11	11-12	12-13	13-14	14-15	15-16	16-17
MidCo 11	MidCo 7	MidCo 6	MidCo 9	MidCo 14	MidCo 1	MidAl 6	WMP 4	MFLP 7	MFLP 20
	FAC EP	FAC EP	FAC EP	FAC EP		FAC 1Qr	FAC P	FAC EPr	FAC EP
FAV 2Q	FAV 2Q	FAV 1P	FAV 2Q	FAV 2Q	FAV QFr	FAV 2P	FAV 4Pr	FAV 3P	FAV 1P

Midland Football League Division Two

BARNT GREEN SPARTEK	The Coppice, Tythe Barn Lane, Shirley, Solihull B90 1PN	07786 983 961
BLOXWICH TOWN	Old Red Lion Ground, Somerfield Road, Walsall, WS3 2EH	07964 941 637
COTON GREEN	New Mill Lane, Fazeley, Tamworth, B78 3RX	07904 587 286
DROITWICH SPA	Walshes Meadow, Harold Davies Drive, Stourport on Severn DY13 0AA	07821 141 568
EARLSWOOD TOWN	The Pavilions, Malthouse Lane, Earlswood, Solihull, B94 5DX	07967 583 896
FAIRFIELD VILLA	Recreation Ground, Stourbridge Road, Fairfield, Bromsgrove, Worcs. B61 9LZ	07834 808 348
FECKENHAM	Studley Sports & Social Club, Eldorado Close, Studley, Warwickshire, B80 7HP	07703 020 499
HAMPTON	Hampton Sports Club, Field Lane, Solihull, B91 2RT	07786 915 274
KNOWLE	The Robins Nest, Hampton Road, Knowle, Solihull, B93 0NX	07738 822 916
MONTPELLIER	The Beehive, Abbeyfields Drive, Studley B80 7BF	07717 731 100
MOORS ACADEMY	Tally Ho Training Centre, Pershore Road, Edgbaston, Birmingham B5 7RZ	07469 875 966
NKF BURBAGE	Kirkby Road Sports Ground, Kirkby Road, Barwell LE9 8FQ	07702 086 427
NORTHFELD TOWN	Shenley Lane Com. Assoc., 472 Shenley Lane, Selly Oak, Birmingham B29 4HZ	07929 232 427
PELSALL VILLA	The Bush Ground, Walsall Road, Walsall, West Midlands WS3 4BP	07982 143 343
REDDITCH BOROUGH	The Meitis & SS Club, Cherry Tree Walk, Batchley, Redditch B97 6PB	07714 460 273
SMITHSWOOD FIRS	The Glades, Lugtrout Lane, Solihull B91 2RX	07785 951 894

CLUB MOVEMENTS
Division Two
Out: Paget Rangers (P), Southam United (W). Sutton United (W).

Division Three
In: Bartestree. Birmingham Tigers. CT Shush. GNP Sports.
Out: Barton United (W).

RESERVE DIVISION	P	W	D	L	F	A	GD	Pts
1 Gresley Res	18	14	1	3	56	26	30	43
2 Walsall Wood Res	18	12	2	4	49	27	22	38
3 Cadbury Athletic Res	18	10	4	4	38	27	11	34
4 Rocester Res	18	9	4	5	53	28	25	31
5 Romulus Res	18	9	2	7	48	50	-2	29
6 Continental Star Res	18	5	6	7	34	35	-1	21
7 Coton Green Res	18	5	4	9	27	34	-7	19
8 Lichfield City Res	18	4	3	11	41	59	-18	15
9 Brocton Res	18	3	4	11	40	58	-18	13
10 Tipton Town Res	18	3	2	13	27	69	-42	11

NORTH WEST COUNTIES LEAGUE

Sponsored by: Hallmark Security
Founded: 1982

Recent Champions: 2014: Norton United
2015: Glossop North End **2016:** Colne

PREMIER DIVISION	P	W	D	L	F	A	GD	Pts	DIVISION ONE	P	W	D	L	F	A	GD	Pts
1 Atherton Collieries	42	32	4	6	103	39	64	100	1 Widnes	42	30	6	6	117	50	67	96
2 Bootle	42	30	2	10	134	57	77	92	2 Charnock Richard	42	29	5	8	117	51	66	92
3 Runcorn Town	42	29	5	8	112	52	60	92	3 Litherland REMYCA	42	27	8	7	107	60	47	89
4 Runcorn Linnets	42	27	9	6	105	45	60	90	4 City of Liverpool FC	42	27	7	8	119	45	74	88
5 1874 Northwich	42	25	7	10	81	50	31	82	5 Whitchurch Alport	42	26	7	9	97	45	52	85
6 West Didsbury & Chorlton	42	21	7	14	106	83	23	70	6 Sandbach United	42	25	6	11	81	51	30	81
7 Padiham	42	21	6	15	85	71	14	69	7 Alsager Town	42	23	5	14	98	66	32	74
8 Irlam	42	19	9	14	65	70	-5	66	8 Prestwich Heys	42	22	3	17	87	62	25	69
9 Ashton Athletic	42	17	9	16	83	74	9	60	9 Chadderton	42	20	7	15	103	80	23	67
10 Hanley Town	42	15	12	15	83	73	10	57	10 Stockport Town	42	19	8	15	92	89	3	64*
11 Barnoldswick Town	42	16	8	18	78	75	3	56	11 Silsden	42	20	2	20	83	77	6	62
12 AFC Liverpool	42	16	9	17	79	84	-5	54*	12 Cheadle Town	42	18	7	17	97	83	14	61
13 Winsford United	42	15	7	20	76	85	-9	52	13 St Helens Town	42	16	8	18	88	95	-7	56
14 Abbey Hey	42	15	7	20	63	76	-13	52	14 Carlisle City	42	16	6	20	72	92	-20	54
15 Maine Road	42	13	10	19	67	72	-5	49	15 FC Oswestry Town	42	16	5	21	73	97	-24	53
16 Congleton Town	42	12	11	19	75	89	-14	47	16 Daisy Hill	42	14	7	21	82	111	-29	49
17 Barnton	42	13	6	23	50	95	-45	45	17 Holker Old Boys	42	12	7	23	65	94	-29	43
18 AFC Darwen	42	10	11	21	50	110	-60	41	18 Bacup Borough	42	11	7	24	45	78	-33	40
19 Squires Gate	42	10	10	22	80	106	-26	40	19 AFC Blackpool	42	7	11	24	48	114	-66	32
20 New Mills	42	8	9	25	65	102	-37	33	20 Atherton LR	42	8	4	30	44	95	-51	28
21 Nelson	42	5	11	26	55	87	-32	25*	21 Eccleshall	42	4	6	32	55	145	-90	18
22 Cammell Laird 1907	42	3	11	28	40	140	-100	20	22 Ashton Town	42	5	2	35	42	132	-90	17

CLUB MOVEMENTS - Premier Division - In: Burscough (R - NPLD1N), Charnock Richard (P), City of Liverpool (P - via play-off), Northwich Victoria (R - NPLD1S), Widnes (P).
Out: Atherton Collieries (P - NPL D1N), Cammell Laird 1907 (R), Nelson (R), New Mills (R).
Division One - In: Abbey HaultonUnited (P - Staffordshire County), Cammell Laird 1907 (R), Nelson (R), New Mills (R).
Out: Charnock Richard (P), City of Liverpool (P - via play-off), Widnes (P).

PREMIER DIVISION	1	2	3	4	5	6	7	8	9	10	11	12	13	14	15	16	17	18	19	20	21	22
1 1874 Northwich		2-0	1-2	3-0	1-3	1-0	2-1	1-1	2-0	5-0	1-3	1-0	1-1	2-0	2-1	2-1	1-2	1-4	3-2	4-1	4-1	0-4
2 Abbey Hey	1-1		1-2	1-1	3-2	1-2	3-2	0-1	2-0	4-0	0-3	0-2	2-1	3-2	7-0	1-1	0-3	0-1	0-2	3-2	2-2	1-3
3 AFC Darwen	1-0	1-0		5-1	1-2	3-1	1-0	1-0	3-0	4-1	5-0	3-0	1-1	1-0	2-2	2-1	2-1	0-1	0-2	1-1	3-1	2-1
4 AFC Liverpool	1-3	1-3	1-5		2-2	0-4	2-0	1-7	0-7	0-0	0-2	1-1	3-2	0-6	0-3	1-1	1-2	0-3	0-3	4-1	3-0	2-2
5 Ashton Athletic	0-1	1-2	1-2	0-2		3-1	1-2	1-4	5-2	4-1	1-0	2-2	3-2	1-2	1-5	1-1	1-0	3-1	1-4	4-2	3-2	2-0
6 Atherton Collieries	3-2	0-1	0-4	1-3	2-2		5-1	0-6	0-4	1-1	6-2	3-2	1-3	2-2	6-0	3-0	3-1	0-3	1-1	2-1	2-3	3-0
7 Barnoldswick Town	1-0	1-1	2-5	1-0	2-1	1-0		0-3	1-0	6-0	0-0	0-4	2-1	1-1	3-3	1-0	1-6	0-4	3-0	0-0	0-3	3-2
8 Barnton	0-0	2-1	3-2	9-0	4-3	3-0	4-2		6-1	6-1	3-2	2-1	1-2	1-0	3-1	3-2	6-1	1-2	3-0	0-2	3-5	5-1
9 Bootle	2-2	3-0	1-2	1-1	5-2	0-0	0-2	1-2		2-0	3-3	2-1	3-0	1-1	2-1	4-2	1-2	0-2	7-2	2-4	1-3	2-1
10 Cammell Laird 1907	1-6	0-2	2-6	4-1	2-2	0-6	0-1	1-7	1-1		2-7	2-1	2-5	1-1	0-0	1-1	0-0	3-3	0-4	1-3	2-7	1-4
11 Congleton Town	2-4	6-1	0-4	3-3	2-2	0-1	3-4	0-2	1-1	1-0		0-0	1-2	3-1	0-3	2-3	2-2	0-0	0-3	3-2	2-1	1-1
12 Hanley Town	0-1	3-0	1-4	3-1	2-2	4-3	4-1	1-7	2-3	3-0	4-1		1-1	2-2	1-1	2-2	0-3	1-3	4-2	1-2	2-0	
13 Irlam	0-1	4-3	1-1	1-3	3-3	1-2	2-1	1-0	1-0	0-2	1-1	2-1		1-0	1-1	1-0	1-1	0-4	2-1	3-1	0-6	1-3
14 Maine Road	1-1	2-2	0-1	2-2	0-2	0-2	1-0	5-4	2-1	1-1	3-2	1-2	2-3		2-0	4-2	2-0	0-2	2-3	6-1	0-3	2-3
15 Nelson	1-3	1-2	0-2	1-2	0-1	2-2	4-0	1-4	1-2	2-2	0-3	1-2	0-2	0-1		7-4	2-2	1-2	1-1	0-0	4-4	0-2
16 New Mills	2-4	2-0	0-5	0-1	1-3	2-2	6-1	0-3	3-0	4-3	2-3	1-1	0-2	2-3	2-1		3-2	2-2	0-1	3-3	1-4	2-1
17 Padiham	1-3	6-3	1-3	1-1	3-0	2-4	2-0	0-3	0-2	4-0	2-1	1-5	3-2	4-1	1-0	4-2		1-0	2-2	1-0	3-1	4-2
18 Runcorn Linnets	1-1	2-2	2-0	8-0	3-0	2-1	5-2	5-0	2-0	3-0	5-2	2-5	4-1	1-0	3-1	4-0	4-2		1-1	4-3	2-2	0-2
19 Runcorn Town	0-2	4-0	2-1	3-1	2-1	2-0	4-1	3-2	3-4	8-0	3-4	3-1	3-0	4-1	1-0	5-0	2-0	3-1		1-1	6-2	4-0
20 Squires Gate	4-1	1-3	3-4	2-3	4-5	1-1	0-2	4-3	2-3	2-0	1-1	4-4	1-1	1-2	4-3	2-0	1-4	3-2	1-6		1-3	3-3
21 West Didsbury & Chorlton	0-1	1-0	1-3	3-0	2-2	2-5	4-1	2-4	3-3	6-1	3-1	1-2	1-2	1-1	1-0	4-3	1-0	1-4	4-1	2-3		4-2
22 Winsford United	1-4	0-2	0-2	1-1	2-0	2-2	2-2	0-3	2-1	6-1	4-2	1-3	2-3	3-2	2-0	3-1	2-5	1-1	0-1	4-2	1-3	

NORTH WEST COUNTIES LEAGUE - STEP 5/6

THE MACRON CUP

HOLDERS: ATHERTON COLLIERIES

ROUND 1
Barnton	v	Nelson	1-2
Carlisle City	v	Ashton Athletic	0-2
Congleton Town	v	Prestwich Heys	3-4 aet
FC Oswestry Town	v	Irlam	1-1, 5-4p
Padiham	v	1874 Northwich	2-3
Runcorn Linnets	v	Daisy Hill	4-2
Sandbach United	v	Stockport Town	4-2
Squires Gate	v	New Mills	0-1
St Helens Town	v	AFC Darwen	4-2
West Didsbury & Chorltonv	v	Barnoldswick Town	1-3
Widnes	v	Alsager Town	5-3
Winsford United	v	Atherton LR	4-0

ROUND 2
1874 Northwich	v	AFC Blackpool	2-1
Bootle	v	AFC Liverpool	3-0
Widnes	v	Cheadle Town	3-0
Ashton Town	v	Abbey Hey	1-3
Barnoldswick Town	v	Cammell Laird 1907	2-1
Eccleshall	v	St Helens Town	3-5
Hanley Town	v	Charnock Richard	2-1
Holker Old Boys	v	Chadderton	3-6
Nelson	v	FC Oswestry Town	1-0
New Mills	v	Silsden	2-8
Prestwich Heys	v	City of Liverpool	1-3
Runcorn Linnets	v	Ashton Athletic	2-3
Runcorn Town	v	Bacup Borough	3-2
Sandbach United	v	Atherton Collieries	1-2
Whitchurch Alport	v	Maine Road	1-2
Winsford United	v	Litherland REMYCA	1-0

ROUND 3
Ashton Athletic	v	Runcorn Town	2-0
Nelson	v	Atherton Collieries	3-0
Maine Road	v	Chadderton	1-3
Silsden	v	1874 Northwich	1-0
City of Liverpool	v	Hanley Town	2-0
Winsford United	v	Widnes	1-2
Barnoldswick Town	v	Abbey Hey	1-1, 4-3p
Bootle	v	St Helens Town	5-1

QUARTER FINALS
Ashton Athletic	v	Bootle	2-5
Nelson	v	Chadderton	1-3
Silsden	v	City of Liverpool	0-2
Widnes	v	Barnoldswick Town	0-1

SEMI FINALS (over two legs)
Barnoldswick Town	v	Bootle	1-0
Bootle	v	Barnoldswick Town	2-3
City of Liverpool	v	Chadderton	0-2
Chadderton	v	City of Liverpool	0-2, 3-4p

FINAL
Barnoldswick Town	v	City of Liverpool	1-1, 2-3p

THE REUSCH FIRST DIVISION CUP

HOLDERS: BARNTON

ROUND 1
AFC Blackpool	v	Carlisle City	2-3
Bacup Borough	v	Chadderton	1-2
Eccleshall	v	Stockport Town	1-7
Holker Old Boys	v	Ashton Town	4-1
Prestwich Heys	v	Litherland REMYCA	2-1
Widnes	v	FC Oswestry Town	4-1

ROUND 2 NORTH
Carlisle City	v	Atherton LR	3-2
Charnock Richard	v	Chadderton	2-0
Holker Old Boys	v	Silsden	3-1
St Helens Town	v	Daisy Hill	2-0

ROUND 2 SOUTH
City of Liverpool	v	Cheadle Town	2-1
Sandbach United	v	Stockport Town	5-0
Whitchurch Alport	v	Alsager Town	4-0
Widnes	v	Prestwich Heys	4-0

QUARTER FINALS
St Helens Town	v	City of Liverpool	0-3
Carlisle City	v	Sandbach United	0-1
Charnock Richard	v	Widnes	1-4
Holker Old Boys	v	Whitchurch Alport	3-2

SEMI FINALS (over two legs)
Widnes	v	City of Liverpool	0-1
City of Liverpool	v	City of Liverpool	3-0
Holker Old Boys	v	Sandbach United	1-3
Sandbach United	v	Holker Old Boys	2-3

FINAL
City of Liverpool	v	Sandbach United	1-0

DIVISION ONE	1	2	3	4	5	6	7	8	9	10	11	12	13	14	15	16	17	18	19	20	21	22
1 AFC Blackpool		1-1	2-1	0-5	2-3	2-3	0-0	1-1	2-2	1-3	0-4	1-1	0-3	0-1	0-5	3-5	2-1	1-3	0-6	0-2	0-1	1-5
2 Alsager Town	1-2		0-2	2-1	1-1	1-0	6-1	0-3	0-1	2-2	1-2	1-2	0-1	0-1	1-0	1-2	1-3	4-2	2-3	0-0	0-1	2-4
3 Ashton Town	6-1	3-1		3-1	5-0	2-0	0-3	2-1	0-2	1-2	4-2	6-1	0-0	1-1	1-2	0-3	3-1	3-1	2-1	3-1	0-1	1-2
4 Atherton LR	3-0	2-3	0-4		1-2	3-2	1-4	1-3	0-1	1-5	2-1	3-3	1-3	2-0	0-2	0-4	0-1	0-2	2-3	0-2	0-9	0-6
5 Bacup Borough	4-0	2-2	0-4	4-0		1-3	0-2	2-3	1-2	1-4	2-1	1-2	0-1	2-0	2-3	0-3	0-2	1-1	2-1	2-1	0-0	0-1
6 Carlisle City	3-1	3-0	5-3	4-2	0-0		0-1	2-1	0-6	2-3	6-2	2-1	2-1	2-2	1-0	1-3	0-3	4-3	2-1	2-2	0-0	0-3
7 Chadderton	7-0	3-5	1-3	5-1	1-0	4-0		1-1	1-3	1-2	5-4	9-0	4-2	3-2	3-3	1-1	1-0	2-5	1-2	2-3	3-0	1-2
8 Charnock Richard	2-2	6-0	1-2	3-0	0-1	2-1	5-4		1-5	2-5	4-0	3-5	1-4	3-1	2-0	0-3	1-2	3-3	5-2	2-0	3-3	1-4
9 Cheadle Town	6-2	8-0	2-0	0-0	3-2	6-1	5-0	1-2		1-1	2-2	4-0	1-0	6-1	4-0	2-4	0-0	5-1	2-1	4-2	2-3	1-2
10 City of Liverpool FC	2-3	2-1	1-4	3-0	3-0	2-2	3-0	6-1	4-3		3-0	3-1	1-0	8-0	5-2	0-1	3-1	1-3	0-0	2-2	2-3	4-2
11 Daisy Hill	1-0	3-2	3-2	2-0	1-2	1-2	2-2	1-4	2-1	0-7		2-1	3-1	2-1	1-4	0-0	3-3	2-2	5-4	5-2	3-7	2-2
12 Eccleshall	0-4	0-1	4-4	5-4	1-2	2-4	1-7	1-5	1-2	0-3	3-3		1-2	1-3	1-2	1-6	0-4	2-4	2-3	0-5	1-3	
13 FC Oswestry Town	2-2	3-1	2-4	3-1	3-0	2-1	4-5	2-1	0-4	0-5	0-1	2-2		4-2	4-0	0-4	1-5	3-2	6-6	0-0	0-3	1-3
14 Holker Old Boys	0-1	2-0	1-2	4-2	1-1	4-3	1-4	2-5	1-2	0-3	3-2	4-1	7-1		1-3	1-0	0-1	2-1	1-2	2-2	3-0	0-1
15 Litherland REMYCA	0-1	6-0	1-2	2-1	5-0	4-0	0-0	2-1	1-0	0-3	2-1	5-2	5-2	5-1		2-3	0-2	3-0	2-0	0-1	1-2	1-3
16 Prestwich Heys	2-2	3-0	4-1	5-1	4-2	3-0	2-2	3-3	2-3	2-3	3-2	3-1	4-2	2-0	0-2		1-1	1-2	1-2	5-3	2-2	6-5
17 Sandbach United	1-0	1-0	3-3	5-1	1-0	1-1	2-0	2-1	2-1	3-1	3-2	3-1	4-1	1-2	1-3	0-2		2-1	2-0	1-3	0-3	3-0
18 Silsden	2-2	3-0	2-2	5-1	0-3	4-4	1-3	4-2	2-2	2-3	4-2	1-0	2-1	4-2	2-4	2-4	2-1		2-6	2-0	2-3	1-1
19 St Helens Town	5-2	2-0	2-1	6-0	2-1	2-1	1-0	0-3	0-2	0-1	7-2	2-1	0-3	3-2	3-2	0-1	1-2	1-4		1-2	0-3	1-4
20 Stockport Town	3-1	3-2	3-2	7-0	1-1	3-1	3-4	1-5	0-10	1-0	3-4	7-1	2-3	2-2	3-1	4-0	2-1	3-1	2-1		1-5	2-3
21 Whitchurch Alport	2-1	2-1	1-2	4-0	3-0	3-1	3-0	0-0	1-2	0-2	2-0	5-0	2-0	3-0	1-3	1-2	1-1	3-0	0-1	2-1		2-5
22 Widnes	7-0	3-0	1-4	3-0	2-0	3-1	1-2	2-1	0-0	2-1	3-1	5-0	5-0	2-2	1-0	2-2	2-0	8-0	1-0	2-2	1-3	

1874 NORTHWICH
Founded: 2012 **Nickname:**

Secretary: Vicki England **(T)** **(E)**
Chairman: Paul Stockton **Manager:** Paul Bowyer & Wayne Goodison **Prog Ed:** programme@1874northwich.com
Ground: Winsford United FC, Wharton Road, Winsford, Cheshire CW7 3AE **(T)** 01606 558 447
Capacity: 6,000 **Seats:** Seats **Covered:** Yes **Midweek Matchday:** Tuesday **Clubhouse:** Yes
Colours(change): Green/black/green (All orange)
Previous Names: None
Previous Leagues: None

HONOURS: FA Comps: None
League: None

10 YEAR RECORD

07-08	08-09	09-10	10-11	11-12	12-13	13-14	14-15	15-16	16-17
						NWC1 3	NWCP 3	NWCP 4	NWCP 5
							FAC Pr	FAC P	FAC Pr
						FAV 1Q	FAV 3P	FAV 2P	FAV 2P

ABBEY HEY
Founded: 1902 **Nickname:** Red Rebels

Secretary: Tony McAllister **(T)** 0161 231 7147 **(E)**
Chairman: James Whittaker **Manager:** Luke Gibson **Prog Ed:** Colin Worrall
Ground: The Abbey Stadium, Goredale Avenue, Gorton, Manchester M18 7HD **(T)** 0161 231 7147
Capacity: 1,000 **Seats:** Yes **Covered:** Yes **Midweek Matchday:** Tuesday **Clubhouse:** Yes
Colours(change): Red/black/red (Blue/white/blue & white)
Previous Names: Abbey Hey W.M.C.
Previous Leagues: Manchester Amateur, South East Lancashire, Manchester.

HONOURS: FA Comps: None
League: Manchester Amateur League 1964-65. South East Lancashire 1966-67, 68-69.
10 YEAR RECORD Manchester League Division One 1970-71, Premier 1981-82, 88-89, 88-89, 91-92, 93-94, 94-95.

07-08	08-09	09-10	10-11	11-12	12-13	13-14	14-15	15-16	16-17
NWC1 17	NWCP 21	NWCP 22	NWC1 15	NWC1 3	NWC1 2	NWCP 20	NWCP 14	NWCP 10	NWCP 14
FAC EP	FAC EPr	FAC EP	FAC EPr		FAC 2Q	FAC EP	FAC EP	FAC 2Q	FAC EP
FAV 1Q	FAV 2P	FAV 2Q	FAV 2Qr	FAV 2Q	FAV 1Q	FAV 1Q	FAV 2Q	FAV 1P	FAV 2Q

AFC DARWEN
Founded: 2009 **Nickname:** Salmoners

Secretary: Elaine Littler **(T)** **(E)**
Chairman: TBC **Manager:** Mark Patterson **Prog Ed:** Steve Hart
Ground: WEC Group Anchor Ground, Anchor Road, Darwen, Lancs BB3 0BB **(T)** 01254 776 193
Capacity: 4,000 **Seats:** Yes **Covered:** Yes **Midweek Matchday:** Wednesday **Clubhouse:** Yes
Colours(change): All red (All navy blue)
Previous Names: None
Previous Leagues: West Lancashire 2009-10.

HONOURS: FA Comps: None
League: None

10 YEAR RECORD

07-08	08-09	09-10	10-11	11-12	12-13	13-14	14-15	15-16	16-17
		WLaP 8	NWC1 13	NWC1 13	NWC1 5	NWC1 9	NWC1 3	NWCP 18	NWCP 18
								FAC EP	FAC EPr
				FAV 1P		FAV 2Q	FAV 2P	FAV 2Q	FAV 1Q

AFC LIVERPOOL
Founded: 2008 **Nickname:** Little Reds

Secretary: Adrian Cork **(T)** **(E)**
Chairman: Chris Stirrup **Manager:** Chris Stammers **Prog Ed:** Paul Smith
Ground: Marine FC, College Road, Crosby, Liverpool L23 3AS **(T)** 0151 9241743 or 0151 286 9101
Capacity: 3,185 **Seats:** 400 **Covered:** 1,400 **Midweek Matchday:** Wednesday **Clubhouse:** Yes **Shop:** Yes
Colours(change): All red (Yellow/black/yellow)
Previous Names: None
Previous Leagues: None

HONOURS: FA Comps: None
League: None

10 YEAR RECORD

07-08	08-09	09-10	10-11	11-12	12-13	13-14	14-15	15-16	16-17
	NWC1 4	NWC1 5	NWC1 4	NWCP 19	NWCP 11	NWCP 7	NWCP 9	NWCP 17	NWCP 12
			FAC EP	FAC EPr	FAC P	FAC P	FAC EP	FAC 1Q	FAC EPr
	FAV 2Q	FAV 3P	FAV 2Qr	FAV 1P	FAV 1Q	FAV 1Q	FAV 2Q	FAV 1Q	FAV 1P

ASHTON ATHLETIC
Founded: 1968   **Nickname:** Yellows

Secretary: J.S. (Taffy) Roberts   **(T)**   **(E)**
Chairman: Jimmy Whyte   **Manager:** Jay Foulds, Ben Kay & Dougie Pitts   **Prog Ed:** Pete Barton
Ground: Brocstedes Park, Downall Green, Ashton in Markerfield WN4 0NR   **(T)** 01942 716 360
Capacity: 600   **Seats:** 100   **Covered:** 300   **Midweek Matchday:** Tuesday   **Clubhouse:** Yes

Colours(change): All yellow. (All blue).
Previous Names: None.
Previous Leagues: Lancashire Combination, Manchester Amateur League

HONOURS: FA Comps: None
League: None

10 YEAR RECORD

07-08	08-09	09-10	10-11	11-12	12-13	13-14	14-15	15-16	16-17
NWC2 3	NWCP 6	NWCP 21	NWCP 22	NWCP 14	NWCP 20	NWCP 6	NWCP 5	NWCP 7	NWCP 9
	FAC EP	FAC EP	FAC EP	FAC Pr	FAC Pr	FAC P	FAC EP	FAC EPr	FAC 2Q
FAV 2P	FAV 1Pr	FAV 1Q	FAV 1Q	FAV 2Q	FAV 1Q	FAV 2Q	FAV 2Q	FAV 1Qr	FAV 2Q

BARNOLDSWICK TOWN
Founded: 1972   **Nickname:** Town or Barlick

Secretary: Alyson Hames   **(T)**   **(E)**
Chairman: Stuart Airdrie   **Manager:** Danny Craig   **Prog Ed:** Anthony Craig
Ground: Silentnight Stadium, West Close Road, Barnoldswick, Colne, BB18 5LJ   **(T)** 07528 410 204
Capacity: **Seats:** Yes   **Covered:** Yes   **Midweek Matchday:** Tuesday   **Clubhouse:** Yes

Colours(change): Yellow & Blue/blue/blue (All red)
Previous Names: Today's club formed after the merger of Barnoldswick United and Barnoldswick Park Rovers in 2003
Previous Leagues: Craven, East Lancashire, West Lancashire.

HONOURS: FA Comps: None
League: West Lancashire Division One 1998-99.

10 YEAR RECORD

07-08	08-09	09-10	10-11	11-12	12-13	13-14	14-15	15-16	16-17
WLaP 10	WLaP 6	NWC1 2	NWCP 7	NWCP 4	NWCP 9	NWCP 16	NWCP 19	NWCP 9	NWCP 11
				FAC EP	FAC EP	FAC EPr	FAC EP	FAC EP	FAC EPr
			FAV 2Q	FAV 2P	FAV 3P	FAV 2Q	FAV 2Q	FAV 2Q	FAV 1P

BARNTON
Founded: 1946   **Nickname:** Villagers

Secretary: Andy Williams   **(T)**   **(E)**
Chairman: Tim Burton   **Manager:** Steve Lloyd   **Prog Ed:** Karl Ladley
Ground: Townfield, Townfield Lane, Barnton, Cheshire CW8 4LH   **(T)** 07484 793 822
Capacity: **Seats:** Yes   **Covered:** Yes   **Midweek Matchday:** Monday   **Clubhouse:** Yes

Colours(change): White & black stripes/black/black (Orange/blue/blue)
Previous Names: None
Previous Leagues: Mid-Cheshire. Cheshire

HONOURS: FA Comps: None
League: Mid-Cheshire/Cheshire 1979-80, 82-83, 88-89, 96-97, 97-98, 98-99, 99-2000, 2000-01, 01-02, 02-03, 04-05, Division Two 2012-13.

10 YEAR RECORD

07-08	08-09	09-10	10-11	11-12	12-13	13-14	14-15	15-16	16-17
Ches1 11	Ches1 16	Ches2 10	Ches2 13	Ches2 13	Ches2 1	Ches1 5	NWC1 7	NWC1 3	NWCP 17
									FAC EP
								FAV 2Q	FAV 2Q

BOOTLE
Founded: 1953   **Nickname:** Bucks

Secretary: Joe Doran   **(T)** 0151 531 0665   **(E)**
Chairman: Bobby Capstick   **Manager:** Joe Doran   **Prog Ed:** Dave Miley Junior
Ground: TDP Solicitors Stadium, Vestey Rd, Off Bridle Road, Bootle L30 1NY   **(T)** 0151 525 4796
Capacity: 1,750   **Seats:**   **Covered:** Yes   **Midweek Matchday:** Tuesday   **Clubhouse:** Yes

Colours(change): All blue (All yellow)
Previous Names: Langton Dock 1953 - 1973.
Previous Leagues: Liverpool Shipping. Lancashire Combination. Cheshire. Liverpool County Combination >2006.

HONOURS: FA Comps: None
League: Liverpool County Combination 1964-65, 65-66, 67-68, 68-69, 69-70, 70-71, 71-72, 72-73, 73-74.
Lancashire Comb. 1975-76, 76-77. Cheshire County Div.2 1978-79. North West Counties Div.1 2008-09.

10 YEAR RECORD

07-08	08-09	09-10	10-11	11-12	12-13	13-14	14-15	15-16	16-17
NWC2 6	NWC1 1	NWCP 3	NWCP 6	NWCP 3	NWCP 3	NWCP 8	NWCP 7	NWCP 8	NWCP 2
FAC EP	FAC 1Q	FAC P	FAC P	FAC P	FAC 1Q	FAC 1Qr	FAC EP	FAC EP	FAC P
FAV 2P	FAV 4P	FAV 4P	FAV 2P	FAV 2Q	FAV 2P	FAV 1P	FAV 1P	FAV 2Q	FAV 3P

BURSCOUGH
Founded: 1946   Nickname: Linnets

Secretary: Steve Halliwell **(T)** **(E)**
Chairman: Mike Swift **Manager:** Dave Sutton **Prog Ed:** Tony Dean
Ground: Victoria Park, Bobby Langton Way, Mart Lane, Burscough L40 0SD **(T)** 01704 896 776
Capacity: 2,500 **Seats:** 270 **Covered:** 1,000 **Midweek Matchday:** Tuesday **Clubhouse:** Yes **Shop:** Yes

Colours(change): White & green/white/white (All sky blue)
Previous Names: None
Previous Leagues: Liverpool County Combination 1946-53, Lancashire Combination 1953-70, Cheshire County 1970-82, North West Counties 1982-98, Northern Premier League 1998-2007, 09-17, Conference 2007-09.
HONOURS: FA Comps: FA Trophy 2002-03.
League: North West Counties Division One 1982-83. Northern Premier Premier Division 2006-07.

10 YEAR RECORD	07-08	08-09	09-10	10-11	11-12	12-13	13-14	14-15	15-16	16-17
	Conf N 8	Conf N 21	NP P 16	NP P 19	NP P 22	NP1N 11	NP1N 14	NP1N 15	NP1N 5	NP1N 22
	FAC 2Q	FAC 2Q	FAC 3Q	FAC 1Q	FAC 1Qr	FAC 1Q	FAC 2Q	FAC 1Q	FAC 3Q	FAC 2Q
	FAT 3Q	FAT 1P	FAT 1Q	FAT 1Q	FAT 1Q	FAT 2Q	FAT 1Qr	FAT P	FAT 1Pr	FAT P

CHARNOCK RICHARD
Founded: 1933   Nickname:

Secretary: David Rowland **(T)** **(E)**
Chairman: Shaun Tootell **Manager:** Andy Westwell **Prog Ed:** Andrew Calvert
Ground: Mossie Park, Charter Lane, Charnock Richard, Chorley PR7 5LZ **(T)** 01257 794 288
Capacity: **Seats:** Yes **Covered:** Yes **Midweek Matchday:** Tuesday **Clubhouse:** Yes

Colours(change): Green & white/green/green & white (Yellow/blue/yellow)
Previous Names: None
Previous Leagues: Chorley Alliance (Sunday). Preston & District. West Lancashire >2016

HONOURS: FA Comps: None
League: Chorley Alliance 1947-48, 56-57. Preston & District 1960-61, 66-67, 67-68, 68-69, 89-90.
West Lancashire Division One 1997-98, Premier 2002-03, 08-09, 11-12, 12-13, 13-14, 14-15.

10 YEAR RECORD	07-08	08-09	09-10	10-11	11-12	12-13	13-14	14-15	15-16	16-17
	WLaP 3	WLaP 1	WLaP 4	WLaP 2	WLaP 1	WLaP 1	WLaP 1	WLaP 1	WLaP 2	NWC1 2
										FAV 2P

CITY OF LIVERPOOL
Founded: 2015   Nickname: The Purps

Secretary: Peter Manning **(T)** **(E)** contact@colfc.co.uk
Chairman: Paul Manning **Manager:** Simon Burton **Prog Ed:** Gary Johansen
Ground: TDP Solicitors Stadium, Vesty Road, off Bridle Road, Bootle, Liverpool L30 1NY **(T)**
Capacity: 1,750 **Seats:** Yes **Covered:** Yes **Midweek Matchday:** Tuesday **Clubhouse:** Yes

Colours(change): All purple (All gold)
Previous Names: None
Previous Leagues: None

HONOURS: FA Comps: None
League: None

10 YEAR RECORD	07-08	08-09	09-10	10-11	11-12	12-13	13-14	14-15	15-16	16-17
										NWC1 4

CONGLETON TOWN
Founded: 1901   Nickname: Bears

Secretary: Ken Mead **(T)** 01260 278 152 **(E)**
Chairman: Steve Burgess **Manager:** Ian Street **Prog Ed:** Ken Mead
Ground: Ivy Gardens, Booth Street, Crescent Road, Congleton, Cheshire CW12 4DG **(T)** 01260 274 460
Capacity: 1,450 **Seats:** 250 **Covered:** 1,200 **Midweek Matchday:** Tuesday **Clubhouse:** Yes **Shop:** Yes

Colours(change): Black & white/black/red. (Black & yellow/yellow/yellow).
Previous Names: Congleton Hornets
Previous Leagues: Crew & District, North Staffs, Macclesfield, Cheshire , Mid Cheshire, NW Co, NPL

HONOURS: FA Comps: None
League: Crewe & District 1901-02, 02-03, 03-04. North Staffs & District 1919-20. Macclesfield & District 1939-40.
Mid Cheshire 1973-74, 75-76, 77-78.

10 YEAR RECORD	07-08	08-09	09-10	10-11	11-12	12-13	13-14	14-15	15-16	16-17
	NWC1 9	NWCP 4	NWCP 5	NWCP 8	NWCP 11	NWCP 7	NWCP 10	NWCP 8	NWCP 6	NWCP 16
	FAC Pr	FAC 1Q	FAC 2Q	FAC Pr	FAC P	FAC P	FAC Pr	FAC Pr	FAC 2Q	FAC P
	FAV 2Qr	FAV 1P	FAV 2P	FAV 1Q	FAV 1Q	FAV 1P	FAV 4P	FAV 2P	FAV 1P	FAV 1P

HANLEY TOWN
Founded: 1966   Nickname:

Secretary: Simon Boswell   (T)   (E)
Chairman: John Powell   **Manager:** Michael Edwards   **Prog Ed:** Bill Knight
Ground: Abbey Lane, Bucknall, Stoke-on-Trent, Staffordshire ST2 8AJ   **(T)** 07875 137 482
Capacity: **Seats:** Yes   **Covered:** Yes   **Midweek Matchday:** Tuesday   **Clubhouse:** Yes

Colours(change): All royal blue (All red)
Previous Names: None
Previous Leagues: London 1966-67. Staffordshire County Senior 1967-76. Mid-Cheshire 1976-88, 96-98. Midland/Staffordshire County 1998-2013.
HONOURS: FA Comps: None
     League: London 1966-67. Staffordshire County Div.2 67-68, Div.1 68-69, Premier 72-73, 75-76. Mid-Cheshire Div.1 81-82. Midland/Staffordshire County Senior 2004-05, 2006-07, 11-12, 12-13. North West Counties Div.1 2015-16.

10 YEAR RECORD

07-08	08-09	09-10	10-11	11-12	12-13	13-14	14-15	15-16	16-17
			StfSP 2	StfSP 1	StfSP 1	NWC1 4	NWC1 4	NWC1 1	NWCP 10
								FAC P	FAC EPr
							FAV 1P	FAV 1Q	FAV 1P

IRLAM
Founded: 1969   Nickname: Mitchells/Shack

Secretary: Warren Dodd   **(T)** 07969 946 277   (E)
Chairman: Steve Nixon   **Manager:** Michael Dodd   **Prog Ed:** Warren Dodd
Ground: Silver Street, Irlam, Manchester M44 6HR   **(T)** 07969 946 277
Capacity: **Seats:** 150   **Covered:** Yes   **Midweek Matchday:** Tuesday   **Clubhouse:** Yes

Colours(change): All blue (Red/black/black)
Previous Names: Mitchell Shackleton.
Previous Leagues: Manchester Amateur. Manchester.
HONOURS: FA Comps: None
     League: Manchester Amateur Division Three 1973-74, Division Two 74-75. Manchester Premier Division 2002-03.

10 YEAR RECORD

07-08	08-09	09-10	10-11	11-12	12-13	13-14	14-15	15-16	16-17
MancP 8	NWC1 8	NWC1 10	NWC1 9	NWC1 10	NWC1 14	NWC1 10	NWC1 14	NWC1 2	NWCP 8
			FAC EP	FAC EP	FAC P				FAC EP
		FAV 2Q	FAV 2P	FAV 1Q	FAV 1Q	FAV 1Q	FAV 1Q	FAV 1Qr	FAV 1P

MAINE ROAD
Founded: 1955   Nickname: Blues

Secretary: Derek Barber   **(T)** 0161 431 8243   (E)
Chairman: Ron Meredith   **Manager:** Chris Hirst   **Prog Ed:** Jeff Newman
Ground: Brantingham Road, Chorlton-cum-Hardy M21 0TT   **(T)** 0161 861 0344
Capacity: 2,000   **Seats:** 200   **Covered:** 700   **Midweek Matchday:** Monday   **Clubhouse:** Yes

Colours(change): All sky blue. (Red & black stripes/black/black).
Previous Names: City Supporters Rusholme 1955-late sixties.
Previous Leagues: Rusholme Sunday 1955-66, Manchester Amateur Sunday 1966-72 & Manchester 1972-87.
HONOURS: FA Comps: None
     League: Manchester Amateur Sunday 1971-72. Manchester Premier 1982-83, 83-84, 84-85, 85-86. North West Counties Division Two 1989-90.

10 YEAR RECORD

07-08	08-09	09-10	10-11	11-12	12-13	13-14	14-15	15-16	16-17
NWC1 4	NWCP 13	NWCP 6	NWCP 13	NWCP 18	NWCP 2	NWCP 4	NWCP 15	NWCP 12	NWCP 15
FAC P	FAC Pr	FAC 1Q	FAC EPr	FAC 1Q	FAC 1Q	FAC EP	FAC EP	FAC P	FAC 1Q
FAV 2Q	FAV 1Pr	FAV 1Q	FAV 1Pr	FAV 2Q	FAV 1P	FAV 2P	FAV 1P	FAV 2Q	FAV 1Q

NORTHWICH VICTORIA
Founded: 1874   Nickname: Vics, Greens

Secretary: Dave Thomas   **(T)** 07798 564 596   **(E)** dave.thomas@northwichvics.co.uk
Chairman: Brian Turner   **Manager:** Paul Moore   **Prog Ed:** Jamie Dewshurst
Ground: Townfield Lane, Barnton, Cheshire CW8 4LH   **(T)** 01606 625 449
Capacity: **Seats:** Yes   **Covered:** Yes   **Midweek Matchday:** Tuesday   **Clubhouse:** Yes

Colours(change): Green and white/green/green (Purple/white/white)
Previous Names: None
Previous Leagues: The Combination 1890-92, 1894-98, Football League 1892-94, Cheshire 1898-1900, Manchester 1900-12 Lancashire 1912-19, Cheshire County 1919-68, Northern Premier 1968-79, Conference 1979-2010
HONOURS: FA Comps: FA Trophy 1983-84.
     League: Manchester 1902-03. Cheshire County 1956-57. Conference North 2005-06.

10 YEAR RECORD

07-08	08-09	09-10	10-11	11-12	12-13	13-14	14-15	15-16	16-17
Conf 19	Conf 22	Conf N 12	NP P 12	NP P 2	NP1S 8	NP1N 9	NP1N 4	NP1N 3	NP1S 22
FAC 1P	FAC 4Q	FAC 2P	FAC 2Qr	FAC 2Q	FAC Pr	FAC 1Q	FAC 1Qr	FAC 2P	FAC P
FAT 1P	FAT 1P	FAT 3P	FAT 1P	FAT 3P	FAT 1Q	FAT 1Pr	FAT 1Qr	FAT 1Q	FAT Pr

PADIHAM

Founded: 1878   **Nickname:** Caldersiders

Secretary: Matthew Ostle   **(T)**   **(E)**
Chairman: Shaun Astin   **Manager:** Steve Wilkes   **Prog Ed:** Rob Moss
Ground: Arbories Memorial Sports Ground, Well Street, Padiham BB12 8LE   **(T)** 01282 773 742
Capacity: 1,688 **Seats:** 159   **Covered:** Yes   **Midweek Matchday:** Wednesday   **Clubhouse:** Yes
Colours(change): All blue. (Red/blue/red).
Previous Names: None
Previous Leagues: Lancashire Comb. East Lancs Am. North East Lancs. West Lancs. North West Counties > 2013. NPL 2013-15.

HONOURS: FA Comps: None
League: West Lancashire Division Two 1971-72, 76-77, Division One 1999-00.

10 YEAR RECORD	North West Counties 2012-13.								
07-08	08-09	09-10	10-11	11-12	12-13	13-14	14-15	15-16	16-17
NWC2 12	NWC1 2	NWCP 10	NWCP 4	NWCP 15	NWCP 1	NP1N 19	NP1N 22	NWCP 11	NWCP 7
FAC EP	FAC P	FAC P	FAC EP	FAC EP	FAC P	FAC 1Q	FAC P	FAC 1Q	FAC P
FAV 2Q	FAV 1Q	FAV 2P	FAV 2Qr	FAV 2P	FAV 1Q	FAT P	FAT 1Q	FAV 1Q	FAV 2P

RUNCORN LINNETS

Founded: 2006   **Nickname:** Linnets

Secretary: Steve Dale   **(T)**   **(E)**
Chairman: Mark Buckley   **Manager:** Michael Ellison   **Prog Ed:** Ellis Clarke
Ground: Millbank Linnets Stadium, Murdishaw Ave, Runcorn, Cheshire WA7 6HP   **(T)** 07050 801733 (Clubline)
Capacity: 1,600 **Seats:** Yes   **Covered:** Yes   **Midweek Matchday:** Tuesday   **Clubhouse:** Yes
Colours(change): Yellow & green/green/yellow (Orange/black/orange)
Previous Names: None
Previous Leagues: None

HONOURS: FA Comps: None
League: None

10 YEAR RECORD									
07-08	08-09	09-10	10-11	11-12	12-13	13-14	14-15	15-16	16-17
NWC1 12	NWCP 11	NWCP 11	NWCP 12	NWCP 5	NWCP 6	NWCP 2	NWCP 2	NWCP 2	NWCP 4
		FAC P	FAC P	FAC 2Q	FAC EPr	FAC 3Q	FAC P	FAC 1Q	FAC EP
FAV 1P	FAV 3P	FAV 2Q	FAV 1P	FAV 1P	FAV 1P	FAV 1P	FAV 1P	FAV 2P	FAV 1P

RUNCORN TOWN

Founded: 1967   **Nickname:** Town

Secretary: Martin Fallon   **(T)**   **(E)**
Chairman: Tony Riley   **Manager:** Chris Herbert   **Prog Ed:** Martin Fallon
Ground: Pavilions Sports Complex, Sandy Lane, Weston Point, Runcorn WA7 4EX   **(T)** 01928 590 508
Capacity: 1,530 **Seats:** Yes   **Covered:** Yes   **Midweek Matchday:** Wednesday   **Clubhouse:** Yes
Colours(change): Navy blue/navy blue/sky blue (All red)
Previous Names: Mond Rangers 1967-2005 (Amalgamated with ICI Weston 1974-75).
Previous Leagues: Runcorn Sunday 1967-73, Warrington & District 1973-84, West Cheshire 1984-10.

HONOURS: FA Comps: None
League: West Cheshire League Division Two 2006-07.

10 YEAR RECORD									
07-08	08-09	09-10	10-11	11-12	12-13	13-14	14-15	15-16	16-17
WCh1 3	WCh1 4	WCh1 3	NWC1 2	NWCP 2	NWCP 4	NWCP 5	NWCP 13	NWCP 13	NWCP 3
				FAC 1Q	FAC 1Q	FAC P	FAC 3Q	FAC P	FAC EP
			FAV 4P	FAV 4Pr	FAV 5P	FAV 2P	FAV 2P	FAV 3Pr	FAV 1P

SQUIRES GATE

Founded: 1948   **Nickname:** Gate

Secretary: John Maguire   **(T)** 01253 348 512   **(E)**
Chairman: Stuart Hopwood   **Manager:** Daniel Penswick   **Prog Ed:** Daniel Hayden
Ground: Brian Addison Stadium, School Road, Marton, Blackpool, Lancs FY4 5DS   **(T)** 01253 348 512
Capacity: 1,000 **Seats:** 100   **Covered:** Yes   **Midweek Matchday:** Tuesday   **Clubhouse:** Yes
Colours(change): All blue. (All red)
Previous Names: Squires Gate British Legion FC >1953.
Previous Leagues: Blackpool & District Amateur 1958-61. West Lancashire 1961-91.

HONOURS: FA Comps: None
League: Blackpool & District Amateur League Division One 1955-56, 56-57.

10 YEAR RECORD	West Lancashire League Division Two 1980-81.								
07-08	08-09	09-10	10-11	11-12	12-13	13-14	14-15	15-16	16-17
NWC1 6	NWCP 10	NWCP 13	NWCP 9	NWCP 16	NWCP 21	NWCP 19	NWCP 6	NWCP 19	NWCP 19
FAC EP	FAC Pr	FAC EPr	FAC EP	FAC 1Qr	FAC EP	FAC EP	FAC 1Qr	FAC EPr	FAC 1Q
FAV 2Pr	FAV 1P	FAV 2Q	FAV 2Q	FAV 3P	FAV 2Q	FAV 2Q	FAV 1Q	FAV 2Q	FAV 1Q

WEST DIDSBURY & CHORLTON

Founded: 1908   **Nickname:** West

Secretary: Rob McKay   **(T)**   **(E)**
Chairman: Glyn Meacher   **Manager:** Steve Settle   **Prog Ed:** John Churchman
Ground: The Recreation Ground, End of Brookburn Road, Chorlton, Manchester M21 8FF   **(T)** 07891 298 441
Capacity: 1,000   **Seats:** Yes   **Covered:** Yes   **Midweek Matchday:** Tuesday   **Clubhouse:** Yes

Colours(change): White & black/black/black (Maroon & sky blue/maroon/maroon)
Previous Names: Christ Church AFC 1908-1920. West Didsbury AFC 1920-2003.
Previous Leagues: Manchester Alliance pre 1920. Lancashire & Cheshire Amateur 1920-2006. Manchester 2006-2012.

HONOURS: FA Comps: None
League: Lancashire & Cheshire Amateur Division Two 1987-88, Division One 88-89
10 YEAR RECORD Manchester League Division One 2010-11.

07-08	08-09	09-10	10-11	11-12	12-13	13-14	14-15	15-16	16-17
Manc1 11	Manc1 5	Manc1 2	Manc1 1	MancP 7	NCE1 3	NWCP 12	NWCP 16	NWCP 5	NWCP 6
						FAC Pr	FAC P	FAC EP	FAC P
				FAV 2Q	FAV 1Q	FAV 1P	FAV 1P	FAV 1P	FAV 2Q

WIDNES

Founded: 2003   **Nickname:** Vikings

Secretary: Russell Stephenson   **(T)**   **(E)**
Chairman: Ian Ross   **Manager:** Joey Dunn   **Prog Ed:** Adam Higgins
Ground: Select Security Stadium, Lower House Lane, Widnes, Cheshire WA8 7DZ   **(T)** 0151 510 6000
Capacity: 13,350 **Seats:** Yes   **Covered:** Yes   **Midweek Matchday:** Monday   **Clubhouse:** Yes

Colours(change): White/black/white (All yellow)
Previous Names: Dragons AFC. Widnes Dragons >2012. Widnes Vikings 2012-14.
Previous Leagues: Junior Leagues 2003-12.

HONOURS: FA Comps: None
League: North West Counties Division One 2016-17.
10 YEAR RECORD

07-08	08-09	09-10	10-11	11-12	12-13	13-14	14-15	15-16	16-17
					WCh3 4	NWC1 14	NWC1 16	NWC1 13	NWC1 1
							FAV 2Q		FAV 2Q

WINSFORD UNITED

Founded: 1883   **Nickname:** Blues

Secretary: Bob Astles   **(T)**   **(E)**
Chairman: Mark Loveless   **Manager:** Lee Duckworth   **Prog Ed:** Bob Astles
Ground: The Barton Stadium, Kingsway, Winsford, Cheshire CW7 3AE   **(T)** 01606 558 447
Capacity: 3,000 **Seats:** 200   **Covered:** 5,000   **Midweek Matchday:** Monday   **Clubhouse:** Yes   **Shop:** Yes

Colours(change): All royal blue (Yellow & black/black/black).
Previous Names: Over Wanderers 1883-1887
Previous Leagues: The Combination 1902-04. Cheshire County 1919-40, 47-82. Northern Premier League 1987-2001.

HONOURS: FA Comps: None
League: Cheshire League 1920-21, 76-77.
10 YEAR RECORD North West Counties League Division Two 2006-07.

07-08	08-09	09-10	10-11	11-12	12-13	13-14	14-15	15-16	16-17
NWC1 10	NWCP 19	NWCP 19	NWCP 3	NWCP 7	NWCP 5	NWCP 14	NWCP 12	NWCP 14	NWCP 13
FAC P	FAC EPr	FAC EPr	FAC EP	FAC EPr	FAC P	FAC P	FAC EP	FAC EPr	FAC 1Qr
FAV 2Q	FAV 2Q	FAV 2P	FAV 2Q	FAV 2P	FAV 3P	FAV 2Pr	FAV 1P	FAV 1P	FAV 1Q

DIVISION ONE

ABBEY HULTON UNITED

Founded: 1947 Nickname:

Secretary: John Wrightman **(T)** **(E)**
Chairman: Lee Savage **Manager:** David Riley **Prog Ed:** L Wightman & D Foulkes
Ground: Birches Head Road, Abbey Hulton, Stoke-on-Trent ST2 8DD **(T)**
Colours(change): Orange/black/black (All grey)
HONOURS: FA Comps: None **League:** Staffordshire County Senior Premier Division 2016-17.

10 YEAR RECORD									
07-08	08-09	09-10	10-11	11-12	12-13	13-14	14-15	15-16	16-17
				StfSP 5	StfSP 4	StfSP 7	StfSP 3	StfSP 8	StfSP 1

AFC BLACKPOOL

Founded: 1947 Nickname: Mechanics

Secretary: Billy Singleton **(T)** **(E)**
Chairman: Stuart Parker **Manager:** Dave Worthington **Prog Ed:** Antony Clegg
Ground: Mechanics Ground, Jepson Way, Common Edge Road, Blackpool, FY4 5DY **(T)** 01253 761 721 **Capacity:** 2,000
Colours(change): Tangerine/Tangerine/white (All blue)
HONOURS: FA Comps: None **League:** West Lancashire League 1960-61, 61-62.
North West Counties League Division Three 1985/86, Division One 2010-11.

10 YEAR RECORD									
07-08	08-09	09-10	10-11	11-12	12-13	13-14	14-15	15-16	16-17
NWC1 9	NWC1 15	NWC1 15	NWC1 1	NWCP 9	NWCP 10	NWCP 13	NWCP 18	NWCP 22	NWC1 19
	FAC EPr			FAC Pr	FAC EP	FAC EP	FAC EP	FAC 1Q	FAC EP
FAV 2Q		FAV 2Q	FAV 2P	FAV 1Q	FAV 2Q	FAV 1P	FAV 1Q	FAV 1Q	FAV 2Q

ALSAGER TOWN

Founded: 1968 Nickname: The Bullets

Secretary: Chris Robinson **(T)** 07888 750 532 **(E)**
Chairman: Terry Greer **Manager:** Wayne Brotherton **Prog Ed:** Dave Proudlove
Ground: Woodpark Stadium, Woodland Court, Alsager ST7 2DP **(T)** 07888 750 532 **Capacity:** 3,000
Colours(change): White & black/black/white. (All red).
HONOURS: FA Comps: None **League:** None

10 YEAR RECORD									
07-08	08-09	09-10	10-11	11-12	12-13	13-14	14-15	15-16	16-17
NP1S 14	NWCP 7	NWCP 18	NWCP 20	NWCP 13	NWCP 15	NWCP 18	NWCP 17	NWCP 20	NWC1 7
FAC P	FAC EP	FAC EP	FAC EP	FAC EP	FAC EP	FAC EP	FAC EP	FAC 1Q	FAC P
FAT P	FAV 2Pr	FAV 2P	FAV 2Q	FAV 1Q	FAV 2Q	FAV 2Q	FAV 1Q	FAV 3P	FAV 2Q

ATHERTON L.R.

Founded: 1956 Nickname: The Panthers

Secretary: Andy Harrison **(T)** **(E)**
Chairman: Jane Wilcock **Manager:** Shaun Lynch **Prog Ed:** Ben Reuven
Ground: Crilly Park, Spa Road, Atherton, Manchester M46 9JX **(T)** 01942 575 173 **Capacity:** 3,000
Colours(change): Yellow/blue/yellow (Orange/black/black).
HONOURS: FA Comps: None **League:** Bolton Combination Division Two A 1965-66.
North West Counties 1992-93, 93-94.

10 YEAR RECORD									
07-08	08-09	09-10	10-11	11-12	12-13	13-14	14-15	15-16	16-17
NWC1 19	NWCP 12	NWCP 20	NWCP 10	NWCP 22	NWC1 13	NWC1 3	NWC1 12	NWC1 17	NWC1 20
FAC EP	FAC 1Q	FAC 1Qr	FAC Pr	FAC P	FAC P				
FAV 2Pr	FAV 1Q	FAV 1Q	FAV 1P	FAV 1P	FAV 1Q	FAV 1P		FAV 2Q	FAV 1P

BACUP BOROUGH

Founded: 1875 Nickname: The Boro

Secretary: Brent Peters **(T)** **(E)**
Chairman: Brent Peters **Manager:** Brent Peters **Prog Ed:** Andrew Walker
Ground: Brian Boys Stadium, Cowtoot Lane, Blackthorn, Bacup, OL13 8EE **(T)** 01706 878 655 **Capacity:** 3,000
Colours(change): Black & white/black/black. (Claret & blue/claret/claret).
HONOURS: FA Comps: None **League:** Lancashire Combination 1946-47.
North West Counties Division Two 2002-03

10 YEAR RECORD									
07-08	08-09	09-10	10-11	11-12	12-13	13-14	14-15	15-16	16-17
NWC1 18	NWCP 8	NWCP 12	NWCP 11	NWCP 17	NWCP 17	NWCP 21	NWCP 21	NWC1 5	NWC1 18
FAC P	FAC 2Q	FAC EPr	FAC 1Q	FAC EP	FAC P			FAC EP	FAC EP
FAV 2Q	FAV 2Q	FAV 2P	FAV 2P	FAV 2P	FAV 1Qr			FAV 2Q	FAV 2Q

CAMMELL LAIRD

Founded: 1907 Nickname: Lairds

Secretary: Anthony 'Toddy' Wood **(T)** 07931 761 429 **(E)** toddywood@hotmail.com
Chairman: Terry Swanicl **Manager:** Mick McGraa **Prog Ed:** Patrick Burke
Ground: Kirklands, St Peter's Road, Rock Ferry, Birkenhead CH42 1PY **(T)** 0151 645 3121 **Capacity:** 2,000
Colours(change): All royal blue (Red & black/red/black)

HONOURS: FA Comps: None **League:** West Cheshire x19 (Firstly in 1954-55 and most recently 2000-01).
North West Counties Division Two 2004-05, Division One 2005-06.

10 YEAR RECORD

07-08	08-09	09-10	10-11	11-12	12-13	13-14	14-15	15-16	16-17
NP1S 2	NP P 18	NP1S 16	NP1N 19	NP1N 22	NP1N 2	NP1N 11	NWC1 2	NWCP 15	NWCP 22
FAC 1Q	FAC 1Q	FAC 2Q	FAC P	FAC 1Q	FAC 1Q	FAC 2Q	FAC EP		
FAT P	FAT 3Qr	FAT 1Q	FAT 1Q	FAT P	FAT 3Q	FAT 1Q	FAV 1Q		

CARLISLE CITY

Founded: 1975 Nickname: Sky Blues

Secretary: Martin Denovellis **(T)** **(E)**
Chairman: Brian Hall **Manager:** James Tose **Prog Ed:** Brian Hall
Ground: Gilford Park, Carlisle CA1 3AF **(T)** 01228 523 777
Colours(change): All sky blue (All navy blue)

HONOURS: FA Comps: None **League:** Northern Alliance Division One 1991-92.

10 YEAR RECORD

07-08	08-09	09-10	10-11	11-12	12-13	13-14	14-15	15-16	16-17
NAI P 13	NAI P 6	NAI P 10	NAI P 6	NAI P 5	NAI P 3	NAI P 2	NAI P 2	NAI P 3	NWC1 14
									FAV 1Q

CHADDERTON

Founded: 1946 Nickname: Chaddy

Secretary: David Shepherd **(T)** 0161 624 9733 **(E)**
Chairman: Bob Sopel **Manager:** Mark Howard **Prog Ed:** Bob Sopel
Ground: Andrew Street, Chadderton, Oldham, Greater Manchester OL9 0JT **(T)** 07506 104 005 (MD)
Colours(change): All red (All white)

HONOURS: FA Comps: None **League:** Manchester Amateur League 1955-56, Division One 1962-63.
Manchester League Division Two 1964-65, Division One 1966-67.

10 YEAR RECORD

07-08	08-09	09-10	10-11	11-12	12-13	13-14	14-15	15-16	16-17
NWC2 5	NWC1 10	NWC1 4	NWC1 6	NWC1 6	NWC1 12	NWC1 13	NWC1 6	NWC1 14	NWC1 9
FAC EP	FAC EP	FAC EPr	FAC P	FAC EP	FAC P			FAC EP	
FAV 2Q	FAV 1Q	FAV 2Qr	FAV 1Q	FAV 2Q	FAV 2Q	FAV 1P	FAV 4P	FAV 2P	FAV 1P

CHEADLE TOWN

Founded: 1961 Nickname:

Secretary: Stuart Crawford **(T)** **(E)**
Chairman: Chris Davies **Manager:** Anthony Trucca **Prog Ed:** Andrew Calvert
Ground: Park Road Stadium, Cheadle, Cheshire SK8 2AN **(T)** 0161 428 2510
Colours(change): Green/black/green (All blue).

HONOURS: FA Comps: None **League:** Manchester Division One 1979-80.

10 YEAR RECORD

07-08	08-09	09-10	10-11	11-12	12-13	13-14	14-15	15-16	16-17
NWC2 14	NWC1 7	NWC1 14	NWC1 10	NWC1 8	NWC1 7	NWC1 11	NWC1 10	NWC1 6	NWC1 12
FAC 2Q	FAC EP	FAC EP	FAC P	FAC P	FAC EPr	FAC EP			FAC 1Q
FAV 2Q	FAV 1Q	FAV 1Pr	FAV 1Q	FAV 1P	FAV 1P	FAV 2P	FAV 1Q	FAV 2Q	FAV 1Q

DAISY HILL

Founded: 1894 Nickname: The Daisies

Secretary: Bob Naylor **(T)** **(E)**
Chairman: Graham Follows **Manager:** Craig & Marc Thomas, Brian Hart **Prog Ed:** Paul Budd
Ground: New Sirs, St James Street, Westhoughton, Bolton BL5 2EB **(T)** 01942 818 544
Colours(change): All royal blue (Red/black/black)

HONOURS: FA Comps: None **League:** Wigan & District 1896-97.
Bolton Combination Premier Division 1962-63, 72-73, 75-76, 77-78.

10 YEAR RECORD

07-08	08-09	09-10	10-11	11-12	12-13	13-14	14-15	15-16	16-17
NWC2 18	NWC1 17	NWC1 11	NWC1 14	NWC1 12	NWC1 16	NWC1 18	NWC1 8	NWC1 12	NWC1 16
FAC EP	FAC EP		FAC EP		FAC EP				
FAV 2Q	FAV 2Q	FAV 2P	FAV 1Q	FAV 1Q	FAV 2Q	FAV 1Q	FAV 1P	FAV 2P	FAV 2Q

ECCLESHALL

Founded: 1971   Nickname: The Eagles

Secretary: Jim Tunney   **(T)**   **(E)**
Chairman: Bob Lloyd   **Manager:** Paul Snape & Peter Griffiths   **Prog Ed:** Richard Marsh
Ground: Pershall Park, Chester Road, Eccleshall ST21 6NE   **(T)** 01785 851 351 (MD)
Colours(change): All royal blue (All red)
HONOURS: FA Comps: None   **League:** Staffordshire County Premier 1982-83. Staffordshire Senior 1989-90. Midland 2001-02, 02-03.

10 YEAR RECORD									
07-08	08-09	09-10	10-11	11-12	12-13	13-14	14-15	15-16	16-17
NWC2 15	NWC1 11	NWC1 9	NWC1 11	NWC1 7	NWC1 15	NWC1 17	NWC1 15	NWC1 16	NWC1 21
FAC EP	FAC EP	FAC EP	FAC 1Q	FAC Pr	FAC EP				
FAV 2Q	FAV 1P	FAV 1Qr	FAV 1P	FAV 1Q	FAV 1P	FAV 2Q	FAV 1P	FAV 2Q	FAV 1Q

FC OSWESTRY TOWN

Founded: 2013   Nickname: Town

Secretary: Andrew Burnett   **(T)**   **(E)**
Chairman: Ian Jones   **Manager:** R Williams-Cooke & R Butcher   **Prog Ed:** Kevin Janes
Ground: The Venue, Burma Road, Oswestry, Shropshire SY11 4AS   **(T)** 01691 684 840
Colours(change): Blue/white/blue (Green & white/green/green)
HONOURS: FA Comps: None   **League:** Mercain Regional Premier Division 2015-16.

10 YEAR RECORD									
07-08	08-09	09-10	10-11	11-12	12-13	13-14	14-15	15-16	16-17
					MerR1 7	MerR1 3	MerRP 5	MerRP 1	NWC1 15
									FAV 1Q

HOLKER OLD BOYS

Founded: 1936   Nickname: Cobs

Secretary: Rachel Cox   **(T)**   **(E)**
Chairman: Maurice Watkin   **Prog Ed:** Dave Smith
Ground: Rakesmoor, Rakesmoor Lane, Hawcoat, Barrow-in-Furness LA14 4QB   **(T)** 01229 828 176
Colours(change): Green/white/green (Blue/white/white)
HONOURS: FA Comps: None   **League:** West Lancashire 1986-87.

10 YEAR RECORD									
07-08	08-09	09-10	10-11	11-12	12-13	13-14	14-15	15-16	16-17
NWC2 16	NWC1 9	NWC1 7	NWC1 3	NWC1 9	NWC1 7	NWC1 6	NWC1 5	NWC1 8	NWC1 17
FAC EP	FAC EPr	FAC EP	FAC P	FAC P	FAC 1Q		FAC EPr	FAC P	
FAV 1Q	FAV 2Qr	FAV 2Q	FAV 2Q	FAV 2Q	FAV 1Q	FAV 1P	FAV 1P	FAV 2Q	FAV 1P

LITHERLAND REMYCA

Founded: 1959   Nickname: The REMY

Secretary: Dave Evans   **(T)**   **(E)**
Chairman: Don Rimmer   **Manager:** Paul McNally   **Prog Ed:** Gary Langley
Ground: Litherland Sports Park, Boundary Road, Litherland, Liverpool L21 7LA   **(T)** 0151 288 6288
Colours(change): Red & white/black/black & red (All navy blue)
HONOURS: FA Comps: None   **League:** Zingari Premier Division 1987-88, 93-94, 94-95, 95-96, Division Two 2005-06. Liverpool County Division Two 2006-07.

10 YEAR RECORD									
07-08	08-09	09-10	10-11	11-12	12-13	13-14	14-15	15-16	16-17
LivCP 4	LivCP 4	LivCP 3	LivCP 13	LivCP 15	LivCP 9	LivCP 5	NWC1 9	NWC1 9	NWC1 3
								FAV 1Q	FAV 1P

NELSON

Founded: 1883   Nickname: Admirals

Secretary: Shane Hudson   **(T)**   **(E)**
Chairman: Fayyaz Ahmed   **Manager:** Alex Norwood   **Prog Ed:** Adam Keizer
Ground: Little Wembley, Lomeshaye Way, Nelson, Lancs BB9 7BN.   **(T)**   **Capacity:** 1500
Colours(change): All blue. (All green).
HONOURS: FA Comps: None   **League:** Lancashire 1895-96. Lancashire Combination 1949-50, 51-52. Football League Division Three North 1922-23. North West Counties Division One 2013-14.

10 YEAR RECORD									
07-08	08-09	09-10	10-11	11-12	12-13	13-14	14-15	15-16	16-17
NWC1 20	NWCP 17	NWCP 17		NWC1 15	NWC1 10	NWC1 1	NWCP 11	NWCP 16	NWCP 21
FAC EP							FAC EP	FAC EP	FAC P
FAV 2Q		FAV 3P			FAV 2Q	FAV 1P	FAV 2Qr	FAV 2Q	FAV 1Q

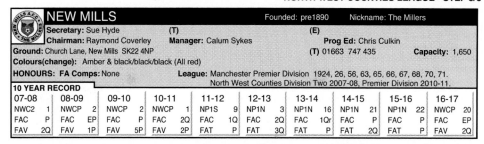

NEW MILLS
Founded: pre1890   Nickname: The Millers

Secretary: Sue Hyde **(T)** **(E)**
Chairman: Raymond Coverley **Manager:** Calum Sykes **Prog Ed:** Chris Culkin
Ground: Church Lane, New Mills SK22 4NP **(T)** 01663 747 435 **Capacity:** 1,650
Colours(change): Amber & black/black/black (All red)
HONOURS: FA Comps: None **League:** Manchester Premier Division 1924, 26, 56, 63, 65, 66, 67, 68, 70, 71.
North West Counties Division Two 2007-08, Premier Division 2010-11.

10 YEAR RECORD

07-08		08-09		09-10		10-11		11-12		12-13		13-14		14-15		15-16		16-17	
NWC2	1	NWCP	2	NWCP	2	NWCP	1	NP1S	9	NP1N	3	NP1N	16	NP1N	21	NP1N	22	NWCP	20
FAC	P	FAC	EP	FAC	P	FAC	2Q	FAC	1Q	FAC	2Q	FAC	1Qr	FAC	P	FAC	P	FAC	EP
FAV	2Q	FAV	1P	FAV	5P	FAV	2P	FAT	P	FAT	3Q	FAT	P	FAT	2Q	FAT	P	FAV	2Q

PRESTWICH HEYS
Founded: 1938   Nickname: The Heys

Secretary: Scott Brady **(T)** **(E)**
Chairman: Neil Gilmore **Manager:** Jon Lyons & Ian Hutchinson **Prog Ed:** Stephen Howard
Ground: Adie Moran Park, Sandgate Road, Whitefield M45 6WG **(T)** 0161 7773 8888 (MD)
Colours(change): Red/white/red (All blue)
HONOURS: FA Comps: None **League:** Lancashire Combination 1970-71. Manchester Division One 1996-97,
Premier Division 2004-05, 04-05, 05-06, 06-07, 15-16.

10 YEAR RECORD

07-08		08-09		09-10		10-11		11-12		12-13		13-14		14-15		15-16		16-17	
MancP	7	MancP	12	MancP	11	MancP	12	MancP	13	MancP	8	MancP	4	MancP	6	MancP	1	NWC1	8

SANDBACH UNITED
Founded: 2004   Nickname:

Secretary: John Clayton **(T)** **(E)**
Chairman: Paul Reel **Manager:** Andy Hockenhull **Prog Ed:** Gary Walker
Ground: Sandbach Community Football Centre, Hind Heath Road, Sandbach CW11 3LZ **(T)** 01270 768 389
Colours(change): Maroon & blue/maroon/maroon (White & blue/blue/blue)
HONOURS: FA Comps: None **League:** None

10 YEAR RECORD

07-08	08-09	09-10	10-11		11-12		12-13		13-14		14-15		15-16		16-17	
			StfSP		Ches2	5	Ches2	6	Ches2	2	ChesP	11	ChesP	4	NWC1	6

SILSDEN
Founded: 1904   Nickname: The Cobbydalers

Secretary: John Barclay **(T)** **(E)**
Chairman: Sean McNulty **Manager:** Danny Forrest **Prog Ed:** Peter Hanson
Ground: Keighley Road, Keighley Road, Silsden BD20 0EH **(T)** 01535 958 850
Colours(change): Red/black/red (White/red/white).
HONOURS: FA Comps: None **League:** Craven Premier Division 1998-99. West Riding County Am. Division Two 99
-2000, Division One 2000-01, Premier Division 2002-03

10 YEAR RECORD

07-08		08-09		09-10		10-11		11-12		12-13		13-14		14-15		15-16		16-17	
NWC1	11	NWCP	9	NWCP	14	NWCP	16	NWCP	12	NWCP	18	NWCP	15	NWCP	10	NWCP	21	NWC1	11
FAC	Pr	FAC	P	FAC	P	FAC	EPr	FAC	Pr	FAC	EP	FAC	EP	FAC	EP	FAC	P	FAC	EPr
FAV	2Q	FAV	2Q	FAV	2Q	FAV	1Q	FAV	1Q			FAV	2Q	FAV	1P	FAV	1P	FAV	2Q

ST HELENS TOWN
Founded: 1946   Nickname: Town or Saints

Secretary: Jeff Voller **(T)** 0151 222 2963 **(E)**
Chairman: Glyn Jones **Manager:** Alan Gillespie **Prog Ed:** Jeff Voller
Ground: Ruskin Drive Sportsground, Ruskin Drive, Dentons Green, St Helens WA10 6RP **(T)** 01942 716 360
Colours(change): All blue (All red).
HONOURS: FA Comps: FA Vase 1986-87. **League:** Lancashire Combination Division Two 1950-51, Premier 1971-72 .

10 YEAR RECORD

07-08		08-09		09-10		10-11		11-12		12-13		13-14		14-15		15-16		16-17	
NWC1	14	NWCP	16	NWCP	9	NWCP	17	NWCP	21	NWCP	19	NWCP	17	NWCP	20	NWC1	7	NWC1	13
FAC	P	FAC	P	FAC	1Q	FAC	Pr	FAC	EP	FAC	EP	FAC	EPr	FAC	EP	FAC	EP		
FAV	1Q	FAV	2Q	FAV	1Q	FAV	3P	FAV	2Q	FAV	1P	FAV	1Q	FAV	3P	FAV	2Q	FAV	1Q

STOCKPORT TOWN

Founded: 2014   Nickname: The Lions

Secretary: Rob Clare   (T)   (E)
Chairman: Seb Rowe   **Manager:** Dave Wild   **Prog Ed:** Andy Calvert
Ground: Lambeth Grove, Woodley, Stockport SK6 1QX   (T) 0161 494 3146
Colours(change): Red & white stripes/blue/red (Purple/white/white)
HONOURS: FA Comps: None   **League:** None

10 YEAR RECORD									
07-08	08-09	09-10	10-11	11-12	12-13	13-14	14-15	15-16	16-17
								NWC1 4	NWC1 10
									FAV 1P

WHITCHURCH ALPORT

Founded: 1946   Nickname:

Secretary: Jamie Harper   (T)   (E)
Chairman: Ryan Jardine   **Manager:** Luke Goddard and Carl Everall   **Prog Ed:** Mark Haller
Ground: Yockings Park, Black Park Road, Whitchurch SY13 1PG   (T)
Colours(change): All red (All blue)
HONOURS: FA Comps: WFA Am Cup 1973-74   **League:** Shrewsbury & District 1947-48. Mid Cheshire 1969-70.

10 YEAR RECORD									
07-08	08-09	09-10	10-11	11-12	12-13	13-14	14-15	15-16	16-17
Ches2 7	Ches2 7	Ches2 9	Ches2 3	Ches2 7	MerRP 11	MerRP 5	MerRP 4	NWC1 18	NWC1 5
									FAV 1Q

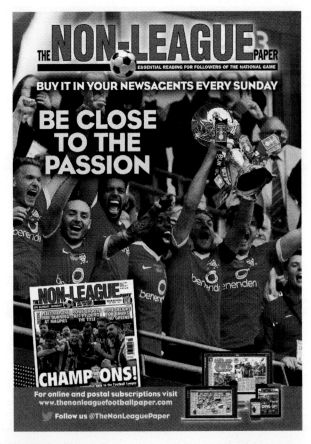

NORTHERN COUNTIES EAST LEAGUE

Sponsored by: Toolstation

Founded: 1982

Recent Champions: 2014: Brighouse Town

2015: Shaw Lane Aquaforce **2016:** Tadcaster Albion

PREMIER DIVISION	P	W	D	L	F	A	GD	Pts
1 Cleethorpes Town	42	35	3	4	144	45	99	108
2 Pickering Town	42	30	7	5	111	39	72	97
3 Bridlington Town	42	28	4	10	112	59	53	88
4 Handsworth Parramore	42	26	5	11	127	52	75	83
5 Thackley	42	23	9	10	81	46	35	78
6 Staveley Miners Welfare	42	20	9	13	96	60	36	69
7 AFC Mansfield	42	20	6	16	79	55	24	66
8 Albion Sports	42	20	6	16	100	99	1	66
9 Hemsworth Miners Welfare	42	19	8	15	92	80	12	65
10 Athersley Recreation	42	17	11	14	76	84	-8	62
11 Liversedge	42	17	8	17	99	73	26	59
12 Bottesford Town	42	17	5	20	86	87	-1	56
13 Worksop Town	42	16	7	19	77	83	-6	55
14 Maltby Main	42	14	12	16	76	92	-16	54
15 Garforth Town	42	16	5	21	68	87	-19	53
16 Clipstone	42	13	10	19	61	83	-22	49
17 Parkgate	42	11	8	23	56	86	-30	41
18 Rainworth Miners Welfare	42	11	5	26	71	107	-36	38
19 Harrogate Railway Athletic	42	11	5	26	60	130	-70	38
20 Barton Town Old Boys	42	9	7	26	57	132	-75	34
21 Armthorpe Welfare	42	6	6	30	47	115	-68	24
22 Retford United (-3)	42	7	6	29	50	132	-82	24

LEAGUE CUP

HOLDERS: CLEETHORPES TOWN

ROUND 1

AFC Emley	v	Pontefract Collieries	2-2, 4-3p
Brigg Town	v	Glasshoughton Welfare	3-4 aet
Eccleshill United	v	Westella & Willerby	3-1
Ollerton Town	v	Worsbrough Bridge Athletic	2-1
Shirebrook Town	v	Rossington Main	1-4
Winterton Rangers	v	Yorkshire Amateur	4-1

ROUND 2

Dronfield Town	v	Worksop Town	0-4
Eccleshill United	v	Hall Road Rangers	1-4
Garforth Town	v	Grimsby Borough	2-0
Handsworth Parramore	v	Cleethorpes Town	1-3
Harrogate Railway Athletic	v	Ollerton Town	3-2 aet
Teversal	v	Athersley Recreation	2-2, 3-2p

ROUND 3

AFC Emley	v	Worksop Town	1-0
Barton Town Old Boys	v	Teversal	2-3
Garforth Town	v	Handsworth Parramore	1-3
Glasshoughton Welfare	v	Nostell Miners Welfare	3-1
Hall Road Rangers	v	Pickering Town	0-2
Hallam	v	Winterton Rangers	10-0
Harrogate Railway Athletic	v	Campion	5-2
Hemsworth Miners Welfare	v	Parkgate	1-0
Knaresborough Town	v	Armthorpe Welfare	2-1
Liversedge	v	Clipstone	2-4 aet
Maltby Main	v	Staveley Miners Welfare	1-5
Rainworth Miners Welfare	v	Bottsford Town	7-3
Retford United	v	Penistone Church	1-2
Rossington Main	v	AFC Mansfield	0-3
Selby Town	v	Albion Sports	2-1
Thackley	v	Bridlington Town	1-2

PREMIER DIVISION	1	2	3	4	5	6	7	8	9	10	11	12	13	14	15	16	17	18	19	20	21	22
1 AFC Mansfield		5-1	2-1	0-1	0-1	3-0	0-2	0-3	5-0	2-1	1-0	0-1	1-1	3-2	2-1	2-2	1-4	4-1	13-0	0-2	1-0	2-1
2 Albion Sports	1-2		4-3	1-0	2-4	5-3	3-0	2-4	3-4	2-4	1-2	4-4	0-4	2-2	2-0	3-0	1-2	4-2	0-2	4-4	2-2	2-0
3 Armthorpe Welfare	1-1	1-3		0-2	3-1	0-4	1-2	1-2	2-4	2-4	0-4	1-2	1-6	2-5	0-3	1-1	1-5	0-2	2-0	1-1	0-2	1-2
4 Athersley Recreation	0-2	2-2	1-0		0-0	0-5	3-1	0-4	1-1	0-2	5-4	1-3	3-3	2-2	2-4	2-0	1-4	2-3	5-2	1-5	0-4	3-0
5 Barton Town Old Boys	1-4	2-3	2-1	2-2		2-5	1-4	0-3	1-2	0-3	1-1	2-2	0-1	0-5	2-2	4-5	0-7	2-0	1-1	1-5	0-4	2-0
6 Bottesford Town	2-1	1-4	2-3	1-2	5-1		1-2	0-3	1-1	4-2	1-4	1-1	3-3	1-2	4-3	0-3	6-1	2-3	6-1	1-0	0-1	2-4
7 Bridlington Town	1-0	4-2	7-1	0-1	1-2	4-2		2-0	1-2	3-0	2-1	5-1	2-4	2-1	6-3	1-2	2-3	6-1	8-0	2-1	1-2	3-0
8 Cleethorpes Town	4-1	0-3	6-1	3-1	6-0	3-2	3-1		1-1	4-0	2-0	10-1	3-0	4-2	4-0	3-0	4-1	4-2	10-0	3-1	2-1	4-1
9 Clipstone	2-2	1-0	1-3	1-1	3-0	2-2	1-5	0-3		0-4	0-2	2-3	3-5	2-1	0-0	3-1	0-0	3-0	2-1	0-3	1-2	3-0
10 Garforth Town	1-0	3-4	4-1	1-3	2-2	4-1	1-3	2-3	2-1		0-5	2-2	3-0	2-0	3-2	1-3	0-3	1-2	1-0	0-0	1-2	1-4
11 Handsworth Parramore	2-1	4-1	2-2	7-1	4-0	4-1	3-4	1-2	2-3	2-0		7-1	0-0	3-3	5-1	5-1	0-1	2-1	10-0	5-1	1-0	0-1
12 Harrogate Railway Athletic	1-2	2-3	2-1	3-4	2-3	0-2	1-3	0-4	1-0	1-2	0-7		2-4	3-2	5-1	2-1	0-5	0-4	5-0	0-2	1-4	0-3
13 Hemsworth Miners Welfare	1-2	2-3	2-3	1-1	3-6	0-1	2-2	0-4	5-2	3-0	0-3	8-1		5-2	2-4	1-1	2-1	5-3	0-2	3-1	2-1	3-2
14 Liversedge	1-1	1-2	5-0	0-0	11-0	4-3	1-2	2-4	1-0	6-0	1-4	3-0	0-0		3-1	0-1	0-1	2-1	3-1	3-3	1-3	3-2
15 Maltby Main	3-1	2-1	1-1	1-3	4-1	1-0	0-0	3-0	5-2	1-5	1-3	2-3	1-1	0-4		2-0	1-1	2-2	3-2	3-3	1-1	
16 Parkgate	2-1	3-3	0-2	1-3	7-0	2-2	0-3	3-3	1-2	1-1	3-5	3-0	0-2	0-1	1-3		1-2	1-0	0-5	1-0	0-0	1-2
17 Pickering Town	2-1	2-4	3-0	2-1	5-0	5-1	1-1	2-0	3-1	3-1	2-0	5-0	0-2	3-1	6-0	5-0		4-0	2-2	2-2	1-1	0-2
18 Rainworth Miners Welfare	2-2	1-5	4-1	2-4	3-2	0-5	2-4	1-2	2-2	0-0	3-0	1-2	1-3	2-2	0-3	3-4		3-4	0-1	0-3	2-0	
19 Retford United	1-3	3-4	0-0	1-5	0-7	0-1	1-2	1-2	1-1	1-3	1-3	2-2	3-0	1-5	3-2	1-2	0-0	4-6		0-2	0-2	
20 Staveley Miners Welfare	2-0	8-0	2-1	2-2	5-0	4-1	1-3	2-6	3-0	3-3	3-3	5-1	2-3	1-2	4-2	2-0	0-1	0-2	3-1		1-0	6-1
21 Thackley	0-3	0-1	4-0	1-1	3-1	1-2	3-3	1-6	2-1	3-0	2-1	2-1	3-1	2-1	1-1	5-1	0-2	3-1	5-0	0-0		1-1
22 Worksop Town	0-2	4-3	5-1	3-4	3-0	2-2	1-4	3-3	2-1	5-1	1-2	5-0	5-2	3-1	3-3	0-0	2-3	0-5	0-3	1-1	0-2	

NORTHERN COUNTIES EAST LEAGUE - STEP 5/6

	DIVISION ONE	P	W	D	L	F	A	GD	Pts
1	Hall Road Rangers	42	30	6	6	107	45	62	96
2	Pontefract Collieries	42	30	5	7	123	48	75	95
3	AFC Emley	42	30	5	7	120	48	72	95
4	Grimsby Borough	42	27	8	7	102	56	46	89
5	Hallam	42	25	7	10	107	48	59	82
6	Penistone Church	42	24	10	8	89	51	38	82
7	Knaresborough Town	42	19	13	10	80	61	19	70
8	Campion	42	20	8	14	98	70	28	68
9	Eccleshill United	42	20	6	16	95	80	15	66
10	Selby Town	42	16	13	13	61	63	-2	61
11	Glasshoughton Welfare	42	17	8	17	82	73	9	59
12	Winterton Rangers	42	18	5	19	77	69	8	59
13	Yorkshire Amateur	42	15	8	19	80	84	-4	53
14	Brigg Town	42	15	4	23	60	102	-42	49
15	Rossington Main	42	12	9	21	57	74	-17	45
16	Teversal	42	13	6	23	59	86	-27	45
17	Ollerton Town	42	12	7	23	57	86	-29	43
18	Shirebrook Town	42	11	6	25	48	95	-47	39
19	Dronfield Town	42	10	5	27	54	98	-44	35
20	Worsbrough Bridge Athletic	42	10	5	27	38	113	-75	35
21	Westella & Willerby	42	7	6	29	45	104	-59	27
22	Nostell Miners Welfare	42	3	6	33	47	132	-85	15

League Cup continued

ROUND 4

AFC Mansfield	v	Knaresborough Town	3-0
Bridlington Town	v	Pickering Town	3-1
Handsworth Parramore	v	Hallam	1-2 aet
Harrogate Railway Athletic	v	Glasshoughton Welfare	3-1

(Harrogate Railway Athletic removed from the cup for fielding ineligible player)

Hemsworth Miners Welfare	v	Rainworth Miners Welfare	0-2
Penistone Church	v	Clipstone	3-2 aet
Selby Town	v	AFC Emley	2-4
Teversal	v	Staveley Miners Welfare	3-1 aet

QUARTER FINALS

Bridlington Town	v	AFC Mansfield	3-1 aet
Hallam	v	Glasshoughton Welfare	1-3
Penistone Church	v	Teversal	5-1
Rainworth Miners Welfare	v	AFC Emley	0-3

SEMI FINALS

Bridlington Town	v	AFC Emley	1-0
Penistone Church	v	Glasshoughton Welfare	3-2

FINAL

Penistone Church	v	Bridlington Town	4-1

CLUB MOVEMENTS

Premier Division - In: Hall Road Rangers (P), Penistone Church (P), Pontefract Collieries (P).
Out: Armthorpe Welfare (R), Retford United (R), Cleethorpes Town (P - NPL D1S).

Division One - In: Armthorpe Welfare (R), East Yorkshire Carnegie (P - Humber Premier), FC Bolsover (P - Centtral Midlands), Retford United (R), Swallownest (P - Sheffield & Hallamshire).
Out: Hall Road Rangers (P), Penistone Church (P), Pontefract Collieries (P), Teversal (S - East Midlands Counties), Westella & Willerby (R - Humber Premier).

DIVISION ONE	1	2	3	4	5	6	7	8	9	10	11	12	13	14	15	16	17	18	19	20	21	22
1 AFC Emley		0-1	4-1	3-0	3-2	3-1	2-1	0-0	2-2	2-0	5-0	2-0	2-1	3-5	4-0	7-1	2-0	5-1	5-0	4-3	6-0	3-1
2 Brigg Town	1-3		1-5	1-1	1-2	0-2	0-2	2-1	1-4	1-0	2-0	3-3	1-6	1-3	4-7	1-2	2-1	2-0	0-1	2-0	2-0	
3 Campion	3-2	3-0		4-1	1-3	3-3	1-2	1-2	2-3	1-6	3-1	1-1	5-1	3-0	5-3	2-2	5-3	3-0	1-1	4-2	1-1	3-0
4 Dronfield Town	2-3	2-5	1-4		3-2	1-2	2-4	1-3	1-5	2-2	1-0	4-0	0-3	1-1	3-2	2-3	1-2	0-1	2-1	0-1	5-0	1-1
5 Eccleshill United	1-5	4-3	3-3	5-1		1-2	3-2	2-3	1-1	1-0	4-2	4-2	1-1	2-3	2-2	0-1	1-2	3-2	5-2	4-0	6-0	2-0
6 Glasshoughton Welfare	1-2	2-0	2-1	4-0	1-3		1-2	0-5	2-3	0-1	3-0	2-1	6-1	1-3	3-2	0-0	6-2	3-4	4-0	3-2	0-0	5-1
7 Grimsby Borough	3-1	7-2	2-2	3-0	1-0	4-1		5-2	1-0	0-0	3-2	3-0	0-1	0-0	4-1	0-0	5-2	3-3	3-2	4-0	3-1	
8 Hall Road Rangers	1-3	4-0	2-1	1-1	3-1	3-2	1-0		1-4	4-3	8-0	5-1	2-1	4-2	3-0	4-1	3-0	1-0	5-0	2-1	2-0	4-1
9 Hallam	0-2	4-0	4-0	1-0	5-0	3-3	0-2	0-1		4-1	4-3	2-3	3-3	1-0	4-0	0-0	2-1	4-2	4-0	4-0	6-0	1-1
10 Knaresborough Town	2-2	4-1	1-0	1-3	1-2	2-2	4-1	2-2	4-3		2-1	2-1	1-1	1-5	0-0	1-1	7-0	2-0	3-0	1-0	2-2	2-4
11 Nostell Miners Welfare	2-9	1-4	2-3	2-3	3-0	2-2	2-3	0-5	0-1	2-2		1-2	1-2	1-5	2-2	1-0	0-1	2-6	0-4	0-2	2-2	1-5
12 Ollerton Town	0-2	6-2	0-2	0-2	2-0	1-0	2-2	1-1	0-3	0-4	5-0		1-4	1-2	1-4	4-0	2-1	1-2	0-1	3-3	1-1	0-1
13 Penistone Church	1-0	4-0	1-1	4-0	1-1	1-0	9-5	0-1	1-1	4-0	3-1		0-2	3-0	1-0	2-1	5-0	3-0	1-0	3-0	1-0	4-2
14 Pontefract Collieries	4-2	0-1	2-0	4-2	5-3	3-0	1-1	4-0	2-0	2-2	7-0	9-0	0-0		2-1	4-1	8-0	5-2	3-1	2-2	5-1	3-0
15 Rossington Main	0-2	0-1	2-0	1-0	3-0	2-0	3-3	0-1	3-0	0-1	2-1	1-4	0-2	0-1		1-1	2-1	3-1	1-1	1-0	1-2	2-2
16 Selby Town	0-0	2-2	0-3	1-0	0-1	2-2	2-1	2-1	1-0	0-0	2-2	0-0	1-1	3-1	3-1		2-1	1-1	5-0	1-0	1-2	1-3
17 Shirebrook Town	1-1	4-0	1-0	2-1	1-1	1-4	0-4	1-1	0-4	1-2	2-1	1-2	0-2	0-1	0-3	0-3		2-0	3-3	0-2	4-1	1-3
18 Teversal	3-1	3-0	0-2	3-0	1-3	2-3	1-2	1-1	0-2	0-1	4-2	1-1	0-0	1-2	3-1	2-1	1-0		1-0	0-0	3-1	2-2
19 Westella & Willerby	2-3	2-3	2-5	2-3	5-4	0-2	0-2	0-5	1-2	0-2	1-1	0-1	1-3	1-3	2-2	0-1	3-0	2-1		0-1	1-0	0-2
20 Winterton Rangers	1-2	0-0	2-0	4-0	0-1	2-0	1-2	2-3	0-5	5-0	4-2	2-0	3-5	3-2	2-1	2-1	4-1	6-1	3-1		1-2	1-2
21 Worsbrough Bridge Athletic	0-5	0-1	0-5	2-0	1-7	1-0	0-2	0-5	1-9	2-0	1-2	3-2	0-1	0-2	3-2	1-4	1-2	3-0	1-2	1-5		0-2
22 Yorkshire Amateur	0-3	4-5	1-5	5-1	2-3	2-2	1-2	1-0	2-2	2-3	3-2	1-2	2-3	2-1	4-0	1-2	3-3	3-0	4-0	2-2	1-2	

AFC MANSFIELD

Founded: 2012   Nickname: The Bulls

Secretary: Paul Hunter   **(T)**   **(E)** afcmansfield@virginmedia.com
Chairman: Andrew Saunders   **Manager:** Rudy Funk   **Prog Ed:** Peter Craggs
Ground: Forest Town Stadium, Clipstone Road West, Forest Town, Mansfield NG19 0EE   **(T)** 07973 491 739
Capacity: **Seats:** Yes   **Covered:** Yes   **Midweek Matchday:** Wednesday   **Clubhouse:** No

Colours(change): All red (Yellow/blue/blue)
Previous Names: None
Previous Leagues: Central Midlands North 2012-14.

HONOURS: FA Comps: None
League: Central Midlands North 2013-14.

10 YEAR RECORD										
07-08	08-09	09-10	10-11	11-12	12-13	13-14	14-15	15-16	16-17	
					CMN 2	CMN 1	NCE1 7	NCE1 2	NCEP 7	
									FAC EP	FAC 3Q
						FAV 2Pr	FAV 5P	FAV 2Pr	FAV 4P	

ALBION SPORTS

Founded: 1974   Nickname: Lions

Secretary: Jaj Singh   **(T)** 07957 206 174   **(E)** singhalbionfc@hotmail.co.uk
Chairman: Kultar Singh   **Manager:** Kulwinder Singh Sandhu   **Prog Ed:** Peter Cusack
Ground: Throstle Nest, Newlands, Farsley, Leeds, LS28 5BE.   **(T)** 0113 255 7292
Capacity: 3,500   **Seats:** 1,750   **Covered:** 1,750   **Midweek Matchday:** Wednesday   **Clubhouse:** n/a

Colours(change): Yellow/royal blue/royal blue (All red)
Previous Names: None
Previous Leagues: Bradford Amateur Sunday 1974-2007. West Riding County Amateur 2007-11.

HONOURS: FA Comps: None
League: Bradford Amateur Sunday Premier Division 1995-96, 99-2000, 00-01, 02-03, 04-05, 05-06.

10 YEAR RECORD	Northern Counties East Division One 2012-13.									
07-08	08-09	09-10	10-11	11-12	12-13	13-14	14-15	15-16	16-17	
			WRCP 2	NCE1 4	NCE1 1	NCEP 6	NCEP 10	NCEP 11	NCEP 8	
						FAC 1Q	FAC P	FAC EPr	FAC EPr	
					FAV 2Q	FAV 2Q	FAV 2Q	FAV 1Q	FAV 1Q	

ATHERSLEY RECREATION

Founded: 1979   Nickname: Penguins

Secretary: Peter Goodlad   **(T)** 07910 121 070   **(E)** petegoodlad@yahoo.co.uk
Chairman: Michael Shepherd   **Manager:** Wayne Thompson   **Prog Ed:** Jamie Wallman
Ground: Sheerien Park, Ollerton Road, Athersley North, Barnsley, S71 3DP   **(T)** 07910 121 070
Capacity: 2,000   **Seats:** 150   **Covered:** 420   **Midweek Matchday:** Wednesday   **Clubhouse:** No   **Shop:** Yes

Colours(change): White & black/black/black (All orange)
Previous Names: Athersley North Juniors 1979-86.
Previous Leagues: Barnsley Junior. Barnsley Association. Sheffield & Hallamshire County Senior 1997-2012.

HONOURS: FA Comps: None
League: Barnsley Junior 1986-87. Barnsley Association 91-92, 92-93, 94-95, 95-96, 96-97. Sheffield & Hallamshire County Senior Division Two 1997-98, Premier Division 1999-2000, 03-04, 04-05, 06-07, 08-09, 11-12

10 YEAR RECORD										
07-08	08-09	09-10	10-11	11-12	12-13	13-14	14-15	15-16	16-17	
SHSP 2	SHSP 1	SHSP 2	SHSP 2	SHSP 1	NCE1 2	NCEP 10	NCEP 13	NCEP 18	NCEP 10	
							FAC P	FAC EP	FAC EP	
						FAV 2P	FAV 2Q	FAV 1P	FAV 1Q	

BARTON TOWN

Founded: 1995   Nickname: Swans

Secretary: Peter Mitchell   **(T)** 07927 623 932   **(E)** bartontown@gmail.com
Chairman: Mark Gregory   **Manager:** Dave Botham   **Prog Ed:** Trevor Richens
Ground: The Easy Buy Ground, Marsh Lane, Barton-on-Humber DN18 5JD   **(T)** 01652 661 809
Capacity: 3,000   **Seats:** 240   **Covered:** 540   **Midweek Matchday:** Tuesday   **Clubhouse:** Yes   **Shop:** No

Colours(change): Sky blue & navy blue/sky blue/navy blue (White & green/green/green)
Previous Names: Barton Town Old Boys >2017.
Previous Leagues: Lincolnshire 1995-2000, Humber (Founder member) 2000-01, Central Midlands 2001-07.

HONOURS: FA Comps: None
League: Lincolnshire 1996-97. Central Midlands Supreme Division 2005-06.

10 YEAR RECORD										
07-08	08-09	09-10	10-11	11-12	12-13	13-14	14-15	15-16	16-17	
NCE1 9	NCE1 5	NCE1 6	NCE1 2	NCEP 11	NCEP 8	NCEP 3	NCEP 5	NCEP 10	NCEP 20	
FAC EP	FAC 1Q	FAC P	FAC P	FAC Pr	FAC P	FAC P	FAC P	FAC P	FAC EP	
FAV 2Q	FAV 2Q	FAV 1Q	FAV 2P	FAV 2P	FAV 2P	FAV 1Q	FAV 2Q	FAV 1Q	FAV 1Q	

BOTTESFORD TOWN
Founded: 1974   Nickname: The Poachers

Secretary: Andrew Allcock   **(T)** 07837 838 630   **(E)** andrew.susworth@googlemail.com
Chairman: Tony Reeve   **Manager:** John Corbett   **Prog Ed:** Rob Barraclough
Ground: Birkdale Park, Ontario Road, Bottesford, Scunthorpe DN17 2TQ   **(T)** 01724 871 883
Capacity: 1,000 **Seats:** 90   **Covered:** 300   **Midweek Matchday:** Wednesday   **Clubhouse:** Yes
Colours(change): All blue & yellow (Green & black/black/black & green)
Previous Names: None
Previous Leagues: Lincolnshire 1974-2000. Central Midlands 2000-07.

HONOURS: FA Comps: None
League: Lincolnshire 1989-90, 90-91, 91-92. Central Midlands Supreme Division 2006-07.

10 YEAR RECORD

07-08		08-09		09-10		10-11		11-12		12-13		13-14		14-15		15-16		16-17	
NCE1	3	NCE1	6	NCE1	9	NCE1	17	NCE1	16	NCE1	15	NCE1	3	NCE1	8	NCE1	3	NCEP	12
FAC	EP	FAC	Pr	FAC	EP	FAC	1Q							FAC	EP	FAC	P	FAC	P
FAV	2Q	FAV	1Q	FAV	1P	FAV	1Q	FAV	2Q	FAV	2P	FAV	1Q	FAV	1Pr	FAV	2Q	FAV	3P

BRIDLINGTON TOWN
Founded: 1918   Nickname: Seasiders

Secretary: Gordon Gillott   **(T)** 07786 879 895   **(E)** gavinbranton@yahoo.co.uk
Chairman: Peter Smurthwaite   **Manager:** Curtis Woodhouse   **Prog Ed:** Dom Taylor
Ground: Neil Hudgell Law Stadium, Queensgate, Bridlington YO16 7LN   **(T)** 01262 606 879
Capacity: 3,000 **Seats:** 500   **Covered:** 500   **Midweek Matchday:** Tuesday   **Clubhouse:** Yes   **Shop:** Yes
Colours(change): All red (All dark blue).
Previous Names: Original Bridlington Town folded in 1994. Greyhound FC changed to Bridlington Town.
Previous Leagues: Yorkshire 1924-39, 59-82, NCEL 1982-90, 99-2003, Northern Premier 1990-94, 2003-08

HONOURS: FA Comps: FA Vase 1992-93
League: Yorkshire League 1974-75. Northern Counties East 1989-90, 2001-02, 09-10, NPL Division One 1992-93.

10 YEAR RECORD

07-08		08-09		09-10		10-11		11-12		12-13		13-14		14-15		15-16		16-17	
NP1N	18	NCEP	4	NCEP	1	NCEP	3	NCEP	2	NCEP	3	NCEP	12	NCEP	8	NCEP	5	NCEP	3
FAC	P	FAC	1Qr	FAC	1Q	FAC	P	FAC	P	FAC	EP	FAC	Pr	FAC	1Q	FAC	EP	FAC	2Qr
FAT	1Q	FAV	2P	FAV	3P	FAV	1Pr	FAV	3P	FAV	1P	FAV	3P	FAV	1Q	FAV	2Q	FAV	1P

CLIPSTONE
Founded: 1928   Nickname: The Cobras

Secretary: Malcolm Holmes   **(T)**   **(E)** clipstonefc@yahoo.co.uk
Chairman: Richard Clarey(Intrim)   **Manager:** Ian Cotton   **Prog Ed:** Nigel Splading
Ground: Worksop Van Hire Stad, Clipstone Rd East, Clipstone Village NG21 9AB   **(T)** 01623 627 262 / 07937 143
Capacity: 500 **Seats:** 60   **Covered:** 200   **Midweek Matchday:** Tuesday   **Clubhouse:** Yes   **Shop:** No
Colours(change): Black & white/black/black (All red)
Previous Names: Clipstone Welfare 1928-2013.
Previous Leagues: Notts Alliance 1991-94. Central Midlands 1994-2012.

HONOURS: FA Comps: None
League: Central Midlands 1993-94, 96-97. Northern Counties East Division One 2014-15.

10 YEAR RECORD

07-08		08-09		09-10		10-11		11-12		12-13		13-14		14-15		15-16		16-17	
CM Su	20	CM Su	9	CM Su	10	CM Su	9	CMN	4	NCE1	11	NCE1	7	NCE1	1	NCEP	13	NCEP	16
														FAC	1Q	FAC	1Q	FAC	EP
												FAV	2Q	FAV	2Q	FAV	1P	FAV	2Q

GARFORTH TOWN
Founded: 1964   Nickname: The Miners

Secretary: Andrew Marsh   **(T)** 07851 815 992   **(E)** secretary@garforthtown.net
Chairman: Brian Close   **Manager:** Rob Hunter   **Prog Ed:** Samuel Bannister
Ground: Community Stadium, Cedar Ridge, Garforth, Leeds LS25 2PF   **(T)** 0113 287 7567
Capacity: 3,000 **Seats:** 278   **Covered:** 200   **Midweek Matchday:** Tuesday   **Clubhouse:** Yes
Colours(change): Yellow/blue/blue
Previous Names: Garforth Miners 1964-85
Previous Leagues: Leeds Sunday Comb. 1972-76, West Yorkshire 1976-78, Yorkshire 1978-82, NCE 1982-2007. Northern Premier 2007-13.

HONOURS: FA Comps: None
League: Northern Counties East Division 1 1997-98

10 YEAR RECORD

07-08		08-09		09-10		10-11		11-12		12-13		13-14		14-15		15-16		16-17	
NP1N	10	NP1N	16	NP1N	20	NP1N	13	NP1N	5	NP1N	22	NCEP	14	NCEP	14	NCEP	16	NCEP	15
FAC	P	FAC	2Qr	FAC	1Q	FAC	P	FAC	1Q	FAC	1Q	FAC	EP	FAC	P	FAC	EP	FAC	EP
FAT	P	FAT	1Qr	FAT	1Q	FAT	1Qr	FAT	1Q	FAT	P	FAV	1P	FAV	2Q	FAV	2P	FAV	1Q

HALL ROAD RANGERS

Founded: 1959   Nickname: Rangers

Secretary: Alan Chaplin   **(T)** 07961 415 884   **(E)** alynn33@alynn33.karoo.co.uk
Chairman: Darren Sunley   **Manager:** David Ricardo   **Prog Ed:** Mike Harker
Ground: Hawroth Park, Dawson Drive, Hull HU6 7DY   **(T)**
Capacity: Seats: 250   Covered: 750   **Midweek Matchday:** Tuesday   **Clubhouse:** Yes   **Shop:** Yes

Colours(change): Blue & white/blue/blue (Yellow & blue/yellow & blue/yellow)
Previous Names: None
Previous Leagues: Sunday League. East Riding County, Yorkshire 1968-82.

HONOURS: FA Comps: None
League: Yorkshire Division Three 1972-73, 79-80. Northern Counties East Division One 2016-17.

10 YEAR RECORD										
07-08	08-09	09-10	10-11	11-12	12-13	13-14	14-15	15-16	16-17
NCE1 2	NCEP 16	NCEP 11	NCEP 14	NCEP 16	NCEP 22	NCE1 11	NCE1 17	NCE1 17	NCE1 1
FAC 1Q	FAC EP	FAC EP	FAC EPr	FAC Pr	FAC EP	FAC EP			
FAV 2Q	FAV 2Q	FAV 1P	FAV 1Q	FAV 2Q	FAV 1P	FAV 1Q	FAV 2Q	FAV 2Q	FAV 2P

HANDSWORTH PARRAMORE

Founded: 1936   Nickname: Amber Parras

Secretary: Max Ross   **(T)** 07500 833 939   **(E)** maxross@blueyonder.co.uk
Chairman: Pete Whitehead   **Manager:** James Collier   **Prog Ed:** Ian Robinson
Ground: The Windsor Foodservice Stadium, Sandy Land, Worksop S80 1UJ   **(T)** 01909 479 955
Capacity: 2,500 **Seats:** 200   Covered: 750   **Midweek Matchday:** Tuesday   **Clubhouse:** Yes   **Shop:** No

Colours(change): Amber & black/black/black (Red & black/red/red)
Previous Names: Parramore Sports > 2010. Sheffield Parramore 2010-2011. Worksop Parramore 2011-14.
Previous Leagues: Sheffield & Hallam County Senior 1985-2008. Central Midlands 2008-11

HONOURS: FA Comps: None
League: Central Midland Supreme Division 2010-11.

10 YEAR RECORD										
07-08	08-09	09-10	10-11	11-12	12-13	13-14	14-15	15-16	16-17
SHS1 5	CM P 4	CM Su 8	CM Su 1	NCE1 3	NCEP 7	NCEP 4	NCEP 7	NCEP 2	NCEP 4
							FAC P	FAC P	FAC 3Q
							FAV 1P	FAV 3P	FAV 1P

HARROGATE RAILWAY ATH.

Founded: 1935   Nickname: The Rail

Secretary: Dave Shepherd   **(T)** 07816 986 799   **(E)**
Chairman: Rob Northfield   **Manager:** Liam Gray
Ground: Station View, Starbeck, Harrogate, North Yorkshire HG2 7JA   **(T)** 01423 883 104
Capacity: 3,500 **Seats:** 300   Covered: 600   **Midweek Matchday:** Tuesday   **Clubhouse:** Yes   **Shop:** Yes

Colours(change): Red/green/red (All blue)
Previous Names: None
Previous Leagues: West Yorkshire, Harrogate & District, Yorkshire 1955-73, 80-82, Northern Counties East 1982-2006. Northern Premier 2006-16

HONOURS: FA Comps: None
League: West Yorkshire 1953-54.

10 YEAR RECORD	Northern Counties East Division Two North 1983-84, Division one 1989-99.									
07-08	08-09	09-10	10-11	11-12	12-13	13-14	14-15	15-16	16-17
NP1N 12	NP1N 18	NP1N 17	NP1N 20	NP1N 21	NP1N 18	NP1N 13	NP1N 8	NP1N 21	NCEP 19
FAC 2P	FAC P	FAC 1Q	FAC P	FAC 1Q	FAC Pr	FAC Pr	FAC 2Q	FAC Pr	FAC 1Q
FAT 1Q	FAT 1Q	FAT 1Q	FAT 3Q	FAT 1Q	FAT 1Q	FAT P	FAT P	FAT P	FAV 2Q

HEMSWORTH M.W.

Founded: 1981   Nickname: Wells

Secretary: Laura Mulroe   **(T)**   **(E)** netsi1@sky.com
Chairman: Richard Norman   **Manager:** Wayne Benn   **Prog Ed:** Shaun Pugh
Ground: Yorkshire NuBuilds Stadium, Wakefield Road, Fitzwilliam, Pontefract WF9 5AJ   **(T)** 01977 614 997
Capacity: 2,000 **Seats:** 100   Covered: 100   **Midweek Matchday:** Tuesday   **Clubhouse:** Yes   **Shop:** Yes

Colours(change): All blue (Volt/black/volt)
Previous Names: None
Previous Leagues: Doncaster Senior. West Riding County Amateur 1995-2008.

HONOURS: FA Comps: None
League: West Riding County Amateur Division One 1996-97.

10 YEAR RECORD	Northern Counties East Division One 2015-16.									
07-08	08-09	09-10	10-11	11-12	12-13	13-14	14-15	15-16	16-17
	NCE1 10	NCE1 7	NCE1 16	NCE1 8	NCE1 13	NCE1 17	NCE1 3	NCE1 1	NCEP 9
			FAC Pr	FAC EP	FAC P			FAC EP	FAC P
		FAV 1P	FAV 1Q	FAV 2Q	FAV 1Q	FAV 2Q	FAV 2Q	FAV 2P	FAV 2P

LIVERSEDGE
Founded: 1910   Nickname: Sedge

Secretary: Bryan Oakes   **(T)** 07855 412 453   **(E)** bryan@bryanoakes.orangehome.co.uk
Chairman: Leigh Bromby   **Manager:** Jonathan Rimmington   **Prog Ed:** Peter Bell
Ground: Clayborn Ground, Quaker Lane, Hightown Road, Cleckheaton WF15 8DF   **(T)** 01274 862 108
Capacity: 2,000 **Seats:** 250   **Covered:** 750   **Midweek Matchday:** Tuesday   **Clubhouse:** Yes   **Shop:** Yes

Colours(change): Sky blue & navy/navy/navy (Red & black/black/black).
Previous Names: None
Previous Leagues: Bradford 1919-22. West Riding Co. Amateur 1922-27, 49-72. Spen Valley 1947-49. Yorkshire 1972-82.

HONOURS: FA Comps: None
League: West Riding County Amateur 1923-24, 25-26, 26-27, 64-65, 65-66, 68-69.
10 YEAR RECORD Spen Valley 1948-49.

07-08	08-09	09-10	10-11	11-12	12-13	13-14	14-15	15-16	16-17
NCEP 4	NCEP 14	NCEP 9	NCEP 17	NCEP 14	NCEP 15	NCEP 20	NCEP 18	NCEP 14	NCEP 11
FAC 2Q	FAC EP	FAC EP	FAC EP	FAC EP	FAC Pr	FAC EP	FAC EP	FAC EP	FAC EP
FAV 2Q	FAV 1P	FAV 1P	FAV 2Qr	FAV 2Q	FAV 2Q	FAV 1P	FAV 2Q	FAV 1Q	FAV 2Q

MALTBY MAIN
Founded: 1916   Nickname: Miners

Secretary: John Mills   **(T)** 07795 693 683   **(E)** john_mills_@hotmail.co.uk
Chairman: Wilf Race   **Prog Ed:** Nick Dunhill
Ground: Muglet Lane, Maltby, Rotherham S66 7JQ.   **(T)** 07795 693 683
Capacity: 2,000 **Seats:** 150   **Covered:** 300   **Midweek Matchday:** Wednesday   **Clubhouse:** No   **Shop:** No

Colours(change): Red/black/black (All blue)
Previous Names: Maltby Miners Welfare 1970-96
Previous Leagues: Sheffield Association 1919-29, 39-41, 45-49, 65-70, 72-73. Rotherham Minor 1929-36. Sheffield Amateur 1936-39. Rotherham Association 1942-45, 55-58. Yorkshire League 1949-55, 73-82. Doncaster & District 1958-65.
HONOURS: FA Comps: None
League: Sheffield Association 1925-26, 26-27.
10 YEAR RECORD

07-08	08-09	09-10	10-11	11-12	12-13	13-14	14-15	15-16	16-17
NCEP 18	NCEP 12	NCEP 16	NCEP 11	NCEP 18	NCEP 14	NCEP 15	NCEP 19	NCEP 7	NCEP 14
FAC EP	FAC EP	FAC EP	FAC P	FAC EP	FAC 1Q	FAC EP	FAC P	FAC 1Q	FAC EP
FAV 1P	FAV 2Q	FAV 2Q	FAV 1Qr	FAV 1Q	FAV 2Q	FAV 1Q	FAV 2Qr	FAV 2P	FAV 1Q

PARKGATE
Founded: 1969   Nickname: The Steelmen

Secretary: Bruce Bickerdike   **(T)** 07831 664 710   **(E)** brucebickerdike@hotmail.co.uk
Chairman: Albert Dudill   **Manager:** Graham Nicholas   **Prog Ed:** Bruce Bickerdike
Ground: Roundwood Sports Complex, Green Lane, Rawmarsh, S62 6LA   **(T)** 01709 826 600
Capacity: 1,000 **Seats:** 300   **Covered:** 300   **Midweek Matchday:** Tuesday   **Clubhouse:** Yes   **Shop:** No

Colours(change): All red & white. (All blue).
Previous Names: BSC Parkgate (1982-86) RES Parkgate (pre 1994)
Previous Leagues: BIR County Senior. Yorkshire 1974-82.

HONOURS: FA Comps: None
League: Northern Counties East Division One 2006-07.
10 YEAR RECORD

07-08	08-09	09-10	10-11	11-12	12-13	13-14	14-15	15-16	16-17
NCEP 8	NCEP 11	NCEP 14	NCEP 2	NCEP 7	NCEP 9	NCEP 19	NCEP 16	NCEP 17	NCEP 17
FAC 1Q	FAC EP	FAC EP	FAC 1Q	FAC 1Q	FAC EP	FAC EP	FAC EP	FAC EP	FAC P
FAV 1P	FAV 2Q	FAV 2Q	FAV 2Q	FAV 3P	FAV 3P	FAV 2P	FAV 1Q	FAV 1Q	FAV 1Q

PENISTON CHURCH
Founded: 1906   Nickname: None

Secretary: David Hampshire   **(T)** 07876 468 975   **(E)** davehampshire@talktalk.net
Chairman: Scott Fairbank   **Manager:** Ian Richards   **Prog Ed:** Andy Green
Ground: Church View Road, Penistone, Sheffield S36 6AT   **(T)**
Capacity: 1,000 **Seats:** 100   **Covered:** Yes   **Midweek Matchday:** Wednesday   **Clubhouse:** Yes

Colours(change): Black & white/black/black (Light blue/dark blue/dark blue)
Previous Names: Formed after the merger of Penistone Choirboys and Penistone Juniors.
Previous Leagues: Sheffield Junior 1906-07. Sheffield Amateur 1907-48. Hatchard League/Sheffield Association 1948-83. Sheffield & Hallamshire County Senior (Founder Members) 1983-14.
HONOURS: FA Comps: None
League: Sheffield & Hallamshire County Senior Division One 1993-94, 2000-01.
10 YEAR RECORD

07-08	08-09	09-10	10-11	11-12	12-13	13-14	14-15	15-16	16-17
Sh&H1 2	Sh&HP 10	Sh&HP 7	Sh&HP 3	Sh&HP 4	Sh&HP 3	Sh&HP 4	NCE1 9	NCE1 5	NCE1 6
								FAC EP	FAC EP
							FAV 1Q	FAV 1Q	FAV 2Q	FAV 1P

PICKERING TOWN
Founded: 1888   Nickname: Pikes

Secretary: Stephen Chapman   **(T)** 07733 056 664   **(E)** pickeringsec@aol.com
Chairman: Keith Usher   **Manager:** Paul Marshall   **Prog Ed:** Peter Dickinson
Ground: Recreation Club, off Mill Lane, Malton Road, Pickering YO18 7DB   **(T)** 01751 473 317
Capacity: 2,000 **Seats:** 200   **Covered:** 500   **Midweek Matchday:** Tuesday   **Clubhouse:** Yes   **Shop:** Yes

Colours(change): All blue (All yellow).
Previous Names: None
Previous Leagues: Beckett, York & District, Scarborough & District, Yorkshire 1972-1982

HONOURS: FA Comps: None
League: Scarborough & District Division One 1930-31, 50-51. York Division Two 1953-54, Division One 55-56, 66-67,
10 YEAR RECORD | 69-70. Yorkshire Division three 1973-74. Northern Counties East Division Two 1987-88.

07-08	08-09	09-10	10-11	11-12	12-13	13-14	14-15	15-16	16-17
NCEP 3	NCEP 9	NCEP 7	NCEP 7	NCEP 12	NCEP 5	NCEP 7	NCEP 11	NCEP 6	NCEP 2
FAC P	FAC 1Q	FAC EP	FAC EP	FAC 1Qr	FAC EPr	FAC EP	FAC EP	FAC P	FAC Pr
FAV 4P	FAV 3P	FAV 4P	FAV 2P	FAV 2Q	FAV 2P	FAV 2Q	FAV 2Q	FAV 1Q	FAV 2P

PONTEFRACT COLLIERIES
Founded: 1958   Nickname: Colls

Secretary: Trevor Waddington   **(T)**   **(E)**
Chairman: Dan Grace   **Manager:** Craig Parry   **Prog Ed:** Trevor Waddington
Ground: Skinner Lane, Pontefract, WF8 4QE   **(T)** 01977 600 818
Capacity: 1,200 **Seats:** 300   **Covered:** 400   **Midweek Matchday:** Wednesday   **Clubhouse:** Yes   **Shop:** Yes

Colours(change): Blue & white/blue & white/blue (Claret & sky blue/claret & sky blue/claret)
Previous Names: None
Previous Leagues: West Yorkshire 1958-79. Yorkshire 1979-82.

HONOURS: FA Comps: None
League: Yorkshire Division Three 1981-82.
10 YEAR RECORD | Northern Counties East Division One North 1983-84.

07-08	08-09	09-10	10-11	11-12	12-13	13-14	14-15	15-16	16-17
NCE1	NCE1 9	NCE1 5	NCE1 5	NCE1 5	NCE1 5	NCE1 9	NCE1 2	NCEP 20	NCE1 2
FAC EPr	FAC EP	FAC EP	FAC EP	FAC EP	FAC EPr	FAC EP	FAC EP	FAC P	FAC 1Q
FAV 1P	FAV 1Q	FAV 2Q	FAV 2Q	FAV 1P	FAV 2Q	FAV 2Q	FAV 1Q	FAV 1Q	FAV 1Q

RAINWORTH M.W.
Founded: 1922   Nickname: The Wrens

Secretary: Les Lee   **(T)** 07889 561 787   **(E)** leslielee7@ntlworld.com
Chairman: Les Lee   **Manager:** Craig Denton   **Prog Ed:** Paul Fryer
Ground: Welfare Ground, Kirklington Road, Rainworth, Mansfield NG21 0JY   **(T)** 01623 792 495
Capacity: 2,201 **Seats:** 221   **Covered:** 350   **Midweek Matchday:** Tuesday   **Clubhouse:** Yes

Colours(change): All white & royal blue (All royal blue).
Previous Names: Rufford Colliery
Previous Leagues: Notts Alliance 1922-03, Central Midlands League 2003-07, Northern Counties East 2007-10. NPL 2010-15.

HONOURS: FA Comps: None
League: Notts Alliance 1971-72, 77-78, 78-79, 79-80, 80-81, 81-82, 82-83, 90-91, 95-96, 96-97.
10 YEAR RECORD |

07-08	08-09	09-10	10-11	11-12	12-13	13-14	14-15	15-16	16-17
NCE1 4	NCE1 2	NCEP 2	NP1S 20	NP1S 19	NP1N 14	NP1S 15	NP1S 21	NCEP 9	NCEP 18
FAC 3Q	FAC 1Qr	FAC 2Q	FAC P	FAC P	FAC 1Qr	FAC Pr	FAC P	FAC EPr	FAC EP
FAV 2P	FAV 1P	FAV 3P	FAT Pr	FAT P	FAT 1Q	FAT P	FAT Pr	FAV 1Q	FAV 1Q

STAVELEY MINERS WELFARE
Founded: 1989   Nickname: The Welfare

Secretary: Ele Reaney   **(T)** 07530 055 849   **(E)** staveleyed@hotmail.co.uk
Chairman: Terry Damms   **Manager:** Brett Marshall   **Prog Ed:** Rich Williams
Ground: Inkersall Road, Staveley, Chesterfield, S43 3JL   **(T)** 01246 471 441
Capacity: 5,000 **Seats:** 220   **Covered:** 400   **Midweek Matchday:** Wednesday   **Clubhouse:** Yes   **Shop:** Yes

Colours(change): Blue & white/white/white (All yellow)
Previous Names: None
Previous Leagues: Chesterfield & District Amateur 1989-91. Sheffield & Hallamshire County Senior 1991-93.

HONOURS: FA Comps: None
League: Sheffield & Hallamshire County Senior Division Three 1991-92, Division Two 1992-93.
10 YEAR RECORD | Northern Counties East Division One 2010-11.

07-08	08-09	09-10	10-11	11-12	12-13	13-14	14-15	15-16	16-17
NCE1 8	NCE1 4	NCE1 4	NCE1 1	NCEP 5	NCEP 13	NCEP 17	NCEP 9	NCEP 8	NCEP 6
FAC P	FAC P	FAC Pr	FAC P	FAC 2Q	FAC Pr	FAC P	FAC 1Q	FAC EP	FAC EP
FAV 2Q	FAV 1Q	FAV 1Q	FAV 4P	FAV SF	FAV 2P	FAV 3P	FAV 1Q	FAV 1Q	FAV 3P

THACKLEY

Founded: 1930   Nickname: Dennyboys

Secretary: Mick Lodge   **(T)** 07961 669 405   **(E)** stuwillingham@hotmail.com
Chairman: Phil Woollias   **Manager:** Chris Reape   **Prog Ed:** Richard Paley
Ground: Dennyfield, Ainsbury Avenue, Thackley, Bradford BD10 0TL   **(T)** 01274 615 571
Capacity: 3000 **Seats:** 300   **Covered:** 600   **Midweek Matchday:** Tuesday   **Clubhouse:** Yes

Colours(change): Red/white/red. (White/black/white).
Previous Names: Thackley Wesleyians 1930-39
Previous Leagues: Bradford Amateur, West Riding County Amateur, West Yorkshire, Yorkshire 1967-82

HONOURS: FA Comps: None
    League: West Riding County Amateur x5. West Yorkshire 1965-66, 66-67. Yorkshire Division Two 1973-74.

10 YEAR RECORD

07-08		08-09		09-10		10-11		11-12		12-13		13-14		14-15		15-16		16-17	
NCEP	16	NCEP	7	NCEP	4	NCEP	8	NCEP	10	NCEP	10	NCEP	13	NCEP	12	NCEP	12	NCEP	5
FAC	EP	FAC	EP	FAC	EP	FAC	2Q	FAC	P	FAC	EP	FAC	EP	FAC	EP	FAC	1Qr	FAC	EP
FAV	1P	FAV	2P	FAV	1Q	FAV	2P	FAV	1P	FAV	3P	FAV	3P	FAV	1Q	FAV	1Qr	FAV	1Q

WORKSOP TOWN

Founded: 1861   Nickname: Tigers

Secretary: David Crisp   **(T)**   **(E)** wtfcsecretary@gmail.com
Chairman: Jason Clark   **Manager:** Ryan Hindley   **Prog Ed:** Jake Brown
Ground: The Windsor Foodservice Stadium, off Sandy Lane, Worksop S80 1UJ   **(T)** 01909 479 955
Capacity: 2,500 **Seats:** 200   **Covered:** 750   **Midweek Matchday:** Wednesday   **Clubhouse:** Yes   **Shop:** Yes

Colours(change): Amber & black/black/amber (All blue)
Previous Names: None
Previous Leagues: Sheffield Association. Midland 1949-60, 61-68, 69-74, Northern Premier 1968-69, 74-2004, 2007-14, Conf. 2004-07

HONOURS: FA Comps: None
    League: Sheffield Association 1898-99 (joint), 47-48, 48-49. Midland 1921-22, 65-66, 72-73.

10 YEAR RECORD

07-08		08-09		09-10		10-11		11-12		12-13		13-14		14-15		15-16		16-17	
NP P	9	NP P	17	NP P	18	NP P	7	NP P	15	NP P	9	NP P	4	NCEP	2	NCEP	4	NCEP	13
FAC	1Q	FAC	2Q	FAC	1Qr	FAC	1Q	FAC	1Q	FAC	1Q	FAC	3Q	FAC	EP	FAC	EP	FAC	Pr
FAT	1Q	FAT	2Q	FAT	1Q	FAT	1Qr	FAT	1P	FAT	2P	FAT	1P	FAT	1Q	FAV	4P	FAV	2P	FAV	2P

NON LEAGUE DAY 07.10.17

DIVISION ONE

AFC EMLEY

Founded: 2005   Nickname: Pewits

Secretary: Andrew Painten   **(T)** 07931 353 515   **(E)** office@afcemley.co.uk
Chairman: Nigel Wakefield   **Manager:** Joe Howson   **Prog Ed:** Dan Brownhill
Ground: The Welfare Ground, Off Upper Lane, Emley, nr Huddersfield HD8 9RE.   **(T)** 01924 849 392   **Capacity:** 2,000
Colours(change): Claret & sky blue/sky blue/claret (Green/black/green)
HONOURS: FA Comps: None   **League:** None

10 YEAR RECORD

07-08		08-09		09-10		10-11		11-12		12-13		13-14		14-15		15-16		16-17	
NCE1	11	NCE1	8	NCE1	8	NCE1	8	NCE1	10	NCE1	7	NCE1	8	NCE1	5	NCE1	4	NCE1	3
FAC	P	FAC	EP	FAC	EP	FAC	P	FAC	EP	FAC	EP	FAC	P	FAC	P	FAC	P	FAC	P
FAV	1P	FAV	2Q	FAV	2Q	FAV	2P	FAV	1P	FAV	4P	FAV	1P	FAV	1P	FAV	2Q	FAV	2P

ARMTHORPE WELFARE

Founded: 1926   Nickname: Wellie

Secretary: Martin turner   **(T)**   **(E)** armthorpe.welfare@hotmail.co.uk
Chairman: Lee Carmody   **Manager:** Michael Carmody   **Prog Ed:** Phil Wiffen
Ground: Welfare Ground, Church Street, Armthorpe, Doncaster DN3 3AG   **(T)**   **Capacity:** 2,500
Colours(change): All royal blue (All red)
HONOURS: FA Comps: None   **League:** Doncaster & District Senior 1952-53, 53-54, 54-55, 56-57, 57-58, 60-61, 61-62, 64 -65, 82-83, Div.3 77-78, Div.2 78-79, Div.1 81-82. NCE Div.1 Central 1984-85.

10 YEAR RECORD

07-08		08-09		09-10		10-11		11-12		12-13		13-14		14-15		15-16		16-17	
NCEP	9	NCEP	15	NCEP	3	NCEP	13	NCEP	13	NCEP	20	NCEP	18	NCEP	17	NCEP	19	NCEP	21
FAC	EP	FAC	Pr	FAC	EP	FAC	P	FAC	1Qr	FAC	EP	FAC	EP	FAC	P	FAC	2Q	FAC	EP
FAV	1P	FAV	2Q	FAV	4Pr	FAV	2Pr	FAV	3P	FAV	2P	FAV	2P	FAV	2Q	FAV	1P	FAV	1Q

BRIGG TOWN

Founded: 1864   Nickname: Zebras

Secretary: Tim Harris   **(T)** 07446 294 837   **(E)** uksoccersafe@gmail.com
Chairman: Tim Harris   **Manager:** Lee Thompson   **Prog Ed:** Tim Harris
Ground: The Hawthorns, Hawthorn Avenue, Brigg DN20 8PG   **(T)** 01652 409 137   **Capacity:** 2,500
Colours(change): Black and white/black/red (Pink/navy/pink)
HONOURS: FA Comps: FAV 1995-96, 2002-03   **League:** Midland Counties 1977-78. Northern Counties East Premier 2000-01. Lincolnshire League x8,

10 YEAR RECORD

07-08		08-09		09-10		10-11		11-12		12-13		13-14		14-15		15-16		16-17	
NP 1	16	NP1S	20	NP1S	15	NP1S	4	NP1S	17	NP1S	13	NP1S	18	NP1S	22	NCEP	21	NCE1	14
FAC	1Q	FAC	1Q	FAC	1Q	FAC	2Qr	FAC	P	FAC	P	FAC	1Qr	FAC	P	FAC	EP	FAC	1Q
FAT	Pr	FAT	1Q	FAT	2Q	FAT	P	FAT	1Q	FAT	P	FAT	2Q	FAT	Pr	FAV	1Q	FAV	1Q

CAMPION

Founded: 1963   Nickname:

Secretary: David Keegan   **(T)**   **(E)** campionafc@gmail.com
Chairman: Richard Holmes   **Manager:** James Bicknell   **Prog Ed:** Richard Holmes
Ground: Scotchman Road, Bradford, BD9 5DB.   **(T)** 01274 491 919
Colours(change): Red & black/black/red (All royal blue)
HONOURS: FA Comps: None   **League:** West Riding Amateur Division Two 1989-90, Division One 92-93.

10 YEAR RECORD

07-08	08-09	09-10	10-11		11-12		12-13		13-14		14-15		15-16		16-17	
			WRCP	3	WRCP	9	WRCP	12	WRCP	3	WRCP	3	WRCP	3	NCE1	8

DRONFIELD TOWN

Founded: 1998   Nickname: None

Secretary: Michael Payne   **(T)**   **(E)** dronfieldtownnfc@yahoo.co.uk
Chairman: Patrick Williams   **Manager:** Chris Millington   **Prog Ed:** Michael Payne
Ground: Stonelow Playing Fields, Stonelow Road, Dronfield, S18 2EU   **(T)**   **Capacity:** 500
Colours(change): Red & black/black with red/red & black (Yellow/blue/yellow)
HONOURS: FA Comps: None   **League:** Hope Valley B Div 2001-02, A Div 2002-03, Prem 2003-04. Midland Regional Alliance Division One 2005-06, Premier 2007-08. Central Midlands North 2012-13.

10 YEAR RECORD

07-08	08-09	09-10		10-11		11-12		12-13		13-14		14-15		15-16		16-17	
		CM P	2	CM Su	7	CMN	3	CMN	1	NCE1	14	NCE1	19	NCE1	15	NCE1	19

NORTHERN COUNTIES EAST LEAGUE - STEP 5/6

EAST YORKSHIRE CARNEGIE
Founded: 2016 **Nickname:** Carnegie, EYC

Secretary: Dave Reader **(T)** **(E)**
Chairman: Dave Reader **Manager:** Jamie Waltham **Prog Ed:** Becky Shipp
Ground: Dunswell Park, Dunswell HU6 0AA **(T)** **Capacity:** 2,000
Colours(change): All black & white (All red & white)
HONOURS: FA Comps: None **League:** None

10 YEAR RECORD

07-08	08-09	09-10	10-11	11-12	12-13	13-14	14-15	15-16	16-17
									HumbP 5

ECCLESHILL UNITED
Founded: 1948 **Nickname:** The Eagles

Secretary: Adrian Benson **(T)** 07767 472 777 **(E)** adrian.benson@btinternet.com
Chairman: Adrian Benson **Manager:** Sean Regan **Prog Ed:** Paul Everett
Ground: Mitton Group Stadium, Kingsway, Wrose, Bradford, BD2 1PN **(T)** 01274 615 739 **Capacity:** 2,225
Colours(change): Blue & white/blue/blue (Red & white/red/red)
HONOURS: FA Comps: None **League:** West Riding County Amateur 1976-77.
Northern Counties East Division One 1996-97.

10 YEAR RECORD

07-08		08-09		09-10		10-11		11-12		12-13		13-14		14-15		15-16		16-17	
NCEP	11	NCEP	20	NCE1	16	NCE1	10	NCE1	6	NCE1	14	NCE1	4	NCE1	13	NCE1	13	NCE1	9
FAC	EP	FAC	EP	FAC	EP			FAC	1Q	FAC	1Q			FAC	EP				
FAV	2Pr	FAV	2Q	FAV	1Q	FAV	2P	FAV	2P	FAV	1Q	FAV	1P	FAV	1Q	FAV	EP	FAV	1Q

FC BOLSOVER
Founded: 2016 **Nickname:** None

Secretary: Christie O'Connor **(T)** **(E)** fcbolsover@gmail.com
Chairman: Benjamin Thomas **Prog Ed:** Phoebe Thomas
Ground: Langwith Road Ground, Langwith Road, Shirebrook, NG20 8TF **(T)** 07950 682 973
Colours(change): Yellow/blue/white (Blue/white/blue)
HONOURS: FA Comps: None **League:** Central Midlands North Division 2016-17.

10 YEAR RECORD

07-08	08-09	09-10	10-11	11-12	12-13	13-14	14-15	15-16	16-17
									CMN 1

GLASSHOUGHTON WELFARE
Founded: 1964 **Nickname:** Welfare or Blues

Secretary: Frank MacLachlan **(T)** 07770 590 359 **(E)** frank.maclachlan@btinternet.com
Chairman: Jon Miles **Manager:** Darren Holmes & Lee Vigars **Prog Ed:** Patrick Monaghan
Ground: Glasshoughton Centre, Leeds Road, Glasshoughton, Castleford WF10 4PF **(T)** 01977 511 234 **Capacity:** 2,000
Colours(change): Royal blue & white/blue/blue (Green & white/white/white)
HONOURS: FA Comps: None **League:** None

10 YEAR RECORD

07-08		08-09		09-10		10-11		11-12		12-13		13-14		14-15		15-16		16-17	
NCEP	20	NCE1	19	NCE1	13	NCE1	7	NCE1	2	NCEP	16	NCEP	16	NCEP	21	NCE1	16	NCE1	11
FAC	EPr	FAC	EPr					FAC	Pr	FAC	EP	FAC	EP	FAC	EP	FAC	EPr		
FAV	2P	FAV	1Q	FAV	1Q	FAV	1Q	FAV	2P	FAV	2Q	FAV	2Q	FAV	1Q	FAV	1Q	FAV	2Qr

GRIMSBY BOROUGH
Founded: 2003 **Nickname:** The Wilderness Boys

Secretary: Nigel Fanthorpe **(T)** 07890 318 054 **(E)** nigelfanthorpe@hotmail.co.uk
Chairman: Tony Legget **Manager:** Daniel Barrett & Andy Liddle **Prog Ed:** Lee Lewis
Ground: The Bradley Football Development Centre, Bradley Road, Grimsby, DN37 0AG **(T)** 07890 318 054 **Capacity:** 1,000
Colours(change): All red (All white)
HONOURS: FA Comps: None **League:** None

10 YEAR RECORD

07-08		08-09		09-10		10-11		11-12		12-13		13-14		14-15		15-16		16-17	
CM Su	12	NCE1	13	NCE1	17	NCE1	15	NCE1	18	NCE1	17	NCE1	16	NCE1	22	NCE1	19	NCE1	4
								FAC	EP										
				FAV	1P	FAV	2Q	FAV	2Q	FAV	1Q	FAV	2Q	FAV	1Q			FAV	2Q

HALLAM

Founded: 1860   **Nickname:** Countrymen

Secretary: Kevin Scott   **(T)** 07889 855 594   **(E)** kevinscottsport@yahoo.co.uk
Chairman: Steve Basford   **Manager:** Scott Bates   **Prog Ed:** Pete Wilding
Ground: Sandygate Road, Crosspool, Sheffield S10 5SE   **(T)** 0114 230 9484   **Capacity:** 1,000
Colours(change): All blue (All yellow)

HONOURS: FA Comps: None   **League:** Hatchard 1902-03, 48-49. Sheffield Amateur 1922-23, 26-27. Sheffield Association 1949-50. Yorkshire Division Two 1960-61.

10 YEAR RECORD

	07-08	08-09	09-10	10-11	11-12	12-13	13-14	14-15	15-16	16-17
	NCEP 6	NCEP 10	NCEP 15	NCEP 19	NCE1 14	NCE1 12	NCE1 20	NCE1 14	NCE1 6	NCE1 5
	FAC 1Q	FAC EP	FAC 1Q	FAC EP	FAC EP	FAC EP				FAC EP
	FAV 3P	FAV 1Pr	FAV 2P	FAV 1P	FAV 1Q	FAV 1Q	FAV 1Q	FAV 2Q	FAV 2P	FAV 2P

KNARESBOROUGH TOWN

Founded: 1902   **Nickname:** The Boro

Secretary: Clare Rudzinski   **(T)** 07702 678 320   **(E)** knaresboroughtownafc@gmail.com
Chairman: Peter Plews   **Manager:** Paul Stansfield   **Prog Ed:** Ian Pickles
Ground: Manse Lane, Knaresborough, HG5 8LF   **(T)** 01423 548 896   **Capacity:** 1,000
Colours(change): Red/black/red (All yellow)

HONOURS: FA Comps: None   **League:** York 1902-03, 03-04, 04-05, 08-09, 24-25, 25-26, 28-29, 33-34, 34-35, Div.2 51-52, Div.1 52-53. Harrogate & District 64-65, 65-66, 66-67. West Yorkshire Prem 2008-09.

10 YEAR RECORD

	07-08	08-09	09-10	10-11	11-12	12-13	13-14	14-15	15-16	16-17
	WYkP 3	WYkP 1	WYkP 4	WYkP 2	WYkP 3	NCE1 8	NCE1 6	NCE1 12	NCE1 8	NCE1 7
								FAC P		
							FAV 2Q	FAV 1Q	FAV 1Q	FAV 1Q

NOSTELL MINERS WELFARE

Founded: 1928   **Nickname:** The Welfare

Secretary: Granville Marshall   **(T)** 01924 864 462   **(E)** nostwellmwfc@hotmail.com
Chairman: Kevin Allsop   **Manager:** Des Hazel   **Prog Ed:** Adam Whiteside
Ground: The Welfare Ground, Crofton Co. Centre, Middle Lane, New Crofton WF4 1LB   **(T)** 01924 866 010   **Capacity:** 1500
Colours(change): Yellow/black/black. (White & blue/blue/blue).

HONOURS: FA Comps: None   **League:** West Yorkshire Premier Division 2004-05

10 YEAR RECORD

	07-08	08-09	09-10	10-11	11-12	12-13	13-14	14-15	15-16	16-17
	NCE1 5	NCEP 13	NCEP 18	NCEP 9	NCEP 17	NCEP 18	NCEP 21	NCEP 15	NCEP 22	NCE1 22
		FAC Pr	FAC P	FAC EPr	FAC EP	FAC EP	FAC EP	FAC EP	FAC EPr	FAC EPr
	FAV 2Q	FAV 3P	FAV 2Q	FAV 1Q	FAV 2Qr	FAV 1P	FAV 1Q	FAV 2Q	FAV 1Q	FAV 2Q

OLLERTON TOWN

Founded: 1988   **Nickname:** The Town

Secretary: Joanne Winter   **(T)**   **(E)**
Chairman: John Thomson   **Manager:** Dave Winter   **Prog Ed:** Liam Kent
Ground: The Lane, Walesby Lane, New Ollerton, Newark NG22 9UT   **(T)**
Colours(change): Red/black/red (All navy)

HONOURS: FA Comps: None   **League:** Notts Alliance Division Two 1992-93, Division One 95-96. Central Midlands Premier Division 2007-08.

10 YEAR RECORD

	07-08	08-09	09-10	10-11	11-12	12-13	13-14	14-15	15-16	16-17
	CM P	CM Su 4	CM Su 3	CM Su 13	CMN 7	CMN 6	CMN 8	CMN 10	CMN 2	NCE1 17
		FAV 1Qr	FAV 2P	FAV 1Q	FAV 2Q	FAV 1Q	FAV 2Q		FAV 1Q	FAV 1Q

RETFORD UNITED

Founded: 1987   **Nickname:** The Badgers

Secretary: S Brammer (Acting)   **(T)** 07980 824 469   **(E)** graham@gtaccounts.com
Chairman: S Brammer (Acting)   **Manager:** Mark Wilson
Ground: Cannon Park, Leverton Road, Retford, Notts DN22 6QF   **(T)** 01777 710 300   **Capacity:** 2,000
Colours(change): Black and white/black/black (Yellow/royal blue/royal blue)

HONOURS: FA Comps: None   **League:** Notts All. Div.1 2000-01. Central Mids Div.1 01-02, Supreme Division 03-04, N.C.E. Prem. Division 06-07, 11-12, N.P.L. Div.1S 07-08, 08-09.

10 YEAR RECORD

	07-08	08-09	09-10	10-11	11-12	12-13	13-14	14-15	15-16	16-17
	NP1S 1	NP1S 1	NP P 6	NP P 22	NCEP 1	NCEP 4	NCEP 9	NCEP 20	NCEP 15	NCEP 22
	FAC P	FAC 4Q	FAC 1Qr	FAC 1Q	FAC EP	FAC 1Q	FAC P	FAC P	FAC EP	FAC EPr
	FAT 1P	FAT P	FAT 1Q	FAT 1Qr	FAV 1Qr	FAV 1P	FAV 1P	FAV 2Q	FAV 2Q	FAV 2Q

ROSSINGTON MAIN

Founded: 1919   Nickname: The Colliery

Secretary: Gerald Parsons   **(T)** 07941 811 217   **(E)** g-parsons2@sky.com
Chairman: Carl Stokes   **Manager:** Chris Glarvey
Ground: Welfare Ground, Oxford Street, Rossington, Doncaster, DN11 0TE   **(T)** 01302 865 524 (MD)   **Capacity:** 2,000
Colours(change): All blue (All red)
HONOURS: FA Comps: None   **League:** Doncaster & District Senior 1944-45.
Central Midlands Premier Division 1984-85.

10 YEAR RECORD

07-08		08-09		09-10		10-11		11-12		12-13		13-14		14-15		15-16		16-17	
NCE1	16	NCE1	11	NCE1	10	NCE1	14	NCE1	7	NCE1	18	NCE1	13	NCE1	15	NCE1	20	NCE1	15
FAC	EPr	FAC	EP	FAC	P	FAC	EP	FAC	EPr	FAC	EP								
FAV	1Q	FAV	1P	FAV	1P	FAV	1P	FAV	2Q	FAV	1Q	FAV	2Q	FAV	2Q	FAV	2Q	FAV	2Q

SELBY TOWN

Founded: 1919   Nickname: The Robins

Secretary: Thomas Arkley   **(T)** 07830 218 657   **(E)** toonarkley@yahoo.co.uk
Chairman: Ralph Pearse   **Manager:** Christian Fox
Ground: The Fairfax Plant Hire Stadium, Richard Street, Scott Road, Selby YO8 4BN   **(T)** 01757 210 900   **Capacity:** 5,000
Colours(change): All red (All blue).
HONOURS: FA Comps: None   **League:** Yorkshire 1934-35, 35-36, 52-53, 53-54.
Northern Counties East Division One 1995-96.

10 YEAR RECORD

07-08		08-09		09-10		10-11		11-12		12-13		13-14		14-15		15-16		16-17	
NCEP	7	NCEP	3	NCEP	13	NCEP	15	NCEP	20	NCE1	16	NCE1	12	NCE1	11	NCE1	10	NCE1	10
FAC	1Q	FAC	1Q	FAC	P	FAC	P	FAC	EP	FAC	EP								
FAT	1P	FAV	1P	FAV	1P	FAV	2Qr	FAV	1P	FAV	2Q	FAV	1Q	FAV	1P	FAV	1P	FAT	EP

SHIREBROOK TOWN

Founded: 1985   Nickname: None

Secretary: Aimee Radford   **(T)** 07983 809 608   **(E)** aimeeradford@yahoo.co.uk
Chairman: Cliff Richard Thomas   **Manager:** Rob Camm   **Prog Ed:** Aimee Radford
Ground: Langwith Road, Shirebrook, Mansfield, NG20 8TF   **(T)** 01623 742 535   **Capacity:** 2,000
Colours(change): Red/black/black (All white)
HONOURS: FA Comps: None   **League:** Central Midlands League Supreme Division 2000-01, 01-02.
Northern Counties East Division One 2003-04.

10 YEAR RECORD

07-08		08-09		09-10		10-11		11-12		12-13		13-14		14-15		15-16		16-17	
NCEP	15	NCEP	17	NCEP	19	NCE1	13	NCE1	13	NCE1	6	NCE1	5	NCE1	4	NCE1	7	NCE1	18
FAC	EP	FAC	P	FAC	P	FAC	1Q	FAC	Pr	FAC	EP	FAC	Pr	FAC	EPr	FAC	EP	FAC	EPr
FAV	1Q	FAV	1Q	FAV	2Q	FAV	1Q	FAV	2Q	FAV	2Pr	FAV	2Q	FAV	1Q	FAV	2P	FAV	2Q

SWALLOWNEST

Founded: 2006   Nickname: None

Secretary: Tony Santoro   **(T)**   **(E)** glennwatts57@gmail.com
Chairman: Glenn Watts
Ground: Rotherham Road, Sheffield S26 4UR.   **(T)** 0114 287 2510
Colours(change): All royal blue (Orange/white/white)
HONOURS: FA Comps: None   **League:** South Yorkshire Amateur Premier Division 2007-08.
Sheffield & Hallamshire County Senior Div.2 2008-09, Prem 10-11, 16-17.

10 YEAR RECORD

07-08		08-09		09-10		10-11		11-12		12-13		13-14		14-15		15-16		16-17	
SYoAP	1	Sh&H2	1	Sh&H1	2	Sh&HP	1	Sh&HP	3	Sh&HP	6	Sh&HP	5	Sh&HP	3	Sh&HP	7	Sh&HP	1

WINTERTON RANGERS

Founded: 1930   Nickname: Rangers

Secretary: Graham Halliday   **(T)** 07753 103 466   **(E)** ghtoon1892@gmail.com
Chairman: Wayne Turtle   **Manager:** Paul Grimes   **Prog Ed:** W. Turtle & M. Girdham
Ground: West Street, Winterton, Scunthorpe DN15 9QF.   **(T)** 01724 732 628   **Capacity:** 3,000
Colours(change): All blue (All red)
HONOURS: FA Comps: None   **League:** Yprkshire Division One 1971-72, 76-77, 78-79.
Northern Counties East Division Two 1989-90, Premier 2007-08.

10 YEAR RECORD

07-08		08-09		09-10		10-11		11-12		12-13		13-14		14-15		15-16		16-17	
NCEP	1	NCEP	5	NCEP	6	NCEP	5	NCEP	6	NCEP	19	NCEP	22	NCE1	18	NCE1	8	NCE1	12
FAC	1Q	FAC	2Qr	FAC	1Q	FAC	1Qr	FAC	EP	FAC	EP	FAC	EP	FAC	P				
FAV	3P	FAV	3P	FAV	1P	FAV	2P	FAV	2Q	FAV	2Q	FAV	2Q	FAV	1P	FAV	1Q	FAV	1Q

WORSBROUGH BRIDGE ATHLETIC

Founded: 1923   Nickname: The Briggers

Secretary: Mark Booth   **(T)**   **(E)**
Chairman: Peter Schofield   **Manager:** Josh Wright   **Prog Ed:** Mark Booth
Ground: Park Road, Worsbrough Bridge, Barnsley S70 5LJ   **(T)** 01226 284 452   **Capacity:** 2,000
Colours(change): All red (All blue)
HONOURS: FA Comps: None   **League:** Barnsley Division One 1952-53, 58-59, 59-60.
Sheffield Association Division One 1965-66, 69-70.

10 YEAR RECORD

07-08	08-09	09-10	10-11	11-12	12-13	13-14	14-15	15-16	16-17
NCE1 15	NCE1 16	NCE1 18	NCE1 12	NCE1 11	NCE1 9	NCE1 10	NCE1 16	NCE1 21	NCE1 20
FAV 1Q	FAV 2Q	FAV 1P	FAV 2Q	FAV 2Q	FAV 1Q	FAV 2Q	FAV 2Q	FAV 1Q	

YORKSHIRE AMATEUR

Founded: 1918   Nickname: Ammers

Secretary: Simon Charlesworth   **(T)**   **(E)** david.g.packham@gmail.com
Chairman: Lincoln Richards   **Manager:** Phil Harding & Lincoln Richards   **Prog Ed:** David Packham
Ground: Bracken Edge, Roxholme Road, Leeds, LS8 4DZ (Sat. Nav. LS7 4JG)   **(T)** 0113 289 2886   **Capacity:** 1,550
Colours(change): White/navy/red (All royal blue)
HONOURS: FA Comps: None   **League:** Yorkshire 1931-32, Division Two 1958-59, Division Three 1977-78.

10 YEAR RECORD

07-08	08-09	09-10	10-11	11-12	12-13	13-14	14-15	15-16	16-17
NCE1 14	NCE1 18	NCE1 14	NCE1 3	NCE1 19	NCE1 21	NCE1 19	NCE1 10	NCE1 11	NCE1 13
FAC EP	FAC EP			FAC EP				FAC EP	
FAV 1Q	FAV 2Q	FAV 1Q	FAV 2Q	FAV 1P	FAV 2Q	FAV 1Q	FAV 1P	FAV 2Q	FAV 1Q

NORTHERN LEAGUE

Sponsored by: Ebac
Founded: 1889

Recent Champions: 2014: Spennymoor Town
2015: Marske United **2016:** Shildon

DIVISION ONE	P	W	D	L	F	A	GD	Pts
1 South Shields	42	34	6	2	127	35	92	108
2 Morpeth Town	42	32	5	5	136	56	80	101
3 North Shields	42	32	5	5	107	39	68	101
4 Shildon	42	29	7	6	112	52	60	94
5 Marske United	42	22	6	14	103	75	28	72
6 Whitley Bay	42	19	13	10	88	70	18	70
7 Consett	42	19	8	15	105	81	24	65
8 Bishop Auckland	42	18	10	14	88	67	21	64
9 Newton Aycliffe	42	19	7	16	78	76	2	64
10 Newcastle Benfield	42	16	10	16	101	71	30	58
11 Sunderland RCA	42	16	9	17	85	79	6	57
12 Penrith	42	17	6	19	67	89	-22	57
13 Jarrow Roofing BCA	42	14	12	16	83	90	-7	54
14 Seaham Red Star	42	15	6	21	78	81	-3	51
15 Dunston UTS	42	14	6	22	77	96	-19	48
16 Ashington	42	13	8	21	73	90	-17	47
17 Ryhope CW	42	11	10	21	82	129	-47	43
18 West Auckland Town	42	11	3	28	60	120	-60	36
19 Washington	42	10	5	27	67	111	-44	35
20 Guisborough Town	42	10	7	25	70	124	-54	34*
21 Chester-Le-Street	42	6	5	31	51	127	-76	23
22 West Allotment Celtic	42	6	4	32	42	122	-80	22

CLUB MOVEMENTS

Division One - In: Billingham Synthonia (P), Stockton Town (P), Team Northumbria (P).
Out: Chester-Le-Street (R), Guisborough Town (R), South Shields (P - NPL D1N), West Allotment Celtic (R).

LEAGUE CUP

HOLDERS: SHILDON
ROUND 1

Alnwick Town	v	Blyth Town	0-3
West Auckland Town	v	Heaton Stannington	2-1
Billingham Synthonia	v	Ashington	1-2
Esh Winning	v	Sunderland RCA	1-5
Hebburn Town	v	Thornaby	2-2, 4-2p
Ryton & Crawcrook Albion	v	Bedlington Terriers	1-2
Washington	v	Brandon United	1-0
West Allotment Celtic	v	Newcastle Benfield	1-5
Willington	v	Penrith	2-4
Easington Colliery	v	Jarrow Roofing BCA	2-2, 4-5p
Bishop Auckland	v	Crook Town	0-0, 3-0p
Tow Law Town	v	Team Northumbria	2-1

ROUND 2

Ashington	v	Ryhope CW	2-1
Billingham Town	v	Washington	2-2, 6-7p
Durham City	v	Chester-Le-Street	1-2
Jarrow Roofing BCA	v	Whickham	0-1
Marske United	v	Guisborough Town	5-2
Newton Aycliffe	v	Shildon	1-1, 6-7p
Seaham Red Star	v	Bishop Auckland	1-4
South Shields	v	Blyth Town	4-2
Sunderland RCA	v	Northallerton Town	2-0
West Auckland Town	v	Stockton Town	0-1
Whitley Bay	v	Bedlington Terriers	5-1
Newcastle Benfield	v	Darlington RA	5-0
North Shields	v	Tow Law Town	4-1
Norton & Stockton Ancients	v	Consett	0-4
Penrith	v	Morpeth Town	1-1, 4-2p
Dunston UTS	v	Hebburn Town	2-0
(Played at Hebburn)			

ROUND 3

Ashington	v	Newcastle Benfield	2-3
Consett	v	Stockton Town	0-2
South Shields	v	Penrith	4-1
Whickham	v	Sunderland RCA	0-5
North Shields	v	Chester-Le-Street	1-1, 4-2p
Shildon	v	Whitley Bay	4-0
Dunston UTS	v	Washington	5-1
Marske United	v	Bishop Auckland	3-2

DIVISION ONE	1	2	3	4	5	6	7	8	9	10	11	12	13	14	15	16	17	18	19	20	21	22
1 Ashington		3-2	3-2	1-1	1-1	1-3	2-3	2-2	1-1	1-5	1-2	1-3	1-2	5-0	2-1	0-1	1-4	3-2	2-4	1-0	2-1	1-1
2 Bishop-Auckland	1-0		4-3	3-0	1-1	3-1	2-2	3-0	3-2	4-4	1-2	0-2	5-0	1-1	3-0	2-3	0-2	1-2	4-2	3-2	6-1	0-0
3 Chester-Le-Street	2-4	2-3		1-3	2-1	1-4	2-2	1-5	0-2	1-1	0-1	1-3	0-2	0-2	2-1	0-6	2-4	0-2	0-1	1-2	1-2	0-4
4 Consett	7-0	3-2	9-0		1-3	4-1	1-1	2-4	2-4	5-3	1-0	2-3	4-0	4-1	2-1	3-2	3-3	0-5	4-1	5-0	2-3	2-2
5 Dunston-UTS	1-1	1-1	2-5	1-2		5-2	3-2	0-5	2-4	6-4	1-0	0-3	3-4	2-0	0-6	1-5	2-4	2-4	0-2	4-1	2-0	0-1
6 Guisborough-Town	4-5	1-4	0-3	3-3	1-2		1-3	1-3	0-5	2-2	0-2	0-8	3-1	2-2	4-5	2-4	2-3	2-2	3-1	3-3	1-3	2-1
7 Jarrow-Roofing-BCA	3-2	2-2	4-2	2-2	2-2	4-1		1-3	4-5	0-4	1-1	3-2	2-2	3-3	1-3	1-1	0-7	1-0	4-0	0-2	1-3	2-2
8 Marske-United	1-1	4-0	3-0	2-2	3-1	0-1	1-3		0-3	4-1	3-0	1-2	3-4	7-1	3-2	2-1	1-2	0-0	3-2	2-0	5-2	0-1
9 Morpeth-Town	5-1	6-3	4-0	2-1	4-2	4-0	4-0	4-2		3-1	5-0	2-0	3-0	7-1	5-2	2-1	0-4	3-2	1-0	8-0	4-1	3-2
10 Newcastle-Benfield	5-2	2-2	3-1	0-2	0-2	2-2	2-1	4-1	3-2		3-3	1-2	1-1	11-1	3-0	0-0	0-1	6-0	6-1	2-0	0-1	0-0
11 Newton-Aycliffe	0-4	1-1	2-0	0-2	1-3	3-2	2-1	5-2	3-1	3-2		1-2	3-4	3-0	1-1	0-1	2-1	2-3	3-2	8-1	2-0	1-3
12 North-Shields	3-1	1-0	5-2	2-1	3-2	6-0	4-2	2-2	1-2	2-0	3-1		2-0	2-0	6-0	3-0	0-1	3-1	1-1	3-0	3-1	3-2
13 Penrith	2-0	0-2	2-1	0-1	2-1	0-4	0-7	2-4	3-0	1-1	2-4	1-2		4-0	1-1	1-3	0-2	0-1	2-1	3-0	1-1	1-4
14 Ryhope-CW	2-1	1-4	2-4	2-2	2-5	5-1	1-4	4-2	1-1	4-3	1-3	1-2	2-2		3-2	4-4	1-2	1-1	4-2	0-1	3-5	4-4
15 Seaham-Red-Star	1-4	0-3	5-0	4-2	2-1	4-0	0-1	0-4	1-3	2-1	1-0	4-0	0-1	1-3		2-2	1-2	0-2	1-3	0-2	5-1	6-1
16 Shildon	3-0	3-1	6-0	6-3	4-1	4-0	3-0	3-0	2-2	2-1	3-2	2-0	5-1	3-3	2-0		0-1	4-1	5-0	3-0	3-2	2-2
17 South-Shields	3-2	1-0	3-0	1-0	3-1	6-0	5-0	4-0	1-1	1-1	4-0	0-1	4-1	6-1	2-1	2-0		2-2	3-1	5-1	5-0	4-2
18 Sunderland-RCA	2-1	2-1	0-0	3-3	1-2	2-4	1-3	2-4	2-2	1-3	0-0	0-0	1-2	2-0	1-1	3-6	1-2		2-1	3-1	3-2	2-0
19 Washington	0-2	1-1	3-3	3-2	1-4	0-0	3-2	1-2	1-4	2-1	5-0	1-6	1-3	1-2	0-3	0-2	2-6	1-10		2-0	9-0	1-3
20 West-Allotment-Celtic	1-0	0-3	3-3	1-2	0-3	0-1	2-1	2-3	0-4	1-5	1-1	1-6	3-6	1-3	0-1	1-4	0-3	2-3			2-3	1-3
21 West-Auckland-Town	2-2	1-2	2-1	3-2	2-3	2-4	0-2	1-3	1-3	0-3	0-3	1-3	1-1	3-4	0-4	1-2	1-4	2-1	3-3	3-2		0-2
22 Whitley-Bay	1-5	2-1	1-2	2-1	2-1	3-1	2-2	2-2	1-2	3-1	3-0	2-2	2-0	5-1	3-3	1-3	3-3	3-2	2-1	2-2	4-0	

DIVISION TWO

		P	W	D	L	F	A	GD	Pts
1	Stockton Town	40	28	9	3	111	37	74	93
2	Team Northumbria	40	28	5	7	98	37	61	89
3	Billingham Synthonia	40	26	8	6	89	37	52	86
4	Heaton Stannington	40	25	4	11	87	44	43	79
5	Billingham Town	40	23	9	8	109	42	67	78
6	Whickham	40	20	9	11	83	51	32	69
7	Easington Colliery	40	20	9	11	84	61	23	69
8	Blyth Town	40	20	8	12	96	56	40	68
9	Northallerton Town	40	17	11	12	90	68	22	62
10	Durham City	40	18	7	15	73	63	10	61
11	Hebburn Town	40	18	7	15	57	59	-2	61
12	Bedlington Terriers	40	16	6	18	76	90	-14	54
13	Tow Law Town	40	15	8	17	68	66	2	53
14	Brandon United	40	9	10	21	46	89	-43	37
15	Alnwick Town	40	10	6	24	72	113	-41	36
16	Thornaby	40	9	7	24	55	102	-47	34
17	Crook Town	40	10	4	26	60	115	-55	34
18	Willington	40	9	5	26	40	94	-54	32
19	Darlington RA	40	9	4	27	61	126	-65	31
20	Ryton & Crawcrook Albion	40	7	9	24	46	93	-47	30
21	Esh Winning	40	7	7	26	53	111	-58	28

Norton & Stockton Ancients withdrew - record expunged.

CLUB MOVEMENTS - Division Two

In: Chester-Le-Street (R), Guisborough Town (R), Jarrow (P - Wearside), West Allotment Celtic (R).

Out: Billingham Synthonia (P), Stockton Town (P), Team Northumbria (P).

J.R. CLEATOR CUP
(2015 League champions v League Cup winners)

Shildon	v	Marske United	4-1

QUARTER FINALS

Sunderland RCA	v	Marske United	2-4
Newcastle Benfield	v	South Shields	1-2
Shildon	v	Stockton Town	3-0
North Shields	v	Dunston UTS	5-0

SEIM FINALS

Marske United	v	North Shields	3-3, 6-7p
Shildon	v	South Shields	1-4

FINAL

North Shields	v	South Shields	0-5

ERNSET ARMSTRONG MEMORIAL CUP

HOLDERS: NORTHALLERTON TOWN

ROUND 1

Billingham Town	v	Alnwick Town	5-0
Whickham	v	Stockton Town	1-3
Blyth Town	v	Heaton Stannington	0-1
Crook Town	v	Tow Law Town	0-4
Hebburn Town	v	Easington Colliery	2-0

ROUND 2

Brandon United	v	Darlington RA	2-0
Hebburn Town	v	Billingham Town	3-3, 3-5p
Heaton Stannington	v	Bedlington Terriers	0-2
Northallerton Town	v	Ryton & Crawcrook Albion	4-0
Thornaby	v	Billingham Synthonia	1-3
Esh Winning	v	Willington	1-2
Team Northumbria	v	Stockton Town	1-4
Tow Law Town	v	Durham City	3-3, 4-5p

QUARTER FINALS

Bedlington Terriers	v	Billingham Synthonia	2-7
Billingham Town	v	Stockton Town	0-1
Brandon United	v	Durham City	0-0, 2-4p
Willington	v	Northallerton Town	2-3

SEMI FINALS

Northallerton Town	v	Billingham Synthonia	2-1
Stockton Town	v	Durham City	2-2, 4-3p

FINAL

Northallerton Town	v	Stockton Town	0-0, 7-6p

DIVISION TWO

		1	2	3	4	5	6	7	8	9	10	11	12	13	14	15	16	17	18	19	20	21
1	Alnwick-Town		1-1	0-1	1-3	2-8	4-4	0-2	6-2	5-5	1-4	5-1	1-2	1-4	2-5	3-2	1-4	0-1	1-0	2-4	0-3	4-0
2	Bedlington-Terriers	0-3		0-1	3-2	0-5	3-2	4-4	4-0	2-2	1-2	3-2	1-3	5-1	0-3	4-1	5-4	0-1	3-0	4-1	0-3	0-0
3	Billingham-Synthonia	3-0	2-1		0-0	3-2	3-0	1-0	6-1	1-0	5-1	2-2	2-2	7-1	2-0	0-1	1-2	2-0	3-2	0-1	2-0	
4	Billingham-Town	3-1	5-0	0-0		4-1	5-0	1-1	2-0	0-1	4-1	5-2	0-1	2-0	2-3	0-1	1-1	0-0	4-1	2-2	7-0	6-0
5	Blyth-Town	3-1	5-0	1-1	4-2		0-0	4-0	4-0	2-1	3-1	2-1	1-2	1-2	2-2	0-0	1-3	3-3	1-2	2-1	0-2	5-1
6	Brandon-United	0-0	3-0	1-4	0-6	1-1		2-2	5-3	1-4	2-2	0-2	0-2	2-1	1-1	2-0	0-3	0-5	3-2	0-1	0-3	1-0
7	Crook-Town	2-6	5-4	1-10	1-6	3-1	1-1		0-2	1-3	1-5	4-1	1-3	0-4	1-2	0-1	1-3	2-3	3-0	0-5	1-2	3-1
8	Darlington-RA	1-1	1-0	2-3	1-4	2-1	4-1	3-2		1-2	3-6	1-1	0-4	0-3	0-2	2-5	0-2	3-4	1-1	0-3	1-4	0-5
9	Durham-City	2-0	0-3	0-2	4-0	1-3	5-3	1-0	4-5		0-2	3-1	0-1	0-0	1-2	3-1	1-2	0-4	2-2	2-2	3-5	3-0
10	Easington-Colliery	4-3	2-3	2-3	0-1	1-0	3-2	3-0	1-1	1-1		2-2	2-0	0-0	3-1	3-0	1-5	1-1	4-2	0-0	2-1	4-0
11	Esh-Winning	2-4	1-2	0-0	2-2	2-3	2-0	5-2	4-2	1-4	1-2		0-6	2-2	4-3	3-2	0-4	0-1	1-5	0-3	1-5	1-1
12	Heaton-Stannington	1-0	4-0	4-1	3-3	3-2	4-1	1-3	8-0	2-0	2-3	2-0		0-1	2-0	5-0	1-1	0-3	1-2	1-2	0-0	3-0
13	Hebburn-Town	5-1	2-1	1-1	2-3	0-5	2-1	2-1	2-0	0-1	0-3	1-2	1-0		0-2	0-1	0-2	0-3	2-1	4-1	3-0	3-0
14	Northallerton-Town	11-1	2-4	0-1	0-3	2-3	1-1	4-2	6-4	1-3	6-0	2-0	0-1	0-0		3-1	0-0	2-2	3-3	3-2	2-0	3-2
15	Ryton-&-Crawcrook-Albion	1-4	1-1	1-2	0-5	0-2	0-1	2-0	1-4	0-0	1-6	2-2	0-4	1-2	3-3		4-4	1-5	4-0	2-3	1-1	1-0
16	Stockton-Town	6-1	3-0	0-2	4-0	1-1	3-0	7-0	5-2	2-4	6-0	3-0	1-1	2-0	1-1		2-1	2-0	3-2	4-0	6-0	6-0
17	Team-Northumbria	3-0	6-1	0-1	2-3	2-1	2-0	5-0	3-4	0-1	2-1	2-1	3-0	2-1	2-1	1-2		5-1	3-0	1-1	6-0	
18	Thornaby	2-2	2-4	0-8	0-5	1-6	2-2	1-4	0-1	2-1	3-6	3-1	6-0	2-0	0-5	3-3	1-2	0-1		0-1	2-1	2-3
19	Tow-Law-Town	3-4	0-3	2-2	0-4	1-1	2-0	3-1	5-1	1-3	0-0	2-0	2-3	1-3	1-1	4-0	1-1	2-0	0-1		1-3	0-1
20	Whickham	2-0	3-3	2-0	2-2	0-1	1-2	2-3	2-0	2-0	0-0	3-0	0-2	7-0	1-3	3-0	2-2	0-3	4-0	3-1		2-2
21	Willington	3-0	2-3	0-2	0-2	2-5	0-1	1-2	4-3	2-1	2-1	5-1	0-3	0-1	1-1	1-0	1-2	0-3	0-0	0-1	0-7	

ASHINGTON

Founded: 1883　　Nickname: The Colliers

Secretary: Gav Perry　　**(T)** 07870 737410　　**(E)** gav@gavperry.co.uk
Chairman: Ian Lavery　　**Manager:** Tim Wade & Steve Harmison　　**Prog Ed:** Ian Jobson
Ground: Woodhorn Lane, Ashington NE63 9FW　　**(T)** 01670 811 991
Capacity: 2,000　**Seats:** 400　**Covered:** 900　**Midweek Matchday:** Tuesday　**Clubhouse:** Yes　**Shop:** Yes

Colours(change): Black & White stripes/black/black (Blue & yellow/yellow/blue)
Previous Names: None
Previous Leagues: East Northumberland. Northern Alliance, Football League, N. Eastern, Midland, Northern Counties, Wearside, N.P.L.

HONOURS: FA Comps: None
League: East Northumberland 1897-98. Northern Alliance 1913-14.
10 YEAR RECORD Northern Division Two 2000-01, 03-04.

07-08		08-09		09-10		10-11		11-12		12-13		13-14		14-15		15-16		16-17	
NL 1	17	NL 1	16	NL 1	6	NL 1	8	NL 1	5	NL 1	7	NL 1	6	NL 1	13	NL 1	12	NL 1	16
FAC	P	FAC	1Q	FAC	EP	FAC	3Q	FAC	4Q	FAC	1Q	FAC	P	FAC	1Qr	FAC	P	FAC	EP
FAV	1Q	FAV	2P	FAV	2Q	FAV	4P	FAV	5P	FAV	4P	FAV	4P	FAV	2P	FAV	2P	FAV	2Q

BILLINGHAM SYNTHONIA

Founded: 1923　　Nickname: Synners

Secretary: Graham Craggs　　**(T)** 07702 530 335　　**(E)** graham.craggs@gb.abb.com
Chairman: David Hillerby　　**Prog Ed:** Graeme Goodman
Ground: Norton (Teesside) Sports Complex, Station Road, Norton TS20 1PE　　**(T)** 01642 530 203
Capacity: 2,000　**Seats:** 200　**Covered:** Yes　**Midweek Matchday:** Wednesday　**Clubhouse:** Yes

Colours(change): Green & white quarters/white/white
Previous Names: Billingham Synthonia Recreation
Previous Leagues: Teesside 1923-the war

HONOURS: FA Comps: None
League: Teeside 1936-37.
10 YEAR RECORD Northern 1956-57, 88-89, 89-90, 95-96. Division Two 86-87.

07-08		08-09		09-10		10-11		11-12		12-13		13-14		14-15		15-16		16-17	
NL 1	9	NL 1	15	NL 1	12	NL 1	12	NL 1	11	NL 1	12	NL 1	20	NL 1	20	NL 2	5	NL 2	3
FAC	P	FAC	P	FAC	P	FAC	P	FAC	P	FAC	EP	FAC	Pr	FAC	EP	FAC	EPr	FAC	1Qr
FAV	3P	FAV	1Q	FAV	2Qr	FAV	5P	FAV	5Pr	FAV	3P	FAV	3P	FAV	1P	FAV	2Q	FAV	1P

BISHOP AUCKLAND

Founded: 1886　　Nickname: Two Blues

Secretary: David Strong　　**(T)** 07768 763 871　　**(E)** secretary@bishopafc.com
Chairman: Nick Postma
Ground: Heritage Park, Bishop Auckland, Co. Durham DL14 9AE　　**(T)** 01388 604 605
Capacity: 2,004　**Seats:** 250　**Covered:** 722　**Midweek Matchday:** Tuesday　**Clubhouse:** Yes

Colours(change): Light & dark blue/blue/blue
Previous Names: Auckland Town 1889-1893
Previous Leagues: Northern Alliance 1890-91, Northern League 1893-1988, Northern Premier 1988-2006

HONOURS: FA Comps: FA Amateur Cup 1895-96, 1899-1900, 1913-14, 20-21, 21-22, 34-35, 38-39, 54-55, 55-56, 56-57.
League: Northern League 1898-99, 1900-01, 01-02, 08-09, 09-10, 11-12, 20-21, 30-31, 38-39, 46-47, 49-50, 50-51,
10 YEAR RECORD 51-52, 53-54, 54-55, 55-56, 66-67, 84-85, 85-86.

07-08		08-09		09-10		10-11		11-12		12-13		13-14		14-15		15-16		16-17	
NL 1	20	NL 1	18	NL 1	13	NL 1	14	NL 1	8	NL 1	6	NL 1	8	NL 1	11	NL 1	8	NL 1	8
FAC	EPr	FAC	Pr	FAC	1Q	FAC	Pr	FAC	EP	FAC	2Q	FAC	1Qr	FAC	1Q	FAC	P	FAC	4Q
FAV	2Q	FAV	2Q	FAV	2Q	FAV	1P	FAV	2Q	FAV	1P	FAV	2Q	FAV	2P	FAV	1P	FAV	2Q

CONSETT

Founded: 1899　　Nickname: Steelman

Secretary: David Pyke　　**(T)** 07889 419 268　　**(E)** david_pyke@hotmail.co.uk
Chairman: Frank Bell　　**Prog Ed:** Gary Welford
Ground: Belle Vue Park, Ashdale Road, Consett DH8 7BF　　**(T)** 01207 588 886
Capacity: 4,000　**Seats:** 400　**Covered:** 1000　**Midweek Matchday:** Tuesday　**Clubhouse:** Yes　**Shop:** No

Colours(change): All Red
Previous Names: Consett Celtic 1899-1922.
Previous Leagues: Northern Alliance 1919-26, 35-37, North Eastern 1926-35, 37-58, 62-64, Midland 1958-60,
Northern Counties 1960-62, Wearside 1964-70.
HONOURS: FA Comps: None
League: North Eastern 1939-40, Division Two 26-27. Northern Counties 1961-62. Northern Division Two 1988-89, 05-06.
10 YEAR RECORD

07-08		08-09		09-10		10-11		11-12		12-13		13-14		14-15		15-16		16-17	
NL 1	2	NL 1	2	NL 1	10	NL 1	2	NL 1	15	NL 1	9	NL 1	11	NL 1	9	NL 1	7	NL 1	7
FAC	2Q	FAC	1Qr	FAC	Pr	FAC	EPr	FAC	EP	FAC	EPr	FAC	EP	FAC	1Q	FAC	2Q	FAC	2Qr
FAV	5P	FAV	2P	FAV	1P	FAV	2Q	FAV	3P	FAV	2P	FAV	2Q	FAV	4P	FAV	2P	FAV	2Q

DUNSTON UTS
Founded: 1975   Nickname: The Fed

Secretary: Bill Montague   **(T)** 07981 194 756   **(E)** w.montague@sky.com
Chairman: Malcolm James   **Prog Ed:** Bill Montague
Ground: UTS Stadium, Wellington Road, Dunston, Gateshead NE11 9JL   **(T)** 0191 493 2935
Capacity: 2,000 **Seats:** 120   **Covered:** 400   **Midweek Matchday:** Wednesday   **Clubhouse:** Yes   **Shop:** No

Colours(change): All blue
Previous Names: Dunston Federation Brewery > 2007. Dunston Federation > 2009.
Previous Leagues: Northern Amateur & Wearside league

HONOURS: FA Comps: FA Vase 2011-12.
League: Wearside 1988-89, 89-90. Northern Division Two 1992-93, Division One 2003-04, 04-05.

10 YEAR RECORD

07-08	08-09	09-10	10-11	11-12	12-13	13-14	14-15	15-16	16-17
NL 1 6	NL 1 6	NL 1 4	NL 1 7	NL 1 3	NL 1 5	NL 1 7	NL 1 6	NL 1 11	NL 1 15
		FAC EPr	FAC 2Q	FAC 1Q	FAC 1Qr	FAC P	FAC 2Q	FAC 1Q	FAC 2Q
		FAV 2P	FAV QF	FAV F	FAV 4P	FAV QF	FAV 5Pr	FAV 5Pr	FAV 3P

GUISBOROUGH TOWN
Founded: 1973   Nickname: Priorymen

Secretary: Keith Smeltzer   **(T)** 07811 850 388   **(E)** keithsmeltzer88@gmail.com
Chairman: Don Cowan   **Manager:** Gary Forster   **Prog Ed:** Danny Clark
Ground: King George V Ground, Howlbeck Road, Guisborough TS14 6LE   **(T)** 01287 636 925
Capacity: **Seats:** Yes   **Covered:** Yes   **Midweek Matchday:** Wednesday   **Clubhouse:** Yes

Colours(change): Red & white stripes/black/red (All purple)
Previous Names: None
Previous Leagues: Middlesbrough & District 1973-77. Northern Alliance 1977-80. Midland 1980-82. Northern Counties East 1982-85.

HONOURS: FA Comps: None
League: Northern Alliance 1979-80.

10 YEAR RECORD

07-08	08-09	09-10	10-11	11-12	12-13	13-14	14-15	15-16	16-17
NL 2 12	NL 2 7	NL 2 5	NL 2 2	NL 1 16	NL 1 11	NL 1 4	NL 1 3	NL 1 3	NL 1 20
FAC EP	FAC EP	FAC 1Q	FAC EP	FAC P	FAC Pr	FAC 3Q	FAC EPr	FAC 1Qr	FAC P
FAV 2Q	FAV 1Pr	FAV 1P	FAV 2Q	FAV 1Pr	FAV 1P	FAV 1P	FAV 2P	FAV 2P	FAV 1P

JARROW ROOFING BOLDON C.A.
Founded: 1987   Nickname: Roofing

Secretary: David Ramsey   **(T)** 07791 707 363   **(E)** secretary@jarrowroofingfc.co.uk
Chairman: Richard McLoughlin   **Prog Ed:** media@jarrowroofingfc.co.uk
Ground: Boldon CA Sports Ground, New Road, Boldon Colliery NE35 9AL   **(T)** 07714 525 549
Capacity: 2,000 **Seats:** 150   **Covered:** 800   **Midweek Matchday:** Tuesday   **Clubhouse:** Yes

Colours(change): Blue and yellow/blue/blue
Previous Names: None
Previous Leagues: South Tyneside Senior 1987-88. Tyneside Amateur 1988-91. Wearside 1991-96.

HONOURS: FA Comps: None
League: None

10 YEAR RECORD

07-08	08-09	09-10	10-11	11-12	12-13	13-14	14-15	15-16	16-17
NL 1 22	NL 2 16	NL 2 3	NL 1 19	NL 1 20	NL 2 4	NL 2 3	NL 1 7	NL 1 15	NL 1 13
FAC 1Qr	FAC Pr	FAC 2Q	FAC P	FAC EP	FAC P	FAC 2Qr	FAC Pr	FAC 1Q	FAC EPr
FAV 2P	FAV 1Q	FAV 2Q	FAV 2Q	FAV 1P	FAV 2P	FAV 3P	FAV 1Q	FAV 2Q	FAV 1P

MARSKE UNITED
Founded: 1956   Nickname: The Seasiders

Secretary: Mark Hathaway   **(T)** 07772 686 794   **(E)** admin@marskeunitedfc.com
Chairman: Mark Harkin   **Prog Ed:** Martin Jobling
Ground: GER Stad., Mount Pleasant Avenue, Marske by the Sea, Redcar TS11 7BW   **(T)** 07772 686 794
Capacity: **Seats:** Yes   **Covered:** Yes   **Midweek Matchday:** Tuesday   **Clubhouse:** Yes

Colours(change): Yellow/blue/blue
Previous Names: None
Previous Leagues: Local leagues 1956-76. Teeside 1976-85. Wearside 1985-97.

HONOURS: FA Comps: None
League: Teesside 1980-81, 84-85. Wearside 1995-96. Northern Division One 2014-15.

10 YEAR RECORD

07-08	08-09	09-10	10-11	11-12	12-13	13-14	14-15	15-16	16-17
NL 2 8	NL 2 5	NL 2 4	NL 2 3	NL 1 18	NL 1 19	NL 1 16	NL 1 1	NL 1 2	NL 1 5
FAC Pr	FAC EP	FAC EP	FAC 1Q	FAC P	FAC P	FAC 4Q	FAC 1Qr	FAC Pr	FAC 1Q
FAV 1P	FAV QF	FAV 5Pr	FAV 2P	FAV 2Q	FAV 1Qr	FAV 1P	FAV 3P	FAV 4P	FAV 2P

MORPETH TOWN
Founded: 1909   Nickname: Highwaymen

Secretary: Lee Crossley   **(T)** 07932 580 810   **(E)** lee.crossleymtfc@yahoo.com
Chairman: Ken Beattie   **Prog Ed:** Andrew McDonnell
Ground: Craik Park, Morpeth Common, Morpeth, Northumberland NE61 2YX   **(T)** 07425 135 301
Capacity: 1,000 **Seats:** 100   **Covered:** Yes   **Midweek Matchday:** Wednesday   **Clubhouse:** Yes

Colours(change): Amber & black/black/black
Previous Names: None
Previous Leagues: Northern Alliance 1936-1994.

HONOURS: FA Comps: FA Vase 2015-16.
    League: Northern Alliance 1983-84, 93-94. Northern Division Two 1995-96.

10 YEAR RECORD

07-08		03-09		09-10		10-11		11-12		12-13		13-14		14-15		15-16		16-17	
NL 1	8	NL 1	12	NL 1	21	NL 2	20	NL 2	4	NL 2	3	NL 2	17	NL 1	8	NL 1	4	NL 1	2
FAC	P	FAC	EP	FAC	1Q	FAC	EP			FAC	EP	FAC	1Q	FAC	EP	FAC	P	FAC	3Q
FAV	2Q	FAV	1Pr	FAV	2P	FAV	2Q	FAV	1Q	FAV	2P	FAV	5P	FAV	2P	FAV	F	FAV	4P

NEWCASTLE BENFIELD
Founded: 1988   Nickname: The Lions

Secretary: Gary Thompson   **(T)** 07525 275 641   **(E)** gctwnphg@gmail.com
Chairman: James Rowe   **Prog Ed:** Ian Cusack
Ground: Sam Smiths Park, Benfield Road, Walkergate NE6 4NU   **(T)** 07525 275 641
Capacity: 2,000 **Seats:** 150   **Covered:** 250   **Midweek Matchday:** Wednesday   **Clubhouse:** Yes

Colours(change): Blue & white hoops/blue/blue
Previous Names: Heaton Corner House. Newcastle Benfield Saints.
Previous Leagues: Northern Alliance 1988-2003

HONOURS: FA Comps: None
    League: Northern Alliance Division Two 1989-90, Division One 1994-95, 2002-03.

10 YEAR RECORD   Northern Division One 2008-09.

07-08		08-09		09-10		10-11		11-12		12-13		13-14		14-15		15-16		16-17	
NL 1	4	NL 1	1	NL 1	5	NL 1	4	NL 1	12	NL 1	21	NL 1	14	NL 1	10	NL 1	18	NL 1	10
FAC	2Q	FAC	3Q	FAC	P	FAC	2Q	FAC	1Q	FAC	EP	FAC	EP	FAC	2Q	FAC	P	FAC	1Q
FAV	3P	FAV	2P	FAV	2P	FAV	2Q	FAV	4P	FAV	2P	FAV	QF	FAV	3P	FAV	1P	FAV	2P

NEWTON AYCLIFFE
Founded: 1965   Nickname: Aycliffe

Secretary: Stephen Cunliffe   **(T)** 07872 985 501   **(E)** stecunliffe@aol.com
Chairman: Alan Oliver   **Prog Ed:** Bob Wood
Ground: Moore Lane Park, Moore Lane, Newton Aycliffe, Co. Durham DL5 5AG   **(T)** 01325 312 768
Capacity: **Seats:** Yes   **Covered:** Yes   **Midweek Matchday:** Wednesday   **Clubhouse:** Yes

Colours(change): Blue & black/blue/blue
Previous Names: None
Previous Leagues: Wearside 1984-94, 2008-09. Darlington & District. Durham Alliance > 2008.

HONOURS: FA Comps: None
    League: Darlington & District Division 'A' 2004-05. Durham Alliance 2007-08. Wearside 2008-09.

10 YEAR RECORD   Northern Division Two 2010-11.

07-08		08-09		09-10		10-11		11-12		12-13		13-14		14-15		15-16		16-17	
DuAl	1	Wear	1	NL 2	9	NL 2	1	NL 1	9	NL 1	17	NL 1	18	NL 1	18	NL 1	6	NL 1	9
								FAC	EP	FAC	EPr	FAC	Pr	FAC	EP	FAC	2Qr	FAC	EPr
						FAV	1Q	FAV	1Qr	FAV	1P	FAV	1Q	FAV	1Q	FAT	5P	FAV	3P

NORTH SHIELDS
Founded: 1896   Nickname: Robins

Secretary: Sean Redford   **(T)** 07929 336 645   **(E)** sean_061@yahoo.co.uk
Chairman: Alan Matthews   **Prog Ed:** Russell Wynn
Ground: Daren Persson Staduim, West Percy Road, Chirton, North Shields NE29 6UA   **(T)**
Capacity: 1,500 **Seats:** Yes   **Covered:** Yes   **Midweek Matchday:**   **Clubhouse:** Yes

Colours(change): All red
Previous Names: North Shields Athletic 1896-15, Preston Colliery 1919-1928, North Shields FC 1928-92. North Shields Athletic 1995-99.
Previous Leagues: Northern Combination. Northern Alliance. North Eastern. Midland. Northern Counties/North Eastern 1960-64.
    Northern 1964-89. Northern Counties East 1989-92. Wearside 1992-2004.
HONOURS: FA Comps: FA Amateur Cup 1968-69. FA Vase 2014-15.
    League: Northern Alliance 1906-07, 07-08. North Eastern Div.2 28-29, Div.1 49-50. Northern Counties 60-61.

10 YEAR RECORD   Northern Div.1 68-69, Div.2 2013-14. Northern Counties East Prem 91-92. Wearside 98-99, 01-02, 03-04.

07-08		08-09		09-10		10-11		11-12		12-13		13-14		14-15		15-16		16-17	
NL 2	17	NL 2	15	NL 2	6	NL 2	4	NL 2	8	NL 2	8	NL 2	1	NL 1	4	NL 1	5	NL 1	3
FAC	EP	FAC	EP			FAC	Pr	FAC	EPr	FAC	EPr	FAC	EP	FAC	Pr	FAC	Pr	FAC	P
FAV	1Q			FAV	2Q	FAV	1Q	FAV	1Q	FAV	1Q	FAV	1Pr	FAV	F	FAV	4P	FAV	3P

PENRITH
Founded: 1894   Nickname: Blues

Secretary: Ian White **(T)** 07960 958 367 **(E)** ianwhite77@hotmail.com
Chairman: Brian Williams
Ground: The Stadium, Frenchfield Park, Frenchfield, Penrith CA11 8UA **(T)** 01768 865 990
Capacity: 1,500 **Seats:** 200 **Covered:** 1,000 **Midweek Matchday:** Tuesday **Clubhouse:** Yes **Shop:** No

Colours(change): White/blue/blue
Previous Names: Penrith 1894-2007. Penrith Town 2007-08. Back to Penrith after a merger with Penrith United.
Previous Leagues: North Eastern. Northern 1947-82. North West Counties 1982-87, 90-97. Northern Premier League 1987-90.

HONOURS: FA Comps: None
League: Northern Division Two 2002-03, 07-08.

10 YEAR RECORD

07-08	08-09	09-10	10-11	11-12	12-13	13-14	14-15	15-16	16-17
NL 2 1	NL 1 7	NL 1 14	NL 1 17	NL 1 19	NL 1 13	NL 1 13	NL 1 14	NL 1 14	NL 1 12
FAC 1Qr	FAC P	FAC P	FAC EP	FAC 1Q	FAC EP	FAC 3Q	FAC EP	FAC EP	FAC Pr
FAV 2Q	FAV 3P	FAV 3P	FAV 2Q	FAV 2Q	FAV 1P	FAV 1P	FAV 1Q	FAV 1Q	FAV 3P

RYHOPE CW
Founded: 1892   Nickname: Colliery Welfare

Secretary: Dougie Benison **(T)** 07901 545 760 **(E)** dougie.benison@btinternet.com
Chairman: Darren Norton **Prog Ed:** Dougie Benison
Ground: Ryhope Recreation Park, Ryhope Street, Ryhope, Sunderland SR2 0AB **(T)** 07901 545 760
Capacity: **Seats:** Yes **Covered:** Yes **Midweek Matchday:** **Clubhouse:** Yes

Colours(change): Red & white/red/red
Previous Names: None
Previous Leagues: Wearside >2012, 2013-14.

HONOURS: FA Comps: None
League: Wearside 1927-28, 61-62, 62-63, 63-64, 65-66, 2010-11, 11-12.

10 YEAR RECORD

07-08	08-09	09-10	10-11	11-12	12-13	13-14	14-15	15-16	16-17
Wear 5	Wear 8	Wear 2	Wear 1	Wear 1	NL 2 2	Wear 2	NL 2 6	NL 2 2	NL 1 17
								FAC EPr	FAC EPr
							FAV 2P	FAV 1Q	FAV 2P

SEAHAM RED STAR
Founded: 1973   Nickname: The Star

Secretary: Dave Copeland **(T)** 07834 473 001 **(E)** davidcopelandc@aol.com
Chairman: Rob Smith **Prog Ed:** Dave Copeland
Ground: Seaham Town Park, Stockton Road, Seaham. Co.Durham SR7 0HY **(T)**
Capacity: 500 **Seats:** Yes **Covered:** Yes **Midweek Matchday:** **Clubhouse:** Yes

Colours(change): Red & white stripes/red/red with white turnover
Previous Names: Seaham Colliery Welfare Red Star 1978-87.
Previous Leagues: Houghton & District 1973-74. Northern Alliance 1974-79. Wearside 1979-83.

HONOURS: FA Comps: None
League: Wearside 1981-82.
10 YEAR RECORD Northern League Division Two 2014-15.

07-08	08-09	09-10	10-11	11-12	12-13	13-14	14-15	15-16	16-17
NL 1 14	NL 1 21	NL 2 12	NL 2 17	NL 2 20	NL 2 10	NL 2 4	NL 2 1	NL 1 9	NL 1 14
FAC EP	FAC EP	FAC EP	FAC EP			FAC EP	FAC P	FAC EPr	FAC EP
FAV 2P	FAV 2Q	FAV 2Q	FAV 1Q	FAV 1Q	FAV 1Q	FAV 1Q	FAV 3P	FAV 3P	FAV 1Q

SHILDON
Founded: 1890   Nickname: Railwaymen

Secretary: Gareth Howe **(T)** 07976 822 453 **(E)** gareth.howe3@btopenworld.com
Chairman: David Dent **Prog Ed:** Martyn Tweddle
Ground: Dean Street, Shildon, Co. Durham DL4 1HA **(T)** 01388 773 877
Capacity: 4,000 **Seats:** 480 **Covered:** 1000 **Midweek Matchday:** Wednesday **Clubhouse:** Yes

Colours(change): Red/black/black
Previous Names: Shildon Athletic > 1923.
Previous Leagues: Auckland & Dist 1892-86, Wear Valley 1896-97, Northern 1903-07, North Eastern 1907-32

HONOURS: FA Comps: None
League: Northern 1933-34, 34-35, 35-36,36-37, 39-40, 2015-16, Division Two 2001-02.

10 YEAR RECORD

07-08	08-09	09-10	10-11	11-12	12-13	13-14	14-15	15-16	16-17
NL 1 5	NL 1 8	NL 1 2	NL 1 5	NL 1 10	NL 1 8	NL 1 3	NL 1 2	NL 1 1	NL 1 4
FAC 1Q	FAC 1Q	FAC P	FAC 3Q	FAC 1Qr	FAC 2Q	FAC P	FAC 4Qr	FAC EPr	FAC 2Q
FAV 2P	FAV 3P	FAV QF	FAV 3P	FAV 1P	FAV SF	FAV 2P	FAV 3P	FAV 1P	FAV 4P

STOCKTON TOWN

Founded: 1979   Nickname:

Secretary: Rob Sexton   **(T)** 07505 900 815   **(E)** 1962.rvs@gmail.com
Chairman: Martin Hillerby   **Prog Ed:** Graham Lipthorpe
Ground: Bishopton Road West, Stockton-on-Tees TS19 0QD   **(T)** 01642 604 915
Capacity: **Seats:** Yes   **Covered:** Yes   **Midweek Matchday:**   **Clubhouse:** Yes

Colours(change): Yellow/blue/yellow
Previous Names: Hartburn Juniors 1979-2003.
Previous Leagues: Teeside 2009-10. Wearside 2010-2016.

HONOURS: FA Comps: None
         League: Wearside 2012-13, 13-14, 14-15,15-16. Northern Division Two 2016-17.

10 YEAR RECORD

07-08	08-09	09-10	10-11	11-12	12-13	13-14	14-15	15-16	16-17
		Tee1 4	Wear 10	Wear 3	Wear 1	Wear 1	Wear 1	Wear 1	NL 2 1
									FAV 2P

SUNDERLAND RYHOPE C.A.

Founded: 1961   Nickname: The CA

Secretary: Colin Wilson   **(T)** 07802 523 533   **(E)** wilsonjohncolin@gmail.com
Chairman: Graham Defty   **Prog Ed:** Colin Wilson
Ground: Meadow Park, Beachbrooke, Stockton Rd, Ryhope, Sunderland SR2 0NZ   **(T)** 07802 523 533
Capacity: 1,500 **Seats:** 150   **Covered:** 200   **Midweek Matchday:** Wednesday   **Clubhouse:** Yes

Colours(change): Red & white/black/red
Previous Names: Ryhope Youth Club 1961-71. Ryhope Community Association 1971-99. Kennek Ryhope CA 1999-2007.
Previous Leagues: Seaham & District. Houghton & District. Northern Alliance 1978-82.

HONOURS: FA Comps: None
         League: None

10 YEAR RECORD

07-08	08-09	09-10	10-11	11-12	12-13	13-14	14-15	15-16	16-17
NL 2 4	NL 2 4	NL 2 2	NL 1 13	NL 1 4	NL 1 22	NL 1 19	NL 1 16	NL 1 13	NL 1 11
FAC EPr	FAC EP	FAC EP	FAC EP	FAC P	FAC EPr	FAC EP	FAC EPr	FAC EPr	FAC EP
FAV 2Q	FAV 1P	FAV 1Q	FAV 1Q	FAV 1P	FAV 2P	FAV 1P	FAV 2P	FAV 5P	FAV 5P

TEAM NORTHUMBRIA

Founded: 1999   Nickname: Team North

Secretary: Tom Robinson   **(T)** 07772 598 192   **(E)** thomas.robinson@northumbria.ac.uk
Chairman: Tony Stokle   **Prog Ed:** Tom Robinson
Ground: Coach Lane, Benton, Newcastle upon Tyne NE7 7XA   **(T)** 0191 215 6575
Capacity: **Seats:** Yes   **Covered:** Yes   **Midweek Matchday:** Monday   **Clubhouse:** Yes

Colours(change): All red
Previous Names: Northumbria University 1999-2003.
Previous Leagues: Northern Alliance 1999-2006.

HONOURS: FA Comps: None
         League: Northern Alliance Premier 2005-06. Northern Division Two 2011-12.

10 YEAR RECORD

07-08	08-09	09-10	10-11	11-12	12-13	13-14	14-15	15-16	16-17
NL 2 19	NL 2 12	NL 2 14	NL 2 5	NL 2 1	NL 1 16	NL 1 21	NL 2 4	NL 2 4	NL 2 2
FAC EP	FAC P	FAC P	FAC EP			FAC 1Q			FAC EP
FAV 2Q	FAV 2Q	FAV 2Q	FAV 1Q		FAV 2Q	FAV 2Q		FAV 3P	FAV 2Q

WASHINGTON

Founded: 1947   Nickname: Mechanics

Secretary: Steve Haywood   **(T)** 0746 541 461   **(E)** stephenhaywood@hotmail.com
Chairman: Rob Cutler   **Prog Ed:** Steve Haywood
Ground: Nissan Sports Complex, Washington Road Sunderland SR5 3NS   **(T)** 0746 541 461
Capacity: 1,000 **Seats:** Yes   **Covered:** Yes   **Midweek Matchday:** Tuesday   **Clubhouse:** Yes

Colours(change): All red
Previous Names: Washington Mechanics, Washington Ikeda Hoover.
Previous Leagues: Gateshead & District, Washington Amateur, Northern Alliance: 1967-68, Wearside: 1968-88

HONOURS: FA Comps: None
         League: North Eastern Division Two 1927-28. Washington Amateur 1955-56, 56-57,57-58, 58-59,59-60,61-62,62-63.

10 YEAR RECORD

07-08	08-09	09-10	10-11	11-12	12-13	13-14	14-15	15-16	16-17
NL 1 21	NL 2 7	NL 2 18	NL 2 16	NL 2 14	NL 2 12	NL 2 9	NL 2 2	NL 1 10	NL 1 19
FAC EP	FAC EPr				FAC EP		FAC P	FAC 2Qr	FAC 1Q
FAV 1P	FAV 1Q	FAV 1Q	FAV 1P	FAV 1Q	FAV 2Q	FAV 2Q	FAV 2Q	FAV 2Q	FAV 1Q

WEST AUCKLAND TOWN   Founded: 1893   Nickname: West

Secretary: Wayne Jones   **(T)** 07951 292 036   **(E)** waynenoj25@hotmail.co.uk
Chairman: Jim Palfreyman   **Prog Ed:** Jim Palfreyman
Ground: Darlington Road, West Auckland, Co. Durham DL14 9AQ   **(T)** 07951 292 036
Capacity: 2,000 **Seats:** 250 **Covered:** 250 **Midweek Matchday:** Tuesday **Clubhouse:** Yes

Colours(change): Yellow/black/yellow
Previous Names: West Auckland 1893-1914.
Previous Leagues: Wear Valley 1896-1900. South Durham Alliance 1900-05. Mid Durham 1905-08.

HONOURS: FA Comps: None
League: Northern 1959-60, 60-61, Division Two 1990-91.

10 YEAR RECORD

07-08		08-09		09-10		10-11		11-12		12-13		13-14		14-15		15-16		16-17	
NL 1	16	NL 1	20	NL 1	16	NL 1	6	NL 1	2	NL 1	4	NL 1	5	NL 1	5	NL 1	17	NL 1	18
FAC	3Qr	FAC	P	FAC	2Q	FAC	EPr	FAC	EPr	FAC	2Qr	FAC	3Qr	FAC	Pr	FAC	P	FAC	P
FAV	2P	FAV	2Q	FAV	3P	FAV	2P	FAV	F	FAV	2P	FAV	F	FAV	2P	FAV	1P	FAV	2P

WHITLEY BAY   Founded: 1897   Nickname: The Seahorses

Secretary: Derek Breakwell   **(T)** 07889 888 187   **(E)** dbreakwell@hotmail.co.uk
Chairman: Paul McIlduff   **Manager:** Marc Nash   **Prog Ed:** Peter Fox
Ground: Hillheads Park, Rink Way, Whitley Bay NE25 8HR   **(T)** 0191 291 3637
Capacity: 4,500 **Seats:** 450 **Covered:** 650 **Midweek Matchday:** Tuesday **Clubhouse:** Yes **Shop:** Yes

Colours(change): Royal blue & white/royal blue/royal blue (All yellow)
Previous Names: Whitley Bay Athletic 1950-58
Previous Leagues: Tyneside 1909-10, Northern Alliance 1950-55, North Eastern 1955-58, Northern 1958-88. Northern Premier League 1988-00.

HONOURS: FA Comps: FA Vase 2001-02, 08-09, 09-10, 10-11.
League: Northern Alliance 1952-53, 53-54. Northern 1964-65, 65-66, 06-07.
10 YEAR RECORD Northern Premier League Division One 1990-91.

07-08		08-09		09-10		10-11		11-12		12-13		13-14		14-15		15-16		16-17	
NL 1	3	NL 1	3	NL 1	3	NL 1	3	NL 1	6	NL 1	3	NL 1	10	NL 1	15	NL 1	16	NL 1	6
FAC	EP	FAC	3Q	FAC	1Q	FAC	3Q	FAC	1Q	FAC	P	FAC	EP	FAC	EPr	FAC	3Q	FAC	EPr
FAV	SF	FAV	F	FAV	F	FAV	F	FAV	5P	FAV	4P	FAV	3P	FAV	3P	FAV	2P	FAV	2Q

DIVISION TWO

ALNWICK TOWN   Founded: 1879   Nickname: Magpies or Wick

Secretary: Cyril Cox   **(T)** 0191 236 6456   **(E)** uk2usa@hotmail.co.uk
Chairman: Tom McKie   **Prog Ed:** Michael Cook
Ground: St. Jame's Park, Weavers Way, Alnwick, Northumberland NE66 1BG   **(T)** 01665 603 162
Colours(change): Black & white stripes/black/black

HONOURS: FA Comps: None   **League:** North Northumberland 1898-99. Nothern Alliance 1937-38, 62-63, 63-64, 65
-66, 67-68, 68-69, 69-70, 70-71, 71-72.

10 YEAR RECORD

07-08		08-09		09-10		10-11		11-12		12-13		13-14		14-15		15-16		16-17	
NAI P	14	NAI P	5	NAI P	11	NAI P	2	NL 2	16	NL 2	21	NL 2	18	NL 2	16	NL 2	17	NL 2	15
										FAV	1Q	FAV	1Q	FAV	2P	FAV	1Qr	FAV	1Q

BEDLINGTON TERRIERS   Founded: 1949   Nickname: Terriers

Secretary: Keith Brown   **(T)** 07930 408 313   **(E)** keithbrown18@hotmail.com
Chairman: Ronan Liddane   **Prog Ed:** Ken Waterhouse
Ground: Doctor Pitt Welfare Park, Park Road, Bedlington NE22 5AT   **(T)** 07935 840 277   **Capacity:** 3,000
Colours(change): All red.
HONOURS: FA Comps: None   **League:** Northern Combination 1954-55. Northern Alliance 1966-67.
Northern DivisioN Two 1993-94, Division One 97-98, 98-99, 99-00, 2000-01, 01-02.
10 YEAR RECORD

07-08		08-09		09-10		10-11		11-12		12-13		13-14		14-15		15-16		16-17	
NL 1	15	NL 1	14	NL 1	7	NL 1	9	NL 1	7	NL 1	15	NL 1	20	NL 1	17	NL 1	22	NL 2	12
FAC	EP	FAC	1Q	FAC	P	FAC	EP	FAC	2Q	FAC	1Q					FAC	EPr	FAC	EP
FAV	1P	FAV	1Pr	FAV	2P	FAV	1P	FAV	2P	FAV	2P					FAV	2Q	FAV	1Q

BILLINGHAM TOWN

Founded: 1967   Nickname: Billy Town

Secretary: Peter Martin   **(T)** 07873 794 768   **(E)** peterwlmartin@hotmail.com
Chairman: John Oliver   **Prog Ed:** Chris Storey
Ground: Bedford Terrace, Billingham, Cleveland TS23 4AE   **(T)** 07873 794 768   **Capacity:** 3,000
Colours(change): All blue & white
HONOURS: FA Comps: None   **League:** Stockton & District Division Two 1968-69. Teesside 1978-79, 81-82.

10 YEAR RECORD

07-08	08-09	09-10	10-11	11-12	12-13	13-14	14-15	15-16	16-17
NL 1 10	NL 1 17	NL 1 19	NL 1 15	NL 1 17	NL 1 20	NL 1 23	NL 2 18	NL 2 11	NL 2 5
FAC 2Q	FAC P	FAC EP	FAC EP	FAC P	FAC P	FAC EP	FAC EP		
FAV 1P	FAV 2Q	FAV 1Q	FAV 1P	FAV 2P	FAV 1Q	FAV 2Qr	FAV 2Q	FAV 1Q	FAV 4P

BLYTH TOWN

Founded: 1995   Nickname:

Secretary: Tracey Elliott   **(T)** 07710 715045   **(E)** barry.elliott8@btinternet.com
Chairman: Barry William Elliott   **Manager:** Andy Bowman & Michael   **Prog Ed:** Chrissie Pringle
Ground: Off Sandringham Avenue, South Newsham, Blyth NE24 3PS   **(T)** 07710 715045
Colours(change): White with blue trim/white/blue hoops (Blue with white trim/blue/blue hoops)
HONOURS: FA Comps: None   **League:** Northern Alliance Division Two 2002-03, Premier 2013-14, 14-15, 15-16.

10 YEAR RECORD

07-08	08-09	09-10	10-11	11-12	12-13	13-14	14-15	15-16	16-17
NAl P 8	NAl P 9	NAl P 4	NAl P 9	NAl P 11	NAl P 2	NAl P 1	NAl P 1	NAl P 1	NL 2 8
									FAV 1Q

BRANDON UNITED

Founded: 1968   Nickname: United

Secretary: Barry Ross   **(T)** 07555 586 305   **(E)** barryross501@gmail.com
Chairman: David Bussey   **Prog Ed:** Dean Johnson
Ground: Welfare Park, Rear Commercial Street, Brandon DH7 7PL   **(T)** 07555 586 305
Colours(change): All red
HONOURS: FA Comps: None   **League:** Durham & District Sunday Div.2 1969-70, Div.1 73-74, 74-75, 75-76, 76-77.
Northern Alliance Div.2 77-78, 78-79. Northern 2002-03, Div.2 84-85, 99-2000.

10 YEAR RECORD

07-08	08-09	09-10	10-11	11-12	12-13	13-14	14-15	15-16	16-17
NL 2 20	NL 2 6	NL 2 15	NL 2 19	NL 2 17	NL 2 18	NL 2 19	NL 2 22	NL 2 15	NL 2 14
FAC EP	FAC EPr	FAC P	FAC EP						
FAV 2Q	FAV 2Q	FAV 1Q	FAV 2Q	FAV 2Q	FAV 1Q		FAV 1Q	FAV 1Q	FAV 1Q

CHESTER-LE-STREET TOWN

Founded: 1972   Nickname: Cestrians

Secretary: Lenny Lauchlan   **(T)** 07938 008 591   **(E)** i.w.lauchlan@durham.ac.uk
Chairman: Joe Burlison   **Prog Ed:** Keith Greener
Ground: Moor Park, Chester Moor, Chester-le-Street, Co.Durham DH2 3RW   **(T)** 07972 419 275
Colours(change): Blue & white hoops/white/white with blue trim
HONOURS: FA Comps: None   **League:** Washington 1975-76. Wearside 1980-81.
Northern Division Two 1983-84, 97-98.

10 YEAR RECORD

07-08	08-09	09-10	10-11	11-12	12-13	13-14	14-15	15-16	16-17
NL 1 18	NL 1 13	NL 1 20	NL 2 8	NL 2 12	NL 2 13	NL 2 11	NL 2 13	NL 2 3	NL 1 21
FAC 1Qr	FAC EP	FAC P	FAC 1Q	FAC EPr	FAC EPr				FAC P
FAV 2Qr	FAV 2Q	FAV 2Q	FAV 2Q	FAV 1Q	FAV 2Q	FAV 1Q	FAV 2Q	FAV 1P	FAV 2P

CROOK TOWN

Founded: 1889   Nickname: Black & Ambers

Secretary: Jonathon Hughes   **(T)** 07801 013 253   **(E)** crooktownafc2015@yahoo.co.uk
Chairman: Vince Kirkup   **Manager:** Wilf Constantine   **Prog Ed:** Jonathon Hughes
Ground: The Sir Tom Cowie Millfield, West Road, Crook, Co.Durham DL15 9PW   **(T)** 01388 762 959   **Capacity:** 1,500
Colours(change): Amber/black/black (All sky blue)
HONOURS: FA Comps: FA Am C 00-01,53-54,   **League:** Northern 1914-15, 26-27, 52-53, 58-59, 62-63, Division Two 2012-13.
58-59, 61-62, 63-64.

10 YEAR RECORD

07-08	08-09	09-10	10-11	11-12	12-13	13-14	14-15	15-16	16-17
NL 2 14	NL 2 9	NL 2 13	NL 2 12	NL 2 10	NL 2 1	NL 1 15	NL 1 22	NL 2 18	NL 2 17
FAC P	FAC 1Q	FAC EP	FAC P	FAC EP	FAC Pr	FAC 1Q	FAC EP	FAC EP	
FAV 2Q	FAV 1P	FAV 3P	FAV 2Q	FAV 2P	FAV 1Q	FAV 2P	FAV 2Q	FAV 1Q	FAV 1Q

DARLINGTON R.A.
Founded: 1993   Nickname: Railwaymen

Secretary: Alan Hamilton   **(T)** 07872 324 808   **(E)** nobbydarlo@ntlworld.com
Chairman: Doug Hawman   Peter Mulcaster   **Prog Ed:** Alan Hamilton
Ground: Brinkburn Road, Darlington, Co. Durham DL3 9LF   **(T)** 01325 468 125
Colours(change): All red (All blue)
HONOURS: FA Comps: None   **League:** Darlington & District 1932-33, 63-64, 67-68, 98-99.
Auckland & District 2000-01. Wearside 2004-05.

10 YEAR RECORD

	07-08	08-09	09-10	10-11	11-12	12-13	13-14	14-15	15-16	16-17
	NL 2 18	NL 2 18	NL 2 19	NL 2 15	NL 2 5	NL 2 5	NL 2 12	NL 2 14	NL 2 13	NL 2 19
	FAC P	FAC EP				FAC EPr	FAC EP			
	FAV 2Q	FAV 2Q	FAV 2Q	FAV 1Q	FAV 1P	FAV 1Q	FAV 2Q	FAV 1Q	FAV 1P	FAV 1Q

DURHAM CITY
Founded: 1949   Nickname: City

Secretary: Fred Usher   **(T)** 07901 804 087   **(E)** fredusher@sky.com
Chairman: Olivier Bernard   **Prog Ed:** Gaz Hutchinson
Ground: Belle View Staduim, Delves Lane, Consett, Co. Durham DH8 7BF   **(T)** 01207 588 886
Colours(change): Yellow/blue/yellow
HONOURS: FA Comps: None   **League:** Northern 1994-95, 2007-08, Division Two 98-99.
Northern Premier Division One North 2008-09.

10 YEAR RECORD

	07-08	08-09	09-10	10-11	11-12	12-13	13-14	14-15	15-16	16-17
	NL 1 1	NP1N 1	NP P 20	NP1N 17	NP1N 9	NL 1 14	NL 1 9	NL 1 12	NL 1 20	NL 2 10
	FAC 1Q	FAC 4Qr	FAC 1Qr	FAC 1Q	FAC P	FAC 1Q	FAC Pr	FAC P	FAC EP	FAC EP
	FAV 2P	FAT 2Pr	FAT 1Q	FAT 1Q	FAT 2Qr	FAV 1P	FAV 2Q	FAV 2Q	FAV 1P	FAV 1Q

EASINGTON COLLIERY
Founded: 1913   Nickname: The Colliery

Secretary: Billy Banks   **(T)** 07967 286 559   **(E)** pa@finishingtouchesteesside.co.uk
Chairman: Paul Adamson   **Prog Ed:** Connor Lamb
Ground: Memorial Avenue, Seaside Lane, Easington Colliery SR8 3PL   **(T)**
Colours(change): All green
HONOURS: FA Comps: None   **League:** Wearside 1929-30, 31-32, 32-33, 47-48, 48-49.

10 YEAR RECORD

	07-08	08-09	09-10	10-11	11-12	12-13	13-14	14-15	15-16	16-17
	Wear 7	Wear 3	Wear 7	Wear 2	NL 2 22	Wear 21	Wear 6	Wear 2	NL 2 6	NL 2 7
										FAC EP
	FAV 2Q	FAV 1Q	FAV 2Q	FAV 1P	FAV 2Q				FAV 2Q	FAV 1P

ESH WINNING
Founded: 1885   Nickname: Stags

Secretary: Matthew Burdess   **(T)** 07432 648 072   **(E)** ewfc1913@outlook.com
Chairman: Charles Ryan   **Manager:** Tony Boakes   **Prog Ed:** Matthew Burdess
Ground: West Terrace, Waterhouse, Durham DH7 9BQ   **(T)** 07432 648 072   **Capacity:** 3,500
Colours(change): Yellow/green/green (Green/green/yellow)
HONOURS: FA Comps: None   **League:** Northern 1912-13.
Durham & District Sunday 1978-79, 79-80, Division Two 72-73.

10 YEAR RECORD

	07-08	08-09	09-10	10-11	11-12	12-13	13-14	14-15	15-16	16-17
	NL 2 13	NL 2 3	NL 1 18	NL 1 21	NL 2 11	NL 2 20	NL 2 22	NL 2 20	NL 2 20	NL 2 21
	FAC P	FAC EP	FAC EPr	FAC EP	FAC EP	FAC P				
	FAV 1Q	FAV 1P	FAV 1Q	FAV 2Qr	FAV 2Q	FAV 2P	FAV 1Q	FAV 2Q	FAV 1Q	FAV 2Q

HEATON STANNINGTON
Founded: 1910   Nickname: The Stan

Secretary: Ken Rodger   **(T)** 07587 690 295   **(E)** kenrodger10@gmail.com
Chairman: Bill Pitt   **Prog Ed:** Kevin Mochrie
Ground: Grounsell Park, Newton Road, High Heaton, Newcastle upon Tyne NE7 7HP   **(T)** 0191 281 9230
Colours(change): Black & white stripes/black/black
HONOURS: FA Comps: None   **League:** Northern Amateur 1936-37, 85-86. Tyneside Amateur 1983-84.
Northern Alliance Premier Division 2011-12, 12-13.

10 YEAR RECORD

	07-08	08-09	09-10	10-11	11-12	12-13	13-14	14-15	15-16	16-17
	NAI P 6	NAI P 8	NAI P 7	NAI P 5	NAI P 1	NAI P 1	NL 2 5	NL 2 9	NL 2 9	NL 2 4
									FAC P	FAC EP
								FAV 2Q	FAV 2Q	FAV 2Q

HEBBURN TOWN

Founded: 1912   Nickname: Hornets

Secretary: David Patterson   **(T)** 07979 033185   **(E)** davepatter@yahoo.co.uk
Chairman: Bill Laffey   **Manager:** Scott Oliver   **Prog Ed:** Richard Bainbridge
Ground: Hebburn Sports & Social, Victoria Rd West, Hebburn, Tyne & Wear NE31 1UN   **(T)** 0191 483 5101
Colours(change): Yellow & black stripes/black/yellow with black hoop (Red & black/black/red & black)
HONOURS: FA Comps: None   **League:** Tyneside1938-39. Northern Combination 1943-44. Wearside 1966-67.

10 YEAR RECORD

07-08		08-09		09-10		10-11		11-12		12-13		13-14		14-15		15-16		16-17	
NL 2	15	NL 2	10	NL 2	16	NL 2	10	NL 2	3	NL 1	18	NL 1	22	NL 2	5	NL 2	10	NL 2	11
FAC	EP	FAC	EP	FAC	P	FAC	EPr	FAC	4Q	FAC	P	FAC	P	FAC	EPr	FAC	EP		
FAV	2P	FAV	2Q	FAV	2Q	FAV	2P	FAV	1P	FAV	2Q	FAV	1Q	FAV	1Q	FAV	1P	FAV	1Q

JARROW

Founded: 1894   Nickname:

Secretary: Susan Topping   **(T)** 07917 416 214   **(E)** jarrowfc@outlook.com
Chairman: Jimmy Kane   **Prog Ed:** Kevin Mullen
Ground: Perth Green Community Assoc., Inverness Road, Jarrow NE32 4AQ   **(T)** 0191 489 3743
Colours(change): Royal blue & white/royal blue/royal blue
HONOURS: FA Comps: None   **League:** Northern Alliance 1898-99. Wearside 2016-17.

10 YEAR RECORD

07-08		08-09		09-10		10-11		11-12		12-13		13-14		14-15		15-16		16-17	
Wear	2	Wear	5	Wear	10	Wear	5	Wear	6	Wear	9	Wear	10	Wear	12	Wear	8	Wear	1

NORTHALLERTON TOWN

Founded: 1994   Nickname: Town

Secretary: Lesley Clark   **(T)** 07891 595 267   **(E)** lesleyclark05@yahoo.co.uk
Chairman: Les Hood   **Prog Ed:** Andrew Pattinson
Ground: The Calvert Stadium, Ainderby Road, Northallerton DL7 8HU   **(T)** 01609 778 337
Colours(change): Black & white stripes/black/black
HONOURS: FA Comps: None   **League:** Northern Division Two 1996-97.

10 YEAR RECORD

07-08		08-09		09-10		10-11		11-12		12-13		13-14		14-15		15-16		16-17	
NL 1	19	NL 1	22	NL 2	8	NL 2	9	NL 2	9	NL 2	6	NL 2	7	NL 2	10	NL 2	8	NL 2	9
FAC	EP	FAC	EP	FAC	EPr	FAC	1Q	FAC	P	FAC	EP	FAC	EP	FAC	P			FAC	P
FAV	3P	FAV	1Q	FAV	1P	FAV	1P	FAV	2Q	FAV	1Pr	FAV	1Q	FAV	1Q	FAV	1Q	FAV	2Q

RYTON & CRAWCROOK ALBION

Founded: 1970   Nickname: The Albion

Secretary: Stevie Carter   **(T)** 07939 573 108   **(E)** racafc@outlook.com
Chairman: Richard Hands   Tony Fawcett   **Prog Ed:** Chris Holt
Ground: Kingsley Park, Stannerford Road, Crawcrook NE40 3SN   **(T)** 0191 413 4448   **Capacity:** 2,000
Colours(change): Black & royal blue stripes/black/royal blue (Yellow/royal blue/yellow)
HONOURS: FA Comps: None   **League:** Northern Alliance Division One 1996-97.

10 YEAR RECORD

07-08		08-09		09-10		10-11		11-12		12-13		13-14		14-15		15-16		16-17	
NAI P	3	NL 1	10	NL 1	17	NL 1	22	NL 2	18	NL 2	14	NL 2	21	NL 2	12	NL 2	16	NL 2	20
FAC	EP	FAC	1Q	FAC	1Q	FAC	EP	FAC	EP										
FAV	1Q	FAV	2Pr	FAV	2Q	FAV	2Q	FAV	2Q	FAV	2Q	FAV	2Q	FAV	1Qr	FAV	1Q	FAV	2Q

THORNABY

Founded: 1980   Nickname: The Blues

Secretary: Trevor Wing   **(T)** 07860 780 446   **(E)** trevor.wing10@btinternet.com
Chairman: Laurence Lyons   **Prog Ed:** Trevor Wing
Ground: Teesdale Park, Acklam Road, Thornaby, Stockton on Tees TS17 7JU   **(T)** 01642 672 896
Colours(change): All blue
HONOURS: FA Comps: None   **League:** Northern Division Two 1987-88, 91-92.

10 YEAR RECORD

07-08		08-09		09-10		10-11		11-12		12-13		13-14		14-15		15-16		16-17	
NL 2	7	NL 2	20	NL 2	17	NL 2	14	NL 2	19	NL 2	19	NL 2	14	NL 2	7	NL 2	7	NL 2	16
FAC	EP	FAC	EP													FAC	EP	FAC	EP
FAV	1P	FAV	2Q	FAV	2Q	FAV	1Q	FAV	1Q	FAV	1Q	FAV	1Q	FAV	1Q	FAV	1Q	FAV	1Q

TOW LAW TOWN

Founded: 1890   Nickname: Lawyers

Secretary: Steve Moralee   **(T)** 07810 238 731   **(E)** stephen.moralee@btinternet.com
Chairman: Russell Manuel   **Prog Ed:** John Dixon
Ground: Ironworks Ground, Tow Law, Bishop Auckland DL13 4EQ   **(T)** 01388 731 443   **Capacity:** 3,000
Colours(change): Black & white stripes/black/black
HONOURS: FA Comps: None   **League:** Northern 1923-24, 24-25, 94-95.

10 YEAR RECORD

07-08		08-09		09-10		10-11		11-12		12-13		13-14		14-15		15-16		16-17	
NL 1	7	NL 1	11	NL 1	9	NL 1	18	NL 1	21	NL 2	11	NL 2	10	NL 2	21	NL 2	14	NL 2	13
FAC	Pr	FAC	P	FAC	EPr	FAC	EP	FAC	EP	FAC	EP	FAC	EP						
FAV	1P	FAV	2Q	FAV	1P	FAV	1P	FAV	2Q	FAV	1Q	FAV	1Q	FAV	1Q	FAV	2Q	FAV	1Q

WEST ALLOTMENT CELTIC

Founded: 1928   Nickname: Celtic

Secretary: Ted Ilderton   **(T)** 07795 246 245   **(E)** tedilderton@gmail.com
Chairman: Jim Wilson   Paul Bennett   **Prog Ed:** Stephen Allott
Ground: Druid Park, Callerton Lane, Woolsington, Newcastle Upon Tyne NE13 8DF   **(T)** 0191 250 7008
Colours(change): Green & white hoops/green/green (Red/red/black)
HONOURS: FA Comps: None   **League:** Northern Am. 1956-57, 57-58, 58-59, 59-60, 81-82, 82-83, Div 2: 38-39.
Northern All. 1986-87, 90-91, 91-92, 97-98, 98-99, 99-2000, 01-02, 03-04. Northern Div 2 2004-05

10 YEAR RECORD

07-08		08-09		09-10		10-11		11-12		12-13		13-14		14-15		15-16		16-17	
NL 1	13	NL 1	9	NL 1	15	NL 1	20	NL 2	7	NL 2	7	NL 2	2	NL 1	19	NL 1	19	NL 1	22
FAC	EP	FAC	P	FAC	Pr	FAC	EP	FAC	EPr	FAC	P	FAC	EP	FAC	1Q	FAC	EP	FAC	EP
FAV	2Q	FAV	1P	FAV	2Q	FAV	2Q	FAV	1Q	FAV	1Q	FAV	2Q	FAV	1P	FAV	2Q	FAV	1Q

WHICKHAM

Founded: 1944   Nickname: The Home Guard

Secretary: Lynn Ready   **(T)** 07775 620 859   **(E)** whickhamfcsecretary@hotmail.co.uk
Chairman: Paul Taylor   **Prog Ed:** Ross Gregory
Ground: Glebe Sports Club, Rectory Lane, Whickham NE11 9NQ   **(T)** 0191 4200 186
Colours(change): Black & white/black/black & white
HONOURS: FA Comps: FA Vase 1980-81.   **League:** Wearside 1977-78, 87-88. Northern Combination 1969-70, 72-73, 73-74.
Northern Division Two 1994-95.

10 YEAR RECORD

07-08		08-09		09-10		10-11		11-12		12-13		13-14		14-15		15-16		16-17	
NL 2	6	NL 2	14	NL 2	10	NL 2	6	NL 2	15	NL 2	16	NL 2	8	NL 2	8	NL 2	12	NL 2	6
FAC	EP	FAC	P	FAC	EP	FAC	EP	FAC	EP					FAC	P	FAC	EP		
FAV	2Q	FAV	1Qr	FAV	2P	FAV	1Q	FAV	1Q			FAV	4P	FAV	2P	FAV	2Q	FAV	1Q

WILLINGTON

Founded: 1906   Nickname: The Blue & Whites

Secretary: Richard Tremewan   **(T)** 07977 427 755   **(E)** richtrem@icloud.com
Chairman: Richard Tremewan   **Prog Ed:** Richard Tremewan
Ground: Hall Lane, Willington, Co. Durham DL15 0QG   **(T)** 01388 745 912   **Capacity:** 7,000
Colours(change): Blue & white/blue/blue
HONOURS: FA Comps: FA Amateur Cup   **League:** Northern 1913-14, 25-26, 29-30.
1949-50.

10 YEAR RECORD

07-08		08-09		09-10		10-11		11-12		12-13		13-14		14-15		15-16		16-17	
Wear	16	Wear	19	Wear	19	Wear	14	Wear	5	Wear	2	NL 2	15	NL 2	11	NL 2	19	NL 2	18
FAV	2Q	FAV	1Q	FAV	2Q	FAV	1Q	FAV	2Q	FAV	2Q	FAV	2Q	FAV	1Q	FAV	1Q	FAV	1Q

SOUTH WEST PENINSULA LEAGUE

Sponsored by: Carlsberg
Founded: 2007

Recent Champions: 2014: Plymouth Parkway
2015: St Austell **2016:** Bodmin Town

PREMIER DIVISION	P	W	D	L	F	A	GD	Pts
1 Tavistock	38	30	5	3	138	39	99	95
2 Saltash United	38	28	6	4	113	26	87	90
3 Bodmin Town	38	27	8	3	117	40	77	89
4 St Austell	38	26	4	8	124	60	64	82
5 Exmouth Town	38	25	4	9	97	43	54	79
6 Plymouth Argyle Res	38	22	8	8	112	40	72	74
7 Plymouth Parkway	38	20	10	8	94	48	46	70
8 Tiverton Town Res	38	17	12	9	97	54	43	63
9 Cullompton Rangers	38	19	4	15	75	71	4	61
10 Falmouth Town	38	16	5	17	84	74	10	53
11 Launceston	38	14	8	16	56	73	-17	50
12 Torpoint Athletic	38	13	8	17	60	64	-4	47
13 Godolphin Atlantic	38	13	3	22	54	92	-38	42
14 Camelford	38	12	6	20	63	103	-40	42
15 Callington Town	38	10	4	24	44	98	-54	34
16 Helston Athletic	38	11	4	23	54	82	-28	31*
17 Ivybridge Town	38	8	5	25	59	122	-63	29
18 Witheridge	38	6	3	29	38	121	-83	21
19 Newquay	38	4	5	29	36	162	-126	17
20 St Blazey	38	1	4	33	42	145	-103	7

DIVISION ONE EAST	P	W	D	L	F	A	GD	Pts
1 Stoke Gabriel	34	22	6	6	107	41	66	72
2 Teignmouth	34	22	5	7	80	50	30	71
3 Appledore AFC	34	21	5	8	91	54	37	68
4 Newton Abbot Spurs	34	19	9	6	80	43	37	66
5 Brixham	34	20	4	10	77	51	26	64
6 Axminster Town AFC	34	17	9	8	62	45	17	60
7 Torridgeside AFC	34	18	3	13	93	66	27	57
8 Crediton United	34	17	6	11	86	64	22	57
9 University of Exeter	34	17	4	13	80	53	27	55
10 St Martins	34	13	4	17	54	59	-5	43
11 Sidmouth Town	34	12	7	15	57	70	-13	43
12 Alphington AFC	34	12	5	17	54	60	-6	41
13 Bovey Tracey	34	11	2	21	69	87	-18	35
14 Galmpton United	34	9	6	19	56	77	-21	33
15 Liverton United	34	10	3	21	42	102	-60	33
16 Totnes & Dartington	34	7	5	22	41	90	-49	26
17 Budleigh Salterton	34	7	4	23	42	112	-70	25
18 Exwick Villa	34	5	7	22	37	84	-47	22

DIVISION ONE WEST	P	W	D	L	F	A	GD	Pts
1 Sticker	34	29	4	1	126	26	100	91
2 Elburton Villa	34	22	7	5	101	45	56	73
3 Plymstock United	34	18	5	11	73	58	15	59
4 Millbrook	34	16	7	11	67	52	15	55
5 Penryn Athletic	34	14	10	10	77	53	24	52
6 Mousehole	34	15	7	12	74	65	9	52
7 St Dennis	34	14	7	13	77	72	5	49
8 Liskeard Athletic	34	13	8	13	65	67	-2	47
9 Illogan RBL	34	13	6	15	72	69	3	45
10 Plymouth Marjons	34	13	6	15	50	68	-18	45
11 Dobwalls	34	13	6	15	70	92	-22	45
12 Porthleven	34	12	7	15	56	63	-7	43
13 Wendron United	34	13	4	17	65	91	-26	43
14 Wadebridge Town	34	12	6	16	72	85	-13	42
15 Holsworthy	34	11	5	18	66	76	-10	38
16 Bude Town AFC	34	9	9	16	63	88	-25	33*
17 Penzance	34	7	8	19	57	105	-48	29
18 Vospers Oak Villa	34	5	2	27	42	98	-56	14*

ADDITIONAL CLUB MOVEMENTS

Premier Division
Out: Tiverton Town Reserves (W).

Division One East- In: Honiton Town (P - Devon & Exeter).
Ilfracombe Town (P -North Devon).
Division One West - In: Ludgvan (P - Cornwall Combination).
St Blazey (R).
Out: Penryn Athletic (W).

	PREMIER DIVISION	1	2	3	4	5	6	7	8	9	10	11	12	13	14	15	16	17	18	19	20
1	Bodmin Town		4-0	2-1	2-0	2-2	6-2	1-0	2-1	1-1	6-1	9-0	3-0	0-0	1-2	4-4	2-0	3-0	3-3	4-2	2-1
2	Callington Town	1-2		0-0	0-2	1-5	1-2	2-2	2-1	2-1	3-1	3-1	1-0	2-3	1-3	0-1	2-1	1-7	0-4	2-1	3-0
3	Camelford	2-1	5-1		1-5	3-1	0-4	4-0	2-1	4-2	3-1	4-0	0-4	2-2	0-2	1-9	3-2	0-4	0-0	1-2	3-1
4	Cullompton Rangers	1-5	6-3	3-2		1-4	3-1	3-1	H-W	4-1	4-0	7-1	1-3	2-3	0-3	2-0	3-1	0-2	0-2	1-0	3-0
5	Exmouth Town	0-1	6-0	4-2	5-1		4-0	0-2	3-1	4-0	3-2	2-1	2-0	2-0	2-2	1-2	3-3	1-3	2-1	2-1	1-2
6	Falmouth Town	1-2	0-0	1-1	0-2	4-1		1-2	3-1	0-2	1-3	5-1	4-1	1-5	0-6	0-1	6-4	1-3	4-2	2-0	5-1
7	Godolphin Atlantic	1-5	2-0	2-1	0-5	0-5	0-3		1-2	1-3	1-3	3-0	3-6	0-2	1-3	0-3	6-3	2-4	2-3	1-0	4-0
8	Helston Athletic	1-2	4-3	3-1	1-4	1-3	2-7	2-1		1-3	1-2	6-0	1-5	0-3	1-1	3-2	3-4	0-1	2-1	3-1	
9	Ivybridge Town	2-8	1-2	2-0	2-3	0-4	0-4	2-3	2-2		1-6	2-1	0-6	0-1	0-6	1-5	2-0	2-5	4-5	2-2	3-5
10	Launceston	0-1	0-0	0-0	2-0	0-5	0-1	1-1	2-0	2-2		1-1	2-2	0-0	0-2	1-2	2-0	1-5	2-1	1-2	2-0
11	Newquay	0-8	4-0	2-4	2-2	1-4	2-2	0-1	0-3	4-0	0-4		1-6	1-5	0-5	1-7	2-3	0-5	0-0	0-2	3-1
12	Plymouth Argyle Res	0-3	2-1	7-1	2-1	0-0	2-1	5-0	2-2	4-1	6-0	7-0		1-1	2-1	6-0	1-0	0-2	0-0	4-0	8-0
13	Plymouth Parkway	2-3	3-0	6-2	6-1	1-0	1-0	4-1	H-W	1-1	2-1	10-2	1-1		0-0	4-5	3-0	2-3	2-3	0-3	10-0
14	Saltash United	0-0	2-0	7-0	1-1	1-0	5-0	6-1	2-0	2-1	2-3	7-0	3-2	3-2		4-0	5-0	1-1	2-2	2-0	6-0
15	St Austell	2-2	3-1	6-0	4-0	0-2	3-2	1-2	2-0	5-2	6-2	10-0	3-1	5-0	0-1		5-1	3-1	1-5	4-1	5-2
16	St Blazey	0-4	1-2	2-5	2-2	1-5	2-3	1-5	0-2	3-5	0-1	1-1	0-6	1-5	1-6	2-5		2-6	0-10	0-2	1-1
17	Tavistock	4-1	4-2	4-0	6-0	1-2	1-1	4-0	10-1	8-0	5-1	10-0	1-1	0-0	3-1	2-0	5-0		6-2	2-1	3-1
18	Tiverton Town Reserves	2-2	3-1	5-1	0-0	1-2	2-1	3-0	1-0	0-5	2-2	8-0	0-0	1-1	1-3	3-3	9-1	1-2		0-2	5-0
19	Torpoint Athletic	1-7	6-0	3-3	3-0	1-2	3-3	1-1	3-0	4-0	0-1	2-0	0-4	1-1	0-3	1-5	2-1	2-2	0-0		4-0
20	Witheridge	0-3	5-1	2-1	0-2	0-3	0-6	0-1	1-1	4-1	0-3	3-4	0-5	0-2	0-3	1-3	5-0	0-1	0-6	1-1	

DIVISION ONE EAST

		1	2	3	4	5	6	7	8	9	10	11	12	13	14	15	16	17	18
1	Alphington AFC		0-3	0-1	3-1	1-2	4-0	1-2	2-3	2-1	2-0	1-5	0-0	1-0	2-2	1-3	2-0	1-3	0-1
2	Appledore AFC	3-0		0-4	4-2	2-0	3-2	5-1	4-0	7-0	9-1	3-4	3-5	1-0	1-1	4-1	3-2	7-2	3-0
3	Axminster Town AFC	1-1	2-0		5-2	2-3	7-1	1-1	1-0	1-1	1-2	1-1	3-1	2-0	0-5	6-1	1-1	0-0	1-0
4	Bovey Tracey	3-2	2-2	2-4		3-0	2-4	2-4	3-0	3-5	3-0	1-2	3-4	3-1	0-3	2-4	1-8	5-0	3-2
5	Brixham	1-0	1-3	1-2	2-0		5-1	2-2	4-2	1-3	5-0	0-0	2-1	1-0	0-5	3-3	1-0	3-0	4-1
6	Budleigh Salterton	3-4	0-4	0-1	1-5	0-4		1-0	2-0	0-5	1-3	2-5	0-1	1-2	1-5	0-5	4-3		0-4
7	Crediton United	5-5	4-0	1-3	4-1	4-5	3-3		3-0	2-1	11-1	3-3	6-0	1-3	1-0	4-3	2-0	1-3	2-1
8	Exwick Villa	1-4	0-2	1-2	1-3	4-2	0-0	1-3		1-4	3-2	1-3	1-2	1-7	1-1	0-1	0-6	3-1	1-2
9	Galmpton United	3-4	0-2	1-0	2-0	3-3	1-3	0-2	4-1		5-0	2-2	1-0	1-2	2-2	0-1	2-3	2-2	2-3
10	Liverton United	1-1	0-1	3-0	1-2	0-4	1-2	3-2	3-2	3-0		1-4	2-4	2-0	2-8	0-3	0-3	1-0	4-3
11	Newton Abbot Spurs	1-0	1-1	0-2	0-3	2-0	9-0	2-3	3-1	4-0	7-0		2-0	0-3	1-0	2-3	4-1	2-1	2-1
12	Sidmouth Town	0-1	3-3	1-1	2-1	1-3	4-0	3-2	2-2	5-1	0-0	2-2		0-0	0-4	1-3	1-5	2-0	0-2
13	St Martins	0-1	1-2	3-0	2-2	0-3	4-1	3-0	1-1	5-2	0-2	0-3	2-3		1-5	1-1	1-5	3-1	3-1
14	Stoke Gabriel	4-1	2-0	4-1	3-0	0-4	6-0	4-1	1-2	2-1	2-1	2-2	3-1	5-1		3-0	7-0	6-0	2-2
15	Teignmouth	2-1	1-1	3-0	3-1	3-0	4-4	3-2	3-0	1-0	1-2	2-0	3-1	2-1	2-4		4-0	5-0	3-1
16	Torridgeside AFC	3-2	1-0	2-2	3-2	1-2	7-2	0-1	1-1	3-4	7-0	3-0	5-1	2-4	5-4	0-2		5-2	2-1
17	Totnes & Dartington	2-1	2-4	2-3	3-2	1-6	2-0	1-1	0-0	2-1	1-1	1-2	0-1	0-1	0-2	4-2	2-3		0-7
18	University of Exeter	0-3	9-1	1-1	3-1	1-0	3-0	0-2	2-2	5-1	3-2	2-2	2-1	4-0	5-3	0-1	5-1	3-0	

DIVISION ONE WEST

		1	2	3	4	5	6	7	8	9	10	11	12	13	14	15	16	17	18
1	Bude Town AFC		0-2	2-2	1-0	4-2	6-2	3-2	0-3	0-7	1-4	1-3	6-3	1-3	6-0	0-5	4-2	2-2	1-1
2	Dobwalls	3-2		2-7	1-3	2-4	0-1	0-1	2-2	5-2	5-4	1-1	5-3	3-1	1-2	0-6	1-0	2-3	3-6
3	Elburton Villa	2-0	3-3		3-1	3-2	4-1	4-2	6-0	3-0	3-0	0-1	2-2	4-2	2-1	1-3	4-1	2-3	7-1
4	Holsworthy	3-3	4-0	0-0		4-1	0-1	1-1	2-2	3-6	0-2	5-0	1-3	0-3	5-3	2-3	2-1	4-3	5-2
5	Illogan RBL	4-1	8-1	2-4	3-1		2-0	1-0	3-1	2-0	3-1	0-3	2-3	2-5	0-0	0-2	4-0	1-3	3-1
6	Liskeard Athletic	5-1	0-5	4-5	1-0	2-2		2-2	0-1	1-1	7-2	0-1	1-2	3-4	2-4	1-4	1-0	0-2	2-0
7	Millbrook	4-0	0-0	1-1	3-1	1-0	2-4		1-4	1-2	4-2	4-0	0-2	2-1	3-0	0-5	4-0	2-1	4-2
8	Mousehole	1-1	1-2	0-4	4-1	1-0	1-1	4-1		0-0	1-2	3-0	1-0	1-1	2-2	0-4	8-1	5-1	3-0
9	Penryn Athletic	7-0	4-2	1-3	5-0	3-3	1-1	1-1	0-2		7-1	4-0	0-0	1-1	4-2	3-3	4-1	1-1	3-0
10	Penzance	1-1	1-1	0-4	1-2	6-4	3-4	2-1	0-6	2-2		2-2	2-2	1-0	3-9	0-8	1-1	1-4	0-2
11	Plymouth Marjons	1-2	1-4	1-4	0-2	3-3	1-1	0-2	3-2	3-0	4-0		1-7	2-0	1-3	0-5	1-2	2-2	4-1
12	Plymstock United	H-W	7-1	1-2	5-4	2-1	0-0	3-2	3-2	3-1	4-2	0-1		1-0	3-2	0-0	3-2	4-1	2-3
13	Porthleven	4-2	4-1	0-6	1-1	1-1	1-3	1-3	3-2	3-1	0-0	1-1	0-1		2-1	0-4	H-W	2-2	3-1
14	St Dennis	1-1	3-0	0-0	1-0	3-3	2-6	1-2	10-3	0-2	2-2	2-1	2-1	2-1		0-4	6-2	2-1	1-2
15	Sticker	4-1	2-2	4-2	5-2	3-0	4-0	1-1	4-1	3-0	3-1	1-2	5-0	3-2	2-0		2-1	7-3	4-0
16	Vospers Oak Villa	0-5	3-4	1-2	1-0	1-2	2-4	2-2	2-3	1-2	3-2	1-3	1-0	3-2	1-4	0-5		3-4	1-2
17	Wadebridge Town	2-2	1-2	1-0	3-4	1-2	2-4	0-3	4-2	0-1	0-4	1-2	2-1	3-1	3-3	1-5	3-2		7-1
18	Wendron United	3-3	2-4	2-2	4-3	3-2	0-0	1-5	1-2	2-1	5-2	2-1	3-2	1-3	1-3	0-3	4-0	6-2	

WALTER C PARSON CUP

HOLDERS: BODMIN TOWN

ROUND 1

Vospers Oak Villa	v	Galmpton United	0-2
Bude Town	v	Newquay	1-2
Mousehole	v	Wadebridge Town	4-2
Illogan RBL	v	Penryn Athletic	2-0
Launceston	v	Holsworthy	0-1
Camelford	v	Bovey Tracey	3-0
St Dennis	v	Penzance	3-1
St Blazey	v	Helston Athletic	4-5
St Martins	v	Tiverton Town Res	2-3
Wendron United	v	Falmouth Town	2-1
Sticker	v	Liskeard Athletic	5-0
Axminster Town	v	Exmouth Town	0-1
Totnes & Dartington	v	Plymouth Argyle Res	2-6
Elburton Villa	v	Plymouth Marjons	3-1
University of Exeter	v	Appledore	4-0
Stoke Gabriel	v	Cullompton Rangers	4-0
Brixham	v	Callington Town	5-1
Liverton United	v	Millbrook	5-1
Newton Abbot Spurs	v	Plymstock United	1-3
Dobwalls	v	Porthleven	1-0
Torridgeside	v	Alphington	1-2
Exwick Villa	v	Ivybridge Town	3-2
Sidmouth Town	v	Crediton United	2-3
Budleigh Salterton	v	Teignmouth	6-2
Plymouth Parkway	v	Exmouth Town	2-4
Plymouth Argyle Res	v	Elburton Villa	3-1
University of Exeter	v	Stoke Gabriel	0-1
Brixham	v	Saltash United	2-7
Liverton United	v	Plymstock United	1-2
St Austell	v	Dobwalls	3-1
Alphington	v	Exwick Villa	0-1
Torpoint Athletic	v	Tavistock	0-1
Crediton United	v	Budleigh Salterton	5-1

ROUND 2

Galmpton United	v	Bodmin Town	0-2
Newquay	v	Godolphin Atlantic	0-3
Mousehole	v	Illogan RBL	1-0
Holsworthy	v	Camelford	3-2
St Dennis	v	Helston Athletic	0-4
Tiverton Town Res	v	Witheridge	4-0
Wendron United	v	Sticker	0-3

ROUND 3

Bodmin Town	v	Godolphin Atlantic	4-0
Mousehole	v	Holsworthy	2-0
Helston Athletic	v	Tiverton Town Res	1-2
Sticker	v	Exmouth Town	1-2 aet
Plymouth Argyle Res	v	Stoke Gabriel	1-0
Saltash United	v	Plymstock United	2-0
St Austell	v	Exwick Villa	HW
Tavistock	v	Crediton United	1-2

QUARTER FINALS

Bodmin Town	v	Mousehole	7-0
Tiverton Town Res	v	Exmouth Town	0-1
Plymouth Argyle Res	v	Saltash United	6-3
St Austell	v	Crediton United	3-2

SEMI FINALS

Bodmin Town	v	Exmouth Town	1-2
Plymouth Argyle Res	v	St Austell	1-4

FINAL

Exmouth Town	v	St Austell	0-1

PREMIER DIVISION

BODMIN TOWN
Founded: 1896   Nickname: Black & Ambers

Secretary: Nick Giles   **(T)**   **(E)** nickgiles@live.co.uk
Chairman: TBC   **Manager:** Darren Gilbert
Ground: Priory Park, Bodmin, Cornwall PL31 2AE   **(T)** 01208 78165
Colours(change): Yellow & black (All white)
HONOURS: FA Comps: None   **League:** Bodmin & District 1922-23, 26-27. South Western 1990-91, 93-94, 2005-06.
South West Peninsula Premier Division 2007-08, 08-09, 11-12, 12-13, 15-16.

10 YEAR RECORD
07-08		08-09		09-10		10-11		11-12		12-13		13-14		14-15		15-16		16-17	
SWPP	1	SWPP	1	SWPP	2	SWPP	2	SWPP	1	SWPP	1	SWPP	7	SWPP	2	SWPP	1	SWPP	3
FAC	1Q	FAC	P	FAC	P	FAC	1Q	FAC	3Qr	FAC	1Qr	FAC	P	FAC	1Qr	FAC	2Q	FAC	Pr
FAV	2Q	FAV	1P	FAV	1P	FAV	4P	FAV	2Pr	FAV	5P	FAV	4P	FAV	4P	FAV	4P	FAV	3P

CALLINGTON TOWN
Founded: 1989   Nickname: The Pasty Men

Secretary: Nick Smith   **(T)** 07808 286 635   **(E)** womble1954@me.com
Chairman: Steve Woolley   **Manager:** Dean Cardew   **Prog Ed:** Andrew Long
Ground: Ginsters Marshfield Parc PL17 7DR   **(T)** 01579 382 647
Colours(change): Red & black (Yellow & blue)
HONOURS: FA Comps: None   **League:** East Cornwall Combination 1997-98, 98-99.
South West Peninsula Division One West 2013-14.

10 YEAR RECORD
07-08		08-09		09-10		10-11		11-12		12-13		13-14		14-15		15-16		16-17	
SW1W	14	SW1W	5	SW1W	10	SW1W	3	SW1W	6	SW1W	5	SW1W	1	SWPP	11	SWPP	16	SWPP	15

CAMELFORD
Founded: 1893   Nickname: Camels

Secretary: Hilary Kent   **(T)**   **(E)** hilarykent35@gmail.com
Chairman: Ollie Rowe   **Manager:** Reg Hambly
Ground: Trefew Park, PL32 9TS   **(T)**
Colours(change): Blue with white trim (Yellow & black)
HONOURS: FA Comps: None   **League:** South West Peninsula Division One West 2010-11.

10 YEAR RECORD
07-08		08-09		09-10		10-11		11-12		12-13		13-14		14-15		15-16		16-17	
SW1W	4	SW1W	8	SW1W	8	SW1W	1	SWPP	9	SWPP	9	SWPP	14	SWPP	17	SWPP	15	SWPP	14
												FAV	2Q	FAV	1Qr	FAV	1P	FAV	1Q

CULLOMPTON RANGERS
Founded: 1945   Nickname: The Cully

Secretary: Alan Slark   **(T)** 07731 939 784   **(E)** alanslark1@tiscali.co.uk
Chairman: Brian Horner   **Manager:** Hedley Steele   Marcus Scott
Ground: Speeds Meadow, Cullompton EX15 1DW   **(T)** 01884 33090
Colours(change): Red & black stripes/black/red (Blue & white stripes/royal blue/royal blue)
HONOURS: FA Comps: None   **League:** East Devon Senior Division One 1950-51, 78-79.
Devon & Exeter Premier Division 1961-62, 63-64.

10 YEAR RECORD
07-08		08-09		09-10		10-11		11-12		12-13		13-14		14-15		15-16		16-17	
SWPP	18	SWPP	8	SWPP	18	SWPP	16	SWPP	15	SWPP	17	SWPP	18	SWPP	12	SWPP	13	SWPP	9
				FAC	EP														
FAV	2Q	FAV	1P	FAV	2Q	FAV	2Q	FAV	2P	FAV	2Q	FAV	2Q	FAV	1Q	FAV	1Q	FAV	2Pr

EXMOUTH TOWN
Founded: 1933   Nickname: The Town

Secretary: Brian Barnden   **(T)**   **(E)** brian7645@btinternet.com
Chairman: Bob Chamberlain   **Manager:** Peter Buckingham
Ground: King George V, Exmouth EX8 3EE   **(T)** 01395 263 348
Colours(change): All royal blue (All red)
HONOURS: FA Comps: None   **League:** Western 1983-84, 85-86.
South West Peninsula Division One East 2012-13.

10 YEAR RECORD
07-08		08-09		09-10		10-11		11-12		12-13		13-14		14-15		15-16		16-17	
SW1E	5	SW1E	15	SW1E	8	SW1E	11	SW1E	5	SW1E	1	SWPP	2	SWPP	8	SWPP	12	SWPP	5
										FAV	1P	FAV	2Q			FAV	2Q	FAV	5P

FALMOUTH TOWN
Founded: 1949   Nickname: The Ambers

Secretary: Wayne Pascoe   **(T)**   **(E)** pascoerichard@hotmail.com
Chairman: Graham Medlin   **Manager:** Andrew Westgarth
Ground: Bickland Park, Bickland Water Road, Falmouth TR11 4PB
    (T) 01326 375 156
Colours(change): Amber & black (White & green)
HONOURS: FA Comps: None   **League:** South Western 1961-62, 65-66, 67-68, 70-71, 71-72, 72-73, 73-74, 85-86, 86-87, 88-89, 89-90, 91-92, 96-97, 99-2000. Western 74-75, 75-76, 76-77, 77-78. Cornwall Comb 83-84.

10 YEAR RECORD

07-08	08-09	09-10	10-11	11-12	12-13	13-14	14-15	15-16	16-17
SWPP 4	SWPP 14	SWPP 3	SWPP 5	SWPP 3	SWPP 16	SWPP 16	SWPP 16	SWPP 11	SWPP 10
FAC EP	FAC P	FAC Pr	FAC EPr	FAC EP					
FAV 2Q	FAV 2Q	FAV 2Q	FAV 1Qr	FAV 3P			FAV 1P	FAV 1Q	

GODOLPHIN ATLANTIC AFC
Founded: 1980   Nickname: G Army

Secretary: Margaret Ashwood   **(T)**   **(E)** godolphin.arms@btconnect.com
Chairman: Tania Semmens   **Manager:** Kevin Richards
Ground: Godolphin Way, Cornwall TR7 3BU   **(T)**
Colours(change): Sky blue & white (Maroon & black)
HONOURS: FA Comps: None   **League:** South West Peninsula Division One West 2012-13.

10 YEAR RECORD

07-08	08-09	09-10	10-11	11-12	12-13	13-14	14-15	15-16	16-17
ECP 2	SW1W 11	SW1W 6	SW1W 2	SW1W 4	SW1W 1	SWPP 5	SWPP 7	SWPP 5	SWPP 13

HELSTON ATHLETIC
Founded: 1896   Nickname: The Blues

Secretary: Paul Hendy   **(T)** 07740 812555   **(E)** paul.m.hendy@btinternet.com
Chairman: Paul Hendy   **Manager:** Steve Massey   **Prog Ed:** Paul Hendy
Ground: Kellaway Park, Helston TR13 8PJ   **(T)** 01326 573742 (Clubhouse)
Colours(change): All blue & white (All grey & white)
HONOURS: FA Comps: None   **League:** Cornwall Senior 1936-37, 37-38, 39-40. Cornwall Comb. 87-88, 2000-01, 10-11. South West Peninsula Division One West 2014-15.

10 YEAR RECORD

07-08	08-09	09-10	10-11	11-12	12-13	13-14	14-15	15-16	16-17
CornC 3	CornC 4	CornC 5	CornC 1	SW1W 2	SW1W 2	SW1W 3	SW1W 1	SWPP 10	SWPP 16
									FAV 1P

IVYBRIDGE TOWN
Founded: 1925   Nickname: The Ivys

Secretary: Paul Cocks   **(T)**   **(E)** secretary@ivybridgefc.com
Chairman: Dave Graddon   **Manager:** Nicky Marker
Ground: Erme Valley, Ermington Road, Ivybridge PL21 9ES   **(T)** 01752 896 686
Colours(change): Green & black (Yellow & blue)
HONOURS: FA Comps: None   **League:** Devon County 2005-06.

10 YEAR RECORD

07-08	08-09	09-10	10-11	11-12	12-13	13-14	14-15	15-16	16-17
SWPP 11	SWPP 4	SWPP 12	SWPP 7	SWPP 19	SWPP 13	SWPP 4	SWPP 4	SWPP 9	SWPP 17
								FAV 2Q	FAV 1Q

LAUNCESTON
Founded: 1891   Nickname: The Clarets

Secretary: Keith Ellacott   **(T)**   **(E)** launcestonfc@aol.com
Chairman: Alan Bradley   **Manager:** Gary Jeffrey
Ground: Pennygillam Ind. Est., Launceston PL15 7ED   **(T)** 01566 773 279
Colours(change): All claret (Sky blue & black)
HONOURS: FA Comps: None   **League:** South Western 1994-95.

10 YEAR RECORD

07-08	08-09	09-10	10-11	11-12	12-13	13-14	14-15	15-16	16-17
SWPP 5	SWPP 10	SWPP 11	SWPP 11	SWPP 5	SWPP 5	SWPP 8	SWPP 10	SWPP 14	SWPP 11
	FAC P	FAC P	FAC EP						
FAV 2Q	FAV 1P	FAV 2Q	FAV 2Q						

NEWQUAY
Founded: 1890   Nickname: The Peppermints

Secretary: Ruth Crick   **(T)**   **(E)** ruth_terry@btinternet.com
Chairman: Don Pratt   **Manager:** Tony MacKellar
Ground: Mount Wise TR7 2BU   **(T)** 01637 872 935
Colours(change): Red & white (Blue & white)
HONOURS: FA Comps: None   **League:** South Western 1958-59, 59-60, 77-78, 79-80, 81-82, 83-84, 87-88.
South West Peninsula Division One West 2011-12.

10 YEAR RECORD

07-08	08-09	09-10	10-11	11-12	12-13	13-14	14-15	15-16	16-17
SW1W 6	SW1W 2	SW1W 5	SW1W 9	SW1W 1	SWPP 12	SWPP 11	SWPP 15	SWPP 18	SWPP 19
FAV 2Q	FAV 1Q	FAV 1P	FAV 1P			FAV EP	FAV 1P	FAV 2Q	

PLYMOUTH ARGYLE RESERVES
Founded: 1886   Nickname: The Pilgrims

Secretary: Glyn Carpenter   **(T)**   **(E)** chippycarps@gmail.com
Chairman: James Brent   **Manager:** Kevin Nancekivell
Ground: Coach Road TQ12 1EJ   **(T)**
Colours(change): Green & white (All yellow)
HONOURS: FA Comps: None   **League:** None

10 YEAR RECORD

07-08	08-09	09-10	10-11	11-12	12-13	13-14	14-15	15-16	16-17
								SW1W 2	SWPP 6

PLYMOUTH PARKWAY AFC
Founded: 1988   Nickname: The Parkway

Secretary: Genny Turner   **(T)**   **(E)** gennyt@sky.com
Chairman: Mark Russell   **Manager:** Lee Hobbs
Ground: Bolitho Park, St Peters Road, Manadon, Plymouth PL5 3JH   **(T)**
Colours(change): Yellow & blue (Red & blue)
HONOURS: FA Comps: None   **League:** Plymouth & District Division Two 1990-91.
South West Peninsula Premier Division 2013-14.

10 YEAR RECORD

07-08	08-09	09-10	10-11	11-12	12-13	13-14	14-15	15-16	16-17
SWPP 3	SWPP 2	SWPP 6	SWPP 3	SWPP 6	SWPP 2	SWPP 1	SWPP 5	SWPP 4	SWPP 7
					FAC 1Qr	FAC 1Q	FAC P	FAC 1Q	FAC 1Q
FAV 3P	FAV 2Q	FAV 4P	FAV 3P	FAV 1P	FAV 1Q	FAV 3P	FAV 2P	FAV 2P	FAV 1Pr

SALTASH UNITED
Founded: 1945   Nickname: The Ashes

Secretary: Steve Ladlow   **(T)** 07341 449 580   **(E)** steve.ladlow57@gmail.com
Chairman: Colin Phillips   **Manager:** Matt Cusack   **Prog Ed:** Colin Wheeler
Ground: Kimberley Stadium, Callington Road, Saltash PL12 6DX   **(T)** 01752 845 746
Colours(change): Red & white stripes/black/red (Yellow/dark blue/dark blue)
HONOURS: FA Comps: None   **League:** South Western 1953-54, 75-76. Western Division One 1976-77, Premier
1984-85, 86-87, 88-89.

10 YEAR RECORD

07-08	08-09	09-10	10-11	11-12	12-13	13-14	14-15	15-16	16-17
SWPP 2	SWPP 5	SWPP 9	SWPP 6	SWPP 4	SWPP 6	SWPP 3	SWPP 3	SWPP 6	SWPP 2
FAC P	FAC EPr	FAC 1Qr	FAC EPr	FAC EP	FAC EP	FAC EP	FAC 1Q	FAC EP	
FAV 2Q	FAV 2P	FAV 2P	FAV 2P	FAV 2P	FAV 1P	FAV 3P	FAV 1P	FAV 1Q	

ST. AUSTELL
Founded: 1890   Nickname: The Lily Whites

Secretary: Neil Powell   **(T)**   **(E)** neilpowell9@aol.com
Chairman: James Hutchings   **Manager:** Jason Chapman & Kelvin Hunkin
Ground: Poltair Park, Trevarthian Road, St Austell PL25 4LR   **(T)** 01726 66099
Colours(change): All white (Yellow & blue)
HONOURS: FA Comps: None   **League:** South Western 1968-69. South West Peninsula Premier 2014-15.

10 YEAR RECORD

07-08	08-09	09-10	10-11	11-12	12-13	13-14	14-15	15-16	16-17
SW1W 16	SW1W 3	SW1W 2	SWPP 10	SWPP 8	SWPP 4	SWPP 9	SWPP 1	SWPP 2	SWPP 4
						FAC EP	FAC P	FAC P	FAC EPr
					FAV 2P	FAV 1Q	FAV SF	FAV 2P	FAV 2Q

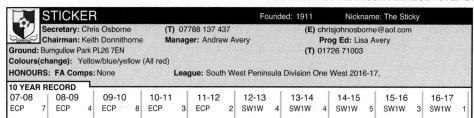

STICKER
Founded: 1911   Nickname: The Sticky
Secretary: Chris Osborne   **(T)** 07788 137 437   **(E)** chrisjohnosborne@aol.com
Chairman: Keith Donnithorne   **Manager:** Andrew Avery   **Prog Ed:** Lisa Avery
Ground: Burngullow Park PL26 7EN   **(T)** 01726 71003
Colours(change): Yellow/blue/yellow (All red)
HONOURS: FA Comps: None   **League:** South West Peninsula Division One West 2016-17.

10 YEAR RECORD
07-08	08-09	09-10	10-11	11-12	12-13	13-14	14-15	15-16	16-17
ECP 7	ECP 4	ECP 8	ECP 3	ECP 2	SW1W 4	SW1W 4	SW1W 5	SW1W 3	SW1W 1

STOKE GABRIEL
Founded: 1905   Nickname: The Railwaymen
Secretary: Kevin Besford   **(T)**   **(E)** kevinbesford@uwclub.net
Chairman: Mike Calf   **Manager:** Stuart Monk
Ground: G J Churchward Memorial TQ9 6RR   **(T)** 01803 782 913
Colours(change): Maroon & blue (Orange & black)
HONOURS: FA Comps: None   **League:** Devon County 1994-95, 96-97.
South West Peninsula Division One East 2013-14, 16-17.

10 YEAR RECORD
07-08	08-09	09-10	10-11	11-12	12-13	13-14	14-15	15-16	16-17
SW1E 4	SW1E 3	SW1E 2	SW1E 3	SW1E 2	SW1E 2	SW1E 1	SWPP 14	SWPP 19	SW1E 1

TAVISTOCK
Founded: 1888   Nickname: The Lambs
Secretary: Shaun Greening   **(T)**   **(E)** secretary@tavistockfc.com
Chairman: Chris Fenner   **Manager:** Stuart Henderson
Ground: Langsford Park, Red & Black Club, Crowndale Road, Tavistock PL19 8JR   **(T)** 01822 614 447
Colours(change): White with red & black (All blue)
HONOURS: FA Comps: None   **League:** Devon 1900-01. Plymouth Combination Division One 1950-51.
South West Peninsula League Division One East 2014-15, Premier 16-17.

10 YEAR RECORD
07-08	08-09	09-10	10-11	11-12	12-13	13-14	14-15	15-16	16-17
SWPP 10	SWPP 6	SWPP 5	SWPP 13	SWPP 10	SWPP 10	SWPP 19	SW1E 1	SWPP 3	SWPP 1
FAC EP	FAC P	FAC EP	FAC P	FAC 1Q	FAC EP	FAC EP			
FAV 2Q	FAV 1P	FAV 2P	FAV 1P	FAV 1P	FAV 1Q	FAV 2P	FAV 1Q		FAV 1P

TORPOINT ATHLETIC
Founded: 1887   Nickname: The Point
Secretary: Robbie Morris   **(T)**   **(E)** robbietafc81@live.co.uk
Chairman: Paul Whitworth   **Manager:** Dan Cole
Ground: The Mill, Mill Lane, Carbeile Road, Torpoint PL11 2RE   **(T)** 01752 812 889
Colours(change): Yellow & black (All blue)
HONOURS: FA Comps: None   **League:** South Western 1964-65, 66-67.

10 YEAR RECORD
07-08	08-09	09-10	10-11	11-12	12-13	13-14	14-15	15-16	16-17
SWPP 6	SWPP 9	SWPP 8	SWPP 4	SWPP 12	SWPP 14	SWPP 10	SWPP 13	SWPP 8	SWPP 12
			FAC 1Q	FAC P	FAC EP				
		FAV 2Q	FAV QF	FAV 2P			FAV 1Q	FAV 2Q	FAV 2P	FAV 3P

WITHERIDGE
Founded: 1920   Nickname: The Withy
Secretary: Chris Cole   **(T)** 07899 981 396   **(E)** chriscole128@hotmail.com
Chairman: Graham Pilsbury   **Manager:** Dave Griffiths   **Prog Ed:** Laurie White & Russell North
Ground: Edge Down Park, Fore Street, Witheridge EX16 8AH   **(T)** 01884 861 511
Colours(change): All blue (All orange)
HONOURS: FA Comps: None   **League:** None

10 YEAR RECORD
07-08	08-09	09-10	10-11	11-12	12-13	13-14	14-15	15-16	16-17
SWPP 9	SWPP 11	SWPP 10	SWPP 14	SWPP 13	SWPP 7	SWPP 6	SWPP 6	SWPP 7	SWPP 18
							FAC P	FAC 1Q	
		FAV 1Q	FAV 1P			FAV 1Q	FAV 2Qr	FAV 1P	FAV 2Q

SOUTH WEST PENINSULA LEAGUE - STEP 6/7

South West Peninsula Division One East

ALPHINGTON	The Chronicles, Church Road, Alphington, Exeter EX2 8SW	01392 279 556
APPLEDORE	Marshford, Churchill Way, Appledore EX39 1PA	01237 475 015
AXMINSTER TOWN	Tiger Way EX13 5HN	
BOVEY TRACEY	Mill Marsh Park, Ashburton Rd, Bovey TQ13 9FF	01626 833 896
BRIXHAM AFC	Wall Park Road TQ5 9UE	
BUDLEIGH SALTERTON	Greenway Lane, Budleigh Salterton EX9 6SG	01395 443 850
CREDITON UNITED	Lords Meadow, Commercial Road, Crediton EX17 1ER	01363 774 671
GALMPTON UNITED AFC	War Memorial Playing Field, Greenway Road, Galmpton, Brixham TQ5 0LN	
HONITON TOWN	Moutbatten Park, Ottery Moor Lane, Honiton EX14 1AW	01404 42379
ILFRACOMBE TOWN	Marlborough Park, Ilfracombe, Devon EX34 8PD	01271 865 939
LIVERTON UNITED	Halford, Liverton TQ12 6JF	
NEWTON ABBOT SPURS	Recreation Ground, Marsh Road, Newton Abbot TQ12 2AR	01626 365 343
SIDMOUTH TOWN	Manstone Recreation Ground, Manstone Lane, Sidmouth EX10 9TF	01395 577 087
ST. MARTINS AFC	Minster Park, Exminster EX6 8AT	
TEIGNMOUTH	Coombe Valley, Coombe Lane, Teignmouth TQ14 9EX	01626 776 688
TORRIDGESIDE	Donnacroft, Torrington EX38 7HT	
TOTNES & DARTINGTON SC	Foxhole Sports Ground, Dartington TQ9 6EB	
UNIVERSITY OF EXETER	University Sports Ground, Topsham Road, Topsham EX3 0LY	01392 879 542

South West Peninsula Division One West

BUDE TOWN	Broadclose Park EX23 8DR	
DOBWALLS	Lantoom Park, Duloe Road, Dobwalls PL14 4LU	07721 689 380
ELBURTON VILLA	Haye Road, Elburton, Plymouth PL9 8HS	01752 480 025
HOLSWORTHY AFC	Upcott Field, North Road, Holsworthy EX22 6HF	01409 254 295
ILLOGAN RBL	Oxland Parc TR16 4DG	01209 216 488
LISKEARD ATHLETIC	Lux Park PL14 3HZ	01579 342 665
LUDGVAN	Jubilee Hall, Fairfield, Ludgvan TR20 8ES	
MILLBROOK AFC	Jenkins Park PL10 1EN	01752 822 113
MOUSEHOLE	Trungle Parc, Paul, Penzance TR19 6UG	01736 731 518
PENZANCE	Penlee Park, Alexandra Place, Penzance TR18 4NE	01736 361 964
PLYMOUTH MAJON	Derriford Road PL6 8BH	
PLYMSTOCK UNITED	Dean Cross, Dean Cross Road, Plymstock PL9 7AZ	01752 406 776
PORTHLEVEN	Gala Parc, Mill Lane, Porthleven TR13 9LQ	01326 569 655
ST. BLAZEY	Blaise Park, Station Road, St Blazey PL24 2ND	01725 814 110
ST. DENNIS	Boscawen Park, St Dennis PL26 8DW	01726 822 635
WADEBRIDGE TOWN	Bodieve Park, Bodieve Road, Wadebridge PL27 6EA	01208 812 537
WENDRON UNITED	Underlane TR13 0EH	01209 860 946

SOUTHERN COMBINATION FOOTBALL LEAGUE

Sponsored by: Macron Store

Founded: 1920 (As Sussex County League >2015)

Recent Champions: 2014: East Preston

2015: Littlehampton Town **2016:** Horsham

PREMIER DIVISION	P	W	D	L	F	A	GD	Pts
1 Shoreham	38	30	2	6	110	30	80	92
2 Haywards Heath Town	38	31	3	4	114	28	86	87*
3 Chichester City	38	26	6	6	94	47	47	84
4 Pagham	38	22	6	10	93	45	48	72
5 Eastbourne Town	38	21	7	10	85	60	25	70
6 Loxwood	38	18	7	13	75	59	16	61
7 Eastbourne United	38	19	2	17	64	67	-3	59
8 Broadbridge Heath	38	18	3	17	71	63	8	57
9 Newhaven	38	15	10	13	85	70	15	55
10 Horsham YMCA	38	15	9	14	67	67	0	54
11 Crawley Down Gatwick	38	15	7	16	95	86	+9	52
12 Lancing	38	15	5	18	74	83	-9	50
13 Hassocks	38	15	3	20	70	68	2	48
14 Peacehaven & Telscombe	38	14	6	18	69	78	-9	48
15 Arundel	38	12	6	20	57	84	-27	42
16 Littlehampton Town	38	12	4	22	61	87	-26	40
17 Worthing United	38	11	4	23	52	104	-52	37
18 AFC Uckfield Town	38	11	2	25	49	95	-46	35
19 Wick	38	8	6	24	53	91	-38	30
20 Hailsham Town	38	2	2	34	32	158	-126	8

CLUB MOVEMENTS

Premier Division - In: East Preston (P), Saltdean United (P), Three Bridges (R - Isthmian D1S).

Out: Hailsham Town (R), Shoreham (P - Isth D1S), Wick (R).

Division One - In: Hailsham Town (R), Wick (R).

Out: East Preston (P), Saltdean United (P).

DIVISION ONE	P	W	D	L	F	A	GD	Pts
1 Saltdean United	34	24	7	3	87	33	54	79
2 Little Common	34	23	6	5	103	49	54	75
3 East Preston	34	23	6	5	85	33	52	75
4 Mile Oak	34	21	6	7	84	48	36	69
5 Lingfield	34	20	3	11	87	65	22	63
6 Steyning Town	34	18	6	10	81	64	17	60
7 Selsey	34	15	8	11	82	69	13	53
8 Langney Wanderers	34	16	3	15	92	87	5	51
9 Midhurst & Easebourne	34	12	8	14	66	72	-6	44
10 Bexhill United	34	13	5	16	60	68	-8	44
11 Southwick	34	12	7	15	65	67	-2	42*
12 Storrington	34	9	10	15	52	70	-18	36*
13 Seaford Town	34	8	7	19	47	68	-21	31
14 Oakwood	34	8	7	19	41	78	-37	31
15 Billingshurst	34	7	7	20	55	86	-31	28
16 Ringmer	34	7	7	20	47	86	-39	28
17 St Francis Rangers	34	6	6	22	43	85	-42	24
18 AFC Varndeanians	34	4	11	19	45	94	-49	23

LEAGUE CUP

HOLDERS: LANCING

ROUND 1

Saltdean United	v	Bexhill United	0-2
Langney Wanderers	v	Little Common	2-0
Storrington	v	Billingshurst	1-0
Ringmer	v	Lingfield	0-3
Seaford Town	v	AFC Varndeanians	0-1
Selsey	v	Steyning Town	6-2

ROUND 2

East Preston	v	Crawley Down Gatwick	5-3
Worthing United	v	Littlehampton Town	2-1
Shoreham	v	Bexhill United	3-0
Pagham	v	Midhurst & Easebourne	4-0
Southwick	v	Langney Wanderers	2-4
Arundel	v	Storrington	6-0
Chichester City	v	Lancing	3-1
St Francis Rangers	v	Newhaven	1-5
Loxwood	v	Oakwood	5-2
Hailsham Town	v	Lingfield	0-5
Hassocks	v	AFC Uckfield Town	1-2
Broadbridge Heath	v	Wick	3-0
Haywards Heath Town	v	Eastbourne Town	3-3, 5-3p
Peacehaven & Telscombe	v	Mile Oak	6-5 aet
Eastbourne United	v	AFC Varndeanians	2-0
Horsham YMCA	v	Selsey	6-1

ROUND 3

East Preston	v	Worthing United	1-3 aet
Shoreham	v	Pagham	2-4 aet
Langney Wanderers	v	Arundel	3-2
Chichester City	v	Newhaven	4-3 aet
Loxwood	v	Lingfield	1-0
AFC Uckfield Town	v	Broadbridge Heath	0-1
Haywards Heath Town	v	Peacehaven & Telscombe	6-2
Eastbourne United	v	Horsham YMCA	3-2 aet

QUARTER FINALS

Worthing United	v	Pagham	0-3
Langney Wanderers	v	Chichester City	3-1
Loxwood	v	Broadbridge Heath	0-2
Haywards Heath Town	v	Eastbourne United	5-0

SEMI FINALS

Pagham	v	Langney Wanderers	8-0
Broadbridge Heath	v	Haywards Heath Town	1-2 aet

FINAL

Pagham	v	Haywards Heath Town	1-0

DIVISION TWO	P	W	D	L	F	A	GD	Pts
1 Bosham	28	21	4	3	102	24	78	67
2 Jarvis Brook	28	19	7	2	108	42	66	64
3 Sidlesham	28	18	6	4	83	28	55	60
4 Lancing United	28	17	4	7	88	45	43	55
5 Upper Beeding	28	13	8	7	86	39	47	47
6 Westfield	28	14	4	10	80	48	32	46
7 Roffey	28	11	8	9	73	37	36	41
8 Cowfold	28	12	5	11	82	54	28	41
9 Rottingdean Village	28	11	4	13	55	71	-16	37
10 Montpelier Villa	28	9	5	14	64	52	12	32
11 Rustington	28	9	5	14	40	56	-16	32
12 Clymping	28	8	6	14	63	75	-12	30
13 Worthing Town Leisure	28	8	2	18	63	72	-9	26
14 Alfold	28	5	2	21	48	106	-58	17
15 Ferring	28	0	0	28	14	300	-286	0

CLUB MOVEMENTS

Division Three - Out: AFC Roffey Club (W - 08/16).

PREMIER DIVISION

AFC UCKFIELD TOWN
Founded: 1988   Nickname: The Oakmen

Secretary: Anthony Scott   **(T)** 07769 114 476   **(E)** antscott7@hotmail.co.uk
Chairman: Tom Parker
Ground: The Oaks, Old Eastbourne Road, Uckfield TN22 5QL   **(T)** 01825 890 905
Capacity: **Seats:** Yes   **Covered:** Yes   **Midweek Matchday:**   **Clubhouse:** Yes

Colours(change): Red & black/black/black (All blue)
Previous Names: Wealden 1988-2010. AFC Uckfield & Uckfield Town merged in 2014.
Previous Leagues: None

HONOURS: FA Comps: None
     League: Sussex County Division Two 2010-11.

10 YEAR RECORD

07-08	08-09	09-10	10-11	11-12	12-13	13-14	14-15	15-16	16-17
SxC2 9	SxC2 15	SxC2 8	SxC2 1	SxC1 8	SxC1 21	SxC1 10	SxC2 2	SCP 15	SCP 18
									FAC EP
								FAV 1Q	FAV 2Q

ARUNDEL
Founded: 1889   Nickname: Mulletts

Secretary: Kathy Wilson   **(T)** 07778 783 294   **(E)** mullets@btinternet.com
Chairman: Bob Marchant   **Prog Ed:** Kathy Wilson
Ground: Mill Road, Arundel, W. Sussex BN18 9QQ   **(T)** 01903 882 548
Capacity: 2,200   **Seats:** 100   **Covered:** 200   **Midweek Matchday:** Tuesday   **Clubhouse:** Yes

Colours(change): Red/white/red (All Blue)
Previous Names: None
Previous Leagues: West Sussex (Founder Members) 1889-1949.

HONOURS: FA Comps: None
     League: Sussex County Division One 1957-58, 58-59, 86-87.

10 YEAR RECORD

07-08	08-09	09-10	10-11	11-12	12-13	13-14	14-15	15-16	16-17
SxC1 3	SxC1 2	SxC1 12	SxC1 9	SxC1 17	SxC1 14	SxC1 12	SxC1 10	SCP 12	SCP 15
FAC 1Q	FAC 1Qr	FAC EP	FAC P	FAC P	FAC EP	FAC EPr	FAC EP	FAC Pr	FAC 1Q
FAV 2P	FAV 3P	FAV 3P	FAV 2Q	FAV 2Q	FAV 2Q	FAV 2Q	FAV 1P	FAV 2Q	FAV 1Q

BROADBRIDGE HEATH
Founded: 1919   Nickname: The Bears

Secretary: Andrew Crisp   **(T)** 07501 057 654   **(E)** crispandy@hotmail.com
Chairman: Keith Soane   **Manager:** Steve Painter   **Prog Ed:** Andrew Crisp
Ground: Broadbridge Leisure Centre, Wickhurst Lane Broadbridge Heath Horsham RH12   **(T)** 01403 211 311
Capacity: **Seats:**   **Covered:**   **Midweek Matchday:**   **Clubhouse:**

Colours(change): All royal blue (White/red/red)
Previous Names: None
Previous Leagues: Horsham & District >1971. West Sussex 1971-79. Southern Counties Combination 1979-83.

HONOURS: FA Comps: None
     League: West Sussex Division One 1975-76.

10 YEAR RECORD

07-08	08-09	09-10	10-11	11-12	12-13	13-14	14-15	15-16	16-17
SxC2 17	SxC2 9	SxC2 14	SxC2 6	SxC2 5	SxC2 6	SxC2 2	SxC1 9	SCP 9	SCP 8
FAV 2Q							FAV 2Q	FAV 2Q	FAV 1Q

CHICHESTER CITY
Founded: 2000   Nickname: Lillywhites

Secretary: Mark Warren   **(T)** 07774 942 643   **(E)** mark@chichestercityfc.co.uk
Chairman: Brent Williams
Ground: Oaklands Park, Chichester, W Sussex PO19 6AR   **(T)** 01243 533 368
Capacity: 2,000 **Seats:** none **Covered:** 200   **Midweek Matchday:** Tuesday   **Clubhouse:** Yes   **Shop:** Yes

Colours(change): White & green/green/white (Orange & black/orange/orange)
Previous Names: Chichester FC (pre 1948), Chichester City 1948-2000. Merged with Portfield in 2000, Chicester City United 2000-09
Previous Leagues: None

HONOURS: FA Comps: None
     League: Sussex County Division One 2003-04.

10 YEAR RECORD

07-08	08-09	09-10	10-11	11-12	12-13	13-14	14-15	15-16	16-17
SxC1 16	SxC1 7	SxC1 3	SxC1 14	SxC1 20	SxC1 19	SxC1 11	SxC1 14	SCP 5	SCP 3
	FAC P	FAC P	FAC EP	FAC EPr	FAC EP	FAC EP	FAC EP	FAC P	FAC EP
FAV 1P	FAV 2P	FAV 1P	FAV 1P	FAV 2P	FAV 2Q	FAV 1Q	FAV 1Q	FAV 1Q	FAV 4P

CRAWLEY DOWN GATWICK
Founded: 1993   Nickname: The Anvils

Secretary: Mick Martin   **(T)** 07973 620 759   **(E)** martinmd@btinternet.com
Chairman: Donal Barrett
Ground: The Haven Centre, Hophurst Lane, Crawley Down RH10 4LJ   **(T)** 01342 717 140
Capacity: 1,000   **Seats:** Yes   **Covered:** 50   **Midweek Matchday:**   **Clubhouse:** Yes

Colours(change): All Red (All blue)
Previous Names: Crawley Down United > 1993. Crawley Down Village > 1999. Crawley Down > 2012.
Previous Leagues: Mid Sussex, Sussex County > 2011. Isthmian 2011-14.

HONOURS: FA Comps: None
    League: Mid-Sussex Premier Division 1994-95. Sussex County Division One 2010-11.

10 YEAR RECORD

07-08		08-09		09-10		10-11		11-12		12-13		13-14		14-15		15-16		16-17	
SxC2	6	SxC2	3	SxC1	8	SxC1	1	Isth1S	16	Isth1S	13	Isth1S	23	SxC1	19	SC1	2	SCP	11
				FAC	EPr	FAC	1Q	FAC	EP	FAC	1Q	FAC	P	FAC	P	FAC	EPr	FAC	EP	FAC	P
FAV	2P	FAV	2Q	FAV	2Q	FAV	1P	FAT	P	FAT	1Q	FAT	1Q	FAV	2P	FAV	1Q	FAV	1Q

EAST PRESTON
Founded: 1966   Nickname: EP

Secretary: Keith Freeman   **(T)** 07986 596 913   **(E)** keweia@btinternet.com
Chairman: Terry Doyle
Ground: Roundstone Recreation Ground, Lashmar Road, East Preston BN16 1ES   **(T)** 01903 776 026
Capacity: **Seats:** Yes   **Covered:** Yes   **Midweek Matchday:**   **Clubhouse:**

Colours(change): Black/black/purple (All purple)
Previous Names: None
Previous Leagues: Worthing & District 1966-68. West Sussex 1968-83.

HONOURS: FA Comps: None
    League: West Sussex Premier Division 1977-78, 80-81, 81-82, 82-83.

10 YEAR RECORD   Sussex County Division Three 1983-84, Division Two 1997-98, 2011-12, Division One 2013-14.

07-08		08-09		09-10		10-11		11-12		12-13		13-14		14-15		15-16		16-17	
SxC1	4	SxC1	18	SxC2	14	SxC2	14	SxC2	1	SxC1	3	SxC1	1	SxC1	11	SCP	19	SC1	3
FAC	Pr	FAC	P	FAC	2Q	FAC	EP			FAC	P	FAC	1Q	FAC	2Q	FAC	EP	FAC	1Q
FAV	1Q	FAV	1P	FAV	1Q	FAV	2Q	FAV	1P	FAV	2Q	FAV	5P	FAV	2P	FAV	1Q	FAV	2Q

EASTBOURNE TOWN
Founded: 1881   Nickname: Town

Secretary: Richard Marsh   **(T)** 07490 860 888   **(E)** rb.marsh@talk21.com
Chairman: David Jenkins
Ground: The Saffrons, Compton Place Road, Eastbourne BN21 1EA   **(T)** 01323 724 328
Capacity: 3,000   **Seats:** 200   **Covered:** Yes   **Midweek Matchday:**   **Clubhouse:** Yes

Colours(change): Yellow/blue/blue (All light blue)
Previous Names: Devonshire Park 1881-89
Previous Leagues: Southern Amateur 1907-46, Corinthian 1960-63, Athenian 1963-76, Sussex County 1976-2007. Isthmian 2007-14.

HONOURS: FA Comps: None
    League: Sussex County 1976-77, 2006-07.

10 YEAR RECORD

07-08		08-09		09-10		10-11		11-12		12-13		13-14		14-15		15-16		16-17	
Isth1S	19	Isth1S	13	Isth1S	22	Isth1S	18	Isth1S	14	Isth1S	11	Isth1S	24	SxC1	4	SCP	2	SCP	5
FAC	1Qr	FAC	1Q	FAC	P	FAC	1Q	FAC	P	FAC	2Q	FAC	2Q	FAC	P	FAC	3Q	FAC	1Q
FAT	1Q	FAT	P	FAT	P	FAT	P	FAT	1Q	FAT	1Q	FAT	1Qr	FAV	1P	FAV	3P	FAV	4P

EASTBOURNE UNITED
Founded: 1894   Nickname: The U's

Secretary: Dean Allchin   **(T)** 07949 588 497   **(E)** deanallchin@hotmail.co.uk
Chairman: Brian Cordingley
Ground: The Oval, Channel View Road, Eastbourne, BN22 7LN   **(T)** 01323 726 989
Capacity: 3,000   **Seats:** 160   **Covered:** 160   **Midweek Matchday:** Tuesday   **Clubhouse:** Yes   **Shop:** Yes

Colours(change): White/black/white (Light blue/white/black).
Previous Names: 1st Sussex Royal Engineers. Eastbourne Old Comrades 1922. Eastbourne United (merged with Shinewater Assoc in 2000)
Previous Leagues: Sussex County 1921-28, 32-56. Spartan 1928-32. Metropolitan 1956-64. Athenian 1964-77. Isthmian 1977-92.

HONOURS: FA Comps: None
    League: Athenian Division Two 1966-67, Division One 68-69. Sussex County Division One 1954-55, 55-56, 2008-09, Division Two 2013-14.

10 YEAR RECORD

07-08		08-09		09-10		10-11		11-12		12-13		13-14		14-15		15-16		16-17	
SxC1	11	SxC1	1	SxC1	6	SxC1	20	SxC2	6	SxC2	4	SxC2	1	SxC1	12	SCP	10	SCP	7
FAC	EP	FAC	EP	FAC	Pr	FAC	EP					FAC	1Q	FAC	P	FAC	1Q	FAC	1Q
FAV	2Q	FAV	1Q	FAV	3P	FAV	2Q			FAV	1Q	FAV	SF	FAV	2P	FAV	2Q	FAV	2P

HASSOCKS
Founded: 1902   Nickname: The Robins

Secretary: Sarah John   **(T)** 07703 346 208   **(E)** sarahajohn@btinternet.com
Chairman: Dave John
Ground: The Beacon, Brighton Road, Hassocks BN6 9NA   **(T)** 01273 846 040
Capacity: 1,800 **Seats:** 270 **Covered:** 100 **Midweek Matchday:** Tuesday **Clubhouse:** Yes

Colours(change): All Red. (All green)
Previous Names: None
Previous Leagues: Mid Sussex, Brighton & Hove & District >1981.

HONOURS: FA Comps: None
League: Brighton, Hove & District Division Two 1965-66, Division One 71-72.
Sussex County Division Three 1991-92.

10 YEAR RECORD									
07-08	08-09	09-10	10-11	11-12	12-13	13-14	14-15	15-16	16-17
SxC1 7	SxC1 16	SxC1 14	SxC1 6	SxC1 4	SxC1 7	SxC1 6	SxC1 15	SCP 13	SCP 13
FAC P	FAC EP	FAC EP	FAC 1Q	FAC EP	FAC EP	FAC 1Q	FAC EP		
FAV 2P	FAV 2Q	FAV 2Q	FAV 1Q	FAV 2Qr	FAV 1P	FAV 1P	FAV 2P		FAV 1Q

HAYWARDS HEATH TOWN
Founded: 1888   Nickname: The Blues

Secretary: Mark Russ   **(T)** 07796 677 661   **(E)** marussy@mac.com
Chairman: Mick Cottingham
Ground: Hanbury Park Stadium, Haywards Heath RH16 4GL   **(T)** 01444 412 837
Capacity: **Seats:** Yes **Covered:** Yes **Midweek Matchday:** **Clubhouse:** Yes

Colours(change): Blue/blue/red (All red)
Previous Names: Haywards Heath Juniors 1888-94. Haywards Heath Excelsior 1894-95. Haywards Heath 1895-1989.
Previous Leagues: Mid-Sussex 1888-1927. Sussex County 1927-52. Metropolitan 1952-61.

HONOURS: FA Comps: None
League: Sussex County/Southern Combination 1949-50, 69-70, Eastern Division 45-46/ Division One 2015-16.

10 YEAR RECORD									
07-08	08-09	09-10	10-11	11-12	12-13	13-14	14-15	15-16	16-17
SxC3 3	SxC3 3	SxC3 3	SxC3 8	SxC3 15	SxC3 2	SxC2 5	SxC2 9	SC1 1	SCP 2
							FAC EP		FAC P
FAV 2Q	FAV 2Q	FAV 1Q		FAV 1Qr		FAV 2Q	FAV 1Q	FAV 2P	FAV 2P

HORSHAM YMCA
Founded: 1898   Nickname: YM's

Secretary: Andy Flack   **(T)** 07775 857 392   **(E)** andy.flack@horsham.gov.uk
Chairman: Geoff Foreman
Ground: Gorings Mead, Horsham, West Sussex RH13 5BP   **(T)** 01403 252 689
Capacity: 1,575 **Seats:** 150 **Covered:** 200 **Midweek Matchday:** **Clubhouse:** Yes

Colours(change): White/black/red (All red)
Previous Names: None
Previous Leagues: Horsham & District, Brighton & Hove, Mid Sussex, Sussex County > 2006, Isthmian 2006-11.

HONOURS: FA Comps: None
League: Sussex County 2004-05, 05-06.

10 YEAR RECORD									
07-08	08-09	09-10	10-11	11-12	12-13	13-14	14-15	15-16	16-17
Isth1S 21	SxC1 3	Isth1S 11	Isth1S 22	SxC1 16	SxC1 10	SxC1 4	SxC1 5	SCP 7	SCP 10
FAC 1Qr	FAC 1Qr	FAC 2Q	FAC P	FAC EPr	FAC EP	FAC EP	FAC Pr	FAC 2Qr	FAC EP
FAT 1Q	FAV 1P	FAT P	FAT P	FAV 1P	FAV 2P	FAV 1Q	FAV 2P	FAV 2Q	FAV 3P

LANCING
Founded: 1941   Nickname: The Lancers

Secretary: John Rea   **(T)** 07598 301 296   **(E)** rea.john@mail.com
Chairman: John Rea
Ground: Culver Road, Lancing, West Sussex BN15 9AX   **(T)** 01903 767 285
Capacity: 2,000 **Seats:** **Covered:** **Midweek Matchday:** **Clubhouse:** Yes

Colours(change): Yellow/blue/yellow (White/black/black)
Previous Names: Lancing Athletic 1941-57
Previous Leagues: Brighton & Hove & District 1946-48.

HONOURS: FA Comps: None
League: Brighton 1946-47, 47-48. Sussex County Division Two 1957-58, 69-70.

10 YEAR RECORD									
07-08	08-09	09-10	10-11	11-12	12-13	13-14	14-15	15-16	16-17
SxC2 12	SxC2 9	SxC2 11	SxC2 2	SxC1 2	SxC1 13	SxC1 18	SxC1 8	SCP 4	SCP 12
FAC EPr	FAC EP	FAC EP	FAC P	FAC P	FAC P	FAC EPr	FAC EP	FAC EP	FAC EPr
FAV 2Q	FAV 2Q	FAV 2Q	FAV 4P	FAV 3P	FAV 1P	FAV 2Q	FAV 2Q	FAV 1P	FAV 2P

LITTLEHAMPTON TOWN

Founded: 1896   **Nickname:** Marigolds

Secretary: Paul Cox   **(T)** 07771 623 224   **(E)** paulcox280458@yahoo.co.uk
Chairman: Robert McAlees
Ground: St Flora Sportsfield, St Flora's Road, Littlehampton BN17 6BD   **(T)** 01903 716 390
Capacity: 4,000   **Seats:** Yes   **Covered:** Yes   **Midweek Matchday:**   **Clubhouse:** Yes

Colours(change): Gold/black/black (Blue/white/red)
Previous Names: Littlehampton 1896-1938.
Previous Leagues: None

HONOURS: FA Comps: None
League: Sussex County Division Two 1996-97, 2003-04, 12-13, Division One 1990-91, 2014-15.

10 YEAR RECORD

07-08		08-09		09-10		10-11		11-12		12-13		13-14		14-15		15-16		16-17	
SxC2	8	SxC2	14	SxC2	12	SxC2	11	SxC2	4	SxC2	1	SxC1	3	SxC1	1	SCP	11	SCP	16
FAC	1Q	FAC	EP	FAC	EPr	FAC	EPr	FAC	EP	FAC	1Q	FAC	1Q	FAC	1Q	FAC	P	FAC	EP
FAV	2Q	FAV	1Q	FAV	1Q	FAV	1Q	FAV	2P	FAV	2Pr	FAV	2P	FAV	3Pr	FAV	1P	FAV	2Qr

LOXWOOD

Founded: 1920   **Nickname:** Magpies

Secretary: John Bellamy   **(T)** 07917 135 212   **(E)** bellas.john@btinternet.com
Chairman: Barry Hunter   **Manager:** David Cocoracchio   **Prog Ed:** Ray Merridew
Ground: Loxwood Sports Ass., Plaistow Road, Loxwood RH14 0RQ   **(T)** 07791 766 857
Capacity: **Seats:** 100   **Covered:** Yes   **Midweek Matchday:**   **Clubhouse:**

Colours(change): White/black/white (Black & yellow stripes/white/black)
Previous Names: None
Previous Leagues: West Sussex 1995-2006.

HONOURS: FA Comps: None
League: West Sussex Division Two North 1998-99, 2001-02.

10 YEAR RECORD Sussex County Division Three 2007-08.

07-08		08-09		09-10		10-11		11-12		12-13		13-14		14-15		15-16		16-17	
SxC3	1	SxC2	10	SxC2	5	SxC2	6	SxC2	5	SxC2	9	SxC2	3	SxC1	6	SCP	8	SCP	6
																FAC	EP	FAC	P
																FAV	2P	FAV	1Q
															FAV	2P				

NEWHAVEN

Founded: 1887   **Nickname:** The Dockers

Secretary: Martin Garry   **(T)** 07768 508 011   **(E)** martin.garry@premierfoods.co.uk
Chairman: Martin Garry   **Manager:** Sean Breach   **Prog Ed:** Lee Robinson
Ground: The Trafalgar Ground, Fort Road Newhaven East Sussex BN9 9DA   **(T)** 01273 513 940
Capacity: **Seats:** Yes   **Covered:** Yes   **Midweek Matchday:**   **Clubhouse:** Yes

Colours(change): Red & yellow/red/red
Previous Names: None
Previous Leagues: Brighton, Hove & District 1887-1920.

HONOURS: FA Comps: None
League: Sussex County Division One 1953-54, 73-74, Division Two 1971-72, 90-91, Division Three 2011-12.

10 YEAR RECORD

07-08		08-09		09-10		10-11		11-12		12-13		13-14		14-15		15-16		16-17	
SxC3	5	SxC3	4	SxC3	9	SxC3	7	SxC3	1	SxC2	2	SxC1	13	SxC1	7	SCP	3	SCP	9
																		FAC	EPr
FAV	1Q	FAV	2Q	FAV	1Q	FAV	1Q	FAV	2Q	FAV	1Q	FAV	1Pr	FAV	1Q	FAV	2P	FAV	3P

PAGHAM

Founded: 1903   **Nickname:** The Lions

Secretary: Marc Hilton   **(T)** 07771 810 757   **(E)** paghamfootballclub@outlook.com
Chairman: Tony Shea
Ground: Nyetimber Lane, Pagham, West Sussex PO21 3JY   **(T)** 01243 266 112
Capacity: 1,500   **Seats:** 200   **Covered:** 200   **Midweek Matchday:**   **Clubhouse:** Yes

Colours(change): Black/black/green & white (Green/white/white)
Previous Names: None
Previous Leagues: Bognor & Chichester 1903-50, West Sussex 50-69

HONOURS: FA Comps: None
League: West Sussex Division One South 1962-63, Prmeier 65-66, 68-69, 69-70.

10 YEAR RECORD Sussex County Division Two 1978-79, 86-87, 2006-07, Division One 80-81, 87-88, 88-89.

07-08		08-09		09-10		10-11		11-12		12-13		13-14		14-15		15-16		16-17	
SxC1	9	SxC1	11	SxC1	17	SxC1	4	SxC1	6	SxC1	5	SxC1	7	SxC1	3	SCP	6	SCP	4
FAC	EPr	FAC	EP	FAC	P	FAC	P	FAC	EP	FAC	1Qr	FAC	EP	FAC	1Q	FAC	1Q	FAC	1Q
FAV	2Q	FAV	2Q	FAV	1P	FAV	2Q	FAV	2P	FAV	1Pr	FAV	2Q	FAV	2P	FAV	2P	FAV	2Q

PEACEHAVEN & TELSCOMBE
Founded: 1923   Nickname: The Tye

Secretary: Dan Palmer   **(T)** 07713 907 630   **(E)** danpalmer2008@hotmail.co.uk
Chairman: Jeremy Avens
Ground: The Sports Park, Piddinghoe Ave, Peacehaven, BN10 8RJ   **(T)** 01273 582 471
Capacity: 3,000 **Seats:** 350   **Covered:** Yes   **Midweek Matchday:**   **Clubhouse:** Yes

Colours(change): Black/black/red & white (Red & white/white/white)
Previous Names: Formed when Peacehaven Rangers and Telscombe Tye merged.
Previous Leagues: Sussex County > 2013. Isthmian 2013-16.

HONOURS: FA Comps: None
League: Brighton, H&D Junior 1951-52, Intermediate 63-64, Senior 68-69. Sussex County Division One 1978-79, 81-82, 82-83, 91-92, 92-93, 94-95, 95-96, 2012-13, Division Three 2005-06, Division Two 2008-09. Isthmian Division One South 2013-14.

10 YEAR RECORD

07-08	08-09	09-10	10-11	11-12	12-13	13-14	14-15	15-16	16-17
SxC2 4	SxC2 1	FAC Pr	SxC1 3	SxC1 5	SxC1 1	Isth1S 1	Isth P 21	Isth1S 24	SCP 14
FAC EP	FAC Pr	FAC EP	FAC P	FAC P	FAC P	FAC 1Q	FAC 1Qr	FAC P	FAC 1Q
FAV 1Q	FAV 2P	FAV 3P	FAV 2P	FAV 3P	FAV 4P	FAT 1Q	FAT 3Q	FAT 1Q	FAV 2Q

SALTDEAN UNITED
Founded: 1966   Nickname: The Tigers

Secretary: Kevin Ratcliffe   **(T)** 07717 501 045   **(E)** kevin.kands@live.co.uk
Chairman: Robert Thomas
Ground: Hill Park, Coombe Vale Saltdean Brighton East Sussex BN2 8HJ   **(T)** 01273 309 898
Capacity: **Seats:**   **Covered:**   **Midweek Matchday:**   **Clubhouse:**

Colours(change): Red & black/black/black (Blue/blue/yellow)
Previous Names: None
Previous Leagues: None

HONOURS: FA Comps: None
League: Sussex County/Southern Combination Division Three 1988-89, Division Two 95-96 / Division One 2016-17.

10 YEAR RECORD

07-08	08-09	09-10	10-11	11-12	12-13	13-14	14-15	15-16	16-17
SxC3 9	SxC3 7	SxC3 8	SxC3 5	SxC3 2	SxC2 18	SxC2 13	SxC2 13	SC1 17	SC1 1
FAC EP									
FAV 1Q	FAV 2Q	FAV 2Q	FAV 2Q	FAV 1Q	FAV 1Q	FAV 1Q	FAV 1Q		FAV 1Q

THREE BRIDGES
Founded: 1901   Nickname: Bridges

Secretary: Lorraine Bonner   **(T)**   **(E)** lorraine.bonner@lw.com
Chairman: Paul Faili   **Prog Ed:** Lorraine Bonner
Ground: Jubilee Walk, Three Bridges Road, Crawley, RH10 1LQ   **(T)** 01293 442 000
Capacity: 3,500 **Seats:** 120   **Covered:** 600   **Midweek Matchday:**   **Clubhouse:** Yes

Colours(change): Orange & black/black/black (All blue)
Previous Names: Three Bridges Worth 1936-52. Three Bridges United 1953-64.
Previous Leagues: Mid Sussex, E Grinstead, Redhill & Dist 36-52. Sussex County >2012. Isthmian 2012-17.

HONOURS: FA Comps: None
League: Sussex County Division One 1953-54, 2011-12.

10 YEAR RECORD

07-08	08-09	09-10	10-11	11-12	12-13	13-14	14-15	15-16	16-17
SxC1 6	SxC1 5	SxC1 7	SxC1 5	SxC1 1	Isth1S 21	Isth1S 19	Isth1S 7	Isth1S 14	Isth1S 23
FAC P	FAC EP	FAC EP	FAC P	FAC EP	FAC P	FAC 1Q	FAC Pr	FAC P	FAC P
FAV 2P	FAV 1Q	FAV 2Q	FAV 3P	FAV 4Pr	FAT 2Q	FAT 2Q	FAT 1Q	FAT P	FAT P

WORTHING UNITED
Founded: 1952   Nickname: Mavericks

Secretary: Mark Sanderson   **(T)** 07968 856 183   **(E)** secretary@worthingunitedfc.co.uk
Chairman: Steve Taylor
Ground: The Robert Albon Memorial Ground, Lyons Way BN14 9JF   **(T)** 01903 234 466
Capacity: **Seats:**   **Covered:** Yes   **Midweek Matchday:**   **Clubhouse:** Yes

Colours(change): Sky blue & white/blue/sky blue (Red & black/black/red)
Previous Names: Wigmore Athletic 1952-88. Amalgamated with Southdown to form Worthing United in 1988.
Previous Leagues: None

HONOURS: FA Comps: None
League: Sussex County Division Two 1973-74, 2014-15, Division Three 1989-90.

10 YEAR RECORD

07-08	08-09	09-10	10-11	11-12	12-13	13-14	14-15	15-16	16-17
SxC1 17	SxC1 20	SxC2 2	SxC2 3	SxC1 14	SxC1 22	SxC1 20	SxC2 1	SCP 14	SCP 17
FAC EP	FAC EP	FAC EP	FAC P			FAC EPr	FAC EP	FAC EPr	FAC EP
FAV 1P	FAV 1Q	FAV 2Q	FAV 2Q		FAV 1Qr	FAV 2Q	FAV 2Q	FAV 1P	FAV 1Q

AFC VARNDEANIANS
Founded: 1929   Nickname:

Secretary: Dave Bridges   **(T)** 07970 114 565   **(E)** dave@fruit-design.co.uk
Chairman: Dave Bridges   **Manager:** Kieran Ridley   **Prog Ed:** Dave Bridges
Ground: Withdean Stadium, Tongdean Lane, Brighton BN1 5JD   **(T)**
Colours(change): Red & black/black/black
HONOURS: FA Comps: None   **League:** Brighton & HD Division One 1973-74, 99-2000, 00-01, 02-03.
Mid Sussex Premier 03-04, 06-07, 08-09. Southern Combination Division Two 15-16.

10 YEAR RECORD

07-08	08-09	09-10	10-11	11-12	12-13	13-14	14-15	15-16	16-17
MSuxP 2	MSuxP 1	MSuxP 7	MSuxP 9	MSuxP 5	MSuxP 7	MSuxP 2	MSuxP 7	SC2 1	SC1 18

BEXHILL UNITED
Founded: 2002   Nickname: The Pirates

Secretary: Simon Dunne   **(T)** 07983 134 245   **(E)** simon_dunne@hotmail.co.uk
Chairman: Bill Harrison
Ground: The Polegrove, Brockley Road, Bexhill on Sea TN39 3EX   **(T)** 07791 368 049
Colours(change): White/black/black (Sky blue/white/white)
HONOURS: FA Comps: None   **League:** Sussex County 1956-57, 65-66, 66-67.

10 YEAR RECORD

07-08	08-09	09-10	10-11	11-12	12-13	13-14	14-15	15-16	16-17
SxC3 2	SxC2 17	SxC3 2	SxC2 4	SxC2 7	SxC2 11	SxC2 8	SxC2 6	SC1 14	SC1 10
								FAC P	
							FAV 2Q	FAV 1Q	FAV 1Q

BILLINGSHURST
Founded: 1891   Nickname: Hurst

Secretary: Jan Tilley   **(T)** 07834 786 750   **(E)** kevtilley@btinternet.com
Chairman: Kevin Tilley
Ground: Jubilee Fields, Newbridge Road, Billingshurst, West Sussex. RH14 9HZ   **(T)** 01403 786 445
Colours(change): Red & black/black/black (All blue)
HONOURS: FA Comps: None   **League:** West Sussex Premier Division 2011-12.

10 YEAR RECORD

07-08	08-09	09-10	10-11	11-12	12-13	13-14	14-15	15-16	16-17
				WSuxP 1	SxC3 4	SxC3 11	SxC3 6	SC2 5	SC1 15

HAILSHAM TOWN
Founded: 1885   Nickname: The Stringers

Secretary: Stuart Fairway   **(T)** 07831 223 874   **(E)** stuartfairway1984@googlemail.com
Chairman: John Nuttall   **Manager:** Jamie Savage   **Prog Ed:** Alan Hook
Ground: The Beaconfield, Western Road, Hailsham BN27 3JF   **(T)** 01323 840 446   **Capacity:** 2,000
Colours(change): Yellow & green/green/green (Light & dark blue/light/light blue)
HONOURS: FA Comps: None   **League:** Southern Counties Combination 1975-76.

10 YEAR RECORD

07-08	08-09	09-10	10-11	11-12	12-13	13-14	14-15	15-16	16-17
SxC1 13	SxC1 15	SxC1 19	SxC1 16	SxC2 2	SxC1 12	SxC1 16	SxC1 17	SCP 18	SCP 20
FAC Pr	FAC P	FAC EP	FAC EP	FAC EP	FAC EP	FAC EP	FAC EP	FAC EP	FAC EP
FAV 1P	FAV 1Q	FAV 1Q	FAV 1Q	FAV 1Q	FAV 1Q	FAV 1Q	FAV 1P	FAV 2P	FAV 1Q

LANGNEY WANDERERS
Founded: 2010   Nickname:

Secretary: Tracey Saunders   **(T)** 07711 811 017   **(E)** saunderstracey@sky.com
Chairman: Stephen Saunders
Ground: Langney Sports Club, Priory Lane, Eastbourne BN23 7QH   **(T)** 01323 766 265   **Capacity:** 4,151
Colours(change): White/red/red (Blue & black/black/black)
HONOURS: FA Comps: None   **League:** East Sussex Premier 2012-13. Sussex County Division Three 2013-14.

10 YEAR RECORD

07-08	08-09	09-10	10-11	11-12	12-13	13-14	14-15	15-16	16-17
					EsSuP 1	SxC3 1	SxC3 3	SC1 9	SC1 8
									FAV 1Qr

LINGFIELD

Founded: 1893   Nickname: The Lingers

Secretary: John Tovey   **(T)** 07778 879 144   **(E)** john.tovey@virginmedia.co.uk
Chairman: Bill Blenkin

Ground: Sports Pavillion, Godstone Road, Lingfield, Surrey RH7 6BT   **(T)** 01342 834 269   **Capacity:** 2,000

Colours(change): Red & Yellow/red/red. (Blue & white/sky blue/sky blue)

HONOURS: FA Comps: None   **League:** POST WAR: Edenbridge & Caterham 1952-53. Surrey Intermediate Prem B 76-77, Prem A 77-78, 78-79. Mid Sussex Prem 92-93. Sussex County Division Three 97-98.

10 YEAR RECORD

07-08		08-09		09-10		10-11		11-12		12-13		13-14		14-15		15-16		16-17	
SxC2	2	SxC1	8	SxC1	10	SxC1	11	SxC1	7	SxC1	6	SxC1	15	SCE	17	SC1	8	SC1	5
		FAC	EP	FAC	1Qr	FAC	P	FAC	1Qr	FAC	1Q	FAC	EP	FAC	EP	FAC	EP		
FAV	1Q	FAV	2Q	FAV	2Q	FAV	1Q	FAV	1Q	FAV	1P	FAV	1P	FAV	3P	FAV	2Q	FAV	1P

LITTLE COMMON

Founded: 1966   Nickname: The Green Lane Boys

Secretary: Daniel Eldridge   **(T)** 07759 125 252   **(E)** danieleldridge11@btinternet.com
Chairman: Daniel Eldridge

Ground: Little Common Recreation Ground, Green Lane, Bexhill on Sea TN39 4PH   **(T)** 01424 845 861

Colours(change): Claret & blue/claret/claret (Yellow & black/black/black)

HONOURS: FA Comps: None   **League:** East Sussex 1975-76, 76-77, 2004-05.

10 YEAR RECORD

07-08		08-09		09-10		10-11		11-12		12-13		13-14		14-15		15-16		16-17	
SxC3	6	SxC3	2	SxC2	4	SxC2	13	SxC2	16	SxC2	3	SxC2	4	SxC2	7	SC1	7	SC1	2
																FAV	1Q	FAV	2Q

MIDHURST & EASEBOURNE

Founded: 1946   Nickname: The Stags

Secretary: Mark Broughton   **(T)** 07736 164 416   **(E)** midhurstfc@gmail.com
Chairman: Mark Broughton

Ground: Rotherfield, Dodsley Lane, Easebourne, Midhurst GU29 9BE   **(T)** 01730 816 557

Colours(change): All blue (Orange/black/orange)

HONOURS: FA Comps: None   **League:** West Sussex 1955-56, 62-63, 64-65, Premier 67-68. Sussex County Division Three 94-95, 2002-03.

10 YEAR RECORD

07-08		08-09		09-10		10-11		11-12		12-13		13-14		14-15		15-16		16-17	
SxC2	10	SxC2	16	SxC2	18	SxC2	15	SxC2	15	SxC2	8	SxC2	14	SxC2	8	SC1	15	SC1	9

MILE OAK

Founded: 1960   Nickname: The Oak

Secretary: Chris Tew   **(T)** 07733 323 453   **(E)** tewey62@virginmedia.com
Chairman: Phil Brotherton   **Manager:** Ben Shoulders   **Prog Ed:** Anthony Whittington

Ground: Mile Oak Recreation Ground, Chalky Road, Portslade BN41 2YU   **(T)** 01273 423 854

Colours(change): Tangerine/black/black (All green)

HONOURS: FA Comps: None   **League:** Brighton & Hove District Div.8 1960-61, Div.4 65-66, Div.2 72-73, Div.1 73-74, Prem 1980-81. Sussex County Division Two 94-95.

10 YEAR RECORD

07-08		08-09		09-10		10-11		11-12		12-13		13-14		14-15		15-16		16-17	
SxC2	5	SxC2	2	SxC1	20	SxC2	7	SxC2	10	SxC2	7	SxC2	7	SxC2	5	SC1	6	SC1	4
FAC	EP	FAC	P	FAC	P	FAC	EP	FAC	EPr							FAC	EP	FAC	EP
FAV	2Qr	FAV	2P	FAV	1Q	FAV	2Q	FAV	2Q			FAV	1Qr	FAV	2Q	FAV	2Q	FAV	2Q

OAKWOOD

Founded: 1962   Nickname: The Oaks

Secretary: Sarah Daly   **(T)** 07762 508 889   **(E)** sarah.daly13@hotmail.co.uk
Chairman: Stuart Lovegrove

Ground: Tinsley Lane, Three Bridges, Crawley RH10 8AJ   **(T)** 01293 515 742

Colours(change): Red & black/black/black (All blue)

HONOURS: FA Comps: None   **League:** Crawley Division One 1973-74. Sussex County Division Three 1984-85, Division Two 2005-06.

10 YEAR RECORD

07-08		08-09		09-10		10-11		11-12		12-13		13-14		14-15		15-16		16-17	
SxC1	18	SxC1	19	SxC2	9	SxC2	17	SxC2	18	SxC2	15	SxC2	12	SxC2	4	SC1	3	SC1	14
				FAC	EP	FAC	EP											FAC	EP
		FAV	1Qr	FAV	1Q	FAV	1Q	FAV	1Q	FAV	1Q	FAV	1Q	FAV	1Q	FAV	2Q	FAV	2Q

RINGMER

Founded: 1906 **Nickname:** Blues

Secretary: Richard Hugall **(T)** 01273 814 929 **(E)** clubsecretary@ringmerfc.co.uk
Chairman: Derek McDougall **Manager:** Ash Bailey **Prog Ed:** Malcolm Crouch
Ground: Caburn Ground, Anchor Field, Ringmer BN8 5QN **(T)** 01273 812 738 **Capacity:** 1,000
Colours(change): All blue. (Green & black).

HONOURS: FA Comps: None **League:** Sussex County Division Two 1968-69, Division One 1970-71.

10 YEAR RECORD

	07-08	08-09	09-10	10-11	11-12	12-13	13-14	14-15	15-16	16-17
	SxC1 10	SxC1 9	SxC1 13	SxC1 10	SxC1 15	SxC1 9	SxC1 9	SxC1 18	SC1 12	SC1 16
	FAC P	FAC P	FAC P	FAC P	FAC EP	FAC P	FAC EP	FAC P	FAC EP	
	FAV 3P	FAV 2Q	FAV 1P	FAV 2Q	FAV 2Pr	FAV 2Q	FAV 2Q	FAV 1P	FAV 1Q	FAV 2Qr

SEAFORD TOWN

Founded: 1888 **Nickname:** The Badgers

Secretary: John Smith **(T)** 07940 511 504 **(E)** johnsmithn@btinternet.com
Chairman: Bob Thomsett
Ground: The Crouch, Bramber Road, Seaford BN25 1AG **(T)** 01323 892 221
Colours(change): All red (Yellow/black/yellow)

HONOURS: FA Comps: None **League:** Lewes 1907-08.
Sussex County Division Three 1985-86, Division Two 1988-89, 2005-06.

10 YEAR RECORD

	07-08	08-09	09-10	10-11	11-12	12-13	13-14	14-15	15-16	16-17
	SxC2 15	SxC2 7	SxC2 10	SxC2 5	SxC2 17	SxC2 12	SxC2 17	SxC2 15	SC1 16	SC1 13
		FAV 2Q			FAV 1P	FAV 2Q	FAV 1Q	FAV 2Q	FAV 1Q	FAV 2Q

SELSEY

Founded: 1903 **Nickname:** Blues

Secretary: Paul Senior **(T)** 07871 060 549 **(E)** selseyfootballclub@yahoo.com
Chairman: David Lee
Ground: The Bunn Leisure Stadium, High Street, Selsey, Chichester, PO20 0QH **(T)** 01243 603 420 **Capacity:** 1,000
Colours(change): All blue (All yellow).

HONOURS: FA Comps: None **League:** West Sussex Division One 1938-39, 54-55, 56-57, 57-58, 58-59, 60-61.
Sussex County Division Two 1963-64, 75-76.

10 YEAR RECORD

	07-08	08-09	09-10	10-11	11-12	12-13	13-14	14-15	15-16	16-17
	SxC1 15	SxC1 10	SxC1 11	SxC1 17	SxC1 12	SxC1 18	SxC1 17	SxC1 20	SC1 13	SC1 7
	FAC 1Q	FAC P	FAC 2Q	FAC EP	FAC P	FAC EP	FAC EP	FAC EP	FAC EP	
	FAV 1Q	FAV 3P	FAV 2Q	FAV 1Q	FAV 1Q	FAV 1Q	FAV 1Q	FAV 1Q	FAV 2Q	FAV 2Q

SOUTHWICK

Founded: 1882 **Nickname:** The Wickers

Secretary: Jackie Royston **(T)** 07958 656 530 **(E)** jackieroyston@gmail.com
Chairman: Alan Petkin
Ground: Old Barn Way, Southwick BN42 4NT **(T)** 01273 701 010
Colours(change): Red & black/black/black (Yellow & black/yellow/yellow)

HONOURS: FA Comps: None **League:** West Sussex Senior 1896-97, 97-98. Sussex County Div.1 25-26, 27-28, 29
-30, 47-48, 68-69, 74-75, Div.2 2000-01, Div.3 14-15. Isthmian D2S 1985-86.

10 YEAR RECORD

	07-08	08-09	09-10	10-11	11-12	12-13	13-14	14-15	15-16	16-17
	SxC2 14	SxC2 11	SxC2 16	SxC2 12	SxC2 8	SxC2 14	SxC3 9	SxC3 1	SC1 5	SC1 11
		FAC EPr	FAC Pr	FAC EP						
	FAV 2Q	FAV 1Qr	FAV 1Q	FAV 2Q		FAV 1Q	FAV 2Q	FAV 2Q	FAV 1Q	FAV 1Q

ST. FRANCIS RANGERS

Founded: 2002 **Nickname:** Saints/Rangers

Secretary: John Goss **(T)** 07748 785 240 **(E)** j.goss@yahoo.co.uk
Chairman: Robert Ward **Prog Ed:** John Goss
Ground: Colwell Ground, Princess Royal Hospital, Lewes Rd, Haywards Hth RH16 4EX **(T)** 01444 474 021 **Capacity:** 1,000
Colours(change): Black & white/black/black (Yellow/white/yellow)

HONOURS: FA Comps: None **League:** None

10 YEAR RECORD

	07-08	08-09	09-10	10-11	11-12	12-13	13-14	14-15	15-16	16-17
	SxC1 14	SxC1 12	SxC1 16	SxC1 19	SxC1 19	SxC1 11	SxC1 10	SxC1 13	SCP 20	SC1 17
			FAC EP	FAC EP	FAC EP	FAC EP	FAC EP	FAC P	FAC EP	FAC EP
		FAV 2P	FAV 1Q	FAV 1P	FAV 1Q	FAV 1P	FAV 1Q	FAV 2Q	FAV 2Q	FAV 1Q

STEYNING TOWN

Founded: 1892   Nickname: The Barrowmen

Secretary: Mark Munns   **(T)** 07769 167 375   **(E)** mark@frmeclad.com
Chairman: Ian Nichols
Ground: The Shooting Field, Steyning, West Sussex BN44 3RQ   **(T)** 01903 814 601
Colours(change): Red & white/red/red (All blue)
HONOURS: FA Comps: None   **League:** Brighton, H&D Division Two 1933-34, 38-39.
Sussex County Division Two 1977-78, Division One 1984-85, 85-86.

10 YEAR RECORD

07-08		08-09		09-10		10-11		11-12		12-13		13-14		14-15		15-16		16-17	
SxC2	11	SxC2	13	SxC2	17	SxC2	16	SxC2	13	SxC2	10	SxC2	11	SxC2	10	SC1	10	SC1	6
		FAV	1Q					FAV	1Q	FAV	1Q	FAV	1Q	FAV	2Q	FAV	2P	FAV	1Q

STORRINGTON

Founded: 1920   Nickname: The Swans

Secretary: Keith Dalmon   **(T)** 07889 367 956   **(E)** keithdalmon@btinternet.com
Chairman: Nigel Dyer
Ground: Recreation Ground, Pulborough Road, Storrington RH20 4HJ   **(T)** 01903 745 860
Colours(change): All blue (All maroon)
HONOURS: FA Comps: None   **League:** Sussex County Division Three 2004-05.

10 YEAR RECORD

07-08		08-09		09-10		10-11		11-12		12-13		13-14		14-15		15-16		16-17	
SxC2	16	SxC2	12	SxC2	7	SxC2	8	SxC2	9	SxC2	10	SxC2	15	SxC2	14	SC1	4	SC1	12

WICK

Founded: 2013   Nickname:

Secretary: Dave Usher   **(T)** 07825 553 909   **(E)** wickfootballclub@outlook.com
Chairman: Dave Usher
Ground: Crabtree Park, Coomes Way, Wick, Littlehampton, W Sussex BN17 7LS   **(T)** 01903 713 535   **Capacity:** 1,000
Colours(change): Red & black/black/red (Yellow/black/black).
HONOURS: FA Comps: None   **League:** Sussex County Division Two 1981-82, 85-86, 89-90, 93-94.

10 YEAR RECORD

07-08		08-09		09-10		10-11		11-12		12-13		13-14		14-15		15-16		16-17	
SxC1	5	SxC1	4	SxC1	4	SxC1	15	SxC1	14	SxC1	16	SxC2	6	SxC2	3	SCP	16	SCP	19
FAC	EPr	FAC	EP	FAC	P	FAC	EP	FAC	EP									FAC	EP
FAV	1P	FAV	1Q	FAV	1P	FAV	1P	FAV	1Q	FAV	2Q							FAV	1P

Southern Combination Division Two

ALFOLD	Recreation Ground, Dunsfold Road, Alfold, Surrey GU6 8JB	07836 553 594
BOSHAM	Recreation Ground, Walton Lane, Bosham, West Sussex PO10 8QF	01243 681 279
CLYMPING	Clymping Village Hall, Clymping, Littlehampton BN17 5GW	07951 196 784
COWFOLD	The Sports Ground, Bolney Road, Cowfold, West Sussex RH13 8AA	07742 281 989
FERRING	The Glebelands, Ferring, West Sussex BN12 5JL	01903 243 618
JARVIS BROOK	Limekiln Playing Fields, Palesgate Lane, Crowborough TN6 3HG	07968 561 226
LANCING UNITED	Croshaw Recreation Ground, Boundstone Lane, Lancing, West Sussex BN15 9LH	07827 356 118
MONTPELLIER VILLA	Falmer Sports Complex, University of Sussex, Pavillion Rd, Brighton BN1 9PJ	07988 692 283
ROFFEY	Bartholomew Way, Horsham RH12 5JL	07763 973 101
ROTTINGDEAN VILLAGE	Rottingdean Sports Centre, Falmer Road, Rottingdean BN2 7DA	01273 306 436
RUSTINGTON	Recreation Ground, Jubilee Avenue, Rustington BN16 3NB	07966 217 603
SIDLESHAM	Recreation Ground, Selsey Road Sidlesham Nr Chichester PO20 7RD	07887 981 257
UPPER BEEDING	Memorial Playing Fields, High Street, Upper Beeding BN44 3WN	07710 900 629
WESTFIELD	The Parish Field, Main Road, Westfield TN35 4SB	07928 176 658
WORTHING TOWN LEISURE	Palatine Park, Palatine Road, Worthing, Sussex BN12 6JN	07710 768 744

SOUTHERN COUNTIES EAST LEAGUE

Sponsored by: None
Founded: As the Kent League in 1966

Recent Champions: 2014: Whyteleafe
2015: Phoenix Sports **2016:** Greenwich Borough

PREMIER DIVISION	P	W	D	L	F	A	GD	Pts
1 Ashford United	38	30	2	6	119	39	80	92
2 Crowborough Athletic	38	28	6	4	96	36	60	90
3 Sevenoaks Town	38	27	3	8	90	35	55	84
4 Cray Valley PM	38	24	3	11	91	57	34	75
5 Whitstable Town	38	22	3	13	82	51	31	69
6 Sheppey United	38	20	8	10	75	55	20	68
7 AFC Croydon Athletic	38	18	11	9	75	62	13	65
8 Hollands & Blair	38	18	8	12	68	55	13	62
9 Canterbury City	38	17	7	14	66	42	24	58
10 Corinthian	38	15	7	16	68	64	4	52
11 Croydon	38	15	3	20	66	83	-17	48
12 Bearsted	38	14	5	19	63	73	-10	47
13 Deal Town	38	11	13	14	66	74	-8	46
14 Rochester United	38	9	10	19	47	79	-32	37
15 Tunbridge Wells	38	10	7	21	41	74	-33	37
16 Lordswood	38	9	7	22	54	101	-47	34
17 Erith Town	38	9	4	25	50	116	-66	31
18 Beckenham Town	38	8	5	25	38	76	-38	29
19 Fisher	38	7	7	24	50	86	-36	28
20 Erith & Belvedere	38	7	5	26	47	94	-47	26

DIVISION ONE	P	W	D	L	F	A	GD	Pts
1 Glebe	36	29	5	2	102	24	78	92
2 Rusthall	36	24	8	4	93	34	59	80
3 Sutton Athletic	36	23	5	8	122	50	72	74
4 Kent Football United	36	24	2	10	85	40	45	71*
5 K Sports	36	20	8	8	97	63	34	68
6 Holmesdale	36	19	6	11	68	53	15	63
7 Bridon Ropes	36	15	10	11	60	59	1	55
8 Snodland Town	36	16	3	17	59	73	-14	51
9 Lydd Town	36	14	7	15	68	79	-11	49
10 Sporting Club Thamesmead	36	12	8	16	60	70	-10	44
11 FC Elmstead	36	11	10	15	55	64	-9	43
12 Forest Hill Park	36	12	7	17	50	75	-25	43
13 Phoenix Sports Reserves	36	13	4	19	65	93	-28	43
14 Orpington	36	10	10	16	45	58	-13	40
15 Eltham Palace	36	10	9	17	65	82	-17	39
16 Gravesham Borough	36	8	8	20	62	84	-22	32
17 Meridian VP	36	9	2	25	45	78	-33	29
18 Crockenhill	36	6	8	22	37	91	-54	26
19 Lewisham Borough	36	4	6	26	45	113	-68	18

CLUB MOVEMENTS

Premier Division - In: Chatham Town (R - Isth D1S).
Out: Ashford United (P - Isth D1S).
Division One - In: Punjab United (P - Kent County), Stansfeld (NC - from Eltham Palace).
Out: Eltham Palace (NC - to Stansfeld), Orpington (W - Kent County).

PREMIER DIVISION		1	2	3	4	5	6	7	8	9	10	11	12	13	14	15	16	17	18	19	20
1	AFC Croydon Athletic		2-2	3-0	2-0	0-4	0-0	4-1	1-1	3-6	2-2	3-0	5-1	2-1	1-3	4-1	1-1	0-4	2-1	1-1	0-3
2	Ashford United	3-3		0-1	4-1	1-0	4-1	2-0	3-1	3-2	4-0	2-1	4-1	3-1	3-1	4-0	7-0	3-2	1-2	2-0	4-2
3	Bearsted	1-5	1-0		2-0	1-0	1-5	0-3	2-3	1-1	1-3	7-1	4-1	3-3	0-1	3-4	2-1	1-2	1-1	3-1	1-2
4	Beckenham Town	1-3	0-2	2-3		0-4	1-0	0-5	1-3	1-3	3-1	2-4	0-1	2-0	0-2	3-0	1-3	1-2	0-2	0-0	0-2
5	Canterbury City	0-1	1-3	0-1	3-0		1-1	4-0	0-0	3-0	3-3	2-1	2-1	2-0	1-1	1-3	0-2	0-2	0-1	5-0	0-1
6	Corinthian	0-2	2-3	2-0	3-0	1-3		3-0	1-3	1-3	1-1	3-1	5-0	3-0	4-4	1-3	3-3	0-4	0-1	5-2	2-2
7	Cray Valley PM	3-0	2-5	2-1	3-3	2-0	2-1		0-3	1-1	5-1	3-2	0-1	2-1	3-2	4-1	1-2	2-0	2-1	2-1	4-1
8	Crowborough Athletic	1-2	2-0	2-1	1-0	4-2	7-1	0-1		0-1	1-1	1-0	2-1	6-1	2-0	2-0	2-0	2-1	3-2	3-0	3-1
9	Croydon	0-3	0-4	4-2	2-1	1-2	1-3	0-3	0-2		1-2	1-0	6-0	3-1	1-0	3-1	3-4	1-6	2-3	2-0	2-2
10	Deal Town	2-2	1-4	3-1	2-2	1-0	1-3	1-1	1-6	5-2		6-0	2-4	2-1	1-2	0-0	0-0	1-0	3-4	4-1	0-2
11	Erith & Belvedere	0-2	2-6	1-2	0-1	1-3	2-1	4-2	0-3	2-6	2-2		4-0	1-1	1-3	1-0	0-0	0-2	0-3	3-2	2-3
12	Erith Town	4-1	2-3	1-2	0-3	1-2	2-1	0-7	1-7	3-2	1-5	2-1		2-3	1-3	3-3	4-2	1-3	0-4	2-2	1-5
13	Fisher	1-1	0-5	0-3	2-0	0-0	3-3	0-3	2-6	1-0	2-3	3-0	10-1		3-4	2-0	0-0	0-2	1-3	1-3	0-2
14	Hollands & Blair	1-2	0-3	1-1	1-1	1-3	1-0	2-4	0-0	3-0	3-0	2-1	2-2	1-3		4-0	2-1	1-0	0-1	0-1	1-0
15	Lordswood	3-3	0-7	1-4	1-3	1-4	0-2	0-7	2-4	1-3	1-1	4-4	4-1	4-1	0-3		2-1	1-1	2-2	3-0	2-1
16	Rochester United	3-0	0-8	1-0	0-1	0-5	0-1	1-4	1-1	3-1	2-2	1-0	0-0	0-4	2-1		3-3	1-0	0-1	3-4	
17	Sevenoaks Town	2-0	4-0	3-2	3-1	4-1	0-1	4-1	1-1	4-0	2-1	5-1	2-0	2-0	5-1	4-0	1-4		2-0	2-0	0-2
18	Sheppey United	1-3	1-0	3-3	2-0	1-1	0-1	3-4	2-3	1-2	1-1	2-2	1-1	3-1	2-2	3-2	3-1	1-2		2-0	1-0
19	Tunbridge Wells	1-3	0-5	2-1	2-2	0-0	1-2	1-2	1-2	1-0	2-1	0-2	3-1	2-0	2-2	1-2	2-1	0-2	3-5		1-0
20	Whitstable Town	3-0	0-2	5-0	3-1	1-4	2-1	1-0	2-3	7-0	2-0	3-0	1-0	4-1	2-4	4-1	2-0	1-2	3-4	1-1	

SOUTHERN COUNTIES EAST LEAGUE - STEP 5/6

LEAGUE CHALLENGE CUP

ROUND 1

Fisher	v	Snodland Town	4-0
Holmesdale	v	Meridian VP	1-0
FC Elmstead	v	Orpington	2-3
Croydon	v	Whitstable Town	0-3
Bearsted	v	Lordswood	4-1
Rusthall	v	Rochester United	1-3
Deal Town	v	Cray Valley PM	2-2, 3-4p

ROUND 2

Fisher	v	Sheppey United	3-4
Holmesdale	v	Tunbridge Wells	3-1
Phoenix Sports Reserves	v	AFC Croydon Athletic	0-1
Hollands & Blair	v	K Sports	2-4
Erith & Belvedere	v	Sporting Club Thamesmead	2-0
Sutton Athletic	v	Glebe	2-1
Corinthian	v	Orpington	7-0
Whitstable Town	v	Kent Football United	1-0
Bridon Ropes	v	Crockenhill	4-1
Crowborough Athletic	v	Eltham Palace	4-1
Beckenham Town	v	Sevenoaks Town	0-2
Gravesham Borough	v	Forest Hill Park	1-0
Bearsted	v	Lydd Town	4-3
Rochester United	v	Cray Valley PM	0-2
Canterbury City	v	Erith Town	4-1
Lewisham Borough	v	Ashford United	0-6

ROUND 3

Sheppey United	v	Holmesdale	1-1, 3-1p
AFC Croydon Athletic	v	K Sports	0-2
Erith & Belvederev	v	Sutton Athletic	2-3
Corinthian	v	Whitstable Town	0-1
Bridon Ropes	v	Crowborough Athletic	1-2
Sevenoaks Town	v	Gravesham Borough	4-0
Bearsted	v	Cray Valley PM	0-4
Canterbury City	v	Ashford United	1-4

QUARTER FINALS

Sheppey United	v	K Sports	2-0
Sutton Athletic	v	Whitstable Town	1-4
Crowborough Athletic	v	Sevenoaks Town	2-3
Cray Valley PM	v	Ashford United	0-2

SEMI FINALS (over two legs)

Sheppey United	v	Whitstable Town	2-2
Whitstable Town	v	Sheppey United	0-2
Sevenoaks Town	v	Ashford United	1-1
Ashford United	v	Sevenoaks Town	0-3

FINAL

Sheppey United	v	Sevenoaks Town	0-2

DIVISION ONE	1	2	3	4	5	6	7	8	9	10	11	12	13	14	15	16	17	18	19
1 Bridon Ropes		1-3	3-2	3-2	1-1	0-0	4-2	0-4	1-2	0-1	2-2	1-0	4-0	1-0	2-2	2-2	5-4	1-0	0-6
2 Crockenhill	0-4		2-2	2-0	1-2	1-3	1-5	1-1	3-3	1-0	0-2	0-3	1-2	0-0	0-6	0-1	0-0		1-4
3 Eltham Palace	1-1	5-2		1-1	0-0	0-4	3-5	0-0	0-6	1-5	2-2	2-2	4-2	3-1	5-0	1-4	1-1	1-2	3-5
4 FC Elmstead	1-2	2-2	3-2		2-1	1-3	2-1	2-2	1-1	0-2	4-1	0-1	1-0	2-2	1-0	0-1	0-1	2-2	1-6
5 Forest Hill Park	3-3	1-3	1-0	1-2		0-2	2-1	1-0	2-2	1-2	3-1	0-1	2-0	2-0	3-3	0-1	2-0	3-2	1-6
6 Glebe	4-1	6-1	3-0	1-2	3-0		4-0	1-1	2-1	4-0	4-1	5-0	4-0	3-1	3-0	0-0	4-0	1-2	2-1
7 Gravesham Borough	0-1	5-1	0-1	2-2	1-1	1-3		0-1	2-2	0-2	2-2	2-4	0-0	2-3	1-0	1-5	1-1	1-4	0-3
8 Holmesdale	2-0	3-0	0-4	2-2	2-1	0-3	2-1		2-0	1-3	8-1	1-3	2-1	1-1	5-0	1-0	2-1	5-3	0-1
9 K Sports	1-1	6-3	1-0	4-1	4-1	0-2	4-1	3-1		2-1	6-2	6-3	2-1	4-2	3-4	1-4	3-0	4-4	2-5
10 Kent Football United	3-0	1-1	5-1	2-1	6-1	0-2	5-0	3-4	0-1		2-1	5-2	2-0	0-1	3-0	2-3	1-0	2-2	0-2
11 Lewisham Borough	0-4	1-2	2-7	1-0	2-2	1-6	4-3	0-2	2-7	2-4		3-2	1-2	3-2	2-3	2-4	1-2	0-0	1-5
12 Lydd Town	1-3	4-0	1-3	3-2	0-1	1-1	2-0	3-2	0-3	1-2	3-1		3-5	3-2	2-1	2-2	5-2	3-3	2-1
13 Meridian VP	0-1	2-0	2-3	2-3	0-1	1-4	1-7	1-2	0-4	0-2	0-0	3-0		4-0	3-5	0-1	0-3	0-1	0-4
14 Orpington	0-0	1-0	2-2	2-2	4-1	1-3	0-0	0-1	3-0	0-2	1-0	2-2	0-2		0-1	0-0	0-3	3-0	1-1
15 Phoenix Sports Reserves	4-3	6-1	3-2	0-4	3-5	2-3	3-4	0-2	0-4	1-7	2-0	5-2	4-1	1-1		0-5	5-1	0-2	2-6
16 Rusthall	1-1	2-0	1-2	3-1	6-1	1-1	2-2	3-1	6-1	2-1	2-1	2-2	1-0	4-0	0-2		3-0	6-0	4-3
17 Snodland Town	2-1	1-0	3-0	2-0	3-0	0-2	2-3	1-2	1-1	0-3	4-0	4-1	4-3	4-3	4-1	1-3		2-1	1-6
18 Sporting Club Thamesmead	3-1	2-2	2-0	0-2	4-2	2-4	2-4	3-2	0-1	0-2	5-2	3-1	2-3	0-2	0-1	0-3	1-0		1-2
19 Sutton Athletic	0-2	4-1	5-1	3-3	4-1	1-2	5-2	6-1	2-2	2-4	5-0	1-1	1-3	0-2	3-1	2-0	9-0	2-2	

AFC CROYDON ATHLETIC

Founded: 2012   Nickname: The Rams

Secretary: Peter Smith   **(T)** 07907 588 496   **(E)** secretary@afccroydonathletic.co.uk
Chairman: Paul Smith   **Manager:** Kevin Raynor   **Prog Ed:** Peter Smith
Ground: Mayfield Stadium, off Mayfield Road, Thornton Heath CR7 6DN   **(T)** 020 8689 5322
Capacity: 3,000 **Seats:** 301   **Covered:** 660   **Midweek Matchday:** Wednesday   **Clubhouse:** Yes   **Shop:** Yes

Colours(change): All maroon (Yellow/dark blue/yellow)
Previous Names: None
Previous Leagues: Combined Counties 2012-15.

HONOURS: FA Comps: None
League: None

10 YEAR RECORD

07-08	08-09	09-10	10-11	11-12	12-13		13-14		14-15		15-16		16-17	
					CC1	8	CC1	7	CC1	2	SCE	11	SCEP	7
							FAC	EP	FAC	EP	FAC	EP	FAC	EP
					FAV	1P	FAV	1P	FAV	2Q	FAV	1Pr	FAV	2Q

BEARSTED

Founded: 1895   Nickname: The Bears

Secretary: Roy Benton   **(T)** 07849 809 875   **(E)** benton951@aol.com
Chairman: Duncan Andrews   **Manager:** Kevin Stevens   **Prog Ed:** Duncan Andrews
Ground: Otham Sports Club, Honey Lane, Otham, Maidstone ME15 8RG   **(T)** 07860 360 280
Capacity: **Seats:** Yes   **Covered:** Yes   **Midweek Matchday:** Tuesday   **Clubhouse:** Yes

Colours(change): White/blue/blue (All yellow)
Previous Names: None
Previous Leagues: Maidstone & District. Kent County 1982-2011. Kent Invicta (Founder Member) 2011-16.

HONOURS: FA Comps: None
League: Maidstone & District Div.6 1961-62, Div.3 73-74, Div.2 74-75, Div.1 77-78, Premier 79-80, 80-81, 81-82.

10 YEAR RECORD | Kent County WD2 82-83, WD1 83-84, WPrem 87-87, WSen 87-88, D1W 96-97, Prem 2000-01, 01-02. Kent Invicta 2015-16.

07-08		08-09		09-10		10-11		11-12		12-13		13-14		14-15		15-16		16-17	
KC P	8	KC P	6	KC P	8	KC P	8	K_lv	7	K_lv	4	K_lv	6	K_lv	2	K_lv	1	SCEP	12
																		FAV	1Q

BECKENHAM TOWN

Founded: 1887   Nickname: Reds

Secretary: Peter Palmer   **(T)** 07774 728 758   **(E)** peterpalmer3@sky.com
Chairman: Paul Fairs   **Manager:** Jason Huntley   **Prog Ed:** Phil English
Ground: Eden Park Avenue, Beckenham Kent BR3 3JL   **(T)** 07774 728 758
Capacity: 4,000 **Seats:** 120   **Covered:** 120   **Midweek Matchday:** Wednesday   **Clubhouse:** Yes   **Shop:** Yes

Colours(change): All red (All blue).
Previous Names: Original club folded in 1969 and reformed based on the Stanhope Rovers Junior team in 1971.
Previous Leagues: London 1923-35, 51-61. Kent County Amateur 1935-51. Aetolian 1961-64. Greater London 1964-69. South East London Amateur 1971-75. London Spartan 1975-82.
HONOURS: FA Comps: None
League: London Division One 1927-28.

10 YEAR RECORD

07-08		08-09		09-10		10-11		11-12		12-13		13-14		14-15		15-16		16-17	
Kent P	3	Kent P	15	Kent P	4	Kent P	10	Kent P	6	Kent P	11	SCE	8	SCE	9	SCE	12	SCEP	18
						FAC	2Q	FAC	2Qr	FAC	1Q	FAC	EP	FAC	EP	FAC	P	FAC	P
				FAV	3P	FAV	3P	FAV	1P	FAV	1P	FAV	3P	FAV	2Q	FAV	2P	FAV	1P

CANTERBURY CITY

Founded: 1904   Nickname:

Secretary: Martyn Sexton   **(T)** 07738 933 683   **(E)** mjsexton@btinternet.com
Chairman: Tim Clark   **Manager:** Ben Smith   **Prog Ed:** Martyn Sexton
Ground: Deal Town FC, The Charles Sportsground, St Leonards Road, Deal CT14 9AU   **(T)** 01304 375 623
Capacity: 2,500 **Seats:** 180   **Covered:** 180   **Midweek Matchday:** Wednesday   **Clubhouse:** Yes   **Shop:** Yes

Colours(change): Burgundy/burgundy/white (All green)
Previous Names: None
Previous Leagues: Kent 1947-59, 94-01, Metropolitan 1959-60, Southern 1960-94, Kent County 2007-11.

HONOURS: FA Comps: None
League: Kent County Division Two East 2007-08, One East 08-09.

10 YEAR RECORD

07-08		08-09		09-10		10-11		11-12		12-13		13-14		14-15		15-16		16-17	
KC2E	1	KC1E	1	KC P	5	KC P	2	Kent P	9	Kent P	9	SCE	12	SCE	12	SCE	8	SCEP	9
												FAC	EP	FAC	P	FAC	P	FAC	Pr
										FAV	1P	FAV	1Q	FAV	1Q	FAV	3P	FAV	2P

CHATHAM TOWN
Founded: 1882   Nickname: Chats

Secretary: Andy Bonneywell   **(T)** 07548 206 955   **(E)** andybon@talktalk.net
Chairman: Kevin Hake   **Manager:** Paul Piggott   **Prog Ed:** Sam Searle
Ground: Maidstone Road Sports Ground, Maidstone Road, Chatham ME4 6LR   **(T)** 01634 812 194
Capacity: 2,000 **Seats:** 600 **Covered:** 600 **Midweek Matchday:** Tuesday **Clubhouse:** Yes **Shop:** Yes

Colours(change): All red & black (All blue & black)
Previous Names: Chatham FC 1882-1974, Medway FC 1974-79
Previous Leagues: Southern 1894-1900, 1920-21, 27-29, 83-88, 2001-06, Kent 1894-96, 1901-1905, 29-59, 68-83, 88-2001, Aetolian 1959-64, Metropolitan 1964-68, ISthmian 2006-17.
HONOURS: FA Comps: None
League: Kent 1894-95, 1903-04, 04-05, 71-72, 73-74, 75-76, 76-77, 79-80, 2000-01. Aetolian 1963-64.

10 YEAR RECORD

07-08	08-09	09-10	10-11	11-12	12-13	13-14	14-15	15-16	16-17
Isth1S 18	Isth1N 10	Isth1S 17	Isth1S 21	Isth1N 15	Isth1N 13	Isth1N 12	Isth1N 21	Isth1S 19	Isth1S 22
FAC 1Q	FAC 1Q	FAC 1Qr	FAC P	FAC 1Q	FAC 1Q	FAC 4Q	FAC P	FAC 2Q	FAC Pr
FAT 1Q	FAT 1Q	FAT P	FAT P	FAT P	FAT 1Q	FAT 2Q	FAT 1Qr	FAT 1Q	FAT P

CORINTHIAN
Founded: 1972   Nickname: The Hoops

Secretary: Sue Billings   **(T)** 07734 855 554   **(E)** corinthians@billingsgroup.com
Chairman: R J Billings   **Manager:** Michael Golding
Ground: Gay Dawn Farm, Valley Road, Longfield DA3 8LY   **(T)** 01474 573 118
Capacity: **Seats:** Yes **Covered:** Yes **Midweek Matchday:** Tuesday **Clubhouse:** Yes

Colours(change): Green & white hoops/white/white (Yellow/green/green)
Previous Names: Welling United Reserves > 2009.
Previous Leagues: Southern 1985-91.

HONOURS: FA Comps: None
League: Southern Counties East 2003-04.

10 YEAR RECORD

07-08	08-09	09-10	10-11	11-12	12-13	13-14	14-15	15-16	16-17
	Kent 2 6	Kent P 14	Kent P 12	Kent P 7	Kent P 4	SCE 5	SCE 6	SCE 6	SCEP 10
				FAC P	FAC P	FAC P	FAC EP	FAC P	FAC EP
			FAV 1P	FAV 2Q	FAV 1Q	FAV 1P	FAV 1P	FAV 1P	FAV 4P

CRAY VALLEY PAPER MILLS
Founded: 1919   Nickname: Millers

Secretary: Jason Taylor   **(T)** 07834 546 213   **(E)** jtaylor171.209@lgflmail.org
Chairman: Frank May   **Prog Ed:** Dave Wilson
Ground: Badgers Sports, Middle Park Avenue, Eltham SE9 5HT   **(T)** 07834 546 213
Capacity: 1,000 **Seats:** 100 **Covered:** Yes **Midweek Matchday:** Wednesday **Clubhouse:** Yes

Colours(change): Green & white/black/black (All sky blue).
Previous Names: None
Previous Leagues: Spartan 1991-97, Spartan South Midlands 1997-98, London Intermediate 1998-01, Kent County 2001-11.

HONOURS: FA Comps: None
League: Sidcup & Kent Division Two 1919-20. South Kent County Division Three (Western) 1933-37, Division One 2002 -03, Premier Division 2004-05. London Alliance Premier Division 1980-81.

10 YEAR RECORD

07-08	08-09	09-10	10-11	11-12	12-13	13-14	14-15	15-16	16-17
KC P 9	KC P 5	KC P 6	KC P 3	Kent P 11	Kent P 8	SCE 7	SCE 7	SCE 10	SCEP 4
						FAC P	FAC EP	FAC P	FAC P
					FAV 1Q	FAV 2Pr	FAV 2Q	FAV 1P	FAV 1Q

CROWBOROUGH ATHLETIC
Founded: 1894   Nickname: The Crows

Secretary: Eric Gillett   **(T)** 07879 434 467   **(E)** emgillett@hotmail.co.uk
Chairman: Simon Colbran   **Manager:** Sean Muggeridge   **Prog Ed:** Malcolm Boyes
Ground: Crowborough Co. Stadium, Alderbrook Rec, Fermor Road, TN6 3DJ   **(T)** 07879 434 467
Capacity: 2,000 **Seats:** 150 **Covered:** 150 **Midweek Matchday:** Tuesday **Clubhouse:** Yes

Colours(change): Navy blue/sky blue/navy blue (All red).
Previous Names:
Previous Leagues: Sussex County 1974-2008. Isthmian 2008-09. Sussex County 2009-14.

HONOURS: FA Comps: None
League: Sussex County Division Two 1992-93, 2004-05, Division Three 2003-04, Division One 2007-08.

10 YEAR RECORD

07-08	08-09	09-10	10-11	11-12	12-13	13-14	14-15	15-16	16-17
SxC1 1	Isth1S 22	SxC1 18	SxC1 12	SxC1 13	SxC1 15	SxC1 5	SCE 10	SCE 7	SCEP 2
FAC 2Q	FAC 3Qr	FAC EPr	FAC EP	FAC EP	FAC P	FAC EPr	FAC EPr	FAC EPr	FAC EP
FAV 5P	FAT 1Q	FAV 2P	FAV 1Q	FAV 1Q	FAV 1Q	FAV 2P	FAV 1Q	FAV 1Q	FAV 5P

CROYDON
Founded: 1953   Nickname: The Trams

Secretary: Judy Wallis   **(T)** 07870 588 886   **(E)** judy@kinetic-foundation.org.uk
Chairman: Martin Burr   **Manager:** Harry Hudson   **Prog Ed:** Simon Hawkins
Ground: Croydon Sports Arena, Albert Road, South Norwood SE25 4QL   **(T)** 02086 545524 (CH-0208 6548555)
Capacity: 8,000 **Seats:** 500   **Covered:** 1,000   **Midweek Matchday:** Wednesday   **Clubhouse:** Yes   **Shop:** Yes

Colours(change): Sky & navy blue/sky & navy/sky (Yellow/black/black)
Previous Names: Croydon Amateurs 1953-73.
Previous Leagues: Surrey Senior 1953-63. Spartan 1963-64. Athenian 1964-74. Isthmian1974- 2006. Kent 2006-09. Combined Counties 2009-14.

HONOURS: FA Comps: None
League: Spartan 1963-64. Athenian Division Two 1965-66. Isthmian Division One 1999-00.

10 YEAR RECORD
07-08	08-09	09-10	10-11	11-12	12-13	13-14	14-15	15-16	16-17
Kent P 12	Kent P 9	CCP 16	CCP 20	CCP 16	CCP 14	CCP 13	SCE 18	SCE 18	SCEP 11
FAC 1Qr	FAC P	FAC EP	FAC P	FAC EP	FAC EP	FAC P	FAC 1Q	FAC 2Q	FAC Pr
FAV 1P	FAV 4P	FAV 2P	FAV 1P	FAV 1P	FAV 1Q	FAV 2Q	FAV 1Qr	FAV 1P	FAV 4P

DEAL TOWN
Founded: 1908   Nickname: The Hoops

Secretary: Fiona Richards   **(T)** 07949 412 467   **(E)** secretary@dealtownfc.co.uk
Chairman: David Chmura   **Manager:** Derek Hares   **Prog Ed:** Danielle Johnson
Ground: Charles Sports Ground, St Leonards Road, Deal CT14 9AU   **(T)** 01304 375 623
Capacity: 2,500 **Seats:** 180   **Covered:** 180   **Midweek Matchday:** Tuesday   **Clubhouse:** Yes   **Shop:** Yes

Colours(change): Black & white/black/white (All red).
Previous Names: Deal Cinque Ports FC > 1920
Previous Leagues: Thanet. East Kent. Kent. Aetolian. Southern. Greater London.

HONOURS: FA Comps: FA Vase 1999-2000
League: Kent 1953-54. Southern Counties East 1999-2000.

10 YEAR RECORD
07-08	08-09	09-10	10-11	11-12	12-13	13-14	14-15	15-16	16-17
Kent P 9	Kent P 12	Kent P 9	Kent P 11	Kent P 15	Kent P 12	SCE 13	SCE 13	SCE 9	SCEP 13
FAC 1Qr	FAC EPr	FAC 1Qr	FAC P	FAC P	FAC EP	FAC P	FAC Pr	FAC 2Q	FAC EP
FAV 2P	FAV 2Q	FAV 1Q	FAV 1Q	FAV 2P	FAV 2P	FAV 1Q	FAV 1Q	FAV 2P	FAV 2Qr

ERITH TOWN
Founded: 1959   Nickname: The Dockers

Secretary: Paul Dale   **(T)** 07877 766 794   **(E)** secretary@erithtown.co.uk
Chairman: Ian Burrell   **Manager:** Adam Woodward   **Prog Ed:** Ian Burrell
Ground: Oakwood, Old Road, Crayford Kent DA1 4DN   **(T)** 07877 766 794
Capacity: **Seats:** Yes   **Covered:** Yes   **Midweek Matchday:** Wednesday   **Clubhouse:** Yes

Colours(change): Red & black stripe/black/black. (Yellow/blue/yellow).
Previous Names: Woolwich Town 1959-89 and 1990-97.
Previous Leagues: London Metropolitan Sunday. London Spartan.

HONOURS: FA Comps: None
League: London Metropolitan Sunday Senior Section 1965-66, 70-71, 74-75.

10 YEAR RECORD
07-08	08-09	09-10	10-11	11-12	12-13	13-14	14-15	15-16	16-17
Kent P 5	Kent P 7	Kent P 12	Kent P 8	Kent P 4	Kent P 3	SCE 3	SCE 19	SCE 13	SCEP 17
FAC 2Q	FAC P	FAC 1Qr	FAC 2Q	FAC 2Q	FAC EP	FAC P	FAC EP	FAC P	FAC P
FAV 2Q	FAV 2Q	FAV 1P	FAV 2Q	FAV 2P	FAV 2P	FAV 3P	FAV 2P	FAV 2Q	FAV 1Q

GLEBE
Founded: 2013   Nickname:

Secretary: Nikola Curtis   **(T)** 07875 036 907   **(E)** glebefc@aol.com
Chairman: Rocky McMillan   **Manager:** Ben Young   **Prog Ed:** Grace McMillan
Ground: Foxbury Avenue, Chislehurst, Bromley BR7 6SD   **(T)** 07903 274 178
Capacity: 1,200 **Seats:** Yes   **Covered:** Yes   **Midweek Matchday:** Tuesday   **Clubhouse:** Yes

Colours(change): Red & black/black/red (All blue & grey)
Previous Names: Glebe Wickham Youth Team founded in 1995 with an adult side formed in 2013.
Previous Leagues: Kent Invicta 2013-16.

HONOURS: FA Comps: None
League: Southern Counties east Division One 2016-17.

10 YEAR RECORD
07-08	08-09	09-10	10-11	11-12	12-13	13-14	14-15	15-16	16-17
						K_lv 10	K_lv 7	K_lv 3	SCE1 1
								FAC EP	FAC EP
						FAV 2Q	FAV 1Q	FAV 1Q	FAV 3P

SOUTHERN COUNTIES EAST LEAGUE - STEP 5/6

HOLLANDS & BLAIR
Founded: 1970   Nickname: Blair

Secretary: Laurence Plummer   **(T)** 07540 841 799   **(E)** laurence.plummer@btinternet.com
Chairman: Barry Peirce   **Manager:** Bryan Greenfield   **Prog Ed:** Richard Day
Ground: Star Meadow Sports Club, Darland Avenue, Gillingham, Kent ME7 3AN   **(T)** 01634 573839
Capacity: **Seats:** Yes   **Covered:** Yes   **Midweek Matchday:** Wednesday   **Clubhouse:** Yes

Colours(change): All red (All blue)
Previous Names: Hollands & Blair United 1970-74
Previous Leagues: Rochester & District 1970-2004. Kent County 2004-11

HONOURS: FA Comps:
League: Rochester & District Premier 1989-90, 93-94, 2002-03, 03-04. Kent County Division Two Easy 2004-05, Division One East 05-06, Premier 08-9, 10-11. Kent Invicta 2013-14, 14-15.

10 YEAR RECORD									
07-08	08-09	09-10	10-11	11-12	12-13	13-14	14-15	15-16	16-17
KC P 5	KC P 1	KC P 2	KC P 1	K_lv 3	K_lv 2	K_lv 1	K_lv 1	SCE 2	SCEP 8
									FAC Pr
								FAV 2Q	FAV 1P

LORDSWOOD
Founded: 1968   Nickname: Lords

Secretary: Steve Lewis   **(T)** 07968 429 941   **(E)** slew1953@hotmail.co.uk
Chairman: Ron Constantine   **Manager:** Richard Styles   **Prog Ed:** Paul Caulfield
Ground: Martyn Grove, Northdane Way, Walderslade, ME5 8YE   **(T)** 01634 669 138
Capacity: 600   **Seats:** 123   **Covered:** 123   **Midweek Matchday:** Tuesday   **Clubhouse:** Yes

Colours(change): Orange & black/black/orange (All sky blue).
Previous Names: None.
Previous Leagues: Rochester & Dist. Kent County.

HONOURS: FA Comps: None
League: None

10 YEAR RECORD									
07-08	08-09	09-10	10-11	11-12	12-13	13-14	14-15	15-16	16-17
Kent P 16	Kent P 16	Kent P 16	Kent P 13	Kent P 12	Kent P 5	Kent P 11	SCE 15	SCE 4	SCEP 16
FAC P	FAC EPr	FAC Pr	FAC EP	FAC P	FAC Pr	FAC EP	FAC Pr	FAC EP	FAC EPr
FAV 2Q	FAV 1P	FAV 1Q	FAV 1P	FAV 1P	FAV 4P	FAV 3P	FAV 1P	FAV 3P	FAV 1P

ROCHESTER UNITED
Founded: 1982   Nickname:

Secretary: Tony Wheeler   **(T)** 07775 735 543   **(E)** tony.wheeler@yahoo.co.uk
Chairman: Lloyd Hume   **Manager:** Matt Hume   **Prog Ed:** Tony Wheeler
Ground: Rochester United Sports Ground, Rede Court Road, Strood, Kent ME2 3TU   **(T)** 07775 735 543
Capacity: **Seats:** Yes   **Covered:** Yes   **Midweek Matchday:** Wednesday   **Clubhouse:** Yes

Colours(change): Red/black/black (Grey/grey/red)
Previous Names: Templars. Bly Spartans.
Previous Leagues: Sunday Medway >1997. Rochester & District 1997-2000. Kent County 2000-2011. Founder Members of Kent Invicta 2011-12.

HONOURS: FA Comps: None
League: Rochester & District Division One 1997-98. Kent County Division One West 2007-08. Kent Invicta 2011-12.

10 YEAR RECORD									
07-08	08-09	09-10	10-11	11-12	12-13	13-14	14-15	15-16	16-17
KC1W 1	KC P 10	KC P 12	KC P 15	K_lv 1	Kent P 13	SCE 15	SCE 20	SCE 15	SCEP 14
								FAC 1Q	FAC Pr
							FAV 1P	FAV 2Q	FAV 2Q

RUSTHALL
Founded: 1899   Nickname: The Rustics

Secretary: Katie Whitmore   **(T)** 07801 296 553   **(E)** katiewhitmore13@hotmail.com
Chairman: Joe Croker   **Manager:** Steve Ashmore   **Prog Ed:** Richard Smith
Ground: Jockey Farm, Nellington Road, Rusthall, Tunbridge Wells, Kent TN4 8SH   **(T)** 07897 427 522
Capacity: **Seats:** Yes   **Covered:** Yes   **Midweek Matchday:** Wednesday   **Clubhouse:** Yes

Colours(change): Green & white stripes/green/green (Red & white stripes/red/red)
Previous Names: None
Previous Leagues: Tunbridge Wells 1899-1983. Kent County 1983-2011. Kent Invicta 2011-16.

HONOURS: FA Comps: None
League: Tunbridge Wells 1904-05, 22-23, 23-24, 24-25, 25-26, 29-30, 30-31, 34-35, 37-38, 38-39, 51-52.

10 YEAR RECORD									
07-08	08-09	09-10	10-11	11-12	12-13	13-14	14-15	15-16	16-17
KC P 6	KC P 11	KC P 7	KC P 14	K_lv 11	K_lv 12	K_lv 7	K_lv	K_lv 19	SCE1 2
									FAV 2Q

510   www.non-leagueclubdirectory.co.uk

SEVENOAKS TOWN

Founded: 1883   Nickname: Town

Secretary: Sam Lansdale   **(T)** 07809 403 688   **(E)** secretary@sevenoakstownfc.co.uk
Chairman: Paul Lansdale   **Manager:** Micky Collins   **Prog Ed:** Paul Lansdale
Ground: Greatness Park, Seal Road, Sevenoaks TN14 5BL   **(T)** 07876 444 274
Capacity: 2,000 **Seats:** 150   **Covered:** 200   **Midweek Matchday:** Tuesday   **Clubhouse:** Yes

Colours(change): Blue & black/black/black (Green & white/green/green).
Previous Names: None.
Previous Leagues: Sevenoaks League. Kent Amateur/County.

HONOURS: FA Comps: None
    League: Kent County 1984-85, 95-96, 2002-03.

10 YEAR RECORD

07-08	08-09	09-10	10-11	11-12	12-13	13-14	14-15	15-16	16-17
Kent P 11	Kent P 14	Kent P 6	Kent P 7	Kent P 14	Kent P 17	SCE 16	SCE 8	SCE 5	SCEP 3
FAC 1Q	FAC Pr	FAC Pr	FAC EP	FAC P	FAC EP	FAC EP	FAC EP	FAC EPr	FAC 2Qr
FAV 1P	FAV 2Q	FAV 1Q	FAV 1Q	FAV 2Q	FAV 1P	FAV 1P	FAV 1Q	FAV 2Q	FAV 2Q

SHEPPEY UNITED

Founded: 1890   Nickname:

Secretary: Jon Longhurst   **(T)** 07713 065 099   **(E)** jon.longhurst@bond-group.co.uk
Chairman: Matt Smith   **Manager:** Ernie Batten   **Prog Ed:** Mike Wood
Ground: Havill Stadium, Holm Park, Queenborough Road ME12 3DB   **(T)** 01795 669 547
Capacity: 1,450 **Seats:** 170   **Covered:** 470   **Midweek Matchday:** Tuesday   **Clubhouse:** Yes

Colours(change): Red & white stripes/black/black (Royal blue & white stripes/royal blue/royal blue)
Previous Names: AFC Sheppy 2007-2010. Sheppey & Sheerness United after merger 2013-14.
Previous Leagues: Kent County > 2014.

HONOURS: FA Comps: None
    League: Kent 1905-06, 06-07, 72-73, 74-75, 78-79, 94-95. Greater London Section B 1964-65.

10 YEAR RECORD

07-08	08-09	09-10	10-11	11-12	12-13	13-14	14-15	15-16	16-17
KC1E 2	KC1E 2	KC1E 11	KC1E 11	KC1E 4	KC P Exp	KC P 2	K_lv 5	K_lv 2	SCEP 6
									FAC EP
								FAV 2Q	FAV 2Q

TUNBRIDGE WELLS

Founded: 1886   Nickname: The Wells

Secretary: Phill Allcorn   **(T)** 07900 243 508   **(E)** secretary@twfcexec.com
Chairman: Scott Bartlett   **Manager:** Jason Bourne   **Prog Ed:** Ian Drury
Ground: Culverden Stadium, Culverden Down, Tunbridge Wells TN4 9SG   **(T)** 07900 243 508
Capacity: 3,750 **Seats:** 250   **Covered:** 1,000   **Midweek Matchday:** Tuesday   **Clubhouse:** Yes

Colours(change): All red (White/black/white)
Previous Names: None.
Previous Leagues: South Eastern. Southern Amateur. Isthmian. Spartan. Kent.

HONOURS: FA Comps: None
    League: Southern Amateur Section B 1909-10. Kent Division One 1984-85.

10 YEAR RECORD

07-08	08-09	09-10	10-11	11-12	12-13	13-14	14-15	15-16	16-17
Kent P 10	Kent P 10	Kent P 7	Kent P 6	Kent P 5	Kent P 7	SCE 4	SCE 5	SCE 14	SCEP 15
FAC EP	FAC P	FAC EPr	FAC 1Q	FAC P	FAC EP	FAC 1Q	FAC EP	FAC Pr	FAC EPr
FAV 1Pr	FAV 2P	FAV 2Q	FAV 3P	FAV 4P	FAV F	FAV 3P	FAV 4Pr	FAV 2P	FAV 1P

WHITSTABLE TOWN

Founded: 1886   Nickname: Oystermen or Natives

Secretary: Helen Spratling   **(T)** 07590 116 735   **(E)** helen.spratling@gmail.com
Chairman: Joe Brownett   **Manager:** Scott Porter   **Prog Ed:** Les Biggs
Ground: The Belmont Ground, Belmont Road, Belmont, Whitstable CT5 1QP   **(T)** 01227 266 012
Capacity: 3,000 **Seats:** 500   **Covered:** 1,000   **Midweek Matchday:** Tuesday   **Clubhouse:** Yes   **Shop:** Yes

Colours(change): Red /white/red (Yellow/yellow/blue)
Previous Names: None
Previous Leagues: East Kent 1897-1909, Kent 1909-59, Aetolian 1959-60, Kent Amateur 1960-62, 63-64, South East Anglian 1962-63,

HONOURS: FA Comps: None
    League: Kent Division Two (Mid Kent) 1927-28, Division Two 33-34, 49-50, Premier Division 2006-07.
10 YEAR RECORD   Kent Amateur Eastern Division 1960-61

07-08	08-09	09-10	10-11	11-12	12-13	13-14	14-15	15-16	16-17
Isth1S 14	Isth1S 16	Isth1S 18	Isth1S 15	Isth1S 18	Isth1S 17	Isth1S 20	Isth1S 8	Isth1S 23	SCEP 5
FAC P	FAC 1Q	FAC 2Q	FAC 2Q	FAC P	FAC P	FAC Pr	FAC 1Q	FAC 1Qr	FAC Pr
FAT P	FAT 1Q	FAT Pr	FAT P	FAT P	FAT 2Q	FAT 2P	FAT P	FAT P	FAV 1Qr

BRIDON ROPES
Founded: 1935   Nickname: The Ropes

Secretary: Clive Smith   **(T)** 07795 966 110   **(E)** cburtonsmith@gmail.com
Chairman: Richard Clements   **Manager:** Mark Murison   **Prog Ed:** Clive Smith
Ground: Meridian Sports & Social Club, Charlton Park Lane, Charlton, London SE7 8QS   **(T)** 0208 856 1923
Colours(change): All blue (All red)
HONOURS: FA Comps: None   **League:** Spartan Division Two 1991-92. Kent County Division One West 2009-10.

10 YEAR RECORD

07-08	08-09	09-10	10-11	11-12	12-13	13-14	14-15	15-16	16-17
KC1W 11	KC1W 3	KC1W 1	KC P 4	K_lv 4	K_lv 7	K_lv 8	K_lv 10	K_lv 5	SCE1 7
									FAC EP
								FAV 1P	FAV 1P

CROCKENHILL
Founded: 1946   Nickname: The Crocks

Secretary: Steve Cullen   **(T)** 07702 886 966   **(E)** steve.cullen@virgin.net
Chairman: Steve Cullen   **Manager:** Kevin Dalrymple   **Prog Ed:** Alan Curnick
Ground: Wested Meadow Ground, Eynsford Road, Crockenhill, Kent BR8 8EJ   **(T)** 01322 666 067
Colours(change): Red & white hoops/black/black (Yellow/blue/blue)
HONOURS: FA Comps: None   **League:** Kent County Division One (Western) 1948-49, Senior (Western) 53-54, 56
-57, Division One West 2000-01, Premier 003-04. Kent 1982-83.

10 YEAR RECORD

07-08	08-09	09-10	10-11	11-12	12-13	13-14	14-15	15-16	16-17
KC P 14	KC1W 10	KC1W 6	KC1W 12	K_lv 14	K_lv 13	K_lv 15	K_lv 14	K_lv 15	SCE1 18

ERITH & BELVEDERE
Founded: 1922   Nickname: Deres

Secretary: Adam Peters   **(T)** 07984 090 805   **(E)** clubsec_erithandbelvederefc@live.com
Chairman: John McFadden   **Manager:** John Wilfort   **Prog Ed:** Brian Spurrell / Martin
Ground: Welling FC, Park View Road, Welling, DA16 1SY   **(T)** 07984 090 805   **Capacity:** 4,000
Colours(change): Blue & white quarters/blue/blue. (Red & white quarters/red/red)
HONOURS: FA Comps: None   **League:** Kent Division One / Premier 1981-82 / 2012-13.

10 YEAR RECORD

07-08	08-09	09-10	10-11	11-12	12-13	13-14	14-15	15-16	16-17
Kent P 7	Kent P 8	Kent P 12	Kent P 5	Kent P 2	Kent P 1	Isth1N 24	SCEP 3	SCEP 16	SCEP 20
FAC 1Q	FAC 2Q	FAC P	FAC 2Q	FAC 1Q	FAC EP	FAC P	FAC Pr	FAC P	FAC EP
FAV 1P	FAV 1P	FAV 2P	FAV 2P	FAV 1Q	FAV 3P	FAT P	FAV QF	FAV 2P	FAV 1Q

FC ELMSTEAD
Founded: 1958   Nickname: The Cocks

Secretary: Tony Aliband   **(T)** 07825 889 120   **(E)** fcelmstead@gmail.com
Chairman: Tony Aliband   **Manager:** Fabio Rossi   **Prog Ed:** Fabio Rossi
Ground: Holmesdale FC, Oakley Rown, Bromley, Kent BR2 8HQ   **(T)**
Colours(change): Blue/red/red (Yellow & blue stripes/blue/blue)
HONOURS: FA Comps: None   **League:** None

10 YEAR RECORD

07-08	08-09	09-10	10-11	11-12	12-13	13-14	14-15	15-16	16-17
						KC3W 2	KC2W 2	K_lv 11	SCE1 11
								FAV 1Q	FAV 1P

FISHER
Founded: 1908   Nickname: The Fish

Secretary: Ian Murphy   **(T)** 07854 172 490   **(E)** ian@fisherfc.co.uk
Chairman: Ben Westmancott   **Manager:** Billy Walton   **Prog Ed:** Jevon Hall
Ground: St Pauls Sports Ground, Salter Road, Rotherhithe, London SE16   **(T)**
Colours(change): Black & white stripe/black/black. (Orange/orange/black).
HONOURS: FA Comps: None   **League:** Southern Southern Division 1982-83, Premier 86-87, Eastern 2004-05.

10 YEAR RECORD

07-08	08-09	09-10	10-11	11-12	12-13	13-14	14-15	15-16	16-17
Conf S 4	Conf S 22	Kent P 13	Kent P 16	Kent P 10	Kent P 14	SCEP 14	SCEP 16	SCEP 17	SCEP 19
FAC 2Q	FAC 2Q			FAC P	FAC EPr	FAC EP	FAC P	FAC EP	
FAT 3Q	FAT 3Q		FAV 1P	FAV 2Q	FAV 2Q	FAV 2Q	FAV 1Pr	FAV 2P	

FOREST HILL PARK

Founded: 1992   Nickname:

Secretary: Clayton Walters   **(T)** 07774 294 236   **(E)** info@fhpfc.co.uk
Chairman: John Simpson   **Manager:** Canturk Yanpur   **Prog Ed:** Canturk Yanpur
Ground: Ladywell Arena, Silvermere Road, Catford, London SE6 4QX   **(T)** 0208 314 1986
Colours(change): All blue (White or red/blue/blue)
HONOURS: FA Comps: None   **League:** South London Alliance Division One 2005-06. Kent County Division Two West 2009-10.

10 YEAR RECORD

07-08	08-09	09-10	10-11	11-12	12-13	13-14	14-15	15-16	16-17
	KC2W 4	KC2W 1	KC1W 9	KC P 6	KC P 7	KC1W 10	KC1W 5	K_lv 13	NCE1 12

GRAVESHAM BOROUGH

Founded: 1927   Nickname: Boro

Secretary: Sam Searle   **(T)** 07859 057 799   **(E)** graveshamboroughfc@aol.co.uk
Chairman: Scott Williamson   **Manager:** Kevin Hake   **Prog Ed:** Sam Searle
Ground: Chatham Town FC, Maidstone Road, Chatham, Kent ME4 6LR   **(T)**
Colours(change): All red (Yellow/black/yellow)
HONOURS: FA Comps: None   **League:** Kent County Senior Division (Western) 1985-86.

10 YEAR RECORD

07-08	08-09	09-10	10-11	11-12	12-13	13-14	14-15	15-16	16-17
KC P 3	KC P 2	KC P 9	KC P 12	KC P 4	KC P 4	K_lv 4	K_lv 8	K_lv 7	SCE1 16
									FAC EP
								FAV 1P	FAV 2Q

HOLMESDALE

Founded: 1956   Nickname: The Dalers

Secretary: Ross Mitchell   **(T)** 07875 730 862   **(E)** mitchell1982@sky.com
Chairman: Mark Harris   **Manager:** Simon Copely   **Prog Ed:** Mark Harris
Ground: Holmesdale Sp.& Soc.Club, 68 Oakley Rd, Bromley BR2 8HQ   **(T)** 020 8462 4440
Colours(change): Green & yellow/green/yellow. (All blue).
HONOURS: FA Comps: None   **League:** Thorton Heath & District Division Six 1956-57, Two 61-62, One 71-72, Premier 86-87. Surrey South Eastern Comb. Prem 92-93. Kent County Div.1W 2005-06, Prem 06-07.

10 YEAR RECORD

07-08	08-09	09-10	10-11	11-12	12-13	13-14	14-15	15-16	16-17
Kent P 15	Kent P 5	Kent P 10	Kent P 14	Kent P 13	Kent P 16	SCE 10	SCE 14	SCE 19	SCE1 6
		FAC P	FAC EP	FAC EP	FAC EP	FAC P	FAC P	FAC P	FAC EP
	FAV 1Qr	FAV 2Q	FAV 1Q	FAV 1Q	FAV 2Q	FAV 2Q	FAV 1Q	FAV 1Qr	FAV 2Q

K SPORTS

Founded: 1919   Nickname: The Paperboys

Secretary: Karen Grieves   **(T)** 07947 797 886   **(E)** karengrieves@aol.com
Chairman: Philip Hudson   **Manager:** Kris Browning
Ground: Cobdown Sports & Social Club, Station Road, Ditton, Aylesford, Kent ME20 6AU   **(T)**
Colours(change): Black & white/black/black & white (All gold)
HONOURS: FA Comps: None   **League:** Kent Division Two 1929-30, 30-31, 31-32, 46-47. Kent County Senior Division West 1959-60, 63-64, Premier West 1990-91.

10 YEAR RECORD

07-08	08-09	09-10	10-11	11-12	12-13	13-14	14-15	15-16	16-17
KC1E 3	KC1E 5	KC1E 5	KC1E 2	KC P 6	KC P 6	KC P 3	KC P 4	K_lv 6	SCE1 5

KENT FOOTBALL UNITED

Founded: 2010   Nickname:

Secretary: Sam McNeil   **(T)** 07860 654 558   **(E)** kentelitefc@hotmail.co.uk
Chairman: Roy McNeil   **Manager:** Ennio Gonnella   **Prog Ed:** Sam McNeil
Ground: Holm Park, Queenborough Road, Sheerness ME12 3DB   **(T)** 07860 654 558
Colours(change): All blue (Yellow/black/yellow)
HONOURS: FA Comps: None   **League:** None

10 YEAR RECORD

07-08	08-09	09-10	10-11	11-12	12-13	13-14	14-15	15-16	16-17
				K_lv 13	K_lv 11	K_lv 11	K_lv 15	K_lv 17	SCE1 4
				FAV 2Q	FAV 1Q	FAV 1Q			

LEWISHAM BOROUGH

Founded: 2003   Nickname: The Boro

Secretary: Ray Simpson   **(T)** 07958 946 236   **(E)** raymondsimpson40@yahoo.com
Chairman: Ray Simpson   **Manager:** Ray Simpson   **Prog Ed:** Juliet Walker
Ground: Ladywell Arena, Silvermere Road, Catford, London SE6 4QX   **(T)**
Colours(change): Blue & white/blue/blue (All red)
HONOURS: FA Comps: None   **League:** Kent County Division One West 2003-04, Premier 2005-06.

10 YEAR RECORD									
07-08	08-09	09-10	10-11	11-12	12-13	13-14	14-15	15-16	16-17
KC P 10	KC P 9	KC P 10	KC P 6	K_lv 8	K_lv 16	K_lv 13	K_lv 16	K_lv 20	SCE1 19

LYDD TOWN

Founded: 1885   Nickname: The Lydders

Secretary: Bruce Marchant   **(T)** 07899 738 108   **(E)** brucemarchant@hotmail.com
Chairman: Pat Lindsey   **Manager:** Liam Smith   **Prog Ed:** Bruce Marchant
Ground: The Lindsey Field, Dengemarsh Road, Lydd, Kent TN29 9JH   **(T)** 01797 321 904
Colours(change): Green/green/red (Yellow & blue/yellow/yellow)
HONOURS: FA Comps: None   **League:** Kent County Premier East 1969-70, 70-71, Senior East 1989-90, 90-91, 91-92, Division One East 92-93, 93-94.

10 YEAR RECORD									
07-08	08-09	09-10	10-11	11-12	12-13	13-14	14-15	15-16	16-17
KC1E 8	KC1E 11	KC2E 11	KC2E 20	K_lv 12	K_lv 6	K_lv 2	K_lv 3	K_lv 8	NCE1 9

MERIDIAN VP

Founded: 1995   Nickname:

Secretary: Mike Rumin   **(T)** 07874 624 638   **(E)** mrumin@gmail.com
Chairman: Dwinder Tamna   **Manager:** Richard Dimmock   **Prog Ed:** Mike Rumin
Ground: Meridian Sports & Social Club, 110 Charlton Park Lane, London SE7 8QS   **(T)** 0208 856 1923
Colours(change): All blue (All red)
HONOURS: FA Comps: None   **League:** None

10 YEAR RECORD									
07-08	08-09	09-10	10-11	11-12	12-13	13-14	14-15	15-16	16-17
KC2W 9	KC2W 12	KC2W 11	KC2W 12	K_lv 15	K_lv 15	K_lv 14	K_lv 12	K_lv 12	SCE1 17
								FAV 1P	FAV 1Q

PHOENIX SPORTS RESERVES

Founded: 1935   Nickname:

Secretary: Alf Levy   **(T)** 07795 182 927   **(E)** alf-levy@sky.com
Chairman: Andy Mortlock   **Manager:** Ben Kotey   **Prog Ed:** Alf Levy
Ground: Phoenix Sports Ground, Mayplace Road East, Barnehurst, Kent DA7 6JT   **(T)** 01322 526 159
Colours(change): Green/black/black (All Red or all green)
HONOURS: FA Comps: None   **League:** Kent Division Two 2011-12. Kent County Division Two West 2013-14.

10 YEAR RECORD									
07-08	08-09	09-10	10-11	11-12	12-13	13-14	14-15	15-16	16-17
				Kent 2 1		KC2W 1	KC1W 8	K_lv 14	SCE1 13

PUNJAB UNITED

Founded: 2003   Nickname:

Secretary: jindi Banwait   **(T)** 07814 995 608   **(E)** jindi_banwait@hotmail.com
Chairman: Jugjit 'Chippie' Sian
Ground: Elite Venue, Hawkins Avenue, Dunkirk Close, Gravesend, Kent DA12 5ND   **(T)** 01474 323 817
Colours(change): Navy & pink/navy/navy (orange & black/black/black)
HONOURS: FA Comps: None   **League:** Kent County Premier 2016-17.

10 YEAR RECORD									
07-08	08-09	09-10	10-11	11-12	12-13	13-14	14-15	15-16	16-17
									KC P 1

SNODLAND TOWN

Founded: 2012   Nickname:

Secretary: Terry Reeves   **(T)** 07894 488 451   **(E)** terry.reeves55@virginmedia.com
Chairman: Mel Rayfield   **Manager:** Gavin Gillies   **Prog Ed:** Alan Totham
Ground: Potyns Field, Paddlesworth Road, Snodland ME6 5DP   **(T)** 07894 488 451
Colours(change): Blue & yellow/blue/blue (Navy & red/navy/navy)
HONOURS: FA Comps: None   **League:** None

10 YEAR RECORD

07-08	08-09	09-10	10-11	11-12	12-13	13-14	14-15	15-16	16-17
					KC P 11	KC P 4	KC P 9	KC1E 3	NCE1 8

SPORTING CLUB THAMESMEAD

Founded: 1900   Nickname: The Acre

Secretary: Lee Hill   **(T)** 07834 583 395   **(E)** lhsasfc@gmail.com
Chairman: Sam Taylor   **Manager:** Lee Hill   **Prog Ed:** Sam Taylor
Ground: Sporting Club Thamesmead, Bayliss Avenue, Thamesmead, London SE28 8NJ   **(T)** 0208 320 4488
Colours(change): Red & black/black/black (Green & yellow/green/green)
HONOURS: FA Comps: None   **League:** South London Alliance Division One 2008-09.

10 YEAR RECORD

07-08	08-09	09-10	10-11	11-12	12-13	13-14	14-15	15-16	16-17
SLAll1 6	SLAll1 1	KC2W 3	KC2W 4	K_lv 10	K_lv 5	K_lv 9	K_lv 6	K_lv 9	SCE1 10
								FAC P	FAC EP
							FAV 1Q	FAV 1Qr	FAV 2P

STANSFELD

Founded: 1961   Nickname: Palace

Secretary: George Lush   **(T)** 07861 885 590   **(E)** georgelush@hotmail.co.uk
Chairman: Ian Rooney   **Prog Ed:** George Lush
Ground: Foxbury Avenue, Chislehurst, Bromley BR7 6HA   **(T)**
Colours(change): Blue/white/blue (All orange)
HONOURS: FA Comps: None   **League:** Kent County Division Two (Western) 1958-59, Premier (Western) 62-63, 63-64, 77 -78, Senior (Western) 84-85, 86-87, 88-89, 89-90, Premier 94-95, 2009-10.

10 YEAR RECORD

07-08	08-09	09-10	10-11	11-12	12-13	13-14	14-15	15-16	16-17
KC1W 2	KC P 3	KC P 1	KC P 13	KC P 2	KC P 9	KC P 6	KC P 2	KC P 4	KC P 9

SUTTON ATHLETIC

Founded: 1898   Nickname:

Secretary: Guy Eldridge   **(T)** 07778 053 433   **(E)** guy.eldridge@btconnect.com
Chairman: John Ball   **Manager:** Ben Young   **Prog Ed:** John Ball
Ground: London Hire Stadium, Lower Road, Hextable, Kent BR8 7RZ   **(T)** 01322 665 377
Colours(change): Green & white/green/green (Black & white stripe/black/white)
HONOURS: FA Comps: None   **League:** Dartford 1952-53, 53-54, 54-55, 56-57, 58-59, 59-60, 60-61, 61-62, 62-63, 63-64, 64 -65. Kent County D2W 68-69, D1W 69-70, PremW 70-71, SeniorW 76-77.

10 YEAR RECORD

07-08	08-09	09-10	10-11	11-12	12-13	13-14	14-15	15-16	16-17
KC1W 8	KC1W 2	KC P 3	KC P 11	K_lv 6	K_lv 8	K_lv 3	K_lv 4	K_lv 4	SCE1 3

SPARTAN SOUTH MIDLANDS LEAGUE

Sponsored by: Molten

Founded: 1998

Recent Champions: 2014: Hanwell Town

2015: Kings Langley **2016:** AFC Dunstable

PREMIER DIVISION	P	W	D	L	F	A	GD	Pts
1 London Colney	42	31	4	7	110	45	65	97
2 Hertford Town	42	28	8	6	91	35	56	92
3 Cockfosters	42	27	7	8	90	48	42	88
4 Wembley	42	23	6	13	115	73	42	75
5 Tring Athletic	42	23	6	13	78	54	24	75
6 Welwyn Garden City	42	21	10	11	87	66	21	73
7 Hoddesdon Town	42	20	9	13	93	69	24	69
8 Berkhamsted	42	21	6	15	77	56	21	69
9 Biggleswade United	42	19	11	12	57	47	10	68
10 Sun Sports	42	18	10	14	77	73	4	64
11 Crawley Green	42	18	6	18	63	76	-13	60
12 Leverstock Green	42	16	10	16	85	76	9	58
13 Stotfold	42	14	10	18	66	77	-11	52
14 Holmer Green	42	13	10	19	56	60	-4	49
15 Oxhey Jets	42	13	10	19	68	84	-16	49
16 Leighton Town	42	14	5	23	68	82	-14	47
17 Edgware Town	42	11	10	21	61	88	-27	43
18 Colney Heath	42	12	7	23	62	100	-38	43
19 Hadley	42	9	12	21	57	79	-22	39
20 St Margaretsbury	42	9	11	22	60	92	-32	38
21 London Tigers	42	8	7	27	46	109	-63	31
22 FC Broxbourne Borough	42	4	5	33	47	125	-78	17

PREMIER DIVISION CUP

HOLDERS: HODDESDON TOWN

ROUND 1

Hoddesdon Town	v	Leverstock Green	2-2, 5-4p
Hertford Town	v	Cockfosters	1-0
Leighton Town	v	Tring Athletic	0-1
Holmer Green	v	FC Broxbourne Borough	3-0
Colney Heath	v	Hadley	0-3
Stotfold	v	London Colney	0-2

ROUND 2

Biggleswade United	v	Hoddesdon Town	1-2
Hertford Town	v	Oxhey Jets	2-0
London Tigers	v	Tring Athletic	0-2
Holmer Green	v	Edgware Town	6-1
Sun Sports	v	Hadley	1-1, 5-4p
Crawley Green	v	Welwyn Garden City	1-5
Berkhamsted	v	St Margaretsbury	6-1
London Colney	v	Wembley	0-3

QUARTER FINALS

Hoddesdon Town	v	Hertford Town	1-0
Tring Athletic	v	Holmer Green	3-2
Sun Sports	v	Welwyn Garden City	4-0
Berkhamsted	v	Wembley	2-3

SEMI FINALS

Hoddesdon Town	v	Tring Athletic	6-3
Sun Sports	v	Wembley	1-4

FINAL

Hoddesdon Town	v	Wembley	1-0

CLUB MOVEMENTS

Premier Division - In: Biggleswade FC (P), Harpenden Town (P).
Out: FC Broxbourne Borough (R), Hertford Town (P - Isth D1N).

Division One - In: Enfield Borough (P), FC Broxbourne Borough (R), St Neots Town Res (P).
Out: Arlesey Town Reserves (W), Biggleswade FC (P), Chesham United Reserves (W), Hadley Wood & Wingate (W), Harpenden Town (P), Kensington Borough (S - Combined Counties), New Bradwell St Peters (P).

Division Two - In: AFC Southgate, Berkhamsted Raiders, Park View.
Out: Enfield Borough (P), New Bradwell St Peter (W), St Neots Town Res (P), Stony Stratford Town (W), Thame Rangers (W).

PREMIER DIVISION	1	2	3	4	5	6	7	8	9	10	11	12	13	14	15	16	17	18	19	20	21	22
1 Berkhamsted		0-2	3-1	0-1	7-2	1-0	6-1	0-1	0-1	0-1	2-0	3-0	2-2	1-5	5-0	1-2	1-0	2-2	2-0	0-1	1-1	3-1
2 Biggleswade United	2-0		1-0	3-1	2-0	0-2	2-0	2-0	2-1	1-2	1-0	0-1	3-2	2-1	0-0	1-0	0-0	1-2	1-0	0-2	1-2	2-4
3 Cockfosters	1-5	2-0		2-2	2-0	1-1	4-2	2-0	2-1	1-2	1-1	4-0	5-1	2-0	6-1	2-0	1-2	1-0	0-2	0-0	1-2	1-3
4 Colney Heath	2-3	0-1	0-3		2-0	2-2	3-1	5-1	1-5	1-6	1-2	0-1	1-4	0-2	2-0	3-2	0-5	3-1	2-2	1-2	2-9	0-5
5 Crawley Green	0-1	1-1	2-0	2-2		2-1	3-1	3-5	1-3	3-2	1-2	2-1	4-0	0-5	2-0	2-0	1-0	0-0	3-2	1-3	0-0	0-5
6 Edgware Town	2-5	2-0	0-2	2-2	3-2		1-2	5-2	0-0	1-2	2-1	1-0	0-2	2-3	0-0	0-2	1-1	3-2	3-3	0-3	1-4	3-3
7 FC Broxbourne Borough	1-2	1-3	0-3	2-6	1-2	1-2		1-2	0-5	0-0	0-2	2-6	3-3	1-6	2-2	1-3	2-2	2-5	2-4	0-1	1-4	4-6
8 Hadley	0-1	2-3	1-2	3-2	1-2	1-2	2-1		1-2	1-1	0-0	1-1	1-1	0-1	1-3	1-2	2-3	0-1	3-3	1-2	3-1	1-3
9 Hertford Town	3-2	0-2	0-2	7-0	2-0	2-0	2-1	1-0		2-0	1-1	5-1	1-1	3-0	3-0	4-1	4-0	1-4	2-0	3-2	0-1	4-1
10 Hoddesdon Town	1-2	3-0	2-4	2-1	2-6	3-2	1-3	1-1	0-0		0-0	4-3	2-0	2-1	1-0	2-2	7-0	6-2	1-3	1-3	1-1	3-2
11 Holmer Green	0-2	2-0	0-0	1-2	0-2	2-1	2-0	1-1	0-3	5-0		3-0	1-4	1-3	2-1	1-1	3-1	2-0	2-0	2-1	1-1	3-4
12 Leighton Town	3-0	1-1	0-2	1-1	2-0	1-0	2-0	1-3	0-3	3-6	2-2		0-3	1-3	4-0	3-1	1-0	1-0	0-1	1-3	2-2	1-3
13 Leverstock Green	2-2	2-1	1-2	0-1	1-2	3-2	4-0	8-1	1-2	2-1	1-0	2-1		4-3	0-1	1-1	5-1	3-3	1-3	1-6	3-0	1-3
14 London Colney	2-0	0-1	2-3	2-1	1-0	6-0	4-0	0-0	1-1	3-1	2-0	2-0	2-2		2-0	2-1	4-0	5-1	2-1	6-2	3-1	2-3
15 London Tigers	3-2	0-1	1-3	1-2	1-2	5-0	1-1	1-1	2-3	1-4	0-4	0-7	1-4	1-9		3-2	1-1	0-3	3-3	0-2		
16 Oxhey Jets	0-0	3-4	3-3	3-2	3-1	2-2	2-3	1-1	1-4	0-0	1-0	5-3	2-1	1-2	3-2		3-3	5-1	1-1	2-3	2-3	1-0
17 St Margaretsbury	0-3	1-1	1-2	1-1	0-2	2-2	2-1	3-3	2-1	1-1	0-3	1-3	2-3	1-2	6-0	1-2		4-3	1-2	1-4	5-2	1-1
18 Stotfold	2-3	2-1	1-1	3-0	1-1	3-2	0-1	1-1	0-1	0-4	2-2	1-4	1-1	0-2	2-0	1-1	3-2		1-2	1-0	2-0	2-2
19 Sun Sports	0-3	1-1	0-2	1-3	3-3	5-1	4-1	0-3	0-2	1-1	2-1	2-1	2-2	2-3	2-3	5-1	3-1	1-2		1-0	1-3	1-1
20 Tring Athletic	0-0	1-1	1-3	1-0	2-1	1-2	3-0	1-1	1-3	1-3	4-2	3-2	1-0	1-1	1-3	1-0	1-1	3-2	0-2		1-1	3-1
21 Welwyn Garden City	2-1	2-1	2-2	2-1	5-0	2-1	2-1	2-1	1-1	2-1	2-0	5-2	2-0	0-1	4-2	4-0	3-1	0-2	0-1	2-3		2-3
22 Wembley	6-0	0-0	4-5	4-0	1-2	2-4	6-0	0-3	0-0	1-6	4-1	2-1	4-3	2-3	1-0	4-0	5-0	6-1	4-4	1-0	4-0	

DIVISION ONE

		P	W	D	L	F	A	GD	Pts
1	Biggleswade FC	40	32	3	5	140	45	95	99
2	Harpenden Town	40	29	6	5	108	37	71	93
3	Baldock Town	40	29	5	6	109	45	64	92
4	Langford	40	24	5	11	109	72	37	77
5	Southall	40	24	4	12	110	64	46	76
6	Risborough Rangers	40	21	8	11	93	58	35	71
7	Wodson Park	40	21	7	12	71	49	22	70
8	Harefield United	40	20	8	12	82	47	35	68
9	Hillingdon Borough	40	21	4	15	114	66	48	67
10	Buckingham Athletic	40	21	3	16	76	68	8	66
11	Broadfields United	40	20	4	16	102	74	28	64
12	Kensington Borough	40	16	8	16	93	83	10	56
13	Codicote	40	13	4	23	65	88	-23	43
14	Ampthill Town	40	13	3	24	73	109	-36	42
15	Chesham United Res	40	12	4	24	70	101	-31	40
16	Winslow United	40	11	5	24	53	111	-58	38
17	Brimsdown	40	10	7	23	84	133	-49	37
18	Hadley Wood & Wingate	40	12	4	24	60	116	-56	37*
19	Bedford	40	10	2	28	42	105	-63	32
20	Hatfield Town	40	9	4	27	57	115	-58	31
21	Arlesey Town Res	40	2	2	36	39	164	-125	8

DIVISION ONE CUP

HOLDERS: CRAWLEY GREEN

ROUND 1

Brimsdown	v	Biggleswade FC	3-5
Broadfields United	v	Harefield United	2-1
Chesham United Res	v	Hillingdon Borough	0-2
Bedford	v	Kensington Borough	1-1, 3-4p
Baldock Town	v	Southall	3-3, 4-3p

ROUND 2

Codicote	v	Biggleswade FC	1-1, 5-4p
Harpenden Town	v	Broadfields United	3-2
Winslow United	v	Wodson Park	0-2
Risborough Rangers	v	Baldock Town	2-3
Arlesey Town Res	v	Langford	3-5
Hillingdon Borough	v	Ampthill Town	2-2, 1-4
Hadley Wood & Wingate	v	Kensington Borough	3-1
Hatfield Town	v	Buckingham Athletic	3-1

QUARTER FINALS

Codicote	v	Harpenden Town	1-2
Wodson Park	v	Baldock Town	3-1
Langford	v	Ampthill Town	6-1
Hadley Wood & Wingate	v	Hatfield Town	0-1

SEMI FINALS

Harpenden Town	v	Wodson Park	1-4
Langford	v	Hatfield Town	3-1

FINAL

Wodson Park	v	Langford	0-1

CHALLENGE TROPHY

HOLDERS: WELWYN GARDEN CITY

ROUND 1

Hale Leys United	v	Langford	0-8
Sun Sports	v	Harpenden Town	3-1
Stony Stratford Town	v	Chesham United Res	AW
MK Gallacticos	v	Wembley	1-3
Southall	v	Stotfold	5-1
Mursley United	v	Old Bradwell United	2-0
Crawley Green	v	Grendon Rangers	4-0
Biggleswade United	v	Pitstone & Ivinghoe	5-1
Kensington Borough	v	Thame Rangers	1-1, 4-5p
Broadfields United	v	Tring Corinthians	6-0
St Neots Town Res	v	Leighton Town	1-2
Amersham Town	v	Risborough Rangers	0-4
St Margaretsbury	v	Hertford Town	0-4
Codicote	v	Hoddesdon Town	2-5
Wodson Park	v	Berkhamsted	1-3
FC Broxbourne Borough	v	Colney Heath	0-2
Clean Slate	v	Arlesey Town Res	3-4
Hadley	v	Harefield United	2-0
Edgware Town	v	London Tigers	2-0
Aston Clinton	v	Tring Athletic	1-4
Baldock Town	v	Oxhey Jets	1-1, 4-1
Hillingdon Borough	v	Loughton Manor	4-0
London Colney	v	Brimsdown	3-1
Biggleswade FC	v	Tring Town	9-1
Totternhoe	v	New Bradwell St Peter	2-2, 4-3p
Holmer Green	v	Leverstock Green	1-2
Hadley Wood & Wingate	v	Bedford	1-2
Cockfosters	v	Hatfield Town	4-1
Buckingham Athletic	v	Enfield Borough	0-1
Ampthill Town	v	Unite MK	1-3
Welwyn Garden City	v	The 61FC (Luton)	2-2, 3-0p

ROUND 2

Langford	v	Sun Sports	4-1
Chesham United Res	v	Wembley	0-3
Southall	v	Mursley United	5-1
Crawley Green	v	Biggleswade United	0-2
Thame Rangers	v	Broadfields United	3-2
Leighton Town	v	Risborough Rangers	1-2
Hertford Town	v	Hoddesdon Town	2-0
Berkhamsted	v	Colney Heath	5-3
Arlesey Town Res	v	Hadley	0-3
Edgware Town	v	Tring Athletic	4-1

DIVISION ONE

		1	2	3	4	5	6	7	8	9	10	11	12	13	14	15	16	17	18	19	20	21
1	Ampthill Town		3-1	0-1	4-0	2-5	6-0	4-1	1-2	1-2	1-4	2-2	1-5	2-0	6-2	0-5	3-5	0-3	2-2	1-3	3-2	1-5
2	Arlesey Town Res	1-3		2-6	3-0	2-9	1-2	0-5	1-4	0-2	3-1	0-2	2-5	1-7	1-5	0-2	1-3	3-4	2-2	0-8	1-1	0-3
3	Baldock Town	5-0	5-0		2-0	2-4	1-0	3-2	2-0	5-1	4-0	5-0	1-0	0-4	5-0	2-0	3-3	3-0	3-2	3-1	6-0	2-0
4	Bedford	4-0	2-1	1-6		1-0	3-3	1-3	1-0	1-2	1-0	0-2	0-2	3-1	4-0	4-2	1-2	1-6	0-3	1-5	0-2	
5	Biggleswade FC	4-1	4-1	3-3	2-1		3-1	3-2	3-2	7-1	8-0	7-1	0-0	1-0	5-1	2-1	2-4	8-1	1-0	1-3	3-1	2-0
6	Brimsdown	3-3	12-1	1-4	5-1	1-7		2-1	3-6	4-2	1-2	4-1	3-3	0-6	3-1	0-7	4-1	1-2	1-5	2-2	3-4	0-3
7	Broadfields United	0-3	8-1	2-1	7-1	2-1	4-1		3-2	2-1	6-1	4-1	1-3	3-2	8-1	0-1	2-1	1-3	3-2	3-1	4-0	1-2
8	Buckingham Athletic	4-1	3-1	0-1	2-0	1-3	3-0	3-1		4-3	3-1	0-1	0-1	2-4	3-2	1-0	3-2	0-0	3-3	4-3	5-0	3-1
9	Chesham United Res	4-2	2-0	2-3	3-3	0-4	4-2	2-3	0-1		2-0	1-2	2-2	1-1	2-3	1-3	1-3	2-3	2-0	3-4	0-1	0-2
10	Codicote	2-1	4-1	0-1	2-0	1-4	1-3	4-1	4-0	4-0		3-0	1-0	1-1	1-4	1-4	2-3	1-5	1-4	5-1	0-1	
11	Hadley Wood & Wingate	0-3	3-0	3-3	1-2	0-5	6-2	4-3	2-1	1-4	3-3		1-3	1-2	4-0	1-6	2-1	0-4	0-3	0-4	4-2	0-0
12	Harefield United	2-1	3-0	2-1	3-0	2-2	7-1	1-3	3-0	0-1	3-0	2-1		1-3	4-0	0-2	1-1	2-4	2-1	1-3	5-0	1-2
13	Harpenden Town	4-0	6-0	1-0	2-1	2-1	1-1	2-1	0-0	6-2	2-1	8-0	1-0		5-1	2-1	3-1	3-1	4-2	2-4	3-1	3-1
14	Hatfield Town	0-2	3-2	0-2	4-1	0-2	3-2	3-1	0-1	2-2	0-3	1-1	0-2	1-4		0-2	1-4	0-7	3-2	1-4	1-1	1-2
15	Hillingdon Borough	4-1	7-1	4-1	3-2	0-1	6-2	1-1	4-1	3-1	2-3	12-0	4-4	0-2	4-3		3-2	4-0	4-5	2-3	4-1	2-2
16	Kensington Borough	2-3	3-1	0-3	5-0	2-6	4-4	2-2	1-0	2-1	3-1	1-2	0-3	1-1	3-2	2-2		1-1	1-3	6-1	2-1	2-2
17	Langford	9-1	4-2	1-3	8-1	0-3	9-1	4-2	2-3	2-1	3-2	1-0	2-2	0-4	3-0	4-3		1-1	1-0	5-0	1-0	
18	Risborough Rangers	2-0	9-0	0-0	2-1	3-4	2-1	2-0	0-1	4-0	1-1	2-1	1-1	1-0	2-1	0-4	1-3	1-3		3-1	2-1	0-3
19	Southall	5-1	1-0	2-3	1-0	0-1	2-2	1-1	5-1	9-2	3-1	4-3	0-2	0-2	5-1	4-1	2-1	4-0	2-2		3-1	1-2
20	Winslow United	2-1	4-1	2-3	2-0	0-8	1-3	2-2	1-2	1-5	2-2	1-3	2-1	0-4	1-3	2-1	1-6	3-1	0-5	2-0		1-0
21	Wodson Park	2-3	4-1	2-2	3-0	0-1	4-0	1-3	4-2	1-3	2-1	2-1	0-0	1-1	3-1	3-1	2-0	1-1	2-3	1-4	0-0	

SPARTAN SOUTH MIDLANDS LEAGUE - STEP 5/6/7

CHALLENGE TROPHY continued...

Baldock Town	v	Hillingdon Borough	2-1
London Colney	v	Biggleswade FC	4-0
Totternhoe	v	Winslow United	2-3
Leverstock Green	v	Bedford	2-1
Cockfosters	v	Enfield Borough	1-1, 2-4p
Unite MK	v	Welwyn Garden City	0-0, 5-4p

ROUND 3
Langford	v	Wembley	1-0
Southall	v	Biggleswade United	3-0
Thame Rangers	v	Risborough Rangers	6-0
Hertford Town	v	Berkhamsted	1-2
Hadley	v	Edgware Town	1-1, 4-2p
Baldock Town	v	London Colney	1-2
Winslow United	v	Leverstock Green	0-3
Enfield Borough	v	Unite MK	7-0

QUARTER FINALS
Langford	v	Southall	5-2
Thame Rangers	v	Berkhamsted	2-2, 4-3p
Hadley	v	London Colney	1-2
Leverstock Green	v	Enfield Borough	4-1

SEMI FINALS
Langford	v	Thame Rangers	1-4
London Colney	v	Leverstock Green	2-0

FINAL
Thame Rangers	v	London Colney	0-3

DIVISION TWO

		P	W	D	L	F	A	GD	Pts
1	Thame Rangers	34	28	2	4	127	38	89	86
2	Totternhoe	34	26	0	8	108	45	63	78
3	Enfield Borough	34	19	7	8	85	37	48	64
4	Aston Clinton	34	21	4	9	81	45	36	64*
5	MK Gallacticos	34	20	3	11	101	70	31	63
6	Old Bradwell United	34	19	4	11	85	63	22	61
7	New Bradwell St Peter	34	17	8	9	85	48	37	59
8	Loughton Manor	34	18	5	11	64	57	7	59
9	St. Neots Town Res	34	17	6	11	80	62	18	57
10	Pitstone & Ivinghoe	34	16	4	14	87	85	2	52
11	The 61FC (Luton)	34	13	8	13	67	64	3	47
12	Unite MK	34	14	3	17	64	85	-21	45
13	Mursley United	34	11	3	20	64	88	-24	36
14	Grendon Rangers	34	9	3	22	46	96	-50	30
15	Tring Corinthians	34	7	8	19	56	96	-40	29
16	Amersham Town	34	6	5	23	49	99	-50	23
17	Tring Town AFC	34	4	2	28	33	110	-77	14
18	Clean Slate	34	2	3	29	39	133	-94	9

Hale Leys United withdrew - record expunged.
Stony Stratford Town withdrew - record expunged.

DIVISION TWO CUP

HOLDERS: HALE LEYS UNITED
ROUND 1
MK Gallacticos	v	Loughton Manor	1-2
Thame Rangers	v	St Neots Town Res	3-1
Enfield Borough	v	Grendon Rangers	2-0
The 61FC (Luton)	v	New Bradwell St Peter	2-1

ROUND 2
Hale Leys United	v	Old Bradwell United	2-6
Mursley United	v	Tring Town	3-1
Clean Slae	v	Stony Stratford Town	HW
Unite MK	v	Loughton Manor	2-2, 4-5p
Thaem Rangers	v	Amersham Town	7-1
Totternhoe	v	Pitstone & Ivinghoe	5-0
Enfield Borough	v	Aston Clinton	3-4
Tring Corinthians	v	The 61FC (Luton)	1-2

QUARTER FINALS
Old Bradwell United	v	Mursley United	1-2
Clean Slate	v	Loughton Manor	2-2, 5-4p
Thame Rangers	v	Totternhoe	1-0
Aston Clinton	v	The 61FC (Luton)	1-1, 5-6p

SEMI FINALS
Mursley United	v	Clean Slate	3-2
Thame Rangers	v	The 61FC (Luton)	0-2

FINAL
Mursley United	v	The 61FC (Luton)	3-1

DIVISION TWO

		1	2	3	4	5	6	7	8	9	10	11	12	13	14	15	16	17	18
1	Amersham Town		0-7	4-1	1-1	5-1	0-2	0-2	1-2	4-2	2-4	2-2	0-2	0-2	2-2	0-4	1-4	1-1	3-3
2	Aston Clinton	3-1		3-0	1-0	4-2	1-2	1-5	1-1	0-3	1-1	2-1	3-3	0-1	1-0	1-3	6-1	2-1	2-0
3	Clean Slate	2-3	0-5		1-6	1-3	0-2	0-2	1-3	3-7	1-6	2-5	1-6	1-8	1-1	3-4	2-1	2-4	1-3
4	Enfield Borough	2-1	2-1	5-1		2-0	3-0	2-4	4-1	2-3	3-0	5-1	0-0	2-1	1-1	4-0	5-0	5-1	2-3
5	Grendon Rangers	4-2	1-2	0-0	0-4		1-5	3-4	2-1	0-3	1-7	0-4	1-2	1-4	0-2	1-6	2-2	2-1	1-2
6	Loughton Manor	3-1	0-4	5-0	2-1	4-1		2-0	3-1	1-1	1-2	0-5	2-0	0-6	2-2	2-0	1-1	2-0	3-1
7	MK Gallacticos	10-4	2-2	8-1	0-3	2-3	4-1		3-2	2-6	1-3	4-3	1-1	3-1	5-2	0-7	3-1	5-2	4-1
8	Mursley United	6-1	1-2	3-1	1-3	0-3	1-3	1-1		1-6	2-4	2-3	4-1	2-4	1-2	1-5	3-2	2-0	2-2
9	New Bradwell St Peter	4-0	0-4	3-0	2-2	6-1	2-2	1-0	5-1		0-1	1-2	1-2	0-0	2-2	3-4	2-0	6-0	3-2
10	Old Bradwell United	1-0	0-2	5-1	1-1	4-1	1-2	4-1	6-2	0-3		3-5	3-2	3-6	0-3	3-1	5-0	2-2	2-1
11	Pitstone & Ivinghoe	4-0	0-1	5-3	1-3	3-3	2-2	1-5	0-2	0-3	5-1		3-1	2-8	1-3	3-2	6-4	5-2	2-4
12	St. Neots Town Reserves	H-W	1-3	7-2	1-5	6-0	2-1	2-4	0-2	3-1	4-2	3-1		2-4	5-1	1-0	3-2	3-0	2-2
13	Thame Rangers	3-0	1-0	4-0	3-2	4-2	5-0	4-0	6-0	2-2	2-3	2-0	5-2		1-0	3-2	2-3	4-0	5-0
14	The 61FC (Luton)	0-1	2-3	4-3	2-2	0-2	3-2	4-3	5-1	0-0	1-5	5-1	1-1	1-5		0-1	2-4	3-0	4-1
15	Totternhoe	4-0	6-1	2-0	2-1	2-1	2-0	2-1	1-0	5-1	3-0	3-4	3-0	0-3	3-1		6-4	6-0	6-0
16	Tring Corinthians	1-3	0-4	3-3	0-0	1-2	2-1	0-5	4-3	0-0	0-0	2-2	3-3	0-6	1-3	1-4		5-1	0-2
17	Tring Town AFC	5-3	0-6	0-1	1-0	0-1	1-3	0-2	0-3	1-3	1-3	1-3	0-6	1-6	2-1	1-5	2-3		1-3
18	Unite MK	5-3	4-2	3-0	0-2	1-0	1-3	0-5	3-6	1-0	2-0	1-2	1-3	4-6	1-4	1-4	3-1	3-1	

BERKHAMSTED

Founded: 2009   Nickname: Comrades

Secretary: Keith Hicks   **(T)** 07767 430 087   **(E)** keith55hicks@gmail.com
Chairman: Steve Davis   **Manager:** Steve Bateman   **Prog Ed:** Grant Hastie
Ground: Broadwater, Lower Kings Road, Berkhamsted HP4 2AL   **(T)** 01442 865 977
Capacity: 2,500 **Seats:** 170 **Covered:** 350 **Midweek Matchday:**   **Clubhouse:** Yes **Shop:** Yes

Colours(change): Yellow/blue/blue
Previous Names: None
Previous Leagues: None

HONOURS: FA Comps: None
    League: Spartan South Midlands Division One 2009-10, 10-11.

10 YEAR RECORD

07-08	08-09	09-10	10-11	11-12	12-13	13-14	14-15	15-16	16-17
		SSM1 1	SSM1 1	SSM P 7	SSM P 11	SSM P 5	SSM P 6	SSM P 5	SSM P 8
				FAC 1Qr	FAC 2Q	FAC 1Q	FAC EP	FAC P	FAC EP
			FAV 2Q	FAV 2Q	FAV 2P	FAV 2P	FAV 1P	FAV 5P	FAV 4P

BIGGLESWADE FC

Founded: 2016   Nickname:

Secretary: Emma Tyrrell   **(T)** 07720 656 580   **(E)** emma-tyrrell@02.co.uk
Chairman: Jeremy Reynolds   **Manager:** David Northfield   **Prog Ed:** Jeremy Reynolds
Ground: Biggleswade Town FC, Langford Road, Biggleswade SG18 9JT   **(T)** 01767 318 202
Capacity: 3,000 **Seats:** 300 **Covered:** Yes **Midweek Matchday:**   **Clubhouse:** Yes

Colours(change): Green & white
Previous Names: Based on Biggleswade Town's U18 side.
Previous Leagues: None

HONOURS: FA Comps: None
    League: Spartan South Midlands Division One 2016-17.

10 YEAR RECORD

07-08	08-09	09-10	10-11	11-12	12-13	13-14	14-15	15-16	16-17
									SSM1 1
									FAV 2P

BIGGLESWADE UNITED

Founded: 1959   Nickname: United

Secretary: Tracey James   **(T)** 07714 661 827   **(E)** info@biggleswadeunited.com
Chairman: Chris Lewis   **Manager:** Cristian Colas-Becerra   **Prog Ed:** Tracey James
Ground: Second Meadow, Fairfield Rd, Biggleswade, Beds SG18 0BS   **(T)** 07714 661 827
Capacity: 2,000 **Seats:** 260 **Covered:** 130 **Midweek Matchday:** Wednesday **Clubhouse:** Yes

Colours(change): Red/navy/red (All royal blue)
Previous Names: None
Previous Leagues: North Hertfordshire 1959-69. Midlands 1969-84. Hertfordshire Senior County 1984-86. Bedford & District 1986-96. South Midlands 1996-97.
HONOURS: FA Comps: None
    League: Bedford & District Division Two 1990-91, Division One 91-92, Premier 94-95, 95-96.

10 YEAR RECORD
South Midlands Division One 1996-97.

07-08	08-09	09-10	10-11	11-12	12-13	13-14	14-15	15-16	16-17
SSM P 18	SSM P 1	SSM P 20	SSM P 20	SSM P 19	SSM P 18	SSM P 17	SSM P 13	SSM P 10	SSM P 9
FAC EPr	FAC 1Q	FAC P	FAC EP	FAC P	FAC P	FAC 1Q	FAC 1Q	FAC 1Q	FAC 1Q
FAV 2p	FAV 2P	FAV 2P	FAV 2Q	FAV 1P	FAV 2Q	FAV 1Q	FAV 2Q	FAV 2P	FAV 2Pr

COCKFOSTERS

Founded: 1921   Nickname: Fosters

Secretary: Graham Bint   **(T)** 07729 709 926   **(E)** graham.bint@btinternet.com
Chairman: Mick Bell
Ground: Cockfosters Sports Ground, Chalk Lane, Cockfosters, Herts EN4 9JG   **(T)** 0208 449 5833
Capacity: **Seats:** Yes **Covered:** Yes **Midweek Matchday:**   **Clubhouse:** Yes

Colours(change): All red (All blue)
Previous Names: Cockfosters Athletic 1921-68.
Previous Leagues: Barnet 1921-30s. Wood Green 1930s-46. Northern Suburban Int. 1946-66. Hertfordshire County 1966-1991. Spartan 1991-97.

HONOURS: FA Comps: None
    League: Wood green DivisioN Two 1931-32, Division One 33-34, Premier 38-39. Northern Suburban Inter. Division One

10 YEAR RECORD
1949-50, 60-61, Premier 61-62. Hertfordshire Senior County Division One 1966-67, Premier 78-79, 80-81, 83-84.

07-08	08-09	09-10	10-11	11-12	12-13	13-14	14-15	15-16	16-17
SSM1 17	SSM1 19	SSM1 11	SSM1 15	SSM1 9	SSM1 2	SSM P 8	SSM P 18	SSM P 9	SSM P 3
FAC Pr	FAC EP	FAC Pr	FAC Pr	FAC P	FAC P	FAC 1Qr	FAC P	FAC 1Q	FAC EP
FAV 2P	FAV 1Q	FAV 1P	FAV 1P	FAV 1Q	FAV 2P	FAV 2P	FAV 1P	FAV 1Qr	FAV 2P

COLNEY HEATH
Founded: 1907   Nickname: Magpies

Secretary: Dean Penny   **(T)** 07920 289 069   **(E)** deanpenny@btinternet.com
Chairman: Martin Marlborough
Ground: The Recreation Ground, High St, Colney Heath, St Albans AL4 0NP   **(T)** 01727 824 325
Capacity: **Seats:** Yes   **Covered:** Yes   **Midweek Matchday:**   **Clubhouse:** Yes
Colours(change): Black & white stripes/black/black (All blue)
Previous Names: None
Previous Leagues: Herts Senior County League 1953-2000

HONOURS: FA Comps: None
    League: Herts County Division Two 1953-54 Division One A 55-56, Prem 58-99, 99-00, Division One 88-89, Spartan South Midlands Division One 2005-06.

10 YEAR RECORD

07-08	08-09	09-10	10-11	11-12	12-13	13-14	14-15	15-16	16-17
SSM P 15	SSM P 12	SSM P 5	SSM P 5	SSM P 8	SSM P 13	SSM P 3	SSM P 14	SSM P 20	SSM P 18
FAC EP	FAC EP	FAC EP	FAC 1Q	FAC	FAC 1Q	FAC EP	FAC P	FAC	
FAV 1P	FAV 2Q	FAV 2Q	FAV 1P	FAV 1Q	FAV 2P	FAV 3Pr	FAV 1P		FAV 1P

CRAWLEY GREEN
Founded: 1992   Nickname:

Secretary: Eddie Downey   **(T)** 07956 107 477   **(E)** eddie.downey@hotmail.com
Chairman: Tony Talbot   **Manager:** Mark Smith
Ground: Barton Rovers FC, Sharpenhoe Road, Barton Le Cay, Beds MK45 4SD   **(T)** 01582 882 398
Capacity: 4,000 **Seats:** 160   **Covered:** Yes   **Midweek Matchday:**   **Clubhouse:** Yes
Colours(change): All maroon
Previous Names: None
Previous Leagues: None

HONOURS: FA Comps: None
    League: Spartan South Midlands Division Two 2004-05.

10 YEAR RECORD

07-08	08-09	09-10	10-11	11-12	12-13	13-14	14-15	15-16	16-17
SSM2 2	SSM1 16	SSM1 8	SSM1 4	SSM1 6	SSM1 4	SSM1 5	SSM1 7	SSM1 2	SSM P 11
		FAC P	FAC 1Qr	FAC EP	FAC EP	FAC P	FAC EP	FAC EP	FAC P
	FAV 2Q	FAV 1Q	FAV 1Q	FAV 2Q	FAV 2Qr	FAV 1Q	FAV 2Q	FAV 2Q	FAV 1P

EDGWARE TOWN
Founded: 1939   Nickname: The Wares

Secretary: Dan Manzi   **(T)**   **(E)** secretary@edgwaretownfc.co.uk
Chairman: Antony Manzi   **Manager:** Fergus Moore & Julian Robinson   **Prog Ed:** Antony Manzi
Ground: Silver Jubilee Park, Townsend Lane, London NW9 7NE   **(T)** 0208 205 1645
Capacity: 1,990 **Seats:** 298   **Covered:**   **Midweek Matchday:**   **Clubhouse:** Yes
Colours(change): All green (Red & black/black/black)
Previous Names: Edgware 1972-87. Original Edgware Town folded in 2008 and re-formed in 2014.
Previous Leagues: Corinthian 1946-63. Athenian 1963-84. Spartan 1984-90, 2006-07. Isthmian 1990-2006, 2007-08.

HONOURS: FA Comps: None
    League: Middlesex Senior 1939-40, 43-44, 44-45 (shared). London Western Section 1945-46. London Spartan Premier 1987-88, 89-90. Isthmian Division Three 1991-92. Spartan South Midlands Premier 2006-07, Division One 2015-16.

10 YEAR RECORD

07-08	08-09	09-10	10-11	11-12	12-13	13-14	14-15	15-16	16-17
Isth1N 8							SSM1 9	SSM1 1	SSM P 17
									FAC P
								FAV 3P	FAV 2Q

HADLEY
Founded: 1882   Nickname:

Secretary: Bob Henderson   **(T)** 07748 267 295   **(E)** gensecretary@hadleyfc.com
Chairman: Guy Slee   **Manager:** Micky Hazard   **Prog Ed:** Guy Slee
Ground: Hadley Sports Ground, Brickfield Lane, Arkley, Barnet EN5 3LD   **(T)** 07905 446 331
Capacity: 2,000 **Seats:** 150   **Covered:** 250   **Midweek Matchday:**   **Clubhouse:** Yes   **Shop:** Yes
Colours(change): Red/black/black (Yellow/white/white)
Previous Names: None
Previous Leagues: Barnet & Dist. 1922-57, North Suburban 1957-70, Mid-Herts 1970-77, Herts Senior County 1977-85, 99-2007, Southern Olymian 1985-99, West Herts 2007-08.
HONOURS: FA Comps: None
    League: Mid-Herts Premier 1975-76, 76-77. Hertfordshire Senior County Division Three 1977-78, Division One 2001-02, Premier 2003-04, 04-05. West Hertfordshire 2007-08.

10 YEAR RECORD

07-08	08-09	09-10	10-11	11-12	12-13	13-14	14-15	15-16	16-17
WHert 1	SSM2 2	SSM1 2	SSM P 14	SSM P 15	SSM P 12	SSM P 13	SSM P 9	SSM P 6	SSM P 19
			FAC EPr	FAC EPr	FAC P	FAC P	FAC EPr	FAC EP	FAC 3Qr
	FAV 2P	FAV 2Q	FAV 1P	FAV 1Pr	FAV P	FAV 2P	FAV 2Qr	FAV 1P	FAV 1Q

HARPENDEN TOWN
Founded: 1891 **Nickname:** Town

Secretary: Stephen Hartnup **(T)** 07796 955 197 **(E)** stephen@hartnup.com
Chairman: Roman Motyczak **Manager:** Danny Plumb **Prog Ed:** Ray Collins
Ground: Rothamstead Park, Amenbury Lane, Harpenden AL5 2EF **(T)** 07734700226/07702604771
Capacity: **Seats:** Yes **Covered:** Yes **Midweek Matchday:** **Clubhouse:** Yes

Colours(change): Yellow & blue
Previous Names: Harpenden FC 1891-1908.
Previous Leagues: Herts Senior County (founder member) 1898-1900, 1908-22, 48-57. Mid-Herts 1900-08. South Midlands 1957-97.

HONOURS: FA Comps: None
League: Herts Senior County Western Division 1910-11, 11-12, 20-21, Premier 50-51, 52-53, 54-55.
10 YEAR RECORD South Midlands Division One 1989-90, Premier 61-62, 64-65.

	07-08	08-09	09-10	10-11	11-12	12-13	13-14	14-15	15-16	16-17
	SSM1 16	SSM1 8	SSM1 12	SSM1 7	SSM1 5	SSM1 7	SSM1 8	SSM1 6	SSM1 4	SSM1 2
										FAC P
	FAV 1P	FAV 1Q	FAV 2Q						FAV 2Q	FAV 1Q

HODDESDON TOWN
Founded: 1879 **Nickname:** Lilywhites

Secretary: Jane Sinden **(T)** 01767 247 526 **(E)** janedsinden@fsmail.net
Chairman: Roger Merton **Manager:** Paul Halsey **Prog Ed:** Jane Sinden
Ground: Wodson Park, Wadesmill Road, Ware, Herts SG12 0UQ **(T)** 01920 462 064
Capacity: 3,000 **Seats:** 100 **Covered:** Yes **Midweek Matchday:** **Clubhouse:** Yes

Colours(change): White/black/black (All blue)
Previous Names: None
Previous Leagues: Hertfordshire County 1920-25. Spartan 1963-75. London Spartan 1975-77. Athenian 1977-84.

HONOURS: FA Comps: FA Vase 1974-75 (1st Winners).
League: Spartan 1970-71, Division One 1935-36, Division Two 'B' 1927-28.
10 YEAR RECORD

	07-08	08-09	09-10	10-11	11-12	12-13	13-14	14-15	15-16	16-17
	SSM1 3	SSM1 5	SSM1 4	SSM1 9	SSM1 3	SSM1 3	SSM1 3	SSM P 6	SSM P 19	SSM P 3	SSM P 7
	FAC EP	FAC EP	FAC P	FAC EP	FAC EP	FAC EPr	FAC EPr	FAC EPr	FAC P	FAC 3Qr	FAC P
	FAV 2Q	FAV 1Q	FAV 3P	FAV 1Q	FAV 1P	FAV 1P	FAV 2Q	FAV P	FAV 2Q	FAV 1P	FAV 3P

HOLMER GREEN
Founded: 1908 **Nickname:** The Greens

Secretary: Matt Brades **(T)** 07801 216 632 **(E)** bradesm@dnb.com
Chairman: Rob Shed **Manager:** Chris Allen **Prog Ed:** John Anderson
Ground: Airedale Park, Watchet Lane, Holmer Green, Bucks HP15 6UF **(T)** 01494 711 485
Capacity: 1,000 **Seats:** 25 **Covered:** yes **Midweek Matchday:** Tuesday **Clubhouse:** Yes

Colours(change): Green & white stripes/green/green
Previous Names: None
Previous Leagues: Chesham & District 1908-38, Wycombe Combination 1984-95, Chiltonian 1995-98.

HONOURS: FA Comps: None
League: Wycombe Combination 1971-72, 73-74, 76-77, 80-81. Chiltonian Prmeier 1984-85, 85-86, 93-94.
10 YEAR RECORD South Midlands Senior 1995-96. Spartan South Midlands 1998-99, Division One 2009-10.

	07-08	08-09	09-10	10-11	11-12	12-13	13-14	14-15	15-16	16-17
	SSM P 20	SSM P 20	SSM1 1	SSM P 17	SSM P 20	SSM P 22	SSM P 12	SSM P 20	SSM P 7	SSM P 14
	FAC EP				FAC EP	FAC EP	FAC EP	FAC Pr	FAC EP	FAC EP
	FAV 1P			FAV 1Q	FAV 1Q	FAV 2Q	FAV 2Q	FAV 1Pr	FAV 1Q	FAV 2P

LEIGHTON TOWN
Founded: 1885 **Nickname:** Reds

Secretary: Sheelah McGregor **(T)** 07967 398 429 **(E)** sheelahm@hotmail.com
Chairman: Iain McGregor **Manager:** Scott Reynolds
Ground: Lake Street, Leighton Buzzard, Beds LU7 1RX **(T)** 01525 373 311
Capacity: 2,800 **Seats:** 400 **Covered:** 300 **Midweek Matchday:** **Clubhouse:** Yes

Colours(change): Red & white
Previous Names: Leighton United 1922-63
Previous Leagues: Leighton & District, South Midlands 1922-24, 26-29, 46-54, 55-56, 76-92, Spartan 1922-53, 67-74,

HONOURS: FA Comps: None
League: South Midlands 1966-67, 91-92. Isthmian Division Two 2003-04.
10 YEAR RECORD

	07-08	08-09	09-10	10-11	11-12	12-13	13-14	14-15	15-16	16-17
	SthM 9	SthM 8	SthM 10	SthC 7	SthC 13	SthC 21	SthC 19	SthC 18	SthC 21	SSM P 16
	FAC 4Q	FAC 2Q	FAC Pr	FAC 1Q	FAC 3Q	FAC Pr	FAC P	FAC P	FAC 1Q	FAC EP
	FAT 1Qr	FAT 1Q	FAT 1Q	FAT P	FAT 1Q	FAT P	FAT P	FAT 1Qr	FAT 1Q	FAV 2Q

LEVERSTOCK GREEN
Founded: 1895   Nickname: The Green

Secretary: Brian Barter   **(T)** 07982 072 783   **(E)** b.barter@btopenworld.com
Chairman: Nicholas Christou   **Manager:** Scott Dash   **Prog Ed:** Brian Barter
Ground: Pancake Lane, Leverstock Green, Hemel Hempstead, Herts HP2 4NQ   **(T)** 01442 246 280
Capacity: 1,500 **Seats:** 50   **Covered:** 100   **Midweek Matchday:** Tuesday   **Clubhouse:** Yes

Colours(change): White/green/green (Gold/black/gold)
Previous Names: None
Previous Leagues: West Herts (pre 1954) & Herts Senior County 1954-91. South Midlands 1991-97.

HONOURS: FA Comps: None
League: Herts Senior County Division One 1978-79.
10 YEAR RECORD South Midlands Senior Division 1996-97.

07-08	08-09	09-10	10-11	11-12	12-13	13-14	14-15	15-16	16-17
SSM P 7	SSM P 6	SSM P 10	SSM P 4	SSM P 11	SSM P 15	SSM P 20	SSM P 15	SSM P 18	SSM P 12
FAC EP	FAC EP	FAC EP	FAC EP	FAC EP	FAC EP	FAC EP	FAC 2Q	FAC EP	FAC EP
FAV 1P	FAV 1P	FAV 1P	FAV 5P	FAV 2Pr	FAV 1Q	FAV 1Q	FAV 2Q	FAV 2Q	FAV 2P

LONDON COLNEY
Founded: 1907   Nickname: Blueboys

Secretary: Johnny Armitt   **(T)**   **(E)**
Chairman: Gareth Davies   **Manager:** Ken Charlery
Ground: Cotlandswick Playing Fields, London Colney, Herts AL2 1DW   **(T)** 01727 822 132
Capacity: 1,000 **Seats:** Yes   **Covered:** Yes   **Midweek Matchday:**   **Clubhouse:** Yes

Colours(change): All royal blue (All red)
Previous Names: None
Previous Leagues: Herts Senior 1955-93.

HONOURS: FA Comps: None
League: Herts Senior County 1956-57, 59-60, 86-87, 88-89. 89-90. South Midlands Senior Division 1994-95. Spartan
10 YEAR RECORD South Midlands Premier Division 2001-02, 16-17, Division One 2011-12.

07-08	08-09	09-10	10-11	11-12	12-13	13-14	14-15	15-16	16-17
SSM P 22	SSM1 9	SSM1 3	SSM1 5	SSM1 1	SSM P 7	SSM P 7	SSM P 2	SSM P 2	SSM P 1
FAC EP	FAC EPr	FAC 1Qr	FAC 1Q	FAC EP	FAC P	FAC EPr	FAC 1Q	FAC P	FAC 1Q
FAV 1Q	FAV 2Q	FAV 2P	FAV 1Q	FAV 1Q	FAV 2Q	FAV 1Q	FAV 3P	FAV 2P	FAV 3P

LONDON TIGERS
Founded: 1986   Nickname: Tigers

Secretary: Mick Wilkins   **(T)** 07802 212 787   **(E)** wilki1@aol.com
Chairman: Mesba Ahmed
Ground: Avenue Park, Western Avenue, Perivale, Greenford UB6 8GA   **(T)** 020 7289 3395 (10am-6pm)
Capacity: **Seats:** Yes   **Covered:** Yes   **Midweek Matchday:**   **Clubhouse:** Yes

Colours(change): Orange/black/black (Yellow & black stripes/black/black)
Previous Names: Marylebone 1986-97. London Tigers then merged with Kingsbury Town 2006. Kingsbury London Tigers 2006-11.
Previous Leagues: None

HONOURS: FA Comps: None
League: None
10 YEAR RECORD

07-08	08-09	09-10	10-11	11-12	12-13	13-14	14-15	15-16	16-17
SSM P 14	SSM P 5	SSM P 8	SSM P 12	SSM P 14	SSM P 20	SSM P 15	SSM P 17	SSM P 13	SSM P 21
	FAC P	FAC 1Q	FAC EP			FAC P	FAC 2Q	FAC EPr	FAC EPr
FAV 2Q	FAV 2Q	FAV 1P	FAV 1Q		FAV 2Q	FAV 1Q	FAV 1Q	FAV 1P	FAV 2Q

OXHEY JETS
Founded: 1972   Nickname: Jets

Secretary: David Fuller   **(T)** 07786 627 659   **(E)** d.g.fuller@ntlworld.com
Chairman: Phil Andrews
Ground: Boundary Stadium, Altham Way, South Oxhey, Watford WD19 6FW   **(T)** 020 8421 6277
Capacity: 1,000 **Seats:** 150   **Covered:** 100   **Midweek Matchday:** Wednesday   **Clubhouse:** Yes   **Shop:** No

Colours(change): All blue
Previous Names: None
Previous Leagues: Youth Leagues > 1981. Herts Senior County 1981-2004.

HONOURS: FA Comps: None
League: Herts Senior County Premier 2000-01, 01-02, 02-03. Spartan South Midladns Division One 2004-2005.
10 YEAR RECORD

07-08	08-09	09-10	10-11	11-12	12-13	13-14	14-15	15-16	16-17
SSM P 19	SSM P 13	SSM P 11	SSM P 19	SSM P 17	SSM P 3	SSM P 18	SSM P 12	SSM P 17	SSM P 15
FAC P	FAC 1Q	FAC EP	FAC 1Q	FAC 2Q	FAC P	FAC EPr	FAC EP	FAC EPr	FAC P
FAV 2Q	FAV 1P	FAV 2Q	FAV 2Q	FAV 1P	FAV 3P	FAV 2P	FAV 2P	FAV 2Q	FAV 1P

ST MARGARETSBURY

Founded: 1894   **Nickname: The Bury**

Secretary: Phil Hayward   **(T)** 07721 415 579   **(E)** smfc@niche-direct.com
Chairman: Gary Stock   **Prog Ed:** Gary Stock
Ground: Recreation Ground, Station Road, St Margarets SG12 8EH   **(T)** 01920 870 473
Capacity: 1,000 **Seats:** 60   **Covered:** 60   **Midweek Matchday:** Tuesday   **Clubhouse:** Yes

Colours(change): Red & black hoops/black/red & black hoops (Yellow & black stripes/yellow/black)
Previous Names: Stanstead Abbots > 1962
Previous Leagues: East Herts, Hertford & District, Waltham & District 1947-48, Herts Senior County 1948-92.

HONOURS: FA Comps: None
League: Spartan 1995-96.

10 YEAR RECORD									
07-08	08-09	09-10	10-11	11-12	12-13	13-14	14-15	15-16	16-17
SSM P 11	SSM P 14	SSM P 14	SSM P 18	SSM P 12	SSM P 4	SSM P 4	SSM P 8	SSM P 19	SSM P 20
FAC P	FAC EP	FAC P	FAC P	FAC EP	FAC 1Q	FAC 1Q	FAC P	FAC P	FAC EP
FAV 1P	FAV 1P	FAV 2Q	FAV 1Q	FAV 2Q	FAV 2Q	FAV 1P	FAV 3P	FAV 1Q	FAV 3P

STOTFOLD

Founded: 1904   **Nickname: The Eagles**

Secretary: Julie Longhurst   **(T)** 07752 430 493   **(E)** julie.longhurst46@virginmedia.com
Chairman: Phil Pateman   **Manager:** Mick Reardon   **Prog Ed:** Phil Pateman
Ground: Roker Park, The Green, Stotfold, Hitchin, Herts SG5 4AN   **(T)** 01462 730 765
Capacity: 5,000 **Seats:** 300   **Covered:** 300   **Midweek Matchday:** Tuesday   **Clubhouse:** Yes

Colours(change): Amber/black/black. (All blue).
Previous Names: Stotfold Athletic.
Previous Leagues: Biggleswade & District, North Herts & South Midlands, United Counties > 2010

HONOURS: FA Comps: None
League: South Midlands 1980-81. United Counties Premier 2007-08.

10 YEAR RECORD									
07-08	08-09	09-10	10-11	11-12	12-13	13-14	14-15	15-16	16-17
UCL P 1	UCL P 2	UCL P 7	SSM P 13	SSM P 9	SSM P 14	SSM P 19	SSM P 16	SSM P 15	SSM P 13
FAC 3Q	FAC 1Q	FAC EP	FAC EP	FAC 1Q	FAC Pr	FAC P	FAC EP	FAC EP	FAC 1Q
FAV 1P	FAV 1P	FAV 4P	FAV 3P	FAV 1Q	FAV 1Q	FAV 1P	FAV 2Q	FAV 2P	FAV 1Qr

SUN SPORTS

Founded: 1898   **Nickname: The Sun**

Secretary: Dave Mason   **(T)**   **(E)**
Chairman: James Kempster   **Manager:** Tim O'Sullivan
Ground: Sun Postal Sports Club, Bellmountwood Avenue, Watford, Herts WD17 3BN   **(T)** 01923 227 453
Capacity: 500 **Seats:** 35   **Covered:** Yes   **Midweek Matchday:**   **Clubhouse:** Yes

Colours(change): Yellow/royal blue/royal blue (All red)
Previous Names: Sun Engraving FC 1898-1935. Sun Sports 1935-95. Sun Postal Sports 1995-2014.
Previous Leagues: Watford & District. Hertfordshire Senior County 1935-2003.

HONOURS: FA Comps: None
League: Herts Senior County 1992-93, 93-94.

10 YEAR RECORD	Spartan South Midlands Division One 2013-14.								
07-08	08-09	09-10	10-11	11-12	12-13	13-14	14-15	15-16	16-17
SSM1 17	SSM1 20	SSM1 14	SSM1 11	SSM1 22	SSM1 17	SSM1 1	SSM P 5	SSM P 14	SSM P 10
								FAC EP	FAC 1Q
FAV 1Q	FAV 1P						FAV 2P	FAV 1Q	FAV 4P

TRING ATHLETIC

Founded: 1958   **Nickname: Athletic**

Secretary: Bob Winter   **(T)** 07979 816 528   **(E)** tringathleticfc@hotmail.com
Chairman: Howard Wells OBE   **Manager:** Ian Richardson
Ground: Grass Roots Stadium, Pendley Sports Centre, Cow Lane, Tring HP23 5NS   **(T)** 01442 891 144
Capacity: 2,000 **Seats:** 125   **Covered:** 100+   **Midweek Matchday:** Tuesday   **Clubhouse:** Yes   **Shop:** Yes

Colours(change): Red/black/black (Yellow/green/green)
Previous Names: Tring Athletic Youth 1958-71.
Previous Leagues: West Herts 1958-88.

HONOURS: FA Comps: None
League: West Herts Division One 1961-62, 64-65, 65-66.

10 YEAR RECORD	Spartan South Midlands Senior Division 1999-2000.								
07-08	08-09	09-10	10-11	11-12	12-13	13-14	14-15	15-16	16-17
SSM P 10	SSM P 8	SSM P 3	SSM P 2	SSM P 6	SSM P 22	SSM P 10	SSM P 10	SSM P 12	SSM P 5
FAC Pr	FAC P	FAC P	FAC 1Q	FAC P	FAC Pr	FAC P	FAC EP	FAC P	FAC EP
FAV 2P	FAV 1Q	FAV 2Q	FAV 3P	FAV 2P	FAV 1Q	FAV 3P	FAV 3P	FAV 1P	FAV 4P

WELWYN GARDEN CITY
Founded: 1921   Nickname: Citizens

Secretary: Karen Fisher   **(T)**   **(E)** welwyngardencityfc@gmail.com
Chairman: Ollie Croft   **Manager:** Adam Fisher   **Prog Ed:** Karen Browne
Ground: Herns Lane, Welwyn Garden City, Herts AL7 1TA   **(T)** 01707 329 358
Capacity: **Seats:** Yes   **Covered:** Yes   **Midweek Matchday:**   **Clubhouse:** Yes

Colours(change): Claret & sky blue
Previous Names: Original club folded in 1935 and was reformed in 1937.
Previous Leagues: Mid-Herts 1922-26, 1944-46. Bedfordshire & District 1926-27. Spartan 1927-35, 37-39, 46-50, 55-59. London 1950-55. Herts Senior County 1959-70. Greater London 1970-71. Metropolitan London (FM) 1971-73. South Midlands 1973-97.
HONOURS: FA Comps: None
League: South Midlands 1973-74, Division One 1981-82. Spartan South Midlands Division One 2014-15.

10 YEAR RECORD

07-08		08-09		09-10		10-11		11-12		12-13		13-14		14-15		15-16		16-17	
SSM P	16	SSM P	9	SSM P	22	SSM1	17	SSM1	17	SSM1	13	SSM1	4	SSM1	1	SSM P	4	SSM P	6
FAC	1Q	FAC	EP	FAC	EP	FAC	EP	FAC	EP							FAC	1Q	FAC	P
FAV	1P	FAV	1Q	FAV	1Q	FAV	2Q	FAV	1Q	FAV	1Q	FAV	3P	FAV	1P	FAV	1P	FAV	3P

WEMBLEY
Founded: 1946   Nickname: The Lions

Secretary: Mrs Jean Gumm   **(T)** 07876 125 784   **(E)** general@wembleyfc.com
Chairman: Brian Gumm
Ground: Vale Farm, Watford Road, Sudbury, Wembley HA0 3HG.   **(T)** 0208 904 8169
Capacity: 2450   **Seats:** 350   **Covered:** 950   **Midweek Matchday:** Tuesday   **Clubhouse:** Yes   **Shop:** No

Colours(change): Red & white
Previous Names: None
Previous Leagues: Middlesex Senior. Spartan. Delphian. Corinthian. Athenian. Isthmian.

HONOURS: FA Comps: None
League: Middlesex Senior 1947-48. Spartan Western Division 1950-51.

10 YEAR RECORD

07-08		08-09		09-10		10-11		11-12		12-13		13-14		14-15		15-16		16-17	
CCP	14	CCP	17	CCP	15	CCP	14	CCP	10	CCP	15	CCP	9	SSM P	7	SSM P	11	SSM P	4
FAC	P	FAC	EPr	FAC	EP	FAC	EP	FAC	1Q	FAC	Pr	FAC	1Q	FAC	EPr	FAC	Pr	FAC	Pr
FAV	3P	FAV	2Q	FAV	2P	FAV	2Q	FAV	2Qr	FAV	1P	FAV	1P	FAV	2P	FAV	1Q	FAV	3P

Spartan South Midlands Division Two

AFC SOUTHGATE	Brickfield Lane, Arkley, Barnet EN5 3LD	020 8360 4273
AMERSHAM TOWN	Spratleys Meadow, School Lane, Amersham, Bucks HP7 0EL	07816 193 109
ASTON CLINTON	Aston Clinton Park, London Road, Aston Clinton HP22 5HL	07890 624 397
BERKHAMSTED RAIDERS	Ashlyns School, Chesham Road, Berkhamsted HP4 3AH	07515 310 059
CLEAN SLATE	The Downs Barn Pavilion, Pannier Place, Downs Barn, Milton Keynes MK14 7QP	01908 617 496
GRENDON RANGERS	The Village Hall, Main Street, Grendon Underwood, Aylesbury, Bucks. HP18 0SP	07979 470 734
LOUGHTON MANOR	Loughton Sports & Social Club, Linceslade Grove, Loughton, Milton Keynes MK5 8DJ	07775 643 830
MK GALACTICOS	North Furzton Sports Ground, Lynmouth Crescent, Milton Keynes MK4 1HD	07739 471 364
MURSLEY UNITED	The Playing Field, Station Road, Mursley MK17 0SA	07512 663 648
OLD BRADWELL UNITED	Stony Stratford FC, Ostlers Lane, Milton Keynes MK11 1AR	07914 012 709
PARK VIEW	New River Stadium, White Hart Lane, Wood Green N22 5QW	
PITSTONE AND IVINGHOE	Pitstone Pavilion & Sports Hall, Marsworth Road, Pitstone LU7 9AP	07732 309 520
THE 61 FC (LUTON)	Kingsway Ground, Beverley Road, Luton LU4 8EU	07749 531 492
TOTTERNHOE	Totternhoe Recreation Ground, Dunstable Road, Totternhoe, Beds LU6 1QP	01582 606 738
TRING CORINTHIANS	Icknield Way, Tring, Herts HP23 5HJ	07886 528 214
TRING TOWN AFC	Miswell Lane Pavilion, Miswell Lane, Tring HP23 4EX	07720 535 355
UNITE MK	MK Irish Club, Manor Fields, Watling Street, Bletchley, Milton Keynes MK2 2HX	01908 375 978

AMPTHILL TOWN
Founded: 1881 Nickname:

Secretary: Eric Turner **(T)** 07887 872 632 **(E)** ericturner789@btinternet.com
Chairman: Lee Roberts **Manager:** Adam Dedman **Prog Ed:** Eric Turner
Ground: Ampthill Park, Woburn Street, Ampthill MK45 2HX **(T)** 01525 404 440
Colours(change): Yellow/blue/blue (Orange/black/black)
HONOURS: FA Comps: None **League:** South Midlands Premier Division 1959-60.

10 YEAR RECORD									
07-08	08-09	09-10	10-11	11-12	12-13	13-14	14-15	15-16	16-17
SSM1 7	SSM1 15	SSM1 13	SSM1 16	SSM1 2	SSM P 5	SSM P 2	SSM P 21	SSM1 14	SSM1 14
	FAC P	FAC EP	FAC EP		FAC EP	FAC P	FAC EP	FAC EP	
FAV 3P	FAV 1Q	FAV 1Q	FAV 2Q	FAV 4P	FAV 5P	FAV QF	FAV 2P	FAV 1Q	FAV 1Q

BALDOCK TOWN
Founded: 1905 Nickname: The Reds

Secretary: Heather Frankland **(T)** 07460 823 414 **(E)**
Chairman: Graham Kingham **Manager:** Luke Gregson
Ground: Arlesey Town FC, Armadillo Stadium, Hitchin Road, Arlesey SG15 6RS **(T)** 07968 215 395
Colours(change): All red (All navy blue)
HONOURS: FA Comps: None **League:** Herts Senior County Northern Div. 1920-21, Div.1 2007-08, Premier 11-12. South
Midlands Div.2 47-38, Div.1 49-50, Premier 27-28, 65-66, 67-68, 69-70.

10 YEAR RECORD									
07-08	08-09	09-10	10-11	11-12	12-13	13-14	14-15	15-16	16-17
Hert1 1	HertP 3	HertP 3	HertP 4	HertP 1	HertP 2	SSM1 7	SSM1 10	SSM1 3	SSM1 3
							FAC P	FAC EP	FAC EP
		FAV 1Q	FAV 1P			FAV 1P	FAV 1P	FAV 2Q	FAV 1P

BEDFORD
Founded: 1957 Nickname: The B's

Secretary: Paolo Riccio **(T)** 07983 396 750 **(E)** paoloriccio@btinternet.com
Chairman: Lui La Mura **Manager:** Russell Jones **Prog Ed:** Paolo Riccio
Ground: McMullen Park, Meadow Lane, Cardington, Bedford, MK44 3SB **(T)** 07831 594 444
Colours(change): Black & white
HONOURS: FA Comps: None **League:** None

10 YEAR RECORD									
07-08	08-09	09-10	10-11	11-12	12-13	13-14	14-15	15-16	16-17
SSM1 9	SSM1 14	SSM1 9	SSM1 13	SSM1 12	SSM1 5	SSM1 3	SSM1 3	SSM P 22	SSM1 19
FAC P	FAC EP	FAC EP	FAC EP	FAC EP			FAC EP	FAC EP	FAC EP
FAV 2Q	FAV 1Q	FAV 2P	FAV 2Q	FAV 2Q		FAV 1Q	FAV 2Q	FAV 1Q	FAV 1Q

BRIMSDOWN
Founded: 2013 Nickname: The Limers

Secretary: Gulay Nil Ermiya **(T)** 07984 409 955 **(E)** gulayermiya1996@googlemail.com
Chairman: Alp Ermiya **Manager:** Halil Hassan
Ground: Haringey Borough FC, Coles Park, White Hart Lane, Tottenham, London N17 7JP **(T)** 0208 889 1415
Colours(change): Yellow & navy
HONOURS: FA Comps: None **League:** None

10 YEAR RECORD									
07-08	08-09	09-10	10-11	11-12	12-13	13-14	14-15	15-16	16-17
						SSM2 13	SSM2 4	SSM1 15	SSM1 17
								FAV 2Q	

BROADFIELDS UNITED
Founded: 1993 Nickname: The Fighting Cocks

Secretary: Chris Webster **(T)** 07944 370 116 **(E)** websterlocke@aol.com
Chairman:
Ground: Harefield United FC, Breakspear Road North, Harefield, Middlesex UB9 6NE **(T)** 01895 823 474
Colours(change): All blue
HONOURS: FA Comps: None **League:** Southern Olympian Division Four 1994-95.
Middlesex County Senior Division 1996-97.

10 YEAR RECORD									
07-08	08-09	09-10	10-11	11-12	12-13	13-14	14-15	15-16	16-17
Midx1W 11	MidxP 9	MidxP Exp	MidxP 5	MidxP 8	MidxP 5	MidxP 15	MidxP 4	SSM1 11	SSM1 11
						FAV 2Q	FAV 1Q	FAV 1Q	FAV 2P

BUCKINGHAM ATHELTIC

Founded: 1933   Nickname: The Ath

Secretary: Colin Howkins   **(T)** 07751 659 769   **(E)** colin@thehowkins.co.uk
Chairman: Tony Checkley   **Manager:** Mark Carter   **Prog Ed:** Tony Checkley
Ground: Stratford Fields, Stratford Road, Buckingham MK18 1NY   **(T)** 01280 816 945 (MD)
Colours(change): Sky blue & navy blue
HONOURS: FA Comps: None   **League:** North Bucks Premier Division 1984-85. South Midlands Division One 1985 -86, 90-91, Spartan South Midlands Division Two 2002-03.

10 YEAR RECORD

07-08	08-09	09-10	10-11	11-12	12-13	13-14	14-15	15-16	16-17
SSM1 13	SSM1 19	SSM1 16	SSM1 18	SSM1 18	SSM1 11	SSM1 13	SSM1 15	SSM1 8	SSM1 10
FAV 2Q	FAV 1Q	FAV 1Q	FAV 1Qr	FAV 1Q	FAV 2Q	FAV 2Q	FAV 1Qr	FAV 2Q	FAV 1Q

CODICOTE

Founded: 1913   Nickname: The Cod

Secretary: Ian Moody   **(T)** 07980 920 674   **(E)** codicote.fc@hotmail.co.uk
Chairman: Jim Bundy   **Manager:** Gifton Noel-Williams & James Tizard
Ground: John Clementsts Memorial Ground, Bury Lane, Codicote SG4 8XY   **(T)** 01438 821 072
Colours(change): Red & black
HONOURS: FA Comps: None   **League:** North Herts Division One 1929-30, 74-75, Division Two 68-69, Premier 77-78

10 YEAR RECORD

07-08	08-09	09-10	10-11	11-12	12-13	13-14	14-15	15-16	16-17
HertP 9	HertP 5	HertP 7	HertP 5	HertP 3	SSM1 8	SSM1 10	SSM1 8	SSM1 10	SSM1 13
						FAC EPr	FAC Pr	FAC EP	
	FAV 1P	FAV 2Q	FAV 1Q	FAV 2Q	FAV 1P	FAV 2Q	FAV 1Q	FAV 1Q	FAV 1Q

ENFIELD BOROUGH

Founded: 2016   Nickname: Panthers

Secretary: Jenny Pittordis   **(T)**   **(E)**
Chairman: Joseph Salih   **Manager:** Marvin Walker
Ground: Enfield Town FC, Donkey Lane, Enfield EN1 3PL   **(T)** 07493 377 484
Colours(change): Red & black
HONOURS: FA Comps: None   **League:** None

10 YEAR RECORD

07-08	08-09	09-10	10-11	11-12	12-13	13-14	14-15	15-16	16-17
									SSM2 3

FC BROXBOURNE BOROUGH

Founded: 1959   Nickname: Boro

Secretary: Graham Dodd   **(T)** 07973 701 515   **(E)** graham@leterboxconsultancy.co.uk
Chairman: John Murphy   **Prog Ed:** Graham Dodd
Ground: Broxbourne Borough V & E Club, Goffs Lane, Cheshunt, Herts EN7 5QN   **(T)** 01992 624 281   **Capacity:** 5,000
Colours(change): All blue
HONOURS: FA Comps: None   **League:** Herts Senior County Division One 1993-94.

10 YEAR RECORD

07-08	08-09	09-10	10-11	11-12	12-13	13-14	14-15	15-16	16-17
SSM P 12	SSM P 4	SSM P 9	SSM P 10	SSM P 13	SSM2 3	SSM1 6	SSM1 2	SSM P 16	SSM P 22
FAC 1Qr	FAC Pr	FAC EP	FAC EP	FAC 1Q				FAC EP	FAC EP
FAV 2Q	FAV 2Q	FAV 1P	FAV 1Q	FAV 1Q		FAV 1Q	FAV 2Q	FAV 3P	FAV 2Q

HAREFIELD UNITED

Founded: 1868   Nickname: Hares

Secretary: Ray Green   **(T)** 07834 771212   **(E)** rayigreen1@btinternet.com
Chairman: Gary South   **Manager:** Jason Shaw   **Prog Ed:** Ray Green
Ground: Preston Park, Breakespeare Road North, Harefield, UB9 6NE   **(T)** 01895 823 474   **Capacity:** 1,200
Colours(change): Red & black
HONOURS: FA Comps: None   **League:** Great Western Comb. Division Two 1947-48, Division One 50-51. Parthenon 1964-65.

10 YEAR RECORD

07-08	08-09	09-10	10-11	11-12	12-13	13-14	14-15	15-16	16-17
SSM P 5	SSM P 2	SSM P 6	SSM P 21	SSM P 18	SSM P 10	SSM P 14	SSM P 4	SSM P 21	SSM1 8
FAC EP	FAC Pr	FAC 2Q	FAC P	FAC Pr	FAC 2Qr	FAC P	FAC P	FAC EPr	FAC 1Q
FAV 4P	FAV 3P	FAV 1P	FAV 2Q	FAV 1Q	FAV 1Q	FAV 1Q	FAV 1P	FAV 1P	FAV 2Q

HATFIELD TOWN

Founded: 1886   Nickname: Blue Boys

Secretary: Joanne Maloney   **(T)** 07725 071 014   **(E)** secretary@hatfieldtownfc.co.uk
Chairman: Chris Maloney   **Manager:** Kev Pearman
Ground: Gosling Sport Park, Stanborough Rd, Welwyn Garden City, Herts AL8 6XE   **(T)** 01707 384 300   **Capacity:** 1,500
Colours(change): All royal blue
HONOURS: FA Comps: None   **League:** Herts Senior Eastern Division 1911-12, 19-20, Premier 1935-36, 37-38, 38-39, 91-92, 2007-08, Division Two 89-90, Division One 90-91, 2001-02, 02-03.

10 YEAR RECORD

07-08	08-09	09-10	10-11	11-12	12-13	13-14	14-15	15-16	16-17
HertP 1	SSM1 3	SSM P 12	SSM P 11	SSM P 22	SSM P 21	SSM P 21	SSM1 4	SSM1 17	SSM1 20
	FAC P	FAC P	FAC EP	FAC 2Q	FAC EP	FAC EP	FAC EP		
FAV 1P	FAV 1Q	FAV 1Q	FAV 1Q	FAV 1Q	FAV 2P	FAV 2Q	FAV 1Q		FAV 1Q

HILLINGDON BOROUGH

Founded: 1990   Nickname: Boro

Secretary: Nicki Gill   **(T)** 07734 472 137   **(E)** accounts@middlesexstadium.com
Chairman: Dee Dhand   **Manager:** Ian Crane   **Prog Ed:** Bart Accardo
Ground: Middlesex Stadium, Breakspear Rd, Ruislip HA4 7SB   **(T)** 01895 639 544   **Capacity:** 1,500
Colours(change): White & royal blue
HONOURS: FA Comps: None   **League:** None

10 YEAR RECORD

07-08	08-09	09-10	10-11	11-12	12-13	13-14	14-15	15-16	16-17
SthW 13	Isth1N 22	SSM P 18	SSM P 16	SSM P 10	SSM P 19	SSM P 11	SSM P 22	SSM1 16	SSM1 9
FAC 3Q	FAC 1Q	FAC EP	FAC EP	FAC EP	FAC EP	FAC P	FAC EP	FAC EPr	
FAT 2Qr	FAT P	FAV 1P	FAV 1P	FAV 1P	FAV 2Q	FAV 1P	FAV 2Q	FAV 1Q	FAV 2Q

LANGFORD

Founded: 1908   Nickname: Reds

Secretary: Ian Chessum   **(T)** 07749 102 060   **(E)** ianchessum@hotmail.com
Chairman: Ian Chessum   **Manager:** Rob Bates   **Prog Ed:** Ian Chessum
Ground: Forde Park, Langford Road, Henlow, Beds SG16 6AF   **(T)** 01462 816 106   **Capacity:** 2,000
Colours(change): Red & white stripes/red/red (All blue).
HONOURS: FA Comps: None   **League:** Bedford & District 1931-32, 49-50. South Midlands Premier Division 1988-89.

10 YEAR RECORD

07-08	08-09	09-10	10-11	11-12	12-13	13-14	14-15	15-16	16-17
SSM P 6	SSM P 11	SSM P 19	SSM P 23	SSM1 10	SSM1 16	SSM1 19	SSM1 13	SSM1 18	SSM1 4
FAC Pr	FAC P	FAC EP	FAC EP	FAC EP					
FAV 1Q	FAV 2Q	FAV 1P	FAV 1P	FAV 1Q	FAV 2Q	FAV 1Q	FAV 1Qr	FAV 1Q	FAV 1Q

LONDON LIONS

Founded: 1995   Nickname: Lions

Secretary: Marta Ghermandi   **(T)**   **(E)** clubsec@londonlions.com
Chairman: Andrew Landesberg   **Manager:** Andrew Landesberg   **Prog Ed:** Dan Jacobs
Ground: Rowley Lane Sports Ground, Rowley Lane, Barnet EN5 3HW   **(T)** 0208 441 6051   **Capacity:** 1,500
Colours(change): All blue (White & blue)
HONOURS: FA Comps: None   **League:** Hertfordshire Senior County Division One 1999-2000, Premier 09-10, 16-17. Spartan South Midlands Division One 2012-13.

10 YEAR RECORD

07-08	08-09	09-10	10-11	11-12	12-13	13-14	14-15	15-16	16-17
HertP 7	HertP 2	HertP 1	SSM1 8	SSM1 7	SSM1 1	SSM P 22	SSM1 17	HertP 5	HertP 1
					FAC 1Q	FAC EPr			
				FAV 1Q	FAV 2P	FAV 2Q			FAV 1Q

RAYNERS LANE

Founded: 1933   Nickname: The Lane

Secretary: Tony Pratt   **(T)** 01895 233 853   **(E)** richard.mitchell@tesco.net
Chairman: Martin Noblett   **Manager:** David Fox   **Prog Ed:** Richard Mitchell
Ground: Tithe Farm Social Club, Rayners Lane, South Harrow HA2 0XH   **(T)** 0208 868 8724
Colours(change): Yellow/green/yellow (Green/blue/green)
HONOURS: FA Comps: None   **League:** Hellenic Division One 1982-83, Division One East 2012-13.

10 YEAR RECORD

07-08	08-09	09-10	10-11	11-12	12-13	13-14	14-15	15-16	16-17
Hel1E 13	Hel1E 14	Hel1E 12	Hel1E 7	Hel1E 3	Hel1E 1	Hel1E 9	Hel1E 7	Hel1E 5	Hel1E 11
								FAV 2Q	FAV 2Q

SPARTAN SOUTH MIDLANDS LEAGUE - STEP 5/6/7

RISBOROUGH RANGERS
Founded: 1971   Nickname: Rangers or Boro

Secretary: Nick Bishop   **(T)** 07855 958 236   **(E)** nick@lloydlatchford.co.uk
Chairman: Richard Woodward   **Manager:** Jamie Rayner   **Prog Ed:** Richard Woodward
Ground: "Windsors" Horsenden Lane, Princes Risborough. Bucks HP27 9NE   **(T)** 07849 843632 (MD only)   **Capacity:** 1,500
Colours(change): All red
HONOURS: FA Comps: None   **League:** None

10 YEAR RECORD

07-08	08-09	09-10	10-11	11-12	12-13	13-14	14-15	15-16	16-17
SSM2 11	SSM2 10	SSM2 10	SSM2 5	SSM2 2	SSM2 4	SSM1 14	SSM1 5	SSM1 7	SSM1 6
								FAC P	FAC EP
							FAV 2Q	FAV 2Q	FAV 1Q

SOUTHALL
Founded: 1871   Nickname:

Secretary: Gurmail Dhaliwal   **(T)**   **(E)** gdhaliwal@southallfc.com
Chairman: Chana Singh Gill   **Manager:** Paul Palmer   **Prog Ed:** Gurmail Dhaliwal
Ground: Hanwell Town FC, Perivale Lane, Perivale, Greenford, Middlesex UB6 8TL   **(T)** 0208 998 1701   **Capacity:** 3,000
Colours(change): Red, white & black
HONOURS: FA Comps: None   **League:** Great Western Suburban 1912-13. Athenian 1926-27.

10 YEAR RECORD

07-08	08-09	09-10	10-11	11-12	12-13	13-14	14-15	15-16	16-17
Midx1SE 2	MidxP 5	MidxP 10	MidxP 8	MidxP 3	SSM1 9	SSM1 11	SSM1 12	SSM1 12	SSM1 5
						FAV 1Q	FAV 2Q	FAV 1P	FAV QF

ST. NEOTS TOWN RESERVES
Founded: 1879   Nickname: Saints

Secretary: Gary Wilson   **(T)** 01480 470 012   **(E)** garygwilson@sky.com
Chairman: Lee Kearns   **Manager:** Mark Gearing
Ground: St. Neots Town FC, Kester Way, St. Neots PE19 6SN   **(T)** 01480 470 012   **Capacity:** 3,000
Colours(change): Blue
HONOURS: FA Comps: None   **League:** United Counties 1956-57.

10 YEAR RECORD

07-08	08-09	09-10	10-11	11-12	12-13	13-14	14-15	15-16	16-17
									SSM2 9

WINSLOW UNITED
Founded: 1891   Nickname: The Ploughmen

Secretary: Gareth Robins   **(T)** 07791 598 346   **(E)** garethrobins75@gmail.com
Chairman: Andy Setterfield   **Manager:** Paul Alleyne   **Prog Ed:** Gareth Robins
Ground: The Recreation Ground, Elmfields Gate, Winslow, Bucks MK18 3JG   **(T)** 01296 713 057   **Capacity:** 2,000
Colours(change): Yellow/blue/yellow (Green & black stripes/black/black)
HONOURS: FA Comps: None   **League:** South Midlands Division One 1974-75.

10 YEAR RECORD

07-08	08-09	09-10	10-11	11-12	12-13	13-14	14-15	15-16	16-17
SSM1 18	SSM1 12		SSM2 4	SSM2 7	SSM1 14	SSM1 9	SSM1 14	SSM1 19	SSM1 16
		FAV 1Q		FAV 1P	FAV 2Q	FAV 2Q	FAV 1Qr	FAV 2Q	FAV 2Q

WODSON PARK
Founded: 1997   Nickname:

Secretary: Lee Cook   **(T)** 07717 458 446   **(E)** lee.cook@wodsonmail.co.uk
Chairman: Lee Cook   **Manager:** Kristian Munt   **Prog Ed:** Lee Cook
Ground: Woodson Park Sports Centre, Wadesmill Road, Herts SG12 0UQ   **(T)** 01920 487 091
Colours(change): Sky & navy blue /navy blue/navy blue (All red)
HONOURS: FA Comps: None   **League:** Hertford & District Division Three 1997-98.

10 YEAR RECORD

07-08	08-09	09-10	10-11	11-12	12-13	13-14	14-15	15-16	16-17
Hert1 2	SSM2 6	SSM2 4	SSM2 14	SSM1 16	SSM1 18	SSM1 17	SSM1 16	SSM1 6	SSM1 7
				FAC EP	FAC EP				
		FAV 1P		FAV 1Q	FAV 1Q				

UNITED COUNTIES LEAGUE

Sponsored by: ChromaSport & Trophies

Founded: 1895

Recent Champions: 2014: Spalding United
2015: AFC Rushden & Dia. **2016:** AFC Kempton Rovers

PREMIER DIVISION	P	W	D	L	F	A	GD	Pts
1 Peterborough Sports	42	36	4	2	150	34	116	112
2 Deeping Rangers	42	29	7	6	123	35	88	94
3 Yaxley	42	28	4	10	106	52	54	88
4 Desborough Town	42	25	9	8	89	53	36	84
5 Eynesbury Rovers	42	26	5	11	119	61	58	83
6 Wisbech Town	42	25	7	10	114	60	54	82
7 Holbeach United	42	22	7	13	99	72	27	73
8 Northampton Sileby Rangers	42	21	7	14	100	79	21	70
9 Wellingborough Town	42	19	8	15	75	85	-10	65
10 Newport Pagnell Town	42	17	12	13	93	56	37	63
11 Harborough Town	42	17	7	18	83	77	6	58
12 Northampton ON Chenecks	42	16	7	19	72	89	-17	55
13 Cogenhoe United	42	14	9	19	67	80	-13	51
14 Sleaford Town	42	15	4	23	73	76	-3	49
15 Peterborough Northern Star	42	13	9	20	50	66	-16	48
16 Rothwell Corinthians	42	13	9	20	57	85	-28	48
17 Leicester Nirvana	42	14	4	24	66	87	-21	46
18 Kirby Muxloe	42	12	4	26	59	103	-44	40
19 Oadby Town	42	10	7	25	62	117	-55	37
20 Boston Town	42	8	10	24	48	94	-46	34
21 Harrowby United	42	5	6	31	35	165	-130	20*
22 Huntingdon Town	42	2	4	36	37	151	-114	10

DIVISION ONE	P	W	D	L	F	A	GD	Pts
1 Daventry Town	36	28	3	5	103	43	60	87
2 Wellingborough Whitworth	36	24	6	6	120	65	55	78
3 Bugbrooke St Michaels	36	24	4	8	113	53	60	76
4 Olney Town	36	22	7	7	101	49	52	73
5 Buckingham Town	36	21	5	10	106	58	48	68
6 Potton United	36	19	7	10	89	49	40	64
7 Raunds Town	36	19	6	11	72	47	25	63
8 Irchester United	36	19	4	13	85	62	23	61
9 Melton Town	36	18	3	15	97	73	24	57
10 Thrapston Town	36	16	7	13	63	64	-1	55
11 Oakham United	36	15	6	15	63	75	-12	51
12 Lutterworth Athletic	36	14	8	14	83	71	12	50
13 Long Buckby AFC	36	14	5	17	71	78	-7	47
14 Blackstones	36	13	7	16	66	77	-11	46
15 Bourne Town	36	11	5	20	62	77	-15	38
16 Rushden and Higham United	36	9	8	19	55	79	-24	35
17 Woodford United	36	3	3	30	34	163	-129	12
18 Stewarts & Lloyds AFC	36	3	0	33	35	127	-92	9
19 Burton Park Wanderers	36	1	4	31	20	128	-108	7

Whittlesey Athletic withdrew - record expunged.

ADDITIONAL CLUB MOVEMENTS

Premier Division - Out: Peterborough Sports (P - NPL - D1S).

Division One - In: Lutterworth Town (P - Leicester Senior), Pinchbeck United (P - Peterborugh & District).

Out: Whittlesey Athletic (W), Woodford United (Northants Combination).

PREMIER DIVISION	1	2	3	4	5	6	7	8	9	10	11	12	13	14	15	16	17	18	19	20	21	22
1 Boston Town		2-2	0-0	1-2	2-3	0-0	1-1	1-3	3-2	0-1	2-2	1-4	1-2	2-3	2-0	1-4	0-3	1-1	1-2	0-1	2-2	0-1
2 Cogenhoe United	4-1		0-2	1-1	1-7	2-1	2-0	2-2	1-1	1-0	1-0	1-2	5-1	4-2	1-2	1-1	2-2	3-1	2-4	0-1	2-3	3-0
3 Deeping Rangers	3-0	2-0		1-0	3-0	5-0	4-1	2-1	8-0	4-0	3-0	0-2	6-0	3-3	8-1	4-1	1-0	6-0	1-1	4-0	2-2	0-0
4 Desborough Town	1-1	5-2	2-1		0-0	1-1	5-0	4-0	4-0	3-2	1-0	0-1	6-4	1-0	3-0	2-1	1-3	4-1	3-2	5-3	0-0	1-2
5 Eynesbury Rovers	1-2	3-0	1-0	2-0		1-4	12-0	0-3	2-1	4-2	7-1	3-1	4-0	5-1	8-0	3-0	2-1	3-2	2-1	5-0	3-2	2-1
6 Harborough Town	2-0	2-0	1-3	2-4	3-4		7-0	2-4	2-0	2-1	2-0	1-1	3-0	0-2	1-1	2-1	0-6	2-1	3-2	2-2	4-1	2-3
7 Harrowby United	2-1	2-0	0-1	0-3	0-8	1-4		0-5	2-1	0-0	3-7	1-2	2-2	1-3	1-4	0-3	1-2	1-3	3-2	0-6	0-5	1-4
8 Holbeach United	3-4	2-2	1-1	1-2	2-0	2-2	9-0		5-4	2-2	3-0	4-2	2-0	3-1	2-2	2-0	1-4	2-1	4-2	1-2	1-3	0-2
9 Huntingdon Town	0-2	1-5	1-9	0-1	1-1	1-3	1-2	1-3		0-2	1-2	0-4	4-4	1-3	0-2	1-3	1-4	0-3	0-0	1-0	0-4	0-1
10 Kirby Muxloe	2-1	2-1	1-4	0-2	2-2	1-3	6-1	3-1	7-2		1-4	1-0	3-0	2-3	4-0	0-2	2-12	0-1	3-1	2-0	0-4	0-4
11 Leicester Nirvana	3-4	3-2	1-2	1-2	2-1	3-2	3-2	2-3	3-2	2-0		3-1	1-2	2-3	3-0	2-3	1-3	3-1	3-1	1-0	0-2	
12 Newport Pagnell Town	1-1	1-1	1-1	1-1	1-1	2-2	10-0	1-1	5-0	3-0	6-0		0-0	6-0	2-0	1-1	2-4	4-0	2-1	1-2	3-5	0-2
13 Northampton ON Chenecks	0-1	2-1	1-4	3-3	2-1	3-2	5-0	0-4	5-0	3-1	0-0	1-4		1-2	3-0	0-1	0-3	1-3	2-0	4-1	0-2	1-3
14 Northampton Sileby Rangers	3-0	4-2	1-4	2-2	4-4	3-2	9-0	3-2	6-0	4-2	0-0	2-2	1-3		3-0	2-1	0-3	2-2	0-3	3-0	1-3	3-1
15 Oadby Town	2-3	1-3	0-4	3-4	2-1	0-2	3-3	0-2	7-1	3-3	2-0	1-5	3-3	3-3		2-2	0-6	3-1	1-4	1-2	2-4	1-3
16 Peterborough Northern Star	3-0	0-1	1-3	0-1	0-1	0-4	2-1	1-5	1-2	2-0	2-1	1-1	0-2	1-0	1-2		0-0	1-2	2-0	1-1	1-4	3-1
17 Peterborough Sports	5-1	5-0	4-1	2-0	4-0	3-1	4-0	2-0	8-1	4-1	5-2	3-1	4-2	2-1	4-0	5-1		0-0	4-2	4-0	1-0	3-1
18 Rothwell Corinthians	5-0	0-2	0-4	1-1	1-5	2-1	1-1	1-2	0-4	3-0	3-1	2-1	0-0	1-0	1-1	1-4		2-2	1-2	1-3	0-5	
19 Sleaford Town	5-1	1-2	1-0	2-3	1-2	1-0	3-2	1-3	3-0	4-0	4-1	2-1	2-3	2-1	4-2	1-1	0-1	1-2		0-3	0-3	0-1
20 Wellingborough Town	3-0	2-2	2-4	1-0	4-2	4-2	2-2	3-0	5-3	2-0	2-1	1-3	1-5	1-5	3-0	2-0	0-7	4-1	1-3		2-2	3-3
21 Wisbech Town	1-1	5-0	3-1	2-4	4-1	2-0	2-0	7-2	8-1	3-0	4-1	3-2	1-3	2-4	3-0	1-1	0-3	4-0	3-1	1-1		1-4
22 Yaxley	6-1	1-0	1-4	3-1	0-2	4-2	10-0	0-1	6-1	5-0	2-1	2-0	5-0	2-1	2-3	0-2	3-3	3-2	2-1	1-1	4-2	

UNITED COUNTIES LEAGUE - STEP 5/6

DIVISION ONE	1	2	3	4	5	6	7	8	9	10	11	12	13	14	15	16	17	18	19
1 Blackstones		0-2	4-3	0-6	2-0	6-2	1-3	3-3	1-1	0-4	1-0	2-2	0-3	1-3	2-2	2-1	2-3	3-4	4-2
2 Bourne Town	0-1		3-4	0-2	2-2	0-2	2-1	1-3	2-1	1-2	4-0	2-3	2-4	1-0	1-0	8-1	2-1	3-3	1-4
3 Buckingham Town	4-1	0-0		2-1	5-2	1-3	2-2	2-0	3-2	4-2	2-0	2-1	2-1	2-3	3-1	4-0	6-0	2-4	9-1
4 Bugbrooke St Michaels	4-2	2-1	3-4		4-0	2-1	3-1	5-3	4-0	2-2	2-0	3-5	2-2	3-0	2-0	7-1	2-1	2-3	10-0
5 Burton Park Wanderers	0-4	1-1	1-4	1-6		0-4	0-3	0-6	1-2	0-3	1-3	0-6	0-6	1-2	1-3	0-2	0-4	1-5	1-1
6 Daventry Town	2-1	3-2	3-1	3-3	8-0		1-1	3-0	2-0	4-2	2-1	4-3	4-0	4-0	3-0	4-1	2-0	3-0	2-0
7 Irchester United	1-1	2-0	4-1	1-0	5-0	0-1		4-0	4-5	3-1	6-1	4-2	1-3	2-0	3-2	1-0	1-3	2-2	7-0
8 Long Buckby AFC	2-1	0-1	0-2	1-2	4-1	1-3	5-3		0-3	4-2	1-3	2-2	0-2	0-2	2-1	4-2	0-2	3-8	2-0
9 Lutterworth Athletic	2-1	1-3	1-1	5-3	2-1	1-1	5-1	2-4		1-2	4-1	1-3	1-1	4-1	1-1	3-0	3-4	2-5	4-0
10 Melton Town	2-3	6-0	0-7	0-1	3-0	4-3	2-3	1-2	4-2		2-1	2-3	2-5	1-1	0-2	4-1	6-0	4-2	12-0
11 Oakham United	0-4	5-3	2-2	2-3	3-1	1-4	3-1	0-0	2-2	4-2		2-2	0-5	0-5	1-0	4-2	0-0	2-0	3-2
12 Olney Town	2-2	5-0	1-0	3-2	7-0	0-2	4-0	2-1	3-1	4-1	0-1		0-1	2-1	3-0	5-1	1-2	3-1	2-0
13 Potton United	3-1	3-1	3-1	1-3	2-1	3-2	1-3	1-2	1-1	0-2	2-2	1-1		0-1	3-2	2-0	0-1	1-1	11-1
14 Raunds Town	3-0	3-1	1-0	1-5	5-1	1-0	2-1	2-0	3-1	2-2	1-2	2-2	3-1		0-0	4-2	0-1	1-1	8-1
15 Rushden and Higham United	1-1	4-4	3-3	2-0	2-0	2-3	4-3	2-5	0-1	1-3	2-7	2-6	0-3	1-1		2-0	1-1	2-3	3-1
16 Stewarts & Lloyds AFC	0-2	3-1	0-6	0-4	0-1	2-7	0-2	0-4	0-2	0-1	1-4	2-5	1-6	0-4	2-3		1-2	1-5	1-2
17 Thrapston Town	0-2	1-0	1-4	2-6	3-0	1-3	2-3	2-2	4-4	3-4	0-1	1-1	0-0	1-0	2-1	3-0		2-2	1-0
18 Wellingborough Whitworth	6-0	3-1	3-2	2-2	5-0	3-4	3-2	5-2	2-1	3-2	4-1	0-3	5-2	3-0	4-0	7-1	4-3		6-0
19 Woodford United	1-5	1-6	1-6	1-2	1-1	0-1	0-1	3-3	2-11	1-5	2-1	1-4	0-6	0-6	1-3	2-6	0-6	2-3	

LEAGUE CUP

HOLDERS: PETERBOROUGH SPORTS

PRELIMINARY ROUND

Woodford United	v	Oakham United	0-4
Leicester Nirvana	v	Newport Pagnell Town	2-1
Bourne Town	v	Yaxley	0-3
Huntingdon Town	v	Bugbrooke St Michaels	3-2
Irchester United	v	Burton Park Wanderers	4-0
Wellingborough Town	v	Oadby Town	1-3 aet
Rushden & Higham United	v	Daventry Town	2-1
Northampton ON Chenecks	v	Melton Town	0-1
Stewarts & Lloyds	v	Kirby Muxloe	0-3
Wisbech Town	v	Potton United	4-1

ROUND 1

Cogenhoe United	v	Oakham United	2-1
Leicester Nirvana	v	Yaxley	0-2
Huntingdon Town	v	Whittlesey Athletic	HW
Irchester United	v	Oadby Town	1-2
Boston Town	v	Harrowby United	5-0
Holbeach United	v	Long Buckby	6-2
Blackstones	v	Eynesbury Rovers	2-4
Olney Town	v	Rushden & Higham United	5-2
Rothwell Corinthians	v	Desborough Town	1-2
Peterborough Northern Star	v	Sleaford Town	2-5
Wellingborough Whitworth	v	Peterborough Sports	2-2, 6-5p
Buckingham Town	v	Lutterworth Athletic	1-3
Melton Town	v	Harborough Town	1-1, 2-3p
Thrapston Town	v	Northampton Sileby Rangers	1-1, 9-8p
Kirby Muxloe	v	Raunds Town	1-3
Wisbech Town	v	Deeping Rangers	3-1

ROUND 2

Cogenhoe United	v	Yaxley	3-5
Huntingdon Town	v	Oadby Town	0-2
Boston Town	v	Holbeach United	0-2
Eynesbury Rovers	v	Olney Town	0-1
Desborough Town	v	Sleaford Town	2-0
Wellingborough Whitworth	v	Lutterworth Athletic	5-1
Harborough Town	v	Thrapston Town	1-2
Raunds Town	v	Wisbech Town	0-3

QUARTER FINALS

Yaxley	v	Oadby Town	6-0
Holbeach United	v	Olney Town	2-4
Desborough Town	v	Wellingborough Whitworth	5-1
Thrapston Town	v	Wisbech Town	1-3

SEMI FINALS

Yaxley	v	Olney Town	1-0
Desborough Town	v	Wisbech Town	2-2, 1-4p

FINAL

Yaxley	v	Wisbech Town	2-1

RESERVE DIVISION

		P	W	D	L	F	A	GD	Pts
1	Lutterworth Athletic Res	32	24	1	7	92	54	38	73
2	Desborough Town Res	32	19	7	6	79	44	35	64
3	Cogenhoe United Res	32	19	7	6	65	38	27	64
4	Wellingborough Whitworth Res	32	18	7	7	90	37	53	61
5	Rothwell Corinthians Res	32	19	3	10	74	54	20	60
6	Olney Town Res	32	15	11	6	71	47	24	56
7	Raunds Town Res	32	17	3	12	75	55	20	54
8	Potton United Res	32	16	5	11	64	54	10	53
9	Eynesbury Rovers Res	32	15	3	14	71	82	-11	48
10	Northampton ON Chenecks Res	32	15	2	15	64	63	1	44*
11	Bugbrooke St Michaels Res	32	13	3	16	70	56	14	42
12	Peterborough Northern Star Res	32	13	3	16	68	81	-13	42
13	Newport Pagnell Town Res	32	12	5	15	72	82	-10	41
14	Irchester United Res	32	7	2	23	45	93	-48	23
15	Harborough Town Res	32	7	0	25	49	91	-42	21
16	Bourne Town Res	32	6	1	25	52	114	-62	19
17	Thrapston Town Res	32	4	3	25	38	94	-56	15

BOSTON TOWN
Founded: 1964   Nickname: Poachers

Secretary: Eddie Graves	**(T)** 07963 418 434
Chairman: Mick Vines	**Manager:** Gary Frost
Ground: DWB Stadium, Tattershall Road, Boston, Lincs PE21 9LR	
Capacity: 6,000 **Seats:** 450 **Covered:** 950	**Midweek Matchday:** Tuesday

(E) btfcsec@hotmail.co.uk
Prog Ed: Eddie Graves
(T) 01205 365 470
Clubhouse: Yes

Colours(change): All blue
Previous Names: Boston 1964-1994
Previous Leagues: Lincolnshire, Central Alliance, Eastern Counties, Midland, Northern Counties East, Central Midlands.

HONOURS: FA Comps: None
League: Lincolnshire 1964-65. Central Alliance 1965-65. Midland 1974-75, 78-79, 80-81.
Central Midlands Supreme 1988-89. United Counties League 1994-95, 2000-01.

10 YEAR RECORD

07-08		08-09		09-10		10-11		11-12		12-13		13-14		14-15		15-16		16-17	
UCL P	6	UCL P	5	UCL P	5	UCL P	7	UCL P	14	UCL P	10	UCL P	14	UCL P	12	UCL P	16	UCL P	20
FAC	1Q	FAC	1Q	FAC	1Q	FAC	Pr	FAC	P	FAC	EP	FAC	P	FAC	1Q	FAC	EP	FAC	EP
FAV	4P	FAV	2P	FAV	2Q	FAV	2Q	FAV	2P	FAV	3P	FAV	1P	FAV	2Q	FAV	1Q	FAV	2Q

COGENHOE UNITED
Founded: 1967   Nickname: Cooks

Secretary: Jon Wright	**(T)** 07793 465 478
Chairman: Derek Wright	**Manager:** Tom Chapman
Ground: Compton Park, Brafield Road, Cogenhoe NN7 1ND	
Capacity: 5,000 **Seats:** 100 **Covered:** 200	**Midweek Matchday:** Tuesday

(E) cogenhoeunited@outlook.com
Prog Ed: Brian Kempster
(T) 01604 890 521
Clubhouse: Yes

Colours(change): All blue
Previous Names: None
Previous Leagues: Central Northants Combination 1967-85.

HONOURS: FA Comps: None
League: Central Northants Combination Division Two 1951-52, Premier 80-81, 82-83, 83-84. United Counties 2004-05.

10 YEAR RECORD

07-08		08-09		09-10		10-11		11-12		12-13		13-14		14-15		15-16		16-17	
UCL P	9	UCL P	9	UCL P	8	UCL P	15	UCL P	12	UCL P	8	UCL P	5	UCL P	5	UCL P	5	UCL P	13
FAC	EP	FAC	EP	FAC	P	FAC	P	FAC	P	FAC	EP	FAC	EPr	FAC	P	FAC	2Q	FAC	P
FAV	3P	FAV	4P	FAV	2P	FAV	1P	FAV	2P	FAV	2Q	FAV	1Q	FAV	1Q	FAV	1P	FAV	1Q

DAVENTRY TOWN
Founded: 1886   Nickname: The Town

Secretary: Brian Porter	**(T)** 07903 859 107
Chairman: Steve Tubb	**Manager:** Arron Parkinson & Ian King
Ground: Communications Park, Browns Road, Daventry, Northants NN11 4NS	
Capacity: 2,000 **Seats:** 250 **Covered:** 250	**Midweek Matchday:**

(E) club.secretary@dtfc.co.uk
Prog Ed: Brian Porter
(T) 01327 311 239
Clubhouse: Yes

Colours(change): Purple/white/purple
Previous Names: None
Previous Leagues: Northampton Town (pre-1987), Central Northways Comb 1987-89, United Counties 1989-2010. Southern 2010-15. Northern Premier 2015-16.
HONOURS: FA Comps: None
League: United Counties Division One 1989-90, 90-91, 2000-01, 2007-08, 16-17, Premier Division 2009-10.

10 YEAR RECORD

07-08		08-09		09-10		10-11		11-12		12-13		13-14		14-15		15-16		16-17	
UCL 1	1	UCL P	7	UCL P	1	SthC	2	SthC	16	SthC	8	SthC	4	SthC	19	NP1S	21	UCL 1	1
				FAC	1Q	FAC	P	FAC	3Q	FAC	2Q	FAC	1P	FAC	1Q	FAC	P	FAC	EP
		FAV	3P	FAV	5P	FAT	2Q	FAT	2Q	FAT	P	FAT	1P	FAT	P	FAT	P	FAV	1P

DEEPING RANGERS
Founded: 1964   Nickname: Rangers

Secretary: Austin Goldsmith	**(T)** 07852 977 095
Chairman: Paul Smith	**Manager:** Michael Goode
Ground: The Haydon Whitham Stadium, Outgang Road, Market Deeping PE6 8LQ	
Capacity: 2,000 **Seats:** 164 **Covered:** 250	**Midweek Matchday:** Tuesday

(E) drfcsecretary@gmail.com
Prog Ed: Lee Holmes
(T) 01778 344 701
Clubhouse: Yes

Colours(change): Claret/blue/claret (Yellow & black/black/yellow)
Previous Names: None
Previous Leagues: Peterborough & District 1966 - 1999.

HONOURS: FA Comps: None
League: United Counties Premier Division 2006-07.

10 YEAR RECORD

07-08		08-09		09-10		10-11		11-12		12-13		13-14		14-15		15-16		16-17	
UCL P	7	UCL P	4	UCL P	4	UCL P	14	UCL P	4	UCL P	5	UCL P	4	UCL P	9	UCL P	10	UCL P	2
FAC	1Q	FAC	P	FAC	EPr	FAC	EP	FAC	2Q	FAC	EP	FAC	EP	FAC	EP	FAC	2Q	FAC	1Q
FAV	1P	FAV	1Q	FAV	1P	FAV	1P	FAV	3P	FAV	2P	FAV	2Q	FAV	3P	FAV	2Q	FAV	1Qr

DESBOROUGH TOWN

Founded: 1896   **Nickname:** Ar Tam

Secretary: John Lee   **(T)** 07545 808 852   **(E)** johnlee@froggerycottage85.fsnet.co.uk
Chairman: Ernie Parsons   **Manager:** Chris Bradshaw   **Prog Ed:** John Lee
Ground: Waterworks Field, Braybrooke Road, Desborough NN14 2LJ   **(T)** 01536 761 350
Capacity: 8,000 **Seats:** 250   **Covered:** 500   **Midweek Matchday:** Tuesday   **Clubhouse:** Yes

Colours(change): All royal blue
Previous Names: None
Previous Leagues: Northamptonshire change name to United Counties in 1934.

HONOURS: FA Comps: None
League: Northamptonshire/United Counties 1900-01, 01-02, 06-07, 20-21, 23-24, 24-25, 27-28 / 48-49, 66-67.

10 YEAR RECORD

	07-08	08-09	09-10	10-11	11-12	12-13	13-14	14-15	15-16	16-17
	UCL P 3	UCL P 11	UCL P 18	UCL P 19	UCL P 16	UCL P 11	UCL P 4	UCL P 14	UCL P 15	UCL P 4
	FAC EPr	FAC EPr	FAC Pr	FAC 1Q	FAC EPr	FAC EPr	FAC P	FAC EP	FAC EP	FAC P
	FAV 2P	FAV 1P	FAV 2Q	FAV 2Q	FAV 1P	FAV 2P	FAV 2P	FAV 2Q	FAV 1Q	FAV 1P

EYNESBURY ROVERS

Founded: 1897   **Nickname:** Rovers

Secretary: Cathy Watts   **(T)** 07787 567 338   **(E)** erfcsecretary@gmail.com
Chairman: Matt Plumb   **Manager:** Mark Ducket   **Prog Ed:** Graham Mills
Ground: Alfred Hall Memorial Ground, Hall Road, Eynesbury, St Neots PE19 2SF   **(T)** 07938 511 581uc
Capacity: **Seats:** Yes   **Covered:** Yes   **Midweek Matchday:**   **Clubhouse:** Yes

Colours(change): Royal blue & white stripes/royal/white
Previous Names: None
Previous Leagues: Biggleswade & District. St Neots Junior. Bed & District. South Midlands 1934-39. United Counties 1946-52. Eastern Counties 1952-63.

HONOURS: FA Comps: None
League: St Neots Junior 1910-11. Bedford & District Division Two 1926-27, 30-31, 31-32.
10 YEAR RECORD United Counties Division 1 1976-77.

	07-08	08-09	09-10	10-11	11-12	12-13	13-14	14-15	15-16	16-17
	UCL 1 13	UCL 1 7	UCL 1 3	UCL 1 6	UCL 1 6	UCL 1 3	UCL 1 2	UCL P 11	UCL P 6	UCL P 5
							FAC EP		FAC EP	FAC 1Q
	FAV 2Q	FAV 2Q	FAV 1P	FAV 2Q	FAV 1Q	FAV 1P	FAV 2P	FAV 1Qr	FAV 1P	FAV 1Q

HARBOROUGH TOWN

Founded: 1976   **Nickname:** The Bees

Secretary: Pauline Winston   **(T)** 07446 415 329   **(E)** p.winston2402@btinternet.com
Chairman: Peter Dougan   **Manager:** Nick Pollard   **Prog Ed:** Peter Wade
Ground: Bowden's Park, Northampton Road, Market Harborough, Leics. LE16 9HF   **(T)** 01858 467 339
Capacity: **Seats:** Yes   **Covered:** Yes   **Midweek Matchday:** Tuesday   **Clubhouse:** Yes

Colours(change): Yellow/black/yellow
Previous Names: Harborough Town Juniors 1976-2008. Juniors merged with adult team Spencer United to form today's club.
Previous Leagues: Northants Combination.

HONOURS: FA Comps: None
League: Northants Combination Premier Division 2009-10.
10 YEAR RECORD

	07-08	08-09	09-10	10-11	11-12	12-13	13-14	14-15	15-16	16-17
	07-08	NhCo 4	NhCo 1	UCL 1 17	UCL 1 2	UCL P 19	UCL P 17	UCL P 20	UCL P 11	UCL P 11
							FAC P	FAC EPr	FAC P	FAC P
					FAV 1Pr	FAV 2Q	FAV 1P	FAV 1Q	FAV 1Q	FAV 1P

HOLBEACH UNITED

Founded: 1929   **Nickname:** Tigers

Secretary: James McMartin   **(T)** 07747 165 701   **(E)** jamesmcmartin3@btinternet.com
Chairman: Dave Dougill   **Manager:** Seb Hayes
Ground: Carters Park, Park Road, Holbeach, Lincs PE12 7EE   **(T)** 01406 424 761
Capacity: 4,000 **Seats:** 200   **Covered:** 450   **Midweek Matchday:** Tuesday   **Clubhouse:** Yes   **Shop:** No

Colours(change): Yellow & black stripes/black/yellow
Previous Names: None
Previous Leagues: King's Lynn. Peterborough & District 1936-46. United Counties 1946-55. Eastern 1955-62. Midland Counties 1962-63.

HONOURS: FA Comps: None
League: United Counties 1989-90, 02-03, 12-13.
10 YEAR RECORD

	07-08	08-09	09-10	10-11	11-12	12-13	13-14	14-15	15-16	16-17
	UCL P 11	UCL P 16	UCL P 16	UCL P 17	UCL P 6	UCL P 1	UCL P 11	UCL P 6	UCL P 4	UCL P 7
	FAC 1Q	FAC EP	FAC EPr	FAC EP	FAC Pr	FAC 1Q	FAC P	FAC P	FAC 2Qr	FAC 1Q
	FAV 1P	FAV 3P	FAV 2Q	FAV 2Q	FAV 1P	FAV 2Q	FAV 1P	FAV 5P	FAV 2P	FAV 2P

KIRBY MUXLOE
Founded: 1910   Nickname:

Secretary: Sean Anderson   **(T)** 07813 255 298   **(E)** kmfcsec@gmail.com
Chairman: Les Warren   **Manager:** John Love   **Prog Ed:** Sean Anderson
Ground: Kirby Muxloe Sports Club, Ratby Lane LE9 2AQ   **(T)** 0116 239 2301
Capacity: 1,000 **Seats:** Yes   **Covered:** Yes   **Midweek Matchday:** Tuesday   **Clubhouse:** Yes

Colours(change): Yellow & blue stripes/blue/blue
Previous Names: None
Previous Leagues: Leicester Mutual. Leicester City. Leics Senior. East Mid Counties 2008-09. Midland All 2009-14. Midland Football 2014-15.

HONOURS: FA Comps: None
League: Leicestershire Senior Premier Division 2007-08.
10 YEAR RECORD | East Midlands Counties 2008-09.

07-08	08-09	09-10	10-11	11-12	12-13	13-14	14-15	15-16	16-17
LeicSP 1	EMC 1	MidAl 10	MidAl 9	MidAl 11	MidAl 12	MidAl 14	MFLP 5	UCL P 9	UCL P 18
		FAC P	FAC P	FAC EP	FAC P	FAC P	FAC P	FAC Pr	FAC 2Q
FAV 1P	FAV 1P	FAV 1P	FAV 1Q	FAV 2Q	FAV 1P	FAV 1P	FAV 2Q	FAV 2Q	FAV 1P

LEICESTER NIRVANA
Founded: 2008   Nickname:

Secretary: Zak Hajat   **(T)** 07811 843 136   **(E)** nirvanafc@hotmail.co.uk
Chairman: Kirk Master   **Manager:** Nick Anderson   **Prog Ed:** Ian Payshorn
Ground: Gleneagles Avenue, Leicester LE5 1LU   **(T)** 01162 660 009
Capacity: **Seats:** Yes   **Covered:** Yes   **Midweek Matchday:**   **Clubhouse:** Yes

Colours(change): All red (All blue)
Previous Names: Thurnby Rangers and Leicester Nirvana merged to form today's club in 2008. Thurnby Nirvana 2008-15.
Previous Leagues: Leicestershire Senior >2010 East Midland Counties 2010-14

HONOURS: FA Comps: None
League: Leicestershire Senior Division One 1997-98, 2000-01, Premier Division 04-05. East Midland Counties 2013-14.
10 YEAR RECORD

07-08	08-09	09-10	10-11	11-12	12-13	13-14	14-15	15-16	16-17
LeicSP 18	LeicSP 6	LeicSP 3	EMC 9	EMC 7	EMC 3	EMC 1	UCL P 2	UCL P 2	UCL P 17
				FAC 1Qr	FAC 1Qr	FAC EPr	FAC P	FAC P	FAC EP
			FAV 1P	FAV 1Q	FAV 1Q	FAV 2Q	FAV 4P	FAV 4P	FAV 2Q

NEWPORT PAGNELL TOWN
Founded: 1963   Nickname: Swans

Secretary: Cindy Stanton   **(T)** 07443 434 487   **(E)** stanton25@sky.com
Chairman: Steve Handley   **Manager:** Darren Lynch   **Prog Ed:** Julie Handley
Ground: Willen Road, Newport Pagnell MK16 0DF   **(T)** 01908 611 993
Capacity: 2,000 **Seats:** 100   **Covered:** 100   **Midweek Matchday:** Tuesday   **Clubhouse:** Yes

Colours(change): White & green stripes/green/green
Previous Names: Newport Pagnell Wanderers > 1972.
Previous Leagues: North Bucks 1963-71. South Midlands 1971-73.

HONOURS: FA Comps: None
League: United Counties Division One 1981-82, 2001-02.
10 YEAR RECORD

07-08	08-09	09-10	10-11	11-12	12-13	13-14	14-15	15-16	16-17
UCL P 15	UCL P 3	UCL P 6	UCL P 3	UCL P 5	UCL P 6	UCL P 16	UCL P 10	UCL P 3	UCL P 10
FAC EP	FAC 2Q	FAC P	FAC 1Q	FAC Pr	FAC 1Q	FAC P	FAC EP	FAC Pr	FAC EP
FAV 1P	FAV 1Qr	FAV 3P	FAV 1P	FAV 4P	FAV 2P	FAV 2Q	FAV 2Q	FAV 1Q	FAV QF

NORTHAMPTON O.N.C.
Founded: 1946   Nickname: The Chens

Secretary: Bryan Lewin   **(T)** 07920 108 300   **(E)** cytrinigan@tesco.net
Chairman: Eddie Slinn   **Manager:** Graham Cottle   **Prog Ed:** Andy Goldsmith
Ground: Old Northamptonians Sports Ground, Billing Road, NN1 5RT   **(T)** 01604 634 045
Capacity: 1,000 **Seats:** Yes   **Covered:** Yes   **Midweek Matchday:**   **Clubhouse:** Yes

Colours(change): White/navy/navy (Red/black/red)
Previous Names: Chenecks FC 1946-60. ON (Old Northamptonians) Chenecks 1960-
Previous Leagues: Northampton Minor 1946-50. Northampton Town 1950-69.

HONOURS: FA Comps: None
League: United Counties Division One 1977-78, 79-80.
10 YEAR RECORD

07-08	08-09	09-10	10-11	11-12	12-13	13-14	14-15	15-16	16-17
UCL 1 6	UCL 1 4	UCL 1 4	UCL 1 14	UCL 1 12	UCL 1 11	UCL 1 6	UCL 1 6	UCL 1 2	UCL P 12
									FAC EPr
								FAV 2Q	FAV 1P

NORTHAMPTON S.R.
Founded: 1968   Nickname: Rangers

Secretary: Dave King   **(T)** 07783 150 082   **(E)** daveron51@yahoo.com
Chairman: Rob Clarke   **Manager:** Andy Hall   **Prog Ed:** Dave Battams
Ground: Fernie Fields Sports Ground, Moulton, Northampton NN3 6FR   **(T)** 01604 670 366
Capacity: **Seats:** Yes   **Covered:** Yes   **Midweek Matchday:** Wednesday   **Clubhouse:** Yes
Colours(change): Red/black/red
Previous Names: Sileby Rangers. Northampton Vanaid.
Previous Leagues: Northampton > 1993.

HONOURS: FA Comps: None
League: Northampton Town 1988-89 89-90. United Counties Division One 1993-94, 2002-03, 04-05, 12-13.

10 YEAR RECORD

07-08	08-09	09-10	10-11	11-12	12-13	13-14	14-15	15-16	16-17
UCL 1 12	UCL 1 3	UCL 1 9	UCL 1 9	UCL 1 16	UCL 1 1	UCL P 15	UCL P 18	UCL P 19	UCL P 8
							FAC 1Q	FAC P	FAC P
FAV 2Q	FAV 2Q	FAV 1Q				FAV 1P	FAV 1Q	FAV 2P	FAV 2P

OADBY TOWN
Founded: 1937   Nickname: The Poachers

Secretary: Kevin Zupp   **(T)** 07580 004 110   **(E)** zuppy101@hotmail.co.uk
Chairman: Pete Hayes   **Manager:** Dave Clay   **Prog Ed:** Dean Leivers
Ground: Freeway Park, Wigston Road, Oadby LE2 5QG   **(T)** 01162 715 728
Capacity: 5,000 **Seats:** 224   **Covered:** 224   **Midweek Matchday:** Tuesday   **Clubhouse:** Yes   **Shop:** Yes
Colours(change): All red (All yellow)
Previous Names: Oadby Imperial > 1951.
Previous Leagues: Leicestershire Senior. Midland Alliance > 2011. East Midlands Counties 2011-12.

HONOURS: FA Comps: None
League: Leicestershire Senior Division Two 1951-52, Premier 63-64, 67-68, 68-69, 72-73, 94-95, 96-97, 97-98, 98-99. Midland Alliance 99-00. United Counties Division One 2013-14.

10 YEAR RECORD

07-08	08-09	09-10	10-11	11-12	12-13	13-14	14-15	15-16	16-17
MidAl 17	MidAl 19	MidAl 14	MidAl 22	EMC 3	UCL 1 4	UCL 1 1	UCL P 13	UCL P 21	UCL P 19
FAC P	FAC P	FAC EP	FAC 2Q	FAC Pr	FAC P	FAC EP	FAC EP	FAC EP	FAC EP
FAV 2Q	FAV 2Q	FAV 2P	FAV 1Q	FAV 5P	FAV 2P	FAV 2P	FAV 1P	FAV 2Q	FAV 1Q

PETERBOROUGH NORTHERN STAR
Founded: 1900   Nickname: Star

Secretary: Rob Zirpolo   **(T)** 07702 809 558   **(E)** clubsecretary@pnsfc.co.uk
Chairman: Tony Zirpolo   **Manager:** Robert Ward   **Prog Ed:** Tim Symonds
Ground: Branch Bros Stadium, Chestnut Avenue, Peterborough, Cambs PE1 4PE   **(T)** 01733 552 416
Capacity: 1,500 **Seats:** Yes   **Covered:** yes   **Midweek Matchday:** Wednesday   **Clubhouse:** Yes
Colours(change): Black & white stripes/black/black
Previous Names: Eye United 1900-31. Northam Star SC 1931-51. Eye United 1951-2005.
Previous Leagues: Peterborough Lge >2003

HONOURS: FA Comps: None
League: Peterborough 2002-03. United Counties League Division One 2008-09.

10 YEAR RECORD

07-08	08-09	09-10	10-11	11-12	12-13	13-14	14-15	15-16	16-17
UCL 1 2	UCL 1 1	UCL 1 2	UCL P 6	UCL P 7	UCL P 13	UCL P 9	UCL P 7	UCL P 17	UCL P 15
					FAC 1Q	FAC P	FAC P	FAC EP	FAC EP
				FAV QF	FAV 2P	FAV 2Q	FAV 3P	FAV 2Q	FAV 1P

ROTHWELL CORINTHIANS
Founded: 1934   Nickname: Corinthians

Secretary: David Rhinds   **(T)** 07955 100 795   **(E)** corinthsofficial@gmail.com
Chairman: Mark Budworth   **Manager:** Shaun Sparrow & Jim Scott   **Prog Ed:** David Rhinds
Ground: Sergeants Lawn, Desborough Road, Rothwell NN14 6JR   **(T)** 01536 711 706
Capacity: **Seats:** 50   **Covered:** 200   **Midweek Matchday:**   **Clubhouse:** Yes
Colours(change): Red/black/black
Previous Names: None
Previous Leagues: Kettering & District Amateur/East Midlands Alliance 1934-95.

HONOURS: FA Comps: None
League: None

10 YEAR RECORD

07-08	08-09	09-10	10-11	11-12	12-13	13-14	14-15	15-16	16-17
UCL 1 3	UCL P 21	UCL P 21	UCL P 21	UCL 1 8	UCL 1 17	UCL 1 15	UCL 1 2	UCL P 14	UCL P 16
	FAC EP	FAC Pr	FAC EP	FAC P	FAC EP			FAC EP	FAC EP
FAV 1Q	FAV 2Q	FAV 1P	FAV 1Qr	FAV 1Q	FAV 1Q	FAV 1Q	FAV 2Q	FAV 2Qr	FAV 2P

SLEAFORD TOWN

Founded: 1968   Nickname: Town

Secretary: Ms Jenny O'Rourke   **(T)** 07777 604 325   **(E)** jennyorourke@btinternet.com
Chairman: Fred Collins   **Manager:** Jamie Shaw   **Prog Ed:** Jamie Shaw
Ground: Eslaforde Park, Boston Road, Sleaford, Lincs NG34 9GH   **(T)** 01529 415 951
Capacity: 1,000 **Seats:** 88   **Covered:** 88   **Midweek Matchday:** Tuesday   **Clubhouse:** Yes

Colours(change): Green/black/green
Previous Names: None
Previous Leagues: Lincolnshire 1968-2003.

HONOURS: FA Comps: None
League: United Counties Division One 2005-06.

10 YEAR RECORD

07-08	08-09	09-10	10-11	11-12	12-13	13-14	14-15	15-16	16-17
UCL P 14	UCL P 15	UCL P 9	UCL P 18	UCL P 19	UCL P 18	UCL P 13	UCL P 19	UCL P 7	UCL P 14
	FAC 1Q	FAC 1Qr	FAC EP	FAC EP	FAC P	FAC 1Q	FAC EP	FAC EP	FAC P
FAV 2P	FAV 1Q	FAV 3P	FAV 1Q	FAV 2Q	FAV 1P	FAV 2Q	FAV 2Q	FAV 4P	FAV 3Pr

ST. ANDREWS

Founded: 1973   Nickname: The Saints

Secretary: Les Botting   **(T)** 07793 500 937   **(E)** standrewsfc@btconnect.com
Chairman: Phil Hodkinson   **Manager:** Jamie Clarke   **Prog Ed:** Bookdesign.com
Ground: Canal Street, Aylestone, Leicester LE2 8LX   **(T)** 0116 283 9298
Capacity: **Seats:** Yes   **Covered:** Yes   **Midweek Matchday:**   **Clubhouse:** Yes

Colours(change): Black & white/black/black
Previous Names: None
Previous Leagues: Leicestershire City League 1973-85. Leicestershire Senior 1985-2008. East Midlands Counties 2008-16. Midland Football League 2016-17.

HONOURS: FA Comps: None
League: Leicestershire City Premier x4. Leicestershire Senior 1989-90, 93-94, 95-96.

10 YEAR RECORD   East Midlands Counties 2015-16.

07-08	08-09	09-10	10-11	11-12	12-13	13-14	14-15	15-16	16-17
LeicSP 7	EMC 9	EMC 15	EMC 17	EMC 4	EMC 16	EMC 7	EMC 2	EMC 1	MFLP 9
		FAC P	FAC EP		FAC EP		FAC EPr	FAC EP	FAC EP
FAV 2Q	FAV 2Qr	FAV 2Q	FAV 2Q	FAV 2P	FAV EP	FAV SF	FAV 2P	FAV 3P	FAV 1P

WELLINGBOROUGH TOWN

Founded: 1867   Nickname: Doughboys

Secretary: Mick Walden   **(T)** 07817 841 752   **(E)** mwalden@dsl.pipex.com
Chairman: M Darnell/D Wingrove   **Manager:** Stuart Goosey   **Prog Ed:** Neil Morris
Ground: Victoria Mill Ground, London Road, Wellingborough NN8 2DP   **(T)** 01933 441 388
Capacity: 2,500 **Seats:** Yes   **Covered:** Yes   **Midweek Matchday:** Tuesday   **Clubhouse:** Yes

Colours(change): Yellow & blue/blue/blue
Previous Names: Original team (Formed 1867) folded in 2002 reforming in 2004
Previous Leagues: Metropolitan. Southern.

HONOURS: FA Comps: None
League: United Counties 1964-65.

10 YEAR RECORD

07-08	08-09	09-10	10-11	11-12	12-13	13-14	14-15	15-16	16-17
UCL P 10	UCL P 18	UCL P 11	UCL P 5	UCL P 8	UCL P 15	UCL P 8	UCL P 15	UCL P 20	UCL P 9
FAC P	FAC P	FAC EP	FAC 1Q	FAC EP	FAC P	FAC EPr	FAC EP	FAC EP	FAC EP
FAV 1Pr	FAV 2P	FAV 2P	FAV 1P	FAV 1Q	FAV 1Q	FAV 2Q	FAV 2Q	FAV 2Q	FAV 2Q

WELLINGBOROUGH WHITWORTH

Founded: 1973   Nickname: Flourmen

Secretary: Julian Souster   **(T)** 07825 632 545   **(E)** whitworthfc@yahoo.co.uk
Chairman: Martin Goodes   **Prog Ed:** Julian Souster
Ground: Victoria Mill Ground, London Road, Wellingborough NN8 2DP   **(T)** 07825 632 545
Capacity: 2,500 **Seats:** Yes   **Covered:** Yes   **Midweek Matchday:**   **Clubhouse:** Yes

Colours(change): Red & black stripes/black/red
Previous Names: None
Previous Leagues: Rushden & District 1973-77. East Midlands Alliance 1977-85.

HONOURS: FA Comps: None
League: Rushden & District 1975-76, 76-77. United Counties Division One 2006-07.

10 YEAR RECORD

07-08	08-09	09-10	10-11	11-12	12-13	13-14	14-15	15-16	16-17
UCL 1 9	UCL 1 8	UCL 1 12	UCL 1 13	UCL 1 4	UCL 1 13	UCL 1 17	UCL 1 7	UCL 1 15	UCL 1 2
					FAC EP			FAC EP	FAC EP
				FAV 1Q	FAV 2Q	FAV 2Q	FAV 1Q	FAV 1Q	FAV 2Q

WISBECH TOWN
Founded: 1920   **Nickname:** Fenmen

Secretary: Gavin Clarey   **(T)** 07919 100 060   **(E)** gav@wisbechtownfc.co.uk
Chairman: P A Brenchley   **Manager:** Dick Creasey   **Prog Ed:** Spencer Larham
Ground: The Elgoods Fenland Stadium, Lynn Road, Wisbech PE14 7AL   **(T)** 01945 581 511
Capacity: **Seats:** 118   **Covered:** Yes   **Midweek Matchday:** Tuesday   **Clubhouse:** Yes

Colours(change): All red (Yellow/green/green)
Previous Names: None
Previous Leagues: Peterborough 1920-35. UCL 1935-50. EC 1950-52, 70-97, 2003-13. Midland 1952-58. Southern 1958-70, 97-2002.

HONOURS: FA Comps: None
     League: United Counties 1946-47, 47-48. Southern Division one 1961-62.
10 YEAR RECORD   Eastern Counties 1971-72, 76-77, 90-91.

07-08		08-09		09-10		10-11		11-12		12-13		13-14		14-15		15-16		16-17	
ECP	12	ECP	16	ECP	11	ECP	4	ECP	2	ECP	2	UCL P	7	UCL P	3	UCL P	8	UCL P	6
FAC	EP	FAC	Pr	FAC	P	FAC	P	FAC	1Q	FAC	1Qr	FAC	EP	FAC	1Q	FAC	P	FAC	P
FAV	2Q	FAV	1P	FAV	2Q	FAV	2P	FAV	4Pr	FAV	4P	FAV	QF	FAV	3P	FAV	1P	FAV	1Qr

YAXLEY
Founded: 1962   **Nickname:** The Cuckoos

Secretary: Chris Howard   **(T)** 07376 430 021   **(E)** yfc.sec@virginmedia.com
Chairman: Malcolm Clements   **Manager:** Brett Whaley   **Prog Ed:** Daniel Tortoise
Ground: In2itive Park, Leading Drove, Holme Road, Yaxley, Peterborough PE7 3NA   **(T)** 01733 244 928
Capacity: 1,500 **Seats:** 150   **Covered:** yes   **Midweek Matchday:** Tuesday   **Clubhouse:** Yes   **Shop:** Yes

Colours(change): All blue
Previous Names: Yaxley British Legion 1963-86. Coalite Yaxley 1986-90. Clarksteel Yaxley 1990.
Previous Leagues: Peterborough & District 1962-88. Eastern Counties (Founder Member) 1988-92. Huntingdonshire 1992-94.
     West Anglia 1994-95.

HONOURS: FA Comps: None
     League: Peterborough & District Division Three South 1968-69, Division Two 70-71, Premier 76-77, 83-84.
10 YEAR RECORD   West Anglia 1994-95. United Counties Division One 1996-97.

07-08		08-09		09-10		10-11		11-12		12-13		13-14		14-15		15-16		16-17	
UCL P	16	UCL P	14	UCL P	19	UCL P	16	UCL P	18	UCL P	12	UCL P	6	UCL P	4	UCL P	12	UCL P	3
FAC	P	FAC	1Qr	FAC	EP	FAC	EP	FAC	EP	FAC	P	FAC	EP	FAC	EP	FAC	1Q	FAC	Pr
FAV	1P	FAV	1Pr	FAV	2Q	FAV	1Q	FAV	1P	FAV	1P	FAV	1Q	FAV	4P	FAV	3P	FAV	1P

Melton Town 2016-17 - 9th in United Counties Division One. Photo: Gordon Whittington.

BLACKSTONES

Founded: 1920   **Nickname:** Stones

Secretary: Ian MacGillivray   **(T)** 07749 620 825   **(E)** imacgilli@outlook.com
Chairman: Gary Peace   **Manager:** Andrew Lodge
Ground: Lincoln Road, Stamford, Lincs PE9 1SH   **(T)** 01780 757 835   **Capacity:** 1,000
Colours(change): Black & green stripes/black/black
HONOURS: FA Comps: None   **League:** Peterborough & District 1918-19, Division Two 1961-62, Division One 75-76.

10 YEAR RECORD

07-08	08-09	09-10	10-11	11-12	12-13	13-14	14-15	15-16	16-17
UCL P 4	UCL P 13	UCL P 13	UCL P 9	UCL P 11	UCL P 20	UCL 1 20	UCL 1 17	UCL 1 10	UCL 1 14
FAC Pr	FAC EP	FAC 1Q	FAC EPr	FAC EP	FAC P	FAC EP			
FAV 4P	FAV 3P	FAV 1P	FAV 2Qr	FAV 1Q	FAV 2Q	FAV 2Q	FAV 2Q	FAV 1P	FAV 2Q

BOURNE TOWN

Founded: 1883   **Nickname:** Wakes

Secretary: Tony Hull   **(T)** 07709 785 273   **(E)** tonyhull2@hotmail.com
Chairman: D Munton & S Elger   **Manager:** Jimmy McDonnell   **Prog Ed:** Tony Hull
Ground: Abbey Lawn, Abbey Road, Bourne, Lincs PE10 9EN   **(T)** 07598 815 357   **Capacity:** 2,000
Colours(change): Claret & sky blue stripes/claret/claret (All claret)
HONOURS: FA Comps: None   **League:** Peterborough & District 1933-34, 39-40, 45-46, 46-47. Central Alliance Division One South 59-60. United Counties Premier 65-66, 68-69, 69-70, 71-72, 90-91.

10 YEAR RECORD

07-08	08-09	09-10	10-11	11-12	12-13	13-14	14-15	15-16	16-17
UCL P 18	UCL P 19	UCL P 17	UCL 1 12	UCL 1 14	UCL 1 10	UCL 1 21	UCL 1 10	UCL 1 5	UCL 1 15
FAC EP	FAC EP	FAC 2Q							
FAV 2Q	FAV 1Q	FAV 1P						FAV 2Q	FAV 1Q

BUCKINGHAM TOWN

Founded: 1883   **Nickname:** Robins

Secretary: Vince Hyde   **(T)** 07787 256 899   **(E)** buckinghamtownfc@hotmail.com
Chairman: Vince Hyde   **Manager:** Gary Ollard   **Prog Ed:** Vince Hyde
Ground: Irish Centre, Manor Fields, Bletchley, Milton Keynes MK2 2HX   **(T)** 01908 375 978   **Capacity:** 2,500
Colours(change): All red
HONOURS: FA Comps: None   **League:** Aylesbury & Dist. 1902-03, 67-68. North Bucks 24-25, 28-29, 33-34, 35-36, 36-37, 38 -39, 48-49, 49-50. Southern Southern Division 90-91. United Counties 83-84, 85-86.

10 YEAR RECORD

07-08	08-09	09-10	10-11	11-12	12-13	13-14	14-15	15-16	16-17
UCL 1 8	UCL 1 9	UCL 1 13	UCL 1 16	UCL 1 11	UCL 1 15	UCL 1 11	UCL 1 16	UCL 1 17	UCL 1 5
FAC EP	FAC EP	FAC EP							
FAV 1Q	FAV 3P	FAV 1Q	FAV 1Q	FAV 2P		FAV 2Q		FAV 1Q	FAV 1P

BUGBROOKE ST MICHAELS

Founded: 1929   **Nickname:** Badgers

Secretary: Graham Connew   **(T)** 07799 492 280   **(E)** graybags05@btinternet.com
Chairman: Kevin Gardner   **Manager:** Nathaniel Liburd & Courtney Herbert   **Prog Ed:** Peter Louch
Ground: Birds Close, Gayton Road, Bugbrooke NN7 3PH   **(T)** 01604 830 707   **Capacity:** 2,500
Colours(change): White/black/black (Yellow & blue stripes/blue/blue)
HONOURS: FA Comps: None   **League:** Central Northants Combination 1968-69, 69-70, 71-72, 76-77, 85-86. United Counties Division One 1998-99.

10 YEAR RECORD

07-08	08-09	09-10	10-11	11-12	12-13	13-14	14-15	15-16	16-17
UCL 1 7	UCL 1 10	UCL 1 7	UCL 1 3	UCL 1 3	UCL 1 7	UCL 1 18	UCL 1 11	UCL 1 18	UCL 1 3
				FAC P	FAC 1Q	FAC EP			
FAV 1P	FAV 2Q	FAV 2P	FAV 2Q	FAV 1P	FAV 2Q	FAV 2Q	FAV 1Q	FAV 1Q	

BURTON PARK WANDERERS

Founded: 1961   **Nickname:** The Wanderers

Secretary: Dave Borrett   **(T)** 07794 959 915   **(E)** daveborrett66@gmail.com
Chairman: Mark Patrick   **Manager:** David Dent   **Prog Ed:** Kirsty Ward
Ground: Burton Park, Polwell Lane, Burton Latimer, Northants NN15 5PS   **(T)** 07980 013 506
Colours(change): Blue & black stripes/black/black (Green/white/green)
HONOURS: FA Comps: None   **League:** None

10 YEAR RECORD

07-08	08-09	09-10	10-11	11-12	12-13	13-14	14-15	15-16	16-17
UCL 1 15	UCL 1 13	UCL 1 15	UCL 1 8	UCL 1 9	UCL 1 19	UCL 1 8	UCL 1 18	UCL 1 19	UCL 1 19
							FAV 2Q	FAV 1Qr	FAV 1Q

HARROWBY UNITED

Founded: 1949   Nickname: The Arrows

Secretary: Michael Atter   **(T)** 07742 077 474   **(E)** mjproperty@fsmail.net
Chairman: Michael Atter   **Manager:** Nick Anderson
Ground: Dickens Road, Grantham NG31 9RB   **(T)** 01476 401 201
Colours(change): TBC
HONOURS: FA Comps: None   **League:** Midlands Regional Alliance Premier Division 1989-90.
United Counties Division One 1991-92.

10 YEAR RECORD

07-08	08-09	09-10	10-11	11-12	12-13	13-14	14-15	15-16	16-17
Lincs 16	CM Su 17	CM Su 18			UCL 1 6	UCL 1 3	UCL P 17	UCL P 18	UCL P 21
							FAC EP	FAC EP	FAC P
						FAV 1P	FAV 2Q	FAV 1P	FAV 1Q

HUNTINGDON TOWN

Founded: 1995   Nickname: The Hunters

Secretary: Russell Yezek   **(T)** 07974 664 818   **(E)** russell.yezek@huntingdontownfc.com
Chairman: Doug Mcilwain   **Manager:** Jimmy Brattan   **Prog Ed:** Doug Mcilwain
Ground: Jubilee Park, Kings Ripton Road,, Huntingdon, Cambridgeshire PE28 2NR   **(T)** 07974 664 818
Colours(change): Red & black stripes/black/red (All blue)
HONOURS: FA Comps: None   **League:** Cambridgeshire Division 1B 1999-2000.
United Counties Division One 2011-12.

10 YEAR RECORD

07-08	08-09	09-10	10-11	11-12	12-13	13-14	14-15	15-16	16-17
UCL 1 4	UCL 1 14	UCL 1 8	UCL 1 5	UCL 1 1	UCL P 4	UCL P 2	UCL P 16	UCL P 22	UCL P 22
				FAC 1Q	FAC 1Q	FAC 1Q	FAC EP	FAC EPr	FAC EP
FAV 1Q	FAV 2Q	FAV 1Q	FAV 2Q	FAV 1Q	FAV 1Q	FAV 3P	FAV 2P	FAV 1Q	FAV 2Q

IRCHESTER UNITED

Founded: 1885   Nickname: The Romans

Secretary: Glynn Cotter   **(T)** 07802 728 736   **(E)** glynn.cotter@btinternet.com
Chairman: Geoff Cotter   **Manager:** Steve Sargent & Matty Freeman   **Prog Ed:** David Cockings
Ground: Alfred Street, Irchester NN29 7DR   **(T)** 01933 312 877   **Capacity:** 1,000
Colours(change): Red/black/black
HONOURS: FA Comps: None   **League:** Rushden & District 1928-29, 29-30, 36-37. Northants / United Counties
Division Two 1930-31, 31-32 / United Counties Division One 2009-10.

10 YEAR RECORD

07-08	08-09	09-10	10-11	11-12	12-13	13-14	14-15	15-16	16-17
UCL 1 16	UCL 1 16	UCL 1 1	UCL P 10	UCL P 20	UCL P 21	UCL 1 19	UCL 1 15	UCL 1 16	UCL 1 8
				FAC EP	FAC EP	FAC EP			
			FAV 1Q	FAV 2Q	FAV 2Q	FAV 2Q	FAV 1P	FAV 1Q	FAV 2Q

LONG BUCKBY AFC

Founded: 1937   Nickname: Bucks

Secretary: Dave Austin   **(T)** 07710 723 477   **(E)** lbafc.dja@gmail.com
Chairman: Dave Austin   **Prog Ed:** Dave Austin
Ground: Station Road, Long Buckby NN6 7QA   **(T)** 07749 393 045   **Capacity:** 2,000
Colours(change): All claret
HONOURS: FA Comps: None   **League:** United Counties Division Three 1969-70, Division Two 70-71, 71-72, Premier
Division 2011-12.

10 YEAR RECORD

07-08	08-09	09-10	10-11	11-12	12-13	13-14	14-15	15-16	16-17
UCL P 2	UCL P 8	UCL P 3	UCL P 4	UCL P 1	UCL P 16	UCL P 18	UCL P 21	UCL 1 6	UCL 1 13
FAC Pr	FAC EP	FAC 1Q	FAC EP	FAC 3Q	FAC EP	FAC EP	FAC EPr	FAC 1Q	
FAV 4P	FAV 3P	FAV 5P	FAV 5P	FAV 3P	FAV 1Pr	FAV 1Q	FAV 2Q	FAV 2Q	FAV 1Q

LUTTERWORTH ATHLETIC

Founded: 1983   Nickname: The Athletic

Secretary: Darren Jones   **(T)** 07836 214 178   **(E)** djones20335783@aol.com
Chairman: Mick English   **Manager:** Mick English   **Prog Ed:** Darren Jones
Ground: Weston Arena, Hall Park, Hall Lane, Bitteswell, Lutterworth LE17 4LN   **(T)** 01455 554 046
Colours(change): Green & white hoops/white/white
HONOURS: FA Comps: None   **League:** Leicester & District Division Two 1994-95, Premier 2004-05.

10 YEAR RECORD

07-08	08-09	09-10	10-11	11-12	12-13	13-14	14-15	15-16	16-17
LeicS1 3	LeicS1 2	LeicSP 6	LeicSP 6	LeicSP 2	EMC 13	UCL 1 5	UCL 1 4	UCL 1 11	UCL 1 12
			FAV 1Q	FAV 1P	FAV 2Q	FAV 1Q		FAV 1Q	FAV 1Q

LUTTERWORTH TOWN

Founded: 1955   Nickname: The Swifts

Secretary: Umesh Chauhan   **(T)** 07872 300 450   **(E)** lutterworthtownfc@hotmail.com
Chairman: Andy Dixon   **Manager:** Josh Dixon   **Prog Ed:** Ashton Carter
Ground: Dunley Way, Lutterworth, Leicestershire, LE17 4NP   **(T)** 07855 836 489
Colours(change): Orange/black/black
HONOURS: FA Comps: None   **League:** Leicestershire Senior Division Two 1980-81, Premier 90-91, 2016-17.

10 YEAR RECORD									
07-08	08-09	09-10	10-11	11-12	12-13	13-14	14-15	15-16	16-17
LeicS1 5	LeicS1 13	LeicS1 8	LeicS1 15	LeicS1 14	LeicS1 6	LeicS1 6	LeicS1 7	LeicS1 3	LeicSP 1

MELTON TOWN

Founded: Nickname:

Secretary: Carol Lewis   **(T)** 07754 472 283   **(E)** secretarymeltonmowbrayfc@hotmail.com
Chairman: Sam Ellis   **Manager:** Stephen Hendey   **Prog Ed:** Graham Hall
Ground: Melton Sports Village, Burton Road, Melton Mowbray LE13 1DR   **(T)** 01664 480 576
Colours(change): Red/black/black
HONOURS: FA Comps: None   **League:** None

10 YEAR RECORD									
07-08	08-09	09-10	10-11	11-12	12-13	13-14	14-15	15-16	16-17
		LeicS1 9	LeicS1 12	LeicS1 6	LeicS1 2	LeicSP 2	LeicSP 2	LeicSP 3	UCL 1 9

OAKHAM UNITED

Founded: 1940s   Nickname: Imps

Secretary: Craig Shuttleworth   **(T)** 07817 578 896   **(E)** info@oakhamunited.co.uk
Chairman: Alistair Forbes   **Manager:** Will Moody   **Prog Ed:** Craig Shuttleworth
Ground: Main Road, Barleythorpe, Oakham, Rutland, LE15 7EE   **(T)** 01572 757 484   **Capacity:** 1,000
Colours(change): Yellow/green/yellow
HONOURS: FA Comps: None   **League:** Peterborough & District Premier Division 2014-15.

10 YEAR RECORD									
07-08	08-09	09-10	10-11	11-12	12-13	13-14	14-15	15-16	16-17
				P&D P 11	P&D P 5	P&D P 11	P&D P 1	UCL 1 12	UCL 1 11

OLNEY TOWN

Founded: 1903   Nickname: The Nurserymen

Secretary: Andrew Baldwin   **(T)** 07932 141 623   **(E)** andew@abaldwin.go-plus.net
Chairman: Paul Tough   **Manager:** Neil Griffiths   **Prog Ed:** Martin Townshend
Ground: Recreation Ground, East Street, Olney, Bucks MK46 4DW   **(T)** 01234 712 227
Colours(change): All green
HONOURS: FA Comps: None   **League:** North Bucks Division Two 1932-33, Division One 61-62. Rushden & District Division One 1957-58, 60-61. United Counties Division One 1972-73.

10 YEAR RECORD									
07-08	08-09	09-10	10-11	11-12	12-13	13-14	14-15	15-16	16-17
UCL 1 10	UCL 1 15	UCL 1 14	UCL 1 4	UCL 1 7	UCL 1 9	UCL 1 7	UCL 1 12	UCL 1 4	UCL 1 4

PINCHBECK UNITED

Founded: Nickname:

Secretary: Richard Withers   **(T)** 07838 231 637   **(E)** wizz6@icloud.com
Chairman: Gary Coomes   **Manager:** Ian Dunn   **Prog Ed:** Gary Coomes
Ground: Sir Harley Stewart Field, Winfrey Avenue, Spalding, PE11 1DA   **(T)** 07508 809 969
Colours(change): All red
HONOURS: FA Comps: None   **League:** Peterborough & District Premier Division 1989-90, 90-91, 2011-12.

10 YEAR RECORD									
07-08	08-09	09-10	10-11	11-12	12-13	13-14	14-15	15-16	16-17
				P&D P 1	P&D P 15	P&D P 15	P&D P 7	P&D P 3	P&D P 2

UNITED COUNTIES LEAGUE - STEP 5/6

POTTON UNITED
Founded: 1943   Nickname: Royals

Secretary: Mrs Bev Strong   **(T)** 07703 442 565   **(E)** bev.strong@tiscali.co.uk
Chairman: Alan Riley   **Manager:** Laurence Revell   **Prog Ed:** Mrs Bev Strong
Ground: The Hollow, Bigglewade Road, Potton, Beds SG19 2LU   **(T)** 01767 261 100   **Capacity:** 2,000
Colours(change): All blue
HONOURS: FA Comps: None   **League:** United Counties 1986-87, 88-89, Division One 2003-04.

10 YEAR RECORD
	07-08	08-09	09-10	10-11	11-12	12-13	13-14	14-15	15-16	16-17
	UCL P 19	UCL P 20	UCL 1 11	UCL 1 15	UCL 1 15	UCL 1 16	UCL 1 10	UCL 1 3	UCL 1 7	UCL 1 6
FAC	P	EP	EPr	EP					EP	
FAV	2P	1P	2Q	1Q	2Q	2Q	1Q	2Q	2Q	1Q

RAUNDS TOWN
Founded: 1946   Nickname: Shopmates

Secretary: David Jones   **(T)** 07763 492 184   **(E)** david.jones180@ntlworld.com
Chairman: Mrs Lesley Jones   **Manager:** James Le Masseur   **Prog Ed:** Carl Mallet
Ground: Kiln Park, London Road, Raunds, Northants NN9 6EQ   **(T)** 01933 623 351   **Capacity:** 3,000
Colours(change): Red & black stripes/black/black
HONOURS: FA Comps: None   **League:** United Counties Division One 1982-83.

10 YEAR RECORD
	07-08	08-09	09-10	10-11	11-12	12-13	13-14	14-15	15-16	16-17
	UCL P 17	UCL P 10	UCL P 20	UCL P 20	UCL 1 13	UCL 1 14	UCL 1 12	UCL 1 9	UCL 1 8	UCL 1 7
FAC	P	1Q	EPr	EP	EP				P	EP
FAV	2Q	2P	1Q	2Q	2Q	2Q		1Q	1P	1Q

RUSHDEN & HIGHAM UNITED
Founded: Formed: 2007   Nickname: The Lankies

Secretary: Scott Freeman   **(T)** 07771 727 265   **(E)** rhufcsec@yahoo.co.uk
Chairman: John O'Connor   **Manager:** Wayne Abbott
Ground: Hayden Road, Rushden, Northants NN10 0HX   **(T)** 01933 410 036   **Capacity:** 1,500
Colours(change): Orange/black/black
HONOURS: FA Comps: None   **League:** None

10 YEAR RECORD
	07-08	08-09	09-10	10-11	11-12	12-13	13-14	14-15	15-16	16-17
	UCL 1 14	UCL 1 6	UCL 1 16	UCL 1 10	UCL 1 5	UCL 1 8	UCL 1 14	UCL 1 13	UCL 1 13	UCL 1 16
FAC					EP	EP	EP			
FAV		2Q	2Q	1Q	2Q	2Q	1Q		1Q	1Q

STEWARTS & LLOYDS CORBY
Founded: 1935   Nickname: The Foundrymen

Secretary: John Davies   **(T)** 07588 018 397   **(E)** foundrychairman@hotmail.co.uk
Chairman: John Davies   **Manager:** Ian Benjamin   **Prog Ed:** Natalie Milne
Ground: Recreation Ground, Occupation Road, Corby NN17 1EH   **(T)** 01536 401 497   **Capacity:** 1,500
Colours(change): Red & black stripes/black/black
HONOURS: FA Comps: None   **League:** United Counties Division One 1973-74, 74-75, Premier 85-86, 08-09.

10 YEAR RECORD
	07-08	08-09	09-10	10-11	11-12	12-13	13-14	14-15	15-16	16-17
	UCL P 12	UCL P 1	UCL P 12	UCL P 8	UCL P 9	UCL P 14	UCL P 19	UCL 1 20	UCL 1 3	UCL 1 18
FAC	EP	2Q	EP	2Qr	EP	EP	EPr			
FAV	2Q	4P	2P	1Q	2P	1P	1P			1Q

THRAPSTON TOWN
Founded: 1960   Nickname: Venturas

Secretary: Steve Vitue   **(T)** 07976 484 507   **(E)** kvnob@aol.com
Chairman: Barry Carter   **Manager:** Ian Walker   **Prog Ed:** Steve Vitue
Ground: Chancery Lane, Thrapston, Northants NN14 4JL   **(T)** 01832 732 470   **Capacity:** 1,000
Colours(change): All blue (Red/black/black)
HONOURS: FA Comps: None   **League:** Kettering Amateur League 1970-71, 72-73, 73-74, 77-78.

10 YEAR RECORD
	07-08	08-09	09-10	10-11	11-12	12-13	13-14	14-15	15-16	16-17
	UCL 1 11	UCL 1 11	UCL 1 6	UCL 1 2	UCL P 21	UCL 1 12	UCL 1 13	UCL 1 8	UCL 1 9	UCL 1 10
FAC					1Q	P			P	
FAV	2Q	1P	2Q	1P	2Q	2Q	2Q	1Q	1Q	1P

WESSEX LEAGUE

Sponsored by: Sydenhams
Founded: 1986

Recent Champions: 2014: Sholing
2015: Petersfield Town **2016:** Salisbury

PREMIER DIVISION	P	W	D	L	F	A	GD	Pts
1 Portland United	42	31	6	5	106	43	63	99
2 Moneyfields	42	32	5	5	103	33	70	98*
3 Sholing	42	25	9	8	80	33	47	84
4 Blackfield & Langley	42	26	5	11	96	47	49	83
5 Alresford Town	42	24	5	13	87	63	24	77
6 Horndean	42	22	10	10	93	64	29	76
7 Team Solent	42	20	7	15	89	62	27	67
8 AFC Portchester	42	19	8	15	81	60	21	65
9 Lymington Town	42	18	7	17	69	59	10	61
10 Brockenhurst	42	16	11	15	70	70	0	59
11 Bemerton Heath Harlequins	42	16	9	17	67	61	6	57
12 Fareham Town	42	16	8	18	78	81	-3	56
13 Andover Town	42	16	6	20	69	61	8	54
14 Bashley	42	15	9	18	66	70	-4	54
15 Newport (IoW)	42	12	17	13	57	62	-5	53
16 Hamworthy United	42	13	6	23	71	89	-18	45
17 Bournemouth	42	9	13	20	52	85	-33	40
18 Cowes Sports	42	10	8	24	46	97	-51	38
19 Amesbury Town	42	9	10	23	60	94	-34	37
20 Fawley	42	11	4	27	61	124	-63	37
21 Whitchurch United	42	8	8	26	50	116	-66	32
22 Verwood Town	42	5	7	30	40	117	-77	22

DIVISION ONE	P	W	D	L	F	A	GD	Pts
1 Hamble Club	40	32	3	5	133	37	96	99
2 Baffins Milton Rovers	40	27	4	9	128	52	76	85
3 Shaftesbury	40	26	4	10	127	65	62	82
4 Christchurch	40	22	10	8	88	57	31	76
5 Ringwood Town	40	23	6	11	90	56	34	75
6 Laverstock & Ford	40	24	0	16	102	71	31	72
7 Tadley Calleva	40	20	8	12	79	58	21	68
8 AFC Stoneham	40	21	4	15	94	65	29	67
9 United Services Portsmouth	40	19	10	11	97	71	26	67
10 Weymouth Res	40	19	7	14	99	63	36	64
11 Downton	40	19	6	15	66	53	13	63
12 Alton	40	19	5	16	82	87	-5	61*
13 Romsey Town	40	17	7	16	71	67	4	58
14 New Milton Town	40	15	6	19	66	94	-28	51
15 Totton & Eling	40	12	11	17	64	68	-4	47
16 Fleet Spurs	40	10	6	24	81	127	-46	36
17 Folland Sports	40	8	6	26	60	120	-60	30
18 Hythe & Dibden	40	6	10	24	38	85	-47	28
19 Andover New Street	40	7	5	28	39	112	-73	26
20 East Cowes Victoria	40	5	8	27	36	120	-84	23
21 Pewsey Vale	40	3	6	31	45	157	-112	15

ADDITIONAL CLUB MOVEMENTS

Premier Division
In: Petersfield Town (R - Southern Division One Central).
Out: Moneyfields (P - Southern Division One Central).

Division One
Out: Fleet Spurs (S - Combined Counties).

PREMIER DIVISION	1	2	3	4	5	6	7	8	9	10	11	12	13	14	15	16	17	18	19	20	21	22
1 AFC Portchester		1-1	2-1	2-0	2-1	3-5	2-5	2-0	2-2	2-0	4-2	5-0	4-1	1-2	1-1	1-3	2-3	0-2	0-1	3-0	1-1	3-1
2 Alresford Town	2-1		5-0	0-2	5-3	2-1	1-2	5-2	4-2	4-3	3-1	0-1	3-1	1-1	1-3	2-2	0-2	0-1	2-1	3-0	3-2
3 Amesbury Town	2-3	1-2		1-2	2-3	1-1	1-4	2-1	0-4	0-0	1-3	2-4	2-1	5-2	1-0	1-2	2-3	0-3	0-6	0-3	1-1	3-3
4 Andover Town	1-2	4-2	3-3		2-0	0-1	1-3	4-1	2-2	5-1	3-5	3-1	0-1	2-2	0-3	0-1	3-2	1-2	0-1	2-0	5-1	1-1
5 Bashley	2-1	1-5	2-2	2-1		1-0	2-1	0-0	2-2	0-0	0-1	1-3	1-0	2-4	1-0	0-1	3-2	5-2	1-1	3-2	4-0	2-4
6 Bemerton Heath Harlequins	0-0	1-2	0-0	0-2	1-1		0-1	2-2	2-2	2-1	2-1	7-0	2-1	1-6	0-1	2-1	0-1	2-2	2-2	2-1	4-0	1-3
7 Blackfield & Langley	1-2	1-0	4-1	2-1	0-4	3-1		2-1	0-1	3-1	1-3	4-1	3-0	1-4	1-0	1-2	1-1	1-3	0-0	1-2	4-0	8-0
8 Bournemouth	0-2	1-2	2-4	1-0	1-1	1-4	2-1		2-1	1-1	1-2	2-3	1-0	0-1	1-3	1-3	1-1	2-2	0-0	0-0	3-2	2-2
9 Brockenhurst	2-0	3-1	2-2	1-3	1-0	0-2	2-1	3-3		1-1	5-3	1-0	1-4	2-1	0-0	0-2	3-2	0-3	0-1	2-0	3-2	2-1
10 Cowes Sports	2-0	0-2	1-0	1-4	1-1	1-2	1-3	2-0	2-0		0-3	2-5	1-4	3-3	3-2	1-5	1-0	1-5	1-3	0-2	4-0	1-0
11 Fareham Town	0-2	1-1	2-3	1-0	0-0	3-0	0-7	2-3	4-0	2-2		3-4	4-0	2-4	0-0	0-1	1-2	2-2	1-1	1-2	2-2	1-0
12 Fawley	0-2	0-2	1-5	0-2	1-3	1-3	0-5	1-3	2-1	3-1	2-7		2-2	0-3	1-3	0-4	1-1	2-4	1-4	1-4	6-4	4-5
13 Hamworthy United	1-1	1-2	4-0	1-1	4-0	1-0	1-3	1-4	7-1	6-3	3-0		2-4	1-5	1-3	0-2	2-2	3-1	1-4	1-3	5-0
14 Horndean	3-2	3-3	2-2	1-1	3-1	2-2	0-1	1-0	3-1	6-0	0-1	3-0	1-1		2-1	0-2	3-0	1-3	3-1	3-2	2-0	2-0
15 Lymington Town	3-1	1-2	1-0	0-4	2-1	2-1	1-2	4-0	1-1	1-2	3-1	2-3	3-0	0-2		0-4	1-1	1-2	1-5	1-3	2-0	5-2
16 Moneyfields	0-2	1-0	4-2	2-0	3-1	2-3	0-0	6-0	2-1	2-0	2-2	7-0	0-1	4-0	1-1		1-0	2-1	3-2	2-0	3-0	6-0
17 Newport (IoW)	0-0	2-5	0-1	1-2	3-2	2-0	2-2	1-1	2-2	0-0	1-2	0-0	3-2	3-3	1-1	2-2		0-1	1-0	1-1	2-0	1-1
18 Portland United	3-2	3-0	4-0	1-0	3-1	2-1	1-2	3-3	3-2	6-0	4-0	3-1	3-0	4-1	2-1	3-0	2-3		1-0	2-0	3-0	1-1
19 Sholing	3-3	1-2	1-0	2-0	1-0	1-0	1-1	5-0	4-0	2-1	3-0	1-1	3-0	3-0	3-1	0-1	3-0	1-0		3-2	3-1	1-0
20 Team Solent	2-1	2-0	3-1	2-0	3-2	1-0	1-5	1-3	1-1	2-0	1-3	3-1	7-0	2-1	1-2	2-2	4-0	2-4	1-1		6-1	9-0
21 Verwood Town	1-4	1-5	2-2	2-0	0-4	1-3	0-2	0-0	1-4	1-2	2-1	3-1	1-3	0-3	1-5	0-4	0-0	0-2	0-4	2-2		3-0
22 Whitchurch United	0-7	0-1	0-3	3-2	0-2	1-4	0-3	3-1	0-3	3-0	1-2	1-3	2-2	2-2	0-1	1-4	0-3	0-4	1-0	2-2	4-3	

LEAGUE CUP

HOLDERS: TEAM SOLENT

ROUND 1

Laverstock & Ford	v Romsey Town	2-1
Bemerton Heath Harlequins	v United Services Portsmouth	3-2
Bashley	v Moneyfields	2-2, 4-3p
Verwood Town	v Alresford Town	0-4
Shaftesbury	v Newport (IOW)	2-1
New Milton Town	v Fareham Town	3-2
East Cowes Victoria	v AFC Stoneham	0-4
Downton	v Bournemouth	5-1
Pewsey Vale	v Totton & Eling	2-2, 1-3p
Team Solent	v Horndean	3-1
Weymouth Res	v Brockenhurst	1-4

ROUND 2

Alton	v Baffins Milton Rovers	0-9
Hythe & Dibden	v Andover Town	1-4
Hamworthy United	v Cowes Sports	8-0
Whitchurch United	v Laverstock & Ford	1-3
Lymington Town	v Bemerton Heath Harlequins	2-4
Bashley	v Fawley	3-0
Folland Sports	v Alresford Town	1-9
Shaftesbury	v New Milton Town	3-0
AFC Stoneham	v Ringwood Town	1-1, 3-4p
AFC Porchester	v Sholing	1-4
Downton	v Totton & Eling	2-2, 4-1p
Fleet Spurs	v Hamble Club	0-3
Andover New Street	v Portland United	1-4
Team Solent	v Brockenhurst	1-1, 5-4p
Tadley Calleva	v Christchurch	3-2
Blackfield & Langley	v Amesbury Town	9-0

ROUND 3

Baffins Milton Rovers	v Andover Town	2-2, 7-6p
Hamworthy United	v Laverstock & Ford	4-1
Bemerton Heath Harlequins	v Bashley	0-1
Alresford Town	v Shaftesbury	4-4, 4-5p
Ringwood Town	v Sholing	2-2, 2-4p
Downton	v Hamble Club	1-1, 1-3p
Portland United	v Team Solent	1-1, 2-4p
Tadley Calleva	v Blackfield & Langley	3-2

QUARTER FINALS

Baffins Milton Rovers	v Hamworthy United	2-1
Bashley	v Shaftesbury	1-3
Sholing	v Hamble Club	1-1, 3-0p
Team Solent	v Tadley Calleva	1-1, 4-1p

SEMI FINALS

TBaffins Milton Rovers	v Shaftesbury	3-2
Sholing	v Team Solent	2-0

FINAL

Baffins Milton Rovers	v Sholing	1-2

DIVISION ONE

		1	2	3	4	5	6	7	8	9	10	11	12	13	14	15	16	17	18	19	20	21
1	AFC Stoneham		5-3	6-2	1-1	1-2	2-3	3-0	6-1	3-2	2-3	2-0	1-2	0-3	4-2	1-0	1-1	2-3	0-2	1-1	3-2	3-2
2	Alton	0-3		5-1	2-0	3-1	3-0	2-2	4-1	4-0	0-3	2-1	0-9	7-0	2-0	3-1	3-2	1-0	2-2	5-0	1-2	1-1
3	Andover New Street	1-5	0-3		3-1	1-1	1-4	5-1	3-2	1-2	0-3	1-1	1-3	3-0	1-2	0-4	0-3	1-0	0-2	0-3		
4	Baffins Milton Rovers	4-2	3-1	9-0		2-2	0-0	6-1	7-1	5-0	0-1	4-0	3-1	2-2	7-0	2-1	2-4	4-5	1-0	6-1	0-3	4-1
5	Christchurch	1-1	4-1	2-1	1-2		2-0	2-1	4-2	4-1	3-2	0-0	3-2	3-3	11-1	1-2	1-0	1-2	2-0	3-1	2-2	2-1
6	Downton	0-2	3-2	2-0	2-3	2-2		5-0	1-1	2-3	2-0	2-1	1-0	2-0	2-0	1-0	3-0	3-1	0-0	0-2	2-2	2-3
7	East Cowes Victoria	0-2	0-1	1-1	1-5	2-2	1-1		1-1	1-0	0-4	1-1	1-7	2-1	4-3	1-2	1-5	1-7	0-6	2-1	3-5	1-2
8	Fleet Spurs	2-3	2-1	2-1	0-5	0-1	4-0	2-1		5-2	0-4	4-3	1-4	3-3	2-2	0-4	0-1	6-4	4-3	2-2	1-3	1-4
9	Folland Sports	0-1	5-2	4-0	0-5	2-4	1-3	2-2	6-3		0-7	1-1	1-8	4-2	4-0	0-4	4-3	2-6	1-4	1-1	2-4	1-2
10	Hamble Club	1-0	8-0	4-0	2-1	3-1	2-1	14-0	4-3	2-1		4-0	2-0	1-3	2-0	1-3	3-3	3-1	2-0	2-2	2-2	2-0
11	Hythe & Dibden	0-2	0-1	1-2	0-4	0-1	1-1	5-1	2-1	1-5			3-2	0-2	1-1	1-1	1-2	0-5	1-0	0-0	4-1	2-2
12	Laverstock & Ford	5-2	1-4	2-0	3-4	2-1	1-0	1-0	5-2	1-0	0-1	2-0		4-5	5-0	2-1	2-1	1-4	2-3	1-0	2-1	3-2
13	New Milton Town	3-0	0-1	2-1	0-4	0-2	1-4	1-2	0-4	1-1	1-3	5-0	0-5		6-1	0-3	3-1	2-1	0-2	1-0	2-4	1-6
14	Pewsey Vale	0-9	4-2	0-0	1-4	1-2	2-5	1-0	5-5	2-2	1-9	2-1	1-2	1-1		2-3	1-3	0-3	1-2	0-4	1-7	1-6
15	Ringwood Town	4-3	3-1	4-1	2-0	2-3	1-0	1-0	4-3	2-1	2-4	4-0	8-3	2-1	8-2		1-2	2-5	0-0	1-1	2-2	1-2
16	Romsey Town	0-3	1-1	1-1	1-2	2-2	2-1	1-0	4-0	3-1	1-0	4-2	4-1	2-3	3-0	2-3		1-1	0-2	1-1	3-2	0-3
17	Shaftesbury	3-2	6-0	7-1	4-3	1-2	4-1	3-0	7-1	5-0	2-3	2-1	1-3	0-1	4-1	2-1	3-1		4-5	0-0	4-4	3-0
18	Tadley Calleva	4-2	3-6	5-1	0-1	1-2	2-1	2-0	1-0	1-1	2-8	2-1	2-4	0-2	7-0	0-0	1-0	2-3		1-1	3-2	2-0
19	Totton & Eling	1-0	7-0	5-1	0-4	3-2	0-2	2-0	1-5	4-0	0-5	5-0	1-2	3-0	3-1	1-4	2-2	1-3	1-2		1-3	1-1
20	United Services Portsmouth	0-1	2-1	3-0	2-4	2-1	1-2	5-1	3-1	4-0	2-2	0-0	5-2	2-2	4-3	1-1	0-1	3-1	0-0	1-4		2-1
21	Weymouth Res	1-4	1-1	3-1	1-4	2-2	0-1	4-0	5-3	6-1	0-2	4-1	1-0	10-0	5-1	1-2	5-1	0-1	1-1	2-2	5-2	

AFC PORTCHESTER — Founded: 1971 — Nickname: Portchy/Royals

Secretary: Andy Girling **(T)** 07824 332 229 **(E)** secretary@afcportchester.co.uk
Chairman: Paul Kelly
Ground: Wicor Recreation Ground Cranleigh Road Portchester Hampshire PO16 9DP **(T)** 01329 233 833 (Clubhouse)
Capacity: **Seats:** Yes **Covered:** Yes **Midweek Matchday:** Tuesday **Clubhouse:** Yes
Colours(change): Tangerine/black/tangerine (All sky blue)
Previous Names: Loyds Sports 1971-73. Colourvison Rangers 1973-76. Wilcor Mill 1976-2003.
Previous Leagues: City of Portsmouth Sunday. Portsmouth & District >1998. Hampshire 1998-2004.

HONOURS: FA Comps: None
League: Portsmouth & Football 1997-98. Hampshire Division One 2001-02.

10 YEAR RECORD

07-08	08-09	09-10	10-11	11-12	12-13	13-14	14-15	15-16	16-17
Wex1 14	Wex1 19	Wex1 6	Wex1 3	Wex1 2	WexP 15	WexP 8	WexP 3	WexP 6	WexP 8
				FAC Pr	FAC EP	FAC 2Q	FAC P	FAC 2Q	FAC 2Q
			FAV 2Q	FAV 2Q	FAV 2Q	FAV 3P	FAV 3P	FAV 1P	FAV 2Q

ALRESFORD TOWN — Founded: 1898 — Nickname: The Magpies

Secretary: Keith Curtis **(T)** 07703 346 672 **(E)** secretary.alresfordtownfc@gmail.com
Chairman: Stuart Munro **Prog Ed:** Gregory Boughton
Ground: Arlebury Park, The Avenue, Alresford, Hants SO24 9EP **(T)** 01962 735 100 or 07703 346
Capacity: **Seats:** Yes **Covered:** Yes **Midweek Matchday:** Tuesday **Clubhouse:** Yes
Colours(change): Black & white stripes/black/black. (All yellow)
Previous Names: None
Previous Leagues: Winchester League, North Hants league, Hampshire League

HONOURS: FA Comps: None
League: North Hampshire 1999-2000.

10 YEAR RECORD

07-08	08-09	09-10	10-11	11-12	12-13	13-14	14-15	15-16	16-17
WexP 21	WexP 18	WexP 17	WexP 15	WexP 15	WexP 2	WexP 2	WexP 16	WexP 20	WexP 5
	FAC EP	FAC P	FAC Pr	FAC P	FAC P	FAC EP	FAC Pr	FAC EP	FAC 2Q
FAV 2Q	FAV 2Q	FAV 1Pr	FAV 1Q	FAV 1P	FAV 2Q	FAV 4P	FAV 3P	FAV 1Q	FAV 2P

AMESBURY TOWN — Founded: 1904 — Nickname: Blues

Secretary: Chris Green **(T)** 07581 245 510 **(E)** amesburytownfc@gmail.com
Chairman: Gino Nardiello **Manager:** Gareth Honer & Carlo Downie **Prog Ed:** Darrell Tolhurst
Ground: Bonnymead Park Recreation Road Amesbury SP4 7BB **(T)** 01980 623 489
Capacity: **Seats:** Yes **Covered:** Yes **Midweek Matchday:** Wednesday **Clubhouse:** Yes
Colours(change): Royal blue & white/royal blue/royal blue (Black & yellow hooped/black/black & yellow hoops)
Previous Names: Amesbury FC 1904-1984.
Previous Leagues: Salisbury & District Junior 1904-06. Salisbury & District 1906-56, 97-98. Wiltshire 1956-71. Wiltshire Combination/County 71-. Western 1994-97. Hampshire 1998-2004.
HONOURS: FA Comps: None
League: Salisbury & District Division Two 1954-55, Division One 55-56. Wiltshire Division One 1959-60.
10 YEAR RECORD Wiltshire Combination/County 1974-75, 79-80 / Division One 90-91, 91-92. Hampshire Premier 1999-2000.

07-08	08-09	09-10	10-11	11-12	12-13	13-14	14-15	15-16	16-17
Wex1 11	Wex1 12	Wex1 11	Wex1 13	Wex1 14	Wex1 14	Wex1 10	Wex1 4	Wex1 2	WexP 19
	FAC EP	FAC EP	FAC EP					FAC EP	FAC P
FAV 2Q	FAV 2Q	FAV 1Q	FAV 1Q	FAV 1Q	FAV 1Q	FAV 1Q	FAV 2Q	FAV 1Q	FAV 1P

ANDOVER TOWN — Founded: 2013 — Nickname:

Secretary: Margaret White **(T)** 07747 389 356 **(E)** secretary@andovertownfc.co.uk
Chairman: John Ward **Manager:** Glenn Burnett **Prog Ed:** Steve White
Ground: Portway Stadium, West Portway, Portway Industrial Estate, Andover SP10 3LF **(T)**
Capacity: 3,000 **Seats:** 250 **Covered:** Yes **Midweek Matchday:** Tuesday **Clubhouse:** Yes
Colours(change): All blue (All orange)
Previous Names: None
Previous Leagues: None

HONOURS: FA Comps: None
League: None

10 YEAR RECORD

07-08	08-09	09-10	10-11	11-12	12-13	13-14	14-15	15-16	16-17
							WexP 12	WexP 4	WexP 13
								FAC Pr	FAC 1Q
							FAV 2Q	FAV 1P	FAV 2P

BAFFINS MILTON ROVERS
Founded: 2011 **Nickname: None**

Secretary: Yvonne Fradgley-Smith **(T)** 07980 403 336 **(E)** baffinsmiltonrovers@hotmail.co.uk
Chairman: Lynne Stagg
Ground: The Kendall Stadium, Eastern Road, Portsmouth PO3 5LY **(T)**
Capacity: **Seats:** 120 **Covered:** Yes **Midweek Matchday:** Tuesday **Clubhouse:** Yes

Colours(change): All royal blue (Yellow/navy/navy)
Previous Names: Formed when Sunday league teams Baffins Milton and Milton Rovers merged.
Previous Leagues: Hampshire Premier >2016

HONOURS: FA Comps: None
League: Portsmouth Saturday Premier Division 2011-12.

10 YEAR RECORD	Hampshire Premier Senior Division , 2013-14, 15-16.								
07-08	08-09	09-10	10-11	11-12	12-13	13-14	14-15	15-16	16-17
				PorS P 1	PorS P 2	HantP 1	HantP 2	HantP 1	Wex1 2

BASHLEY
Founded: 1947 **Nickname: The Bash**

Secretary: Mike Cranidge **(T)** 07591 187 663 **(E)** footballsecretary@bashleyfc.org.uk
Chairman: Laurence Flanagan
Ground: Bashley Road Ground, Bashley Road, New Milton, Hampshire BH25 5RY **(T)** 01425 620 280
Capacity: 4,250 **Seats:** 250 **Covered:** 1,200 **Midweek Matchday:** Tuesday **Clubhouse:** Yes **Shop:** Yes

Colours(change): Gold/black/black (White/blue/blue)
Previous Names: None
Previous Leagues: Bournemouth 1953-83, Hampshire 1983-86, Wessex 1986-89, Southern 1989-2004, 06-16. Isthmian 2004-06

HONOURS: FA Comps: None
League: Hampshire Division Three 1984-85. Wessex 1986-87, 87-88, 88-89. Southern Southern Division 1989-90,

10 YEAR RECORD	Division One South & West 2006-07.								
07-08	08-09	09-10	10-11	11-12	12-13	13-14	14-15	15-16	16-17
SthP 5	SthP 14	SthP 7	SthP 11	SthP 13	SthP 17	SthP 23	Sthsw 22	Sthsw 22	WexP 14
FAC 3Q	FAC 3Qr	FAC 2Q	FAC 3Q	FAC 1Q	FAC 1Qr	FAC 2Q	FAC P	FAC P	FAC EP
FAT 1P	FAT 1Pr	FAT 1P	FAT 1P	FAT 1Q	FAT 1Qr	FAT 1Q	FAT P	FAT 1Q	FAV 2Q

BEMERTON HEATH HARLEQUINS
Founded: 1989 **Nickname: Quins**

Secretary: Andy Hardwick **(T)** 07561 164 068 **(E)** sec.bhhfc@hotmail.co.uk
Chairman: Steve Slade
Ground: The Clubhouse, Western Way, Bemerton Heath Salisbury SP2 9DT **(T)** 01722 331 925
Capacity: 2,100 **Seats:** 250 **Covered:** 350 **Midweek Matchday:** Tuesday **Clubhouse:** Yes

Colours(change): Black & white/black/black & white (All orange)
Previous Names: Bemerton Athletic, Moon FC & Bemerton Boys merged in 1989
Previous Leagues: Salisbury & Wilts Combination, Salisbury & Andover Sunday.

HONOURS: FA Comps: None
League: None

10 YEAR RECORD									
07-08	08-09	09-10	10-11	11-12	12-13	13-14	14-15	15-16	16-17
WexP 13	WexP 12	WexP 3	WexP 2	WexP 2	WexP 5	WexP 7	WexP 13	WexP 9	WexP 11
FAC P	FAC EP	FAC P	FAC EP	FAC EP	FAC EP	FAC EP	FAC 1Q	FAC P	FAC 1Q
FAV 2P	FAV 2P	FAV 2P	FAV 4P	FAV 3P	FAV 5P	FAV 2P	FAV 2P	FAV 2Q	FAV 3P

BLACKFIELD & LANGLEY
Founded: 1935 **Nickname: Watersiders**

Secretary: Doug Sangster **(T)** 07899 927 165 **(E)** bandlfc@hotmail.com
Chairman: Claire Sinclair
Ground: Gang Warily Rec., Newlands Rd, Southampton SO45 1GA **(T)** 02380 893 603
Capacity: 2,500 **Seats:** 180 **Covered:** Yes **Midweek Matchday:** Tuesday **Clubhouse:** Yes

Colours(change): Green & white/white/green & white (All maroon).
Previous Names: None
Previous Leagues: Southampton Junior. Southampton Senior. Hampshire 1950-2000.

HONOURS: FA Comps: None
League: Southampton Junior Division One 1945-46. Southampton West Division 1946-47. Hampshire Division Three

10 YEAR RECORD	West 1951-52, Division Two 1984-85, Premier Division 97-98. Wessex Premier Division 2012-13.								
07-08	08-09	09-10	10-11	11-12	12-13	13-14	14-15	15-16	16-17
Wex1 10	Wex1 2	WexP 8	WexP 14	WexP 16	WexP 1	WexP 6	WexP 5	WexP 3	WexP 4
		FAC EP	FAC P	FAC 1Q	FAC 4Q	FAC EP	FAC 2Qr	FAC 3Q	FAC P
FAV 2Q	FAV 2Q	FAV 2Q	FAV 1P	FAV 2P	FAV 4P	FAV 4P	FAV 3P	FAV 1P	FAV 3P

BOURNEMOUTH

Founded: 1875   Nickname: Poppies

Secretary: Patricia Painter   **(T)** 07894 948 267   **(E)** bournemouthwessex@gmail.com
Chairman: Bob Corbin
Ground: Victoria Park, Namu Road, Winton, Bournemouth BH9 2RA   **(T)** 01202 515 123
Capacity: 3,000 **Seats:** 205   **Covered:** 205   **Midweek Matchday:** Tuesday   **Clubhouse:** Yes   **Shop:** Yes

Colours(change): Red/white/red (Yellow & blue/blue/blue)
Previous Names: Bournemouth Rovers, Bournemouth Wanderers, Bournemouth Dean Park.
Previous Leagues: Hampshire

HONOURS: FA Comps: None
         League: None

10 YEAR RECORD

	07-08		08-09		09-10		10-11		11-12		12-13		13-14		14-15		15-16		16-17	
WexP	5	WexP	15	WexP	4	WexP	5	WexP	9	WexP	13	WexP	15	WexP	18	WexP	18	WexP	17
FAC	EP	FAC	P	FAC	EP	FAC	P	FAC	2Qr	FAC	EP	FAC	P	FAC	Pr	FAC	EP	FAC	EP
FAV	1P	FAV	1Q	FAV	2Q	FAV	3P	FAV	QF	FAV	2P	FAV	1Q	FAV	2Q	FAV	2Q	FAV	1P

BROCKENHURST

Founded: 1898   Nickname: The Badgers

Secretary: Matt Parfect   **(T)** 07903 620 495   **(E)** info@brockenhurstfc.co.uk
Chairman: Ian Allen   **Manager:** Pat McManus   **Prog Ed:** Ian Claxton
Ground: Grigg Lane, Brockenhurst, Hants SO42 7RE   **(T)** 01590 623 544
Capacity: 2,000 **Seats:** 200   **Covered:** 300   **Midweek Matchday:** Tuesday   **Clubhouse:** Yes

Colours(change): All blue (All green).
Previous Names: None
Previous Leagues: Hampshire

HONOURS: FA Comps: None
         League: Hampshire Division Three 1959-60, Division Two 70-71, Division One 75-76. Wessex Division One 2012-13.

10 YEAR RECORD

	07-08		08-09		09-10		10-11		11-12		12-13		13-14		14-15		15-16		16-17	
WexP	6	WexP	5	WexP	13	WexP	22	Wex1	5	Wex1	1	WexP	11	WexP	14	WexP	14	WexP	10
FAC	2Q	FAC	Pr	FAC	1Q	FAC	EP	FAC	1Q	FAC	EP	FAC	1Q	FAC	EP	FAC	3Q	FAC	P
FAV	3P	FAV	1Q	FAV	3P	FAV	2Q	FAV	1P	FAV	1Q	FAV	2Q	FAV	1Q	FAV	1Q	FAV	2Q

COWES SPORTS

Founded: 1881   Nickname: Yachtsmen

Secretary: Bill Murray   **(T)** 01983 245 720   **(E)** secretary.cowessportsfc@outlook.com
Chairman: Ian Lee
Ground: Westwood Park Reynolds Close off Park Rd Cowes Isle of Wight PO31 7NT   **(T)** 01983 718 277
Capacity: **Seats:** Yes   **Covered:** Yes   **Midweek Matchday:** Tuesday   **Clubhouse:** Yes

Colours(change): Blue & White/black/blue (Purple/white/red)
Previous Names: None
Previous Leagues: Hampshire (Founding members) 1896-98, 1903-94. Southern 1898-1900.

HONOURS: FA Comps: None
         League: Hampshire Division One 1896-97, 1926-27, 27-28, 30-31, 36-37, 55-56, 93-94, Division Two 1974-75.
         Southern Division Two South West 1998-99.

10 YEAR RECORD

	07-08		08-09		09-10		10-11		11-12		12-13		13-14		14-15		15-16		16-17	
WexP	9	WexP	13	WexP	22	Wex1	8	Wex1	6	Wex1	4	Wex1	3	Wex1	2	WexP	11	WexP	18
FAC	EP	FAC	1Q	FAC	EP	FAC	EP	FAC	EP	FAC	EP	FAC	P	FAC	P	FAC	P	FAC	EP
FAV	3P	FAV	2Q	FAV	2Q	FAV	2Q	FAV	2Q	FAV	3P	FAV	2Q	FAV	2Q	FAV	1P	FAV	2Q

FAREHAM TOWN

Founded: 1947   Nickname: Creeksiders

Secretary: Paul Procter   **(T)** 07445 805 122   **(E)** farehamtnfc@gmail.com
Chairman: Nick Ralls   **Manager:** Pete Stiles   **Prog Ed:** Paul Procter
Ground: Cams Alders, Palmerston Drive, Fareham, Hants PO14 1RH   **(T)** 07445 805 122
Capacity: 2,000 **Seats:** 450   **Covered:** 500   **Midweek Matchday:** Tuesday   **Clubhouse:** Yes   **Shop:** Yes

Colours(change): Red & black stripes/black/red (Blue & black stripes/blue/blue)
Previous Names: Formed when Fareham FC, Fareham Brotherhood and Fareham Youth Centre merged.
Previous Leagues: Portsmouth 1946-49. Hampshire 1949-79. Southern 1979-98.

HONOURS: FA Comps: None
         League: Hampshire League Division 3 East 1949-50, Premier 1959-60, 62-63, 63-64, 64-65, 65-66, 72-73, 74-75.

10 YEAR RECORD

	07-08		08-09		09-10		10-11		11-12		12-13		13-14		14-15		15-16		16-17	
WexP	8	WexP	10	WexP	6	WexP	8	WexP	12	WexP	9	WexP	10	WexP	19	WexP	12	WexP	12
FAC	Pr	FAC	EP	FAC	EP	FAC	P	FAC	EP	FAC	2Q	FAC	1Q	FAC	P	FAC	EP	FAC	1Qr
FAV	1Q	FAV	1Pr	FAV	2P	FAV	2Q	FAV	1P	FAV	2Q	FAV	2P	FAV	1P	FAV	1Q	FAV	2Q

HAMBLE CLUB
Founded: 1969   Nickname: The Monks

Secretary: Colin Williams   **(T)** 07977 324 923   **(E)** secretary.hambleclubfc@gmail.com
Chairman: Mike Clarke
Ground: Hamble Community Facility, Hamble Lane SO31 4TS   **(T)** 07977 324 923
Capacity: **Seats:** Yes   **Covered:** Yes   **Midweek Matchday:**   **Clubhouse:** Yes

Colours(change): All yellow (All red)
Previous Names: None
Previous Leagues: Hampshire Premier 1993-2016.

HONOURS: FA Comps: None
League: Hampshire Premier 2014-15. Wessex Division One 2016-17.

10 YEAR RECORD
07-08	08-09	09-10	10-11	11-12	12-13	13-14	14-15	15-16	16-17
HantP 14	HantP 17	HantP 12	HantP 16	HantP 15	HantP Exp	Hant1 2	HantP 1	HantP 3	Wex1 1

HAMWORTHY UNITED
Founded: 1926   Nickname: The Hammers

Secretary: Kevin Keets   **(T)** 07540 142276   **(E)** hamworthyutdsecretary@gmail.com
Chairman: Steve Harvey   **Manager:** Brendon King   **Prog Ed:** Stuart Tanner
Ground: The County Ground, Blandford Close, Hamworthy, Poole BH15 4BF   **(T)** 01202 674 974
Capacity: 2,000 **Seats:**   **Covered:** Yes   **Midweek Matchday:** Tuesday   **Clubhouse:** Yes   **Shop:** No

Colours(change): Maroon & sky blue (Orange & black)
Previous Names: Hamworthy St. Michael merged with Trinidad Old Boys 1926
Previous Leagues: Dorset Combination (Founder Member) / Dorset Premier 1957-2004.

HONOURS: FA Comps: None
League: Dorset Premier 2002-03, 03-04.

10 YEAR RECORD
07-08	08-09	09-10	10-11	11-12	12-13	13-14	14-15	15-16	16-17
WexP 10	WexP 8	WexP 16	WexP 9	WexP 7	WexP 10	WexP 12	WexP 10	WexP 16	WexP 16
FAC 2Q	FAC 2Q	FAC 1Q	FAC Pr	FAC EP	FAC P	FAC 2Q	FAC 2Q	FAC 1Q	FAC 1Q
FAV 2P	FAV 3P	FAV 1Q	FAV 2Q	FAV 1Q	FAV 2Q	FAV 1P	FAV 2Q	FAV 1Q	FAV 1Q

HORNDEAN
Founded: 1887   Nickname: Deans

Secretary: Mandy Winter   **(T)** 07900 384588   **(E)** horndeanfc1887@gmail.com
Chairman: David Sagar
Ground: Five Heads Park Five Heads Road Horndean Hampshire PO8 9NZ   **(T)** 02392 591 363
Capacity: **Seats:** Yes   **Covered:** Yes   **Midweek Matchday:** Tuesday   **Clubhouse:** Yes

Colours(change): All red (All yellow)
Previous Names: None
Previous Leagues: Waterlooville & District. Portsmouth. Hampshire 1972-86, 1995-2004. Wessex 1986-95

HONOURS: FA Comps:
League: Waterlooville & District 1926-27, 29-30, 30-31, 31-32. Portsmouth Division Two 1953-54, Premier 68-69, 69-70, 70-71. Hampshire Division Four 1974-75, Division Three 75-76, Division Two 79-80.

10 YEAR RECORD
07-08	08-09	09-10	10-11	11-12	12-13	13-14	14-15	15-16	16-17
WexP 11	WexP 22	Wex1 12	Wex1 2	WexP 17	WexP 11	WexP 17	WexP 11	WexP 5	WexP 6
				FAC 1Q	FAC 1Q	FAC 1Q	FAC 1Q	FAC EP	FAC EP
			FAV 1Q	FAV 2Q	FAV 3P	FAV 2Q	FAV 2P	FAV 1P	FAV 1P

LYMINGTON TOWN
Founded: 1998   Nickname: Town

Secretary: Barry Torah   **(T)** 07849 645 234   **(E)** Secretary.lymingtontownfc@yahoo.com
Chairman: George Shaw   **Prog Ed:** Barry Torah
Ground: The Sports Ground, Southampton Road, Lymington SO41 9ZG   **(T)** 01590 671 305
Capacity: 3,000 **Seats:** 200   **Covered:** 300   **Midweek Matchday:** Tuesday   **Clubhouse:** Yes

Colours(change): Red/black/red (Yellow/blue/blue)
Previous Names: None
Previous Leagues: Hampshire 1998-2004.

HONOURS: FA Comps: None
League: Wessex Division Two 2004-05.

10 YEAR RECORD
07-08	08-09	09-10	10-11	11-12	12-13	13-14	14-15	15-16	16-17
WexP 20	WexP 18	WexP 20	WexP 11	WexP 14	WexP 19	WexP 14	WexP 9	WexP 13	WexP 9
FAC P	FAC P	FAC Pr	FAC EP	FAC Pr	FAC EP	FAC P	FAC EP	FAC EP	FAC EPr
FAV 4P	FAV 2P	FAV 2Q	FAV 1P	FAV 1Q	FAV 2Q	FAV 1P	FAV 2Qr	FAV 2P	FAV 1Q

NEWPORT (I.O.W.)

Founded: 1888   Nickname: The Port

Secretary: Lisa Woodward   **(T)** 07917 043 152   **(E)** secretary.newport.iwfc@gmail.com
Chairman: Stuart Ross
Ground: St George's Park, St George's Way, Newport PO30 2QH   **(T)** 01983 525 027
Capacity: 4,000 **Seats:** 300 **Covered:** 1,000 **Midweek Matchday:** Tuesday   **Clubhouse:** Yes   **Shop:** Yes

Colours(change): Yellow/blue/blue (Red/white/red)
Previous Names: None
Previous Leagues: I.O.W. 1896-28. Hants 28-86. Wessex 86-90.

HONOURS: FA Comps: None
League: Isle of Wight 1907-08, 08-09, 09-10, 23-24. Hampshire 1929-30, 32-33, 38-39, 47-48, 49-50, 52-53, 53-54, 56
10 YEAR RECORD -57, 79-79, 79-80, 80-81. Southern Eastern Division 2000-01.

07-08		08-09		09-10		10-11		11-12		12-13		13-14		14-15		15-16		16-17	
SthS	22	WexP	6	WexP	9	WexP	10	WexP	13	WexP	6	WexP	4	WexP	7	WexP	10	WexP	15
FAC	P	FAC	EP	FAC	P	FAC	1Q	FAC	1Q	FAC	2Q	FAC	P	FAC	2Qr	FAC	EP	FAC	EP
FAT	P	FAV	1P	FAV	2Q	FAV	3P	FAV	1Q	FAV	5Pr	FAV	2P	FAV	3P	FAV	4P	FAV	2P

PETERSFIELD TOWN

Founded: 1993   Nickname: Rams

Secretary: Mark Nicoll   **(T)** 07949 328 240   **(E)** secretary.petersfieldtownfc@outlook.com
Chairman: Gaeme Moir   **Prog Ed:** Graeme Moir
Ground: Love Lane, Petersfield, Hampshire GU31 4BW   **(T)** 01730 233 416
Capacity: 3000 **Seats:** 250 **Covered:** 250 **Midweek Matchday:** Tuesday   **Clubhouse:** Yes

Colours(change): Red & black/black/red (All sky blue)
Previous Names: Petersfield United folded in 1993. Petersfield Town reformed 1993 to join Wessex League.
Previous Leagues: Hampshire 1980-84. Isthmian 1984-93. Wessex 1993-2015, Southern 2015-17.

HONOURS: FA Comps: None
League: Wessex Division One 2013-14, Premier Division 2014-15.
10 YEAR RECORD

07-08		08-09		09-10		10-11		11-12		12-13		13-14		14-15		15-16		16-17	
Wex1	8	Wex1	4	Wex1	8	Wex1	11	Wex1	12	Wex1	6	Wex1	1	WexP	1	SthC	13	SthC	22
				FAC	EP	FAC	EP	FAC	EP	FAC	EPr	FAC	P	FAC	EP	FAC	3Q	FAC	P
		FAV	2Q	FAV	1Q	FAV	1Q	FAV	2Q	FAV	1P	FAV	1P	FAV	2Q	FAT	P	FAT	Pr

PORTLAND UNITED

Founded: 1921   Nickname: Blues

Secretary: Randle Gates   **(T)** 07928 341 060   **(E)** secretary.portlandutdfc@aol.com
Chairman: Robin Satherley
Ground: New Grove Corner, Grove Road, Portland DT5 1DP   **(T)** 01305 861 489
Capacity: 2,000 **Seats:** Yes **Covered:** Yes **Midweek Matchday:** Tuesday   **Clubhouse:** Yes

Colours(change): All royal blue (White/black/black)
Previous Names: None
Previous Leagues: Western 1925-70. Dorset Combination 1970-76, 77-2001, Dorset Premier 2006-07. Wessex 2001-02.

HONOURS: FA Comps: None
League: Western Division Two 1930-31, 31-32. Dorset Combination 1998-99, 99-2000, Dorset Premier 2007-08, 08-09,
10 YEAR RECORD 12-13, 13-14. Wessex Division One 2015-16, Premier 2016-17.

07-08		08-09		09-10		10-11		11-12		12-13		13-14		14-15		15-16		16-17	
Dor P	1	Dor P	1	Dor P	8	Dor P	4	Dor P	3	Dor P	1	Dor P	1	Dor P	2	Wex1	1	WexP	1
																		FAV	2P

SHAFTESBURY

Founded: 1888   Nickname: The Rockies

Secretary: Dave Burford   **(T)** 01747 855 051   **(E)** secretary@shaftesburyfc.co.uk
Chairman: Steven Coffen
Ground: Cockrams, Coppice Street, Shaftesbury SP7 8PF   **(T)** 07917 652 438
Capacity: **Seats:** Yes **Covered:** Yes **Midweek Matchday:** Tuesday   **Clubhouse:** Yes

Colours(change): Red & white/black/black (All blue)
Previous Names: Shaftesbury Town.
Previous Leagues: Dorset Junior. Dorset Senior 1931-57. Dorset Combination 1957-62, 76-2004. Wessex 2004-11. Dorset Premier 2011-16.

HONOURS: FA Comps: None
League: Dorset Junior 1905-06, 62-63. Dorset Senior 1932-33. Dorset Combination 1988-89, 96-97.
10 YEAR RECORD Dorset Premier 2015-16. Wessex Division One 2016-17.

07-08		08-09		09-10		10-11		11-12		12-13		13-14		14-15		15-16		16-17	
Wex1	12	Wex1	15	Wex1	20	Wex1	19	Dor P	18	Dor P	11	Dor P	14	Dor P	4	Dor P	1	Wex1	3
FAC	EPr	FAC	EPr	FAC	EP														
FAV	1Q	FAV	1P	FAV	2Q	FAV	2Q									FAV	2Q	FAV	2P

SHOLING

Founded: 1884   Nickname: The Boatmen

Secretary: Greg Dickson   **(T)** 07496 804 555   **(E)** secretary@sholingfc.com
Chairman: Gerry Roberts   **Manager:** Dave Diaper   **Prog Ed:** Greg Dickson
Ground: The Universal Stadium, Portsmouth Road, Sholing, SO19 9PW   **(T)** 02380 403 829
Capacity: 1,000   **Seats:** Yes   **Covered:** Yes   **Midweek Matchday:** Tuesday   **Clubhouse:** Yes

Colours(change): Red & white stripes/black/black (Blue & white stripes/blue/blue)
Previous Names: Woolston Works, Thornycrofts (Woolston) 1918-52, Vospers 1960-2003, Vosper Thorneycroft FC/VTFC 2003-10
Previous Leagues: Hampshire 1991-2004, Wessex 2004-09, 2013-14. Southern 2009-13, 2014-15.

HONOURS: FA Comps: FA Vase 2013-14.
      League: Hampshire Premier Division 2000-01, 03-04.
      Wessex Premier 2013-14.

10 YEAR RECORD

07-08		08-09		09-10		10-11		11-12		12-13		13-14		14-15		15-16		16-17	
WexP	2	WexP	2	Sthsw	4	Sthsw	2	Sthsw	4	Sthsw	7	WexP	1	Sthsw	17	WexP	2	WexP	3
FAC	1Qr	FAC	EP	FAC	2Q	FAC	2Qr	FAC	2Q	FAC	3Q	FAC	2Q	FAC	1Q	FAC	P	FAC	1Q
FAV	3Pr	FAV	4P	FAV	P	FAT	P	FAT	1Q	FAT	3Q	FAV	F	FAT	3Q	FAV	2P	FAV	1P

TEAM SOLENT

Founded: 2007   Nickname: The Sparks

Secretary: Liam Dell   **(T)** 07881 014 588   **(E)** secretary.teamsolent@solent.ac.uk
Chairman: Bill Moore
Ground: Test Park, Lower Broomhill Road, Southampton SO16 9BP   **(T)**
Capacity: **Seats:** Yes   **Covered:** Yes   **Midweek Matchday:** Monday   **Clubhouse:** Yes

Colours(change): All red (All white).
Previous Names: None
Previous Leagues: Hampshire Premier 2007-11.

HONOURS: FA Comps: None
      League: Wessex Division One 2014-15.

10 YEAR RECORD

07-08		08-09		09-10		10-11		11-12		12-13		13-14		14-15		15-16		16-17	
HantP	7	HantP	3	HantP	2	HantP	2	Wex1	3	Wex1	3	Wex1	6	Wex1	1	WexP	7	WexP	7
												FAC	EP	FAC	EP	FAC	EP	FAC	P
										FAV	1Q	FAV	1Q	FAV	1Qr	FAV	1P	FAV	5P

AFC STONEHAM
Founded: 1919   Nickname: The Purples

Secretary: Luke Smith   **(T)** 07771 884 997   **(E)** secretary@afcstoneham.co.uk
Chairman: Mark Stupple
Ground: The HP Arena, Jubilee Park, Chestnut Avenue, Eastleigh SO50 9PF   **(T)** 07765 046 429
Colours(change): All purple (Pink/black/black)
HONOURS: FA Comps: None   **League:** Southampton Senior 1982-83, 92-93, 96-97. Hampshire Premier 2007-08.

10 YEAR RECORD

07-08	08-09	09-10	10-11	11-12	12-13	13-14	14-15	15-16	16-17
HantP 1	HantP 4	HantP 6	HantP 8	HantP 4	HantP 2	HantP 12	HantP 4	Wex1 8	Wex1 8
									FAV 1P

ALTON TOWN
Founded: 1947   Nickname: The Brewers

Secretary: Wayne Dickson   **(T)** 07709 715 322   **(E)** secretary.altontownfc@hotmail.com
Chairman: Jim McKell   **Manager:** Mark Corbett   **Prog Ed:** Carl Saunders
Ground: Alton (Bass) Sports Ground, Anstey Road, Alton, Hants GU34 2RL   **(T)**   **Capacity:** 2,000
Colours(change): White/black/black (All red)
HONOURS: FA Comps: None   **League:** Athenian Division Two 1973-74. Hampshire Division Two 1986-87, Division One 98-99, Premier 2001-02.

10 YEAR RECORD

07-08	08-09	09-10	10-11	11-12	12-13	13-14	14-15	15-16	16-17
WexP 14	WexP 19	WexP 18	WexP 13	WexP 10	WexP 18	CCP 21	CC1 13	Wex1 7	Wex1 12
FAC EP	FAC EP	FAC P	FAC 2Qr	FAC P	FAC P	FAC P	FAC 1Q	FAC EP	
FAV 1Q	FAV 2Q	FAV 2Q	FAV 2Q	FAV 2Pr	FAV 1P	FAV 1Q	FAV 1Q	FAV 1P	FAV 1P

ANDOVER NEW STREET
Founded: 1895   Nickname: The Street

Secretary: Kerry Tobin   **(T)** 07976 630 218   **(E)** andovernewstreetfc@hotmail.co.uk
Chairman: Martin Tobin   **Manager:** John Smith & Ian Meechan
Ground: Foxcotte Park Charlton Andover Hampshire SP11 0TA   **(T)** 01264 358 358
Colours(change): Green & black stripes/black/black (All white)
HONOURS: FA Comps: None   **League:** None

10 YEAR RECORD

07-08	08-09	09-10	10-11	11-12	12-13	13-14	14-15	15-16	16-17
Wex1 19	Wex1 20	Wex1 19	Wex1 17	Wex1 10	Wex1 15	Wex1 15	Wex1 13	Wex1 16	Wex1 19
FAV 2Q	FAV 2Q		FAV 1P	FAV 2Q	FAV 1Q			FAV 1Q	FAV 1Q

CHRISTCHURCH
Founded: 1885   Nickname: The Church

Secretary: Sian Corbin   **(T)** 07766 913 571   **(E)** secretary@christchurchfc.co.uk
Chairman: Fiona Clements
Ground: Hurn Bridge S.C, Avon Causeway, Christchurch BH23 6DY   **(T)** 01202 473 792   **Capacity:** 1,200
Colours(change): All Blue (All yellow)
HONOURS: FA Comps: None   **League:** Hampshire Division Two 1937-38, 47-48, 85-86, Division Three 52-53.

10 YEAR RECORD

07-08	08-09	09-10	10-11	11-12	12-13	13-14	14-15	15-16	16-17
WexP 16	WexP 7	WexP 5	WexP 6	WexP 3	WexP 3	WexP 16	WexP 21	Wex1 6	Wex1 4
FAC P	FAC P	FAC EP	FAC EP	FAC EP	FAC 1Q	FAC EP	FAC EPr	FAC P	FAC EP
FAV 2P	FAV 5P	FAV 2P	FAV 1Pr	FAV 3P	FAV 1P	FAV 1Pr	FAV 2Q	FAV 1Q	FAV 2Q

DOWNTON
Founded: 1905   Nickname: The Robins

Secretary: Cara Lewis   **(T)** 07788 535 359   **(E)** info@downtonfc.com
Chairman: Ian Drinkwater
Ground: Brian Whitehead Sports Ground Wick Lane Downton Wiltshire SP5 3NF   **(T)** 01725 512 162   **Capacity:** 2,000
Colours(change): All red (Yellow/blue/blue)
HONOURS: FA Comps: None   **League:** Wessex League Division One 2010-11.

10 YEAR RECORD

07-08	08-09	09-10	10-11	11-12	12-13	13-14	14-15	15-16	16-17
WexP 23	Wex1 17	Wex1 4	Wex1 1	WexP 6	WexP 8	WexP 21	Wex1 12	Wex1 10	Wex1 11
FAC Pr	FAC 1Q	FAC EPr	FAC EP	FAC EPr	FAC EP	FAC EP	FAC EP		
FAV 2Q	FAV 1Q	FAV 1P	FAV 2P	FAV 2P	FAV 3P	FAV 2Q		FAV 1Q	FAV 1Q

EAST COWES VICTORIA ATHLETIC
Founded: 1885   **Nickname:** The Vics

Secretary: Darren Dyer   **(T)** 07725 128 701   **(E)** ecvafc@outlook.com
Chairman: Paul Phelps   **Prog Ed:** Darren Dyer
Ground: Beatrice Avenue Whippingham East Cowes Isle of Wight PO32 6PA   **(T)** 01983 297 165   **Capacity:** 1,000
Colours(change): Red & white/black/black (Orange/black/orange)
HONOURS: FA Comps: None   **League:** Hampshire Division Two 1947-48, 63-64, 71-72, Division One 85-86, 86-87.

10 YEAR RECORD

07-08	08-09	09-10	10-11	11-12	12-13	13-14	14-15	15-16	16-17
Wex1 18	Wex1 18	Wex1 17	Wex1 15	Wex1 4	Wex1 8	Wex1 16	Wex1 15	Wex1 18	Wex1 20
					FAC P	FAC EP			
			FAV 2Q	FAV 1Q	FAV 1Q	FAV 2Q	FAV 2Q	FAV 1Q	FAV 2Q

FAWLEY
Founded: 1923   **Nickname:** Oilers

Secretary: Scott Johnson   **(T)** 07825 550 624   **(E)** fawleyafc@aol.com
Chairman: Kevin Mitchell
Ground: Waterside Spts & Soc. club, 179 Long Lane, Holbury, Soto, SO45 2PA   **(T)** 02380 893 750 (Club)
Colours(change): All blue (All red)
HONOURS: FA Comps: None   **League:** Hampshire Division Three 1994-95.

10 YEAR RECORD

07-08	08-09	09-10	10-11	11-12	12-13	13-14	14-15	15-16	16-17
Wex1 6	Wex1 9	Wex1 2	WexP 20	WexP 19	WexP 17	WexP 20	WexP 17	WexP 19	WexP 20
					FAC EP	FAC EP	FAC EP	FAC EP	FAC EP
				FAV 2P	FAV 1P	FAV 2Q	FAV 1Q	FAV 1Q	FAV 1Q

FOLLAND SPORTS
Founded: 1938   **Nickname:** Planemakers

Secretary: Garry Budden   **(T)** 07972 283 272   **(E)** follandsportsfc@hotmail.co.uk
Chairman: Roy Kingdon
Ground: Folland Park, Kings Ave, Hamble, Southampton SO31 4NF   **(T)** 02380 452 173   **Capacity:** 1,000
Colours(change): All red (All blue)
HONOURS: FA Comps: None   **League:** Hampshire 1941-42, Division Four 79-80, Division Three 80-81.
Southampton Senior 1961-62, 67-68. Wessex Division One 2009-10.

10 YEAR RECORD

07-08	08-09	09-10	10-11	11-12	12-13	13-14	14-15	15-16	16-17
WexP 17	WexP 21	Wex1 1	WexP 12	WexP 5	WexP 7	WexP 3	WexP 8	WexP 21	Wex1 17
FAC P	FAC EPr	FAC EPr	FAC 3Q	FAC EP	FAC P	FAC P	FAC 2Qr	FAC EP	FAC EP
FAV 1P	FAV 1Q	FAV 2P	FAV 1P	FAV 2Q	FAV 3P	FAV 2P	FAV 2P	FAV 2Q	FAV 1Q

HYTHE & DIBDEN
Founded: 1902   **Nickname:** The Boatmen

Secretary: Vanessa Cox   **(T)** 07789 266 473   **(E)** hythedibdenfc@aol.com
Chairman: Dave Cox
Ground: Clayfields, Claypit Lane, Dibden SO45 5TN   **(T)** 07825 550 624
Colours(change): Green/white/green (All blue)
HONOURS: FA Comps: None   **League:** Hampshire Division Three West 1949-50.
Southampton Division Two 1970-71, 75-76.

10 YEAR RECORD

07-08	08-09	09-10	10-11	11-12	12-13	13-14	14-15	15-16	16-17
Wex1 20	Wex1 7	Wex1 16	Wex1 14	Wex1 18	Wex1 16	Wex1 4	Wex1 7	Wex1 11	Wex1 18
							FAC EP	FAC EP	
			FAV 2Q		FAV 1Q	FAV 1P	FAV 1Q	FAV 2Q	FAV 1Q

LAVERSTOCK & FORD
Founded: 1956   **Nickname:** The Stock

Secretary: Matthew McMahon   **(T)** 07795 665 731   **(E)** sec.laverstockandfordfc@gmail.com
Chairman: John Pike
Ground: The Dell, Church Road, Laverstock, Salisbury, Wilts SP1 1QX   **(T)** 01722 327 401
Colours(change): Green & white hoops/green/green (Yellow/blue/white)
HONOURS: FA Comps: None   **League:** Hampshire Division Two 2002-03.

10 YEAR RECORD

07-08	08-09	09-10	10-11	11-12	12-13	13-14	14-15	15-16	16-17
Wex1 2	WexP 20	WexP 21	WexP 17	WexP 22	Wex1 13	Wex1 9	Wex1 8	Wex1 5	Wex1 6
		FAC EP	FAC P						FAC EP
	FAV 2Q	FAV 1P	FAV 1P		FAV 1Q	FAV 1P	FAV 2Q	FAV 1P	FAV 1Q

NEW MILTON TOWN
Founded: 1998 Nickname: The Linnets

Secretary: Viv Williams **(T)** 07803 424 835 **(E)** enquiries@newmiltontownfc.com
Chairman: Scott McFarlane

Ground: Fawcetts Fields, Christchurch Road, New Milton BH25 6QB **(T)** 01425 628 191 **Capacity:** 1,500

Colours(change): Maroon & blue stripes/blue/blue (White/black/white)

HONOURS: FA Comps: None **League:** Wessex 1998-99, 2004-05.

10 YEAR RECORD

07-08		08-09		09-10		10-11		11-12		12-13		13-14		14-15		15-16		16-17	
WexP	19	WexP	19	WexP	19	WexP	19	WexP	20	WexP	21	Wex1	11	Wex1	6	Wex1	14	Wex1	14
FAC	EP	FAC	P	FAC	P	FAC	EPr	FAC	EPr	FAC	EP					FAC	EP		
FAV	1P	FAV	3P	FAV	2Q	FAV	1Q	FAV	2Q	FAV	2P			FAV	2Q	FAV	1P	FAV	1Q

RINGWOOD TOWN
Founded: 1879 Nickname: The Peckers

Secretary: Aubrey Hodder **(T)** 07754 460 501 **(E)** ringwoodtownfc@live.co.uk
Chairman: Phil King **Prog Ed:** Phil King

Ground: The Canotec Stadium, Long Lane, Ringwood, Hampshire BH24 3BX **(T)** 01425 473 448 **Capacity:** 1,000

Colours(change): Red with white trim/red/red (Orange/black/orange)

HONOURS: FA Comps: None **League:** Hampshire Division three 1995-96.

10 YEAR RECORD

07-08		08-09		09-10		10-11		11-12		12-13		13-14		14-15		15-16		16-17	
WexP	22	Wex1	11	Wex1	5	Wex1	6	Wex1	9	Wex1	9	Wex1	13	Wex1	11	Wex1	13	Wex1	5
		FAC	Pr	FAC	P	FAC	1Q	FAC	EP	FAC	EP								
FAV	1Q	FAV	1Q	FAV	2Q	FAV	1Q	FAV	2Q	FAV	1Q	FAV	1Q	FAV	1P	FAV	2Q	FAV	1Q

ROMSEY TOWN
Founded: 1886 Nickname: Town

Secretary: Clare Crossland **(T)** 07864 877 274 **(E)** romseytownfc@gmail.com
Chairman: Ken Jacobs

Ground: The By-Pass Ground, South Front, Romsey SO51 8GJ **(T)** 01794 516 691 **Capacity:** 1,500

Colours(change): Red & black/white/black (Yellow/royal blue/royal blue)

HONOURS: FA Comps: None **League:** Post War: Southampton West 1951-52, Senior Div.2 72-73, Senior Div.1 73-74, 76 -77, Prem 80-81, 83-84. Hampshire Div.4 75-76, Div.2 78-79. Wessex 89-90.

10 YEAR RECORD

07-08		08-09		09-10		10-11		11-12		12-13		13-14		14-15		15-16		16-17	
WexP	18	WexP	11	WexP	10	WexP	16	WexP	8	WexP	20	WexP	22	Wex1	14	Wex1	9	Wex1	13
				FAC	P	FAC	EPr	FAC	EP	FAC	P	FAC	EP	FAC	EP				
		FAV	1Q	FAV	1Q	FAV	2Q	FAV	2Q	FAV	2Q	FAV	2Q	FAV	1Q	FAV	2Q	FAV	1P

TADLEY CALLEVA
Founded: 1989 Nickname: The Tadders

Secretary: Dean Newton **(T)** 07926 830 806 **(E)** secretarytcfc@gmail.com
Chairman: Sandy Russell

Ground: Barlows Park Silchester Road Tadley Hampshire RG26 3PX **(T)** 07787 501 028 **Capacity:** 1,000

Colours(change): All yellow (All white)

HONOURS: FA Comps: None **League:** Wessex Division One 2007-08.

10 YEAR RECORD

07-08		08-09		09-10		10-11		11-12		12-13		13-14		14-15		15-16		16-17	
Wex1	1	Wex1	16	Wex1	15	Wex1	16	Wex1	17	Wex1	7	Wex1	5	Wex1	3	Wex1	3	Wex1	7
												FAC	P	FAC	EPr	FAC	EP	FAC	EP
		FAV	1Q							FAV	1Q	FAV	2Q	FAV	2Q	FAV	3Pr	FAV	1Q

TOTTON & ELING
Founded: 1925 Nickname: The Millers

Secretary: Rob Lornax **(T)** 02380 861 590 **(E)** tandemillers2@gmail.com
Chairman: Andy Tipp **Manager:** Jay Keating **Prog Ed:** Andy Tipp

Ground: Millers Park,Little Tesrwood Farm Salisbury Road Totton SO40 2RW **(T)** 07545 182 379 **Capacity:** 1,500

Colours(change): Red & black stripes/black/red & black (Blue/blue/yellow)

HONOURS: FA Comps: None **League:** Hampshire Division three 1974-75, Division One 1987-88, 88-89. Wessex Division One 2008-09.

10 YEAR RECORD

07-08		08-09		09-10		10-11		11-12		12-13		13-14		14-15		15-16		16-17	
Wex1	5	Wex1	1	WexP	7	WexP	18	WexP	11	WexP	12	WexP	8	WexP	20	Wex1	15	Wex1	15
				FAC	P	FAC	1Q	FAC	P	FAC	1Qr	FAC	Pr	FAC	EP				
		FAV	1P	FAV	2Q	FAV	1Q	FAV	1Q	FAV	1Q	FAV	1Q	FAV	1Q				

UNITED SERVICES PORTSMOUTH

Founded: 1962   Nickname: The Navy

Secretary: Bob Brady   **(T)** 07887 541 782   **(E)** usportsmouthfc@hotmail.co.uk
Chairman: Richard Stephenson   **Prog Ed:** Charlie Read
Ground: Victory Stadium HMS Temeraire Burnaby Road Portsmouth PO1 2HB   **(T)** 02392 573 041 (Gr'sman)
Colours(change): Royal blue & red stripes/royal blue/royal blue (All white)
HONOURS: FA Comps: None   **League:** Hampshire Division Two 1967-68, 77-78, 80-81.

10 YEAR RECORD

07-08	08-09	09-10	10-11	11-12	12-13	13-14	14-15	15-16	16-17
Wex1 9	Wex1 3	Wex1 9	Wex1 5	Wex1 13	Wex1 12	Wex1 7	Wex1 5	Wex1 4	Wex1 9
								FAC EP	FAC P
FAV 1Qr	FAV 2Q	FAV 1P	FAV 1Q	FAV 2Q	FAV 2Q	FAV 2Q	FAV 2P	FAV 2Qr	FAV 1Q

VERWOOD TOWN

Founded: 1920   Nickname: The Potters

Secretary: Nigel Watts   **(T)** 07517 077 566   **(E)** secretary@vtfc.co.uk
Chairman: Martin Gilham
Ground: Potterne Park Potterne Way Verwood Dorset BH21 6RS   **(T)** 01202 814 007
Colours(change): Red & black/red/black (Royal blue & black stripes/royal blue/royal blue)
HONOURS: FA Comps: None   **League:** Wessex Division One 2011-12.

10 YEAR RECORD

07-08	08-09	09-10	10-11	11-12	12-13	13-14	14-15	15-16	16-17
Wex1 4	Wex1 13	Wex1 7	Wex1 9	Wex1 1	WexP 14	WexP 19	WexP 15	WexP 17	WexP 22
			FAC EPr	FAC EP	FAC EP	FAC EP	FAC EP	FAC P	FAC Pr
		FAV 1P	FAV 3P	FAV 1Q	FAV 1Qr	FAV 2P	FAV 3P	FAV 2Q	FAV 1Q

WEYMOUTH RESERVES

Founded: 1896   Nickname: The Terras

Secretary: Ray Pearce   **(T)** 07801 697 474   **(E)** wfcresec@btopenworld.com
Chairman: Steve Mills
Ground: Bob Lucas Stadium, Radipole Lane, Weymouth DT4 9XJ   **(T)** 01305 785 558
Colours(change): Claret/white/white (All yellow)
HONOURS: FA Comps: None   **League:** Western Division One 1953-54. Dorset Combination 1989-90.

10 YEAR RECORD

07-08	08-09	09-10	10-11	11-12	12-13	13-14	14-15	15-16	16-17
		Dor P 7	Dor P 2	Dor P 12	Dor P 6	SomP 2	Dor P 5	Dor P 3	Wex1 10

WHITCHURCH UNITED

Founded: 1903   Nickname: Jam Boys

Secretary: Adam Williams   **(T)** 07547 077 007   **(E)** secretary.wufc@gmail.com
Chairman: Peter Adams   **Prog Ed:** John Rutledge
Ground: Longmeadow Winchester Road Whitchurch Hampshire RG28 7RB   **(T)** 01256 892 493   **Capacity:** 1,500
Colours(change): Red & white stripes/red/red (All blue)
HONOURS: FA Comps: None   **League:** Hampshire Division Two 1989-90.

10 YEAR RECORD

07-08	08-09	09-10	10-11	11-12	12-13	13-14	14-15	15-16	16-17
Wex1 17	Wex1 6	Wex1 10	Wex1 7	Wex1 8	Wex1 2	WexP 13	WexP 6	WexP 15	WexP 21
				FAC 2Q	FAC EP	FAC EPr	FAC EPr	FAC EPr	FAC P
			FAV 1Q	FAV 2Q	FAV 2Q	FAV 1Q	FAV 2Q	FAV 1Pr	FAV 2Q

WEST MIDLANDS (REGIONAL) LEAGUE
ADDITIONAL CLUB MOVEMENTS
Premier Division - In: Tividale (R - Midland League).
Out: Haughmond (P - Midland League), Willenhall Town (R).
Division One - In: Allscott (P), Willenhall Town (R).
Out: FC Stafford (W), Hereford Lads Club (P), Wednesfield (P).
Division Two - In: AFC Bilbrook, AFC Bridgnorth Dev, AFC Wednesbury, Church Stretton, FC Darlaston, Ludlow,
Market Drayton Town Res, Oldbury United, Rock Rovers.
Out: Allscott (P), Tipton Youth (W), Malvern Town Res (W), Emerald Athletic (W),
Azaad Sports (Wolverhampton & District Sunday Lge), West Brom United (W).

WEST MIDLANDS (REGIONAL) LEAGUE

Sponsored by: None
Founded: 1889

Recent Champions: 2014: Lye Town
2015: Sporting Khalsa **2016:** Shawbury United

PREMIER DIVISION		P	W	D	L	F	A	GD	Pts
1	Haughmond	38	32	3	3	135	42	93	99
2	Wolverhampton Casuals	38	27	3	8	122	70	52	84
3	Wolverhampton Sporting Community	38	24	10	4	122	43	79	81*
4	Malvern Town	38	25	4	9	120	56	64	79
5	Wellington	38	20	8	10	95	65	30	68
6	Bewdley Town	38	20	6	12	118	82	36	66
7	Ellesmere Rangers	38	20	5	13	97	77	20	65
8	AFC Bridgnorth	38	17	4	17	67	76	-9	55
9	Pegasus Juniors	38	17	3	18	85	74	11	54
10	Cradley Town	38	16	5	17	76	70	6	53
11	Shifnal Town	38	15	8	15	76	76	0	53
12	Stone Old Alleynians	38	12	13	13	70	64	6	49
13	Black Country Rangers	38	13	10	15	73	72	1	49
14	Willenhall Town	38	15	3	20	74	99	-25	48
15	Bilston Town Community	38	12	7	19	73	90	-17	43
16	Smethwick	38	12	4	22	53	91	-38	40
17	Dudley Sports	38	9	7	22	49	92	-43	34
18	Dudley Town	38	9	4	25	52	114	-62	31
19	Wellington Amateurs	38	7	2	29	45	147	-102	20*
20	Gornal Athletic	38	2	3	33	28	130	-102	9

DIVISION ONE		P	W	D	L	F	A	GD	Pts
1	Hereford Lads Club	30	26	2	2	121	32	89	80
2	Wednesfield	30	22	3	5	114	45	69	69
3	Worcester Raiders	30	18	5	7	83	61	22	59
4	Newport Town	30	18	4	8	89	54	35	58
5	Old Wulfrunians	30	17	5	8	78	52	26	56
6	Tipton Town	30	17	4	9	61	52	9	55
7	Darlaston Town (1874)	30	13	5	12	53	50	3	44
8	St Martins	30	11	2	17	65	94	-29	35
9	Wem Town	30	9	6	15	59	78	-19	33
10	Bustleholme	30	9	4	17	58	77	-19	31
11	Wrens Nest	30	8	6	16	55	82	-27	30
12	Bromyard Town	30	8	4	18	48	79	-31	28
13	Wyrley	30	7	6	17	38	87	-49	27
14	F C Stafford	30	8	5	17	67	98	-31	26*
15	Kington Town	30	7	4	19	53	80	-27	25
16	Team Dudley	30	7	5	18	53	74	-21	23*

Penncroft withdrew - record expunged.
Shenstone Pathfinder withdrew - record expunged.

DIVISION TWO		P	W	D	L	F	A	GD	Pts
1	Telford Juniors	26	18	3	5	100	40	60	57
2	West Brom United	26	18	3	5	79	29	50	57
3	Allscott	26	16	7	3	79	36	43	52*
4	AFC Broseley	26	14	2	10	53	51	2	44
5	Gornal Colts	26	12	3	11	60	51	9	39
6	Warstone Wanderers	26	12	3	11	66	63	3	39
7	Sikh Hunters	26	10	4	12	60	77	-17	34
8	Wolverhampton United	26	11	1	14	60	89	-29	31*
9	Wonder Vaults	26	10	3	13	57	66	-9	30*
10	Tipton Youth	26	8	6	12	52	65	-13	30
11	Malvern Town Res	26	8	5	13	53	64	-11	29
12	Bewdley Town Res	26	8	3	15	58	69	-11	27
13	Emerald Athletic	26	7	6	13	44	83	-39	27
14	Azaad Sports	26	4	3	19	40	78	-38	12*

Premier Division League Cup Final

Haughmond	v	Smethwick	1-0

Division One League Cup Final

Old Wulfrunians	v	Wednesfield	1-3

Divison Two League Cup Final

West Bromwich United	v	Telford Juniors	3-1

PREMIER DIVISION		1	2	3	4	5	6	7	8	9	10	11	12	13	14	15	16	17	18	19	20
1	AFC Bridgnorth		4-5	3-3	1-0	2-0	5-1	2-0	4-1	2-1	1-3	1-5	4-1	3-4	0-5	3-3	0-1	0-1	1-0	3-0	3-1
2	Bewdley Town	3-2		3-2	1-2	3-3	2-2	10-0	2-1	6-0	4-5	0-3	4-3	6-1	4-2	1-1	2-5	7-4	8-3	7-0	3-1
3	Bilston Town Community	2-3	1-4		1-2	0-1	2-1	2-1	0-6	5-0	0-3	1-2	1-4	3-4	0-1	4-2	2-6	0-1	5-0	5-4	1-2
4	Black Country Rangers	2-2	1-1	2-2		1-2	3-2	1-1	5-1	5-0	0-0	3-2	1-3	0-2	3-3	1-1	4-1	0-1	1-3	4-0	1-6
5	Cradley Town	0-2	3-2	2-2	1-1		3-0	3-1	6-1	6-1	1-2	2-3	2-1	0-0	0-2	1-3	5-3	1-7	0-1	3-2	4-1
6	Dudley Sports	0-2	2-0	0-4	0-2	2-7		1-2	4-2	1-0	0-4	2-2	2-0	2-2	4-1	2-2	1-3	1-5	0-5	2-0	1-2
7	Dudley Town	0-3	1-4	1-7	2-1	4-2	1-1		4-3	3-1	0-4	0-1	3-1	2-4	1-2	0-0	2-5	0-6	1-1	1-4	2-1
8	Ellesmere Rangers	2-0	2-0	1-1	2-1	3-2	0-0	3-1		4-1	3-2	2-5	2-1	3-0	7-0	3-2	2-1	1-3	0-3	1-3	4-2
9	Gornal Athletic	0-4	1-2	1-3	1-3	1-5	0-2	0-5	2-3		1-3	2-0	0-1	0-3	2-0	1-1	0-6	2-4	1-3	0-2	0-3
10	Haughmond	3-0	4-2	9-0	3-0	5-0	5-1	3-1	3-2	5-0		4-0	3-1	3-2	4-2	4-1	3-0	1-3	4-1	4-1	7-1
11	Malvern Town	4-0	1-1	3-0	3-1	0-0	1-2	4-1	4-3	6-0	5-0		5-0	4-2	5-3	4-3	4-4	2-0	0-2	7-2	8-0
12	Pegasus Juniors	5-1	3-2	0-1	5-3	3-1	2-0	6-1	0-2	4-6	1-0		0-1	6-1	1-4	0-2	3-3	3-1	4-0	1-2
13	Shifnal Town	1-1	3-0	3-3	4-2	2-1	2-0	2-1	1-3	1-1	1-1	2-4	3-2		0-1	3-0	0-4	2-2	2-2	1-2
14	Smethwick	3-1	1-5	2-1	0-2	2-1	3-0	1-0	0-6	2-2	0-1	0-5	0-1	2-1		1-3	3-4	1-1	1-2	2-3	0-2
15	Stone Old Alleynians	0-1	1-1	2-2	1-1	0-2	1-1	4-3	1-2	1-0	0-2	3-1	1-0	1-2	1-0		2-0	3-2	3-3	2-2	1-1
16	Wolverhampton Casuals	2-1	4-5	2-1	4-3	1-0	5-2	7-0	5-3	8-2	1-3	3-2	2-2	1-0	3-2	3-1		2-1	4-1	3-0	3-0
17	Wolverhampton Sporting Community	6-0	5-1	1-1	3-1	3-0	3-0	7-0	2-2	6-1	0-0	6-2	5-0	6-2	2-2	2-1	2-2		1-1	6-0	1-0
18	Wellington	3-0	5-0	6-0	1-1	1-0	2-0	2-1	4-4	5-0	2-6	0-4	2-2	3-1	6-0	3-1	3-2	1-1		9-0	2-3
19	Wellington Amateurs	0-2	0-4	0-2	3-5	1-4	2-5	3-0	0-5	2-0	0-4	0-7	0-7	1-9	2-1	1-9	2-3	0-6	1-2		1-4
20	Willenhall Town	5-0	0-3	2-3	3-4	1-2	5-2	2-5	2-2	4-2	1-9	0-2	2-3	3-1	0-1	0-4	2-8	2-2	3-1	3-1	

PREMIER DIVISION

AFC BRIDGNORTH
Founded: 2013 **Nickname:** Meadow Men

Secretary: Steve Groome **(T)** 07748 302 650 **(E)** steve_groome2003@yahoo.co.uk
Chairman: Stan Parkes
Ground: Crown Meadow, Innage Lane, Bridgnorth WV16 4HS **(T)** 07748 302 650 **Capacity:** 2,000
Colours(change): Blue & white
HONOURS: FA Comps: None **League:** West Midlands (Reg) Division One 2013-14.

10 YEAR RECORD

07-08	08-09	09-10	10-11	11-12	12-13	13-14	14-15	15-16	16-17
						WM1 1	WMP 2	WMP 2	WMP 8
								FAC P	FAC EP
							FAV 1P	FAV 2P	FAV 1Q

BEWDLEY TOWN
Founded: 1978 **Nickname:** None

Secretary: Steve Godfrey **(T)** 07739 626 169 **(E)** stevegodfrey09@gmail.com
Chairman: Geoff Edwards **Manager:** Phil Mullen **Prog Ed:** Derry Thompson
Ground: Ribbesford Meadows, Ribbesford, Bewdley, Worcs DY12 2TJ **(T)** 07739 626 169
Colours(change): Royal blue & yellow/royal blue/royal blue (Yellow & royal blue/yellow/yellow)
HONOURS: FA Comps: None **League:** West Midlands (Reg) Division One South 2002-03, Division One 2004-05.

10 YEAR RECORD

07-08	08-09	09-10	10-11	11-12	12-13	13-14	14-15	15-16	16-17
WMP 3	WMP 3	WMP 12	WMP 6	WMP 4	WMP 8	WMP 7	WMP 17	WMP 16	WMP 6
		FAC EP	FAC P	FAC 1Q	FAC 1Q	FAC EP	FAC EP		
FAV 2P	FAV 2Q	FAV 2P	FAV 2Q	FAV 1Q	FAV 1P	FAV 1Q	FAV 1Q	FAV 1Q	FAV 2Q

BILSTON TOWN COMMUNITY
Founded: 1894 **Nickname:** The Steelmen

Secretary: Paul lloyd **(T)** 07908 452 956 **(E)** paulelloyd@hotmail.co.uk
Chairman: Graham Hodson
Ground: Queen Street Stadium, Queen Street, Bilston WV14 7EX **(T)** 07725 816 043 **Capacity:** 4,000
Colours(change): Orange & black
HONOURS: FA Comps: None **League:** Walsall & District 1895-96, 1900-01, 01-02, 32-33, 35-36, 47-48. Birmingham
& District/West Mids (Reg) Division One 1956-57, Premier 60-61, 72-73.

10 YEAR RECORD

07-08	08-09	09-10	10-11	11-12	12-13	13-14	14-15	15-16	16-17
WM2 2	WM1 5	WM1 12	WM1 9	WM1 9	WM1 2	WMP 16	WMP 13	WMP 20	WMP 15
					FAV 1P	FAV 2Q	FAV 1Q	FAV 2Q	FAV 2Q

BLACK COUNTRY RANGERS
Founded: 1996 **Nickname:**

Secretary: Andy Harris **(T)** 07891 128 896 **(E)** bcrfc@outlook.com
Chairman: Paul Garner
Ground: Halesowen Town F C, The Grove, Old Hawne Lane, Halesowen B63 3TB **(T)** 07891 128 896
Colours(change): Red
HONOURS: FA Comps: None **League:** West Midlands (Reg) Division Two 2009-10, Division One 10-11.

10 YEAR RECORD

07-08	08-09	09-10	10-11	11-12	12-13	13-14	14-15	15-16	16-17
WM2 11	WM2 5	WM2 1	WM1 1	WMP 2	WMP 5	WMP 5	WMP 10	WMP 15	WMP 13
						FAC P	FAC EP		
					FAV 2P	FAV 1Q	FAV 1Q	FAV 1Pr	FAV 2Q

CRADLEY TOWN
Founded: 1948 **Nickname:** The Lukes or Hammers

Secretary: David Attwood **(T)** 07708 659 636 **(E)** d.attwood@sky.com
Chairman: Trevor Thomas **Manager:** Andy Wyton **Prog Ed:** David Attwood
Ground: The Beeches, Beeches View Avenue, Cradley, Halesowen B63 2HB **(T)** 07708 659 636 **Capacity:** 3,000
Colours(change): Red/black/red (All blue)
HONOURS: FA Comps: None **League:** West Midlands (Reg) Division One 1990-91.

10 YEAR RECORD

07-08	08-09	09-10	10-11	11-12	12-13	13-14	14-15	15-16	16-17
MidAl 22	MidAl 16	MidAl 22	WMP 8	WMP 8	WMP 9	WMP 10	WMP 15	WMP 8	WMP 10
FAC EP	FAC 2Q	FAC 1Q	FAC EP	FAC EPr	FAC Pr	FAC EP			FAC EPr
FAV 2P	FAV 2Q	FAV 2Q	FAV 1Q	FAV 1Q	FAV 2Q	FAV 1P	FAV 2Q	FAV 1P	FAV 1Q

DUDLEY SPORTS

Founded: 1925 Nickname: The Piemen

Secretary: John Lewis **(T)** 07737 099 385 **(E)** kath-john.lewis@blueyonder.co.uk
Chairman: Kathryn Conroy
Ground: Hillcrest Avenue, Brierley Hill, West Mids DY5 3QH **(T)** 01384 349 413 **Capacity:** 2,000
Colours(change): Green & white
HONOURS: FA Comps: None **League:** None

10 YEAR RECORD

07-08		08-09		09-10		10-11		11-12		12-13		13-14		14-15		15-16		16-17	
WMP	8	WMP	12	WMP	15	WMP	14	WMP	12	WMP	17	WMP	17	WMP	12	WMP	6	WMP	17
		FAC	EP	FAC	1Q					FAC	EPr							FAC	P
FAV	1Q	FAV	1Q	FAV	1Q	FAV	1Q	FAV	2Q	FAV	1Q	FAV	2Q	FAV	1Q	FAV	2Q	FAV	2Q

DUDLEY TOWN

Founded: 1888 Nickname: The Duds or Robins

Secretary: David Ferrier **(T)** 07986 549 675 **(E)** davef.dtfc@blueyonder.co.uk
Chairman: Stephen Austin
Ground: The Dell Stadium, Bryce Road, Brierley Hill, West Mids DY5 4NE **(T)** 07986 549 675
Colours(change): Red & black
HONOURS: FA Comps: None **League:** Birmingham Combination 1933-34. Southern Midland Division 1984-85.

10 YEAR RECORD

07-08		08-09		09-10		10-11		11-12		12-13		13-14		14-15		15-16		16-17	
WMP	5	WMP	5	WMP	5	WMP	13	WMP	7	WMP	6	WMP	9	WMP	14	WMP	13	WMP	18
FAC	EPr	FAC	EP	FAC	Pr	FAC	P			FAC	1Q	FAC	EPr	FAC	P				
FAV	2Q	FAV	2P	FAV	2Qr	FAV	2Qr	FAV	2Q	FAV	1Q	FAV	2P	FAV	2Q	FAV	1Q	FAV	1Q

ELLESMERE RANGERS

Founded: 1969 Nickname: The Rangers

Secretary: John Edge **(T)** 07947 864 357 **(E)** john.edge2@homecall.co.uk
Chairman: Neil Williams
Ground: Beech Grove, Ellesmere, Shropshire SY12 0BT **(T)** 07947 864 357 **Capacity:** 1,250
Colours(change): Sky blue & navy blue
HONOURS: FA Comps: None **League:** West Midlands (Reg) Division One 2005-06, Premier 2009-10.

10 YEAR RECORD

07-08		08-09		09-10		10-11		11-12		12-13		13-14		14-15		15-16		16-17	
WMP	7	WMP	4	WMP	1	MidAl	13	MidAl	15	MidAl	22	WMP	11	WMP	4	WMP	10	WMP	7
		FAC	1Qr	FAC	EP	FAC	EP	FAC	EP	FAC	EP	FAC	P	FAC	EP	FAC	EP		
FAV	2Q	FAV	2Q	FAV	1Q	FAV	2Q	FAV	2P	FAV	1Qr	FAV	2Q	FAV	EP	FAV	1P	FAV	1Q

HEREFORD LADS CLUB

Founded: 1925 Nickname:

Secretary: Stacie Franklyn **(T)** 07542 581 976 **(E)** stevenbelly@icloud.com
Chairman: Danny Moon
Ground: Hereford Lads Club, Widemarsh Common, Hereford HR4 9NA **(T)** 07837 665 745
Colours(change):
HONOURS: FA Comps: None **League:** Herefordshire Division One 2002-03.
West Midlands Division One 2016-17.

10 YEAR RECORD

07-08		08-09	09-10	10-11	11-12		12-13		13-14		14-15		15-16		16-17	
HerefP	5				WM2	2	WM2	3	WM1	10	WM1	5	WM1	2	WM1	1

MALVERN TOWN

Founded: 1947 Nickname: The Hillsiders

Secretary: Margaret Scott **(T)** 07944 110 402 **(E)** marg@malverntown.co.uk
Chairman: Christopher Pinder
Ground: HD anywhere Community Stadium, Lamgland Avenue, Malvern WR14 2EQ **(T)** 07944 110 402 **Capacity:** 2,500
Colours(change): Sky blue and claret
HONOURS: FA Comps: None **League:** Midland Combination Division One 1955-56.

10 YEAR RECORD

07-08		08-09		09-10		10-11		11-12		12-13		13-14		14-15		15-16		16-17	
SthC	20	SthC	22	MidAl	19	MidAl	23	WMP	13	WMP	13	WMP	14	WMP	5	WMP	3	WMP	4
FAC	1Q	FAC	P	FAC	Pr	FAC	P	FAC	EPr							FAC	EP	FAC	EP
FAT	P	FAT	P	FAV	1P	FAV	1P	FAV	1Q	FAV	1Q	FAV	1Q	FAV	1Q	FAV	2Q	FAV	1P

PEGASUS JUNIORS

Founded: 1955 Nickname: The Redmen

Secretary: Nik Marsh **(T)** 07816 121 248 **(E)** nikmarsh1982@gmail.com
Chairman: **Manager:** Mick Panniers **Prog Ed:** Kevin Bishop
Ground: Old School Lane, Hereford HR1 1EX **(T)** 07816 121 248 **Capacity:** 1,000
Colours(change): Red/white/red (Sky blue/white/sky blue)
HONOURS: FA Comps: None **League:** Hellenic Division One 1984-85, 98-99.

10 YEAR RECORD

07-08		08-09		09-10		10-11		11-12		12-13		13-14		14-15		15-16		16-17	
Hel P		Hel P	10	Hel P	14	Hel P	22	WMP	17	WMP	7	WMP	2	WMP	9	WMP	9	WMP	9
FAC	EPr	FAC	EP	FAC	2Q	FAC	EPr	FAC	EPr	FAC	P	FAC	EP	FAC	EPr	FAC	EP		
FAV	1P	FAV	1Q	FAV	2Q	FAV	2Q	FAV	1Q	FAV	1P	FAV	1Q	FAV	2P	FAV	1Q	FAV	2Q

SHIFNAL TOWN

Founded: 1964 Nickname: The Town or Reds

Secretary: Ron Finney **(T)** 07986 563 156 **(E)** eve.ronfinney@hotmail.co.uk
Chairman: Peter Bradley **Manager:** Mark Wells **Prog Ed:** Peter Bradley
Ground: Phoenix Park, Coppice Green Lane, Shifnal, Shrops TF11 8PD **(T)** 07986 563 156
Colours(change): Red & white stripes/black/red (Pale blue/navy/navy)
HONOURS: FA Comps: None **League:** West Midlands (Regional) Division One 1978-79, 2015-16, Premier Division 2006-07.

10 YEAR RECORD

07-08		08-09		09-10		10-11		11-12		12-13		13-14		14-15		15-16		16-17	
MidAl	15	MidAl	8	MidAl	21	WMP	9	WMP	16	WMP	19	WMP	19	WMP	21	WM1	1	WMP	11
FAC	P	FAC	1Q	FAC	EP	FAC	EPr	FAC	EPr	FAC	EP								
FAV	1P	FAV	1P	FAV	1Q	FAV	2Pr	FAV	1Q	FAV	1P	FAV	1Q	FAV	2Q	FAV	1Q	FAV	1P

SMETHWICK

Founded: 1977 Nickname:

Secretary: TBC **(T)** **(E)**
Chairman: TBC
Ground: Hillcrest Avenue, Brierley Hill, West Mids. DY5 3QH **(T)** 01384 826 420 **Capacity:** 2,000
Colours(change): Blue & yellow
HONOURS: FA Comps: None **League:** Midland Combination Division Three 2007-08. West Midlands Division One 2012-13.

10 YEAR RECORD

07-08		08-09		09-10		10-11		11-12		12-13		13-14		14-15		15-16		16-17	
MCm3	1	MCm2	6	MCm2	10	WM2	4	WM1	4	WM1	1	WMP	12	WMP	19	WMP	12	WMP	16
																		FAV	1Q

STONE OLD ALLEYNIANS

Founded: 1962 Nickname:

Secretary: Philip Johnson **(T)** 07813 553 087 **(E)** phil.johnson2016@hotmail.com
Chairman: Dave Mardling
Ground: Wellbeing Park, Yarnfield Lane, Yarnfield ST15 0NF **(T)** 07813 553 087 **Capacity:** 2,000
Colours(change): White & black
HONOURS: FA Comps: None **League:** Mid Staffordshire Division Two 1965-66, 80-81, Division One 71-72, 74-75, 78-79.

10 YEAR RECORD

07-08		08-09		09-10		10-11		11-12		12-13		13-14		14-15		15-16		16-17	
WM2	6	WM2	3	WM2	4	WM1	6	WM1	5	WM1	10	WM1	8	WM1	2	WMP	14	WMP	12
														FAV	2Q	FAV	2Q	FAV	2Qr

TIVIDALE

Founded: 1953 Nickname: The Dale

Secretary: Leon Murray **(T)** 07939 234 813 **(E)** leon@tividalefc.com
Chairman: Christopher Dudley
Ground: The Beeches, Packwood Road, Tividale, West Mids B69 1UL **(T)** 01384 211 743 **Capacity:** 3,000
Colours(change): All yellow
HONOURS: FA Comps: None **League:** Warwickshire & West Midlands Alliance Premier 1964-65. West Midlands (Reg) Division One 1972-73, Premier Division 2010-11. Midland Alliance 2013-14.

10 YEAR RECORD

07-08		08-09		09-10		10-11		11-12		12-13		13-14		14-15		15-16		16-17	
WMP	11	WMP	13	WMP	7	WMP	1	MidAl	4	MidAl	8	MidAl	1	NP1S	8	NP1S	22	MFLP	22
FAC	EP	FAC	EP	FAC	1Qr	FAC	EP	FAC	EP	FAC	2Q	FAC	1Q	FAC	2Qr	FAC	1Q	FAC	P
FAV	1Q	FAV	2Q	FAV	2P	FAV	1P	FAV	5P	FAV	2Q	FAV	2Q	FAT	P	FAT	P	FAV	1Q

WEDNESFIELD

Founded: 1961   Nickname: The Cottagers

Secretary: Meredith Gill   **(T)** 07807 868 763   **(E)** meridithgill@gmail.com
Chairman: Darren Giddins
Ground: Cottage Ground, Amos Lane, Wednesfield WV11 1ND   **(T)** 07807 868 763
Colours(change): Red & white stripes/black/black
HONOURS: FA Comps: None   **League:** West Midlands Division One A 1976-77, Division One 77-78, Premier 95-96, 96-97.

10 YEAR RECORD									
07-08	08-09	09-10	10-11	11-12	12-13	13-14	14-15	15-16	16-17
WMP 4	WMP 9	WMP 11	WMP 4	WMP 6	WMP 18	WMP 15	WMP 22	WM1 4	WM1 2
		FAC EP	FAC 2Q						
	FAV 2Q	FAV 1P	FAV 2P		FAV 1Q	FAV 1Q	FAV 1Q	FAV 1Q	FAV 1Q

WELLINGTON

Founded: 1968   Nickname: The Wellies

Secretary: Michael Perkins   **(T)** 07842 186 643   **(E)** perkinsmj49@gmail.com
Chairman: Phillip Smith
Ground: Wellington Playing Field, Wellington, Hereford HR4 8AZ   **(T)** 07842 186 643 (MD)   **Capacity:** 1,000
Colours(change): Orange
HONOURS: FA Comps: None   **League:** West Midlands (Reg) Division One South 1998-99.

10 YEAR RECORD									
07-08	08-09	09-10	10-11	11-12	12-13	13-14	14-15	15-16	16-17
WMP 13	WMP 6	WMP 6	WMP 10	WMP 11	WMP 15	WMP 8	WMP 11	WMP 11	WMP 5
FAC P	FAC EP	FAC EP	FAC EPr	FAC EP	FAC P		FAC P		
FAV 2P	FAV 1Q	FAV EP	FAV 3P	FAV 1Q	FAV 2Q	FAV 1Q	FAV 1P	FAV 2Q	FAV 2Q

WELLINGTON AMATEURS

Founded: 1950   Nickname: The Ams

Secretary: Ben Coates   **(T)** 07738 715 038   **(E)** bcoates9@icloud.com
Chairman: Dave Gregory   **Manager:** Mark Taylor   **Prog Ed:** Dave Gregory
Ground: Fortis Stadium, School grove, Oakengates, Telford, Shrops TF2 6BQ   **(T)** 07738 715 038
Colours(change): Red/black/black (All blue)
HONOURS: FA Comps: None   **League:** Wellington Division Two 1954-55, 60-61. Shropshire County Premier 1982-83, 88-89. West Midlands (Reg) Division Two 2007-08, Division One 08-09, 09-10, 11-12.

10 YEAR RECORD									
07-08	08-09	09-10	10-11	11-12	12-13	13-14	14-15	15-16	16-17
WM2 1	WM1 1	WM1 1	WM1 2	WM1 1	WMP 12	WMP 13	WMP 20	WMP 19	WMP 19
							FAV 1Q		FAV 2Q

WOLVERHAMPTON CASUALS

Founded: 1899   Nickname: The Cassies

Secretary: Michael Green   **(T)** 07870 737 229   **(E)** mickgreen7@hotmail.com
Chairman: Garath Deacon
Ground: Brinsford Stadium, Brinsford Lane, Wolverhampton WV10 7PR   **(T)** 07870 737 229
Colours(change): Green
HONOURS: FA Comps: None   **League:** West Midlands (Reg) Division One 1994-95.

10 YEAR RECORD									
07-08	08-09	09-10	10-11	11-12	12-13	13-14	14-15	15-16	16-17
WMP 18	WMP 19	WMP 16	WMP 12	WMP 3	WMP 3	WMP 3	WMP 6	WMP 7	WMP 2
				FAC EP	FAC 1Qr	FAC P	FAC EP	FAC EP	FAC EPr
FAV 2Q	FAV 1Q	FAV 1P	FAV 1P	FAV 1Q	FAV 1Q	FAV 2Q	FAV 1Q	FAV 2Q	FAV 2P

WOLVERHAMPTON SPORTING CFC

Founded: 2001   Nickname: Wolves Sporting

Secretary: Mark Hobson   **(T)** 07966 505 425   **(E)** wolvessporting@yahoo.co.uk
Chairman: John Quarry
Ground: Pride Park, Hazel Lane, Great Wyrley, Staffs WS6 6AA   **(T)** 07966 505 425
Colours(change): Black & orange
HONOURS: FA Comps: None   **League:** West Midlands (Reg) Division Two 2006-07.

10 YEAR RECORD									
07-08	08-09	09-10	10-11	11-12	12-13	13-14	14-15	15-16	16-17
WM1 3	WMP 8	WMP 20	WMP 18	WMP 19	WMP 10	WMP 18	WMP 16	WMP 4	WMP 3
									FAC EP
			FAV 1P	FAV 2Q	FAV 2Q	FAV 1Q	FAV 1Q	FAV 1Q	FAV 1P

West Midlands (Regional) Division One		
ALLSCOTT	Allscott S&S Club, Shawbirch Road, Allscott, Shropshire TF6 5EQ	07791 621 481
BROMYARD TOWN	Delahay Meadow, Stourport Road, Bromyard HR7 4NT	07885 849 948
BUSTLEHOLME	Tipton Town F C, Wednesbury Oak Road, Tipton, West Mid. DY4 0BS	07805 829 354
DARLASTON TOWN (1874)	Bentley Leisure Pavilion, Bentley Road North, Bentley, Walsall. WS2 0EA	0759 3281 513
GORNAL ATHLETIC	Garden Walk Stadium, Garden Walk, Lower Gornal, Dudley DY3 2NR	07762 585 149
KINGTON TOWN	Mill Street, Kington, Herefordshire. HR5 3AL	07900 310 020
NEWPORT TOWN	Shuker Playing Fields, Shuker Close, Newport,Shropshire TF10 7SG	07961 017 524
OLD WULFRUNIANS	Memorial Ground, Castlecroft Road, Wolverhampton WV3 8NA	07875 688 730
ST MARTINS	The Venue, Burma Road, Parkhall, Oswestry, Shrops. SY11 4AS	07903 756 790
TEAM DUDLEY	Priory Road - 3G Complex, Priory Road, Dudley, West Midlands DY1 4AD	07940 842 782
TELFORD JUNIORS	Doseley Road, Dawley, Telford, Shropshire TF4 3AB	07810 871 660
TIPTON TOWN	Tipton Sports Academy, Wednesbury Oak Road, Tipton DY4 0BS	07535 975 142
WEM TOWN	Butler Sports Centre, Bowens Field, Wem SY4 5AP	07790 426 152
WILLENHALL TOWN	Queen Street Stadium, Queen Street, Bilston, Wolverhampton. WV14 7EX	07901 560 691
WORCESTER RAIDERS	Claines Lane, Worcestershire WR3 7SS	07532 266 897
WRENS NEST	The Beeches, Packwood Road, Tividale B69 1UL	07963 935 601
WYRLEY	Long Lane, Essington, Wolverhampton. WS6 6AT	07899 960 806

WESTERN LEAGUE

Sponsored by: Toolstation
Founded: 1892

Recent Champions: 2014: Larkhall Athletic
2015: Melksham Town **2016:** Odd Down (Bath)

PREMIER DIVISION	P	W	D	L	F	A	GD	Pts
1 Bristol Manor Farm	38	33	3	2	118	33	85	102
2 Street	38	29	5	4	112	46	66	92
3 Melksham Town	38	26	7	5	105	43	62	85
4 Buckland Athletic	38	26	5	7	98	49	49	83
5 Bradford Town	38	20	8	10	90	56	34	68
6 Willand Rovers	38	20	7	11	69	52	17	67
7 Odd Down (Bath)	38	19	7	12	89	64	25	64
8 Cribbs	38	18	7	13	77	54	23	61
9 Gillingham Town	38	18	6	14	80	54	26	60
10 Brislington	38	16	5	17	78	74	4	53
11 Cadbury Heath	38	16	5	17	75	75	0	53
12 Shepton Mallet	38	13	9	16	67	71	-4	48
13 Chipping Sodbury Town	38	12	6	20	55	83	-28	42
14 Clevedon Town	38	12	4	22	70	87	-17	40
15 Wells City	38	10	10	18	67	90	-23	40
16 Bridport	38	10	7	21	63	86	-23	37
17 Longwell Green Sports	38	11	1	26	40	113	-73	34
18 Hallen	38	6	4	28	39	97	-58	22
19 Bitton	38	5	4	29	41	97	-56	19
20 Sherborne Town	38	3	4	31	41	150	-109	13

DIVISION ONE	P	W	D	L	F	A	GD	Pts
1 Wellington	42	27	11	4	92	36	56	92
2 Hengrove Athletic	42	27	7	8	105	37	68	88
3 Cheddar	42	24	10	8	92	52	40	82
4 Keynsham Town	42	26	3	13	82	50	32	81
5 Radstock Town	42	21	11	10	85	47	38	74
6 Bishops Lydeard	42	20	8	14	77	67	10	68
7 Ashton & Backwell United	42	19	7	16	71	69	2	64
8 Chippenham Park	42	19	9	14	74	78	-4	63*
9 Malmesbury Victoria	42	18	7	17	82	82	0	61
10 Chard Town	42	16	11	15	74	74	0	59
11 Devizes Town	42	16	10	16	72	81	-9	58
12 Westbury United	42	18	4	20	60	73	-13	58
13 Wincanton Town	42	16	8	18	83	79	4	56
14 Portishead Town	42	16	7	19	48	58	-10	55
15 Roman Glass St George	42	16	4	22	72	96	-24	52
16 Bishop Sutton	42	15	6	21	60	63	-3	51
17 Oldland Abbotonians	42	15	5	22	60	85	-25	50
18 Warminster Town	42	12	11	19	68	75	-7	47
19 Corsham Town	42	11	9	22	61	83	-22	42
20 Welton Rovers	42	10	7	25	54	95	-41	37
21 Calne Town	42	10	4	28	50	99	-49	34
22 Almondsbury UWE	42	7	7	28	67	110	-43	28

ADDITIONAL CLUB MOVEMENTS

Premier Division

In: Bridgwater Town (R - Southern D1S&W).
Out: Bristol Manor Farm (P - Southern D1S&W),
Gillingham Town (W - Dorset Premier).

Division One

In: Bristol Telephones (P - Gloucester County).

PREMIER DIVISION	1	2	3	4	5	6	7	8	9	10	11	12	13	14	15	16	17	18	19	20
1 Bitton		1-2	1-2	0-4	0-2	1-2	1-2	1-7	0-1	0-1	3-6	3-1	0-1	0-6	1-3	1-0	2-1	1-2	1-2	3-3
2 Bradford Town	3-1		3-1	5-3	1-4	1-2	1-1	3-0	1-1	1-2	2-1	3-1	4-1	2-3	6-2	1-1	5-0	1-5	1-1	1-1
3 Bridport	3-2	3-3		0-0	1-3	0-1	1-4	4-0	2-0	0-2	1-3	2-3	3-2	0-1	2-2	1-2	5-1	0-4	2-2	5-3
4 Brislington	4-0	0-1	2-2		1-4	3-1	3-1	3-1	2-0	1-4	2-1	3-0	4-3	2-5	0-2	1-2	0-2	4-5	2-2	3-1
5 Bristol Manor Farm	4-1	4-1	3-0	4-2		4-1	1-1	3-1	2-1	1-0	2-1	3-1	8-0	3-1	4-0	6-1	5-0	0-0	5-1	2-0
6 Buckland Athletic	3-0	2-2	3-1	4-1	3-1		3-0	3-2	0-2	1-2	1-1	5-0	3-1	1-3	4-1	3-1	5-1	2-0	5-2	4-0
7 Cadbury Heath	3-2	2-4	3-0	3-1	0-5	2-3		2-0	4-0	2-1	0-5	0-1	3-1	1-1	2-3	2-3	6-0	2-4	1-5	3-4
8 Chipping Sodbury Town	2-1	0-5	5-0	1-0	1-2	2-2	1-2		3-4	2-1	1-2	0-0	1-1	0-3	0-4	0-4	3-2	0-2	4-3	0-3
9 Clevedon Town	2-4	1-3	1-2	2-2	1-2	4-3	2-4	1-1		1-3	2-1	3-0	7-0	2-5	1-4	2-2	9-0	1-3	4-3	0-2
10 Cribbs	0-1	1-3	4-3	1-2	1-1	0-6	2-1	0-1	1-0		0-0	6-2	7-2	0-1	2-0	5-1	8-0	3-1	2-2	2-2
11 Gillingham Town	5-3	0-1	1-0	2-3	1-2	0-2	2-0	2-2	4-1	4-3		0-1	8-0	2-3	3-2	1-1	2-1	1-1	2-3	1-3
12 Hallen	3-2	1-2	1-3	1-3	0-2	1-3	2-5	0-1	1-5	0-0	0-4		4-1	1-2	1-3	2-2	4-1	1-6	1-2	1-5
13 Longwell Green Sports	1-0	0-5	0-3	3-2	2-5	0-3	2-0	2-0	1-2	1-2	0-2	1-0		0-8	1-2	3-2	2-0	0-5	0-2	0-2
14 Melksham Town	2-0	1-0	3-0	4-1	2-1	3-0	2-0	2-2	6-0	2-0	0-1	1-0	3-1		3-3	0-2	5-0	2-3	5-1	1-1
15 Odd Down (Bath)	4-0	2-1	4-2	0-0	1-2	3-3	1-1	6-0	3-2	1-3	2-0	4-0	0-1	3-3		5-0	4-3	1-3	1-0	0-2
16 Shepton Mallet	3-0	0-2	3-1	1-3	0-1	2-4	0-1	1-2	1-0	2-2	1-5	4-1	1-3	3-1	0-0		10-1	1-3	2-2	2-0
17 Sherborne Town	2-2	1-8	2-2	1-8	0-6	0-2	1-3	2-4	1-2	2-2	1-2	3-1	1-2	2-4	0-5	2-2		0-2	4-2	1-2
18 Street	3-0	4-1	5-3	4-1	2-3	2-2	3-1	4-2	2-1	3-1	2-3	1-0	3-0	2-2	3-0	1-1	6-1		2-1	2-0
19 Wells City	1-1	1-1	2-2	0-2	2-4	0-2	2-5	1-2	4-2	0-3	1-1	1-0	4-1	3-3	3-8	2-3	2-1	1-4		0-1
20 Willand Rovers	1-1	1-0	2-1	1-0	1-4	0-1	2-2	2-1	5-0	1-0	1-0	2-2	4-0	0-3	2-0	1-0	6-0	2-5	0-1	

WESTERN LEAGUE - STEP 5/6

DIVISION ONE	1	2	3	4	5	6	7	8	9	10	11	12	13	14	15	16	17	18	19	20	21	22
1 Almondsbury UWE		1-2	2-2	1-2	3-1	2-2	2-4	1-5	2-4	1-5	0-4	0-1	2-3	3-2	1-3	1-3	2-1	1-2	3-4	4-3	0-1	3-4
2 Ashton & Backwell United	2-0		4-1	0-0	3-0	3-0	4-2	3-5	2-2	2-8	1-4	2-1	0-2	2-1	0-2	0-0	3-2	5-1	1-1	1-0	0-1	1-2
3 Bishop Sutton	6-0	2-0		1-2	5-1	3-2	0-1	2-3	0-4	3-0	0-2	0-1	0-1	1-1	1-0	1-2	0-3	1-1	0-2	0-1	0-1	2-0
4 Bishops Lydeard	3-0	2-1	2-3		0-1	2-1	2-3	3-0	2-2	1-0	2-1	2-4	4-0	2-1	1-0	1-1	1-3	2-0	0-0	5-0	1-1	3-3
5 Calne Town	1-2	1-2	1-4	1-3		4-0	1-1	0-2	3-2	1-3	1-2	0-2	3-1	2-3	1-2	3-2	1-0	1-1	1-4	1-1	4-0	1-2
6 Chard Town	3-3	0-2	1-1	2-3	2-1		1-1	1-1	5-2	0-3	2-0	4-2	5-1	3-0	1-0	1-0	2-1	3-2	0-3	3-0	1-0	3-3
7 Cheddar	6-1	1-2	2-0	2-4	3-0	2-2		4-0	3-1	5-0	3-1	2-0	1-2	3-2	2-1	1-0	2-2	4-0	1-1	4-0	3-2	2-1
8 Chippenham Park	2-1	3-2	2-0	4-1	1-1	3-3	1-1		4-4	0-1	0-2	2-1	2-1	2-5	1-0	2-1	2-1	1-1	1-0	1-0	0-3	1-3
9 Corsham Town	1-1	0-1	3-4	3-3	2-5	1-0	3-0	1-3		2-0	1-2	1-1	2-0	1-4	0-1	1-5	2-3	2-2	1-0	2-0	0-2	0-1
10 Devizes Town	2-9	1-0	1-1	1-4	2-0	2-1	2-0	3-3	0-0		0-2	2-0	4-4	3-3	0-2	0-2	5-1	3-1	1-1	2-1	0-2	3-1
11 Hengrove Athletic	3-0	1-1	1-1	3-0	6-0	2-5	1-1	6-0	4-0			1-0	1-0	0-1	2-1	4-0	4-0	2-3	6-0	9-0	4-3	
12 Keynsham Town	3-2	2-0	3-0	2-0	4-0	4-0	2-0	3-0	1-2	7-0	2-1		5-4	1-3	1-2	2-2	2-1	3-0	2-0	3-3	0-2	3-2
13 Malmesbury Victoria	2-1	1-2	0-4	4-2	6-0	2-2	2-2	0-0	2-1	2-2	0-0	3-0		A-W	2-0	6-1	2-3	3-2	3-4	6-0	1-3	2-4
14 Oldland Abbotonians	2-0	3-3	1-0	0-1	0-1	1-3	0-2	0-0	3-1	1-3	0-4	0-1	1-5		0-2	1-0	3-1	1-7	0-3	4-2	4-1	2-1
15 Portishead Town	1-1	1-1	1-2	2-0	3-1	3-2	0-2	3-2	0-1	2-1	1-1	1-2	2-3	0-1		0-5	3-2	1-3	2-0	0-0	0-2	1-1
16 Radstock Town	1-1	3-0	3-0	1-1	3-0	1-1	1-0	4-1	0-2	0-0	3-1	2-1					8-3	1-0	2-3	1-0	3-1	6-2
17 Roman Glass St George	4-3	1-4	3-0	4-3	2-1	0-2	1-4	3-0	2-1	1-0	0-3	0-6	3-1	0-1	2-0	2-5		2-2	1-1	4-1	1-1	3-2
18 Warminster Town	1-2	1-0	0-3	1-2	0-2	3-1	1-1	2-4	2-1	1-1	1-2	1-2	5-1	2-0	5-0	1-1	4-1		1-3	1-1	1-1	2-3
19 Wellington	1-1	2-1	3-1	4-1	4-0	3-1	4-0	6-3	3-0	0-0	1-1	2-0	4-0	2-2	2-0	1-1	2-0	2-0		2-1	5-3	3-0
20 Welton Rovers	4-3	3-4	0-3	2-1	2-1	0-0	0-3	3-2	1-2	2-2	2-3	3-0	1-2	3-2	1-1	0-5	4-1	0-2	0-1		5-1	2-3
21 Westbury United	3-1	1-2	0-1	3-0	1-2	3-0	1-4	1-2	3-2	0-4	1-1	0-1	0-1	3-1	1-2	1-2	2-1	1-3	0-3	2-0		3-1
22 Wincanton Town	1-0	4-2	2-1	1-3	7-1	1-3	0-2	1-2	0-0	4-1	1-4	0-1	5-0	7-0	1-1	0-0	1-3	2-2	0-0	1-2	2-1	

LES PHILLIPS CUP

HOLDERS: HENGROVE ATHLETIC

PRELIMINARY ROUND

Roman Glass St George v Chippenham Park	6-2
Longwell Green Sports v Keynsham Town	3-1
Calne Town v Gillingham Town	1-3
Radstock Town v Malmesbury Victoria	2-2, 4-2p
Bishop Sutton v Bitton	2-1
Chard Town v Welton Rovers	2-1
Cribbs v Sherborne Town	3-1
Odd Down (Bath) v Bridport	1-5
Cadbury Heath v Oldland Abbotonians	3-1
Street v Wincanton Town	4-1

ROUND 1

Roman Glass St George v Longwell Green Sports	2-1
Bristol Manor Farm v Devizes Town	10-0
Bishops Lydeard v Gillingham Town	4-6
Brislington v Bradford Town	0-2
Radstock Town v Warminster Town	0-3
Melksham Town v Bishop Sutton	2-0
Buckland Athletic v Chard Town	5-2
Chipping Sodbury Town v Clevedon Town	4-2
Wells City v Ashton & Backwell United	0-4
Almondsbury UWE v Shepton Mallet	1-2
Portishead Town v Hallen	0-2
Corsham Town v Cribbs	0-1
Cheddar v Westbury United	2-3
Willand Rovers v Bridport	3-1
Cadbury Heath v Hengrove Athletic	0-4
Wellington v Street	1-0

ROUND 2

Roman Glass St George v Bristol Manor Farm	1-0
Gillingham Town v Bradford Town	2-1
Warminster Town v Melksham Town	2-3
Buckland Athletic v Chipping Sodbury Town	2-1
Ashton & Backwell United v Shepton Mallet	0-2
Hallen v Cribbs	1-4
Westbury United v Willand Rovers	0-2
Hengrove Athletic v Wellington	1-0

QUARTER-FINALS

Roman Glass St George v Gillingham Town	1-3
Melksham Town v Buckland Athletic	1-0
Shepton Mallet v Cribbs	1-3
Willand Rovers v Hengrove Athletic	1-0

SEMI-FINALS

Gillingham Town v Melksham Town	0-1
Cribbs v Willand Rovers	1-1, 11-10p

FINAL

Melksham Town v Cribbs	0-0, 5-4p

BITTON

Founded: 1892 Nickname: The Ton

Secretary: Daniel Langdon **(T)** 07816 399 956 **(E)** dan_langdon@hotmail.co.uk
Chairman: John Langdon **Manager:** Daniel Langdon
Ground: Rapid Solicitors Ground, Bath Road, Bitton, Bristol BS30 6HX. **(T)** 01179 323 222
Capacity: 1,000 **Seats:** 48 **Covered:** 200 **Midweek Matchday:** Tuesday **Clubhouse:** Yes

Colours(change): Red & white/black/black (Yellow/green/yellow)
Previous Names: None
Previous Leagues: Avon Premier Combination, Gloucestershire County 1995-97.

HONOURS: FA Comps: None
League: Western League Premier Division 2008-09.

10 YEAR RECORD

07-08		08-09		09-10		10-11		11-12		12-13		13-14		14-15		15-16		16-17	
WestP	7	WestP	1	WestP	8	WestP	2	WestP	2	WestP	7	WestP	6	WestP	7	WestP	14	WestP	19
FAC	1Q	FAC	2Q	FAC	EPr	FAC	1Q	FAC	EPr	FAC	P	FAC	P	FAC	EP	FAC	P	FAC	P
FAV	4P	FAV	5P	FAV	2P	FAV	4P	FAV	4P	FAV	4P	FAV	3P	FAV	1Q	FAV	2Q	FAV	2Q

BRADFORD TOWN

Founded: 1992 Nickname: Bobcats

Secretary: Richard Tucker **(T)** 07712 286 230 **(E)** bradfordtownfc@gmail.com
Chairman: Mark Hodkinson **Manager:** Danny Greaves **Prog Ed:** Andy Meadon
Ground: Bradford Sports & Social Club, Trowbridge Rd, Bradford on Avon BA15 1EE **(T)** 07801 499 168
Capacity: **Seats:** Yes **Covered:** Yes **Midweek Matchday:** Wednesday **Clubhouse:** Yes

Colours(change): All royal blue (All sky blue)
Previous Names: None
Previous Leagues: Wiltshire County 1992-2005.

HONOURS: FA Comps: None
League: Western Division One 2013-14.

10 YEAR RECORD

07-08		08-09		09-10		10-11		11-12		12-13		13-14		14-15		15-16		16-17	
West1	13	West1	3	West1	4	West1	6	West1	5	West1	3	West1	1	WestP	8	WestP	8	WestP	5
						FAC	EPr	FAC	EP	FAC	EP	FAC	EP	FAC	1Q	FAC	2Q	FAC	EP
				FAV	2P	FAV	2Q	FAV	1P	FAV	2Q	FAV	1P	FAV	5P	FAV	4P	FAV	4P

BRIDGWATER TOWN

Founded: 1984 Nickname: The Robins

Secretary: Ian Barber **(T)** 07968 970 418 **(E)** ianbarber4@gmail.com
Chairman: Adrian Byrne **Manager:** Karl Baggaley & Dave Pearse
Ground: Fairfax Park, College Way, Bath Road, Bridgwater, Somerset TA6 4TZ **(T)** 01278 446 899
Capacity: 2,000 **Seats:** 128 **Covered:** 500 **Midweek Matchday:** Tuesday **Clubhouse:** Yes **Shop:** Yes

Colours(change): Red & white stripes/black/red (Blue & white)
Previous Names: Bridgwater Town
Previous Leagues: Somerset Senior 1984-94. Western 1994-2007. Southern 2007-2017.

HONOURS: FA Comps: None
League: Somerset Senior Division One 1986-87, Premier 89-90, 90-91, 91-92. Western Division One 1995-96.

10 YEAR RECORD

07-08		08-09		09-10		10-11		11-12		12-13		13-14		14-15		15-16		16-17	
Sthsw	6	Sthsw	7	Sthsw	3	Sthsw	18	Sthsw	15	Sthsw	19	Sthsw	14	Sthsw	12	Sthsw	19	Sthsw	22
FAC	1Q	FAC	1Q	FAC	3Q	FAC	1Q	FAC	1Q	FAC	P	FAC	3Q	FAC	2Q	FAC	P	FAC	P
FAT	P	FAT	P	FAT	1Qr	FAT	1Q	FAT	1Q	FAT	P	FAT	2Q	FAT	1Q	FAT	P	FAT	Pr

BRIDPORT

Founded: 1885 Nickname: Bees

Secretary: Chris Tozer **(T)** 07500 064 317 **(E)** sevie@tiscali.co.uk
Chairman: Adrian Scadding **Manager:** Adam Fricker
Ground: St Mary's Field, Bridport, Dorset DT6 5LN **(T)** 01308 423 834
Capacity: 2,000 **Seats:** 150 **Covered:** Yes **Midweek Matchday:** Wednesday **Clubhouse:** Yes

Colours(change): Red/black/black (All yellow)
Previous Names: None
Previous Leagues: Dorset. South Dorset. West Dorset. Perry Street. Dorset Combination (Founding Memeber) 1957-61, 84-88. Western 1961-84.

HONOURS: FA Comps: None
League: Dorset Combination 1985-86, 86-87, 87-88.

10 YEAR RECORD

07-08		08-09		09-10		10-11		11-12		12-13		13-14		14-15		15-16		16-17	
West1	18	West1	13	West1	10	West1	3	WestP	14	WestP	14	WestP	12	WestP	14	WestP	16	WestP	16
FAC	EP	FAC	1Q	FAC	1Qr	FAC	P	FAC	P	FAC	EP	FAC	P	FAC	EP	FAC	1Q	FAC	EP
FAV	2Q	FAV	1Q	FAV	2Q	FAV	1P	FAV	1P	FAV	2Q	FAV	1Q	FAV	2P	FAV	1P	FAV	1Q

BRISLINGTON
Founded: 1956   Nickname: Bris

Secretary: Angela Hazel   **(T)** 07724 829 090   **(E)** brislingtonsecretary@gmail.com
Chairman: Steve Jenkins   **Manager:** Lee Perkes
Ground: Ironmould Lane, Brislington, Bristol BS4 4TZ   **(T)** 01179 774 030
Capacity: 2,000 **Seats:** 144   **Covered:** 1,500   **Midweek Matchday:** Tuesday   **Clubhouse:** Yes

Colours(change): Red & black/black/black. (All royal blue)
Previous Names: Foremd as an U16 team.
Previous Leagues: Bristol Church of England. Bristol & Suburban. Somerset Senior until 1991.

HONOURS: FA Comps: None
       League: Somerset Senior 1988-89. Western Division One 1994-95.

10 YEAR RECORD

07-08	08-09	09-10	10-11	11-12	12-13	13-14	14-15	15-16	16-17
WestP 13	WestP 10	WestP 9	WestP 15	WestP 7	WestP 2	WestP 10	WestP 10	WestP 11	WestP 10
FAC P	FAC P	FAC EPr	FAC EP	FAC 1Q	FAC EP	FAC 4Q	FAC P	FAC EP	FAC 2Q
FAV 1P	FAV 2P	FAV 2P	FAV 1P	FAV 1Q	FAV 1P	FAV 2P	FAV 1P	FAV 1Q	FAV 2Q

BUCKLAND ATHLETIC
Founded: 1977   Nickname: The Bucks

Secretary: Christine Holmes   **(T)** 07856 525 730   **(E)** phardingham@virginmedia.com
Chairman: Roy Holmes   **Manager:** Ellis Laight
Ground: Homers Heath, South Quarry, Kingskerswell Road, Newton Abbot TQ12 5JU   **(T)** 01626 361 020
Capacity: 1,000 **Seats:** Yes   **Covered:** Yes   **Midweek Matchday:** Wednesday   **Clubhouse:** Yes

Colours(change): Yellow with black trim/yellow/yellow (Navy blue & yellow/navy/navy)
Previous Names: None
Previous Leagues: Torbay Pioneer 1977-87. Devon & Exeter 1987-2000. Devon County 2000-07. South West Peninsula 2007-12.

HONOURS: FA Comps: None
       League: Devon & Exeter Senior Third Division 1987-88, Premier 94-95, 99-00.

10 YEAR RECORD   South West Peninsula Premier 2009-10, 10-11.

07-08	08-09	09-10	10-11	11-12	12-13	13-14	14-15	15-16	16-17
SWPP 14	SWPP 3	SWPP 1	SWPP 1	SWPP 2	WestP 10	WestP 11	WestP 2	WestP 4	WestP 4
		FAC EPr	FAC EPr	FAC Pr	FAC 2Q	FAC EP	FAC EP	FAC P	FAC EP
	FAV 2Q	FAV 2Q	FAV 2Q	FAV 1P	FAV 2P	FAV 2P	FAV 3P	FAV 3P	FAV QF

CADBURY HEATH
Founded: 1894   Nickname: The Heathens

Secretary: Martin Painter   **(T)** 07971 399 268   **(E)** martinbristol1955@hotmail.com
Chairman: Steve Plenty   **Manager:** Robert Mallett
Ground: Springfield, Cadbury Heath Road, Bristol BS30 8BX   **(T)** 07971 399 268
Capacity: 2,000 **Seats:** Yes   **Covered:** Yes   **Midweek Matchday:** Wednesday   **Clubhouse:** Yes

Colours(change): Red & white/red/red (Yellow/blue/blue)
Previous Names: None
Previous Leagues: Gloucestershire County 1968-75, 80-2000. Midland Combination 1975-77.

HONOURS: FA Comps: None
       League: Gloucestershire County 1970-71, 71-72, 72-73, 73-74, 93-94, 97-98, 98-99.

10 YEAR RECORD   Western League Division One 2011-12.

07-08	08-09	09-10	10-11	11-12	12-13	13-14	14-15	15-16	16-17
West1 5	West1 4	West1 11	West1 4	West1 1	WestP 4	WestP 13	WestP 11	WestP 12	WestP 11
				FAC 2Q	FAC P	FAC EP	FAC EP	FAC EP	FAC 3Q
		FAV 4P	FAV 2P	FAV 2P	FAV 2P	FAV 1P	FAV 2Q	FAV 2P	FAV 2Q

CHIPPING SODBURY TOWN
Founded: 1885   Nickname: The Sods

Secretary: Geoff Endicott   **(T)** 0778 678 823   **(E)** g.endicott@btopenworld.com
Chairman: Mike Fox
Ground: The Ridings, Wickwar Road, Chipping Sodbury, Bristol BS37 6BQ   **(T)**
Capacity: **Seats:** Yes   **Covered:** Yes   **Midweek Matchday:** Tuesday   **Clubhouse:** Yes

Colours(change): Black & white stripes/black/black (Yellow/blue/yellow)
Previous Names: None
Previous Leagues: Gloucester County 2008-2015.

HONOURS: FA Comps: None
       League: Western Division One 2015-16.

10 YEAR RECORD

07-08	08-09	09-10	10-11	11-12	12-13	13-14	14-15	15-16	16-17
	GlCo 17	GlCo 8	GlCo 3	GlCo 18	GlCo 15	GlCo 11	GlCo 3	West1 1	WestP 13
									FAV 1Q

CLEVEDON TOWN

Founded: 1880   Nickname: Seasiders

Secretary: Brian Rose   **(T)** 07768 100 632   **(E)** brian.rose@blueyonder.co.uk
Chairman: Mark Lewis   **Manager:** Micky Bell
Ground: Hand Stadium, Davis Lane, Clevedon BS21 6TG   **(T)** 07768 100 632
Capacity: 3,500   **Seats:** 300   **Covered:** 1,600   **Midweek Matchday:** Wednesday   **Clubhouse:** Yes   **Shop:** Yes

Colours(change): Blue with white stripes/blue/blue (Yellow & black/black/yellow)
Previous Names: Clevedon FC and Ashtonians merged in 1974
Previous Leagues: Western (Founder Members 1892), 1945-58, 73-93. Bristol & District. Bristol Suburban. Somerset Senior. Southern 1993-2015.

HONOURS: FA Comps: None
League: Bristol & Suburban 1925-26, 27-28, 28-29. Somerset Senior 36-37. Bristol Charity 37-38, 40-41. Western 92-93.
10 YEAR RECORD   Southern Midland Division 98-99, Divions 1W 2005-06.

07-08	08-09	09-10	10-11	11-12	12-13	13-14	14-15	15-16	16-17
SthP 11	SthP 18	SthP 21	Sthsw 20	Sthsw 20	Sthsw 15	Sthsw 17	Sthsw 18	WestP 19	WestP 14
FAC 3Q	FAC 2Q	FAC 2Q	FAC 3Q	FAC 2Q	FAC 2Q	FAC 3Qr	FAC P	FAC 3Q	FAC P
FAT 2Q	FAT 1Q	FAT 1Q	FAT P	FAT P	FAT Pr	FAT 2Q	FAT P	FAV 1Q	FAV 2P

CRIBBS

Founded: 1976   Nickname: Cribbs

Secretary: Simon Hartley   **(T)** 07970 744063   **(E)** welshwizard1973@aol.com
Chairman: Dave Nelson   **Manager:** Tony Beecham
Ground: The Lawns, Station Road, Henbury, Bristol BS10 7TB   **(T)** 0117 950 2303
Capacity: 1,000   **Seats:** 100   **Covered:** Yes   **Midweek Matchday:** Tuesday   **Clubhouse:** Yes

Colours(change): Blue/blue/red & white (Red/black/white & red)
Previous Names: Sun Life Assurance 1976. AXA>2011. Cribbs Friends Life 2011-13
Previous Leagues: Bristol & Avon. Avon Premier Combination. Gloucestershire County > 2012.

HONOURS: FA Comps: None
League: Gloucester County 2011-12.
10 YEAR RECORD

07-08	08-09	09-10	10-11	11-12	12-13	13-14	14-15	15-16	16-17
GlCo 5	GlCo 6	GlCo 11	GlCo 2	GlCo 1	West1 8	West1 5	West1 3	WestP 5	WestP 8
							FAC P	FAC EP	FAC EPr
						FAV 2Q	FAV 1Q	FAV 1Q	FAV 1Q

HALLEN

Founded: 1949   Nickname: The Armadillos

Secretary: Richard Stokes   **(T)** 07791 492 640   **(E)** sinbad88@hotmail.co.uk
Chairman: Lee Fairman   **Manager:** Ben Willshire   **Prog Ed:** Ray Bright
Ground: Hallen Centre, Moorhouse Lane, Hallen Bristol BS10 7RU   **(T)** 01179 505 559
Capacity: 2,000   **Seats:** 200   **Covered:** 200   **Midweek Matchday:** Tuesday   **Clubhouse:** Yes

Colours(change): Blue/black/blue (All yellow)
Previous Names: Lawrence Weston Athletic, Lawrence Weston Hallen
Previous Leagues: Bristol & District. Bristol Premier. Gloucestershire County 1987-92. Hellenic 1992-2000.

HONOURS: FA Comps: None
League: Gloucestershire County 1988-89, 92-93. Hellenic Division One 1996-97. Western Division One 2003-04.
10 YEAR RECORD

07-08	08-09	09-10	10-11	11-12	12-13	13-14	14-15	15-16	16-17
WestP 15	WestP 9	WestP 12	WestP 16	WestP 4	WestP 9	WestP 15	WestP 17	WestP 17	WestP 18
FAC 2Q	FAC EP	FAC 2Q	FAC P	FAC 1Qr	FAC P	FAC 1Q	FAC P	FAC EPr	FAC EP
FAV 2P	FAV 2Q	FAV 2Q	FAV 2Qr	FAV 2Q	FAV 1P	FAV 5P	FAV 2P	FAV 2P	FAV 2Q

HENGROVE ATHLETIC

Founded: 1948   Nickname: The Grove

Secretary: Martin McConachie   **(T)** 07432 614 494   **(E)** secretary@hengroveathletic.com
Chairman: Mike Greatbanks   **Manager:** John Durbin
Ground: Norton Lane, Whitchurch, Bristol BS14 9TB   **(T)** 07884 492 217
Capacity: **Seats:** Yes   **Covered:** Yes   **Midweek Matchday:** Wednesday   **Clubhouse:** Yes

Colours(change): Green & white stripes/green/green (Blue & yellow/yellow/yellow)
Previous Names: None
Previous Leagues: Bristol & Suburban >1974. Somerset County 1974-2006.

HONOURS: FA Comps: None
League: Somerset County Premier Division 2005-06.
10 YEAR RECORD

07-08	08-09	09-10	10-11	11-12	12-13	13-14	14-15	15-16	16-17
West1 6	West1 6	West1 7	West1 10	West1 10	West1 2	WestP 21	West1 12	West1 7	West1 2
				FAC EP	FAC P	FAC EP	FAC EP		FAC EPr
			FAV 2Pr	FAV 2Q	FAV 2Q	FAV 2Q	FAV 2Q	FAV 3P	FAV 1P

LONGWELL GREEN SPORTS
Founded: 1966   Nickname: The Green

Secretary: David Heal   **(T)** 07954 466 599   **(E)** daveheal04@gmail.com
Chairman: John Gibbs   **Manager:** Martin Grimshaw
Ground: Longwell Green Com. Centre, Shellards Road BS30 9AD   **(T)** 01179 323 722
Capacity: 1,000 **Seats:** 75   **Covered:** 100   **Midweek Matchday:** Tuesday   **Clubhouse:** Yes   **Shop:** Yes
Colours(change):   Blue & white/black/black (Yellow/blue/blue)
Previous Names: None
Previous Leagues: Bristol & District. Gloucestershire County.

HONOURS: FA Comps: None
             League: Bristol & District Division Four 1982-83.

10 YEAR RECORD									
07-08	08-09	09-10	10-11	11-12	12-13	13-14	14-15	15-16	16-17
West1 8	West1 2	WestP 11	WestP 17	WestP 13	WestP 15	WestP 14	WestP 16	WestP 18	WestP 17
		FAC EP	FAC P	FAC P	FAC EPr	FAC Pr	FAC 1Q	FAC P	FAC EP
	FAV 1P	FAV 2P	FAV 2Q	FAV 1Qr	FAV 2Pr	FAV 1P	FAV 1P	FAV 2Qr	FAV 2Q

MELKSHAM TOWN
Founded: 1876   Nickname: Town

Secretary: Mark Jeffery   **(T)** 07739 905 575   **(E)** markmtfc@virginmedia.com
Chairman: Darren Perrin   **Manager:** Kieran Baggs
Ground: Oakfield Stadium, Eastern Way, Melksham SN12 7GU   **(T)**
Capacity: **Seats:** Yes   **Covered:** Yes   **Midweek Matchday:** Monday   **Clubhouse:** Yes
Colours(change):   Yellow/black/black (All red)
Previous Names: Melksham FC 1876-1951.
Previous Leagues: Wiltshire (Founder Members) 1894-1974.

HONOURS: FA Comps: None
             League: Wiltshire 1903-04, Premier 1993-94.

10 YEAR RECORD	Western Division One 1979-80, 96-97, Premier Division 2014-15.								
07-08	08-09	09-10	10-11	11-12	12-13	13-14	14-15	15-16	16-17
WestP 11	WestP 11	WestP 19	WestP 8	West1 2	WestP 13	WestP 7	WestP 1	WestP 5	WestP 3
FAC 1Q	FAC EP	FAC EP	FAC EP	FAC P	FAC 1Q	FAC EPr	FAC EPr	FAC EPr	FAC EP
FAV 3P	FAV 1P	FAV 1P	FAV 2P	FAV 2P	FAV 2Q	FAV 2Q	FAV 4P	FAV 2P	FAV 4Pr

ODD DOWN (BATH)
Founded: 1901   Nickname: The Down

Secretary: Lorraine Brown   **(T)** 07734 924 435   **(E)** lorrainebrown@btinternet.com
Chairman: Dave Loxton   **Manager:** Ray Johnston
Ground: Lew Hill Memorial Ground, Combe Hay Lane, Odd Down BA2 8PA   **(T)** 01225 832 491
Capacity: 1,000 **Seats:** 160   **Covered:** 250   **Midweek Matchday:** Tuesday   **Clubhouse:** Yes
Colours(change):   All blue
Previous Names: None
Previous Leagues: Bath & District. Wiltshire. Somerset Senior. Mid-Somerset.

HONOURS: FA Comps: None
             League: Western Division One 1992-93, Premier Division 2015-16.

10 YEAR RECORD									
07-08	08-09	09-10	10-11	11-12	12-13	13-14	14-15	15-16	16-17
WestP 21	West1 19	West1 2	WestP 8	WestP 9	WestP 8	WestP 4	WestP 5	WestP 1	WestP 7
FAC P	FAC P	FAC Pr	FAC Pr	FAC P	FAC P	FAC EPr	FAC P	FAC P	FAC P
FAV 2Q	FAV 2Q	FAV 2Q	FAV 2P	FAV 2Q	FAV 2P	FAV 2P	FAV 3P	FAV 2P	FAV 2P

SHEPTON MALLET
Founded: 1986   Nickname: The Mallet

Secretary: Gary Banfield   **(T)** 07762 880 705   **(E)** gkrkb@tiscali.co.uk
Chairman: John Hugill   **Manager:** Craig Loxton & Jon Burr   **Prog Ed:** Gary Banfield
Ground: Playing Fields, Old Wells Road, West Shepton, Shepton Mallet BA4 5XN   **(T)** 01749 344 609
Capacity: 2,500 **Seats:** 120   **Covered:** Yes   **Midweek Matchday:** Tuesday   **Clubhouse:** Yes
Colours(change):   Black & white/black/red (Yellow/navy/yellow)
Previous Names: None
Previous Leagues: Somerset Senior.

HONOURS: FA Comps: None
             League: Somerset Senior League 2000-01.

10 YEAR RECORD									
07-08	08-09	09-10	10-11	11-12	12-13	13-14	14-15	15-16	16-17
West1 11	West1 17	West1 17	West1 14	West1 16	West1 7	West1 2	WestP 9	WestP 10	WestP 12
FAC P	FAC EP	FAC EP				FAC EPr	FAC Pr	FAC EP	FAC P
FAV 1P	FAV 2Q	FAV 2Q	FAV 2Q	FAV 1Q	FAV 1Q	FAV 2P	FAV 3P	FAV 2Q	FAV 1Q

STREET
Founded: 1880   Nickname: The Cobblers

Secretary: Richard Palette   **(T)** 07721 679 681   **(E)** streetfootballclub@outlook.com
Chairman: James Court   **Manager:** Richard Fey
Ground: The Tannery Ground, Middlebrooks, Street BA16 0TA   **(T)** 01458 445 987
Capacity: 1,000 **Seats:** 150 **Covered:** 25 **Midweek Matchday:** Tuesday **Clubhouse:** Yes
Colours(change): All green (All red)
Previous Names: None
Previous Leagues: Somerset Senior 1880-1911, 22-30, 60-98. Western 1911-22, 30-39, 46-60.

HONOURS: FA Comps: None
League: Somerset Senior 1892-93, 95-96, 97-98, 98-99, 1909-10, 63-64, 65-66, 1996-97, Division Three 93-94.

10 YEAR RECORD

	07-08	08-09	09-10	10-11	11-12	12-13	13-14	14-15	15-16	16-17
	WestP 18	WestP 13	WestP	WestP 13	WestP 10	WestP 6	WestP 5	WestP 13	WestP 7	WestP 2
FAC	EP	Pr	EPr		EP	EP	EP	1Q	EPr	P	1Q
FAV	2P	3Pr	2Q	2Q	1Q	1P	2Q	2Q	1Q	1P

WELLINGTON
Founded: 1892   Nickname: Wellie

Secretary: David Derrick   **(T)** 07519 843 737   **(E)** david230275@googlemail.com
Chairman: Mike Hall   **Prog Ed:** Mrs Jane Brown
Ground: Wellington Playing Field, North Street, Wellington TA21 8LY   **(T)** 01823 664 810
Capacity: 1,500 **Seats:** 200 **Covered:** 200 **Midweek Matchday:** Wednesday **Clubhouse:** Yes
Colours(change): Orange/black/orange (Claret/blue/claret)
Previous Names: None
Previous Leagues: Taunton Saturday, Somerset Senior.

HONOURS: FA Comps: None
League: Western Division One 2007-08, 16-17.

10 YEAR RECORD

	07-08	08-09	09-10	10-11	11-12	12-13	13-14	14-15	15-16	16-17
	West1 1	WestP 7	WestP 13	WestP 18	West1 18	West1 18	West1 8	West1 6	West1 12	West1 1
FAC			EP	P	EP	FAT 2Q				
FAV	1P	2Q	3P	2P	2Q			2Q		1Q

WELLS CITY
Founded: 1890   Nickname:

Secretary: David Green   **(T)** 07584 045 238   **(E)** daveg55@hotmail.co.uk
Chairman: Steve Loxton
Ground: Athletic Ground, Rowdens Road, Wells, Somerset BA5 1TU   **(T)** 01749 679 971
Capacity: 1,500 **Seats:** Yes **Covered:** Yes **Midweek Matchday:** Tuesday **Clubhouse:** Yes
Colours(change): All blue (All yellow)
Previous Names: None
Previous Leagues: Western 1929-60. Somerset Senior 1960-2008.

HONOURS: FA Comps: None
League: Western Division One 1949-50, 2009-10.

10 YEAR RECORD

	07-08	08-09	09-10	10-11	11-12	12-13	13-14	14-15	15-16	16-17
	SomP 2	West1 10	West1 1	West1 9	WestP 12	WestP 19	West1 6	West1 19	West1 2	WestP 15
FAC					2Q	P	1Q			EPr
FAV			2P	1Q	1P	2Q	1Q	1Q	1P	2Q

WILLAND ROVERS
Founded: 1946   Nickname: Rovers

Secretary: Dom Clark   **(T)** 07546 561 212   **(E)** domclarkwillandrovers@gmail.com
Chairman: Mike Mitchell   **Manager:** Russell Jee
Ground: Silver Street, Willand, Collumpton, Devon EX15 2RG   **(T)** 01884 33885
Capacity: 1,000 **Seats:** 75 **Covered:** 150 **Midweek Matchday:** Wednesday **Clubhouse:** Yes
Colours(change): White/dark blue/dark blue (Yellow/royal blue/yellow)
Previous Names: None.
Previous Leagues: Devon & Exeter >1992. Devon County (Founder Members) 1992-2001.

HONOURS: FA Comps: None
League: Devon County 1998-99, 00-01, Western Division One 2004-05.

10 YEAR RECORD

	07-08	08-09	09-10	10-11	11-12	12-13	13-14	14-15	15-16	16-17
	WestP 3	WestP 3	WestP 2	WestP 4	WestP 5	WestP 11	WestP 8	WestP 6	WestP 6	WestP 6
FAC	P	P	2Q	1Q	EP	EP	EP	4Q	EP	EPr
FAV	2P	3P	5Pr	4P	4P	2P	1P	1Q	2Q	1P

DIVISION ONE

ALMONDSBURY U.W.E.

Founded: 1969   **Nickname:** The Almonds

Secretary: Douglas Coles   **(T)** 07748 655 399   **(E)** doug2004.coles@blueyonder.co.uk
Chairman: Mike Blessing   **Manager:** Neil Bailey
Ground: The Field, Almondsbury, Bristol BS32 4AA   **(T)** 01454 612 240   **Capacity:** 1,000
Colours(change): Green & white hoops/green/green (Yellow & blue)
HONOURS: FA Comps: None   **League:** Bristol Suburban Premier Division 1990-91. Gloucestershire County 2003-04.

10 YEAR RECORD

07-08	08-09	09-10	10-11	11-12	12-13	13-14	14-15	15-16	16-17
West1 20	West1 18	West1 13	West1 12	West1 9	West1 10	West1 9	West1 5	West1 11	West1 22
			FAC P	FAC EP	FAC 1Q		FAC EP	FAC 1Q	
		FAV 1Q	FAV 2Q	FAV 1Q	FAV 1Q	FAV 1P	FAV 1Q	FAV 2Q	FAV 2Q

ASHTON & BACKWELL UNITED

Founded: 2010   **Nickname:** The Stags

Secretary: Miss Charlie Cole   **(T)** 07866 024 499   **(E)** ashtonbackwellunited@btconnect.com
Chairman: Jim Biggins   **Manager:** Paul Wearing
Ground: The Lancer Scott Stadium, West Town Road, Backwell. BS48 3HQ   **(T)** 01275 461 273   **Capacity:** 1,000
Colours(change): Maroon & blue/blue/blue (Yellow)
HONOURS: FA Comps: None   **League:** None

10 YEAR RECORD

07-08	08-09	09-10	10-11	11-12	12-13	13-14	14-15	15-16	16-17
			SomP 7	SomP 3	SomP 3	West1 14	West1 8	West1 8	West1 7
								FAC EP	FAC EP
				FAV 2Q	FAV 2Q	FAV 1P	FAV 2Q	FAV 2Q	FAV 2Q

BISHOP SUTTON

Founded: 1977   **Nickname:** Bishops

Secretary: Malcolm Hunt   **(T)** 07799 623 901   **(E)** bishopsuttonafcsecretary@hotmail.co.uk
Chairman: George Williams   **Manager:** David Stone
Ground: Lakeview, Wick Road, Bishops Sutton, Bristol BS39 5XN.   **(T)** 07532 126 483   **Capacity:** 1,500
Colours(change): All blue (All yellow)
HONOURS: FA Comps: None   **League:** Western Division One 1997-98, Premier Division 2012-13.

10 YEAR RECORD

07-08	08-09	09-10	10-11	11-12	12-13	13-14	14-15	15-16	16-17
WestP 19	WestP 15	WestP 4	WestP 5	WestP 6	WestP 1	WestP 9	WestP 19	West1 21	West1 16
FAC EP	FAC EP	FAC EP	FAC P	FAC 1Q	FAC Pr	FAC P	FAC EP	FAC EP	
FAV 1Q	FAV 1Q	FAV 1P	FAV 1Pr	FAV 2P	FAV 2Q	FAV 1P	FAV 1Q	FAV 1P	FAV 2Q

BISHOPS LYDEARD

Founded: 1912   **Nickname:**

Secretary: Paul Brown   **(T)** 07548 125 292   **(E)** itspeebee@gmail.com
Chairman: Gary Brown   **Manager:** Brett Andrews
Ground: Cottlestone Road, Bishops Lydeard, Taunton, TA4 3BA   **(T)** 07956 682 367   **Capacity:** 1,000
Colours(change): Red & black stripes/black/black (Yellow/blue/blue)
HONOURS: FA Comps: None   **League:** Somerset County Division One 2004-05, Premier Division 15-16.

10 YEAR RECORD

07-08	08-09	09-10	10-11	11-12	12-13	13-14	14-15	15-16	16-17
Som1 1	SomP 4	SomP 2	SomP 12	SomP 11	SomP 13	SomP 10	SthP 6	SomP 1	West1 6

BRISTOL TELEPHONES

Founded: 1948   **Nickname:** The Phones

Secretary: Steve Watkins   **(T)** 0789 4787 193   **(E)** steve.watkins56@talktalk.net
Chairman: Shaun Collins   **Manager:** Shaun Collins
Ground: BTRA Sports Ground, Stockwood Lane, Stockwood, Bristol BS14 8SJ   **(T)** 01275 891 776
Colours(change): All pale blue (All orange)
HONOURS: FA Comps: None   **League:** Bristol & Suburban Premier Division 2010-11, 12-13. Gloucestershire County 2016-17.

10 YEAR RECORD

07-08	08-09	09-10	10-11	11-12	12-13	13-14	14-15	15-16	16-17
	Br&SuP2 11	Br&SuP2 3	Br&SuP1 1	Br&SuP1 3	Br&SuP1 1	GlCo 3	GlCo 8	GlCo 10	GlCo 1

CALNE TOWN
Founded: 1886   Nickname: Lilywhites

The Lilywhites

Secretary: Wayne McLaughlin   **(T)** 07795 833 702   **(E)** wmm498@msn.com
Chairman: Trudy East   **Manager:** Ben Redford & Clive McDaid
Ground: Bremhill View, Calne, Wiltshire SN11 9EE   **(T)** 07795 833 702   **Capacity:** 2,500
Colours(change): White/black/black (All yellow)
HONOURS: FA Comps: None   **League:** None

10 YEAR RECORD

	07-08	08-09	09-10	10-11	11-12	12-13	13-14	14-15	15-16	16-17
	WestP 14	WestP 16	WestP 20	West1 11	West1 4	West1 9	West1 13	West1 15	West1 15	West1 21
FAC	EPr	1Q	P	EP	EP	EP	EP			
FAV	2Q	1P	1P	1Q	1P	2Q	1Q	2Q	1P	1P

CHARD TOWN
Founded: 1920   Nickname: The Robins

Secretary: Clare Gage   **(T)** 07771 848 148   **(E)** chardtownfcsecretary@outlook.com
Chairman: Lyndsey Gage   **Manager:** Paul Down
Ground: Denning Sports Field, Zembard Lane, Chard, Somerset TA20 1JL   **(T)** 01460 61402   **Capacity:** 1,500
Colours(change): Red/white/red (Blue/blue/white)
HONOURS: FA Comps: None   **League:** Perry Street & District 1939-40.
Somerset Senior 1949-50, 53-54, 59-60, 67-68, 69-70.

10 YEAR RECORD

	07-08	08-09	09-10	10-11	11-12	12-13	13-14	14-15	15-16	16-17
	WestP 20	WestP 20	West1 16	West1 13	West1 6	West1 6	West1 15	West1 7	West1 3	West1 10
FAC	EP	EPr	EP			EP	P			
FAV	2Q	2Q	2Q	2Q	2Q	1Q	1Q			

CHEDDAR
Founded: 1892   Nickname: The Cheesemen

Secretary: Alan Cooper   **(T)** 0784 587 08121   **(E)** alancooper7@sky.com
Chairman: Matt Postins   **Manager:** Jared Greenhalgh   Simon Childs
Ground: Bowdens Park, Draycott Road, Cheddar BS27 3RL   **(T)** 01934 707 271   **Capacity:** 1,105
Colours(change): Yellow/black/yellow (All blue)
HONOURS: FA Comps: None   **League:** Cheddar Valley 1910-11.
Somerset Senior Division One 2003-04.

10 YEAR RECORD

	07-08	08-09	09-10	10-11	11-12	12-13	13-14	14-15	15-16	16-17
	SomP 8	SomP 8	SomP 7	SomP 4	SomP 2	West1 11	West1 17	West1 10	WestP 5	West1 3
FAC										EPr
FAV							1Q	1Q	1Q	2Q

CHIPPENHAM PARK
Founded: 2012   Nickname: The Park

Secretary: Tim Smith   **(T)** 07528 796 837   **(E)** smithallantim@hotmail.com
Chairman: Damien Coulter   **Manager:** Tim Smith & Brett Partner
Ground: Hardenhuish Park, Bristol Road, Chippenham SN14 6LR   **(T)** 01249 650 400   **Capacity:** 2,800
Colours(change): All blue (All green)
HONOURS: FA Comps: None   **League:** None

10 YEAR RECORD

	07-08	08-09	09-10	10-11	11-12	12-13	13-14	14-15	15-16	16-17
						Wilt 3	West1 10	West1 11	West1 14	West1 8
FAV							1Q	2P	2Q	1Q

CORSHAM TOWN
Founded: 1883   Nickname: The Peacocks

Secretary: Leslie Bateman   **(T)** 07941 523 954   **(E)** les.bateman63@btinternet.com
Chairman: Chris Perry   **Manager:** Jamie Harrison
Ground: Southbank Ground, Lacock Road, Corsham SN13 9HS   **(T)** 07963 030 652   **Capacity:** 1,200
Colours(change): Red & white/red/red (Yellow & blue/blue/yellow)
HONOURS: FA Comps: None   **League:** Wiltshire Division Two 1960-61, Division One 97-98.
Western Premier Division 2006-07.

10 YEAR RECORD

	07-08	08-09	09-10	10-11	11-12	12-13	13-14	14-15	15-16	16-17
	WestP 5	WestP 19	WestP 17	WestP 10	WestP 18	West1 4	West1 7	West1 9	West1 10	West1 19
FAC	2Q	EP	EP	P	EP	EP	1Qr	EP		
FAV	1P	1Q	1P	2Q	1Qr	1Q	2Q	2Q	1P	2Q

DEVIZES TOWN

Founded: 1885   Nickname: The Town

Secretary: Neil Fautley   **(T)** 07891 341 344   **(E)** neil@hallmarkflooring.co.uk
Chairman: Shaun Moffat   **Manager:** Darren Walters
Ground: Nursteed Road, Devizes, Wiltshire SN10 3DX   **(T)** 01380 722 817   **Capacity:** 2,500
Colours(change): Red & white stripes/black/black (All blue)
HONOURS: FA Comps: None   **League:** Wiltshire Senior 1895-96, 89-99, 35-36, 48-49, 51-52, 53-54, Premier 61-62, 63-64. Western Premier Division 1972-73, Division One 99-2000.

10 YEAR RECORD

07-08		08-09		09-10		10-11		11-12		12-13		13-14		14-15		15-16		16-17	
WestP	10	WestP	21	West1	19	West1	5	West1	19	West1	21	West1	11	West1	18	West1	19	West1	11
FAC	EP	FAC	EP	FAC	EPr			FAC	EP										
FAV	2Q	FAV	2Q	FAV	2Q	FAV	2Q	FAV	1P	FAV	1Q	FAV	1Q	FAV	1Q	FAV	1Q	FAV	1P

KEYNSHAM TOWN

Founded: 1895   Nickname: K's

Secretary: Julian French   **(T)** 07814 609 853   **(E)** Julian.French@friendslifeservices.co.uk
Chairman: Malcolm Trainer   **Manager:** John Allen
Ground: AJN Stadium, Bristol Road, Keynsham BS31 2BE   **(T)** 07814 609 853   **Capacity:** 3,000
Colours(change): Amber/black/Amber (All maroon)
HONOURS: FA Comps: None   **League:** Western Division One 1977-78.

10 YEAR RECORD

07-08		08-09		09-10		10-11		11-12		12-13		13-14		14-15		15-16		16-17	
West1	14	West1	5	West1	8	West1	16	West1	13	West1	13	West1	19	West1	17	West1	9	West1	4
FAC	EP	FAC	EP	FAC	EP	FAC	EP											FAC	EP
FAV	1Q	FAV	2Q	FAV	1P	FAV	2P	FAV	2Q	FAV	1Q	FAV	2Q	FAV	2Q	FAV	2Qr	FAV	2Q

MALMESBURY VICTORIA

Founded: 1896   Nickname: The Vics

Secretary: Brendon Rice   **(T)** 07825 172 500   **(E)** brendon@innov.co.uk
Chairman: Bernie Davies   **Manager:** Kevin Bridgeman
Ground: Flying Monk Ground, Gloucester Road, SN16 0AJ   **(T)** 01666 822 141
Colours(change): Black & white stripes/black/red (Red & black stripes/red/black)
HONOURS: FA Comps: None   **League:** Wiltshire Premier 1999-00, 2014-15.

10 YEAR RECORD

07-08		08-09		09-10		10-11		11-12		12-13		13-14		14-15		15-16		16-17	
Hel1W	16	Hel1W	2	Hel P	19	Hel1W	13	Hel1W	16	Hel1W	15	Hel1W	12	Wilt	1	Wilt	3	West1	9
FAV	1Q	FAV	1P	FAV	2Q	FAV	1Q					FAV	1Q	FAV	1P	FAV	2Q	FAV	1Q

OLDLAND ABBOTONIANS

Founded: 1910   Nickname: The O's

Secretary: Tom Shepherd   **(T)** 07808 299 133   **(E)** secretary@oldlandfootball.com
Chairman: Derek Jones   **Manager:** Scott Armstrong
Ground: Aitchison Playing Field, Castle Road, Oldland Common, Bristol BS30 9SZ   **(T)** 01179 328 263
Colours(change): Blue & white/blue/blue (All yellow)
HONOURS: FA Comps: None   **League:** Somerset County Division One 2004-05.

10 YEAR RECORD

07-08		08-09		09-10		10-11		11-12		12-13		13-14		14-15		15-16		16-17	
West1	12	West1	7	West1	6	West1	2	West1	11	West1	5	West1	21	West1	14	West1	4	West1	17
												FAC	EP					FAC	P
										FAV	1Q	FAV	1Q	FAV	1Q	FAV	2Q	FAV	2Q

PORTISHEAD TOWN

Founded: 1912   Nickname: Posset

Secretary: Jean Harrison   **(T)** 07969 045 310   **(E)** jemaha11@talktalk.net
Chairman: Adrian Green
Ground: Bristol Road, Portishead, Bristol BS20 6QG   **(T)** 01275 817 600   **Capacity:** 1,400
Colours(change): White/black/black (All red)
HONOURS: FA Comps: None   **League:** Somerset County 1993-94, 94-95, 95-96, 97-98.

10 YEAR RECORD

07-08		08-09		09-10		10-11		11-12		12-13		13-14		14-15		15-16		16-17	
West1	9	West1	11	West1	12	West1	18	West1	12	West1	14	West1	22	West1	21	West1	6	West1	14
				FAC	P	FAC	EP											FAC	1Q
		FAV	2Q	FAV	1Q	FAV	2Q	FAV	1Q	FAV	1Q	FAV	1Q	FAV	2Q	FAV	1P	FAV	2Q

RADSTOCK TOWN

Founded: 1895   Nickname: The Miners

Secretary: Debbie Smith   **(T)** 07828 665 636   **(E)** rtfcsecretary@outlook.com
Chairman: Simon Wilkinson   **Manager:** Shane Smith
Ground: Southfields Recreation Ground, Southfields, Radstock BA3 2NZ   **(T)** 01761 435 004   **Capacity:** 1,250
Colours(change): Red/black/red (All yellow)
HONOURS: FA Comps: None   **League:** Somerset Senior Division One 1996-97.

10 YEAR RECORD

07-08		08-09		09-10		10-11		11-12		12-13		13-14		14-15		15-16		16-17	
WestP	17	WestP	17	WestP	16	WestP	12	WestP	16	WestP	17	WestP	1	West1	13	West1	13	West1	5
FAC	EPr	FAC	EP	FAC	EP	FAC	P	FAC	P	FAC	EP	FAC	EP	FAC	EP				
FAV	1Q	FAV	2Q	FAV	1Q	FAV	1P	FAV	1Q	FAV	2Q	FAV	2Q	FAV	1P	FAV	2Q	FAV	1Q

ROMAN GLASS ST GEORGE

Founded: 1872   Nickname: The Glass

Secretary: Emily Baldwin   **(T)** 07708 277 592   **(E)** emilyjaynebaldwin@outlook.com
Chairman: Roger Hudd   **Manager:** Andy Gurney
Ground: Oaklands Park, Gloucester Road, Alomndsbury BS32 4AG   **(T)** 01454 612 220   **Capacity:** 2,000
Colours(change): White/black/black (All red)
HONOURS: FA Comps: None   **League:** Bristol & District Div.1 1949-50. Bristol Premier Com. Div.1 1963-64, 64-65, 65-66, 66-67, 67-68, 88-89, Prem 92-93. .Gloucestershire County 1969-70, 2001-02, 06-07.

10 YEAR RECORD

07-08		08-09		09-10		10-11		11-12		12-13		13-14		14-15		15-16		16-17	
West1	10	West1	16	West1	18	West1	15	West1	8	West1	17	West1	12	West1	20	West1	18	West1	15
										FAV	2Q	FAV	2Q	FAV	2Q	FAV	1Qr	FAV	2Q

SHERBORNE TOWN

Founded: 1894   Nickname:

Secretary: Colin Goodland   **(T)** 07929 090 612   **(E)** colingoodland@live.co.uk
Chairman: John Bowers   **Manager:** Gerry Pearson
Ground: Raleigh Grove, Terrace Playing Field, Sherbone DT9 5NS   **(T)** 01935 816 110   **Capacity:** 1,200
Colours(change): Black & white/black/black (Green/white/white).
HONOURS: FA Comps: None   **League:** Dorset Premier 1981-82. Western Division One 2012-13.

10 YEAR RECORD

07-08		08-09		09-10		10-11		11-12		12-13		13-14		14-15		15-16		16-17	
West1	2	WestP	12	WestP	18	WestP	14	WestP	17	West1	1	WestP	9	WestP	12	WestP	13	WestP	20
FAC	1Q	FAC	EP	FAC	P	FAC	2Q	FAC	EP	FAC	1Q	FAC	P	FAC	1Q	FAC	Pr	FAC	EP
FAV	3P	FAV	1P	FAV	2Q	FAV	1Pr	FAV	2Q	FAV	2P	FAV	2Q	FAV	1P	FAV	1Q	FAV	1P

WARMINSTER TOWN

Founded: 1878   Nickname: The Red & Blacks

Secretary: Chris Robbins   **(T)** 07734 025 196   **(E)** Chrisjrobbins1@virginmedia.com
Chairman: Pete Russell   **Manager:** Mark Breffit
Ground: Weymouth Street, Warminster BA12 9NS   **(T)** 01985 217 828
Colours(change): Red & black stripes/black/red & black (All blue)
HONOURS: FA Comps: None   **League:** None

10 YEAR RECORD

07-08		08-09		09-10		10-11		11-12		12-13		13-14		14-15		15-16		16-17	
Wex1	7	Wex1	5	Wex1	14	Wex1	12	Wex1	16	West1	15	West1	18	West1	16	West1	17	West1	18
				FAC	Pr	FAC	EP												
		FAV	1P	FAV	1Q	FAV	2Q			FAV	2Q	FAV	1P	FAV	1Q	FAV	2Q	FAV	1Q

WELTON ROVERS

Founded: 1887   Nickname: Rovers

Secretary: Malcolm Price   **(T)** 07970 791 644   **(E)** malcolm@weltonr.plus.com
Chairman: Malcolm Price   Gareth Paisey
Ground: West Clewes, North Road, Midsomer Norton, Bath BA3 2QD   **(T)** 02762 412 097   **Capacity:** 2,400
Colours(change): Green & white/green/green (Yellow/blue/blue).
HONOURS: FA Comps: None   **League:** Western 1911-12, 64-65, 65-66, 66-67, 73-74, Division One 59-60, 87-88.

10 YEAR RECORD

07-08		08-09		09-10		10-11		11-12		12-13		13-14		14-15		15-16		16-17	
WestP	9	WestP	8	WestP	5	WestP	19	West1	7	West1	16	West1	6	West1	2	WestP	20	West1	20
FAC	1Q	FAC	EP	FAC	EP	FAC	EP	FAC	EP	FAC	EP			FAC	EP	FAC	EP	FAC	EP
FAV	2Qr	FAV	2Q	FAV	3P	FAV	1Q	FAV	1Q	FAV	2Q	FAV	1Q	FAV	2P	FAV	3P	FAV	1Q

WESTBURY UNITED

Founded: 1920   Nickname: White Horse Men

Secretary: Greg Coulson   **(T)** 07814 956 428   **(E)** secretary@westburyunited.co.uk
Chairman: Matt Bright   **Manager:** Neil Kirkpatrick
Ground: Meadow Lane, Westbury, Wiltshire BA13 3QA   **(T)** 01373 764 197
Colours(change): Green/black/white (Al navy blue)
HONOURS: FA Comps: None   **League:** Wiltshire 1934-35, 37-38, 38-39, 49-50, 50-51, 55-56.
Western Division 1991-92.

10 YEAR RECORD

07-08		08-09		09-10		10-11		11-12		12-13		13-14		14-15		15-16		16-17	
West1	7	West1	9	West1	5	West1	17	West1	17	West1	19	West1	20	West1	22	West1	22	West1	12
FAC	EP	FAC	P	FAC	EPr	FAC	P												
FAV	2Q	FAV	2Qr	FAV	1P	FAV	1Q	FAV	1Q	FAV	1P	FAV	1Q	FAV	1Q	FAV	1Q	FAV	2Q

WINCANTON TOWN

Founded: 1890   Nickname: Winky

Secretary: Chris Martin   **(T)** 07828 987 712   **(E)** cmartin10101981@gmail.com
Chairman: Terry Wise   **Manager:** Chris Wise
Ground: Wincanton Sports Ground, Moor Lane, Wincanton. BA9 9RA   **(T)** 01963 31815
Colours(change): Yellow & black/black/black (Green & white/green/green)
HONOURS: FA Comps: None   **League:** Yeovil & District Division Two 1988-89, Division One 89-90, Premier 90-91.
Dorset Senior Division 2006-07.

10 YEAR RECORD

07-08		08-09		09-10		10-11		11-12		12-13		13-14		14-15		15-16		16-17	
Dor P	5	Dor P	8	Dor P	9	Dor P	7	Dor P	4	Dor P	2	West1	4	West1	4	West1	16	West1	13
																FAC	P		
														FAV	1Q	FAV	EP	FAV	1Q

A dramatic injury-time winner from Phil Matthews gives Flitwick Town a 2-1 win over Marston Shelton Rovers and thereby clinch their first ever Bedfordshire County Premier Division title. Photo: Gordon Whittington.

Hardwick 2016-17 - 1st in Cambridgshire Premier Division. Photo: Gordon Whittington.

ANGLIAN COMBINATION

Sponsored by: Hadley & Ottaway
Founded: 1964
Recent Champions:
2014: Acle United
2015: Acle United **2016:** Acle United
angliancombination.org.uk

PREMIER DIVISION	P	W	D	L	F	A	GD	Pts
1 Spixworth	30	28	1	1	100	20	80	85
2 Harleston Town	30	26	2	2	100	19	81	80
3 Mulbarton Wanderers	30	16	7	7	60	36	24	55
4 Acle United	30	15	8	7	59	40	19	53
5 Waveney	30	14	8	8	76	54	22	50
6 Blofield United	30	12	7	11	49	49	0	43
7 Mattishall	30	13	4	13	60	62	-2	43
8 Stalham Town	30	12	6	12	66	61	5	42
9 St Andrews	30	11	8	11	58	49	9	41
10 Wroxham Res	30	12	5	13	57	60	-3	40*
11 Long Stratton	30	10	8	12	52	47	5	38
12 Norwich CEYMS	30	10	3	17	48	58	-10	33
13 Reepham Town	30	9	5	16	52	82	-30	32
14 Caister	30	9	4	17	65	71	-6	31
15 Kirkley & Pakefield Res	30	2	5	23	26	89	-63	11
16 Cromer Town	30	0	1	29	22	153	-131	0*

Out: Spixworth now Norwich CMS (P - Eastern Counties).

DIVISION ONE	P	W	D	L	F	A	GD	Pts
1 Bradenham Wanderers	28	18	7	3	79	35	44	61
2 Beccles Town	28	19	4	5	78	37	41	61
3 Hellesdon	28	17	5	6	80	45	35	56
4 Bungay Town	28	16	5	7	61	36	25	53
5 Aylsham	28	15	7	6	77	50	27	52
6 North Walsham Town	28	15	2	11	77	53	24	47
7 Attleborough Town	28	12	8	8	60	45	15	44
8 Loddon United	28	12	2	14	59	73	-14	38
9 Wymondham Town	28	10	7	11	64	62	2	37
10 Mundford	28	12	1	15	59	63	-4	37
11 Sheringham	28	11	3	14	68	65	3	36
12 Hindringham	28	5	6	17	46	83	-37	21
13 Scole United	28	6	3	19	42	81	-39	21
14 Dersingham Rovers	28	6	2	20	45	102	-57	20
15 Holt United	28	3	4	21	28	93	-65	13

DON FROST CUP

(Premier Division champions v Mummery Cup holders)

Acle United	v	Spixworth	2-2, 4-3p

MUMMERY CUP
(Premier and Division One Clubs)

HOLDERS: SPIXWORTH

ROUND 1

Cromer Town	v	Kirkley & Pakefield Res	1-4
Loddon United	v	Mundford	3-5
Blofield United	v	Hellesdon	4-3
Scole United	v	Waveney	1-4
Wymondham Town	v	Mattishall	0-1
Stalham Town	v	Acle United	0-1
Foulsham	v	Caister	0-2
Norwich CEYMS	v	Beccles Town	3-1
Bradenham Wanderers	v	St Andrews	4-6 aet
Bungay Town	v	Harleston Town	AW
Attleborough Town	v	Aylsham	3-1
Sheringham	v	Mulbarton Wanderers	2-3 aet
Holt United	v	Spixworth	1-6
Dersingham Rovers	v	Wroxham Res	1-5
Hindringham	v	North Walsham Town	0-0, 8-7p
Reepham Town	v	Long Stratton	4-1

ROUND 2

Kirkley & Pakefield Res	v	Mundford	0-4
Blofield United	v	Waveney	1-1, 3-4p
Mattishall	v	Acle United	2-2, 2-4p
Caister	v	Norwich CEYMS	0-4
St Andrews	v	Harleston Town	0-4
Attleborough Town	v	Mulbarton Wanderers	1-2
Spixworth	v	Wroxham Res	1-4
Hindringham	v	Reepham Town	1-3

QUARTER-FINALS

Mundford	v	Waveney	2-1
Acle United	v	Norwich CEYMS	3-1
Harleston Town	v	Mulbarton Wanderers	0-2
Wroxham Res	v	Reepham Town	2-5

SEMI-FINALS

Mundford	v	Acle United	0-2
Mulbarton Wanderers	v	Reepham Town	3-1

FINAL

Acle United	v	Mulbarton Wanderers	1-2

CYRIL BALLYN TROPHY
(Division Two, Three, Four, Five and Six first teams and external league reserve sides)

FINAL		**HOLDERS:** MUNDFORD	
Poringland Wanderers	v	UEA	0-4

CS MORLEY CUP
(Anglian Combination reserve teams)

FINAL		**HOLDERS:** GORLESTON RESERVES	
Attleborough Town Res	v	Gorleston Res	0-3

PREMIER DIVISION	1	2	3	4	5	6	7	8	9	10	11	12	13	14	15	16
1 Acle United		2-0	5-2	5-0	0-5	2-3	0-0	5-0	2-0	2-1	3-1	0-3	4-1	2-2	0-2	1-2
2 Blofield United	0-0		3-2	9-1	0-2	3-1	2-1	2-1	2-2	0-2	1-0	0-3	3-0	1-4	1-3	0-0
3 Caister	0-2	3-0		11-0	2-3	1-1	2-2	3-2	0-1	2-1	0-0	0-3	1-3	1-1	1-6	1-2
4 Cromer Town	0-4	2-5	2-12		0-2	0-2	0-2	4-5	0-1	0-4	0-3	A-W	1-10	3-4	1-5	0-6
5 Harleston Town	5-0	6-0	7-2	9-0		2-1	4-2	3-0	6-0	1-0	2-2	0-2	2-0	4-2	2-0	8-0
6 Kirkley & Pakefield Res	0-0	0-1	0-3	0-0	1-2		0-3	1-2	3-7	1-2	0-1	1-7	0-5	0-4	1-5	3-3
7 Long Stratton	0-0	1-1	4-2	4-0	2-2	6-2		1-2	1-5	0-2	6-0	0-3	0-0	4-2	1-2	0-0
8 Mattishall	0-1	3-1	3-1	8-0	0-4	5-1	2-0		0-1	2-1	0-1	0-3	3-2	1-1	1-4	H-W
9 Mulbarton Wanderers	2-2	1-1	4-0	5-0	0-1	1-1	2-0	1-0		1-0	4-0	1-2	0-0	2-1	1-3	5-0
10 Norwich CEYMS	2-2	1-2	0-3	4-1	0-3	3-1	0-1	2-3	4-1		4-1	1-4	2-5	1-3	0-0	1-3
11 Reepham Town	0-3	1-5	2-4	8-0	3-0	2-0	0-5	4-4	2-2	5-2		1-4	3-1	0-7	0-4	4-1
12 Spixworth	1-1	2-1	8-0	6-0	2-0	3-0	2-0	6-3	1-0	4-0	5-0		1-3	4-1	4-3	3-1
13 St Andrews	3-2	1-1	1-0	1-6	0-2	0-1	3-2	1-3	1-1	0-3	0-4			2-2	1-1	1-0
14 Stalham Town	2-3	1-0	0-4	4-0	0-4	4-0	3-2	2-4	1-1	3-1	4-3	1-2	0-3		0-3	3-4
15 Waveney	2-3	3-3	3-2	4-2	0-4	5-1	0-1	3-3	2-4	1-3	4-4	1-4	1-0	2-2		1-1
16 Wroxham Res	1-3	0-1	2-0	5-3	1-3	4-1	5-1	2-1	0-2	2-3	4-1	1-4	4-1	0-2	3-3	

ANGLIAN COMBINATION - STEP 7

Anglian Combination Premier Division

ACLE UNITED	Bridewell Lane, Acle, Norwich NR13 3RA	01493 752 989
BECCLES TOWN	College Meadow, Ken Markland Way, Common Lane, Beccles NR34 9BU	07500 484 442
BLOFIELD UNITED	Old Yarmouth Road, Blofield, Norwich NR13 4LE	07748 863 203
BRADENHAM WANDERERS	Hale Road, Bradenham IP25 7RA	07786 165 522
CAISTER	Caister Playing Fields, off Allendale Road, Caister-on-Sea NR30 5ES	07852 212 210
HARLESTON TOWN	Harleston Recreation Ground, Wilderness Lane, Harleston IP20 9DD	07887 781 603
HELLESDON	Hellesdon Community Centre, Woodview Road, Hellesdon, Norwich NR6 5QB	01603 483 823
LONG STRATTON	Long Stratton Playing Field, Long Stratton, Manor Road NR15 2XR	07806 792 840
MATTISHALL	Mattishall Playing Fields, South Green, Mattishall, Norwich NR20 3JY	01362 850 246
MULBARTON WANDERERS	Mulberry Park #1, Mulbarton, Norfolk NR14 8AE	07738 668 407
NORWICH CEYMS	Hilltops Sports Centre, Main Road, Swardeston, Norwich NR14 8DU	01508 578 826
REEPHAM TOWN	Stimpsons Piece, Station Road, Reepham NR10 4LJ	07887 442 470
ST ANDREWS	Thorpe Recreation Ground, Laundry Lane, Thorpe St Andrew, Norwich NR7 0XQ	01603 300 316
STALHAM TOWN	Rivers Park Stalham, Stepping Stone Lane, Stalham, Norfolk NR12 9ER	07818 418 677
WAVENEY	Saturn Close Sports Ground, Station Road, Lowestoft NR32 4TD	07711 710 533
WROXHAM RESERVES	Trafford Park, Skinners Lane, Wroxham NR12 8SJ	01603 783 538

DIVISION TWO

		P	W	D	L	F	A	GD	Pts
1	UEA	30	22	3	5	88	24	64	69
2	Yelverton	30	21	4	5	70	30	40	67
3	Watton United	30	19	8	3	70	35	35	65
4	Hoveton Wherrymen	30	19	6	5	63	27	36	63
5	East Harling	30	18	5	7	72	38	34	59
6	Easton	30	16	5	9	88	52	36	53
7	Wells Town	30	17	1	12	68	56	12	52
8	Martham	30	14	6	10	70	48	22	48
9	Poringland Wanderers	30	10	12	8	47	37	10	42
10	Caister Res	30	11	4	15	51	65	-14	36*
11	Mattishall Res	30	8	4	18	56	87	-31	27*
12	Thetford Rovers	30	7	3	20	50	78	-28	24
13	Acle United Res	30	6	4	20	37	79	-42	22
14	Sprowston Athletic	30	6	4	20	39	78	-39	21*
15	Hempnall	30	5	4	21	40	82	-42	19
16	Blofield United Res	30	3	3	24	35	128	-93	11*

DIVISION THREE

		P	W	D	L	F	A	GD	Pts
1	Gayton United	28	20	4	4	97	32	65	64
2	Fakenham Town Res	28	18	3	7	75	30	45	56*
3	Brandon Town	28	17	4	7	74	35	39	55
4	Horsford United	28	14	8	6	48	38	10	50
5	Redgate Rangers	28	14	5	9	51	41	10	47
6	Freethorpe	28	13	4	11	60	61	-1	43
7	South Walsham	28	12	7	9	57	63	-6	43
8	Long Stratton Res	28	12	4	12	52	60	-8	40
9	Buxton	28	12	4	12	44	54	-10	39*
10	Hemsby	28	11	5	12	47	57	-10	38
11	Swaffham Town Res	28	10	5	13	60	73	-13	35
12	Beccles Caxton	28	8	4	16	45	67	-22	28
13	Norwich CEYMS Res	28	7	5	16	40	62	-22	26
14	Sheringham Res	28	7	2	19	48	84	-36	18*
15	Loddon United Res (W)	28	2	2	24	18	59	-41	-2*

DIVISION FOUR

		P	W	D	L	F	A	GD	Pts
1	Gorleston Res	28	24	2	2	176	22	154	74
2	Earsham	28	22	3	3	126	27	99	69
3	Hingham Athletic	28	19	2	7	135	53	82	59
4	Costessey Sports	28	18	4	6	90	42	48	58
5	Bungay Town Res	28	16	4	8	89	53	36	52
6	Reepham Town Res	28	16	4	8	73	61	12	52
7	Bradenham Wanderers Res	28	12	5	11	76	70	6	41
8	St Andrews Res	28	12	4	12	69	76	-7	40
9	Downham Town Res	28	11	2	15	58	60	-2	35
10	Stalham Town Res	28	8	6	14	63	78	-15	30
11	North Walsham Town Res	28	9	2	17	63	79	-16	27*
12	Wymondham Town Res	28	8	1	19	35	106	-71	25
13	Dersingham Rovers Res	28	7	3	18	52	97	-45	24
14	Thorpe Village	28	5	3	20	42	115	-73	18
15	Horsford United Res	28	0	1	27	15	223	-208	-2*

DIVISION FIVE NORTH

		P	W	D	L	F	A	GD	Pts
1	Aylsham Res	26	23	1	2	116	12	104	70
2	Heacham	26	19	3	4	79	30	49	60
3	Gayton United Res	26	18	3	5	76	49	27	57
4	Castle Acre Swifts	26	18	2	6	114	42	72	56
5	Hellesdon Res	26	16	2	8	108	62	46	50
6	UEA Res	26	15	3	8	119	41	78	47*
7	Hindringham Res	26	9	5	12	63	69	-6	32
8	Narborough	26	8	6	12	47	68	-21	30
9	Easton Res	26	8	5	13	39	64	-25	28*
10	Necton	26	6	3	17	55	93	-38	21
11	Mundford Res	26	6	3	17	40	133	-93	21
12	South Walsham Res	26	6	2	18	37	108	-71	18*
13	Wells Town Res	26	4	5	17	42	98	-56	16*
14	Martham Res	26	4	1	21	38	104	-66	11*

DIVISION FIVE SOUTH

		P	W	D	L	F	A	GD	Pts
1	Gt Yarmouth Town Res	26	22	3	1	112	18	94	69
2	Waveney Res	26	19	3	4	86	30	56	60
3	Mulbarton Wanderers Res	26	17	6	3	85	34	51	57
4	Harleston Town Res	26	17	3	6	96	39	57	54
5	Belton	26	17	2	7	98	42	56	53
6	Attleborough Town Res	26	16	4	6	91	39	52	52
7	East Harling Res	26	13	2	11	90	69	21	41
8	Beccles Town Res	26	14	0	12	76	56	20	41*
9	Poringland Wanderers Res	26	8	2	16	51	95	-44	23*
10	Yelverton Res	26	7	1	18	37	101	-64	22
11	Thetford Rovers Res	26	5	2	19	34	125	-91	16*
12	Scole United Res	26	5	3	18	37	75	-38	14*
13	Newton Flotman	26	3	4	19	41	125	-84	13
14	Freethorpe Res	26	1	1	24	26	112	-86	4

CLUB MOVEMENTS

FIVE NORTH:
In: Dussindale Rovers (P - Norwich & District)
Norwich Eagles (P - Norwich & District)
Redgate Rangers Res (N).

FIVE SOUTH:
In: AC Mill Lane (P - Lowestoft & District)
Tacolneston (P - South Norfolk)

BEDFORDSHIRE COUNTY LEAGUE

Sponsored by: No sponsor
Founded: 1904
Recent Champions:
2014: AFC Oakley M&DH
2015: Renhold United
2016: AFC Oakley M&DH
bedfordshirefootballleague.co.uk

BRITANNIA CUP

HOLDERS: AFC OAKLEY M&DH
ROUND 1

Sandy	v	Wootton Blue Cross	0-2
Wilstead	v	AFC Oakley M&DH	1-2
Sharnbrook	v	Shefford Town & Campton	0-5
Ickwell & Old Warden	v	Caldecote	1-2
Ampthill Town Res	v	Kempston Rovers Dev	6-1
Renhold United	v	Stevington	4-3
Flitwick Town	v	AFC Kempston Town & B.C. 3-3, 4-5p	
Cranfield United	v	Marston Shelton Rovers	0-3

QUARTER-FINALS

Wootton Blue Cross	v	AFC Oakley M&DH	1-2
Shefford Town & Campton	v	Caldecote	0-2
Ampthill Town Res	v	Renhold United	1-0
AFC Kempston Town & B.C.	v	Marston Shelton Rovers	1-2

SEMI-FINALS

AFC Oakley M&DH	v	Caldecote	1-1, 5-6p
Ampthill Town Res	v	Marston Shelton Rovers	0-2

FINAL

Caldecote	v	Marston Shelton Rovers	0-3

PREMIER DIVISION

	PREMIER DIVISION	P	W	D	L	F	A	GD	Pts
1	Flitwick Town	30	22	1	7	81	51	30	66*
2	AFC Kempston Town & Bedford College	30	21	1	8	99	49	50	64
3	AFC Oakley M&DH	30	19	5	6	84	40	44	62
4	Caldecote	30	18	6	6	68	48	20	60
5	Wilstead	30	18	3	9	89	56	33	57
6	Renhold United	30	15	4	11	58	55	3	46*
7	Shefford Town & Campton	30	14	3	13	59	51	8	45
8	Stevington	30	11	7	12	52	53	-1	40
9	Cranfield United	30	12	4	14	53	56	-3	40
10	Marston Shelton Rovers	30	11	4	15	48	47	1	37
11	Wootton Blue Cross	30	9	8	13	62	67	-5	35
12	Ickwell & Old Warden	30	11	3	16	56	74	-18	35*
13	Sharnbrook	30	10	4	16	47	62	-15	33*
14	Ampthill Town Res	30	8	4	18	36	64	-28	26*
15	Kempston Rovers Dev	30	7	5	18	50	83	-33	22*
16	Sandy	30	1	4	25	25	111	-86	6*

In: Crawley Green Res (P)

Out: Ampthill Town Res (W).

DIVISION ONE

	DIVISION ONE	P	W	D	L	F	A	GD	Pts
1	Queens Park Crescents	24	17	5	2	67	26	41	56
2	Totternhoe Res	24	17	3	4	64	31	33	54
3	Crawley Green Res	24	13	5	6	54	42	12	44
4	Henlow	24	12	8	4	56	34	22	43*
5	AFC Kempston Tn & Bedford Coll Res	24	13	1	10	59	42	17	40
6	M&DH Clapham Sports	24	10	6	8	56	48	8	32*
7	Shefford Town & Campton Res	24	10	3	11	42	42	0	31*
8	The 61 FC (Luton) Res	24	8	3	13	42	63	-21	26*
9	Westoning	24	8	1	15	42	47	-5	22*
	(withdrew having played 79% of their matches - remaining fixtures awarded to opponents)								
10	Cople & Bedford SA	24	7	2	15	52	71	-19	22*
11	Meltis Albion	24	7	2	15	43	63	-20	20*
	(withdrew having played 92% of their matches - remaining fixtures awarded to opponents)								
12	Elstow Abbey	24	3	6	15	34	77	-43	13*
13	Old Bradwell United Res	24	4	9	11	36	61	-25	9*
	Ickleford withdrew - record expunged.								

IN: Biggleswade FC Res (N), Meltis Albion (N).

	PREMIER DIVISION	1	2	3	4	5	6	7	8	9	10	11	12	13	14	15	16
1	AFC Kempston Town & Bedford College		1-4	3-2	4-3	2-1	2-3	2-1	7-2	6-0	8-3	8-1	2-3	0-0	4-0	2-3	4-0
2	AFC Oakley M&DH	2-1		2-1	7-1	0-1	1-2	3-1	7-0	4-2	2-1	8-1	2-1	1-2	1-2	1-5	8-4
3	Ampthill Town Reserves	0-2	2-2		0-2	0-2	2-0	0-5	H-W	3-2	H-W	5-1	2-0	0-1	1-2	0-3	1-1
4	Caldecote	2-1	1-1	4-1		2-4	1-7	5-1	2-1	2-1	2-1	3-0	2-1	3-2	5-2	3-0	0-0
5	Cranfield United	1-3	0-5	3-1	2-0		2-3	5-0	1-1	0-1	0-2	3-0	0-1	2-1	0-1	3-4	1-1
6	Flitwick Town	2-1	3-4	3-2	1-2	4-2		H-W	5-4	1-3	3-2	2-0	3-2	4-2	1-0	0-2	3-1
7	Ickwell & Old Warden	2-6	1-3	4-3	0-2	3-0	0-3		1-5	2-2	1-3	5-1	4-2	3-2	2-1	1-2	4-3
8	Kempston Rovers Development	1-6	3-3	1-1	0-4	3-5	0-3	1-3		2-1	1-2	A-W	H-W	2-1	2-3	5-0	1-3
9	Marston Shelton Rovers	0-1	0-1	6-0	2-0	0-1	1-2	0-1	6-0		0-0	2-0	4-1	2-1	1-2	2-0	2-2
10	Renhold United	3-2	3-1	4-1	1-1	3-0	3-4	2-1	0-0	1-2		4-2	1-2	4-2	2-1	1-6	1-1
11	Sandy	0-3	0-2	0-0	1-6	3-3	0-7	2-4	1-4	0-3	0-1		0-2	1-2	2-2	1-3	3-4
12	Sharnbrook	1-4	0-2	1-2	1-1	2-2	1-4	2-1	2-4	4-0	4-2	2-2		4-2	0-3	1-3	3-2
13	Shefford Town & Campton	2-3	0-2	3-1	0-0	4-3	0-3	5-1	4-1	1-0	1-3	4-0	1-1		3-0	2-1	3-1
14	Stevington	3-4	0-0	3-1	0-1	1-2	2-2	3-3	2-2	1-1	1-2	6-2	0-2	0-3		3-3	2-0
15	Wilstead	3-4	0-4	3-2	3-3	4-1	4-2	5-0	6-1	6-1	2-3	8-1	2-0	2-3	1-3		2-0
16	Wootton Blue Cross	1-3	1-1	1-2	3-5	1-3	5-1	1-1	4-3	2-1	4-0	5-0	5-1	3-2	0-3	3-3	

BEDFORDSHIRE COUNTY LEAGUE - STEP 7

Bedfordshire County Premier Division

AFC KEMPSTON & BEDFORD COL.	Football Turf 3G, AFC Kempston, Hillgrounds Road, Kempston
AFC OAKLEY SPORTS M&DH	Oakley Village Sports Centre, Oakley, Bedford MK43 7RU
CALDECOTE	The Playing Fields, Harvey Close, Upper Caldecote SG18 9BQ
CRANFIELD UNITED	Crawley Road, Cranfield, Bedfordshire MK43 0AA 01234 751 444
CRAWLEY GREEN RESERVES	Crawley Green Recreation Ground, Crawley Green Road, Luton LU2 9AG
FLITWICK TOWN	Flitwick Community Football Centre, Ampthill Road, Flitwick MK45 1BA
ICKWELL & OLD WARDEN	Ickwell Green, Ickwell, Bedfordshire SG18 9EE
KEMPSTON ROVERS DEV.	Hillgrounds Stadium, Hillgrounds Road, Kemspton, Bedfordshire MK42 8SZ 01234 852 346
MARSTON SHELTON ROVERS	Bedford Road, Marston Moretaine, Bedford MK43 0LE
QUEENS PARK CRESCENTS	Bedford Park
RENHOLD UNITED	Renhold Playing Fields, Renhold, Bedford MK41 0LR
SHARNBROOK	Playing Fields, Lodge Road, Sharnbrook MK44 1JP
SHEFFORD TOWN & CAMPTON	Shefford Sports Club, Hitchin Road, Shefford SG17 5JD
STEVINGTON	Pavenham Playing Field, Pavenham, Bedfordshire MK43 7PE
WILSTEAD	Jubilee Playing Fields, Bedford Road, Wilstead MK45 3HE
WOOTTON BLUE CROSS	Weston Park, Bedford Road., Wootton MK43 9JT

DIVISION TWO

		P	W	D	L	F	A	GD	Pts
1	Riseley Sports	20	14	4	2	52	23	29	46
2	Wixams	20	12	7	1	59	25	34	43
3	Lea Sports PSG	20	10	7	3	41	27	14	36*
4	Cranfield United Res	20	11	2	7	40	38	2	35
5	Flitwick Town Res	20	8	6	6	36	29	7	30
6	Atletico Europa	20	9	1	10	45	51	-6	28
7	Caldecote Res	20	5	5	10	35	45	-10	20
8	AFC Oakley M&DH Res	20	6	2	12	29	53	-24	19*
9	Houghton Athletic	20	4	7	9	33	42	-9	17*
10	Sundon Park Rovers	20	4	4	12	30	54	-24	16
11	Potton Town	20	2	5	13	25	38	-13	-6*

Kempston Hammers Sports withdrew - record expunged.

IN: Luton Leagreave (N). Westoning (N).

Out: Old Bradwell United Res (W).

DIVISION THREE

		P	W	D	L	F	A	GD	Pts
1	Renhold United Res	18	12	3	3	50	26	24	39
2	Wilstead Res	18	9	5	4	49	32	17	32
3	Bedford Albion	18	9	6	3	49	24	25	31*
4	Marston Shelton Rovers Res	18	9	3	6	51	33	18	30
5	Kempston Athletic	18	7	4	7	59	62	-3	25
6	Sandy Albion	18	8	4	6	32	38	-6	25*
7	Caldecote A	18	7	1	10	45	56	-11	22
8	Shefford Town & Campton 'A'	18	5	0	13	31	60	-29	15
9	Wootton Village	18	3	4	11	17	41	-24	12*
10	White Eagles	18	4	4	10	36	47	-11	10*

AFC Dunton withdrew - record expunged.

DIVISION FOUR

		P	W	D	L	F	A	GD	Pts
1	CS Rovers	18	14	2	2	68	26	42	44
2	Henlow Reserves	18	12	2	4	59	24	35	38
3	Clifton	18	11	2	5	43	30	13	35
4	Harlington	18	8	5	5	65	40	25	25*
5	AFC Kempston Tn & Bedford Coll 'A'	18	7	3	8	49	53	-4	24
6	Dinamo Flitwick	18	7	2	9	33	68	-35	23
7	Flitwick Town 'A'	18	7	1	10	40	48	-8	18*
8	Sandy Reserves	18	5	2	11	41	56	-15	17
9	Stevington Reserves	18	5	2	11	32	57	-25	17
10	Lidlington United Sports	18	3	1	14	29	57	-28	9*

No Division Four for 2017-18 - Division Three made up of:
AFC Kempston Town & Bedford College 'A'; Bedford Albion Reserves (N); Black Swan [Luton] (N); Caldecote A'; Clifton; Dinamo Flitwick; Flitwick Town 'A'; Harlington; Kempston Athletic; Lidlington United Sports; Sandy Reserves; Shefford Town & Campton 'A'; Stevington Reserves; White Eagles; Wootton Village.
Out: Potton Town (W), Sandy Albion (W).

CENTENARY CUP		
FINAL	**HOLDERS:** QUEENS PARK CRESCENTS	
Totternhoe Res	v Queens Park Crescents	1-2

JUBILEE CUP		
FINAL	**HOLDERS:** CRANFIELD UNITED RES	
Wixams	v Sundon Park Rovers	0-1

WATSON SHIELD		
FINAL	**HOLDERS:** RENHOLD UNITED RES	
Marston Shelton Rovers Res v	AFC Oakley M&DH Res	1-3

CAMBRIDGESHIRE COUNTY LEAGUE

Sponsored by: Kershaw Mechanical Services Ltd
Founded: 1891
Recent Champions:
2014: Over Sports
2015: Great Shelford **2016:** Great Shelford

PREMIER DIVISION	P	W	D	L	F	A	GD	Pts
1 Hardwick	34	28	1	5	135	38	97	85
2 Great Shelford	34	25	5	4	116	51	65	80
3 Lakenheath	34	22	2	10	102	59	43	68
4 Eaton Socon	34	20	8	6	88	46	42	68
5 Chatteris Town	34	18	5	11	80	48	32	59
6 West Wratting	34	16	7	11	74	51	23	55
7 Linton Granta	34	14	9	11	65	64	1	51
8 Fulbourn Institute	34	15	6	13	61	71	-10	51
9 Cherry Hinton	34	15	5	14	67	68	-1	50
10 Gamlingay United	34	13	7	14	61	70	-9	46
11 Brampton	34	14	3	17	73	80	-7	45
12 Outwell Swifts	34	11	6	17	47	77	-30	39
13 Cambridge City Reserves	34	9	8	17	64	87	-23	35
14 Sawston United	34	7	10	17	48	79	-31	31
15 Foxton	34	9	2	23	50	96	-46	29
16 Hemingfords United	34	9	3	22	55	83	-28	27*
17 Fowlmere	34	9	3	22	56	97	-41	24*
18 Over Sports	34	5	4	25	34	111	-77	19

Out: Hardwick (W - took up place of Reserves in Division One A)

PREMIER DIVISION CUP

HOLDERS: GAMLINGAY UNITED

ROUND 1

Great Shelford	v	West Wratting	2-3
Hardwick	v	Lakenheath	2-4

ROUND 2

Fulbourn Institute	v	West Wratting	0-0, 9-8p
Brampton	v	Chatteris Town	1-3
Fowlmere	v	Over Sports	4-3
Eaton Socon	v	Hemingfords United	4-0
Foxton	v	Outwell Swifts	3-2
Lakenheath	v	Cherry Hinton	4-1
Linton Granta	v	Gamlingay United	5-1
Sawston United	v	Cambridge City Res	4-2

QUARTER-FINALS

Fulbourn Institute	v	Chatteris Town	3-1
Fowlmere	v	Eaton Socon	1-4
Foxton	v	Lakenheath	1-4
Linton Granta	v	Sawston United	3-1

SEMI-FINALS

Fulbourn Institute	v	Eaton Socon	1-3
Lakenheath	v	Linton Granta	4-3

FINAL

Eaton Socon	v	Lakenheath	1-4

PREMIER DIVISION	1	2	3	4	5	6	7	8	9	10	11	12	13	14	15	16	17	18
1 Brampton		4-0	2-2	1-0	3-1	2-4	1-0	6-4	4-0	2-4	1-8	4-2	2-1	1-3	0-2	3-1	3-0	3-2
2 Cambridge City FC Reserves	1-0		0-1	3-1	1-4	3-3	4-3	1-2	2-2	4-6	1-7	0-2	5-3	0-0	4-3	3-0	8-2	1-4
3 Chatteris Town	3-0	6-3		2-1	1-2	6-0	3-0	6-0	3-0	3-1	0-2	1-2	0-1	0-1	1-1	3-2	5-0	2-1
4 Cherry Hinton	4-2	3-1	4-3		1-2	0-3	4-2	3-5	3-1	1-5	1-5	3-1	1-3	0-1	6-0	1-0	2-2	3-1
5 Eaton Socon	3-2	1-1	0-0	4-0		7-3	1-0	2-3	1-1	1-2	3-2	2-1	3-2	4-1	4-0	3-0	1-1	3-1
6 Fowlmere	1-0	3-1	0-2	0-3	1-1		3-5	1-2	5-3	1-4	1-2	0-1	2-5	4-1	1-2	1-3	1-4	0-4
7 Foxton	3-5	1-0	1-2	0-2	1-6	1-2		3-4	2-1	0-0	2-5	5-2	2-6	1-2	2-3	4-1	1-0	1-4
8 Fulbourn Institute	4-0	4-0	2-4	0-4	0-2	1-2	4-0		2-1	2-1	1-4	2-3	0-4	2-1	2-2	4-0	1-1	2-0
9 Gamlingay United	1-1	2-0	4-1	1-2	2-1	4-1	2-1	2-0		1-3	1-3	5-4	3-1	0-2	1-0	2-2	1-2	1-1
10 Great Shelford	6-3	2-2	5-1	2-2	3-3	4-0	5-0	2-1	2-2		1-2	3-1	2-0	3-2	6-1	7-2	3-0	2-4
11 Hardwick	3-2	5-4	2-1	2-0	1-1	7-2	7-1	9-0	2-3	2-3		6-1	2-3	2-1	9-0	4-0	3-1	2-0
12 Hemingfords United	5-3	2-3	1-2	1-1	1-5	3-3	1-2	0-1	2-4	1-2	0-1		1-3	2-3	3-0	2-0	1-2	1-6
13 Lakenheath	3-0	3-0	3-2	2-3	3-3	2-0	8-2	3-0	7-1	2-5	1-3	1-3		6-2	2-0	3-1	5-0	3-2
14 Linton Granta	3-2	3-3	3-0	4-0	3-2	3-4	1-1	1-1	4-2	0-2	1-7	1-1	3-0		2-0	3-4	1-1	0-3
15 Outwell Swifts	2-1	1-2	2-2	5-2	0-4	1-0	0-1	0-0	4-0	2-6	0-4	4-0	2-3	0-0		2-0	0-3	3-2
16 Over Sports	0-4	2-1	1-7	1-3	0-4	2-1	1-2	1-1	1-4	0-7	0-7	2-1	2-2	2-5	1-4		0-4	0-3
17 Sawston United	3-3	1-1	0-4	1-1	2-3	5-3	4-0	1-3	1-3	2-3	0-5	0-2	1-5	1-1	0-0	1-1		2-3
18 West Wratting	1-3	1-1	1-1	2-2	3-1	3-0	2-0	1-1	0-0	1-4	1-0	3-1	1-3	3-3	3-1	5-1	2-0	

CAMBRIDGESHIRE COUNTY LEAGUE - STEP 7

Cambridgeshire County Premier Division

BRAMPTON	Thrapston Road Playing Fields, Brampton, Huntingdon PE28 4TB
CAMBRIDGE CITY RESERVES	Cottenham Village College, High Street, Cottenham, Cambridge CB24 8UA
CHATTERIS TOWN	West Street, Chatteris, Cambridgeshire PE16 6HW
CHERRY HINTON	Recreation Ground, High Street, Cherry Hinton Cambridge CB1 9HZ
EATON SOCON	River Road, Eaton Ford, St Neots PE19 3AU
FOWLMERE	Fowlmere Village Hall #1, Chrishall Road, Fowlmere, Royston SG8 7RE
FOXTON	Hardman Road, off High Street, Foxton CB22 6RP
FULBOURN INSTITUTE	Fulbourn Recreation, Home End, Fulbourn CB21 5HS
GAMLINGAY UNITED	Gamlingay Community Centre, Stocks Lane, Gamlingay, Cambridgeshire SG19 3JR
GREAT SHELFORD	Recreation Ground, Woollards Lane, Great Shelford CB2 5LZ
HARDWICK	Egremont Road, Hardwick, Cambridge CB3 7XR
HEMINGFORDS UNITED	Peace Memorial Playing Field #1, Manor Road, Hemingford Grey PE28 9BX
LAKENHEATH	The Pit, Wings Road, Lakenheath IP27 9HN
LINTON GRANTA	Recreation Ground, Meadow Lane, Linton, Cambridge CB21 6HX
OUTWELL SWIFTS	Outwell Playing Field The Nest, Wisbech Road, Outwell, Wisbechech PE14 8PA
OVER SPORTS	Over Recreation Ground, The Doles, Over, Cambridge CB4 5NW
SAWSTON UNITED	Spicers Sports Ground, New Road, Sawston CB22 4BW
WEST WRATTING	Recreation Ground, Bull Lane, West Wratting CB21 5NJ

WILLIAM COCKELL CUP

FINAL   **HOLDERS:** CHATTERIS TOWN
Comerton United   v   Orwell   4-1

SENIOR DIVISION A

		P	W	D	L	F	A	GD	Pts
1	Comberton United	28	21	4	3	125	31	94	67
2	Cambridge University Press	28	21	3	4	94	41	53	66
3	Milton	28	20	3	5	95	48	47	63
4	Soham United	28	14	5	9	87	59	28	47
5	Burwell Swifts	28	15	2	11	69	71	-2	47
6	Orwell	28	12	8	8	96	63	33	44
7	Ely City Res	28	13	5	10	63	53	10	44
8	Cottenham United	28	11	5	12	65	53	12	38
9	Hundon	28	10	8	10	47	43	4	38
10	Somersham Town	28	9	6	13	62	49	13	33
11	Girton United	28	9	5	14	61	63	-2	32
12	Soham Town Rangers Res	28	9	3	16	47	73	-26	30
13	Fulbourn Institute Res	28	9	2	17	50	89	-39	29
14	Royston Town A	28	2	6	20	41	87	-46	12
15	Great Paxton	28	2	1	25	16	195	-179	7

In: Great Paxton (W took up place of Reserves in Division Three A)

DIVISION ONE A

		P	W	D	L	F	A	GD	Pts
1	Steeple Bumpstead	24	17	1	6	78	34	44	52
2	Great Chishill	24	14	7	3	65	32	33	49
3	Cherry Hinton Res	24	15	2	7	63	41	22	47
4	Mildenhall Town Res	24	13	5	6	74	49	25	44
5	Exning United	24	11	5	8	66	65	1	38
6	Steeple Morden	24	10	7	7	57	45	12	37
7	Balsham	24	11	4	9	50	58	-8	37
8	Milton Res	24	9	5	10	65	62	3	32
9	Duxford United	24	10	2	12	53	65	-12	32
10	Linton Granta Res	24	6	4	14	50	66	-16	22
11	Debden	24	6	3	15	52	71	-19	21
12	Sawston United Res	24	4	3	17	37	83	-46	15
13	Over Sports Res	24	5	2	17	37	76	-39	14*

Histon Hornets Sports withrew - record expunged.
Out: Mildenhall Town Res (S - D1B).

PERCY OLDHAM CUP

FINAL   **HOLDERS:** COMBERTON UNITED
Wisbech St Mary Res   v   Sawston Rovers   2-0

SENIOR DIVISION B

		P	W	D	L	F	A	GD	Pts
1	Bar Hill	30	24	5	1	90	28	62	77
2	Haverhill Borough Res	30	21	4	5	93	36	57	67
3	Whittlesford United	30	21	3	6	77	47	30	66
4	Wisbech St Mary Res	30	18	7	5	95	45	50	61
5	Red Lodge	30	18	2	10	82	58	24	56
6	Bluntisham Rangers	30	14	4	12	67	63	4	46
7	Needingworth United	30	12	7	11	76	67	9	43
8	Witchford 96	30	13	3	14	60	56	4	42
9	Lakenheath Res	30	10	10	10	51	58	-7	40
10	Cambridge University Press Res	30	10	6	14	46	65	-19	36
11	Godmanchester Rovers Res	30	10	4	16	56	75	-19	31*
12	Sawston Rovers	30	8	4	18	50	76	-26	28
13	Buckden	30	7	6	17	58	91	-33	27
14	Ashdon Villa	30	9	3	18	48	83	-35	24*
15	Hardwick Res	30	4	4	22	33	84	-51	16
16	West Wratting Res	30	3	4	23	28	78	-50	7*

In: Newmarket Town Res (N).

DIVISION ONE B

		P	W	D	L	F	A	GD	Pts
1	Huntingdon United	24	22	2	0	110	16	94	68
2	March Town United Res	24	17	4	3	62	22	40	55
3	Chatteris Town Res	24	14	4	6	70	34	36	46
4	Houghton & Wyton	24	14	3	7	71	37	34	45
5	Fordham	24	12	3	9	40	38	2	39
6	Eaton Socon Res	24	11	3	10	66	46	20	36
7	Hemingfords United Res	24	10	4	10	39	64	-25	34
8	Alconbury	24	8	5	11	66	58	8	29
9	Littleport Town	24	9	2	13	52	64	-12	29
10	Fenstanton	24	7	6	11	44	62	-18	27
11	St Ives Rangers	24	7	1	16	34	77	-43	22
12	Swavesey Institute	24	4	1	19	53	81	-28	13
13	Manea United	24	2	0	22	26	134	-108	6

In: Mildenhall Town Res (S - D1A)

DIVISION TWO A	P	W	D	L	F	A	GD	Pts
1 Clare Town	22	17	0	5	77	43	34	51
2 Thaxted Rangers	22	14	2	6	60	34	26	44
3 Cambourne Rovers	22	13	2	7	52	29	23	41
4 Bar Hill Res	22	13	2	7	77	38	39	38*
5 Papworth	22	11	5	6	64	37	27	38
6 City Life	22	10	4	8	59	45	14	34
7 Bassingbourn	22	10	4	8	53	50	3	34
8 Great Shelford Res	22	8	3	11	49	53	-4	27
9 Gamlingay United Res	22	6	8	8	56	53	3	26
10 Litlington Athletic	22	5	2	15	32	94	-62	17
11 Abington United	22	3	3	16	33	81	-48	12
12 Saffron Crocus	22	4	1	17	26	81	-55	7*

Fowlmere Reserves withdrew - record expunged.

DIVISION TWO B	P	W	D	L	F	A	GD	Pts
1 AFC Barley Mow	24	21	1	2	106	33	73	64
2 Little Downham Swifts	24	19	2	3	83	33	50	59
3 Wimblington	24	12	5	7	70	47	23	41
4 Brampton Res	24	13	2	9	52	38	14	41
5 Ramsey Pavilion	24	11	6	7	73	60	13	39
6 Soham United Res	24	11	5	8	48	36	12	38
7 Mepal Sports	24	10	2	12	48	61	-13	32
8 Wisbech St Mary A	24	8	3	13	38	50	-12	27
9 Isleham United	24	7	4	13	30	48	-18	25
10 March Rangers	24	7	3	14	42	74	-32	24
11 Mildenhall United	24	5	4	15	38	68	-30	18
12 Upwell Town	24	5	3	16	44	81	-37	18
13 Ely Crusaders	24	4	6	14	28	71	-43	18

DIVISION THREE A	P	W	D	L	F	A	GD	Pts
1 Whittlesford United Res	22	18	2	2	104	41	63	56
2 Linton Granta A	22	14	5	3	67	23	44	47
3 Mott MacDonald	22	14	4	4	62	25	37	46
4 Melbourn	22	12	2	8	66	44	22	38
5 Girton United Res	22	11	5	6	49	45	4	38
6 Meldreth	22	11	2	9	56	54	2	35
7 Hundon Res	22	9	7	6	45	44	1	34
8 Eaton Socon A	22	9	2	11	54	61	-7	29
9 Foxton Res	22	6	3	13	44	62	-18	21
10 Cherry Hinton A	22	3	2	17	36	92	-56	11
11 Duxford United Res	22	3	1	18	28	71	-43	10
12 Great Paxton Res	22	4	1	17	26	75	-49	7*

In: Offord United (S - D3A).

DIVISION THREE B	P	W	D	L	F	A	GD	Pts
1 Tuddenham 08	24	21	0	3	90	25	65	63
2 Doddington United	24	18	3	3	96	35	61	57
3 Burwell Swifts Res	24	14	5	5	73	51	22	47
4 The Eagle	24	14	3	7	61	43	18	45
5 Earith United	24	14	2	8	73	52	21	44
6 Offord United	24	12	1	11	52	55	-3	37
7 Benwick Athletic	24	10	3	11	67	67	0	33
8 Cottenham United Res	24	7	2	15	42	81	-39	23
9 Alconbury Res	24	6	7	11	38	52	-14	22*
10 Chatteris Fen Tigers	24	5	5	14	39	55	-16	20
11 Lakenheath Casuals	24	8	1	15	39	56	-17	19*
12 Bluntisham Rangers Res	24	5	4	15	37	72	-35	19
13 Wisbech St Mary B	24	4	0	20	37	100	-63	12

In: Burwell Tigers (P), Guyhirn (P). Somersham Town Res (N). Wisbech Town Acorns (NC from Upwell Town. Out: Offord United (S - D3A)

DIVISION FOUR A	P	W	D	L	F	A	GD	Pts
1 Haverhill Rovers Res	24	19	3	2	132	37	95	60
2 Comberton United Res	24	15	6	3	101	52	49	51
3 Steeple Morden Res	24	16	3	5	73	42	31	51
4 Suffolk Punch Haverhill	24	14	1	9	52	55	-3	43
5 Wickhambrook	23	12	5	6	67	54	13	41
6 Saffron Dynamos	24	10	5	9	70	54	16	35
7 Papworth Res	24	9	4	11	79	61	18	31
8 Kedington	23	10	1	12	75	77	-2	31
9 Sawston Rovers Res	24	9	1	14	55	78	-23	28
10 Cambridge Ambassadors	24	7	4	13	51	75	-24	25
11 Milton A	24	7	3	14	44	81	-37	24
12 Buckden Reserves	24	5	1	18	47	114	-67	16
13 Guilden Morden	24	3	1	20	39	105	-66	10

Sawston United A Team withdrew - record expunged.
In: Great Paxton (NC from great Paxton Res).

DIVISION FOUR B	P	W	D	L	F	A	GD	Pts
1 Wisbech St Mary C	24	21	1	2	93	22	71	64
2 Guyhirn	24	18	1	5	72	33	39	55
3 Burwell Tigers	24	18	0	6	89	34	55	54
4 Fordham Res	24	13	3	8	72	37	35	42
5 Witchford 96 Res	24	12	3	9	65	54	11	39
6 Ely Crusaders Res	24	12	3	9	51	43	8	39
7 Isleham United Res	24	11	5	8	37	41	-4	38
8 Chatteris Town A	24	11	3	10	50	49	1	36
9 Hemingfords United A	24	8	1	15	55	69	-14	22*
10 Wimblington Res	24	7	4	13	49	63	-14	22*
11 March Rangers Res	24	5	2	17	41	74	-33	17
12 Coldham United	24	3	0	21	35	135	-100	9
13 Upwell Town Res	24	3	2	19	38	93	-55	8*

Out: Burwell Tigers (P), Guyhirn (P).

DIVISION FIVE A	P	W	D	L	F	A	GD	Pts
1 Harston Bostocks	18	13	3	2	81	24	57	42
2 Fulbourn Institute A	18	12	1	5	65	28	37	37
3 Bassingbourn Res	18	10	4	4	53	25	28	34
4 Barrington	18	10	3	5	90	33	57	33
5 Clare Town Res	18	11	0	7	74	42	32	33
6 Histon Hornets Sports Res	18	10	2	6	79	50	29	32
7 Thaxted Rangers Res	18	9	5	4	52	24	28	32
8 Bottisham	18	3	0	15	27	160	-133	9
9 Barton Mills	18	1	1	16	33	87	-54	1*
10 Steeple Morden A	18	1	1	16	18	99	-81	-2*

Lakenheath Casuals Res withdrew - record expunged.
Saffron Crocus Res withdrew - record expunged

In: Hardwick Res (N), Harston Bostocks Res (N), Longstanton (N), Oakington Vikings (N), Orwell Res (N), Steeple Bumpstead Res (N).
Out: Steeple Morden Res (W),

DIVISION FIVE B	P	W	D	L	F	A	GD	Pts
1 Houghton & Wyton Res	22	17	3	2	78	25	53	54
2 Needingworth United Res	22	17	0	5	111	39	72	51
3 Outwell Swifts Reserves	22	14	6	2	72	33	39	48
4 Huntingdon United Res	22	15	2	5	91	29	62	47
5 Coldham United Res	22	10	3	9	63	49	14	33
6 AFC Christchurch	22	9	4	9	45	47	-2	31
7 Wicken	22	10	3	9	58	58	0	30*
8 Manchester United	22	9	1	12	51	69	-18	28
9 Fenstanton Res	22	8	2	12	50	54	-4	26
10 Benwick Athletic Res	22	4	2	16	24	90	-66	14
11 Cottenham United A	22	4	1	17	27	62	-35	10*
12 Chatteris Town B	22	1	2	19	18	133	-115	4

In: Chatteris Fen Tigers Res (N), Little Downham Swifts Res (N), Littleport Town Res (N), March Soccer School (N), Somersham Town 'A' (N), St Ives Rangers Res (N). Out: Chatteris Town B (W).

CENTRAL MIDLANDS LEAGUE

Sponsored by: Abacus Lighting   **Founded:** 1971
Recent Champions: 2014: (N) AFC Mansfield (S) Clifton All Whites
2015: Bilsthorpe (N) Mickleover Royals (S) **2016:** Glapwell (N) Selston (S)

NORTH DIVISION

		P	W	D	L	F	A	GD	Pts
1	FC Bolsover	30	22	5	3	148	31	117	71
2	Clay Cross Town	30	23	0	7	121	46	75	69
3	AFC Bentley	30	20	3	7	79	34	45	63
4	Collingham	30	19	2	9	91	52	39	59
5	Tideswell United	30	18	3	9	80	48	32	57
6	Retford	30	15	6	9	92	53	39	50*
7	Newark Town	30	14	7	9	67	52	15	49
8	Appleby Frodingham	30	15	4	11	62	50	12	49
9	Dronfield Town Res	30	13	5	12	63	54	9	44
10	Harworth C	30	13	4	13	73	60	13	43
11	Askern	30	11	7	12	58	57	1	40
12	Phoenix	30	11	4	15	75	97	-22	34*
13	Bilsthorpe	30	7	1	22	41	81	-40	22
14	Dinnington Town	30	5	2	23	42	125	-83	17
15	Thorne Colliery	30	2	4	24	40	142	-102	10
16	Welbeck Lions	30	2	3	25	33	183	-150	9

SOUTH DIVISION

		P	W	D	L	F	A	GD	Pts
1	Selston	28	21	3	4	71	29	42	66
2	Eastwood Community	28	20	5	3	86	41	45	65
3	Sherwood Colliery	28	19	4	5	81	31	50	61
4	Hucknall Town	28	17	5	6	83	23	60	56
5	Swanwick Pentrich Road	28	14	6	8	67	35	32	48
6	South Normanton	28	15	3	10	68	59	9	48
7	Matlock Town Res	28	13	6	9	74	55	19	45
8	Mickleover RBL	28	12	2	14	62	56	6	38
9	Linby Colliery	28	11	3	14	51	68	-17	36
10	Southwell City	28	9	5	14	52	67	-15	32
11	Pinxton	28	8	5	15	47	64	-17	29
12	Blidworth Welfare	28	8	4	16	54	81	-27	28
13	Holbrook St Michaels	28	5	3	20	32	97	-65	18
14	Keyworth United	28	4	3	21	39	105	-66	15
15	Teversal Res	28	3	5	20	32	88	-56	14

LEAGUE CHALLENGE CUP

HOLDERS: HUCKNALL ROLLS LEISURE

ROUND 1

Southwell City	v	Bilsthorpe	5-3
Retford	v	Matlock Town Res	2-5
Sherwood Colliery	v	Mickleover RBL	6-2
Tideswell United	v	Appleby Frodingham	2-1
Harworth CI	v	Pinxton	3-1
Selston	v	Keyworth United	9-0
Dronfield Town Res	v	Welbeck Lions	12-1
Newark Town	v	Thorne Colliery	2-0
Swanwick Pentrich Road	v	Askern	3-1
Collingham	v	Teversal Res	1-3
FC Bolsover	v	Clay Cross Town	5-1
Hucknall Town	v	Blidworth Welfare	7-1
Linby Colliery	v	AFC Bentley	2-1
Dinnington Town	v	South Normanton	1-3
Phoenix	v	Eastwood Community	2-6

ROUND 2

Southwell City	v	Matlock Town Res	0-4
Sherwood Colliery	v	Tideswell United	2-1
Harworth CI	v	Selston	2-3
Dronfield Town Res	v	Newark Town	2-0
Holbrook St Michaels	v	Swanwick Pentrich Road	1-4

DIVISION NORTH

		1	2	3	4	5	6	7	8	9	10	11	12	13	14	15	16
1	AFC Bentley		2-0	0-2	5-2	1-2	1-2	3-1	1-0	0-7	2-0	2-1	2-0	4-2	1-0	3-1	12-2
2	Appleby Frodingham	2-0		4-0	2-1	1-2	3-1	6-1	2-2	3-3	0-3	0-2	2-3	0-5	3-2	2-0	4-1
3	Askern	1-0	3-1		3-1	0-1	2-3	4-0	3-2	0-4	1-3	1-1	0-4	3-3	3-1	0-2	1-1
4	Bilsthorpe	0-3	0-2	1-3		3-2	0-2	2-5	0-1	0-2	2-3	3-5	0-0	2-1	4-2	1-2	3-2
5	Clay Cross Town	3-0	6-0	8-0	7-0		1-0	3-2	3-0	1-5	4-3	6-0	5-2	1-3	6-2	7-1	8-1
6	Collingham	2-2	2-1	2-1	3-1	5-4		0-0	2-1	0-3	3-2	1-2	5-1	2-3	23-1	1-5	5-1
7	Dinnington Town	0-11	1-1	0-2	1-4	0-13	0-3		1-2	0-10	1-4	1-5	0-1	1-5	1-2	1-4	11-1
8	Dronfield Town Res	1-3	3-2	5-5	H-W	3-0	1-2	1-3		1-1	2-1	2-1	3-1	0-1	5-0	3-1	4-0
9	FC Bolsover	1-2	0-2	2-2	6-1	5-1	3-2	11-2	5-1		7-2	1-1	11-0	2-2	10-0	1-0	6-0
10	Harworth CI	0-0	1-2	3-1	3-2	0-3	1-2	6-0	5-3	1-2		2-0	3-3	1-5	5-1	0-3	13-0
11	Newark Town	0-3	1-1	1-1	4-0	2-3	2-3	4-1	2-2	1-0	1-1		3-4	3-2	5-0	1-3	6-2
12	Phoenix	0-2	1-6	1-0	2-3	0-4	2-4	3-2	2-2	2-12	5-0	0-2		4-2	4-0	3-6	17-1
13	Retford	0-0	2-0	2-0	2-0	1-2	0-2	5-0	4-0	0-7	1-2	3-3	5-3		5-5	0-2	4-1
14	Thorne Colliery	0-8	1-4	0-6	1-3	1-4	4-3	2-3	0-3	2-3	1-4	2-4	2-2	0-8		3-4	1-1
15	Tideswell United	2-0	1-3	0-0	4-1	1-3	4-2	6-1	3-2	1-3	2-0	1-2	7-1	1-1	2-2		2-1
16	Welbeck Lions	0-2	0-3	1-10	3-1	0-8	0-4	1-2	0-8	1-15	1-1	1-2	2-15	5-2	0-9		

DIVISION SOUTH

		1	2	3	4	5	6	7	8	9	10	11	12	13	14	15
1	Blidworth Welfare		2-2	0-2	0-5	2-1	1-3	1-5	2-3	0-3	2-3	1-1	2-4	2-2	2-2	6-0
2	Eastwood Community	6-2		6-1	1-1	6-4	3-2	3-0	4-1	4-0	3-1	1-2	1-2	7-2	3-1	3-1
3	Holbrook St Michaels	3-6	1-2		2-1	2-2	0-3	1-3	2-0	1-5	1-2	0-5	1-4	3-2	3-4	2-1
4	Hucknall Town	6-0	0-1	7-0		4-0	5-0	2-3	5-0	3-0	1-2	1-1	6-0	7-0	1-0	4-0
5	Keyworth United	2-0	1-3	4-0	2-2		0-4	4-4	0-5	2-0	1-2	1-2	3-7	0-3	0-5	3-1
6	Linby Colliery	4-1	1-5	4-1	0-3	2-1		1-3	2-2	3-3	1-1	2-1	3-2	2-1	2-3	1-0
7	Matlock Town Res	1-3	1-2	2-0	1-1	6-2	7-1		2-4	2-0	2-3	1-3	3-3	6-4	1-0	1-1
8	Mickleover RBL	6-2	0-3	6-0	0-1	7-0	2-1	0-6		0-1	0-2	1-2	1-2	3-1	2-1	5-0
9	Pinxton	2-5	3-3	5-0	0-4	6-1	5-2	3-4	1-3		1-1	0-6	0-2	0-2	0-0	5-3
10	Selston	4-0	2-4	4-1	2-2	5-0	6-0	2-1	3-1	1-0		3-0	2-1	1-0	1-4	3-0
11	Sherwood Colliery	1-2	3-1	9-3	2-1	13-0	2-1	3-0	0-1	0-1	0-1		2-0	2-0	4-0	5-1
12	South Normanton	3-2	0-1	3-1	2-3	5-2	1-0	2-2	6-5	3-2	0-1	4-4		1-2	2-0	1-4
13	Southwell City	4-2	1-1	7-1	1-2	3-2	0-4	1-1	3-1	1-2	0-5	3-1	1-4		0-1	4-2
14	Swanwick Pentrich Road	1-3	3-3	0-0	3-0	4-0	7-1	2-0	2-0	5-0	2-1	1-2	3-0	3-3		9-0
15	Teversal Res	2-3	3-4	0-0	0-5	2-1	2-1	3-5	1-3	0-0	1-7	0-1	2-4	1-1	1-1	

LEAGUE CHALLENGE CUP

Teversal Res	v	FC Bolsover	2-5
Hucknall Town	v	Linby Colliery	2-1 aet
South Normanton	v	Eastwood Community	3-4

SEMI-FINALS

Sherwood Colliery	v	Selston	1-2
FC Bolsover	v	Hucknall Town	0-4

QUARTER-FINALS

Matlock Town Res	v	Sherwood Colliery	0-2
Selston	v	Dronfield Town Res	4-1
Swanwick Pentrich Road	v	FC Bolsover	2-3 aet
Hucknall Town	v	Eastwood Community	2-0

FINAL

Selston	v	Hucknall Town	2-0

Central Midlands Division North

AFC BENTLEY	Bentley MW, 105 The Avenue, Bentley, Doncaster, Sth Yorks DN5 0PN	01302 874 420
APPLEBY FRODINGHAM	Brumby Hall Sports Ground, Ashby Road, Scunthorpe, DN16 1AA	01724 402134
ASKERN	Welfare Sports Ground, Manor Way, Doncaster Road, Askern, DN6 0AJ	
BRODSWORTH WELFARE	Welfare Ground, Woodlands, Nr. Doncaster, DN6 7PP	01302 728 380
CLAY CROSS TOWN	The 'I WANT PET FOODS' Ground, Clay Cross, Chesterfield, Derbyshire S45 9QF	07542 715 705
COLLINGHAM	Collingham FC, Station Road, Collingham, Newark, Notts NG23 7RA	01636 892 303
DINNINGTON TOWN	Phoenix Park, 131 Laughton Road, Dinnington, Nr Sheffield S25 2PP	07854 722 465
DRONFIELD TOWN RESERVES	The H E Barnes Stadium, Stonelow Road, Dronfield S18 2EU	
HARWORTH COLLIERY	Recreation Ground, Scrooby Road, Bircotes, Doncaster DN11 8JT	01302 750614
LINCOLN MOORLANDS RAILWAY	Moorland Sports Ground, Newark Road, Lincoln LN6 8RT	01522 874 111
NEWARK TOWN	Collingham FC, Station Road, Collingham NG23 7RA	01636 892303
PHOENIX	Phoenix Sports Complex, Bawtry Road, Brinsworth, Rotherham S60 5PA	01709 363 788
RENISHAW RANGERS	Hard Lane Kiveton	
RETFORD	Babworth Road, Retford	
STAVELEY M.W. RES	Inkersall Road, Staveley, Chesterfield, S43 3JL	01246 471 441
THORNE COLLIERY	Moorends Welfare, Grange Road, Moorends, Thorne, Doncaster DN8 4LU	07855 545221
TIDESWELL UNITED	Tideswell Sports Complex, St Johns Road, Tideswell SK1 8NZ	
WELBECK LIONS	Elkesley Road, Meden Vale, Mansfield, Nottinghamshire NG20 9P	

CLUB MOVEMENTS - NORTH In: In: Brodsworth Welfare (P - Doncaster Senior), Lincoln Moorlands Railway (P - Lincolnshire League), Renishaw Rangers (Sheffield & Hallamshire Senior), Staveley Miners Welfare Res (P - CMFL Reserve Division). **Out:** Bilsthorpe (S - Notts Senior). FC Bolsover - (P - Northern Counties East). **SOUTH In:** AFC Kilburn (Midlands Regional Alliance), Aslockton & Orston - formerley Aslockton Cranmers (Notts Senior), Greenwood Meadows (R - East Midlands Co), Hilton Harriers (Staffordshire County Senior). **Out:** Selston (P - East Midlands Counties), Southwell City (Notts Senior).

Central Midlands Division South

AFC KILBURN	Kilburn Welfare, Chapel Street DE56 0NR	
ASLOCKTON & ORSTON	Orston Recreation Ground, Spa Lane NG13 9PL	
BLIDWORTH WELFARE	Blidworth Welfare Miners SC, Mansfield Road, Blidworth, Mansfield NG21 0LR	01623 793 361
EASTWOOD COMMUNITY	Corination Park, Chewton Street, Eastwood NG16 3HB	
GREENWOOD MEADOWS	Lenton Lane Ground, Lenton Lane, Nr Clifton Bridge, Nottingham NG7 2SA	07740 797 261
HILTON HARRIERS	The Mease, Hilton, Derbyshire, DE65 5LS	
HOLBROOK ST MICHAELS	Holbrook Park, Mackney Road, Holbrook, Belper, Derbyshire DE56 0T	
HUCKNALL TOWN AFC	Watnall Road, Hucknall, Nottingham, Nottinghamshire NG15 6E	
KEYWORTH UNITED	Platt Lane Sports Complex, Keyworth NG12 5GE	
LINBY COLLIERY WELFARE	Linby Colliery Welfare Ground, Church Lane, Linby, Nottinghamshire NG15 8A	
MATLOCK TOWN RESERVES	DCJ Group Insurance Arena, Causeway Lane, Matlock, Derbyshire DE4 3AR	
MICKLEOVER RBL	Mickleover RBL, Poppyfields Drive, Mickleover, Derby DE3 9GQ	01332 513 548
PINXTON	Van Elle Welfare Arena, Wharf Road, Pinxton NG16 6LG	01773 810 650
SHERWOOD COLLIERY	Debdale Lane, Mansfield Woodhouse, Mansfield, Nottinghamshire NG19 7N	01623 631 747
SOUTH NORMANTON	M J Robinson Structures Arena, Lees Lane, South Normanton, Derbyshire DE55 2AD	07834 206 253
SWANWICK PENTRICH ROAD	Highfield Road, Swanwick, Alfreton, Derbyshire DE55 1BW	
TEVERSAL RESERVES	Teversal Grange Spts and So.Centre, Carnarvon St, Teversal, NG17 3HJ	

CHESHIRE LEAGUE

Sponsored by: Hallmark Security
Founded: 1919
Recent Champions:
2014: Garswood United
2015: Linotype Cheadle HN
2016: Knutsford

PREMIER DIVISION	P	W	D	L	F	A	GD	Pts
1 Whaley Bridge	30	23	0	7	68	36	32	69
2 Poynton	30	20	4	6	85	44	41	64
3 Denton Town	30	19	3	8	74	33	41	60
4 Knutsford	30	15	7	8	67	38	29	52
5 Linotype Cheadle HN	30	16	4	10	57	41	16	52
6 Altrincham Res	30	14	8	8	67	42	25	50
7 Wythenshawe Town	30	14	8	8	61	41	20	50
8 Congleton Vale	30	15	5	10	57	38	19	50
9 Crewe	30	10	5	15	54	58	-4	35
10 Rylands	30	9	8	13	51	62	-11	35
11 Eagle Sports	30	10	5	15	41	65	-24	35
12 Greenalls Padgate St Oswalds	30	8	7	15	38	58	-20	31
13 Malpas	30	8	4	18	53	80	-27	28
14 Rudheath Social	30	8	3	19	58	82	-24	27
15 Styal	30	6	6	18	28	65	-37	24
16 Garswood United	30	5	3	22	22	98	-76	18

DIVISION ONE	P	W	D	L	F	A	GD	Pts
1 Billinge	30	23	3	4	87	36	51	72
2 Warrington Town Res	30	22	5	3	89	36	53	71
3 Pilkington	30	20	1	9	93	54	39	61
4 AFC Macclesfield	30	19	4	7	80	47	33	61
5 FC St Helens	30	14	9	7	59	51	8	51
6 West Didsbury & Chorlton Res	30	14	7	9	66	65	1	49
7 Mersey Valley	30	14	3	13	63	70	-7	45
8 Middlewich Town	30	11	8	11	73	59	14	41
9 Lostock Gralam	30	12	5	13	78	75	3	41
10 Daten	30	11	7	12	56	58	-2	40
11 Egerton	30	11	2	17	71	90	-19	35
12 Golborne Sports	30	9	6	15	63	80	-17	33
13 Halebank	30	9	3	18	58	88	-30	30
14 Cheadle Town Res	30	7	1	22	61	93	-32	22
15 Tarporley Victoria	30	4	4	22	47	82	-35	16
16 Grappenhall Sports	30	4	4	22	42	102	-60	13*

PREMIER DIVISION CHALLENGE CUP

HOLDERS: WHALEY BRIDGE
ROUND 1

Linotype Cheadle HN	v	Poynton	3-3, 4-5p
Eagle Sports	v	Rylands	0-3
Rudheath Social	v	Greenalls Padgate St Oswalds	5-1
Denton Town	v	Malpas	3-0
Altrincham Res	v	Whaley Bridge	0-4
Styal	v	Wythenshawe Town	1-2
Garswood United	v	Knutsford	1-4
Crewe	v	Congleton Vale	1-2

QUARTER-FINALS

Poynton	v	Rylands	2-0
Rudheath Social	v	Denton Town	5-3
Whaley Bridge	v	Wythenshawe Town	2-0
Knutsford	v	Congleton Vale	0-2

SEMI-FINALS

Poynton	v	Rudheath Social	4-1
Whaley Bridge	v	Congleton Vale	2-0

FINAL

Poynton	v	Whaley Bridge	1-3

MEMORIAL CUP

FINAL   **HOLDERS:** LINOTYPE CHEADLE HN

Knutsford	v	Whaley Bridge	6-0

DIVISION ONE & TWO CHALLENGE CUP

FINAL

Cheadle Town Res	v	Warrington Town Res	0-2

DIVISION TWO	P	W	D	L	F	A	GD	Pts
1 Windle Labour	22	16	4	2	61	31	30	52
2 Deva Christleton	22	13	4	5	54	23	31	43
3 Winstanley Warriors	22	11	5	6	56	52	4	38
4 Ford Motors	22	11	4	7	61	36	25	37
5 Orford	22	11	4	7	43	46	-3	37
6 Broadheath Central	22	9	4	9	54	44	10	31
7 Unicorn Athletic	22	8	5	9	53	47	6	29
8 Cuddington	22	7	4	11	47	61	-14	25
9 Maine Road Res	22	7	2	13	45	52	-7	23
10 Moore United	22	6	3	13	37	58	-21	21
11 Barnton Res	22	4	7	11	36	61	-25	19
12 Sandbach United Res	22	3	6	13	34	70	-36	15

In: Blacon Youth Club (P - Chester & Wirral), Buxton Res (N), St Helens Town Res (N), Vulcan FC (P - Warrington & District).

	PREMIER DIVISION	1	2	3	4	5	6	7	8	9	10	11	12	13	14	15	16
1	Altrincham FC Res		3-0	1-1	2-3	0-1	4-2	4-0	2-2	2-2	3-3	2-0	6-0	3-0	5-0	2-0	1-1
2	Congleton Vale	3-0		1-0	1-2	5-0	3-1	1-4	2-2	4-0	6-1	2-0	3-2	3-0	1-0	0-1	0-4
3	Crewe	2-4	0-2		3-6	2-2	1-0	4-1	2-4	2-1	5-0	2-2	3-5	1-1	1-0	1-2	1-0
4	Denton Town	2-0	1-3	2-2		2-1	4-0	0-0	1-2	1-0	11-0	1-3	6-0	4-1	1-1	2-1	1-2
5	Eagle Sports	1-3	0-5	1-4		0-1	4-2	0-0	0-2	2-0	0-6	3-1	2-3	1-1	0-2	4-2	
6	Garswood United	0-4	0-0	3-2	0-2	2-6		1-2	0-8	0-2	2-1	0-4	0-3	1-4	1-1	0-1	1-1
7	Greenalls Padgate St Oswalds	2-0	2-2	2-1	0-1	1-3	0-2		2-2	3-0	2-4	0-3	2-1	1-1	2-2	1-2	1-2
8	Knutsford	1-1	3-1	0-3	0-2	0-1	4-0	2-1		1-2	3-1	2-1	5-1	2-2	3-0	6-0	1-4
9	Linotype Cheadle HN	4-0	1-0	3-1	1-2	4-0	1-0	0-0	0-2		1-0	3-5	4-0	2-0	4-1	2-1	2-2
10	Malpas	0-2	3-0	0-2	1-0	6-1	9-1	1-2	0-4	1-1		4-3	2-3	1-1	1-3	1-6	2-3
11	Poynton	2-2	3-2	6-4	3-1	2-1	1-0	6-0	1-0	4-1	2-1		3-1	2-2	4-1	4-2	1-4
12	Rudheath Social	2-4	1-2	1-3	0-6	1-1	16-0	1-2	0-4	0-4	5-4	1-1		2-3	2-3	1-4	2-0
13	Rylands	1-1	1-3	2-3	3-0	1-1	2-0	1-1	2-2	2-5	1-3	1-6	1-3		10-0	1-0	0-4
14	Styal	1-3	1-1	2-1	0-2	2-0	0-1	3-2	1-1	0-3	1-2	0-2	0-1	3-0		0-1	0-2
15	Whaley Bridge	2-1	1-0	3-1	2-1	3-0	9-2	3-0	4-1	1-0	3-0	3-2	2-1	2-3	2-1		3-1
16	Wythenshawe Town	4-2	1-1	1-0	0-3	2-4	3-1	0-0	2-0	6-2	1-1	1-3	1-1	5-0	1-2		

Cheshire League Premier Division		
ALTRINCHAM RESERVES	Egerton Youth Club FC, Egerton Youth Club, Mereheath Lane, Knutsford WA16 6SL	
ASHTON TOWN	The Ashton Town Stadium, Edge Green St, Ashton-in-Makerfield, Wigan, WN4 8SL	01942 724 448
BILLINGE	Billinge Comm. Spts/Soccer Cte , Carrmill Road , Billinge WN5 7TX	01744 893 533
CONGLETON VALE	Congleton High School, Box Lane, Congleton, Cheshire CW12 4NS	
CREWE	Cumberland Arena, Thomas Street, Crewe CW1 2BD	
DENTON TOWN	Whittles Park, Heather Lea, Denton M34 6EJ	
EAGLE SPORTS	Eagle Sports Club, Thornton Road, Great Sankey, Warrington WA5 2SZ	
GREENALLS PADGATE ST OS'WLD	Carlsberg Tetley Social Club, Long Lane, Warrington WA2 8PU	
KNUTSFORD	Manchester Road, Knutsford WA16 0NT	
LINOTYPE & CHEADLE HN	The Heath, Norbreck Avenue, Cheadle, Stockport SK8 2ET	
MALPAS	Malpas & District Sports Club, Wrexham Road, Malpas, Cheshire SY14 7EJ	
POYNTON	Poynton Sports Club, London Road North, Poynton, Cheshire SK12 1AG	
RUDHEATH SOCIAL	Lostock Gralam FC, Park Stad, Manchester Rd, Lostock Gralam, Northwich CW9 7PJ	
RYLANDS	Rylands Recreation Club, Gorsey Lane, Warrington WA2 7RZ	
WARRINGTON TOWN RES		
WHALEY BRIDGE	Horwich Park, Park Road, Whaley Bridge, High Peak SK23 7DJ	
WYTHENSHAWE TOWN	Ericstan Park, Timpson Road, Wythenshawe M23 9LL	0161 998 5076

In: Ashton Town (R - North West Counties).

DORSET PREMIER LEAGUE

Sponsored by: BeSpoke Teamwear
Founded: 1957
Recent Champions: 2014: Portland United
2015: Hamorthy Recreation **2016:** Shaftesbury Town

		P	W	D	L	F	A	GD	Pts
1	Holt United	32	26	1	5	99	31	68	79
2	Balti Sports	32	22	4	6	104	49	55	70
3	Hamworthy Recreation	32	23	3	6	107	38	69	69*
4	Merley Cobham Sports	32	21	4	7	98	50	48	67
5	Westland Sports	32	20	5	7	104	46	58	65
6	Swanage Town & Herston	32	19	6	7	104	47	57	63
7	Dorchester Sports	32	18	5	9	86	69	17	59
8	Gillingham Town Res	32	16	6	10	77	54	23	54
9	Parley Sports	32	15	6	11	63	50	13	51
10	Blandford United	32	12	3	17	62	85	-23	39
11	Wareham Rangers	32	9	5	18	55	89	-34	32
12	Mere Town	32	8	6	18	53	87	-34	30
13	Sturminster Newton	32	9	2	21	45	84	-39	29
14	Bridport Res	32	7	7	18	52	82	-30	28
15	Hamworthy United Res	32	5	5	22	45	97	-52	20
16	Sherborne Town Res	32	3	5	24	37	102	-65	14
17	Cranborne	32	2	1	29	35	166	-131	7

In: Gillingham Town take their Reserve team's place. Milburn Sports and Shaftesbury Res (P - Dorset Football Lge). **Out:** Cranborne (R).

LEAGUE CUP

HOLDERS: MERLEY COBHAM SPORTS
ROUND 1
Sherborne Town Res	v	Gillingham Town Res		0-3

ROUND 2
Parley Sports	v	Balti Sports		2-1
Bridport Res	v	Swanage Town & Herston		3-6 aet
Hamworthy Recreation	v	Mere Town		4-5
Holt United	v	Dorchester Sports		4-0
Hamworthy United Res	v	Gillingham Town Res		1-2
Blandford United	v	Sturminster Newton		2-4
Westland Sports	v	Merley Cobham Sports		1-5
Wareham Rangers	v	Cranborne		10-0

QUARTER-FINALS
Parley Sports	v	Swanage Town & Herston		2-3
Mere Town	v	Holt United		1-2
Gillingham Town Res	v	Sturminster Newton		4-0
Merley Cobham Sports	v	Wareham Rangers		3-3, 5-4p

SEMI-FINALS
Swanage Town & Herston	v	Holt United		2-0
Gillingham Town Res	v	Merley Cobham Sports		2-1 aet

FINAL
Gillingham Town Res	v	Swanage Town & Herston		0-2

PREMIER DIVISION

		1	2	3	4	5	6	7	8	9	10	11	12	13	14	15	16	17
1	Balti Sports		1-4	5-0	4-2	6-1	4-2	2-1	8-2	0-1	5-2	5-1	3-1	5-2	2-1	4-1	5-1	1-5
2	Blandford United	2-4		4-4	4-1	2-4	2-3	0-10	2-3	1-3	4-1	0-2	1-2	5-1	2-1	3-1	1-4	1-4
3	Bridport Res	0-2	2-2		5-2	3-0	2-3	1-3	2-2	0-1	2-2	1-4	0-0	6-5	0-1	1-3	3-2	3-3
4	Cranborne	2-10	0-5	2-4		2-11	1-9	0-6	0-3	0-9	3-4	0-2	1-2	3-2	3-1	1-4	2-6	1-3
5	Dorchester Sports	3-0	0-1	2-0	7-0		4-3	3-2	4-3	0-3	3-2	0-5	3-2	0-0	4-2	2-2	6-1	4-1
6	Gillingham Town Reserves	0-1	6-0	2-2	3-2	0-1		1-1	5-1	1-3	1-1	3-3	2-1	2-1	5-1	2-0	5-2	2-5
7	Hamworthy Recreation	3-2	1-3	5-0	7-1	3-3	4-1		3-2	2-0	7-0	2-1	1-0	9-1	7-1	4-3	6-0	1-0
8	Hamworthy United Res	1-1	0-3	5-0	5-2	2-2	0-1	0-3		0-3	0-1	0-4	0-2	1-1	2-2	0-6	1-6	0-4
9	Holt United	4-0	3-0	2-1	3-0	2-1	2-1	1-3	5-1		2-1	2-3	7-0	8-1	4-2	1-2	2-0	4-6
10	Mere Town	1-1	0-2	2-3	1-1	3-4	1-1	1-3	4-2	0-3		2-2	3-2	2-1	2-4	2-5	0-1	
11	Merley Cobham Sports	2-3	3-0	2-0	8-1	7-1	4-2	2-1	4-1	2-3	6-5		1-1	4-0	2-1	1-2	9-2	1-0
12	Parley Sports	0-0	6-3	5-2	2-0	1-2	2-0	2-0	3-1	0-3	3-1	2-3		3-2	1-2	2-2	4-1	5-2
13	Sherborne Town Res	1-2	3-1	0-3	3-1	4-2	0-2	1-1	0-4	0-3	0-1	2-4	0-3		0-1	1-11	1-1	0-3
14	Sturminster Newton	0-4	0-1	4-2	5-1	1-3	0-2	0-2	3-2	1-3	2-0	1-3	2-1	3-2		0-4	1-3	1-3
15	Swanage Town & Herston	2-4	6-0	2-0	6-0	5-3	1-1	4-2	5-0	0-3	6-2	4-2	1-1	6-0	6-0		1-1	1-3
16	Wareham Rangers	0-9	2-2	2-0	2-0	0-1	1-3	1-2	3-0	0-4	1-4	0-0	0-3	2-1	3-3	0-2		2-3
17	Westland Sports	1-1	4-1	3-0	20-0	1-3	1-3	1-2	5-1	2-2	6-0	3-1	2-1	3-1	5-1	1-1	3-1	

Dorset Premier League

BALTI SPORTS	Weymouth Collage, Cranford Avenue, Weymouth, Dorset DT4 7LA	01305 761 100
BLANDFORD UNITED	Blandford Recreation Ground, Park Road, Blandford Forum DT11 7BX	07932 414 524
BRIDPORT RESERVES	St Marys Field, Skilling Hill Road, Bridport DT6 5LA	01308 423 834
DORCHESTER SPORTS	The Avenue Stadium, Weymouth Avenue, Dorchester, Dorset DT1 2RY	01305 262 451
GILLINGHAM TOWN	Hardings Lane, Gillingham, Dorset SP8 4HX	01747 823 673
HAMWORTHY RECREATION	Hamworthy Rec. Club, Magna Road, Canford Magna, Wimborne BH21 3AE	01202 881 922
HAMWORTHY UNITED RESERVES	The County Ground, Blandford Close, Hamworthy, Poole BH15 4BF	01202 674 974
HOLT UNITED	Petersham Lane, Gaunts Common, Holt, Wimborne BH21 4JR	01258 840 379
MERE TOWN	Mere Recreation Ground, Queens Road, Mere BA12 6EW	07725 031 587
MERLEY COBHAM SPORTS	Cobham Sports & Social Club, Merley House Lane, Wimborne BH21 3AA	01202 885 773
MILBORNE PORT	Memorial Playing Field, Springfield Road, Milborne Port, Sherborne DT9 5RE	
PARLEY SPORTS	Parley Sports Club, Christchurch Road, West Parley BH22 8SQ	01202 573 345
SHAFTESBURY TOWN RES	Cockrams, Coppice Street, Shaftesbury SP7 8PF	07917 652 438
SHERBORNE TOWN RESERVES	Raleigh Grove, The Terrace Playing Fields, Sherborne DT9 5NS	01935 816 110
STURMINSTER NEWTON	Barnetts Field, Honeymead Lane, Sturminster Newton, Dorset DT10 1EW	01258 471 406
SWANAGE TOWN & HERSTON	Day's Park, off De Moulham Road, Swanage BH19 2JW	01929 424 673
WAREHAM RANGERS	Purbeck Sports Centre, Worgret Road, Wareham, Dorset BH20 4PH	01929 556 454
WESTLAND SPORTS	Alvington Development Centre, Alvington Lane, Yeovil, BA22 8UX	07977 102799

ESSEX & SUFFOLK BORDER LEAGUE

Sponsored by: Andreas Carter
Founded: 1911
Recent Champions: 2014: Gas Recreation. **2015:** West Bergholt. **2016:** Coggeshall Town.

PREMIER DIVISION	P	W	D	L	F	A	GD	Pts
1 Little Oakley	24	20	2	2	75	16	59	62
2 Gas Recreation	24	19	1	4	90	27	63	58
3 West Bergholt	24	16	4	4	75	43	32	52
4 Alresford Colne Rangers	24	15	1	8	64	43	21	46
5 Coggeshall Town Res	24	13	3	8	51	31	20	42
6 Harwich & Parkeston	24	10	3	11	52	38	14	33
7 White Notley	24	10	2	12	47	55	-8	32
8 Weeley Athletic	24	9	3	12	47	55	-8	30
9 Hatfield Peverel	24	9	3	12	51	60	-9	30
10 Brantham Athletic Res	24	7	4	13	40	61	-21	25
11 Earls Colne	24	7	3	14	48	69	-21	24
12 Holland Res	24	3	2	19	20	96	-76	11
13 Barnston	24	1	3	20	23	89	-66	6

Cinque Port withdrew - record expunged.
Ipswich Wanderers Reserves - withdrew - record expunged.
Tollesbury withdrew - record expunged.
University of Essex withdrew - record expunged.

DIVISION ONE	P	W	D	L	F	A	GD	Pts
1 Dedham Old Boys	24	17	2	5	70	37	33	53
2 Wormingford Wanderers	24	16	3	5	71	40	31	51
3 Hedinghams United	24	15	5	4	55	33	22	50
4 Kelvedon Social	24	14	5	5	54	36	18	47
5 Cressing United	24	11	7	6	66	34	32	40
6 Little Oakley Res	24	11	7	6	58	44	14	40
7 Gas Recreation Res	24	12	3	9	55	40	15	39
8 Tiptree Jobserve	24	10	2	12	45	55	-10	32
9 Alresford Colne Rangers Res	24	8	1	15	33	59	-26	25
10 Boxted Lodgers	24	6	4	14	40	57	-17	22
11 FC Clacton Res	24	6	2	16	41	71	-30	20
12 West Bergholt Res	24	5	3	16	52	76	-24	18
13 Lawford Lads	24	1	4	19	26	84	-58	7

University of Essex Res withdrew - record expunged.

DIVISION TWO	P	W	D	L	F	A	GD	Pts
1 Great Bentley	20	17	1	2	110	20	90	52
2 Tiptree Park	20	17	1	2	96	13	83	52
3 Little Oakley A	20	15	1	4	44	22	22	46
4 Brightlingsea Regent A	20	10	3	7	68	31	37	33
5 Bradfield Rovers	20	10	2	8	58	46	12	32
6 Hatfield Peverel Res	20	10	2	8	58	49	9	32
7 Mersea Island	20	10	2	8	50	63	-13	32
8 Boxted Lodgers Res	20	6	1	13	44	68	-24	19
9 Brantham Athletic 'A'	20	4	3	13	30	81	-51	15
10 Lawford Lads Res	20	1	2	17	16	93	-77	5
11 Kelvedon Social Res	20	1	0	19	16	104	-88	3

Colchester Athletic withdrew - record expunged.
Earls Colne Res withdrew - record expunged.

DIVISION THREE	P	W	D	L	F	A	GD	Pts
1 Flitch United	22	18	2	2	84	18	66	56
2 Connaught Red Star	22	18	1	3	89	26	63	55
3 Tiptree Heath	22	16	2	4	109	33	76	50
4 Bures United	22	14	3	5	67	20	47	45
5 Belle Vue Social Club	22	13	2	7	87	40	47	41
6 Colne Engaine	22	11	2	9	81	59	22	35
7 Holland A	22	10	2	10	51	56	-5	32
8 Weeley Athletic Res	22	8	0	14	46	95	-49	24
9 Great Bentley Res	22	5	4	13	46	71	-25	19
10 Dedham Old Boys Res	22	5	4	13	31	58	-27	19
11 Barnston Res	22	1	3	18	17	98	-81	6
12 Bradfield Rovers Res	22	0	1	21	22	156	-134	1

CLUB MOVEMENTS
PREMIER DIVISION - In: Little Oakley Res (P).
Out: Holland Res (R), Little Oakley (P - Eastern Counties),
Holland FC (P - Eastern Counties), Lawford Lads (R).

DIVISION ONE - In: Holland Res (R).

DIVISION THREE - In: Colne Athletic, Hedinghams Res,
New Field, Oyster, Tollesbury Res and Wormingford Wanderers
Res (P - Colchester & East Essex), Ramsey Mill, Rowhedge,
Tiptree Jobserve Res.

PREMIER DIVISION		1	2	3	4	5	6	7	8	9	10	11	12	13
1	Alresford Colne Rangers		9-3	4-2	0-5	4-2	3-2	2-1	3-1	1-1	0-2	1-4	4-1	1-0
2	Barnston	0-5		2-4	1-2	0-12	0-8	0-0	1-3	3-1	0-2	0-2	1-5	1-4
3	Brantham Athletic F.C. Res	1-0	H-W		2-2	1-3	1-3	0-1	1-4	5-1	0-3	1-2	3-3	1-0
4	Coggeshall Town Res	1-0	3-2	3-1		5-1	A-W	4-1	1-2	A-W	1-0	0-0	3-3	1-3
5	Earls Colne	2-7	0-0	2-2	0-3		2-6	0-4	1-4	2-0	2-4	4-3	1-6	2-3
6	Gas Recreation	3-0	4-0	4-0	1-0	3-1		4-1	4-3	9-0	4-2	5-0	2-5	0-1
7	Harwich & Parkeston	1-3	H-W	2-3	1-3	7-1	0-2		4-0	7-0	0-2	1-2	3-3	3-0
8	Hatfield Peverel	1-7	1-1	7-1	2-1	1-3	2-3	4-4		H-W	0-2	5-1	1-5	4-2
9	Holland Res	2-3	3-0	1-6	1-2	0-3	1-9	0-4	2-1		0-8	0-1	2-4	1-1
10	Little Oakley	2-1	4-1	2-1	2-0	1-1	3-1	1-0	4-0	9-0		2-1	3-2	9-0
11	Weeley Athletic	2-3	6-0	2-2	1-2	2-0	1-8	2-0	1-1	7-2	0-3		2-3	1-4
12	West Bergholt	3-1	4-0	2-0	5-3	2-1	1-1	1-3	4-1	2-0	0-4	3-2		3-2
13	White Notley	1-2	5-1	2-0	0-4	1-2	0-4	1-4	4-3	7-0	1-1	5-2	0-5	

LEAGUE CUP

HOLDERS: COGGESHALL TOWN

ROUND 1

FC Clacton Res	v	University of Essex	2-3
Bures United	v	Tollesbury	HW
Cinque Port	v	Tiptree Heath	3-4
Belle Vue Social Club	v	Hedinghams United	2-4
Holland Res	v	Earls Colne	0-1
Coggeshall Town Res	v	Cressing United	5-2

ROUND 2

Bradfield Rovers	v	University of Essex	1-0
Brantham Athletic Res	v	Bures United	3-3, 3-4p
Hatfield Peverel	v	Colne Engaine	3-1
Deham Old Boys	v	Tiptree Heath	1-2
Barnston	v	Brightlingsea Regent A	1-5
Kelvedon Social	v	Lawford Lads	0-1
Tiptree Jobserve	v	Wormingford Wanderers	0-4
Mersea Island	v	Weeley Athletic	1-1, 3-0p
Little Oakley	v	Colchester Athletic	6-0
Great Bentley	v	West Bergholt	3-0
Hedinghams United	v	Flitch United	3-4
Earls Colne	v	Tiptree Park	2-2, 4-3p
Boxted Lodgers	v	Coggeshall Town Res	0-3
Gas Recreation	v	White Notley	4-2
Alresford Colne Rangers	v	Ipswich Wanderers Res	HW
Connaught Red Star	v	Harwich & Parkeston	0-3

ROUND 3

Bradfield Rovers	v	Bures United	0-0, 3-4p
Hatfield Peverel	v	Tiptree Heath	3-1
Brightlingsea Regent A	v	Lawford Lads	9-1
Wormingford Wanderers	v	Mersea Island	4-0
Little Oakley	v	Great Bentley	3-2 aet
Flitch United	v	Earls Colne	2-2, 3-5p
Coggeshall Town Res	v	Gas Recreation	7-4
Alresford Colne Rangers	v	Harwich & Parkeston	3-2

QUARTER-FINALS

Bures United	v	Hatfield Peverel	1-5
Brightlingsea Regent A	v	Wormingford Wanderers	0-3
Little Oakley	v	Earls Colne	3-0
Coggeshall Town Res	v	Alresford Colne Rangers	2-1

SEMI-FINALS

Hatfield Peverel	v	Wormingford Wanderers	1-0 aet
Little Oakley	v	Coggeshall Town Res	4-2 aet

FINAL

Hatfield Peverel	v	Little Oakley	1-2

TOMMY THOMPSON CUP

QUARTER-FINALS

Connaught Red Star	v	Dedham Old Boys Res	3-0
Colne Engaine	v	Tiptree Heath	6-4
Belle Vue Social Club	v	Great Bentley	5-0
Tiptree Park	v	Little Oakley A	4-2

SEMI-FINALS

Connaught Red Star	v	Colne Engaine	2-0
Belle Vue Social Club	v	Tiptree Park	1-5

FINAL

Connaught Red Star	v	Tiptree Park	0-1

RESERVE CUP

QUARTER-FINALS

University of Essex Res	v	Little Oakley Res	AW
Bradfield Rovers Res	v	Barnston Res	0-3
Holland A	v	Gas Recreation Res	7-2
Boxted Lodgers Res	v	Alresford Colne Rangers Res	2-8

SEMI-FINALS

Little Oakley Res	v	Barnston Res	4-1
Holland A	v	Alresford Colne Rangers Res	HW

FINAL

Little Oakley Res	v	Holland A	0-0, 4-5p

Essex & Suffolk Border League Premier Division

ALRESFORD COLNE RANGERS	Ford Lane, Alresford, Colchester CO7 8AU	07896 54 122
BARNSTON	High Easter Road, Barnston, Dunmow CM6 1LZ	07712 129 459
BRANTHAM ATHLETIC RES.	Brantham Leisure Centre, New Village, Brantham CO11 1RZ	01206 392 506
COGGESHALL TOWN RESERVES	West Street, Coggeshall, Essex CO6 1NT	01376 562 843
DEDHAM OLD BOYS	Southfields, The Drift, Dedham CO7 6AH	07713 579 821
EARLS COLNE	Green Farm Meadow, Halstead Road, Earls Colne, Colchester CO6 2NG	01787 223 584
GAS RECREATION	Bromley Road, Colchester CO4 3JE	07557 358 886
HARWICH & PARKESTON	Royal Oak, Main Road, Dovercourt, Harwich CO12 4AA	01255 503 643
HATFIELD PEVEREL	The Keith Bigden Memorial Ground, Wickham Bishops Rd, Hatfield Peverel CM3 2JL	07799 146 518
HEDINGHAMS UNITED	Lawn Meadow, Yeldham Road, Sible Hedingham, Halstead, Essex CO9 3QJ	07970 721 309
KELVEDON SOCIAL	The Chase, Kelvedon, Essex CO5 9AB	01376 516 593
LITTLE OAKLEY RESERVES	War Memorial Club Ground, Harwich Road, Little Oakley, Harwich CO12 5ED	01255 880 370
WEELEY ATHLETIC	Vista Road Recreation Ground, Clacton on Sea, Essex CO15 6DB	07815 422 294
WEST BERGHOLT	Lorkin Daniel Field, Lexden Road, West Bergholt, Colchester CO6 3BW	01206 241 525
WHITE NOTLEY	Oak Farm, Faulkbourne, Witham CM8 1SF	01376 519 864
WORMINGFORD WANDERERS	Wormingford, Playing Field, Robletts Ways, Wormingford, Colchester, Essex CO6 3AX	01206 543 934

ESSEX OLYMPIAN LEAGUE

Sponsored by: ProKit UK
Founded: 1966
Recent Champions:
2014: Southminster St. Leonards
2015: Harold Wood Athletic
2016: Kelvedon Hatch

	PREMIER DIVISION	P	W	D	L	F	A	GD	Pts
1	Springfield	26	18	4	4	67	35	32	58
2	Hannakins Farm	26	16	4	6	55	36	19	52
3	May & Baker E.C.	26	13	7	6	66	51	15	46
4	Manford Way	26	13	5	8	48	41	7	44
5	Frenford Senior	26	11	10	5	58	42	16	43
6	Harold Wood Athletic	26	12	4	10	47	46	1	40
7	Kelvedon Hatch	26	9	12	5	47	32	15	39
8	Bishops Stortford Swifts	26	10	3	13	52	61	-9	36*
9	Leigh Ramblers	26	8	6	12	53	54	-1	30
10	Rayleigh Town	26	8	8	10	50	48	2	29*
11	Canning Town	26	6	8	12	57	66	-9	26
12	White Ensign	26	6	5	15	40	63	-23	23
13	Buckhurst Hill	26	4	6	16	37	61	-24	18
14	Harold Hill	26	4	6	16	40	81	-41	18

SENIOR CUP

HOLDERS: KELVDON HATCH

ROUND 1

Ramsden Scotia	v	Epping	1-2
Snaresbrook	v	FC Hamlets	0-3
Basildon Town	v	Rochford Town	2-1
Benfleet	v	Old Chelmsfordians	2-1
Leytonstone United	v	Hutton	0-2
Toby	v	Great Baddow	1-0
Shenfield AFC	v	Ongar Town	3-1
Westhamians	v	Newbury Forest	2-3
Brentwood Town Res	v	Dagenham United	AW
Sungate	v	Galleywood	1-3
Runwell Sports	v	Debden Sports	3-0
Herongate Athletic	v	Old Barkabbeyans	7-2
London APSA	v	Old Southendian	4-1
Ryan	v	Newham United	5-0
Southend Sports	v	Lakeside	2-3
Roydon	v	Broomfield	2-1
Upminster	v	Catholic United	1-7

ROUND 2

May & Baker E.C.	v	Epping	6-1
Buckhurst Hill	v	FC Hamlets	0-2
Manford Way	v	Basildon Town	0-1

	PREMIER DIVISION	1	2	3	4	5	6	7	8	9	10	11	12	13	14
1	Bishops Stortford Swifts		5-2	1-4	2-6	3-0	2-2	3-1	2-2	3-1	7-2	2-3	0-1	3-2	1-2
2	Buckhurst Hill	2-1		0-2	3-1	0-1	0-2	3-4	1-5	0-2	4-4	3-0	0-0	0-2	5-5
3	Frenford Senior	0-1	0-0		3-0	4-3	3-1	0-2	1-3	1-0	2-1	4-2	1-2	0-3	0-2
4	Hannakins Farm	0-1	3-0	3-4		0-1	1-2	1-1	3-2	0-3	2-0	5-3	1-1	3-2	3-1
5	Harold Hill	2-3	1-2	3-3	3-5		2-0	0-2	1-1	1-0	2-1	0-3	1-0	0-1	1-3
6	Harold Wood Athletic	3-2	6-0	1-0	5-0	2-1		2-0	1-3	0-1	3-0	2-4	1-0	1-2	4-2
7	Kelvedon Hatch	2-0	1-1	2-1	1-0	2-0	3-0		2-3	3-3	1-0	4-0	3-0	1-1	1-2
8	Manford Way	3-1	3-2	0-2	1-1	1-0	0-2	2-3		5-1	4-1	3-2	1-1	3-1	3-2
9	May & Baker E.C.	2-2	2-2	2-1	2-2	3-3	1-1	1-3	1-7		2-2	1-2	2-2	2-3	3-5
10	Newbury Forest	2-5	1-2	0-0	2-3	0-3	0-4	0-4	1-2	2-2		5-1	1-4	2-3	1-3
11	Newham United	2-4	1-4	1-3	1-1	2-0	4-3	1-5	1-5	1-2	1-3		2-5	1-2	3-2
12	Rayleigh Town	1-2	0-2	1-0	0-1	4-0	3-4	1-3	2-3	2-1	5-1	3-1		1-1	2-4
13	Springfield	3-1	0-3	2-1	4-0	5-3	0-3	1-2	4-3	0-1	3-1	4-1	2-0		0-4
14	White Ensign	1-2	4-2	0-1	1-0	1-0	1-2	3-0	0-0	5-0	4-3	3-2	2-2	1-2	

Essex Olympian League Premier Division

BASILDON TOWN	Basildon Leisure Club, Gardiners Lane South, Gardiners Way, Basildon, SS14 3AP	01268 883 128
BISHOP'S STORTFORD SWIFTS	Silver Leys, Hadham Road (A1250), Bishop's Stortford CM23 2QE	07815 718 249
CANNING TOWN	West Ham Foundation, 60A Albastross Close London E6 5NX	020 7511 4477
CATHOLIC UNITED	South East Essex College, Wellstead Gardens, Westcliff-on-Sea SS0 0AY	01702 348 786
FRENFORD	Frenford Clubs, The Drive, Ilford, Essex, IG1 3PS	020 8518 0992
HAROLD WOOD ATHLETIC	Harold Wood Recreation Park, Harold View, Harold Wood RM3 0LX	01708 375 698
KELVEDON HATCH	New Hall, School Road, Kelvedon Hatch, Brentwood CM15 0DH	07950 807 419
LEIGH RAMBLERS	Belfairs Park, Eastwood Road North, Leigh on Sea, Essex SS9 4LR	07732 672 280
MANFORD WAY	London Marathon Sports Ground, Forest Road, Hainault IG6 3HJ	0208 500 3486
MAY & BAKER E.C.	Barking Rugby Club, Gale Street, Dagenham, RM9 4TX	0208 595 7324
RAYLEIGH TOWN	Rayleigh Town Sports/Soc. Club, London Road, Rayleigh SS6 9DT	01268 784 001
SPRINGFIELD	Springfield Hall Park, Arun Close, Springfield CM1 7QE	01245 492 441
WHITE ENSIGN	The Fen Forge Centre, Eastwoodbury Lane, Southend on Sea SS2 6UD	01702 520 482

SENIOR CHALLENGE CUP
(Premier Champions v Senior Cup Holders)

FINAL

Kelvedon Hatch	v	Manford Way	1-0

DIVISION ONE

		P	W	D	L	F	A	GD	Pts
1	Basildon Town	24	21	1	2	90	20	70	64
2	Catholic United	24	19	0	5	74	30	44	57
3	Shenfield A.F.C.	24	11	3	10	53	48	5	38*
4	Great Baddow	24	12	3	9	55	41	14	37*
5	Runwell Sports	24	10	4	10	53	56	-3	34
6	Newbury Forest	24	10	3	11	54	70	-16	33
7	Old Southendian	24	8	7	9	36	41	-5	31
8	Hutton	24	9	4	11	43	55	-12	31
9	Galleywood	24	9	1	14	38	57	-19	31*
10	Snaresbrook	24	9	4	11	49	57	-8	30*
11	Old Chelmsfordians	24	8	4	12	61	63	-2	28
12	London APSA	24	7	1	16	33	59	-26	20*
13	Newham United	24	4	3	17	27	69	-42	6*

DIVISION TWO

		P	W	D	L	F	A	GD	Pts
1	Sungate	22	15	5	2	53	27	26	50
2	FC Hamlets	22	15	4	3	70	27	43	49
3	Benfleet	22	13	3	6	58	36	22	42
4	Toby	22	10	7	5	44	21	23	37
5	Herongate Athletic	22	10	4	8	62	46	16	34
6	Ryan F.C.	22	8	5	9	52	56	-4	28*
7	Ongar Town	22	8	3	11	27	45	-18	27
8	Upminster	22	7	2	13	32	46	-14	25*
9	Lakeside	22	7	5	10	39	53	-14	24*
10	Ramsden Scotia	22	6	5	11	34	46	-12	23
11	Rochford Town	22	5	3	14	42	59	-17	18
12	Old Barkabbeyans	22	3	4	15	29	80	-51	11*

DIVISION THREE

		P	W	D	L	F	A	GD	Pts
1	May & Baker E.C. Res	18	16	1	1	56	13	43	49
2	Rayleigh Town Res	18	9	3	6	46	33	13	33*
3	Shoebury Town	18	11	0	7	55	33	22	30*
4	Hutton Res	18	9	2	7	43	29	14	29
5	Harold Wood Athletic Res	18	6	5	7	32	32	0	23
6	Old Chelmsfordians Res	18	8	2	8	29	24	5	22*
7	Debden Sports	18	6	3	9	26	42	-16	21
8	Frenford Senior Res	18	5	4	9	46	63	-17	19
9	Roydon	18	5	3	10	31	49	-18	18
10	Leytonstone United	18	3	1	14	30	76	-46	10

Brentwood Town Res withdrew - record expunged.

DIVISION FOUR

		P	W	D	L	F	A	GD	Pts
1	Manford Way Res	20	12	3	5	62	27	35	39
2	White Ensign Res	20	11	4	5	59	41	18	37
3	Southend Sports	20	11	3	6	50	34	16	36
4	Old Southendian Res	20	12	5	3	51	31	20	35*
5	Galleywood Res	20	9	3	8	50	54	-4	30
6	Toby Res	20	8	5	7	46	39	7	29
7	Harold Hill Res	20	7	4	9	38	46	-8	25
8	Runwell Sports Res	20	6	5	9	31	38	-7	23
9	Canning Town Res	20	4	6	10	35	62	-27	21*
10	Leigh Ramblers Res	20	2	6	12	32	69	-37	15*
11	Kelvedon Hatch Res	20	4	4	12	28	41	-13	12*

SENIOR CUP continued...

Rayleigh Town	v	Benfleet	3-1
Shoebury Town	v	Hutton	4-1
Toby	v	Shenfield AFC	0-2
Frenford Senior	v	Newbury Forest	4-0
Harold Wood Athletic	v	Dagenham United	12-0
Harold Hill	v	Leigh Ramblers	2-1
Galleywood	v	Bishops Stortford Swifts	0-1
Hannakins Farm	v	Runwell Sports	0-2
Kelvedon Hatch	v	Canning Town	3-1
White Ensign	v	Herongate Athletic	6-1
Springfield	v	London APSA	3-1
Ryan	v	Lakeside	5-1
Roydon	v	Catholic United	0-4

ROUND 3

May & Baker E.C.	v	FC Hamlets	1-2 aet
Basildon Town	v	Rayleigh Town	3-0
Shoebury Town	v	Shenfield AFC	0-4
Frenford Senior	v	Harold Wood Athletic	3-1
Harold Hill	v	Bishops Stortford Swifts	5-3 aet
Runwell Sports	v	Kelvedon Hatch	2-3
White Ensign	v	Springfield	3-3, 4-5p
Ryan	v	Catholic United	0-3

QUARTER-FINALS

FC Hamlets	v	Basildon Town	0-1
Shenfield AFC	v	Frenford Senior	2-2, 4-5p
Harold Hill	v	Kelvedon Hatch	0-2
Springfield	v	Catholic United	1-2

SEMI-FINALS

Basildon Town	v	Frenford Senior	2-2, 4-3p
Kelvedon Hatch	v	Catholic United	1-0

FINAL

Basildon Town	v	Kelvedon Hatch	4-1

DIVISION FIVE

		P	W	D	L	F	A	GD	Pts
1	Basildon Town Res	20	16	4	0	75	24	51	52
2	Sungate Res	20	15	2	3	53	25	28	47
3	Catholic United Res	20	14	1	5	65	31	34	43
4	Shenfield A.F.C. Res	20	13	1	6	65	31	34	41*
5	Southend Sports Res	20	8	5	7	44	42	2	29
6	Dagenham United	20	9	1	10	52	49	3	25*
7	Bishops Stortford Swifts Res	20	8	1	11	49	49	0	21*
8	Springfield Res	20	8	3	9	36	46	-10	17*
9	Newbury Forest Res	20	6	0	14	28	64	-36	14*
10	Herongate Athletic Res	20	3	1	16	29	61	-32	8*
11	Leytonstone United Res	20	0	1	19	17	91	-74	-7*

CLUB MOVEMENTS

Premier Division:
Out: Hannakins Farm (F).
Division One:
Out London APSA (W).
Division Three:
In: Beacon Hill Rovers, Leigh Town, Leytonstone United.
Division Four:
In: Chingford Athletic, Epping.
Out: Harold Hill Res (W).
Division Five:
In: Academy Soccer, Old Barkabbeyans Res, Westhamians.

RESERVE LEAGUE CUP

FINAL

May & Baker E.C. Res	v	Basildon Town Res	0-1

GLOUCESTERSHIRE COUNTY LEAGUE

Sponsored by: Marcliff
Founded: 1968
Recent Champions: 2014: Longlevens
2015: Cheltenham Civil Service
2016: AEK Boco

		P	W	D	L	F	A	GD	Pts
1	Bristol Telephones	32	24	2	6	105	52	53	74
2	Frampton United	32	20	5	7	85	41	44	65
3	Stonehouse Town	32	19	7	6	77	41	36	64
4	Thornbury Town	32	18	5	9	67	43	24	59
5	Kingswood	32	18	3	11	68	51	17	57
6	Rockleaze Rangers	32	17	6	9	58	48	10	54*
7	AEK Boco	32	16	5	11	61	49	12	53
8	Hardwicke	32	16	5	11	70	58	12	52*
9	Little Stoke	32	13	9	10	53	46	7	48
10	Lebeq United	32	14	5	13	71	67	4	47
11	Patchway Town	32	13	7	12	53	44	9	46
12	Broadwell Amateurs	32	14	3	15	57	49	8	45
13	Henbury	32	7	8	17	55	62	-7	29
14	Bishops Cleeve Res	32	7	7	18	33	80	-47	25*
15	Gala Wilton	32	5	2	25	36	92	-56	17
16	Hanham Athletic	32	3	6	23	23	92	-69	15
17	Southmead CS Athletic	32	3	5	24	31	88	-57	14

Cheltenham Civil Service withdrew - record expunged.

LES JAMES LEAGUE CUP

HOLDERS: HARDWICKE

PRELIMINARY ROUND

Patchway Town	v	Broadwell Amateurs	0-2
Stonehouse Town	v	Gala Wilton	4-1

ROUND 1

Frampton United	v	Hardwicke	1-1, 2-4p
Lebeq United	v	Southmead CS Athletic	2-1
Rockleaze Rangers	v	Bristol Telephones	2-6
Hanham Athletic	v	Broadwell Amateurs	0-1
AEK Boco	v	Stonehouse Town	5-3
Bishops Cleeve Res	v	Cheltenham Civil Service	4-2
Kingswood	v	Thornbury Town	2-1
Henbury	v	Little Stoke	4-1

QUARTER-FINALS

Hardwicke	v	Lebeq United	3-5
Bristol Telephones	v	Broadwell Amateurs	1-4
AEK Boco	v	Bishops Cleeve Res	6-1
Kingswood	v	Henbury	2-4

SEMI-FINALS

Lebeq United	v	Broadwell Amateurs	2-5
AEK Boco	v	Henbury	1-0

FINAL

Broadwell Amateurs	v	AEK Boco	0-3

		1	2	3	4	5	6	7	8	9	10	11	12	13	14	15	16	17
1	AEK Boco		2-0	3-0	0-2	0-4	3-1	1-1	1-3	3-1	0-3	5-0	2-2	1-0	3-2	2-2	1-0	1-1
2	Bishops Cleeve Res	0-3		1-3	1-3	1-2	1-1	1-0	0-4	0-0	2-1	1-1	1-3	6-5	0-2	0-4	1-1	1-4
3	Bristol Telephones	3-1	10-0		2-1	2-2	6-1	3-1	0-1	4-3	3-1	3-2	5-0	5-3	3-4	3-2	4-0	3-1
4	Broadwell Amateurs	1-3	2-1	3-5		1-2	3-1	4-2	0-2	3-1	3-1	3-2	1-2	0-0	1-1	6-0	0-2	0-1
5	Frampton United	2-1	3-0	1-2	1-3		9-1	7-1	7-2	3-1	6-0	4-2	2-2	2-1	0-2	5-1	2-2	2-3
6	Gala Wilton	2-0	0-2	1-5	0-1	2-3		3-1	1-2	1-5	3-4	1-2	1-2	0-3	0-2	2-1	2-4	0-7
7	Hanham Athletic	0-6	0-0	1-9	1-1	1-3	0-1		0-1	1-0	0-3	1-5	1-1	1-0	0-1	1-1	1-8	0-1
8	Hardwicke	1-3	2-2	2-5	2-1	0-1	3-2	3-0		2-2	2-0	2-0	4-1	1-0	3-4	7-0	1-1	2-2
9	Henbury	0-1	6-0	5-2	2-4	0-2	3-0	4-1	1-3		0-3	1-4	2-1	0-0	0-3	8-1	2-2	1-2
10	Kingswood	1-2	2-0	3-1	2-1	3-3	2-0	5-1	4-2	1-0		2-2	1-1	2-4	1-2	4-0	3-2	1-2
11	Lebeq United	4-3	6-0	1-4	3-1	1-0	5-1	3-0	2-4	2-2	2-6		2-1	4-1	2-3	2-1	1-3	0-0
12	Little Stoke	2-2	3-2	1-3	2-0	0-0	1-0	4-0	4-4	6-1	1-0	0-1		0-1	2-3	3-2	0-0	1-0
13	Patchway Town	2-0	3-0	0-1	1-3	3-0	2-3	3-2	2-0	1-1	0-1	3-3	2-1		1-0	3-1	1-3	0-0
14	Rockleaze Rangers	0-1	1-4	1-1	3-2	0-1	4-3	1-1	2-1	1-1	0-2	3-2	0-0	1-1		2-0	1-4	4-3
15	Southmead CS Athletic	2-4	0-1	0-1	0-2	0-2	2-2	0-3	2-1	1-1	1-4	2-1	0-3	1-3	1-3		1-1	0-3
16	Stonehouse Town	3-1	2-2	5-1	1-0	1-3	3-0	2-0	5-1	1-0	4-0	5-1	2-1	0-3	2-1	3-1		2-3
17	Thornbury Town	4-2	1-2	1-3	2-1	2-1	1-0	7-0	3-2	3-1	1-2	1-3	1-2	1-1	2-1	2-1	2-3	

BRISTOL TELEPHONES - LEAGUE CHAMPIONS Standing (L to R): Ryan Hicks, Lee Pitman, Dave Johnson (Asst.Mgr), Mike Alvis, Keiron Golding, Ben Griffiths, Leon Britton, Neil Osborne (Asst. Mgr) Billie Downes, Pete Sarre (Committee), Kyran Hunt, Jamie Sheppard, Steve Watkins (President and Secretary), Gerry Holmes (V.Chairman), Shaun Collins (Chairman and Manager). Kneeling: Dhani Golding, Sam Sarre, Martin Blacker (Capt), Will Osborne, Alex Graham, Scott Saunders.

GLOUCESTERSHIRE COUNTY LEAGUE - STEP 7

AEK BOCO – LES JAMES LEAGUE CUP WINNERS
Back row (L to R): Rich Sperring, Jordan Scott, Joe Reeves, Brad Wheadon, Jack Madge, Darren Werrett, Sam Abraham, Gary Lancaster (Manager).
Front row: Liam Jenkins, Austin Shopland, Harrison Kyte, Jack Green, Callum Ball.

Gloucestershire County League		
AEK BOCO	True Clarity Pavilion, Greenbank Road, Hanham, Bristol BS15 3RZ	01179 477 331
BROADWELL AMATEURS	The Hawthorns, Broadwell, Gloucestershire GL16 7BE	01594 837 097
FRAMPTON UNITED	The Bell Field, Bridge Road, Frampton on Severn, Gloucestershire GL2 7HA	07817 486 933
GALA WILTON	The Gala Club, Fairmile Gardens, Tewkesbury Road, Longford, Glou GL2 9EB	01452 524 447
HANHAM ATHLETIC	The Playing Fields Pavilion, 16 Vicarage Road, Hanham, Bristol BS15 3AH	01179 678 291
HARDWICKE AFC	Hardwicke Playing Field, Green Lane, GL2 4QA	01452 540 998
HENBURY	Arnell Drive Playing Field, Lorain Walk, Henbury, Bristol BS10 7AS	0117 959 0475
KINGSWOOD	Kingswood PF, Wickwar Road, Kingswood, Wotton-under-Edge GL12 8RF	07971 682 091
LEBEQ UNITED	Oaklands Park, Almondsbury, Bristol BS32 4AG	01454 615 888
LITTLE STOKE	Little Stoke Playing Fields, Little Stoke Lane, Bristol BS34 6HR	01454 865 202
PATCHWAY TOWN	Scott Park, Coniston Road, Patchway, Bristol BS34 5JR	0117 949 3952
ROCKLEAZE RANGERS	Pen Park Sports Pavillion, Jarratts Road, Bristol BS10 6WF	07834 505 786
RUARDEAN HILL RANGERS	The Recreation Ground, Ruardean Hill, GL17 9AR	01594 544 871
SOUTHMEAD CS ATHLETIC	Pen Park Sports Pavillion, Jarratts Road, Bristol BS10 6WF	0117 9508 362
STONEHOUSE TOWN	Oldends Lane, Stonehouse, Glos GL10 2DG	07849 551 656
THORNBURY TOWN	Mundy Playing Fields, Kington Lane, Thornbury BS35 1NA	01454 413 645
WICK	Wick Sports Ground, Oldbury Lane,, Wick, Bristol BS30 5RJ	07801 129 560

CLUB MOVEMENTS
in: Ruardean Hill Rangers (P - Gloucestershire Northern Senior), Wick (P - Bristol Premier Combination).
Out: Bishops Cleeve Res (W), Bristol Telephones (P - Western League).

HAMPSHIRE PREMIER LEAGUE

Sponsored by: New Forest Care
Founded: 2007
Recent Champions:
2014: Baffins Milton Rovers
2015: Hamble Club
2016: Baffins Milton Rovers

SENIOR DIVISION	P	W	D	L	F	A	GD	Pts
1 Bush Hill	28	24	1	3	79	29	50	73
2 Fleetlands	28	17	4	7	69	47	22	55
3 Liphook United	28	15	7	6	79	43	36	52
4 Paulsgrove	28	16	3	9	65	49	16	51
5 QK Southampton	28	13	7	8	68	46	22	46
6 Hayling United	28	14	4	10	63	47	16	46
7 Clanfield	28	14	2	12	61	51	10	44
8 Locks Heath	28	13	5	10	66	59	7	44
9 Colden Common	28	11	4	13	47	55	-8	37
10 Winchester Castle	28	11	2	15	57	67	-10	35
11 Liss Athletic	28	8	7	13	57	60	-3	31
12 Infinity	28	9	1	18	43	70	-27	25*
13 Hedge End Rangers	28	6	7	15	42	78	-36	25
14 Overton United	28	5	6	17	33	68	-35	21
15 Stockbridge	28	3	2	23	27	87	-60	11

Andover Lions withdrew - record expunged.

In: Sway (P).

DIVISION ONE	P	W	D	L	F	A	GD	Pts
1 Four Marks	24	18	5	1	70	17	53	59
2 Sway	24	15	6	3	82	30	52	51
3 Upham	24	15	2	7	51	28	23	47
4 Netley Central Sports	24	13	2	9	60	48	12	41
5 South Wonston Swifts	24	7	6	11	33	40	-7	27
6 Lyndhurst	24	7	6	11	33	57	-24	27
7 Michelmersh & Timsbury	24	7	3	14	42	68	-26	24
8 Headley United	24	5	3	16	32	60	-28	18
9 AFC Petersfield	24	3	3	18	33	88	-55	12

SENIOR CUP

HOLDERS: HAMBLE CLUB

ROUND 1

Upham	v	AFC Petersfield	0-1
Bush Hill	v	Liphook United	1-1, 4-5p
Stocksbridge	v	Hedge End Rangers	0-3
Fleetlands	v	Lynhurst	2-1
Winchester Castle	v	Michelmersh & Timsbury	1-2
Colden Common	v	Sway	1-4
Locks Heath	v	Netley Central Sports	HW
South Wonston Swifts	v	Overton United	3-2
Four Marks	v	Andover Lions	0-3

ROUND 2

AFC Petersfield	v	Liphook United	1-4
Hedge End Rangers	v	Infinity	0-3
Fleetlands	v	Michelmersh & Timsbury	3-2
Liss Athletic	v	QK Southampton	1-2
Clanfield	v	Sway	4-2
Locks Heath	v	Paulsgrove	0-3
Headley United	v	Hayling United	0-3
South Wonston Swifts	v	Andover Lions	2-0

QUARTER-FINALS

Liphook United	v	Infinity	0-2
Fleetlands	v	QK Southampton	1-5
Clanfield	v	Paulsgrove	4-1
Hayling United	v	South Wonston Swifts	3-0

SEMI-FINALS

Infinity	v	QK Southampton	0-2
Clanfield	v	Hayling United	2-3

FINAL

QK Southampton	v	Hayling United	2-3

SENIOR DIVISION		1	2	3	4	5	6	7	8	9	10	11	12	13	14	15
1	Bush Hill		6-1	3-0	0-1	3-1	5-1	H-W	3-1	1-4	2-0	3-0	4-1	3-1	4-3	3-1
2	Clanfield	2-4		3-0	1-3	0-1	2-0	3-1	0-2	2-2	2-0	5-0	2-1	3-2	H-W	4-0
3	Colden Common	1-2	3-5		2-1	2-0	3-2	3-1	1-7	2-2	4-2	2-3	1-2	1-6	3-1	2-1
4	Fleetlands	2-4	2-0	2-0		3-1	5-1	H-W	1-5	1-0	3-3	4-1	5-2	0-2	3-0	7-2
5	Hayling United	1-2	3-2	2-1	4-0		3-3	1-2	1-3	5-2	3-0	1-2	1-2	5-1	1-3	
6	Hedge End Rangers	0-5	2-0	2-1	2-2	1-3		1-3	1-1	3-2	3-2	0-0	1-0	1-3	0-0	3-3
7	Infinity	A-W	1-7	0-0	2-6	1-7	2-1		1-2	2-1	0-3	6-2	2-4	2-3	6-0	1-0
8	Liphook United	2-2	7-2	0-0	1-3	2-2	8-2	2-0		1-2	3-3	3-2	4-0	2-2	H-W	5-2
9	Liss Athletic	0-2	1-2	2-1	0-2	2-2	7-1	2-1	1-2		3-3	2-2	1-4	3-2	8-0	3-5
10	Locks Heath	0-4	3-1	0-0	3-2	2-0	6-3	4-3	5-2	6-3		3-4	0-1	0-0	H-W	3-1
11	Overton United	0-1	1-3	0-2	2-3	0-1	5-3	2-3	1-1	0-0	0-5		2-3	0-2	3-1	2-3
12	Paulsgrove	2-3	2-1	2-1	1-1	2-4	3-2	3-1	3-0	2-1	4-0	0-0		2-2	4-1	6-2
13	QK Southampton	2-5	2-2	1-2	5-1	2-2	1-1	0-2	2-3	1-1	5-3	0-1	4-1		2-1	4-1
14	Stockbridge	0-2	0-5	3-5	1-4	0-1	1-2	4-0	0-10	4-0	1-2	0-0	1-7	1-7		1-3
15	Winchester Castle	2-1	2-1	0-4	2-2	2-3	2-0	7-0	1-0	1-2	1-3	6-0	2-1	1-3	1-2	

Hampshire Premier League		
BUSH HILL	Mansel Park, Evenlode Road, Millbrook, Southampton SO16 9LT	07896 969 493
CLANFIELD	Peel Park, Chalton Lane, Clanfield, Waterlooville PO8 0RJ	07765 238 231
COLDEN COMMON	Colden Common Rec., Main Road, Colden Common, Winchester SO21 1RP	07506 459 508
FLEETLANDS	DARA Fleetlands, Lederle Lane, Gosport PO13 0AA	01329 239 723
HAYLING UNITED	Hayling College, Church Road, Hayling Island, Hampshire PO11 0NU	07584 196 719
HEDGE END RANGERS	Norman Rodaway Rec Grd, Heathouse Lane, Hedge End, Southampton SO30 0LE	07876 037 653
INFINITY	Knowle Village Community Hall, Knowle Avenue, Knowle, Fareham PO17 5LG	07718 152 473
LIPHOOK UNITED	Recreation Ground, London Road, Liphook GU30 7AN	07721 521 126
LISS ATHLETIC	Newman Collard Playing Fields Liss GU33 7LH	07725 133 233
LOCKS HEATH	Locksheath Rec, 419 Warsash Rd, Titchfield Common, Fareham PO14 4JX	07732 663 053
OVERTON UNITED	Overton Recreation Centre, Bridge Street, Overton RG25 3HD	01256 770 561
PAULSGROVE	Paulsgrove Social Club, Marsden Road, Paulsgrove, Portsmouth PO6 4JB	07901 655 485
QK SOUTHAMPTON	Lordshill Recreation Ground, Redbridge Lane, Lordshill, Southampton SO16 0XN	07801 550 337
STOCKBRIDGE	Stockbridge Recreation Ground, High Street, Stockbridge SO20 6EU	07768 266 288
SWAY	Jubilee Field, Station Road, Sway Hampshire SO41 6BE ·	0777 386 8988
WINCHESTER CASTLE	Hants Co. Council Spts Grd, Petersfield Rd (A31),Chilcombe, Winchester SO23 8ZB	01962 866989

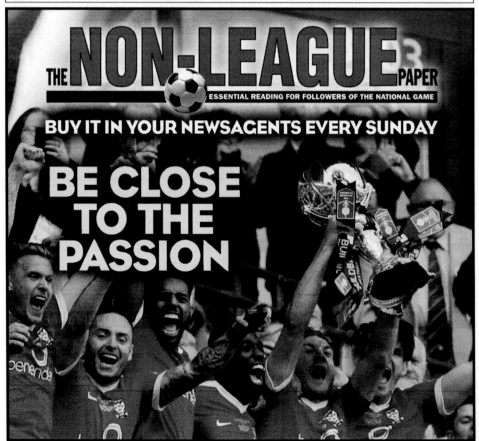

HERTS SENIOR COUNTY LEAGUE

Sponsored by: HertSavers Credit Union
Founded: 1898 reformed 1935
Recent Champions:
2014: Bedmond Sports & S.C.
2015: Belstone
2016: Standon and Puckeridge

PREMIER DIVISION

		P	W	D	L	F	A	GD	Pts
1	London Lions	30	26	2	2	112	31	81	80
2	Bovingdon	30	18	3	9	83	55	28	57
3	Letchworth Garden City Eagles	30	16	6	8	78	38	40	54
4	Ware Sports	30	17	3	10	75	55	20	54
5	Bushey Sports Club	30	15	7	8	73	55	18	52
6	Belstone	30	13	8	9	75	66	9	47
7	Sandridge Rovers	30	13	6	11	46	40	6	45
8	Wormley Rovers	30	13	5	12	43	53	-10	44
9	Knebworth	30	11	4	15	54	68	-14	37
10	Standon and Puckeridge	30	11	3	16	57	62	-5	36
11	Cuffley	30	10	6	14	58	64	-6	36
12	Buntingford Town	30	11	3	16	60	83	-23	36
13	Chipperfield Corinthians	30	10	4	16	63	77	-14	34
14	Evergreen	30	8	4	18	52	84	-32	28
15	Hatfield Social	30	7	5	18	42	101	-59	26
16	Sarratt	30	3	7	20	31	70	-39	16

DIVISION ONE

		P	W	D	L	F	A	GD	Pts
1	AFC Oaklands	30	23	3	4	101	28	73	72
2	FC Lemsford	30	19	8	3	69	39	30	65
3	Broadfields	30	21	1	8	107	41	66	64
4	Harefield United Res	30	19	4	7	93	56	37	61
5	Bengeo Trinity	30	17	7	6	77	38	39	58
6	Hampstead Heath	30	17	2	11	58	57	1	53
7	Ickleford	30	14	4	12	100	71	29	46
8	Sun Sports Res	30	12	5	13	73	62	11	41
9	Hinton	30	11	7	12	64	66	-2	40
10	Lemsford	30	11	5	14	60	82	-22	38
11	Baldock Town Res	30	10	7	13	55	76	-21	37
12	Stevenage Community	30	9	5	16	53	67	-14	32
13	AFC Hatfield	30	8	5	17	78	100	-22	29
14	Croxley Community	30	6	5	19	56	110	-54	23
15	Cuffley Res	30	4	2	24	42	103	-61	14
16	Hatfield Town Res	30	2	4	24	32	122	-90	10

Lings Elite withdrew - record expunged.

AUBERY CUP

HOLDERS: BELSTONE

ROUND 1

Bengeo Trinity	v	Standon and Puckeridge	5-4
Cuffley	v	Chipperfield Corinthians	0-5
Letchworth Garden City Eagles	v	Evergreen	4-1
Wormley Rovers	v	Hinton	2-7
Lemsford	v	Bushey Sports Club	0-3
AFC Hatfield	v	Sandridge Rovers	1-4
Knebworth	v	Ickleford	3-1
Croxley Community	v	Buntingford Town	AW
Lings Elite	v	FC Lemsford	AW
Harefield United Res	v	AFC Oaklands	2-2, 6-5p
Sun Sports Res	v	Hatfield Social	2-7
Hatfield Town Res	v	Baldock Town Res	1-2
Broadfields	v	London Lions	1-3
Bovingdon	v	Stevenage Community	5-0
Belstone	v	Sarratt	5-1
Hampstead Heath	v	Ware Sports	1-4

ROUND 2

Bengeo Trinity	v	Chipperfield Corinthians	2-5
Letchworth Garden City Eagles	v	Hinton	3-0
Bushey Sports Club	v	Sandridge Rovers	0-2 aet
Knebworth	v	Buntingford Town	5-2
FC Lemsford	v	Harefield United Res	3-2
Hatfield Social	v	Baldock Town Res	2-1
London Lions	v	Bovingdon	8-1
Belstone	v	Ware Sports	4-2

QUARTER-FINALS

Chipperfield Corinthians	v	Letchworth Garden City Eagles	1-3
Sandridge Rovers	v	Knebworth	1-2
FC Lemsford	v	Hatfield Social	4-2
London Lions	v	Belstone	10-2

SEMI-FINALS

Letchworth Garden City Eagles	v	Knebworth	1-0
FC Lemsford	v	London Lions	0-4

FINAL

Letchworth Garden City Eagles	v	London Lions	1-7

PREMIER DIVISION

		1	2	3	4	5	6	7	8	9	10	11	12	13	14	15	16
1	Belstone		1-1	7-4	3-3	2-2	3-0	5-3	2-3	1-1	0-1	1-4	2-1	1-1	2-1	5-1	3-0
2	Bovingdon	2-3		7-2	3-3	3-1	7-1	7-1	6-1	3-0	0-1	1-4	1-0	6-0	H-W	3-1	H-W
3	Buntingford Town	3-3	0-3		2-4	4-2	2-4	3-1	4-0	1-0	2-1	1-7	1-1	2-0	2-1	2-1	2-3
4	Bushey Sports Club	0-2	7-0	1-0		6-1	2-4	5-2	5-0	4-5	0-3	1-1	2-2	2-0	4-3	2-4	2-2
5	Chipperfield Corinthians	2-4	2-1	5-2	1-1		2-4	3-0	11-1	0-1	2-1	1-4	1-4	4-1	4-1	0-2	1-3
6	Cuffley	4-2	0-2	2-3	1-2	2-2		0-1	2-0	2-1	3-3	1-2	2-2	1-1	H-W	0-0	1-1
7	Evergreen	5-1	2-4	3-4	1-2	0-0	3-1		1-2	3-2	2-4	2-8	1-2	2-0	H-W	2-3	3-1
8	Hatfield Social	3-1	4-3	4-1	1-1	3-2	1-6	3-3		4-2	1-6	0-5	1-1	2-3	H-W	4-4	0-3
9	Knebworth	2-3	1-4	4-1	0-2	4-3	3-1	1-2	4-2		2-2	1-3	H-W	3-2	2-2	1-2	4-1
10	Letchworth Garden City Eagles	1-1	4-1	2-3	5-1	5-0	5-0	6-2	8-0	3-0		1-2	1-0	4-1	0-1	1-2	0-0
11	London Lions	9-1	2-5	3-1	3-0	4-1	3-2	6-1	3-0	2-1	4-1		5-1	2-0	9-0	2-1	4-0
12	Sandridge Rovers	1-0	1-3	2-1	0-1	0-3	1-3	1-0	3-0	2-1	1-0	2-2		4-0	1-2	2-1	4-0
13	Sarratt	2-2	0-0	3-2	4-5	1-2	1-7	1-2	0-0	2-3	1-2	A-W	1-1		3-0	0-2	1-2
14	Standon and Puckeridge	0-6	9-3	5-3	A-W	5-1	4-1	3-1	3-1	4-2	3-3	2-1	5-1	1-1		0-1	0-3
15	Ware Sports	5-1	2-3	3-1	1-5	5-1	4-3	4-2	5-2	6-0	3-3	2-4	0-2	3-0	3-1		2-3
16	Wormley Rovers	1-7	2-1	1-1	1-0	4-2	1-0	1-1	2-0	1-2	0-1	0-4	0-3	3-1	4-1	0-2	

Herts Senior County League Premier Division

AFC OAKLANDS	Oaklands College Main Pitch, Smallford Campus, ST ALBANS, Hertfordshire AL4 0JA	
BELSTONE	The Medburn Ground, Watling Street, Radlett WD6 3AB	020 8207 2395
BOVINGDON	Green Lane, Bovingdon, Hemel Hempstead HP3 0LA	01442 832 628
BROADFIELDS	Tithe Farm Sports and Social Club, 151 Rayners Lane, HARROW, London HA2 0XH	
BUNTINGFORD TOWN	The Bury Sainsbury Distribution Centre, London Road, Buntingford SG9 9HZ	01763 271 522
BUSHEY SPORTS CLUB	Met Police Sports Club, Aldenham Road, Bushey, Watford WD2 3TR	01923 243 947
CHIPPERFIELD CORINTHIANS	Queens Street, Chipperfield, Kings Langley WD4 9BT	01923 269 554
CUFFLEY	King George's Playing Fields, Northaw Road East, Cuffley EN6 4LU	07815 174 434
EVERGREEN	Southway, Abbots Langley, WATFORD, Hertfordshire WD4 8PN	
FC LEMSFORD	Roe Hill Playing Fields, Briars Lane, HATFIELD, Herts AL10 8EY	
KNEBWORTH	Knebworth Recreation Ground, Watton Road, Knebworth, Hertfordshire SG3 6AH	
LETCHWORTH GC EAGLES	Pixmore Playing Fields, Ledgers Lane, Baldock Road, Letchworth SG6 2EN	07855 337 175
SANDRIDGE ROVERS	Spencer Recreation Ground, Sandridge, St Albans AL4 9DD	01727 835 506
STANDON & PUCKERIDGE	Station Road, Standon, Ware SG11 1QT	01920 823 460
WARE SPORTS	Wodson Park Sports Centre, Wadesmill Road, WARE, Hertfordshire SG12 0RB	
WORMLEY ROVERS	Wormley Sports Club, Church Lane, Wormley EN10 7QF	01992 460 650

ADDITIONAL CLUB MOVEMENTS
Premier Division
Out: London Lions (P - Spartan South Midlands)

Division One
In: Bovington Res (P), Cheshunt U21s (N), Hadley Res (N), Kinja FC (N), Oxhey Jets Res (N), Rayners Lane Res (N), Wodson Park (N), Weston (N - Hitchin Sunday Lge).

Out: Hatfield United Res (W), Ickleford (W), Baldock Town Res (W), Croxley Community (W), Cuffley Res (W), Hatfield Town Res (W).

RESERVE & DEV DIVISION	P	W	D	L	F	A	GD	Pts
1 Bovingdon Res	24	18	3	3	83	35	48	57
2 Hadley A	24	17	4	3	69	25	44	55
3 Lings Elite U21s	24	15	3	6	51	36	15	48
4 Old Parmiterians	24	13	3	8	58	48	10	42
5 Sarratt Res	24	11	5	8	57	38	19	38
6 Buntingford Town Res	24	10	4	10	38	37	1	34
7 Letchworth Garden City Eagles Res	24	10	4	10	50	50	0	34
8 Knebworth Res	24	9	3	12	43	54	-11	30
9 Sandridge Rovers Res	24	8	2	14	47	53	-6	26
10 Wormley Rovers Res	24	7	4	13	36	53	-17	25
11 Lemsford Res	24	7	2	15	40	53	-13	23
12 Evergreen Res	24	5	4	15	26	72	-46	19
13 Chipperfield Corinthians Res	24	5	1	18	39	83	-44	16

HUMBER PREMIER LEAGUE

Sponsored by: No sponsor
Founded: 2000
Recent Champions:
2014: Beverley Town
2015: Sculcoates Amateurs
2016: Wawne United

PREMIER DIVISION	P	W	D	L	F	A	GD	Pts
1 Crown FC	28	21	3	4	79	33	46	66
2 Sculcoates Amateurs	28	18	5	5	86	33	53	59
3 Chalk Lane	28	17	2	9	57	41	16	53
4 Pocklington Town	28	15	5	8	86	49	37	50
5 East Yorkshire Carnegie	28	15	4	9	65	51	14	49
6 Hessle Rangers	28	13	9	6	73	63	10	48
7 Reckitts AFC	28	14	3	11	66	57	9	45
8 East Riding Rangers	28	13	5	10	54	47	7	44
9 Beverley Town	28	12	6	10	56	41	15	42
10 South Cave	28	9	4	15	58	63	-5	31
11 Goole United	28	9	3	16	54	88	-34	30
12 North Ferriby Athletic	28	6	7	15	32	47	-15	25
13 Hedon Rangers	28	6	7	15	51	90	-39	25
14 Hanson Jewellers	28	5	4	19	42	101	-59	19
15 Easington United	28	2	3	23	45	100	-55	9

DIVISION ONE	P	W	D	L	F	A	GD	Pts
1 Hornsea Town	20	16	1	3	69	29	40	49
2 Walkington	20	15	2	3	62	23	39	47
3 Bridlington Town Res	20	9	4	7	40	34	6	31
4 Driffield Evening Institute	20	8	2	10	44	50	-6	26
5 LIV Supplies AFC	20	7	4	9	38	38	0	25
6 Hall Road Rangers Res	20	7	4	9	33	55	-22	25
7 Howden AFC	20	6	5	9	33	48	-15	23
8 Brandesburton	20	5	7	8	46	54	-8	22
9 Westella & Willerby	20	6	4	10	36	45	-9	22
10 Hull United	20	6	3	11	39	51	-12	21
11 Hessle Sporting United	20	6	2	12	39	52	-13	20

LEAGUE CUP

HOLDERS: WALKINGTON

ROUND 1

Sculcoates Amateurs	v	Hull United AFC	8-0
Goole United	v	Pocklington Town	1-3
North Ferriby Athletic	v	Easington United	0-1
Brandesburton	v	Reckitts AFC	1-6
Hanson Jewellers	v	Walkington	2-7
Driffield Evening Institute	v	East Yorkshire Carnegie	1-4
South Cave	v	Westella & Willerby	6-1
Hedon Rangers	v	East Riding Rangers	0-2
LIV Supplies AFC	v	Howden AFC	4-1
Hornsea Town	v	Hall Road Rangers Res	2-2, 5-3p

ROUND 2

Sculcoates Amateurs	v	Pocklington Town	3-0
Easington United	v	Bridlington Town Res	1-1, 3-1p
Crown FC	v	Reckitts AFC	2-0
Hessle Rangers	v	Beverley Town	3-3, 3-4p
Walkington	v	Hessle Sporting United	2-0
East Yorkshire Carnegie	v	South Cave	2-3
East Riding Rangers	v	LIV Supplies AFC	1-2
Chalk Lane	v	Hornsea Town	2-1

QUARTER-FINALS

Sculcoates Amateurs	v	Easington United	8-2
Crown FC	v	Beverley Town	4-1
Walkington	v	South Cave	0-5
LIV Supplies AFC	v	Chalk Lane	3-0

SEMI-FINALS

Sculcoates Amateurs	v	Crown FC	2-3 aet
South Cave	v	LIV Supplies AFC	1-2

FINAL

Crown FC	v	LIV Supplies AFC	0-2

PREMIER DIVISION	1	2	3	4	5	6	7	8	9	10	11	12	13	14	15	16
1 Beverley Town		3-1	0-1	4-2	2-2	2-0	3-1	1-3	1-1	0-2	4-0	3-4	2-1	0-2	1-1
2 Chalk Lane	2-1		3-2	3-1	1-2	0-1	0-2	3-0	4-2	2-2	4-2	1-2	3-2	1-2	4-1
3 Crown FC	2-2	1-2		0-1	2-0	1-0	3-0	1-1	3-1	2-3	1-1	4-1	2-0	3-2	2-1
4 Easington United	2-4	0-2	3-4		1-2	1-3	5-6	3-3	0-1	2-3	2-2	2-6	0-3	1-2	3-8
5 East Riding Rangers	0-1	4-0	0-3	2-1		4-2	1-3	5-1	2-2	2-5	2-0	3-2	1-3	1-1	8-0
6 East Yorkshire Carnegie	1-1	2-1	2-4	4-3	1-1		7-0	5-3	3-0	5-3	3-1	1-0	2-3	0-5	2-1
7 Goole United	0-5	0-0	1-5	3-0	0-2	5-3		2-3	5-1	1-1	1-0	2-8	1-6	1-7	1-6
8 Hanson Jewellers FC	0-7	1-3	1-7	2-3	1-2	4-1	0-7		0-2	4-4	1-2	2-1	2-6	0-7	2-3
9 Hedon Rangers	2-2	3-1	1-7	1-1	1-2	2-7	5-4	4-2		5-5	1-5	4-5	2-2	1-6	1-5
10 Hessle Rangers	2-0	0-3	4-6	2-1	3-2	3-3	2-1	2-2	2-4		4-0	3-2	3-5	0-5	4-2
11 North Ferriby Athletic	1-2	1-2	1-4	5-0	1-1	0-1	1-0	2-0	1-1	0-0		2-3	0-1	0-0	2-1
12 Pocklington Town	2-0	0-2	0-2	9-3	4-0	0-1	4-2	10-0	3-0	1-1	3-0		5-1	1-1	2-2
13 Reckitts AFC	2-1	1-3	0-2	10-4	0-2	0-3	1-1	1-2	3-2	1-1	2-1	3-4		2-1	1-0
14 Sculcoates Amateurs	3-2	1-3	1-3	1-0	4-0	2-1	8-1	5-1	7-0	0-6	0-0	3-3	4-1		3-0
15 South Cave	1-2	2-3	1-2	5-0	2-1	1-1	1-3	2-1	2-1	2-3	3-1	1-1	3-5	1-3	

KENT COUNTY LEAGUE

Sponsored by: NRG	
Founded: 1922	
Recent Champions:	
2014: Metrogas	
2015: Metrogas	
2016: Faversham Strike Force Seniors	

PREMIER DIVISION

		P	W	D	L	F	A	GD	Pts
1	Punjab United	30	23	4	3	104	32	72	73
2	Greenways	30	21	3	6	89	40	49	66
3	Peckham Town	29	19	3	7	70	27	43	59*
4	Kennington	29	18	5	6	81	43	38	58*
5	Fleetdown United	30	17	7	6	66	37	29	58
6	Borden Village	30	17	4	9	83	42	41	54*
7	Faversham Strike Force Seniors	29	17	4	8	67	46	21	54*
8	Bexley	30	16	4	10	72	42	30	52
9	Stansfeld (Oxford & Bermondsey)	28	10	9	9	57	54	3	39
10	Lydd Town Res	30	10	4	16	65	90	-25	34
11	Staplehurst Monarchs United	29	10	2	17	60	84	-24	32
12	Erith 147 Sports	30	7	6	17	49	80	-31	27
13	Farnborough OB Guild	29	7	4	18	41	83	-42	25
14	Metrogas	30	7	1	22	58	92	-34	21*
15	Hildenborough Athletic	30	6	2	22	36	91	-55	20
16	Guru Nanak	29	0	0	29	22	137	-115	-1*

DIVISION ONE CENTRAL & EAST

		P	W	D	L	F	A	GD	Pts
1	New Romney	20	14	3	3	40	22	18	45
2	Hawkinge Town	20	12	3	5	47	24	23	39
3	Kings Hill	20	11	3	6	48	35	13	32*
4	Ide Hill	19	9	4	6	46	42	4	31
5	K Sports Res	20	8	2	10	44	54	-10	26
6	East Kent College	20	8	2	10	50	41	9	25*
7	Rolvenden	20	7	4	9	36	40	-4	24*
8	Deal Community Sports	19	6	4	9	34	46	-12	22
9	Hollands & Blair Res	20	7	1	12	35	45	-10	21*
10	Sutton Athletic Res	20	6	3	11	40	46	-6	20*
11	South Darenth	20	5	3	12	28	53	-25	18

DIVISION ONE WEST

		P	W	D	L	F	A	GD	Pts
1	Lewisham Athletic	24	19	1	4	89	30	59	58
2	Otford United	24	18	4	2	58	15	43	58
3	Chipstead	24	15	2	7	65	31	34	47
4	Old Roan	24	13	1	10	60	49	11	40
5	Club Langley	24	12	4	8	46	42	4	40
6	Halstead United	24	11	3	10	54	40	14	36
7	Long Lane	24	11	3	10	67	55	12	36
8	Halls AFC	24	9	5	10	47	40	7	32
9	Bexlians	24	9	5	10	53	49	4	32
10	Stansfeld (Oxford & Bermondsey) Res	24	9	4	11	44	69	-25	30*
11	AFC Mottingham	24	6	1	17	16	67	-51	19
12	Orpington Res	24	6	1	17	30	84	-54	16*
13	AFC Morzinga	24	0	2	22	22	80	-58	1*

BILL MANKLOW INTER REGIONAL CHALLENGE CUP

HOLDERS: EAST KENT COLLEGE

ROUND 1

Peckham Town	v	Hildenborough Athletic	2-0
South Darenth	v	Guru Nanak	3-4
Staplehurst Monarchs United	v	Faversham Strike Force	5-2
Halls AFC	v	Halstead United	2-1
Kennington	v	Hawkinge Town	3-3, 3-4p
Fleetdown United	v	Bexlians	4-0
Bexley	v	Lewisham Athletic	2-3
Old Roan	v	Chipstead	3-1

ROUND 2

AFC Mottingham	v	Peckham Town	0-3
AFC Morzinga	v	Erith 147 Sports	3-6
Punjab United	v	Guru Nanak	6-0
Staplehurst Monarchs United	v	Borden Village	3-2
Farnborough OBG	v	Orpington Res	1-0
Otford United	v	Halls AFC	3-1
New Romney	v	K Sports Res	3-2
Hawkinge Town	v	Sutton Athletic Res	5-2
Rolvenden	v	East Kent College	0-3
Kings Hill	v	Ide Hill	1-2
Fleetdown United	v	Stansfeld O&B	2-2, 4-1p
Lewisham Athletic	Bye		
Greenways	v	Lydd Town Res	1-0
Deal Community Sports	v	Hollands & Blair Res	2-1
Club Langley	v	Long Lane	0-1
Metrogas	v	Old Roan	4-1

ROUND 3

Peckham Town	v	Erith 147 Sports	2-3
Punjab United	v	Staplehurst Monarchs United	5-0
Farnborough OBG	v	Otford United	1-3
New Romney	v	Hawkinge Town	2-0
East Kent College	v	Ide Hill	HW
Fleetdown United	v	Lewisham Athletic	1-2
Greenways	v	Deal Community Sports	4-2
Long Lane	v	Metrogas	4-1

QUARTER-FINALS

Erith 147 Sports	v	Punjab United	0-2
Otford United	v	New Romney	3-2
East Kent College	v	Lewisham Athletic	1-2
Greenways	v	Long Lane	5-0

SEMI-FINALS

Punjab United	v	Otford United	3-1
Lewisham Athletic	v	Greenways	0-2

FINAL

Punjab United	v	Greenways	0-1

PREMIER DIVISION

		1	2	3	4	5	6	7	8	9	10	11	12	13	14	15	16
1	Bexley		2-0	4-1	3-1	1-2	2-0	1-3	4-0	2-1	H-W	1-1	3-2	3-4	0-1	0-0	4-2
2	Borden Village	2-1		1-1	1-3	2-2	3-4	4-0	3-0	5-0	1-4	4-3	7-2	0-2	4-0	2-2	7-1
3	Erith 147 Sports	1-5	0-2		1-1	1-5	0-2	1-3	6-3	2-2	1-2	1-2	1-2	0-2	1-5	2-0	2-1
4	Farnborough OB Guild	2-5	1-1	1-1		0-2	0-4	0-5	3-1	1-2	2-3	0-3	5-3	0-5	0-5	V-V	1-3
5	Faversham Strike Force Seniors	3-1	0-2	3-2	4-3		0-2	0-2	3-1	5-0	4-4	3-1	2-1	0-1	1-2	3-1	2-1
6	Fleetdown United	2-1	2-0	1-0	3-2	2-2		1-0	6-0	2-2	3-1	2-2	2-0	1-2	1-1	0-0	1-1
7	Greenways	1-0	1-2	5-4	4-1	1-0	2-0		4-1	2-0	4-0	2-4	4-2	1-1	0-5	5-2	7-0
8	Guru Nanak	2-10	0-7	0-4	1-2	V-V	0-10	0-6		2-4	1-3	1-3	2-3	1-3	0-5	1-6	1-6
9	Hildenborough Athletic	0-3	0-4	4-0	0-3	0-5	1-3	0-3	5-0		1-3	2-3	0-3	1-4	0-2	5-3	0-3
10	Kennington	0-0	2-1	1-3	3-0	1-3	2-0	4-3	6-0	4-0		7-1	5-3	1-0	1-0	3-0	V-V
11	Lydd Town Reserves	1-2	1-6	3-4	1-2	3-5	0-2	1-9	3-1	7-1	3-3		4-1	2-4	2-2	3-1	3-4
12	Metrogas	1-6	2-5	1-1	2-3	1-2	2-3	1-2	5-1	5-1	2-7	3-1		0-1	2-3	1-2	1-5
13	Peckham Town	0-0	1-2	4-1	3-0	3-0	3-0	0-2	4-0	4-1	3-3	7-1	4-0		0-1	V-V	1-4
14	Punjab United	4-3	5-2	11-2	9-0	3-1	6-1	0-0	5-0	4-0	1-0	6-0	5-2	3-1		2-5	2-0
15	Stansfeld (Oxford & Bermondsey)	1-3	H-W	1-2	2-2	2-2	1-1	2-2	4-1	3-1	3-3	4-2	0-3	H-W	2-2		5-3
16	Staplehurst Monarchs United	4-2	0-3	3-3	3-2	2-3	1-5	3-6	8-1	1-2	0-5	0-1	5-2	2-1	1-4	0-5	

Kent County League Premier Division

BEXLEY	STC Sports Ground, Ivor Grove, New Eltham, London SE9 2AJ	0208 858 2057
BORDEN VILLAGE	Borden Playstool, Wises Lane, Borden, Sittingbourne Kent ME9 8LP	07817 955 823
FARNBOROUGH OBG	Farnborough Sports Club, Farrow Field, Off High Street, Farnborough, Kent BR6 7BA	01689 862 949
FAVERSHAM STRIKE FORCE	Sittingbourne Community College, (3G Pitch), Swanstree Avenue, Kent ME10 4NL	01795 425 825
FLEETDOWN UNITED	Heath Lane Open Space, Heath Lane (Lower), Dartford DA1 2QH	01322 273 848
GREENWAYS	Old Southfields, Nursery Mews, Off Cedar Avenue, Gravesend DA12 5JT	07805 406 003
KENNINGTON	The Julie Rose Stadium, Willesborough Road, Kennington, Ashford, Kent TN24 9QX	01233 613 131
LEWISHAM ATHLETIC	Warren Avenue Playing Fields, Warren Avenue, Bromley, Kent BR1 4BP	07918 600 852
LYDD TOWN RESERVES	The Lindsey Field, Dengemarsh Road, Lydd, Kent TN29 9JH	01797 321 904
METROGAS	Marathon Playing Fields, Forty Foot Way, Avery Hill Road, New Eltham SE9 2EX	020 8859 1579
NEW ROMNEY	The Maude Pavilion, Station Road, New Romney, Kent TN28 8LQ	07710 077 702
OTFORD UNITED	Otford Recreation Ground, Off Otford High Street, Otford, Kent TN14 5PG	07802 736 279
PECKHAM TOWN	Pynners Close, Dulwich Common, London SE21 7HA	07715 386 547
STANSFELD O & B CLUB	Marathon Playing Fields, Forty Foot Way, Avery Hill Road, New Eltham SE9 2EX	020 8859 1579
STAPLEHURST & MONARCHS UTD	Jubilee Sports Ground, Headcorn Road, Staplehurst TN12 0DS	01580 892 292
TUDOR SPORTS	Oxford Road, Sidcup, Kent DA14 6LW	0208 300 2987

CLUB MOVEMENTS
Premier Division - Out: Punjab United (P – Southern Counties East Div 1); Hildenborough Ath (R); Guru Nanak (R).
In: New Romney (P); Lewisham Athletic (P); Otford Utd (P).
Division One Central & East - Out: New Romney (P); Ide Hill & Sutton Athletic Reserves (Transferred to Div 1 West); South Darenth (Relegated to Div 2 West).
In: Hildenborough Ath (R); Guru Nanak (R); Cuxton 91 (P); Willesborough Athletic (P); Herne Bay Reserves (Placed).
Division One West - Out: Lewisham Athletic (P); Otford Utd (P)
In: Old Bromleians (P); Welling Park (P); Ide Hill & Sutton Athletic Reserves (Transferred from Div 1 West).
Division Two Central & East -Out: Cuxton 91 (P); Willesborough Athletic (P); Aylesford (R).
In: Wateringbury (P); Burgess Hodgson (P); Rusthall Reserves (P); Tonbridge Invicta (P) Rochester City (P); Lordswood Reserves (Placed).

Division Two West - Out: Old Bromleians (P); Welling Park (P).
In: South Darenth (Relegated from Div 1 C&E); Sydenham Sports (P); Welling Town (P); Metrogas Reserves (P).
Division Three Central & East - Out: Wateringbury (P); Burgess Hodgson (P); Rusthall Reserves (P); Tonbridge Invicta (P) Rochester City (P).
In: Aylesford (R); Faversham Town Reserves; Woodnesborough; Deal Town Rangers; AFC Ashford Athletic; Bromley Green; Tenterden Town; Deal Sports Reserves; CC Sport.
Division Three West - Out: Sydenham Sports (P); Welling Town (P); Metrogas Reserves (P).
In: Red Velvet; Old Bromleians Reserves; AFC Lewisham; South East Athletic Reserves.

CLUBS RENAMED FOR 2017/18:
Tudor Sports formerly Erith 147 Sports
Deal Sports formerly Deal Community Sports

DIVISION TWO CENTRAL & EAST

		P	W	D	L	F	A	GD	Pts
1	Cuxton 91	18	16	1	1	75	12	63	49
2	Willesborough Athletic	18	15	2	1	97	32	65	47
3	Snodland Town Res	18	11	1	6	43	44	-1	34
4	West Farleigh	18	10	2	6	54	27	27	32
5	Deal Town Res	18	8	0	10	37	52	-15	24
6	New Romney Res	18	6	1	11	28	55	-27	19
7	Sheppey United Res	18	4	4	10	25	50	-25	16
8	Ashford	18	4	3	11	28	47	-19	15
9	Larkfield & New Hythe Wanderers	18	3	4	11	19	48	-29	13
10	Aylesford	18	3	2	13	19	58	-39	5*

DIVISION TWO WEST

		P	W	D	L	F	A	GD	Pts
1	Old Bromleians	20	14	3	3	69	33	36	45
2	Welling Park	20	12	1	7	48	50	-2	36*
3	Nomads	20	10	4	6	58	46	12	34
4	Crayford Arrows	20	11	1	8	51	41	10	34
5	South East Athletic	20	10	3	7	51	36	15	33
6	Fleetdown United Res	20	9	3	8	31	31	0	30
7	Long Lane Res	20	7	3	10	30	48	-18	24
8	FC Elmstead Res	20	7	2	11	27	33	-6	23
9	Johnson & Phillips	20	6	2	12	33	42	-9	20
10	Dulwich Village	20	5	4	11	30	46	-16	19
11	Belvedere	20	5	2	13	29	51	-22	17

LES LECKIE CUP

FINAL   HOLDERS: LARKFIELD & NEW HYTHE WANDERERS

Cuxton 91	v	Rochester City		0-2

DIVISION THREE CENTRAL & EAST

		P	W	D	L	F	A	GD	Pts
1	Wateringbury	16	12	1	3	58	25	33	37
2	Burgess Hodgson	16	10	3	3	68	34	34	33
3	Rusthall Res	16	10	2	4	47	30	17	32
4	Tonbridge Invicta	16	8	3	5	39	21	18	27
5	Rochester City	16	7	4	5	41	37	4	25
6	AEI Sports	16	7	3	6	35	33	2	24
7	University of Kent	16	4	2	10	31	54	-23	14
8	Guru Nanak Res	16	3	2	11	22	53	-31	8*
9	Staplehurst Monarchs United Res	16	1	0	15	13	67	-54	3

BARRY BUNDOCK WEST KENT SHIELD

FINAL   HOLDERS: LEWISHAM ATHLETIC

FC Elmstead Res	v	Welling Town		0-4

DIVISION THREE WEST

		P	W	D	L	F	A	GD	PTS
1	Sydenham Sports	26	22	3	1	104	18	86	69
2	Welling Town	26	18	3	5	80	43	37	57
3	Metrogas Reserves	26	18	1	7	90	42	48	55
4	Parkwood Rangers	26	15	6	5	58	37	21	51
5	Drummond Athletic	26	12	6	8	66	57	9	44*
6	AFC Bexley	26	13	1	12	62	60	2	40
7	HFSP & Ten-Em-Be	26	11	4	11	52	47	5	36*
8	Peckham Town Res	26	10	4	12	49	64	-15	34
9	Meridian VP Res	26	10	3	13	75	75	0	33
10	Bridon Ropes Res	26	7	6	13	48	65	-17	27
11	Farnborough OB Guild Res	26	8	1	17	51	79	-28	24*
12	Sporting Club Thamesmead	26	6	5	15	39	83	-44	23
13	Bexley Res	25	4	2	19	35	91	-56	14
14	Halls AFC Res	25	2	5	18	24	72	-48	10*

SEASON 2016-2017

Punjab United FC
Premier Division Champions
'Bill Manklow' Inter- Regional Challenge Cup Finalists

Greenways FC
Premier Division Runners-Up
'Bill Manklow' Inter- Regional Challenge Cup Winners

Rob Jeffrey - Greenways FC
Aford Awards Manager of the Year

Lewisham Athletic FC
Division One West Champions

Willesborough Athletic FC
Division Two Central & East Runners Up
Invitation Cup Winners

Welling Town FC
Division Three West Runners Up
'Barry Bundock' West Kent Challenge Shield Winners

Sydenham Sports FC
Division Three West Winners

Karim Habibi - West Farleigh FC
Secretary of the Year

Rochester City FC
Eastern Section 'Les Leckie' Cup Winners

Philip Smith
League Personality of the Year

Fair Play Award Winners
Overall Winner - West Farleigh FC

Abraham Opoku – Peckham Town FC
Leading Goal Scorer

League Management Committee

Peter Wilson - Referee of the Year

LEAGUE CONTACT
Philip Smith - Marketing & Communications Officer
Telephone: 07939 046182
Email: philip.smith@kentcountyfootballleague.co.uk

LEICESTERSHIRE SENIOR LEAGUE

Sponsored by: Everards Brewery
Founded: 1919
Recent Champions:
2014: Allexton & New Parks
2015: Sileby Town
2016: Birstall United

PREMIER DIVISION

		P	W	D	L	F	A	GD	Pts
1	Lutterworth Town	26	25	1	0	128	23	105	76
2	Saffron Dynamo	26	16	3	7	79	48	31	51
3	Friar Lane & Epworth	26	15	6	5	73	49	24	51
4	Bardon Hill	26	16	3	7	70	46	24	51
5	Coalville Town Dev	26	16	1	9	59	52	7	49
6	Sileby Town	26	13	4	9	50	37	13	43
7	Ingles	26	11	6	9	51	49	2	39
8	Barlestone St Giles	26	12	4	10	49	50	-1	36*
9	Blaby & Whetstone Athletic Res	26	10	3	13	55	80	-25	27*
10	Cottesmore Amateurs	26	8	1	17	37	66	-29	25
11	GNG	26	7	2	17	40	61	-21	23
12	Kirby Muxloe Res	26	5	2	19	41	73	-32	17
13	Ashby Ivanhoe Res	26	4	3	19	34	75	-41	12*
14	Allexton & New Parks	26	4	1	21	39	96	-57	10*

Shelthorpe Dynamo withdrew - record expunged.

CHAMPIONSHIP DIVISION

		P	W	D	L	F	A	GD	Pts
1	Hathern	28	19	4	5	95	37	58	61
2	FC Khalsa GAD	28	18	7	3	86	34	52	61
3	Oadby Town Res	28	19	4	5	72	30	42	58*
4	Ibstock United	28	18	2	8	91	44	47	56
5	County Hall	28	17	5	6	74	34	40	56
6	Birstall United Res	28	15	5	8	68	49	19	50
7	Aylestone Park OB Res	28	15	4	9	68	44	24	40*
8	Barrow Town Res	28	12	3	13	85	71	14	39
9	Desford	28	10	2	16	61	71	-10	32
10	Highfield Rangers	28	9	3	16	64	93	-29	30
11	Holwell Sports Res	28	9	2	17	64	84	-20	29
12	Anstey Town	28	9	1	18	48	95	-47	28
13	Ratby Sports	28	9	3	16	40	60	-20	27*
14	Anstey Nomads Res	28	5	0	23	47	102	-55	15
15	Loughborough FC	28	3	1	24	27	142	-115	7*

Leicester Road Dev withdrew - record expunged.

DIVISION ONE

		P	W	D	L	F	A	GD	Pts
1	Lutterworth Town Res	15	15	0	0	92	11	81	45
2	Friar Lane & Epworth Res	18	14	0	4	78	32	46	42
3	Desford Res	17	10	3	4	55	26	29	32*
4	Ingles Res	17	8	3	6	47	42	5	27
5	Sileby Town Res	17	9	2	6	68	23	45	25*
6	Barlestone St Giles Res	18	7	1	10	34	46	-12	22
7	GNG Res	17	6	3	8	43	60	-17	21
8	Cottesmore Amateurs Res	16	2	4	10	27	50	-23	10
9	Ibstock Utd Res	14	1	2	11	18	71	-53	5
10	Loughborough FC Res	17	2	0	15	15	116	-101	2*

BEACON BITTER CUP

HOLDERS: IBSTOCK UNITED

ROUND 1

Earl Shilton Albion	v	Barlestone St Giles		AW
Shelthorpe Dynamo	v	Kirby Muxloe Res		1-2
Aylestone Park OB Res	v	Birstall United Res		2-1
Ibstock United	v	Hathern		1-2
GNG	v	Blaby & Whetstone Athletic Res		HW
Lutterworth Town	v	Saffron Dynamo		2-1
Sileby Town	v	Cottesmore Amateurs		5-2
Coalville Town Dev	v	Bardon Hill		7-2
Alexton & New Parks	v	Ingles		1-0
Ashby Ivanhoe Res	v	Friar Lane & Epworth		1-5
Desford	v	County Hall		0-5
Holwell Sports Res	v	Leicester Road Dev		HW
Anstey Town	v	FC Khalsa GTB		0-2
Anstey Nomads Res	v	Barrow Town Res		0-6
Loughborough FC	v	Highfield Rangers		3-5
Ratby Sports	v	Oadby Town Res		0-1

ROUND 2

Barlestone St Giles	v	kirby Muxloe Res	1-0
Aylestone Park OB Res	v	Hathern	4-5
GNG	v	Lutterworth Town	0-4
Sileby Town	v	Coalville Town Dev	0-2
Alexton & New Parks	v	Friar Lane & Epworth	1-6
County Hall	v	Holwell Sports Res	4-1
FC Khalsa GTB	v	Barrow Town Res	3-1
Highfield Rangers	v	Oadby Town Res	0-1

QUARTER-FINALS

Barlestone St Giles	v	Hathern	2-1
Lutterworth Town	v	Coalville Town Dev	3-2
Friar Lane & Epworth	v	County Hall	1-3
FC Khalsa GTB	v	Oadby Town Res	1-0

SEMI-FINALS

Barlestone St Giles	v	Lutterworth Town	3-2
County Hall	v	FC Khalsa GTB	1-3

FINAL

Barlestone St Giles	v	FC Khalsa GTB	2-0

PRESIDENT'S TROPHY

HOLDERS: FRIAR LANE & EPWORTH RESERVES

FINAL

Ingles Res	v	Lutterworth Town Res	0-6

PREMIER DIVISION	1	2	3	4	5	6	7	8	9	10	11	12	13	14
1 Allexton & New Parks		4-2	1-2	2-1	2-0	2-4	2-3	0-5	2-5	1-3	1-6	1-7	0-4	2-3
2 Ashby Ivanhoe Res	4-3		0-1	2-3	4-4	0-4	1-5	2-4	1-0	3-3	3-0	0-10	0-3	1-2
3 Bardon Hill	5-0	2-1		3-3	5-1	4-2	3-0	2-2	5-2	1-2	4-2	1-2	4-3	1-2
4 Barlestone St Giles	3-1	3-1	3-1		1-2	1-2	4-0	2-2	2-0	1-1	5-4	0-5	0-6	2-2
5 Blaby & Whetstone Athletic Res	2-1	3-1	3-2	4-3		1-2	3-1	3-5	5-0	0-6	2-1	2-4	0-8	2-3
6 Coalville Town Development Squad	3-2	1-0	1-4	0-1	5-2		2-1	3-3	3-0	2-1	2-1	0-3	1-4	2-0
7 Cottesmore Amateurs	2-0	1-3	2-3	1-2	3-3	2-1		2-5	3-1	3-1	2-0	1-6	1-2	3-1
8 Friar Lane & Epworth	2-0	1-1	3-2	3-1	3-4	5-2	3-1		6-3	2-3	3-2	1-3	3-2	1-1
9 GNG	6-2	3-0	3-3	2-1	0-1	0-2	2-0	2-4		1-1	2-0	1-3	3-4	1-3
10 Ingles	3-3	2-1	0-2	1-2	4-4	0-3	5-0	2-0	1-0		3-1	2-2	0-3	0-3
11 Kirby Muxloe Res	0-4	2-1	1-2	1-4	4-2	2-4	3-0	0-4	0-1	1-4		2-5	1-3	3-2
12 Lutterworth Town	11-0	2-1	6-2	3-0	7-1	6-1	5-0	4-0	4-2	6-0	6-0		6-1	2-0
13 Saffron Dynamo	4-3	4-1	1-3	1-0	3-0	6-3	3-0	2-2	3-0	2-3	2-2	3-7		1-1
14 Sileby Town	6-0	5-0	0-3	0-1	2-1	1-4	2-0	0-1	2-0	2-0	2-2	1-3	4-1	

Leicestershire Senior League Premier Division

ALLEXTON & NEW PARKS	New College, Glenfield Road, Leicester LE3 6DN	0116 287 1759
ASHBY IVANHOE RESERVES	The NFU Sports Ground, Lower Packington Rd, Ashby de la Zouch, LE65 1TS	01530 413 140
BARDON HILL	Bardon Close, Coalville, Leicester LE67 4BS	01530 815 569
BARLESTONE ST GILES	Barton Road, Barlestone, Nuneaton CV13 0EP	01455 291 392
COALVILLE TOWN DEV.	Owen Street Sports Ground, Owen St, Coalville LE67 3DA	01530 833 365
COTTESMORE AMATEURS	Rogues Park, Main Street, Cottesmore, Oakham LE15 4DH	07764 193 475
ELLISTOWN	Terrace Road, Ellistown, Leicestershire LE67 1GD	01530 230 152
FC KHALSA GAD	Judge Meadow Community College, Marydene Drive, Evingron, Leicester LE5 5UA	0116 241 7580
FRIAR LANE & EPWORTH	Whittier Road, Leicester. LE2 6FT	0116 283 3629
GNG	Riverside Football Ground, Braunstone Lane East, Leicester LE3 2FW	07968 829 858
HATHERN	Pasture Lane, Hathern, Leicestershire LE12 5LJ	
IBSTOCK UNITED	The Welfare Ground, Leicester Road, Ibstock, Leicestershire LE67 6HN	01530 260 656
INGLES	The Dovecote, Butthole Lane, Shepshed, Leicestershire. LE12 9BN	01509 650 992
KIRBY MUXLOE RESERVES	Ratby Lane, Kirby Muxloe, Leicester LE9 9AQ	0116 239 2301
SAFFRON DYNAMO	Cambridge Road, Whetstone LE8 3LG	07957 151 630
SILEBY TOWN	Sileby Sports Club, 3 Southfield Avenue, Sileby, Leicestershire LE12 7WL	07708 231 563

CLUB MOVEMENTS

Premier Division

Out: Blaby & Whetstone Athletic Res (W), Lutterworth Town (P - United Counties).

Division One (formerly Championship Division)

In: Asfordby, Caterpillar, Earl Shilton Albion, Melton Town Dev, Rugby Borough, St Andrews Res, Thurnby Rangers.

Out: Oadby Town Res (W).

Combination (formerley Division One)

In: Allexton & New Parks Dev, Hathern Res, Saffron Dynamo Res.

Out: Friar Lane & Epworth Res (W), Ibstock United (W).

LIVERPOOL COUNTY PREMIER LEAGUE

Sponsored by: No sponsor	
Founded: 2006	
Recent Champions:	
2014: Aigburth Peoples Hall	
2015: Aigburth Peoples Hall	
2016: Aigburth Peoples Hall	

PREMIER DIVISION

		P	W	D	L	F	A	GD	Pts
1	Aigburth Peoples Hall	24	21	1	2	88	27	61	64
2	Lower Breck	24	20	1	3	114	39	75	61
3	Waterloo Dock	24	17	2	5	92	42	50	53
4	Liverpool Nalgo	24	13	2	9	53	57	-4	41
5	East Villa	24	12	2	10	44	43	1	38
6	Waterloo Grammar School Old Boys	24	11	3	10	55	67	-12	36
7	Old Xaverians	24	9	5	10	50	53	-3	32
8	Byrom	24	10	1	13	52	60	-8	31
9	Page Celtic	24	9	3	12	46	53	-7	30
10	Warbreck	24	7	1	16	43	80	-37	22
11	South Sefton Borough	24	6	2	16	27	58	-31	20
12	Alumni	24	5	2	17	36	71	-35	17
13	MSB Woolton	24	3	1	20	34	84	-50	10

Walton Community withdrew - record expunged.
West Everton Xaviers withdrew - record exunged.

DIVISION ONE

		P	W	D	L	F	A	GD	Pts
1	Old Xaverians Res	22	18	3	1	82	20	62	57
2	Custy's	22	16	0	6	71	49	22	48
3	Alder	22	14	4	4	73	38	35	46
4	Salisbury Athletic	22	13	2	7	47	40	7	41
5	Netherley Woodlane Legion	22	12	2	8	58	45	13	38
6	British Rail	22	11	4	7	65	40	25	37
7	BRNESC	22	8	3	10	39	50	-11	27*
8	Liver Academy	22	7	4	11	43	61	-18	24*
9	Edge Hill Boys Club Old Boys	22	6	4	12	41	63	-22	22
10	ROMA	22	3	3	16	32	61	-29	14*
11	Eli Lilly	22	3	3	15	34	88	-54	12*
12	Copperas Hill	22	3	2	17	31	61	-30	11

ZINGARI CUP

HOLDERS: AIGBURTH PEOPLES HALL

ROUND 1

East Villa	v	Aigburth Peoples Hall	1-3
Warbreck	v	Waterloo Grammar School OB	1-3
MSB Woolton	v	Lower Breck	1-6
Old Xaverians	v	Waterloo Dock	2-5
Byrom	v	Walton Community	HW
South Sefton Borough	v	Liverpool Nalgo	3-5

QUARTER-FINALS

Aigburth Peoples Hall	v	Waterloo Grammar School OB	4-1
Lower Breck	v	Waterloo Dock	3-2 aet
Page Celtic	v	Byrom	HW
Alumni	v	Liverpool Nalgo	2-3

SEMI-FINALS

Aigburth Peoples Hall	v	Lower Breck	1-5
Page Celtic	v	Liverpool Nalgo	1-0

FINAL

Lower Breck	v	Page Celtic	3-1

DIVISION TWO

		P	W	D	L	F	A	GD	Pts
1	Bankfield Old Boys	22	19	0	2	105	28	77	57*
2	Waterloo Dock Res	22	15	3	3	86	34	52	48*
3	South Garston	22	12	3	7	48	39	9	42*
4	Mount Athletic	22	12	3	6	75	52	23	39*
5	Lower Breck Res	22	12	2	8	59	53	6	38
6	Red Rum	22	9	4	9	78	58	20	31
7	AFC Kirkby	22	10	1	10	57	54	3	31*
8	Litherland REMYCA 'A'	22	9	4	9	55	55	0	31
9	Botanic	22	9	4	9	61	62	-1	31
10	Knowsley North	22	4	3	15	47	89	-42	15
11	Aintree Villa	22	4	1	17	28	72	-44	10*
12	Leighbridge	22	0	2	20	22	125	-103	2

PREMIER DIVISION

		1	2	3	4	5	6	7	8	9	10	11	12	13
1	Aigburth Peoples Hall		5-1	2-0	2-1	10-0	1-3	6-0	6-2	3-0	7-0	2-0	1-2	1-5
2	Alumni	1-2		2-2	1-2	0-2	2-6	2-3	1-1	3-4	1-0	4-1	3-1	2-4
3	Byrom	1-4	0-1		2-1	1-2	0-5	3-0	4-2	2-1	0-1	2-3	4-2	11-3
4	East Villa	0-2	2-1	1-0		5-1	2-4	2-1	2-0	2-0	3-1	3-2	3-4	2-1
5	Liverpool Nalgo	0-2	5-1	2-1	0-2		0-2	4-2	1-1	2-2	1-0	4-2	2-0	1-4
6	Lower Breck	1-2	9-1	6-2	5-3	4-5		5-2	H-W	3-1	5-0	2-2	6-3	10-2
7	MSB Woolton	3-5	5-1	2-5	0-1	3-7	0-6		1-3	1-2	1-2	3-5	0-9	0-2
8	Old Xaverians	2-4	0-3	4-0	1-1	2-4	2-6	2-2		3-1	5-1	8-1	0-5	2-2
9	Page Celtic	2-6	2-1	1-3	4-0	4-1	1-3	3-1	0-3		2-2	5-1	4-7	0-1
10	South Sefton Borough	1-4	3-2	3-6	2-0	1-2	0-4	2-0	0-4	1-1		5-0	0-2	1-2
11	Warbreck	3-6	5-2	A-W	4-2	1-4	1-5	4-1	A-W	1-2	1-0		1-5	1-6
12	Waterloo Dock	2-3	4-0	6-1	2-2	6-3	5-3	2-1	7-0	2-0	3-0	7-1		3-1
13	Waterloo Grammar School Old Boys	1-2	3-0	6-2	3-2	1-0	2-11	1-2	1-3	1-4	2-1	2-3	3-3	

GEORGE MAHON CUP

HOLDERS: WEST EVERTON XAVIERS

PRELIMINARY ROUND

Leighbridge	v	Litherland REMYCA 'A'	2-9
Botanic	v	AFC Kirkby	2-4
Bankfield Old Boys	v	Knowsley North	6-0
Red Rum	v	South Garston	2-6
Aintree Villa	v	Mount Athletic	1-4

ROUND 1

Litherland REMYCA 'A'	v	Warbreck	0-3
British Rail	v	Page Celtic	3-6
AFC Kirkby	v	Netherley Woodlane Legion	1-4
Copperas Hill	v	Walton Community	HW
Bankfield Old Boys	v	Aigburth Peoples Hall	0-6
Old Xaverians	v	Waterloo Grammar School OB	3-2 aet
Leyfield	v	East Villa	AW
Liverpool Nalgo	v	South Sefton Borough	3-2
Liver Academy	v	ROMA	2-1 aet
Eli Lilly	v	Edge Hill Boys Club Old Boys	5-5, 4-5p
Lower Breck	Bye		
Byrom	v	South Garston	4-3
Mount Athletic	v	Salisbury Athletic	AW
Custys	v	BRNESC	3-3, 5-6p
Alumni	v	Alder	1-1, 6-5p
Waterloo Dock	v	MSB Woolton	8-3

ROUND 2

Warbreck	v	Page Celtic	5-2
Netherley Woodlane Legion	v	Copperas Hill	1-2
Aigburth Peoples Hall	v	Old Xaverians	3-0
East Villa	v	Liverpool Nalgo	2-0
Liver Academy	v	Edge Hill Boys Club Old Boys	5-7
Lower Breck	v	Byrom	6-0
Salisbury Athletic	v	BRNESC	3-2
Alumni	v	Waterloo Dock	0-6

QUARTER-FINALS

Warbreck	v	Copperas Hill	2-2, 5-3p
Aigburth Peoples Hall	v	East Villa	3-0
Edge Hill Boys Club Old Boys	v	Lower Breck	0-6
Salisbury Athletic	v	Waterloo Dock	3-2

SEMI-FINALS

Copperas Hill	v	Aigburth Peoples Hall	0-8
Lower Breck	v	Salisbury Athletic	2-1

FINAL

Aigburth Peoples Hall	v	Lower Breck	0-2

Youth Division (U18)	P	W	D	L	F	A	GD	Pts
1 Finn Harps U18	24	20	2	2	112	35	77	64*
2 Old Xaverians U18	24	20	1	2	107	10	97	61*
3 Whiston Juniors U18	24	17	4	3	116	31	85	55
4 Liverton U18	24	13	2	8	86	50	36	41*
5 West Derby Pumas U18	23	11	5	4	62	39	23	38*
6 Geneva U18	24	11	3	10	59	44	15	36
7 Rosemont Athletic U18	24	10	3	11	62	63	-1	33
8 Checkemlads U18	24	9	3	12	48	47	1	29*
9 Mersey Batteries U18	24	7	2	10	34	39	-5	23*
10 Real Vikings U18	24	4	2	16	38	96	-58	14*
11 Childwall Valley U18	24	4	1	17	31	103	-72	13*
12 Rosemont U18	23	4	1	18	23	102	-79	13
13 BRNESC U18	24	2	3	19	23	142	-119	9

CLUB MOVEMENTS

Premier Division - In: AFC Liverpool Res, Alder (P), Custy's (P). **Out:** Blaby & Whetstone Athletic Res (W), Lutterworth Town (P - United Counties), Page Celtic (West Cheshire). **Division One - In:** Asfordby, Caterpillar, Earl Shilton Albion, Melton Town Dev, Rugby Borough, St Andrews Res, Thurnby Rangers. **Out:** Alder (P), Custy's (P), Eli Lilly (W), Salisbury Athletic (W), Old Xaverians Res (W). **Division Two - In:** City of Liverpool Res (West Cheshire), Fantail, Leyfield, Liverpool Baltic, Liverpool Medics, Roby and Waterloo GSOB Res (Liverpool OB Lge).**Out:** Leighbridge (W), Litherland REMYCA 'A' (W).

Liverpool County Premier League Premier Division

AFC LIVERPOOL RESERVES		
AIGBURTH PEOPLE'S HALL	Wavertree Sports Park 3G pitch, Wellington Road L15 4LE	
ALDER	Alder Sports Club L12 2AY	
ALUMNI	Wavertree Sports Park 3G pitch, Wellington Road L15 4LE	
BYROM	Archbishop Beck	
CUSTY'S		
EAST VILLA	Scargreen Park, Scargreen Avenue, Liverpool	
LIVERPOOL NALGO	Alder Sports Club, Alder Road, Liverpool L12 2BA	0151 228 5250
LOWER BRECK	Lower Breck 3G	
MSB WOOLTON	Wavertree Sports Park 3G pitch, Wellington Road L15 4LE	
OLD XAVERIANS	St Francis Xaviers College, Beconsfield Road, Liverpool L25 6EG	0151 428 2829
SOUTH SEFTON BOROUGH	Mill Dam Field behind the Punch Bowl Pub, Bridges Lane, Sefton L29 7WA	
WARBRECK	St John Bosco 3G	
WATERLOO DOCK	Lower Breck 3G	
WATERLOO GSOB	Archbishop Beck	

MANCHESTER LEAGUE

Sponsored by: FBT Europe	**GILGRYST CUP**
Founded: 1893	

Recent Champions:
2014: Hindsford
2015: Stockport Georgians
2016: Prestwich Heys

GILGRYST CUP

HOLDERS: PRESTWISH HEYS
PRELIMINARY ROUND

Westbury Sports Club	v	Royton Town	1-6
Bolton County	v	Hindsford	0-2
Uppermill	v	Manchester Central	0-4

QUALIFYING ROUND

Elton Vale	v	Heywood St James	6-1
Prestwich Heys Res	v	Walshaw Sports	1-0
Royton Town	v	Breightmet United	5-2
Old Altrinchamians	v	Altrincham Hale	4-1
Wythenshawe Amateurs	v	Irlam Steel	3-0
Heyside	v	Hindsford	3-6
Dukinfield Town	v	Boothstown	2-1
Atherton Town	v	Rochdale Sacred Heart	1-5
Manchester Gregorians	v	Wilmslow Albion	2-2, 2-4p
Beechfield United	v	Chapel Town	2-2, 4-3p
Chadderton Res	v	Springhead	1-2
AVRO	v	East Manchester	2-2, 4-3p
Hollinwood	Bye		
Manchester Central	v	Leigh Athletic	1-2
Govan Athletic	v	Stockport Georgians	1-2
Pennington	v	AFC Monton	4-7

ROUND 1

Elton Vale	v	Prestwich Heys Res	2-2, 1-3p
Royton Town	v	Old Altrinchamians	3-0
Wythenshawe Amateurs	v	Hindsford	1-2
Dukinfield Town	v	Rochdale Sacred Heart	0-3
Wilmslow Albion	v	Beechfield United	1-1, 4-2p
Springhead	v	AVRO	2-2, 4-5p
Hollinwood	v	Leigh Athletic	3-3, 3-4p
Stockport Georgians	v	AFC Monton	2-2, 2-4p

PREMIER DIVISION

		P	W	D	L	F	A	GD	Pts
1	Rochdale Sacred Heart	28	21	2	5	101	44	57	65
2	Wythenshawe Amateurs	28	21	2	5	71	39	32	61*
3	Springhead	28	14	6	8	59	48	11	48
4	Manchester Gregorians	28	14	5	9	52	44	8	47
5	Hindsford	28	14	4	10	71	53	18	46
6	AFC Monton	28	15	2	11	61	48	13	43*
7	Royton Town	28	12	7	9	59	49	10	43
8	Stockport Georgians	28	12	6	10	70	41	29	42
9	Walshaw Sports	28	12	5	11	53	50	3	41
10	East Manchester	28	11	5	12	56	63	-7	38
11	AVRO	28	10	5	13	59	64	-5	34*
12	Dukinfield Town	28	10	4	14	47	49	-2	33*
13	Old Altrinchamians	28	8	2	18	44	61	-17	26
14	Elton Vale	28	5	3	20	34	101	-67	18
15	Wilmslow Albion	28	2	0	26	20	103	-83	6

Rochdale Town folded before the start of the season.

DIVISION ONE

		P	W	D	L	F	A	GD	Pts
1	Prestwich Heys Res	36	26	6	4	111	51	60	84
2	Heyside	36	24	6	6	107	45	62	78
3	Bolton County	36	24	4	8	108	46	62	76
4	Atherton Town	36	20	6	10	65	41	24	66
5	Manchester Central	36	19	8	9	86	53	33	65
6	Beechfield United	36	19	4	13	104	79	25	61
7	Boothstown	36	16	9	11	86	76	10	54*
8	Chadderton Res	36	14	9	13	99	90	9	51
9	Leigh Athletic	36	16	4	16	78	76	2	51*
10	Pennington	36	15	6	15	82	102	-20	51
11	Westbury Sports Club	36	14	6	16	99	107	-8	48
12	Hollinwood	36	16	3	17	104	98	6	46*
13	Chapel Town	36	12	8	16	81	91	-10	44
14	Breightmet United	36	13	3	20	56	81	-25	42
15	Altrincham Hale	36	10	10	16	80	86	-6	40
16	Irlam Steel	36	12	4	20	73	100	-27	31*
17	Heywood St James	36	8	5	23	78	118	-40	26*
18	Govan Athletic	36	6	5	25	57	111	-54	23
19	Uppermill	36	2	6	28	44	147	-103	12

DIVISION TWO

		P	W	D	L	F	A	GD	Pts
1	Stockport Georgians Res	28	23	3	2	104	28	76	72
2	Hindsford Res	28	21	1	6	87	38	49	64
3	Rochdale Sacred Heart Res	28	19	1	8	111	43	68	58
4	Springhead Res	28	16	1	11	89	62	27	49
5	Manchester Gregorians Res	28	15	3	10	66	63	3	47*
6	Royton Town Res	28	15	1	12	89	78	11	46
7	Dukinfield Town Res	28	12	5	11	62	65	-3	41
8	Wythenshawe Amateurs Res	28	12	2	14	65	68	-3	38
9	Atherton Town Res	28	10	2	16	57	71	-14	32
10	Walshaw Sports Res	28	9	4	15	59	86	-27	31
11	AVRO Res	28	12	0	16	67	67	0	29*
12	Wilmslow Albion Res	28	10	0	18	48	78	-30	29*
13	AFC Monton Res	28	8	4	16	45	76	-31	28
14	Elton Vale Res	28	8	3	17	69	95	-26	27
15	Hollinwood Res	28	4	2	22	48	148	-100	13*

PREMIER DIVISION

		1	2	3	4	5	6	7	8	9	10	11	12	13	14	15
1	AFC Monton		6-2	1-2	3-2	2-1	1-3	4-2	2-0	2-6	2-0	1-1	1-0	1-3	5-1	0-3
2	AVRO	3-1		1-1	1-4	7-1	1-2	2-5	1-0	1-2	3-3	1-1	3-3	1-4	4-3	0-1
3	Dukinfield Town	1-0	1-1		0-2	3-4	2-1	3-4	2-0	2-5	0-1	0-2	2-3	0-1	3-0	1-2
4	East Manchester	3-3	2-1	2-4		3-2	4-2	0-3	2-4	2-4	1-4	3-4	2-1	1-0	4-0	0-1
5	Elton Vale	0-1	2-12	1-1	4-2		3-3	0-2	0-6	4-2	1-4	1-2	0-8	0-2	1-0	0-2
6	Hindsford	3-2	0-1	4-2	3-1	4-1		3-1	0-1	4-3	0-4	4-1	1-2	3-2	5-0	3-3
7	Manchester Gregorians	0-4	1-0	4-3	1-1	6-0	4-1		1-0	1-4	1-1	1-3	1-0	2-2	2-3	3-2
8	Old Altrinchamians	0-5	1-2	1-2	3-0	0-4	2-0			2-4	0-2	1-0	4-0	0-3	8-1	0-1
9	Rochdale Sacred Heart	3-0	1-5	H-W	8-0	6-0	4-3	2-0	4-0		4-0	4-2	1-1	2-1	8-0	2-5
10	Royton Town	1-0	1-2	2-0	2-2	5-5	2-2	2-3	2-1	2-0		5-1	0-3	0-3	4-1	2-3
11	Springhead	3-0	6-1	1-1	1-1	2-0	1-3	0-1	6-1	0-6	5-4		1-2	2-2	4-2	2-1
12	Stockport Georgians	1-3	3-1	1-3	1-1	6-0	2-1	1-1	1-1	1-3	2-2	1-2		6-1	5-2	0-3
13	Walshaw Sports	1-3	3-1	1-3	1-2	1-2	2-2	1-0	6-3	2-2	2-2	0-3	3-1		2-1	2-5
14	Wilmslow Albion	1-4	0-1	0-3	0-5	2-0	0-5	0-2	2-4	1-3	0-2	0-2	0-9	0-1		0-4
15	Wythenshawe Amateurs	2-4	6-0	4-2	3-1	4-1	3-2	0-0	0-3	3-8	0-1	1-0	3-2	2-1	3-0	

DIVISION THREE

		P	W	D	L	F	A	GD	Pts
1	Westbury Sports Club Res	28	23	3	2	118	35	83	72
2	Leigh Athletic Res	28	18	6	4	97	71	26	60
3	Chapel Town Res	28	19	2	7	86	59	27	57*
4	Rochdale Sacred Heart A	28	17	5	6	118	65	53	56
5	East Manchester Academy	28	16	3	9	109	70	39	51
6	Irlam Steel Res	28	15	4	9	79	66	13	48*
7	Heyside Res	28	12	5	11	98	88	10	40*
8	Bolton County Res	28	12	3	13	70	81	-11	39
9	Old Altrinchamians Res	28	11	5	12	65	74	-9	38
10	Pennington Res	28	9	6	13	75	74	1	33
11	Boothstown Res	28	9	2	17	60	90	-30	28*
12	Breightmet United Res	28	8	2	18	53	91	-38	25*
13	Springhead A	28	8	3	17	61	93	-32	23*
14	Govan Athletic Res	28	3	4	21	53	101	-48	11*
15	Atherton Town A	28	2	3	23	32	116	-84	8*

NEW CONSTITUTIONS FOR 2017-18

DIVISION ONE
Atherton Town, Beechfield United, Boothstown, Chadderton Reserves, Chapel Town, Elton Vale, Hollinwood, Leigh Athletic, Manchester Central, Pennington, Westbury Sports Club, Wilmslow Albion.

DIVISION TWO
Altrincham Hale, Atherton LR Development (N), Bolton Lads and Girls Club (Lancashire Amateur), Breightmet United, Govan Athletic, Heywood St James, Hindley Juniors (Bolton & Bury Junior), Irlam Steel, Radcliffe Juniors (Lancashire Amateur), Tintwistle Athletic (Lancs & Cheshire League), Uppermill.

DIVISION THREE
Atherton Town Res, Avro Res, Dukinfield Town Res, Hindsford Res, Manchester Gregorians Res, Rochdale Sacred Heart Res, Royton Town Res, Springhead Res, Stockport Georgians Res, Walshaw Sports Res, Wilmslow Albion Res, Wythenshawe Amateurs Res.

DIVISION FOUR
AFC Monton Res, Bolton County Res, Chapel Town Res, East Manchester Academy, Elton Vale Res, Heyside Res, Hollinwood Res, Irlam Steel Res, Leigh Athletic Res, Old Altrinchamians Res, Pennington Res, Rochdale Sacred Heart A.

DIVISION FIVE
Altrincham Hale Res (Altrincham & District), Atherton Town A Bolton Lads and Girls Club Res (Lancashire Amateur), Boothstown Res, Breightmet United Res, Chadderton EDS (North West Youth Alliance), Heywood St James Res (Reformed), Govan Athletic Res, Springhead A, Tintwistle Athletic Res (Lancs & Cheshire), Uppermill Res (Huddersfield & District).

GILGRYST CUP continued...

QUARTER-FINALS

Prestwich Heys Res	v	Royton Town	0-4
Hindsford	v	Rochdale Sacred Heart	2-3
Wilmslow Albion	v	AVRO	1-4
Leigh Athletic	v	AFC Monton	1-2

SEMI-FINALS

Royton Town	v	Rochdale Sacred Heart	2-5
AVRO	v	AFC Monton	1-2

FINAL

Rochdale Sacred Heart	v	AFC Monton	1-0

NORMAN NODEN CUP

HOLDERS: STOCKPORT GEORGIANS
FINAL - Premier Division Winners v Gilcrist Cup Winners 30/07/16

Royton Town	v	Manchester Gregorians	2-0

TERRY WOOD CUP

HOLDERS: OLD ALTRINCHAMIANS
FINAL - Division One Winners v Murray Shield Winners 30/07/16

East Manchester	v	Elton Vale	5-1

MURRAY SHIELD

HOLDERS: EAST MANCHESTER
FINAL

East Manchester	v	Manchester Central	2-2, 4-3p

OPEN CUP

HOLDERS: PRESTWICH HEYS RES
FINAL

Walshaw Sports Res	v	Rochdale Sacred Heart Res	0-2

BRIDGWATER CUP

HOLDERS: UPPERMILL RES
FINAL

Westbury Sports Club Res	v	Bolton County Res	1-1, 5-4p

Manchester League Premier Division

AFC MONTON	New Alder Park, Off Worsley Road, Winton, Salford M30 8JN	07836 321 193
AVRO	Vestacare Stadium, White Bank Road, Oldham OL8 3JH	
BOLTON COUNTY	Radcliffe Road, Darcy Lever, Bolton, Lancashire BL3 1AN	
DUKINFIELD TOWN	Woodhams Park, Birch Lane, Dukinfield SK16 5AP	07748 634 862
EAST MANCHESTER	Wright Robinson Sports College, Abbey Hey Lane, Gorton M18 8RL	
HEYSIDE	Rochdale Road, Shaw, OLDHAM, Lancashire OL2 7HS	
HINDSFORD	Squires Lane, Tyldesley M29 8JF	
MANCHESTER GREGORIANS	MCFC, Platt Lane Complex, Yew Tree Road, Fallowfield M14 7UU	
OLD ALTRINCHAMIANS	Crossford Bridge Sports Ground, Danefield Road, Sale M33 7WR	
PRESTWICH HEYS RESERVES	Adie Moran Park, Sandgate Road, Whitefield M45 6WG	0161 7773 8888 (MD)
ROCHDALE SACRED HEART	Fox Park, Belfield Mill Lane, Rochdale OL16 2UB	01706 869 640
ROYTON TOWN	Oldham Academy North, Broadway OL2 5BF	
SPRINGHEAD	Ashfield Crescent PF, St John Street, Lees, Oldham OL4 3DR	
STOCKPORT GEORGIANS	Cromley Road, Woodsmoor, Stockport SK2 7DT	
WALSHAW SPORTS	Walshaw Sports Club, Sycamore Road, Tottington, Bury BL8 3EG	07843 761 182
WYTHENSHAWE AMATEUR	Hollyhedge Park, Altrincham Road, Wythenshawe M22 4US	07902 240 224

MIDDLESEX COUNTY LEAGUE

Sponsored by: Cherry Red Books
Founded: 1984
Recent Champions:
2014: Sporting Hackney
2015: Hillingdon
2016: West Essex

ALEC SMITH PREMIER DIVISION CUP

HOLDERS: HILLINGDON
PRELIMINARY ROUND

British Airways	v	AFC Wembley	3-3, 10-9p
Brentham	v	Cricklewood Wanderers	3-1
CB Hounslow United Res	v	Hillingdon	1-3
Sporting Hackney	v	FC Assyria	2-3
FC Deportivo Galicia	v	LPOSSA	HW
Tooting & Mitcham Wanderers	v	Indian Gymkhana Club	1-2
Southall Res	v	Pitshanger Dynamo	1-3
South Kilburn	v	Kensington Dragons	0-3

QUARTER-FINALS

British Airways	v	Indian Gymkhana Club	6-3
FC Deportivo Galicia	v	Kensington Dragons	3-2
Hillingdon	v	FC Assyria	1-5
Brentham	v	Pitshanger Dynamo	1-1, HWp

SEMI-FINALS

British Airways	v	FC Assyria	3-4
FC Deportivo Galicia	v	Brentham	1-0

FINAL

FC Assyria	v	FC Deportivo Galicia	3-0

PREMIER DIVISION	P	W	D	L	F	A	GD	Pts
1 FC Deportivo Galicia	26	21	3	2	63	25	38	66
2 British Airways	26	19	4	3	88	31	57	61
3 FC Assyria	26	19	1	6	113	43	70	58
4 Indian Gymkhana Club	26	10	8	8	43	37	6	38
5 Pitshanger Dynamo	26	12	2	12	71	66	5	38
6 Kensington Dragons	26	10	6	10	58	54	4	36
7 Hillingdon	26	10	6	10	50	48	2	36
8 Cricklewood Wanderers	26	9	7	10	44	62	-18	34
9 Brentham	26	10	3	13	55	69	-14	33
10 AFC Wembley	26	8	8	10	50	54	-4	32
11 Tooting & Mitcham Wanderers	26	7	9	10	30	50	-20	30
12 Sporting Hackney	26	8	2	16	46	73	-27	26
13 C.B. Hounslow United Res	26	4	4	18	25	67	-42	16
14 South Kilburn	26	1	5	20	22	79	-57	8

LPOSSA withdrew - record expunged.
Southall Res withdrew - record expunged.

PREMIER DIVISION		1	2	3	4	5	6	7	8	9	10	11	12	13	14
1	AFC Wembley		2-3	1-2	2-3	1-1	2-6	1-2	1-1	1-1	5-2	3-0	2-0	2-2	4-0
2	Brentham	2-2		1-3	2-3	1-1	6-1	0-4	2-0	0-2	3-2	1-2	3-2	1-4	1-2
3	British Airways	4-1	4-0		6-0	5-1	2-3	2-1	2-1	1-1	2-4	3-4	4-2	5-1	D
4	C.B. Hounslow United Res	0-2	2-3	0-5		0-2	1-5	1-2	0-2	0-0	5-2	1-6	D	1-5	D
5	Cricklewood Wanderers	0-3	3-2	3-7	1-1		1-2	1-3	3-2	2-1	3-5	4-2	4-2	3-0	1-3
6	FC Assyria	7-1	10-1	1-2	6-1	4-0		1-1	5-0	3-2	3-0	5-6	3-0	12-1	3-1
7	FC Deportivo Galicia	4-1	3-1	1-1	2-1	4-0	4-2		3-2	1-0	4-1	3-0	4-0	HW	3-0
8	Hillingdon	1-1	AW	1-1	4-3	6-0	2-5	1-2		4-2	0-6	0-3	4-1	4-0	2-1
9	Indian Gymkhana Club	3-1	3-3	2-4	2-0	1-2	0-4	1-1	1-1		3-1	3-1	3-0	2-2	4-0
10	Kensington Dragons	2-2	3-1	0-5	0-1	2-2	HW	3-0	3-3	1-2		3-0	D	0-2	3-0
11	Pitshanger Dynamo	4-5	3-5	1-4	4-0	1-1	0-5	2-4	1-4	4-3	2-2		7-0	6-0	5-3
12	South Kilburn	1-2	3-7	1-5	2-1	D	2-8	1-3	1-2	0-1	2-7	0-3		1-4	1-1
13	Sporting Hackney	2-1	2-4	0-5	1-0	2-3	3-6	2-3	0-2	AW	2-4	3-4	1-0		1-4
14	Tooting & Mitcham Wanderers	1-1	3-2	0-4	1-0	2-2	4-3	0-1	1-1	0-0	2-2	1-0	0-0	0-6	

DIVISION ONE CENTRAL & EAST	P	W	D	L	F	A	GD	Pts
1 AFC United	18	14	1	3	59	36	23	43
2 Stonewall	18	13	3	2	43	18	25	42
3 Tottenham Hale Rangers	18	13	2	3	53	26	27	41
4 AEK London	18	11	3	4	42	25	17	36
5 Mile End Park Rangers	18	9	1	8	49	32	17	28
6 J L Rovers	18	7	4	7	52	46	6	25
7 Hackney Wick	18	5	1	12	39	53	-14	16
8 The Wilberforce Wanderers	18	4	3	11	36	42	-6	15
9 Fire United Christian	18	2	2	14	26	74	-48	8
10 WARSA	18	2	0	16	37	84	-47	6

DIVISION ONE WEST	P	W	D	L	F	A	GD	Pts
1 Lampton Park	18	15	0	3	73	16	57	45
2 Spartan Youth	18	12	2	4	35	19	16	38
3 Kodak (Harrow)	18	10	5	3	30	17	13	35
4 Larkspur Rovers	18	9	4	5	36	26	10	31
5 VOS	18	7	1	9	36	24	12	22
6 Alpha & Omega	18	6	3	8	38	42	-4	21
7 New Hanford	18	6	2	10	30	44	-14	20
8 Hillingdon Abbots	18	6	1	11	19	46	-27	19
9 Hounslow Wanderers	18	3	5	10	16	48	-32	14
10 Evergreen	18	1	5	12	21	52	-31	8

DIVISION TWO	P	W	D	L	F	A	GD	Pts
1 PFC Victoria London	16	13	1	2	58	16	42	40
2 Hayes MBFC	16	11	1	4	61	43	18	34
3 AFC Hanwell & Hayes	16	9	0	7	53	35	18	27
4 Heston Bombers	16	7	2	7	28	36	-8	23
5 Cranford Park	16	6	4	6	30	36	-6	22
6 C.B. Hounslow United 3rds	16	7	1	8	20	35	-15	22
7 Harrow Rangers	16	5	4	7	30	47	-17	19
8 Ealing Casuals	16	5	1	10	31	21	10	16
9 Centenary Park	16	2	0	14	15	57	-42	6

MCFL COMBINATION	P	W	D	L	F	A	GD	Pts
1 Harrow Bhoys	22	17	1	4	79	29	50	52
2 Hilltop	22	17	1	4	73	32	41	52
3 St Nicholas	22	14	1	7	53	44	9	43
4 Sudbury Court	22	13	2	7	60	42	18	41
5 Lampton Park Res	22	13	1	8	60	27	33	40
6 C.B. Hounslow United 5ths	22	9	3	10	44	48	-4	30
7 LNER	22	10	0	12	61	70	-9	30
8 Ruislip	22	7	8	7	54	45	+9	29
9 Som Academy	22	8	1	13	38	39	-1	25
10 AFC Heathrow	22	6	2	14	39	84	-45	20
11 Hillingdon 3rds	22	3	2	17	29	69	-40	11
12 Barnet and Harrow	22	3	2	17	22	83	-61	11

SENIOR RESERVE DIVISION	P	W	D	L	F	A	GD	Pts
1 South Kilburn Res	18	14	2	2	73	30	43	44
2 Indian Gymkhana Club Res	18	14	2	2	58	20	38	44
3 FC Deportivo Galicia Res	18	11	4	3	63	32	31	37
4 Pitshanger Dynamo Res	18	9	2	7	57	40	17	29
5 Soccer Ed	18	8	2	8	60	62	-2	26
6 LPOSSA Res	18	8	0	10	64	54	10	24
7 Brentham Res	18	6	5	7	24	39	-15	23
8 Stonewall Res	18	6	0	12	27	53	-26	18
9 Kensington Dragons Res	18	3	2	13	33	59	-26	11
10 C.B. Hounslow United 4ths	18	1	1	16	24	94	-70	4

Tooting & Mitcham Wanderers 2016-17.
11th in Middlesex County Premier Division.
Photo: Roger Turner.

Middlesex County League Premier Division

BRENTHAM	Meadvale Road, Ealing, London W5 1NP	020 8997 2624
BRITISH AIRWAYS	Short Lane Stadium, Stanwell, Staines TW19 7BH	
C.B. HOUNSLOW UNITED RES.	TBC	
CRICKLEWOOD WANDERERS	Vale Farm Sports Centre, Watford Road, North Wembley, London HA0 3HE	
FC ASSYRIA	Osterley Sports Club, Tentelow Lane, Norwood Green, Middlesex UB2 4LW	020 8574 7055
HILLINGDON	Brunel Uni. Sports Complex, Kingston Park, Kingston Lane, Hillingdon UB8 3PW	
INDIAN GYMKHANA	Indian Gymkhana Club, Thornbury Avenue, Osterley TW7 4NQ	020 8568 4009
KENSINGTON DRAGONS	Linford Christie Stadium, Artillery Lane, off Du Cane Road W12 0DF	
LAMPTON PARK	Osterley Sports Club, Tentelow Lane, Norwood Green, Middlesex UB2 4LW	020 8574 7055
PITSHANGER DYNAMO	Hanwell Town FC, Perivale Lane, Perivale, Greenford Middlesex UB6 8TL	
SOUTH KILBURN	Vale Farm, Watford Road, North Wembley HA0 3HE	
SPORTING HACKNEY	Hackney Marshes, Homerton Road, Hackney, London E9 5PF	020 8986 7955
STONEWALL	Barn Elms Playing Fields, Queen Elizabeth Walk, Barnes SW13 0DG	020 8876 7685
TOOTING & MITCHAM WANDERERS	Raynes Park Vale FC, Grand Drive, Raynes Park SW20 9NB	02085 408 843
TOTTENHAM HALE RANGERS	Fredrick Knight Sports Ground, Willoughby Lane, Tottenham, London N17 0SL	020 8801 8233

CLUB MOVEMENTS
Premier Division - In: Lampton Park (P), Stonewall (P), Tottenham Hale Rangers (P). **Out: AFC Wembley (W),** FC Deportivo Galicia (P - Combined Counties).

Division One Central & East - In: Chape London, Hackey Wick Res, London Samurai United, London United, St Panteleimon.
Out: WARSA (W).

Division One West - In: FC Deportivo Galicia Res, FC IGK (formerly Indian Gymkana Res), Hayes MBFC (P), PFC Victoria London (P), South Kilburn 3rds.
Out: Hillingdon Abbots (R), Spartan Youth (W).

Division Two - In: Hillingdon Abbots (R), West SL Benfica, Western Athletic.
Out: Ealing Casuals (W).

NORTH RIDING (formerly Teesside) LEAGUE

DIVISION ONE

		P	W	D	L	F	A	GD	Pts
1	Boro Rangers	22	20	1	1	89	22	67	61
2	BEADS FC	22	17	2	3	83	42	41	53
3	Stockton West End	22	13	1	8	75	55	20	40
4	Redcar Town	22	10	4	8	37	34	3	34
5	Redcar Newmarket	22	11	1	10	54	52	2	34
6	Fishburn Park	22	8	5	9	50	56	-6	29
7	Thornaby Dubliners	22	8	2	12	44	56	-12	26
8	Guisborough Three Fiddles	22	8	2	12	43	59	-16	26
9	Staithes Athletic	22	7	2	13	45	59	-14	23
10	Nunthorpe Ath	22	7	2	13	37	60	-23	23
11	Billingham Town Res	22	5	4	13	44	58	-14	19
12	St Mary's Yarm	22	3	4	15	28	76	-48	13

Grangetown Boys Club withdrew - record expunged.

Whinney Banks YCC withdrew - record expunged.

Sponsored by: Jack Hatfield Sports
Founded: 1891
Recent Champions: 2014: Whinney Banks YCC
2015: Whinney Banks YCC **2016:** Boro Rangers

MACMILLAN BOWL LEAGUE CUP

QUARTER FINALS		HOLDERS: WHINNEY BANKS YCC
BEADS SC	v Stockton West End	3-1
Staithes Athletic	v Fishburn Park	1-2
Nunthorpe Athletic	v Boro Rangers	0-4
Billingham Town Res	v Grangetown BC	HW
SEMI FINALS		
BEADS SC	v Fishburn Park	2-1
Boro Rangers	v Billingham Town Res	0-2
FINAL		
BEADS SC	v Billingham Town Res	3-2

LOU MOORE MEMORIAL TROPHY

FINAL		HOLDERS: REDCAR NEWMARKET
BEADS SC	v Redcar Town	2-4 aet

DIVISION ONE

		1	2	3	4	5	6	7	8	9	10	11	12
1	BEADS FC		7-4	3-6	5-1	4-0	7-3	4-2	4-1	6-0	4-3	2-5	6-1
2	Billingham Town Res	1-2		1-3	2-2	2-5	2-2	6-5	1-2	3-2	4-3	2-3	2-2
3	Boro Rangers	1-1	3-1		6-1	5-1	2-0	5-2	3-0	3-0	3-0	2-3	4-1
4	Fishburn Park	3-2	3-3	1-2		1-3	3-4	5-1	1-0	2-0	2-4	4-7	1-0
5	Guisborough Three Fiddles	1-2	3-1	2-8	2-2		0-4	4-0	1-3	0-2	1-4	3-2	3-4
6	Nunthorpe Athletic	1-2	2-1	1-9	1-4	0-2		1-6	0-1	0-2	3-1	4-3	2-1
7	Redcar Newmarket	0-1	1-0	2-6	2-1	6-3	2-0		1-3	2-2	1-0	4-1	3-1
8	Redcar Town	1-1	2-0	1-4	3-3	2-0	1-1	1-2		4-0	3-2	1-0	2-0
9	St Mary's Yarm	1-7	2-1	0-4	1-5	0-3	1-3	0-4	4-4		1-3	3-3	2-7
10	Staithes Athletic	2-4	2-3	0-3	1-2	2-2	3-2	2-1	2-1	2-2		3-5	3-4
11	Stockton West End	4-7	0-3	0-3	5-1	4-2	4-2	5-1	1-0	7-1	8-1		4-3
12	Thornaby Dubliners	1-2	2-1	1-4	2-2	1-2	3-1	1-6	3-1	3-2	0-2	3-1	

North Riding League Premier Division

BEADS FC	Beechwood & Easterside Social Club, Marton Road, Middlesbrough TS4 3PP
BILLINGHAM TOWN RESERVES	Bedford Terrace, Billingham, Cleveland TS23 4AE
BORO RANGERS	Eston Leisure Complex #2, Normanby Road, Eston, Middlesbrough TS6 9AE
FISHBURN PARK	Eskdale School, Broomfield Park, Whitby, N Yorkshire YO22 4EB
GRANGETOWN BOYS CLUB	Grangetown Youth & C. Centre 1, Trunk Road, Grangetown, Middlesbrough TS6 7HP
GUISBOROUGH UNITED	King George V Playing Fields 1, Howlbeck Road, Guisborough TS14 6LE
NUNTHORPE ATHLETIC	Nunthorpe Recreation Club, Guisborough Road, Nunthorpe, Middlesbrough TS7 0LE
REDCAR NEWMARKET	Rye Hill School, Redcar Lane, Redcar TS10 2HN
REDCAR TOWN	Mo Mowlam Park #2, Trunk Road, Redcar TS10 5BW
ST MARY'S 1947	Conyers School #1, Green Lane, Yarm TS15 9ET
STAITHES ATHLETIC	Staithes Athletic Social Club, Seaton Crescent, Staithes, Saltburn TS13 5AY
STOCKTON WEST END	North Shore Health Academy, Talbot Street, Stockton TS20 2AY
THORNABY DUBLINERS	Harold Wilson Sports Complex, Bader Avenue, Thornaby TS17 8PH
YARM & EAGLESCLIFFE	

NORTHAMPTONSHIRE COMBINATION

Sponsored by: MDH Teamwear
Founded: N/K
Recent Champions:
2014: Brixworth All Saints
2015: Corby Eagles
2016: James King Blisworth
northantscombination.co.uk

PREMIER DIVISION	P	W	D	L	F	A	GD	Pts
1 James King Blisworth	26	23	0	3	101	28	73	69
2 Harpole	26	22	0	4	89	37	52	66
3 Kettering Nomads	26	20	1	5	92	29	63	61
4 Roade	26	18	3	5	68	33	35	57
5 Heyford Athletic	26	12	4	10	55	51	4	40
6 Moulton	26	10	3	13	50	58	-8	33
7 Brixworth All Saints	26	10	3	13	39	60	-21	33
8 Corby S&L Khalsa	26	9	5	12	64	81	-17	32
9 Medbourne	26	9	3	14	49	65	-16	30
10 Earls Barton United	26	9	2	15	41	60	-19	29
11 Corby Pegasus	26	7	6	13	51	72	-21	27
12 Wollaston Victoria	26	7	3	16	40	84	-44	24
13 Spratton	26	6	3	17	36	74	-38	21
14 Wellingborough Rising Sun	26	1	2	23	24	67	-43	-4*

Milton withdrew - record expunged.and joined Division One.

PREMIER DIVISION CUP

HOLDERS: HARPOLE
ROUND 1
Wellingborough Rising Sun v James King Blisworth 1-7
Roade Bye
Harpole v Corby S&L Khalsa 4-2
Wollaston Victoria v Brixworth All Saints 1-2
Spratton v Corby Pegasus 1-1, 0-3p
Medbourne Bye
Kettering Nomads v Earls Barton United 8-1
Moulton v Heyford Athletic 2-1

QUARTER-FINALS
James King Blisworth v Roade 2-2, 5-4p
Harpole v Brixworth All Saints 3-1
Corby Pegasus v Medbourne 0-6
Kettering Nomads v Moulton 4-1

SeMI-FINALS
James King Blisworth v Harpole 4-2
Medbourne v Kettering Nomads 1-3

FINAL
James King Blisworth v Kettering Nomads 5-0

PREMIER DIVISION		1	2	3	4	5	6	7	8	9	10	11	12	13	14
1	Brixworth All Saints		3-2	2-4	1-0	1-4	1-4	0-4	0-1	1-0	1-2	1-4	3-0	2-1	5-1
2	Corby Pegasus	1-1		3-2	0-0	0-4	1-8	1-5	0-3	5-5	0-3	0-0	2-0	11-1	3-1
3	Corby S&L Khalsa	3-3	4-4		2-3	1-4	3-2	5-4	3-3	2-2	3-0	3-5	1-4	2-3	4-1
4	Earls Barton United	7-0	3-2	2-1		3-5	1-3	0-4	0-5	1-2	0-4	0-4	3-4	1-0	0-1
5	Harpole	2-0	5-2	1-0	3-1		4-1	4-1	0-6	4-0	2-1	2-3	5-1	5-4	4-1
6	Heyford Athletic	0-1	3-1	2-3	4-2	0-3		0-4	2-1	3-2	1-3	1-4	4-1	2-0	2-2
7	James King Blisworth	5-1	5-2	8-1	3-1	2-0	2-0		0-3	1-0	5-0	3-1	4-0	5-1	8-2
8	Kettering Nomads	4-2	4-0	12-3	5-1	1-3	6-1	A-W		3-2	3-0	2-0	5-1	3-2	1-0
9	Medbourne	2-0	4-0	1-2	0-2	1-4	0-0	0-6	2-4		2-4	2-5	1-2	H-W	6-4
10	Moulton	3-0	2-2	2-2	0-3	1-2	1-5	0-5	2-1	5-6		5-3	1-2	5-1	1-2
11	Roade	2-2	2-0	3-1	4-2	3-1	1-1	1-4	2-0	5-0	1-0		5-1	H-W	1-2
12	Spratton	1-3	1-3	1-4	2-2	2-5	1-2	3-7	0-2	0-4	0-2	1-3		2-2	1-1
13	Wellingborough Rising Sun	2-3	2-4	A-W	A-W	0-4	1-2	A-W	0-6	1-3	1-1	1-3	0-1		1-2
14	Wollaston Victoria	1-2	1-2	6-5	1-5	1-9	2-2	0-5	2-6	1-2	5-2	0-3	0-4	H-W	

DIVISION ONE	P	W	D	L	F	A	GD	Pts
1 Gretton	22	16	2	4	91	35	56	50
2 Burton United	22	16	1	5	70	25	45	49
3 Roade Res	22	15	2	5	72	29	43	47
4 Wootton St George	22	15	2	5	72	43	29	47
5 Corby Eagles	22	13	2	7	82	51	31	35*
6 Desborough & Rothwell United	22	10	5	7	67	54	13	35
7 Milton	22	9	5	8	34	44	-10	32
8 West Haddon Albion	22	8	3	11	29	39	-10	27
9 Woodford Wolves	22	6	2	14	53	83	-30	20
10 Stanion United	22	4	3	15	40	78	-38	12*
11 Finedon Volta	22	3	2	17	29	80	-51	11
12 Kettering Orchard Park	22	1	3	18	19	97	-78	3*

DIVISION TWO	P	W	D	L	F	A	GD	Pts
1 Mereway	20	19	0	1	75	16	59	57
2 Corby Kingswood	20	15	3	2	77	41	36	48
3 AFC Houghton Magna	20	12	3	5	63	40	23	39
4 Wellingborough Aztecs	20	9	4	7	53	52	1	31
5 Corby Pegasus Res	20	8	3	9	42	45	-3	27
6 Bugbrooke St Michaels 'A'	20	7	5	8	39	51	-12	26
7 Corby Strip Mills	20	7	2	11	44	56	-12	23
8 Higham Town	20	5	3	12	29	57	-28	18
9 Daventry Drayton Grange	20	5	2	13	38	62	-24	17
10 Corby Locos	20	4	4	12	26	50	-24	16
11 Northampton Spartak	20	4	1	15	31	47	-16	13

NORTHANTS COMBINATION LEAGUE - STEP 7

Northamptonshire Combination Premier Division

BRIXWORTH ALL SAINTS	St Davids Close, off Froxhill Crescent, Brixworth NN6 9EA
BURTON ALBION	Toll Bar Road, Islip NN14 3LH
CORBY PEGASUS	West Glebe South Pitch 3 NN17 1SZ
EARLS BARTON UNITED	The Grange, Northampton Road, Earls Barton, Northants NN6 0HA
GRETTON	Gretton Recreation Ground, Kirby Road, Gretton, Northants. NN17 3DB
HARPOLE	Playing Field, Larkhall Lane, Harpole NN7 4DP
HEYFORD ATHLETIC	Nether Heyford PF NN7 3LL
JAMES KING BLISWORTH	Blisworth Playing Field, Courteenhall Road, Blisworth NN7 3DD
KETTERING NOMADS	Isham Cricket Club NN14 1HW
MEDBOURNE	Medbourne S&S Club LE16 8DR
MOULTON	Brunting Road, Moulton, Northampton NN3 7QF
ROADE	Connolly Way, Hyde Road, Roade NN7 2LU
SPRATTON	Smith Street, Spratton NN6 8HW
WOLLASTON VICTORIA	Wollaston PF NN29 7QP
WOODFORD UNITED	Byfield Road, Woodford Halse, Daventry, Northants NN11 3QS

01327 263 734

DIVISION THREE

		P	W	D	L	F	A	GD	Pts
1	Weedon	24	18	2	4	95	46	49	56
2	Kislingbury JLB FC	24	16	3	5	97	49	48	51
3	Kettering Nomads Res	24	15	3	6	53	41	12	48
4	Bugbrooke St Michaels 'B'	24	15	0	9	71	55	16	45
5	FC FotoGold	24	14	2	8	67	53	14	44
6	Wollaston Victoria Res	24	11	3	10	58	42	16	36
7	Brixworth All Saints Res	24	10	6	8	63	75	-12	36
8	Corby Kingswood Res	24	8	7	9	53	47	6	31
9	Earls Barton United Res	24	9	3	12	49	58	-9	30
10	Corby Ravens	24	9	3	12	58	77	-19	30
11	Medbourne Res	24	6	3	15	36	83	-47	21
12	Daventry Rangers	24	5	2	17	47	58	-11	14*
13	Irthlingborough Town	24	1	1	22	19	82	-63	-5*

DIVISION FOUR

		P	W	D	L	F	A	GD	Pts
1	Harpole Res	18	16	2	0	74	18	56	50
2	Burton Band	18	14	1	3	76	21	55	43
3	Corby United	18	12	0	6	76	30	46	36
4	Yelvertoft	18	9	4	5	45	29	16	31
5	Desborough & Rothwell United Res	18	7	2	9	40	61	-21	23
6	Heyford Athletic Res	18	6	3	9	41	61	-20	21
7	Stanwick Rovers	18	5	4	9	32	39	-7	19
8	Corby Siam	18	4	4	10	36	59	-23	16
9	Finedon Volta Res	18	4	3	11	34	68	-34	15
10	Wilby	18	1	1	16	19	87	-68	1*

DIVISION FIVE

		P	W	D	L	F	A	GD	Pts
1	Irthlingborough Rangers	26	18	4	4	60	49	11	58
2	Spratton Res	26	18	1	7	76	36	40	55
3	Corby Ravens Res	26	15	5	6	83	47	36	50
4	Stanion United Res	26	16	4	6	98	44	54	46*
5	Corby Strip Mills Res	26	14	3	9	70	49	21	45
6	Moulton Res	26	13	4	9	76	65	11	43
7	Corby United Res	26	12	4	10	63	56	7	40
8	Corby Hellenic Fisher	26	10	5	11	59	49	10	32*
9	Higham Town Res	26	9	5	12	40	55	-15	32
10	Wellingborough Rising Sun Res	26	12	1	13	83	39	44	28*
11	Great Doddington	26	7	3	16	48	83	-35	24
12	West Haddon Albion Res	26	9	0	17	42	78	-36	24*
13	Corby Trades & Labour	26	6	2	18	56	77	-21	20
14	Daventry Rangers Res	26	2	1	23	25	152	-127	4*

ADDITIONAL CLUB MOVEMENTS

Premier Division
Out: Corby S&L Khalsa (W).

Division One
In: AFC Houghton Magna (P), Bugbrooke St Michaels 'A' (P), Corby Pegasus Res (P), Highham Aztec, Weedon (P - D3), Weldon United.
Out: Corby Eagles (W), Woodford Wolves (W).

Division Two
In: Corby Ravens (P), Daventry Cummins, Harpole Res (P - D4).
Out: AFC Houghton Magna (P), Bugbrooke St Michaels 'A' (P), Corby Kingswood (W), Corby Pegasus Res (P), Mereway (W).

Division Three
In: Burton Band (P), Corby United (P), Yelvertoft (P), Desborough & Rothwell United Res (P), Heyford Athletic Res (P), Stanwick Rovers (P), Corby Siam (P), Fonedon Volta Res (P), Irthlingborough Rangers (P - D5), Spratton Res (P - D3).
Out: Corby Ravens (P), Weedon (P - D1).

Division Four
In: Corby Ravens Res (P), Stanion United Res (P), Corby Strip Mills Res (P), Moulton Res (P), Corby United Res (P), Corby Hellenic Fisher (P), Higham Town Res (P), Great Doddington (P), West Haddon Albion Res (P), Corby Trades & Labour (P).
Out: Harpole Res (P - D2), Burton Band (P), Corby United (P), Yelvertoft (P), Desborough & Rothwell United Res (P), Heyford Athletic Res (P), Stanwick Rovers (P), Corby Siam (P), Fonedon Volta Res (P).

Division Five
In: No Division Five for 2017-18.
Out: Irthlingborough Rangers (P - D3), Spratton Res (P - D3), Corby Ravens Res (P), Stanion United Res (P), Corby Strip Mills Res (P), Moulton Res (P), Corby United Res (P), Corby Hellenic Fisher (P), Higham Town Res (P), Wellingborough Rising Sun Res (W), Great Doddington (P), West Haddon Albion Res (P), Corby Trades & Labour (P).

NORTHERN ALLIANCE

Sponsored by: Bay Plastics Ltd
Founded: 1890
Recent Champions:
2014: Blyth Town **2015:** Blyth Town
2016: Blyth Town

PREMIER DIVISION		P	W	D	L	F	A	GD	Pts
1	Killingworth Town	28	20	4	4	63	27	36	64
2	Newcastle University	28	17	7	4	76	37	39	58
3	North Shields Athletic	28	16	4	8	76	49	27	52
4	Ponteland United	28	16	2	10	62	49	13	50
5	Walker Central	28	17	2	9	86	49	37	47*
6	Whitley Bay A	28	14	5	9	69	54	15	47
7	Shankhouse	28	11	5	12	48	65	-17	38
8	Birtley Town	28	11	4	13	64	69	-5	37
9	Seaton Delaval AFC	28	8	10	10	51	53	-2	34
10	Wallington	28	10	4	14	51	67	-16	34
11	AFC Newbiggin	28	9	6	13	45	73	-28	33
12	Percy Main Amateurs	28	8	5	15	49	67	-18	29
13	Ashington Colliers	28	8	2	18	50	66	-16	26
14	Gateshead Rutherford	28	6	7	15	47	55	-8	25
15	Northbank Carlisle	28	4	3	21	28	85	-57	12*

Redhouse Farm withdrew - record expunged.

CHALLENGE CUP

HOLDERS: BLYTH TOWN
ROUND 1

Whitley Bay A	v	Seaton Delaval AFC	0-3
Newcastle University	v	Red House Farm	3-1
Killingworth Town	v	North Shields Athletic	4-2
Wallington	v	Shankhouse	2-1
Ashington Colliers	v	Ponteland United	0-3
Gateshead Rutherford	v	Percy Main Amateurs	3-1
AFC Newbiggin	v	Birtley Town	0-6
Northbank Carlisle	v	Walker Central	0-5

QUARTER-FINALS

Seaton Delaval AFC	v	Newcastle University	2-6
Killingworth Town	v	Wallington	3-0
Ponteland United	v	Gateshead Rutherford	3-2
Birtley Town	v	Walker Central	2-3

SEMI-FINALS

Newcastle University	v	Killingworth Town	0-3
Ponteland United	v	Walker Central	3-2

FINAL

Killingworth Town	v	Ponteland United	3-4

PREMIER DIVISION		1	2	3	4	5	6	7	8	9	10	11	12	13	14	15
1	AFC Newbiggin		1-0	3-1	2-2	3-4	0-5	1-3	3-1	2-0	0-6	2-2	2-4	2-3	0-2	2-2
2	Ashington Colliers	1-2		1-3	2-4	1-3	4-0	5-2	4-1	2-2	4-1	4-2	3-1	1-3	1-2	1-3
3	Birtley Town	0-1	4-0		3-0	0-3	1-3	2-6	5-0	2-1	2-2	1-1	1-3	1-5	3-1	3-2
4	Gateshead Rutherford	0-1	3-0	2-4		1-4	2-1	0-3	7-0	1-4	0-1	1-2	4-0	1-4	1-1	3-4
5	Killingworth Town	3-0	4-0	5-3	2-1		0-0	1-1	1-0	2-2	0-2	3-0	6-2	2-1	2-0	1-0
6	Newcastle University	11-2	2-1	5-1	2-2	2-0		2-0	6-1	4-3	4-1	1-1	2-1	2-3	3-4	3-0
7	North Shields Athletic	3-2	3-1	6-3	1-1	1-3	1-1		4-0	1-0	5-0	3-1	6-0	1-5	3-4	1-3
8	Northbank Carlisle	2-1	3-1	2-4	2-0	1-5	1-1	1-4		3-3	0-2	2-4	1-1	3-6	2-0	0-3
9	Percy Main Amateurs	5-2	4-2	2-3	4-3	0-1	0-2	1-4	2-0		1-5	1-0	3-2	0-3	1-0	1-2
10	Ponteland United	4-0	1-0	4-2	2-2	1-0	2-5	2-0	3-0	6-0		2-1	1-2	2-1	4-2	0-3
11	Seaton Delaval AFC	2-2	2-2	1-4	0-0	0-2	0-0	1-1	2-1	2-2	5-1		1-1	0-3	6-2	4-3
12	Shankhouse	2-2	2-0	4-3	2-0	2-2	1-1	4-3	1-0	3-1	2-1	1-5		1-5	1-3	1-2
13	Walker Central	0-1	2-4	2-2	3-2	0-1	1-2	2-4	4-0	3-0	3-2	1-3	4-1		6-3	8-1
14	Wallington	3-4	3-5	1-1	0-3	3-2	0-1	1-2	2-1	3-2	2-4	4-2	1-0	3-3		0-0
15	Whitley Bay A	2-2	3-0	3-2	1-1	0-1	4-5	2-4	6-0	4-4	3-0	3-1	2-3	4-2	4-1	

DIVISION ONE		P	W	D	L	F	A	GD	Pts
1	Gateshead FC A	30	26	2	2	126	28	98	80
2	Grainger Park B C	30	23	2	5	101	45	56	71
3	Hexham	30	19	4	7	85	51	34	61
4	Cullercoats	30	19	2	9	85	57	28	58*
5	Wallsend Labour Club	30	18	1	11	73	63	10	55
6	Monkseaton	30	15	5	10	68	53	15	50
7	Heaton Stannington A	30	15	1	14	82	79	3	46
8	Felling Magpies	30	13	6	11	69	49	20	45
9	Seaton Burn	30	12	4	14	56	62	-6	40
10	Hebburn Reyrolle	30	11	2	17	63	95	-32	35
11	Wallsend Boys Club	30	10	3	17	51	67	-16	33
12	Cramlington Town	30	10	3	17	48	79	-31	33
13	New Fordley	30	7	3	20	48	81	-33	24
14	Gosforth Bohemians	30	6	4	20	42	74	-32	22
15	Alnmouth United	30	8	1	21	34	80	-46	22*
16	Gateshead Redheugh 1957	30	4	3	23	34	102	-68	15

Name Changes: Newcastle Chemfica formerley Heaton Stannington A.
Wallsend Community formerly Wallsend Boys Club.

DIVISION TWO		P	W	D	L	F	A	GD	Pts
1	Killingworth YPC	28	21	4	3	108	21	87	61*
2	Forest Hall	28	19	1	8	99	31	68	58
3	Hazlerigg Victory	28	17	5	6	91	34	57	56
4	Red Row Welfare	28	18	3	7	91	41	50	54*
5	Willington Quay Saints	28	14	6	8	61	57	4	48
6	Cramlington United	28	14	3	11	59	57	2	45
7	Blyth Town A	28	13	5	10	77	57	20	44
8	Prudhoe Youth Club Seniors	28	13	5	10	81	60	21	41*
9	Spittal Rovers	28	13	1	14	54	53	1	40
10	Bedlington Town	28	12	4	12	62	64	-2	40
11	Whitburn Athletic	28	8	8	12	57	75	-18	32
12	Whitley Bay Boys Club Seniors	28	9	4	15	55	78	-23	31
13	Blyth FC	28	6	1	21	24	109	-85	16*
14	Wideopen and District	28	2	4	22	32	132	-100	10
15	Ryton and Crawcrook Albion A	28	2	4	22	35	117	-82	7*

In: Blyth Spartans Res (N), Coundon & Leeholme (N),
Seghill (P - Newcastle Corinthians Lge).
Name Change: Winlaton Vulcans formerly Ryton & Crawcrook A.

Northern Alliance Premier Division

AFC NEWBIGGIN	Newbiggin Sports Centre, Newbiggin by the Sea NE64 6HG	07528 608 807
ASHINGTON COLLIERS	Ashington FC, Hirst Welfare, Alexandra Road, Ashington NE63 9HF	07745 344 502
BIRTLEY TOWN	Birtley Sports Complex, Durham Road, Birtley DH3 2TB	07958 540 389
GATESHEAD FC A	Heworth Leisure Centre, Gateshead NE10 0PD	07912 869 943
GATESHEAD RUTHERFORD	Farnacres, Beggarswood Park, Coach Road, Lobley Hill, Gateshead NE16 1OH	07557 331 721
GRAINGER PARK B C	Grainger Park Boys Club, Denton Road, Scotswood, Newcastle NE15 7HB	07876 358 299
KILLINGWORTH TOWN	West Moor Community Centre, Benton Lane, West Moor, Newcastle NE12 7NP	07896 262 944
NEWCASTLE UNIVERSITY	Cochrane Park, Etherstone Avenue, Newcastle upon Tyne NE7 7JX	07971 852 468
NORTH SHIELDS ATHLETIC	John Spence Community High School, Preston Road, North Shields NE29 9PU	07813 590 965
NORTHBANK CARLISLE	Sheepmount Sports Complex, Sheepmount, Carlisle CA3 8XL	07761 416 331
PERCY MAIN AMATEURS	Purvis Park, St Johns Green, Percy Main, North Shields NE29 6HS	07960 189 667
PONTELAND UNITED	Ponteland Leisure Centre, Callerton Lane, Ponteland NE20 9EG	07774 523 762
SEATON DELAVAL AMATEURS	Wheatridge Park, Seaton Delaval, Whitley Bay NE25 0QH	07969 551 513
SHANKHOUSE	Action Park, Dudley NE23 7HY	01670 361 929
WALLINGTON	Oakford Park, Scots Gap, Morpeth NE61 4EJ	07920 099 416
WHITLEY BAY A	Hillheads Park, Rink Way, off Hillheads Road, Whitley Bay NE25 8HR	07534 711 921

GEORGE DOBBIN LEAGUE CUP

HOLDERS: PONTELAND UNITED

ROUND 1

Alnmouth United	v	Wallsend Labour Club	1-0
Gateshead FC A	v	Spittal Rovers	9-1
Whitley Bay Boys Club Senior	Bye		
Monkseaton	Bye		
Hazlerigg Victory	Bye		
Shankhouse	v	Red House Farm	1-3
Birtley Town	v	Wallsend Boys Club	3-1
New Fordley	v	Wallington	3-5
Cullercoats	v	Gateshead Rutherford	3-2
Cramlington United	v	Hebburn Reyrolle	5-2
Grainger Park B C	v	Whitley Bay A	2-1
Wideopen & District	Bye		
Red Row Welfare	v	Prudhoe Youth Club Senior	0-2
Seaton Burn	v	Blyth Town A	2-1
Percy Main Amateurs	v	Seaton Delaval AFC	2-1
Bedlington Town	Bye		
Heaton Stannington A	Bye		
Killingworth YPC	Bye		
Gosforth Bohemians	Bye		
Ryton and Crawcrook Albion	v	Felling Magpies	1-2
Ponteland United	Bye		
Blyth FC	Bye		
Walker Central	v	Forest Hall	7-4
Ashington Colliers	Bye		
AFC Newbiggin	v	Cramlington Town	7-3
Gateshead Redheugh 1957	Bye		
Willington Quay Saints	Bye		
Shilbottle C W	Bye		
North Shields Athletic	v	Newcastle University	2-3
Northbank Carlisle	v	Whitburn Athletic	6-0
Killingworth Town	Bye		
Hexham	Bye		

ROUND 2

Alnmouth United	v	Gateshead FC A	1-0
Whitley Bay Boys Club Senior	v	Monkseaton	0-1
Hazlerigg Victory	v	Red House Farm	0-4
Birtley Town	v	Wallington	4-2
Cullercoats	v	Cramlington United	1-2
Grainger Park B C	v	Wideopen & District	4-1
Prudhoe Youth Club Senior	v	Seaton Burn	2-1
Percy Main Amateurs	v	Bedlington Town	5-0

Heaton Stannington A	v	Killingworth YPC	0-1
Gosforth Bohemians	v	Felling Magpies	3-1
Ponteland United	v	Blyth FC	10-0
Walker Central	v	Ashington Colliers	3-0
AFC Newbiggin	v	Gateshead Redheugh 1957	6-2
Willington Quay Saints	Bye		
Newcastle University	v	Northbank Carlisle	8-0
Killingworth Town	v	Hexham	5-0

ROUND 3

Alnmouth United	v	Monkseaton	1-2
Red House Farm	v	Birtley Town	0-5
Cramlington United	v	Grainger Park B C	1-3
Prudhoe Youth Club Senior	v	Percy Main Amateurs	2-5
Killingworth YPC	v	Gosforth Bohemians	6-3
Ponteland United	v	Walker Central	1-2
AFC Newbiggin	v	Willington Quay Saints	3-2
Newcastle University	v	Killingworth Town	1-0

QUARTER-FINALS

Monkseaton	v	Birtley Town	0-1
Grainger Park B C	v	Percy Main Amateurs	4-5
Killingworth YPC	v	Walker Central	1-2
AFC Newbiggin	v	Newcastle University	1-4

SEMI-FINALS

Birtley Town	v	Percy Main Amateurs	7-3
Walker Central	v	Newcastle University	3-2

FINAL

Birtley Town	v	Walker Central	0-1

COMBINATION CUP

FINAL	**HOLDERS:** NEWCASTLE UNIVERSITY		
Gateshead FC A	v	Seaton Burn	0-1

AMATEUR CUP

FINAL	**HOLDERS:** GATESHEAD FC A		
Cramlington United	v	Hazlerigg Victory	0-6

BILL GARDNER CUP

FINAL	**HOLDERS:** CARLISLE CITY		
Seaton Delaval AFC	v	Whitley Bay A	4-3

NOTTINGHAMSHIRE SENIOR LEAGUE

Sponsored by: Precision
Founded: 2004
Recent Champions:
2014: Selston **2015:** Wollaton
2016: Ruddington Village

SENIOR CUP

HOLDERS: AWSWORTH VILLA

ROUND 1

Gedling Southbank	v	Bingham Town	0-1
Ravenshead	v	Greenwood Meadows AFC	6-4 aet
Unity	v	Netherfield Albion	4-1

ROUND 2

Bingham Town	v	Ravenshead	2-3
Unity	v	Bilborough Town	1-0
Calverton Miners Welfare	v	Underwood Villa	3-2
Ashland Rovers	v	Newark Flowserve	2-4
Kirton Brickworks	v	Sandiacre Town	4-6
Magdala Amateurs	v	Nottingham Trent University	3-7 aet
Ruddington Village	v	Bilborough United	4-3
AFC Bridgford	v	FC Cavaliers	1-2
AFC Dunkirk	v	Beeston	HW
Cotgrave	v	Real United	1-1, 5-4p
Birchover Park	v	AFC Clifton	2-1
Aslockton Cranmers	v	Aston United	0-1
Wollaton	v	Attenborough	5-1
Greyhounds	v	Team DNF	2-3 aet
Basford United Community	v	Clifton All Whites	1-4
Mansfield Hosiery Mills	v	Awsworth Villa	0-13

SENIOR DIVISION

		P	W	D	L	F	A	GD	Pts
1	Clifton All Whites	36	28	1	7	110	40	70	85
2	Awsworth Villa	36	24	7	5	97	48	49	79
3	AFC Dunkirk	36	20	8	8	101	53	48	68
4	Bilborough Town	36	21	5	10	71	53	18	68
5	Wollaton	36	20	5	11	114	77	37	65
6	Aston United	36	19	5	12	70	63	7	62
7	Basford Utd Community	36	18	7	11	97	60	37	58*
8	Real United	36	16	7	13	96	84	12	55
9	Cotgrave	36	16	6	14	79	64	15	54
10	Nottingham Trent University	36	13	8	15	78	84	-6	47
11	Newark Flowserve	36	14	3	19	73	99	-26	45
12	Ruddington Village	36	12	6	18	65	96	-31	42
13	Bingham Town	36	11	7	18	60	74	-14	40
14	Magdala Amateurs	36	11	7	18	68	104	-36	40
15	FC Cavaliers	36	9	8	19	48	67	-19	35
16	Attenborough	36	10	4	22	61	104	-43	34
17	Sandiacre Town	36	9	5	22	54	86	-32	32
18	Underwood Villa	36	6	12	18	42	91	-49	30
19	Unity	36	8	3	25	51	88	-37	27

Beeston AFC withdrew - record expunged.

SENIOR DIVISION

		1	2	3	4	5	6	7	8	9	10	11	12	13	14	15	16	17	18	19
1	AFC Dunkirk		5-5	5-0	1-1	1-1	4-0	4-1	0-1	0-1	0-0	3-0	3-2	5-1	4-2	5-0	3-1	3-0	2-0	1-2
2	Aston United	3-2		2-1	2-3	H-W	3-1	3-1	5-3	2-2	2-0	4-0	3-1	3-2	3-2	0-1	2-0	H-W	3-3
3	Attenborough	3-1	0-2		1-2	3-2	2-9	1-2	1-3	1-3	1-1	6-2	7-2	1-5	1-1	5-3	5-1	1-3	4-3	1-6
4	Awsworth Villa	1-1	1-0	1-2		6-3	2-0	4-2	1-2	6-1	5-1	5-3	3-1	2-2	3-2	0-0	1-0	3-1	4-0	3-4
5	Basford United Community	3-3	5-1	4-0	5-2		4-1	2-0	4-2	2-0	2-1	9-0	2-1	1-2	4-2	4-1	5-2	6-2	4-2	2-2
6	Bilborough Town	0-5	3-2	2-0	2-2	2-0		3-0	0-1	2-1	2-0	2-0	2-3	3-1	2-1	2-1	1-1	4-0	1-0	2-4
7	Bingham Town	4-1	2-0	0-1	1-0	1-1	0-1		1-3	1-3	0-1	3-3	0-3	4-1	3-5	5-2	2-2	3-1	1-1	2-3
8	Clifton All Whites	1-3	2-3	5-0	0-0	3-2	1-2	2-1		1-2	3-0	2-0	5-1	4-2	4-0	4-0	4-2	6-0	2-3	1-4
9	Cotgrave	0-2	1-1	5-0	0-2	3-0	3-1	6-0	1-4		5-2	1-1	5-2	1-1	2-2	1-2	2-2	8-0	2-0	5-5
10	FC Cavaliers	0-2	0-2	3-1	0-1	0-0	0-3	0-2	0-1	4-0		0-0	2-2	1-2	0-0	9-3	2-1	5-0	0-3	2-2
11	Magdala Amateurs	0-4	0-1	4-2	3-7	3-2	2-2	4-2	1-3	4-2		4-1	1-3	2-5	1-2	4-2	2-2	1-3	2-2	4-1
12	Newark Flowserve	4-4	2-1	1-0	0-4	3-2	4-2	0-2	0-3	A-W	1-2	2-2		1-4	3-2	7-3	3-6	3-2	3-0	3-1
13	Nottingham Trent University	5-3	4-2	5-1	2-3	3-3	1-4	1-1	0-9	1-2	3-2	4-5	6-2		0-2	0-3	2-0	2-2	4-1	2-3
14	Real United	2-4	2-0	2-4	1-1	1-1	2-2	2-2	0-6	0-5	3-1	7-3	4-3	H-W		5-0	6-1	3-1	5-1	3-8
15	Ruddington Village	3-4	2-3	1-1	0-3	0-4	0-0	2-1	1-3	3-0	4-0	4-3	3-0	1-1	3-1		1-3	1-1	3-2	2-8
16	Sandiacre Town	0-3	0-4	4-2	1-2	0-2	2-2	1-2	1-0	0-1	1-3	6-1	3-1	0-8	1-3		0-1	2-2	2-1
17	Underwood Villa	1-1	2-2	0-0	1-5	2-1	2-1	2-2	1-3	1-2	2-1	1-1	0-2	1-1	3-4	1-1	1-1		3-3	1-6
18	Unity	3-2	A-W	2-0	1-2	1-4	0-1	1-6	0-5	3-2	4-1	4-1	1-3	2-3	1-5	2-4	1-4	2-0		A-W
19	Wollaton	2-7	5-0	7-2	2-6	4-1	1-2	5-0	0-4	3-2	1-2	5-0	2-4	2-2	3-4	3-1	2-0	0-1	4-2	

DIVISION ONE

		P	W	D	L	F	A	GD	Pts
1	Calverton Miners Welfare	28	22	2	4	99	31	68	68
2	Kimberley Miners Welfare Res	28	17	6	5	73	45	28	57
3	Ashland Rovers	28	16	5	7	81	43	38	53
4	Wollaton Reserves	28	14	8	6	56	41	15	50
5	Gedling Southbank	28	14	5	9	70	51	19	47
6	Awsworth Villa Res	28	13	7	8	68	69	-1	46
7	Kirton Brickworks	28	13	7	8	58	50	8	45*
8	Southwell City Res	28	12	6	10	71	62	9	42
9	Ruddington Village Res	28	10	6	12	55	44	11	36
10	AFC Bridgford	28	8	5	15	42	42	0	29
11	Netherfield Albion	28	9	2	17	55	94	-39	29
12	Keyworth United Res	28	8	4	16	46	82	-36	28
13	Birchover Park	28	7	5	16	40	55	-15	26
14	Bilborough United	28	5	10	13	43	67	-24	25
15	AFC Clifton	28	3	0	25	36	117	-81	9

Clifton All Whites Res withdrew - record expunged.
Greenwood Meadows Res withdrew - record expunged.

DIVISION TWO

		P	W	D	L	F	A	GD	Pts
1	Team DNF	20	18	0	2	76	25	51	54
2	Ravenshead	20	15	2	3	63	32	31	47
3	Selston Res	20	13	1	6	53	35	18	40
4	Aslockton Cranmers	20	9	7	4	49	30	19	34
5	West Bridgford AFC	20	7	5	8	46	49	-3	26
6	Basford Utd Community Res	20	7	2	11	38	46	-8	23
7	Bilsthorpe Res	20	6	4	10	39	50	-11	22
8	Underwood Villa Res	20	7	1	12	31	63	-32	22
9	Mansfield Hosiery Mills	20	6	3	11	36	48	-12	21
10	Greyhounds	20	4	4	12	41	61	-20	16
11	Bingham Town Res	20	2	3	15	23	56	-33	9

Beeston Res withdrew - record expunged.
Radcliffe Olympic Res withdrew - record expunged.
Unity Res withdrew - record expunged.

SENIOR CUP

ROUND 3

Ravenshead	v	Unity	6-1
Calverton Miners Welfare	v	Newark Flowserve	1-5
Sandiacre Town	v	Nottingham Trent University	5-5, 3-4p
Ruddington Village	v	FC Cavaliers	2-4
AFC Dunkirk	v	Cotgrave	1-2
Birchover Park	v	Aston United	0-5
Wollaton	v	Team DNF	4-0
Clifton All Whites	v	Awsworth Villa	3-1

QUARTER-FINALS

Ravenshead	v	Newark Flowserve	0-2
Nottingham Trent University	v	FC Cavaliers	4-0
Cotgrave	v	Aston United	4-2 aet
Wollaton	v	Clifton All Whites	2-3

SEMI-FINALS

Newark Flowserve	v	Nottingham Trent University	2-2, 2-4p
Cotgrave	v	Clifton All Whites	2-1 aet

FINAL

Nottingham Trent University	v	Cotgrave	2-3

JUNIOR CUP

HOLDERS: KIMBERLEY MINERS WELFARE RES

QUARTER-FINALS

Kimberley Miners Welfare Res	v	Underwood Villa Res	1-0
Selston Res	v	Bingham Town Res	3-1 aet
Awsworth Villa Res	v	Bilsthorpe Res	3-1
West Bridgford AFC	v	Wollaton Res	3-1

SEMI-FINALS

Kimberley Miners Welfare Res	v	Selston Res	6-0
Awsworth Villa Res	v	West Bridgford AFC	2-2, 6-5p

FINAL

Kimberley Miners Welfare Res	v	Awsworth Villa Res	0-4

Nottinghamshire Senior Premier Division

AFC DUNKIRK	Ron Steel Sports Ground, Lenton Lane, Nottingham NG7 2SA	
ATTENBOROUGH	Village Green, The Strand, Attenborough, Nottingham NG9 6AU	0115 9257 439
AWSWORTH VILLA	The Shilo, Attewell Road, Awsworth, Nottingham NG16 2SY	
BASFORD UNITED COMMUNITY	Greenwich Avenue	
BILBOROUGH TOWN	Harvey Hadden	
BINGHAM TOWN	Butt Field, Bingham, Nottingham NG13 8GG	
CALVERTON MINERS WELFARE	Calverton Miners Welfare, Hollinwood Lane, Calverton NG14 6NR	0115 965 4390
COTGRAVE	Woodview, Cotgrave Welfare, Woodview, Cotgrave, Nottingham NG12	
FC CAVALIERS	The Forest. #1, Gregory Boulevard, Nottingham NG7 2SA	
GEDLING SOUTHBANK	Hollinwood Lane 1, Calverton, Nottingham NG14 6NR	
KIMBERLEY M.W. RESERVES	The Stag Ground, Kimberley, Nottingham NG16 2NB	07572 863 155
MAGDALA AMATEURS	Roko, Wilford Lane, West Bridgford, Nottingham NG2 7RN	
NEWARK FLOWSERVE	Hawton Lane, Newark, Nottinghamshire NG24 3BU	
RUDDINGTON VILLAGE	Elms Park, Ruddington, Nottingham	07545 388439
SANDIACRE TOWN	St Giles	
SOUTHWELL CITY	War Memorial Recreation Ground, Bishop's Drive, Southwell NG25 0JP	01636 814 386
UNDERWOOD VILLA	Bracken Park, Felly Mill Lane, North, Off Mansfield Road, Underwood NG16 5FG	
WOLLATON	Wollaton Sports Association, 753 Wollaton Road, Wollaton, NG8 2AN	

ADDITIONAL CLUB MOVEMENTS
Premier Division
In: Gedling Southbank (P), Southwell City (S - Central Midlands League).
Out: Ashton United (W), Nottingham Trent Unisversity (R), Real United (R), Unity (W).

Division One
In: Beeston Rylands (P - Notts Amateur), Bilsthorpe (S - Central Midlands), Mansfield Hoslery Mills (P), Nottingham Trent Unisversity (R),
Real United (R).
Out: Birchover Park (W), Gedling Southbank (P).

Division Two
In: Barrowby (P - Grantham & District), Bridgford United (P - Midland Amateur Alliance D1), Burton Joyce, Gedling Southbank Res,
Kirton Brickworks Res, Magdala Amateurs Res, Newark Flowserve Res, Nottingham City, Real United Res, Sneinton Town (P - Notts Amateur Alliance),
Stapleford Town, Welbeck Lions Res, Woodthorpe Park Rangers (P - Notts Amateur Alliance).
Out: Aslockton Cranmers (S - Central Midlands), Basford United Community Res (W), Bilsthorpe Res (W), West Bridgford Res (W),
Mansfield Hoslery Mills (P).

OXFORDSHIRE SENIOR LEAGUE

Sponsored by: No sponsor
Founded: N/K
Recent Champions:
2014: Oakley United
2015: Oakley United
2016: OUP

PRESIDENTS CUP

HOLDERS: ADDERBURY PARK

ROUND 1

Middleton Cheney	v	Heyford Athletic	0-4
Eynsham	Bye		
Garsington	v	OUP	4-1
Kennington Athletic	v	Charlton	0-2
Horspath	Bye		
Zubry Oxford FC	v	Oxford Irish	HW
Mansfield Road	v	Chinnor FC Res	5-1
Adderbury Park	v	Marston Saints	10-1
Kidlington Old Boys	v	Chalgrove	AW
Northway	v	Cropedy	4-3 aet
Yarnton	Bye		
Launton Sports	v	Freeland	1-2

ROUND 2

Heyford Athletic	v	Eynsham	7-2
Garsington	Bye		
Charlton	v	Horspath	2-0
Zubry Oxford FC	v	Mansfield Road	1-4
Adderbury Park	v	Chalgrove	3-1
Northway	Bye		
Yarnton	Bye		
Freeland	Bye		

QUARTER-FINALS

Heyford Athletic	v	Garsington	7-0
Charlton	v	Mansfield Road	2-3
Adderbury Park	v	Northway	6-1
Yarnton	v	Freeland	0-6

SEMI-FINALS

Heyford Athletic	v	Mansfield Road	4-0
Adderbury Park	v	Freeland	2-0

FINAL

Heyford Athletic	v	Adderbury Park	1-0

PREMIER DIVISION

		P	W	D	L	F	A	GD	Pts
1	Adderbury Park	24	21	1	2	67	20	47	64
2	Heyford Athletic	24	18	4	2	69	18	51	58
3	Freeland	24	16	1	7	87	39	48	49
4	Mansfield Rd	24	15	1	8	81	52	29	46
5	Cropedy	24	10	2	12	46	57	-11	32
6	Chalgrove	24	8	7	9	48	46	2	31
7	OUP	24	9	3	12	52	62	-10	30
8	Marston Sts	24	9	3	12	50	72	-22	30
9	Horspath	24	7	6	11	49	49	0	27
10	Launton Sports	24	7	4	13	38	66	-28	25
11	Yarnton	24	6	6	12	32	46	-14	24
12	Garsington	24	5	2	17	53	96	-43	17
13	Eynsham	24	4	2	18	24	73	-49	14

PREMIER DIVISION

		1	2	3	4	5	6	7	8	9	10	11	12	13
1	Adderbury Park		1-1	1-0	3-0	4-0	5-1	1-0	2-1	5-1	H-W	3-0	3-1	1-0
2	Chalgrove	0-1		2-0	1-2	0-2	4-1	1-2	2-2	1-0	2-4	1-1	3-2	0-0
3	Cropedy	1-5	5-3		4-1	1-4	4-1	0-5	1-1	4-1	4-1	4-1	2-4	4-0
4	Eynsham	1-9	0-2	0-2		0-5	0-4	0-4	1-1	1-2	0-3	4-1	0-1	0-1
5	Freeland	2-3	4-3	5-0	3-1		7-0	0-3	5-1	8-1	2-1	2-2	4-0	4-1
6	Garsington	4-6	2-2	1-2	2-0	0-8		1-5	2-3	5-3	2-5	3-7	4-1	1-1
7	Heyford Athletic	2-1	2-2	2-1	8-1	3-1	H-W		3-1	5-0	4-2	7-0	1-0	4-0
8	Horspath	1-3	0-1	2-0	3-3	4-3	8-2	2-2		0-1	1-5	5-0	1-2	0-1
9	Launton Sports	0-1	2-7	0-0	1-2	0-5	5-2	0-0	1-1		2-1	3-2	4-1	1-1
10	Mansfield Rd	0-2	5-3	4-0	5-2	3-6	6-4	3-2	3-1	7-5		7-1	2-2	2-1
11	Marston Sts	1-2	3-1	4-2	3-1	3-2	7-4	0-3	1-4	4-2	0-6		2-1	1-2
12	OUP	2-1	4-5	7-2	0-4	4-3	4-3	1-2	3-2	1-3	4-3	3-3		0-1
13	Yarnton	1-4	1-1	2-3	5-0	1-2	3-4	0-0	2-4	2-0	2-3	0-3	4-4	

DIVISION ONE

		P	W	D	L	F	A	GD	Pts
1	Kennington Athletic	14	11	2	1	39	17	22	35
2	Charlton	14	10	1	3	30	13	17	31
3	Middleton Cheney	14	9	1	4	34	16	18	28
4	Adderbury Res	14	9	0	5	31	29	2	27
5	Northway	14	6	1	7	26	28	-2	19
6	Chinnor FC Res	14	3	2	9	25	28	-3	11
7	Zubry Oxford FC	14	3	2	9	23	39	-16	11
8	Mansfield Rd Res	14	0	1	13	10	48	-38	1

DIVISION TWO

		P	W	D	L	F	A	GD	Pts
1	OUP Res	16	15	0	1	62	19	43	45
2	Marston Sts Res	16	10	1	5	43	31	12	31
3	Launton Sports Res	16	8	3	5	54	30	24	27
4	Chalgrove Res	16	7	3	6	42	32	10	24
5	Freeland Res	16	7	1	8	33	38	-5	22
6	Charlton Res	16	7	1	8	32	43	-11	22
7	Horspath Res	16	5	2	9	35	53	-18	17
8	Yarnton Res	16	4	3	9	25	55	-30	15
9	Garsington Res	16	2	0	14	20	45	-25	6

Eynsham Res withdrew - record expunged.

PETERBOROUGH & DISTRICT LEAGUE

Sponsored by: ChromaSport
Founded: 1902
Recent Champions:
2014: Kings Lynn Town Res. **2015:** Oakham United
2016: Moulton Harrox

PREMIER DIVISION	P	W	D	L	F	A	GD	Pts
1 Peterborough Sports Res	34	31	1	2	146	33	113	94
2 Pinchbeck United	34	27	3	3	119	40	79	87*
3 Moulton Harrox	34	23	6	4	121	43	78	78*
4 Netherton United	34	22	5	5	113	36	77	77*
5 Stamford Lions	34	22	3	9	110	58	52	62*
6 Peterborough ICA Sports	34	19	2	13	81	56	25	59
7 Ketton	34	16	2	16	89	68	21	50
8 Langtoft United	34	15	5	14	65	69	-4	50
9 Holbeach United Res	34	14	2	18	72	92	-20	44
10 AFC Stanground Sports	34	13	3	18	91	119	-28	42
11 Wisbech Town Res	34	12	5	15	66	65	1	39*
12 Sawtry	34	11	5	18	61	94	-33	38
13 Deeping Rangers Res	34	9	6	19	64	89	-25	33
14 Leverington Sports	34	8	4	21	44	87	-43	31*
15 Thorney	34	8	3	22	39	104	-65	26*
16 Stilton United	34	9	1	23	56	106	-50	22*
17 Uppingham Town	34	6	2	26	35	131	-96	20
18 Crowland Town	34	6	2	25	50	132	-82	19*

PREMIER SHIELD

HOLDERS: PINCHBECK UNITED

ROUND 1

Stamford Lions	v	AFC Stanground Sports	5-1
Leverington Sports	v	Pinchbeck United	1-6

ROUND 2

Stamford Lions	v	Netherton United	2-4
Thorney	v	Peterborough Sports Res	0-7
Wisbech Town Res	v	Holbeach United Res	3-2
Moulton Harrox	v	Sawtry	4-1
Crowland Town	v	Ketton	1-4
Deeping Rangers Res	v	Uppingham Town	3-0
Stilton United	v	Pinchbeck United	1-4
Peterborough ICA Sports	v	Langtoft United	3-2

QUARTER-FINALS

Netherton United	v	Peterborough Sports Res	3-1
Wisbech Town Res	v	Moulton Harrox	2-4
Ketton	v	Deeping Rangers Res	2-1
Pinchbeck United	v	Peterborough ICA Sports	2-1

SEMI-FINALS

Netherton United	v	Moulton Harrox	3-2
Ketton	v	Pinchbeck United	1-2

FINAL

Netherton United	v	Pinchbeck United	0-1

PREMIER DIVISION	1	2	3	4	5	6	7	8	9	10	11	12	13	14	15	16	17	18
1 AFC Stanground		7-2	3-2	2-1	2-3	2-2	8-1	0-4	0-4	4-4	1-4	1-3	11-0	5-3	4-8	2-2	4-1	0-3
2 Crowland Town	0-4		2-1	1-0	0-3	1-1	2-3	0-7	1-4	1-10	2-8	2-6	7-0	1-1	1-1	4-5	1-6	1-3
3 Deeping Rangers Reserves	2-1	1-1		2-0	9-0	1-2	7-2	V-V	1-3	0-3	1-4	0-6	9-3	4-2	1-3	1-3	7-1	1-3
4 Holbeach United Reserves	4-2	4-1	8-1		2-2	1-1	6-1	0-3	3-2	1-1	2-2	5-0	2-0	5-2	3-1	3-0	3-0	2-1
5 Ketton	4-0	5-2	3-0	2-2		0-3	9-0	1-4	2-2	0-0	1-2	1-2	5-2	4-0	1-1	3-1	1-1	1-3
6 Langtoft United	1-3	V-V	3-0	1-0	1-2		2-1	1-2	1-6	0-2	1-0	0-2	1-1	2-2	3-0	0-2	2-4	1-5
7 Leverington Sports	3-1	1-4	2-2	0-8	2-2	1-4		1-7	1-2	0-1	0-5	0-1	5-1	1-2	0-3	0-5	0-1	0-6
8 Moulton Harrox	5-1	5-0	11-0	3-1	5-0	3-0	8-0		1-1	4-0	4-2	4-1	5-4	4-0	6-1	3-0	7-0	0-3
9 Netherton United	7-0	7-2	2-1	7-0	2-0	4-0	10-0	1-1		5-1	2-3	3-2	1-0	9-2	5-0	1-1	1-1	0-0
10 Peterborough ICA Sports	0-4	9-1	1-1	1-0	2-1	0-3	6-0	3-6	0-3		1-2	1-4	5-0	4-1	1-0	2-2	4-0	0-3
11 Peterborough Sports Reserves	11-0	6-0	3-1	2-2	1-1	2-0	3-1	1-2	1-3	0-0		3-0	2-0	2-2	7-1	5-1	3-1	0-2
12 Pinchbeck United	4-1	4-1	6-0	3-1	2-0	2-1	2-2	3-2	1-1				V-V	7-0	5-0	1-3	5-1	0-1
13 Riverside	0-11	0-1	0-1	2-9	0-6	1-4	0-9	1-5	0-10	0-2	2-3	0-6		2-2	0-4	3-4	0-4	0-3
14 Sawtry	1-0	3-0	1-3	1-2	1-2	0-2	1-0	0-9	2-6	2-5	0-4	0-2	1-1		2-1	1-0	0-2	0-5
15 Stilton United	3-1	0-2	1-1	3-2	0-1	6-1	2-2	1-5	2-6	2-1	0-1	3-5	8-2	4-0		3-4	4-1	0-2
16 Thorney	3-1	2-3	2-4	1-1	0-2	1-0	2-3	1-3	V-V	1-2	4-8	1-3	4-0	1-2	4-1		2-4	0-3
17 Uppingham Town	2-2	2-1	5-3	0-4	1-8	1-2	9-0	1-5	1-2	0-3		0-0						0-3
18 Whittlesey Athletic	8-1	6-0	6-0	1-0	2-0	4-0	5-0	0-2	0-0	3-0	3-0	0-1	9-1	3-0	3-4	2-2	3-0	

DIVISION ONE	P	W	D	L	F	A	GD	Pts
1 Moulton Harrox Res	30	25	1	2	114	26	88	82*
2 Warboys Town	30	21	5	4	126	51	75	68
3 Sutton Bridge United	30	21	4	5	116	48	68	67
4 Whittlesey Athletic Res	30	14	4	6	111	39	72	64*
5 Wittering Harriers	30	13	6	10	92	77	15	48*
6 Peterborough Polonia	30	13	3	13	73	55	18	45*
7 Oundle Town	30	13	5	12	92	79	13	44
8 Long Sutton Athletic	30	12	5	12	77	82	-5	44*
9 Oakham United Res	30	13	4	11	78	66	12	40*
10 Glinton & Northborough	30	12	2	16	85	83	2	36*
11 Stamford Belvedere	30	11	4	14	67	77	-10	36*
12 Kings Cliffe	30	11	2	17	64	75	-11	35
13 Netherton United Res	30	8	5	17	51	106	-55	29
14 Riverside	30	5	4	21	50	143	-93	19
15 Baston	30	4	2	20	38	124	-86	10*
16 Spalding United Res	30	3	2	24	41	144	-103	10*

DIVISION TWO	P	W	D	L	F	A	GD	Pts
1 Ramsey Town	24	20	1	3	109	22	87	61
2 Whittlesey Athletic 'A'	24	18	4	2	95	28	67	58
3 AFC Stanground Sports Res	24	17	3	4	98	34	64	54
4 Tydd St Mary	24	12	6	6	65	47	18	42
5 Parkway Eagles	24	11	2	11	70	67	3	35
6 Langtoft United Res	24	10	3	11	69	61	8	33
7 Crowland Town Res	24	9	2	12	44	52	-8	28*
8 Peterborough ICA Sports Res	24	6	4	12	41	86	-45	28*
9 Netherton United 'A'	24	7	5	12	49	81	-32	26
10 Stamford Lions Reserves	24	7	3	14	42	78	-36	24
11 Spalding Town	24	6	5	12	45	73	-28	22*
12 Ketton Reserves	24	6	2	16	41	70	-29	18*
13 Leverington Sports Res	24	4	2	18	31	100	-69	14

Peterborough & District League Premier Division

AFC STANGROUND SPORTS	In2itive Park, Leading Drove, Holme Road Yaxley, PE7 3NA	01733 821 430
DEEPING RANGERS RESERVES	Haydon Whitham Stadium, Outgang Road, Market Deeping, Lincolnshire, PE6 8LQ	01778 344 701
HOLBEACH UNITED RESERVES	Carters Park, Park Road, Holbeach Spalding PE12 7EE	07983 342 962
KETTON	Ketton Sports and Community Centre, Pit Lane, Ketton, Stamford, PE9 3SZ	01780 721 507
LANGTOFT UNITED	Manor Way, Sports Ground, Langtoft, Peterborough PE6 9NB	01778 347 253
LEVERINGTON SPORTS	Church Road, Leverington, Wisbech PE13 5DE	01945 465 082
MOULTON HARROX	Broad Lane, Moulton, Spalding PE12 6PN	07714 700 940
NETHERTON UNITED	The Grange, Charlotte Way, Peterborough PE3 9TT	07808 774 302
PETERBOROUGH ICA SPORTS	Ringwood, South Bretton PE3 9SH	07827 446 844
PETERBOROUGH SPORTS RES.	651 Lincoln Road, Peterborough PE1 3HA	07894 445 991
SAWTRY	Greenfield, Straight Drove, Sawtry, Cambridgeshire PE28 5XE	01487 831 797
STAMFORD LIONS	Borderville Sports Centre, Ryhall Road, Stamford, Lincolnshire, PE9 1US	07809 321 383
STILTON UNITED	Yaxley FC, Leading Drove, PE7 3NA	07756 778 154
SUTTON BRIDGE UNITED	Memorial Park, Bridge Road, Sutton Bridge, PE12 9SA	07960 465 233
THORNEY	Thorney Park, Tavistock Close, Thorney PE6 0SP	07743 296 505
WARBOYS TOWN	The Sports Field, Forge Way, Warboys, PE28 2TN	07983 342 962
WISBECH TOWN RESERVES	The Elgoods Fenland Stadium, Lynn Road, Wisbech, PE14 7AL	01945 581 511

DIVISION THREE

		P	W	D	L	F	A	GD	Pts
1	Bretton North End	22	13	2	1	87	18	69	55*
2	FC Peterborough	22	15	1	5	70	33	37	49*
3	Eye United	22	12	3	5	93	37	56	45*
4	Brotherhood Sports	22	13	0	9	82	56	26	39
5	Sawtry Reserves	22	11	2	6	62	49	13	36*
6	Farcet United	22	12	0	10	59	63	-4	36
7	Stamford Belvedere Res	22	9	3	9	46	55	-9	33*
8	AFC Stanground Sports 'A'	22	8	1	11	64	76	-12	27*
9	Oundle Town Reserves	22	7	0	12	62	77	-15	22*
10	Whittlesey Athletic 'B'	22	6	1	15	51	98	-47	19
11	Thorpe Wood Rangers	22	5	0	11	32	51	-19	13*
12	Uppingham Town Res	22	1	1	18	38	133	-95	2*

DIVISION FOUR

		P	W	D	L	F	A	GD	Pts
1	Premiair	28	24	2	2	144	31	113	74
2	Cardea	28	18	4	6	121	64	57	58
3	Feeder	28	15	4	7	105	53	52	55*
4	Whaplode Drove	28	16	2	9	94	57	37	53*
5	Holbeach Bank	28	16	1	11	72	61	11	49
6	AFC Stanground Sports 'B'	28	14	2	11	53	58	-5	43*
7	Whittlesey Athletic 'C'	28	10	5	10	64	57	7	36*
8	Stamford Lions 'A'	28	10	6	12	55	57	-2	36
9	Parkside	28	11	3	14	63	76	-13	36
10	FC Peterborough Rese	28	10	4	13	60	74	-14	34*
11	Long Sutton Athletic Res	28	9	3	14	54	69	-15	32*
12	Tydd St Mary Res	28	9	1	15	48	94	-46	29*
13	Huntingdon Rovers	28	5	6	16	54	99	-45	24*
14	Netherton United 'B'	28	6	2	19	48	126	-78	23*
15	Wittering Harriers Res	28	4	5	18	51	110	-59	16*

DIVISION FIVE A

		P	W	D	L	F	A	GD	Pts
1	Peterborough NECI	12	10	2	0	49	14	35	32
2	Eunice Huntingdon	12	7	1	3	31	20	11	25*
3	Ramsey Town Res	12	5	0	5	19	19	0	21*
4	Holbeach United 'A'	12	5	0	6	29	27	2	14*
5	Orton Rangers	12	4	0	8	23	38	-15	12
6	Feeder Res	12	2	2	8	26	43	-17	8
7	Glinton & Northborough Res	12	3	1	6	22	38	-16	5*

DIVISION FIVE B

		P	W	D	L	F	A	GD	Pts
1	British School of Sport	10	7	2	1	39	20	19	23
2	AFC Orton	10	7	1	2	35	13	22	22
3	Kings Cliffe Reserves	10	4	1	4	26	18	8	16*
4	Wisbech Town Acorns U21	10	6	0	4	33	31	2	16*
5	Riverside Reserves	10	3	0	6	22	36	-14	8*
6	Leverington Sports 'A'	10	0	0	10	5	42	-37	0

ADDITIONAL CLUB MOVEMENTS

Premier Division
In: Sutton Bridge United (P), Warboys Town (P).
Out: Pincheck United (P - United Counties).

Division One
In: AFC Stanground Sports Res (P), Tydd St Mary (P) Whittlesey Athletic Res become Whittlesey Athletic.
Out: Baston (W), Riverside (W), Sutton Bridge United (P), Warboys Town (P).

Division Two
In: Rippingale & Folkingham (N), Sawtry Res (P), Whittlesey Athletic A become Whittlesey Athletic Res.
Out: AFC Stanground Sports Res (P), Peterborough ICA Sports Res (W), Tydd St Mary (P).

Division Three
In: Whittlesey Athletic B become Whittlesey Athletic A.
Out: AFC Stanguard Sports A (R), Sawtry Res (P).

Division Four
In: AFC Stanground Sports A (R) Whittlesey Athletic C become Whittlesey Athletic B.
Out: .AFC Stanground Sports B (W).

Division Five - Glinton & Northborough Res, AFC Orton, Kings Cliffe Res, Leverington Sports A, will be joined by: Dreams & Peterborough Rangers, FC Peterborough A, Gunthorpe Harriers, Hampton, Pincheck United Res, Premiair Res, Spalding United A and Wittering Res.
Out: .British School of Sport (W), Wisbech Town Acorns U21 (W), Riverside Res (W).

SHEFFIELD & HALLAMSHIRE SENIOR LEAGUE

Sponsored by: Pete's Patisserie

Recent Champions: 2014: Handsworth FC **2015:** Swinton Athletic **2016:** Frecheville CA FC

PREMIER DIVISION	P	W	D	L	F	A	GD	Pts
1 Swallownest FC	26	22	1	3	77	20	57	67
2 Swinton Athletic	26	17	3	6	74	40	34	54
3 Frecheville CA FC	26	15	6	5	62	37	25	51
4 Stocksbridge Park Steels Res	26	15	5	6	52	32	20	50
5 AFC Penistone Church	26	15	3	8	76	39	37	48
6 Handsworth Parramore Res	26	14	5	7	49	31	18	47
7 Jubilee Sports	26	13	5	8	65	64	1	44
8 Houghton Main	26	11	7	8	52	37	15	40
9 North Gawber Colliery	26	10	3	13	56	51	5	33
10 Wombwell Main	26	8	4	14	42	64	-22	28
11 Athersley Recreation Res	26	6	6	14	51	58	-7	24
12 Millmoor Juniors	26	5	1	20	35	101	-66	16
13 Denaby United	26	3	3	20	40	82	-42	12
14 Denaby Main	26	1	2	23	22	97	-75	5

Out: Athersley Recreation Res merged with Grimethorpe Sports, Swallownest (P - Northern Counties East).

DIVISION ONE	P	W	D	L	F	A	GD	Pts
1 Grimethorpe Sports	26	18	1	7	110	62	48	55
2 South Kirkby Colliery	26	17	2	7	60	34	26	53
3 Oughtibridge WMFC	26	16	4	6	69	29	40	52
4 Ecclesfield Red Rose 1915	26	16	3	7	66	41	25	51
5 Wickersley	26	13	4	9	68	40	28	43
6 Caribbean Sports	26	13	4	9	60	55	5	43
7 Brinsworth Whitehill	26	13	4	9	56	53	3	43
8 High Green Villa	26	12	4	10	63	64	-1	40
9 Sheffield Bankers	26	11	6	9	58	44	14	39
10 AFC Dronfield	26	11	4	11	62	51	11	37
11 Silkstone United	26	9	5	12	53	64	-11	32
12 Davy FC	26	5	4	17	42	91	-49	19
13 Hemsworth MW Res	26	3	2	21	37	109	-72	11
14 Millmoor Juniors Res	26	1	1	24	23	90	-67	4

Out: Millmoor Juniors Res (F).

SENIOR DIVISION		1	2	3	4	5	6	7	8	9	10	11	12	13	14
1	AFC Penistone Church		2-1	6-0	5-0	0-0	1-2	2-1	7-0	10-2	1-1	3-1	0-1	3-1	1-0
2	Athersley Recreation Res	1-4		8-0	2-2	2-3	1-4	2-2	2-2	4-1	3-7	2-3	1-2	2-1	1-4
3	Denaby Main	1-11	1-2		1-3	3-3	0-2	1-3	1-3	1-2	0-2	1-2	1-3	1-2	3-3
4	Denaby United	1-3	0-5	5-2		1-3	1-6	4-5	1-3	3-2	2-2	2-3	1-5	1-4	1-3
5	Frecheville CA FC	5-0	2-0	7-1	4-1		2-0	1-1	5-5	4-0	2-1	1-0	0-3	5-2	4-2
6	Handsworth Parramore Res	3-2	3-1	2-0	2-1	1-1		1-1	5-1	1-3	4-3	0-3	0-3	0-0	4-1
7	Houghton Main	2-0	4-1	3-1	3-3	5-0	0-0		1-1	4-0	1-2	0-2	0-1	3-3	4-1
8	Jubilee Sports	1-5	3-2	4-0	3-1	2-1	1-2	0-2		9-2	2-1	2-1	1-4	5-0	3-3
9	Millmoor Juniors	2-1	3-3	1-2	3-1	1-3	0-2	3-1	0-1		1-4	0-3	1-5	1-10	2-3
10	North Gawber Colliery	1-2	0-3	4-0	3-2	2-3	1-0	2-3	2-3	5-2		0-3	3-4	2-0	3-0
11	Stocksbridge Park Steels Res	2-2	3-1	4-0	1-0	1-0	1-1	3-2	2-2	6-0	1-1		2-1	2-1	1-3
12	Swallownest FC	2-0	0-0	6-1	2-0	1-0	1-0	1-0	8-1	3-0	5-2	2-1		1-2	12-1
13	Swinton Athletic	6-2	2-1	3-0	4-1	1-1	2-0	2-0	6-3	9-2	2-1	4-0	2-0		3-2
14	Wombwell Main	2-3	0-0	3-0	3-2	1-2	0-4	0-1	0-4	3-1	2-1	1-1	0-1	1-2	

Sheffield & Hallamshire Senior League Premier Division

DENABY MAIN	Tickhill Square, Denaby. Doncaster, South Yorkshire DN12 4AW	
DENABY UNITED	Balby Carr Community Academy, Weston Road, Balby DN4 8ND	
FRECHEVILLE C.A.	Frecheville S & SC, Silkstone Road, Sheffield S12 4RH	
GRIMETHORPE SPORTS	Shafton Welfare Park, off High Street, Shafton, Barnsley S72 8QA	
HANDSWORTH PARRAMORE RES	Handsworth Junior Sports Club, Olivers Mount, Sheffield S9 4PA	
HOUGHTON MAIN	Middlecliffe Lane	
JUBILEE SPORTS	Chaucer School, Wordsworth Avenue, Sheffield S5 8NH	
MILLMOOR JUNIORS	Grange Park Football Ground, Droppingwell Road, Kimberworth, Rotherham S61 2RB	
NORTH GAWBER COLLIERY	Woolley MW, Wolley Colliery Road, Darton, Barnsley S75 5JA	
OUGHTIBRIDGE WAR MEMORIAL	Oughtibridge War Mem. Grd, off Waterside Gardens, Oughtibridge, Sheffield S35 0JS	
PENISTONE CHURCH RESERVES	Memorial Ground, Church View, Penistone, Sheffield S36 6AT	
SOUTH KIRBY COLLIERY	South Kirkby MW Ground, Millars Walk, South Kirkby WF9 3UZ	
STOCKSBRIDGE P.S. RESERVES	Look Local Stadium, Bracken Moor Lane, Stocksbridge, Sheffield S36 2AN	
SWINTON ATHLETIC	Mexborough Athletic Ground, New Oxford Road, Mexborough S64 0JL	
WOMBWELL MAIN	Rockingham Comm. Centre, Sheffield Road, Hoyland Common, Barnsley S74 0DQ	

SHEFFIELD & HALAMSHIRE SENIOR LEAGUE - STEP 7

DIVISION TWO NORTH	P	W	D	L	F	A	GD	Pts
1 Dodworth MWFC	20	15	3	2	80	20	60	48
2 Hepworth United	20	15	2	3	83	15	68	47
3 Stocksbridge PS Dev	20	15	2	3	67	20	47	47
4 Euroglaze FC	20	13	2	5	55	28	27	41
5 FC Graceholme	20	11	1	8	57	27	30	34
6 Houghton Main Res	20	10	1	9	38	42	-4	31
7 South Kirkby Colliery Res	20	6	3	11	29	67	-38	21
8 Bawtry Town FC	20	5	3	12	31	61	-30	18
9 Wombwell Main Dev	20	5	1	14	41	72	-31	16
10 Worsbrough Bridge Athletic Dev	20	3	3	14	23	78	-55	12
11 Working Wonders	20	1	1	18	18	92	-74	4

Single Division Two for 2017-18
In: Boynton Sports (N), Burngreave (N), Manor Hotel (N), Thurcroft Miners Institute (N).
Out: FC Graceholme (F), Euroglaze (F), Houghton Main Res (F), Bawtry Town (F), Renshaw Rangers (S - Central Midlands), Millmoor Juniors Dev (F), Sheffield Lane Top (F), Davy Reserves (F).

DIVISION TWO NORTH	P	W	D	L	F	A	GD	Pts
1 Sheffield Medics	22	15	2	5	79	29	50	47
2 Caribbean Sports Res	22	13	4	5	65	33	32	43
3 Kiveton Park	22	13	4	5	58	36	22	43
4 Swinton Athletic Res	22	13	1	8	56	32	24	40
5 Davy FC Reserves	22	13	0	9	61	52	9	39
6 New Bohemians	22	10	4	8	40	48	-8	34
7 AFC Dronfield Res	22	7	4	11	43	48	-5	25
8 Maltby Main Reserves	22	7	4	11	44	65	-21	25
9 Sheffield Lane Top	22	7	2	13	37	62	-25	23
10 Sheffield Bankers Res	22	6	4	12	38	53	-15	22
11 Millmoor Juniors Dev	22	6	4	12	38	60	-22	22
12 Renishaw Rangers	22	5	1	16	33	74	-41	16

Out: Kiveton Park (P).

LEAGUE CUP

HOLDERS: JUBILEE SPORTS

ROUND 1

FC Graceholme	v	AFC Dronfield Res	HW
Hepworth United	v	Hemsworth MW Res	2-0 aet
Jubilee Sports	v	Stocksbridge Park Steels Res	2-1
AFC Penistone Church	v	Silkstone United	4-1
Athersley Recreation Res	v	North Gawber Colliery	4-3 aet
Renishaw Rangers	v	Davy FC	2-1
Kiveton Park	v	AFC Dronfield	2-1 aet
South Kirkby Colliery	v	Sheffield Lane Top	6-1
Grimethorpe Sports	v	Working Wonders	4-3
Maltby Main Res	v	Millmoor Juniors Res	HW
Denaby Main	v	Frecheville CA FC	1-2
Millmoor Juniors Dev	v	Sheffield Bankers Res	1-2
Sheffield Bankers	v	Swinton Athletic	2-1
New Bohemians	v	Brinsworth Whitehill	1-3
Swinton Athletic Res	v	Wombwell Main Dev	5-3
Dodworth MWFC	v	High Green Villa	3-0
Bawtry Town FC	v	Stocksbridge PS Dev	1-3
Millmoor Juniors	v	Swallownest FC	AW
Denaby United	v	Houghton Main Res	7-1

ROUND 2

Euroglaze FC	v	Worsbrough Bridge Athletic Dev	2-1
Sheffield Bankers Res	v	Kiveton Park	0-1
Brinsworth Whitehill	v	Denaby United	4-2
Wombwell Main	v	FC Graceholme	3-1
Sheffield Medics	v	Jubilee Sports	3-1
Houghton Main	v	Stocksbridge PS Dev	2-1
Davy FC Res	v	Caribbean Sports	1-3
Maltby Main Res	v	Grimethorpe Sports	2-4
Wickersley	v	South Kirkby Colliery	7-3
Caribbean Sports Res	v	Sheffield Bankers	3-2
South Kirkby Colliery Res	v	Dodworth MWFC	0-4
Frecheville CA FC	v	Swinton Athletic Reserves	5-1
Ecclesfield Red Rose 1915 v		Oughtibridge WMFC	2-1
Athersley Recreation Res	v	Handsworth Parramore Res	2-0
AFC Penistone Church	v	Hepworth United	2-1
Swallownest FC	v	Renishaw Rangers	7-2

ROUND 3

Sheffield Medics	v	Frecheville CA FC	4-2
Athersley Recreation Res	v	Kiveton Park	3-1
Wombwell Main	v	AFC Penistone Church	1-2
Dodworth MWFC	v	Houghton Main	0-1
Caribbean Sports	v	Swallownest FC	0-4
Caribbean Sports Res	v	Brinsworth Whitehill	3-4
Wickersley	v	Ecclesfield Red Rose 1915	6-4
Euroglaze FC	v	Grimethorpe Sports	4-1

QUARTER FINALS

Brinsworth Whitehill	v	AFC Penistone Church	6-4 aet
Houghton Main	v	Athersley Recreation Res	1-4
Sheffield Medics	v	Wickersley	3-1
Swallownest FC	v	Euroglaze FC	6-1

SEMI FINALS

Athersley Recreation Res	v	Brinsworth Whitehill	0-0, 10-11p
Sheffield Medics	v	Swallownest FC	0-1

FINAL

Swallownest FC	v	Brinsworth Whitehill	5-1

SOMERSET COUNTY LEAGUE

Sponsored by: Errea
Founded: 1890
Recent Champions:
2014: Nailsea United. **2015:** Shirehampton. **2016:** Bishops Lydeard

PREMIER DIVISION

	PREMIER DIVISION	P	W	D	L	F	A	GD	Pts
1	Watchet Town	32	21	7	4	79	32	47	70
2	Shirehampton	32	21	3	8	93	51	42	66
3	Nailsea & Tickenham	32	20	7	5	75	26	49	64*
4	Stockwood Wanderers	32	19	4	9	62	37	25	61
5	Middlezoy Rovers	32	16	5	11	58	57	1	53
6	Chilcompton Sports	32	13	11	8	67	60	7	50
7	Odd Down (BATH) Res	32	16	2	14	58	62	-4	50
8	Staplegrove	32	15	3	14	64	54	10	48
9	Nailsea United	32	13	7	12	61	51	10	46
10	Fry Club	32	13	4	15	42	48	-6	43
11	Wells City Reserves	32	12	5	15	45	51	-6	41
12	Bridgwater Town FC Res	32	10	6	16	51	70	-19	36
13	Shepton Mallet Res	32	8	9	15	55	65	-10	33
14	Wrington Redhill	32	8	5	19	43	77	-34	29
15	Clevedon United	32	6	8	18	38	69	-31	26
16	Berrow	32	7	6	19	38	78	-40	24*
17	Yatton Athletic	32	6	4	22	62	103	-41	22

Out: Berrow merged with Highbridge (D1W). Shepton Mallet Res (W), Yatton Athletic merged with Cleeve United (D1W)

PREMIER & FIRST DIVISION CUP

HOLDERS: WRINGTON REDHILL
ROUND 1

Wells City Res	v	Clevedon United	2-1
Berrow	v	Peasdown Miners Welfare	2-1
Winscombe	v	Fry Club	1-2
Street Res	v	Ilminster Town	2-2, 4-2p
Watchet Town	v	Brislington Res	2-0
Congresbury	v	Bridgwater Town Res	0-6
Stockwood Green	v	Clutton	1-1, 4-5p
Somerton Town	v	Odd Down (BATH) Res	5-1
Stockwood Wanderers	v	Chilcompton Sports	0-1
Minehead AFC	v	Middlezoy Rovers	0-1
Wrington Redhill	v	Yatton Athletic	6-1
Timsbury Athletic	v	Nailsea & Tickenham	3-3, 4-5p
Broad Plain House	v	Shepton Mallet Res	3-4
Shirehampton	v	Larkhall Athletic Res	0-0, 6-5p
Staplegrove	v	Uphill Castle	2-1
Nailsea United	v	Westfield	6-2

PREMIER DIVISION

	PREMIER DIVISION	1	2	3	4	5	6	7	8	9	10	11	12	13	14	15	16	17
1	Berrow		3-0	1-5	1-1	0-0	0-1	0-3	3-5	1-2	0-0	1-6	2-0	1-6	0-3	1-1	4-0	3-6
2	Bridgwater Town FC Res	2-2		6-1	5-3	1-1	2-1	0-4	3-2	3-4	0-0	0-3	0-2	0-1	2-3	2-0	1-2	2-1
3	Chilcompton Sports	2-1	2-2		1-0	4-2	2-0	0-2	5-2	1-1	2-3	7-3	6-3	2-2	0-0	2-0	2-2	6-1
4	Clevedon United	3-0	0-2	3-3		1-0	0-2	1-2	2-4	1-2	1-4	2-1	4-2	2-1	1-1	1-1	0-3	1-1
5	Fry Club	2-1	1-0	2-2	2-0		2-0	1-3	2-2	0-2	2-1	3-1	2-1	0-4	0-2	0-1	2-0	2-3
6	Middlezoy Rovers	1-0	1-2	1-0	2-0	0-2		1-3	1-0	4-0	3-2	2-4	2-1	2-5	1-5	3-1	2-0	3-0
7	Nailsea & Tickenham	4-0	6-2	0-0	1-0	1-0	2-2		1-1	0-1	2-2	3-3	3-2	2-0	1-1	5-0	1-1	5-1
8	Nailsea United	1-0	6-0	0-0	3-4	2-0	2-3	1-0		3-2	0-0	3-1	4-2	0-1	2-3	0-2	4-0	1-1
9	Odd Down (BATH) Res	0-1	0-1	1-1	4-1	3-0	3-3	1-0	1-2		0-4	0-5	3-2	2-0	4-2	0-1	2-1	7-4
10	Shepton Mallet Res	1-2	2-5	1-3	0-0	2-1	4-4	0-5	2-1	2-3		2-3	1-2	0-3	1-4	3-2	3-0	3-1
11	Shirehampton	7-0	2-1	3-0	5-1	0-2	5-1	0-4	2-0	4-0	2-2		3-1	1-1	4-1	4-1	6-3	2-0
12	Staplegrove	1-2	4-1	4-0	0-0	2-1	2-3	0-2	1-1	3-0	3-2	1-2		3-2	1-0	2-1	7-0	2-3
13	Stockwood Wanderers	4-0	4-1	3-0	4-2	0-2	2-0	1-0	0-3	3-1	3-2	1-1			0-2	2-1	5-3	2-0
14	Watchet Town	2-2	3-1	5-0	5-0	3-1	3-1	3-0	1-1	1-0	2-2	1-0	0-1	0-0		2-1	1-0	7-2
15	Wells City Res	3-0	0-0	2-2	4-2	2-1	1-1	1-0	2-0	5-2	3-0	2-3	0-2	0-1	1-3		0-1	0-3
16	Wrington Redhill	4-2	2-0	1-3	1-1	1-2	1-1	1-5	1-2	3-1	3-2	1-2	2-4	0-1	0-6	0-2		2-2
17	Yatton Athletic	2-4	4-4	2-3	2-0	3-4	3-4	0-4	4-6	3-2	0-4	2-4	1-2	1-2	2-4	3-4	1-4	

DIVISION ONE EAST

		P	W	D	L	F	A	GD	Pts
1	Clutton	28	21	6	1	96	21	75	69
2	Stockwood Green	28	20	8	0	99	12	87	68
3	Timsbury Athletic	28	18	5	5	81	27	54	59
4	Brislington Res	28	18	5	5	85	34	51	56*
5	Westfield	28	16	4	8	90	55	35	52
6	Larkhall Athletic FC Res	28	14	6	8	62	45	17	48
7	Keynsham Town Res	28	15	0	13	58	57	1	45
8	Imperial	28	13	2	13	66	67	-1	41
9	Purnell Sports	28	9	5	14	52	64	-12	32
10	Frome Town Sports	28	9	2	17	47	76	-29	29
11	Welton Rovers Res	28	8	1	19	32	100	-68	25
12	Peasedown Miners Welfare	28	7	6	15	33	54	-21	24*
13	Broad Plain House	28	7	3	18	51	85	-34	24
14	Castle Cary	28	6	2	20	45	86	-41	20
15	Cutters Friday	28	1	1	26	26	140	-114	4

DIVISION ONE WEST

		P	W	D	L	F	A	GD	Pts
1	Ilminster Town	24	14	5	5	58	29	29	47
2	Portishead Town Res	24	18	3	3	78	25	53	45*
3	Winscombe	24	14	3	7	47	30	17	45
4	Somerton Town	24	13	4	7	59	26	33	43
5	Minehead AFC	24	13	2	9	59	40	19	41
6	Street Res	24	11	7	6	45	36	9	40
7	Uphill Castle	24	10	7	7	51	44	7	37
8	Burnham United	24	9	4	11	46	45	1	31
9	Cleeve West Town	24	7	5	12	34	46	-12	26
10	Highbridge Town	24	7	6	11	49	62	-13	24*
11	Glastonbury	24	6	3	15	21	51	-30	21
12	Combe St Nicholas	24	4	3	17	27	66	-39	15
13	Congresbury	24	3	2	19	23	97	-74	8*

DIVISION TWO EAST

		P	W	D	L	F	A	GD	Pts
1	Saltford	20	12	7	1	52	22	30	43
2	Fry Club Res	20	13	4	3	46	22	24	43
3	Long Ashton	20	12	4	4	59	35	24	40
4	Hengrove Athletic Res	20	11	6	3	46	16	30	39
5	Mendip Broadwalk	20	11	5	4	55	20	35	38
6	AFC Brislington	20	7	6	7	42	29	13	27
7	Radstock Town Res	20	7	5	8	27	35	-8	26
8	Pensford	20	5	5	10	39	50	-11	20
9	Chew Magna	20	5	4	11	29	55	-26	19
10	Stockwood Green Res	20	2	1	17	26	74	-48	7
11	Tunley Athletic	20	1	1	18	23	86	-63	1*

DIVISION TWO WEST

		P	W	D	L	F	A	GD	Pts
1	Nailsea & Tickenham Res	23	19	3	1	69	21	48	60
2	Worle	24	17	4	3	97	35	62	55
3	Weston St Johns	24	16	1	7	64	44	20	49
4	Ashton & Backwell United Res	24	11	3	10	49	48	1	36
5	Winscombe Res	24	8	11	5	41	32	9	35
6	Clevedon United Res	24	9	6	9	39	41	-2	33
7	Churchill Club 70	24	9	4	11	46	53	-7	31
8	Banwell	24	8	4	12	51	60	-9	28
9	1610 Taunton United	23	8	4	11	48	65	-17	28
10	Cheddar Reserves	24	7	4	13	33	51	-18	25
11	Nailsea United Res	24	6	6	12	36	59	-23	24
12	Burnham United Res	24	4	5	15	30	62	-32	14*
13	Kewstoke Lions	24	3	5	16	30	62	-32	14

Additional Club Movements:

Out: Clevedon United Res (P), Churchill Club 70 (P)

PREMIER & FIRST DIVISION CUP

ROUND 2

Wells City Res	v	Berrow	3-4
Fry Club	v	Street Res	5-0
Watchet Town	v	Bridgwater Town Res	5-2
Clutton	v	Somerton Town	2-0
Chilcompton Sports	v	Middlezoy Rovers	8-2
Wrington Redhill	v	Nailsea & Tickenham	0-0, 2-4p
Shepton Mallet Res	v	Shirehampton	1-0
Staplegrove	v	Nailsea United	2-1

QUARTER-FINALS

Berrow	v	Fry Club	0-3
Watchet Town	v	Clutton	2-2, 2-4p
Chilcompton Sports	v	Nailsea & Tickenham	2-2, 3-4p
Shepton Mallet Res	v	Staplegrove	4-2

SEMI-FINALS

Fry Club	v	Clutton	3-2
Nailsea & Tickenham	v	Shepton Mallet Res	3-0

FINAL

Fry Club	v	Nailsea & Tickenham	0-0, 5-4p

DIVISION TWO CUP

HOLDERS: HIGHBRIDGE TOWN

QUARTER-FINALS

Worle	v	Hengrove Athletic Res	4-2
Chew Magna	v	Fry Club Res	2-2, 4-2p
Long Ashton	v	Mendip Broadwalk	3-1
Radstock Town Res	v	Saltford	5-1

SEMI-FINALS

Worle	v	Chew Magna	2-0
Long Ashton	v	Radstock Town Res	3-0

FINAL

Worle	v	Long Ashton	4-0

Somerset County League Premier Division

BRIDGWATER TOWN RESEVES	Fairfax Park, College Way, Bath Road, Bridgwater TA6 4TZ	01278 446 899
CHILCOMPTON SPORTS	Chilcompton Sports Ground, Bennell Wells Road, Chilcompton BA3 4EZ	01761 232 117
CLEVEDON UNITED	Coleridge Vale, Clevedon, North Somerset	01275 871 878
CLUTTON	Warwick Fields, Upper Bristol Rd , Behind Warwick Arms, Clutton, Bristol BS39 5TA	07778 779 759
FRY CLUB	Somerdale Pavilion, Cross Street, Keynsham, Bristol BS31 2FW	0117 986 5787
ILMINSTER TOWN	The Archie Gooch Pavilion, Canal Way, Ilminster TA19 9FE	07875 378 663
MIDDLEZOY ROVERS	The Aerodrome, Westonzoyland, Somerset TA7 0ES	07881 504 050
NAILSEA AND TICKENHAM	Fryth Way, Pound Lane, Nailsea BS48 2AS	07446 962 091
NAILSEA UNITED	Grove Sports Ground, Old Church, Nailsea BS48 4ND	01275 856 892
ODD DOWN RESERVES	Lew Hill Memorial Ground, Combe Hay Lane, Odd Down, Bath BA2 8PH	01225 832 491
SHIREHAMPTON	Recreation Ground, Penpole Lane, Shirehampton, Bristol BS11 0EA	0117 923 5461
STAPLEGROVE	Staplegrove Sports Ground, Manor Road, Staplegrove, Taunton TA2 6EG	01823 352 574
STOCKWOOD GREEN	Hursley Lane, Woolard Lane, Whitchurch, Bristol BS14 0QY	07780 727 179
STOCKWOOD WANDERERS	Stockers Stadium, Stockwood lane, Bristol BS14 8SJ	07504 311 071
WATCHET TOWN	Memorial Ground, Doniford Road, Watchet TA23 0TE	01984 631 041
WELLS CITY RESERVES	Athletic Ground, Rowdens Road, Wells, Somerset BA5 1TU	01749 679 971
WRINGTON REDHILL	The Recreation Field, Silver Street, Wrington, Bristol BS40 5QN	07918 192 544

STAFFORDSHIRE COUNTY SENIOR LEAGUE

Sponsored by: No sponsor   **Founded:** 1957

Recent Champions: 2014: Wolstanton United **2015:** Wolstanton United. **2016:** Leek CSOB

PREMIER DIVISION	P	W	D	L	F	A	GD	Pts
1 Abbey Hulton United	30	23	2	5	91	32	59	71
2 Wolstanton United	30	21	2	7	79	37	42	65
3 Silverdale Athletic	30	16	9	5	79	38	41	57
4 Leek CSOB	30	17	5	8	57	36	21	56
5 Redgate Clayton	30	16	7	7	78	42	36	55
6 Ball Haye Green	30	16	4	10	83	62	21	52
7 Newcastle Town Res	30	13	7	10	67	54	13	46
8 Ashbourne	30	12	6	12	56	53	3	42
9 Florence	30	11	8	11	58	57	1	41
10 Hilton Harriers Athletic	30	10	9	11	57	59	-2	39
11 Hanley Town Res	30	9	11	10	44	52	-8	38
12 Walsall Phoenix	30	10	4	16	56	71	-15	34
13 Cheadle Town	30	9	5	16	43	63	-20	32
14 Knypersley Victoria	30	8	3	19	54	109	-55	27
15 Eccleshall Res	30	3	4	23	36	109	-73	13
16 Alsager Town Res	30	2	2	26	37	101	-64	8

Cheadle SMU withdrew - record expunged.

DIVISION ONE	P	W	D	L	F	A	GD	Pts
1 Foley Meir	26	20	2	4	83	33	50	62
2 Stone Dominoes	26	19	3	4	81	33	48	60
3 Eastwood Hanley	26	16	5	5	74	41	33	53
4 MMU Cheshire	26	16	2	8	84	32	52	50
5 Penkridge	26	16	0	10	93	58	35	48
6 Keele University	26	13	3	10	79	52	27	42
7 Market Drayton Tigers	26	12	6	8	64	59	5	42
8 Milton United	26	11	2	13	72	55	17	35
9 Audley & District	26	10	5	11	60	59	1	35
10 Redgate Clayton Res	26	10	3	13	55	62	-7	33
11 Wolverhampton SC U21	26	8	1	17	44	72	-28	25
12 Abbey Hulton United Res	26	4	7	15	32	87	-55	19
13 Staffordshire LA	26	4	2	20	37	153	-116	14
14 Cheadle Town Res	26	2	1	23	28	90	-62	7

Hawkins Sports withdrew - record expunged.

Division Two North	P	W	D	L	F	A	GD	Pts
1 Tunstall Town	24	22	1	1	130	36	94	67
2 Foley Meir Res	24	20	0	4	72	29	43	60
3 Leek CSOB Res	24	15	3	6	71	39	32	48
4 Chesterton	24	11	3	10	58	55	3	36
5 Goldenhill Wanderers	24	10	5	9	66	52	14	35
6 AFC Alsager	24	11	2	11	60	62	-2	35
7 Norton Athletic	24	8	6	10	58	56	+2	30
8 Staffordshire Moorlands	24	9	2	13	46	58	-12	29
9 HDFC	24	8	4	12	51	58	-7	28
10 Milton United Res	24	8	1	15	31	81	-50	25
11 Audley & District Res	24	6	3	15	29	62	-33	21
12 Keele University Res	24	5	3	16	38	76	-38	18
13 Congleton Rovers	24	4	5	15	41	87	-46	17

Division Two South	P	W	D	L	F	A	GD	Pts
1 Pathfinder	21	18	1	2	77	13	64	55
2 Brereton Social	21	16	3	2	53	19	34	51
3 Walsall Phoenix U21s	21	8	5	8	54	50	4	29
4 Cannock United	21	8	4	9	40	52	-12	28
5 Acorn Albion	21	7	5	9	39	39	0	26
6 Red Star Alma	21	7	2	12	28	49	-21	23
7 Whittington	21	4	2	15	29	62	-33	14
8 Hilton Harriers Athletic Res	21	4	2	15	24	60	-36	14

Stoke Old Alleynians Res withdrew - record expunged.

Additional Club Movements

Premier - Out: Abbey Hulton United (P - North West Counties), Hilton Harriers Athletic (W).

Division One - Pathfinder now Shenstone Pathfinder and Tunstall Town now OSSMA Bluton TT.

Staffordshire County Senior League Premier Division

ALSAGER TOWN RESERVES — Wood Park Stadium, Woodland Court, Alsager, Staffordshire ST7 2DP

ASHBOURNE — Rocester FC, Mill Street, Rocester, Staffordshire ST14 5JX

BALL HAYE GREEN — Ball Haye Green WMC, Ball Haye Green, Leek ST13 6BH

CHEADLE TOWN — Thorley Drive, Cheadle, Staffordshire. ST10 1SA

EASTWOOD HANLEY — Wellbeing Park, Yarnfield Lane, Yarnfield, Staffordshire ST15 0NF

ECCLESHALL RESERVES — Pershall Park, Chester Road, Eccleshall ST21 6NE

FLORENCE — Florence Sports & Social, Lightwood Road, Longton, Stoke-on-Trent ST7 4JS

FOLEY MEIR — Macintosh Arena, Whitcombe Road, Meir, Staffordshire ST3 6AO

HANLEY TOWN RESERVES — Potteries Park, Abbey Lane, Bucknall, Staffordshire ST2 8AU

KNYPERSLEY VICTORIA — Knypersley Sports, Tunstall Road, Staffordshire ST8 6JP

LEEK CSOB — Knypersley Sports, Tunstall Road, Staffordshire ST8 6JP

NEWCASTLE TOWN RESERVES — Drayton Beaumont Stadium, Buckmaster Avenue, Clayton, Staffordshire ST5 3BX

REDGATE CLAYTON — Clayton Comm. Centre, Northwood Lane, Clayton, Newcastle-under-Lyme ST5 4BN

SILVERDALE ATHLETIC — Kents Lane Football Ground, Sutton Ave, Staffordshire ST5 6TA

STONE DOMINOES — Stone Wellbeing Centre, Stone Dominoes, Staffordshire ST15 0NF

WALSALL PHOENIX — The Green, off Little Aston Road, Aldridge, Staffordshire WS9 8NH

WOLSTANTON UNITED — Bradwell Comm. Centre, Riceyman Road, Bradwell, Newcastle-under-Lyme ST5 8LD

SUFFOLK & IPSWICH LEAGUE

Sponsored by: TouchlineSIL

Founded: 1896

Recent Champions:

2014: Achilles

2015: Crane Sports

2016: Crane Sports

SENIOR DIVISION	P	W	D	L	F	A	GD	Pts
1 Henley Athletic	30	26	0	4	89	24	65	78
2 Achilles	30	25	1	4	132	46	86	76
3 Crane Sports	30	20	4	6	82	28	54	64
4 Bramford United	30	19	4	7	75	47	28	61
5 Coplestonians	30	16	3	11	62	42	20	51
6 East Bergholt United	30	10	9	11	49	57	-8	39
7 Leiston St Margarets	30	12	3	15	39	54	-15	39
8 Felixstowe Harpers United	30	11	6	13	64	61	3	37*
9 Ransomes Sports	30	10	6	14	67	79	-12	36
10 Haughley United	30	9	7	14	56	69	-13	34
11 Capel Plough	30	7	10	13	50	64	-14	31
12 Grundisburgh	30	10	1	19	41	89	-48	31
13 Wenhaston United	30	8	6	16	47	64	-17	30
14 Westerfield United	30	6	11	13	36	61	-25	29
15 Stanton	30	6	7	17	49	72	-23	25
16 Ipswich Athletic	30	3	6	21	34	115	-81	15

DIVISION ONE	P	W	D	L	F	A	GD	Pts
1 Benhall St Mary	26	18	5	3	101	30	71	59
2 AFC Hoxne	26	18	3	5	86	28	58	57
3 Sporting '87	26	17	5	4	71	21	50	56
4 Claydon	26	17	4	5	76	30	46	55
5 Trimley Red Devils	25	12	5	8	78	39	39	41
6 Stowupland Falcons	26	13	1	12	70	70	0	40
7 AFC Kesgrave	26	11	6	9	67	40	27	39
8 Bacton United '89	26	11	4	11	53	42	11	37
9 Wickham Market	26	10	6	10	60	49	11	36
10 Mendlesham	26	10	4	12	53	70	-17	34
11 Trimley Athletic	26	6	5	15	42	50	-8	23
12 Old Newton United	26	7	1	18	58	82	-24	22
13 Ipswich Exiles	25	4	4	17	36	89	-53	14*
14 Ipswich Valley Rangers	26	0	1	25	12	223	-211	-5*

BOB COLEMAN CUP

HOLDERS: ACHILLES

ROUND 1

Adastral Park	v	Stage Event Security	7-0

ROUND 2

Trimley Red Devils	v	Halesworth Town	3-2
Coddenham Athletic	v	Adastral Park	0-3
Old Newton United	v	Witnesham Wasps	2-4
East Bergholt United	Bye		
Bramford United	Bye		
Achilles	Bye		
Leiston St Margarets	Bye		
Grundisburgh	Bye		
Barham Athletic	v	Stonham Aspal	4-3
Chantry Grasshoppers	v	Cedars Park	0-6
Somersham	v	Stowupland Falcons	2-3
Coplestonians	Bye		
Shotley	v	AFC Hoxne	2-1
Capel Plough	Bye		
Trimley Athletic	v	Ipswich Exiles	2-6
Bacton United 89	v	AFC Kesgrave	2-4 aet
BROB	v	Kesgrave Kestrels	2-4 aet
Wenhaston United	Bye		
Bartons Willows	v	ipswich Valley Rangers	4-2
Westerfield United	Bye		
Wickham Market	v	Mendlesham	0-1
Saxmundham Sports	v	Benhall St Mary	0-7
Henley Athletic	Bye		
Felixstowe Harpers United	Bye		
Ufford Sports	v	Sporting 87	3-5
Claydon	v	Sproughton Sports	13-1
Ipswich Athletic	Bye		
Stanton	Bye		
Ransomes Sports	Bye		
Crane Sports	Bye		
Bildeston Rangers	v	Tacket Street BBOB	5-1
Haughley United	Bye		

ROUND 3

Trimley Red Devils	v	Adastral Park	3-2
Witnesham Wasps	v	East Bergholt United	1-5
Bramford United	v	Achilles	0-4
Leiston St Margarets	v	Grundisburgh	2-4
Barham Athletic	v	Cedars Park	2-4
Stowupland Falcons	v	Coplestonians	3-3, 0-3p
Shotley	v	Capel Plough	2-2, 3-5p
ipswich Exiles	v	AFC Kesgrave	0-7
Kesgrave Kestrels	v	Wenhaston United	1-2
Bartons Willows	v	Westerfield United	2-6
Mendlesham	v	Benhall St Mary	2-3
Henley Athletic	v	Felixstowe Harpers United	0-4
Sporting 87	v	Claydon	1-3
Ipswich Athletic	v	Stanton	1-2
Ransomes Sports	v	Crane Sports	3-5
Bildeston Rangers	v	Haughley United	0-7

SENIOR DIVISION		1	2	3	4	5	6	7	8	9	10	11	12	13	14	15	16
1	Achilles		5-1	3-2	3-1	2-3	5-2	4-2	5-1	6-1	2-0	5-0	7-2	15-2	3-3	5-2	3-0
2	Bramford United	1-7		2-0	1-1	1-4	4-0	3-1	0-1	3-1	1-2	3-2	4-0	1-1	2-1	3-1	1-0
3	Capel Plough	2-5	1-1		1-0	1-3	0-0	0-0	1-2	1-2	2-3	10-0	0-1	3-3	2-2	2-1	3-1
4	Coplestonians	5-4	0-1	4-1		1-3	1-2	1-1	4-0	1-2	1-2	3-0	1-2	1-2	5-1	1-0	1-1
5	Crane Sports	0-1	3-1	7-0	0-1		2-0	2-2	11-0	1-0	1-3	4-1	0-1	7-0	2-1	1-0	3-1
6	East Bergholt United	3-7	2-2	3-4	1-3	1-1		2-1	1-1	2-1	1-3	3-3	1-0	3-1	2-2	0-3	0-0
7	Felixstowe Harpers United	2-1	4-0	2-0	2-9	0-4	2-1		1-2	2-3	0-4	7-2	1-2	2-3	2-2	5-3	1-1
8	Grundisburgh	2-5	2-4	1-3	0-1	1-5	0-6	1-4		0-4	0-4	1-0	6-3	4-2	3-2	3-1	0-2
9	Haughley United	1-2	3-6	2-2	1-2	4-2	1-2	0-3	3-1		1-3	2-2	2-1	4-4	3-2	0-3	2-2
10	Henley Athletic	2-1	1-2	5-0	5-1	2-0	2-1	2-0	6-1	0-1		9-1	2-0	2-1	4-1	4-0	5-1
11	Ipswich Athletic	0-9	2-5	1-1	1-3	0-6	2-0	4-4	1-4	3-3	0-1		0-0	0-5	3-1	1-4	1-2
12	Leiston St Margarets	1-3	0-6	4-1	1-2	0-1	0-1	1-0	1-0	1-0	0-2	5-1		0-3	2-3	1-3	1-1
13	Ransomes Sports	2-4	2-3	3-3	3-1	1-2	1-2	3-2	3-0	4-4	0-2	8-0	1-2		3-1	3-2	0-2
14	Stanton	1-5	0-4	0-1	0-2	0-2	1-1	0-2	1-4	0-0	0-1	1-5	3-1			2-2	3-0
15	Wenhaston United	1-3	0-3	2-2	1-3	0-0	2-2	0-4	0-3	4-2	3-1	4-1	0-0	3-1	0-5		2-2
16	Westerfield United	1-2	0-6	1-1	0-2	2-2	2-4	1-5	2-1	1-1	1-3	2-1	1-2	1-1	4-4	1-0	

SUFFOLK & IPSWICH LEAGUE - STEP 7

DIVISION TWO

		P	W	D	L	F	A	GD	Pts
1	Barham Athletic	26	19	4	3	97	29	68	61
2	Bildeston Rangers	26	19	3	4	103	41	62	60
3	Shotley	26	19	1	6	85	37	48	58
4	Cedars Park	26	17	3	6	79	35	44	54
5	BROB	26	14	3	9	62	43	19	45
6	Stonham Aspal	26	13	1	12	80	57	23	40
7	Witnesham Wasps	26	12	1	13	64	70	-6	37
8	Tacket Street BBOB	26	11	1	14	51	62	-11	34
9	Somersham	26	8	7	11	47	65	-18	31
10	Halesworth Town	26	9	3	14	37	66	-29	30
11	Coddenham Athletic	26	8	3	15	41	64	-23	27
12	Bartons Willows	26	8	1	17	37	75	-38	25
13	Sproughton Sports	26	4	2	20	27	108	-81	12*
14	Chantry Grasshoppers	26	3	3	20	45	103	-58	8*

DIVISION THREE

		P	W	D	L	F	A	GD	Pts
1	Adastral Park	20	18	1	1	105	18	87	55
2	Cockfield United	20	17	2	1	108	25	83	53
3	Saxmundham Sports	20	14	2	4	103	33	70	44
4	Kesgrave Kestrels	20	11	2	7	76	57	19	35
5	Tattingstone United	20	9	2	9	54	68	-14	29
6	Ufford Sports	20	8	3	9	34	39	-5	27
7	Elmswell	20	7	2	11	49	69	-20	23
8	Sutton Heath Saxons	20	5	3	12	41	72	-31	18
9	Woolverstone United	20	4	3	13	41	63	-22	15
10	Newton Road	20	4	3	13	38	72	-34	15
11	Salvation Army	20	1	1	18	23	156	-133	2*

DIVISION FOUR

		P	W	D	L	F	A	GD	Pts
1	AFC YourShirts	24	23	1	0	134	24	110	70
2	Felixstowe Rangers	24	19	2	3	125	42	83	59
3	Thurston	24	16	3	5	102	38	64	51
4	Barham Athletic Res	24	14	4	6	86	44	42	46
5	Cedars Park 'A'	24	13	2	9	72	54	18	41
6	Kesgrave Kestrels Res	24	12	1	11	60	60	0	37
7	Sproughton United	24	9	5	10	57	55	2	29*
8	Needham Market Phoenix	24	9	2	13	71	70	1	29
9	Ufford Sports Res	24	9	3	12	44	67	-23	28*
10	Wortham	24	6	2	16	55	88	-33	20
11	BROB Res	24	7	1	16	42	106	-64	20*
12	Bacton United '89 'A'	24	5	1	18	34	114	-80	10*
13	Chantry Grasshoppers Res	24	0	1	23	18	138	-120	-1*.

BOB COLEMAN CUP

ROUND 4

Trimley Red Devils	v	East Bergholt United	1-3
Achilles	v	Grundisburgh	2-0
Cedars Park	v	Coplestonians	0-2
Capel Plough	v	AFC Kesgrave	0-3
Wenhaston United	v	Westerfield United	1-1, 4-2p
Benhall St Mary	v	Felixstowe Harpers United	2-1
Claydon	v	Stanton	3-1
Crane Sports	v	Haughley United	3-0

QUARTER-FINALS

East Bergholt United	v	Achilles	2-3 aet
Coplestonians	v	AFC Kesgrave	2-4
Wenhaston United	v	Benhall St Mary	0-2
Claydon	v	Crane Sports	2-1

SEMI-FINALS

Achilles	v	AFC Kesgrave	1-0
Benhall St Mary	v	Claydon	2-1

FINAL

Achilles	v	Benhall St Mary	2-3

INTERMEDIATE A

		P	W	D	L	F	A	GD	Pts
1	AFC Hoxne Res	22	19	2	1	93	18	75	59
2	Westerfield United Res	22	17	4	1	81	29	52	55
3	Achilles Res	22	15	2	5	83	37	46	47
4	East Bergholt United Res	22	14	1	7	70	34	36	43
5	Framlingham Town Res	22	10	4	8	62	39	23	34
6	Sporting '87 Res	22	8	2	12	47	56	-9	26
7	Wenhaston United Res	22	7	4	11	26	51	-25	25
8	Coplestonians Res	22	6	4	12	51	54	-3	22
9	Old Newton United Res	22	6	4	12	33	79	-46	20*
10	Ipswich Athletic Res	22	4	4	14	42	88	-46	14*
11	Mendlesham Res	22	3	3	16	35	102	-67	10*
12	Cranes Sports Res	22	5	2	15	45	81	-36	5*

INTERMEDIATE B

		P	W	D	L	F	A	GD	Pts
1	Bramford United Res	24	18	1	5	55	27	28	55
2	Coplestonians 'A'	24	16	3	5	63	24	39	51
3	Henley Athletic Res	24	14	2	8	55	36	19	44
4	Bacton United '89 Res	24	13	2	9	56	43	13	41
5	Trimley Athletic Res	24	12	2	10	61	59	2	38
6	Haughley United Res	24	13	3	8	65	38	27	36*
7	Trimley Red Devils Res	24	10	3	11	61	54	7	33
8	Stonham Aspal Res	24	8	5	11	52	66	-14	29
9	East Bergholt United 'A'	24	8	1	15	51	79	-28	25
10	Stowupland Falcons Res	24	6	6	12	42	65	-23	24
11	Benhall St Mary Res	23	7	3	13	35	64	-29	24
12	Claydon Res	24	5	6	13	45	60	-15	21
13	Capel Plough Res	23	5	3	15	32	58	-26	11*

INTERMEDIATE C

		P	W	D	L	F	A	GD	Pts
1	Wickham Market Res	26	22	1	3	99	23	76	67
2	Cedars Park Res	25	18	0	7	84	34	50	54
3	Cockfield United Res	26	17	2	7	84	44	40	53
4	Debenham LC Res	26	15	5	6	81	45	36	50
5	Witnesham Wasps Res	26	15	2	9	75	56	19	47
6	Ransomes Sports Res	24	14	4	6	60	57	3	33*
7	Stowupland Falcons 'A'	26	11	0	15	50	79	-29	33
8	AFC Kesgrave Res	26	11	1	14	66	75	-9	32*
9	Stonham Aspal 'A'	26	10	2	14	60	92	-32	32
10	Leiston St Margarets Res	24	9	3	12	48	50	-2	30
11	Somersham Res	26	8	1	17	47	84	-37	25
12	Halesworth Town Res	26	7	2	17	37	83	-46	18*
13	Sporting '87 'A'	25	5	3	17	49	77	-28	16*
14	Sproughton Sports Res	24	4	1	17	40	81	-41	7*

SURREY ELITE INTERMEDIATE LEAGUE

Sponsored by: No Sponsor
Founded: 2008
Recent Champions:
2014: N P L **2015:** Horsley **2016:** Horsley

INTERMEDIATE DIVISION	P	W	D	L	F	A	GD	Pts
1 Virginia Water	26	20	2	4	64	21	43	62
2 Tooting Bec	26	19	3	4	88	29	59	60
3 Horsley	26	15	5	6	64	36	28	50
4 AFC Spelthorne Sports	26	14	7	5	55	38	17	49
5 Ripley Village	26	15	1	10	51	37	14	46
6 Westside	26	12	5	9	58	51	7	43*
7 N P L	26	12	6	8	56	50	6	42
8 Battersea Ironsides	26	12	2	12	69	58	11	34*
9 Laleham	26	9	4	13	42	43	-1	31
10 Godalming & Farncombe Athletic	26	9	4	13	59	61	-2	31
11 Merrow	26	8	5	13	40	57	-17	29
12 AFC Cubo	26	7	6	13	58	65	-7	24*
13 Yateley United	26	2	2	22	24	88	-64	11*
14 Reigate Priory	26	2	0	24	25	119	-94	6

Project Clapham withdrew - record expunged.
Warlingham withdrew - record expunged.

INTERMEDIATE LEAGUE CHALLENGE CUP

HOLDERS: HORSLEY
ROUND 1

Battersea Ironsides	v	AFC Spelthorne Sports	2-2, AWp
Yateley United	v	N P L	1-2
Reigate Priory	v	Ripley Village	2-1
Laleham	v	Warlingham	HW
Tooting Bec	v	Westside	3-1
Merrow	v	Project Clapham	HW
Godalming & Farncombe Athletic	v	Horsley	3-5
AFC Cubo	v	Virginia Water	0-4

QUARTER-FINALS

AFC Spelthorne Sports	v	Horsley	3-1
Laleham	v	Virginia Water	0-2
N P L	v	Tooting Bec	2-3
Reigate Priory	v	Merrow	0-8

SEMI-FINALS

Merrow	v	AFC Spelthorne Sports	1-2
Tooting Bec	v	Virginia Water	0-1

FINAL

AFC Spelthorne Sports	v	Virginia Water	0-1

INTERMEDIATE DIVISION

		1	2	3	4	5	6	7	8	9	10	11	12	13	14
1	AFC Cubo		2-4	1-3	1-3	0-2	0-2	4-1	0-2	5-0	0-2	6-4	0-1	2-2	4-1
2	AFC Spelthorne Sports	1-1		2-0	5-2	1-0	2-2	4-0	1-3	5-2	1-0	1-1	4-2	0-1	4-1
3	Battersea Ironsides	5-2	2-3		3-2	2-3	3-1	1-1	0-4	10-1	2-1	1-5	2-6	2-2	11-0
4	Godalming & Farncombe Athletic	4-4	2-2	5-2		1-4	2-0	1-1	5-1	5-0	2-3	2-2	1-3	1-3	3-1
5	Horsley	2-3	3-1	1-0	2-3		3-1	3-0	2-1	8-0	2-1	3-2	2-2	4-4	5-1
6	Laleham	3-3	0-0	3-1	3-2	0-3		1-1	3-0	4-0	2-0	1-2	1-2	0-1	4-3
7	Merrow	5-3	3-1	0-4	3-2	0-0	2-3		0-1	2-1	0-3	1-3	0-3	4-2	2-1
8	N P L	2-2	1-1	2-0	HW	2-2	3-2	2-2		5-2	3-0	2-2	0-3	1-3	2-2
9	Reigate Priory	2-3	2-6	1-3	1-5	0-3	2-0	2-3	2-6		0-5	1-11	0-9	0-4	0-1
10	Ripley Village	4-3	0-0	0-2	2-0	3-2	3-1	2-1	6-2	5-0		0-3	3-2	2-1	1-0
11	Tooting Bec	2-1	7-1	7-1	4-1	2-0	HW	5-2	5-1	5-0	2-1		0-1	3-0	7-0
12	Virginia Water	2-0	0-1	3-2	4-1	2-0	1-0	1-0	3-2	2-1	1-0	0-1		3-0	5-0
13	Westside	3-3	1-4	2-5	6-0	2-2	4-2	3-2	2-4	4-1	0-3	1-0	0-3		3-0
14	Yateley United	3-5	AW	0-2	1-4	2-3	0-3	1-4	0-4	0-4	5-1	1-3	0-0	0-4	

Surrey Elite Intermediate League

AFC CUBO	Barn Elms Sports Ground, Queen Elizabeth Walk, Barnes SW13 0DG
AFC SPELTHORNE SPORTS	296 Staines Road West, Ahford Common, Ashford TW15 1RY
BATTERSEA IRONSIDES	Battersea Ironsides S&S Club, Burntwood Lane, Earlsfield SW17 0AW
CHESSINGTON KC	Tolworth Court Sports Ground, Old Kingston Road, Tolworth KT4 7QH
GODALMING & FARNCOMBE ATH	From Surrey County League (Western)
LALEHAM	Laleham Recreation Ground, The Broadway, Laleham, Staines. TW18 1RZ
MERROW	The Urnfield, Downside Road, Guildford, Surrey, GU4 8PH
NPL	NPL Sports Club, Queens Road, Teddington, TW11 0LW
REIGATE PRIORY	Reigate Priory Cricket Club, off Park Lane, Reigate RH2 8JX
RIPLEY VILLAGE	The Green, Ripley, Woking GU23 6AN
ROYAL HOLLOWAY OLD BOYS	Royal Holloway College Sports Centre (Nobles Fields), Prune Hill, Egham TW20 0ES
SPARTAN YOUTH	Carville Hall Park North, 52 Carville Cres, Brentford TW8 9RD
TOOTING BEC	Raynes Park Sports Ground, Taunton Avenue SW20 0BH
WESTSIDE	The Memorial Ground, Westway Close, Raynes Park SW20 9LN

Club Movements - Out: Virginia Water (P - Hellenic), Horsley (Surrey County Intermediate Western), Yateley United (Surrey County Intermediate Western).
In - Chessington KC (P - Surrey South Eastern Combination), Royal Holloway Old Boys (P - Surrey County Intermediate Western), Spartan Youth (Middlesex County.

THAMES VALLEY PREMIER LEAGUE

Formerly the Reading Football League > 2014
Founded: 1988
Recent Champions:
2014: Highmoor Ibis Reserves **2015:** Marlow United
2016: Reading YMCA

PREMIER DIVISION		P	W	D	L	F	A	GD	Pts
1	Reading YMCA	26	22	4	0	94	16	78	70
2	Marlow United	26	19	2	5	96	40	56	59
3	Newbury FC	25	17	2	6	73	29	44	53
4	Woodcote Stoke Row	26	16	4	6	76	42	34	52
5	Cookham Dean	26	14	3	9	69	49	20	45
6	Mortimer	26	11	3	12	43	54	-11	36
7	Wraysbury Village	26	10	4	12	39	56	-17	34
8	Woodley United Res	26	10	2	14	28	58	-30	32
9	Highmoor Ibis Res	25	9	7	9	49	49	0	31
10	Unity	26	9	2	15	36	42	-6	29
11	Berks County FC	26	8	3	15	34	65	-31	27
12	Taplow United	26	6	4	16	44	72	-28	22
13	Rotherfield United	26	2	8	16	27	67	-40	16
14	Hurst	26	3	2	21	22	91	-69	11

In: Woodley United Royals (NC - from Woodley Utd Res), Wright & Unity Sports (NC - from Unity, Wokingham & Emmbrook Res (Hellenic D2E).

DIVISION ONE		P	W	D	L	F	A	GD	Pts
1	Westwood United	16	12	2	2	46	21	25	38
2	Reading YMCA Rapids	18	12	2	4	56	38	18	38
3	Maidenhead Magpies	17	12	1	4	58	27	31	37
4	Eldon Celtic	17	11	1	5	54	24	30	34
5	Maidenhead Town	18	9	4	5	42	32	10	31
6	Frilsham & Yattendon	18	7	2	9	37	40	-3	23
7	FC Imaan Lions	18	5	5	8	41	39	2	20
8	Cookham Dean Res	18	6	1	11	29	37	-8	19
9	Mortimer Res	18	3	3	12	30	64	-34	12
10	AFC Corinthians	18	0	1	17	11	82	-71	-1

In: Richings Park (East Berkshire).

SENIOR CUP

HOLDERS: COOKHAM DEAN
ROUND 1
Maidenhead Magpies	v	Newbury FC	0-8
Berks County FC	v	Winnersh Rangers	0-4
Unity	v	AFC Corinthians	2-1
Taplow United	v	Hurst	2-2, 5-6p
Highmoor Ibis Res	v	Westwood United	3-2
Marlow United	v	Frilsham & Yattendon	5-2

ROUND 2
Newbury FC	v	Winnersh Rangers	0-2
Unity	v	Woodcote Stoke Row	3-4
Wraysbury Village	v	Cookham Dean	1-3
Eldon Celtic	v	Maidenhead Town	5-3
Rotherfield United	v	Reading YMCA	0-2 aet
FC Imaan Lions	v	Mortimer	3-4
Woodley United Res	v	Hurst	3-1 aet
Highmoor Ibis Res	v	Marlow United	0-1

QUARTER-FINALS
Winnersh Rangers	v	Woodcote Stoke Row	4-6 aet
Cookham Dean	v	Eldon Celtic	8-1
Reading YMCA	v	Mortimer	4-0
Woodley United Res	v	Marlow United	3-5

SEMI-FINALS
Woodcote Stoke Row	v	Cookham Dean	2-3 aet
Reading YMCA	v	Marlow United	2-1

FINAL
Cookham Dean	v	Reading YMCA	4-1

INTERMEDIATE CUP

HOLDERS: FC IMAAN LIONS
FINAL
Burghfield FC	v	Finchampstead Res	0-2

JUNIOR CUP

HOLDERS: HURST RES
FINAL
Twyford & Ruscombe	v	South Reading	1-2

SENIOR DIVISION		1	2	3	4	5	6	7	8	9	10	11	12	13	14
1	Berks County FC		0-4	3-3	1-4	1-5	0-3	2-1	0-2	0-0	2-1	1-0	1-2	3-1	1-0
2	Cookham Dean	2-1		5-1	7-0	2-6	5-2	2-0	0-1	4-0	4-0	2-1	1-1	4-1	1-2
3	Highmoor Ibis Res	1-1	2-2		5-2	1-3	1-1	H-W	3-4	2-2	1-0	1-2	1-2	4-0	0-0
4	Hurst	0-3	1-3	2-1		1-5	0-2	2-2	0-6	1-0	3-3	1-5	1-4	0-2	0-2
5	Marlow United	3-2	5-2	8-3	3-1		7-2	1-0	0-3	5-1	5-1	1-2	6-2	4-0	5-0
6	Mortimer	3-2	0-4	1-3	3-2	1-6		0-3	0-1	2-2	3-0	3-2	0-5	2-0	3-0
7	Newbury FC	8-1	5-3	A-A	4-0	4-1	2-1		1-2	4-1	3-1	2-0	5-0	6-1	1-0
8	Reading YMCA	4-1	4-1	1-1	8-0	1-0	1-1	3-3		H-W	10-0	3-1	4-1	8-0	6-0
9	Rotherfield United	3-2	1-4	2-3	2-1	2-6	1-4	1-4	0-3		0-5	0-0	1-4	1-2	1-1
10	Taplow United	6-2	3-2	0-1	2-0	3-3	0-1	2-4	1-3	2-2		1-0	2-4	0-1	5-3
11	Unity	1-2	0-0	4-3	4-0	0-3	1-0	0-4	0-4	3-0	5-1		0-1	2-0	1-2
12	Woodcote Stoke Row	5-1	8-0	1-5	8-0	1-1	0-2	4-0	2-2	1-1	4-2	3-1		7-0	1-0
13	Woodley United Res	0-1	0-2	2-0	4-0	3-2	2-1	0-2	0-2	2-1	2-2	1-0	2-3		2-1
14	Wraysbury Village	3-0	4-3	1-3	2-0	1-2	4-2	1-5	0-8	2-2	4-1	3-1	3-2	0-0	

DIVISION TWO

		P	W	D	L	F	A	GD	Pts
1	Burghfield FC	20	16	0	4	54	25	29	48
2	Westwood United Res	20	15	2	3	69	24	45	47
3	Finchampstead Res.	20	14	1	5	66	27	39	43
4	White Eagles	19	12	4	3	62	32	30	40
5	Wargrave	20	9	2	9	37	55	-18	29
6	Barkham Athletic	20	7	4	9	45	57	-12	24
7	Woodcote Stoke Row Res	20	5	5	10	42	60	-18	23
8	Maidenhead Magpies Res	20	6	2	12	31	34	-3	20
9	Goring United	20	6	2	12	36	59	-23	20
10	Highmoor U21	19	5	1	13	21	47	-26	12
11	Taplow United Res	20	1	3	16	20	63	-43	8

In: Finchampstead (NC from Finchampstead Res).

DIVISION THREE

		P	W	D	L	F	A	GD	Pts
1	Berks County Res	20	19	0	1	86	25	61	54
2	Harchester Hawks	20	12	2	6	51	41	10	38
3	Newbury FC Res	20	11	1	8	48	34	14	34
4	Ashridge Park	20	8	2	10	67	54	13	28
5	Maidenhead Town Res	20	7	4	9	48	48	0	28
6	Hurst Res	20	7	5	8	44	48	-4	25
7	Woodley United "A"	20	7	4	9	63	73	-10	25
8	Brimpton	20	7	3	10	63	53	10	24
9	Unity Res	20	7	3	10	32	47	-15	24
10	Rotherfield United Res	19	5	2	12	27	59	-32	17
11	White Eagles Reserves	19	3	6	10	34	81	-47	15

In: Braybrooke (P).

DIVISION FOUR

		P	W	D	L	F	A	GD	Pts
1	South Reading	22	18	4	0	88	28	60	58
2	Braybrooke	22	15	4	3	69	31	38	49
3	Hurst "A"	22	15	2	5	88	38	50	44
4	Twyford & Ruscombe	22	11	5	6	83	47	36	41
5	Berks County FC Rovers	22	13	1	8	72	40	32	40
6	AFC Corinthians A	22	12	2	8	61	40	21	35
7	Woodley United "B"	22	8	3	11	49	49	0	27
8	Goring Utd Res	22	7	3	12	51	67	-16	24
9	Wargrave Res	22	6	2	14	41	64	-23	23
10	Taplow United "A"	22	6	3	13	47	72	-25	21
11	The Hop Leaf	22	3	2	17	23	116	-93	11
12	Harchester Hawks Res	22	1	3	18	23	103	-80	6

Thames Valley Premier League

BERKS COUNTY	Bracknell Leisure Centre	
COOKHAM DEAN	Alfred Major Rec Ground, Hillcrest Avenue, Cookham Rise , Maidenhead SL6 9NB	
HIGHMOOR-IBIS RESERVES	Palmer Park Stadium, Wokingham Road, Reading RG6 1LF	
MARLOW UNITED	Bisham Abbey National Sports Centre, Abbey Way, Marlow, Bucks SL7 1RR	
MORTIMER	Alfred Palmer Memorial PF, West End Road, Mortimer, Reading RG7 3TW	
NEWBURY	Faraday Road, Newbury RG14 2AD	01635 41031
READING YMCA	Padworth Village Hall, Padworth, Reading, Berkshire RG7 4HY	
TAPLOW UNITED	Stanley Jones Field, Berry Hill, Taplow SL6 0DA	
WESTWOOD UNITED	Bobbin Lane, Westwood BA15 2DL	
WOKINGHAM & EMMBROOK RES	Emmbrook Sports & Social Club, Lowther Road, Wokingham RG41 1JB	01189 780 209
WOODCOTE & STOKE ROW	Woodcote Recreation Ground, Woodcote, Reading RG8 0QY	
WOODLEY UNITED ROYALS	Bulmershe Pavilion, Woodlands Avenue, Woodley, Reading RG5 3EU	
WRAYSBURY VILLAGE	Wraysbury Village	
WRIGHT & UNITY SPORTS	Cintra Park, Cintra Avenue, Reading RG2 7AU	

WEARSIDE LEAGUE

	Sponsored by: TWR
	Founded: 1892
	Recent Champions:
	2014: Stockton Town 2015: Stockton Town
	2016: Stockton Town

		P	W	D	L	F	A	GD	Pts
1	Jarrow FC	38	29	4	5	94	36	58	91
2	Redcar Athletic	38	27	6	5	125	46	79	87
3	Cleator Moor Celtic	38	25	5	8	104	48	56	80
4	Richmond Town	38	24	5	9	112	51	61	77
5	Boldon CA	38	22	8	8	71	47	24	74
6	Silksworth Colliery Welfare	38	22	6	10	92	45	47	72
7	Hartlepool FC	38	18	7	13	95	76	19	61
8	Coxhoe Athletic	38	19	3	16	87	80	7	60
9	South Shields Res	38	17	6	15	63	67	-4	57
10	Sunderland West End	38	17	4	17	78	84	-6	55
11	Darlington Reserves	38	16	3	19	80	91	-11	51
12	Gateshead Leam Rangers	38	14	3	21	82	94	-12	45
13	Prudhoe Town	38	12	9	17	66	78	-12	45
14	Stokesley SC	38	13	5	20	73	89	-16	44
15	Ashbrooke Belford House	38	13	1	24	63	116	-53	40
16	Annfield Plain	38	10	8	20	66	114	-48	38
17	Wolviston FC	38	9	8	21	59	93	-34	35
18	Windscale FC	38	8	5	25	61	93	-32	29
19	Harton and Westoe CW	38	7	4	27	55	115	-60	25
20	Seaham Red Star Res	38	6	4	28	41	104	-63	22

Out: Jarrow FC (P - Northern League), Ashbrooke Belford House (F),
Seaham Red Star Res (F).
In: Hebburn Town Res.

ALAN HOOD CHARITY CUP

PRELIMINARY ROUND

Boldon CA	v	Hartlepool FC
Gateshead Lean Rangers	v	Darlington Res
Seham Red Star Res	v	Annfield Plain
Silksworth Colliery Welfare	v	Harton and Westoe CW

ROUND 1

Coxhoe Athletic	v	Prudhoe Town
Redcar Athletic	v	South Shields Res
Richmond Town	v	Jarrow FC
Stokesley SC	v	Wolviston FC
Ashbrooke Belford House	v	Boldon CA
Cleator Moor Celtic	v	Gateshead Leam Rangers
Windscale FC	v	Silksworth Colliery Welfare
Seaham Red Star Res	v	Sunderland West End

QUARTER-FINALS

Coxhoe Athletic	v	Redcar Athletic
Windscale FC	v	Richmond Town
Wolviston FC	v	Sunderland West End
Cleator Moor Celtic	v	Boldon CA

SEMI-FINALS

Redcar Athletic	v	Wolviston FC
Richmond Town	v	Boldon CA

FINAL

Redcar Athletic	v	Boldon CA	2-0

MONKWEARMOUTH CHARITY CUP

FINAL   **HOLDERS: STOCKTON TOWN**

Sunderland West End	v	Redcar Athletic	1-2

SUNDERLAND SHIPOWNERS CUP

FINAL   **HOLDERS: STOCKTON TOWN**

Richmond Town	v	Cleator Moor Celtic	2-4

DURHAM TROPHY

FINAL   **HOLDERS: SILKSWORTH COLLIERY WELFARE**

Ashbrooke Belford House	v	Jarrow FC	4-1

Wearside League

ANNFIELD PLAIN	Derwent Park , West Road , Annfield Plain DH9 8PZ
BOLDON C.A.	Boldon Colliery Welfare, New Road, Boldon Colliery NE35 9DS
CLEATOR MOOR CELTIC	McGrath Park, Birks Road, Cleator Moor, Cumbria CA25 5HR
COXHOE ATHLETIC	Beechfield Park Commercial Road East Coxhoe County Durham DH6 4LF
DARLINGTON RESERVES	Eastbourne Sports Complex 4G Pitch, Bourne Ave, Darlington DL1 1LJ
GATESHEAD LEAM RANGERS	Hilltop Playing Field, Gateshead, Tyne and Wear NE10 8LT
HARTLEPOOL	Grayfields Enclosure, Jesmond Gardens, Hartlepool TS24 8QS
HARTON AND WESTOE	Welfare Ground, Low Lane, South Shields NE34 ONA
HEBBURN TOWN RESERVES	Castle View Enterprise Academy, Cartwright Road
PRUDHOE TOWN	Kimberley Park, Broomhouse Road, Prudhoe NE42 5EH
REDCAR ATHLETIC	Green Lane, Redcar TS10 3RW
RICHMOND TOWN	Earls Orchard Playing Field. DL10 4RH
SILKSWORTH COLLIERY WELFARE	Silksworth Welfare Park, Blind Lane, Silksworth, Sunderland SR3 1AX
SOUTH SHIELDS RESERVES	Harton & Westoe FC, Welfare Ground, Low Lane, South Shields NE34 ONA
STOKESLEY SPORTS CLUB	Stokesley Sports Club, Broughton Road, Stokesley TS9 5NY
SUNDERLAND WEST END	Ford Quarry, Keelmans Lane, Pennywell, Sunderland
WINDSCALE	Falcon Complex, Croadalla Avenue Egremont Cumbria CA22 2QN
WOLVISTON	Metcalfe Park, Wynyard Road, Wolviston, Billingham TS22 5NE

WEST CHESHIRE LEAGUE

Sponsored by: Carlsberg

Founded: 1892

Recent Champions:

2014: Maghull

2015: South Liverpool

2016: South Liverpool

	DIVISION ONE	P	W	D	L	F	A	GD	Pts
1	Newton	30	23	2	5	79	35	44	71
2	Mossley Hill Athletic	30	19	5	6	76	44	32	62
3	South Liverpool	30	18	5	7	78	50	28	59
4	Rainhill Town	30	18	1	11	66	53	13	55
5	Maghull	30	14	10	6	67	42	25	52
6	Redgate Rovers	30	14	4	12	66	56	10	46
7	Richmond Raith Rovers	30	14	3	13	80	71	9	45
8	Vauxhall Motors	30	13	5	12	72	61	11	44
9	Capenhurst Villa	30	13	4	13	49	66	-17	43
10	Upton AA	30	11	9	10	76	53	23	42
11	Heswall	30	11	7	12	49	40	9	40
12	Chester Nomads	30	10	6	14	50	65	-15	36
13	Helsby	30	8	3	19	41	59	-18	27
14	West Kirby	30	5	9	16	47	79	-32	24
15	Cammell Laird 1907 Res	30	7	1	22	35	83	-48	22
16	Mallaby	30	4	2	24	34	108	-74	14

Out: Cammell Laird 1907 Res (W), Capenhurst Villa replacing Res in D2), Helsby (W).

PYKE CUP

HOLDERS: SOUTH LIVERPOOL

ROUND 1

Maghull	v	Chester Nomads	1-4
Mallaby	v	Heswall	0-3
Cammell Laird 1907 Res	v	Rainhill Town	AW
Helsby	v	Richmond Raith Rovers	1-3
Newton	v	Vauxhall Motors	2-1
Capenhurst Villa	v	Redgate Rovers	2-3
West Kirby	v	Upton A.A.	1-2
South Liverpool	v	Mossley Hill Athletic	0-1

QUARTER-FINALS

Chester Nomads	v	Heswall	0-2
Rainhill Town	v	Richmond Raith Rovers	2-4
Upton A.A.	v	Mossley Hill Athletic	1-0
Newton	v	Redgate Rovers	1-2

SEMI-FINALS

Heswall	v	Richmond Raith Rovers	3-1
Redgate Rovers	v	Upton A.A.	3-2

FINAL

Heswall	v	Redgate Rovers	2-2, 3-4p

	DIVISION ONE	1	2	3	4	5	6	7	8	9	10	11	12	13	14	15	16
1	Cammell Laird 1907 Res		0-2	3-1	2-3	0-5	1-3	6-3	1-5	1-5	1-4	2-1	2-2	A-W	0-5	2-0	2-4
2	Capenhurst Villa	3-1		0-2	1-0	0-0	1-1	H-W	1-7	0-2	2-0	1-2	5-1	1-1	2-1	1-0	3-4
3	Chester Nomads	H-W	3-4		1-0	1-1	2-2	7-1	1-3	0-3	1-3	1-6	4-3	0-3	1-1	2-3	1-1
4	Helsby	H-W	3-0	0-1		0-4	1-1	8-0	2-1	1-3	1-3	1-4	H-W	A-W	1-1	2-0	2-2
5	Heswall	0-2	3-1	0-1	2-1		4-0	3-0	1-2	0-1	0-2	2-1	3-5	2-2	0-0	3-2	3-0
6	Maghull	3-0	5-1	4-1	4-0	3-0		7-0	1-1	1-4	0-2	1-3	5-1	0-3	2-2	2-2	1-1
7	Mallaby	0-3	A-W	0-4	4-3	1-1	2-3		3-3	3-6	2-10	2-7	A-W	0-6	1-8	0-2	5-1
8	Mossley Hill Athletic	4-0	2-1	3-3	2-1	3-0	2-3	H-W		2-0	3-1	6-0	3-2	4-2	2-1	2-3	1-1
9	Newton	3-1	4-2	4-1	3-1	1-1	1-1	4-0	1-2		1-0	2-0	H-W	5-1	4-2	4-1	3-0
10	Rainhill Town	7-1	1-2	1-3	3-2	H-W	0-1	H-W	0-3	2-1		1-4	4-3	4-3	2-5	0-3	2-1
11	Redgate Rovers	H-W	6-2	0-2	H-W	3-2	0-2	1-2	0-2	1-0	1-2		6-3	1-4	3-3	1-1	2-3
12	Richmond Raith Rovers	4-0	8-3	5-1	7-2	2-1	2-2	H-W	7-2	2-3	1-2	0-4		4-2	2-1	4-3	5-1
13	South Liverpool	6-0	3-3	4-1	4-3	2-1	3-2	1-0	2-0	1-3	3-1	4-2	1-3		1-1	3-0	2-2
14	Upton AA	6-1	2-1	3-1	2-0	1-2	1-1	6-1	1-2	2-3	0-3	2-2	4-1	3-4		3-1	4-1
15	Vauxhall Motors	4-0	3-4	2-2	3-1	1-3	0-1	7-2	2-1	2-3	2-2	2-2	7-3	3-2	6-3		3-2
16	West Kirby	0-3	1-2	2-1	1-2	2-2	1-5	1-2	3-3	4-2	3-4	1-3	0-0	1-5	2-2	1-4	

West Cheshire League Division One

ASHVILLE	Villa Park, Cross Lane, Wallasey Village, Wallasey CH45 8RH
CHESTER NOMADS	Boughton Hall Cricket Club, Boughton, Chester, CH3 5EL
HESWALL	Gayton Park, Brimstage Road, Heswall CH60 1XG
MAGHULL	Old Hall Field, Hall Lane, Maghull L31 7DY
MALLABY	Wirral Tennis Centre, Valley Road, Birkenhead, Wirral CH41 7EJ
MARSHALLS	I.M.Marsh Campus, Barkhill Road, Liverpool L17 6BD
MOSSLEY HILL ATHLETIC	Mossley Hill Athletic Club, Mossley Hill Road, Liverpool L18 8BX
NESTON NOMADS	Vauxhall Sports & Social Club, Rivacre Road, Hooton, South Wirral CH66 1NJ
NEWTON	Millcroft, Frankby Road, Greasby CH49 3PE
RAINHILL TOWN	Sutton Leisure Centre WA9 5AO
REDGATE ROVERS	JMO Sports Park, Blaguegate Playing Fields, Liverpool Road,, Skelmersdale WN8 8RX
RICHMOND RAITH ROVERS	St John Bosco School, Storrington Avenue, Liverpool L11 9DQ
SOUTH LIVERPOOL	North Field, Jericho Lane, Aigburth, Liverpool L17 5AR
UPTON A.A.	Chester County Sports & Social Club, Plas Newton Lane, Chester CH2 1PR
VAUXHALL MOTORS	Vauxhall Sports Ground, Rivacre Road, Hooton, Ellesmere Port CH66 1NJ
WEST KIRBY	Marine Park, Greenbank Road, West Kirby CH48 5HL

DIVISION TWO	P	W	D	L	F	A	GD	Pts
1 Ashville	28	24	1	3	88	27	61	73
2 Marshalls	28	23	3	2	90	28	62	72
3 Maghull Reserves	28	16	8	4	64	32	32	56
4 Mossley Hill Athletic Res	28	13	7	8	62	45	17	46
5 South Liverpool Res	28	12	9	7	69	48	21	45
6 Neston Nomads	28	13	5	10	68	50	18	44
7 Hale	28	12	6	10	62	51	11	42
8 Prescot Cables Res	28	12	6	10	64	59	5	42
9 Kirkby Town Railway	28	11	7	10	84	65	19	40
10 Bootle Reserves	28	10	7	11	48	52	-4	37
11 West Kirby Reserves	28	7	2	19	38	98	-60	23
12 Heswall Reserves	28	4	9	15	29	59	-30	21
13 Vauxhall Motors Res	28	6	3	19	47	86	-39	21
14 Willaston	28	6	3	19	45	85	-40	21
15 Southport Trinity	28	3	0	25	42	115	-73	9

Out: Kirkby Town Railway (W), Bootle Res (W)., Neston Nomads (P).

DIVISION THREE	P	W	D	L	F	A	GD	Pts
1 Rainhill Town Res	28	19	5	4	77	25	52	62
2 Capenhurst Villa Res	27	18	5	4	61	31	30	59
3 Cheshire Lines	27	18	5	4	62	34	28	58*
4 Ellesmere Port Town	28	16	7	5	74	38	36	55
5 Ashville Res	28	16	5	7	86	49	37	53
6 Litherland REMYCA Res	28	16	5	7	90	55	35	53
7 Redgate Rovers Res	28	13	1	14	63	48	15	40
8 Marshalls Res	28	11	6	11	54	55	-1	39
9 Chester Nomads Res	28	10	5	13	49	52	-3	35
10 Upton AA Res	28	9	6	13	61	57	4	33
11 Neston Nomads Res	28	8	3	17	44	63	-19	27
12 City of Liverpool Res	28	8	4	16	42	49	-7	25*
13 Mersey Royal	28	8	1	19	49	97	-48	25
14 Cammell Laird 1907 Dev	28	5	4	19	33	66	-33	19
15 Helsby Res	28	3	0	25	17	143	-126	9

In: Burscough Dynamo (Mid Lancs League), Capenhurst Villa Res, Cheshire Lines Res, Ellesmere Port Town Res (Chester & Wirral League), Poulton Royal, The Celts, Wirral SB (Sunday football).

YOUTH DIVISION	P	W	D	L	F	A	GD	Pts
1 South Liverpool Youth	16	12	2	2	58	24	34	38
2 Mossley Hill Athletic Youth	16	12	2	2	44	25	19	38
3 Litherland REMYCA Youth	16	9	2	5	48	29	19	29
4 Maghull Youth	16	8	4	4	59	36	23	28
5 Maghull Town Youth	16	9	1	6	44	32	12	28
6 Vauxhall Motors Youth	16	7	1	8	32	31	1	22
7 Ellesmere Port Town Youth	16	4	1	11	30	53	-23	13
8 Princes Villa Youth	16	3	1	12	33	51	-18	10
9 Chester Nomads Youth	16	1	0	15	16	83	-67	3

WEST LANCASHIRE LEAGUE

Sponsored by: Bay Radio
Founded: 1904
Recent Champions:
2014: Charnock Richard **2015:** Charnock Richard **2016:** Blackpool Wren Rovers

PREMIER DIVISION

		P	W	D	L	F	A	GD	Pts
1	Longridge Town	32	27	2	3	99	30	69	83
2	Blackpool Wren Rovers	32	25	5	2	126	33	93	74*
3	Fulwood Amateurs	32	19	4	9	78	46	32	61
4	Garstang	32	15	8	9	69	47	22	53
5	Euxton Villa	32	17	6	9	64	49	15	51*
6	Tempest United	32	15	5	12	66	60	6	50
7	Hesketh Bank	32	14	3	15	64	69	-5	45
8	Vickerstown	32	13	4	15	57	69	-12	43
9	Turton	32	12	4	16	55	56	-1	40
10	Coppull United	32	12	3	17	51	75	-24	39
11	Slyne with Hest	32	11	5	16	57	77	-20	38
12	Southport Hesketh	32	9	9	14	73	66	7	36
13	Thornton Cleveleys	32	11	6	15	56	66	-10	36*
14	Whitehaven	32	9	5	18	54	90	-36	32
15	Lostock St Gerards	32	8	6	18	58	92	-34	27*
16	Crooklands Casuals	32	7	5	20	48	99	-51	26
17	Eagley	32	7	2	23	57	108	-51	23

DIVISION ONE

		P	W	D	L	F	A	GD	Pts
1	Haslingden St Marys	28	18	5	5	82	43	39	59
2	Burscough Richmond	28	17	6	5	68	37	31	57
3	Hurst Green	28	17	4	7	68	46	22	55
4	Poulton	28	17	2	9	80	48	32	53
5	CMB	28	16	4	8	73	45	28	52
6	Milnthorpe Corinthians	28	16	3	9	73	55	18	51
7	Hawcoat Park	28	13	4	11	40	41	-1	43
8	Askam United	28	11	4	13	47	51	-4	37
9	Lytham Town	28	11	3	14	57	48	9	36
10	Stoneclough	28	11	2	15	56	63	-7	35
11	Wyre Villa	28	7	5	16	55	77	-22	26
12	GSK Ulverston Rangers	28	8	2	18	47	82	-35	23*
13	Mill Hill St Peters	28	6	2	20	42	72	-30	20
14	Ladybridge	28	10	6	12	53	85	-32	20*
15	Dalton United	28	5	2	21	39	87	-48	17

DIVISION TWO

		P	W	D	L	F	A	GD	Pts
1	CMB	22	17	3	2	82	36	46	54
1	Fulwood Amateurs Res	30	24	4	2	86	45	41	76
2	Kendal County	30	22	3	5	87	35	52	69
3	Leyland United	29	22	1	6	93	34	59	67
4	Croston Sports	30	18	4	8	62	35	27	58
5	Millom	30	16	7	7	76	55	21	49*
6	Blackpool Wren Rovers Res	30	13	7	10	83	54	29	46
7	Furness Rovers	30	11	5	14	59	66	-7	38
8	Garstang Res	30	11	5	14	56	64	-8	38
9	Euxton Villa Res	30	12	2	16	55	66	-11	38
10	Furness Cavaliers	30	9	7	14	65	74	-9	34
11	Thornton Cleveleys Res	30	10	7	13	65	70	-5	31*
12	Burscough Richmond Res	30	9	2	19	47	78	-31	29
13	Hurst Green Res	30	8	4	18	51	72	-21	28
14	Walney Island	29	7	7	15	52	75	-23	28
15	Coppull United Res	30	5	5	20	39	105	-66	20
16	Swarthmoor	30	5	4	21	46	94	-48	19

DIVISION THREE

		P	W	D	L	F	A	GD	Pts
1	Tempest United Res	28	20	5	3	118	50	68	65
2	Haslingden St Marys Res	28	18	6	4	86	46	40	60
3	Poulton Res	28	20	4	4	85	32	53	58*
4	Lostock St Gerards Res	28	17	3	8	79	50	29	54
5	Lytham Town Res	28	15	2	11	71	65	6	47
6	CMB Res	28	14	4	10	76	68	8	46
7	Croston Sports Res	28	12	4	12	48	63	-15	40
8	Hesketh Bank Res	28	11	6	11	67	63	4	39
9	Turton Res	28	9	7	12	70	79	-9	34
10	Mill Hill St Peters Res	28	8	3	17	55	79	-24	27
11	Fulwood Amateurs Res A	28	6	8	14	49	87	-38	26
12	Milnthorpe Corinthians Res	28	7	4	17	60	77	-17	25
13	Stoneclough Res	28	6	9	13	59	82	-23	24*
14	Wyre Villa Res	28	6	4	18	51	85	-34	22
15	Eagley Res	28	6	1	21	51	99	-48	19

Out: Lostock St Gerrards Res (P).

PREMIER DIVISION

		1	2	3	4	5	6	7	8	9	10	11	12	13	14	15	16	17
1	Blackpool Wren Rovers		4-0	11-0	4-0	3-0	3-3	2-1	1-0	0-1	9-1	5-1	3-3	4-1	5-1	5-0	6-1	7-2
2	Coppull United	0-2		0-0	7-0	1-3	1-2	2-1	1-2	0-3	2-0	3-1	0-2	1-5	1-4	1-1	1-3	1-3
3	Crooklands Casuals	1-5	1-2		4-5	0-2	1-3	3-3	1-2	0-5	3-2	1-3	3-5	1-2	1-1	2-1	3-1	3-2
4	Eagley	2-5	0-1	4-3		0-1	1-6	1-6	3-4	2-4	3-4	1-2	2-1	3-4	3-1	3-2	3-1	4-0
5	Euxton Villa	1-1	1-3	2-4	4-2		2-1	0-0	3-0	1-3	5-1	4-0	1-0	2-0	3-1	3-1	0-0	1-1
6	Fulwood Amateurs	0-4	0-1	3-1	3-0	6-2		3-3	4-1	1-1	3-0	2-0	3-2	1-2	4-1	1-0	7-2	6-0
7	Garstang	0-3	3-2	7-1	2-1	1-1	0-2		3-1	2-1	3-0	0-2	2-2	2-0	2-2	0-1	1-0	3-1
8	Hesketh Bank	3-6	2-4	1-0	5-2	0-1	5-1	2-1		1-2	1-1	3-1	2-2	3-1	4-0	1-2	5-2	2-1
9	Longridge Town	2-1	8-2	9-0	6-3	0-3	2-0	4-0	3-0		2-1	1-0	4-3	2-2	4-0	3-0	2-0	1-0
10	Lostock St Gerards	4-4	2-3	1-1	6-2	1-2	2-4	1-1	1-4			1-1	0-4	0-5	1-3	4-2	2-3	3-3
11	Slyne with Hest	0-6	3-1	4-0	6-1	1-5	0-4	0-5	3-3	0-3	0-0		3-3	0-1	1-4	3-3	6-2	3-2
12	Southport Hesketh	1-8	7-1	1-3	4-0	0-1	2-2	3-3	1-2	3-0	7-1	1-4		0-1	2-3	0-0	1-2	6-1
13	Tempest United	2-3	2-3	2-4	2-2	1-3	4-0	2-2	0-3	1-7	3-2	5-1	1-3		1-1	0-2	2-0	3-1
14	Thornton Cleveleys	0-1	1-1	3-1		0-1	0-1	4-0	0-6	2-4	1-0	1-1	1-1			1-2	1-3	4-1
15	Turton	0-2	5-2	3-0	3-0	5-3	1-2	1-2	4-0	0-1	1-3	0-2	2-1	1-3	1-2		2-2	5-0
16	Vickerstown	1-2	4-1	3-1	1-1	3-1	1-0	2-0	3-2	2-3	2-1	2-3	1-1	2-4	4-3	1-2		3-1
17	Whitehaven	1-1	0-2	1-1	3-1	2-2	2-4	0-6	4-3	1-2	4-2	4-3	6-1	0-3	3-2	3-2	1-0	

West Lancashire League Premier Division

BLACKPOOL WREN ROVERS	Bruce Park, School Road, Marton, Blackpool FY4 5DX	07876 013 181
BURSCOUGH RICHMOND	Richmond Park, Junction Lane, Burscough, West Lancashire L40 5SN	07976 896 195
COPPULL UNITED	Springfield Road, Coppull PR7 5EJ	07719 577 717
EUXTON VILLA	Jim Fowler Memorial Ground, Runshaw Hall Lane, Euxton, Chorley PR7 6HH	07851 603 350
FULWOOD AMATEURS	Lightfoot Lane, Fulwood, Preston PR2 3LP	07952 743 475
GARSTANG	The Riverside, High Street, Garstang PR3 1EB	07967 337 411
HASLINGDEN ST MARYS	South Shore Street, Haslingden, Lancs BB4 5DX	01706 221 814
HESKETH BANK	Centenary Sports Ground, Station Road, Hesketh Bank, Preston PR4 6SR	07713 158 393
LONGRIDGE TOWN	Inglewhite Road, Longridge, Preston PR3 2NA	
SLYNE WITH HEST	Bottomdale Road, Slyne, Lancaster LA2 6BG	07775 777 835
SOUTHPORT HESKETH	Bankfield Lane, Southport, Merseyside PR9 7NJ	07927 325 585
TEMPEST UNITED	Tempest Road, Chew Moor Village, Lostock, Bolton BL6 4HL	01942 811 938
THORNTON CLEVELEYS	Bourne Road, Cleveleys, Thornton Cleveleys FY5 4QA	
TURTON	Thomasson Fold, Turton, Bolton BL7 0PD	07814 317 295
VICKERSTOWN CC	Park Vale, Mill Lane, Walney, Barrow-in-Furness LA14 3NB	07446 112 716
WHITEHAVEN	Focus Scaffolding Sports Complex, Coach Road, Whitehaven, CA28 9DB	07876 612 277

WLFL RICHARDSON CUP

ROUND 1

Eagley	v	Coppull United	5-4

ROUND 2

Euxton Villa	v	Crooklands Casuals	8-2
Hesketh Bank	v	Fulwood Amateurs	1-4
Lostock St Gerards	v	Southport Hesketh	2-2, 4-2p
Slyne with Hest	v	Garstang	0-4
Tempest United	v	Whitehaven	5-1
Vickerstown	v	Longridge Town	2-1
Blackpool Wren Rovers	v	Thornton Cleveleys	2-1
Turton	v	Eagley	3-1

QUARTER-FINALS

Tempest United	v	Lostock St Gerards	HW
Vickerstown	v	Garstang	0-2
Blackpool Wren Rovers	v	Exuton Villa	4-2
Fulwood Amateurs	v	Turton	4-2

SEMI-FINALS

Blackpool Wren Rovers	v	Fulwood Amateurs	6-1
Tempest United	v	Garstang	1-2

FINAL

Blackpool Wren Rovers	v	Garstang	2-0

WLFL PRESIDENTS CUP

FINAL

Haslingden St Marys	v	Hawcoat Park	1-1, 4-5p

WLFL CHALLENGE CUP

FINAL

Fulwood Amateurs Res	v	Leyland United	4-1

WLFL STEWART ROWE MEMORIAL CUP

FINAL

CMB Res	v	Mill Hill St Peters Res	0-1

WEST YORKSHIRE LEAGUE

Sponsored by: Active 8
Founded: 1928
Recent Champions:
2014: Bardsey **2015:** Field
2016: Beeston St Anthony's

PREMIER DIVISION	P	W	D	L	F	A	GD	Pts
1 Carlton Athletic	30	27	0	3	120	25	95	81
2 Leeds City	30	18	4	8	80	44	36	58
3 Beeston St Anthony's	30	18	4	8	74	52	22	58
4 Field	30	17	6	7	65	38	27	54*
5 Pool	30	14	5	11	61	53	8	47
6 Headingley	30	15	3	12	59	61	-2	45*
7 Horbury Town	30	13	5	12	71	56	15	44
8 Shelley	30	13	5	12	44	45	-1	44
9 Sherburn White Rose	30	13	4	13	59	73	-14	43
10 Hunslet Club	30	12	5	13	59	59	0	41
11 Knaresborough Town	30	12	4	14	52	56	-4	40
12 Ilkley Town	30	10	4	16	45	51	-6	34
13 Robin Hood Athletic	30	9	6	15	48	60	-12	33
14 Oxenhope Recreation	30	8	1	21	43	92	-49	22*
15 Wetherby Athletic	30	4	6	20	34	95	-61	18
16 Brighouse Old Boys	30	4	4	22	43	97	-54	16

DIVISION ONE	P	W	D	L	F	A	GD	Pts
1 Hall Green United	28	22	3	3	86	29	57	69
2 Hartshead	28	17	7	4	89	37	52	58
3 Huddersfield Amateur	28	17	6	5	80	50	30	57
4 Aberford Albion	28	15	3	10	73	54	19	48
5 Kippax	28	15	3	10	62	56	6	48
6 Leeds Modernians	28	15	3	10	71	67	4	48
7 Wyke Wanderers	28	12	5	11	54	55	-1	41
8 Howden Clough	28	12	2	14	63	82	-19	38
9 Whitkirk Wanderers	28	11	4	13	51	62	-11	37
10 Featherstone Colliery	28	10	6	12	55	57	-2	36
11 East End Park	28	9	8	11	65	66	-1	35
12 Boroughbridge	28	9	4	15	46	63	-17	31
13 Old Centralians	28	7	5	16	44	69	-25	26
14 Swillington Saints	28	3	4	21	48	88	-40	13
15 Otley Town	28	4	1	23	33	85	-52	13

DIVISION TWO	P	W	D	L	F	A	GD	Pts
1 Rawdon Old Boys	22	20	0	2	117	13	104	60
2 Rothwell	22	15	2	5	78	43	35	47
3 Altofts	22	15	2	5	70	40	30	47
4 AFC Horsforth	22	13	2	7	99	54	45	41
5 Ossett Albion	22	13	1	8	65	43	22	40
6 Nostell Miners Welfare	22	9	6	7	67	59	8	33
7 Kellingley Welfare	22	9	4	9	47	54	-7	31
8 Ripon City	22	8	3	11	63	62	1	27
9 Baildon Trinity Athletic	22	7	3	12	38	55	-17	24
10 Garforth Rangers	22	7	2	13	36	82	-46	23
11 Middleton Park	22	1	3	18	28	88	-60	6
12 Great Preston	22	0	2	20	21	136	-115	2

LEAGUE CUP

HOLDERS: BEESTON ST ANTHONY'S

ROUND 1
Leeds Modemians	v	Huddersfield Amateur	3-0
Kellingley Welfare	v	Ossett Albion	1-2
Great Preston	v	Old Centralians	0-10
Altofts	v	Otley Town	5-0
Hall Green United	v	Rothwell	5-0
Wyke Wanderers	v	Boroughbridge	3-3, 4-2p
Featherstone Colliery	v	Howden Clough	2-0 aet
Kippax	v	Rawdon Old Boys	1-1, 5-6p
Swillington Saints	v	Whitkirk Wanderers	7-5
Garforth Rangers	v	Nostell Miners Welfare	2-4
Ripon City	v	AFC Horsforth	2-0
Aberford Albion	v	Thornhill	HW

ROUND 2
Beeston St Anthony's	v	East End Park	5-3
Leeds Modemians	v	Hunslet Club	4-3
Ossett Albion	v	Old Centralians	1-2
Altofts	v	Hall Green United	1-1, 4-2p
Middleton Park	v	Horbury Town	0-9
Oxenhope Recreation	v	Pool	2-3 aet
Ilkley Town	v	Wyke Wanderers	6-1
Shelley	v	Brighouse Old Boys	3-5
Featherstone Colliery	v	Rawdon Old Boys	5-2 aet
Sherburn White Rose	v	Swillington Saints	4-1
Nostell Miners Welfare	v	Robin Hood Athletic	0-4
Hartshead	v	Leeds City	3-1
Ripon City	v	Aberford Albion	2-3
Wetherby Athletic	v	Baildon Trinity Athletic	8-1
Field	v	Knaresborough Town	2-0
Headingley	v	Carlton Athletic	0-3

ROUND 3
Beeston St Anthony's	v	Leeds Modemians	4-2
Old Centralians	v	Altofts	1-2
Horbury Town	v	Pool	1-0
Ilkley Town	v	Brighouse Old Boys	4-1
Featherstone Colliery	v	Sherburn White Rose	0-2
Robin Hood Athletic	v	Hartshead	1-0
Aberford Albion	v	Wetherby Athletic	4-2
Field	v	Carlton Athletic	0-3

QUARTER-FINALS
Beeston St Anthony's	v	Altofts	4-0
Horbury Town	v	Ilkley Town	2-0
Sherburn White Rose	v	Robin Hood Athletic	3-1
Aberford Albion	v	Carlton Athletic	1-3

SEMI-FINALS
Beeston St Anthony's	v	Horbury Town	3-0
Sherburn White Rose	v	Carlton Athletic	0-4

FINAL
Beeston St Anthony's	v	Carlton Athletic	2-4

PREMIER DIVISION	1	2	3	4	5	6	7	8	9	10	11	12	13	14	15	16
1 Beeston St Anthony's		5-2	1-2	3-7	1-2	2-1	4-1	2-1	3-0	3-2	H-W	2-1	4-0	2-0	1-2	1-1
2 Brighouse Old Boys	2-2		0-10	3-4	0-2	1-3	0-4	5-2	1-4	1-8	1-3	1-1	1-2	0-1	1-4	5-3
3 Carlton Athletic	2-3	3-1		2-0	3-0	6-1	5-1	4-0	3-1	4-2	6-0	8-1	2-1	6-3	2-0	6-0
4 Field	0-0	4-2	A-W		3-0	2-0	0-0	3-1	1-1	0-3	8-1	1-0	0-1	0-1	3-0	1-1
5 Headingley	3-2	2-0	2-4	2-4		2-1	1-1	1-3	1-2	2-1	2-3	3-2	3-2	2-0	1-5	5-1
6 Horbury Town	3-2	4-0	1-0	1-2	1-1		0-2	3-3	2-3	3-2	1-0	4-2	4-2	3-0	5-1	
7 Hunslet Club	3-1	2-2	0-4	1-2	4-1	2-1		2-1	3-2	0-2	1-2	2-3	7-4	1-3	4-1	1-1
8 Ilkley Town	2-2	3-0	0-4	0-1	2-2	4-2	2-1		2-0	1-2	2-1	1-2	0-0	1-2	0-1	1-0
9 Knaresborough Town	1-4	3-1	1-4	1-3	6-0	3-2	2-1	1-0		3-3	1-2	1-0	2-1	1-2	1-0	0-1
10 Leeds City	1-3	1-1	1-2	1-1	5-1	1-1	2-2	0-2	4-1		4-3	1-2	2-0	2-1	7-2	2-1
11 Oxenhope Recreation	1-3	4-1	0-5	0-4	1-4	1-6	3-4	4-1	2-1	0-5		3-2	0-2	1-1	2-3	3-4
12 Pool	3-4	2-1	3-2	2-2	2-3	3-1	3-0	2-1	2-2	2-3	5-1		2-1	1-0	1-1	2-1
13 Robin Hood Athletic	1-4	3-4	1-4	4-1	1-2	2-2	1-2	1-0	1-0	2-1	4-0	2-2		0-0	0-4	3-0
14 Shelley	2-4	1-2	1-3	2-3	H-W	1-3	2-2	2-1	0-0	0-2	4-0	3-2	2-1		1-1	3-0
15 Sherburn White Rose	3-4	5-2	0-6	4-1	1-3	3-0	2-1	1-7	3-4	1-6	3-0	1-6	2-2	1-0		3-3
16 Wetherby Athletic	3-2	1-4	0-8	1-4	0-6	0-9	2-5	0-1	1-4	1-3	2-0	0-2	3-3	1-1	1-2	

WEST YORKSHIRE LEAGUE - STEP 7

West Yorkshire League Premier Division

BEESTON ST ANTHONY'S	St Antony's Road, Beeston, Leeds LS11 8DP
CARLTON ATHLETIC	Carlton Cricket Club, Town Street, Carlton WF3 3QU
FIELD	Field Sports & Social Club, Hollingwood Lane, Bradford BD7 2RE
HALL GREEN UNITED	Crigglestone Sports Club, Painthorpe Lane, Hall Green, Wakefield WF4 3LA
HARTSHEAD	Princess Mary's Athletics Track, Bradford Road, Liversedge WF15 6LW
HEADINGLEY	Weetwood Playing Fields, Weetwood, Leeds LS16 5AU
HORBURY TOWN	Slazengers Sports Complex, Southfields, Horbury WF4 5BH
HUDDERSFIELD AMATEUR	Old Earth, Lower Edge, Elland HX5 9ES
HUNSLET CLUB	The Hunslet Club, Hillidge Road LS10 1BP
ILKLEY TOWN	Ben Rhydding Sports Club, Leeds Road, ILKLEY LS29 8AW
KNARESBOROUGH TOWN	Knaresborough Town A.F.C., Manse Lane, Knaresborough HG5 8LF
LEEDS CITY	Adel War Memorial Association, Church Lane, Adel, Leeds LS16 8DE
POOL	Arthington Lane, Pool-in-Wharfedale LS21 1LE
ROBIN HOOD ATHLETIC	Behind Coach & Horses Hotel, Rothwell Haigh LS26 0SF
SHELLEY	Storthes Hall, Huddersfield HD8 0WA
SHERBURN WHITE ROSE	Finkle Hill, Recreation Ground, Finkle Hill, Sherburn-in-Elmet LS25 6EL

	ALLIANCE DIVISION ONE	P	W	D	L	F	A	GD	Pts		ALLIANCE DIVISION TWO	P	W	D	L	F	A	GD	Pts
1	Beeston St. Anthony's Res	30	24	4	2	115	39	76	76	1	Shelley Res	24	21	2	1	98	24	74	65
2	Leeds City Res	30	21	4	5	89	37	52	67	2	Kippax Res	24	15	1	8	74	60	14	46
3	Field Res	30	21	1	8	98	51	47	64	3	Hartshead Res	24	12	5	7	70	53	17	41
4	Robin Hood Athletic Res	30	17	4	9	89	54	35	55	4	Old Centralians Res	24	12	4	8	58	45	13	40
5	Carlton Athletic Res	30	16	6	8	85	66	19	54	5	Aberford Albion Res	24	11	6	7	50	43	7	39
6	Horbury Town Res	30	15	4	11	85	65	20	49	6	Whitkirk Wanderers Res	24	11	5	8	64	57	7	38
7	East End Park Res	30	14	4	12	80	81	-1	46	7	Altofts Res	24	11	2	11	55	60	-5	35
8	Headingley Res	30	12	5	13	61	70	-9	41	8	Hall Green United Res	24	10	4	10	68	55	13	34
9	Hunslet Club Res	30	11	7	12	75	70	5	40	9	AFC Horsforth Res	24	9	7	8	57	54	3	34
10	Huddersfield Amateur Res	30	11	5	14	65	75	-10	38	10	Howden Clough Res	24	8	6	10	67	65	2	30
11	Pool Res	30	11	3	16	67	93	-26	36	11	Ilkley Town Res	24	7	3	14	49	73	-24	24
12	Leeds Modernians Res	30	11	1	18	59	79	-20	34	12	Otley Town Res	24	3	1	20	37	89	-52	10
13	Oxenhope Recreation Res	30	10	3	17	78	91	-13	33	13	Sherburn White Rose Res	24	2	2	20	33	102	-69	8
14	Boroughbridge Res	30	6	3	21	45	81	-36	21										
15	Brighouse Old Boys Res	30	7	0	23	49	130	-81	21										
16	Wyke Wanderers Res	30	5	2	23	41	99	-58	17										

WYAFL TROPHY

HOLDERS: FIELD RES
FINAL

Leeds City Res	v	Shelley Res	1-0

WILTSHIRE LEAGUE

Sponsored by: No sponsor

Founded: 1928
Recent Champions:
2014: Southbrook **2015:** Malmesbury Victoria
2016: Trowbridge Town

PREMIER DIVISION

	PREMIER DIVISION	P	W	D	L	F	A	GD	Pts
1	Wroughton FC	26	22	2	2	87	27	60	68
2	Shrewton United	26	20	2	4	89	37	52	62
3	Melksham Town Res	26	18	3	5	87	51	36	57
4	Marlborough Town	26	17	1	8	82	45	37	52
5	Trowbridge Town	26	14	4	8	56	54	2	46
6	Cricklade Town	26	14	2	10	91	63	28	44
7	Ludgershall Sports	26	13	5	8	68	53	15	44
8	Wilts Calne Town	26	10	3	13	56	68	-12	33
9	Royal Wootton Bassett Town Res	26	8	5	13	56	67	-11	29
10	Corsham Town Res	26	8	4	14	48	67	-19	28
11	Bromham FC	26	8	4	14	40	73	-33	28
12	Malmesbury Victoria Dev	26	5	3	18	40	82	-42	18
13	Devizes Town Res	26	4	2	20	38	72	-34	14
14	Pewsey Vale Dev	26	1	0	25	27	106	-79	3

Lydiard Millicent changed their name to Beversbrook FC and then subsequently withdrew - record expunged.
Chippenham Park Dev withdrew before the season started.

SENIOR CUP

ROUND 1   **HOLDERS:** WROUGHTON FC

Malmesbury Victoria Dev	v	Ludgershall Sports	1-0
Cricklade Town	v	Marlborough Town	6-2
Bromham FC	v	Shrewton United	1-7
Beversbrook FC	v	Wilts Calne Town	1-2
Royal Wootton Bassett Town	v	Devizes Town Reserves	4-4, 2-4p
Chippenham Park Dev.	v	Trowbridge Town	AW
Corsham Town Res	v	Wroughton FC	3-4
Melksham Town Res	v	Pewsey Vale Dev	13-1

QUARTER-FINALS

Malmesbury Victoria Dev	v	Cricklade Town	0-3
Shrewton United	v	Wilts Calne Town	HW
Devizes Town Res	v	Trowbridge Town	3-0
Wroughton FC	v	Melksham Town Res	3-2 aet

SEMI-FINALS

Cricklade Town	v	Shrewton United	0-2
Devizes Town Res	v	Wroughton FC	1-3

FINAL

Shrewton United	v	Wroughton FC	1-3

CLUB MOVEMENTS - In: Bassett Bulldogs (P - Swindon & District), Bremhill View (P - Chippenham Sunday Lge), Kintbury Rangers (North Berks), Westbury United Res (Trowbridge).
Out: Wilts Calne Town (W).

PREMIER DIVISION

	PREMIER DIVISION	1	2	3	4	5	6	7	8	9	10	11	12	13	14
1	Bromham FC		1-2	1-7	4-3	2-0	1-1	1-8	2-2	1-0	6-2	1-2	3-1	0-2	0-4
2	Corsham Town Res	1-1		4-1	0-0	2-4	2-4	0-4	1-2	3-2	0-0	3-2	2-5	2-2	2-4
3	Cricklade Town	3-4	4-3		5-4	9-1	9-2	2-1	3-3	6-1	4-3	2-0	3-3	4-1	2-3
4	Devizes Town Res	2-0	0-1	0-2		0-3	0-1	1-3	2-5	8-1	3-3	0-4	1-2	4-5	2-6
5	Ludgershall Sports	3-0	2-0	4-2	2-0		2-5	5-2	1-3	5-0	0-0	1-2	4-1	4-1	2-2
6	Malmesbury Victoria Dev	0-0	1-2	2-4	0-1	2-2		1-3	2-5	2-3	2-6	1-5	2-1	1-3	1-3
7	Marlborough Town	3-1	7-1	2-0	9-1	4-2	5-1		5-2	2-1	2-2	1-3	2-3	3-1	0-3
8	Melksham Town Res	5-2	4-3	7-2	3-2	3-2	6-0	3-2		5-0	5-2	3-6	1-2	2-1	0-3
9	Pewsey Vale Dev	1-3	2-3	2-8	0-1	2-4	1-3	2-4	1-6		0-3	1-7	0-1	2-8	1-2
10	Royal Wootton Bassett Town Res	4-0	2-7	3-2	1-0	1-4	4-1	0-2	2-4	5-1		2-3	3-4	3-1	0-2
11	Shrewton United	5-3	3-1	4-2	4-0	2-2	3-0	4-1	1-1	7-2	1-0		7-0	3-4	2-3
12	Trowbridge Town	2-1	4-0	2-1	3-1	3-3	5-2	1-3	0-3	5-0	2-2	0-3		4-1	0-5
13	Wilts Calne Town	0-1	3-2	1-3	3-2	1-5	3-1	1-3	3-4	2-1	4-2	1-3	1-1		1-6
14	Wroughton FC	10-1	3-1	2-1	2-0	4-1	3-2	3-1	1-0	2-0	7-1	2-3	0-1	2-2	

Wiltshire League Premier Division

BASSETT BULLDOGS	Beversbrook Sports Facility, Calne SN11 9FL	07794 552 298
BREMHILL	Beversbrook Sports Facility, Calne SN11 9FL	
BROMHAM	Station Road, Sway, Lymington SO41 6BE	
CORSHAM TOWN RESERVES	Southbank Ground, Lacock Road, Corsham	
CRICKLADE TOWN	Cricklade Leisure Centre, Stones Lane, Cricklade SN6 6JW	
DEVIZES TOWN RESERVES	Nursteed Road, Devizes SN10 3DX	
KINTBURY RANGERS	Recreation Ground, Inkpen Road RG17 9TY.	07771 636 594
LUDGERSHALL SPORTS	Astor Crescent, Ludgershall SP11 9QE	
MALMESBURY VICTORIA DEV.	Flying Monk Ground Gloucester Road SN16 9JS	
MARLBOROUGH TOWN	Elcot Lane, Marlborough, SN8 2BG	
MELKSHAM TOWN RESERVES	The Conigre, Melksham	
PEWSEY VALE DEVELOPMENT	Recreation Ground, Ball Road, Pewsey, Nr Marlborough	01672 562 990
PURTON	The Red House, Church Street, Purton SN5 4DY	07774 086 421 (MD)
SHREWTON UNITED	Shrewton Recreation Ground, Mill Lane, Shrewton SP3 4JY	
TROWBRIDGE TOWN	Woodmarsh, Bradley Road, Trowbridge BA14 0SB	
WESTBURY UNITED RESERVES	Meadow Lane, Westbury	
WOOTTON BASSETT TOWN DEV.	Gerrard Buxton Sports Ground, Rylands Way, Royal Wootton Bassett SN4 8AW	
WROUGHTON	The Weir Field Ground, Devizes Road, Wroughton, Wiltshire	

YORK LEAGUE

Sponsored by: Minster Engineering
Founded: 1897
Recent Champions:
2014: Old Malton St. Mary's **2015:** Riccall United **2016:** Old Malton St. Mary's

	PREMIER DIVISION	P	W	D	L	F	A	GD	Pts
1	Wigginton Grasshoppers	28	23	2	3	116	29	87	71
2	Old Malton	28	16	11	1	71	29	42	59
3	Huntington Rovers	28	17	6	5	81	41	40	57
4	Dringhouses	28	17	3	8	75	44	31	54
5	Dunnington	28	16	4	8	68	36	32	52
6	Sporting Knavesmire	28	15	5	8	66	47	19	50
7	Malton & Norton	28	15	3	10	60	41	19	48
8	Church Fenton FC	28	11	5	12	60	51	9	38
9	F1 Racing	28	11	3	14	80	62	18	36
10	Osbaldwick	28	8	7	13	44	52	-8	31
11	York RI	28	10	1	17	56	95	-39	31
12	Tadcaster Magnets	28	6	6	16	31	68	-37	24
13	Copmanthorpe	28	6	4	18	45	84	-39	22
14	Riccall United	28	5	4	19	43	99	-56	19
15	Brooklyn FC	28	1	2	25	15	133	-118	2*

In: Hemingbrough United (P).

	DIVISION ONE	P	W	D	L	F	A	GD	Pts
1	Poppleton United	20	17	1	2	71	23	48	52
2	Pocklington Town Res	20	15	4	1	67	23	44	49
3	Hemingbrough United	20	14	3	3	74	32	42	45
4	Thorpe United	20	10	3	7	71	43	28	33
5	Harrison Signs FC	20	9	2	9	48	42	6	26*
6	Tockwith AFC	20	8	2	10	42	52	-10	26
7	Kirkbymoorside	20	7	4	9	52	53	-1	25
8	Rawcliffe	20	6	5	9	41	43	-2	23
9	Cliffe	20	3	2	15	25	86	-61	11
10	York St Johns University	20	7	2	11	45	70	-25	8*
11	Heslington	20	0	0	20	19	88	-69	0

Out: Hemingbrough United (P).

	DIVISION TWO	P	W	D	L	F	A	GD	Pts
1	Wilberfoss	16	13	1	2	58	26	32	40
2	Easingwold Town	16	10	0	6	51	33	18	30
3	Bishopthorpe United	16	10	0	6	42	37	5	30
4	Barmby Moor	16	9	1	6	44	34	10	28
5	Strensall	16	9	1	6	54	46	8	28
6	Stamford Bridge	16	7	1	8	35	38	-3	22
7	Civil Service	16	6	1	9	47	44	3	19
8	Haxby United	16	3	2	11	39	50	-11	11
9	Fulford FC	16	1	1	14	15	77	-62	4

	DIVISION THREE	P	W	D	L	F	A	GD	Pts
1	Heworth AFC	16	14	0	2	70	21	49	42
2	Huby United	16	13	0	3	68	33	35	39
3	Rufforth United	16	10	0	6	68	32	36	30
4	South Milford	16	11	0	5	69	47	22	30*
5	Selby Olympia	16	6	3	7	47	46	1	21
6	The Raj FC	16	6	1	9	26	51	-25	19
7	Cawood	16	3	3	10	52	76	-24	12
8	Moor Lane	16	2	2	12	35	81	-46	8
9	Jorvik Blades	16	2	1	13	25	73	-48	7

Howden AFC YORK withdrew - record expunged.

	PREMIER DIVISION	1	2	3	4	5	6	7	8	9	10	11	12	13	14	15
1	Brooklyn FC		0-3	0-2	0-2	0-4	0-4	0-3	0-5	2-5	0-3	1-1	1-4	2-1	0-3	3-5
2	Church Fenton	6-0		6-1	3-6	0-2	4-2	1-1	2-1	1-2	4-1	1-3	2-2	1-0	0-5	4-2
3	Copmanthorpe	7-0	1-6		1-2	3-3	1-5	3-3	3-0	1-1	1-0	2-1	1-4	2-3	0-4	1-4
4	Dringhouses	4-0	1-0	3-0		0-1	4-3	4-0	3-1	0-2	3-3	5-2	5-0	8-2	0-8	3-1
5	Dunnington	7-0	3-1	4-0	0-2		1-3	2-1	0-1	0-0	2-1	7-0	2-2	3-2	1-2	8-0
6	F1 Racing	14-0	1-1	5-2	3-2	5-0		1-4	1-2	0-4	1-1	3-2	1-2	2-3	1-5	5-1
7	Huntington Rovers	5-2	2-0	2-3	3-2	3-0	4-2		0-0	3-3	7-2	7-0	2-1	3-0	1-2	3-3
8	Malton and Norton	7-0	2-0	5-3	0-1	0-2	4-1	1-3		1-1	2-0	2-0	0-4	3-0	0-4	2-1
9	Old Malton St Marys	2-0	1-1	4-2	2-1	2-3	3-1	1-1	1-1		0-0	1-1	5-1	3-1	2-0	10-1
10	Osbaldwick	5-0	1-4	4-0	1-5	0-0	2-1	2-3	3-0	2-2		0-3	2-2	0-0	2-1	1-0
11	Riccall United	5-0	2-6	6-2	0-4	1-5	1-1	1-3	0-8	1-5	1-4		1-3	0-0	1-2	4-7
12	Sporting Knavesmire	9-0	4-0	2-2	3-3	3-0	2-0	4-3	1-2	1-2	2-1	3-1		1-0	0-3	1-0
13	Tadcaster Magnets	1-1	0-0	1-0	0-0	0-3	1-7	1-3	2-5	0-2	2-0	1-3	3-1		2-1	2-2
14	Wigginton Grasshoppers	13-2	2-1	3-1	2-0	4-3	6-2	1-1	4-2	0-0	4-3	12-1	5-1	6-0		8-1
15	York Railway Institute	3-1	3-2	3-0	3-2	0-2	0-5	1-7	1-3	3-5	2-0	4-1	0-3	6-3	1-6	

York League Premier Division

CHURCH FENTON	Church Fenton Sportsground, Busk Lane, Church Fenton, Nr Tadcaster LS24 9RF
COPMANTHORPE	Hamilton Way, Acomb, York YO24 4NX
DRINGHOUSE	Dringhouses Sports & Social Club, St Helens Road, Dringhouses, York YO24 1HR
DUNNINGTON	Dunnington Sports Club, Common Road, Dunnington, York YO19 5NG
F1 RACING	White Rose Avenue, New Earswick, York YO32 4BA
HEMINGBROUGH UNITED	Selby Town, Richard St, Scott Road, Selby YO8 4BN
HUNTINGTON ROVERS	Huntington SportsClub, North Lane, Huntington, York YO32 9RU
MALTON & NORTON	Norton College, Langton Road, Norton on Derwent, Nr Malton YO17 9PZ
OLD MALTON	FitzWilliam Sportsfield Old Malton YO17 7EY
OSBALDWICK	Osbaldwick Sports club, The Leyes, Osbaldwick, York YO10 3PR
POPPLETON UNITED	The Poppleton Centre, Main Street, Poppleton, York YO26 6JT
SPORTING KNAVESMIRE	Poppleton Com. Sports Pavilion, Millfield Lane, Nether Poppleton, Nr York YO26 6LY
TADCASTER MAGNETS	Magnets Sports Ground, Leeds Road, Tadcaster, North Yorkshire LS24 9HD
WIGGINTON GRASSHOPPERS	Mill Lane, Wigginton, York YO32 2PY
YORK RI	Hamilton Way, Acomb, York YO24 4NX

DIVISION FOUR

		P	W	D	L	F	A	GD	Pts
1	Malt Shovel	20	14	3	3	101	48	53	45
2	Wetherby Athletic B	20	13	5	2	78	34	44	44
3	Bubwith White Swan	20	13	1	6	72	40	32	40
4	Bramham	20	13	1	6	65	39	26	37*
5	Pollington	20	12	3	5	80	50	30	36*
6	Huntington	20	9	4	7	72	38	34	31
7	Swinton AFC	20	5	3	12	27	74	-47	18
8	St Clements	20	8	2	10	55	72	-17	17*
9	AFC Crayke	20	6	1	13	37	72	-35	16*
10	Wheldrake	20	1	2	17	23	95	-72	5
11	LNER Builders	20	3	1	16	33	81	-48	4*

In: Clifford FC, Elm Bank, Stillington S&C (Beckett), Wistow.

RESERVE A DIVISION

		P	W	D	L	F	A	GD	Pts
1	Huntington Rovers Res	20	19	0	1	101	30	71	57
2	Dunnington Res	20	13	0	7	93	40	53	39
3	Wigginton Grasshoppers Res	20	9	4	7	63	69	-6	31
4	Thorpe United Res	20	9	2	9	41	41	0	29
5	Old Malton Res	20	11	1	8	52	50	2	28*
6	Malton & Norton Res	20	7	6	7	41	49	-8	27
7	Hemingbrough Utd Res	20	7	2	11	52	60	-8	23
8	Copmanthorpe Res	20	7	3	10	48	61	-13	21*
9	Church Fenton Res	20	7	0	13	46	69	-23	21
10	Tadcaster Magnets Res	20	5	3	12	35	75	-40	18
11	Dringhouses Res	20	3	5	12	29	57	-28	8*

RESERVE B DIVISION

		P	W	D	L	F	A	GD	Pts
1	Pocklington Town 3rd	20	17	2	1	83	13	70	50*
2	Easingwold Town Res	20	13	3	4	49	42	7	42
3	F1 Racing Res	20	13	2	5	62	33	29	41
4	Osbaldwick Res	20	10	2	8	64	49	15	32
5	Riccall United Res	20	9	5	6	59	49	10	29*
6	Tockwith AFC Res	20	9	2	9	47	48	-1	29
7	Haxby Town Res	20	8	2	10	39	52	-13	26
8	Harrison Signs Res	20	8	1	11	41	70	-29	19*
9	Bishopthorpe United Res	20	4	4	12	29	47	-18	16
10	Stamford Bridge Res	20	2	4	14	27	53	-26	10
11	Brooklyn Res	20	2	3	15	27	71	-44	9

RESERVE C DIVISION

		P	W	D	L	F	A	GD	Pts
1	Poppleton United Res	20	16	3	1	82	22	60	51
2	Heworth AFC Res	20	15	3	2	86	30	56	48
3	York Railway Institute Res	20	15	3	2	84	36	48	47
4	Wilberfoss Res	20	11	2	7	73	62	11	35
5	Selby Olympia Res	20	10	1	9	62	60	2	31
6	Malt Shovel Res	20	7	1	12	45	67	-22	22
7	Civil Service Res	20	7	0	13	52	62	-10	21
8	Wetherby Athletic Res	20	6	3	11	46	66	-20	21
9	Rufforth United Res	20	7	1	12	39	79	-40	19*
10	Cliffe Res	20	4	2	14	36	71	-35	11*
11	Fulford Res	20	1	4	15	28	78	-50	4*

LEAGUE TABLES 2016-17

ALDERSHOT & DISTRICT LEAGUE

ALTRINCHAM & DISTRICT AMATEUR LEAGUE

AMATEUR FOOTBALL COMBINATION

ARMY ASSOCIATION

ARTHURIAN LEAGUE

AYLESBURY & DISTRICT LEAGUE

BANBURY DISTRICT & LORD JERSEY LEAGUE

BASINGSTOKE & DISTRICT LEAGUE

BIRMINGHAM & DISTRICT FOOTBALL LEAGUE

BISHOP'S STORTFORD, STANSTED & DISTRICT LEAGUE

BLACKBURN & DISTRICT FOOTBALL COMBINATION

BOURNEMOUTH HAYWARD SATURDAY LEAGUE

BRIGHTON, WORTHING & DISTRICT LEAGUE

BRISTOL & SUBURBAN LEAGUE

BRISTOL AND DISTRICT LEAGUE

BRISTOL DOWNS ASSOCIATION FOOTBALL LEAGUE

BRISTOL PREMIER COMBINATION

CENTRAL & SOUTH NORFOLK LEAGUE

CENTRAL MIDLANDS LEAGUE RESERVE DIVISION

CHELTENHAM ASSOCIATION FOOTBALL LEAGUE

CHESHIRE LEAGUE RESERVES DIVISIONS

CHESTER & WIRRAL FOOTBALL LEAGUE

CIRENCESTER & DISTRICT LEAGUE

COLCHESTER & EAST ESSEX FOOTBALL LEAGUE

CORNWALL COMBINATION

CRAVEN & DISTRICT FOOTBALL LEAGUE

CREWE & DISTRICT FOOTBALL LEAGUE

CROOK & DISTRICT LEAGUE

DEVON & EXETER FOOTBALL LEAGUE

DORSET FOOTBALL LEAGUE

DUCHY LEAGUE

DURHAM FOOTBALL ALLIANCE

EAST BERKSHIRE FOOTBALL LEAGUE

EAST LINCOLNSHIRE LEAGUE

EAST RIDING COUNTY LEAGUE

ESSEX OLYPIAN LEAGUE U21 DIVISION

FURNESS PREMIER LEAGUE

GLOUCESTERSHIRE NORTHERN SENIOR LEAGUE

GREAT YARMOUTH & DISTRICT LEAGUE

GUERNSEY FOOTBALL ASSOCIATION LEAGUE

GUILDFORD & WOKING ALLIANCE LEAGUE

HALIFAX & DISTRICT AFL

HAMPSHIRE PREMIER LEAGUE COMBINATION

HARROGATE AND DISTRICT FOOTBALL LEAGUE

HEREFORDSHIRE FA COUNTY LEAGUE

HOPE VALLEY AMATEUR LEAGUE

HUDDERSFIELD AND DISTRICT ASSOCIATION FOOTBALL LEAGUE

ISLE OF MAN SENIOR LEAGUES

ISLE OF WIGHT SATURDAY LEAGUE

JERSEY FOOTBALL COMBINATION

KINGSTON AND DISTRICT SATURDAY LEAGUE

LANCASHIRE & CHESHIRE AFL

LANCASHIRE AMATEUR LEAGUE

LANCASHIRE FOOTBALL LEAGUE

LEICESTER & DISTRICT FOOTBALL LEAGUE

LINCOLNSHIRE FOOTBALL LEAGUE

LUTON DISTRICT & SOUTH BEDS FOOTBALL LEAGUE

MAIDSTONE & DISTRICT FOOTBALL LEAGUE

MERCIAN REGIONAL FOOTBALL LEAGUE

MID ESSEX LEAGUE

MID LANCS FOOTBALL LEAGUE

MID SOMERSET LEAGUE

MID SUSSEX FOOTBALL LEAGUE

MIDLAND AMATEUR ALLIANCE

MIDLANDS REGIONAL ALLIANCE

NORTH BERKSHIRE LEAGUE

NORTH BUCKS AND DISTRICT FOOTBALL LEAGUE

NORTH DEVON FOOTBALL LEAGUE

NORTH EAST NORFOLK LEAGUE

NORTH GLOUCESTERSHIRE ASSOCIATION FOOTBALL LEAGUE

NORTH WEST NORFOLK LEAGUE

NORWICH & DISTRICT SATURDAY FOOTBALL LEAGUE

NOTTS AMATEUR ALLIANCE

PERRY STREET AND DISTRICT LEAGUE

PLYMOUTH & WEST DEVON LEAGUE

PORTSMOUTH SATURDAY FOOTBALL LEAGUE

REDHILL & DISTRICT LEAGUE

ROMFORD & DISTRICT FOOTBALL LEAGUE

SALISBURY & DISTRICT LEAGUE

SCUNTHORPE & DISTRICT FOOTBALL LEAGUE

SOUTH DEVON FOOTBALL LEAGUE

SOUTH LONDON FOOTBALL ALLIANCE

SOUTHAMPTON SATURDAY FOOTBALL LEAGUE

SOUTHEND BOROUGH & DISTRICT FOOTBALL COMBINATION

SOUTHERN AMATEUR LEAGUE

ST HELENS AND DISTRICT COMBINATION LEAGUE

STRATFORD UPON AVON FOOTBALL ALLIANCE

STROUD & DISTRICT FOOTBALL LEAGUE

SURREY COUNTY INTERMEDIATE LEAGUE (WESTERN)

SWINDON & DISTRICT FOOTBALL LEAGUE

TAUNTON & DISTRICT SATURDAY FOOTBALL LEAGUE

TROWBRIDGE & DISTRICT FOOTBALL LEAGUE

WAKEFIELD & DISTRICT FA LEAGUE

WEST RIDING COUNTY AMATEUR FOOTBALL LEAGUE

WEST SUSSEX FOOTBALL LEAGUE

WESTMORLAND ASSOCIATION FOOTBALL LEAGUE

WESTON SUPER MARE AND DISTRICT FOOTBALL LEAGUE

WIGAN & DISTRICT AMATEUR LEAGUE

YEOVIL AND DISTRICT LEAGUE

YORKSHIRE AMATEUR LEAGUE

ALDERSHOT & DISTRICT LEAGUE

Senior Division	P	W	D	L	F	A	GD	Pts
1 Rushmoor Community	14	12	1	1	50	11	39	37
2 Frimley Select	14	9	4	1	56	21	35	31
3 Hartley Wintney A	14	6	3	5	31	31	0	21
4 Ropley	14	6	1	7	23	33	-10	19
5 Wey Valley	14	5	2	7	33	33	0	17
6 Alton	14	4	3	7	21	36	-15	15
7 Fleet Spurs Res	14	4	0	10	24	38	-14	12
8 Bagshot Res	14	2	2	10	20	55	-35	8

Division One	P	W	D	L	F	A	GD	Pts
1 Hale Rovers	16	11	2	3	50	23	27	35
2 Yateley United A	16	10	2	4	35	33	2	32
3 Spartans	16	9	1	6	61	31	30	28
4 Fleet Spurs A	16	9	1	6	31	27	4	28
5 Traco Athletic	16	8	3	5	31	28	3	27
6 Mytchett Athletic	16	8	2	6	39	38	1	26
7 Sandhurst Sports	16	5	1	10	30	43	-13	16
8 AFC Laffans	16	3	1	12	19	46	-27	10
9 Hindhead Athletic	16	2	1	13	15	42	-27	7

Division Two	P	W	D	L	F	A	GD	Pts
1 Normandy	15	15	0	0	91	20	71	45
2 Wey Valley Res	15	7	1	7	53	62	-9	22
3 Fleet Spurs Vet	15	6	3	6	43	48	-5	21
4 Letef Select	15	6	2	7	36	43	-7	20
5 Yateley United B	15	5	1	9	49	57	-8	16
6 AFC Laffans Res	15	2	1	12	30	72	-42	7

ALTRINCHAM & DISTRICT AMATEUR LEAGUE

	P	W	D	L	F	A	GD	Pts
1 Club AZ	24	18	1	5	90	27	63	55
2 Sale Amateurs	24	15	3	6	63	46	17	48
3 Wythenshawe Amateur	24	14	4	6	77	54	23	46
4 Sale UNT	24	14	4	6	73	55	18	46
5 Altrincham-Hale A	24	15	1	8	73	61	12	46
6 Kartel Sports	24	13	3	8	54	39	15	42
7 Partington Rovers	24	12	4	8	87	49	38	40
8 Old Altrinchamians	24	10	3	11	58	57	1	33
9 Broadheath Central FC	24	9	3	12	52	57	-5	30
10 Altrincham Hale	24	8	3	13	55	61	-6	27
11 Unicorn Athletic	24	7	2	15	48	97	-49	23
12 Flixton AFC	24	2	4	18	40	98	-58	10
13 Govan Athletic A	24	1	1	22	20	89	-69	4

AMATEUR FOOTBALL COMBINATION

Premier	P	W	D	L	F	A	GD	Pts
1 Old Meadonians	20	16	1	3	61	22	39	49
2 Old Parmiterians	20	14	3	3	61	30	31	45
3 Old Suttonians	20	10	3	7	47	38	9	33
4 Dorkinians	20	8	7	5	40	32	8	31
5 Old Wokingians	20	10	0	10	32	35	-3	30
6 UCL Academicals	20	8	3	9	39	44	-5	27
7 Old Minchendenians	20	7	4	9	36	44	-8	25
8 Old Thorntonians	20	7	1	12	24	34	-10	22
9 Honorable Artillery Company	20	5	6	9	28	38	-10	21
10 Old Hamptonians	20	5	5	10	34	36	-2	20
11 Old Salvatorians	20	2	3	15	20	69	-49	9

Wandsworth Borough VI withdrew

Senior One	P	W	D	L	F	A	GD	Pts
1 Park View	22	19	1	2	83	29	54	58
2 Clapham Old Xaverians	22	14	5	3	72	41	31	47
3 Bealonians	22	11	7	4	49	28	21	40
4 Economicals	22	11	5	6	56	40	16	38
5 Fulham Compton Old Boys	22	11	3	8	49	36	13	36
6 Southgate Olympic	22	11	1	10	51	46	5	34
7 Old Ignatians	22	8	4	10	65	54	11	28
8 Kings Old Boys	22	8	3	11	39	59	-20	27
9 Old Aloysians	22	6	5	11	47	71	-24	20*
10 Enfield Old Grammarians	22	5	5	12	43	69	-26	20
11 Old Pauline	22	5	3	14	41	64	-23	18
12 London Lawyers	22	2	0	20	25	83	-58	1*

Senior Two North	P	W	D	L	F	A	GD	Pts
1 Queen Mary College Old Boys	18	12	3	3	51	22	29	39
2 Old Manorians	18	12	2	4	55	29	26	38
3 Hale End Athletic	18	12	1	5	47	34	13	37
4 Albanian	18	11	3	4	48	23	25	36
5 IB Albion	18	9	4	5	45	26	19	31
6 Sloane	18	9	2	7	50	33	17	29
7 Latymer Old Boys	18	7	4	7	52	45	7	25
8 Old Woodhouseians	18	4	1	13	42	45	-3	13
9 Spaniards	18	2	3	13	32	64	-32	9
10 Old Aloysians II	18	0	1	17	16	117	-101	-2*

Senior Two South	P	W	D	L	F	A	GD	Pts
1 Reigatians	20	12	5	3	52	25	27	41
2 Wandsworth Borough	20	10	7	3	36	21	15	37
3 Fitzwilliam Old Boys	20	10	4	6	39	21	18	34
4 Glyn Old Boys	20	10	3	7	44	40	4	33
5 Shene Old Grammarians	20	9	3	8	36	44	-8	30
6 Old Tenisonians	20	7	6	7	32	28	4	27
7 Old Meadonians II	20	7	4	9	39	39	0	25
8 Worcester College Old Boys	20	6	7	7	29	36	-7	25
9 Honorable Artillery Company II	20	6	5	9	39	42	-3	23
10 Economicals II	20	4	3	13	30	48	-18	15
11 Old Sedcopians	20	4	3	13	38	70	-32	15

Senior Three North	P	W	D	L	F	A	GD	Pts
1 UCL Academicals II	18	12	2	4	50	21	29	38
2 Southgate County	18	11	3	4	54	29	25	36
3 Hale End Athletic II	18	8	5	5	42	30	12	29
4 Old Salvatorians II	18	8	5	5	37	33	4	29
5 Globe Rangers	18	8	4	6	41	32	9	28
6 Old Ignatians II	18	8	4	6	42	43	-1	28
7 Bealonians II	18	8	2	8	29	28	1	26
8 Albanian II	18	5	3	10	26	48	-22	18
9 Southgate Olympic II	18	4	2	12	39	56	-17	14
10 Old Tollingtonians	18	2	2	14	25	65	-40	8

LEAGUE TABLES

Senior Three South

		P	W	D	L	F	A	GD	Pts
1	Old Hamptonians II	20	13	1	6	45	32	13	40
2	Old Thorntonians II	20	10	6	4	40	26	14	36
3	Royal Bank of Scotland	20	10	3	7	72	41	31	33
4	Old Strand Academicals	20	9	4	7	47	43	4	31
5	Mickleham Old Boxhillians	20	9	3	8	40	37	3	30
6	Old Suttonians II	20	8	4	8	43	41	2	28
7	Citigroup	20	8	4	8	43	53	-10	27*
8	Economicals III	20	9	0	11	45	54	-9	24*
9	Old Vaughanians	20	7	3	10	50	61	-11	24*
10	Old Meadonians III	20	5	6	9	37	41	-4	21
11	Sinjuns Grammarians	20	4	2	14	28	61	-33	14

Intermediate North

		P	W	D	L	F	A	GD	Pts
1	Old Minchendenians II	16	12	0	4	81	35	46	36
2	Enfield Old Grammarians II	16	11	1	4	52	35	17	34
3	Old Manorians II	16	10	1	5	53	34	19	31
4	Lea Valley	16	7	2	7	42	58	-16	23
5	Old Uffingtonians	16	6	3	7	57	49	8	21
6	UCL Academicals III	16	5	5	6	36	41	-5	20
7	Wood Green Old Boys	16	5	3	8	31	44	-13	18
8	Old Parmiterians II	16	5	0	11	38	66	-28	15
9	Old Salvatorians III	16	1	5	10	25	53	-28	8

Intermediate South

		P	W	D	L	F	A	GD	Pts
1	New-Magdalen AFC	18	12	4	2	49	28	21	40
2	Old St Marys	18	11	2	5	34	19	15	35
3	Dorkinians II	18	11	1	6	40	27	13	34
4	Royal Bank of Scotland II	18	10	3	5	49	34	15	33
5	Witan	18	7	0	11	24	34	-10	21
6	Old Wokingians II	18	5	5	8	29	38	-9	20
7	Old Isleworthians	18	6	4	8	36	37	-1	19*
8	City of London	18	5	4	9	28	42	-14	19
9	Hampstead Heathens	18	5	4	9	31	35	-4	13*
10	Economicals IV	18	4	1	13	22	48	-26	11*

One North

		P	W	D	L	F	A	GD	Pts
1	Bealonians III	16	10	3	3	48	26	22	33
2	Somerville Old Boys	16	9	3	4	57	40	17	30
3	Leyton County Old Boys	16	9	2	5	50	31	19	29
4	Queen Mary College Old Boys II	16	7	4	5	51	40	11	25
5	Latymer Old Boys II	16	7	2	7	35	38	-3	23
6	University of Hertfordshire	16	6	4	6	57	58	-1	22
7	Old Manorians III	16	5	3	8	43	57	-14	18
8	Old Parmiterians III	16	4	1	11	28	51	-23	13
9	Old Magdalenians	16	3	2	11	40	68	-28	11

One South

		P	W	D	L	F	A	GD	Pts
1	London Welsh	18	14	2	2	58	25	33	44
2	Reigatians II	18	12	1	5	54	39	15	37
3	Heathrow Seniors	18	9	2	7	35	29	6	29
4	Old Meadonians IV	18	9	2	7	32	35	-3	29
5	Old Pauline II	18	9	0	9	34	27	7	27
6	Old Thorntonians III	18	9	0	9	46	42	4	27
7	Old Tiffinians	18	7	3	8	33	32	1	24
8	Glyn Old Boys II	18	6	3	9	34	40	-6	21
9	Old Sedcopians II	18	4	3	11	35	56	-21	15
10	Old Suttonians III	18	2	2	14	24	60	-36	8

Two North

		P	W	D	L	F	A	GD	Pts
1	Old Kingsburians	16	11	1	4	48	27	21	34
2	UCL Academicals IV	16	10	1	5	53	32	21	31
3	Albanian III	16	8	3	5	50	55	-5	27
4	Venceremos FC	16	8	2	6	46	34	12	26
5	Old Parmiterians IV	16	7	2	7	45	40	5	23
6	Hale End Athletic III	16	6	2	8	44	47	-3	20
7	Southgate Olympic III	16	5	3	8	41	50	-9	18
8	Old Minchendenians III	16	4	2	10	36	54	-18	14
9	Egbertian II	16	3	4	9	33	57	-24	13

Two South

		P	W	D	L	F	A	GD	Pts
1	Clapham Old Xaverians II	20	16	2	2	58	24	34	50
2	Old Tenisonians II	20	13	2	5	75	32	43	41
3	Wandsworth Borough II	20	12	2	6	47	30	17	38
4	Dorkinians III	20	9	6	5	53	37	16	33
5	Kings Old Boys II	20	8	4	8	40	44	-4	28
6	Brent	20	8	2	10	50	52	-2	26
7	Old Guildfordians	20	8	2	10	36	50	-14	26
8	Old Pauline III	20	7	3	10	40	49	-9	24
9	Tilburg Regents	20	7	1	12	39	60	-21	22
10	Old Meadonians V	20	5	2	13	44	75	-31	17
11	Sinjuns Grammarians II	20	3	2	15	28	57	-29	11

Three North

		P	W	D	L	F	A	GD	Pts
1	Old Parmiterians V	18	15	2	1	65	24	41	47
2	Hinton & Finchley Revolution OB	18	12	3	3	59	38	21	39
3	Mill Hill Village	18	12	0	6	81	55	26	36
4	Old Woodhouseians II	18	9	3	6	55	40	15	30
5	Mayfield Athletic	18	8	2	8	60	59	1	26
6	Southgate Olympic IV	18	7	3	8	48	45	3	24
7	Queen Mary College Old Boys III	18	7	2	9	37	42	-5	23
8	Southgate County II	18	3	2	13	33	57	-24	11
9	Old Ignatians III	18	2	4	12	39	63	-24	10
10	Old Aloysians III	18	4	1	13	38	92	-54	10*

Three South

		P	W	D	L	F	A	GD	Pts
1	Old Whitgiftian	20	15	0	5	61	31	30	45
2	Fulham Compton Old Boys II	20	14	1	5	46	29	17	43
3	Old Wokingians III	20	12	3	5	62	42	20	39
4	Old St Marys II	20	12	1	7	55	45	10	37
5	Old Meadonians VI	20	10	2	8	39	38	1	32
6	Old Thorntonians IV	20	8	2	10	47	45	2	26
7	Reigatians III	20	6	4	10	43	51	-8	22
8	Old Boilers	20	5	5	10	41	53	-12	20
9	National Westminster Bank	20	4	7	9	34	56	-22	19
10	Old Suttonians IV	20	5	3	12	41	54	-13	18
11	Old Crosbeians	20	3	4	13	32	57	-25	10*

Four North

		P	W	D	L	F	A	GD	Pts
1	Old Kingsburians II	18	11	4	3	51	29	22	34*
2	Old Challoners	18	10	4	4	40	27	13	34
3	Old Salvatorians IV	18	10	1	7	51	46	5	28*
4	Egbertian III	18	7	6	5	43	32	11	27
5	Old Vaughanians II	18	8	3	7	40	46	-6	27
6	Bealonians IV	18	7	3	8	42	49	-7	24
7	Parkfield	18	6	5	7	47	43	4	23
8	Enfield Old Grammarians III	18	6	2	10	38	54	-16	20
9	Albanian IV	18	5	3	10	31	31	0	18
10	Latymer Old Boys III	18	4	1	13	29	55	-26	13

Four South

		P	W	D	L	F	A	GD	Pts
1	Shene Old Grammarians II	20	15	4	1	65	30	35	49
2	Royal Sun Alliance	20	13	3	4	78	49	29	42
3	Old Hamptonians	20	11	5	4	64	40	24	38
4	Fulham Compton Old Boys II	20	12	1	7	55	33	22	37
5	Wandsworth Borough III	20	8	6	6	37	35	2	30
6	Old Thorntonians V	20	7	4	9	43	60	-17	25
7	Old Sedcopians III	20	7	3	10	43	50	-7	24
8	Dorkinians IV	20	6	4	10	39	45	-6	22
9	Old Meadonians VII	20	7	0	13	38	55	-17	21
10	Old Wokingians IV	20	4	2	14	35	66	-31	14
11	City of London II	20	3	2	15	30	64	-34	11

Five North

		P	W	D	L	F	A	GD	Pts
1	Wood Green Old Boys II	18	15	1	2	99	34	65	46
2	Old Manorians IV	18	14	2	2	79	36	43	44
3	Old Tollingtonians II	18	9	2	7	51	43	8	26*
4	London Hospital Old Boys	18	7	1	10	49	66	-17	18*
5	Latymer Old Boys IV	18	6	0	12	47	87	-40	18
6	Old Parmiterians VI	18	4	1	13	44	64	-20	13
7	Old Aloysians IV	18	4	1	13	40	79	-39	9*

Five South

		P	W	D	L	F	A	GD	Pts
1	Glyn Old Boys III	20	18	1	1	55	16	39	55
2	London Welsh II	20	16	3	1	70	28	42	51
3	Shene Old Grammarians III	20	11	3	6	65	38	27	36
4	Witan II	20	10	4	6	49	35	14	34
5	John Fisher Old Boys	20	7	5	8	48	51	-3	26
6	Old Tiffinians II	20	7	4	9	49	60	-11	25
7	Old Tenisonians III	20	6	6	8	40	45	-5	24
8	Clapham Old Xaverians III	20	6	4	10	56	51	5	22
9	Old Suttonians V	20	4	3	13	23	56	-33	15
10	Old Wokingians V	20	5	0	15	39	78	-39	15
11	Old Grantonians	20	3	1	16	52	88	-36	9*

Six North

		P	W	D	L	F	A	GD	Pts
1	Bealonians VI	18	12	3	3	65	36	29	39
2	Old Tollingtonians III	18	11	3	4	58	34	24	36
3	UCL Academicals V	18	11	3	4	53	31	22	36
4	Old Woodhouseians III	18	10	3	5	59	39	20	33
5	Southgate Olympic V	18	9	2	7	46	39	7	29
6	Mill Hill Village II	18	8	2	8	66	45	21	26
7	Leyton County Old Boys II	18	7	3	8	55	57	-2	23*
8	Old Ignatians IV	18	3	4	11	39	67	-28	13
9	Wood Green Old Boys III	18	4	1	13	37	77	-40	13
10	Old Manorians V	18	2	2	14	36	89	-53	8

Six South

		P	W	D	L	F	A	GD	Pts
1	Old Suttonians VI	18	16	1	1	99	24	75	49
2	Clapham Old Xaverians IV	18	15	0	3	86	24	62	45
3	Old Wokingians VI	18	11	2	5	50	38	12	35
4	Dorkinians V	18	9	3	6	51	39	12	30
5	Mickleham Old Boxhillians II	18	9	1	8	37	45	-8	28
6	Brent II	18	7	0	11	44	62	-18	21
7	Glyn Old Boys IV	18	6	2	10	35	58	-23	20
8	Old Meadonians VIII	18	4	2	12	28	64	-36	14
9	Reigatians IV	18	3	1	14	33	66	-33	10
10	John Fisher Old Boys II	18	2	4	12	22	65	-43	6*

Seven North

		P	W	D	L	F	A	GD	Pts
1	University of Hertfordshire II	16	14	1	1	110	19	91	43
2	Old Pegasonians	16	13	1	2	77	26	51	40
3	Old Kingsburians III	16	8	1	7	54	25	29	25
4	Old Parmiterians VII	16	7	3	6	45	51	-6	24
5	Old Salvatorians V	16	7	4	5	41	35	6	22*
6	Old Minchendenians IV	16	5	2	9	29	65	-36	17
7	Southgate Olympic VI	16	3	3	10	28	64	-36	12
8	Latymer Old Boys V	16	4	1	11	34	73	-39	10*
9	Old Woodhouseians IV	16	3	0	13	24	84	-60	9

Seven South

		P	W	D	L	F	A	GD	Pts
1	Wandsworth Borough IV	20	14	2	4	77	26	51	44
2	Old Wokingians IV	20	12	4	4	76	44	32	40
3	Sinjuns Grammarians III	20	12	3	5	54	49	5	39
4	Old Pauline IV	20	10	5	5	65	41	24	35
5	Brent III	20	10	2	8	47	49	-2	32
6	Old Thorntonians VI	20	9	2	9	41	52	-11	29
7	Dorkinians VI	20	8	1	11	48	54	-6	25
8	Reigatians V	20	7	3	10	30	49	-19	24
9	Old Suttonians VII	20	6	4	10	43	49	-6	22
10	Old Tiffinians III	20	3	3	14	35	64	-29	12
11	Old Guildfordians II	20	4	2	14	40	79	-39	8*

Eight North

		P	W	D	L	F	A	GD	Pts
1	Old Parmiterians VIII	20	16	0	4	88	30	58	48
2	Old Kingsburians IV	20	15	2	3	85	32	53	47
3	UCL Academicals VI	20	14	1	5	77	46	31	43
4	Southgate Olympic VII	20	12	2	6	71	44	27	38
5	Ravenscroft Old Boys	20	11	1	8	66	48	18	34
6	Enfield Old Grammarians IV	20	10	2	8	55	37	18	29*
7	Bealonians VII	20	7	2	11	47	62	-15	23
8	Southgate County III	20	6	2	12	46	63	-17	20
9	Old Challoners II	20	5	3	12	36	64	-28	18
10	Old Vaughanians III	20	4	3	13	44	87	-43	15
11	Old Ignatians V	20	0	2	18	21	123	-102	2

Eight South

		P	W	D	L	F	A	GD	Pts
1	City of London III	18	14	2	2	87	25	62	44
2	Shene Old Grammarians IV	18	13	3	2	82	22	60	42
3	Wandsworth Borough V	18	8	5	5	42	34	8	29
4	Old Whitgiftian II	18	7	6	5	58	41	17	27
5	Old Tiffinians IV	18	6	6	6	58	55	3	24
6	Reigatians VI	18	6	5	7	49	50	-1	23
7	Old Sedcopians IV	18	6	5	7	37	51	-14	23
8	Old St Marys III	18	7	1	10	38	50	-12	22
9	Old Meadonians IX	18	4	1	13	30	68	-38	13
10	Old Wokingians VIII	18	2	0	16	21	106	-85	6

LEAGUE TABLES

ARMY ASSOCIATION

Massey Trophy - Division One

		P	W	D	L	F	A	GD	Pts
1	RLC	12	10	2	0	44	14	30	32
2	RE	12	7	3	2	39	20	19	24
3	R Sigs	12	6	1	5	32	19	13	19
4	Royal Artillery	12	6	1	5	18	32	-14	19
5	REME	12	5	2	5	31	24	7	17
6	AAC	12	2	0	10	23	41	-18	6
7	RAPTC	12	1	1	10	12	49	-37	4

Massey Trophy - Division Two

		P	W	D	L	F	A	GD	Pts
1	Inf Men	8	6	2	0	30	6	24	20
2	AGC - Men	8	5	2	1	19	5	14	17
3	AMS - Men	8	2	2	4	10	22	-12	8
4	INT CORPS	8	1	3	4	2	17	-15	6
5	RAC - Men	8	0	3	5	3	14	-11	3

ARTHURIAN LEAGUE

Premeir Division

		P	W	D	L	F	A	GD	Pts
1	Old Carthusians	18	16	1	1	79	21	58	49
2	Old Foresters	18	11	3	4	39	26	13	36
3	Kings College Wimbledon	18	9	3	6	41	34	7	30
4	Old Etonians	18	7	6	5	29	28	1	27
5	Old Salopians	18	8	2	8	49	41	8	26
6	Old Tonbridgians	18	8	0	10	35	43	-8	24
7	Lancing Old Boys	18	7	1	10	39	49	-10	22
8	Old Marlburians	18	5	4	9	34	46	-12	19
9	Old Harrovians	18	3	4	11	23	52	-29	13
10	Old Brentwoods	18	3	2	13	21	49	-28	11

Division One

		P	W	D	L	F	A	GD	Pts
1	Old Wykehamists	18	13	1	4	54	23	31	40
2	Old Chigwellians	18	13	1	4	50	23	27	40
3	Old Bradfieldians	18	11	3	4	47	35	12	33*
4	Old Cholmeleians	18	9	3	6	54	41	13	27*
5	Old Reptonians	18	6	3	9	31	44	-13	21
6	Old Malvernians	18	6	1	11	32	52	-20	19
7	Old Aldenhamians	18	5	3	10	35	48	-13	18
8	Old Wellingtonians	18	5	3	10	32	47	-15	18
9	Old Millfieldians	18	5	4	9	44	46	-2	16*
10	Old Radleians	18	4	4	10	38	58	-20	16

Division Two

		P	W	D	L	F	A	GD	Pts
1	Lancing Old Boys II	16	9	3	4	36	25	11	30
2	Old Carthusians III	16	8	5	3	43	27	16	29
3	Old Berkhamstedians	16	7	3	6	39	35	4	24
4	Old Westminsters	16	7	2	7	44	41	3	23
5	Old Etonians II	16	6	3	7	32	28	4	21
6	Kings College Wimbledon II	16	6	3	7	29	32	-3	21
7	Old Carthusians II	16	5	5	6	26	30	-4	20
8	Old Foresters II	16	5	2	9	21	36	-15	17
9	Old Sennockians	16	5	2	9	19	35	-16	17

Division Three

		P	W	D	L	F	A	GD	Pts
1	Old Alleynians AFC	14	11	1	2	49	24	25	34
2	Old Harrovians II	14	11	1	2	45	21	24	34
3	Old Chigwellians II	14	8	2	4	29	25	4	26
4	Old Citizens	14	6	1	7	30	30	0	19
5	Old Epsomians	14	5	2	7	33	32	1	17
6	Old Salopians II	14	4	1	9	23	45	-22	13
7	Old Eastbournians	14	3	2	9	27	38	-11	11
8	Old Aldenhamians II	14	2	2	10	20	41	-21	8

Division Four

		P	W	D	L	F	A	GD	Pts
1	Old Merchant Taylors	14	9	3	2	37	22	15	30
2	Old Tonbridgians II	14	9	2	3	43	26	17	29
3	Old Haberdashers	14	7	0	7	39	39	0	21
4	Old Bancroftians AFC	14	6	2	6	31	24	7	20
5	Old Suttonians SV	14	5	4	5	46	47	-1	19
6	Old Stoics	14	5	4	5	32	37	-5	19
7	Old Wykehamists II	14	3	3	8	29	44	-15	12
8	Old Cholmeleians II	14	2	2	10	24	42	-18	8

Division Five North

		P	W	D	L	F	A	GD	Pts
1	Old Merchant Taylors II	15	9	2	4	39	25	14	29
2	Old Chigwellians III	15	8	4	3	36	22	14	28
3	Old Brentwoods II	15	7	4	4	27	26	1	25
4	Old Foresters III	15	6	3	6	38	33	5	21
5	Old Brentwoods III	15	4	2	9	24	29	-5	14
6	Old Cholmeleians III	15	3	1	11	13	42	-29	10

Division Five South

		P	W	D	L	F	A	GD	Pts
1	Old Rugbeians	14	10	2	2	44	18	26	32
2	Old Johnians FC	14	9	1	4	50	23	27	28
3	Old Alleynians AFC II	14	6	4	4	47	43	4	22
4	Kings College Wimbledon III	14	6	1	7	27	28	-1	19
5	Old Amplefordians	14	4	5	5	43	45	-2	17
6	Old Westminsters II	14	4	4	6	29	39	-10	16
7	Old Malvernians II	14	2	4	8	26	45	-19	10
8	Old Harrovians III	14	3	3	8	24	49	-25	9*

AYLESBURY & DISTRICT LEAGUE

Premier Division

		P	W	D	L	F	A	GD	Pts
1	Aylesbury Dynamos	18	14	1	3	68	21	47	43
2	Long Crendon	17	14	1	2	49	23	26	43
3	Wendover	18	12	1	5	66	45	21	37
4	New Zealand	17	11	0	6	54	36	18	33
5	APBS	18	8	2	8	45	39	6	26
6	Elmhurst	18	6	3	9	41	41	0	21
7	Pond Park Rangers	18	6	0	12	31	54	-23	18
8	FC Mandeville	18	5	1	12	39	62	-23	16
9	Haddenham United	18	5	0	13	39	47	-8	15
10	Long Marston	18	3	1	14	31	95	-64	10

Division One

		P	W	D	L	F	A	GD	Pts
1	Quainton	16	13	0	3	57	20	37	39
2	Bucks CC	16	11	1	4	38	28	10	34
3	Wingrave	16	10	3	3	53	26	27	33
4	Ludgershall	16	7	3	6	25	23	2	24
5	Rivets Sports	16	6	4	6	28	29	-1	22
6	Oving	16	7	1	8	37	39	-2	22
7	Bedgrove Dynamos	16	3	5	8	19	44	-25	14
8	Haddenham United Res	16	2	3	11	17	43	-26	9
9	FC Mandeville Res	16	2	2	12	27	49	-22	8

Division Two

		P	W	D	L	F	A	GD	Pts
1	Tetsworth	16	12	3	1	65	24	41	39
2	Bedgrove United	16	12	1	3	55	19	36	37
3	Rivets Sports Res	16	10	2	4	64	33	31	32
4	Long Crendon Res	16	9	3	4	33	29	4	30
5	Wendover Res	16	5	2	9	48	47	1	17
6	FC Spandits	16	4	3	9	36	51	-15	15
7	Bucks CC Res	16	4	2	10	34	56	-22	14
8	Quainton Res	16	4	1	11	27	61	-34	13
9	Long Marston Res	16	2	3	11	26	68	-42	9

Division Three

		P	W	D	L	F	A	GD	Pts
1	Bedgrove United Res	16	13	1	2	49	18	31	40
2	AC Meadowcroft	16	10	2	4	45	22	23	32
3	Aylesbury Dynamos Res	16	8	4	4	50	27	23	28
4	Tetsworth Res	16	8	4	4	46	27	19	28
5	Wingrave Res	16	5	4	7	26	28	-2	19
6	Bedgrove Dynamos Res	16	5	3	8	24	41	-17	18
7	Great Milton	16	4	2	10	32	55	-23	14
8	Oving Res	16	4	1	11	30	55	-25	13
9	Ludgershall Res	16	3	3	10	20	49	-29	12

BANBURY DISTRICT & LORD JERSEY LEAGUE

Premier Division

		P	W	D	L	F	A	GD	Pts
1	Woodford United	18	16	2	0	60	17	43	50
2	KEA	18	13	3	2	63	23	40	42
3	Broughton & North Newington	18	12	3	3	53	25	28	39
4	Deddington Town	18	8	1	9	34	32	2	25
5	Bishops Itchington	18	7	3	8	36	36	0	24
6	Sinclair Utd	18	8	0	10	33	46	-13	24
7	Croughton	18	7	2	9	39	38	1	23
8	Middleton Cheney	18	4	2	12	31	67	-36	14
9	Diverse	18	4	0	14	22	57	-35	12
10	Hornton	18	2	2	14	28	58	-30	8

Division One

		P	W	D	L	F	A	GD	Pts
1	AFC Bicester	18	16	1	1	66	24	42	49
2	Chasewell Park	18	14	2	2	56	20	36	44
3	Wroxton Sports	18	10	3	5	48	35	13	33
4	Bloxham	18	8	4	6	41	37	4	28
5	Charlton & District	18	8	2	8	52	40	12	26
6	Chesterton	18	6	4	8	36	49	-13	22
7	Heyford Athletic	18	6	4	8	26	42	-16	22
8	Finmere	18	4	4	10	37	48	-11	16
9	Banbury United Youth	18	2	3	13	16	36	-20	9
10	Deddington Town Res	18	2	1	15	17	64	-47	7

Division Two

		P	W	D	L	F	A	GD	Pts
1	Byfield Athletic	14	12	0	2	49	26	23	36
2	Bicester United	14	8	2	4	52	36	16	26
3	SWIS	14	6	2	6	29	28	1	20
4	Bishops Itchington Res	14	6	3	5	41	39	2	18*
5	Steeple Aston	14	5	2	7	27	30	-3	17
6	Bodicote Sports	14	5	2	7	28	39	-11	17
7	Bloxham Res	14	4	3	7	36	37	-1	15
8	Chacombe	14	2	2	10	21	48	-27	8

Division Three

		P	W	D	L	F	A	GD	Pts
1	KEA Res	18	16	0	2	101	23	78	48
2	AFC BANBURY	18	11	5	2	84	36	48	38
3	Banbury Sports	18	11	2	5	57	31	26	35
4	Kings Sutton	18	10	2	6	50	42	8	32
5	Banbury Galaxy	18	7	4	7	49	36	13	25
6	Heyford United	18	6	5	7	63	43	20	23
7	Magna Exteriors	18	6	3	9	39	81	-42	21
8	Kingsmere United	18	4	2	12	35	49	-14	14
9	Brill United	18	4	1	13	39	91	-52	13
10	BANBURY CROSS	18	3	0	15	18	103	-85	9

Division Four

		P	W	D	L	F	A	GD	Pts
1	Broughton & North Newington Res	18	14	2	2	76	20	56	44
2	Wroxton Sports Res	18	13	3	2	57	23	34	42
3	Bloxbury Athletic	18	9	5	4	53	30	23	32
4	Steeple Aston Res	18	8	6	4	42	30	12	30
5	SWIS Res	18	8	1	9	40	46	-6	25
6	Bodicote Sports Res	18	7	1	10	41	50	-9	22
7	Chasewell Park Res	18	6	2	10	45	62	-17	20
8	Charlton & District Second	18	6	1	11	42	55	-13	19
9	Kings Sutton Res	18	6	1	11	46	73	-27	19
10	Finmere Res	18	1	2	15	28	81	-53	5

BASINGSTOKE & DISTRICT LEAGUE

Division One

		P	W	D	L	F	A	GD	Pts
1	Hook	14	11	2	1	51	20	31	35
2	Twentyten	14	10	1	3	49	24	25	31
3	DC UK	14	7	3	4	46	31	15	24
4	Tadley Calleva A Team	14	7	3	4	45	38	7	24
5	Basingstoke Royals	14	5	2	7	33	31	2	17
6	AFC Aldermaston Res	14	5	2	7	24	46	-22	17
7	Bounty United	14	3	2	9	28	53	-25	11
8	Basingstoke Athletic	14	0	1	13	16	49	-33	1

Division Two

		P	W	D	L	F	A	GD	PTS
1	Herriard Sports	18	17	1	0	83	10	73	52
2	Winklebury Wizards	18	11	3	4	63	35	28	36
3	Basingstoke Labour	18	10	5	3	68	26	42	35
4	Overton United 'B'	18	10	5	3	60	25	35	35
5	AFC Berg	18	10	4	4	58	32	26	34
6	AFC Aldermaston A Team	18	7	3	8	36	49	-13	24
7	Twentyten Res	18	5	3	10	28	61	-33	18
8	Long Dog Soldiers	18	3	2	13	24	56	-32	11
9	Origin Headley	18	3	0	15	26	88	-62	9
10	Chineham Sat	18	1	0	17	17	81	-64	3

LEAGUE TABLES
BIRMINGHAM & DISTRICT FOOTBALL LEAGUE

Premier Division

		P	W	D	L	F	A	GD	Pts
1	Wake Green Amateurs 'A'	22	14	7	1	51	22	29	49
2	Village A	22	15	3	4	55	27	28	48
3	Silhill 'A'	22	13	5	4	47	25	22	41*
4	Birmingham Irish	22	11	8	3	39	22	17	41
5	Kings Heath Old Boys	22	10	6	6	39	25	14	36
6	CPA 1sts	22	9	5	8	33	35	-2	32
7	Premier A	22	9	4	9	47	42	5	31
8	AFC Somers	22	7	4	11	36	49	-13	25
9	Handsworth GSOB 'A'	22	4	9	9	54	55	-1	21
10	Old Hill	22	5	3	14	34	57	-23	15*
11	Crusaders	22	3	3	16	30	71	-41	12
12	Bartley Green Continental	22	2	3	17	31	66	-35	9

Division One

		P	W	D	L	F	A	GD	PTS
1	Birmingham Medics A	20	14	4	2	60	27	33	46
2	Sutton United A	20	11	5	4	58	40	18	38
3	Silhill B	20	9	6	5	53	38	15	33
4	CT Shush	20	9	3	8	27	27	0	30
5	Old Wulfrunians 'A'	20	9	2	9	34	27	7	29
6	Bearwood Athletic	20	8	2	10	42	46	-4	26
7	Two Gates	20	8	2	10	34	42	-8	26
8	Wake Green Amateurs B	20	7	3	10	36	43	-7	24
9	Village B	20	6	3	11	31	40	-9	21
10	Folsom	20	5	5	10	30	55	-25	20
11	BNJS	20	4	5	11	30	50	-20	14*

Division Two

		P	W	D	L	F	A	GD	PTS
1	Amanah	22	15	4	3	82	32	50	49
2	Desi	22	13	3	6	62	50	12	42
3	Dosthill Rovers	22	10	7	5	59	44	15	37
4	Kinver	22	11	4	7	58	49	9	37
5	Boldmere Sports & Social 'A'	22	11	4	7	46	39	7	37
6	Calthorpe United	22	12	1	9	64	40	24	34*
7	Sportsco A	22	9	2	11	55	43	12	29
8	Flamengo	22	8	4	10	32	39	-7	28
9	St Georges Warriors	22	7	3	12	39	54	-15	24
10	Castlecroft Rangers	22	6	3	13	26	60	-34	21
11	Wake Green Amateurs C	22	6	1	15	44	81	-37	19
12	Halesowen	22	4	4	14	30	66	-36	16

Division Three

		P	W	D	L	F	A	GD	PTS
1	Chelmsley Wood	24	21	0	3	90	26	64	63
2	Crown F.M.N	24	20	3	1	94	34	60	63
3	Kingstanding Celtic	24	15	3	6	72	41	31	48
4	AFC Glebe United	24	12	4	8	64	49	15	37*
5	Wake Green Amateurs D	24	11	3	10	69	54	15	36
6	Lodgefield Park	24	10	6	8	49	56	-7	36
7	Birmingham Tigers	24	11	2	11	53	43	10	35
8	Cresconians	24	10	1	13	54	54	0	31
9	Silhill C	24	9	1	14	53	78	-25	28
10	CPA 2nds	24	8	2	14	53	60	-7	26
11	Coleshill North Warwick	24	5	7	12	38	52	-14	22
12	Premier B	24	3	4	17	34	115	-81	13
13	Lapal Athletic	24	1	4	19	23	84	-61	7

Division Four

		P	W	D	L	F	A	GD	PTS
1	Hampton	24	22	2	0	108	14	94	68
2	Handsworth GSOB B	24	13	4	7	56	41	15	43
3	Hall Green United	24	12	5	7	64	57	7	41
4	Sutton United B	24	12	3	9	68	48	20	39
5	BT	24	11	5	8	70	61	9	38
6	Village C	24	10	5	9	53	52	1	35
7	AFC Vesey	24	11	2	11	51	56	-5	35
8	Codsall High Old Boys	24	11	1	12	50	66	-16	34
9	Birmingham Citadel	24	10	1	13	64	57	7	31
10	Silhill D	24	9	2	13	63	79	-16	29
11	Old Wulfrunians B	24	5	5	14	61	83	-22	17*
12	Real Riverside A	24	5	5	14	34	65	-31	14*
13	Wood Wanderers	24	3	4	17	28	91	-63	10*

Division Five

		P	W	D	L	F	A	GD	PTS
1	Wednesbury Athletic	26	20	0	6	88	31	57	60
2	Sporting Sandwell	26	16	5	5	88	32	56	53
3	Old Horns	26	16	5	5	68	34	34	53
4	Coldfield Rangers	26	15	7	4	65	28	37	52
5	Norton Canes	26	13	6	7	83	53	30	45
6	Birmingham Medics B	26	11	6	9	56	50	6	39
7	Garden House Rangers	26	10	7	9	54	52	2	37
8	Peel	26	10	6	10	60	69	-9	36
9	Real Riverside B	26	9	3	14	41	38	3	30
10	AFC Solihull Res	26	9	3	14	45	68	-23	24*
11	Walsall Phoenix	26	6	5	15	52	74	-22	23
12	Whittington U21	26	5	5	16	27	82	-55	20
13	Handsworth GSOB C	26	5	4	17	26	78	-52	19
14	Smethwick Vaults	26	4	4	18	35	99	-64	16

Division Six

		P	W	D	L	F	A	GD	PTS
1	Aston	28	22	5	1	124	33	91	71
2	Wake Green Amateurs E	28	22	0	6	91	43	48	66
3	Bartley Reds United	28	19	4	5	101	55	46	58*
4	CT Shush U21	28	17	3	8	105	42	63	54
5	Coldlands U21	28	17	3	8	111	59	52	54
6	Sutton United 'C'	28	16	2	10	94	58	36	50
7	Gillway Boys U21	28	15	3	10	89	51	38	48
8	FC Birmingham	28	12	7	9	88	92	-4	43
9	Bluepool	28	10	6	12	77	90	-13	36
10	Village 'D'	28	9	3	16	67	90	-23	30
11	Silhill E	28	9	1	18	82	96	-14	28
12	Handsworth GSOB 'D'	28	9	3	16	62	102	-40	27*
13	FC Lozells	28	7	3	18	65	117	-52	21*
14	Whittington	28	2	2	24	26	131	-105	8
15	Olton Ravens U21	28	1	1	26	22	145	-123	4

BISHOP'S STORTFORD, STANSTED & DISTRICT LEAGUE

Premier Division

		P	W	D	L	F	A	GD	Pts
1	Atletico Corinthians	14	11	1	2	36	11	25	34
2	Alemite Athletic	14	10	1	3	49	24	25	31
3	Northolt	14	10	0	4	46	34	12	30
4	North Weald	14	8	1	5	42	35	7	25
5	Sheering	14	6	0	8	76	38	38	18
6	Town Mead	14	5	1	8	32	38	-6	16
7	Hatfield Heath	14	2	0	12	15	41	-26	6
8	Hertfordshire Rangers	14	2	0	12	19	94	-75	6

Division One

		P	W	D	L	F	A	GD	PTS
1	Alemite Athletic Res	19	13	5	1	48	15	33	44
2	Avondale Rangers	21	12	4	5	60	30	30	40
3	Lower Street	21	10	2	9	59	53	6	32
4	Heath Rovers Stansted Res	20	9	3	8	34	31	3	30
5	E F Lakers	20	7	5	8	37	55	-18	26
6	Albury	20	7	3	10	38	50	-12	24
7	S C Birchanger	21	6	3	12	40	53	-13	21
8	Sheering Res	16	2	1	13	21	50	-29	7

BLACKBURN & DISTRICT FOOTBALL COMBINATION

Premier Division

		P	W	D	L	F	A	GD	Pts
1	Longshaw	18	14	2	2	69	22	47	44
2	Euro Garages	18	14	1	1	56	16	40	44*
3	Rishton United	18	11	0	7	50	37	13	33
4	Cabin End	18	8	2	8	48	59	-11	20*
5	Clayton Park Rangers	18	6	0	11	44	58	-14	18*
6	Blackburn United	18	3	2	13	21	59	-38	11
7	Anchor	18	2	0	16	21	58	-37	6

Division Two

		P	W	D	L	F	A	GD	PTS
1	The Ivy Veterans	18	17	0	1	96	17	79	51
2	Lord Raglan	18	15	0	3	75	29	46	45
3	Walker Preston	18	10	1	7	51	53	-2	31
4	Rishton Rovers	18	9	2	7	52	42	10	29
5	Blackburn Eagles	18	9	2	7	60	55	5	29
6	The Lion	18	6	4	8	54	57	-3	19*
7	Blackburn United Res	18	5	3	10	37	50	-13	18
8	Blackburn Olympic	18	4	2	12	29	63	-34	14
9	Worth Avenue	18	4	4	10	51	76	-25	13*
10	Islington	18	1	2	15	22	85	-63	5

Division Three

		P	W	D	L	F	A	GD	PTS
1	Hole I'th Wall	18	18	0	0	113	19	94	54
2	Blackburn Elite	18	14	1	3	77	28	49	43
3	Great Harwood Town	18	11	2	5	62	30	32	35
4	St. Marys C.O.B.	18	5	2	11	27	62	-35	17
5	Abbey	18	4	2	12	36	74	-38	14
6	Globe Bullough Park	18	3	4	11	30	89	-59	13
7	Darwen Alexandra	18	2	1	15	35	78	-43	7

BOURNEMOUTH HAYWARD SATURDAY LEAGUE

Premier Division

		P	W	D	L	F	A	GD	Pts
1	Bournemouth Manor	18	14	2	2	73	31	42	44
2	Bournemouth Sports	18	12	3	3	55	25	30	39
3	Bournemouth Electric	18	10	1	7	43	35	8	31
4	Alderholt	18	8	4	6	46	28	18	28
5	Westover Bournemouth	18	8	4	6	30	25	5	28
6	Hamworthy Recreation Res	18	7	3	8	56	57	-1	21*
7	AFC Burton (Sat)	18	6	3	9	44	50	-6	21
8	Parley Sports BFA Team	18	4	6	8	49	61	-12	18
9	Merley Cobham Sports Res	18	5	2	11	32	62	-30	17
10	Redlynch and Woodfalls	18	1	2	15	22	76	-54	8*

Division One

		P	W	D	L	F	A	GD	PTS
1	Lower Parkstone CFC	20	14	3	3	78	38	40	45
2	Sway Res	20	12	4	4	62	33	29	40
3	Bournemouth Electric Res	20	13	1	6	58	30	28	40
4	Bournemouth Manor Res	20	10	7	3	58	31	27	37
5	Boldre Royals	20	9	1	10	47	60	-13	28
6	Bournemouth Sports Res	20	8	3	9	45	53	-8	27
7	Portcastrian	20	8	1	11	52	68	-16	25
8	Fordingbridge Turks	20	6	2	12	39	49	-10	20
9	Bisterne United Res	20	5	5	10	31	62	-31	20
10	Alderholt Res	20	5	3	12	34	64	-30	18
11	Queens Park Athletic	20	4	2	14	33	49	-16	14

Division Two

		P	W	D	L	F	A	GD	PTS
1	Mudeford Mens	22	17	2	3	71	31	40	53
2	AFC Burton Res	22	14	2	6	63	39	24	44
3	Bransgore United	22	13	2	7	51	45	6	41
4	Fordingbridge Turks Res	22	12	4	6	72	45	27	40
5	Westover Bournemouth Res	22	11	3	8	47	38	9	36
6	AFC Pennington	22	11	2	9	54	37	17	35
7	West Howe Saturday	22	9	3	10	58	62	-4	30
8	Poole Borough Res	22	9	1	12	46	55	-9	28
9	Bisterne United	22	7	1	14	59	75	-16	22
10	New Milton Eagles	22	7	1	14	40	67	-27	22
11	AFC Bransgore	22	6	1	15	49	80	-31	19
12	Talbot Rise United	22	4	2	16	37	73	-36	14

Division Three

		P	W	D	L	F	A	GD	PTS
1	Redlynch and Woodfalls Res	18	13	3	2	48	20	28	42
2	Bournemouth Manor A Team	18	11	3	4	51	19	32	36
3	Magpies (Saturday)	18	10	3	5	50	27	23	33
4	FC Barolo	18	8	5	5	28	37	-9	29
5	Cherry Bees	18	8	5	5	40	24	16	28*
6	Milford	18	2	1	15	16	55	-39	7
7	Burley	18	1	0	17	17	68	-51	3

LEAGUE TABLES

BRIGHTON, WORTHING & DISTRICT LEAGUE

Premier Division	P	W	D	L	F	A	GD	Pts
1 Worthing BCOB	16	13	0	3	51	25	26	39
2 Ovingdean	16	12	1	3	47	20	27	37
3 Hangleton	16	12	0	4	48	21	27	36
4 Sompting	16	10	3	3	60	20	40	33
5 Brighton Electricity	16	6	3	7	43	36	7	21
6 Worthing Dynamos	16	5	3	8	26	40	-14	18
7 Goring-by-Sea Cricket Club	16	5	0	11	35	31	4	15
8 Midway	16	3	1	12	20	28	-8	10
9 Ferring Res	16	0	1	15	9	118	-109	1

Southwick Rangers withdrew - record expunged.

Division One East	P	W	D	L	F	A	GD	Pts
1 Woodingdean Wanderers	16	14	2	0	64	24	40	44
2 Romans United	16	14	0	2	81	22	59	42
3 The View	16	8	2	6	43	34	9	26
4 Diversity United	16	7	3	6	44	31	13	24
5 The Lecturn	16	6	4	6	37	36	1	22
6 St Peters	16	5	1	10	26	46	-20	16
7 Boys Brigade Old Boys	16	4	2	10	32	44	-12	14
8 Hangleton FC Res	16	4	2	10	28	50	-22	14
9 Southwich Rangers Res	16	1	2	13	21	89	-68	5

Division One West	P	W	D	L	F	A	GD	Pts
1 FC MSR All Stars	22	18	2	2	80	23	57	56
2 AFC Sparta	22	15	4	3	105	32	73	49
3 Worthign Town Leisure 3	22	16	1	5	76	28	48	49
4 Worthing BCOB Res	22	14	2	6	69	44	25	44
5 Northbrook	22	11	4	7	59	55	4	37
6 Maybridge	22	9	6	7	71	51	20	33
7 Broadwater Athletic	22	10	2	10	66	56	10	32
8 AFC Boadwater	22	8	3	11	83	75	8	27
9 Goring Cricket Club Res	22	7	4	11	61	74	-13	25
10 St Marys	22	4	4	14	30	83	-53	16
11 Goring St Theresas	22	3	0	19	25	94	-69	9
12 Littlehampton Town Ath. Res	22	0	2	20	21	131	-110	2

BRISTOL AND DISTRICT LEAGUE

Senior Division	P	W	D	L	F	A	GD	Pts
1 Stapleton	24	22	0	2	108	24	84	66
2 Shirehampton Res	24	17	3	4	71	33	38	54
3 Bradley Stoke Town	24	16	2	6	91	38	53	50
4 Iron Acton	24	11	5	8	69	45	24	38
5 Cribbs 'A'	24	12	1	11	63	59	4	37
6 Bristol Barcelona	24	11	3	10	54	42	12	36
7 Patchway Town Res	24	11	3	10	50	51	-1	36
8 Pucklechurch Sports	24	9	3	12	48	50	-2	30
9 Lebeq (Saturday) FC.Res	24	9	2	13	38	94	-56	29
10 Mendip Broadwalk Res	24	8	3	13	55	67	-12	27
11 Wick Res	24	9	0	15	43	72	-29	27
12 Longwell Green Sports 'A'	24	4	3	17	33	88	-55	15
13 Brimsham Green	24	2	2	20	19	79	-60	8

Division One	P	W	D	L	F	A	GD	PTS
1 Hillfields Old Boys	26	23	2	1	111	27	84	71
2 Nicholas Wanderers	26	21	4	1	74	18	56	67
3 AEK Boco 'A'	26	19	2	5	82	33	49	59
4 AFC Mangotsfield	26	17	2	7	58	36	22	53
5 Rangeworthy	26	14	2	10	67	54	13	44
6 Henbury Res	26	12	4	10	72	50	22	40
7 Seymour United Res	26	12	2	12	54	70	-16	38
8 Greyfriars Athletic Res	26	10	2	14	60	73	-13	32
9 Made for Ever	26	10	1	15	53	64	-11	31
10 Totterdown United Res	26	10	0	16	45	63	-18	30
11 Soundwell Victoria	26	7	2	17	45	80	-35	23
12 Frys Club 'A'	26	6	2	18	54	88	-34	20
13 Hanham Athletic Res	26	4	2	20	15	78	-63	14
14 Frampton Athletic Res	26	3	1	22	33	89	-56	10

Division Two	P	W	D	L	F	A	GD	PTS
1 Yate Athletic	24	17	4	3	82	28	54	55
2 Stapleton Res	24	13	7	4	70	44	26	46
3 Sea Mills Park Res	24	14	4	6	70	48	22	46
4 Nicholas Wanderers Res	24	14	3	7	49	40	9	45
5 Tormarton	24	13	3	8	58	52	6	42
6 Chipping Sodbury Town 'A'	24	11	7	6	52	41	11	40
7 Old Sodbury Res	24	10	4	10	44	49	-5	34
8 Olveston United Res	24	8	5	11	48	51	-3	29
9 Bendix	24	7	7	10	42	47	-5	28
10 Hartcliffe	24	7	5	12	41	51	-10	26
11 Iron Acton Res	24	7	3	14	26	46	-20	24
12 Highridge United Res	24	4	3	17	34	94	-60	15
13 Horfield United	24	2	3	19	17	42	-25	9

Division Three	P	W	D	L	F	A	GD	PTS
1 Lawrence Rovers	26	20	3	3	95	37	58	63
2 Bradley Stoke Town Res	26	17	2	7	68	39	29	53
3 Bromley Heath United (Fishponds)	26	17	1	8	92	54	38	52
4 Bristol Barcelona Res	26	16	3	7	69	44	25	51
5 Hambrook Res	26	13	5	8	52	43	9	44
6 Westerleigh Sports	26	13	1	12	71	67	4	40
7 Roman Glass St George 'A'	26	10	6	10	49	54	-5	36
8 Greyfriars Athletic 'A'	26	9	4	13	72	81	-9	31
9 Talbot Knowle United	26	9	2	15	60	76	-16	29
10 Rangeworthy Res	26	8	4	14	53	58	-5	28
11 Mendip Broadwalk 'A'	26	8	4	14	44	88	-44	28
12 Wick 'A'	26	7	5	14	53	60	-7	26
13 Pucklechurch Sports Res	26	7	1	18	46	67	-21	22
14 Frys Club 'B'	26	5	5	16	37	93	-56	20

Division Four	P	W	D	L	F	A	GD	PTS
1 De Veys Res	21	17	0	4	64	22	42	51
2 Real Thornbury Res	21	12	2	7	70	34	36	38
3 Crosscourt United	21	12	1	8	75	49	26	37
4 Cribbs 'B'	21	11	3	7	50	47	3	36
5 Winterbourne United Res	21	10	0	11	50	40	10	30
6 Yate Athletic Res	21	7	6	8	44	58	-14	27
7 Cutters Friday	21	4	1	16	26	69	-43	13
8 DRG Frenchay Res	21	3	3	15	25	85	-60	12

Division Five	P	W	D	L	F	A	GD	PTS
1 Hillfields OB Res	20	18	1	1	98	24	74	55
2 Hanham Abbotonians	20	15	2	3	67	32	35	47
3 Nicholas Wanderers 'A'	19	14	0	5	74	38	36	42
4 Bristol Eagles	20	13	0	7	69	41	28	39
5 AFC Grace	19	10	0	9	55	54	1	30
6 Seymour United 'A'	20	9	1	10	34	57	-23	28
7 Bristol Barcelona 'A'	20	8	0	12	45	58	-13	24
8 Bradley Stoke Town 'A'	19	7	1	11	42	59	-17	22
9 Sea Mills Park 'A'	15	4	1	10	23	50	-27	13
10 Shaftesbury Crusade Res	19	2	0	17	33	68	-35	6
11 Greyfriars Athletic 'B'	19	2	0	17	19	78	-59	6

BRISTOL DOWNS ASSOCIATION FOOTBALL LEAGUE

Division One	P	W	D	L	F	A	GD	Pts
1 Sneyd Park	24	19	1	4	85	19	66	58
2 Old Elizabethans	24	18	2	4	80	33	47	56
3 Clifton St Vincents	24	17	2	5	70	38	32	53
4 Torpedo	24	15	5	4	85	24	61	50
5 Ashley	24	14	2	8	50	33	17	44
6 Saints Old Boys	24	13	3	8	49	35	14	42
7 Old Cliftonians	24	10	4	10	56	69	-13	34
8 AFC Bohemia	24	8	4	12	43	51	-8	28
9 Wellington Wanderers	24	7	2	15	38	57	-19	23
10 Portland Old Boys	24	6	5	13	45	68	-23	23
11 Jamaica Bell	24	4	5	15	31	54	-23	17
12 Sporting Greyhound	24	2	6	16	26	74	-48	12
13 St Andrews	24	2	1	21	24	127	-103	7

Division Two	P	W	D	L	F	A	GD	Pts
1 Jersey Rangers	22	17	3	2	95	27	68	54
2 Sneyd Park Res	22	16	4	2	67	28	39	52
3 Torpedo Res	22	12	5	5	54	26	28	41
4 Clifton St Vincents Res	22	11	4	7	55	34	21	37
5 DAC Beachcroft	22	9	6	7	54	46	8	33
6 Saints Old Boys Res	22	8	7	7	57	62	-5	31
7 Retainers	22	9	3	10	40	58	-18	30
8 Lion FC	22	6	5	11	43	54	-11	23
9 Clifton Rockets	22	6	5	11	51	63	-12	23
10 Tebby AFC	22	6	3	13	49	70	-21	21
11 Evergreen	22	5	3	14	46	79	-33	18
12 Bengal Tigers	22	2	2	18	31	95	-64	8

Division Three	P	W	D	L	F	A	GD	Pts
1 Old Cliftonians Res	26	19	3	4	85	32	53	60
2 Saints Old Boys A Team	26	18	3	5	88	46	42	57
3 Sneyd Park A Team	26	17	2	7	80	40	40	53
4 Torpedo A Team	26	16	2	8	59	32	27	50
5 Old Elizabethans Res	26	14	5	7	64	48	16	47
6 Club Corinthians	26	12	4	10	60	47	13	40
7 Greens Park Rangers	26	12	4	10	59	51	8	40
8 Clifton St Vincents A Team	26	12	1	13	71	68	3	37
9 Helios FC	26	10	3	13	56	54	2	33
10 Sporting Greyhound Res	26	9	5	12	46	57	-11	32
11 Ashley Res	26	9	3	14	49	54	-5	30
12 Portland Old Boys Res	26	8	1	17	55	80	-25	25
13 West Town United	26	5	3	18	37	98	-61	18
14 Clifton Rockets Res	26	1	1	24	33	135	-102	4

Division Four	P	W	D	L	F	A	GD	Pts
1 Jersey Rangers Res	26	15	8	3	73	39	34	53
2 Saints Old Boys B Team	26	16	4	6	66	43	23	52
3 Tebby AFC Res	26	16	4	6	71	51	20	52
4 Redcliffe Raiders	26	15	5	6	102	54	48	50
5 Southmead Hospital	26	13	4	9	68	49	19	43
6 Durdham Down Rangers	26	13	2	11	57	49	8	41
7 Retainers Res	26	11	5	10	39	52	-13	38
8 Torpedo B Team	26	9	6	11	49	50	-1	33
9 Sneyd Park B Team	26	8	8	10	49	45	4	32
10 Lion FC Res	26	10	2	14	46	64	-18	32
11 Cotham Old Boys	26	8	4	14	47	66	-19	28
12 Clifton Vale	26	7	5	14	58	63	-5	26
13 Clifton St Vincents B Team	26	7	1	18	43	86	-43	22
14 NCSF United	26	3	4	19	32	89	-57	13

BRISTOL PREMIER COMBINATION

Premier Division	P	W	D	L	F	A	GD	Pts
1 Cribbs Res	26	23	2	1	90	27	63	71
2 Wick	26	22	2	2	69	29	40	68
3 Olveston United	26	17	4	5	76	31	45	52*
4 Sea Mills Park	26	16	2	8	83	46	37	50
5 AEK Boco Res	26	10	5	11	56	57	-1	35
6 Hallen Res	26	10	4	12	58	66	-8	34
7 Winterbourne United	26	11	2	13	69	80	-11	32*
8 Totterdown United	26	9	5	12	42	56	-14	32
9 Talbot Knowle Utd	26	9	2	15	72	66	6	29
10 Lebeq (Saturday) FC	26	9	1	16	52	71	-19	28
11 Old Sodbury	26	8	3	15	58	80	-22	27
12 Longwell Green Res	26	8	3	15	49	74	-25	27
13 Highridge United	26	8	3	15	39	79	-40	27
14 Bitton Res	26	3	0	23	27	78	-51	9

Premier One	P	W	D	L	F	A	GD	Pts
1 Shaftesbury Crusade	24	20	0	4	67	28	39	60
2 Chipping Sodbury Town Res	24	19	2	3	94	41	53	59
3 Roman Glass/St George Res	24	15	2	7	77	46	31	47
4 Real Thornbury	24	14	4	6	107	34	73	46
5 St. Pancras	24	14	4	6	80	48	32	46
6 Hambrook	24	13	2	9	51	45	6	41
7 Seymour United	24	12	2	10	61	47	14	38
8 De Veys	24	11	4	9	76	66	10	37
9 Greyfriars Athletic	24	6	5	13	47	62	-15	23
10 Frampton Athletic	24	6	0	18	55	86	-31	18
11 Bristol Manor Farm Res	24	5	2	17	43	102	-59	17
12 Oldland Abbotonians Res	24	4	1	19	29	105	-76	13
13 D R G (Frenchay)	24	2	2	20	16	93	-77	8

BRISTOL & SUBURBAN LEAGUE

Premier Division One	P	W	D	L	F	A	GD	Pts
1 St Aldhelms	24	16	4	4	57	23	34	52
2 Sartan United	24	13	5	6	61	38	23	44
3 Bristol Bilbao	24	12	8	4	46	23	23	44
4 Easton Cowboys	24	12	6	6	39	34	5	42
5 AFC Mangotsfield	24	10	6	8	61	62	-1	36
6 Lawrence Weston	24	10	4	10	46	48	-2	34
7 Mangotsfield Sports	24	8	5	11	28	43	-15	29
8 Filton Athletic	24	8	4	12	43	41	2	28
9 Old Georgians	24	8	3	13	38	53	-15	27
10 Avonmouth	24	8	3	13	46	68	-22	27
11 Downend	24	7	5	12	43	50	-7	26
12 Ashton United	24	5	8	11	41	51	-10	23
13 Stoke Gifford United	24	5	7	12	35	50	-15	20

LEAGUE TABLES

Premier Division Two

		P	W	D	L	F	A	GD	Pts
1	Fishponds Old Boys	22	16	3	3	61	30	31	51
2	Rockleaze Rangers Res	22	15	4	3	75	28	47	49
3	Old Cothamians	22	14	1	7	55	34	21	43
4	Port of Bristol	22	12	6	4	42	28	14	41
5	Parson Street Old Boys	22	12	4	6	86	44	42	40
6	AFC Hartcliffe	22	9	2	11	54	61	-7	29
7	Almondsbury UWE Res	22	6	8	8	46	50	-4	26
8	Glenside 5 Old Boys	22	8	2	12	37	43	-6	26
9	Ridings High	22	7	5	10	36	49	-13	26
10	Cadbury Heath Res	22	7	4	11	47	40	7	25
11	AFC Brislington Res	22	5	0	17	29	97	-68	15
12	Kellaway Rangers	22	1	1	20	26	90	-64	4

Division One

		P	W	D	L	F	A	GD	Pts
1	AFC Mangotsfield Res	20	17	3	0	76	21	55	54
2	Bromley Heath United	20	17	1	2	86	13	73	52
3	Ashton United Res	20	15	2	3	70	26	44	47
4	Fry's Club OB	20	11	2	7	77	46	31	35
5	Rockleaze Rangers 'A'	20	8	5	7	60	43	17	29
6	St Aldhelms Res	20	7	5	8	57	44	13	26
7	Easton Cowboys Res	20	8	2	10	38	50	-12	26
8	Ridings High Res	20	5	3	12	38	55	-17	18
9	Avonmouth Res	20	3	2	15	28	78	-50	11
10	Bristol Telephones Res	20	3	1	16	24	121	-97	10
11	Wanderers	20	1	4	15	26	83	-57	7

Division Two

		P	W	D	L	F	A	GD	Pts
1	Wessex Wanderers	22	20	0	2	72	19	53	60
2	North Bristol United	22	15	2	5	93	45	48	47
3	Oldbury FC	22	13	3	6	104	45	59	42
4	Bristol Spartak	22	12	3	7	51	46	5	39
5	Stockwood Wanderers Res	22	11	4	7	58	44	14	37
6	Sartan United Res	22	11	2	9	64	39	25	35
7	Old Cothamians Res	22	9	1	12	60	72	-12	28
8	Fishponds Old Boys Res	22	7	6	9	45	40	5	27
9	Long Ashton Res	22	7	4	11	40	59	-19	25
10	AEK Boco Colts	22	5	2	15	36	104	-68	16
11	Hydez Futebol Clube	22	3	3	16	29	99	-70	12
12	Almondsbury UWE A	22	2	4	16	22	62	-40	10

Division Three

		P	W	D	L	F	A	GD	Pts
1	North Bristol Trust	20	16	1	3	78	25	53	49
2	Corinthian Sports	20	12	4	4	54	33	21	40
3	Kingswood	20	10	3	7	63	41	22	33
4	Keynsham Town A	20	10	3	7	55	48	7	33
5	Bromley Heath United Res	20	10	2	8	51	42	9	32
6	Park Knowle	20	7	6	7	47	49	-2	27
7	Little Stoke Res	20	7	5	8	36	52	-16	26
8	Rockleaze Rangers B	20	7	2	11	47	63	-16	23
9	Filton Athletic Res	20	5	6	9	25	51	-26	21
10	Old Georgians Res	20	4	4	12	26	54	-28	16
11	Glenside 5 Old Boys Res	20	4	0	16	29	53	-24	12

Division Four

		P	W	D	L	F	A	GD	Pts
1	Cosmos	20	19	0	1	103	30	73	57
2	Fry's Club OB Res	20	17	0	3	119	31	88	51
3	Bedminster Cricketers	20	15	1	4	106	35	71	46
4	Imperial Res	20	11	1	8	64	46	18	34
5	Stoke Gifford United Res	20	10	3	7	67	53	14	33
6	AFC Mangotsfield 'A'	20	8	2	10	52	51	1	26
7	RR Athletic	20	8	0	12	72	77	-5	24
8	Easton Cowboys A	20	7	1	12	55	77	-22	22
9	Brandon Sports	20	5	1	14	36	99	-63	16
10	Long Ashton 'A'	20	5	0	15	48	80	-32	15
11	Avonmouth 'A'	20	0	1	19	19	162	-143	1

Division Five

		P	W	D	L	F	A	GD	Pts
1	Oldbury FC Res	24	19	3	2	81	36	45	60
2	North Bristol Trust Res	24	18	2	4	62	24	38	56
3	Bristol Spartak Res	24	16	1	7	81	50	31	49
4	St Aldhelms A	24	15	3	6	73	39	34	48
5	Port of Bristol Res	24	14	3	7	76	38	38	45
6	Lockleaze Community	24	12	6	6	65	49	16	42
7	TC Sports	24	12	2	10	71	55	16	38
8	Parson Street OB Res	24	10	3	11	50	59	-9	33
9	Cosmos Res	24	7	1	16	35	73	-38	22
10	AFC Mangotsfield B	24	6	3	15	40	72	-32	21
11	Corinthian Sports Res	24	5	3	16	46	59	-13	18
12	Kellaway Rangers Res	24	2	4	18	31	74	-43	10
13	Wessex Wanderers Res	24	2	2	20	34	117	-83	8

CENTRAL & SOUTH NORFOLK LEAGUE

Division One

		P	W	D	L	F	A	GD	Pts
1	Tacolneston	20	19	0	1	91	21	70	57
2	Morley Village	20	15	1	4	59	28	31	46
3	Marham Wanderers	20	13	2	5	76	47	29	41
4	Hethersett Athletic	20	11	2	7	49	35	14	35
5	Attleborough Town A	20	10	2	8	50	36	14	32
6	Rockland Utd.	20	8	2	10	50	69	-19	26
7	North Elmham	20	7	2	11	45	60	-15	23
8	Watton Utd. Res.	20	5	3	12	36	59	-23	18
9	Sporle	20	5	1	14	55	81	-26	16
10	Mulbarton Wanderers A	20	4	2	14	31	71	-40	14
11	Shipdham	20	3	3	14	44	79	-35	12

Division Two

		P	W	D	L	F	A	GD	Pts
1	Dereham Taverners	18	16	1	1	79	14	65	49
2	Longham	18	16	0	2	106	26	80	48
3	Castle Acre Swifts Res.	18	11	1	6	63	40	23	34
4	Brandon Town Res.	18	9	2	7	42	45	-3	29
5	Yaxham	18	9	1	8	61	52	9	28
6	Bridgham Utd.	18	8	1	9	50	58	-8	25
7	Tacolneston Res.	18	8	0	10	59	58	1	24
8	Bar 33	18	6	1	11	42	62	-20	19
9	Bowthorpe Rovers	18	2	1	15	29	89	-60	7
10	Rampant Horse	18	1	0	17	18	105	-87	3

Division Three

		P	W	D	L	F	A	GD	Pts
1	Dereham Taverners Res.	18	15	1	2	79	31	48	46
2	Rockland Utd. Res.	18	12	3	3	66	36	30	39
3	Hingham Athletic Res.	18	12	2	4	74	39	35	38
4	Redgrave Rangers	18	12	2	4	54	34	20	38
5	Colkirk	18	8	2	8	48	49	-1	26
6	Gressenhall Res.*	18	7	2	9	43	58	-15	20
7	Cockers	18	5	3	10	41	47	-6	18
8	Narborough Res.	18	4	4	10	43	55	-12	16
9	Morley Village Res.	18	5	0	13	26	52	-26	15
10	Necton Res.	18	0	1	17	22	95	-73	1

CENTRAL MIDLANDS LEAGUE

Reserve Division

		P	W	D	L	F	A	GD	Pts
1	Sherwood Colliery Res	26	22	1	3	97	28	69	67
2	Hucknall Town Res	26	19	4	3	92	23	69	61
3	Staveley MW Res	26	16	5	5	95	23	72	53
4	Eastwood Community Res	26	16	2	8	76	45	31	50
5	Radford Res	26	15	0	11	67	40	27	45
6	Mickleover Sports Res	26	13	2	11	74	43	31	41
7	Mickleover RBL Res	26	12	4	10	45	52	-7	39*
8	Swanwick Pentrich Road Res	26	12	2	12	55	44	11	36*
9	Linby Colliery Res	26	11	2	13	54	63	-9	35
10	Holbrook Sports Res	26	11	1	14	57	93	-36	34
11	Harworth CI Res	26	8	2	16	41	72	-31	26
12	Holbrook St Michaels Res	26	5	4	17	36	103	-67	19
13	Belper Town Res	26	3	2	21	34	103	-69	11
14	Belper Utd Res	26	2	3	21	27	118	-91	8*

CHELTENHAM ASSOCIATION FOOTBALL LEAGUE

Division One

		P	W	D	L	F	A	GD	Pts
1	Falcons	18	14	0	4	45	23	22	42
2	Welland	18	13	3	2	42	20	22	42
3	Cheltenham Civil Service Res	18	11	3	4	51	27	24	36
4	Bishops Cleeve FC Thirds	18	7	4	7	32	35	-3	25
5	RSG	18	7	3	8	45	33	12	24
6	Staunton & Corse	18	6	4	8	37	42	-5	22
7	Leckhampton Rovers	18	6	3	9	33	38	-5	21
8	Upton Town	18	5	3	10	23	36	-13	18
9	Kings	18	5	2	11	27	40	-13	17
10	FC Barometrics Res	18	3	1	14	23	64	-41	10

Division Two

		P	W	D	L	F	A	GD	Pts
1	Andoversford	22	17	2	3	89	26	63	53
2	Dowty Dynamos	22	17	2	3	57	19	38	53
3	Whaddon United Res	22	17	1	4	73	29	44	51*
4	Newton	22	13	2	7	67	52	15	41
5	Tewkesbury Town	22	10	4	8	49	32	17	34
6	Shurdington Rovers	22	9	1	12	58	56	2	28
7	Cheltenham Civil Service 3rds	22	9	1	12	37	48	-11	28
8	Gloucester Elmleaze	22	7	3	12	37	57	-20	24
9	Prestbury Rovers	22	5	1	16	38	66	-28	16
10	Newlands Athletic FC	22	10	3	9	44	49	-5	12*
11	Southside Star FC Res	22	2	3	17	29	98	-69	8*
12	Brockworth Albion Res	22	4	1	17	34	80	-46	4*

Division Three

		P	W	D	L	F	A	GD	Pts
1	FC Barometrics Thirds	20	15	2	3	71	31	40	47
2	Bredon Res	20	14	3	3	51	19	32	45
3	Apperley	20	13	4	3	53	22	31	43
4	Hanley Swan	20	12	5	3	100	32	68	41
5	Gala Wilton Thirds	20	8	2	10	33	58	-25	26
6	Kings Res	20	6	5	9	32	53	-21	23
7	Bourton Rovers Thirds	20	6	4	10	50	39	11	21*
8	Falcons Res	20	5	6	9	36	42	-6	21
9	Fintan	20	6	2	12	39	52	-13	20
10	Andoversford Res	20	4	4	12	40	61	-21	16
11	Smiths Athletic Res	20	2	1	17	24	120	-96	7

Division Four

		P	W	D	L	F	A	GD	Pts
1	Cheltenham Civil Service 4ths	22	16	4	2	95	36	59	52
2	Windyridge Rovers	22	15	5	2	89	44	45	50
3	Charlton Rovers Res	22	15	3	4	92	33	59	48
4	FC Lakeside Res	22	14	2	6	53	46	7	44
5	Leckhampton Rovers Res	22	12	4	6	59	44	15	40
6	Pittville United	22	10	2	10	54	59	-5	32
7	Dowty Dynamos Res	22	8	4	10	52	59	-7	28
8	Cheltenham United	22	8	2	12	59	60	-1	26
9	Regency Town	22	8	1	13	57	91	-34	25
10	Apperley Res	22	5	4	13	37	76	-39	18*
11	Malvern Vale	22	2	2	18	36	88	-52	8
12	Staunton & Corse Res	22	2	1	19	34	81	-47	7

Division Five

		P	W	D	L	F	A	GD	Pts
1	St Pauls United	24	21	3	0	155	20	135	66
2	AFC Renegades	24	19	4	1	154	28	126	61
3	Prestbury Rovers Res	24	15	2	7	78	49	29	47
4	Welland Res	24	15	1	8	93	77	16	46
5	Gala Wilton Fourths	24	14	3	7	68	47	21	45
6	Fintan Res	24	13	0	11	71	82	-11	39
7	FC Brizen	24	10	4	10	65	78	-13	33*
8	Cheltenham Saracens Res	24	7	3	14	60	78	-18	24
9	Charlton Rovers Thirds	24	8	3	13	57	104	-47	24*
10	Malvern Vale Res	24	5	8	11	45	75	-30	23
11	Andoversford Thirds	24	4	3	17	39	91	-52	15
12	Winchcombe Town Res	24	2	4	18	36	109	-73	10
13	Regency Town Res	24	2	4	18	51	134	-83	6*

CHESTER & WIRRAL FOOTBALL LEAGUE

Premier Division

		P	W	D	L	F	A	GD	Pts
1	Blacon Youth FC	22	18	2	2	95	26	69	56
2	Birkenhead Town FC	22	18	2	2	47	23	24	56
3	Newton Athletic FC	22	15	1	6	85	52	33	46
4	Christleton Celtic FC	22	12	5	5	53	45	8	41
5	Shaftsbury Youth FC	22	12	4	6	59	41	18	40
6	Higher Bebington Kelma FC	22	10	3	9	48	44	4	33
7	Ellesmere Port FC	22	11	0	11	56	56	0	33
8	Lodge Bar FC	22	8	4	10	47	48	-1	28
9	MBNA FC	22	4	3	15	38	71	-33	15
10	Kelsall FC	22	3	3	16	35	81	-46	12
11	Chester Nomads III FC	22	2	4	16	34	70	-36	10
12	Ellesmere Port Town FC A	22	2	3	17	44	84	-40	9

Division One

		P	W	D	L	F	A	GD	PTS
1	AFC ESSAR	20	15	1	4	65	37	28	46
2	Franklyn's FC	20	14	1	5	78	27	51	43
3	Clubbies AFC	20	12	2	6	55	29	26	38
4	Cestrian Alex FC	20	11	4	5	76	39	37	37
5	New Ferry Rangers FC	20	11	3	6	64	57	7	36
6	Neston Nomads III FC	20	8	2	10	51	60	-9	26
7	Hoole Rangers FC	20	6	7	7	48	47	1	25
8	FC UBER	20	7	3	10	55	60	-5	24
9	Elton Athletic FC	20	6	2	12	26	53	-27	20
10	Eastham Athletic FC	20	4	2	14	27	62	-35	14
11	Whitby Athletic FC	20	0	5	15	21	95	-74	5

LEAGUE TABLES

Division Two

		P	W	D	L	F	A	GD	PTS
1	Sutton Athletic FC	24	22	0	2	113	19	94	66
2	St Saviours FC	24	20	0	4	94	34	60	60
3	Overpool Athletic FC	24	17	1	6	113	27	86	52
4	Upton JFC	24	14	3	7	76	39	37	45
5	Blacon Youth Res FC	24	12	4	8	84	36	48	40
6	Princes Villa FC	24	11	6	7	88	50	38	39
7	Chester Argyle FC	24	11	5	8	78	71	7	38
8	Orange Athletic Chester FC	24	8	5	11	63	52	11	29
9	Crossway FC	24	8	5	11	52	61	-9	29
10	Elton Rigger FC	24	7	1	16	41	80	-39	22
11	Beehive FC	24	6	1	17	38	127	-89	19
12	Hoole Youth FC	24	3	3	18	41	111	-70	12
13	Upton Rangers FC	24	0	0	24	24	198	-174	0

CIRENCESTER & DISTRICT LEAGUE

Division One

		P	W	D	L	F	A	GD	Pts
1	Intel FC	16	13	0	3	70	23	47	39
2	The Beeches	16	13	0	3	58	13	45	39
3	Hatherop	16	7	2	7	48	51	-3	23
4	Poulton	16	7	2	7	42	49	-7	23
5	South Cerney	16	7	1	8	41	53	-12	22
6	Ashton Keynes	16	6	3	7	34	46	-12	18*
7	Wheatsheaf	16	5	1	10	48	53	-5	16
8	Siddington	16	5	1	10	38	55	-17	16
9	Lechlade FC 87	16	3	2	11	30	66	-36	8*

Division Two

		P	W	D	L	F	A	GD	Pts
1	Blunsdon FC	16	11	3	2	60	30	30	36
2	Sherston	16	10	1	5	59	35	24	31
3	Oaksey	16	10	1	5	41	29	12	31
4	Minety	16	9	0	7	55	37	18	27
5	Kingshill Sports	16	8	1	7	51	40	11	25
6	Stratton United	16	7	2	7	46	39	7	23
7	Down Ampney	16	5	2	9	39	54	-15	17
8	Sherborne Harriers	16	2	3	11	25	61	-36	9
9	Ashton Keynes Res	16	2	3	11	14	65	-51	9

COLCHESTER & EAST ESSEX FOOTBALL LEAGUE

Premier Division

		P	W	D	L	F	A	GD	Pts
1	Cavendish	18	16	0	2	70	19	51	48
2	Harwich Rangers	18	13	2	3	64	30	34	38*
3	Tollesbury	18	10	2	6	57	45	12	32
4	Oyster	18	8	3	7	55	51	4	27
5	Nayland Rangers	18	8	3	7	43	42	1	27
6	New Field	18	7	4	7	47	40	7	25
7	Mistley	18	5	2	11	25	53	-28	20*
8	Wormingford Wanderers Res	18	5	3	10	48	63	-15	18
9	Sporting Rebels	18	4	1	13	40	78	-38	13
10	Langham Lodgers	18	2	4	12	32	60	-28	10

Division One

		P	W	D	L	F	A	GD	Pts
1	Tavern	16	12	2	2	55	21	34	38
2	Tiptree Park Res	16	12	1	3	55	25	30	37
3	Riverbank Athletic	16	11	2	3	56	22	34	35
4	Abbey Fields	16	10	3	3	53	18	35	33
5	Cavendish Res	16	4	4	8	29	42	-13	19*
6	Stoke by Nayland	16	6	1	9	28	42	-14	19
7	New Field Res	16	4	0	12	34	66	-32	12
8	Marks Tey	16	3	1	12	23	65	-42	10
9	Oyster Res	16	2	2	12	34	66	-32	8

CORNWALL COMBINATION

		P	W	D	L	F	A	GD	Pts
1	Carharrack	38	30	6	2	147	44	103	98*
2	Ludgvan	38	26	8	4	113	40	73	86
3	St Agnes	38	26	4	8	146	60	86	82
4	St Ives Town	38	22	11	5	130	53	77	77
5	St Day	38	21	5	12	100	78	22	68
6	Helston Athletic Res	38	20	3	15	115	67	48	63
7	Perranwell	38	17	6	15	82	76	6	59*
8	Hayle	38	17	4	17	93	102	-9	55
9	St Just	38	15	6	17	84	99	-15	51
10	Porthleven Res	38	15	5	18	79	77	2	50
11	Goonhavern Athletic	38	15	5	18	60	78	-18	50
12	Penryn Athletic Res	38	12	9	17	56	75	-19	47*
13	Perranporth	38	14	4	20	62	101	-39	46
14	Redruth United	37	13	4	20	60	68	-8	43
15	Holman SC	38	12	6	20	61	91	-30	42
16	RNAS Culdrose	38	14	0	24	61	101	-40	42
17	Illogan RBL Res	38	11	8	19	72	110	-38	40*
18	Falmouth Town Res	38	11	1	26	54	118	-64	34
19	Mullion	38	8	9	21	47	87	-40	32*
20	Newquay Res	37	4	8	25	40	137	-97	1*

CRAVEN & DISTRICT FOOTBALL LEAGUE

Premier Division

		P	W	D	L	F	A	GD	Pts
1	Skipton LMS	20	18	2	0	82	29	53	56
2	Trawden Celtic	20	13	5	2	47	24	23	44
3	Settle Utd	20	13	4	3	49	17	32	43
4	Rolls	20	11	2	7	81	44	37	35
5	Grassington Utd	20	10	4	6	44	41	3	34
6	Wilsden Athletic	20	9	2	9	45	49	-4	29
7	Silsden Whitestar	20	6	4	10	34	42	-8	22
8	Cross Hills	20	6	1	13	34	63	-29	19
9	Earby Town	20	4	1	15	27	57	-30	13
10	Gargrave	20	3	2	15	28	59	-31	11
11	Grindleton	20	3	1	16	21	67	-46	10

Division One

		P	W	D	L	F	A	GD	Pts
1	Cowling	20	15	4	1	75	29	46	49
2	Rolls Res	20	13	1	6	58	35	23	40
3	Manningham Allstars JFC	20	11	1	8	66	42	24	34
4	Carleton	20	9	5	6	57	41	16	32
5	Broomhill	20	10	2	8	43	41	2	32
6	Skipton Town	20	10	1	9	59	41	18	31
7	AFC Colne	20	9	4	7	58	49	9	31
8	Chatburn	20	8	2	10	47	50	-3	26
9	Bradley	20	5	5	10	42	75	-33	20
10	Bingley Town First	20	4	5	11	36	75	-39	17
11	Oxenhope Recreation	20	0	2	18	25	88	-63	2

Division Two	P	W	D	L	F	A	GD	Pts
1 Settle Utd Res	22	17	1	4	73	34	39	52
2 Hellifield Sports FC	22	14	4	4	90	41	49	46
3 Cononley Sports	22	11	5	6	71	55	16	38
4 Salts	22	11	3	8	73	55	18	36
5 Trawden Celtic Res	22	11	3	8	78	73	5	36
6 Pendle Renegades Res	22	10	4	8	47	61	-14	34
7 Grassington Utd Res	22	9	4	9	66	67	-1	31
8 AFC Barnoldswick	22	9	2	11	65	58	7	29
9 Barnoldswick Barons	22	7	3	12	49	72	-23	24
10 Skipton Town Res	22	6	4	12	60	80	-20	22
11 Cross Hills Res	22	6	3	13	42	53	-11	21
12 Otley Town	22	3	0	19	33	98	-65	9

Division Three	P	W	D	L	F	A	GD	Pts
1 Ilkley	23	17	3	3	117	44	73	54
2 Silsden Whitestar Res	24	17	3	4	86	39	47	54
3 Barlick Wanderers	24	14	4	6	93	53	40	46
4 Salts Res	22	14	1	7	88	25	63	43
5 Horton	24	14	0	10	54	53	1	42
6 Bingley Town Res	24	13	0	11	72	74	-2	39
7 Cowling Res	24	11	2	11	66	64	2	35
8 Settle Utd 3rds FC	24	10	3	11	53	75	-22	33
9 Broomhill Res	24	10	3	11	49	99	-50	33
10 Sutton	23	8	4	11	71	57	14	28
11 Addingham	24	6	3	15	55	66	-11	21
12 Earby Town Res	24	3	1	20	32	137	-105	10
13 Bradley Res	24	2	3	19	44	94	-50	9

CREWE & DISTRICT FOOTBALL LEAGUE

Premier Division	P	W	D	L	F	A	GD	Pts
1 Winsford Saxons FC	20	14	4	2	80	38	42	46
2 Sandbach Town	20	13	5	2	53	33	20	44
3 Barnton Wanderers	20	10	4	6	46	31	15	34
4 Tarvin	20	10	4	6	52	40	12	34
5 Mary Dendy	20	11	1	8	45	49	-4	34
6 Over 3 Grange FC	20	8	2	10	37	47	-10	26
7 Sandbach Curshaws	20	7	4	9	59	52	7	25
8 Winsford United Res	20	7	4	9	36	34	2	25
9 Winnington Avenue 1994	20	6	5	9	36	40	-4	23
10 Tarporley Victoria Res	20	3	3	14	20	48	-28	12
11 Winnington Avenue	20	2	2	16	28	80	-52	8

CROOK & DISTRICT LEAGUE

Division One	P	W	D	L	F	A	GD	Pts
1 Shildon Railway	16	12	1	3	52	16	36	37
2 Bowes	16	10	5	1	45	21	24	35
3 Wear Valley	16	8	2	6	36	24	12	26
4 Middlestone Moor Masons Arms	16	6	5	5	39	29	10	23
5 Howden-Le-Wear Australian	16	7	1	8	34	39	-5	22
6 Willington W.M.C.	16	5	3	8	26	46	-20	18
7 Alston Moor Sports Club	16	5	4	7	27	32	-5	16*
8 Evenwood Town	16	3	3	10	20	50	-30	12
9 Bishop Auckland Hogans	16	3	2	11	36	58	-22	11

Division Two	P	W	D	L	F	A	GD	Pts
1 Heighington	16	13	2	1	98	27	71	41
2 Newton Aycliffe Navy Club	16	13	2	1	61	20	41	38*
3 Darlington Travellers Rest	16	9	4	3	50	32	18	31
4 Wolsingham	16	9	3	4	50	31	19	30
5 Crook Town Wanderers	16	5	2	9	36	52	-16	17
6 Barnard Castle Glaxo Rangers	16	6	2	8	33	53	-20	17*
7 Stanhope Town S&S Club	16	3	1	12	28	68	-40	10
8 Ferryhill Town	16	4	0	12	47	67	-20	9*
9 Wearhead United	16	1	2	13	15	68	-53	2*

DEVON & EXETER FOOTBALL LEAGUE

Premier Division	P	W	D	L	F	A	GD	Pts
1 Honiton Town	28	21	6	1	101	22	79	69
2 Newtown	28	23	0	5	87	39	48	69
3 Elmore	28	21	1	6	81	29	52	64
4 Heavitree United	28	19	2	7	80	34	46	59
5 Okehampton Argyle	28	15	6	7	77	54	23	51
6 Seaton Town	28	13	4	11	53	53	0	43
7 Feniton	28	11	4	13	74	76	-2	37
8 Beer Albion	28	11	4	13	62	68	-6	37
9 Topsham Town	28	5	13	6	67	61	6	35
10 Upottery	28	10	4	14	49	53	-4	34
11 Clyst Valley	28	8	4	16	47	85	-38	28
12 Newton St Cyres	28	7	5	16	54	87	-33	26
13 Exmouth Amateurs	28	8	3	17	31	67	-36	26*
14 Hatherleigh Town	28	5	4	19	39	68	-29	19
15 Bow Amateur Athletic Club	28	0	4	24	34	140	-106	4

Division One	P	W	D	L	F	A	GD	Pts
1 Cronies	20	17	2	1	87	15	72	53
2 University of Exeter Res	20	11	5	4	45	26	19	38
3 Exmouth Town Res	20	10	5	5	46	31	15	35
4 Witheridge Res	20	11	2	7	50	45	5	35
5 Sidmouth Town Res	20	10	4	6	48	35	13	34
6 Lyme Regis	20	9	2	9	48	38	10	29
7 Colyton	20	8	3	9	43	45	-2	27
8 Wellington Town Res	20	5	4	11	27	57	-30	19
9 Alphington Res	20	3	6	11	28	56	-28	15
10 Willand Rovers Res	20	3	5	12	29	62	-33	14
11 Bickleigh	20	2	4	14	22	63	-41	10.

Division Two	P	W	D	L	F	A	GD	Pts
1 Lapford	26	21	4	1	111	20	91	67
2 Cullompton Rangers 2nds	26	18	3	5	86	32	54	57
3 Chagford	26	16	2	8	81	54	27	50
4 Heavitree United 2nds	26	14	3	9	84	62	22	45
5 Dawlish United	26	14	2	10	53	50	3	44
6 University 3rds	26	13	2	11	65	52	13	41
7 Woodbury	26	11	6	9	62	52	10	39
8 Axmouth United	26	12	2	12	51	61	-10	38
9 Dawlish	26	9	3	14	60	78	-18	30
10 Halwill	26	8	4	14	45	67	-22	28
11 Newtown 2nds	26	8	2	16	52	75	-23	26
12 Tipton St John	26	6	5	15	45	78	-33	23
13 Lympstone	26	7	2	17	40	91	-51	23
14 Budleigh Salterton 2nds	26	4	2	20	25	88	-63	13*

LEAGUE TABLES

Division Three

		P	W	D	L	F	A	GD	Pts
1	Perry Street	20	17	2	1	110	26	84	53
2	University 4ths	20	14	2	4	64	25	39	44
3	Bampton	20	13	3	4	92	40	52	42
4	Axminster Town 2nds	20	10	5	5	84	49	35	35
5	Honiton Town 2nds	20	9	3	8	54	58	-4	30
6	East Budleigh	20	9	2	9	53	52	1	29
7	Newton Poppleford	20	8	0	12	60	66	-6	24
8	Tedburn St Mary	20	7	2	11	48	65	-17	23
9	Clyst Valley 2nds	20	4	4	12	38	71	-33	16
10	Exmouth Amateurs 2nds	20	5	2	13	27	87	-60	16*
11	Culm United	20	1	1	18	20	111	-91	4

Division Four

		P	W	D	L	F	A	GD	Pts
1	Kentisbeare	24	21	3	0	61	18	43	66
2	Thorverton	24	18	4	2	87	32	55	58
3	Uplowman Athletic	24	15	3	6	74	33	41	48
4	University 5ths	24	12	4	8	68	52	16	40
5	Ottery St Mary	24	10	6	8	51	49	2	36
6	Priory	24	11	2	11	69	61	8	35
7	Countess Wear Dynamoes	24	11	0	13	54	61	-7	33
8	Sandford	24	9	5	10	57	53	4	32
9	Pinhoe	24	9	3	12	49	61	-12	30
10	Otterton	24	9	3	12	44	56	-12	30
11	Morchard Bishop	24	5	1	18	43	75	-32	15*
12	St Martins 2nds	24	3	4	17	25	84	-59	12*
13	Sampford Peverell	24	2	4	18	29	76	-47	10

Division Five

		P	W	D	L	F	A	GD	Pts
1	Royal Oak	24	22	2	0	117	30	87	68
2	Crediton United 2nds	24	20	3	1	105	25	80	63
3	Whipton & Pinhoe	24	16	3	5	104	42	62	51
4	Winchester	24	15	3	6	83	52	31	48
5	Millwey Rise	24	11	1	12	57	52	5	34
6	South Zeal United	24	9	1	14	58	75	-17	27*
7	North Tawton	24	7	6	11	48	65	-17	27
8	Beer Albion 2nds	24	8	2	14	55	86	-31	26
9	Newton St Cyres 2nds	24	6	7	11	37	80	-43	25
10	Feniton 2nds	24	7	2	15	39	73	-34	22*
11	Starcross Generals	24	6	4	14	47	89	-42	22
12	Alphington 3rds	24	4	5	15	42	89	-47	16*
13	Awliscombe United	24	2	7	15	30	64	-34	13

Division Six

		P	W	D	L	F	A	GD	Pts
1	Winkleigh	24	22	1	1	129	38	91	67
2	Exwick Village	24	17	2	5	98	46	52	53
3	Lyme Regis 2nds	24	17	0	7	76	31	45	51
4	Central FC	24	14	3	7	84	57	27	45
5	Halwill 2nds	24	13	3	8	80	56	24	42
6	Hemyock	24	13	1	10	82	48	34	40
7	Offwell Rangers	24	12	4	8	61	45	16	39*
8	Elmore 2nds	24	12	1	11	73	53	20	37
9	Tivvy Park Rangers	24	7	2	15	51	76	-25	23
10	Stoke Hill	24	7	2	15	58	100	-42	22*
11	Dunkeswell Rovers	24	5	3	16	32	85	-53	18
12	Hatherleigh Town 2nds	24	3	2	19	32	124	-92	10*
13	Silverton	24	1	2	21	36	133	-97	5

Division Seven

		P	W	D	L	F	A	GD	Pts
1	Ilminster Town 2nds	22	18	2	2	69	28	41	56
2	Cranbrook	22	17	3	2	81	24	57	54
3	Wellington Town 3rds	22	16	3	3	72	46	26	51
4	Sidmouth Town 3rds	22	13	3	6	79	42	37	42
5	Exmouth Spartans	22	12	1	9	61	57	4	37
6	Bickleigh 2nds	22	9	2	11	60	60	0	29
7	K&M Polonia Exeter	22	7	4	11	42	56	-14	25
8	Cheriton Fitzpaine	22	7	2	13	48	62	-14	23
9	Woodbury 2nds	22	7	2	13	44	77	-33	23
10	Seaton Town 2nds	22	6	3	13	42	45	-3	20*
11	Colyton 2nds	22	3	4	15	37	71	-34	13
12	H T Dons	22	2	1	19	26	93	-67	7

Division Eight

		P	W	D	L	F	A	GD	Pts
1	Upottery 2nds	22	17	3	2	77	18	59	54
2	Bravehearts	22	16	4	2	99	28	71	52
3	Axminster Town 3rds	22	14	3	5	76	37	39	44*
4	Queens Head	22	11	4	7	63	54	9	37
5	Bampton 2nds	22	11	3	8	69	50	19	36
6	Kentisbeare 2nds	22	9	7	6	77	53	24	34
7	Lapford 2nds	22	11	1	10	53	37	16	34
8	Newton Poppleford 2nds	22	8	2	12	63	78	-15	26
9	Amory Green Rovers	22	5	5	12	41	70	-29	20
10	Seven Stars Kennford	22	4	1	17	35	98	-63	12*
11	Bradninch	22	4	3	15	37	93	-56	11*
12	Sandford 2nds	22	3	2	17	26	100	-74	11

Division Nine

		P	W	D	L	F	A	GD	Pts
1	St Martins 3rds	18	11	4	3	42	26	16	37
2	Witheridge 3rds	18	11	2	5	59	33	26	35
3	Chagford 2nds	18	11	1	6	60	33	27	34
4	Millwey Rise 2nds	18	8	5	5	40	27	13	29
5	East Budleigh 2nds	18	8	5	5	42	33	9	29
6	Honiton Town 3rds	18	9	2	7	55	47	8	29
7	Tedburn St Mary 2nds	18	6	3	9	40	48	-8	21
8	Amory Green Rovers 2nds	18	6	2	10	41	50	-9	20
9	Central FC 2nds	18	4	3	11	29	59	-30	15
10	Feniton 3rds	18	2	1	15	27	79	-52	7

DORSET FOOTBALL LEAGUE

Senior

		P	W	D	L	F	A	GD	Pts
	Senior Division	P	W	D	L	F	A	GD	PTS
1	Witchampton United	26	21	3	2	82	28	54	66
2	Shaftesbury Town Res	26	20	3	3	77	35	42	63
3	Dorchester Sports Res	26	17	4	5	78	41	37	55
4	Milborne Port	26	12	6	8	64	48	16	42
5	Chickerell United	26	13	3	10	62	53	9	42
6	Corfe Mullen United	26	10	8	8	57	47	10	38
7	Allendale	26	12	1	13	62	61	1	37
8	Portland United Res	26	11	3	12	58	55	3	36
9	Wincanton Town Res	26	9	5	12	53	66	-13	32
10	Poole Borough	26	8	2	16	44	66	-22	26
11	Piddletrenthide United	26	7	4	15	39	67	-28	24*
12	Westland Sports Res	26	7	3	16	36	69	-33	23*
13	Blandford United Res	26	4	5	17	34	66	-32	16*
14	Boscombe Polonia	26	4	4	18	36	80	-44	16

Division One

		P	W	D	L	F	A	GD	PTS
1	Corfe Castle	26	19	3	4	99	39	60	60
2	Broadstone	26	19	2	5	69	37	32	59
3	AFC Blandford	26	18	4	4	89	39	50	58
4	Wareham Rangers Res	26	16	5	5	89	47	42	53
5	Mere Town Res	26	14	4	8	75	45	30	46
6	Canford United	26	11	6	9	54	47	7	39
7	Tisbury	26	11	2	13	50	61	-11	34*
8	Wool & Winfrith	26	9	6	11	61	71	-10	33
9	Swanage Town & Herston Res	26	8	5	13	47	69	-22	28*
10	Parley Sports Res	26	9	1	16	26	48	-22	28
11	Balti Sports Res	26	8	1	17	51	75	-24	24*
12	Weymouth A	26	7	3	16	62	94	-32	24
13	Portland United Youth	26	6	5	15	48	74	-26	19*
14	Portland Town	26	2	3	21	31	105	-74	9

Division Two

		P	W	D	L	F	A	GD	PTS
1	Allendale Res	20	15	1	4	69	23	46	46
2	Stalbridge	20	12	3	5	60	32	28	39
3	Piddlehinton Utd	20	12	3	5	49	32	17	39
4	Broadmayne	20	12	2	6	71	39	32	38
5	Maiden Newton & Cattistock	20	12	2	6	42	31	11	38
6	Portesham Utd	20	6	6	8	31	38	-7	24
7	Sturminster Newton United Res	20	7	4	9	39	50	-11	24*
8	Owermoigne	20	6	4	10	36	57	-21	21*
9	Broadstone Res	20	5	2	13	35	54	-19	17
10	Chickerell Utd Res	20	4	3	13	30	66	-36	15
11	Milborne Port Res	20	3	2	15	22	62	-40	8*

Division Three

		P	W	D	L	F	A	GD	PTS
1	Sturminster Marshall	22	20	1	1	114	18	96	61
2	Okeford United	22	16	3	3	87	28	59	51
3	Allendale A	22	12	3	7	72	54	18	39
4	Marnhull	22	10	6	6	69	53	16	36
5	AFC Blandford Res	22	10	3	9	68	50	18	33
6	Handley Sports	22	10	3	9	60	60	0	32*
7	Donhead Utd	22	8	3	11	62	60	2	27
8	South Cheriton United	21	8	2	11	47	67	-20	23*
9	Pimperne Sports Society	22	6	4	12	47	70	-23	22
10	Portland Town A	22	6	3	13	39	80	-41	21
11	Corfe Mullen United Res	22	4	5	13	33	82	-49	17
12	Wool & Winfrith Res	21	3	0	18	27	103	-76	9

Division Four

		P	W	D	L	F	A	GD	PTS
1	Bridport A	22	19	2	1	104	20	84	59
2	Swanage RBL	22	17	2	3	90	33	57	52*
3	Corfe Castle Res	22	16	4	2	65	26	39	52
4	Chickerell United A	22	13	2	7	75	54	21	41
5	Portesham United Res	22	9	4	9	61	65	-4	31
6	Portland Town B	22	9	3	10	49	61	-12	30
7	Lytchett and Upton Red Triangle	22	8	2	12	55	72	-17	26
8	Shillingstone	22	6	3	13	56	78	-22	21
9	Wincanton Town A	22	7	1	14	53	64	-11	20*
10	Marnhull Res	22	6	2	14	55	65	-10	19*
11	Wool & Winfrith A	22	5	1	16	43	99	-56	12*
12	Crossways Spitfires	22	3	2	17	23	92	-69	11

DUCHY LEAGUE

Premier Division

		P	W	D	L	F	A	GD	Pts
1	St Minver	22	18	1	3	84	24	60	55
2	St Stephen	22	14	5	3	101	45	56	47
3	Torpoint Athletic Thirds	22	14	1	7	88	48	40	43
4	LC Phoenix	22	13	4	5	52	29	23	43
5	Saltash United Thirds	22	11	3	8	72	52	20	36
6	North Petherwin	22	9	7	6	60	44	16	34
7	Lostwithiel	22	10	2	10	56	59	-3	32
8	Edgcumbe FC	22	9	4	9	65	49	16	31
9	Biscovey	22	9	2	11	70	70	0	20*
10	Foxhole Stars	22	6	2	14	51	56	-5	20
11	Pelynt	22	2	2	18	23	124	-101	8
12	Callington Town Thirds	22	0	1	21	23	145	-122	-2*

Division One

		P	W	D	L	F	A	GD	PTS
1	St Dennis Res	22	19	2	1	83	38	45	59
2	Veryan	22	17	1	4	69	27	42	52
3	Gerrans & St Mawes Utd	22	16	1	5	81	39	42	49
4	Sticker Res	22	14	3	5	68	30	38	45
5	St Mawgan	22	13	3	6	57	43	14	42
6	Gunnislake	22	7	3	12	52	84	-32	24
7	AFC Bodmin	22	6	5	11	44	43	1	23
8	Holywell and Cubert	22	7	2	13	50	71	-21	23
9	St Dominick	22	5	4	13	44	60	-16	19
10	Grampound	22	6	1	15	41	58	-17	19
11	St Columb Major	22	5	3	14	38	70	-32	18
12	Altarnun	22	2	2	18	37	101	-64	5*

Division Two

		P	W	D	L	F	A	GD	PTS
1	Godolphin Atlantic Res	22	18	1	3	91	32	59	55
2	Boscastle	22	14	1	7	57	43	14	43
3	North Hill	22	12	5	5	73	38	35	41
4	Queens Rangers	22	11	4	7	60	43	17	37
5	St Merryn	22	11	3	8	53	44	9	36
6	St Newlyn East	22	11	1	10	79	62	17	34
7	St Cleer	22	10	3	9	57	59	-2	33
8	Tregrehan Mills	22	7	3	12	56	65	-9	27*
9	St Breward	22	6	6	10	44	62	-18	24
10	Tintagel	22	4	5	13	45	78	-33	17
11	Mevagissey Res	22	7	1	14	44	85	-41	16*
12	Lifton	22	3	3	16	43	91	-48	9*

Division Three

		P	W	D	L	F	A	GD	PTS
1	St Minver Res	22	16	2	4	84	37	47	50
2	Lanivet Inn	22	15	2	5	81	36	45	47
3	Pensilva Res	22	15	1	6	85	45	40	46
4	Gorran	22	13	6	3	101	43	58	45
5	Calstock	22	13	4	5	72	52	20	37*
6	Saltash United Fourths	22	11	4	7	62	50	12	37
7	Stoke Climsland	22	10	1	11	60	57	3	31
8	Delabole United	22	7	2	13	48	65	-17	20*
9	High Street	22	5	4	13	46	83	-37	19
10	Grampound Res	22	6	1	15	44	104	-60	19
11	North Petherwin Res	22	4	3	15	46	86	-40	15
12	Tregony	22	1	2	19	38	109	-71	2*

Division Four

		P	W	D	L	F	A	GD	PTS
1	Dobwalls Res	18	14	3	1	67	23	44	45
2	Roche Res	18	12	2	4	43	28	15	38
3	AFC Par	18	10	3	5	55	42	13	33
4	Foxhole Stars Res	18	10	2	6	52	38	14	32
5	Rame Peninsula FC	18	9	3	6	60	34	26	27*
6	St Stephen Res	18	7	2	9	34	44	-10	23
7	St Dennis Thirds	18	7	0	11	34	41	-7	21
8	Lanreath Res	18	6	2	10	28	52	-24	20
9	St Mawgan Res	18	4	0	14	26	58	-32	12
10	St Teath	18	2	1	15	22	61	-39	4*

LEAGUE TABLES

Division Five

		P	W	D	L	F	A	GD	PTS
1	Lamerton Community FC	20	15	3	2	89	36	53	48
2	St Eval Spitfires	20	13	3	4	99	42	57	42
3	Liskeard Athletic Thirds	20	14	1	5	63	27	36	40*
4	Southgate Seniors	20	12	3	5	72	35	37	36*
5	Wadebridge Town Thirds	20	11	1	8	56	52	4	34
6	Lostwithiel Res	20	8	7	5	45	36	9	31
7	Polperro	20	8	5	7	63	56	7	29
8	Week St Mary	20	7	1	12	37	60	-23	22
9	Looe Town Res	20	6	2	12	23	40	-17	20
10	Boscastle Res	20	2	0	18	18	82	-64	6
11	St Anns Chapel	20	1	0	19	16	115	-99	3

DURHAM FOOTBALL ALLIANCE COMBINATION

		P	W	D	L	F	A	GD	Pts
1	Wheatley Hill WMC	12	8	2	2	44	21	23	26
2	Sunderland Hall Farm Glasshus	12	8	1	3	40	18	22	25
3	West Auckland Tunns	12	6	1	5	25	19	6	19
4	Bishop Auckland Res	12	5	3	4	21	23	-2	18
5	Durham City Res	12	4	3	5	28	29	-1	15
6	Blackhill & Ebbchester	12	2	5	5	33	42	-9	11
7	Billingham	12	0	3	9	15	54	-39	3

EAST BERKSHIRE FOOTBALL LEAGUE

Premier Division

		P	W	D	L	F	A	GD	Pts
1	Langley FC	18	11	4	3	43	24	19	37
2	FC Beaconsfield	18	11	3	4	37	23	14	36
3	Delaford	18	10	5	3	68	41	27	35
4	Richings Park	18	9	3	6	41	38	3	30
5	Chalvey (WMC) Sports Res	18	9	2	7	41	51	-10	29
6	Old Windsor	18	8	2	8	40	47	-7	26
7	Iver Heath Rovers	18	7	2	9	40	31	9	23
8	Slough Heating Laurencians	18	5	3	10	43	46	-3	18
9	Eton Wick	18	3	3	12	27	52	-25	12
10	KS Gryf	18	3	1	14	30	57	-27	10

Division One

		P	W	D	L	F	A	GD	PTS
1	Frontline	16	12	2	2	53	19	34	38
2	Stoke Poges Saints FC	16	10	3	3	48	27	21	33
3	Slough Heating Laurencians Res	16	9	0	7	34	47	-13	27
4	Iver Heath Rovers Res	16	8	1	7	47	20	27	25
5	Richings Park Res	16	7	3	6	31	33	-2	24
6	Windsor Great Park	16	6	1	9	35	36	-1	19
7	The Swan FC	16	5	3	8	35	35	0	18
8	Real Saracens	16	4	3	9	36	53	-17	15
9	Langley Galaxy	16	3	0	13	26	75	-49	9

Division Two

		P	W	D	L	F	A	GD	PTS
1	Signcraft FC	14	11	2	1	51	21	30	35
2	FC Slough	14	11	1	2	56	26	30	34
3	Eton Wick Res	14	6	2	6	36	36	0	20
4	Robertswood	14	5	4	5	36	31	5	19
5	Phoenix Old Boys FC	14	5	2	7	38	34	4	17
6	Willow Wanderers	14	4	3	7	29	39	-10	15
7	Hillingdon Legion FC	14	4	2	8	30	40	-10	14
8	Falcons	14	1	2	11	18	67	-49	5

Division Three

		P	W	D	L	F	A	GD	PTS
1	KS Gryf Res	20	15	1	4	64	29	35	46
2	Langley Galaxy FC Res	20	12	4	4	74	41	33	40
3	Frontline Res	20	11	4	5	50	37	13	37
4	Chalvey (WMC) Sports A	20	11	3	6	52	31	21	36
5	Harefield St Mary's	20	10	3	7	63	46	17	33
6	Stoke Poges Saints FC Res	20	10	3	7	61	49	12	33
7	Mercian United	20	8	2	10	49	62	-13	26
8	Phoenix Old Boys Res	20	7	3	10	36	41	-5	24
9	Townmead	20	7	3	10	42	60	-18	24
10	Langley Hornets	20	4	1	15	21	59	-38	13
11	St Peter's Iver	20	1	1	18	39	96	-57	4

EAST LINCOLNSHIRE LEAGUE

Division One

		P	W	D	L	F	A	GD	PTS
1	Tetney Rovers	14	12	2	0	62	13	49	38
2	All-Star Panthers	14	9	2	3	52	16	36	29
3	North Somercotes United	14	9	1	4	50	15	35	28
4	A.F.C. Holton Le Clay	14	9	1	4	52	22	30	28
5	Cleethorpes Town 'A'	14	6	2	6	31	33	-2	20
6	Louth Old Boys	14	3	1	10	21	48	-27	10
7	Louth Town Res	14	2	1	11	15	52	-37	7
8	Mablethorpe Athletic	14	1	0	13	14	98	-84	3

Division Two

		P	W	D	L	F	A	GD	PTS
1	Skegness United	14	12	1	1	58	15	43	37
2	North Thoresby	14	9	1	4	25	21	4	28
3	Sutton Rovers	14	8	0	6	47	30	17	24
4	Alford Town	14	6	2	6	37	42	-5	20
5	Scamblesby	14	6	0	8	31	37	-6	18
6	Chapel Swifts	14	5	1	8	33	40	-7	16
7	Ludford Rovers	14	5	1	8	24	33	-9	16
8	North Somercotes United Res	14	2	0	12	21	58	-37	6

Division Three

		P	W	D	L	F	A	GD	PTS
1	Grimsby Borough Dev	20	17	1	2	68	31	37	52
2	Immingham Town Devt	20	16	1	3	80	31	49	49
3	North Cotes	20	13	1	6	71	32	39	40
4	Manby	20	10	2	8	72	47	25	32
5	Susies Star's	20	8	4	8	49	39	10	28
6	Burgh Athletic	20	7	4	9	49	47	2	25
7	Market Rasen Dev	20	8	1	11	45	47	-2	25
8	Sutton Rovers Res	20	7	1	12	50	75	-25	22
9	Louth Old Boys Vets	20	6	3	11	42	78	-36	21
10	The Tache FC	20	5	4	11	35	60	-25	19
11	Alford Town Res	20	2	0	18	24	98	-74	6

EAST RIDING COUNTY LEAGUE

Premier Division

		P	W	D	L	F	A	GD	Pts
1	North Ferriby United Academy	20	16	2	2	72	37	35	50
2	AFC Orchard	20	14	2	4	54	42	12	44
3	Wawne United	20	11	4	5	49	32	17	37
4	Holme Rovers	20	9	3	8	55	46	9	30
5	Leven Members Club	20	8	4	8	43	36	7	30*
6	Beverley Town Res	20	9	2	9	48	56	-8	29
7	North Cave	20	8	4	8	38	37	1	28
8	St George's FC	20	7	2	11	44	56	-12	23
9	Bridlington SC County	20	5	3	12	38	49	-11	18
10	Ridings FC	20	4	4	12	38	49	-11	16
11	Sculcoates Amateurs Res	20	2	4	14	27	66	-39	9*

Division One

		P	W	D	L	F	A	GD	PTS
1	Queens County	22	17	1	4	83	30	53	52
2	AFC North	22	12	6	4	87	43	44	44*
3	Hutton Cranswick SRA	22	13	3	6	74	26	48	42
4	Hodgsons AFC	22	13	2	7	68	52	16	41
5	East Riding Rangers Res	22	13	2	7	64	56	8	41
6	West Hull Amateurs	22	12	3	7	62	54	8	39
7	Middleton Rovers	22	11	2	9	54	32	22	35
8	Bridlington Town County	22	8	2	12	51	60	-9	26
9	Hedon Rangers Res	22	6	4	12	52	64	-12	22
10	Beverley Town Academy	22	5	5	12	44	66	-22	19*
11	Hornsea Town Res	22	4	1	17	44	113	-69	13
12	Hanson Jewellers Res	22	1	3	18	25	112	-87	6

Division Two

		P	W	D	L	F	A	GD	PTS
1	Harchester United	18	15	1	2	66	14	52	46
2	Lambwath FC	18	12	3	3	62	36	26	39
3	Withernsea	18	10	2	6	63	44	19	32
4	Skirlaugh	18	9	4	5	61	49	12	31
5	Roos	18	8	2	8	52	53	-1	26
6	Haltemprice	18	7	4	7	51	52	-1	25
7	Driffield Evening Institute Res	18	6	1	11	35	59	-24	19
8	South Cave Utd Res	18	5	2	11	38	55	-17	17
9	Eastern Raiders	18	4	2	12	35	71	-36	14
10	Apollo Rangers	18	2	3	13	37	67	-30	9

Division Three

		P	W	D	L	F	A	GD	PTS
1	AFC Gulls	18	14	3	1	68	30	38	45
2	Skirlaugh Res	18	11	5	2	64	29	35	38
3	Waterloo	18	12	1	5	64	40	24	37
4	Hessle Rangers Juniors	18	10	2	6	72	44	28	32
5	Reckitts Res	18	10	1	7	67	41	26	31
6	Bridlington SC County Res	18	7	4	7	44	44	0	25
7	Easington United Res	18	7	1	10	34	64	-30	22
8	Orchard Park	18	4	4	10	43	66	-23	16
9	Gilberdyke Phoenix	18	3	1	14	32	63	-31	10
10	FC Georgies Bar	18	1	0	17	33	100	-67	3

Division Four

		P	W	D	L	F	A	GD	PTS
1	Hedon Rangers 3rds	18	12	2	4	67	36	31	38
2	Langtoft	18	11	3	4	60	41	19	36
3	Holme Rovers Res	18	9	6	3	48	34	14	33
4	Little Driffield AFC	18	10	3	5	53	47	6	33
5	East Riding Rangers 3rds	18	9	1	8	45	44	1	28
6	Malt Shovel Hawthorn	18	8	1	9	66	48	18	25
7	AFC Duke of York	18	7	4	7	44	47	-3	25
8	Long Riston	18	6	3	9	55	66	-11	21
9	Eastrington Village	18	5	1	12	33	51	-18	16
10	Driffield Town	18	1	0	17	26	83	-57	3

Division Five

		P	W	D	L	F	A	GD	PTS
1	Patrington	18	15	2	1	53	25	28	47
2	Hessle Rangers Res	18	15	0	3	86	30	56	45
3	Market Weighton United	18	12	0	6	90	50	40	36
4	Kingston Hull	18	10	1	7	64	54	10	31
5	Brandesburton Res	18	9	2	7	64	47	17	29
6	Cottingham Rangers	18	9	1	8	61	48	13	28
7	Leven Members Club Res	18	7	2	9	68	43	25	23
8	AFC North Res	18	4	1	13	23	68	-45	13
9	Orchard Park Res	18	4	1	13	28	86	-58	13
10	Easington United Casuals	18	0	0	18	17	103	-86	0

Division Six

		P	W	D	L	F	A	GD	PTS
1	Marist Rovers	18	15	1	2	103	39	64	46
2	South Park Rangers	18	14	3	1	64	24	40	45
3	Griffin Athletic	18	13	0	5	75	33	42	39
4	East Riding Rangers 4ths	18	10	1	7	63	56	7	31
5	Market Weighton United Res	18	8	1	9	52	53	-1	25
6	Withernsea Res	18	8	1	9	57	83	-26	25
7	Howden Academy	18	8	0	10	60	45	15	24
8	Banks Harbour	18	6	1	11	56	56	0	19
9	Courtland Raiders	18	3	0	15	31	101	-70	9
10	Window Doctor AFC	18	1	0	17	33	104	-71	3

ESSEX OLYMPIAN LEAGUE

Under 21 Division

		P	W	D	L	F	A	GD	Pts
1	Lakeside U21	24	19	2	3	123	27	96	62*
2	Corinthians U21	24	21	2	1	88	28	60	62*
3	Buckhurst Hill U21	24	18	2	4	114	49	65	53*
4	May & Baker E.C. U21	24	15	2	7	77	45	32	47
5	Southend Manor U21	24	13	3	8	87	50	37	40*
6	Redbridge U21	24	10	2	12	47	72	-25	35*
7	Collier Row U21	24	10	4	10	79	70	9	34
8	Harold Hill U21	24	10	3	11	68	63	5	33
9	Forest Glade U21	24	8	5	11	55	59	-4	29
10	Old Southendian U21	24	8	2	14	45	73	-28	24*
11	Frenford Senior U21	24	5	0	19	29	91	-62	13*
12	Academy Soccer U21	24	5	0	19	35	77	-42	9*
13	Westhamians U21	24	0	1	23	33	176	-143	-5*

FURNESS PREMIER LEAGUE

Premier Division

		P	W	D	L	F	A	GD	Pts
1	Croftlands Park	28	19	4	5	97	52	45	61
2	Barrow Celtic	28	18	4	6	105	59	46	58
3	Hawcoat Park Res	28	18	2	8	93	46	47	56
4	Kirkby United	28	16	6	6	107	42	65	54
5	Vickerstown CC Res	28	15	6	7	78	56	22	51
6	Holker Old Boys Res	28	15	3	10	81	54	27	48
7	Haverigg United	28	14	5	9	73	51	22	47
8	Millom Res	28	15	2	11	81	66	15	47
9	Bootle	28	13	2	13	60	51	9	41
10	GSK Ulverston Rangers Res	28	10	2	16	56	79	-23	32
11	Britannia	28	9	4	15	84	111	-27	31
12	Furness Cavaliers Res	28	8	1	19	45	91	-46	25
13	Walney Island Res	28	6	3	19	31	81	-50	21
14	Swarthmoor Social Res	28	5	3	20	40	103	-63	15*
15	Furness Rovers Res	28	3	5	20	47	136	-89	-2*

LEAGUE TABLES

Division One

		P	W	D	L	F	A	GD	PTS
1	Coniston	20	14	3	3	73	26	47	45
2	Dalton United Res	20	13	2	5	69	40	29	41
3	Crooklands Casuals Res	20	11	3	6	51	46	5	36
4	Hawcoat Park A	20	11	3	6	71	42	29	33*
5	Barrow Wanderers	20	10	3	7	60	45	15	33
6	Askam United Res	20	9	3	8	62	64	-2	30
7	Ormsgill North End	20	8	2	10	51	40	11	26
8	Vickerstown CC A	20	8	1	11	50	46	4	22*
9	Haverigg United Res	20	5	4	11	17	61	-44	19
10	Holker Old Boys A	20	7	2	11	38	60	-22	17*
11	Barrow Celtic Res	20	0	2	18	34	106	-72	-1*

Division Two

		P	W	D	L	F	A	GD	PTS
1	Millom A	16	13	0	3	67	25	42	39
2	Bridge United	16	11	2	3	66	33	33	35
3	Dalton United A	16	8	4	4	45	44	1	28
4	Coniston Res	16	7	0	9	33	66	-33	21
5	Kirkby United Res	16	6	2	8	40	39	1	20
6	Britannia Res	16	6	2	8	42	48	-6	20
7	FC Barrow Island	16	7	2	7	51	37	14	14*
8	Walney Island A	16	4	2	10	27	52	-25	14
9	Bootle Res	16	3	0	13	30	57	-27	9

GLOUCESTERSHIRE NORTHERN SENIOR LEAGUE

Division One

		P	W	D	L	F	A	GD	Pts
1	Ruardean Hill Rangers	28	22	4	2	103	23	80	70
2	Cam Bulldogs	28	19	3	6	56	39	17	60
3	Sharpness	28	17	4	7	63	44	19	55
4	Charlton Rovers	28	17	1	10	89	41	48	52
5	Brockworth Albion	28	15	6	7	52	44	8	51
6	Taverners	28	10	6	12	46	49	-3	36
7	Newent Town	28	10	5	13	57	67	-10	35
8	Tuffley Rovers Res	28	10	4	14	61	57	4	34
9	Southside Star	28	9	7	12	59	72	-13	34
10	Berkeley Town	28	10	4	14	48	85	-37	34
11	Harrow Hill	28	8	8	12	42	60	-18	32
12	Bibury	28	7	6	15	55	85	-30	27
13	FC Barometrics	28	5	11	12	45	53	-8	26
14	Leonard Stanley	28	6	7	15	36	62	-26	25*
15	Bredon	28	3	8	17	32	65	-33	17

Division Two

		P	W	D	L	F	A	GD	Pts
1	Chalford	30	24	6	0	74	21	53	78
2	Quedgeley Wanderers	30	20	4	6	101	34	67	64
3	Longlevens Res	30	18	8	4	63	31	32	62
4	Stroud Harriers	30	17	3	10	70	51	19	53*
5	Lydbrook Athletic	30	15	6	9	69	48	21	51
6	Whaddon United	30	15	5	10	53	37	16	50
7	FC Lakeside	30	13	4	13	65	59	6	43
8	Woolaston	30	13	4	13	42	45	-3	43
9	English Bicknor	30	12	5	13	61	51	10	41
10	Lydney Town Res	30	11	7	12	71	70	1	40
11	Mitcheldean	30	11	7	12	48	61	-13	40
12	Winchcombe Town	30	11	5	14	55	69	-14	38
13	Dursley Town	30	8	6	16	51	68	-17	30
14	Abbeymead Rovers	30	6	1	23	37	108	-71	19
15	Smiths Athletic	30	4	5	21	38	92	-54	17
16	Wotton Rovers	30	2	4	24	30	86	-56	10

GUILDFORD & WOKING ALLIANCE LEAGUE

Premier Division

		P	W	D	L	F	A	GD	Pts
1	Parkside United	16	15	1	0	61	10	51	46
2	Guildford Park	16	10	1	5	31	20	11	31
3	Swinley Forest	16	9	2	5	48	36	12	29
4	Chertsey Old Salesians	16	8	4	4	38	44	-6	28
5	University of Surrey A	16	5	2	9	53	47	6	17
6	Heathervale	16	5	1	10	30	37	-7	16
7	Holmbury St Mary	16	5	1	10	25	37	-12	16
8	AFC Westend	16	4	2	10	27	38	-11	14
9	Shalford	16	3	2	11	18	62	-44	11

Division One

		P	W	D	L	F	A	GD	Pts
1	Bookham	14	9	2	3	25	12	13	29
2	Woking & Maybury	14	8	3	3	42	25	17	27
3	West Byfleet Albion	14	8	3	3	36	22	14	27
4	Ottershaw	14	6	2	6	35	27	8	20
5	Woking Tigers	14	6	1	7	38	38	0	19
6	Elstead	14	6	1	7	33	42	-9	19
7	Windlesham & Lightwater A	14	6	0	8	36	55	-19	18
8	Laleham Res	14	1	0	13	8	32	-24	3

Division Two

		P	W	D	L	F	A	GD	Pts
1	Hersham Villa	22	17	3	2	73	27	46	54
2	Deepcut Community	22	15	4	3	88	39	49	49
3	Wrecclesham	22	14	0	8	75	49	26	42
4	Staines Lammas Res	22	10	4	8	61	46	15	34
5	AFC Westend Res	22	9	5	8	61	54	7	32
6	Horsley A	22	10	2	10	54	56	-2	32
7	Woking Corinthians	22	8	4	10	51	74	-23	28
8	Farncombe Athletic	22	8	3	11	60	74	-14	27
9	Byfleet	22	7	4	11	55	64	-9	25
10	Merrow A	22	8	1	13	36	51	-15	25
11	Dunsfold	22	5	4	13	36	65	-29	19
12	Surrey Athletic	22	3	2	17	47	98	-51	11

Division Three

		P	W	D	L	F	A	GD	Pts
1	Pirbright	20	19	0	1	67	7	60	57
2	Laleham Athletic	20	13	2	5	48	22	26	41
3	Worplesdon Phoenix A	20	13	0	7	52	32	20	39
4	Bourne Blades	20	12	1	7	51	32	19	37
5	Burpham Res	20	10	3	7	36	34	2	33
6	Farncombe Athletic Res	20	10	1	9	34	36	-2	31
7	Virginia Water A	20	9	1	10	39	39	0	28
8	Ockham Res	20	5	3	12	28	41	-13	15
9	Guildford Park Res	20	4	3	13	26	49	-23	15
10	Shalford Res	20	4	1	15	20	92	-72	13
11	FC Staines	20	3	1	16	26	43	-17	10

Division Four

		P	W	D	L	F	A	GD	Pts
1	Hersham	16	14	1	1	86	16	70	43
2	Woking & Horsell A	16	11	2	3	75	32	43	35
3	University of Surrey B	16	10	2	4	101	29	72	32
4	Knaphill Athletic A	16	10	1	5	62	40	22	31
5	Guildford Barbarians	16	6	2	8	43	79	-36	20
6	Burpham A	16	4	4	8	32	48	-16	15*
7	Hambledon A	16	4	3	9	31	51	-20	15
8	Wrecclesham Res	16	3	3	10	42	68	-26	12
9	Farncombe Athletic A	16	1	0	15	20	129	-109	3

GREAT YARMOUTH & DISTRICT LEAGUE

		P	W	D	L	F	A	GD	Pts
1	Great Yarmouth Town Hall	18	16	1	1	97	19	78	49
2	Old Hall	18	13	3	2	79	27	52	42
3	Prostar Windows	18	11	4	3	63	30	33	37
4	Hemsby Res	18	10	2	6	30	32	-2	32
5	Mariners	18	8	2	8	52	62	-10	26
6	Caister B	18	6	2	10	28	58	-30	20
7	Bohemians Res	18	5	2	11	35	59	-24	17
8	Apollo Tavern	18	5	1	12	35	65	-30	16
9	Filby & Runham	18	3	2	13	21	58	-37	9*
10	Bohemians	18	2	3	13	18	48	-30	8*

GUERNSEY FOOTBALL ASSOCIATION LEAGUE

Priaulx League

		P	W	D	L	F	A	GD	Pts
1	Rovers AC	21	14	3	4	65	35	30	45
2	North A C	21	13	5	3	47	29	18	44
3	St Martins FC	21	13	4	4	52	24	28	43
4	UCF Sylvans	21	8	5	8	58	46	12	29
5	Alderney FC	21	8	3	10	35	45	-10	27
6	Rangers	21	6	5	10	46	56	-10	23
7	Vale Recreation	21	5	6	10	48	44	4	21
8	Belgrave Wanderers	21	1	1	19	22	94	-72	4

Jackson League

		P	W	D	L	F	A	GD	PTS
1	Rovers AC	16	15	0	1	43	8	35	45
2	Captains	16	9	4	3	41	21	20	31
3	BWB Rangers FC	16	10	1	5	36	28	8	31
4	St Martins AC	16	8	0	8	26	33	-7	24
5	Manzur	16	7	1	8	41	21	20	22
6	Vale Recreation	16	6	2	8	39	36	3	20
7	Belgrave Wanderers	16	5	1	10	22	44	-22	16
8	North AC	16	4	2	10	17	23	-6	14
9	UCF Sylvans	16	2	1	13	17	68	-51	7

Lancashire Railway League One

		P	W	D	L	F	A	GD	PTS
1	Manzur	18	12	5	1	47	21	26	41
2	Rangers	18	8	2	8	38	40	-2	26
3	Rovers AC	18	7	4	7	44	30	14	25
4	Vale Recreation	18	6	3	9	44	41	3	21
5	Northerners	18	6	3	9	39	52	-13	21
6	RBFC A	18	5	6	7	30	46	-16	21
7	UCF Sylvans	18	5	5	8	29	41	-12	20

Lancashire Railway League Two

		P	W	D	L	F	A	GD	PTS
1	Last Post	18	14	2	2	72	15	57	44
2	Rocquaine Pirates	18	10	2	6	57	32	25	32
3	Manor Farm Saints	18	8	4	6	41	38	3	28
4	RBFC B	18	6	5	7	31	39	-8	23
5	Centrals	18	6	3	9	43	55	-12	21
6	Herm Island Bels	18	4	4	10	31	56	-25	16
7	United F C	18	5	0	13	26	66	-40	15

HALIFAX & DISTRICT AFL

Premier Division

		P	W	D	L	F	A	GD	Pts
1	Illingworth St Marys	20	19	1	0	107	24	83	58
2	Northowram	20	12	2	6	52	36	16	38
3	Calder 76	20	12	2	6	61	48	13	38
4	Ryburn United	20	11	4	5	65	19	46	37
5	Warley Rangers Halifax	20	10	1	9	67	56	11	31
6	Midgley United	20	9	3	8	54	53	1	30
7	Hebden Royd RS	20	6	4	10	51	64	-13	22
8	Sowerby United	20	6	3	11	49	66	-17	21
9	Shelf United	20	5	3	12	36	55	-19	18
10	Greetland AFC	20	4	6	10	41	73	-32	18
11	Copley United	20	0	3	17	19	108	-89	3

Division One

		P	W	D	L	F	A	GD	Pts
1	Shelf FC	22	20	0	2	106	26	80	60
2	Sowerby Bridge	22	18	2	2	102	37	65	56
3	Denholme United	22	14	2	6	79	59	20	44
4	Ryburn United Res	22	13	4	5	75	53	22	43
5	Calder 76 Res	22	10	2	10	45	73	-28	32
6	Brighouse Sports AFC	22	9	4	9	44	51	-7	31
7	Holmfield	22	10	1	11	39	46	-7	31
8	Elland Allstars	22	8	5	9	59	50	9	29
9	Salem	22	7	2	13	47	65	-18	23
10	AFC Crossleys	22	7	2	13	59	87	-28	23
11	Greetland AFC Res	22	2	1	19	34	105	-71	7
12	Midgley United Res	22	1	1	20	24	61	-37	4

Division Two

		P	W	D	L	F	A	GD	Pts
1	The Ivy House FC	22	18	2	2	114	31	83	56
2	Illingworth St Marys Res	22	18	1	3	117	41	76	55
3	Junction Inn	22	16	3	3	77	43	34	51
4	St Columbas	22	14	3	5	69	37	32	45
5	Northowram Res	22	13	0	9	73	56	17	39
6	FC Plummet Line	22	11	1	10	66	51	15	34
7	AFC Crossleys Res	22	8	3	11	68	97	-29	27
8	Sowerby United Res	22	8	1	13	55	81	-26	25
9	Shelf United Res	22	7	2	13	59	77	-18	23
10	Sowerby Bridge Res	22	4	1	17	40	91	-51	13
11	Hebden Royd RS Res	22	3	1	18	48	106	-58	10
12	Salem Res	22	3	0	19	39	114	-75	9

HAMPSHIRE PREMIER LEAGUE

Combination

		P	W	D	L	F	A	GD	Pts
1	Paulsgrove Res	24	19	1	4	77	19	58	58
2	Bush Hill Res	24	15	5	4	68	37	31	50
3	Fleetlands Res	24	12	6	6	71	32	39	42
4	Liphook United Res	24	13	3	8	55	46	9	42
5	Overton United Res	24	12	5	7	61	48	13	41
6	Winchester Castle Res	24	12	3	9	63	45	18	39
7	Clanfield Res	24	10	5	9	51	53	-2	35
8	Hedge End Rangers Res	24	10	3	11	46	42	4	33
9	Hayling United Res	24	10	2	12	58	68	-10	32
10	QK Southampton Res	24	9	3	12	37	48	-11	30
11	Four Marks Res	24	8	2	14	48	67	-19	26
12	Headley United Res	24	3	4	17	33	68	-35	13
13	Michelmersh & Timsbury Res	24	1	2	21	20	115	-95	5

LEAGUE TABLES

HARROGATE AND DISTRICT FOOTBALL LEAGUE

Premier Division

		P	W	D	L	F	A	GD	Pts
1	Kirk Deighton Rangers	16	13	1	2	52	18	34	40
2	Knaresborough Celtic	16	11	3	2	62	30	32	36
3	Beckwithshaw Saints	16	9	4	3	40	25	15	31
4	Bedale Town	16	8	3	5	47	29	18	27
5	Hampsthwaite United	16	6	4	6	53	44	9	22
6	Harlow Hill	16	5	3	8	42	43	-1	18
7	Burley Trojans	16	4	0	12	29	67	-38	12
8	Kirkby Malzeard	16	3	1	12	24	64	-40	10
9	Pannal Sports	16	2	3	11	20	49	-29	9

Division One

		P	W	D	L	F	A	GD	PTS
1	Thirsk Falcons	20	19	0	1	122	28	94	57
2	Pateley Bridge	20	14	3	3	71	32	39	45
3	Knaresborough Celtic Res	20	13	2	5	67	52	15	41
4	Helperby United	20	10	3	7	72	54	18	33
5	Bramhope	20	10	0	10	60	56	4	30
6	Dalton Athletic	20	7	3	10	57	72	-15	24
7	Hampsthwaite HC	20	7	2	11	46	58	-12	23
8	Bardsey	20	5	5	10	41	75	-34	20
9	Addingham	20	5	3	12	51	83	-32	18
10	Beckwithshaw Saints Res	20	4	3	13	35	69	-34	15
11	Boroughbridge A	20	2	4	14	26	69	-43	10

Division Two

		P	W	D	L	F	A	GD	PTS
1	Kirk Deighton Rangers Res	16	12	1	3	53	31	22	37
2	Richmond Town Res	16	12	0	4	64	25	39	36
3	FC United Knaresborough	16	9	3	4	52	30	22	30
4	Ripon City Res	16	7	3	6	37	37	0	24
5	Bedale Town Res	16	7	3	6	34	41	-7	24
6	Pannal Sports Res	16	5	1	10	43	55	-12	16
7	Kirkby Malzeard Res	16	5	0	11	38	51	-13	15
8	Hampsthwaite United Res	16	5	0	11	27	43	-16	15
9	Pool A	16	4	1	11	33	68	-35	13

HERTFORDSHIRE FA COUNTY FOOTBALL LEAGUE

Premier Division

		P	W	D	L	F	A	GD	PTS
1	Hinton	24	17	5	2	61	23	38	56
2	Bartestree	24	14	4	6	77	49	28	46
3	Tenbury United	24	14	3	7	63	38	25	42*
4	Westfields Res	24	13	3	8	56	44	12	39*
5	Fownhope	24	10	7	7	49	37	12	37
6	Orleton Colts	24	11	3	10	61	53	8	36
7	Ewyas Harold	24	10	5	9	55	37	18	35
8	Holme Lacy	24	10	3	11	56	61	-5	33
9	Hereford Lads Club Res	24	8	4	12	38	78	-40	25*
10	Wellington Res	24	8	3	13	70	74	-4	24*
11	Ledbury Town	24	7	1	16	52	87	-35	22
12	Leominster Town	24	6	3	15	49	73	-24	21
13	Pegasus Res	24	4	4	16	30	63	-33	7*

Division One

		P	W	D	L	F	A	GD	PTS
1	Tenbury Town	24	17	3	4	92	38	54	54
2	Kington Town Res	24	17	2	5	83	33	50	53
3	Hereford City	24	15	2	7	49	35	14	47
4	Woofferton	24	14	4	6	86	48	38	43*
5	Holme Lacy Res	24	12	4	8	61	56	5	40
6	Wellington Colts	24	13	6	5	77	40	37	39*
7	Ewyas Harold Res	24	8	3	13	46	54	-8	27
8	Ludlow Colts	24	7	5	12	56	58	-2	26
9	Ledbury Town Res	24	9	5	10	54	66	-12	26*
10	Fownhope Res	24	10	1	13	54	79	-25	25*
11	Weobley	24	8	0	16	56	67	-11	21*
12	Hinton Res	24	7	3	14	48	71	-23	21*
13	Orleton Colts Res	24	0	0	24	28	145	-117	0

Division Two

		P	W	D	L	F	A	GD	PTS
1	Burghill Rangers	22	17	2	3	86	29	57	53
2	Kingstone Rovers	22	14	6	2	101	31	70	48
3	Dore Valley	22	13	2	7	69	41	28	41
4	Bartestree Res	22	11	5	6	64	38	26	38
5	Toros	22	11	3	8	86	46	40	36
6	Weston	22	11	3	8	66	40	26	36
7	Ross Juniors	22	10	6	6	64	56	8	36
8	Civil Service	22	6	4	12	51	63	-12	22
9	Withington	22	6	1	15	36	74	-38	19
10	Leominster Res	22	7	2	13	30	64	-34	17*
11	Shobdon	22	4	2	16	49	70	-21	8*
12	Hereford City Res	22	3	2	17	32	182	-150	7*

HOPE VALLEY AMATEUR LEAGUE

Premier Division

		P	W	D	L	F	A	GD	Pts
1	Bakewell Town	20	15	2	3	58	16	42	47
2	Dove Holes	20	13	2	5	48	30	18	41
3	Furness Vale	20	12	3	5	59	31	28	39
4	High Lane	20	10	3	7	46	42	4	33
5	Dronfield Old Boys	20	9	5	6	41	29	12	32
6	Bradwell	20	8	6	6	45	38	7	30
7	Dronfield Town A	20	8	3	9	39	48	-9	27
8	Hathersage	20	7	3	10	35	44	-9	24
9	Ashover FC	20	6	3	11	50	47	3	21
10	Tideswell United Res	20	5	2	13	33	59	-26	17
11	Buxworth	20	1	0	19	25	95	-70	3

A Division

		P	W	D	L	F	A	GD	PTS
1	Cote Heath	20	16	0	4	76	27	49	48
2	Buxton Town	20	14	1	5	70	39	31	43
3	Baslow	20	12	3	5	72	34	38	39
4	Grindleford	20	12	2	6	63	50	13	38
5	Blazing Rag	20	9	2	9	57	61	-4	29
6	Youlgrave United	20	8	4	8	64	53	11	28
7	Darley Dale Lions	20	8	2	10	67	60	7	26
8	Eyam	20	7	2	11	37	63	-26	23
9	Dove Holes Res	20	7	3	10	49	38	11	21*
10	Railway FC	20	6	1	13	48	76	-28	19
11	FC Trunk	20	1	0	19	31	133	-102	-3*

B Division	P	W	D	L	F	A	GD	PTS
1 Bamford	18	10	4	4	62	42	20	34
2 Fairfield FC	18	9	5	4	50	31	19	32
3 Dale	18	10	0	8	51	46	5	30
4 Calver	18	9	1	8	55	47	8	28
5 Stoney Middleton	18	7	5	6	38	42	-4	26
6 Bradwell Res	18	11	2	5	46	32	14	23*
7 Bakewell Town Res	18	7	1	10	35	46	-11	22
8 Dronfield Woodhouse	18	5	3	10	43	56	-13	18
9 Chinley	18	5	2	11	38	57	-19	17
10 Buxworth Res	18	5	1	12	32	51	-19	16

HUDDERSFIELD AND DISTRICT ASSOCIATION FOOTBALL LEAGUE

Division One	P	W	D	L	F	A	GD	Pts
1 Meltham Athletic	22	16	4	2	82	34	48	52
2 Holmbridge	22	15	3	4	49	33	16	48
3 Heywood Irish Centre FC	21	15	2	4	79	43	36	47
4 Newsome	22	12	3	7	60	48	12	39
5 Diggle	22	12	2	8	82	39	43	38
6 Kirkheaton Rovers	22	11	1	10	45	38	7	34
7 Shepley	22	11	1	10	48	42	6	34
8 Hepworth Utd	22	9	3	10	45	54	-9	30
9 Skelmanthorpe	21	7	4	10	48	52	-4	25
10 Britannia Sports	22	3	4	15	35	89	-54	13
11 Shelley	22	3	3	16	33	74	-41	12
12 Aimbry	22	2	0	20	15	75	-60	6

Division Two	P	W	D	L	F	A	GD	PTS
1 Berry Brow	26	19	6	1	85	45	40	63
2 Linthwaite Athletic	26	19	3	4	105	54	51	60
3 AFC Lindley	26	17	6	3	73	39	34	57
4 Colne Valley	26	17	4	5	98	45	53	55
5 Slaithwaite Utd	26	15	4	7	83	49	34	49
6 Honley	26	12	6	8	64	58	6	42
7 Lepton Highlanders	26	12	3	11	63	55	8	39
8 Scholes	26	9	7	10	48	49	-1	34
9 Marsden	26	8	6	12	66	78	-12	30
10 H.V.Academicals	26	6	8	12	43	59	-16	26
11 Netherton	26	7	2	17	48	79	-31	23
12 Holmfirth Town	26	4	3	19	33	97	-64	15
13 Cumberworth	26	3	2	21	31	66	-35	11
14 Scissett	26	1	6	19	28	95	-67	9

Division Three	P	W	D	L	F	A	GD	PTS
1 Almondbury Woolpack	22	15	2	5	83	50	33	47
2 Moorside	22	14	3	5	73	32	41	45
3 AFC Dalton	21	12	5	4	77	41	36	41
4 Brook Motors	21	13	2	6	74	45	29	41
5 3D Dynamos	22	12	5	5	60	42	18	41
6 Brighouse Athletic	22	9	4	9	55	71	-16	31
7 Junction	22	8	4	10	51	67	-16	28
8 Hade Edge	22	6	8	8	42	51	-9	26
9 Uppermill	22	7	4	11	54	54	0	25
10 Almondbury WMC	22	6	4	12	60	68	-8	22
11 Wooldale Wanderers	22	4	5	13	55	91	-36	17
12 Flockton FC	22	0	4	18	25	97	-72	4

Division Four	P	W	D	L	F	A	GD	PTS
1 Dalton Dynamos	26	23	3	0	133	24	109	72
2 Fothergill-Whittles	26	21	2	3	135	25	110	65
3 Littleborough	26	17	5	4	136	49	87	56
4 Cask	26	18	2	6	103	43	60	56
5 Deighton FC	26	15	3	8	87	59	28	48
6 Golcar Utd	26	12	4	10	58	76	-18	40
7 Heyside FC	26	13	1	12	76	99	-23	40
8 Thornhill United	26	8	4	14	84	104	-20	28
9 Cartworth Moor	26	8	3	15	79	120	-41	27
10 Westend	26	7	4	15	58	129	-71	25
11 Kirkburton	26	6	3	17	53	86	-33	21
12 Cavalry Arms	26	5	4	17	50	73	-23	19
13 Rose and Crown	26	5	2	19	54	118	-64	17
14 Mount	26	3	2	21	40	141	-101	11

ISLE OF MAN SENIOR LEAGUES

Premier Division	P	W	D	L	F	A	GD	Pts
1 St Georges	24	23	0	1	138	18	120	69
2 Corinthians	24	18	1	5	106	45	61	55
3 St Marys	24	16	3	5	87	40	47	51
4 Rushen Utd	24	15	3	6	87	44	43	48
5 Peel	24	13	5	6	86	29	57	44
6 DHSOB	24	13	3	8	61	42	19	42
7 St Johns Utd	24	13	2	9	55	42	13	41
8 Laxey	24	10	4	10	78	57	21	34
9 Colby	24	7	2	15	48	81	-33	23
10 Douglas Athletic	24	6	2	16	46	79	-33	20
11 Ramsey	24	3	5	16	31	88	-57	14
12 Union Mills	24	1	4	19	35	111	-76	7
13 Ayre United	24	0	2	22	27	209	-182	-1*

Division Two	P	W	D	L	F	A	GD	PTS
1 Braddan	24	20	2	2	126	24	102	62
2 Douglas Royal	24	19	0	5	117	50	67	57
3 Foxdale	24	16	3	5	121	49	72	51
4 Onchan	24	15	3	6	55	38	17	48
5 Castletown	24	14	3	7	74	58	16	45
6 Marown	24	13	0	11	73	58	15	39
7 Pulrose United	24	12	2	10	94	60	34	38
8 Gymnasium	24	11	2	11	75	63	12	35
9 RYCOB	24	10	1	13	68	78	-10	31
10 Douglas & District	24	6	2	16	53	85	-32	20
11 Governors Athletic	24	5	1	18	40	132	-92	16
12 Malew	24	3	3	18	28	107	-79	12
13 Michael United	24	0	2	22	11	133	-122	2

ISLE OF WIGHT SATURDAY LEAGUE

Division One	P	W	D	L	F	A	GD	Pts
1 Whitecroft & Barton	22	17	2	3	72	15	57	53
2 Ventnor FC	22	15	5	2	83	31	52	50
3 Brading Town	22	15	4	3	62	27	35	49
4 Shanklin	22	15	3	4	64	28	36	48
5 Binstead & COB	22	12	3	7	36	33	3	39
6 West Wight	22	11	2	9	55	25	30	35
7 E.C.S.	22	10	3	9	50	45	5	33
8 Ryde Saints	22	8	0	14	34	48	-14	24
9 Cowes Sports Res	22	5	1	16	38	72	-34	16
10 Brighstone	22	4	3	15	31	74	-43	15
11 Oakfield	22	4	0	18	31	81	-50	12
12 Bembridge	22	2	2	18	33	110	-77	8

LEAGUE TABLES

Division Two

	P	W	D	L	F	A	GD	PTS
1 Sandown	18	15	1	2	103	28	75	46
2 Northwood St Johns	18	14	3	1	99	21	78	45
3 Osborne Coburg	18	12	3	3	58	17	41	39
4 Pan Sports	18	12	1	5	77	32	45	37
5 Carisbrooke Utd	18	10	2	6	75	39	36	32
6 Niton Community	18	6	3	9	34	48	-14	21
7 Newport IOW A	18	6	2	10	46	68	-22	18*
8 East Cowes Vics Res	18	3	0	15	24	75	-51	12*
9 AFC Wootton	18	2	1	15	19	123	-104	7
10 Yarmouth & Calb	18	1	2	15	24	108	-84	5

Division Three

	P	W	D	L	F	A	GD	PTS
1 St Helens BS	12	10	2	0	43	18	25	32
2 Seaview	12	9	1	2	40	22	18	28
3 Wroxall	12	7	2	3	39	20	19	23
4 Newchurch	12	5	0	7	16	29	-13	15
5 Kyngs Towne	12	4	2	6	34	32	2	14
6 Ryde Saints A	12	2	0	10	16	48	-32	6
7 Brading Town A	12	1	1	10	13	32	-19	4

Combination One

	P	W	D	L	F	A	GD	PTS
1 E.C.S. Res	20	18	0	2	94	29	65	54
2 Whitecroft & Barton Sports Res	20	16	0	4	54	22	32	48
3 West Wight Res	20	13	2	5	64	25	39	41
4 Brading Town Res	20	11	2	7	36	33	3	35
5 Shanklin Res	20	11	0	9	24	33	-9	33
6 Ryde Saints Res	20	7	2	11	44	46	-2	23
7 Osborne Coburg Res	20	7	2	11	43	51	-8	23
8 Binstead & COB	20	7	2	11	37	48	-11	23
9 Northwood St Johns Res	20	6	2	12	51	51	0	20
10 Oakfield Res	20	5	3	12	30	70	-40	18
11 Bembridge Res	20	1	1	18	16	85	-69	4

Combination Two

	P	W	D	L	F	A	GD	PTS
1 Carisbrooke Utd Res	14	13	0	1	68	27	41	39
2 Sandown Res	14	12	0	2	74	18	56	36
3 Kyngs Towne Res	14	7	1	6	47	41	6	22
4 Brighstone Res	14	7	0	7	47	28	19	21
5 Ventnor Res	14	6	0	4	70	23	47	18*
6 Seaview Res	14	2	2	10	23	75	-52	8
7 Yarmouth & Calb Res	14	1	1	12	19	98	-79	4
8 Niton Community Res	14	1	2	11	22	60	-38	3*

JERSEY FOOTBALL COMBINATION

Premiership

	P	W	D	L	F	A	GD	Pts
1 St Paul's	21	18	3	0	88	17	71	54*
2 JTC Jersey Wanderers	21	13	1	7	47	31	16	40
3 Jersey Scottish	21	10	4	7	54	27	27	34
4 St Ouen	21	10	1	10	46	45	1	31
5 St Peter	21	6	7	8	38	39	-1	25
6 Rozel Rovers	21	6	4	11	35	51	-16	22
7 Trinity	21	5	5	11	30	58	-28	20
8 Jersey Portuguese	21	2	3	16	18	88	-70	9

Championship

	P	W	D	L	F	A	GD	PTS
1 St Clement	18	17	1	0	82	13	69	52
2 Grouville	18	12	2	4	65	26	39	38
3 St Brelade	18	9	4	5	64	34	30	31
4 St Lawrence	18	9	3	6	29	25	4	30
5 First Tower Utd	18	5	0	13	23	60	-37	15
6 St John	18	4	1	13	17	63	-46	13
7 Sporting Academics	18	1	1	16	17	76	-59	4

Division One

	P	W	D	L	F	A	GD	PTS
1 St Peter Res	14	12	0	2	53	11	42	36
2 St Paul's Res	14	12	0	2	48	10	38	36
3 St Clement Res	14	8	1	5	31	21	10	25
4 St Ouen Res	14	8	0	6	35	25	10	24
5 JTC Jersey Wanderers Res	14	7	1	6	26	24	2	22
6 Grouville Res	14	5	1	8	17	28	-11	16
7 Rozel Rovers Res	14	1	2	11	19	56	-37	5
8 Jersey Portuguese Res	14	0	1	13	8	62	-54	1

Division Two

	P	W	D	L	F	A	GD	PTS
1 Trinity Res	16	13	1	2	47	21	26	40
2 St Peter C	16	12	0	4	44	24	20	36
3 St Clement C	16	11	2	3	64	20	44	35
4 St Brelade Res	16	7	2	7	33	44	-11	26*
5 St Ouen C	16	8	3	5	50	29	21	24*
6 St John Res	16	5	0	11	29	58	-29	15
7 JTC Jersey Wanderers C	16	4	2	10	27	31	-4	14
8 St Lawrence Res	16	3	4	9	31	43	-12	13
9 Sporting Academics Res	16	1	2	13	20	75	-55	2*

KINGSTON AND DISTRICT SATURDAY LEAGUE

Premier Division

	P	W	D	L	F	A	GD	PTS
1 Old Wimbledonians	16	13	2	1	54	13	41	40*
2 K.G.C	16	10	2	4	46	26	20	32
3 Lennox	16	9	3	4	51	34	17	30
4 Petersham Pumas	16	9	1	6	29	32	-3	28
5 Kingston Albion	16	7	1	8	33	32	1	22
6 M.C United	16	6	2	8	30	38	-8	20
7 Teddington	16	5	3	8	33	33	0	17*
8 Barnslake	16	3	2	11	24	62	-38	11
9 Darkside	16	1	2	13	24	54	-30	5

Division One

	P	W	D	L	F	A	GD	PTS
1 SuttonTown	18	16	2	0	79	17	62	50*
2 Surbiton Eagles	18	11	3	4	61	30	31	36
3 Corinthians 12	18	10	3	5	51	38	13	33
4 Feltham Rangers	18	9	2	7	48	47	1	29
5 N.P.L	18	8	2	8	44	42	2	26
6 Lower Green	18	7	4	7	34	27	7	25
7 Dynamo Kingston	18	6	4	8	40	42	-2	22
8 Sutton Celtic	18	4	2	12	30	70	-40	14
9 AFC North Leatherhead	18	2	4	12	13	40	-27	10
10 St Martins	18	2	4	12	20	68	-48	10

Division Two

		P	W	D	L	F	A	GD	PTS
1	Thornton Heath	14	9	1	4	40	15	25	28
2	Old Rutlishians	14	8	3	3	44	37	7	27
3	N.P.L Res	14	8	2	4	38	28	10	26
4	Chessington KC	14	6	1	7	31	36	-5	19
5	Epsom Casuals	14	5	2	7	26	31	-5	17
6	AFC Hampton	14	5	2	7	30	39	-9	17
7	Hook Venturers	14	5	1	8	32	50	-18	16
8	Petersham Pumas Res	14	3	2	9	22	27	-5	11

LANCASHIRE & CHESHIRE AFL

Premier Division

		P	W	D	L	F	A	GD	Pts
1	Mellor	24	21	1	2	95	27	68	64
2	Whalley Range	24	21	1	2	91	40	51	64
3	Tintwistle Athletic	24	14	1	9	75	54	21	43
4	Old Trafford and Gorse Hill	24	13	2	9	83	55	28	41
5	Rochdalians AFC	24	11	5	8	61	42	19	38
6	Parrswood Celtic	24	12	1	11	65	66	-1	37
7	South Manchester	24	10	6	8	57	53	4	36
8	Abacus Media	24	10	3	11	63	63	0	33
9	High Lane	24	9	4	11	64	57	7	31
10	Old Ashtonians	24	8	4	12	53	65	-12	28
11	Newton	24	7	2	15	55	69	-14	23
12	Bedians AFC	24	4	1	19	36	101	-65	13
13	Moston Brook	24	0	1	23	32	138	-106	1

Division One

		P	W	D	L	F	A	GD	PTS
1	Moorside Rangers	22	19	1	2	76	32	44	58
2	Newton Heath	22	14	4	4	96	67	29	46
3	Signol Athletic	22	14	3	5	87	45	42	45
4	Stoconians	22	14	1	7	79	66	13	43
5	Trafford United	22	14	0	8	81	56	25	42
6	Milton	22	10	5	7	55	43	12	35
7	Old Stretfordians	22	10	2	10	68	61	7	32
8	Bury Amateur AFC	22	6	2	14	40	72	-32	20
9	Oldham Victoria	22	6	0	16	60	95	-35	18
10	Didsbury FC	22	5	1	16	48	81	-33	16
11	Salford Victoria	22	4	3	15	43	72	-29	15
12	Swinton	22	4	2	16	36	79	-43	14

Division Two

		P	W	D	L	F	A	GD	PTS
1	Mellor Res	22	19	0	3	87	38	49	57
2	Waterloo FC	22	18	0	4	100	40	60	54
3	Hooley Bridge Celtic	22	15	2	5	90	50	40	47
4	Whalley Range Res	22	13	2	7	92	71	21	41
5	AFC Oldham 2005	22	9	5	8	51	57	-6	32
6	South Manchester Res	22	7	4	11	43	58	-15	25
7	Chorltonians	22	7	3	12	60	67	-7	24
8	Newton Res	22	7	3	12	44	65	-21	24
9	Parrswood Celtic Res	22	8	2	12	49	65	-16	23*
10	Spurley Hey	22	6	2	14	46	69	-23	20
11	Staly Lions	22	5	3	14	43	75	-32	18
12	Moston Brook Res	22	4	2	16	46	96	-50	14

Division Three

		P	W	D	L	F	A	GD	PTS
1	Didsbury FC Second	20	15	2	3	53	27	26	47
2	Chorltonians Res	20	14	3	3	62	31	31	45
3	Salford Victoria Res	20	11	5	4	68	36	32	38
4	Newton Heath 2nd Team	20	10	1	9	67	53	14	31
5	Santos	20	9	2	9	54	54	0	29
6	Hooley Bridge Celtic Res	20	8	1	11	46	59	-13	25
7	Heaton Mersey	20	8	0	12	31	51	-20	24
8	Rochdalians AFC Second	20	6	5	9	55	62	-7	23
9	Cheadle Hulme Athletic	20	7	0	13	47	57	-10	21
10	Manchester Polonia	20	5	3	12	36	71	-35	18
11	Chadderton Park	20	4	4	12	36	54	-18	16

LANCASHIRE AMATEUR LEAGUE

Premier Division

		P	W	D	L	F	A	GD	Pts
1	Failsworth Dynamos	26	22	3	1	95	19	76	69
2	Old Boltonians	26	16	4	6	86	45	41	52
3	Blackrod Town	26	15	5	6	65	38	27	50
4	Horwich St Mary's Victoria	26	16	1	9	74	40	34	49
5	Mostonians	26	13	5	8	51	42	9	44
6	Little Lever SC	26	10	6	10	71	59	12	36
7	Old Mancunians	26	10	5	11	53	44	9	35
8	Rochdale St Clements	26	9	8	9	65	68	-3	35
9	Oldham Hulmeians	26	9	5	12	69	75	-6	28*
10	Howe Bridge Mills	26	8	3	15	69	115	-46	27
11	Bury GSOB	26	7	4	15	45	82	-37	25
12	Old Blackburnians	26	7	3	16	39	74	-35	24
13	Whitworth Valley	26	5	6	15	59	87	-28	21
14	Tottington United	26	3	6	17	50	103	-53	15

Division One

		P	W	D	L	F	A	GD	PTS
1	Roach Dynamos	26	20	4	2	109	39	70	64
2	Prestwich	26	20	3	3	104	39	65	63
3	Rossendale FC	26	20	3	3	87	31	56	63
4	Ashtonians	26	15	3	8	61	48	13	48
5	Bolton Wyresdale	26	13	5	8	55	39	16	44
6	Failsworth Dynamos Res	26	12	3	11	52	56	-4	39
7	Thornleigh	26	11	5	10	68	59	9	38
8	Accrington Amateurs	26	12	2	12	66	70	-4	38
9	Castle Hill	26	10	2	14	56	77	-21	32
10	Wardle	26	8	3	15	76	84	-8	27
11	Old Boltonians Res	26	7	4	15	61	90	-29	25
12	Hesketh Casuals	26	7	1	18	51	88	-37	22
13	Radcliffe St Mary's	26	2	1	23	34	123	-89	7
14	Chaddertonians	26	4	3	19	41	78	-37	3*

Division Two

		P	W	D	L	F	A	GD	PTS
1	AFC Dobbies	26	20	4	2	82	49	33	64
2	Mostonians Res	26	19	3	4	88	38	50	60
3	Rochdale St Clements Res	26	17	2	7	78	55	23	53
4	Valley United FC	26	13	7	6	79	48	31	46
5	Astley & Tyldesley FC	26	12	5	9	65	58	7	41
6	Radcliffe JFC	26	10	6	10	79	68	11	36
7	Radcliffe Town	26	10	6	10	52	44	8	36
8	Horwich RMI	26	9	6	11	55	64	-9	33
9	Ainsworth	26	10	3	13	64	64	-11	33
10	Bolton Nomads	26	9	3	14	57	67	-10	30
11	Accrington Amateurs Res	26	5	9	12	50	62	-12	24
12	Bury GSOB Res	26	4	11	11	38	54	-16	23
13	Littleborough	26	5	3	18	39	90	-51	18
14	Oldham Hulmeians Res	26	2	6	18	37	91	-54	12

LEAGUE TABLES

Division Three

		P	W	D	L	F	A	GD	PTS
1	Horwich St Mary's Victoria Res	24	19	4	1	104	37	67	61
2	Old Blackburnians Res	24	18	3	3	83	26	57	57
3	Old Mancunians Res	24	18	0	6	71	41	30	54
4	Radcliffe Town Res	24	9	7	8	69	61	8	34
5	Bolton Lads Club	24	11	1	12	57	65	-8	34
6	Little Lever SC Res	24	10	3	11	76	82	-6	33
7	Thornleigh Res	24	10	3	11	61	74	-13	33
8	Old Boltonians A	24	10	2	12	53	72	-19	32
9	Rossendale FC Res	24	8	4	12	61	62	-1	28
10	Radcliffe Boys	24	8	3	13	65	68	-3	27
11	Rochdale St Clements A	24	6	6	12	55	71	-16	24
12	Hesketh Casuals Res	24	5	1	18	51	100	-49	16
13	Howe Bridge Mills Res	24	3	5	16	55	102	-47	14

Division Four

		P	W	D	L	F	A	GD	PTS
1	Old Blackburnians A	20	16	2	2	76	34	42	50
2	Blackrod Town Res	20	14	4	2	71	36	35	46
3	Lymm	20	13	2	5	85	30	55	41
4	Whitworth Valley Res	20	12	3	5	58	44	14	39
5	Old Mancunians A	20	11	3	6	69	50	19	36
6	Thornleigh A	20	10	1	9	60	50	10	31
7	Ashtonians Res	20	5	1	14	37	51	-14	16
8	Wardle Res	20	4	3	13	34	72	-38	15
9	Radcliffe St Mary's Res	20	4	2	14	52	86	-34	14
10	Little Lever SC A	20	6	0	14	43	113	-70	14*
11	Ainsworth Res	20	4	1	15	45	64	-19	13

Division Five

		P	W	D	L	F	A	GD	PTS
1	Howe Bridge Mills A	22	16	2	4	85	44	41	50
2	Radcliffe Town A	22	15	0	7	77	43	34	45
3	Oldham Hulmeians A	22	14	3	5	64	31	33	45
4	Bury GSOB A	22	12	3	7	67	52	15	39
5	Lymm Res	22	9	4	9	49	48	1	31
6	Old Mancunians B	22	10	1	11	52	58	-6	31
7	Tottington United Res	22	9	2	11	49	50	-1	29
8	Horwich RMI Res	22	8	4	10	46	48	-2	28
9	Bolton Wyresdale Res	22	8	3	11	54	61	-7	27
10	Rochdale St Clements B	22	6	3	13	31	63	-32	21
11	Astley & Tyldesley FC Res	22	6	3	13	29	64	-35	21
12	Wardle A	22	5	0	17	40	81	-41	15

Division Six

		P	W	D	L	F	A	GD	PTS
1	Radcliffe Boys Res	16	15	0	1	83	25	58	45
2	Lymm A	16	12	1	3	58	27	31	37
3	Thornleigh B	16	9	0	7	49	46	3	27
4	Oldham Hulmeians B	16	8	0	8	39	40	-1	24
5	Tottington United A	16	7	2	7	42	29	13	23
6	Old Boltonians B	16	7	1	8	37	38	-1	22
7	Bolton Wyresdale A	16	6	2	8	49	45	4	20
8	Radcliffe Town B	16	2	2	12	23	62	-39	8
9	Littleborough Res	16	2	0	14	34	102	-68	6

LANCASHIRE FOOTBALL LEAGUE

East

		P	W	D	L	F	A	GD	Pts
1	Yorkshire Amateur	14	10	2	2	40	14	26	32
2	Bradford RIASA	14	9	0	5	55	32	23	27
3	Brighouse Town	14	7	1	6	34	27	7	22
4	Thackley	14	7	1	6	38	35	3	22
5	Ossett Town	14	6	2	6	35	28	7	20
6	Liversedge	14	5	2	7	28	40	-12	17
7	Silsden	14	4	1	9	20	48	-28	13
8	RIASA East	14	3	1	10	27	53	-26	10

West Division

		P	W	D	L	F	A	GD	PTS
1	Chorley	16	11	0	5	49	27	22	33
2	AFC Fylde	16	10	1	5	60	36	24	31
3	Bamber Bridge	16	10	1	5	48	40	8	31
4	Barnoldswick Town	16	9	2	5	52	33	19	29
5	Colne	16	9	2	5	46	34	12	29
6	Charnock Richard	16	7	1	8	33	50	-17	22
7	Workington	16	5	3	8	28	37	-9	18
8	Ashton Athletic	16	4	2	10	34	50	-16	14
9	AFC Darwen	16	0	2	14	9	52	-43	2

South Division

		P	W	D	L	F	A	GD	PTS
1	Hyde	14	11	1	2	50	27	23	34
2	Curzon Ashton Dev	14	9	0	5	46	26	20	27
3	Stalybridge Celtic	15	7	3	5	37	28	9	24
4	RIASA South	15	7	2	6	42	42	0	23
5	FC United of Manchester	15	7	1	7	45	43	2	22
6	Buxton	15	5	2	8	34	46	-12	17
7	Witton Albion Dev	14	3	1	10	24	49	-25	10
8	Ashton United	14	2	3	9	23	43	-20	9
9	Stockport County	4	2	1	1	12	9	3	7

LEICESTER & DISTRICT FOOTBALL LEAGUE

Premier Division

		P	W	D	L	F	A	GD	Pts
1	Thurnby Rangers	22	18	3	1	90	30	60	57
2	Beaumont Town	22	18	0	4	64	39	25	54
3	Houghton Rangers	22	14	4	4	58	28	30	46
4	Cosby United	22	12	4	6	64	38	26	40
5	Magna 73	22	11	4	7	50	43	7	37
6	Thurlaston	22	8	3	11	47	41	6	27
7	Kingsway Rangers	22	8	2	12	41	54	-13	21*
8	Glen Villa	22	5	5	12	42	78	-36	20
9	Huncote	22	5	3	14	40	56	-16	18
10	Queniborough	22	6	1	15	46	67	-21	16*
11	Kibworth Town	22	4	4	14	39	71	-32	16
12	Burbage Old Boys	22	3	7	12	29	65	-36	16

Division One

		P	W	D	L	F	A	GD	PTS
1	Birstall RBL	22	19	0	3	87	32	55	57
2	Glenfield Town	22	17	1	4	92	22	70	52
3	Fleckney Athletic	22	15	1	6	93	32	61	46
4	Studs FC	22	14	1	7	78	45	33	43
5	Dunton & Broughton Utd	22	10	3	9	57	57	0	33
6	Cosby United Res	22	10	2	10	45	67	-22	32
7	Old Aylestone	22	8	6	8	61	78	-17	30
8	New Parks Social 2015	22	8	1	13	55	57	-2	19*
9	Belgrave	22	5	2	15	36	72	-36	15*
10	Ashby Road	22	4	3	15	33	82	-49	15
11	Beaumont Town Res	22	6	3	13	33	67	-34	12*
12	Leicester Three Lions	22	3	3	16	27	86	-59	6*

Division Two

		P	W	D	L	F	A	GD	PTS
1	Dunton & Broughton Utd Res	22	16	2	4	57	34	23	50
2	St Patricks	22	14	6	2	67	19	48	48
3	Northfield Emerald 2013	22	13	2	7	58	45	13	41
4	Huncote Res	22	11	4	7	53	47	6	37
5	Whetstone Athletic	22	11	2	9	56	52	4	35
6	Label Apeel FC	22	10	2	10	52	53	-1	32
7	Narborough Foxes	22	9	4	9	51	40	11	31
8	IQRA	22	9	2	11	70	68	2	29
9	Forest East	22	6	9	7	44	45	-1	27
10	Magna 73 Res	22	7	4	11	61	75	-14	25
11	North Kilworth	22	4	1	17	28	64	-36	13
12	Leicester Polska	22	2	2	18	41	96	-55	3*

Division Three

		P	W	D	L	F	A	GD	PTS
1	North Kilworth Res	20	16	2	2	82	28	54	50
2	Studs FC Res	20	16	0	4	61	20	41	39*
3	Glen Villa Res	20	12	3	5	61	40	21	36*
4	Lutterworth Athletic Dev	20	9	5	6	51	36	15	32
5	AFC Andrews	20	9	4	7	39	32	7	31
6	Glenfield Town Res	20	9	3	8	43	51	-8	30
7	Queniborough Res	20	8	2	10	51	52	-1	23*
8	Dunton & Broughton Dev	20	6	3	11	52	67	-15	21
9	Kibworth Town Res	20	5	1	14	37	75	-38	16
10	CFA FC	20	2	5	13	22	59	-37	11
11	St Patricks Res	20	3	2	15	35	74	-39	8*

LINCOLNSHIRE FOOTBALL LEAGUE

Premier Division

		P	W	D	L	F	A	GD	Pts
1	Skegness Town	28	23	0	5	114	25	89	69
2	Hykeham Town	28	21	3	4	79	36	43	66
3	Wyberton	28	18	1	9	75	42	33	55
4	Lincoln Moorlands Railway AFC	28	18	1	9	71	44	27	55
5	Horncastle Town	28	17	1	10	60	43	17	52
6	Immingham Town	28	14	4	10	69	58	11	46
7	Sleaford Sports Amateurs	28	13	3	12	55	56	-1	42
8	Grimsby Borough Res	28	12	5	11	61	48	13	41
9	Brigg Town FC Res	28	11	6	11	57	57	0	39
10	Louth Town	28	10	5	13	52	67	-15	35
11	CGB Humbertherm	28	10	4	14	37	73	-36	34
12	Nettleham	28	9	2	17	40	55	-15	29
13	Sleaford Town Res	28	6	3	19	35	101	-66	21
14	Market Rasen Town	28	4	2	22	25	84	-59	14
15	Ruston Sports	28	3	2	23	22	63	-41	11

LOWESTOFT & DISTRICT LEAGUE

Division One

		P	W	D	L	F	A	GD	Pts
1.	Mutford & Wrentham	22	18	3	1	73	23	50	57
2.	Oulton Broad	22	15	4	3	79	21	58	49
3.	AC Mill Lane	22	15	0	7	75	36	39	45
4.	Spexhall	22	10	4	8	53	44	9	34
5.	Norton Athletic	22	9	4	9	64	49	15	31
6.	The Crown	22	10	1	11	50	60	-10	31
7.	Barsham	22	8	5	9	49	52	-3	29
8.	Kirkley & Pakefield 'A'	22	7	7	8	35	50	-15	28
9.	Southwold Town	22	8	1	13	45	57	-12	25
10.	Hearts of Oak	22	7	3	12	39	80	-41	24
11.	First & Last	22	6	5	11	33	42	-9	23
12.	Ellingham	22	0	1	21	22	107	-85	-2

Division Two

		P	W	D	L	F	A	GD	Pts
1	Stanford	20	16	1	3	107	30	77	49
2	"Caister ""A"""	20	15	2	3	62	28	34	47
3	The Crown Res	20	12	3	5	74	45	29	39
4	Crusaders	20	10	3	7	51	52	-1	33
5	Kirkley & Pakefield B	20	9	3	8	59	52	7	30
6	Tudor Rose	20	8	4	8	51	62	-11	28
7	Bungay Town A	20	6	4	10	47	47	0	22
8	Spexhall Res	20	7	1	12	46	73	-27	22
9	Norton Athletic Res	20	5	6	9	28	47	-19	21
10	"Waveney ""A"""	20	5	3	12	34	49	-15	18
11	Carlton Colville Town	20	1	2	17	13	87	-74	2*

Division Three

		P	W	D	L	F	A	GD	Pts
1	Oxford Arms	18	17	1	0	98	11	87	52
2	Hopton	18	14	1	3	95	20	75	43
3	Belton Res	18	12	0	6	87	29	58	36
4	Art Eternal	18	10	1	7	53	37	16	31
5	Beccles Caxton Res	18	9	2	7	76	30	46	29
6	Gentlemens Club	18	7	4	7	53	45	8	22*
7	East Coast	18	6	2	10	41	56	-15	20
8	AC Mill Lane Res	18	5	2	11	35	94	-59	14*
9	Redwood United	18	3	1	14	28	71	-43	10
10	Nirvana Athletic	18	0	0	18	11	184	-173	0

LUTON DISTRICT & SOUTH BEDS FOOTBALL LEAGUE

Premier Division

		P	W	D	L	F	A	GD	Pts
1	Farley Boys	14	12	0	2	54	13	41	36
2	Houghton Rangers	14	11	1	2	51	22	29	34
3	North Sundon Wanderers	14	6	2	6	25	39	-14	20
4	Christians in Sport	14	6	1	7	40	47	-7	19
5	Sporting Lewsey Park	14	5	3	6	37	34	3	18
6	St Josephs	14	4	2	8	33	40	-7	14
7	Square FC	14	4	0	10	28	40	-12	12
8	Luton Leagrave AFC	14	3	1	10	27	60	-33	10

Division One

		P	W	D	L	F	A	GD	Pts
1	Jedenastka	14	10	2	2	56	32	24	32
2	Christians in Sport 2nd XI	14	10	1	3	70	27	43	31
3	Square FC 2nd X1	14	9	3	2	50	18	32	30
4	FC Kokan	14	9	2	3	52	27	25	29
5	Farley Boys 2nd X1	14	6	0	8	30	58	-28	18
6	FC Polonia	14	4	1	9	29	44	-15	13
7	Houghton Hatters	14	2	0	12	22	77	-55	6
8	Luton Aces	14	1	1	12	15	41	-26	4

LEAGUE TABLES

MERCIAN REGIONAL FOOTBALL LEAGUE

Premier Division

		P	W	D	L	F	A	GD	Pts
1	Oakengates Athletic	22	15	2	5	72	33	39	47
2	Rock Rovers	22	14	4	4	60	36	24	46
3	Church Stretton	22	12	4	6	58	38	20	40
4	Clee Hill United	22	13	1	8	68	53	15	40
5	Childs Ercall	22	11	2	9	56	44	12	35
6	Prees	22	10	3	9	64	59	5	33
7	Gobowen Celtic	22	10	3	9	62	67	-5	33
8	Madeley Sports	22	7	7	8	35	39	-4	28
9	Shifnal United 97	22	7	2	13	44	66	-22	23
10	Wrockwardine Wood	22	6	6	10	40	58	-18	21*
11	FC Hodnet	22	4	4	14	29	56	-27	16
12	AFC Bridgnorth Res	22	3	2	17	22	61	-39	11

Division One

		P	W	D	L	F	A	GD	Pts
1	Shrewsbury Juniors	32	24	2	6	151	38	113	74
2	Stoke Heath	32	22	6	4	150	61	89	72
3	Newport Town Res	32	23	2	7	92	36	56	71
4	Oakengates Rangers	32	22	4	6	140	56	84	70
5	Craven Arms Town	32	19	6	7	139	58	81	63
6	St Martins Village	32	18	5	9	111	66	45	59
7	FC Oswestry Res	32	18	3	11	87	82	5	57
8	Madeley Sports Res	32	17	5	10	81	56	25	56
9	Coven Utd	32	16	4	12	91	69	22	52
10	St Georges United	32	15	3	14	70	56	14	48
11	Riverside	32	11	4	17	53	74	-21	37
12	Brown Clee	32	11	3	18	73	79	-6	36
13	Whitchurch Alport Juniors	32	8	5	19	76	85	-9	29
14	AFC Broseley	32	9	1	22	42	128	-86	28
15	Albrighton FC	32	6	4	22	56	126	-70	22
16	Denso	32	3	1	28	33	237	-204	10
17	AFC Shifnal	32	1	0	31	38	176	-138	3

MID ESSEX FOOTBALL LEAGUE

Premier Division

		P	W	D	L	F	A	GD	Pts
1	Beacon Hill Rovers	21	14	4	3	61	34	27	46
2	Braintree & Bocking United	21	14	5	2	66	32	34	44*
3	CT 66	21	13	3	5	64	47	17	42
4	Haver Town	21	11	3	7	52	28	24	36
5	Bridge Hill	21	7	2	12	42	52	-10	20*
6	Silver End United	21	5	2	14	27	50	-23	17
7	Harold Wood Athletic A	21	5	2	14	29	61	-32	14*
8	Felsted Rovers	21	3	3	15	25	62	-37	12

Division One

		P	W	D	L	F	A	GD	Pts
1	St Clere's	24	19	2	3	91	30	61	59
2	Great Baddow Res	24	20	1	3	73	33	40	58*
3	Great Leighs Athletic	24	13	6	5	54	35	19	45
4	Dunmow Rhodes	24	13	2	9	55	32	23	41
5	Brentwood Athletic	24	12	4	8	67	36	31	40
6	Haver Town Res	24	8	2	14	45	53	-8	23*
7	South Woodham Ferrers United	24	6	3	15	32	57	-25	21
8	United Chelmsford Churches	24	5	0	19	41	85	-44	15
9	Rayleigh Town A	24	2	0	22	25	122	-97	3*

Division Two

		P	W	D	L	F	A	GD	Pts
1	Emeronians	20	15	3	2	46	18	28	48
2	Sandon Royals	20	13	3	4	44	31	13	42
3	Extreme United	20	13	2	5	58	28	30	41
4	Kenson	20	12	4	4	52	30	22	40
5	Stock United	20	9	4	7	42	25	17	31
6	Harold Wood Athletic B	20	9	4	7	30	33	-3	31
7	Mayland Village	20	7	5	8	33	31	2	26
8	Gosfield United	20	5	2	13	31	53	-22	17
9	Writtle Saturday	20	3	3	14	30	56	-26	12
10	CT 66 Res	20	4	3	13	36	57	-21	9*
11	Mundon Vics	20	1	5	14	23	63	-40	8

Division Three

		P	W	D	L	F	A	GD	Pts
1	Orsett & Thurrock Cricket Club	18	15	2	1	70	25	45	47
2	Writtle Res	18	13	1	4	42	31	11	40
3	Brentwood Athletic Res	18	13	3	2	54	14	40	39*
4	Hutton A	18	7	5	6	38	40	-2	23*
5	Boreham	18	6	4	8	28	32	-4	22
6	White Notley Res	18	6	1	11	38	51	-13	19
7	Dunmow Rhodes Res	18	7	1	10	47	40	7	16*
8	Beacon Hill Rovers Res	18	4	3	11	22	62	-40	15
9	Southminster St Leonards	18	6	2	10	40	39	1	14*
10	Silver End United Res	18	1	2	15	12	57	-45	-4*

Division Four

		P	W	D	L	F	A	GD	Pts
1	Writtle A	22	15	3	4	72	38	34	48
2	Baddow Athletic	22	15	1	6	60	36	24	46
3	Durning	22	14	2	6	57	30	27	44
4	Writtle Manor	22	13	4	5	58	42	16	43
5	Old Chelmsfordians A	22	12	4	6	48	38	10	40
6	Maldon Saints	22	10	4	8	55	50	5	34
7	Leigh Ramblers A	22	8	5	9	40	44	-4	29
8	Royal Oak	22	11	1	10	46	36	10	28*
9	Flitch United Res	22	6	2	14	40	58	-18	20
10	Gosfield United Res	22	4	5	13	46	64	-18	17
11	Marconi Athletic	22	3	1	18	24	74	-50	10
12	Tillingham Hotspur	22	5	0	17	38	74	-36	0*

Division Five

		P	W	D	L	F	A	GD	Pts
1	Southminster St Leonards Res	22	16	3	3	84	33	51	51
2	Braintree & Bocking United Res	22	15	1	6	73	30	43	46
3	United Chelmsford Churches Res	22	14	2	6	52	27	25	44
4	Burnham Ramblers A	22	14	1	7	66	35	31	40*
5	Old Chelmsfordians B	22	12	0	10	51	44	7	33*
6	Haver Town B	22	12	1	9	67	48	19	31*
7	Felsted Rovers Res	22	9	3	10	47	56	-9	30
8	Mundon Vics Res	22	9	1	12	44	66	-22	28
9	Valley Green	22	8	2	12	63	64	-1	23*
10	Beaulieu Park	22	6	2	14	34	54	-20	20
11	Kelvedon Social A	22	6	0	16	38	81	-43	18
12	Marconi Athletic Res	22	3	0	19	19	100	-81	6*

MAIDSTONE & DISTRICT FOOTBALL LEAGUE

Premier Division	P	W	D	L	F	A	GD	Pts
1 Malgo	16	11	3	2	62	30	32	36
2 Hunton	16	11	0	5	53	33	20	33
3 Hollingbourne	16	10	2	4	44	32	12	32
4 Lenham Wanderers	16	9	4	3	49	34	15	31
5 Mangravet	16	7	1	8	39	25	14	22
6 Marden Minors	16	6	1	9	36	43	-7	19
7 Headcorn	16	4	1	11	24	44	-20	13
8 Eccles	15	3	3	9	17	47	-30	12
9 Sittingbourne Lions	15	2	1	12	22	58	-36	7

10 Leybourne Athletic withdrew - record expunged.

Division One	P	W	D	L	F	A	GD	Pts
1 Ashford Ath Res	18	16	2	0	74	17	57	50
2 Eccles Res	18	12	3	3	79	26	53	39
3 Maidstone Athletic	18	9	3	6	62	58	4	30
4 Parkwood Jupitors	18	8	3	7	47	53	-6	27
5 Lenham Wanderers Res	18	7	5	6	46	31	15	26
6 Town Malling Club	18	6	8	4	38	32	6	26
7 Kings Hill Res	18	7	5	6	39	39	0	26
8 Ditton Minors	18	4	4	10	29	53	-24	16
9 West Farleigh Res	18	2	4	12	24	47	-23	10
10 Phoenix United	18	0	1	17	19	101	-82	1

MID LANCS FOOTBALL LEAGUE

Premier Division	P	W	D	L	F	A	GD	Pts
1 Southport & Ainsdale Amateurs	15	14	1	0	69	13	56	43
2 Bolton United	17	12	2	3	71	28	43	38
3 Standish St.Wilfrids	17	11	3	3	53	22	31	36
4 Eccleston & Heskin	17	11	1	5	53	31	22	34
5 Preston Wanderers	19	10	3	6	63	40	23	33
6 Fleetwood Hesketh	18	7	4	7	44	58	-14	25
7 Newman College	19	7	3	9	40	50	-10	24
8 Broughton Amateurs	19	5	4	10	40	56	-16	19
9 Hoole United	17	4	5	8	24	37	-13	17
10 Ribble Wanderers	15	4	1	10	30	54	-24	13
11 Walmer Bridge	17	3	0	14	30	51	-21	9
12 Penwortham Town	16	1	1	14	19	96	-77	4

MID-SOMERSET LEAGUE

Premier Division	P	W	D	L	F	A	GD	Pts
1 Coleford Athletic	18	16	0	2	80	21	59	48
2 Westfield Res	18	14	1	3	68	26	42	43
3 Frome Collegians	18	13	1	4	68	24	44	40
4 Radstock Town A	18	9	3	6	49	45	4	29*
5 Temple Cloud	18	7	3	8	38	33	5	24
6 Wells City A	18	6	3	9	36	57	-21	21
7 Mells & Vobster Utd	18	6	2	10	42	65	-23	20
8 Interhound,	18	6	2	10	31	54	-23	20
9 Purnell Sports Res	18	4	3	11	32	65	-33	15
10 Welton Arsenal,	18	0	0	18	26	80	-54	-1*

Division One	P	W	D	L	F	A	GD	Pts
1 Victoria Sports	18	16	2	0	84	16	68	50
2 Baltonsborough	18	12	3	3	66	25	41	39
3 Westhill Sports	18	12	2	4	55	27	28	38
4 Chilcompton Sports Res	18	9	1	8	46	38	8	28
5 Belrose	18	6	4	8	28	32	-4	21*
6 Chew Magna Res	18	6	2	10	36	49	-13	20
7 Clutton Res	18	5	3	10	30	49	-19	18
8 PILTON UNITED	18	4	3	11	26	56	-30	15
9 High Littleton	18	4	3	11	31	55	-24	11*
10 Meadow Rangers	18	3	3	12	24	79	-55	9*

Division Two	P	W	D	L	F	A	GD	Pts
1 Peasedown Albion	20	19	1	0	97	13	84	58
2 Bath Villa	20	15	3	2	78	30	48	48
3 Somer Valley Sports	20	13	1	6	54	42	12	40
4 Evercreech Rovers	20	10	4	6	59	38	21	34
5 Saltford Res	20	9	3	8	35	31	4	30
6 Coleford Athletic Res	20	7	2	11	36	42	-6	23
7 Frome Town Sports Res	20	5	4	11	32	62	-30	19
8 Westhill Sports Res	20	5	4	11	28	64	-36	19
9 Mells & Vobster Utd Res	20	5	3	12	38	63	-25	18
10 Pensford Res	20	5	4	11	41	56	-15	15*
11 Glastonbury Res	20	2	1	17	28	85	-57	3*

Division Three	P	W	D	L	F	A	GD	Pts
1 Peasedown Albion Res	16	11	3	2	67	24	43	36
2 Wessex	16	10	3	3	50	30	20	32*
3 Timsbury Athletic Res	16	7	7	2	57	27	30	28
4 Weston	16	8	3	5	51	33	18	27
5 Farrington Gurney	16	6	5	5	42	39	3	20*
6 Westfield A	16	5	3	8	32	51	-19	18
7 Purnell Sports A	16	4	4	8	33	42	-9	16
8 Chilcompton United	16	2	6	8	29	60	-31	9*
9 Pilton United Res	16	0	4	12	19	74	-55	4

MID SUSSEX FOOTBALL LEAGUE

Premier Division	P	W	D	L	F	A	GD	Pts
1 Lindfield	28	22	0	6	101	34	67	66
2 Willingdon Athletic	28	20	4	4	80	23	57	64
3 Balcombe	28	16	5	7	76	42	34	53
4 Cuckfield	28	16	5	7	78	47	31	53
5 Forest Row	28	13	9	6	64	42	22	48
6 Dormansland Rockets	28	14	3	11	74	65	9	45
7 Copthorne	28	13	5	10	71	53	18	44
8 Buxted	28	13	2	13	53	62	-9	41
9 AFC Varndeanians II	28	12	3	13	58	65	-7	39
10 Smallfield	28	11	5	12	53	55	-2	38
11 AFC Ringmer	28	10	5	13	44	71	-27	35
12 Rotherfield	28	8	8	12	43	56	-13	32
13 Peacehaven & Telscombe II	28	6	4	18	43	82	-39	22
14 Portslade Athletic	28	3	3	22	39	109	-70	12
15 Ditchling	28	0	5	23	17	88	-71	5

LEAGUE TABLES

Championship

		P	W	D	L	F	A	GD	Pts
1	Sporting Lindfield	18	12	3	3	66	33	33	39
2	Copthorne II	18	10	5	3	64	26	38	35
3	Nutley	18	9	5	4	57	31	26	32
4	AFC Uckfield Town II	18	8	3	7	52	46	6	27
5	Polegate Town	18	8	3	7	46	47	-1	27
6	AFC Haywards	18	7	5	6	33	33	0	26
7	Barcombe	18	7	2	9	38	54	-16	23
8	Ashurst Wood	18	6	2	10	27	48	-21	20
9	Roffey II	18	4	1	13	32	69	-37	13
10	Furnace Green Rovers	18	2	5	11	20	48	-28	11

Division One

		P	W	D	L	F	A	GD	Pts
1	Burgess Hill Albion	18	15	3	0	78	14	64	48
2	DCK Maidenbower	18	14	0	4	67	22	45	42
3	Hurstpierpoint	18	11	0	7	48	47	1	33
4	Ardingly	18	9	2	7	37	34	3	29
5	Ansty Sports & Social Club	18	9	1	8	49	40	9	28
6	Brighton & Sussex Medical School	18	8	3	7	46	41	5	27
7	Montpelier Villa AFC II	18	8	1	9	41	42	-1	25
8	AFC Varndeanians III	18	6	0	12	39	51	-12	18
9	Wivelsfield Green Pilgrims	18	2	1	15	28	77	-49	7
10	Alliance	18	2	1	15	21	86	-65	7

Division Two

		P	W	D	L	F	A	GD	Pts
1	West Hoathly	18	16	1	1	76	7	69	49
2	Crawley Devils	18	12	3	3	46	24	22	39
3	Copthorne III	18	9	4	5	43	31	12	31
4	Handcross Village	18	8	2	8	57	44	13	26
5	Plumpton Athletic	18	8	0	10	45	49	-4	24
6	Cuckfield Town	18	8	0	10	38	47	-9	24
7	Eastbourne Rangers II	18	6	3	9	40	45	-5	21
8	Felbridge	18	5	2	11	19	39	-20	17
9	Crawley Athletic	18	5	1	12	33	57	-24	16
10	Buxted II	18	4	2	12	21	75	-54	14

Division Three

		P	W	D	L	F	A	GD	Pts
1	Jarvis Brook II	16	12	3	1	69	12	57	39
2	Balcombe II	16	10	4	2	38	22	16	34
3	Willingdon Athletic II	16	9	3	4	35	26	9	30
4	Cuckfield II	16	8	2	6	32	27	5	26
5	Lindfield II	16	7	3	6	37	36	1	24
6	AFC Haywards II	16	6	2	8	29	41	-12	20
7	Dormansland Rockets II	16	5	3	8	29	42	-13	18
8	East Court	16	3	1	12	33	50	-17	10
9	Chagossian & Mauritian Association	16	1	1	14	18	64	-46	4

Division Four

		P	W	D	L	F	A	GD	Pts
1	Ridgewood	18	18	0	0	94	24	70	54
2	Stones	18	11	2	5	58	35	23	35
3	Montpelier Villa AFC III	18	10	3	5	65	35	30	33
4	Ashurst Wood II	18	9	4	5	55	52	3	31
5	Copthorne IV	18	8	4	6	40	42	-2	28
6	AFC Hurst	18	8	3	7	42	40	2	27
7	Rotherfield II	18	4	3	11	30	63	-33	15
8	Peacehaven & Telscombe III	18	4	3	11	26	59	-33	15
9	Wisdom Sports	18	4	1	13	32	58	-26	13
10	Portslade Athletic II	18	1	3	14	17	51	-34	6

Division Five

		P	W	D	L	F	A	GD	Pts
1	Burgess Hill Rhinos	16	12	1	3	59	28	31	37
2	Ifield Albion	16	11	2	3	51	29	22	35
3	Roffey III	16	10	1	5	39	20	19	31
4	Fletching	16	10	1	5	51	34	17	31
5	Polegate Town II	16	10	1	5	32	28	4	31
6	Ansty Sports & Social Club II	16	6	3	7	46	46	0	21
7	AFC Ringmer II	16	5	0	11	25	36	-11	15
8	Willingdon Athletic III	16	2	1	13	16	46	-30	7
9	East Row First	16	1	0	15	15	67	-52	3

Division Six

		P	W	D	L	F	A	GD	Pts
1	Bolney Rovers	18	15	2	1	85	16	69	47
2	Forest Row II	18	12	1	5	74	42	32	37
3	AFC Uckfield Town III	18	11	3	4	48	25	23	36
4	Burgess Hill Albion II	18	10	3	5	60	31	29	33
5	Scaynes Hill	18	10	3	5	51	33	18	33
6	Burgess Hill Athletic	18	9	3	6	50	44	6	30
7	Fairfield	18	4	1	13	26	60	-34	13
8	Ditchling II	18	3	3	12	19	66	-47	12
9	Plumpton Athletic II	18	4	0	14	26	88	-62	12
10	Newick	18	2	1	15	19	53	-34	7

Division Seven

		P	W	D	L	F	A	GD	Pts
1	AFC Bolnore	16	13	1	2	47	16	31	40
2	Nutley II	16	10	3	3	56	24	32	33
3	Ifield Galaxy Saturday	16	10	3	3	49	23	26	33
4	Maresfield Village II	16	7	2	7	31	37	-6	23
5	Furngate	16	6	2	8	38	42	-4	20
6	Handcross Village II	16	5	4	7	33	48	-15	19
7	Lindfield III	16	4	2	10	27	36	-9	14
8	Hartfield	16	4	2	10	23	46	-23	14
9	Ardingly II	16	3	1	12	26	58	-32	10

Division Eight

		P	W	D	L	F	A	GD	Pts
1	Crawley Panthers	16	13	1	2	63	30	33	40
2	DCK Maidenbower II	16	10	1	5	45	27	18	31
3	East Grinstead Town III	16	9	2	5	52	26	26	29
4	Cuckfield Developement	16	7	1	8	26	34	-8	22
5	AFC Uckfield Town IV	16	6	1	9	25	26	-1	19
6	Crawley United	16	5	4	7	41	51	-10	19
7	East Grinstead Meads	16	6	0	10	44	53	-9	18
8	Barcombe II	16	5	2	9	35	55	-20	17
9	Handcross Village III	16	4	2	10	30	59	-29	14

Division Nine

		P	W	D	L	F	A	GD	Pts
1	Keymer & Hassocks	18	16	1	1	64	21	43	49
2	Ringmer III	18	13	1	4	51	26	25	40
3	Stones II	18	10	5	3	64	43	21	35
4	Heath Rangers	18	10	1	7	56	42	14	31
5	Fletching II	18	9	1	8	41	46	-5	28
6	West Hoathly II	18	6	3	9	37	35	2	21
7	Fairwarp II	18	5	4	9	34	51	-17	19
8	Ashurst Wood III	18	4	3	11	44	51	-7	15
9	Scaynes Hill II	18	4	0	14	17	82	-65	12
10	Buxted III	18	2	3	13	25	36	-11	7

MIDLAND AMATEUR ALLIANCE

Premier Division

		P	W	D	L	F	A	GD	Pts
1	Old Elizabethans	20	19	1	0	98	20	78	58
2	Alvaston United	20	12	4	4	59	39	20	40
3	Nottinghamshire FC	20	10	4	6	76	39	37	34
4	Beeston Old Boys Association	20	10	4	6	50	28	22	34
5	Polonia Nottingham United	20	8	6	6	60	55	5	30
6	Derbyshire Amateurs	20	8	4	8	41	58	-17	28
7	Trent Vineyard	20	8	3	9	45	49	-4	27
8	Kirkby Athletic	20	7	2	11	37	65	-28	23
9	Ravenshead II	20	5	1	14	31	60	-29	16
10	Wollaton III	20	3	3	14	31	85	-54	12
11	Old Bemrosians	20	3	2	15	43	73	-30	10*

Division One

		P	W	D	L	F	A	GD	Pts
1	Bridgford United	26	19	3	4	96	39	57	60
2	Shirebrook Wanderers	26	18	3	5	119	30	89	57
3	Sutton Travellers	26	18	2	6	112	45	67	55*
4	Robin Hood Colts	26	17	3	6	89	38	51	54
5	ASHA FC	26	11	5	10	80	45	35	38
6	United Worksop	26	12	3	11	52	56	-4	38*
7	Manor FC	26	11	5	10	64	53	11	36*
8	Wollaton IV	26	11	3	12	79	77	2	35*
9	Ripley Town Res	26	9	6	11	78	66	12	33
10	Blidworth Welfare Red	26	8	6	12	54	70	-16	30
11	Nottinghamshire FC II	26	8	4	14	43	71	-28	28
12	AFC Bull Farm	26	8	2	16	68	117	-49	26
13	Ashfield FC	26	7	3	16	65	98	-33	24
14	Kirkby Athletic II	26	1	0	25	14	208	-194	3

MIDLANDS REGIONAL ALLIANCE

Premier Division

		P	W	D	L	F	A	GD	Pts
1	Rowsley 86	18	16	1	1	74	22	52	49
2	Derby Singh Brothers	18	12	2	4	35	23	12	38
3	Wirksworth Town	18	11	2	5	46	35	11	35
4	Allenton United	18	10	3	5	47	19	28	33
5	Wirksworth Ivanhoe	18	6	5	7	38	39	-1	23
6	Shirebrook Rangers	18	6	5	7	39	44	-5	23
7	Newhall United	18	4	5	9	33	42	-9	17
8	AFC Kilburn	18	4	5	9	29	45	-16	17
9	Cromford	18	3	4	11	18	45	-27	13
10	Allestree	18	1	2	15	17	62	-45	5

Division One

		P	W	D	L	F	A	GD	Pts
1	Castle Donington Cobras	18	14	3	1	70	23	47	45
2	Melbourne Dynamo	18	13	4	1	53	24	29	43
3	Chesterfield Town	18	12	2	4	58	29	29	38
4	Rowsley 86 Res	18	10	2	6	54	49	5	32
5	Matlock United	18	9	5	4	36	31	5	32
6	Little Eaton	18	7	3	8	37	45	-8	24
7	Moira United	18	5	3	10	27	35	-8	18
8	AFC Kilburn Res	18	2	5	11	22	52	-30	11
9	Sherwin Athletic	18	2	2	14	21	50	-29	8
10	Wirksworth Town Res	18	0	3	15	21	61	-40	3

Division Two

		P	W	D	L	F	A	GD	Pts
1	Burton Town	20	16	0	4	88	39	49	48
2	Mayfield	20	14	2	4	85	35	50	44
3	Willington Sports	20	13	2	5	51	24	27	41
4	Melbourne Dynamo Res	20	11	4	5	73	45	28	37
5	Matlock Town ADS	20	11	3	6	71	49	22	36
6	Rolls-Royce Leisure	20	9	1	10	40	41	-1	28
7	Punjab United	20	7	5	8	48	55	-7	26
8	Wirksworth Ivanhoe Res	20	7	1	12	40	45	-5	22
9	Littleover Dazzlers	20	5	4	11	49	46	3	19
10	Little Eaton Res	20	6	0	14	53	71	-18	18
11	Dimple	20	0	0	20	16	164	-148	0

NORTH BERKS FOOTBALL LEAGUE

Division One

		P	W	D	L	F	A	GD	Pts
1	Berinsfield	16	14	1	1	64	19	45	43
2	Saxton Rovers	16	12	1	3	42	27	15	37
3	Wallingford Town AFC	16	8	3	5	30	20	10	27
4	Kintbury Rangers	16	7	3	6	34	27	7	24
5	Long Wittenham Athletic	16	7	0	9	26	37	-11	21
6	Stanford-in-The-Vale	16	6	1	9	32	46	-14	19
7	East Hendred AFC	16	4	3	9	34	40	-6	15
8	Burghclere	16	3	5	8	35	41	-6	14
9	Lambourn Sports	16	2	1	13	17	57	-40	7

Division Two

		P	W	D	L	F	A	GD	Pts
1	Hungerford Town FC Swifts	18	17	1	0	74	18	56	52
2	Westminster	18	13	1	4	60	29	31	40
3	Steventon	18	12	0	6	51	30	21	36
4	Harwell Village	18	10	1	7	55	41	14	31
5	North Oxford	18	10	1	7	44	34	10	31
6	Hanney United	18	5	4	9	27	34	-7	19
7	Dorchester	18	6	1	11	30	45	-15	19
8	Kintbury Rangers Res	18	5	2	11	22	52	-30	17
9	Sutton Courtenay	18	4	2	12	26	43	-17	14
10	Faringdon Town Res	18	1	1	16	15	78	-63	4

Division Three

		P	W	D	L	F	A	GD	Pts
1	Watlington Town	18	13	3	2	57	28	29	42
2	Benson Lions	18	12	1	5	48	17	31	37
3	Ardington & Lockinge	18	11	3	4	60	34	26	36
4	Saxton Rovers Res	18	10	2	6	50	25	25	32
5	Compton	18	9	1	8	40	59	-19	28
6	Grove Rangers	18	8	1	9	42	37	5	25
7	Wallingford Town AFC Res	18	8	0	10	36	41	-5	24
8	Marcham	18	6	0	12	24	48	-24	18
9	Uffington United	18	5	1	12	28	58	-30	16
10	Highworth Town Dev	18	1	2	15	15	53	-38	5

Division Four

		P	W	D	L	F	A	GD	Pts
1	Blewbury	20	16	0	4	80	28	52	48
2	Burghclere Res	20	15	1	4	77	32	45	46
3	Coleshill United	19	13	1	5	80	38	42	40
4	Long Wittenham Athletic Res	20	13	0	7	56	35	21	39
5	Drayton	20	11	1	8	56	43	13	34
6	North Oxford Res	20	11	0	9	56	39	17	33
7	Lambourn Sports Res	19	10	2	7	22	40	-18	32
8	Stanford-in-The-Vale Res	20	6	1	13	38	64	-26	19
9	Berinsfield Res	20	4	3	13	39	82	-43	15
10	Dorchester Res	20	2	2	16	24	76	-52	8
11	Hagbourne United	20	1	3	16	25	76	-51	6

LEAGUE TABLES

Division Five

		P	W	D	L	F	A	GD	Pts
1	Grove Rangers Res	20	20	0	0	74	15	59	60
2	Wallingford Town AFC A	20	16	1	3	52	24	28	49
3	Coleshill United Res	20	12	1	7	63	45	18	37
4	Faringdon Town 'A'	20	10	3	7	46	45	1	33
5	Marcham Res	20	8	4	8	58	50	8	28
6	Hanney 66 Club	20	9	1	10	47	69	-22	28
7	Didcot Eagles	20	8	0	12	52	53	-1	24
8	Steventon Res	20	7	0	13	41	41	0	21
9	Sutton Courtenay Res	20	5	4	11	48	36	12	19
10	Uffington United Res	20	3	2	15	23	74	-51	11
11	Cumnor Minors	20	3	2	15	27	79	-52	11

Division Two

		P	W	D	L	F	A	GD	Pts
1	Hanslope Res.	26	20	5	1	123	30	93	65
2	Willen Res.	26	19	2	5	75	34	41	59
3	Wing Village Res	26	19	1	6	107	63	44	58
4	Silverstone Res.	26	18	1	7	94	56	38	55
5	Deanshanger Athletic Res.	26	17	3	6	100	35	65	54
6	Tattenhoe Res.	26	14	4	8	90	54	36	46
7	MK Wanderers Res.	26	11	5	10	53	42	11	38*
8	Buckingham United Res.	26	11	5	10	51	62	-11	38
9	Westbury	26	10	3	13	62	69	-7	33
10	Yardley Gobion Res.	26	7	4	15	59	92	-33	25*
11	Marsh Gibbon Res.	26	5	2	19	32	109	-77	17
12	Brackley Sports Res.	26	5	1	20	33	87	-54	16
13	Steeple Claydon Res.	26	3	3	20	30	87	-57	12*
14	Padbury Village Res.	26	2	3	21	25	114	-89	9*

NORTH BUCKS AND DISTRICT FOOTBALL LEAGUE

Premier Division

		P	W	D	L	F	A	GD	Pts
1	Potterspury	24	20	1	3	82	30	52	61
2	Stewkley	24	17	2	5	60	27	33	53
3	Great Horwood	24	16	3	5	88	37	51	51
4	Great Linford	24	14	3	7	51	37	14	45
5	Silverstone	23	14	3	6	47	39	8	45
6	Duston Dynamo's	24	11	4	9	61	40	21	37
7	Towcester Town	24	9	4	11	45	39	6	31
8	Deanshanger Athletic	24	8	5	11	50	49	1	29
9	Hanslope	23	8	5	10	46	45	1	29
10	Twyford United	24	6	5	13	47	64	-17	23
11	Brackley Sports	24	6	1	17	38	75	-37	19
12	Southcott Village R.A.	24	4	1	19	31	86	-55	13
13	Marsh Gibbon	24	3	1	20	28	106	-78	10

Intermediate Division

		P	W	D	L	F	A	GD	Pts
1	Wing Village	24	22	0	2	110	36	74	66
2	Willen	24	19	0	5	97	37	60	57*
3	Stoke Hammond Wanderers	24	15	0	9	90	51	39	45
4	Stony Stratford Town	24	13	4	7	73	46	27	43
5	Wicken Sports	24	13	2	9	63	56	7	41
6	AFC Santander	24	12	1	11	55	61	-6	37*
7	Yardley Gobion	24	10	4	10	57	60	-3	34
8	Potterspury Res.	24	10	1	13	50	73	-23	31*
9	Grendon Rangers Res.	23	7	2	14	42	75	-33	23
10	Great Horwood Res.	24	5	6	13	49	92	-43	21
11	MK Gallactico Res.	24	5	3	16	40	66	-26	18
12	Clean Slate Res	23	5	3	15	36	69	-33	18
13	MK Wanderers	24	5	2	17	37	77	-40	17

Syresham withdrew - record expunged.

Division One

		P	W	D	L	F	A	GD	Pts
1	City Colts	19	17	2	0	90	23	67	53
2	Olney	20	16	3	1	99	30	69	51
3	Steeple Claydon	20	12	3	5	40	32	8	39
4	Scot	21	11	5	5	59	42	17	38
5	Buckingham United	19	9	4	6	52	36	16	31
6	Tattenhoe	19	9	3	7	59	41	18	30
7	Padbury Village	21	6	3	12	30	50	-20	21
8	Great Linford Res.	19	6	1	12	40	52	-12	19
9	Stewkley Res.	19	5	0	14	33	84	-51	15
10	Towcester Town Res.	12	4	1	7	28	18	10	13
11	Southcott Village R.A. Res.	10	1	0	8	9	45	-37	3
12	University of Buckingham	19	0	1	18	14	99	-85	1

Stony Stratford Town Res. withdrew - record expunged.

NORTH DEVON FOOTBALL LEAGUE

Premier Division

		P	W	D	L	F	A	GD	Pts
1	Ilfracombe Town	28	25	2	1	150	20	130	77
2	Shamwickshire Rovers	28	22	1	5	122	39	83	67
3	Braunton	28	21	3	4	100	40	60	66
4	Boca Seniors	28	20	3	5	131	32	99	63
5	Park United	28	20	2	6	139	40	99	62
6	Bradworthy	28	16	3	9	77	75	2	51
7	Torrington	28	10	4	14	59	66	-7	34
8	North Molton Sports Club	28	10	6	12	79	89	-10	33*
9	Hartland	28	10	3	15	66	81	-15	33
10	Shebbear United	28	10	1	17	54	108	-54	31
11	Fremington	28	8	2	18	65	108	-43	26
12	Bideford Community AFC	28	7	4	17	43	90	-47	25
13	Landkey Town	28	6	2	20	57	102	-45	17*
14	Barnstaple FC	28	2	2	24	35	146	-111	8
15	Georgeham & Croyde	28	3	2	23	42	183	-141	8*

Division One

		P	W	D	L	F	A	GD	Pts
1	Ilfracombe Town Res	28	25	2	1	146	39	107	77
2	Sporting Barum	28	23	5	0	137	32	105	74
3	Braunton Res	28	22	1	5	121	36	85	67
4	Torridgeside Res	28	16	5	7	72	64	8	53
5	Shamwickshire Rovers Res	28	15	4	9	88	67	21	47
6	Kilkhampton	28	14	3	11	67	67	0	45
7	Merton	28	14	1	13	60	63	-3	40*
8	Pilton Academicals	28	12	1	15	72	67	5	37
9	Chittlehampton	28	9	3	16	65	92	-27	30
10	Stratton United	28	9	1	18	50	101	-51	28
11	High Bickington	28	8	2	18	40	89	-49	23*
12	Chivenor	28	6	4	18	60	98	-38	22
13	Northam Lions	28	6	4	18	56	96	-40	22
14	Combe Martin	28	6	2	20	51	101	-50	20*
15	Putford	28	6	2	20	38	111	-73	17*

Intermediate One

		P	W	D	L	F	A	GD	Pts
1	Appledore Res	26	21	0	5	121	34	87	63
2	Braunton Thirds	26	20	3	3	105	35	70	63
3	Ilfracombe Town Thirds	26	19	2	5	149	43	106	59
4	Fremington Res	26	17	4	5	106	43	63	55
5	Hartland Clovelly Res	26	14	0	12	86	74	12	42
6	Haxton Rangers	26	14	1	11	85	76	9	40*
7	Bideford CAFC Res	26	13	1	12	76	75	1	37*
8	South Molton	26	10	5	11	66	72	-6	35
9	Barnstaple FC Res	26	9	3	14	84	94	-10	30
10	Torrington Res	26	7	4	15	57	102	-45	25
11	Equalizers	26	7	2	17	59	120	-61	23
12	North Molton Sports Club Res	26	7	3	16	47	112	-65	21*
13	Morwenstow Res	26	4	5	17	58	117	-59	14*
14	Lynton & Lynmouth	26	3	1	22	42	144	-102	4*

Intermediate Two

		P	W	D	L	F	A	GD	Pts
1	Bridgerule	24	19	2	3	127	48	79	59
2	Northam Lions Res	24	19	2	3	110	38	72	59
3	Holsworthy Res	24	19	1	4	70	24	46	58
4	Braunton Fourths	24	13	3	8	68	53	15	42
5	Appledore Lions	24	13	2	9	90	53	37	41
6	Shebbear United Res	24	11	1	12	57	74	-17	34
7	Hartland Clovelly Thirds	24	11	1	12	79	54	25	31*
8	Georgeham & Croyde Res	24	10	1	13	82	86	-4	31
9	Woolsery	24	9	3	12	41	79	-38	30
10	Combe Martin Res	24	6	4	14	53	66	-13	19*
11	Bradworthy Res	24	6	2	16	48	101	-53	17*
12	Torridgeside Thirds	24	6	2	16	34	71	-37	14*
13	Park Rangers	24	1	2	21	32	144	-112	5

NORTH EAST NORFOLK LEAGUE

Division One

		P	W	D	L	F	A	GD	Pts
1	Runton United	20	20	0	0	124	14	110	60
2	Haisboro Athletic	20	18	0	2	96	30	66	54
3	Gimingham United	20	11	1	8	71	42	29	34
4	Cromer Youth Old Boys	20	10	3	7	48	39	9	33
5	Southrepps	20	8	1	11	39	58	-19	25
6	East Ruston	20	7	4	9	46	49	-3	24*
7	Aylsham A	20	7	2	11	39	61	-22	23
8	Holt United Res	20	5	4	11	31	66	-35	19
9	Felmingham	20	5	3	12	39	69	-30	17*
10	Hickling	20	5	3	12	31	75	-44	17*
11	Erpingham United	20	3	1	16	33	94	-61	10

Division Two

		P	W	D	L	F	A	GD	Pts
1	Briston	16	16	0	0	104	15	89	48
2	North Walsham Town A	16	11	2	3	57	26	31	35
3	Gimingham United Res	16	11	2	3	50	36	14	34*
4	Bacton	16	10	0	6	61	34	27	30
5	Stalham Town A	16	9	1	6	38	36	2	28
6	Southrepps Res	16	6	0	10	37	47	-10	17*
7	Holt United Colts	16	3	1	12	28	72	-44	9*
8	Greshams	16	1	3	12	19	40	-21	1*
9	Erpingham United Res	16	0	1	15	14	102	-88	-1*

NORTH GLOUCESTERSHIRE ASSOCIATION FOOTBALL LEAGUE

Premier Division

		P	W	D	L	F	A	GD	Pts
1	Whitecroft	24	18	3	3	86	24	62	57
2	Redbrook Rovers	24	16	5	3	92	42	50	53
3	Broadwell Res	24	17	2	5	65	34	31	53
4	Ellwood Res	24	15	5	4	61	31	30	50
5	Yorkley	24	12	2	10	40	40	0	38
6	Soudley	24	12	1	11	57	51	6	37
7	Bream Amts	24	9	5	10	68	58	10	32
8	Howle Hill	24	9	3	12	57	60	-3	30
9	Huntley	24	6	7	11	45	54	-9	25
10	Coleford Town	24	6	4	14	41	53	-12	22
11	Westbury Utd	24	5	6	13	37	65	-28	21
12	Ruardean Hill Rangers Res	24	4	3	17	23	80	-57	15
13	Viney St Swithins	24	3	2	19	22	102	-80	11

Division One

		P	W	D	L	F	A	GD	Pts
1	Harrow Hill Res	18	14	2	2	66	25	41	44
2	Lydbrook Athletic Res	18	12	5	1	54	37	17	41
3	Lydney Town A	18	11	4	3	56	30	26	37
4	Mushet & Coalway Utd	18	12	1	5	48	26	22	37
5	Tidenham	18	7	2	9	46	48	-2	23
6	Whitecroft Res	18	5	5	8	41	53	-12	20
7	Redmarley	18	6	1	11	37	56	-19	19
8	Blakeney	18	5	3	10	26	39	-13	18
9	Woolaston Res	18	4	1	13	30	57	-27	13
10	Westbury Utd Res	18	1	2	15	20	53	-33	5

Division Two

		P	W	D	L	F	A	GD	Pts
1	Worrall Hill	20	17	2	1	87	29	58	53
2	Mitcheldean Res	20	16	1	3	69	24	45	49
3	Newent Town Res	20	14	2	4	70	27	43	44
4	English Bicknor Res	20	12	3	5	43	24	19	39
5	Harrow Hill A	20	12	1	7	54	38	16	37
6	Coleford Town Res	20	8	4	8	49	51	-2	28
7	Lydbrook Athletic A	20	5	2	13	26	60	-34	17
8	Whitecroft A	20	5	1	14	25	67	-42	16
9	Longhope	20	4	1	15	31	65	-34	13
10	Ruardean Utd	20	3	3	14	24	68	-44	12
11	Ruardean Hill Rangers A	20	3	2	15	19	44	-25	11

Division Three

		P	W	D	L	F	A	GD	Pts
1	Milkwall	22	20	1	1	108	25	83	61
2	Ross Juniors	22	16	2	4	67	31	36	50
3	Puma FC	22	11	7	4	77	52	25	40
4	Rank Outsiders	22	12	2	8	55	38	17	38
5	Mushet & Coalway Utd Res	22	11	4	7	56	46	10	37
6	Redbrook Rovers Res	22	11	1	10	58	70	-12	34
7	Bream Amts Res	22	8	4	10	55	59	-4	28
8	Broadwell A	22	8	0	14	41	54	-13	24
9	St Briavels	22	7	0	15	53	69	-16	21
10	Newent Town A	22	5	2	15	38	87	-49	17
11	Weston	22	4	4	14	31	54	-23	16
12	Yorkley Res	22	4	3	15	39	93	-54	15

LEAGUE TABLES

Division Four

		P	W	D	L	F	A	GD	Pts
1	Sedbury Utd	20	18	1	1	107	25	82	43*
2	Milkwall Res	20	13	3	4	61	35	26	42
3	Newnham Utd	20	12	1	7	90	42	48	37
4	Tidenham Res	20	11	3	6	61	44	17	36
5	Mitcheldean A	20	11	0	9	54	51	3	33
6	Littledean	20	9	3	8	57	69	-12	30
7	Lydney Town B	20	8	2	10	49	47	2	26
8	Harrow Hill B	20	7	2	11	37	79	-42	23
9	Sling	20	6	1	13	37	50	-13	19
10	Blakeney Res	20	4	3	13	38	69	-31	15
11	Rank Outsiders Res	20	1	1	18	11	91	-80	4

Division Three

		P	W	D	L	F	A	GD	Pts
1	FC Polonia	22	18	2	2	111	37	74	56
2	East Leake Robins	22	16	4	2	93	45	48	52
3	Loughborough Emmanuel	22	15	2	5	86	36	50	47
4	Sileby Victoria Res	22	13	3	6	76	45	31	39*
5	Shepshed Amateurs Res	22	9	5	8	52	46	6	32
6	Loughborough United Res	22	10	3	9	63	72	-9	30*
7	Greenhill YC 'A'	22	6	5	11	55	74	-19	23
8	Woodhouse Imperial Res	22	7	4	11	46	60	-14	22*
9	Bottesford FC Res	22	6	4	12	46	90	-44	21*
10	Loughborough FC 'A'	22	8	1	13	60	75	-15	20*
11	Shepborough United	22	3	6	13	41	76	-35	15
12	Mountsorrel FC	22	1	1	20	25	98	-73	2*

NORTH LEICESTERSHIRE FOOTBALL LEAGUE

Premier Division

		P	W	D	L	F	A	GD	Pts
1	Caterpillar FC	18	12	4	2	56	22	34	40
2	Greenhill YC	18	11	3	4	49	29	20	36
3	East Leake FC	18	10	4	4	52	27	25	34
4	Mountsorrel Amateurs	18	10	2	6	59	35	24	32
5	Falcons FC	18	7	2	9	51	51	0	23
6	Sileby Victoria	18	6	2	10	38	49	-11	20
7	Ravenstone United	18	7	3	8	40	44	-4	18*
8	Sutton Bonington	18	5	3	10	31	69	-38	18
9	Sutton Bonington Academicals	18	7	0	11	38	55	-17	15*
10	Bottesford FC	18	2	3	13	31	64	-33	9

North West Norfolk League

Division One

		P	W	D	L	F	A	GD	Pts
1	AFC Lynn	24	22	2	0	127	22	105	68
2	Terrington	24	19	2	3	77	23	54	59
3	Redgate Rangers Res	24	16	2	6	77	41	36	50
4	Birchwood	24	14	4	6	83	33	50	46
5	Heacham Res	24	13	3	8	74	66	8	42
6	Bishops Lynn	24	13	2	9	74	50	24	41
7	Ingoldisthorpe	24	13	2	9	55	42	13	41
8	West Lynn	24	8	2	14	53	65	-12	26
9	Castle Rising	24	7	2	15	56	95	-39	23
10	River Lane Rangers	24	6	2	16	41	67	-26	20
11	Thornham	24	4	2	18	30	65	-35	14
12	Hunstanton	24	4	2	18	34	120	-86	14
13	Woottons (The)	24	3	1	20	29	121	-92	10

Division One

		P	W	D	L	F	A	GD	Pts
1	Wymeswold FC	20	17	1	2	73	29	44	52
2	Sporting Markfield	20	15	2	3	56	21	35	47
3	Cossington Saints	20	11	4	5	81	41	40	37
4	Castle Donington	20	11	3	6	51	36	15	36
5	Shepshed Amateurs	20	7	4	9	46	57	-11	25
6	Loughborough United	20	8	1	11	47	60	-13	25
7	Belton Villa	20	7	3	10	49	43	6	24
8	Greenhill YC Res	20	5	2	13	30	58	-28	17
9	Mountsorrel Amateurs Res	20	4	2	14	34	90	-56	13*
10	Thringstone MW	20	7	3	10	43	49	-6	12*
11	Caterpillar FC Res	20	3	5	12	33	59	-26	-1*

Division Two

		P	W	D	L	F	A	GD	Pts
1	Snettisham	26	23	2	1	101	31	70	71
2	Denver	26	19	1	6	87	38	49	58
3	Marshland Saints	26	19	0	7	71	29	42	57
4	Docking	26	17	3	6	82	32	50	54
5	South Creake	26	14	6	6	82	52	30	48
6	Heacham A	26	15	2	9	70	72	-2	47
7	Watlington Sports & Social Club	26	13	2	11	71	48	23	41
8	Pentney	26	10	2	14	55	72	-17	32
9	Gayton United A	26	8	6	12	56	55	1	30
10	Woottons (The) Res	26	8	5	13	49	53	-4	29
11	Ingoldisthorpe Res	26	8	5	13	61	75	-14	29
12	Birchwood Res	26	4	2	20	47	91	-44	14
13	Hungate Rovers	26	4	0	22	30	153	-123	12
14	Hunstanton Res	26	1	2	23	16	77	-61	

Division Two

		P	W	D	L	F	A	GD	Pts
1	Kegworth Imperial	18	17	0	1	77	28	49	51
2	Shelthorpe Dynamo	18	13	1	4	73	27	46	40
3	CK Dons	18	11	3	4	67	29	38	36
4	FC Coalville	18	11	3	4	62	32	30	36
5	Measham Welfare	18	8	1	9	59	62	-3	25
6	Market Bosworth	18	7	1	10	56	65	-9	22
7	Woodhouse Imperial	18	5	2	11	41	63	-22	17
8	Holwell Sports Dev	18	5	2	11	50	69	-19	13*
9	Castle Donington Res	18	3	2	13	27	68	-41	11
10	Birstall Old Boys	18	1	3	14	30	99	-69	-3*

NORWICH & DISTRICT SATURDAY FOOTBALL LEAGUE

Division One

		P	W	D	L	F	A	GD	Pts
1	Dussindale Rovers	20	17	2	1	109	20	89	53
2	Hethersett Athletic Old Boys	20	17	2	1	88	21	67	53
3	Norwich Eagles	20	13	1	6	93	38	55	40
4	Norman Wanderers	20	11	2	7	72	45	27	35
5	UEA A	20	10	4	6	57	43	14	34
6	Norwich Medics	20	9	2	9	47	39	8	29
7	Taverham	20	7	3	10	44	68	-24	24
8	Earsham Res	20	7	0	13	41	59	-18	17*
9	Heartsease Athletic	20	4	1	15	33	88	-55	13
10	Wensum Albion	20	1	5	14	37	97	-60	8
11	Home Care United	20	1	4	15	18	121	-103	7

NOTTS AMATEUR ALLIANCE

Premier Division

		P	W	D	L	F	A	GD	Pts
1	Beeston Rylands	26	22	1	3	118	44	74	67
2	Woodthorpe Park Rangers	26	20	4	2	95	43	52	64
3	Strelley Rose	26	17	2	7	103	58	45	53
4	Wollaton Hall & Bramcote	26	15	2	9	65	51	14	47
5	Premium	26	12	6	8	54	63	-9	42
6	Cranmer Arms	26	12	3	11	84	58	26	39
7	Sneinton Town	26	11	6	9	67	65	2	39
8	Arnold Saints	26	11	4	11	61	62	-1	37
9	Skegby United	26	9	4	13	52	62	-10	31
10	FC Geordie	26	9	2	15	62	89	-27	29
11	AC Wollaton	26	7	2	17	47	60	-13	23
12	Gedling Southbank Colts	26	6	5	15	52	78	-26	23
13	Arnold Samba	26	7	0	19	57	100	-43	21
14	Netherfield Seniors	26	3	1	22	50	134	-84	10

Division One

		P	W	D	L	F	A	GD	Pts
1	AFC Top Valley	24	21	2	1	114	23	91	56*
2	Nottingham Community	24	18	0	6	90	38	52	54
3	Corner Pin	24	16	5	3	83	47	36	53
4	AFC Villa	24	15	2	7	92	54	38	47
5	Nottingham Riverside United	24	14	2	8	95	65	30	44
6	Gedling Southbank A	24	11	4	9	80	61	19	37
7	Sneinton Town Pythian	24	9	4	11	65	69	-4	31
8	Beston	24	9	3	12	61	80	-19	30
9	Victory	24	7	3	14	61	95	-34	24
10	AFC Bridgford Res.	24	4	4	16	43	85	-42	19*
11	Mapperley	24	5	2	17	27	71	-44	17
12	Forest Park	24	5	1	18	38	89	-51	16
13	United Approach	24	4	4	16	37	109	-72	16

PERRY STREET AND DISTRICT LEAGUE

Premier Division

		P	W	D	L	F	A	GD	Pts
1	Barrington	18	14	2	2	59	23	36	44
2	South Petherton	18	12	4	2	59	19	40	40
3	Beaminster	18	12	1	5	70	24	46	37
4	Misterton	18	10	3	5	56	24	32	33
5	Shepton Beauchamp	18	10	2	6	36	29	7	32
6	Winsham	18	7	2	9	25	44	-19	23
7	Chard Utd.	18	6	3	9	38	46	-8	21
8	West & Middle Chinnock	18	3	4	11	26	46	-20	13
9	Netherbury	18	3	0	15	12	79	-67	9
10	Combe Res	18	2	1	15	17	64	-47	6*

Division One

		P	W	D	L	F	A	GD	Pts
1	Merriott Rovers	18	11	6	1	64	21	43	39
2	Pymore	18	11	3	4	55	26	29	36
3	Waytown Hounds	18	11	2	5	46	26	20	35
4	Forton Rangers	18	10	3	5	64	30	34	33
5	Hawkchurch	18	10	2	6	63	34	29	32
6	Ilminster Colts	18	10	2	6	37	27	10	32
7	Uplyme	18	7	2	9	51	40	11	23
8	Shepton Res	18	5	0	13	39	69	-30	14*
9	Combe A	18	2	2	14	36	69	-33	6*
10	South Petherton Res	18	1	2	15	22	135	-113	5

Division Two

		P	W	D	L	F	A	GD	Pts
1	Halstock	18	15	0	3	84	23	61	45
2	Chard Rangers	18	11	3	4	61	35	26	36
3	Farway United	18	11	3	4	61	35	26	36
4	Winsham Res	18	10	2	6	60	46	14	32
5	Charmouth	18	8	2	8	56	40	16	26
6	Dowlish & Donyatt	18	6	4	8	37	53	-16	22
7	Crewkerne Rangers	18	6	2	10	52	54	-2	20
8	Kingsbury	18	5	2	11	34	64	-30	17
9	Thorncombe	18	3	7	8	49	64	-15	16
10	Chard Utd. Res	18	2	1	15	23	103	-80	7

Division Three

		P	W	D	L	F	A	GD	Pts
1	Misterton Res	22	18	2	2	123	30	93	56
2	Forton Rangers Res	22	18	1	3	112	42	70	55
3	Uplyme Res	22	18	0	4	100	34	66	54
4	Thorncombe Res	22	10	3	9	60	57	3	33
5	Lyme Rovers	22	10	3	9	82	60	22	32*
6	Merriott Dynamos	22	9	3	10	56	70	-14	30
7	Crewkerne Rangers Res	22	8	5	9	57	50	7	29
8	Ilminster Town A	22	7	7	8	43	65	-22	28
9	Donyatt United	22	8	4	10	44	73	-29	28
10	Farway Res	22	4	4	14	47	85	-38	16
11	Chard Rangers Res	22	3	2	17	44	95	-51	11
12	Chard United All Stars	22	2	0	20	19	126	-107	5*

PLYMOUTH & WEST DEVON LEAGUE

Premier Division

		P	W	D	L	F	A	GD	Pts
1	The Windmill FC (Devon)	22	16	2	4	68	28	40	50
2	Plympton Athletic	22	15	4	3	72	33	39	49
3	Mount Gould FC	22	12	4	6	64	32	32	40
4	Bluebird United	22	11	4	7	52	43	9	37
5	Millbridge	22	10	5	7	61	54	7	35
6	University of Plymouth	22	11	0	10	55	46	9	31*
7	The Navy Inn	22	9	2	11	49	51	-2	29
8	Tavistock Community	22	8	3	11	39	53	-14	27
9	Chaddlewood Miners Old Boys	22	7	3	12	47	56	-9	24
10	WMOV DRDE Trust	22	8	0	14	40	81	-41	24
11	Maristow	22	2	3	17	33	91	-58	9
12	Roborough	22	6	3	13	39	51	-12	6*

Division One

		P	W	D	L	F	A	Gd	Pts
1	Lakeside Athletic	20	16	1	3	81	31	50	49
2	Morley Rangers	20	16	1	3	64	29	35	49
3	Millbridge 2nd	20	14	2	4	68	28	40	44
4	Plympton Athletic 2nd	19	10	2	7	62	40	22	32
5	Signal Box Oak Villa	20	9	2	9	42	45	-3	32*
6	DC Auto Repairs	20	8	4	8	47	58	-11	28
7	Plymouth Hope	20	8	2	10	54	54	0	23*
8	Pennycross SC	19	9	1	9	60	46	14	22*
9	Princetown	20	4	2	14	34	84	-50	14
10	Belgrave	20	3	2	15	26	73	-47	9
11	Hooe Rovers	20	2	2	16	25	75	-50	8

LEAGUE TABLES

Division Two

		P	W	D	L	F	A	GD	Pts
1	Chaddlewood Inn	14	11	1	2	59	20	39	34
2	Signal Box Frankfort 2nd	14	9	0	5	36	21	15	27
3	Melbourne Inn	14	7	1	6	38	35	3	22
4	WMOV DRDE Trust 2nd	14	6	3	5	23	35	-12	21
5	Woodford	14	5	0	9	23	40	-17	15
6	Staddiscombe Colts	14	4	2	8	27	46	-19	14
7	Millbridge 3rd	14	5	1	8	28	24	4	13*
8	Kitto FC	14	2	6	6	22	35	-13	12

Division Three

		P	W	D	L	F	A	GD	Pts
1	Lakeside Athletic 2nd	18	16	0	2	102	32	70	48
2	University of Plymouth 2nds	18	14	1	3	69	23	46	43
3	Signal Box Frankfort 3rds	18	9	2	7	76	54	22	29
4	Devonport FC	18	10	2	6	59	55	4	29*
5	Friary Vaults	18	8	3	7	47	49	-2	27
6	Victoria Park Rangers FC	18	8	1	9	51	47	4	25
7	Maristow 2nd	18	8	1	9	50	49	1	22*
8	Belgrave 2nd	18	5	1	12	38	60	-22	16
9	Tavistock Rovers	18	5	1	12	41	67	-26	13*
10	Princetown 2nd	18	1	0	17	23	120	-97	0*

PORTSMOUTH SATURDAY FOOTBALL LEAGUE

Premier Division

		P	W	D	L	F	A	GD	Pts
1	Horndean Hawks	12	8	3	1	35	14	21	24*
2	Wymering	12	6	3	3	34	23	11	21
3	Southsea Utd	12	3	3	6	36	40	-4	12
4	Bishops Waltham Dynamos	12	4	0	8	26	39	-13	12
5	Widbrook Utd	12	3	3	6	17	32	-15	12

Division One

		P	W	D	L	F	A	GD	Pts
1	Portchester Rovers	20	14	2	4	80	43	37	45*
2	AFC Ventora	21	13	2	6	81	50	31	41
3	Burrfields FC	20	11	2	7	70	55	15	36*
4	Segensworth FC	21	10	5	6	72	53	19	34*
5	Horndean Utd	21	10	2	9	75	60	15	32
6	Carberry	21	10	2	9	51	49	2	32
7	Fareport Town	21	4	1	16	35	87	-52	13
8	Drayton Town	21	2	2	17	30	97	-67	8

REDHILL & DISTRICT LEAGUE

Premier Division

		P	W	D	L	F	A	GD	Pts
1	Woodmansterne Hyde	14	11	1	2	61	19	42	34
2	Charlwood	14	10	1	3	50	26	24	31
3	South Godstone	14	8	2	4	42	37	5	26
4	AFC Walcountians	14	7	2	5	34	31	3	23
5	Holland Sports	14	5	2	7	33	35	-2	17
6	South Park A	14	5	2	7	29	46	-17	17
7	Walton Heath	14	2	1	11	23	49	-26	7
8	Nutfield	14	2	1	11	20	49	-29	7

Division One

		P	W	D	L	F	A	GD	Pts
1	AFC Hamsey Rangers	12	9	0	2	40	14	26	27*
2	South Park B	12	6	2	4	22	23	-1	20
3	Nomads Res	12	6	1	5	23	25	-2	19
4	Woodmansterne Hyde Res	12	6	0	5	20	22	-2	18*
5	Perrywood Sports	12	5	0	7	18	25	-7	15
6	Horley AFC	12	4	2	6	25	36	-11	14
7	Warlingham Res	12	2	1	9	18	21	-3	7

Division Two

		P	W	D	L	F	A	GD	Pts
1	Chipstead Res	16	14	2	0	68	17	51	44
2	Reigate OB	16	13	1	2	76	15	61	40
3	Warlingham A	16	11	2	3	54	29	25	35
4	Brockham	16	8	0	8	26	37	-11	24
5	Nutfield Res	16	7	1	8	40	41	-1	22
6	RH Athletic A	16	7	1	8	44	56	-12	22
7	Nomads A	16	3	0	13	27	56	-29	9
8	Horley AFC Res	16	2	2	12	22	77	-55	8
9	Oxted A	16	2	1	13	26	55	-29	7

ROMFORD & DISTRICT FOOTBALL LEAGUE

Division One

		P	W	D	L	F	A	GD	Pts
1	L Mac Spartans	12	11	0	1	60	12	48	33
2	AAH Romford	12	10	0	2	40	10	30	30
3	Lionside United	12	7	0	5	32	34	-2	21
4	Brentwood United	12	6	2	4	45	12	33	20
5	Gatcliffe FC	12	3	3	6	25	41	-16	12
6	New Star Soccer FC	12	1	1	10	21	54	-33	4
7	Upminster A	12	1	0	11	15	75	-60	3

SALISBURY & DISTRICT LEAGUE

Premier Division

		P	W	D	L	F	A	GD	Pts
1	D.I.UTD	15	11	3	1	54	18	36	36
2	Porton Sports	15	11	1	3	81	25	56	34
3	Sarum Youth (Sen)	15	9	2	4	55	33	22	29
4	Chalke Valley	15	7	2	6	33	30	3	23
5	Railway Social Club	15	3	0	12	27	54	-27	9
6	Value Cars	15	0	0	15	17	107	-90	0

SCUNTHORPE & DISTRICT FOOTBALL LEAGUE

Division One

		P	W	D	L	F	A	GD	Pts
1	Brumby	14	13	1	0	75	10	65	40
2	Crowle Town Colts	14	9	1	4	40	23	17	28
3	Limestone Rangers	14	7	1	6	34	35	-1	22
4	Barnetby United	14	6	3	5	33	21	12	21
5	Epworth Town	14	6	1	7	27	24	3	19
6	College Wanderers	14	5	3	6	28	20	8	18
7	Scunthonians	14	4	2	8	27	34	-7	14
8	Bottesford Town Res	14	0	0	14	9	106	-97	0

Division Two

		P	W	D	L	F	A	GD	Pts
1	Epworth Town Colts	16	13	1	2	60	20	40	40
2	Scotter United	16	12	1	3	58	16	42	37
3	The Butchers Arms	16	11	3	2	68	17	51	36
4	Ashby RAOB	16	9	1	6	46	35	11	28
5	East Drayton	16	7	2	7	39	43	-4	23
6	New Holland Villa	16	6	0	10	36	72	-36	18
7	Epworth Town Res	16	3	2	11	23	56	-33	11
8	Crosby Colts	16	3	1	12	24	67	-43	10
9	Limestone Rangers Res	16	2	1	13	29	57	-28	7

Division Three

		P	W	D	L	F	A	GD	Pts
1	Shape Changers	16	14	2	0	123	14	109	44
2	A.F.C. Blades	16	12	0	4	63	33	30	36
3	A.F.C. Queensway	16	11	0	5	40	34	6	33
4	Barnetby United Res	16	8	2	6	47	47	0	26
5	Briggensians	16	7	3	6	40	47	-7	24
6	Crosby Colts Res	16	5	4	7	36	52	-16	19
7	Scotter United Res	16	3	3	10	23	48	-25	12
8	Epworth Colts Blues	16	3	1	12	31	60	-29	10
9	Santon	16	1	1	14	24	92	-68	4

SOUTH DEVON FOOTBALL LEAGUE

Premier Division

		P	W	D	L	F	A	GD	Pts
1	Buckland Athletic 2nd	26	24	0	2	115	33	82	72
2	Waldon Athletic	26	19	2	5	77	48	29	59
3	East Allington United	26	15	2	9	67	40	27	47
4	Ashburton	26	13	5	8	70	46	24	44
5	Dartmouth AFC	26	12	5	9	64	45	19	41
6	Kingsteignton Athletic	26	12	5	9	53	45	8	41
7	Watcombe Wanderers	26	12	2	12	72	54	18	38
8	Upton Athletic	26	10	4	12	60	67	-7	34
9	Brixham AFC 2nds	26	9	3	14	47	73	-26	30
10	Ivybridge Town 2nd	26	8	5	13	53	72	-19	26*
11	Kingskerswell & Chelston	26	7	5	14	42	63	-21	26
12	Loddiswell Athletic	26	7	3	16	45	92	-47	24
13	Ipplepen Athletic	26	6	4	16	49	98	-49	22
14	Newton Abbot Spurs 2nd	26	4	3	19	40	78	-38	15

Division One

		P	W	D	L	F	A	GD	Pts
1	Roselands	24	23	0	1	110	21	89	69
2	Buckland Athletic 3rd	24	19	1	4	63	29	34	58
3	Paignton Villa	24	18	3	3	111	33	78	57
4	Newton Abbot 66	24	13	5	6	84	47	37	44
5	Harbertonford	24	13	3	8	77	40	37	42
6	Beesands Rovers	24	11	3	10	61	57	4	36
7	Chudleigh Athletic	24	11	2	11	57	49	8	35
8	Totnes & Dartington 2nds	24	8	5	11	51	76	-25	29
9	Stoke Gabriel 2nd	24	7	3	14	41	68	-27	21*
10	Babbacombe Corinthians	24	5	3	16	40	79	-39	18
11	Watcombe Wanderers 2nds	24	5	2	17	34	73	-39	14*
12	Bovey Tracey 2nds	24	4	0	20	36	102	-66	9*
13	Kingskerswell & Chelston 2nds	24	3	2	19	25	116	-91	8*

Division Two

		P	W	D	L	F	A	GD	Pts
1	Paignton Saints	26	20	4	2	106	36	70	64
2	Salcombe Town	26	18	4	4	107	44	63	58
3	Buckfastleigh Rangers	26	16	4	6	85	46	39	52
4	Liverton United 2nd	26	13	5	8	53	37	16	44
5	Brixham Town	26	12	5	9	92	57	35	41
6	Kingsteignton Athletic 2nds	26	13	2	11	63	60	3	41
7	AFC Staverton	26	13	2	11	68	46	22	38*
8	Hookhills United	26	11	5	10	74	64	10	38
9	Stoke Gabriel 3rds	26	9	8	9	59	51	8	32*
10	Teignmouth 2nd	26	9	2	15	40	105	-65	26*
11	Bishopsteignton United	26	7	2	17	56	101	-45	23
12	Newton United	26	5	5	16	53	94	-41	20
13	Dartmouth AFC 2nd	26	6	2	18	52	95	-43	20
14	Waldon Athletic 2nd	26	4	2	20	30	102	-72	14

Division Three

		P	W	D	L	F	A	GD	Pts
1	Torbay Police	24	20	1	3	135	37	98	61
2	Broadmeadow	24	17	2	5	69	29	40	53
3	Riviera United	24	17	1	6	83	36	47	52
4	Roselands 2nds	24	16	0	8	59	37	22	48
5	Meadowbrook Athletic	24	14	2	8	58	46	12	44
6	Chudleigh Athletic 2nds	24	13	0	11	54	70	-16	39
7	Harbertonford 2nd	24	12	1	11	55	45	10	37
8	Abbotskerswell	24	8	3	13	52	62	-10	27
9	Teign Village	24	7	3	14	45	87	-42	24
10	Ipplepen Athletic 2nds	24	7	1	16	50	61	-11	22
11	Upton Athletic 2nds	24	6	1	17	42	94	-52	19
12	East Allington United 2nd	24	5	3	16	41	79	-38	18
13	Buckfastleigh Rangers 2nds	24	4	2	18	31	91	-60	14

Division Four

		P	W	D	L	F	A	GD	Pts
1	Ashburton 2nd	27	23	2	2	130	43	87	71
2	Barton Athletic	27	19	2	6	93	44	49	59
3	Torbay Police 2nds	27	14	5	8	74	58	16	47
4	Kingsbridge & Kellaton United	27	14	3	10	69	68	1	45
5	Paignton Villa 2nds	27	12	3	12	77	85	-8	39
6	Newton Abbot 66 2nd	27	12	2	13	85	88	-3	38
7	Newton Rovers	27	9	5	13	59	59	0	32
8	Torquay Town	27	9	2	16	38	70	-32	29
9	Dittisham United	27	6	2	19	36	88	-52	17*
10	Broadhempston United	27	3	2	22	36	94	-58	11

Division Five

		P	W	D	L	F	A	GD	Pts
1	Bishopsteignton United 2nds	24	23	0	1	133	23	110	69
2	Riviera United 2nds	24	16	2	6	89	50	39	50
3	Babbacombe Corinthians 2nds	24	15	4	5	71	42	29	49
4	Paignton Saints 2nds	24	14	1	9	84	75	9	43
5	Newton United 2nd	24	12	4	8	63	50	13	40
6	Ilsington Villa	24	11	4	9	59	51	8	37
7	Stoke Fleming & Strete	24	10	6	8	65	44	21	36
8	Barton Athletic 2nds	24	9	3	12	72	91	-19	30
9	Watts Blake & Bearne AFC	24	9	1	14	64	80	-16	28
10	Chudleigh Athletic 3rds	24	7	5	12	66	92	-26	26
11	Brixham AFC 3rds	24	7	2	15	55	82	-27	23
12	Newton Rovers 2nds	24	3	3	18	37	96	-59	12
13	Malborough United	24	2	1	21	36	118	-82	7

SOUTH LONDON FOOTBALL ALLIANCE

Premier Division

		P	W	D	L	F	A	GD	Pts
1	Red Velvet	16	14	2	0	50	14	36	44
2	West Bromley Albion	16	12	0	4	60	34	26	36
3	Tudor Sports	16	10	0	6	40	30	10	30
4	Thames Borough	16	9	1	6	56	44	12	28
5	Croydon BR FC	16	7	1	8	28	33	-5	22
6	Kingsdale	16	6	0	10	35	47	-12	18
7	Our Lady Seniors	16	5	1	10	29	42	-13	16
8	Lewisham Athletic Res	16	4	0	12	30	56	-26	12
9	Golden Lion	16	2	1	13	24	52	-28	7

LEAGUE TABLES

Division One

		P	W	D	L	F	A	GD	Pts
1	Eltham Town	18	16	1	1	67	17	50	49
2	Old Bromleians Res	18	15	0	3	80	27	53	45
3	Old Colfeians	18	9	3	6	51	40	11	30
4	Johnson and Philips Res	18	8	2	8	36	39	-3	26
5	Farnborough O.B.G. 'A'	18	7	2	9	45	48	-3	23
6	Croydon BR Res	18	7	2	9	36	65	-29	23
7	Shirley Town	18	7	1	10	36	29	7	22
8	Seven Acre Sports	18	7	0	11	33	58	-25	21
9	Iron Tugboat City	18	5	1	12	44	60	-16	16
10	Danson Sports	18	2	2	14	21	66	-45	8

SOUTHAMPTON SATURDAY FOOTBALL LEAGUE

Premier Division

		P	W	D	L	F	A	GD	Pts
1	BTC Southampton	18	15	2	1	65	16	49	47
2	Chamberlayne Athletic	18	14	0	4	50	21	29	42
3	Nursling	18	9	3	6	52	40	12	30
4	AFC Gulf Western	18	9	2	7	35	21	14	29
5	Park Sports	18	8	5	5	28	22	6	29
6	Comrades	18	7	2	9	31	45	-14	23
7	Braishfield	18	6	4	8	43	45	-2	22
8	Southampton University	18	5	2	11	40	52	-12	17
9	Hedge End Town	18	4	1	13	29	57	-28	13
10	Durley	18	2	1	15	26	80	-54	7

Senior One

		P	W	D	L	F	A	GD	Pts
1	Bishops Waltham Dynamo's	14	11	2	1	43	19	24	35
2	Athletico Romsey	14	10	2	2	34	15	19	32
3	Alderbury	14	10	0	4	53	28	25	30
4	Montefiore Halls	14	7	1	6	44	34	10	22
5	Warsash Wasps	14	6	3	5	35	34	1	21
6	Priory Rovers	14	3	2	9	25	33	-8	11
7	AFC Botley	14	3	0	11	17	50	-33	9
8	Comrades Res	14	1	0	13	6	44	-38	3

Junior One

		P	W	D	L	F	A	GD	Pts
1	Upham Res	14	11	3	0	58	27	31	36
2	Park Phoenix	14	9	1	4	37	39	-2	28
3	Compton	14	8	1	5	51	26	25	25
4	Capital	14	8	1	5	46	32	14	25
5	Knightwood Utd	14	6	3	5	32	29	3	21
6	Langley Manor	14	4	0	10	25	45	-20	12
7	AFC Phoenix XI	14	3	2	9	31	51	-20	11
8	Shamblehurst	14	1	1	12	15	46	-31	4

Junior Two

		P	W	D	L	F	A	GD	Pts
1	FC Independence	14	11	1	2	60	13	47	34
2	West Totton	14	10	1	3	43	20	23	31
3	Hamble Utd	14	7	3	4	42	38	4	24
4	Soton Medics	14	6	2	6	41	36	5	20
5	Forest Edge Rovers	14	6	1	7	34	38	-4	19
6	BTC Soton Res	14	6	1	7	22	35	-13	19
7	London Airways	14	2	2	10	15	48	-33	8
8	Durley Res	14	1	3	10	15	44	-29	6

Junior Three

		P	W	D	L	F	A	GD	Pts
1	Athletico Romsey Res	14	8	4	2	29	15	14	28
2	AFC Testwood	14	8	2	4	37	25	12	26
3	Hedge End Tn Res	14	7	4	3	37	28	9	25
4	AFC Hiltingbury	14	7	2	5	28	33	-5	23
5	West End Rovers	14	7	1	6	38	28	10	22
6	Hythe Aztecs	14	4	3	7	39	42	-3	15
7	Nomansland & Landford	14	4	0	10	23	48	-25	12
8	Inmar	14	1	4	9	27	39	-12	7

Junior Four

		P	W	D	L	F	A	GD	Pts
1	Sporting Wessex	16	12	0	4	60	20	40	36
2	Athletico Romsey A	16	12	0	4	55	19	36	36
3	Hythe Aztecs Res	16	10	2	4	54	27	27	32
4	Michelmersh & Timsbury	16	10	2	4	47	29	18	32
5	Braishfield Res	16	8	2	6	39	33	6	26
6	AFC Station	16	7	2	7	37	35	2	23
7	Compton Res	16	3	1	12	21	66	-45	10
8	Hamble Utd Res	16	3	0	13	19	52	-33	9
9	Botley Village	16	2	1	13	29	80	-51	7

SOUTHERN AMATEUR LEAGUE

Senior Division One

		P	W	D	L	F	A	GD	Pts
1	Polytechnic	20	15	4	1	51	18	33	49
2	Alleyn Old Boys	20	10	7	3	35	20	15	37
3	Nottsborough	20	10	2	8	29	31	-2	32
4	Old Wilsonians	20	9	2	9	32	37	-5	29
5	Old Owens	20	8	4	8	37	37	0	28
6	West Wickham	20	6	8	6	25	25	0	26
7	Old Garchonians	20	7	3	10	34	37	-3	24
8	Old Parkonians	20	7	3	10	27	34	-7	24
9	Winchmore Hill	20	5	6	9	29	33	-4	21
10	Crouch End Vampires	20	5	4	11	29	44	-15	19
11	NUFC Oilers	20	4	5	11	22	34	-12	17

Senior Division Two

		P	W	D	L	F	A	GD	Pts
1	East Barnet Old Grammarians	20	13	4	3	59	29	30	43
2	Bank of England	20	11	5	4	58	30	28	38
3	Actonians Association	20	10	5	5	40	23	17	35
4	Old Finchleians	20	8	6	6	39	38	1	30
5	Civil Service	20	8	5	7	24	26	-2	29
6	Merton	20	7	7	6	32	31	1	28
7	Ibis Eagles	20	7	4	9	39	43	-4	25
8	Alexandra Park	20	6	5	9	41	46	-5	23
9	HSBC	20	6	8	6	35	41	-6	23*
10	Weirside Rangers	20	5	3	12	28	50	-22	18
11	South Bank Cuaco	20	2	2	16	26	64	-38	8

Senior Division Three

		P	W	D	L	F	A	GD	Pts
1	Norsemen	24	21	0	3	80	34	46	60*
2	Old Lyonians	24	15	3	6	72	44	28	45*
3	Kew Association	24	13	3	8	68	41	27	42
4	Carshalton	24	13	5	6	56	33	23	41*
5	Broomfield	24	10	2	12	53	36	17	32
6	Old Blues	24	6	3	15	33	61	-28	21
7	AFC Oldsmiths	24	7	0	17	34	73	-39	21
8	Old Stationers	24	8	2	14	54	77	-23	20*
9	Old Salesians	24	5	2	17	36	87	-51	14*

Intermediate Division One

		P	W	D	L	F	A	GD	Pts
1	NUFC Oilers Res	18	13	3	2	51	25	26	42
2	West Wickham Res	18	11	4	3	41	26	15	37
3	Polytechnic Res	18	10	0	8	40	33	7	30
4	Alleyn Old Boys Res	18	6	4	8	29	36	-7	22
5	Nottsborough Res	18	6	4	8	28	41	-13	22
6	Old Garchonians Res	18	6	3	9	41	42	-1	21
7	Old Wilsonians Res	18	6	3	9	38	44	-6	21
8	Civil Service Res	18	6	3	9	23	32	-9	21
9	Actonians Association Res	18	6	2	10	25	27	-2	20
10	Old Parkonians Res	18	5	4	9	30	40	-10	19

Intermediate Division Two

		P	W	D	L	F	A	GD	Pts
1	Winchmore Hill Res	16	11	3	2	46	27	19	36
2	East Barnet Old Grammarians Res	16	7	4	5	41	28	13	25
3	Old Finchleians Res	16	8	1	7	43	47	-4	25
4	Ibis Eagles Res	16	8	0	8	35	44	-9	24
5	Crouch End Vampires Res	16	6	3	7	40	34	6	21
6	Bank of England Res	16	6	2	8	39	40	-1	20
7	Old Lyonians Res	16	6	2	8	39	43	-4	20
8	Alexandra Park Res	16	5	4	7	34	44	-10	19
9	Norsemen Res	16	5	1	10	30	40	-10	16

Intermediate Division Three

		P	W	D	L	F	A	GD	Pts
1	South Bank Cuaco Res	16	10	5	1	37	23	14	35
2	AFC Oldsmiths Res	16	10	1	5	37	26	11	31
3	HSBC Res	16	9	2	5	56	26	30	29
4	St James' Old Boys	16	8	1	7	36	24	12	25
5	Weirside Rangers Res	16	7	4	5	30	26	4	25
6	Merton Res	16	7	3	6	34	25	9	24
7	The Warren Res	16	6	1	9	29	29	0	19
8	Old Blues Res	16	3	1	12	14	48	-34	10
9	Kew Association Res	16	1	4	11	21	67	-46	4*

Junior Division One

		P	W	D	L	F	A	GD	Pts
1	Winchmore Hill 3rd	16	11	4	1	42	19	23	37
2	Nottsborough 3rd	16	9	4	3	38	25	13	31
3	Polytechnic 3rd	16	7	5	4	47	33	14	26
4	West Wickham 3rd	16	7	3	6	28	22	6	24
5	Old Parkonians 3rd	16	6	3	7	37	52	-15	21
6	Civil Service 3rd	16	5	2	9	43	41	2	17
7	Alleyn Old Boys 3rd	16	5	1	10	27	36	-9	16
8	Actonians Association 3rd	16	4	4	8	26	37	-11	16
9	Old Garchonians 3rd	16	4	2	10	32	55	-23	14

Junior Division Two

		P	W	D	L	F	A	GD	Pts
1	Alexandra Park 3rd	16	12	0	4	48	27	21	36
2	Old Finchleians 3rd	16	11	1	4	53	42	11	34
3	Carshalton 3rd	16	8	1	7	35	43	-8	25
4	Nottsborough 4th	16	6	4	6	40	32	8	22
5	Old Owens 3rd	16	8	1	7	36	41	-5	22*
6	Civil Service 4th	16	6	3	7	31	31	0	21
7	Old Parkonians 4th	16	5	3	8	36	45	-9	18
8	Old Wilsonians 3rd	16	4	3	9	38	45	-7	15
9	Merton 3rd	16	4	0	12	30	41	-11	12

Junior Division Three

		P	W	D	L	F	A	GD	Pts
1	Bank of England 3rd	18	15	2	1	75	30	45	47
2	South Bank Cuaco 3rd	18	11	1	6	55	44	11	34
3	HSBC 3rd	18	10	2	6	55	49	6	32
4	Old Finchleians 4th	18	8	7	3	69	45	24	31
5	East Barnet Old Grammarians 3rd	18	9	2	7	59	54	5	29
6	Winchmore Hill 4th	18	8	2	8	48	50	-2	26
7	Old Garchonians 4th	18	7	0	11	43	61	-18	21
8	Crouch End Vampires 3rd	18	6	2	10	49	55	-6	20
9	Actonians Association 4th	18	4	1	13	39	48	-9	13
10	Old Blues 3rd	18	2	1	15	24	80	-56	7

Junior Division Four

		P	W	D	L	F	A	GD	Pts
1	Alleyn Old Boys 4th	16	12	0	4	63	25	38	36
2	Old Parkonians 5th	16	8	4	4	45	23	22	28
3	Polytechnic 4th	16	9	1	6	37	23	14	28
4	Ibis Eagles 3rd	16	7	4	5	45	33	12	25
5	AFC Oldsmiths 3rd	16	7	4	5	30	30	0	25
6	Alexandra Park 4th	16	6	4	6	31	40	-9	22
7	Civil Service 5th	16	5	4	7	42	42	0	19
8	Winchmore Hill 5th	16	6	0	10	38	39	-1	18
9	St James' Old Boys Res	16	1	1	14	20	96	-76	4

Minor Division One North

		P	W	D	L	F	A	GD	PTS
1	Norsemen 4th	16	15	0	1	71	21	50	45
2	Alexandra Park 5th	16	7	4	5	44	24	20	25
3	Winchmore Hill 6th	16	6	5	5	35	30	5	23
4	Old Parkonians 7th	16	7	2	7	28	40	-12	23
5	Old Owens 4th	16	6	4	6	47	45	2	22
6	Old Finchleians 5th	16	7	3	6	40	33	7	21*
7	Crouch End Vampires 4th	16	6	1	9	40	46	-6	19
8	Old Parkonians 6th	16	4	4	8	34	37	-3	16
9	East Barnet Old Grammarians 4th	16	1	3	12	24	87	-63	6

Minor Division Two North

		P	W	D	L	F	A	GD	PTS
1	Alexandra Park 6th	16	12	2	2	75	33	42	38
2	Norsemen 5th	16	11	0	5	52	32	20	33
3	Old Lyonians 3rd	16	9	3	4	61	34	27	30
4	Old Finchleians 6th	16	8	2	6	61	40	21	26
5	Broomfield Res	16	7	2	7	48	45	3	23
6	Broomfield 3rd	16	6	1	9	41	59	-18	19
7	Old Stationers Res	16	7	0	9	45	48	-3	18*
8	Old Lyonians 4th	16	4	3	9	25	51	-26	15
9	Winchmore Hill 7th	16	1	1	14	20	86	-66	4

Minor Division Three North

		P	W	D	L	F	A	GD	PTS
1	East Barnet Old Grammarians 5th	18	16	1	1	89	32	57	49
2	Winchmore Hill 8th	18	12	4	2	78	35	43	38
3	Norsemen 6th	18	10	3	5	64	43	21	33
4	Alexandra Park 7th	18	7	2	9	42	45	-3	23
5	Old Parkonians 9th	18	7	2	9	54	58	-4	23
6	Old Parkonians 8th	18	7	2	9	47	54	-7	23
7	Old Stationers 3rd	18	6	5	7	43	66	-23	22*
8	Alexandra Park 8th	18	6	2	10	43	75	-32	20
9	Crouch End Vampires 5th	18	4	5	9	30	42	-12	17
10	Old Finchleians 7th	18	1	4	13	36	76	-40	7

LEAGUE TABLES

Minor Division Four North

		P	W	D	L	F	A	GD	PTS
1	Old Owens 5th	18	12	3	3	72	34	38	39
2	Alexandra Park 10th	18	12	1	5	62	47	15	37
3	Norsemen 7th	18	11	2	5	66	40	26	35
4	Winchmore Hill 9th	18	7	4	7	64	58	6	25
5	Old Lyonians 5th	18	6	3	9	43	57	-14	21
6	Alexandra Park 9th	18	5	2	11	47	64	-17	14*
7	Crouch End Vampires 6th	18	2	1	15	32	86	-54	7

Minor Division One South

		P	W	D	L	F	A	GD	PTS
1	West Wickham 4th	16	14	2	0	55	10	45	44
2	Polytechnic 5th	16	11	2	3	66	21	45	35
3	Weirside Rangers 3rd	16	9	2	5	31	36	-5	29
4	Old Wilsonians 4th	16	8	1	7	33	28	5	25
5	Alleyn Old Boys 5th	16	5	3	8	27	29	-2	18
6	Actonians Association 5th	16	5	3	8	27	39	-12	18
7	Ibis Eagles 4th	16	4	3	9	22	34	-12	15
8	HSBC 4th	16	4	2	10	27	61	-34	14
9	HSBC 5th	16	2	2	12	22	52	-30	8

Minor Division Two South

		P	W	D	L	F	A	GD	PTS
1	Carshalton 4th	18	17	0	1	83	21	62	51
2	Actonians Association 6th	18	13	1	4	64	26	38	40
3	Polytechnic 6th	18	12	1	5	64	30	34	37
4	Ibis Eagles 5th	18	10	2	6	43	36	7	32
5	West Wickham 5th	18	8	3	7	33	27	6	27
6	Old Wilsonians 5th	18	6	2	10	39	55	-16	20
7	Bank of England 4th	18	6	0	12	34	51	-17	18
8	Civil Service 6th	18	5	2	11	25	57	-32	17
9	Merton 4th	18	4	0	14	35	52	-17	12
10	Lloyds Warren 3rd	18	3	1	14	21	86	-65	10

Minor Division Three South

		P	W	D	L	F	A	GD	PTS
1	Carshalton 5th	16	12	1	3	65	29	36	37
2	Alleyn Old Boys 6th	16	10	2	4	61	23	38	32
3	Old Salesians Res	16	8	5	3	53	34	19	29
4	Actonians Association 7th	16	8	5	3	32	27	5	29
5	Polytechnic 7th	16	6	5	5	45	35	10	23
6	West Wickham 6th	16	5	2	9	42	44	-2	17
7	South Bank Cuaco 4th	16	4	2	10	30	48	-18	14
8	Old Wilsonians 6th	16	4	2	10	25	52	-27	14
9	HSBC 6th	16	3	0	13	24	85	-61	9

Minor Division Four South

		P	W	D	L	F	A	GD	PTS
1	Polytechnic 9th	18	14	2	2	59	30	29	44
2	Kew Association 3rd	18	11	2	5	61	45	16	35
3	Ibis Eagles 6th	18	10	1	7	59	34	25	31
4	Actonians Association 8th	18	9	3	6	41	41	0	30
5	Merton 5th	18	9	2	7	33	38	-5	29
6	Civil Service 7th	18	7	3	8	43	38	5	24
7	South Bank Cuaco 5th	18	5	3	10	34	37	-3	18
8	Old Wilsonians 7th	18	5	3	10	29	44	-15	18
9	Polytechnic 8th	18	3	6	9	27	37	-10	15
10	HSBC 7th	18	4	1	13	28	70	-42	13

Minor Division Five South

		P	W	D	L	F	A	GD	PTS
1	Carshalton 6th	20	18	1	1	124	20	104	55
2	Civil Service 8th	20	14	1	5	78	36	42	43
3	Merton 6th	20	12	1	7	62	49	13	37
4	Alleyn Old Boys 7th	20	11	4	5	57	44	13	37
5	Old Blues 4th	20	8	4	8	48	54	-6	28
6	Merton 7th	20	8	4	8	47	63	-16	28
7	Bank of England 5th	20	8	1	11	47	45	2	25
8	Old Wilsonians 8th	20	7	4	9	45	57	-12	25
9	Old Salesians 3rd	20	7	2	11	39	56	-17	20*
10	South Bank Cuaco 6th	20	5	2	13	38	62	-24	17
11	Old Wilsonians 9th	20	0	0	20	12	111	-99	0

SOUTHEND BOROUGH & DISTRICT FOOTBALL COMBINATION

Premier Division

		P	W	D	L	F	A	GD	Pts
1	Leigh Town	16	10	5	1	33	15	18	35
2	Christchurch	16	11	1	4	40	22	18	34
3	Laindon Orient	16	11	0	5	45	22	23	33
4	Shoebury Town Res	16	9	2	5	33	34	-1	29
5	Railway Academicals	16	9	1	6	46	25	21	28
6	Bridgemarsh	16	7	3	6	37	31	6	24
7	Corinthians	16	6	2	8	30	26	4	20
8	Rochford Town Res	16	1	0	15	16	59	-43	3
9	Southend Rangers	16	1	0	15	14	60	-46	3

Division One

		P	W	D	L	F	A	GD	Pts
1	B.K.S. Sports	18	17	0	1	91	14	77	51
2	Leigh Town Res	18	13	3	2	61	30	31	42
3	Laindon Orient Res	18	11	3	4	77	31	46	36
4	Corinthians Res	18	12	0	6	53	39	14	36
5	Pitsea Athletic	18	7	2	9	51	49	2	23
6	Parkway Sports	17	5	6	6	29	41	-12	21
7	Rochford Town A	17	6	2	9	41	52	-11	20
8	Ashingdon Res	18	3	3	12	36	58	-22	12
9	Old Southendian A	18	3	1	14	15	86	-71	10
10	Southend Collegians	18	2	0	16	32	86	-54	6

Division Two

		P	W	D	L	F	A	GD	Pts
1	Bridgemarsh Res	18	14	1	3	54	23	31	43
2	Railway Academicals Res	18	13	1	4	81	33	48	40
3	Wakebury	18	12	3	3	54	22	32	39
4	Shoebury Town A	17	8	5	4	50	27	23	29
5	Laindon Orient Res	18	9	0	9	57	42	15	27
6	Ashingdon A	17	7	3	7	43	47	-4	24
7	Ekco Whitecaps	18	7	1	10	34	41	-7	22
8	Southend Sports A	18	5	3	10	39	57	-18	18
9	Weir Sports	18	4	3	11	51	71	-20	15
10	Southend Collegians Res	18	0	0	18	19	119	-100	0

Division Three

		P	W	D	L	F	A	GD	Pts
1	Earls Hall United	22	17	5	0	112	34	78	56
2	Leigh Town B	22	16	6	0	96	39	57	54
3	Ashingdon B	22	14	3	5	65	36	29	45
4	Southend Sports B	22	13	4	5	61	42	19	43
5	Thundersley Athletic	22	13	3	6	90	49	41	42
6	Landwick	22	8	5	9	69	58	11	29
7	Southend Rangers Res	22	8	2	12	47	57	-10	26
8	BKS Sports A	22	6	5	11	53	55	-2	23
9	Old Southendian B	22	7	2	13	61	70	-9	23
10	Railway Academicals A	22	4	3	15	45	96	-51	19
11	J.M.C. Athletic	22	3	4	15	40	95	-55	13
12	Southend Collegians A	22	0	1	21	17	125	-108	1

STROUD & DISTRICT FOOTBALL LEAGUE

Division One

		P	W	D	L	F	A	GD	Pts
1	Upton St Leonards	24	15	7	2	61	23	38	52
2	Old Richians	24	14	5	5	54	27	27	47
3	St Nicholas Old Boys	24	12	5	7	57	46	11	41
4	Barnwood United	24	11	4	9	42	29	13	37
5	Kings Stanley	24	11	3	10	43	36	7	36
6	Tetbury Town	24	10	5	9	51	33	18	35
7	Stroud United	24	10	7	7	47	45	2	34*
8	Charfield	24	9	7	8	38	44	-6	34
9	Stonehouse Town Res	24	8	6	10	45	51	-6	30
10	Tredworth Tigers	24	7	7	10	59	53	6	28
11	Frampton United Res	24	8	4	12	45	55	-10	28
12	Randwick	24	7	4	13	42	67	-25	25
13	Longford	24	1	2	21	14	89	-75	5

Division Two

		P	W	D	L	F	A	GD	Pts
1	Kingswood Res	24	18	4	2	76	29	47	58
2	Hardwicke Res	24	16	3	5	73	36	37	51
3	Horsley United	24	14	3	7	68	48	20	45
4	Quedgeley Wanderers Res	24	13	2	9	64	46	18	41
5	Cam Bulldogs Res	24	12	3	9	54	45	9	39
6	Tibberton United	24	10	5	9	57	55	2	32*
7	Didmarton	24	8	7	9	47	48	-1	31
8	Sharpness Res	24	9	4	11	56	58	-2	31
9	Bush	24	8	6	10	48	60	-12	30
10	Longlevens 3rds	24	7	3	14	59	87	-28	24
11	Eastcombe	24	5	5	14	46	88	-42	20
12	Tuffley Rovers 3rds	24	4	7	13	44	66	-22	19
13	AFC Phoenix	24	5	2	17	53	79	-26	17

Division Three

		P	W	D	L	F	A	GD	Pts
1	Minchinhampton	22	19	3	0	78	18	60	60
2	Rodborough Old Boys	22	16	4	2	77	26	51	52
3	Trident	22	14	6	2	56	29	27	48
4	Thornbury Town Res	22	11	3	8	56	38	18	36
5	Chalford Res	22	10	3	9	48	37	11	33
6	Arlingham	22	9	6	7	45	43	2	33
7	Whitminster Res	22	8	4	10	52	65	-13	25*
8	Uley	22	8	1	13	49	77	-28	25
9	McCadam	22	6	6	10	43	50	-7	24
10	Cotswold Rangers	22	4	3	15	39	78	-39	15
11	Tetbury Town Res	22	3	4	15	38	73	-35	13
12	Dursley Town Res	22	2	1	19	37	84	-47	4*

Division Four

		P	W	D	L	F	A	GD	Pts
1	Ramblers	24	18	4	2	74	24	50	58
2	Taverners Res	24	18	1	5	80	34	46	55
3	Upton St Leonards Res	24	16	3	5	77	27	50	51
4	Quedgeley Wanderers 3rds	24	13	5	6	58	30	28	44
5	Abbeymead Rovers Res	24	12	4	8	78	59	19	40
6	Hardwicke 3rds	24	8	4	12	39	48	-9	28
7	Frampton United 3rds	24	9	5	10	53	46	7	26*
8	Alkerton Rangers	24	9	2	13	41	77	-36	26*
9	Wickwar Wanderers	24	9	3	12	64	52	12	24*
10	Old Richians Res	24	8	0	16	33	71	-38	24
11	Avonvale United	24	8	2	14	47	64	-17	23*
12	Stonehouse Town 3rds	24	6	4	14	48	59	-11	22
13	Longford Res	24	3	1	20	32	133	-101	7*

Division Five

		P	W	D	L	F	A	GD	Pts
1	Kingsway Rovers	26	22	2	2	148	23	125	68
2	Tredworth Tigers Res	26	21	2	3	97	35	62	65
3	Tuffley Rovers 4ths	26	18	2	6	70	33	37	56
4	Barnwood United Res	26	17	2	7	103	39	64	53
5	Saintbridge	26	16	3	7	88	56	32	48*
6	Leonard Stanley Res	26	16	0	10	76	63	13	48
7	Wotton Rovers Res	26	14	3	9	70	56	14	45
8	Randwick Res	26	9	3	14	74	90	-16	30
9	Charfield Res	26	8	2	16	49	80	-31	26
10	Longlevens 4ths	26	11	1	14	61	75	-14	25*
11	Chalford 3rds	26	7	4	15	55	86	-31	25*
12	Berkeley Town Res	26	4	1	21	42	122	-80	13*
13	Horsley United Res	26	2	2	22	22	124	-102	5*
14	Brockworth Albion 3rds	26	3	1	22	22	95	-73	4*

Division Six

		P	W	D	L	F	A	GD	Pts
1	Painswick	24	18	2	4	87	31	56	56
2	Stroud Harriers Res	24	16	0	8	83	49	34	48
3	Kings Stanley Res	24	15	4	5	84	53	31	46*
4	Rodborough Old Boys Res	24	15	0	9	72	46	26	45
5	North Nibley	24	13	2	9	57	47	10	41
6	Cam Bulldogs 3rds	24	13	2	9	61	55	6	41
7	Uley Res	24	11	4	9	49	54	-5	37
8	Eastcombe Res	24	9	5	10	59	70	-11	32
9	Minchinhampton Res	24	9	3	12	63	59	4	30
10	Stroud United Res	24	6	4	14	61	87	-26	22
11	Sharpness 3rds	24	7	3	14	48	80	-32	21*
12	Cashes Green	24	4	0	20	37	104	-67	12
13	Longlevens 5ths	24	5	1	18	44	70	-26	10*

Division Seven

		P	W	D	L	F	A	GD	Pts
1	Bridgeway	24	18	5	1	128	27	101	59
2	Gloster Rovers	24	17	2	5	135	40	95	53
3	Kingsway Rovers Res	24	15	5	4	114	43	71	50
4	Abbeymead Rovers 3rds	24	15	3	6	72	59	13	45*
5	Cotswold Rangers Res	24	13	3	8	80	58	22	42*
6	Tuffley Rovers 5ths	24	13	1	10	60	46	14	40*
7	Cam Everside Wanderers	24	10	6	8	78	67	11	36
8	Tetbury Town 3rds	24	11	1	12	63	70	-7	34
9	Stonehouse Town 4ths	24	12	1	11	49	80	-31	34*
10	Rodborough Old Boys 3rds	24	6	2	16	41	74	-33	20
11	Randwick 3rds	24	5	0	19	47	95	-48	12*
12	Woodchester	24	4	0	20	49	142	-93	12
13	Uley 3rds	24	2	1	21	34	149	-115	7

STRATFORD UPON AVON FOOTBALL ALLIANCE

Division One

		P	W	D	L	F	A	GD	Pts
1	Badsey United	24	19	1	4	82	29	53	58
2	Claverdon AFC	24	18	4	2	83	32	51	58
3	Henley Forest	24	12	3	9	61	44	17	39
4	Feckenham Res	24	11	3	10	45	48	-3	36
5	Northfield Athletic	24	8	8	8	41	42	-1	32
6	Ilmington United	24	9	3	12	53	56	-3	30
7	Quinton	24	8	6	10	61	82	-21	30
8	Alcester Town Res	24	9	3	12	46	69	-23	30
9	Studley United	24	9	5	10	57	43	14	29*
10	South Redditch Athletic	24	9	2	13	54	60	-6	29
11	FISSC	24	7	6	11	45	50	-5	24
12	Alveston	24	7	4	13	49	74	-25	25
13	Shipston Excelsior Res	24	3	6	15	39	87	-48	15

LEAGUE TABLES

Division Two

		P	W	D	L	F	A	GD	Pts
1	FC Wickhamford	26	21	3	2	164	48	116	66
2	Central Ajax	26	19	2	5	100	29	71	59
3	Inkberrow A	26	17	5	4	121	40	81	56
4	Studley Rangers	26	17	5	4	96	41	55	56
5	Henley Forest Res	26	17	1	8	89	50	39	52
6	FC Stratford A	26	14	3	9	94	62	32	42*
7	Welford	26	12	4	10	101	54	47	40
8	Inkberrow Res	26	12	3	11	74	60	14	39
9	Bretforton Old Boys	26	11	2	13	81	93	-12	35
10	White Eagles	26	9	2	15	73	105	-32	29
11	Tysoe United	26	5	2	19	58	117	-59	17
12	Shipston Excelsior Colts	26	5	0	21	38	125	-87	15
13	Blockley Sports	26	4	0	22	32	193	-161	12
14	FISSC Res	26	3	0	23	32	136	-104	9

SURREY COUNTY INTERMEDIATE LEAGUE (WESTERN)

Premier Division

		P	W	D	L	F	A	GD	Pts
1	Royal Holloway Old Boys	24	16	6	2	62	27	35	54
2	University of Surrey	24	17	0	7	105	44	61	51
3	Chertsey Curfews	24	15	4	5	91	44	47	49
4	West End Village	24	14	2	8	81	58	23	44
5	Chobham Burymead	24	13	5	6	58	39	19	44
6	Cranleigh	24	13	4	7	58	39	19	40*
7	Knaphill Athletic	24	12	3	9	68	63	5	39
8	Woking & Horsell	24	10	4	10	48	42	6	34
9	Milford & Witley	24	7	1	16	32	73	-41	22
10	Shottermill & Haslemere	24	5	4	15	33	63	-30	19
11	Chiddingfold	24	5	4	15	39	77	-38	19
12	Windlesham & Lightwater	24	5	3	16	32	59	-27	18
13	Farnborough North End	24	1	6	17	33	112	-79	8*

Division One

		P	W	D	L	F	A	GD	Pts
1	Lyne Seniors	20	15	3	2	62	20	42	48
2	Worplesdon Phoenix	20	13	3	4	47	30	17	42
3	Manorcroft United	20	12	3	5	33	14	19	39
4	Keens Park Rangers	20	12	2	6	49	32	17	38
5	Hambledon	20	11	3	6	49	34	15	36
6	Guildford United	20	10	3	7	36	30	6	33
7	Old Salesians	20	7	4	9	43	39	4	25
8	Egham Athletic	20	4	3	13	37	51	-14	15
9	Weysiders	20	4	3	13	30	63	-33	15
10	Burpham	20	4	2	14	18	55	-37	14
11	Millmead	20	2	3	15	25	61	-36	9

SWINDON & DISTRICT FOOTBALL LEAGUE

Premier Division

		P	W	D	L	F	A	GD	Pts
1	Tawny Owl	20	20	0	0	117	22	95	60
2	Deers Leap	20	13	2	5	69	29	40	41
3	Bassett Bulldogs	20	13	0	7	57	36	21	39
4	Sportz Central	20	12	1	7	60	50	10	37
5	Swindon Spitfires	20	9	5	6	77	56	21	32
6	FC Dorcan	20	9	2	9	56	59	-3	29
7	Ramsbury	20	8	2	10	39	55	-16	26
8	Swindon Centurians	20	8	1	11	49	72	-23	25
9	Village Inn	20	4	3	13	37	64	-27	15
10	North Swindon WMC	20	4	1	15	36	97	-61	13
11	Spectrum	20	1	1	18	24	81	-57	4

Division One

		P	W	D	L	F	A	GD	Pts
1	Sport 4 Pinehurst	23	19	1	3	106	32	74	58
2	Old Town United	24	17	4	3	93	39	54	55
3	Lyneham	23	16	2	5	91	30	61	50
4	Lower Stratton	24	15	4	5	85	49	36	49
5	Stratton Juniors	24	11	4	9	55	52	3	37
6	Wroughton Res	24	11	3	10	67	47	20	36
7	Core Construction	24	10	4	10	77	63	14	34
8	New Town All Stars	24	10	1	13	47	74	-27	31
9	Marlborough Res	24	8	4	12	50	56	-6	28
10	Moredon	24	7	2	15	32	76	-44	23
11	Haydon Wick	23	5	7	11	44	67	-23	22
12	Chiseldon	24	3	1	20	35	96	-61	10
13	Swindon AFC	23	2	3	18	32	133	-101	9

TAUNTON & DISTRICT SATURDAY FOOTBALL LEAGUE

Division One

		P	W	D	L	F	A	GD	Pts
1	Bridgwater Sports	18	14	1	3	53	20	33	37*
2	Alcombe Rovers	18	10	2	6	38	20	18	32
3	Middlezoy Rovers Res	18	9	2	7	35	42	-7	29
4	Bishops Lydeard Res	18	7	3	8	48	37	11	24
5	Westonzoyland	18	6	5	7	36	21	15	23
6	Morganians	18	6	1	11	37	58	-21	19
7	Porlock	18	3	2	13	24	73	-49	8*

Division Two

		P	W	D	L	F	A	GD	Pts
1	Wembdon	20	14	4	2	48	21	27	46
2	Ash Rangers	20	14	3	3	62	29	33	45
3	North Petherton	20	12	3	5	53	32	21	39
4	Creech FC	20	11	5	4	58	38	20	38
5	Bridgwater Sports Res	20	8	5	7	49	47	2	29
6	Milverton Rangers	20	8	2	10	51	52	-1	26
7	Woolavington	20	8	5	7	47	49	-2	26*
8	Dulverton Town	20	5	5	10	36	60	-24	20
9	Watchet Town Res	20	5	4	11	45	51	-6	19
10	Stogursey	20	2	5	13	30	62	-32	11
11	Norton Fitzwarren	20	2	1	17	27	65	-38	7

Division Three

		P	W	D	L	F	A	GD	Pts
1	Bishops Lydeard Colts	16	11	2	3	63	28	35	35
2	Galmington Dragons	16	10	2	4	61	39	22	32
3	Bridgwater Grasshoppers	16	10	1	5	62	37	25	31
4	Bridgwater Wolves	16	10	1	5	48	31	17	31
5	Minehead Res	16	10	1	5	44	27	17	31
6	Redgate	16	7	1	8	35	33	2	22
7	Porlock Res	16	3	1	12	16	68	-52	10
8	Butlins FC	16	2	3	11	23	45	-22	9
9	Exmoor Rangers	16	2	2	12	21	65	-44	5*

Division Four

		P	W	D	L	F	A	GD	Pts
1	Staplegrove Res	20	15	2	3	69	31	38	47
2	White Eagles	20	14	0	6	69	40	29	42
3	North Curry	20	8	5	7	54	43	11	29
4	Nether Stowey	20	9	2	9	45	42	3	29
5	Bridgwater Sports Colts	20	9	1	10	62	47	15	28
6	Middlezoy Athletic	20	7	6	7	50	48	2	27
7	Norton Fitzwarren Res	20	8	5	7	53	48	5	26*
8	Berrow & Highbridge Town Res	20	7	3	10	51	58	-7	24
9	Hamilton Athletic Foxes	20	7	1	12	59	79	-20	22
10	North Petherton Res	20	5	4	11	38	62	-24	19
11	Morganians Res	20	5	3	12	41	93	-52	18

TROWBRIDGE & DISTRICT FOOTBALL LEAGUE

Division One

		P	W	D	L	F	A	GD	Pts
1	Melksham Town 'A'	20	17	1	2	69	16	53	52
2	Luxol St Andrews FC	20	15	3	2	62	17	45	48
3	Freshford United	20	14	3	3	77	27	50	45
4	Stockton & Codford FC	20	11	4	5	56	26	30	36*
5	Westbury Town	20	8	5	7	50	44	6	29
6	Warminster Town Res	20	7	4	9	52	44	8	25
7	Hilperton United	20	6	7	7	42	49	-7	25
8	Semington Magpies	20	3	6	11	29	45	-16	15
9	Trowbridge Town Res	20	3	6	11	25	74	-49	15
10	Westbury United Res	20	2	3	15	29	63	-34	9
11	Heytesbury	20	2	2	16	19	105	-86	8

Division Two

		P	W	D	L	F	A	Gd	Pts
1	Three Daggers FC	18	16	1	1	108	26	82	49
2	Calne Eagles	18	16	1	1	91	23	68	49
3	Trowbridge Town 'A' FC	18	11	1	6	42	27	15	34
4	Bradford Town Youth FC	18	11	1	6	63	27	36	32*
5	Warminster Town 'A' FC	18	9	0	9	61	62	-1	27
6	Aces FC	18	8	3	7	41	51	-10	27
7	Melksham Town 'B' FC	18	5	2	11	47	66	-19	17
8	Zeals FC	18	3	2	13	45	94	-49	11
9	The Stiffs	18	3	0	15	25	87	-62	9
10	Trowbridge Wanderers Dev	18	2	1	15	23	83	-60	7

WAKEFIELD & DISTRICT FA LEAGUE

Premier Division

		P	W	D	L	F	A	GD	Pts
1	Real Moor	16	15	1	0	104	29	75	43*
2	Crown Gawthorpe	16	9	3	4	65	30	35	30
3	Crackenedge	16	9	1	6	72	38	34	28
4	Eastmoor	16	7	1	8	42	39	3	22
5	Healdfield	16	7	1	8	49	50	-1	22
6	Prince of Wales (OCR)	16	8	0	8	52	53	-1	21*
7	Halton Moor	16	6	1	9	37	67	-30	19
8	Crofton Sports	16	4	2	10	31	56	-25	14
9	Fieldhead Hospital	16	1	2	13	19	109	-90	2*

Division One

		P	W	D	L	F	A	GD	Pts
1	Rock Inn	22	21	1	0	92	21	71	64
2	Royston Cross	22	18	2	2	98	23	75	56
3	FC Prince	22	16	2	4	76	32	44	50
4	Stanley United	22	13	4	5	50	52	-2	43
5	AFC Junction (Normanton)	22	12	3	7	69	40	29	39
6	Ossett Dynamos	22	8	2	12	34	63	-29	26
7	Durkar	22	10	1	11	49	48	1	25*
8	Ryhill	22	9	1	12	57	65	-8	25*
9	Red Lion Alverthorpe	22	6	0	16	37	83	-46	18
10	Pontefract Sports & Social	22	3	2	17	33	68	-35	11
11	Snydale Athletic	22	2	4	16	17	71	-54	10
12	Nostell Miners Welfare	22	1	4	17	25	71	-46	7

Division Two

		P	W	D	L	F	A	GD	Pts
1	New Pot Oil	24	19	3	2	97	25	72	60
2	Fox & Hounds (Batley)	24	17	2	5	111	54	57	53
3	Waterloo	24	15	4	5	97	37	60	49
4	Horbury Athletic	24	15	2	7	95	38	57	47
5	Overthorpe SC (Wfd)	24	11	3	10	62	64	-2	36
6	West End Terriers	24	12	2	10	88	61	27	35*
7	Henry Boons	24	11	2	11	60	55	5	35
8	Wakefield City	24	10	1	13	69	129	-60	31
9	Crofton Sports Res	24	8	4	12	65	83	-18	25*
10	Thornesians AFC	24	7	4	13	57	87	-30	22*
11	Snydale Athletic Res	24	7	4	13	55	86	-31	22*
12	Middleton Old Boys	24	3	2	19	44	113	-69	11
13	New Carlton	24	4	1	19	46	114	-68	7*

WEST RIDING COUNTY AMATEUR FOOTBALL LEAGUE

Premier Division

		P	W	D	L	F	A	GD	Pts
1	Lower Hopton	22	16	3	3	67	33	34	51
2	Newsome FC	22	15	5	2	70	24	46	50
3	Steeton	22	12	4	6	54	38	16	40
4	Littletown	21	12	3	6	56	42	14	39
5	Golcar United	22	10	5	7	61	45	16	37*
6	Lepton Highlanders	21	9	4	8	59	55	4	31
7	Huddersfield YMCA	22	8	5	9	61	48	13	29
8	Salts	22	9	1	12	47	54	-7	28
9	Honley FC	22	7	4	11	52	62	-10	24*
10	Campion	22	5	9	8	43	56	-13	24
11	D.R.A.M. Community FC	22	3	0	19	32	88	-56	9
12	Overthorpe Sports Club	22	2	3	17	30	87	-57	9

Division One

		P	W	D	L	F	A	GD	Pts
1	Thornton United	26	18	4	4	115	46	69	60*
2	Wakefield City	26	19	3	4	91	54	37	60
3	Route One Rovers	25	18	3	4	98	42	56	57
4	Holmfirth Town FC	26	16	4	6	96	43	53	52
5	Golcar United Res	26	15	5	6	67	40	27	50
6	Britannia Sports FC	26	14	5	7	75	47	28	47
7	West Horton	26	14	3	9	99	62	37	45
8	Wibsey	26	11	6	9	71	67	4	39
9	Ventus/Yeadon Celtic	25	9	0	16	54	83	-29	27
10	Steeton Res	26	7	5	14	52	68	-16	26
11	Tyersal	26	5	3	18	51	105	-54	15*
12	Churwell Lions FC	26	4	3	19	37	104	-67	15
13	Hunsworth	26	4	3	19	37	95	-58	14*
14	Westbrook YMCA	26	3	2	21	24	111	-87	12*

LEAGUE TABLES

Division Two

		P	W	D	L	F	A	GD	Pts
1	T V R United	14	11	2	1	97	30	67	37*
2	Salts Res	14	10	2	2	51	25	26	32
3	Bradford FC	14	8	2	4	58	37	21	26
4	Thornton United Res	14	7	1	6	50	56	-6	22
5	Littletown Res	14	6	1	7	44	63	-19	19
6	Tingley Athletic	14	4	1	9	37	46	-9	13
7	Lower Hopton Res	13	3	1	10	41	55	-14	10
8	Tyersal Res	14	1	2	11	21	87	-66	4*

WEST SUSSEX FOOTBALL LEAGUE

Premier Division

		P	W	D	L	F	A	GD	Pts
1	Nyetimber Pirates	22	17	4	1	68	23	45	55
2	Lavant	22	14	4	4	52	26	26	46
3	Henfield	22	10	4	8	67	66	1	34
4	T D Shipley	22	10	3	9	50	40	10	33
5	Newtown Villa	22	9	6	7	43	43	0	33
6	Rogate 08 FC	22	9	4	9	52	44	8	31
7	West Chiltington	22	10	0	12	53	56	-3	30
8	Wisborough Green	22	7	6	9	44	61	-17	27
9	Predators	22	8	2	12	29	46	-17	26
10	Hunston Community Club	22	7	4	11	43	55	-12	25
11	Petworth	22	6	3	13	36	55	-19	21
12	Holbrook	22	3	4	15	34	56	-22	13

Brockham FC withdrew - record expunged.

Championship North

		P	W	D	L	F	A	GD	PTS
1	Ashington Rovers	18	14	2	2	50	28	22	44
2	Southwater	18	10	4	4	55	36	19	34
3	Worthing Borough	18	10	3	5	51	28	23	33
4	Partridge Green	18	10	3	5	38	30	8	33
5	Pulborough	18	9	2	7	20	26	-6	29
6	Billingshurst Res	18	6	6	6	40	32	8	24
7	Alfold Res	18	8	0	10	44	45	-1	24
8	Upper Beeding Res	18	5	4	9	35	42	-7	19
9	Cowfold Res	18	3	3	12	22	47	-25	12
10	Horsham Trinity	18	1	1	16	21	62	-41	4

Championship South

		P	W	D	L	F	A	GD	PTS
1	Angmering Seniors	16	13	3	0	72	19	53	42
2	Stedham United	16	7	5	4	34	26	8	26
3	East Dean	16	6	7	3	51	37	14	25
4	Lancing United Res	16	7	4	5	40	47	-7	25
5	Harting	16	5	4	7	31	33	-2	19
6	Worthing Leisure	16	5	4	7	32	41	-9	19
7	Newtown Villa Res	16	5	3	8	36	44	-8	18
8	Fernhurst Sports	16	4	3	9	25	41	-16	15
9	Sidlesham Res	16	3	1	12	21	54	-33	10

Division Two North

		P	W	D	L	F	A	GD	PTS
1	Border Wanderers	16	11	3	2	45	19	26	36
2	Capel	16	10	5	1	57	19	38	35
3	Barns Green	16	10	5	1	44	23	21	35
4	Ewhurst	16	9	3	4	33	19	14	30
5	Rudgwick	16	5	3	8	45	44	1	18
6	Horsham Olympic	16	4	4	8	34	41	-7	16
7	Horsham Crusaders	16	4	3	9	21	50	-29	15
8	Holbrook Res	16	4	1	11	21	45	-24	13
9	Billingshurst 3rds	16	1	1	14	13	53	-40	4

Division Two South

		P	W	D	L	F	A	GD	PTS
1	The Unicorn	14	11	1	2	49	17	32	34
2	Angmering FC	14	10	2	2	52	20	32	32
3	Coal Exchange	14	8	2	4	44	27	17	26
4	Lavant Res	14	6	3	5	33	30	3	21
5	Hammer United	14	4	3	7	26	33	-7	15
6	The Crown FC	14	4	0	10	23	41	-18	12
7	Yapton	14	4	0	10	28	52	-24	12
8	Clymping Res	14	3	1	10	18	53	-35	10

Division Three North

		P	W	D	L	F	A	GD	PTS
1	Westcott 1935 FC	16	14	1	1	64	15	49	43
2	Henfield Res	16	11	3	2	53	34	19	36
3	Horsham Bap & Am	16	9	3	4	46	32	14	30
4	Thakeham Village	16	8	2	6	42	31	11	26
5	Newdigate	16	7	2	7	36	37	-1	23
6	Holbrook 3rds	16	5	3	8	34	38	-4	18
7	Slinfold	16	4	3	9	33	52	-19	15
8	Southwater Res	16	4	1	11	35	71	-36	13
9	Cowfold 3rds	16	1	0	15	20	53	-33	3

Division Three South

		P	W	D	L	F	A	GD	PTS
1	Nyetimber Pirates Res	16	13	2	1	53	14	39	41
2	Elmer FC	16	13	0	3	57	21	36	39
3	Yapton Res	16	7	3	6	50	30	20	24
4	Felpham Colts	16	5	6	5	42	45	-3	21
5	West Chiltington Res	16	6	1	9	26	43	-17	19
6	Why United	16	4	6	6	26	31	-5	18
7	Milland	16	4	5	7	30	44	-14	17
8	Hunston Community Club Res	16	3	3	10	19	45	-26	12
9	Beaumont Park	16	2	4	10	21	51	-30	10

Division Four North

		P	W	D	L	F	A	GD	PTS
1	Rowfant Village	18	14	3	1	88	20	68	45
2	Ewhurst Res	18	11	4	3	57	23	34	37
3	Wisborough Green Res	18	10	2	6	43	33	10	32
4	T D Shipley Res	18	9	2	7	44	25	19	29
5	Plaistow	18	8	5	5	45	38	7	29
6	Rudgwick Res	18	9	2	7	46	42	4	29
7	Partridge Green Res	18	6	4	8	38	45	-7	22
8	Newdigate Res	18	4	3	11	31	53	-22	15
9	Horsham Bap & Am Res	18	2	3	13	18	79	-61	9
10	Border Wanderers Res	18	2	2	14	15	67	-52	8

Division Four South

		P	W	D	L	F	A	GD	PTS
1	Watersfield	16	12	1	3	52	27	25	37
2	Fittleworth	16	11	4	1	48	23	25	37
3	Chapel	16	8	5	3	49	34	15	29
4	Barnham Trojans	16	7	5	4	39	28	11	26
5	Stedham United Res	16	5	2	9	40	33	7	17
6	Tangmere	16	4	5	7	20	30	-10	17
7	Ambassadors	16	3	5	8	29	47	-18	14
8	Fernhurst Sports Res	16	3	3	10	27	45	-18	12
9	Petworth Res	16	2	4	10	20	57	-37	10

LEAGUE TABLES

Division Five North

		P	W	D	L	F	A	GD	PTS
1	Capel Res	20	14	3	3	80	35	45	45
2	Southwater Royals	20	13	6	1	65	26	39	45
3	Westcott 1935 FC Res	20	14	1	5	82	42	40	43
4	Watersfield Res	20	11	3	6	63	28	35	36
5	Pulborough Patriots	20	9	3	8	50	52	-2	30
6	Holbrook 4ths	20	9	1	10	41	43	-2	28
7	Barns Green Res	20	7	4	9	48	63	-15	25
8	Southwater 3rds	20	6	4	10	40	59	-19	22
9	Slinfold Res	20	6	1	13	40	55	-15	19
10	Horsham Crusaders Res	20	5	1	14	25	68	-43	16
11	Horsham Olympic Res	20	1	3	16	33	96	-63	6

Division Five South

		P	W	D	L	F	A	GD	PTS
1	Lancing United 3rds	22	20	1	1	98	25	73	61
2	Littlehampton Town Athletic	22	15	1	6	59	37	22	46
3	Boxgrove	22	14	4	4	68	36	32	43*
4	Rogate 08 FC Res	22	15	1	6	77	33	44	37*
5	Angmering Seniors Res	22	11	4	7	77	49	28	37
6	Barnham Trojans Res	22	10	3	9	64	43	21	33
7	Harting Res	22	9	2	11	52	70	-18	29
8	Del United	22	8	2	12	49	57	-8	26
9	Milland Res	22	8	1	13	48	66	-18	25
10	Why United Res	22	5	1	16	34	56	-22	16
11	Lodsworth Res	22	5	1	16	27	99	-72	16
12	Fittleworth Res	22	1	1	20	18	100	-82	4

Arun Church withdrew - record expunged.

WESTMORLAND ASSOCIATION FOOTBALL LEAGUE

Division One

		P	W	D	L	F	A	GD	Pts
1	Pirelli	22	19	0	3	76	40	36	57
2	Keswick	22	16	4	2	65	27	38	52
3	Appleby	22	14	2	6	49	33	16	44
4	Windermere SC	22	12	2	8	50	38	12	38
5	Wetheriggs Utd	22	10	4	8	50	36	14	34
6	Kirkoswald	22	10	3	9	45	46	-1	33
7	Kendal Utd	22	7	9	6	44	43	1	30
8	Sedbergh Wanderers	22	8	5	9	39	39	0	29
9	Ibis	22	7	2	13	44	53	-9	23
10	Penrith Res	22	7	1	14	36	52	-16	22
11	Kendal County Res	22	3	2	17	28	68	-40	11
12	Ambleside Utd	22	1	2	19	23	74	-51	5

Division Two

		P	W	D	L	F	A	GD	Pts
1	Endmoor KGR	28	22	3	3	92	23	69	69
2	Shap	28	20	4	4	102	44	58	64
3	Kendal Utd Res	28	17	4	7	59	49	10	55
4	Eden Thistle	28	16	3	9	73	52	21	51
5	Castletown Utd	28	15	3	10	104	75	29	48
6	Keswick Res	28	13	2	13	58	53	5	44*
7	Carleton Banks	28	12	6	10	67	66	1	42
8	Wetheriggs Utd Res	28	14	0	14	83	87	-4	42
9	Dent	28	13	4	11	81	66	15	37*
10	Braithwaite	28	9	7	12	68	81	-13	34
11	Windermere SC Res	28	9	4	15	50	66	-16	31
12	Greystoke	28	7	5	16	62	84	-22	26
13	Staveley Utd	28	7	2	19	38	76	-38	23
14	Ullswater Utd	28	6	3	19	57	96	-39	21
15	Langwathby Utd	28	3	4	21	44	120	-76	13

Division Three

		P	W	D	L	F	A	GD	Pts
1	Appleby Res	26	21	1	4	106	44	62	64
2	AFC Carlisle	26	21	4	1	109	29	80	61*
3	Ambleside Town	26	18	2	6	105	44	61	56
4	Ibis Res	26	14	2	10	73	59	14	44
5	Sedbergh Wanderers Res	26	12	3	11	65	64	1	39
6	Endmoor KGR Res	26	11	5	10	93	63	30	38
7	Lunesdale Utd	26	12	1	13	66	70	-4	37
8	Penrith Royal	26	10	3	13	73	71	2	36*
9	Burneside Res	26	11	3	12	75	76	-1	36
10	Penrith Town	26	10	0	16	50	85	-35	30
11	Penrith Academy	26	9	2	15	54	87	-33	29
12	Kirkoswald Res	26	8	3	17	45	82	-37	21
13	Ambleside Utd Res	26	11	0	15	62	86	-24	15*
14	Penrith Saints	26	1	1	24	34	150	-116	4

WESTON SUPER MARE AND DISTRICT FOOTBALL LEAGUE

Division One

		P	W	D	L	F	A	GD	Pts
1	Draycott	18	14	3	1	83	28	55	45
2	Hutton	18	12	2	4	61	26	35	38
3	Locking Park	18	8	6	4	45	53	-8	30
4	Wrington Red Hill Res	18	8	1	9	47	46	1	25
5	Portishead Town A	18	6	5	7	40	41	-1	23
6	Sporting Weston	18	6	5	7	49	53	-4	23
7	Nailsea Utd A	18	5	5	8	50	48	2	20
8	K V F C	18	5	4	9	35	58	-23	19
9	Uphill Castle Res	18	4	4	10	47	62	-15	16
10	Cleeve West Town Res	18	2	5	11	32	74	-42	11

Division Two

		P	W	D	L	F	A	GD	Pts
1	Portishead Caledonian Thistle	18	17	1	0	99	31	68	52
2	Westend	18	14	3	1	81	26	55	45
3	Wedmore	18	10	2	6	68	48	20	32
4	South Park Rangers	18	7	3	8	52	53	-1	24
5	St George (EIG)	18	9	1	8	52	44	8	22*
6	Winscombe A	18	5	1	12	34	86	-52	15*
7	Worle Rangers	18	4	2	12	34	54	-20	14
8	Clapton in Gordano	18	4	2	12	41	72	-31	14
9	Yatton Ath Res	18	5	0	13	39	88	-49	14*
10	Berrow Res	18	7	1	10	50	48	2	12*

Division Three

		P	W	D	L	F	A	GD	Pts
1	Worle Res	18	10	6	2	58	27	31	36
2	Churchill Club 70 Res	18	11	3	4	52	34	18	36
3	Banwell Res	18	10	3	5	50	42	8	33
4	Axbridge Town	18	9	3	6	59	28	31	30
5	Locking Park Res	18	7	4	7	41	28	13	25
6	Cleeve West Town A	18	9	2	7	52	43	9	24*
7	Congresbury Res	18	7	3	8	46	49	-3	24
8	Worle Rangers Res	18	4	3	11	37	76	-39	15
9	AFC Nailsea	18	4	2	12	31	49	-18	14
10	Kewstoke Lions Res	18	3	3	12	33	83	-50	6*

LEAGUE TABLES

Division Four

		P	W	D	L	F	A	GD	Pts
1	Nailsea Utd B	16	12	1	3	61	23	38	37
2	St George (EIG) Res	16	11	0	5	44	29	15	33
3	Selkirk Utd	16	10	1	5	48	32	16	31
4	Shipham	16	10	2	4	53	39	14	31*
5	Portishead Town B	16	7	0	9	48	41	7	21
6	Wrington Redhill A	16	6	4	6	42	42	0	21*
7	Cheddar A	16	4	3	9	29	40	-11	15
8	Burnham Utd A	16	4	3	9	25	51	-26	15
9	AFC Nailsea Res	16	1	0	15	17	70	-53	3

Division Five

		P	W	D	L	F	A	GD	Pts
1	Uphill Castle A	18	15	2	1	76	31	45	47
2	Hutton Res	18	12	2	4	72	37	35	38
3	St Pauls Church FC	18	11	3	4	91	48	43	33*
4	Banwell A	18	10	2	6	55	47	8	29*
5	Congresbury A	18	7	2	9	49	76	-27	22*
6	Sporting Weston Res	18	6	3	9	62	66	-4	21
7	South Park Rangers Res	18	7	0	11	56	63	-7	21
8	Portishead Town Colts	18	5	5	8	45	51	-6	17*
9	Axbridge Town Res	18	4	4	10	36	61	-25	16
10	Wedmore Res	18	0	3	15	37	99	-62	3

WIGAN & DISTRICT AMATEUR LEAGUE

Premier Division

		P	W	D	L	F	A	GD	Pts
1	Winstanley St.Aidans	22	20	1	1	66	14	52	61
2	Digmoor	22	14	1	7	57	32	25	43
3	Hurlston Hall	22	13	2	7	54	38	16	41
4	Pemberton	22	10	5	7	49	43	6	35
5	Shevington	22	9	5	8	49	41	8	32
6	Newburgh Harrock United	22	9	4	9	53	38	15	31
7	Gidlow Athletic	22	8	4	10	53	54	-1	28
8	St.Judes	22	7	6	9	39	37	2	27
9	Bickerstaffe	22	7	2	13	43	49	-6	23
10	Ince Central	22	5	5	12	34	59	-25	20
11	Hindley Town	22	5	3	14	40	84	-44	18
12	Wigan Rovers	22	6	0	16	24	72	-48	18

Division One

		P	W	D	L	F	A	GD	Pts
1	Higher Ince	20	16	3	1	90	26	64	51
2	Leigh Foundry	20	15	3	2	65	28	37	48
3	AFC Scholes	20	11	3	6	64	37	27	36
4	AFC Tyldesley	20	9	6	5	47	38	9	33
5	Goose Green United	20	10	2	8	56	58	-2	32
6	AFC Coachouse	20	7	4	9	44	42	2	25
7	Sutton Junction	20	8	1	11	47	59	-12	25
8	Leigh Rangers	20	5	7	8	47	56	-9	22
9	Punchbowl	20	6	2	12	51	66	-15	20
10	Winstanley Warriors	20	5	0	15	27	67	-40	15
11	Black Bull	20	2	1	17	40	101	-61	7

Division Two

		P	W	D	L	F	A	GD	Pts
1	Rainford United	18	15	3	0	66	18	48	48
2	Tanner Athletic	18	11	3	4	50	37	13	35*
3	Winstanley Warriors Res	18	10	2	6	40	32	8	32
4	Daten 3rd	18	8	3	7	32	50	-18	27
5	HMP Hindley	18	8	2	8	48	31	17	26
6	Hag Fold	18	6	6	6	29	28	1	24
7	Ormskirk	18	7	2	9	44	45	-1	23
8	Ecclesfield	18	6	3	9	40	48	-8	21
9	The Village Inn	18	4	2	12	23	41	-18	13*
10	Whelley	18	1	2	15	24	66	-42	5

Division Three

		P	W	D	L	F	A	GD	Pts
1	Pemberton Athletic	22	19	0	3	120	24	96	57
2	Abram	22	20	0	2	113	42	71	57*
3	Gidlow Athletic Res	22	16	2	4	100	41	59	50
4	Newtown AFC	22	13	1	8	83	46	37	40
5	Tyldesley United	22	12	1	9	70	45	25	37
6	Wigan Rovers Res	22	11	1	10	60	61	-1	34
7	Sutton Junction Res	22	10	3	9	84	57	27	33
8	Ashton Villa	22	7	3	12	59	64	-5	24
9	Billinge Community	22	6	3	13	56	83	-27	21
10	Daten 4th	22	4	3	15	38	56	-18	15
11	Burscough Dynamo	22	3	3	16	31	105	-74	12
12	Red Lions	22	1	0	21	19	209	-190	3

YEOVIL AND DISTRICT LEAGUE

Premier Division

		P	W	D	L	F	A	GD	Pts
1	Templecombe Rovers	20	16	1	3	64	19	45	49
2	Normalair	20	14	1	5	87	46	41	42*
3	Montacute	20	13	2	5	53	27	26	41
4	Somerton Town Res	20	9	2	9	54	49	5	29
5	Wagtail Athletic	20	8	3	9	41	41	0	27
6	East Coker	20	7	5	8	49	52	-3	26
7	Martock United	20	7	3	10	48	80	-32	24
8	Castle Cary Res	20	7	1	12	35	51	-16	22
9	Ashcott	20	6	3	11	38	53	-15	21
10	Stoke	20	6	3	11	41	63	-22	21
11	Ilchester	20	4	2	14	40	69	-29	14

Division One

		P	W	D	L	F	A	GD	Pts
1	AFC Camel	22	20	1	1	126	33	93	61
2	Pen Mill	22	19	0	3	115	25	90	57
3	Keinton Park Rangers	22	14	3	5	84	46	38	45
4	Barwick & Stoford	22	12	2	8	54	52	2	38
5	Bradford Abbas	22	9	5	8	62	55	7	32
6	Charlton	22	8	4	10	52	72	-20	28
7	Ashcott Res	22	7	4	11	48	65	-17	25
8	Bruton United	22	7	4	11	49	67	-18	25
9	Aller Park Rangers	22	7	4	11	45	65	-20	25
10	Manor Athletic	22	7	1	14	48	73	-25	22
11	Mudford	22	6	4	12	38	73	-35	22
12	Odcombe	22	0	0	22	14	109	-95	0

Division Two

		P	W	D	L	F	A	GD	Pts
1	Brhoden United	22	17	2	3	108	34	74	53
2	Pen Mill Athletic	22	17	2	3	81	32	49	53
3	Perry Street Res	22	17	2	3	73	32	41	53
4	Odcombe Res	22	12	5	5	55	31	24	41
5	Pen Mill Res	22	12	1	9	62	57	5	37
6	Huish AFC	22	11	0	11	64	46	18	30*
7	Martock United Res	22	8	2	12	41	53	-12	26
8	Ilchester Res	22	8	3	11	47	62	-15	26*
9	Keinton Park Rangers Res	22	6	3	13	44	95	-51	21
10	Milborne Port A	22	4	6	12	34	49	-15	18
11	Stoke Res	22	4	2	16	28	77	-49	10*
12	Ashcott A	22	1	2	19	24	93	-69	5

YORKSHIRE AMATEUR LEAGUE

Premier Division

		P	W	D	L	F	A	GD	Pts
1	Farsley Celtic Juniors	20	15	2	3	67	25	42	47
2	Leeds Medics & Dentists	20	11	4	5	64	28	36	37
3	Stanley United	20	10	7	3	47	32	15	37
4	Alwoodley FC	20	10	4	6	44	37	7	34
5	Grangefield OB	20	9	3	8	53	48	5	30
6	Ealandians	20	9	3	8	56	43	13	27*
7	St. Nicholas	20	8	3	9	30	39	-9	27
8	Beeston Juniors	20	7	2	11	44	58	-14	23
9	Stanningley OB	20	6	4	10	35	49	-14	22
10	Farnley Sports	20	5	5	10	34	46	-12	20
11	Trinity & All Saints COB	20	1	1	18	22	91	-69	4

Championship

		P	W	D	L	F	A	GD	Pts
1	Drighlington FC	20	18	2	0	68	19	49	56
2	Morley Town AFC	20	13	1	6	75	40	35	40
3	Mount St. Mary's	20	13	1	6	57	26	31	40
4	Leeds Medics & Dentists Res	20	12	3	5	54	28	26	39
5	Wortley	20	10	2	8	48	52	-4	29*
6	Collingham Juniors OB	20	7	4	9	44	50	-6	25
7	Shire Academics	20	7	3	10	33	45	-12	24
8	Calverley United	20	5	3	12	35	47	-12	18
9	Beeston St. Anthony's	20	5	4	11	41	61	-20	16*
10	Thornesians	20	4	0	16	26	72	-46	12
11	Alwoodley FC Res	20	4	1	15	24	65	-41	10*

Division One

		P	W	D	L	F	A	GD	Pts
1	Gildersome Spurs OB	20	15	3	2	84	31	53	42*
2	St. Bedes AFC	20	13	3	4	60	32	28	42
3	Horsforth St. Margaret's	20	13	3	4	62	35	27	42
4	Leeds Independent	20	11	7	2	55	28	27	40
5	Huddersfield YMCA	20	12	2	6	46	35	11	35*
6	Garforth Rangers	20	6	3	11	43	48	-5	18*
7	Dewsbury Rangers FC	20	4	4	12	31	54	-23	16
8	Old Batelians	20	6	1	13	40	71	-31	16*
9	Rothwell	20	4	4	12	31	75	-44	16
10	Leeds Medics & Dentists III	20	3	6	11	36	56	-20	15
11	Farsley Celtic Juniors Res	20	4	2	14	38	61	-23	14

Division Two

		P	W	D	L	F	A	GD	Pts
1	Idle FC	20	17	1	2	82	32	50	52
2	Leeds City OB	20	13	3	4	76	37	39	42
3	Collegians	20	12	4	4	79	46	33	40
4	Ealandians Res	20	12	2	6	54	37	17	38
5	Colton Athletic	20	11	1	8	64	61	3	34
6	Sandal Wanderers	20	9	4	7	79	56	23	31
7	Morley Town AFC Res	20	8	2	10	51	63	-12	26
8	Woodkirk Valley	20	6	1	13	53	64	-11	19
9	Wheelwright OB	20	6	1	13	52	61	-9	16*
10	Lepton Highlanders	20	5	1	14	47	96	-49	16
11	Old Centralians	20	0	2	18	32	116	-84	2

Division Three

		P	W	D	L	F	A	GD	Pts
1	East Ardsley Wanderers	22	17	3	2	94	41	53	54
2	Fairbank United	22	16	5	1	96	35	61	53
3	Farnley Sports Res	22	13	2	7	84	61	23	41
4	Huddersfield Amateur	22	9	7	6	65	46	19	34
5	Norristhorpe	22	10	3	9	73	67	6	33
6	Leeds City OB Res	22	10	3	9	63	57	6	33
7	Leeds Medics & Dentists IV	22	10	3	9	51	64	-13	33
8	Leeds Modernians	22	9	2	11	61	68	-7	29
9	Shire Academics Res	22	8	4	10	56	67	-11	28
10	Churwell Lions	22	6	4	12	54	52	2	16*
11	Thornesians Res	22	2	1	19	36	122	-86	4*
12	FC Headingley	22	2	3	17	22	75	-53	3*

Division Four

		P	W	D	L	F	A	GD	Pts
1	Morley Town AFC III	18	13	2	3	54	28	26	41
2	Rodillian	18	13	1	4	51	26	25	40
3	Horsforth St. Margaret's Res	17	12	2	3	72	25	47	38
4	Colton Athletic Res	18	7	4	7	54	69	-15	25
5	North Leeds	18	6	4	8	51	65	-14	22
6	Ealandians III	17	6	2	9	44	58	-14	20
7	Trinity & All Saints COB Res	18	7	1	10	40	48	-8	19*
8	Beeston Juniors Res	18	6	2	10	43	42	1	17*
9	Woodhouse Moor Methodists	18	4	4	10	34	43	-9	13*
10	Wortley Res	18	3	2	13	26	65	-39	5*

Division Five

		P	W	D	L	F	A	GD	Pts
1	Garforth Crusaders	20	16	1	3	76	19	57	49
2	Leeds City OB III	20	13	2	5	81	47	34	41
3	Horsforth St. Margaret's III	20	13	0	7	60	33	27	36*
4	Drighlington FC Res	20	11	3	6	53	41	12	36
5	Shire Academics III	20	12	0	8	48	42	6	36
6	Methley United	20	9	2	9	50	58	-8	26*
7	Dewsbury Rangers FC Res	20	7	3	10	46	59	-13	24
8	Norristhorpe Res	20	7	1	12	64	78	-14	22
9	Woodkirk Valley Mens Res	20	6	1	13	61	73	-12	16*
10	St. Bedes AFC Res	20	4	2	14	45	77	-32	14
11	North Leeds Res	20	3	3	14	37	94	-57	12

Division Six

		P	W	D	L	F	A	GD	Pts
1	Morley United	20	16	3	1	87	22	65	51
2	Middleton Park	20	15	3	2	73	26	47	48
3	Rothwell Res	20	12	4	4	57	32	25	40
4	West End Park	20	13	1	6	66	49	17	40
5	Old Centralians Res	20	7	3	10	52	62	-10	24
6	Leeds City OB IV	20	7	3	10	48	70	-22	24
7	Old Batelians Res	20	8	2	10	49	62	-13	23*
8	Shire Academics IV	20	6	3	11	41	57	-16	18*
9	Huddersfield Amateur Res	20	5	1	14	45	59	-14	16
10	Leeds Modernians Res	20	4	4	12	33	54	-21	16
11	Thornesians III	20	2	3	15	30	88	-58	9

NORTHERN IRELAND TABLES 2016-17

IRELAND FOOTBALL ASSOCIATION

Premiership

		P	W	D	L	F	A	GD	Pts
1	Linfield	37	26	8	3	84	23	61	86
2	Crusaders	37	26	6	5	77	35	42	84
3	Coleraine	37	18	10	9	55	41	14	64
4	Cliftonville	37	17	7	13	54	47	7	58
5	Ballymena United	37	18	4	15	74	72	2	58
6	Glenavon	37	13	13	11	54	49	5	52
7	Dungannon Swifts	37	13	10	14	65	59	6	49
8	Ards	37	13	7	17	60	69	-9	46
9	Glentoran	37	12	9	16	44	52	-8	45
10	Ballinamallard United	37	9	5	23	41	71	-30	32
11	Carrick Rangers	37	5	7	25	30	75	-45	22
12	Portadown	37	7	4	26	28	73	-45	13*

Championship

		P	W	D	L	F	A	GD	Pts
1	Warrenpoint Town	31	21	6	4	74	34	40	69
2	Institute	31	15	9	7	60	37	23	54
3	Ballyclare Comrades	31	15	6	10	62	52	10	51
4	HW Welders	31	14	6	11	48	40	8	48
5	PSNI	31	12	10	9	45	43	2	46
6	Knockbreda	31	13	4	14	54	51	3	43
7	Dergview	31	12	6	13	66	51	15	42
8	Larne	31	11	7	13	51	48	3	40
9	Loughgall	31	12	3	16	53	55	-2	39
10	Lurgan Celtic	31	12	3	16	55	67	-12	39
11	Armagh City	31	9	7	15	40	53	-13	34
12	Annagh United	31	3	7	21	29	106	-77	16

Premier Intermediate League

		P	W	D	L	F	A	GD	Pts
1	Limavady United	26	17	4	5	63	26	37	55
2	Newry City	26	15	3	8	56	32	24	48
3	Donegal Celtic	26	13	6	7	51	42	9	45
4	Moyola Park	26	12	5	9	43	37	6	41
5	Banbridge Town	26	11	2	13	36	40	-4	35
6	Dundela	26	9	7	10	44	46	-2	34
7	Lisburn Distillery	26	10	4	12	43	49	-6	34
8	Tobermore United	26	10	4	12	39	45	-6	34
9	Newington	26	10	2	14	35	48	-13	32
10	Queens University	26	10	1	15	30	42	-12	31
11	Bangor	26	8	5	13	46	57	-11	29
12	Sport & Leisure Swifts	26	8	3	15	30	52	-22	27

BALLYMENA & PROVINCIAL LEAGUE

Intermediate Division

		P	W	D	L	F	A	GD	Pts
1	Coagh United	20	16	1	3	54	25	29	49
2	Wakehurst	20	14	3	3	53	28	25	45
3	Glebe Rangers	20	12	5	3	46	19	27	41
4	Newtowne	20	13	2	5	49	32	17	41
5	Ballynure OB	20	9	2	9	42	45	-3	29
6	Sofia Farm	20	9	1	10	35	37	-2	28
7	Brantwood	20	6	6	8	36	38	-2	24
8	Desertmartin	20	7	3	10	32	44	-12	24
9	Magherafelt Sky Blues	20	5	2	13	34	52	-18	17
10	Dunloy	20	5	1	14	37	59	-22	16
11	Chimney Corner	20	1	0	19	28	67	-39	3

Woodlands withdrew.

Junior Division Two

		P	W	D	L	F	A	GD	Pts
1	3rd Ballyclare OB	16	12	2	2	52	25	27	38
2	Remo FC	16	11	2	3	46	28	18	35
3	Ballynure OB B	16	8	5	3	45	28	17	29
4	Clough Rangers Athletic	16	8	0	8	39	45	-6	24
5	Wakehurst Strollers	16	7	2	7	42	33	9	23
6	Castle Star	16	6	1	9	47	44	3	19
7	68th OB A	16	4	3	9	38	65	-27	15
8	Mountainview FC	16	4	1	11	28	42	-14	13
9	Cookstown RBL Reserves	16	4	0	12	32	59	-27	12

Carnmoney FC withdrew .

Junior Division Three

		P	W	D	L	F	A	GD	Pts
1	Brantwood III	16	14	0	2	59	21	38	42
2	Antrim Rovers Swifts	16	12	1	3	70	32	38	37
3	Whitehead Rangers	16	11	0	5	48	25	23	33
4	Carnlough Swifts	16	6	4	6	42	44	-2	22
5	Red Star (Carrick)	16	6	3	7	34	43	-9	21
6	1st Carrickfergus Old Boys	16	6	1	9	37	45	-8	19
7	Ballyclare North End	16	5	4	7	32	51	-19	19
8	68th OB B	16	2	3	11	23	48	-25	9
9	Shore Road YM	16	1	2	13	22	58	-36	5

18th Newtownabbey OB III withdrew.

NORTHERN IRELAND FOOTBALL

MID ULSTER LEAGUE

Intermediate A

		P	W	D	L	F	A	GD	Pts
1	Dollingstown	24	19	2	3	63	28	35	59
2	Valley Rangers	24	15	3	6	83	38	45	48
3	Windmill Stars	24	13	5	6	60	36	24	44
4	Fivemiletown United	24	13	5	6	50	34	16	44
5	Tandragee Rovers	24	13	4	7	60	36	24	43
6	Moneyslane	24	13	4	7	55	34	21	43
7	Banbridge Rangers	24	13	4	7	62	42	20	43
8	Hanover	24	12	3	9	64	39	25	39
9	Crewe United	24	12	3	9	58	40	18	39
10	St Marys	24	8	1	15	29	45	-16	25
11	Ballymacash Rangers	24	5	1	18	23	60	-37	16
12	Camlough Rovers	24	2	0	22	27	114	-87	6
13	Seapatrick	24	0	1	23	21	109	-88	1

Intermediate B

		P	W	D	L	F	A	GD	Pts
1	Richhill AFC	26	20	4	2	84	21	63	64
2	AFC Silverwood	26	18	6	2	74	33	41	60
3	Dungannon Tigers	26	14	2	10	52	44	8	44
4	Lurgan Town	26	13	4	9	58	41	17	43
5	Craigavon City	26	12	4	10	60	51	9	40
6	Bourneview Mill	26	11	6	9	47	38	9	39
7	Lower Maze	26	11	4	11	56	60	-4	37
8	Tullyvallen	26	10	5	11	58	59	-1	35
9	Oxford Sunnyside	26	10	3	13	44	52	-8	33
10	Markethill Swifts	26	10	2	14	52	70	-18	32
11	Laurelvale	26	6	8	12	44	61	-17	26
12	Dungannon Rovers	26	6	7	13	43	66	-23	25
13	Seagoe	26	7	2	17	39	65	-26	23
14	Broomhedge Maghaberry	26	4	3	19	33	83	-50	15

Division One

		P	W	D	L	F	A	GD	Pts
1	Hill Street	18	15	2	1	89	20	69	47
2	Ballyoran	18	14	3	1	62	26	36	45
3	Rectory Rangers	18	9	3	6	44	41	3	30
4	Coalisland Athletic	18	9	1	8	67	49	18	28
5	Sandy Hill	18	8	3	7	52	47	5	27
6	Portadown BBOB	18	8	3	7	33	53	-20	27
7	Ambassadors	18	6	1	11	40	59	-19	19
8	Armagh Rovers	18	5	2	11	48	53	-5	17
9	Red Star	18	4	3	11	31	61	-30	15
10	Derryhirk United	18	1	1	16	19	76	-57	4

Division Two

		P	W	D	L	F	A	GD	Pts
1	Donaghmore	16	14	1	1	60	10	50	43
2	Caledon Rovers	16	13	2	1	56	14	42	41
3	Glenavy	16	7	4	5	45	32	13	25
4	Lurgan BBOB	16	7	3	6	46	46	0	24
5	Keady Celtic	16	7	2	7	50	46	4	23
6	Armagh Celtic	16	5	3	8	44	56	-12	18
7	Knockmenagh Swifts	16	6	0	10	39	60	-21	18
8	Lurgan United	16	3	1	12	22	54	-32	10
9	Scarva Rangers	16	2	0	14	25	69	-44	6

Division Three

		P	W	D	L	F	A	GD	Pts
1	Aghalee Village	18	18	0	0	83	17	66	54
2	Goodyear	18	14	0	4	62	34	28	42
3	Stranmillis	18	11	1	6	57	35	22	34
4	West End Hibs	18	10	1	7	45	41	4	31
5	Hillsborough Boys	18	9	2	7	55	38	17	29
6	Donacloney	18	7	3	8	33	43	-10	24
7	Newmills	18	5	2	11	30	45	-15	17
8	White City	18	5	2	11	36	55	-19	17
9	Gilford Crusaders	18	3	2	13	29	72	-43	11
10	Moira Albion	18	1	1	16	14	64	-50	4

Division Four

		P	W	D	L	F	A	GD	Pts
1	Banbridge YCOB	18	15	3	0	66	16	50	48
2	United LT	18	14	2	2	67	31	36	44
3	Santos FC	18	10	4	4	66	46	20	34
4	The Dons	18	10	3	5	38	32	6	33
5	Armagh Blues	18	8	1	9	56	43	13	25
6	Union Lusa FC	18	6	2	10	42	57	-15	20
7	Sporting Lisburn	18	4	6	8	47	43	4	18
8	Damolly	18	5	2	11	44	68	-24	17
9	Annalong	18	4	3	11	35	67	-32	15
10	Southside	18	1	0	17	20	78	-58	3

NORTHERN AMATEUR LEAGUE

Premier Division

		P	W	D	L	F	A	GD	Pts
1	Crumlin Star	24	17	6	1	81	20	61	57
2	Downpatrick F.C.	24	15	6	3	69	34	35	51
3	Rathfriland Rangers	24	15	5	4	64	25	39	50
4	Ards Rangers	24	14	6	4	74	40	34	48
5	Immaculata F.C.	24	11	5	8	57	43	14	38
6	Crumlin United	24	9	3	12	51	50	1	30
7	Lisburn Rangers	24	8	6	10	38	52	-14	30
8	Albert Foundry F.C.	24	8	5	11	55	48	7	29
9	Shankill United	24	9	2	13	47	58	-11	29
10	Drumaness Mills	24	8	2	14	36	53	-17	26
11	Derriaghy C C	24	7	4	13	35	54	-19	25
12	Malachians	24	5	6	13	30	52	-22	21
13	Ardglass	24	2	0	22	20	128	-108	6

Division One A

		P	W	D	L	F	A	GD	Pts
1	East Belfast	26	17	6	3	61	31	30	57
2	1st Bangor Old Boys	26	18	3	5	63	39	24	57
3	Larne Tech O.B.	26	15	6	5	70	34	36	51
4	Abbey Villa	26	16	2	8	78	47	31	50
5	Comber Rec F.C.	26	14	4	8	60	45	15	46
6	Newcastle	26	13	6	7	66	49	17	45
7	Islandmagee	26	13	3	10	63	45	18	42
8	Ballynahinch Olympic	26	12	4	10	46	35	11	40
9	St Patricks Y.M. F.C.	26	9	3	14	52	67	-15	30
10	Orangefield Old Boys	26	8	4	14	40	51	-11	28
11	Dunmurry Rec	26	9	1	16	45	55	-10	25*
12	Killyleagh Y.C	26	6	14	42	56	-14	24	
13	Kilmore Rec	26	6	4	16	30	49	-19	22
14	Dundonald	26	0	0	26	16	129	-113	0

NORTHERN IRELAND FOOTBALL

Division One B

	P	W	D	L	F	A	GD	Pts
1 Rathfern Rangers	26	20	3	3	83	26	57	63
2 Sirocco Wks	26	19	3	4	83	34	49	60
3 Rosario Y.C.	26	17	3	6	52	32	20	54
4 Dromara Village	26	15	8	3	75	40	35	53
5 University of Ulster at Jordanstown	26	16	3	7	72	39	33	51
6 Barn United	26	13	3	10	56	48	8	42
7 Downshire YM	26	12	6	8	52	49	3	42
8 Mossley F.C.	26	10	4	12	66	60	6	34
9 Grove United	26	9	4	13	52	63	-11	31
10 Ballywalter Rec. F.C.	26	7	4	15	43	68	-25	25
11 Portaferry Rovers	26	6	5	15	42	71	-29	23
12 Colin Valley F.C.	26	5	5	16	46	75	-29	20
13 Ballynahinch United	26	3	4	19	36	55	-19	13
14 Wellington Rec	26	1	3	22	28	126	-98	6

Division One C

	P	W	D	L	F	A	GD	Pts
1 St Lukes F.C.	24	20	3	1	81	25	56	63
2 Dunmurry Y. M.	24	19	0	5	97	43	54	57
3 18th Newtownabbey O.B.	24	17	4	3	85	44	41	55
4 Shorts FC	24	17	3	4	95	48	47	54
5 Bangor Swifts	24	10	5	9	50	51	-1	35
6 Bryansburn Rangers	24	9	5	10	51	53	-2	32
7 Bangor Amateurs F.C.	24	9	3	12	49	60	-11	30
8 Bloomfield F.C.	24	7	8	9	46	49	-3	29
9 Holywood F.C.	24	6	7	11	57	76	-19	25
10 Saintfield United	24	8	3	13	43	57	-14	24*
11 Iveagh United	24	5	5	14	43	68	-25	20
12 Groomsport	24	4	1	19	38	91	-53	13
13 Dromore Amateurs	24	1	1	22	21	91	-70	4

Division Two A

	P	W	D	L	F	A	GD	Pts
1 Rosemount Rec	20	14	2	4	56	24	32	44
2 Suffolk F.C.	20	12	6	2	45	26	19	42
3 Woodvale F.C.	20	11	4	5	57	30	27	37
4 Tullycarnet FC	20	10	4	6	57	37	20	34
5 Ford	20	9	6	5	52	27	25	33
6 Finaghy F.C.	20	9	6	5	40	24	16	33
7 St Oliver Plunkett F.C.	20	9	3	8	50	44	6	30
8 Greenisland F.C.	20	7	6	7	38	37	1	27
9 Queens Grads.	20	5	5	10	41	50	-9	20
10 Kircubbin F.C.	20	1	2	17	22	75	-53	5
11 Newington Rangers	20	0	2	18	13	97	-84	2

Division Two B

	P	W	D	L	F	A	GD	Pts
1 Ballysillan Swifts	20	14	4	2	76	34	42	46
2 Lower Shankill FC	20	13	4	3	63	31	32	43
3 Aquinas FC	20	12	4	4	61	28	33	40
4 Bangor Rangers	20	12	4	4	55	32	23	40
5 Ardoyne	20	9	6	5	66	50	16	33
6 Bangor Y.M.	20	8	3	9	41	50	-9	27
7 Queens University	20	7	3	10	45	40	5	24
8 Newtownbreda F C	20	7	1	12	42	71	-29	22
9 Portavogie Rangers F.C.	20	4	5	11	27	54	-27	17
10 Civil Service	20	4	1	15	25	63	-38	13
11 Kelvin Old Boys	20	2	1	17	31	79	-48	7

Division Two C

	P	W	D	L	F	A	GD	Pts
1 Castlewellan Town FC	22	19	2	1	90	20	70	59
2 Donaghadee F.C.	22	16	2	4	86	34	52	50
3 Shamrock FC	22	15	4	3	93	43	50	49
4 Drumbo F.C.	22	12	7	3	54	33	21	43
5 St Teresas Y.C.	22	14	1	7	56	46	10	43
6 Whitehead Eagles	22	7	4	11	43	61	-18	25
7 Ravenhill YM FC	22	6	6	10	34	57	-23	24
8 Ballynagross F.C.	22	6	5	11	34	66	-32	23
9 Grange Rangers	22	5	2	15	41	69	-28	17
10 Rooftop	22	4	4	14	39	77	-38	16
11 4th Newtownabbey F.C.	22	5	0	17	34	63	-29	15
12 Suffolk Swifts	22	3	3	16	34	69	-35	12

Division Three A

	P	W	D	L	F	A	GD	Pts
1 Crumlin Star	26	16	4	6	83	44	39	52
2 Woodvale F.C.	26	15	5	6	66	36	30	50
3 Comber Rec F.C.	26	16	1	9	61	45	16	49
4 Ards Rangers	26	13	7	6	62	48	14	46
5 Albert Foundry F.C.	26	15	1	10	71	66	5	46
6 Immaculata F.C.	26	14	5	7	85	46	39	44*
7 Rosario Y.C.	26	12	1	13	64	59	5	37
8 Lisburn Rgs	26	11	4	11	74	74	0	37
9 Crumlin Utd	26	10	5	11	52	59	-7	35
10 Malachians	26	9	3	14	59	70	-11	30
11 St Lukes F.C.	26	8	5	13	79	82	-3	29
12 St Patricks YM	26	9	2	15	66	86	-20	29
13 Rathfern Rgs	26	6	4	16	38	73	-35	22
14 Orangefield O.B.	26	4	1	21	45	117	-72	13

Division Three B

	P	W	D	L	F	A	GD	Pts
1 Barn Utd	24	18	1	5	90	30	60	55
2 St Oliver Plunkett F.C.	24	16	4	4	93	28	65	52
3 Larne Tech O.B.	24	15	2	7	56	25	31	47
4 Sirocco Wks	24	13	2	9	69	46	23	41
5 Derriaghy CC	24	12	5	7	52	40	12	41
6 Tullycarnet FC	24	12	3	9	58	62	-4	39
7 Bangor Swifts	24	11	3	10	53	53	0	36
8 Grove Utd	24	11	1	12	58	65	-7	34
9 Dunmurry Rec	24	9	4	11	57	78	-21	31
10 U.U.Jordanstown	24	8	4	12	35	51	-16	28
11 Bloomfield F.C.	24	7	6	11	44	51	-7	27
12 Killyleagh Y.C.	24	5	3	16	37	66	-29	18
13 Wellington Rec	24	0	0	24	24	131	-107	0

Division Three C

	P	W	D	L	F	A	GD	Pts
1 Lower Shankill	20	15	1	4	68	38	30	46
2 Shankill Utd.	20	15	1	4	56	34	22	46
3 Islandmagee	20	12	2	6	49	38	11	38
4 Abbey Villa II	20	10	1	9	44	36	8	31
5 Dunmurry Y.M.	20	8	4	8	45	48	-3	28
6 Bangor Rgs	20	8	2	10	51	55	-4	26
7 Ford F.C.	20	7	5	8	38	43	-5	26
8 Saintfield Utd	20	7	3	10	48	60	-12	24
9 Colin Valley F.C.	20	6	3	11	45	53	-8	21
10 Shorts	20	6	0	14	55	66	-11	18
11 Queens Grads	20	4	2	14	32	60	-28	14

Division Three D	P	W	D	L	F	A	GD	Pts
1 East Belfast FC	22	20	1	1	96	22	74	61
2 Shamrock FC	22	15	3	4	88	38	50	48
3 1st Bangor Old Boys	22	14	2	6	68	38	30	44
4 Bangor YM	22	12	3	7	51	49	2	39
5 Suffolk FC	22	10	4	8	51	51	0	34
6 Ballywalter Rec. F.C.	22	9	4	9	44	47	-3	31
7 Mossley FC	22	8	3	11	53	52	1	27
8 Iveagh Utd	22	6	4	12	43	61	-18	22
9 St Teresas Y.C.	22	5	6	11	48	73	-25	21
10 Portaferry Rovers	22	5	3	14	41	78	-37	18
11 Downshire YM.	22	4	4	14	53	88	-35	16
12 Bryansburn Rgs.	22	5	1	16	54	93	-39	16

Division Three E	P	W	D	L	F	A	GD	Pts
1 Aquinas FC	20	17	1	2	121	22	99	52
2 Bangor Amateurs	20	15	2	3	69	31	38	47
3 18th Newtownabbey O.B.	20	13	4	3	67	42	25	40*
4 Rosemount Rec	19	11	1	7	63	41	22	31*
5 Queens Colts	20	9	2	9	53	56	-3	29
6 Drumbo F.C.	20	8	2	10	48	48	0	26
7 Civil Service	19	8	4	7	38	46	-8	25*
8 Ravenhill YM FC	20	4	5	11	37	75	-38	17
9 Kelvin OB	20	5	1	14	38	83	-45	16
10 Newtownbreda	20	4	3	13	45	78	-33	15
11 Dromore Amateurs	20	1	3	16	18	75	-57	6

Division Three F	P	W	D	L	F	A	GD	Pts
1 Greenisland F.C.	20	17	3	0	101	27	74	54
2 Ballysillan Swifts	20	15	3	2	84	33	51	48
3 Holywood F.C.	20	14	5	1	78	28	50	47
4 4th Newtownabbey O.B.	20	11	3	6	51	46	5	36
5 Donaghadee FC	20	9	2	9	58	54	4	29
6 Whitehead Eagles	20	7	2	11	57	48	9	23
7 Suffolk Swifts 11"s	20	7	1	12	48	68	-20	22
8 Groomsport	20	6	2	12	40	80	-40	20
9 Finaghy F.C.	20	4	3	13	24	61	-37	15
10 Rooftop	20	4	1	15	40	77	-37	13
11 Grange Rgs	20	3	1	16	40	99	-59	10

NORTHERN IRELAND INTERMEDIATE LEAGUE

	P	W	D	L	F	A	GD	Pts
1 Portstewart	16	11	4	1	26	10	16	37
2 Ardstraw	16	9	2	5	32	20	12	29
3 Strabane Athletic	16	9	2	5	42	32	10	29
4 Trojans	16	8	2	6	37	19	18	26
5 Oxford United Stars	16	7	5	4	28	18	10	26
6 Maiden City	16	7	1	8	39	29	10	22
7 Ballymoney United	16	5	3	8	32	48	-16	18
8 Newbuildings United	16	4	0	12	24	53	-29	12
9 Dungiven	16	1	3	12	18	49	-31	6

BELFAST & DISTRICT LEAGUE

Premier Division	P	W	D	L	F	A	GD	Pts
1 Willowbank	16	14	2	0	60	20	40	44
2 St James Swifts	16	13	1	2	67	25	42	40
3 Cumann Spoirt an Phobail	16	9	3	4	51	39	12	30
4 Belfast Celtic	16	7	3	6	42	38	4	24
5 Tullymore Swifts	16	6	2	8	38	38	0	20
6 St Matthews	16	6	2	8	30	34	-4	20
7 Bheann Mhadigan	16	5	2	9	35	44	-9	17
8 St Marys	16	3	1	12	29	65	-36	10
9 Ligoniel WMC	16	1	0	15	23	72	-49	3
Berlin Swifts withdrew.								

Division One	P	W	D	L	F	A	GD	Pts
1 Newhill	22	16	2	4	71	29	42	50
2 22nd OB	22	16	1	5	54	26	28	49
3 Willowbank II	22	14	4	4	56	40	16	46
4 Tullymore Swifts II	22	11	3	8	62	51	11	36
5 Realtá	22	10	4	8	57	44	13	34
6 Kashmir Bilbao	22	10	2	10	49	49	0	32
7 St Malachys OB	22	10	1	11	54	56	-2	31
8 Holylands	22	7	4	11	57	57	0	25
9 Belfast Celtic II	22	7	2	13	45	64	-19	23
10 New Santos	22	7	2	13	45	74	-29	23
11 Cumann Spoirt an Phobail II	22	7	1	14	56	71	-15	22
12 St Matthews II	22	3	2	17	25	70	-45	11

Division Two	P	W	D	L	F	A	GD	Pts
1 St James Swifts II	18	13	4	1	71	27	44	43
2 St Marys II	18	12	1	5	67	47	20	37
3 Westland YM	18	11	3	4	50	39	11	36
4 Newhill II	18	9	1	8	61	60	1	28
5 Glencairn	18	8	3	7	50	46	4	27
6 Rock Athletic	18	8	2	8	52	55	-3	26
7 Bheann Mhadigan II	18	7	2	9	47	51	-4	23
8 Sporting Belfast	18	5	3	10	38	50	-12	18
9 Glenpark	18	4	2	12	53	75	-22	14
10 22nd OB B	18	1	3	14	30	69	-39	6
11 Colin Bhoys withdrew.								

Division Three	P	W	D	L	F	A	GD	Pts
1 St Paul's	26	20	4	2	136	34	102	64
2 Crosscollyer	26	20	3	3	83	28	55	63
3 Realtá II	26	16	3	7	103	49	54	51
4 Willowbank III	26	15	4	7	117	78	39	49
5 Belfast Deaf United	26	14	4	8	110	60	50	46
6 Ballysillan Swifts III	26	15	1	10	73	50	23	46
7 Glanville Rec	26	12	4	10	87	70	17	40
8 Shankill Elim	26	12	1	13	66	60	6	37
9 New Santos II	26	11	2	13	59	69	-10	35
10 St Malachys OB II	26	9	6	11	64	69	-5	33
11 Clarawood FC	26	9	3	14	75	76	-1	30
12 Rock Athletic II	26	5	1	20	71	96	-25	16
13 Glencairn II	26	2	4	20	31	131	-100	10
14 Cartoon Army	26	1	2	23	24	229	-205	5

IRISH CUP

HOLDERS: GLENAVON

FIRST ROUND

Newington	v Bangor	3–2
Windmill Stars	v Tullyvallen Rangers	5–0
18th Newtownabbey OB	v Bangor Amateurs	5–3
Abbey Villa	v Holywood	5–0
Ballynure OB	v Albert Foundry	4–1
Ballywalter Rec	v Ardstraw	1–2
Banbridge Rangers	v Derriaghy CC	4-4, 3-4p
Bloomfield	v Seapatrick	3–4
Brantwood	v Comber Rec	3-3, 1-3p
Chimney Corner	v Crewe United	0–5
Coagh United	v Malachians	2–1
Craigavon City	v Grove United	1–6
Desertmartin	v Newcastle	2–0
Dollingstown	v Newbuildings United	4–2
Donegal Celtic	v Oxford United Stars	1–3
Downshire YM	v Rathfern Rangers	4–0
Dungiven	v Saintfield United	1–0
Dunloy	v Wellington Rec	3–0
East Belfast	v Dundonald	5–2
Fivemiletown United	v Killymoon Rangers	HW
Glebe Rangers	v Iveagh United	4–0
Islandmagee	v Ballymacash Rangers	4–1
Lisburn Distillery	v Rosario YC	4–0
Limavady United	v Banbridge Town	2–0
Lurgan Town	v Laurelvale	2–1
Moneyslane	v Magherafelt Sky Blues	6–1
Newry City	v Oxford Sunnyside	7–0
Portaferry Rovers	v A.F.C. Silverwood	2–3
Queen's University	v Dromore Amateurs	14–0
Rathfriland Rangers	v Moyola Park	3-3, 4-2p
St Patrick's Young Men	v Markethill Swifts	5–4
Shankill United	v Crumlin United	0–4
Sirocco Works	v Hanover	2-2, 4-1p
Sport & Leisure Swifts	v Ballynahinch Olympic	3–2
Trojans	v Immaculata	3–1
UUJ	v Dungannon Rovers	4–0
Valley Rangers	v Newtowne	3–1
Sofia Farmer	v Lower Maze	2–1

SECOND ROUND

18th Newtownabbey OB	v Ballynahinch United	2–1
Abbey Villa	v Dungiven	4–1
Ards Rangers	v Lurgan Town	2–0
Barn United	v Dundela	2–1
Camlough Rovers	v Dromara Village	0–5
Coagh United	v Derriaghy CC	0-0, 2-3p
Comber Rec	v Ardstraw	5–2
Crewe United	v Ardglass	5–1
Crumlin Star	v Trojans	1–2
Crumlin United	v Ballymoney United	2–3
Downshire YM	v UUJ	2-2, 3-2p
Fivemiletown United	v Sirocco Works	4–1
Glebe Rangers	v A.F.C. Silverwood	3–2
Grove United	v Rathfriland Rangers	4-4, 3-1p
Islandmagee	v Killyleagh YC	5–3

(Islandmages removed from teh competition for playing an inelligble player, Killyleagh YC reinstated)

Larne Tech OB	v Wakehurst	1–2
Lisburn Rangers	v Ballynure OB	4–2
Moneyslane	v Portstewart	0–2
Mossley	v St Luke's	1–4
Newry City A.F.C.	v Newington	1–3
Queen's University	v Lisburn Distillery	0–1
Richhill A.F.C.	v Nortel	HW
Seapatrick	v Drumaness Mills	0–2
Shorts	v Dunloy	8–0
Sofia Farmer	v Limavady United	2–0
Sport & Leisure Swifts	v St. Patrick's	2–1
St Mary's YC	v Oxford United Stars	4–5
Strabane Athletic	v East Belfast	4–5
Tobermore United	v Desertmartin	6–0
Valley Rangers	v Seagoe	7–0
Windmill Stars	v Donard Hospital	HW

THIRD ROUND

Abbey Villa	v Dollingstown	2–3
Comber Rec	v St Luke's	2–3
Crewe United	v Ballymoney United	3–1
Derriaghy CC	v Valley Rangers	2–0
Dromara Village	v Drumaness Mills	1–2
Dundela	v Downshire YM	3–2
East Belfast	v Shorts	0–2
Fivemiletown United	v Newington	5–4
Glebe Rangers	v Grove United	0-0, 3-4p
Killyleagh YC	v Portstewart	0–5
Lisburn Rangers	v Lisburn Distillery	0–1
Richhill A.F.C.	v Oxford United Stars	1–0
Sofia Farmer	v Windmill Stars	0–2
Sport & Leisure Swifts	v Ards Rangers	3–2
Tobermore United	v Wakehurst	2–1
Trojans	v 18th Newtownabbey OB	HW

FOURTH ROUND

Derriaghy CC	v	Portstewart	2–4
Dundela	v	Fivemiletown United	3–4
Lisburn Distillery	v	St Luke's	3–0
Richhill A.F.C.	v	Grove United	6–2
Sport & Leisure Swifts	v	Dollingstown	1–3
Tobermore United	v	Shorts	6–0
Trojans	v	Drumaness Mills	3–1
Windmill Stars	v	Crewe United	3–4

FIFTH ROUND

Annagh United	v	Tobermore United	0–2
Armagh City	v	Trojans	2–1
Ballyclare Comrades	v	Institute	2–4
Ballymena United	v	Cliftonville	1-1, 4-3p
Coleraine	v	Carrick Rangers	5–1
Crusaders	v	Ards	2–0
Dungannon Swifts	v	Dergview	3–0
Glenavon	v	Portstewart	4–1
Glentoran	v	Linfield	1-2 aet
Harland & Wolff Welders	v	Lurgan Celtic	1–0
Knockbreda	v	Crewe United	1–2
Larne	v	Portadown	1–2
Loughgall	v	Fivemiletown United	3–0
PSNI	v	Lisburn Distillery	2–1
Richhill A.F.C.	v	Dollingstown	1–4
Warrenpoint Town	v	Ballinamallard United 0-0, 5-4p	

SIXTH ROUND

Armagh City	v	Glenavon	0–2
Coleraine	v	Tobermore United	1–0
Crusaders	v	PSNI	2–0
Dungannon Swifts	v	Dollingstown	4–1
Harland & Wolff Welders	v	Ballymena United	1–3
Institute	v	Linfield	0–2
Loughgall	v	Portadown	1–2
Warrenpoint Town	v	Crewe United	5–0

QUARTER FINALS

Ballymena United	v	Coleraine	0–4
Crusaders	v	Linfield	0–2
Dungannon Swifts	v	Warrenpoint Town	2-1 aet
Portadown	v	Glenavon	0–5

SEMI FINALS

Linfield	v	Dungannon Swifts	1–0
Coleraine	v	Glenavon	2–1

FINAL

Saturday 6th May 2017

Coleraine	v	Linfield	0-3

SCOTTISH TABLES 2016-17

HIGHLAND LEAGUE

		P	W	D	L	F	A	GD	Pts
1	Buckie Thistle	34	26	4	4	130	36	94	82
2	Cove Rangers	34	25	7	2	109	30	79	82
3	Brora Rangers	34	26	3	5	116	36	80	81
4	Formartine United	34	22	7	5	82	47	35	73
5	Fraserburgh	34	19	6	9	77	48	29	63
6	Forres Mechanics	34	17	7	10	84	63	21	58
7	Turriff United	34	18	4	12	56	42	14	58
8	Wick Academy	34	15	8	11	75	52	23	53
9	Inverurie Loco Works	34	14	8	12	71	53	18	50
10	Keith	34	15	2	17	74	88	-14	47
11	Clachnacuddin	34	11	8	15	53	77	-24	41
12	Lossiemouth	34	11	5	18	52	70	-18	38
13	Nairn County	34	9	7	18	57	74	-17	34
14	Huntly	34	9	7	18	54	97	-43	34
15	Deveronvale	34	9	3	22	51	75	-24	30
16	Rothes	34	7	5	22	37	106	-69	26
17	Fort William	34	3	2	29	44	136	-92	11
18	Strathspey Thistle	34	2	3	29	28	120	-92	9

NORTH CALEDONIAN LEAGUE

		P	W	D	L	F	A	GD	Pts
1	Invergordon	14	11	1	2	34	18	16	34
2	Orkney FC	14	10	1	3	29	13	16	31
3	Halkirk United	14	9	1	4	33	17	16	28
4	Golspie Sutherland	14	6	2	6	33	33	0	20
5	Thurso	14	5	3	6	22	18	4	18
6	St.Duthus	14	4	2	8	22	30	-8	14
7	Inverness Athletic	14	2	2	10	27	39	-12	8
8	Alness United	14	2	2	10	19	51	-32	8

EAST OF SCOTLAND LEAGUE

Premier Division	P	W	D	L	F	A	GD	Pts
1 Lothian Thistle Hutchison Vale	20	17	2	1	85	16	69	53
2 Leith Athletic	20	15	2	3	80	18	62	47
3 Tynecastle	20	14	1	5	56	26	30	43
4 Heriot Watt University	20	12	3	5	61	30	31	39
5 Coldstream	20	9	4	7	39	51	-12	31
6 Stirling University	20	9	3	8	55	36	19	30
7 Eyemouth United	20	7	2	11	34	53	-19	23
8 Peebles Rovers	20	6	1	13	28	45	-17	19
9 Ormiston	20	4	0	16	25	57	-32	12
10 Tweedmouth Rangers	20	3	3	14	28	77	-49	12
11 Burntisland Shipyard	20	3	1	16	12	94	-82	10

LOWLAND LEAGUE

		P	W	D	L	F	A	GD	Pts
1	East Kilbride	30	24	3	3	89	21	68	75
2	East Stirlingshire	30	21	5	4	107	43	64	68
3	Spartans	30	17	5	8	69	30	39	56
4	University of Stirling	30	16	5	9	60	53	7	53
5	Dalbeattie Star	30	14	5	11	60	50	10	47
6	Cumbernauld Colts	30	13	8	9	51	43	8	47
7	BSC Glasgow	30	12	6	12	63	56	7	42
8	Whitehill Welfare	30	13	1	16	53	64	-11	40
9	Gretna 2008	30	12	4	14	44	65	-21	40
10	Gala Fairydean Rovers	30	11	7	12	55	77	-22	40
11	Edinburgh University	30	10	7	13	40	42	-2	37
12	Civil Service Strollers	30	10	7	13	59	68	-9	37
13	Vale of Leithen	30	11	4	15	52	66	-14	37
14	Hawick Royal Albert	30	8	1	21	58	93	-35	25
15	Selkirk	30	6	5	19	58	86	-28	23
16	Preston Athletic	30	5	1	24	41	102	-61	16

SJFA EAST REGION

Superleague		P	W	D	L	F	A	GD	Pts
1	Kelty Hearts	30	25	3	2	84	29	55	78
2	Bonnyrigg Rose	30	23	0	7	70	25	45	69
3	Boness United	30	17	4	9	73	34	39	55
4	Penicuik Athletic	30	14	7	9	65	47	18	49
5	Lochee United	30	15	4	11	53	48	5	49
6	Dundonald Bluebell	30	13	6	11	65	58	7	45
7	Broughty Athletic	30	12	7	11	46	55	-9	43
8	Broxburn Athletic	30	12	6	12	69	57	12	42
9	Linlithgow Rose	30	11	7	12	39	37	2	40
10	Hill of Beath Hawthorn	30	9	7	14	42	53	-11	34
11	Carnoustie Panmure	30	9	6	15	43	76	-33	33
12	Camelon Juniors	30	7	11	12	34	52	-18	32
13	Jeanfield Swifts	30	8	8	14	51	74	-23	32
14	Newtongrange Star	30	7	9	14	43	62	-19	30
15	Musselburgh Athletic	30	6	11	13	42	48	-6	29
16	Fauldhouse United	30	3	2	25	25	89	-64	11

Play-off

Newtongrange Star 1 - 0 Forfar West End

Forfar West End 3 - 1 Newtongrange Star

Forfar West End win 3-2 on aggregate and are promoted to the Superleague whilst Newtongrange Star are relegated to the Premier League.

Premier Division

		P	W	D	L	F	A	GD	Pts
1	Sauchie Juniors	28	21	3	4	77	27	50	66
2	Kennoway Star Hearts	28	19	3	6	75	42	33	60
3	Forfar West End	28	18	4	6	54	29	25	58
4	Tranent Juniors	28	14	6	8	51	41	10	48
5	Tayport	28	13	8	7	55	38	17	47
6	Arniston Rangers	28	13	8	7	43	41	2	47
7	Dalkeith Thistle	28	13	4	11	49	41	8	43
8	Bathgate Thistle	28	11	8	9	56	45	11	41
9	Haddington Athletic	28	10	6	12	58	52	6	36
10	Downfield	28	9	6	13	47	63	-16	33
11	Glenrothes	28	10	3	15	42	62	-20	33
12	Whitburn Juniors	28	5	9	14	50	60	-10	24
13	St Andrews United	28	5	8	15	37	56	-19	23
14	Dundee Violet	28	4	4	20	41	85	-44	16
15	Armadale Thistle	28	3	4	21	26	79	-53	13

North Division

		P	W	D	L	F	A	GD	Pts
1	Kirriemuir Thistle	28	21	5	2	126	32	94	68
2	Thornton Hibs	28	21	5	2	100	25	75	68
3	Dundee North End	28	17	6	5	82	38	44	57
4	Kinnoull	28	16	8	4	75	39	36	56
5	East Craigie	28	16	6	6	77	38	39	54
6	Scone Thistle	28	16	5	7	70	43	27	53
7	Luncarty	28	14	8	6	81	44	37	50
8	Blairgowrie	28	13	5	10	72	60	12	44
9	Lochee Harp	28	9	5	14	59	69	-10	32
10	Coupar Angus	28	9	4	15	56	81	-25	31
11	Arbroath Vics	28	8	3	17	50	82	-32	27
12	Newburgh	28	5	3	20	52	92	-40	18
13	Brechin Vics	28	4	2	22	36	107	-71	14
14	Lochore Welfare	28	4	2	22	39	114	-75	14
15	Forfar Albion	28	1	5	22	28	139	-111	8

South Division

		P	W	D	L	F	A	GD	Pts
1	Dunbar United	26	22	1	3	90	21	69	67
2	Blackburn United	26	21	2	3	72	22	50	65
3	Pumpherston Juniors	26	20	2	4	96	40	56	62
4	Lochgelly Albert	26	17	6	3	65	31	34	57
5	Easthouses Lily MW	26	12	3	11	50	59	-9	39
6	West Calder United	26	11	5	10	53	49	4	38
7	Edinburgh United	26	10	7	9	67	59	8	37
8	Rosyth	26	11	4	11	47	47	0	37
9	Oakley United	26	9	4	13	50	71	-21	31
10	Craigroyston	26	6	5	15	47	69	-22	23
11	Livingston United	26	5	5	16	39	77	-38	20
12	Crossgates Primrose	26	4	5	17	47	80	-33	17
13	Stoneyburn Juniors	26	4	3	19	25	69	-44	15
14	Kirkcaldy YM	26	1	6	19	31	85	-54	9

SJFA NORTH REGION

Superleague

		P	W	D	L	F	A	GD	Pts
1	Banks o' Dee	26	22	2	2	83	20	63	68
2	Dyce Juniors	26	17	7	2	77	24	53	58
3	Culter	26	17	5	4	62	34	28	56
4	Stonehaven	26	16	7	3	68	28	40	55
5	Hall Russell United	26	13	5	8	53	36	17	44
6	Newburgh Thistle	26	12	3	11	62	55	7	39
7	Colony Park	26	11	2	13	49	55	-6	35
8	Hermes	26	10	3	13	56	53	3	33
9	Banchory St Ternan	26	9	4	13	49	74	-25	31
10	Inverness City	26	8	1	17	44	76	-32	25
11	Maud	26	6	6	14	48	69	-21	24
12	Dufftown	26	6	2	18	47	84	-37	20
13	Buckie Rovers	26	5	4	17	39	81	-42	19
14	Deveronside	26	2	5	19	31	79	-48	11

Division One East

		P	W	D	L	F	A	GD	Pts
1	Ellon United	20	15	3	2	54	29	25	48
2	Sunnybank	20	13	4	3	42	16	26	43
3	East End	20	13	3	4	54	22	32	42
4	Stoneywood Parkvale	20	11	6	3	50	32	18	39
5	Longside	20	7	5	8	38	32	6	26
6	Buchanhaven Hearts	20	7	4	9	23	32	-9	25
7	Fraserburgh United	20	6	4	10	27	35	-8	22
8	Aberdeen University	20	7	1	12	36	46	-10	22
9	Lewis United	20	5	5	10	27	33	-6	20
10	Glentanar	20	5	1	14	23	56	-33	16
11	Cruden Bay	20	2	2	16	19	60	-41	8

Division One West

		P	W	D	L	F	A	GD	Pts
1	Spey Valley United	18	16	1	1	73	22	51	49
2	Montrose Roselea	18	15	1	2	93	14	79	46
3	Nairn St Ninian	18	13	1	4	64	28	36	40
4	Islavale	18	10	3	5	67	32	35	33
5	Forres Thistle	18	9	0	9	43	40	3	27
6	Burghead Thistle	18	6	2	10	32	55	-23	20
7	New Elgin	18	4	4	10	29	48	-19	16
8	Whitehills	18	4	2	12	24	67	-43	14
9	Newmachar United	18	3	3	12	26	50	-24	12
10	Fochabers	18	1	1	16	16	111	-95	4

SJFA WESTERN REGION

Super League Premier

		P	W	D	L	F	A	GD	Pts
1	Glenafton Athletic	22	14	4	4	35	21	14	46
2	Kirkintilloch Rob Roy	22	13	4	5	37	21	16	43
3	Beith Juniors	22	11	9	2	44	26	18	42
4	Auchinleck Talbot	22	12	4	6	26	17	9	40
5	Hurlford United	22	7	9	6	37	41	-4	30
6	Cumnock Juniors	22	8	5	9	36	31	5	29
7	Arthurlie	22	9	2	11	37	48	-11	29
8	Pollok	22	7	5	10	41	33	8	26
9	Kilbirnie Ladeside	22	7	5	9	29	34	-5	26
10	Kilwinning Rangers	22	7	3	12	29	38	-9	24
11	Largs Thistle	22	6	1	15	30	50	-20	19
12	Troon	22	5	1	16	28	49	-21	16

Play-off

Kilsyth Rangers 0-1 Kilwinning Rangers I Kilwinning Rangers 2-2 Kilsyth Rangers

Kilwinning Rangers retain their place in the Super League Premier with a 3-2 aggregate win.

SCOTTISH FOOTBALL

Division One

		P	W	D	L	F	A	GD	Pts
1	Girvan	26	16	4	6	59	30	29	52
2	Clydebank	26	16	2	8	58	33	25	50
3	Kilsyth Rangers	26	13	10	3	67	32	35	49
4	Petershill	26	14	6	6	70	33	37	48
5	Rutherglen Glencairn	26	12	9	5	50	32	18	45
6	Irvine Meadow XI	26	11	7	8	37	31	6	40
7	Shettleston	26	12	4	10	43	44	-1	40
8	Renfrew	26	10	6	10	43	38	5	36
9	Cumbernauld United	26	9	5	12	38	64	-26	32
10	Maryhill	26	9	4	13	35	60	-25	31
11	Yoker Athletic	26	8	6	12	46	58	-12	30
12	Shotts Bon Accord	26	8	0	18	30	65	-35	24
13	Blantyre Victoria	26	5	4	17	33	64	-31	19
14	Irvine Victoria	26	4	3	19	31	56	-25	15

Central District Division One

		P	W	D	L	F	A	GD	Pts
1	Cambuslang Rangers	26	18	3	5	94	37	57	57
2	Larkhall Thistle	26	18	3	5	66	41	25	57
3	St Roch's	26	16	4	6	58	34	24	52
4	Thorniewood United	26	12	5	9	62	50	12	43*
5	Rossvale	26	12	6	8	53	43	10	42
6	Wishaw Juniors	26	13	3	10	49	43	6	42
7	Neilston Juniors	26	12	4	10	48	47	1	40
8	Benburb	26	10	6	10	57	54	3	36
9	Greenock Juniors	26	10	5	11	41	49	-8	35
10	Forth Wanderers	26	8	4	14	50	73	-23	28
11	Lesmahagow Juniors	26	7	5	14	42	63	-21	26
12	Vale of Clyde	26	6	8	12	28	50	-22	25*
13	Bellshill Athletic	26	6	2	18	49	72	-23	20
14	Johnstone Burgh	26	2	6	18	31	72	-41	12

Central District Division Two

		P	W	D	L	F	A	GD	Pts
1	Glasgow Perthshire	22	15	3	4	72	33	39	48
2	Port Glasgow Juniors	22	13	2	7	42	26	16	41
3	East Kilbride Thistle	22	12	3	7	41	37	4	39
4	Lanark United	22	11	5	6	46	34	12	38
5	Carluke Rovers	22	12	2	8	59	49	10	38
6	Vale of Leven	22	9	6	7	40	34	6	33
7	Gartcairn Juniors	22	11	0	11	47	42	5	33
8	Dunipace Juniors	22	8	5	9	28	35	-7	29
9	Ashfield	22	6	5	11	33	50	-17	23
10	Royal Albert	22	6	4	12	41	53	-12	22
11	St Anthony's	22	5	6	11	32	46	-14	21
12	Newmains United	22	3	1	18	23	65	-42	10

Ayrshire District League

		P	W	D	L	F	A	GD	Pts
1	Darvel	22	18	3	1	56	23	33	57
2	Kello Rovers	22	16	2	4	62	38	24	50
3	Ardrossan Winton Rovers	22	15	2	5	73	28	45	47
4	Whitletts Victoria	22	14	0	8	58	34	24	42
5	Annbank United	22	13	2	7	58	34	24	41
6	Dalry Thistle	22	13	1	8	57	41	16	40
7	Maybole Juniors	22	11	2	9	53	43	10	35
8	Craigmark Burntonians	22	8	1	13	42	57	-15	25
9	Ardeer Thistle	22	7	3	12	40	45	-5	24
10	Saltcoats Victoria	22	3	0	19	30	81	-51	9
11	Lugar Boswell Thistle	22	2	3	17	28	86	-58	9
12	Muirkirk Juniors	22	2	1	19	21	68	-47	7

SOUTH OF SCOTLAND LEAGUE

		P	W	D	L	F	A	GD	Pts
1	Edusports Academy	26	22	2	2	88	28	60	68
2	Wigtown & Bladnoch	26	21	3	2	74	29	45	66
3	St Cuthbert Wanderers	26	19	3	4	110	54	56	60
4	Threave Rovers	26	11	7	8	62	32	30	40
5	Mid-Annandale	26	12	4	10	79	72	7	40
6	Newton Stewart	26	12	3	11	70	59	11	39
7	Heston Rovers	26	12	2	12	68	61	7	38
8	Abbey Vale	26	11	5	10	61	54	7	38
9	Lochar Thistle	26	11	2	13	62	52	10	35
10	Creetown	26	10	1	15	49	67	-18	31
11	Lochmaben	26	8	2	16	46	65	-19	26
12	Upper Annandale	26	5	6	15	45	69	-24	21
13	Nithsdale Wanderers	26	6	3	17	53	84	-31	21
14	Dumfries YMCA	26	0	1	25	22	163	-141	1

SCOTTISH AMATEUR FOOTBALL LEAGUE

Premier Division

		P	W	D	L	F	A	GD	Pts
1	St. Joseph's FP	18	15	1	2	68	24	44	46
2	Oban Saints	17	11	1	5	55	30	25	34*
3	Goldenhill	18	11	0	7	46	27	19	33
4	East Kilbride FC	18	10	3	5	42	27	15	33
5	Shawlands FP	18	7	2	9	31	35	-4	23*
6	Motherwell Thistle	18	6	4	8	38	51	-13	22
7	Inverclyde	17	6	2	9	37	45	-8	20
8	Drumchapel Colts	18	4	4	9	29	55	-26	19*
9	Campbeltown Pupils	18	4	2	11	31	51	-20	14*
10	Ferguslie Star	18	4	1	13	34	66	-32	13

ABERDEENSHIRE AMATEUR FOOTBALL ASSOCIATION

Premier Division

		P	W	D	L	F	A	GD	Pts
1	Woodside	26	19	2	5	91	41	50	59
2	Sportsmans Club	26	18	5	3	69	27	42	59
3	Rothie Rovers	26	15	3	8	72	50	22	48
4	MS United	26	15	1	10	79	61	18	46
5	Westhill	26	12	4	10	60	44	16	40
6	RGU	26	12	2	12	63	57	6	38
7	University	26	12	5	9	44	39	5	38*
8	Newtonhill	26	9	5	12	44	55	-11	32
9	Ellon Amateurs	26	9	3	14	54	61	-7	30
10	Echt	26	9	2	15	39	57	-18	29
11	Kincorth	26	7	7	12	46	72	-26	28
12	AC Mill	26	7	5	14	43	71	-28	26
13	Torry Amateurs	26	8	1	17	53	83	-30	25
14	Westdyke	26	5	5	16	47	86	-39	20

Division One North

		P	W	D	L	F	A	GD	Pts
1	Cove Thistle	26	18	6	2	89	42	47	60
2	Old Aberdonians	26	18	2	6	73	34	39	56
3	Beacon Rangers	26	16	4	6	83	56	27	52
4	Granite City	26	15	4	7	86	49	37	49
5	St Laurence	26	12	4	10	53	54	-1	40
6	Glendale	26	11	3	12	43	59	-16	36
7	Nicolls Amateurs	26	10	5	11	45	61	-16	35
8	Bon Accord City	26	10	4	12	62	56	6	34
9	Bervie Caledonian	26	10	3	13	63	67	-4	33
10	Kaimhill United	26	10	5	11	61	58	3	29*
11	Stonehaven Athletic	26	8	4	14	46	65	-19	28
12	Turriff Thistle	26	7	4	15	48	74	-26	25
13	Dyce ITC Hydraulics	26	6	3	17	46	79	-33	21
14	West End	26	3	5	18	40	84	-44	14

Division One East

		P	W	D	L	F	A	GD	Pts
1	Cowie Thistle	24	17	3	4	103	44	59	54
2	Banchory Amateurs	24	16	4	4	76	50	26	52
3	Alford	24	13	4	7	50	32	18	43
4	Tarves	24	13	4	7	63	49	14	43
5	Insch	24	12	4	8	58	36	22	40
6	Stoneywood East End	24	14	6	4	55	33	22	34*
7	Halliburton	24	10	5	9	44	49	-5	32*
8	Rattrays XI	24	8	7	9	45	63	-18	31
9	Ellon Thistle	24	8	4	12	33	49	-16	28
10	Cammachmore	24	6	3	15	52	72	-20	21
11	Blackburn	24	5	3	16	41	72	-31	18
12	Great Western United	24	5	5	14	48	69	-21	17*
13	Formartine United	24	3	0	21	39	89	-50	9

Division Two North

		P	W	D	L	F	A	GD	Pts
1	Newburgh Thistle	26	21	2	3	97	27	70	65
2	Don Athletic	26	20	2	4	85	36	49	62
3	Burghmuir	26	19	4	3	84	28	56	61
4	Northern United	26	16	2	8	79	52	27	50
5	BSFC	26	15	3	8	81	48	33	48
6	Kintore	26	11	4	11	49	60	-11	37
7	FC Polska	26	11	3	12	62	78	-16	36
8	Balmedie	26	10	6	10	62	59	3	32*
9	Glendale XI	26	10	2	14	66	76	-10	32
10	Huntly Amateurs	26	7	5	14	56	69	-13	26
11	Fintray Thistle	26	7	3	16	46	75	-29	24
12	Monymusk	26	5	5	16	54	93	-39	20
13	Kemnay Youth	26	4	4	18	31	77	-46	16
14	Theologians	26	2	3	21	39	113	-74	9

Division Two East

		P	W	D	L	F	A	GD	Pts
1	Bridge of Don	26	19	3	4	73	41	32	60
2	Sheddocksley	26	17	4	5	71	36	35	55
3	Westdyce	26	16	4	6	79	36	43	52
4	Lads Club Amateurs	26	15	5	6	74	54	20	50
5	JS XI	26	12	7	7	69	52	17	43
6	Auchnagatt Barons	26	10	7	9	46	51	-5	37
7	Glentanar Reflex	26	11	2	13	59	72	-13	35
8	Torphins	26	10	3	13	57	58	-1	33
9	University Strollers	26	10	3	13	53	59	-6	33
10	Aboyne	26	10	3	13	51	65	-14	33
11	Highland Hotel	26	7	3	16	36	60	-24	24
12	Jesus House	26	6	4	16	37	63	-26	22
13	Grammar FP's	26	6	3	17	52	86	-34	21
14	Glendale Youth	26	5	5	16	48	72	-24	20

Division Three

		P	W	D	L	F	A	GD	Pts
1	Faithlie United	24	20	2	2	115	25	90	62
2	Tolbooth	24	19	3	2	136	35	101	60
3	Continental	24	13	4	7	53	37	16	43
4	McTeagle	24	14	4	6	81	58	23	40*
5	Postal ALC	24	12	4	8	77	51	26	40
6	Colony Park	24	10	7	7	60	50	10	37
7	University Colts	24	11	3	10	54	54	0	36
8	St Marnans	24	9	3	12	64	63	1	30
9	Feughside	24	8	4	12	58	65	-7	28
10	Ferryhill	24	6	4	14	60	86	-26	22
11	AFC Murdos	24	5	5	14	50	79	-29	20
12	Bon Accord Thistle	24	3	4	17	49	128	-79	13
13	Middlefield Wasps	24	2	1	21	31	157	-126	-5*

BORDER AMATEUR LEAGUE

A League

		P	W	D	L	F	A	GD	Pts
1	Chirnside Utd	18	15	0	3	51	30	21	45
2	Greenlaw	18	12	2	4	56	38	18	38
3	West Barns Star	18	11	1	6	61	36	25	34
4	Hawick Waverley	18	9	3	6	48	41	7	30
5	Tweeddale Rovers	18	8	2	8	35	39	-4	26
6	Jed Legion	18	7	4	7	41	36	5	25
7	Stow	18	5	3	10	34	39	-5	18
8	Gordon	18	4	3	11	37	54	-17	15
9	Langholm Legion	18	4	3	11	33	55	-22	15
10	Tweedmouth Ams	18	3	3	12	27	55	-28	12

B League

		P	W	D	L	F	A	GD	Pts
1	Hawick Utd	18	15	1	2	81	32	49	46
2	Newtown	18	12	2	4	67	32	35	38
3	Coldstream Ams	18	12	1	5	52	38	14	37
4	Hawick Legion	18	10	3	5	54	33	21	33
5	Biggar Utd	18	7	3	8	48	48	0	24
6	Kelso Thistle	18	5	4	9	33	49	-16	19
7	Earlston Rhymers	18	6	1	11	32	66	-34	19
8	Linton Hotspur	18	5	3	10	39	58	-19	18
9	Gala Hotspur	18	3	5	10	27	43	-16	14
10	Leithen Rovers	18	2	3	13	36	70	-34	9

SCOTTISH FOOTBALL

C League

	C League	P	W	D	L	F	A	GD	Pts
1	St.Boswells	18	14	1	3	55	39	16	43
2	Duns Ams	18	12	3	3	65	37	28	39
3	Lauder	18	11	3	4	60	29	31	36
4	Melrose	18	8	2	8	57	61	-4	26
5	CFC Bowholm	18	7	3	8	52	38	14	24
6	Berwick Colts	18	6	4	8	48	50	-2	22
7	Hawick Legion Rovers	18	5	4	9	48	62	-14	19
8	Kelso Ams	18	6	1	11	38	60	-22	19
9	Ancrum	18	5	2	11	33	60	-27	17
10	Selkirk Victoria	18	4	1	13	37	57	-20	13

SCOTTISH JUNIOR CUP

HOLDERS: Beith Juniors

ROUND 1

Arbroath Victoria	v	Crossgates Primrose	4-4
Ardeer Thistle	v	East Kilbride Thistle	0-1
Ardrossan Winton Rovers	v	Dundonald Bluebell	2-1
Armadale Thistle	v	Kennoway Star Hearts	1-3
Bo'ness United	v	Bellshill Athletic	3-3
Broxburn Athletic	v	Glenafton Athletic	3-3
Buchanhaven Hearts	v	Culter	0-2
Camelon Juniors	v	Whitburn	3-4
Dundee East Craigie	v	Bathgate Thistle	1-3
Ellon United	v	Glasgow Perthshire	0-1
Haddington Athletic	v	Troon	1-0
Irvine Victoria	v	Newtongrange Star	2-1
Jeanfield Swifts	v	Lugar Boswell Thistle	3-0
Kilbirnie Ladeside	v	Banchory St. Ternan	6-0
Kirriemuir Thistle	v	Easthouses Lily M.W.	4-0
Largs Thistle	v	Blantyre Victoria	0-1
Lesmahagow Juniors	v	Irvine Meadow XI	0-2
Livingston United	v	Cruden Bay	7-0
Lochee United	v	Hurlford United	2-1
New Elgin	v	Dundee North End	1-8
Newburgh	v	Hermes	0-5
Newburgh Thistle JFC	v	Sauchie	0-5
Port Glasgow Juniors	v	Whitehills	5-0
Pumpherston	v	Kirkcaldy Y.M.C.A.	3-0
Saltcoats Victoria	v	Renfrew	0-2
St. Roch's	v	Kilwinning Rangers	0-1
Thornton Hibs	v	Dunbar United	2-2
Vale of Clyde	v	Sunnybank	8-0
West Calder United	v	Stoneywood-Parkvale FC	3-0
Whitletts Victoria	v	Buckie Rovers	5-2
Wishaw Juniors	v	Cumnock Juniors	2-0

REPLAYS

Bellshill Athletic	v	Bo'ness United	1-6
Crossgates Primrose	v	Arbroath Victoria	1-3
Dunbar United	v	Thornton Hibs	3-3, 4-3p
Glenafton Athletic	v	Broxburn Athletic	3-1

ROUND 2

Annbank United	v	Auchinleck Talbot	1-2
Arbroath Victoria	v	Whitburn	3-4
Ashfield	v	Stoneyburn	1-1
Benburb	v	Dyce	5-3
Blantyre Victoria	v	Tayport	2-0
Brechin Victoria	v	Sauchie	1-4
Burghead Thistle	v	Stonehaven	0-3
Cambuslang Rangers	v	Lochgelly Albert	1-2
Carluke Rovers	v	Deveronside	1-0
Colony Park JFC	v	Kirkintilloch Rob Roy	0-4
Coupar Angus	v	Forth Wanderers	3-5
Craigmark Burntonians	v	Penicuik Athletic	0-4
Cumbernauld United	v	Rutherglen Glencairn	2-1
Dalry Thistle	v	Bo'ness United	0-4
Darvel Juniors	v	Ardrossan Winton Rovers	1-1
Downfield	v	Nairn St. Ninian	1-0
Dufftown J.	v	Pumpherston	3-2
Dunbar United	v	Kennoway Star Hearts	5-0
Dundee North End	v	Wishaw Juniors	5-0
Dundee Violet	v	Blairgowrie	4-1
East End	v	Lochee United	0-6
East Kilbride Thistle	v	Forres Thistle	3-1
Edinburgh United	v	Dunipace	3-1
Fauldhouse United	v	St. Anthony's	5-0
Forfar Albion	v	Blackburn United	0-11
Forfar West End	v	Culter	0-2
Gartcairn	v	Newmachar United JFC	5-0
Girvan	v	Muirkirk Juniors	5-2
Glenafton Athletic	v	Livingston United	8-1
Glenrothes	v	Hill of Beath Hawthorn	1-6
Greenock Juniors	v	Vale of Leven	2-1
Hall Russell United	v	Maybole Juniors	0-2
Inverness City FC	v	Scone Thistle	2-5
Irvine Meadow XI	v	Oakley United	4-0
Islavale	v	Fochabers	9-0
Jeanfield Swifts	v	St. Andrews United	1-0
Johnstone Burgh	v	Broughty Athletic	1-2
Kello Rovers	v	Carnoustie Panmure	1-2
Kelty Hearts	v	Aberdeen University JFC	6-1
Kilwinning Rangers	v	Arthurlie	0-0
Kinnoull	v	Glasgow Perthshire	1-2
Kirriemuir Thistle	v	Whitletts Victoria	3-1
Lanark United	v	Neilston Juniors	0-0
Lewis United	v	Rosyth	1-3
Lochee Harp	v	Maryhill	3-5
Lochore Welfare	v	Kilsyth Rangers	0-4
Luncarty	v	Fraserburgh United	4-1
Maud	v	Spey Valley United FC	5-1
Musselburgh Athletic	v	Craigroyston	8-4
Newmains United Comm FC	v	Hermes	1-1
Petershill	v	Dalkeith Thistle	2-1
Pollok	v	Glentanar J.	4-0
Renfrew	v	Bathgate Thistle	6-4
Royal Albert	v	Larkhall Thistle	1-3
Shettleston	v	Montrose Roselea	2-0
Shotts Bon Accord	v	Haddington Athletic	3-3
Tranent	v	Longside	4-3
West Calder United	v	Arniston Rangers	0-2
Yoker Athletic	v	Irvine Victoria	2-3

Port Glasgow Juniors	v	Thorniewood United	1-1

REPLAYS

Ardrossan Winton Rovers	v	Darvel Juniors	1-2
Arthurlie	v	Kilwinning Rangers	1-3
Bonnyrigg Rose Athletic	v	Rossvale JFC	3-1
Haddington Athletic	v	Shotts Bon Accord	3-3
Hermes	v	Newmains United Comm FC	6-0
Linlithgow Rose	v	Clydebank	3-0
Neilston Juniors	v	Lanark United	2-1
Stoneyburn	v	Ashfield	1-2
Thorniewood United	v	Port Glasgow Juniors	3-1
Vale of Clyde	v	Beith Juniors	0-3
Banks O'Dee	v	Kilbirnie Ladeside	1-0

ROUND 3

Banks O'Dee	v	Sauchie	0-5
Beith Juniors	v	Islavale	9-0
Blackburn United	v	Girvan	2-5
Cumbernauld United	v	Tranent	2-1
Darvel Juniors	v	Irvine Meadow XI	1-1
Dufftown J.	v	Dunbar United	1-2
Edinburgh United	v	Maud	2-1
Gartcairn	v	Whitburn	3-0
Glasgow Perthshire	v	Kirkintilloch Rob Roy	3-4
Haddington Athletic	v	Neilston Juniors	2-1
Irvine Victoria	v	Carluke Rovers	1-2
Kelty Hearts	v	Ashfield	7-1
Kilsyth Rangers	v	Lochgelly Albert	3-0
Kilwinning Rangers	v	Shettleston	5-2
Larkhall Thistle	v	Fauldhouse United	1-2
Maryhill	v	Forth Wanderers	2-0
Maybole Juniors	v	Benburb	2-3
Penicuik Athletic	v	Scone Thistle	2-0
Petershill	v	Carnoustie Panmure	1-0
Pollok	v	Auchinleck Talbot	1-1
Renfrew	v	Arniston Rangers	1-0
Thorniewood United	v	Bonnyrigg Rose Athletic	1-1
Auchinleck Talbot	v	Pollok	4-0
Blantyre Victoria	v	Bo'ness United	2-2
Downfield	v	Broughty Athletic	1-5
Dundee North End	v	Linlithgow Rose	0-5
Dundee Violet	v	Glenafton Athletic	0-2
East Kilbride Thistle	v	Culter	1-1
Irvine Meadow XI	v	Darvel Juniors	5-3
Jeanfield Swifts	v	Hermes	2-3
Kirriemuir Thistle	v	Hill of Beath Hawthorn	1-4
Lochee United	v	Musselburgh Athletic	2-3
Luncarty	v	Rosyth	3-2
Stonehaven	v	Greenock Juniors	1-1

REPLAYS

Bo'ness United	v	Blantyre Victoria	2-2, 3-4p
Bonnyrigg Rose Athletic	v	Thorniewood United	4-0
Culter	v	East Kilbride Thistle	1-3
Greenock Juniors	v	Stonehaven	3-2

ROUND 4

Beith Juniors	v	Auchinleck Talbot	0-1
Broughty Athletic	v	Sauchie	0-4
Carluke Rovers	v	Irvine Meadow XI	1-0
Cumbernauld United	v	Luncarty	1-3
Dunbar United	v	Benburb	3-1
East Kilbride Thistle	v	Glenafton Athletic	0-4
Edinburgh United	v	Kilwinning Rangers	0-2
Fauldhouse United	v	Maryhill	0-0
Gartcairn	v	Hermes	1-1
Girvan	v	Penicuik Athletic	2-3
Kelty Hearts	v	Hill of Beath Hawthorn	5-0
Kirkintilloch Rob Roy	v	Musselburgh Athletic	2-1
Linlithgow Rose	v	Blantyre Victoria	4-0
Petershill	v	Haddington Athletic	7-1
Renfrew	v	Greenock Juniors	2-0
Kilsyth Rangers	v	Bonnyrigg Rose Athletic	2-2

REPLAYS

Bonnyrigg Rose Athletic	v	Kilsyth Rangers	3-0
Maryhill	v	Fauldhouse United	1-1, HWp
Hermes	v	Gartcairn	2-2, AWp

ROUND 5

Auchinleck Talbot	v	Luncarty	4-0
Dunbar United	v	Glenafton Athletic	0-3
Gartcairn	v	Carluke Rovers	2-2
Kelty Hearts	v	Kilwinning Rangers	1-2
Maryhill	v	Linlithgow Rose	2-4
Penicuik Athletic	v	Kirkintilloch Rob Roy	3-4
Petershill	v	Bonnyrigg Rose Athletic	0-2
Renfrew	v	Sauchie	2-4

REPLAY

Carluke Rovers	v	Gartcairn	2-3

QUARTER FINALS

Auchinleck Talbot	v	Kilwinning Rangers	2-0
Bonnyrigg Rose Athletic	v	Kirkintilloch Rob Roy	2-0
Glenafton Athletic	v	Sauchie	1-0
Linlithgow Rose	v	Gartcairn	7-0

SEMI FINALS 1st LEG

Glenafton Athletic	v	Bonnyrigg Rose Athletic	1-0
Linlithgow Rose	v	Auchinleck Talbot	0-0

SEMI FINALS 2nd LEG

Auchinleck Talbot	v	Linlithgow Rose	1-0
Bonnyrigg Rose Athletic	v	Glenafton Athletic	0-0

FINAL

Auchinleck Talbot	v	Glenafton Athletic	1-2

WELSH TABLES 2016-17

WELSH PREMIER

		P	W	D	L	F	A	GD	Pts
1	The New Saints	32	28	1	3	101	26	75	85
2	Gap Connah's Quay	32	16	10	6	45	24	21	58
3	Bala Town FC	32	16	9	7	61	46	15	57
4	Bangor City	32	16	4	12	53	53	0	52
5	Carmarthen Town AFC	32	10	9	13	40	46	-6	39
6	Cardiff Metropolitan University	32	10	6	16	41	41	0	36
7	Newtown	32	12	9	11	59	41	18	45
8	Cefn Druids	32	9	12	11	40	48	-8	39
9	Llandudno FC	32	7	14	11	31	45	-14	35
10	Aberystwyth Town	32	10	4	18	41	63	-22	34
11	Rhyl FC	32	8	6	18	38	76	-38	30
12	Airbus UK Broughton	32	5	6	21	37	78	-41	21

Ater 22 games the League splits into two. The top six then play each other twice again and the bottom six do the same. However, once split, no team can climb back into the top six no matter what points they finish on.

CYMRU ALLIANCE

		P	W	D	L	F	A	GD	Pts
1	Prestatyn Town	30	26	2	2	114	35	79	80
2	Caernarfon Town	30	19	7	4	83	45	38	64
3	Gresford Athletic	30	18	2	10	67	47	20	56
4	Porthmadog	30	16	2	12	64	48	16	50
5	Holywell Town	30	14	8	8	52	45	7	50
6	Flint Town United	30	14	6	10	62	47	15	48
7	Caersws	30	15	3	12	61	59	2	48
8	Guilsfield	30	12	7	11	53	46	7	43
9	Holyhead Hotspur	30	12	6	12	58	52	6	42
10	Denbigh Town	30	10	8	12	57	62	-5	38
11	Ruthin Town	30	10	3	17	49	72	-23	33
12	Penrhyncoch	30	9	7	14	39	48	-9	31*
13	Llanfair United	30	7	4	19	36	69	-33	25
14	Mold Alexandra	30	7	4	19	44	91	-47	25
15	Conwy Borough	30	7	3	20	53	83	-30	24
16	Buckley Town	30	6	4	20	38	81	-43	22

WELSH LEAGUE

Division One

		P	W	D	L	F	A	GD	Pts
1	Barry Town United	30	20	6	4	69	18	51	66
2	Penybont	30	19	4	7	73	41	32	61
3	Goytre	30	18	4	8	80	49	31	58
4	Haverfordwest County	30	16	6	8	55	47	8	54
5	Caerau (Ely)	30	13	9	8	57	50	7	48
6	Cwmbran Celtic	30	14	3	13	60	50	10	45
7	Undy Athletic	30	13	2	15	53	53	0	41
8	Afan Lido	30	13	5	12	46	49	-3	41*
9	Taffs Well	30	12	4	14	40	48	-8	40
10	Goytre United	30	10	9	11	44	37	7	39
11	Cambrian & Clydach	30	10	7	13	41	49	-8	37
12	Ton Pentre	30	10	6	14	51	61	-10	36
13	Port Talbot Town	30	10	5	15	41	57	-16	35
14	Monmouth Town	30	9	6	15	49	74	-25	33
15	Caldicot Town	30	7	2	21	36	65	-29	23
16	Risca United	30	6	2	22	38	85	-47	20

Division Two

		P	W	D	L	F	A	GD	Pts
1	Llanelli Town	30	23	7	0	108	29	79	76
2	Briton Ferry Llansawel	30	18	8	4	57	33	24	62
3	Cwmamman United	30	18	4	8	74	49	25	58
4	Pontypridd Town	30	16	9	5	66	38	28	57
5	AFC Porth	30	15	7	8	70	42	28	52
6	Ammanford	30	15	5	10	66	47	19	50
7	Aberdare Town	30	11	8	11	46	42	4	41
8	AFC Llwydcoed	30	12	1	17	49	75	-26	37
9	Croesyceiliog	30	10	6	14	39	50	-11	36
10	Pontardawe Town	30	9	7	14	47	58	-11	34
11	Abergavenny Town	30	9	5	16	45	57	-12	32
12	Dinas Powys	30	10	1	19	42	67	-25	31
13	Garden Village	30	8	4	18	45	58	-13	28
14	West End	30	8	7	15	40	72	-32	28
15	Aberbargoed Buds	30	7	6	17	39	64	-25	27
16	Newport City	30	6	5	19	28	80	-52	20*

Division Three

		P	W	D	L	F	A	GD	Pts
1	Llantwit Major	30	22	6	2	68	24	44	72
2	STM Sports	30	21	4	5	91	38	53	64*
3	Caerau	30	16	2	12	71	65	6	50
4	Chepstow Town	29	14	5	10	66	57	9	47
5	Treharris Athletic Western	29	14	5	10	53	50	3	47
6	Panteg	30	15	1	14	67	63	4	46
7	Penrhiwceiber Rangers	30	13	5	12	50	60	-10	44
8	Bridgend Street	30	12	7	11	64	41	23	43
9	Ely Rangers	30	11	7	12	67	70	-3	40
10	Treowen Stars	30	11	6	13	45	59	-14	39
11	Trethomas Bluebirds	30	11	5	14	49	61	-12	38
12	Trefelin Boys & Girls Club	30	8	12	10	48	49	-1	36
13	Ynysygerwn	30	9	5	16	46	61	-15	32
14	Tredegar Town	30	9	2	19	42	66	-24	29
15	Caerleon	30	7	3	20	39	81	-42	24
16	Cwm Welfare	30	6	5	19	50	71	-21	23

WELSH NATIONAL LEAGUE

Premier

		P	W	D	L	F	A	GD	Pts
1	FC Queens Park	26	22	1	3	113	34	79	67
2	Brickfield Rangers	26	18	5	3	85	26	59	59
3	Llanuwchllyn	26	17	4	5	73	39	34	55
4	Corwen	26	17	4	5	58	28	30	55
5	Chirk AAA	26	16	4	6	67	40	27	52
6	FC Nomads of Connah's Quay	26	14	3	9	63	51	12	45
7	Hawarden Rangers	26	11	5	10	57	37	20	38
8	Saltney Town	26	11	3	12	44	44	0	36
9	Cefn Albion	26	10	5	11	63	67	-4	35
10	Penycae	26	6	4	16	55	77	-22	22
11	Llay Welfare	26	5	5	16	36	67	-31	20
12	Coedpoeth United	26	5	3	18	34	90	-56	18
13	Brymbo	26	4	5	17	30	77	-47	17
14	Overton Recreational	26	0	1	25	20	121	-101	1

Division One

		P	W	D	L	F	A	GD	Pts
1	Lex Glyndwr	22	17	3	2	104	24	80	54
2	Rhostyllen	22	16	2	4	114	35	79	50
3	Penley	22	16	2	4	104	31	73	50
4	Rhydymwyn	22	13	4	5	76	22	54	43
5	Llangollen Town	22	12	3	7	70	44	26	39
6	Castell Alun Colts	22	12	2	8	80	49	31	38
7	New Brighton Villa	22	12	1	9	75	45	30	37
8	Rhos Aelwyd	22	9	5	8	44	36	8	32
9	Point of Ayr	22	5	2	15	47	84	-37	17
10	Johnstown Youth	22	3	3	16	26	92	-66	9*
11	Maesgwyn	22	1	1	20	23	161	-138	4
12	Acrefair Youth	22	2	0	20	23	163	-140	3*

AFC Brynford withdrew - record expunged.

NORTH EAST WALES LEAGUE

Division One

		P	W	D	L	F	A	GD	Pts
1	CPD Sychdyn	26	20	4	2	97	21	76	64
2	Mynydd Isa Spartans	26	18	4	4	84	33	51	58
3	Cefn Mawr Rangers	26	18	2	6	100	34	66	56
4	Gap Connah's Quay Res	26	16	5	5	108	51	57	53
5	Offa Athletic	26	16	5	5	79	40	39	53
6	Flint Mountain	26	15	4	7	89	60	29	49
7	Acton	26	12	3	11	63	56	7	39
8	Halkyn United	26	11	2	13	76	89	-13	35
9	Mold Town United	26	9	5	12	60	64	-4	32
10	Caerwys	26	9	4	13	48	58	-10	31
11	Aston Park Rangers	26	8	3	15	61	89	-28	27
12	Mostyn Dragons	26	4	5	17	27	82	-55	17
13	Hawkesbury Bell	26	1	2	23	12	133	-121	5
14	Bradley Park	26	0	2	24	21	115	-94	212

Tanyfron United withdrew - record expunged.

WELSH ALLIANCE

Division One

		P	W	D	L	F	A	GD	Pts
1	Glantraeth	30	23	4	3	90	29	61	73
2	Llandudno Junction	30	18	3	9	79	47	32	57
3	Llangefni Town	30	17	6	7	69	37	32	57
4	Llanrug United	30	16	6	8	77	52	25	54
5	Greenfield	30	15	5	10	57	44	13	50
6	Penrhyndeudraeth	30	14	7	9	66	46	20	49
7	Trearddur Bay	30	14	4	12	58	58	0	46
8	Llandyrnog United	30	12	8	10	55	55	0	44
9	Nantlle Vale	30	11	6	13	67	64	+3	39
10	St Asaph City	30	11	5	14	60	61	-1	38
11	Llanberis	30	10	5	15	44	59	-15	35
12	Abergele Town	30	10	7	13	45	62	-17	34*
13	Pwllheli	30	9	5	16	61	76	-15	32
14	Barmouth & Dyffryn United	30	9	5	16	51	79	-28	32
15	Llanrwst United	30	7	5	18	28	68	-40	26
16	Glan Conwy	30	2	3	25	35	105	-70	9

Division Two

		P	W	D	L	F	A	GD	Pts
1	Llandudno Albion	26	20	1	5	90	36	54	61
2	Mynydd Llandegai	26	19	1	6	90	50	40	58
3	Prestatyn Sports	26	17	2	7	93	51	42	50*
4	Mochdre Sports	26	15	3	8	52	37	15	48
5	Amlwch Town	26	13	5	8	54	39	15	44
6	Meliden	26	13	3	10	61	54	7	42
7	Penmaenmawr Phoenix	26	13	1	12	56	59	-3	40
8	Gaerwen	26	11	5	10	53	55	-2	38
9	Cemaes Bay	26	9	5	12	53	58	-5	32
10	Y Felinheli	26	8	5	13	47	57	-10	29
11	Llanfairpwll	26	8	1	17	40	77	-37	25
12	Pentraeth	26	6	2	18	37	73	-36	20
13	Llanerchymedd	26	5	4	17	35	67	-32	19
14	Blaenau Ffestiniog Amt	26	5	2	19	28	76	-48	17

Llanllyfni withdrew - record expunged.

GWYNEDD LEAGUE

		P	W	D	L	F	A	GD	Pts
1	Bodedern Athletic	22	18	2	2	81	25	56	56
2	Aberffraw	22	18	0	4	73	31	42	54
3	Bontnewydd	22	15	5	2	77	34	43	50
4	Bro Goronwy	22	11	5	6	52	45	7	38
5	Menai Bridge Tigers	22	10	4	8	57	49	8	34
6	Nefyn United	22	10	4	8	59	59	0	34
7	Llanystumdwy	22	9	4	9	62	49	13	31
8	Waunfawr	22	6	6	10	41	41	0	24
9	Beaumaris Town	22	6	3	13	46	75	-29	21
10	Talysarn Celts	22	6	1	15	36	56	-20	19
11	Harlech Town	22	2	6	14	33	65	-32	12
12	Bethesda	22	0	2	20	26	114	-88	2

ANGLESEY LEAGUE

		P	W	D	L	F	A	GD	Pts
1	Holyhead Town	14	12	2	0	50	19	31	38
2	Llangoed & District	14	11	1	2	45	16	29	34
3	Bryngwran Bulls	14	9	0	5	50	27	23	27
4	Mynydd Llandegai Res	14	8	1	5	47	29	18	25
5	Valley Athletic	14	6	2	6	39	33	6	20
6	Pentraeth Res	14	3	2	9	18	36	-18	11
7	Bodorgan	14	2	1	11	18	55	-37	7
8	Bethesda Res	14	0	1	13	11	63	-52	-2*

WELSH FOOTBALL

MID WALES LEAGUE

Division One

		P	W	D	L	F	A	GD	Pts
1	Rhayader Town	28	21	3	4	70	25	45	66
2	Carno	28	17	8	3	67	34	33	59
3	Berriew	28	17	6	5	89	39	50	57
4	Llanrhaeadr Ym Mochant	28	17	3	8	70	42	28	54
5	Llanidloes Town	28	15	5	8	54	40	14	50
6	Knighton Town	28	15	5	8	44	36	8	50
7	Hay St Mary's	28	12	6	10	66	52	14	42
8	Aberaeron	28	11	9	8	47	41	6	42
9	Bow Street	28	12	4	12	63	45	18	40
10	Llandrindod Wells	28	11	6	11	54	58	-4	39
11	Radnor Valley	28	7	7	14	44	55	-11	28
12	Machynlleth	28	7	2	19	36	82	-46	23
13	Welshpool Town	28	6	4	18	29	61	-32	22
14	Tywyn Bryncrug	28	4	2	22	43	92	-49	14
15	Montgomery Town	28	3	0	25	22	96	-74	9

Division Two

		P	W	D	L	F	A	GD	Pts
1	Kerry	24	17	4	3	61	24	37	55
2	Churchstoke	24	15	4	5	66	38	28	49
3	Borth United	24	15	4	5	59	38	21	49
4	Dolgellau Athletic	24	12	6	6	56	42	14	42
5	Newbridge-on-Wye	24	12	5	7	67	54	13	41
6	Aberystwyth University	24	10	4	10	42	42	0	34
7	Dyffryn Banw	24	10	3	11	37	42	-5	33
8	Builth Wells	24	9	4	11	49	64	-15	31
9	Abermule	24	8	6	10	52	41	11	30
10	Llansantffraid Village	24	9	3	12	37	39	-2	30
11	Presteigne St. Andrews	24	4	7	13	39	67	-28	19
12	Four Crosses	24	5	3	16	25	50	-25	18
13	Penybont	24	1	5	18	30	79	-49	8

VALE OF CLYWD & CONWY LEAGUE

Premier Division

		P	W	D	L	F	A	GD	Pts
1	Llanefydd	16	14	1	1	54	15	39	43
2	Llanfairfechan Town	16	11	1	4	52	43	9	34
3	Abergele	16	8	3	5	46	34	12	27
4	Rhyl Town	16	5	4	7	30	40	-10	19
5	Llansannan	16	5	3	8	32	35	-3	18
6	Old Colwyn	16	3	8	5	35	48	-13	17
7	Rhyl Athletic	16	7	1	8	44	34	10	16*
8	Machno United	16	4	3	9	47	56	-9	15
9	Rhyl Rovers	16	2	2	12	22	57	-35	8

Division One

		P	W	D	L	F	A	GD	PTS
1	Cerrig-y-Drudion	22	20	1	1	104	24	80	61
2	Rhyl Youth	22	17	2	3	80	30	50	53
3	Y Glannau	22	16	2	4	77	37	40	50
4	Bro Cernyw	22	14	3	5	60	31	29	45
5	Llandudno Athletic	22	12	4	6	82	63	19	40
6	Llysfaen	22	9	3	10	51	60	-9	30
7	Llanfairfechan Town Reserves	22	9	1	12	66	59	7	28
8	Betws-y-Coed	22	5	4	13	38	87	-49	19
9	Denbigh Albion	22	5	1	16	47	91	-44	16
10	Cymru Hotspur	22	5	3	14	42	70	-28	12*
11	St Asaph City Youth	22	3	2	17	27	89	-62	11
12	Rhos United	22	2	4	16	41	74	-33	10

NEWPORT & DISTRICT FOOTBALL LEAGUE

Premier X

		P	W	D	L	F	A	GD	Pts
1	Cwmcarn Athletic	20	18	2	0	96	22	+74	56
2	AC Pontymister	20	16	1	3	82	26	+56	49
3	Villa Dino Christchurch	20	13	0	7	86	58	+28	39
4	Docks Cons	20	11	1	8	57	40	+17	34
5	Fairwater FC	20	11	0	9	67	57	+10	33
6	FC Boilermaker	20	9	2	9	64	56	+8	29
7	Riverside Rovers	20	6	3	11	42	73	-21	21
8	Llanyrafon AFC	20	6	3	11	35	60	-25	21
9	Whiteheads United	20	5	6	9	43	70	-27	21
10	Pontnewydd United	20	3	0	17	36	101	-65	9
11	Malpas United	20	1	4	15	34	89	-55	7

Spytty AFC withdrew - record expunged.
Cwmbran FC withdrew - record expunged.

Premier Y

		P	W	D	L	F	A	Gd	Pts
1	Albion Rovers	18	13	2	3	99	33	+66	41
2	Cwmbran Celtic	18	11	1	6	77	50	+27	34
3	Trethomas Bluebirds	18	11	0	7	72	55	+17	33
4	Newport Corinthians	18	10	1	7	69	61	+8	31
5	Coed Eva Athletic	18	9	1	8	59	65	-6	28
6	Pill AFC	18	8	1	9	55	54	+1	25
7	Lliswerry FC	18	7	4	7	61	62	-1	25
8	Cromwell AFC	18	7	3	8	72	65	+7	24
9	Rogerstone AFC	18	5	3	10	53	92	-39	18
10	Lucas Cwmbran	18	1	0	17	20	100	-80	3

Marshfield AFC withdrew - record expunged.
Cwmbran Town withdrew - record expunged.
Spencer Boys Club withdrew - record expunged.

Division One

		P	W	D	L	F	A	Gd	Pts
1	Croesyceiliog Athletic	22	16	5	1	88	36	+52	53
2	West of St Julians	22	14	1	7	86	57	+29	43
3	Caerleon Town	22	13	2	7	58	41	+17	41
4	Albion Rovers	22	10	7	5	86	48	+38	37
5	River Usk AFC	22	10	2	10	66	61	+5	32
6	Newport Corinthians	22	8	7	7	62	61	-+1	31
7	Cwmcarn Athletic	22	8	5	9	64	66	-2	29
8	Machen FC	22	7	5	10	71	60	+11	26
9	AC Pontymister	22	6	7	9	58	59	-1	25
10	Villa Dino C/Church	22	6	3	13	47	74	-27	18
11	The Docks Cons	22	4	6	12	37	67	-30	18
12	Upper Cwmbran	22	3	3	16	41	131	-90	12

Cross Hands FC withdrew - record expunged.

Division Two

		P	W	D	L	F	A	Gd	Pts
1	Recrite Scffolding FC	22	17	2	2	118	34	+84	53
2	Glenside Rovers	22	17	1	4	119	48	+71	52
3	Newport Corinthians	22	16	2	4	133	58	+75	50
4	Llanyrafon AFC	22	15	1	6	103	50	+53	46
5	Glan Usk FC	22	13	5	4	96	51	+45	44
6	ictory Church AFC	22	12	2	8	74	63	+11	38
7	Lliswerry	22	8	3	11	53	70	-17	27
8	Rogerstone	22	7	1	14	78	86	-8	22
9	Caerleon Town	22	7	1	14	40	79	-39	22
10	Cromwell Youth	22	5	0	17	41	90	-49	15
11	Newport Eagles	22	3	0	19	43	149	-106	9
12	Albion Rovers	22	3	0	19	46	166	-120	9

Andy Stephens (Bala)
scores from the spot
against BCardiff Met.
Photo: Keith Clayton.

Below: Defence on
top during Bangor City
v Bala Town.
Photo: Bill Wheatcroft.

Above: Midfield action from the Bangor
City v Bala Town WPL match early in
the season.

Right: Llandudno's Marc Williams
stretches but can't get his header on
target against Aberystwyth.
Photos: Bill Wheatcroft.

Ryan Woolacott
(Aberystwyth) scores
against Caersws.
Photo: Keith Clayton.

WELSH FOOTBALL

PEMBROKESHIRE LEAGUE

Division One

		P	W	D	L	F	A	GD	Pts
1	Hakin United	26	22	3	1	150	32	118	69
2	Merlins Bridge	26	20	2	4	111	43	68	62
3	West Dragons	26	19	5	2	101	40	61	62
4	Goodwick United	26	16	4	6	87	31	56	52
5	Lamphey	26	13	4	9	67	62	5	43
6	Carew	26	13	2	11	86	49	37	41
7	Neyland	26	12	1	13	85	98	-13	37
8	Tenby	26	8	6	12	102	87	15	30
9	Angle	26	8	5	13	51	86	-35	29
10	Pennar Robins	26	7	5	14	55	68	-13	26
11	Monkton Swifts	26	8	3	15	70	85	-15	26
12	Milford United	26	5	4	17	52	88	-36	19
13	Narberth	26	5	4	17	35	113	-78	19
14	Johnston	26	2	0	24	23	193	-170	6

Division Two

		P	W	D	L	F	A	GD	Pts
1	Clarbeston Road	26	19	6	1	110	41	69	63
2	Herbrandston	26	17	3	6	97	41	56	54
3	Fishguard Sports	26	15	4	7	74	40	34	48
4	St Ishmaels	26	13	7	6	52	40	12	46
5	Hakin United II	26	12	5	9	76	56	20	41
6	Hundleton	26	11	5	10	74	69	5	38
7	Prendergast Villa	26	11	5	10	61	60	1	36
8	Merlins Bridge II	26	11	3	12	65	69	-4	36
9	St Clears	26	11	3	12	58	69	-11	36
10	Saundersfoot Sports	26	9	5	12	60	58	2	32
11	Solva	26	7	9	10	70	80	-10	30
12	Lawrenny	26	6	7	13	47	76	-29	25
13	Letterston	26	3	4	19	48	119	-71	13
14	Goodwick United II	26	4	0	22	30	104	-74	12

Division Three

		P	W	D	L	F	A	GD	Pts
1	Kilgetty	22	17	3	2	79	23	56	53
2	Llangwm	22	15	4	3	81	34	47	49
3	Broad Haven	22	14	6	2	79	28	51	48
4	Camrose	22	12	4	6	57	42	15	40
5	Carew II	22	11	2	9	53	47	6	35
6	Pendine	22	9	3	10	71	61	10	30
7	Pennar Robins II	22	8	3	11	55	52	3	27
8	Milford United II	22	8	2	12	60	68	-8	26
9	Manorbier United	22	7	1	14	60	85	-25	22
10	Clarbeston Road II	22	5	4	13	48	78	-30	19
11	Milford Athletic	22	5	2	15	33	80	-47	17
12	Narberth II	22	3	2	17	29	107	-78	8

Division Four

		P	W	D	L	F	A	GD	Pts
1	West Dragons II	26	21	4	1	104	36	68	67
2	St Florence	25	18	2	5	109	50	59	56
3	Pembroke Boro	26	15	4	7	107	55	52	49
4	Pennar Robins III	25	14	4	7	72	47	25	43
5	Lamphey II	26	15	3	8	108	60	48	41
6	Fishguard Sports II	26	11	3	12	69	67	2	36
7	Hubberston	26	11	3	12	92	87	5	33
8	St Ishmaels II	26	10	4	12	71	93	-22	28
9	Angle II	26	8	6	12	51	89	-38	27
10	Prendergast Villa II	26	8	5	13	59	76	-17	26
11	Herbrandston II	25	5	10	11	62	81	-19	25
12	Neyland II	26	5	4	17	51	117	-66	19
13	Solva II	26	7	3	16	64	114	-50	15
14	St Clears II	26	3	5	18	41	88	-47	14

Division Five

		P	W	D	L	F	A	GD	Pts
1	Monkton Swifts II	22	21	1	0	154	33	121	61
2	Broad Haven II	22	17	2	3	89	32	57	53
3	Kilgetty II	22	13	2	7	79	58	21	41
4	Llangwm II	22	12	3	7	84	50	34	39
5	Hundleton II	22	11	4	7	63	53	10	37
6	Letterston II	22	9	4	9	60	54	6	31
7	Milford Athletic II	22	7	3	12	46	76	-30	24
8	Carew III	22	6	5	11	36	70	-34	23
9	Lawrenny II	22	6	2	14	36	73	-37	20
10	Camrose II	22	5	4	13	45	93	-48	19
11	Pembroke Boro II	22	4	3	15	47	97	-50	15
12	Milford United III	22	3	3	16	44	94	-50	12

WELSH CUP

HOLDERS: THE NEW SAINTS

FIRST QUALIFYING ROUND

Llansantffraid Village	v	Abermule	3–4
AFC Brynford	v	Cefn Albion	6–3
Coedpoeth United	v	Acton	3–2
FC Penley	v	Sychdyn	1–2
Lex Gwyndwr	v	Rhostyllen	4–1
Mynydd Isa Spartans	v	Greenfield	1–5
Rhydymwyn	v	Castell Alun Colts	4–1
Amlwch Town	v	Mochdre Sports	1–2
Cemaes Bay	v	Blaenau Ffestiniog	4–2
Dyffryn Nantlle	v	Pwllheli	3–2
Gaerwen	v	Llanfairfechan	3-2 aet
Llandudno Albion	v	Llanfairpwll	7–1
Llanllyfni	v	Llanystumdwy	7–3
Llanrwst United	v	Penmaenmawr Phoenix	1–4
Meliden	v	Pentraeth	1–3
Prestatyn Sports	v	Gwalchmai	HW
Y Felinheli	v	Llandyrnog United	6–5
Berriew	v	Trewern	5–0
Brecon Corries	v	Kerry	3–1
Montgomery Town	v	Tywyn Bryncrug	3–2
Presteigne St Andrews	v	Borth United	2–3
Waterloo Rovers	v	Newbridge-on-Wye	4-4, 6-7p
Bettws	v	CP Suburbs	HW
Cefn Cribbwr	v	Trefelin BGC	2–4
Ely Rangers	v	Llandovery	7–0

Hirwaun	v	Penlan Social	0–2
Newcastle Emlyn	v	Porthcawl	0–6
Llangynwyd Rangers	v	Pontyclun	1–2
Llantwit Major	v	Garw	2–0
Penrhiwfer	v	Hirwaun Sports	2–5
Pontypridd Town	v	Team Swansea	4–0
Ynysgerwyn	v	Treforest	4–1
Abergavenny Town	v	Chepstow Town	6–4
Abertillery Bluebirds	v	Treowen Stars	2–3
AFC Perthcelyn	v	Aber Valley	0–4
Bridgend Street	v	AFC Butetown	4–1
Caerleon	v	Cwm Welfare	5–3
Dynamo Aber	v	Penrhiwceiber Rangers	5–3
Gelli Hibernian	v	Dinas Powys	0–6
Llanrumney United	v	Cwmbrân Town	2-1 aet
Merthyr Saints	v	Cardiff Hibernian	5–2
Newport YMCA	v	Cardiff Corinthians	4–1
Risca Whiteheads	v	Nelson Cavaliers	0–3
STM Sports	v	Llantwit Fardre	2–0
Sully Sports	v	Clwb Cymric	4–0
Tiger Bay	v	Blaenavon Blues	2–1
Trethomas Bluebirds	v	Panteg	3–2
Wattsville	v	Tredegar Town	0–4
Llangollen Town	v	Llanuwchllyn	3–4
RTB Ebbw Vale	v	Newport City	3–1
Caerau	v	West End	1–0
Blaenrhondda	v	Ynysddu Welfare	1–0
Mynydd Llandegai	v	Menai Bridge Tigers	5–0

SECOND QUALIFYING ROUND

Aberdare Town	v	Trethomas Bluebirds	0–1
Aberbargoed Buds	v	Dynamo Aber	4–2
Abergavenny Town	v	Aber Valley	4-3 aet
AFC Porth	v	AFC Llywdcoed	2-1 aet
Ammanford	v	Ynysgerwyn	0–1
Bettws	v	Trefelin BGC	1–11
Bridgend Street	v	STM Sports	2–0
Caerau	v	Briton Ferry Llansawel	2–0
Cwmamman United	v	Porthcawl Town Athletic	5–1
Ely Rangers	v	Croesyceiliog	1–4
Dinas Powys	v	Merthyr Saints	0–1
Hirwaun Sports	v	Pontardawe Town	2-2, 3-4p
Llanelli Town	v	Pontypridd Town	3–1
Pontyclun	v	Garden Village	4-3 aet
Llantwit Major	v	Penlan Social	2-1 aet
Nelson Cavaliers	v	Blaenrhondda	0–4
RTB Ebbw Vale	v	Llanrumney United	2–1
Newport YMCA	v	Caerleon	3–2
Sully Sports	v	Tiger Bay	4–1
Treowen Stars	v	Tredegar Town	1–0
Abergele Town	v	Pentraeth	7–3
Brymbo	v	Llay Welfare	6–1
Cemaes Bay	v	Prestatyn Sports	1–5
Coedpoeth United	v	AFC Brynford	2–0
Corwen	v	FC Queens Park	4–1
Dyffryn Nantlle	v	Glan Conwy	5–3
FC Nomads of Connah's Quay	v	Brickfield Rangers	3–1
Gaerwen	v	Llangefni Town	0–1
Lex XI	v	Chirk AAA	3–2
Llanberis	v	Penmaenmawr Phoenix	7–2
Llandudno Albion	v	Llanllyfni	4–2
Llandudno Junction	v	Mynydd Llandegai	2–3
Llanrug United	v	Penrhyndeudraeth	4–0
Mochdre Sports	v	St. Asaph City	0–3
Rhydymwyn	v	Hawarden Rangers	1–3
Saltney Town	v	Penycae	2–4
Sychdyn	v	Greenfield	0–7

Trearddur Bay United	v	Glantraeth	0–1
Y Felinheli	v	Barmouth & Dyffryn United	2–3
Aberaeron	v	Montgomery Town	2–1
Abermule	v	Llanuwchllyn	1–6
Borth United	v	Welshpool Town	1–3
Bow Street	v	Brecon Corries	0–2
Carno	v	Knighton Town	3–0
Hay St Marys	v	Llanrhaeadr Ym Mochnant	1–2
Llanidloes Town	v	Berriew	4–2
Newbridge-on-Wye	v	Llandrindod Wells	2–6
Rhayader Town	v	Machynlleth	6–2

ROUND 1

Guilsfield	v	Welshpool Town	6–3
Conwy Borough	v	Caernarfon Town	1–5
Trethomas Bluebirds	v	Llanelli Town	0–6
Aberaeron	v	Caldicot Town	1–4
Merthyr Saints	v	Llandrindod Wells	2–3
Sully Sports	v	Llantwit Major	2–6
Croesyceiliog	v	Goytre United	1-1, 2-4p
Cambrian & Clydach	v	Trefelin BGC	1–3
Aberbargoed Buds	v	Barry Town United	0–5
Afan Lido	v	Pontyclun	4–1
Newport YMCA	v	Haverfordwest County	1–2
Ton Pentre	v	Abergavenny Town	4–2
RTB Ebbw Vale	v	Ynysygerwyn	1–2
Pen-y-Bont	v	AFC Porth	3–1
Undy Athletic	v	Blaenrhondda	3–0
Bridgend Street	v	Goytre	2-2, 4-5p
Mold Alexandra	v	Llanberis	4–0
St. Asaph City	v	Prestatyn Town	0–8
Llanrhaeadr y Mochnant	v	Prestatyn Sports	5–3
Greenfield	v	Llandudno Albion	3–2
Dyffryn Nantle Vale	v	Holyhead Hotspur	0–3
Lex XI	v	Corwen	1–2
Flint Town United	v	Penycae	6–0
Hawarden Rangers	v	Carno	2–1
Abergele	v	Llanrug United	0–2
Gresford Athletic	v	Denbigh Town	3–0
Llanuwchlyn	v	Ruthin Town	0–3
Llangefni Town	v	Brymbo	4–0
Glantraeth	v	Mynydd Llandegai	3–5
Coedpoeth United	v	Holywell Town	0–8
Porthmadog	v	Caersws	4–0
Llanidloes Town	v	Llanfair United	0–2
Monmouth Town	v	Brecon Corries	1–0
Penrhyncoch	v	FC Nomads of Connah's Quay	2–0
Rhayader Town	v	Caerau (Ely)	4–3
Taff's Well	v	Port Talbot Town	0-0, 5-3p
Barmouth & Dyffryn United	v	Buckley Town	0–2
Pontardawe Town	v	Cwmbran Celtic	1–0
Cwmamman United	v	Caerau	2–0
Treowen Stars	v	Risca United	4–1

WELSH FOOTBALL

ROUND 2

Afan Lido	v	Pontardawe Town	1–0
Taff's Well	v	Llanelli Town	2–3
Mold Alexandra	v	Guilsfield	2-4 aet
Llangefni Town	v	Caernarfon Town	4-4, 3-4p
Hawarden Rangers	v	Prestatyn Town	1–4
Buckley Town	v	Corwen	1–6
Holywell Town	v	Llanrhaeadr y Mochnant	6–0
Penrhyncoch	v	Ruthin Town	3–0
Porthmadog	v	Gresford Athletic	2-2, 3-1p
Mynydd Llandegai	v	Greenfield	0–3
Flint Town United	v	Llanfair United	3–4
Holyhead Hotspur	v	Llanrug United	2–1
Rhayader Town	v	Goytre	1–2
Haverfordwest County	v	Undy Athletic	3–2
Llantwit Major	v	Llandrindod Wells	1–0
Treowen Stars	v	Ton Pentre	1–2
Trefelin BGC	v	Goytre United	0-1 aet
Ynysygerwyn	v	Monmouth Town	7–3
Barry Town United	v	Pen-y-Bont	0–3
Caldicot Town	v	Cwmamman United	2–0

ROUND 3

Llanelli Town	v	Ynysygerwyn	5–1
Greenfield	v	Guilsfield	0–3
Caernarfon Town	v	Carmarthen Town	3–1
Prestatyn Town	v	Holyhead Hotspur	2–1
Pen-y-Bont	v	Airbus UK Broughton	4–1
Aberystwyth Town	v	Holywell Town	2–0
Llanfair United	v	Corwen	1–0
Haverfordwest County	v	Afan Lido	1–0
Rhyl	v	Penrhyncoch	6–0
Bala Town	v	Caldicot Town	6–1
Cardiff Met University	v	Porthmadog	4–0
Newtown	v	The New Saints	0–3
Connah's Quay Nomads	v	Goytre United	3–2
Llandudno	v	Goytre	0–2
Ton Pentre	v	Bangor City	0–2
Cefn Druids	v	Llantwit Major	2–0

ROUND 4

Aberystwyth Town	v	Prestatyn Town	1–5
Llanfair United	v	Cefn Druids	4–1
Bangor City	v	Llandudno	4–0
Bala Town	v	Pen-y-Bont	4–1
Guilsfield	v	Cardiff Met University	4–2
Haverfordwest County	v	Connah's Quay Nomads	1–5
The New Saints	v	Llanelli Town	7–0
Caernarfon Town	v	Rhyl	3–2

QUARTER FINALS

The New Saints	v	Bangor City	2-1 aet
Llanfair United	v	Caernarfon Town	0–7
Guilsfield	v	Bala Town	0–3
Prestatyn Town	v	Connah's Quay Nomads	2-2, 3-4p

SEMI FINALS

Caernarfon Town	v	Bala Town	1–3
Connah's Quay Nomads	v	The New Saints	0–3

FINAL

Bala Town	v	The New Saints	2–1

HOLDERS: ABERGAVENNY TOWN

ROUND 1

Gelli Hibernian	v	CRC Rangers	0-10
Cwmaman Workmans Club	v	Clydach Wasps	3-5 aet
FC Cwmaman	v	Penrhiwfer	2-1
Tonypandy Albion	v	FC Tredegar	5-2
Glamorgan	v	Villa Dino Christchurch	0-4
Llanrumney United	v	Hirwaun	1-3
Lucas Cwmbran	v	Maerdy Social	5-1
Aberffraw	v	Mardy AFC	2-2, 4-2p
Nelson Cavaliers	v	Carnetown	2-3
CPD Llansannan	v	Beaumaris Town	2-2, 3-4p
Cardiff Hibernian	v	North End	2-1
Llanystumdwy	v	Cefn Mawr Rangers	2-3
Tynte Rovers	v	Penclawdd	1-2
Offa Athletic	v	Clwb Pel Droed Bro Cernyw	2-0
Pentwynmawr Athletic	v	Pencoed Athletic Amateur	1-3 aet
Old Colwyn	v	CPD Sychdyn	1-2
West of StJulians	v	Llandovery	8-1
Mynydd Isa Spartans	v	Menai Bridge Tigers	0-6
AFC Perthcelyn	v	Cwmbach Royal Stars	0-3
Blaenrhondda	v	Garw SBGC	0-1
Cefn Cribwr Boys Club	v	Hirwaun Sports	3-2

ROUND 2

Blaenau Ffestiniog	v	Gaerwen	3-2
Bryn Rovers	v	Trefelin BGC	1-3
Tonypandy Albion	v	RTB Ebbw Vale	1-4
Penrhyndeudraeth	v	Cemaes Bay	
Seaside AFC	v	Penlan	0-4
Treforrest	v	Treharris Western Athletic	2-4
CRC Rangers	v	Llangynwydd Rangers	0-2
FC Cwmaman	v	Cwmfelin Press	3-0
AFC Butetown	v	Ton & Gelli Boys Club	2-3
Morriston Olympic	v	Ynystawe Athletic	3-0 aet
Castell Alun Colts	v	Corwen	0-6
Dyffryn Nantlle Vale	v	Llanllyfni	3-4
AC Pontymister	v	Aber Valley YMCA	7-2
Aberffraw	v	Llanrug United	3-2
Abergele Town	v	Amlwch Town	2-1
Acrefair Youth	v	Hawarden Rangers	1-17
New Brighton Villa	v	FC Nomads of Connah's Quay	0-4
Clwb Cymric	v	Merthyr Saints	3-2
Offa Athletic	v	Brymbo	1-8
Overton Recreational	v	Greenfield	0-2
Chirk AAA	v	Rhydymwyn	5-1
Villa Dino Christchurch	v	Abertillery Bluebirds	4-0
Cwmbran Town	v	STM Sports	2-4
Coedpoeth United	v	AFC Brynford	3-3, 3-4p
Bow Street	v	Carno	0-3
Pentraeth	v	Llanwrst United	3-3, 2-4p
Churchstoke	v	Knighton Town	2-0
Llanrhaeadr Ym Mochnant	v	Dolgellau Athletic Amateur	4-3
Garw SBGC	v	Cwmbach Royal Stars	4-3
Prestatyn Sports	v	Pwllheli	4-6
Llandudno Junction	v	Glantraeth	5-2
Llansantffraid Village	v	Llanidloes Town	1-2
Goodwick United	v	Penclawdd	3-1
Rhos Aelwyd	v	Johnstown Youth	3-0
Llandyrnog United	v	Beaumaris Town	3-1
Llanuwchllyn	v	Berriew	3-0
Grange Albion	v	Carnetown	7-3
Saltney Town	v	Lex Glyndwr	2-4

Llanfairfechan	v	Llandudno Albion	3-6
Machynlleth	v	Llandrindod Wells	3-1
Hakin Utd	v	Cefn Cribwr	7-2 aet
St Asaph City	v	Penamenmawr Phoenix	8-0
Llanfairpwll	v	Trearddur Bay United	0-6
Presteigne St Andrews	v	Radnor Valley	0-1
Hirwaun	v	Team Swansea	0-9
Sychdyn	v	Cefn Albion	4-5 aet
Llangefni Town	v	Menai Bridge Tigers	9-1
Tywyn Bryncrug	v	Montgomery Town	3-2 aet
Kilvey United	v	Merlin's Bridge	4-5
Llangollen Town	v	Cefn Mawr Rangers	0-4
Lucas Cwmbran	v	Clydach Wasps	4-3
Llay Welfare	v	Penycae	0-3
Baglan Red Dragons	v	Llantwit Major	3-1
Meliden	v	Y Felinheli	4-1
Mochdre Sports	v	Glan Conwy	5-0
Pontllotyn	v	West of St Julians	5-3 aet
Blaenavon Blues	v	Cardiff Hibernian	7-3
Mochdre Sports	v	Glan Conwy	5-0
Rockspur	v	Maltsters Sports	2-4
Bonymaen Colts	v	Pencoed Athletic Amateur	1-5
Mynydd Llandegai	v	Llanberis	3-2
Brecon Corrinthians	v	Mardy AFC	8-0

ROUND 3

Greenfield	v	FC Nomads of Connah's Quay	1-3
STM Sports	v	Lucas Cwmbran	5-3
Ton & Gelli Boys Club	v	Treharris Western Athletic	2-1
Chirk AAA	v	AFC Brynford	5-1
Baglan Red Dragons	v	Penlan Social	1-2 aet
Churchstoke	v	Radnor Valley	1-6
Blaenavon Blues	v	Pontllotyn	3-1
FC Queens Park	v	Rhos Aelwyd	5-3
Pencoed Athletic Amateur	v	Morriston Olympic	6-0
Llangynwyd Rangers	v	Brecon Corries	1-2
Hawarden Rangers	v	Cefn Albion	3-1 aet
Goodwick United	v	Hakin United	2-0
Lex Glyndwr	v	Penycae	1-2
Grange Albion	v	Clwb Cymric	3-1
Llandudno Junction	v	Blaenau Ffestiniog	6-1
Maltsters Sports	v	FC Cwmaman	2-1
Llandyrnog United	v	St Asaph City	2-2, 3-5p
Merlin's Bridge	v	Trefelin BGC	1-3
Llangefni Town	v	Meliden	3-1
Llanllyfni	v	Aberffraw	2-5
Team Swansea	v	Garw SGBC	6-4
Llanrwst United	v	Penrhyndeudraeth	1-0
Llanuwchllyn	v	Llanrhaeadr Ym Mochnant	2-3
RTB Ebbw Vale	v	Villa Dino Christchurch	6-3
Mynydd Llandegai	v	Llandudno Albion	3-2
Abergele Town	v	Trearddur Bay United	2-4 aet
Pwllheli	v	Mochdre Sports	2-0 aet
Tywyn Bryncrug	v	Machynlleth	1-2
Llanidloes Town	v	Carno	1-2
AC Pontymister	v	Sully Sports	1-2
Cefn Mawr Rangers	v	Rhostyllen	4-2 aet
Brymbo	v	Corwen	1-2

ROUND 4

STM Sports	v	RTB Ebbw Vale	6-3
Llangefni Town	v	Pwllheli	4-1
Llanrhaeadr Ym Mochnant	v	Brecon Corries	2-4
Machynlleth	v	Trearddur Bay United	2-4
Penycae	v	Carno	0-3
Radnor Valley	v	Chirk AAA	1-3
St Asaph City	v	FC Queens Park	2-1
Goodwick United	v	Pencoed Athletic Amateur	0-1
Sully Sports	v	Maltsters Sports	3-2
Team Swansea	v	Grange Albion	9-1
Ton & Gelli Boys Club	v	Penlan Social	0-2
Trefelin BGC	v	Blaenavon Blues	5-1
Aberffraw	v	Llanrwst United	1-3
Cefn Mawr Rangers	v	FC Nomads of Connah's Quay	3-6 aet
Hawarden Rangers	v	Mynydd Llandegai	6-2
Llandudno Junction	v	Corwen	1-2

ROUND 5

Team Swansea	v	Brecon Corries	4-3
Llanrwst United	v	Chirk AAA	1-2
Trearddur Bay United	v	Corwen	1-2
Llangefni Town	v	St Asaph City	10-0
Hawarden Rangers	v	FC Nomads of Connah's Quay	0-1
Sully Sports	v	Carno	4-1
Pencoed Athletic Amateur	v	Trefelin BGC	0-0, 3-4p
Penlan Social	v	STM Sports	3-2

QUARTER FINALS

Trefelin BGC	v	Penlan Social	1-1, 1-4p
Sully Sports	v	Team Swansea	1-0
Llangefni Town	v	FC Nomads of Connah's Quay	1-0
Corwen	v	Chirk AAA	1-2

SEMI FINALS

Llangefni Town	v	Chirk AAA	0-1
Sully Sports	v	Penlan	0-1

FINAL

Chirk AAA	v	Penlan Social	2-1 aet

the
FOOTBALL
ASSOCIATION
COMPETITIONS

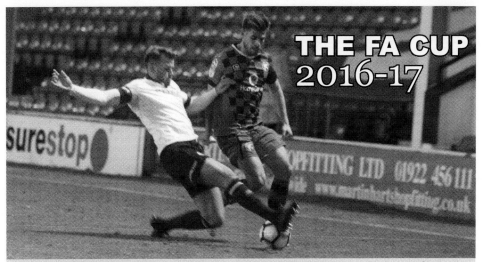

THE FA CUP 2016-17

FAC1P - Halls (Macclesfield) tackles Edwaeds (Walsall) during the 'Silkmen's' 0-1 victory. Photo: Keith Clayton

FAC1Q - Fabian McCarthy (left), Highworth Town, and Eastbourne United's Dean Stevens battle for the ball. Photo: Roger Turner.

FACEP - Hailsham Town No.9, Sam Divall, beats Andy Greaves, Crawley Down Gatwick's goalkeeper to score. Photo: Roger Turner.

EXTRA PRELIMINARY ROUND
SATURDAY 6 AUGUST 2016 - WINNING CLUBS TO RECEIVE £1,500

#	Home		Away	Score	Att
1	Ashington	v	Nelson	1-2	216
2	Heaton Stannington	v	West Auckland Town	2-3	280
3	Harrogate Railway Athletic	v	Albion Sports	1-1	107
	Albion Sports	v	Harrogate Railway Athletic (10/8)	0-3	108
4	Easington Colliery	v	Northallerton Town	0-1	
5	West Allotment Celtic	v	Consett (7/8)	0-2	156
	(at Heaton Stannington FC)				
6	Shildon	v	Bedlington Terriers	6-1	165
7	Seaham Red Star	v	Morpeth Town	1-3	160
8	Thornaby	v	Bishop Auckland	0-4	136
9	Liversedge	v	Guisborough Town	2-5	138
10	North Shields	v	Jarrow Roofing Boldon CA	0-0	276
	Jarrow Roofing Boldon CA	v	North Shields (9/8)	0-2	178
11	Bridlington Town	v	Silsden	1-1	141
	Silsden	v	Bridlington Town (9/8)	1-3	137
12	Newcastle Benfield	v	Thackley	2-0	72
13	Whitley Bay	v	Norton & Stockton Ancients	2-2	222
	Norton & Stockton Ancients	v	Whitley Bay (10/8)	2-1	91
14	Chester-Le-Street Town	v	Garforth Town	3-0	127
15	Sunderland Ryhope CW	v	Pickering Town	2-2	68
	Pickering Town	v	Sunderland Ryhope CW (9/8)	3-3aet	142
	(Pickering Town won 2-1 on kicks from the penalty mark)				
16	Padiham	v	Team Northumbria	1-0	141
17	Marske United	v	South Shields	3-1	411
18	Penrith	v	Sunderland RCA	1-0	126
19	Washington	v	Newton Aycliffe	2-2	104
	Newton Aycliffe	v	Washington (9/8)	0-2	
20	Durham City	v	Billingham Synthonia	0-4	101
	(at Billingham Synthonia FC)				
21	Barnoldswick Town	v	Dunston UTS	2-2	201
	Dunston UTS	v	Barnoldswick Town (9/8)	4-0	242
22	Armthorpe Welfare	v	Handsworth Parramore	0-2	88
23	Maltby Main	v	Squires Gate	0-1	68
24	Penistone Church	v	Cheadle Town	1-3	175
25	Alsager Town	v	Barton Town Old Boys	4-1	82
26	Pontefract Collieries	v	Runcorn Town	3-2	92
27	Parkgate	v	Irlam	2-1	
28	Maine Road	v	Nostell MW	3-3	130
	Nostell MW	v	Maine Road (9/8)	2-3	92
29	Congleton Town	v	New Mills	3-0	195
30	West Didsbury & Chorlton	v	AFC Liverpool	0-0	178
	AFC Liverpool	v	West Didsbury & Chorlton (10/8)	0-1	161
31	Hemsworth MW	v	Runcorn Linnets	2-1	157
32	AFC Blackpool	v	Ashton Athletic	0-1	303
33	Atherton Collieries	v	Bacup Borough	3-2	146
34	AFC Emley	v	Athersley Recreation (7/8)	2-1	
35	AFC Darwen	v	Cammell Laird 1907	3-3	120
	Cammell Laird	v	AFC Darwen (9/8)	3-2	62
36	Abbey Hey	v	Bootle	1-3	103
37	1874 Northwich	v	Barnton	2-1	360
38	Worksop Town	v	Hallam	4-2	421
39	Staveley MW	v	Winsford United	1-2	171
40	Lichfield City	v	Wolverhampton Casuals	0-0	151
	Wolverhampton Casuals	v	Lichfield City (9/8)	1-2	100
41	Haughmond	v	Alvechurch	0-2	127
42	AFC Bridgnorth	v	Boldmere St Michaels	0-3	121
43	Heath Hayes	v	Bromsgrove Sporting	0-3	178
44	Coleshill Town	v	Cradley Town	2-2	90
	Cradley Town	v	Coleshill Town (9/8)	1-4	80
45	Brocton	v	Walsall Wood	2-1	80
46	Lye Town	v	AFC Wulfrunians	3-2	120
47	Sporting Khalsa	v	Hanley Town	1-1	86
	Hanley Town	v	Sporting Khalsa (9/8)	1-3	86
48	Tividale	v	Wolverhampton SC	2-1	93
49	Coventry Sphinx	v	Highgate United	0-5	140
50	Stourport Swifts	v	Westfields	3-4	119
51	Coventry United	v	Shawbury United (7/8)	1-1	205
	Shawbury United	v	Coventry United (10/8)		
	(tie abandoned after 82 mins due to an issue with the floodlights, 0-1)				
	(tie awarded to Coventry United – Shawbury United removed)				
52	Dudley Sports	v	Nuneaton Griff	1-1	84
	Nuneaton Griff	v	Dudley Sports (10/8)	3-3aet	110
	(Dudley Sports won 6-5 on kicks from the penalty mark)				
53	Malvern Town	v	Rocester	1-2	201
54	Brigg Town	v	Clipstone	2-1	78
55	Oadby Town	v	Long Eaton United	1-2	
56	Loughborough University	v	Shirebrook Town	4-4	113
	Shirebrook Town	v	Loughborough University (9/8)	0-3	
57	Bottesford Town	v	Radford	1-0	74
58	South Normanton Athletic	v	Aylestone Park	2-0	50
59	Shepshed Dynamo	v	AFC Mansfield	0-4	168
60	Hinckley	v	Heanor Town (5/8)	1-1	308
	Heanor Town	v	Hinckley (10/8)	5-1	
61	Blaby & Whetstone Athletic	v	St Andrews	2-0	68
62	Leicester Nirvana	v	Dunkirk	1-2	34
63	Anstey Nomads	v	Harborough Town	1-3	74
64	Retford United	v	Leicester Road	1-1	
	Leicester Road	v	Retford United (9/8)	4-2	
65	Ashby Ivanhoe	v	Quorn	4-3	328
66	Bardon Hill	v	Kirby Muxloe		
	(walkover for Kirby Muxloe – Bardon Hill withdrawn)				
67	Rainworth MW	v	Cleethorpes Town	1-3	127
68	Holbeach United	v	Swaffham Town	4-1	125
69	Boston Town	v	Wisbech Town	1-4	73
70	Kirkley & Pakefield	v	Walsham Le Willows	0-0	84
	Walsham Le Willows	v	Kirkley & Pakefield (10/8)	1-2	86
71	Peterborough Sports	v	Gorleston	8-0	146
72	Harrowby United	v	Thetford Town	2-1	69
73	Yaxley	v	Huntingdon Town	12-0	94
74	Ely City	v	Deeping Rangers	1-4	90
75	Fakenham Town	v	Sleaford Town	0-1	76
76	Godmanchester Rovers	v	Great Yarmouth Town	2-0	124
77	Eynesbury Rovers	v	Peterborough Northern Star	3-1	84
78	Haverhill Rovers	v	Hertford Town	1-2	257
79	Redbridge	v	Waltham Forest	1-5	70
80	Brantham Athletic	v	Hadley	0-1	40
81	Enfield 1893	v	Tower Hamlets	2-4	44
82	FC Clacton	v	Eton Manor	3-5	93
83	Sporting Bengal United	v	Ipswich Wanderers (7/8)	0-0	52
	(at Waltham Forest FC, Wadham Lodge)				
	Ipswich Wanderers	v	Sporting Bengal United (9/8)	0-2	96
84	Wivenhoe Town	v	Hullbridge Sports	0-2	109
85	Barkingside	v	Hadleigh United (7/8)	2-1	105
86	Whitton United	v	Basildon United	0-0	49
	Basildon United	v	Whitton United (9/8)	5-0	72
87	London Bari	v	Clapton	1-3	
88	Barking	v	Takeley	2-0	78
89	Sawbridgeworth Town	v	Southend Manor	0-0	122
	Southend Manor	v	Sawbridgeworth Town (9/8)	2-2aet	76
	(Sawbridgeworth Town won 4-3 on kicks from the penalty mark)				
90	Stanway Rovers	v	FC Romania	1-0	79
91	Ilford	v	Burnham Ramblers	0-9	47
92	FC Broxbourne Borough	v	Felixstowe & Walton United	1-5	72
93	Halstead Town	v	Newmarket Town (9/8)	2-1	163
	(7/8 – tie abandoned after 32 mins due to serious injury to player, 1-0)				

EXTRA PRELIMINARY ROUND

94	St Margaretsbury	v	Long Melford (7/8)	2-5	
95	Hoddesdon Town	v	Stansted	1-0	98
96	Saffron Walden Town	v	Mildenhall Town	1-0	289
97	Edgware Town	v	Holmer Green	5-1	102
98	Flackwell Heath	v	Baldock Town	6-3	75
99	Crawley Green	v	Rothwell Corinthians (7/8)	2-1	81
100	London Tigers	v	Sun Sports	1-1	
	Sun Sports	v	London Tigers (9/8)	2-0	
101	Leighton Town	v	Northampton Sileby Rangers	1-2	116
102	Tring Athletic	v	Desborough Town	0-1	87
103	Wellingborough Town	v	Stotfold	1-3	114
104	Burnham	v	Oxhey Jets	0-2	45
105	Cogenhoe United	v	Berkhamsted	1-0	65
106	Bedford	v	Welwyn Garden City	1-2	59
107	Cockfosters	v	Harpenden Town	1-2	62
108	Newport Pagnell Town	v	Biggleswade United	0-1	146
109	Wembley	v	Daventry Town	4-0	
110	Harefield United	v	Northampton On Chenecks	1-1	80
	Northampton On Chenecks	v	Harefield United (10/8)	1-1aet	
	(Harefield United won 9-8 on kicks from the penalty mark - at Cogenhoe United FC)				
111	Leverstock Green	v	London Colney	1-2	95
112	Ascot United	v	Milton United (5/8)	2-0	156
113	Abingdon United	v	AFC Hayes	0-0	45
	AFC Hayes	v	Abingdon United (9/8)	6-1	59
114	Thame United	v	Abbey Rangers (5/8)	3-0	141
115	Binfield	v	North Greenford United	0-1	96
116	Thatcham Town	v	Bracknell Town	2-3	109
117	Spelthorne Sports	v	Hartley Wintney	4-3	90
118	Carterton	v	Highmoor Ibis	1-2	
119	Camberley Town	v	Cove	6-1	81
120	Chertsey Town	v	Hook Norton	2-0	84
121	Brimscombe & Thrupp	v	Henley Town	3-1	63
122	Longlevens	v	Bedfont & Feltham	4-2	202
123	Bedfont Sports	v	Windsor	3-2	76
124	Ardley United	v	Tuffley Rovers	3-2	71
125	Highworth Town	v	Tadley Calleva (7/8)	2-1	
126	Andover Town	v	Royal Wootton Bassett	5-2	96
127	Hanworth Villa	v	Knaphill	2-2	103
	Knaphill	v	Hanworth Villa (9/8)	2-3	141
128	Fairford Town	v	CB Hounslow United	1-5	
129	Horsham YMCA	v	Hollands & Blair	2-3	
130	Sevenoaks Town	v	Sporting Club Thamesmead	2-1	72
131	Holmesdale	v	Haywards Heath Town	0-2	45
132	Chessington & Hook United	v	Wick	3-1	133
133	Littlehampton Town	v	Pagham (7/8)	1-3	
134	Hailsham Town	v	Crawley Down Gatwick	5-7	63
135	Beckenham Town	v	Lancing	1-1	110
	Lancing	v	Beckenham Town (9/8)	3-4	128
136	Colliers Wood United	v	AFC Croydon Athletic	5-2	88
137	Croydon	v	AFC Uckfield Town	2-1	41
138	Epsom & Ewell	v	Gravesham Borough (7/8)	5-2	125
139	Erith & Belvedere	v	Loxwood	0-1	64
140	Deal Town	v	Banstead Athletic	0-1	98
141	Peacehaven & Telscombe	v	Lordswood	3-3	177
	Lordswood	v	Peacehaven & Telscombe (9/8)	1-3	110
142	Tunbridge Wells	v	Eastbourne United	1-1	315
	Eastbourne United	v	Tunbridge Wells (9/8)	2-1	219
143	Newhaven	v	Rochester United	0-0	119
	Rochester United	v	Newhaven (10/8)	1-4aet	99
144	Mile Oak	v	Guildford City	0-3	96
145	Bridon Ropes	v	Canterbury City	0-3	210
146	Raynes Park Vale	v	Eastbourne Town	0-2	50
147	Worthing United	v	Shoreham	0-3	94

148	East Preston	v	Horley Town	4-1	110
149	Whitstable Town	v	Oakwood	4-0	154
150	Southwick	v	Cray Valley (PM)	0-4	70
151	Crowborough Athletic	v	Farnham Town	1-3	
152	Redhill	v	St Francis Rangers	4-1	
	(at St Francis Rangers FC)				
153	Sheppey United	v	Badshot Lea	0-1	393
154	Ashford United	v	Corinthian	2-0	235
155	Erith Town	v	Sutton Common Rovers	2-2	50
	Sutton Common Rovers	v	Erith Town (8/8)	0-2	
156	Westfield	v	Walton & Hersham	0-1	92
157	Arundel	v	Chichester City	4-3	124
158	Moneyfields	v	Christchurch	4-3	43
159	Sholing	v	Bournemouth (5/8)	4-1	131
160	Bemerton Heath Harlequins	v	Keynsham Town	1-0	46
161	Cadbury Heath	v	Folland Sports	7-0	56
162	Hengrove Athletic	v	Verwood Town	2-2	30
	Verwood Town	v	Hengrove Athletic (10/8)	3-1	
163	Oldland Abbotonians	v	Newport (IW)	1-0	58
164	Lydney Town	v	Team Solent	0-6	
165	Lymington Town	v	Hamworthy United (5/8)	0-0	78
	(at Bashley FC)				
	Hamworthy United	v	Lymington Town (9/8)	1-0	81
	(at Christchurch FC)				
166	Bradford Town	v	Fareham Town	1-3	105
167	Whitchurch United	v	Cribbs	0-0	
	Cribbs	v	Whitchurch United (9/8)	0-1	61
168	Brockenhurst	v	Laverstock & Ford	2-1	
169	United Services Portsmouth	v	Melksham Town	2-1	84
	(at AFC Portchester FC)				
170	Odd Down	v	Longwell Green Sports	2-0	51
171	Sherborne Town	v	Amesbury Town	0-2	74
172	Bashley	v	Horndean	2-1	138
173	Cowes Sports	v	Brislington	0-3	93
174	Fawley	v	AFC Portchester (7/8)	0-3	
175	Bridport	v	Alresford Town	1-2	146
176	Blackfield & Langley	v	Hallen	2-0	59
177	Bristol Manor Farm	v	Gillingham Town	1-1	111
	Gillingham Town	v	Bristol Manor Farm (9/8)	4-3	79
178	Welton Rovers	v	Bitton	0-2	86
179	AFC St Austell	v	Street	2-2	208
	Street	v	AFC St Austell (9/8)	3-0	111
180	Clevedon Town	v	Ashton & Backwell United	2-1	83
181	Wells City	v	Portishead Town	2-2	64
	Portishead Town	v	Wells City (9/8)	2-1	65
182	Shepton Mallet	v	Willand Rovers	1-1	96
	Willand Rovers	v	Shepton Mallet (10/8)	0-2	
183	Buckland Athletic	v	Plymouth Parkway	2-3	184
184	Bodmin Town	v	Cheddar	2-2	
	Cheddar	v	Bodmin Town (9/8)	2-3aet	

FACEP - Goal mouth action between AFC Emley and Athersley Rec. Photo: Bill Wheatcroft.

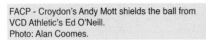

FACEP - Barkingside's Paul Wright clears from
Hadliegh United's Ben Golding.
Photo: Alan Coomes.

FACP - Croydon's Andy Mott shields the ball from
VCD Athletic's Ed O'Neill.
Photo: Alan Coomes.

PRELIMINARY ROUND
SATURDAY 20 AUGUST 2016 - WINNERS RECEIVE £1,925

#	Home	v	Away	Score	Att	#	Home	v	Away	Score	Att
1	Harrogate Railway Athletic	v	Norton & Stockton Ancients	3-1	99	45	Westfields	v	Tividale	5-1	
2	Billingham Synthonia	v	Northallerton Town	6-0	119	46	Dunkirk	v	Cleethorpes Town	2-0	60
3	Dunston UTS	v	Penrith	3-3	188	47	Heanor Town	v	Long Eaton United (19/8)	3-2	
	Penrith	v	Dunston UTS (24/8)	1-2	203	48	Lincoln United	v	Carlton Town	2-1	115
4	Shildon	v	Kendal Town	2-0	150	49	Loughborough Dynamo	v	Ashby Ivanhoe	1-3	115
5	Padiham	v	Newcastle Benfield	1-2		50	Basford United	v	Belper Town	2-4	183
6	Nelson	v	Bishop Auckland	1-4		51	AFC Mansfield	v	South Normanton Athletic	2-0	76
7	Chester-Le-Street Town	v	Marske United	0-4		52	Brigg Town	v	Blaby & Whetstone Athletic	2-1	
8	West Auckland Town	v	Lancaster City	1-5		53	Leicester Road	v	Harborough Town	3-1	
9	Clitheroe	v	Consett	0-1		54	Bottesford Town	v	Kirby Muxloe	1-2	53
10	Guisborough Town	v	Bridlington Town	2-3	160	55	Loughborough University	v	Gresley	1-4	
11	Washington	v	Pickering Town	2-2	70	56	Sleaford Town	v	Stamford	0-3	
	Pickering Town	v	Washington (23/8)	1-2	151	57	Yaxley	v	Dereham Town	4-4	
12	Tadcaster Albion	v	Scarborough Athletic	3-2	612		Dereham Town	v	Yaxley (23/8)	1-0	153
13	North Shields	v	Morpeth Town	0-1		58	Soham Town Rangers	v	Harrowby United	4-1	123
14	Droylsden	v	Radcliffe Borough	4-4	167	59	Kirkley & Pakefield	v	Holbeach United	3-4	64
	Radcliffe Borough	v	Droylsden (23/8)	2-1		60	Deeping Rangers	v	Wroxham	2-1	85
15	Prescot Cables	v	Trafford	0-1	228	61	Wisbech Town	v	Peterborough Sports	1-4	
16	Handsworth Parramore	v	Stocksbridge Park Steels	4-1	129	62	Norwich United	v	Histon	1-2	140
17	Congleton Town	v	Farsley Celtic	0-6	148	63	Eynesbury Rovers	v	Godmanchester Rovers	1-1	
18	Alsager Town	v	Winsford United	1-6			Godmanchester Rovers	v	Eynesbury Rovers (24/8)	1-3	
19	Ramsbottom United	v	Sheffield	1-2	144	64	Bury Town	v	Spalding United	0-3	
20	Worksop Town	v	Ashton Athletic (21/8)	2-2	486	65	Ware	v	Maldon & Tiptree	0-2	64
	Ashton Athletic	v	Worksop Town (23/8)	2-2aet	140	66	Thurrock	v	Halstead Town	2-3	74
	(Ashton Athletic won 4-1 on kicks from the penalty mark)					67	Witham Town	v	Eton Manor	3-0	89
21	Parkgate	v	Burscough	1-4		68	Waltham Forest	v	Hoddesdon Town	4-0	
22	Ossett Town	v	Goole	2-1	90	69	Haringey Borough	v	Barkingside	7-2	
23	West Didsbury & Chorlton	v	Squires Gate	2-3		70	Waltham Abbey	v	Bowers & Pitsea	2-2	97
24	Atherton Collieries	v	Witton Albion	1-3			Bowers & Pitsea	v	Waltham Abbey (23/8)	2-4	167
25	Mossley	v	Hemsworth MW	4-0	131	71	Brentwood Town	v	Tilbury	1-2	115
26	Hyde United	v	Cammell Laird 1907	4-0	204	72	Sporting Bengal United	v	Clapton	2-0	
27	Glossop North End	v	Brighouse Town	2-2	290	73	Long Melford	v	Saffron Walden Town	0-2	
	Brighouse Town	v	Glossop North End (22/8)	4-2	312	74	Romford	v	Hullbridge Sports (21/8)	4-3	
28	Maine Road	v	AFC Emley	3-2		75	Barking	v	Stanway Rovers	0-0	
29	Shaw Lane Association	v	Colwyn Bay	0-1	139		Stanway Rovers	v	Barking (23/8)	3-2	75
30	Colne	v	1874 Northwich	2-2	190	76	Ilford	v	Felixstowe & Walton United	0-2	
	1874 Northwich	v	Colne (23/8)	1-3	254	77	Brightlingsea Regent	v	Great Wakering Rovers	2-1	103
31	Northwich Victoria	v	Cheadle Town	2-4		78	Sawbridgeworth Town	v	Tower Hamlets	4-2	
32	Bamber Bridge	v	Ossett Albion	2-5	157	79	Aveley	v	AFC Hornchurch (19/8)	0-1	171
33	Pontefract Collieries	v	Bootle	2-1		80	Hertford Town	v	Hadley	0-1	
34	Coleshill Town	v	Dudley Sports	4-0	59	81	Royston Town	v	Heybridge Swifts	1-4	
35	Bedworth United	v	Rocester	3-2	119	82	Cheshunt	v	Basildon United	8-0	
36	Kidsgrove Athletic	v	Lye Town	2-0	101	83	Kempston Rovers	v	Oxhey Jets	1-0	97
37	Coventry United	v	Lichfield City	5-1	99	84	Stotfold	v	Welwyn Garden City	3-2	
38	Hereford	v	Alvechurch	4-2	2624	85	Crawley Green	v	Uxbridge	0-3	
39	Rugby Town	v	Bromsgrove Sporting	1-0	228	86	Bedford Town	v	AFC Dunstable	1-2	
40	Leek Town	v	Newcastle Town	3-2	262	87	Sun Sports	v	Northwood	2-0	
41	Highgate United	v	Boldmere St Michaels	1-0		88	Arlesey Town	v	Potters Bar Town	1-1	117
42	Market Drayton Town	v	Evesham United	0-2			Potters Bar Town	v	Arlesey Town (23/8)	4-1	122
43	Sporting Khalsa	v	Romulus	1-2		89	AFC Rushden & Diamonds	v	Northampton Sileby Rangers	4-3	
44	Chasetown	v	Brocton	9-0	183	90	Desborough Town	v	London Colney	0-1	

FACEP - Goal mouth action from the tie between Staveley and Winsford. Photo: Bill Wheatcroft.

FACEP - Staveley v Winsford. Photo: Bill Wheatcroft.

FAC2Q - Chesham's Toby Little and Sevenoaks Harrington Carnagie compete for the ball.
Photo: Alan Coomes.

FACP - Shortwood United's No.7 shapes up to shoot at the Ashford Town (Mddx) goal. Photo: Peter Barnes.

PRELIMINARY ROUND
SATURDAY 20 AUGUST 2016 - WINNERS RECEIVE £1,925

91	Chalfont St Peter	v	Harpenden Town	2-0	74
92	Edgware Town	v	Barton Rovers	1-3	107
93	Aylesbury United	v	Biggleswade United (21/8)	0-1	172
94	Cogenhoe United	v	Flackwell Heath	1-5	66
95	Beaconsfield SYCOB	v	Marlow (21/8)	2-2	204
	Marlow	v	Beaconsfield SYCOB (23/8)	3-3aet	114
	(Beaconsfield SYCOB won 4-3 on kicks from the penalty mark)				
96	Aylesbury	v	Hanwell Town	4-2	
97	Wembley	v	Harefield United	1-1	
	Harefield United	v	Wembley (23/8)	2-1	
98	Bishop's Cleeve	v	Camberley Town	1-1	
	Camberley Town	v	Bishop's Cleeve (23/8)	2-0	129
99	Highmoor Ibis	v	Brimscombe & Thrupp	1-2	32
100	Thame United	v	North Leigh	1-7	81
101	Wantage Town	v	Hanworth Villa	4-2	
102	North Greenford United	v	Kidlington	4-1	68
103	CB Hounslow United	v	Petersfield Town	2-1	191
104	Egham Town	v	Bracknell Town	2-1	72
105	Spelthorne Sports	v	Andover Town	2-3	74
106	Farnborough	v	Longlevens	5-1	213
107	Ascot United	v	Didcot Town	4-3	77
108	Slimbridge	v	Bedfont Sports	3-0	46
109	Chertsey Town	v	AFC Hayes	3-0	
110	Yate Town	v	Fleet Town	1-2	125
111	Shortwood United	v	Ashford Town (Middx)	0-2	
112	Ardley United	v	Highworth Town	0-3	
113	Canterbury City	v	Pagham (21/8)	1-1	62
	Pagham	v	Canterbury City (24/8)	2-1aet	
114	Cray Valley (PM)	v	Hastings United (21/8)	0-2	
115	Shoreham	v	Dorking Wanderers	3-4	93
116	Greenwich Borough	v	Walton & Hersham	1-1	125
	Walton & Hersham	v	Greenwich Borough (23/8)	0-3	115
117	Hollands & Blair	v	Whyteleafe	1-1	128
	Whyteleafe	v	Hollands & Blair (23/8)	4-2	130
118	Peacehaven & Telscombe	v	Haywards Heath Town	2-0	
119	Redhill	v	Lewes	1-6	
	(at Lewes FC)				
120	Badshot Lea	v	Cray Wanderers	0-4	52
121	Crawley Down Gatwick	v	Corinthian Casuals	2-3	118
122	Loxwood	v	Arundel	0-2	
123	Carshalton Athletic	v	Farnham Town	3-0	115
124	Whitstable Town	v	Eastbourne Town	0-0	
	Eastbourne Town	v	Whitstable Town (23/8)	1-1aet	
	(Eastbourne Town won 3-1 on kicks from the penalty mark)				
125	Chipstead	v	Beckenham Town	2-1	44
126	South Park	v	Phoenix Sports	2-0	78
127	Eastbourne United	v	Newhaven	2-2	152
	Newhaven	v	Eastbourne United (23/8)	1-2	
128	Ashford United	v	Three Bridges	1-0	
129	Herne Bay	v	East Grinstead Town	1-0	

130	Molesey	v	Godalming Town	0-2	79
131	Faversham Town	v	Epsom & Ewell	2-1	155
132	VCD Athletic	v	Croydon	0-0	57
	Croydon	v	VCD Athletic (24/8)	1-2	81
133	Sevenoaks Town	v	Horsham	4-2	
134	Tooting & Mitcham United	v	East Preston	0-1	159
135	Guernsey	v	Thamesmead Town	2-2	1142
	Thamesmead Town	v	Guernsey (23/8)	1-1aet	147
	(Thamesmead Town won 4-2 on kicks from the penalty mark)				
136	Walton Casuals	v	Chatham Town	3-3	43
	Chatham Town	v	Walton Casuals (22/8)	1-2	152
137	Ramsgate	v	Erith Town	1-0	144
138	Banstead Athletic	v	Colliers Wood United	3-3	
	Colliers Wood United	v	Banstead Athletic (24/8)	3-0	
139	Sittingbourne	v	Hythe Town	1-1	158
	Hythe Town	v	Sittingbourne (23/8)	5-0	209
140	Guildford City	v	Chessington & Hook United	1-1	91
	Chessington & Hook United	v	Guildford City (23/8)	1-2	
141	Gillingham Town	v	AFC Totton	2-0	144
142	Bashley	v	Sholing	1-2	179
143	Amesbury Town	v	Bemerton Heath Harlequins	1-3	64
144	Blackfield & Langley	v	Paulton Rovers	1-2	78
145	Cadbury Heath	v	Team Solent	4-1	48
146	AFC Portchester	v	Mangotsfield United	2-0	
147	Whitchurch United	v	Moneyfields	0-3	
148	Wimborne Town	v	Alresford Town	1-1	238
	Alresford Town	v	Wimborne Town (24/8)	1-0aet	142
149	United Services Portsmouth	v	Winchester City	0-3	88
150	Verwood Town	v	Fareham Town	2-2	
	Fareham Town	v	Verwood Town (23/8)	4-0	95
151	Swindon Supermarine	v	Odd Down	5-1	133
152	Oldland Abbotonians	v	Brislington	2-3	77
153	Hamworthy United	v	Brockenhurst	2-1	118
	(at Brockenhurst FC)				
154	Salisbury	v	Bitton	5-0	561
155	Street	v	Larkhall Athletic	4-2	96
156	Bideford	v	Bodmin Town	1-1	205
	Bodmin Town	v	Bideford (24/8)	1-2	200
157	Taunton Town	v	Tiverton Town	4-4	432
	Tiverton Town	v	Taunton Town (23/8)	0-2	406
158	Bridgwater Town	v	Plymouth Parkway	0-6	160
159	Portishead Town	v	Shepton Mallet	2-0	77
160	Clevedon Town	v	Barnstaple Town	0-1	

FACEP - (Above) The ball travels goalbound during this tie between AFC Emley and Athersley Rec.

Whilst (left) this Athersley player gets his shot away despite the challenge from the AFC Emley player.
Photo: Bill Wheatcroft.

FACP - Goal mouth action from Shortwood United's home tie against Ashford Town (Mddx).
Photo: Peter Barnes.

FIRST QUALIFYING ROUND
SATURDAY 3 SEPTEMBER 2016 - WINNERS RECEIVE £3,000

#	Home		Away	Score	Att
1	Washington	v	Shildon	2-5	157
2	Ashton United	v	Nantwich Town	0-3	213
3	Brighouse Town	v	Lancaster City	0-3	380
4	Blyth Spartans	v	Frickley Athletic	3-1	667
5	Hyde United	v	Colne	1-0	271
6	Bishop Auckland	v	Ossett Albion	5-1	328
7	Whitby Town	v	Winsford United	3-3	239
	Winsford Town	v	Whitby Town (5/9)	1-2	
8	Sheffield	v	Farsley Celtic	0-3	325
9	Marske United	v	Marine	0-2	264
10	Newcastle Benfield	v	Bridlington Town	0-2	107
11	Morpeth Town	v	Colwyn Bay	4-1	220
12	Harrogate Railway Athletic	v	Consett	0-5	168
13	Dunston UTS	v	Skelmersdale United	2-2	249
	Skelmersdale United	v	Dunston UTS (6/9)	1-2	223
14	Ashton Athletic	v	Mossley	7-2	152
15	Squires Gate	v	Handsworth Parramore	2-5	88
16	Witton Albion	v	Buxton	3-0	324
17	Billingham Synthonia	v	Ossett Town	2-2	165
	Ossett Town	v	Billingham Synthonia (6/9)	3-2	132
18	Pontefract Collieries	v	Tadcaster Albion	2-3	298
19	Burscough	v	Maine Road	4-3	116
20	Trafford	v	Cheadle Town	5-2	318
21	Workington	v	Warrington Town	3-0	448
22	Radcliffe Borough	v	Spennymoor Town	3-5	175
23	Leek Town	v	Kettering Town	2-3	416
24	Hednesford Town	v	Belper Town	1-2	391
25	King's Lynn Town	v	Brigg Town	6-1	511
26	AFC Mansfield	v	Stratford Town	2-1	95
27	Rushall Olympic	v	Soham Town Rangers	2-2	161
	Soham Town Rangers	v	Rushall Olympic (6/9)	0-1	169
28	Matlock Town	v	Heanor Town	4-2	423
29	Chasetown	v	Grantham Town	1-1	233
	Grantham Town	v	Chasetown (6/9)	2-2aet	261
	(Chasetown won 6-5 on kicks from the penalty mark)				
30	Evesham United	v	Barwell	2-2	237
	Barwell	v	Evesham United (6/9)	2-0	204
31	Peterborough Sports	v	Stourbridge	1-3	206
32	Ashby Ivanhoe	v	Ilkeston	0-6	693
33	St Neots Town	v	Stamford	1-1	351
	Stamford	v	St Neots Town (6/9)	4-1	273
34	Westfields	v	St Ives Town	4-0	190
35	Lincoln United	v	Dunkirk	6-1	161
36	Halesowen Town	v	Coleshill Town	3-0	376
37	Highgate United	v	Leamington	3-1	231
38	Leicester Road	v	Kirby Muxloe	0-0	159
	Kirby Muxloe	v	Leicester Road (6/9)	3-2aet	
39	Coalville Town	v	Redditch United	2-1	161
40	Coventry United	v	Bedworth United	0-2	347
41	Mickleover Sports	v	Spalding United	3-2	172
42	Deeping Rangers	v	Gresley	2-6	152
43	Romulus	v	Hereford	1-1	713
	Hereford	v	Romulus (6/9)	3-0	2240
44	Rugby Town	v	Corby Town	1-0	312
45	Dereham Town	v	Holbeach United	2-1	191
46	Eynesbury Rovers	v	Sutton Coldfield Town	1-3	190
47	Stafford Rangers	v	Kidsgrove Athletic	1-2	659
48	Brightlingsea Regent	v	Billericay Town	1-2	146
49	Hadley	v	London Colney	1-0	103
50	Haringey Borough	v	Witham Town	0-3	136
51	Kempston Rovers	v	Harefield United	3-2	138
52	Hanwell Town	v	Enfield Town	1-0	212
53	Sun Sports	v	Hayes & Yeading United	0-2	155
54	Hendon	v	Cheshunt	5-2	257
55	Maldon & Tiptree	v	Biggleswade Town	0-1	115
56	Heybridge Swifts	v	AFC Dunstable	2-2	103
	AFC Dunstable	v	Heybridge Swifts (7/9)	2-1	117
57	Chesham United	v	Saffron Walden Town	5-0	325
58	Harrow Borough	v	Sawbridgeworth Town	4-1	118
59	AFC Sudbury	v	Halstead Town	6-0	420
60	Kings Langley	v	Sporting Bengal United	6-1	101
61	Felixstowe & Walton United	v	Tilbury	2-1	247
62	Chalfont St Peter	v	Potters Bar Town	0-3	130
63	Uxbridge	v	Needham Market	2-0	109
64	Cambridge City	v	Flackwell Heath	3-1	136
65	Harlow Town	v	Romford	3-1	313
66	Stanway Rovers	v	Barton Rovers	0-1	87
67	Canvey Island	v	Dunstable Town	2-1	238
68	Hitchin Town	v	Biggleswade United	4-2	708
69	Leiston	v	Grays Athletic	4-1	253
70	Waltham Forest	v	Stotfold	2-1	95
71	AFC Rushden & Diamonds	v	AFC Hornchurch	2-0	436
72	Lowestoft Town	v	Histon	0-2	407
73	Waltham Abbey	v	Wingate & Finchley	0-5	130
74	Colliers Wood United	v	Eastbourne Town	2-0	102
75	Hythe Town	v	Leatherhead	1-0	255
76	East Preston	v	Merstham	1-4	158
77	Camberley Town	v	Hastings United	0-2	159
78	South Park	v	Dorking Wanderers (2/9)	2-1	274
79	Walton Casuals	v	Greenwich Borough	3-2	71
80	Burgess Hill Town	v	Ashford United	2-1	325
81	Fleet Town	v	Slimbridge	1-1	111
	Slimbridge	v	Fleet Town (7/9)	1-0aet	119
82	Andover Town	v	Farnborough	0-5	256
83	Brimscombe & Thrupp	v	Peacehaven & Telscombe	3-0	162
84	Staines Town	v	Godalming Town	4-0	241
85	CB Hounslow United	v	Metropolitan Police	1-3	166
86	Herne Bay	v	Ashford Town (Middx)	3-1	217
87	Eastbourne United	v	Highworth Town	0-3	139
88	Faversham Town	v	Cray Wanderers	1-0	195
89	Pagham	v	Dulwich Hamlet	0-3	230
90	Ascot United	v	Tonbridge Angels (4/8)	2-2	430
	Tonbridge Angels	v	Ascot United (6/9)	7-0	376
91	Arundel	v	Egham Town	1-5	122
92	Worthing	v	Carshalton Athletic	3-3	561
	Carshalton Athletic	v	Worthing (5/9)	2-6	
93	Lewes	v	Sevenoaks Town	0-0	490
	Sevenoaks Town	v	Lewes (7/9)	2-1	280
94	Wantage Town	v	Beaconsfield SYCOB	1-1	80
	Beaconsfield SYCOB	v	Wantage Town (5/9)	6-1	118
95	VCD Athletic	v	Kingstonian	4-1	98
96	Slough Town	v	Chipstead	6-1	472
97	Thamesmead Town	v	Chertsey Town	1-0	78
98	Corinthian Casuals	v	North Leigh	2-3	168
99	Folkestone Invicta	v	North Greenford United	3-1	337
100	Bognor Regis Town	v	Guildford City	5-1	396
101	Ramsgate	v	Whyteleafe	1-2	196
102	Taunton Town	v	Cinderford Town	2-0	242
103	Alresford Town	v	Fareham Town	1-1	100
	Fareham Town	v	Alresford Town (6/9)	2-4	167
104	Barnstaple Town	v	Merthyr Town	0-4	210
105	Weymouth	v	Paulton Rovers (6/9)	2-1	472
	(3/8 - tie abandoned after 50 mins due to waterlogged pitch, 1-1)				
106	Winchester City	v	Street	4-2	154
107	Sholing	v	Havant & Waterlooville	0-2	301
108	Salisbury	v	Frome Town	2-0	832
109	Portishead Town	v	Swindon Supermarine	1-4	166
110	Gillingham Town	v	Cirencester Town	0-2	110
111	Cadbury Heath	v	Plymouth Parkway	3-0	86
112	Chippenham Town	v	Moneyfields	9-0	282
113	Basingstoke Town	v	Bemerton Heath Harlequins	4-0	237
114	Dorchester Town	v	Banbury United	0-3	249
115	Bideford	v	AFC Portchester	1-2	189
116	Brislington	v	Hamworthy United	5-2	60

SECOND QUALIFYING ROUND
SATURDAY 17 SEPTEMBER 2016 - WINNERS RECEIVE £4,500

No	Home		Away	Score	Att
1	Bridlington Town	v	Harrogate Town	1-1	298
	Harrogate Town	v	Bridlington Town (20/9)	3-2	446
2	Handsworth Parramore	v	Burscough	2-0	98
3	Witton Albion	v	Stalybridge Celtic	1-1	316
	Stalybridge Celtic	v	Witton Albion (20/9)	2-1	241
	(at Mossley AFC)				
4	Blyth Spartans	v	Morpeth Town	2-4	1065
5	Bishop Auckland	v	Trafford	1-0	457
6	Nantwich Town	v	Marine	2-2	403
	Marine	v	Nantwich Town (20/9)	2-3	279
7	Ashton Athletic	v	FC Halifax Town	0-5	479
8	Curzon Ashton	v	Consett	1-1	208
	Consett	v	Curzon Ashton (20/9)	0-1	709
9	Altrincham	v	Gainsborough Trinity	3-2	516
10	Kidsgrove Athletic	v	Matlock Town	1-2	257
11	Lancaster City	v	Darlington 1883	2-1	580
12	Alfreton Town	v	AFC Fylde	1-0	263
13	Tadcaster Albion	v	Farsley Celtic	0-2	464
14	Bradford (Park Avenue)	v	Salford City	0-1	427
15	Workington	v	Shildon	3-1	563
16	Dunston UTS	v	Chorley	0-2	333
17	Stockport County	v	Hyde United	2-0	1425
18	Ossett Town	v	FC United Of Manchester	1-7	694
19	Spennymoor Town	v	Whitby Town	1-0	607
20	Rushall Olympic	v	Kettering Town	1-2	241
21	Kirby Muxloe	v	Boston United	1-2	330
22	Sutton Coldfield Town	v	Hereford	2-3	823
23	Brackley Town	v	Rugby Town	6-0	305
24	Coalville Town	v	AFC Mansfield	0-1	139
25	Mickleover Sports	v	Stourbridge	1-2	256
26	Westfields	v	Highgate United	4-2	239
27	Kidderminster Harriers	v	Tamworth	4-0	1050
28	Nuneaton Town	v	Lincoln United	1-2	438
29	Halesowen Town	v	Belper Town	1-0	318
30	Gresley	v	Stamford	1-1	294
	Stamford	v	Gresley (20/9)	1-0	314
31	Barwell	v	Ilkeston	0-1	214
32	Chasetown	v	Bedworth United	0-1	334
33	Worcester City	v	AFC Telford United	0-0	721
	AFC Telford United	v	Worcester City (20/9)	1-3	661
34	Sevenoaks Town	v	Chesham United	2-2	426
	Chesham United	v	Sevenoaks Town (20/9)	2-1	273
35	Concord Rangers	v	AFC Rushden & Diamonds	1-3	192
36	Beaconsfield SYCOB	v	Witham Town	3-1	84
37	Egham Town	v	VCD Athletic	2-1	78
38	Dulwich Hamlet	v	Hendon	0-2	822
39	Hythe Town	v	Walton Casuals	2-4	221
40	Dereham Town	v	St Albans City	1-2	243
41	Wingate & Finchley	v	Tonbridge Angels	0-3	167
42	AFC Dunstable	v	Hampton & Richmond Borough	1-7	173
43	Wealdstone	v	Histon	4-0	327
44	Chelmsford City	v	Dartford	2-3	675
45	Staines Town	v	Maidenhead United	1-0	414
46	Hayes & Yeading United	v	Worthing	0-2	175
47	Hemel Hempstead Town	v	Herne Bay	1-1	320
	Herne Bay	v	Hemel Hempstead Town (20/9)	1-5	262
48	Eastbourne Borough	v	Metropolitan Police	2-1	441
49	Kempston Rovers	v	Burgess Hill Town	1-1	167
	Burgess Hill Town	v	Kempston Rovers (20/9)	3-1	258
50	South Park	v	Leiston	1-4	124
51	Hadley	v	Kings Langley	2-1	125
52	Ebbsfleet United	v	AFC Sudbury	5-0	855
53	Felixstowe & Walton United	v	Bishop's Stortford	2-1	416
54	Cambridge City	v	Slough Town	1-3	205
55	Folkestone Invicta	v	Waltham Forest	3-1	290
56	Uxbridge	v	Harrow Borough	1-2	178
57	East Thurrock United	v	Whitehawk	2-3	223
58	Canvey Island	v	Potters Bar Town	2-2	251
	Potters Bar Town	v	Canvey Island (20/9)	3-2	218
59	Whyteleafe	v	Welling United	0-2	231
60	King's Lynn Town	v	Harlow Town	1-0	674
61	Billericay Town	v	Bognor Regis Town	2-1	366
62	Faversham Town	v	Hitchin Town	2-2	295
	Hitchin Town	v	Faversham Town (19/9)	0-1	
63	Hanwell Town	v	Thamesmead Town	1-1	146
	Thamesmead Town	v	Hanwell Town (20/9)	4-2aet	35
64	Merstham	v	Colliers Wood United	0-0	148
	Colliers Wood United	v	Merstham (21/9)	1-2aet	146
65	Margate	v	Biggleswade Town	2-0	466
66	Barton Rovers	v	Hastings United	0-1	145
67	Swindon Supermarine	v	Farnborough	1-0	209
68	Winchester City	v	Truro City	4-0	210
69	Havant & Waterlooville	v	Highworth Town	5-1	329
70	Alresford Town	v	Cadbury Heath	1-3	138
71	Chippenham Town	v	Poole Town	4-1	436
72	Salisbury	v	Gloucester City	1-2	945
73	Cirencester Town	v	Banbury United	1-6	155
74	Basingstoke Town	v	Hungerford Town	0-1	347
75	Weymouth	v	Gosport Borough	3-2	527
76	AFC Portchester	v	Merthyr Town	0-2	217
77	Taunton Town	v	Slimbridge	2-0	375
78	Brislington	v	Brimscombe & Thrupp	1-2	110
79	Bath City	v	Oxford City	1-1	482
	Oxford City	v	Bath City (20/9)	1-2aet	228
80	North Leigh	v	Weston Super Mare	2-1	175

THIRD QUALIFYING ROUND
SATURDAY 1 OCTOBER 2016 - WINNERS RECEIVE £7,500

#	Home		Away	Score	Att
1	Halesowen Town	v	Nantwich Town	1-1	534
	Nantwich Town	v	Halesowen Town (4/10)	2-1	362
2	Kettering Town	v	Boston United	2-0	628
3	Lincoln United	v	Handsworth Parramore	3-1	318
4	Farsley Celtic	v	Bishop Auckland	0-1	357
5	FC Halifax Town	v	Stalybridge Celtic	2-1	965
6	Worcester City	v	Brackley Town	0-3	628
7	King's Lynn Town	v	Alfreton Town	0-2	847
8	Curzon Ashton	v	Bedworth United	4-0	207
9	Ilkeston	v	Stourbridge	1-2	413
10	Lancaster City	v	Kidderminster Harriers	2-3	570
11	Matlock Town	v	Workington	1-1	489
	Workington	v	Matlock Town (4/10)	1-3	562
12	Stockport County	v	Salford City	2-0	3181
13	Spennymoor Town	v	Chorley	1-0	713
14	FC United Of Manchester	v	Harrogate Town	3-3	1541
	Harrogate Town	v	FC United Of Manchester (4/10)	2-0	
15	Altrincham	v	Morpeth Town	3-0	658
16	AFC Mansfield	v	Stamford	1-2	220
17	Faversham Town	v	Egham Town	1-1	442
	Egham Town	v	Faversham Town (4/10)	1-0	147
18	North Leigh	v	Folkestone Invicta	3-1	202
19	Ebbsfleet United	v	Havant & Waterlooville	7-0	742
20	Hungerford Town	v	Leiston	1-4	245
21	Potters Bar Town	v	Bath City	0-0	338
	Bath City	v	Potters Bar Town (4/10)	1-1aet	
	(Potters Bar Town won 4-3 on kicks from the penalty mark)				
22	Hendon	v	AFC Rushden & Diamonds	3-0	417
23	Margate	v	Hastings United (4/10)	2-2	385
	Hastings United	v	Margate (11/10)	1-2aet	530
24	Taunton Town	v	Hampton & Richmond Borough	2-1	630
25	Weymouth	v	Brimscombe & Thrupp	6-0	643
26	St Albans City	v	Worthing	6-0	678
27	Wealdstone	v	Banbury United	2-1	457
28	Tonbridge Angels	v	Hereford	4-2	1112
29	Beaconsfield SYCOB	v	Felixstowe & Walton United	3-0	273
30	Whitehawk	v	Merthyr Town	2-0	292
31	Chesham United	v	Staines Town	2-0	354
32	Burgess Hill Town	v	Cadbury Heath	6-1	333
33	Slough Town	v	Dartford	2-3	733
34	Billericay Town	v	Chippenham Town	3-2	482
35	Welling United	v	Swindon Supermarine	7-1	325
36	Gloucester City	v	Hemel Hempstead Town	2-2	489
	Hemel Hempstead Town	v	Gloucester City (4/10)	2-0	
37	Westfields	v	Walton Casuals	4-0	349
38	Eastbourne Borough	v	Hadley	0-0	416
	Hadley	v	Eastbourne Borough	1-4	297
39	Merstham	v	Thamesmead Town	5-1	188
40	Harrow Borough	v	Winchester City	2-1	177

FOURTH QUALIFYING ROUND
SATURDAY 15 OCTOBER 2016 - WINNERS RECEIVE £12,500

#	Home		Away	Score	Att
1	Southport	v	Chester	1-0	1674
2	Alfreton Town	v	Gateshead	2-2	457
	Gateshead	v	Alfreton Town (19/10)	2-3aet	465
3	North Ferriby United	v	Macclesfield Town	1-4	395
4	Harrogate Town	v	FC Halifax Town	0-2	1791
5	Stockport County	v	Bishop Auckland	2-0	2770
6	Barrow	v	Tranmere Rovers	2-1	2133
7	Nantwich Town	v	Stourbridge	1-3	754
8	Altrincham	v	Matlock Town	3-1	1071
9	Lincoln City	v	Guiseley	0-0	2629
	Guiseley	v	Lincoln City (18/10)	1-2	765
10	Lincoln United	v	Spennymoor Town	0-3	578
11	Stamford	v	Wrexham	1-1	1264
	Wrexham	v	Stamford (18/10)	2-3aet	1598
12	York City	v	Curzon Ashton	1-1	1307
	Curzon Ashton	v	York City (17/10)	2-1	467
13	Welling United	v	Whitehawk	0-1	515
14	Westfields	v	Leiston	2-1	741
15	Sutton United	v	Forest Green Rovers	2-1	751
16	Chesham United	v	Potters Bar Town	1-0	777
17	Dagenham & Redbridge	v	Wealdstone	3-1	1224
18	Torquay United	v	Woking	1-1	1348
	Woking	v	Torquay United (18/10)	2-1	791
19	Taunton Town	v	Hemel Hempstead Town	0-0	1282
	Hemel Hempstead Town	v	Taunton Town (18/10)	0-1	631
20	Braintree Town	v	Bromley	4-2	343
21	Beaconsfield SYCOB	v	Brackley Town	0-5	495
22	Tonbridge Angels	v	Dartford	0-3	1391
23	Egham Town	v	St Albans City	0-1	327
24	Boreham Wood	v	Hendon	3-0	457
25	Aldershot Town	v	Eastbourne Borough	1-2	1443
26	Harrow Borough	v	Margate	2-2	309
	Margate	v	Harrow Borough (18/10)	1-3	574
27	Maidstone United	v	Billericay Town	3-1	1428
28	Kidderminster Harriers	v	Weymouth	6-0	1394
29	Solihull Moors	v	Kettering Town	3-1	769
30	Burgess Hill Town	v	Dover Athletic	0-5	629
31	Merstham	v	Ebbsfleet United	2-1	646
32	Eastleigh	v	North Leigh	6-0	889

FIRST ROUND PROPER
SATURDAY 5 NOVEMBER 2016 - WINNERS RECEIVE £18,000

1	Sheffield United	v	Leyton Orient (6/11)	6-0	6099
2	Millwall	v	Southend United (4/11)	1-0	4502
3	Dagenham & Redbridge	v	FC Halifax Town	0-0	1387
	FC Halifax Town	v	Dagenham & Redbridge (15/11)	2-1	1465
4	Merstham	v	Oxford United	0-5	1920
5	Taunton Town	v	Barrow (6/11)	2-2	2297
	Barrow	v	Taunton Town (15/11)	2-1	1717
6	Southport	v	Fleetwood Town (7/11)	0-0	2265
	Fleetwood Town	v	Southport (15/11)	4-1aet	1609
7	Yeovil Town	v	Solihull Moors	2-2	2118
	Solihull Moors	v	Yeovil Town (15/11)	1-1aet	1460
	(Solihull Moors won 4-2 on kicks from the penalty mark)				
8	Stockport County	v	Woking	2-4	4025
9	Dartford	v	Sutton United	3-6	1689
10	Walsall	v	Macclesfield Town	0-1	2334
11	Port Vale	v	Stevenage	1-0	3093
12	Northampton Town	v	Harrow Borough	6-0	3306
13	Cambridge United	v	Dover Athletic	1-1	2620
	Dover Athletic	v	Cambridge United (17/11)	2-4aet	1158
14	Westfields	v	Curzon Ashton	1-1	1178
	Curzon Ashton	v	Westfields (14/11)	3-1	1075
15	Milton Keynes Dons	v	Spennymoor Town	3-2	4099
16	Gillingham	v	Brackley Town	2-2	2410
	Brackley Town	v	Gillingham (16/11)	4-3aet	1654
17	Alfreton Town	v	Newport County (6/11)	1-1	1109
	Newport County	v	Alfreton Town (15/11)	4-1aet	1189
18	Portsmouth	v	Wycombe Wanderers	1-2	8130
19	Maidstone United	v	Rochdale (6/11)	1-1	2227
	Rochdale	v	Maidstone United (15/11)	2-0	1350

20	Bury	v	AFC Wimbledon	2-2	2346
	AFC Wimbledon	v	Bury (15/11)	5-0	2316
21	St Albans City	v	Carlisle United (6/11)	3-5	3473
22	Boreham Wood	v	Notts County (6/11)	2-2	1201
	Notts County	v	Boreham Wood (15/11)	2-0	1762
23	Mansfield Town	v	Plymouth Argyle	1-2	2318
24	Braintree Town	v	Eastbourne Borough	7-0	645
25	Hartlepool United	v	Stamford (6/11)	3-0	2461
26	Bolton Wanderers	v	Grimsby Town	1-0	7173
27	Bradford City	v	Accrington Stanley	1-2	4985
28	Oldham Athletic	v	Doncaster Rovers	2-1	2984
29	Eastleigh	v	Swindon Town (4/11)	1-1	3312
	Swindon Town	v	Eastleigh (15/11)	1-3	4321
30	Shrewsbury Town	v	Barnet	3-0	3120
31	Morecambe	v	Coventry City (6/11)	1-1	1732
	Coventry City	v	Morecambe (15/11)	2-1	2275
32	Crawley Town	v	Bristol Rovers	1-1	2251
	Bristol Rovers	v	Crawley Town (15/11)	4-2aet	3676
33	Whitehawk	v	Stourbridge	1-1	726
	Stourbridge	v	Whitehawk (14/11)	3-0	1993
34	Colchester United	v	Chesterfield	1-2	1840
35	Lincoln City	v	Altrincham	2-1	3529
36	Exeter City	v	Luton Town	1-3	2972
37	Charlton Athletic	v	Scunthorpe United	3-1	4123
38	Cheltenham Town	v	Crewe Alexandra	1-1	2880
	Crewe Alexandra	v	Cheltenham Town (15/11)	1-4	1711
39	Peterborough United	v	Chesham United	2-1	4328
40	Blackpool	v	Kidderminster Harriers (6/11)	2-0	1963

SECOND ROUND PROPER
SATURDAY 3 DECEMBER 2016 - WINNERS RECEIVE £27,000

1	Curzon Ashton	v	AFC Wimbledon (4/12)	3-4	1831
2	Chesterfield	v	Wycombe Wanderers	0-5	3685
3	Millwall	v	Braintree Town (4/12)	5-2	3345
4	Macclesfield Town	v	Oxford United (2/12)	0-0	2566
	Oxford United	v	Macclesfield Town (13/12)	3-0	3642
5	Bolton Wanderers	v	Sheffield United (4/12)	3-2	7027
6	Blackpool	v	Brackley Town	1-0	1764
7	Stourbridge	v	Northampton Town (13/12)	1-0	2520
8	Notts County	v	Peterborough United (4/12)	2-2	3940
	Peterborough United	v	Notts County (20/12)	2-0	7796
9	Cambridge United	v	Coventry City (4/12)	4-0	4283
10	Port Vale	v	Hartlepool United (4/12)	4-0	3514

11	Bristol Rovers	v	Barrow (4/12)	1-2	4570
12	Woking	v	Accrington Stanley (4/12)	0-3	3718
13	Lincoln City	v	Oldham Athletic (5/12)	3-2	7012
14	Luton Town	v	Solihull Moors	6-2	3512
15	Sutton United	v	Cheltenham Town	2-1	2224
16	Eastleigh	v	FC Halifax Town (4/12)	3-3	2098
	FC Halifax Town	v	Eastleigh (13/12)	0-2	1539
17	Shrewsbury Town	v	Fleetwood Town	0-0	2886
	Fleetwood Town	v	Shrewsbury Town (13/12)	3-2	1279
18	Charlton Athletic	v	Milton Keynes Dons	0-0	4902
	Milton Keynes Dons	v	Charlton Athletic (13/12)	3-1aet	3655
19	Plymouth Argyle	v	Newport County	0-0	5071
	Newport County	v	Plymouth Argyle (21/12)	0-1aet	5121
20	Carlisle United	v	Rochdale	0-2	4426

THIRD ROUND PROPER
SATURDAY 7 JANUARY 2016 - WINNERS RECEIVE £67,500

1	Ipswich Town	v	Lincoln City	2-2	16027
	Lincoln City	v	Ipswich Town (17/1)	1-0	9069
2	Barrow	v	Rochdale	0-2	4414
3	Manchester United	v	Reading	4-0	74396
4	Hull City	v	Swansea City	2-0	6608
5	Sunderland	v	Burnley	0-0	17632
	Burnley	v	Sunderland (17/1)	2-0	12257
6	Queens Park Rangers	v	Blackburn Rovers	1-2	7482
7	Millwall	v	AFC Bournemouth	3-0	9471
8	West Ham United	v	Manchester City (6/1)	0-5	56975
9	Brighton & Hove Albion	v	Milton Keynes Dons	2-0	11091
10	Blackpool	v	Barnsley	0-0	4875
	Barnsley	v	Blackpool (17/1)	1-2aet	5558
11	Wigan Athletic	v	Nottingham Forest	2-0	5163
12	Birmingham City	v	Newcastle United	1-1	13171
	Newcastle United	v	Birmingham City (18/1)	3-1	34896
13	Chelsea	v	Peterborough United (8/1)	4-1	41003
14	Middlesbrough	v	Sheffield Wednesday (8/1)	3-0	23661
15	West Bromwich Albion	v	Derby County	1-2	25288
16	Everton	v	Leicester City	1-2	35493

17	Liverpool	v	Plymouth Argyle (8/1)	0-0	52692
	Plymouth Argyle	v	Liverpool (18/1)	0-1	17048
18	Wycombe Wanderers	v	Stourbridge	2-1	6312
19	Watford	v	Burton Albion	2-0	13270
20	Preston North End	v	Arsenal	1-2	22185
21	Cardiff City	v	Fulham (8/1)	1-2	5199
22	Stoke City	v	Wolverhampton Wanderers	0-2	21479
23	Cambridge United	v	Leeds United (9/1)	1-2	7973
24	Bristol City	v	Fleetwood Town	0-0	10301
	Fleetwood Town	v	Bristol City (17/1)	0-1	2115
25	Huddersfield Town	v	Port Vale	4-0	11715
26	Tottenham Hotspur	v	Aston Villa (8/1)	2-0	31182
27	Brentford	v	Eastleigh	5-1	7537
28	Bolton Wanderers	v	Crystal Palace	0-0	11683
	Crystal Palace	v	Bolton Wanderers (17/1)	2-1	7149
29	Norwich City	v	Southampton	2-2	12449
	Southampton	v	Norwich City (18/1)	1-0	13517
30	Sutton United	v	AFC Wimbledon	0-0	5013
	AFC Wimbledon	v	Sutton United (17/1)	1-3	4768
31	Accrington Stanley	v	Luton Town	2-1	1717
32	Rotherham United	v	Oxford United	2-3	5618

FOURTH ROUND PROPER
SATURDAY 28 JANUARY 2017 - WINNERS RECEIVE £90,000

1	Tottenham Hotspur	v	Wycombe Wanderers	4-3	31440	9	Manchester United	v	Wigan Athletic (29/1)	4-0	75229
2	Derby County	v	Leicester City (27/1)	2-2	25079	10	Millwall	v	Watford (29/1)	1-0	9722
	Leicester City	v	Derby County (8/2)	3-1aet	29648	11	Rochdale	v	Huddersfield Town	0-4	7431
3	Oxford United	v	Newcastle United	3-0	11810	12	Burnley	v	Bristol City	2-0	14921
4	**Sutton United**	v	Leeds United (29/1)	1-0	4997	13	Blackburn Rovers	v	Blackpool	2-0	9327
5	Liverpool	v	Wolverhampton Wanderers	1-2	52469	14	Fulham	v	Hull City (29/1)	4-1	15143
6	Southampton	v	Arsenal	0-5	31288	15	Middlesbrough	v	Accrington Stanley	1-0	24040
7	**Lincoln City**	v	**Brighton & Hove Albion**	3-1	9469	16	Crystal Palace	v	Manchester City	0-3	13979
8	Chelsea	v	Brentford	4-0	41042						

FIFTH ROUND PROPER
SATURDAY 18 FEBRUARY 20167 - WINNERS RECEIVE £180,000

1	Burnley	v	Lincoln City	0-1	19185	5	Middlesbrough	v	Oxford United	3-2	28198
2	Fulham	v	Tottenham (19/2)	0-3	22557	6	Wolverhampton Wanderers	v	Chelsea	0-3	30193
3	Blackburn Rovers	v	Manchester United (19/2)	1-2	23130	7	Huddersfield Town	v	Manchester City	0-0	24129
							Manchester City	v	Huddersfield Town (1/3)	5-1	42425
4	**Sutton United**	v	Arsenal (20/2)	0-2	5013	8	Millwall	v	Leicester City	1-0	18012

QUARTER-FINALS
SATURDAY 11 MARCH 2017 - WINNERS RECEIVE £360,000

1	Chelsea	v	Manchester United (13/3)	1-0	40081	3	Tottenham Hotspur	v	Millwall (12/3)	6-0	31137
2	Middlesbrough	v	Manchester City	0-2	32228	4	Arsenal	v	Lincoln City	5-0	59454

SEMI-FINALS
WINNERS RECEIVE £900,000   RUNNERS-UP £450,000

SATURDAY 22 APRIL 2017 - at Wembley Stadium						SUNDAY 23 APRIL 2017 - at Wembley Stadium					
1	Chelsea	v	Tottenham Hotspur (22/4)	4-2	86355	2	Arsenal	v	Manchester City (23/4)	2-1aet	85725

THE FINAL
SATURDAY 27 MAY 2017 - at Wembley Stadium   WINNERS RECEIVE £1.8m   RUNNERS-UP £900,000

ARSENAL	2	1	CHELSEA	89472

FAC1P - Ross (Macclesfield) takes the ball off the foot of Jackson (Walsall), to maintain the clean sheet that would help the 'Silkmen' claim a League club scalp. Photo: Keith Clayton.

PRELIMINARY ROUND DRAW
SATURDAY 19 AUGUST 2017

1	Albion Sports / Nelson	v	Newton A / Chester-L-S
2	South Shields	v	Bridlington / Bill'ham Syn
3	Bill'ham T / Pickering	v	Clitheroe
4	Sund RCA / Garforth	v	Ashington / Sunderland Ryhope CW
5	Guisborough / Stockton Town	v	Shildon / Morpeth
6	Goole AFC	v	Newcastle BBP / West Allot C
7	Barn'wick / Jarr RBCA	v	Washington / Dunston UTS
8	Tadcaster Albion	v	Colne
9	Thackley / Harrogate R	v	Kendal Town
10	Scarborough Athletic	v	Marske / Nth Shields
11	Consett AFC / Bishop Auck	v	Team Northumbria / Heaton Stannington
12	Penrith AFC / West Auck	v	Seaham RS / Whitley Bay
13	Irlam / Abbey Hey	v	Maine Road / Winsford
14	Sheffield	v	Ossett Town
15	Charnock Richard / Penistone Church	v	Litherland Remyca / AFC L'pool
16	Bamber Bridge	v	Brighouse Town
17	Hallam / Bootle	v	Atherton Collieries
18	Frickley Athletic	v	Runcorn T / AFC Darwen
19	Ramsbottom United	v	Armthorpe / Liversedge
20	Pontefract / Alsager	v	Skelmersdale United
21	Squires G / Ashton Ath	v	Runcorn L / Hemsworth
22	Parkgate / Barnton	v	Widnes / Handsworth Parramore
23	Trafford	v	Kidsgrove Athletic
24	Prescot Cables	v	Padiham / City of Liverpool
25	Northwich / 1874 Northwich_	v	Athersley Recreation_ / West Didsbury & Chorlton AFC
26	Glossop North End	v	Mossley AFC
27	Hyde United	v	Congleton / New Mills
28	Ossett Albion	v	Droylsden
29	Colwyn Bay	v	Stocksbridge Park Steels
30	Radcliffe Borough	v	AFC Emley / Burscough
31	Leek Town	v	Cammell Laird 1907 / Maltby Main
32	Sporting Khalsa / Stourport	v	Market Drayton Town
33	Alvechurch	v	Hanley Town / Atherstone
34	Walsall W / Whitchurch Alport	v	Tividale / Highgate U
35	Bedworth United	v	Wolv SC / Haughmond
36	Coventry United / Rugby Town	v	Romulus
37	Bromsgrove Sporting / Rocesterv		Coleshill / Wellington
38	Wolv Cas / Malvern	v	Coventry S / Boldmere
39	Daventry T / Worcester	v	Chasetown
40	Brocton / Cadbury Ath	v	Gresley
41	Newcastle Town	v	Evesham United
42	AFC Wulf's / Shawbury U	v	Westfields / Bewdley
43	Birstall United / South Normanton Athletic	v	Cleethorpes Town
44	Rainworth / Shepshed D	v	Kimberley MW / Blaby & Whetstone Athletic
45	Kirby Mux / Barton T	v	Dunkirk / Thurn Nirv
46	Harrowby United / Grimsby B	v	Leicester Road / Sleaford
47	Oadby Town / St Andrews	v	Loughborough Dynamo
48	Worksop / Hinckley AFC	v	Heanor Town / Aylestone Park
49	Retford / Quorn	v	AFC Mansfield / Hall Rd Ran
50	Staveley MW / Loughboro U	v	Basford United
51	Boston Town / Radford	v	Carlton Town
52	Lincoln United	v	Belper Town
53	Bottesford / L Eaton U	v	Clipstone / West Bridgford
54	Biggleswade / Wisbech T	v	Spalding United
55	Dereham Town	v	Corby Town
56	Cambridge City	v	Stamford AFC
57	Barton Rovers	v	Peterborough Northern Star / Deeping Rangers
58	Raunds Town / Yaxley	v	Northampton Sileby Rangers / Harborough Town
59	Ely City / Holbeach U	v	Histon / Northampton On Chenecks
60	Potton U / Bigg'wade U	v	AFC Dunstable
61	Huntingdon T / Newport Pag	v	Kempston Rovers
62	Arlesey Town	v	Wellingborough Whitworths / Desborough
63	Soham Town Rangers	v	Cogenhoe / Godmanchester
64	Eynesbury Rovers / Thetford T	v	Peterborough Sports
65	Fakenham / W'Boro Twn	v	AFC Rushden & Diamonds
66	Bedford Town	v	Swaffham / Rothwell C
67	St Marg / Burnham R	v	Hullbridge / Ipswich W
68	Bury Town	v	Tilbury
69	Southend M / Wroxham	v	Stanway R / Gorleston
70	Bowers & Pitsea	v	Haringey Borough
71	Maldon & Tiptree	v	Waltham Abbey
72	AFC Hornchurch	v	Brentwood Town
73	Canvey Island	v	Witham Town
74	FC Clacton / Clapton	v	Norwich United
75	Framlingham Town / Wadham Lodgev		Mildenhall Town
76	Hoddesdon / Haverhill R	v	Heybridge Swifts
77	Newmarket / Gt Wakering	v	Ware
78	FC Broxbourne Borough / Bethnal Grn	v	Takeley / Wivenhoe

79	Felixstowe / Brantham	v	Cheshunt
80	Barkingside / Stowmarket	v	Romford
81	AFC Sudbury	v	Aveley
82	Ilford / Woodbridge	v	Enf'ld 1893 / Haverhill Borough
83	Hertford Town	v	Hadleigh U / S Bengal U
84	Gt Yarmouth / Diss Town	v	Walsham LW / Basildon
85	Grays Athletic	v	Redbridge / Stansted
86	Hackney Wick / L Melford	v	FC Romania / Waltham F
87	Barking	v	Kirk & Pake / Saff Wald
88	Potters Bar Town	v	Sawbridgewth / West Essex
89	Slimbridge AFC	v	Cinderford Town
90	Flackwell H / Burnham	v	Didcot Town
91	Ardley Utd / Baldock Town	v	Welwyn GC / N Greenford
92	Chalfont St Peter	v	Beaconsfield Town
93	Ashford Town (Middx)	v	Windsor / Wembley
94	Colney Hth / Tring Ath	v	Shortwood United
95	Kidlington	v	Lydney Town / Wantage T
96	Swindon Supermarine	v	Northwood
97	Hayes & Yeading United	v	Brimscombe & Thrupp / Sun Sports
98	Leighton T / Oxhey Jets	v	Woodley United / Tuffley Rovers
99	Wootton Bass / Crawley Grn	v	Stotfold / Berkhamsted
100	Chipping Sodbury Town / Brackley Town Saints	v	Bishop's Cleeve
101	Edgware Town / Leverstock G	v	Aylesbury United
102	Southall / Harpenden Town	v	Langford / Hadley
103	Aylesbury	v	Cirencester Town
104	Uxbridge	v	Thame United
105	Highworth T / London Col	v	Marlow
106	Hanwell Town	v	Fairford / Longlevens AFC
107	Highmoor Ibis / Buckingham Town	v	North Leigh
108	Cockfosters / Risborough Rangers	v	Holmer Grn / AFC Hayes
109	Arundel / Pagham	v	Sittingbourne
110	Hassocks / Hollands & Blair	v	Crowborough / Lingfield
111	Erith & Bel / Wick	v	Abbey Rangers / Cray Valley (PM)
112	Whyteleafe	v	Rochester United / Erith Town
113	Carshalton Athletic	v	Walt Hers / Mile Oak
114	Haywards Heath Town / Bedfont Sp	v	South Park
115	Colliers W'd / AFC U'field	v	Shoreham
116	Mole V / Canterbury City_	v	E'bourne Tn / Bearsted
117	Corinthian-Casuals	v	Hythe Town
118	Greenwich Borough	v	Horsh YMCA / Three Bdges
119	Corinthian / Deal Town	v	Glebe / Lordswood
120	Walton Casuals	v	Molesey
121	Hailsham T / Redhill	v	Ashford United_
122	Ramsgate	v	Hanworth V / Bedfont & Feltham

123	East Grinstead Town	v	VCD Athletic
124	Cray Wanderers	v	Sevenoaks / Broadbridge Heath
125	Epsom & E / Banstead	v	Loxwood / Holmesdale
126	E Preston / Saltdean United	v	Thamesmead Town
127	Chatham / Littlehampton	v	Little Common / Eastbourne United
128	Chipstead	v	Horley Town / Raynes Park
129	Tun Wells / Beckenham	v	Rusthall / CB Hounslow United
130	Worthing United / Steyning Town	v	Phoenix Sports
131	Spelthorne Sports / Chertsey	v	Horsham
132	Herne Bay	v	Chessington / Lancing
133	Lewes	v	Newhaven / P'Hav & Tel
134	Sheppey United_ / AFC Croydon Athletic	v	Hastings United
135	Whitstable / Croydon	v	Faversham Town
136	AC London / Crawley D	v	Egham Town
137	Bracknell / Cowes	v	Winchester City
138	Fleet Town	v	AFC Totton
139	Lymington / Andover Town	v	Wimborne Town
140	Godalming / Westfield	v	Farnham / Fawley
141	Christchurch / AFC P'hester	v	Amesbury Town / Eversley & California
142	Hamworthy / Bemerton	v	Ringwood / Ascot Utd
143	Binfield / Chichester	v	Horndean / Melksham
144	Team Solent / Brock'hurst	v	Hartley Wintney
145	Newport IW / Guildford C	v	Camberley / Blackfield
146	Salisbury	v	Bashley / Fareham
147	Badshot Lea / Verwood	v	Moneyfields
148	Whitchurch / Laverstock & Ford	v	Knaphill / Bournemouth
149	Sholing / Alresford	v	Thatcham T / Petersfield
150	Plymouth Parkway / Portland United	v	Paulton Rovers
151	Barnstaple Town	v	Clevedon / Bitton AFC
152	Shepton M / Tavistock	v	Shaftesbury / Exmouth Town
153	Bideford AFC	v	Wells City / Cribbs
154	Cadbury H / Longwell GS	v	Yate Town
155	Bridgwater / Keynsham Town	v	Brislington / Sherborne
156	Wellington / Hengrove A	v	Buckland / Bodmin Town
157	Cheddar_ / Willand	v	Bristol Manor Farm
158	Bradford T / Odd Down	v	Mangotsfield United
159	Taunton Town	v	Larkhall Athletic
160	AFC St Austell / Bridport	v	Street / Hallen

THE FA TROPHY 2016-17

PRELIMINARY ROUND
SATURDAY 8 OCTOBER 2016 - WINNERS RECEIVE £2,500

#	Home		Away	Score	Att
1	Witton Albion	v	Brighouse Town	5-2	235
2	Glossop North End	v	Tadcaster Albion	2-0	369
3	Prescot Cables	v	Ossett Albion	1-1	290
	Ossett Albion	v	Prescot Cables (11/10)	0-1	87
4	Colne	v	Trafford	1-2	181
5	Burscough	v	Kendal Town	1-2	110
6	Clitheroe	v	Stocksbridge Park Steels	0-5	
7	Colwyn Bay	v	Hyde United	1-0	268
8	Northwich Victoria	v	Mossley (9/10)	1-1	
	Mossley	v	Northwich Victoria (11/10)	3-2	65
9	Shaw Lane Association	v	Scarborough Athletic	2-0	304
10	Belper Town	v	Goole	1-2	
11	Radcliffe Borough	v	Farsley Celtic	1-3	119
12	Lancaster City	v	Droylsden	1-1	233
	Droylsden	v	Lancaster City (11/10)	1-3	102
13	Ramsbottom United	v	Sheffield	3-1	
14	Ossett Town	v	Bamber Bridge	0-1	141
15	Bedworth United	v	Rugby Town	3-3	223
	Rugby Town	v	Bedworth United (11/10)	0-2	131
16	Stamford	v	Basford United	1-0	
17	AFC Rushden & Diamonds	v	Histon	1-1	333
	Histon	v	AFC Rushden & Diamonds (11/10)	1-6	151
18	Gresley	v	Spalding United	4-1	243
19	Carlton Town	v	Chasetown	3-1	
20	Newcastle Town	v	Soham Town Rangers	1-3	132
21	Loughborough Dynamo	v	Leek Town	1-2	
22	Lincoln United	v	Romulus	2-2	171
	Romulus	v	Lincoln United (11/10)	1-3aet	
23	Aylesbury	v	Ware	1-3	56
24	Sittingbourne	v	Bury Town	0-2	150
25	Maldon & Tiptree	v	Great Wakering Rovers	3-1	
26	East Grinstead Town	v	Three Bridges	4-0	141
27	Witham Town	v	Aveley	2-1	
28	Cray Wanderers	v	Carshalton Athletic (26/10)	3-0	91
	(9/10 – tie ordered to be replayed, 3-3)				
29	Potters Bar Town	v	Horsham	0-2	131
30	Thurrock	v	Bowers & Pitsea	1-2	83
31	Chipstead	v	Kempston Rovers	3-3	65
	Kempston Rovers	v	Chipstead (11/10)	2-0	88
32	Aylesbury United	v	Chatham Town	4-1	99
33	Uxbridge	v	AFC Dunstable	4-0	
34	Lewes	v	Tilbury	1-1	
	Tilbury	v	Lewes (11/10)	0-3	
35	South Park	v	Guernsey	2-0	112
36	Whyteleafe	v	Cheshunt	1-3	
37	Haringey Borough	v	Hythe Town	1-2	86
38	Dorking Wanderers	v	Northwood	3-6	
39	Wroxham	v	Godalming Town	3-0	71
40	Norwich United	v	Tooting & Mitcham United	0-2	156
41	Ramsgate	v	Hastings United	0-3	192
42	AFC Hornchurch	v	Ashford Town (Middx)	2-3	162
43	Molesey	v	Romford	1-3	
44	Brentwood Town	v	Marlow	1-2	92
45	Arlesey Town	v	Chalfont St Peter	2-2	72
	Chalfont St Peter	v	Arlesey Town (11/10)	6-0	
	(at AFC Hayes)				
46	Corinthian Casuals	v	Thamesmead Town	2-1	121
47	Brightlingsea Regent	v	Dereham Town	2-1	102
48	VCD Athletic	v	Greenwich Borough	1-1	127
	Greenwich Borough	v	VCD Athletic (11/10)	1-2	
49	Royston Town	v	Egham Town	3-0	144
50	Hanwell Town	v	Bedford Town	4-0	123
51	Barton Rovers	v	Herne Bay	0-1	101
52	Slimbridge	v	Swindon Supermarine	1-3	60
53	Bridgwater Town	v	North Leigh	2-2	109
	North Leigh	v	Bridgwater Town (11/10)	4-1	
54	Winchester City	v	Petersfield Town	1-1	140
	Petersfield Town	v	Winchester City (11/10)	1-3aet	115
55	Wimborne Town	v	AFC Totton	2-2	264
	AFC Totton	v	Wimborne Town (11/10)	1-2	184
56	Salisbury	v	Hereford	4-3	1225
57	Paulton Rovers	v	Tiverton Town	1-6	
58	Bishop's Cleeve	v	Didcot Town	1-0	80
59	Mangotsfield United	v	Yate Town	0-2	310
60	Farnborough	v	Barnstaple Town	1-5	172
61	Fleet Town	v	Bideford	2-1	
62	Kidlington	v	Wantage Town	2-3	79
63	Taunton Town	v	Larkhall Athletic	6-2	
64	Shortwood United	v	Evesham United	0-1	

FAT1Q - Hastings United put pressure on Aylesbury United's defence. Photo: Roger Turner.

FAT1Q - Goal mouth action from Havant & Waterlloville's 1-2 win over Cirencester Town. Photo: Peter Barnes.

FAT2P - Alfreton's No.3 gets to ball before Boreham Wood's 'keeper to send his header goal bound.
Photo: Bill Wheatcroft.

FIRST QUALIFYING ROUND
SATURDAY 29 OCTOBER 2016 - WINNERS RECEIVE £2,700

1	Goole	v	Blyth Spartans	1-1	252	38	Metropolitan Police	v	Brightlingsea Regent	2-6	124
	Blyth Spartans	v	Goole (1/11)	7-1		39	Needham Market	v	Wroxham	2-0	205
2	Spennymoor Town	v	Matlock Town	1-2	393	40	Slough Town	v	Bognor Regis Town	4-1	435
3	Warrington Town	v	Nantwich Town	0-2	274	41	Grays Athletic	v	Wingate & Finchley (30/10)	1-1	146
4	Stocksbridge Park Steels	v	Lancaster City	2-1	128		Wingate & Finchley	v	Grays Athletic (1/11)	2-0	96
5	Whitby Town	v	Workington	4-3	321	42	Worthing	v	Kempston Rovers	3-1	418
6	Skelmersdale United	v	Kendal Town	1-3		43	AFC Sudbury	v	Bowers & Pitsea	4-0	196
7	Colwyn Bay	v	Witton Albion	1-1	298	44	Tonbridge Angels	v	Ashford Town (Middx)	3-3	
	Witton Albion	v	Colwyn Bay (1/11)	3-1	257		Ashford Town (Middx)	v	Tonbridge Angels (1/11)	1-4	158
8	Mossley	v	Farsley Celtic	1-3	124	45	Kings Langley	v	Heybridge Swifts	1-0	
9	Ramsbottom United	v	Prescot Cables	2-1	216	46	Leiston	v	Hendon	5-0	173
10	Bamber Bridge	v	Trafford	0-2	169	47	VCD Athletic	v	Ware	1-3	68
11	Buxton	v	Glossop North End	2-0	518	48	Enfield Town	v	Canvey Island	3-2	273
12	Ashton United	v	Marine	0-4	124	49	Tooting & Mitcham United	v	Dunstable Town	2-4	
13	Shaw Lane Association	v	Frickley Athletic	6-2	276	50	Billericay Town	v	Maldon & Tiptree	2-0	337
14	Stratford Town	v	Grantham Town	2-2		51	Chalfont St Peter	v	Corinthian Casuals	3-2	
	Grantham Town	v	Stratford Town (1/11)	4-0			(at Chesham United FC)				
15	Leamington	v	Mickleover Sports	0-1	352	52	Cray Wanderers	v	Marlow	4-0	75
16	Kidsgrove Athletic	v	Soham Town Rangers	5-3	151	53	Cheshunt	v	Folkestone Invicta	1-3	144
17	Rushall Olympic	v	Halesowen Town	1-2		54	Royston Town	v	Northwood	2-2	155
18	Ilkeston	v	Barwell	0-2			Northwood	v	Royston Town (1/11)	1-4	
19	Carlton Town	v	St Ives Town	1-4	93	55	Lowestoft Town	v	Dulwich Hamlet	1-2	428
20	Stourbridge	v	King's Lynn Town	1-2	465	56	Biggleswade Town	v	Witham Town	1-0	
21	Corby Town	v	Stafford Rangers	0-2	435	57	Faversham Town	v	South Park	3-4	175
22	Kettering Town	v	Market Drayton Town	5-1	357	58	Uxbridge	v	Harlow Town	0-1	
23	Redditch United	v	Cambridge City	3-1	242	59	Herne Bay	v	Harrow Borough	2-2	
24	Stamford	v	Hednesford Town	1-4			Harrow Borough	v	Herne Bay (1/11)	3-0	96
25	Leek Town	v	Sutton Coldfield Town	2-1		60	Hayes & Yeading United	v	Hitchin Town	0-1	127
26	AFC Rushden & Diamonds	v	Coalville Town	1-0			(at Beaconsfield SYCOB FC)				
27	Bedworth United	v	St Neots Town	2-3	122	61	Evesham United	v	Frome Town	1-1	235
28	Lincoln United	v	Gresley	4-2	202		Frome Town	v	Evesham United (2/11)	1-0	152
29	Horsham	v	Romford (30/10)	1-3	291	62	Yate Town	v	North Leigh	1-6	118
30	East Grinstead Town	v	Phoenix Sports+	2-3	95	63	Salisbury	v	Chippenham Town	2-3	904
31	Kingstonian	v	Lewes (30/10)	2-1	245	64	Taunton Town	v	Swindon Supermarine	5-0	493
32	Hastings United	v	Aylesbury United	4-0		65	Tiverton Town	v	Wimborne Town	0-1	
33	Hythe Town	v	Walton Casuals	3-2	179	66	Cirencester Town	v	Havant & Waterlooville	1-2	147
34	Burgess Hill Town	v	Beaconsfield SYCOB	5-1		67	Merthyr Town	v	Cinderford Town	6-1	273
35	Leatherhead	v	Chesham United	2-3	255	68	Banbury United	v	Bishop's Cleeve	0-1	220
36	Waltham Abbey	v	Merstham	0-5		69	Fleet Town	v	Winchester City	1-2	93
37	Hanwell Town	v	Bury Town	2-1	116	70	Weymouth	v	Wantage Town	4-0	402
						71	Dorchester Town	v	Barnstaple Town	3-1	344
						72	Staines Town	v	Basingstoke Town	1-4	291

SECOND QUALIFYING ROUND
SATURDAY 12 NOVEMBER 2016 - WINNERS RECEIVE £3,250

1	Nantwich Town	v	Kendal Town	2-0	
2	Blyth Spartans	v	Halesowen Town	4-3	
3	Buxton	v	King's Lynn Town	1-3	302
4	Marine	v	St Neots Town	1-1	288
	St Neots Town	v	Marine (15/11)	2-4aet	
5	Hednesford Town	v	Stafford Rangers	1-1	910
	Stafford Rangers	v	Hednesford Town (15/11)	2-1aet	
6	St Ives Town	v	Leek Town	2-1	160
7	Shaw Lane Association	v	Whitby Town	3-0	
8	Ramsbottom United	v	Redditch United (15/11)	4-1	139
9	Kidsgrove Athletic	v	Stocksbridge Park Steels	3-5	
10	Barwell	v	Farsley Celtic	2-3	159
11	Grantham Town	v	Matlock Town	0-2	259
12	Trafford	v	Mickleover Sports	0-1	206
13	AFC Rushden & Diamonds	v	Lincoln United	3-3	485
	Lincoln United	v	AFC Rushden & Diamonds (15/11)	2-0	229
14	Witton Albion	v	Kettering Town	2-1	339
15	Kings Langley	v	Enfield Town	1-0	
16	Bishop's Cleeve	v	Taunton Town	0-1	72
17	Dunstable Town	v	Weymouth	1-4	106
18	Dorchester Town	v	Basingstoke Town	0-3	306
19	Merthyr Town	v	Slough Town	2-2	370
	Slough Town	v	Merthyr Town (15/11)	2-0	429
20	Havant & Waterlooville	v	Billericay Town	5-0	256
21	Brightlingsea Regent	v	Harlow Town (15/11)	1-1	
	Harlow Town	v	Brightlingsea Regent (22/11)	2-1	228
	(12/11 - tie abandoned after 45 mins due to floodlight failure, 0-0)				
22	Hanwell Town	v	Frome Town	0-1	104
23	Chippenham Town	v	Leiston	0-1	306
24	Dulwich Hamlet	v	Chesham United	4-0	716
25	Merstham	v	Hythe Town (15/11)	0-3	105
26	Burgess Hill Town	v	Chalfont St Peter (15/11)	2-2	
	Chalfont St Peter	v	Burgess Hill Town (22/11)	1-1aet	
	(Burgess Hill Town won 8-7 on kicks from the penalty mark)				
27	Biggleswade Town	v	Hitchin Town	1-1	
	Hitchin Town	v	Biggleswade Town	3-2	
28	Folkestone Invicta	v	North Leigh	2-3	
29	Royston Town	v	Wimborne Town	4-0	180
30	Needham Market	v	Harrow Borough	1-2	203
31	Cray Wanderers	v	Worthing (13/11)	1-2	
32	Phoenix Sports	v	Winchester City	1-3	67
33	Hastings United	v	South Park	1-1	
	South Park	v	Hastings United (16/11)	3-2aet	84
34	AFC Sudbury	v	Romford	4-0	
35	Kingstonian	v	Tonbridge Angels	1-1	318
	Tonbridge Angels	v	Kingstonian (15/11)	1-2	
36	Ware	v	Wingate & Finchley	0-2	

THIRD QUALIFYING ROUND
SATURDAY 26 NOVEMBER 2016 - WINNERS RECEIVE £4,000

1	Stocksbridge Park Steels	v	Stalybridge Celtic	2-2	
	Stalybridge Celtic	v	Stocksbridge Park Steels (6/12)	2-3	140
2	Harrogate Town	v	Salford City	2-2	
	Salford City	v	Harrogate Town (6/12)	0-3	283
3	Witton Albion	v	Boston United (6/12)	4-2	194
	(26/11 – tie abandoned after 45 mins due to fog, 1-0)				
4	Mickleover Sports	v	Brackley Town	1-1	
	Brackley Town	v	Mickleover Sports (29/11)	3-1	140
5	Gainsborough Trinity	v	Alfreton Town	0-0	308
	Alfreton Town	v	Gainsborough Trinity (30/11)	4-1aet	
6	King's Lynn Town	v	St Ives Town	1-0	
7	Shaw Lane Association	v	Nantwich Town	3-1	215
	(tie awarded to Nantwich Town – Shaw Lane Association removed)				
8	Altrincham	v	Blyth Spartans (6/12)	2-2	
	Blyth Spartans	v	Altrincham (10/12)	2-3	
9	Ramsbottom United	v	AFC Telford United	0-2	319
10	Matlock Town	v	FC Halifax Town	1-1	
	FC Halifax Town	v	Matlock Town (29/11)	2-3	479
11	Farsley Celtic	v	Tamworth	2-2	227
	Tamworth	v	Farsley Celtic (29/11)	0-4	371
12	Chorley	v	Stafford Rangers (6/12)	1-0	466
13	Kidderminster Harriers	v	Lincoln United	3-1	916
14	Curzon Ashton	v	Worcester City (28/11)	1-2	193
15	FC United Of Manchester	v	Nuneaton Town (6/12)	1-5	736
16	Stockport County	v	Bradford (Park Avenue)	2-0	1164
17	Gloucester City	v	AFC Fylde	2-3	240
18	Darlington 1883	v	Marine (27/11)	2-2	743
	Marine	v	Darlington 1883 (6/12)	3-2	308
19	Ebbsfleet United	v	Harrow Borough	4-2	613
20	Slough Town	v	Wingate & Finchley	2-4	352
21	Truro City	v	Frome Town	6-1	269
22	Hampton & Richmond Boro	v	Royston Town	0-0	
	Royston Town	v	Hampton & Richmond Boro (6/12)	2-1	198
23	Concord Rangers	v	Welling United	0-1	161
24	Kings Langley	v	AFC Sudbury	1-3	151
25	Weston Super Mare	v	Dartford	2-4	
26	Worthing	v	Hemel Hempstead Town	1-1	505
	Hemel Hempstead Town	v	Worthing (29/11)	0-1	157
27	Hungerford Town	v	Gosport Borough	0-1	144
28	Oxford City	v	South Park	1-2	
29	Bath City	v	Basingstoke Town	2-0	366
30	Chelmsford City	v	Taunton Town	1-0	507
31	Margate	v	East Thurrock United	1-1	
	East Thurrock United	v	Margate (29/11)	2-0	
32	Leiston	v	Eastbourne Borough	1-1	212
	Eastbourne Borough	v	Leiston (6/12)	2-2aet	262
	(Leiston won 5-3 on kicks from the penalty mark)				
33	Poole Town	v	Weymouth	1-1	755
	Weymouth	v	Poole Town (29/11)	2-0	441
34	Havant & Waterlooville	v	Harlow Town	1-3	197
35	Winchester City	v	Dulwich Hamlet	0-1	
36	Maidenhead United	v	Wealdstone	2-2	555
	Wealdstone	v	Maidenhead United (29/11)	2-1	
37	Burgess Hill Town	v	Hitchin Town	0-3	
38	Whitehawk	v	St Albans City	1-1	326
	St Albans City	v	Whitehawk (29/11)	0-1	
39	North Leigh	v	Kingstonian	1-0	203
40	Hythe Town	v	Bishop's Stortford	4-2	234

FIRST ROUND PROPER
SATURDAY 10 DECEMBER 2016 - WINNERS RECEIVE £5,000

#	Home		Away	Score	Att
1	Gateshead	v	King's Lynn Town	2-0	277
2	Farsley Celtic	v	Southport	0-4	352
3	Solihull Moors	v	Matlock Town	1-2	336
4	Nantwich Town	v	Lincoln City+ (20/12)	1-2	482
5	Alfreton Town	v	North Ferriby United	1-0	290
6	Kidderminster Harriers	v	AFC Telford United	4-0	
7	Nuneaton Town	v	Stocksbridge Park Steels	3-1	356
8	Harrogate Town	v	Barrow	3-3	
	Barrow	v	Harrogate Town (13/12)	4-2aet	819
9	AFC Fylde	v	Brackley Town	1-1	641
	Brackley Town	v	AFC Fylde (13/12)	4-0	146
10	York City	v	Worcester City	3-1	
11	Chorley	v	Guiseley	0-1	612
12	Witton Albion	v	Chester	1-1	883
	Chester	v	Witton Albion (13/12)	2-1	921
13	Wrexham	v	Tranmere Rovers+	0-1	2159
14	Altrincham	v	Macclesfield Town (20/12)	1-1	717
	Macclesfield Town	v	Altrincham (4/1)	2-1	548
15	Stockport County	v	Marine	3-2	
16	Ebbsfleet United	v	Woking	1-1	825
	Woking	v	Ebbsfleet United (13/12)	0-1	613
17	Chelmsford City	v	Hitchin Town	1-0	469
18	Dagenham & Redbridge	v	Worthing	1-2	597
19	Harlow Town	v	Eastleigh	2-0	482
20	Whitehawk	v	Weymouth	2-2	253
	Weymouth	v	Whitehawk (13/12)	1-2	401
21	Braintree Town	v	Torquay United	2-0	301
22	East Thurrock United	v	Aldershot Town	1-1	
	Aldershot Town	v	East Thurrock United (12/12)	3-4aet	566
23	Dulwich Hamlet	v	Royston Town	2-2	
	Royston Town	v	Dulwich Hamlet (13/12)	0-1	312
24	Welling United	v	Hythe Town	8-1	355
25	Wealdstone	v	Wingate & Finchley	2-2	364
	Wingate & Finchley	v	Wealdstone (13/12)	1-2aet	280
26	Dartford	v	Dover Athletic	1-1	813
	Dover Athletic	v	Dartford (13/12)	1-2	
27	South Park	v	North Leigh	1-1	148
	North Leigh	v	South Park	1-3	157
28	AFC Sudbury	v	Gosport Borough	2-1	641
29	Sutton United	v	Bath City	1-0	524
30	Forest Green Rovers	v	Truro City	1-1	
	Truro City	v	Forest Green Rovers (13/12)	0-1aet	
31	Boreham Wood	v	Maidstone United	0-0	201
	Maidstone United	v	Boreham Wood (13/12)	2-3	
32	Bromley	v	Leiston	1-1	411
	Leiston	v	Bromley (13/12)	3-5	306

SECOND ROUND PROPER
SATURDAY 14 JANUARY 2017 - WINNERS RECEIVE £6,000

#	Home		Away	Score	Att
1	Worthing	v	Sutton United	2-2	1398
	Sutton United	v	Worthing (24/1)	3-2aet	496
2	Tranmere Rovers	v	South Park	4-1	2801
3	Bromley	v	Welling United	1-2	519
4	East Thurrock United	v	Braintree Town	2-5	
5	Nuneaton Town	v	Guiseley	6-1	554
6	Boreham Wood	v	Alfreton Town	2-1	201
7	Barrow	v	Matlock Town	3-2	976
8	Southport	v	Wealdstone	1-2	744
9	Gateshead	v	Lincoln City	1-3	528
10	Dartford	v	Chelmsford City	0-1	918
11	Kidderminster Harriers	v	Ebbsfleet United	3-0	1078
12	Harlow Town	v	York City	1-2	816
13	AFC Sudbury	v	Macclesfield Town	1-3	
14	Whitehawk	v	Dulwich Hamlet	1-4	530
15	Chester	v	Forest Green Rovers	0-2	1250
16	Stockport County	v	Brackley Town	1-1	1605
	Brackley Town	v	Stockport County (17/1)	2-0	294

THIRD ROUND PROPER
SATURDAY 4 FEBRUARY 2017 - WINNERS RECEIVE £7,000

#	Home		Away	Score	Att
1	Welling United	v	Lincoln City	1-3	743
2	Braintree Town	v	Dulwich Hamlet	0-0	608
	Dulwich Hamlet	v	Braintree Town (7/2)	5-2	860
3	Barrow	v	Kidderminster Harriers	1-0	1173
4	Tranmere Rovers	v	Chelmsford City	1-1	2473
	Chelmsford City	v	Tranmere Rovers (8/2)	1-4	923
5	Macclesfield Town	v	Forest Green Rovers	1-0	967
6	Wealdstone	v	Brackley Town	1-4	620
7	Nuneaton Town	v	York City	0-3	687
8	Sutton United	v	Boreham Wood	0-0	879
	Boreham Wood	v	Sutton United (7/2)	5-0	269

FOURTH ROUND PROPER
SATURDAY 25 FEBRUARY 2017 - WINNERS RECEIVE £8,000

#	Home		Away	Score	Att
1	Dulwich Hamlet	v	Macclesfield Town	2-2	2834
	Macclesfield Town	v	Dulwich Hamlet (7/3)	2-0	1071
2	York City	v	Brackley Town	1-0	1994
3	Boreham Wood	v	Lincoln City	0-2	901
4	Tranmere Rovers	v	Barrow	5-1	3487

SEMI FINALS
1ST LEG SATURDAY 11 & 14 MARCH / 2ND LEG SATURDAY 18 MARCH 2017 - WINNERS RECEIVE £16,000

Home		Away	Score	Att
Macclesfield Town	v	Tranmere Rovers	1-1	2358
Tranmere Rovers	v	Macclesfield Town	0-1	6100
Macclesfield Town through 2-1 on aggregate.				8458
York City	v	Lincoln City	2-1	3294
Lincoln City	v	York City	1-1 aet	8409
York City through 3-2 on aggregate.				11703

THE FINAL...

MACCLESFIELD TOWN   2
(McManus 48)

YORK CITY   3
(McManus 48)

Wembley Stadium   **Att: 38,224**
*combined Trophy/Vase attendance

THE SQUADS

MACCLESFIELD TOWN	YORK CITY
Scott Flinders	Kyle Letheren
Andy Halls	Asa Hall (sub 69)
David Fitzpatrick Neill	Yan Klukowski (sub 46)
Byrne (sub 68)	Hamza Bencherif
George Pilkington	Danny Holmes (sub 76)
Rhys Browne	Amari Morgan-Smith
Chris Holroyd	Simon Heslop
Kingsley James	Sean Newton
Ollie Norburn (sub 89)	Daniel Parslow
Mitch Hancox (sub 86)	Jon Parkin
Danny Whitaker	Vadaine Oliver
Substitutes	**Substitutes**
John McCombe (68)	Adriano Moke (46)
Luke Summerfield (86)	Aidan Connolly (69)
Anthony Dudley (89)	Shaun Rooney (76)
Craig Ross	Luke Simpson
Danny Whitehead	Scott Fenwick

Referee Paul Tierney.
Assisted by Ian Hussin and Edward Smart.
Fourth official Ben Toner.

There was some surprise at the results of the semi-final stage of this competition when the two teams, Lincoln City, promoted to League Two as National League winners, and Tranmere Rovers, a participant in the play offs, were, even though established as favourites to make it to the Wembley final, beaten by their lower ranked opponents, Macclesfield and York, over two legs. No matter their surprise at their semi-final victories there was no sign that either the Minstermen or the Silkmen were merely content to be satisfied with making an appearance at the national stadium for they both contributed to one of the better Trophy finals, giving their own fans and neutrals plenty to enjoy and admire on a lovely early summer sunny afternoon.

A late goal from substitute Aidan Connolly gained the victory for York City who had previously led twice, only to be pegged back on both occasions by Macclesfield in an entertaining game between two well matched teams. As one of the sides relegated from the National League at the end of a previously disappointing season this victory would have brought some consolation to the Minstermen and their loyal supporters. For the Silkmen, as the very first winners of the competition in 1970, and having finished the season much higher in the table than their opponents, it will have brought disappointment since they had started as favourites.

York took the lead in the 8th minute when the evergreen Jon Parkin cleverly backheaded home a cross from Danny Holmes. Within five minutes the teams were back on level terms. When a Mitch Hancox free kick was only half cleared Rhys Browne was able to pick up the loose ball and shoot home from just inside the area, past goalkeeper Kyle Letheren, who may well have been left helpless by a defender's deflection. Back came the Minstermen to regain the lead in the 22nd minute, the lively Vadaine Oliver being on hand at the far post to slide home Sean, later to be judged man of the match, Newton's low cross from the left. This was evidently not going to be one of those tentative finals where both teams show more concern about preventing the opposition scoring than making chances for themselves. No, this was the sort of football that spectators enjoy. Those who chose to leave at the end of the Vase final missed out.

Rhys Browne equalises for Macclesfield against York City. Photo: Alan Coomes

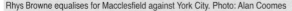

Macclesfield, behind for a second time, retaliated with a powerful long range effort from Danny Whitaker which Letheren was just able to tip over, the goalie then saving from the same player at point blank range. Another Silkmen effort came from the nippy Browne. With a tricky run across the area he forged a good chance only to ruin it by firing wildly over. Deservedly, on the balance of the number of scoring opportunities they were engineering, Macclesfield drew level, on virtually the stroke of half time, with a wonder goal. From thirty five yards out Ollie Norburn, completely out of the blue, left Letheren helplessly stranded, scoring with a lightning strike high into the net to send in the teams level at the interval and spectators looking forward to the resumption.

Oliver (York) gives the lead back to York.
Photo: Keith Clayton.

The second half opened with Whitaker's shot on target but straight at Letheren, before a clearance header from a corner fell at Whitaker's feet. His goalward shot rolled slowly past the helpless keeper but, more regretfully for him, also past the post. At this point Macclesfield were having decidedly the better of the play. Chris Holroyd made a chance for Hancox whose shot Letheren just managed to parry clear of any onrushing opponent. The powerful Hamza Bencherif blocked a Kingsley James effort on the line and Letheren, by far the busier of the keepers, thwarted Browne as he sought to complete successfully a Silkmen men move involving several players. York were decidedly on the defensive.

At the other end, in an increasingly rare York attack, Sean Newton fired a low ball across the six yard area with no attacker on hand to take advantage. The dreaded extra time loomed ever closer. Macclesfield were certainly having the better of the play but then fate intervened. Seemingly out of nothing, with five minutes of normal time left, 35 year old Parkin, very worthy of his place in the team, used his powerful physique to make the most of a through ball. His shot deflected off a defender's boot, and lurched goalwards, sub Connolly being fortuitously on hand to ensure no defender was able to clear and make certain that the ball crossed the line.

There was little time left for the Silkmen to grab a third equaliser. Try as they might, the towering Bencherif and his defensive brethren were in no mood to allow any further danger to threaten Letheren's goal and the final whistle from Paul Tierney signalled that the Trophy would soon be securely in skipper Simon Heslop's grasp and making its way to Yorkshire and not Cheshire.

Arthur Evans

PAST FINALS

1970 MACCLESFIELD TOWN 2 (Lyons, B Fidler)   **TELFORD UNITED** 0   Att: 28,000
Northern Premier League   *Southern League*
Macclesfield: Cooke, Sievwright, Bennett, Beaumont, Collins, Roberts, Lyons, B Fidler,Young, Corfield, D Fidler.
Telford: Irvine, Harris, Croft, Flowers, Coton, Ray,Fudge, Hart, Bentley, Murray, Jagger.   Ref: K Walker

1971 TELFORD UTD 3 (Owen, Bentley, Fudge)   **HILLINGDON BORO.** 2 (Reeve, Bishop)   Att: 29,500
Southern League   *Southern League*
Telford: Irvine, Harris, Croft, Ray, Coton, Carr, Fudge, Owen, Bentley, Jagger ,Murray.
Hillingdon B.: Lowe, Batt, Langley, Higginson, Newcombe, Moore, Fairchild,Bishop, Reeve, Carter, Knox.   Ref: D Smith

1972 STAFFORD RANGERS 3 (Williams 2, Cullerton)   **BARNET** 0   Att: 24,000
Northern Premier League   *Southern League*
Stafford R.: Aleksic, Chadwick, Clayton, Sargeant, Aston, Machin, Cullerton, Chapman,Williams, Bayley, Jones.
Barnet: McClelland, Lye, Jenkins, Ward, Embrey, King, Powell, Ferry, Flatt, Easton, Plume .   Ref: P Partridge

1973 SCARBOROUGH 2 (Leask, Thompson)   **WIGAN ATHLETIC** 1 (Rogers) aet   Att:23,000
Northern Premier League   *Northern Premier League*
Scarborough: Garrow, Appleton, Shoulder, Dunn, Siddle, Fagan, Donoghue, Franks,Leask (Barmby), Thompson, Hewitt.
Wigan: Reeves, Morris, Sutherland, Taylor,Jackson, Gillibrand, Clements, Oats (McCunnell), Rogers, King, Worswick.   Ref: H Hackney

1974 MORECAMBE 2 (Richmond, Sutton)   **DARTFORD** 1 (Cunningham)   Att: 19,000
Northern Premier League   *Southern League*
Morecambe: Coates, Pearson, Bennett, Sutton, Street, Baldwin, Done, Webber,Roberts (Galley), Kershaw, Richmond.
Dartford: Morton, Read, Payne, Carr, Burns,Binks, Light, Glozier, Robinson (Hearne), Cunningham, Halleday.   Ref: B Homewood

1975(1) MATLOCK TOWN 4 (Oxley, Dawson, T Fenoughty, N Fenoughty) **SCARBOROUGH** 0   Att: 21,000
Northern Premier League   *Northern Premier League*
Matlock: Fell, McKay, Smith, Stuart, Dawson, Swan, Oxley, N Fenoughty, Scott, T Fenoughty, M Fenoughty.
Scarborough: Williams, Hewitt, Rettitt, Dunn, Marshall, Todd, Houghton, Woodall, Davidson, Barnby, Aveyard.   Ref: K Styles

1976 SCARBOROUGH 3 (Woodall, Abbey, Marshall(p)) **STAFFORD R.** 2 (Jones 2) aet   Att: 21,000
Northern Premier League   *Northern Premier League*
Scarborough: Barnard, Jackson, Marshall, H Dunn, Ayre (Donoghue), HA Dunn, Dale,Barmby, Woodall, Abbey, Hilley.
Stafford: Arnold, Ritchie, Richards, Sargeant,Seddon, Morris, Chapman, Lowe, Jones, Hutchinson, Chadwick.   Ref: R Challis

1977 SCARBOROUGH 2 (Dunn(p), Abbey)   **DAGENHAM** 1 (Harris)   Att: 21,500
Northern Premier League   *Isthmian League*
Scarborough: Chapman, Smith, Marshall (Barmby), Dunn, Ayre, Deere, Aveyard,Donoghue, Woodall, Abbey, Dunn.
Dagenham: Hutley, Wellman, P Currie, Dunwell,Moore, W Currie, Harkins, Saul, Fox, Harris, Holder.   Ref: G Courtney

1978 ALTRINCHAM 3 (King, Johnson, Rogers)   **LEATHERHEAD** 1 (Cook)   Att: 20,000
Northern Premier League   *Isthmian League*
Altrincham: Eales, Allan, Crossley, Bailey, Owens, King, Morris, Heathcote,Johnson, Rogers, Davidson (Flaherty).
Leatherhead: Swannell, Cooper, Eaton, Davies,Reid, Malley, Cook, Salkeld, Baker, Boyle (Bailey).   Ref: A Grey

1979 STAFFORD RANGERS 2 (A Wood 2)   **KETTERING TOWN** 0   Att: 32,000
Northern Premier League   *Southern League*
Stafford: Arnold, F Wood, Willis, Sargeant, Seddon, Ritchie, Secker, Chapman, A Wood, Cullerton, Chadwick (Jones).
Kettering: Lane, Ashby, Lee, Eastell, Dixey,Suddards, Flannagan, Kellock, Phipps, Clayton, Evans (Hughes).   Ref: D Richardson

1980(2) DAGENHAM 2 (Duck, Maycock)   **MOSSLEY** 1 (Smith)   Att: 26,000
Isthmian League   *Northern Premier League*
Dagenham: Huttley, Wellman, Scales, Dunwell, Moore, Durrell, Maycock, Horan,Duck, Kidd, Jones (Holder).
Mossley: Fitton, Brown, Vaughan, Gorman, Salter, Polliot, Smith, Moore, Skeete, O'Connor, Keelan (Wilson).   Ref: K Baker

1981(3) BISHOP'S STORTFORD 1 (Sullivan)   **SUTTON UNITED** 0   Att: 22,578
Isthmian League   *Isthmian League*
Bishop's Stortford: Moore, Blackman, Brame, Smith (Worrell), Bradford, Abery, Sullivan,Knapman, Radford, Simmonds, Mitchell.
Sutton Utd.: Collyer, Rogers, Green, J Rains,T Rains, Stephens (Sunnucks), Waldon, Pritchard, Cornwell, Parsons, Dennis.   Ref: J Worrall

1982 ENFIELD 1 (Taylor)   **ALTRINCHAM** 0   Att: 18,678
Alliance Premier League   *Alliance Premier League*
Enfield: Jacobs, Barrett, Tone, Jennings, Waite, Ironton, Ashford, Taylor,Holmes, Oliver (Flint), King.
Altrincham: Connaughton, Crossley, Davison, Bailey, Cuddy, King (Whitbread), Allan, Heathcote, Johnson, Rogers, Howard.   Ref: B Stevens

Notes:
1   The only occasion three members of the same family played in the same FA Trophy Final team.
2   The first of the Amateurs from the Isthmian League to win the FA Trophy.
3   Goalkeeper Terry Moore had also won an Amateur Cup Winners Medal with Bishop's Stortford in 1974.
     All games played at Wembley (old & new) unless stated.

1983 TELFORD UTD 2 (Mather 2)
Alliance Premier League

NORTHWICH VICTORIA 1 (Bennett)
Alliance Premier League

Att: 22,071

Telford: Charlton, Lewis, Turner, Mayman (Joseph), Walker, Easton, Barnett,Williams, Mather, Hogan, Alcock.
Northwich: Ryan, Fretwell, Murphy, Jones, Forshaw, Ward, Anderson, Abel (Bennett), Reid, Chesters, Wilson.

Ref: B Hill

1984 NORTHWICH VICTORIA 1 (Chester)
Replay NORTHWICH VICTORIA 2 (Chesters(p), Anderson)
Alliance Premier League

BANGOR CITY 1 (Whelan)
BANGOR CITY 1 (Lunn)
Alliance Premier League

Att: 14,200
Att: 5,805 (at Stoke)

Northwich: Ryan, Fretwell, Dean, Jones, Forshaw (Power 65), Bennett, Anderson,Abel, Reid, Chesters, Wilson.   Ref: J Martin
Bangor: Letheren, Cavanagh, Gray, Whelan, Banks,Lunn, Urqhart, Morris, Carter, Howat, Sutcliffe (Westwood 105) . Same in replay.

1985 WEALDSTONE 2 (Graham, Holmes)
Alliance Premier League

BOSTON UNITED 1 (Cook)
Alliance Premier League

Att: 20,775

Wealdstone: Iles, Perkins, Bowgett, Byatt, Davies, Greenaway, Holmes, Wainwright,Donnellan, Graham (N Cordice 89), A Cordice.
Boston: Blackwell, Casey, Ladd,Creane, O'Brien, Thommson, Laverick (Mallender 78), Simpsom, Gilbert, Lee, Cook.

Ref: J Bray

1986 ALTRINCHAM 1 (Farrelly)
Gola League

RUNCORN 0
Gola League

Att: 15,700

Altrincham: Wealands, Gardner, Densmore, Johnson, Farrelly, Conning, Cuddy,Davison, Reid, Ellis, Anderson. Sub: Newton.
Runcorn: McBride, Lee, Roberts,Jones, Fraser, Smith, S Crompton (A Crompton), Imrie, Carter, Mather, Carrodus.

Ref: A Ward

1987 KIDDERMINSTER HARRIERS 0
Replay KIDDERMINSTER HARRIERS 2 (Davies 2)
Conference

BURTON ALBION 0
BURTON ALBION 1 (Groves)
Southern League

Att: 23,617
Att: 15,685 (at West Brom)

Kidderminster: Arnold, Barton, Boxall, Brazier (sub Hazlewood in rep), Collins (sub Pearson 90 at Wembley), Woodall, McKenzie,
O'Dowd, Tuohy, Casey, Davies. sub:Jones.
Burton: New, Essex, Kamara, Vaughan, Simms, Groves, Bancroft, Land, Dorsett, Redfern, (sub Wood in replay), Gauden.
Sub: Patterson.   Ref: D Shaw

1988 ENFIELD 0
Replay ENFIELD 3 (Furlong 2, Howell)
Conference

TELFORD UNITED 0
TELFORD UNITED 2 (Biggins, Norris(p))
Conference

Att: 20,161
Att: 6,912 (at W Brom)

Enfield: Pape, Cottington, Howell, Keen (sub Edmonds in rep), Sparrow (sub Hayzleden at Wembley), Lewis (sub Edmonds at
Wembley), Harding, Cooper, King,Furlong, Francis.
Telford: Charlton, McGinty, Storton, Nelson, Wiggins, Mayman (sub Cunningham in rep (sub Hancock)), Sankey, Joseph, Stringer (sub
Griffiths at Wembley, Griffiths in replay), Biggins, Norris.   Ref: L Dilkes

1989 TELFORD UNITED 1 (Crawley)
Conference

MACCLESFIELD TOWN 0
Conference

Att: 18,102

Telford: Charlton, Lee, Brindley, Hancock, Wiggins, Mayman, Grainger, Joseph, Nelson, Lloyd, Stringer. Subs: Crawley, Griffiths.
Macclesfield: Zelem, Roberts, Tobin, Edwards, Hardman, Askey, Lake, Hanton, Imrie, Burr, Timmons. Subs: Devonshire, Kendall.

1990 BARROW 3 (Gordon 2, Cowperthwaite)
Conference

LEEK TOWN 0
Northern Premier League

Att: 19,011

Barrow: McDonnell, Higgins, Chilton, Skivington, Gordon, Proctor, Doherty (Burgess), Farrell (Gilmore), Cowperthwaite, Lowe, Ferris.
Leek: Simpson, Elsby (Smith), Pearce, McMullen, Clowes, Coleman (Russell),Mellor, Somerville, Sutton, Millington, Norris   Ref: T Simpson

1991 WYCOMBE W. 2 (Scott, West)
Conference

KIDDERMINSTER HARRIERS 1 (Hadley)
Conference

Att: 34,842

Wycombe: Granville, Crossley, Cash, Kerr, Creaser, Carroll, Ryan, Stapleton,West, Scott, Guppy (Hutchinson).   Ref: J Watson
Kidderminster: Jones, Kurila, McGrath, Weir, Barnett, Forsyth, Joseph (Wilcox), Howell (Whitehouse), Hadley, Lilwall, Humphries

1992 COLCHESTER UTD* 3 (Masters, Smith, McGavin)
Conference

WITTON ALBION 1 (Lutkevitch)
Conference

Att: 27,806

Colchester: Barrett, Donald, Roberts, Knsella, English, Martin, Cook, Masters,McDonough (Bennett 65), McGavin, Smith.   Ref: K P Barratt
Witton: Mason, Halliday, Coathup, McNeilis, Jim Connor, Anderson, Thomas, Rose, Alford, Grimshaw (Joe Connor), Lutkevitch (McCluskie)

1993 WYCOMBE W*. 4 (Cousins, Kerr, Thompson, Carroll)
Conference

RUNCORN 1 (Shaughnessy)
Conference

Att: 32,968

Wycombe: Hyde, Cousins, Cooper, Kerr, Crossley, Thompson (Hayrettin 65),Carroll, Ryan, Hutchinson, Scott, Guppy. Sub: Casey.
Runcorn: Williams, Bates, Robertson, Hill, Harold (Connor 62), Anderson, Brady (Parker 72), Brown, Shaughnessy, McKenna, Brabin

1994 WOKING 2 (D Brown, Hay)
Conference

RUNCORN 1 (Shaw (pen))
Conference

Att: 15,818

Woking: Batty, Tucker, L Wye, Berry, Brown, Clement, Brown (Rattray 32), Fielder, Steele, Hay (Puckett 46), Walker.   Ref: Paul Durkin
Runcorn: Williams, Bates, Robertson, Shaw, Lee, Anderson, Thomas, Connor, McInerney (Hill 71), McKenna, Brabin. Sub: Parker

1995 WOKING 2 (Steele, Fielder)
Conference

KIDDERMINSTER HARRIERS 1 aet (Davies)
Conference

Att: 17,815

Woking: Batty, Tucker, L Wye, Fielder, Brown, Crumplin (Rattray 42), S Wye, Ellis, Steele, Hay (Newberry 112), Walker. (Sub: Read(gk))
Kidderminster: Rose, Hodson, Bancroft, Webb, Brindley (Cartwright 94), Forsyth, Deakin, Yates, Humphreys (Hughes 105), Davies,
Purdie. Sub: Dearlove (gk)
Ref: D J Gallagher

THE FA TROPHY

1996 MACCLESFIELD TOWN 3 (Payne, OG, Hemmings) **NORTHWICH VICTORIA 1 (Williams)** Att: 8,672
Conference *Conference*
Macclesfield: Price, Edey, Gardiner, Payne, Howarth(C), Sorvel, Lyons, Wood (Hulme 83), Coates, Power, Hemmings (Cavell 88).
Northwich: Greygoose, Ward, Duffy, Burgess (Simpson 87), Abel (Steele), Walters, Williams, Butler (C), Cooke, Humphries, Vicary.
Ref: M Reed

1997 WOKING 1 (Hay 112) **DAGENHAM & REDBRIDGE 0** Att: 24,376
Conference *Isthmian League*
Woking: Batty, Brown, Howard, Foster, Taylor, S Wye, Thompson (sub Jones 115), Ellis, Steele (L Wye 108), Walker, Jackson (Hay 77).
Dagenham: Gothard, Culverhouse, Connor, Creaser, Jacques (sub Double 75), Davidson, Pratt (Naylor 81), Parratt, Broom, Rogers,
Stimson (John 65). Ref: J Winter

1998 CHELTENHAM TOWN 1 (Eaton 74) **SOUTHPORT 0** Att: 26,387
Conference *Conference*
Cheltenham: Book, Duff, Freeman, Banks, Victory, Knight (Smith 78), Howells, Bloomer, Walker (sub Milton 78), Eaton, Watkins. Sub:
Wright.
Southport: Stewart, Horner, Futcher, Ryan, Farley, Kielty, Butler, Gamble, Formby (sub Whittaker 80), Thompson (sub Bollard 88),
Ross. Sub: Mitten. Ref: G S Willard

1999 KINGSTONIAN 1 (Mustafa 49) **FOREST GREEN ROVERS 0** Att: 20,037
Conference *Conference*
Kingstonian: Farrelly, Mustafa, Luckett, Crossley, Stewart, Harris, Patterson, Pitcher, Rattray, Leworthy (Francis 87), Akuamoah. Subs
(not used): John, Corbett, Brown, Tranter
Forest Green Rovers: Shuttleworth, Hedges, Forbes, Bailey (Smart 76), Kilgour, Wigg (Cook 58), Honor (Winter 58), Drysdale,
McGregor, Mehew, Sykes. Subs (not used): Perrin, Coupe Ref: A B Wilkie

2000 KINGSTONIAN 3 (Akuamoah 40, 69, Simba 75) **KETTERING TOWN** 2 (Vowden 55, Norman 64p) Att: 20,034
Conference *Conference*
Kingstonian: Farelly, Mustafa, Luckett, Crossley, Stewart (Saunders 77), Harris, Kadi (Leworthy 83), Pitcher, Green (Basford 86),
Smiba, Akuamoah. Subs (not used): Hurst, Allan
Kettering Town: Sollit, McNamara, Adams, Perkins, Vowden, Norman (Duik 76), Fisher, Brown, Shutt, Watkins (Hudson 46), Setchell
(Hopkins 81). Subs (not used): Ridgway, Wilson Ref: S W Dunn

2001 CANVEY ISLAND 1 (Chenery) **FOREST GREEN ROVERS 0** Att: 10,007
Isthmian League *Conference* at Villa Park
Forest Green Rovers: Perrin, Cousins, Lockwood, Foster, Clark, Burns, Daley, Drysdale (Bennett 46), Foster (Hunt 75), Meecham,
Slater. Subs (not used): Hedges, Prince, Ghent
Canvey Island: Harrison, Duffy, Chenery, Bodley, Ward, Tilson, Stimson (Tanner 83), Gregory, Vaughan (Jones 76), Parmenter. Subs
(not used): Bennett, Miller, Thompson. Ref: A G Wiley

2002 YEOVIL TOWN 2 (Alford, Stansfield) **STEVENAGE BOROUGH 0** Att: 18,809
Conference *Conference* at Villa Park
Yeovil Town: Weale, Lockwood, Tonkin, Skiverton, Pluck (White 51), Way, Stansfield, Johnson, Alford (Giles 86), Crittenden (Lindegaard
83), McIndoe. Subs (not used): O'Brien, Sheffield
Stevenage Borough: Wilkerson, Hamsher, Goodliffe, Trott, Fraser, Fisher, Wormull (Stirling 71), Evers (Williams 56), Jackson, Sigere
(Campbell 74), Clarke. Subs (not used): Campbell, Greygoose Ref: N S Barry

2003 BURSCOUGH 2 (Martindale 25, 55) **TAMWORTH 1 (Cooper 78)** Att: 14,265
Northern Premier *Southern Premier* at Villa Park
Burscough: Taylor, Teale, Taylor, Macauley (White 77), Lawless, Bowen, Wright, Norman, Martindale (McHale 80), Byrne (Bluck 84),
Burns. Subs (not used): McGuire (g/k) Molyneux.
Tamworth: Acton, Warner, Follett, Robinson, Walsh, Cooper, Colley, Evans (Turner 64), Rickards (Hatton 88), McGorry,
Sale (Hallam 54). Subs (not used): Grocutt, Barnes (g/k). Ref: U D Rennie

2004 HEDNESFORD TOWN 3 (Maguire 28, Hines 53, Brindley 87) **CANVEY ISLAND 2 (Boylan 46, Brindley 48 og)** Att: 6,635
Southern Premier *Isthmian Premier Champions* at Villa Park
Hednesford Town: Young, Simkin, Hines, King, Brindley, Ryder (Barrow 59), Palmer, Anthrobus, Danks (Piearce 78), Maguire,
Charie (Evans 55). Subs (not used): Evans (g/k) McGhee.
Canvey Island: Potter, Kennedy, Duffy, Chenery, Cowan, Gooden (Dobinson 89), Minton, Gregory (McDougald 80), Boylan,
Midgley (Berquez 73), Ward. Subs (not used): Theobald, Harrison (g/k).
Ref: M L Dean

2005 GRAYS ATHLETIC 1 (Martin 65) Pens: 6 **HUCKNALL TOWN 1 (Ricketts 75) Pens: 5** Att: 8,116
Conference South *Conference North* at Villa Park
Grays Athletic: Bayes, Brennan, Nutter, Stuart, Matthews, Thurgood, Oli (Powell 80), Hopper (Carthy 120), Battersby (sub West 61),
Martin, Cole. Subs (not used): Emberson, Bruce..
Hucknall Town: Smith, Asher, Barrick (Plummer 30), Hunter, Timons, Cooke, Smith (Ward 120), Palmer (Heathcote 94), Ricketts,
Bacon, Todd. Subs (not used): Winder, Lindley. Ref: P Dowd

2006 GRAYS ATHLETIC 2 (Oli, Poole) **WOKING 0** Att: 13,997
Conference *Conference* at Upton Park
Grays Athletic: Bayes, Sambrook, Nutter, Stuart, Hanson, Kightly (Williamson 90), Thurgood, Martin, Poole, Oli, McLean.
Subs (not used): Eyre (g/k), Hooper, Olayinka, Mawer.
Woking: Jalal, Jackson, MacDonald, Nethercott (Watson 60), Hutchinson, Murray, Smith (Cockerill 60), Evans (Blackman 85),
Ferguson, McAllister, Justin Richards. Subs (not used): Davis (g/k), El-Salahi.

Ref: Howard Webb (Sheffield)

2007 **STEVENAGE BOROUGH** 3 (Cole, Dobson, Morrison) **KIDDERMINSTER HARRIERS** 2 (Constable 2) Att: 53,262
Conference   *Conference*   **(New Trophy record)**
Stevenage Borough: Julian, Fuller, Nutter, Oliver, Gaia, Miller, Cole, Morrison, Guppy (Dobson 63), Henry, Beard.
Subs not used: Potter, Slabber, Nurse, McMahon.
Kidderminster Harriers: Bevan, Kenna, Hurren, Creighton, Whitehead, Blackwood, Russell, Penn, Smikle (Reynolds 90),
Christie (White 75) , Constable.
Subs not used: Taylor, Sedgemore, McGrath.
                                                            Ref: Chris Foy (Merseyside)

2008 **EBBSFLEET UNITED** 1 (McPhee)   **TORQUAY UNITED** 0   Att: 40,186
Blue Square Premier   *Blue Square Premier*
Ebbsfleet United: Cronin, Hawkins, McCarthy, Smith, Opinel, McPhee, Barrett, Bostwick, Long (MacDonald 84), Moore, Akinde.
Subs not used: Eribenne, Purcell, Ricketts, Mott.
Torquay United: Rice, Mansell, Todd, Woods, Nicholson, D'Sane (Benyon 66), Hargreaves, Adams, Zebroski, Sills (Hill 88),
Phillips (Stevens 46). Subs not used: Hockley and Robertson.
                                                            Ref: Martin Atkinson (West Riding)

2009 **STEVENAGE BOROUGH** 2 (Morison, Boylan)   **YORK CITY** 0   Att: 27,102
Blue Square Premier   *Blue Square Premier*
Stevenage Borough: Day, Henry, Bostwick, Roberts, Wilson, Mills, Murphy, Drury, Vincenti (Anaclet 86), Boylan, Morison.
Subs not used: Bayes, Albrighton, Maamria and Willock.
York City:Ingham, Purkiss, McGurk, Parslow, Pejic, Mackin, Greaves(McWilliams 74), Rusk (Russell 80), Brodie, McBreen (Sodje 60),
Boyes. Subs not used – Mimms and Robinson.
                                                            Referee: Michael Jones.

2010 **BARROW** 2 (McEvilly 79, Walker 117)   **STEVENAGE BOROUGH** 1 (Drury 10)   Att: 21,223
Blue Square Premier   *Blue Square Premier*
Barrow: Stuart Tomlinson, Simon Spender, Paul Jones, Phil Bolland, Paul Edwards, Simon Wiles (sub Carlos Logan 63rd min),
Robin Hulbert, Andy Bond, Paul Rutherford (sub Mark Boyd 109th min), Jason Walker, Gregg Blundell (sub Lee McEvilly 73rd min).
Subs not used – Tim Deasy and Mike Pearson.
Stevenage Borough: Chris Day (sub Ashley Bayes 90th min), Ronnie Henry, Jon Ashton, Mark Roberts, Scott Laird,
Joel Byrom (sub Lawrie Wilson 58th min), David Bridges, Michael Bostwick, Andy Drury, Chris Beardsley (sub Charlie Griffin 64th min),
Yemi Odubade. Subs not used – Stacey Long and Peter Vincenti.
Man of the match - Paul Rutherford.
                                                            Referee Lee Probert.

2011 **DARLINGTON** 1 (Senior 120)   **MANSFIELD TOWN** 0   Att: 24,668
Blue Square Premier   *Blue Square Premier*
Darlington: Sam Russell, Paul Arnison, Ian Miller, Liam Hatch, Aaron Brown, Jamie Chandler, Chris Moore, Marc Bridge-Wilkinson (sub
Paul Terry 100th min), Gary Smith (sub Arman Verma 38th min), John Campbell (sub Chris Senior 75th min), Tommy Wright.
Subs not used – Danzelle St Louis-Hamilton (gk) and Phil Gray.
Mansfield Town: Alan Marriott, Gary Silk, Stephen Foster, Tom Naylor, Dan Spence, Louis Briscoe, Tyrone Thompson, Kyle Nix, Adam
Smith (sub Ashley Cain 95th min), Adam Murray (sub Danny Mitchley 108th min), Paul Connor
Subs not used – Paul Stonehouse and Neil Collett (gk)
Man of the match - Jamie Chandler.
                                                            Referee Stuart Atwell

2012 **YORK CITY** 2 (Blair 61, Oyebanjo 68)   **NEWPORT COUNTY** 0   Att: 19,844
Blue Square Premier   *Blue Square Premier*
York City: Michael Ingham, Jon Challinor, Chris Smith, Daniel Parslow, Ben Gibson, Matty Blair, Lanre Oyebanjo, Patrick McLaughlan
(sub Jamal Fyfield 82nd min), James Meredith, Ashley Chambers (Adriano Moke (89th min), Jason Walker (Jamie Reed 90th min).
Subs not used – Paul Musselwhite (g/k), Michael Potts.
Newport County: Glyn Thompson, David Pipe, Ismail Yakubu, Gary Warren, Andrew Hughes, Sam Foley, Lee Evans, Nat Jarvis (sub
Jake Harris 68th min), Max Porter (sub Darryl Knights 79th min), Romone Rose (sub Elliott Buchanan 68th min), Lee Minshull.
Subs not used – Matthew Swan (g/k), Paul Rodgers.
Man of the match - Lanre Oyebanjo.
                                                            Referee Anthony Taylor

2013 **WREXHAM** 1 (Thornton 82 (pen))   **GRIMSBY TOWN** 1 (Cook 71)   Att: 35,226
Wrexham won 4-1 on kicks from the penalty mark after extra time.
Blue Square Premier   *Blue Square Premier*
Wrexham: Chris Maxwell, Stephen Wright, Martin Riley, Jay Harris, Danny Wright, Brett Ormerod (Robert Ogleby 77 min),
Andy Morrell (Adrian Cieslewicz 61 min), Dean Keates, Johnny Hunt, Chris Westwood, Kevin Thornton (Joe Clarke 89 min).
Subs not used - Andy Coughlin (gk) Glen Little.
Grimsby Town: Sam Hatton, Aswad Thomas, Shaun Pearson, Ian Miller, Joe Colbeck, Craig Disley, Frankie Artus, Andy Cook, James
McKeown, Ross Hannah (Andi Thanoj 55 min), Marcus Marshall (Richard Brodie 87 min).
Subs not used - Jamie Devitt, Bradley Wood, Lenell John-Lewis.
                                                            Referee Jonathan Moss

2014 **CAMBRIDGE UNITED** 4 (Bird 38, Donaldson 50,59, Berry 78 (pen)) **GOSPORT BOROUGH** 0   Att: 18,120
Conference Premier   *Conference South*
Cambridge United: Will Norris, Greg Taylor, Jock Coulson (Tom Bonner 87 min), Ian Miller, Ryan Donaldson, Tom Champion,
Richard Tait, Liam Hughes (Nathan Arnold 73 min), Luke Berry, Ryan Bird, Josh Gillies (Andy Pugh 61 min).
Subs not used - Kevin Roberts, Mitch Austin.
Gosport Borough: Nathan Ashmore, Lee Molyneaux, Andy Forbes, Jamie Brown (Rory Williams 57 min), Brett Poate, Sam Pearce,
Josh Carmichael, Danny Smith, Tim Sills (Dan Woodward 57 min), Justin Bennett, Michael Gosney (Dan Wooden 72 min).
Subs not used - Ryan Scott, Adam Wilde.
                                                            Referee Craig Pawson

THE FA TROPHY

2015 **NORTH FERRIBY UNITED** 3 (King 76 (pen), Kendall 86, 111) **WREXHAM** 3 (Moult 11, 118, Harris 59) **Att: 14,548**
Conference North *Conference National*

North Ferriby United: Adam Nicklin, Sam Topliss, Danny Hone, Matt Wilson, Josh Wilde (Nathan Peat 90), Liam King,
Adam Bolder (Nathan Jarman 62), Russell Fry (Ryan Kendall 80), Danny Clarke, Tom Denton, Jason St Juste.
Subs not used - Tom Nicholson and Mark Gray.
Wrexham: Andy Coughlin, Steve Tomassen, Manny Smith, Blaine Hudson, Neil Ashton, Jay Harris, Dean Keates (Robbie Evans 73),
Joe Clarke (Andy Bishop 102), Kieron Morris (Wes York 87), Louis Moult, Connor Jennings.
Subs not used - Mark Carrington and Luke Waterfall.

Referee Michael Oliver

2016 **FC HALIFAX TOWN** 1 (McManus 48) **GRIMSBY TOWN** 0 **Att: 46,781** (Inaugural Non-League finals day)
Conference National *Conference National*

North Ferriby United: Sam Johnson, Matty Brown, Hamza Bencherif, Kevin Roberts, James Bolton, Nicky Wroe, Jake Hibbs,
Scott McManus (Kingsley James 73), Josh McDonald (Sam Walker 63), Jordan Burrow, Richard Peniket (Connor Hughes 86).
Subs not used - Jordan Porter and Shaquille McDonald.
Grimsby Town: James McKeown, Richard Tait (Danny East 81), Shaun Pearson, Aristote Nsiala, Gregor Robertson,
Andy Monkhouse (Jon-Paul Pitman 68), Craig Disley, Craig Clay (Nathan Arnold 63), Jon Nolan, Omar Bogle, Padraig Amond.
Subs not used - Josh Gowling and Josh Venney.

Referee Lee Mason

All Finals at Wembley unless otherwise stated.

PRELIMINARY ROUND 2017-18
SATURDAY 7 OCTOBER 2017

1	Ossett Albion	v	Droylsden
2	Ramsbottom United	v	Colwyn Bay
3	Bamber Bridge	v	Brighouse Town
4	Cleethorpes Town	v	Hyde United
5	Mossley AFC	v	Skelmersdale United
6	Kendal Town	v	Radcliffe Borough
7	Stocksbridge Park Steels	v	Atherton Collieries
8	Scarborough Athletic	v	South Shields
9	Tadcaster Albion	v	Glossop North End
10	Ossett Town	v	Goole AFC
11	Prescot Cables	v	Trafford
12	Clitheroe	v	Colne
13	Sheffield	v	Frickley Athletic
14	Romulus	v	Corby Town
15	Newcastle Town	v	Soham Town Rangers
16	Chasetown	v	Market Drayton Town
17	AFC Rushden & Diamonds	v	Kidsgrove Athletic
18	Basford United	v	Peterborough Sports
19	Stamford AFC	v	Loughborough Dynamo
20	Belper Town	v	Alvechurch
21	Gresley	v	Bedworth United
22	Leek Town	v	Lincoln United
23	Thamesmead Town	v	AFC Hornchurch
24	Greenwich Borough	v	Hanwell Town
25	Heybridge Swifts	v	Carshalton Athletic
27	Kempston Rovers	v	Hythe Town
28	Potters Bar Town	v	Tilbury
29	Ashford United_	v	Sittingbourne
30	Egham Town	v	Shoreham
31	Northwood	v	Maldon & Tiptree
32	AFC Sudbury	v	Aylesbury United
33	Waltham Abbey	v	Faversham Town
34	Romford	v	Hastings United
35	VCD Athletic	v	Bedford Town
36	Haringey Borough	v	Whyteleafe
37	Bowers & Pitsea	v	Dereham Town
38	Cray Wanderers	v	Horsham
39	Chipstead	v	Barking
40	East Grinstead Town	v	Lewes
41	Corinthian-Casuals	v	AFC Dunstable
42	Cheshunt	v	Herne Bay
43	Ramsgate	v	Bury Town
44	Hayes & Yeading United	v	Barton Rovers
45	Brentwood Town	v	South Park
46	Walton Casuals	v	Canvey Island
47	Phoenix Sports	v	Chalfont St Peter
48	Ashford Town (Middx)	v	Uxbridge
49	Grays Athletic	v	Norwich United
50	Aylesbury	v	Molesey
51	Marlow	v	Aveley
52	Taunton Town	v	AFC Totton
53	Mangotsfield United	v	Thame United
54	Bishop's Cleeve	v	Larkhall Athletic
55	Shortwood United	v	Didcot Town
56	Fleet Town	v	Yate Town
57	Evesham United	v	Cirencester Town
58	North Leigh	v	Wimborne Town
59	Moneyfields	v	Bideford AFC
60	Swindon Supermarine	v	Barnstaple Town
61	Salisbury	v	Paulton Rovers
62	Slimbridge AFC	v	Hartley Wintney
63	Bristol Manor Farm	v	Cinderford Town
64	Kidlington	v	Winchester City

FIRST QUALIFYING ROUND 2017-18
SATURDAY 28 OCTOBER 2017

1	Ashton United	v	Sheffield / Frickley A
2	Tadcaster / Glossop NE	v	Matlock Town
3	Mossley AFC / Skelm Utd	v	Lancaster City
4	Ossett Town / Goole AFC	v	Ossett / Droylsden
5	Altrincham	v	Clitheroe / Colne
6	Farsley Celtic	v	Scarboro A / S Shields
7	Buxton	v	Cleethorpes Town / Hyde United
8	Warrington Town	v	Bamber B / Brighouse
9	Shaw Lane Association	v	Ramsbottom / Colwyn Bay
10	Whitby Town	v	Marine
11	Precot C / Trafford	v	Stalybridge Celtic
12	Kendal Town / Radcliffe B	v	Stck Pk Stl / Atherton
13	Workington AFC	v	Witton Albion
14	Grantham Town	v	Halesowen Town
15	Rushall Olympic	v	Nantwich Town
16	Hednesford Town	v	Mickleover Sports
17	Newcastle T / Soham Town	v	AFC Rushden & Diamonds / Kidsgrove
18	Stratford Town	v	Gresley / Bedworth
19	Chasetown / Mark Dray	v	Spalding United
20	Stafford Rangers	v	St Ives Town
21	Barwell	v	Carlton Town
22	Stamford / Loughboro D	v	Sutton Coldfield Town
23	St Neots Town	v	Romulus / Corby Town
24	Redditch United	v	Coalville Town
25	Cambridge City	v	Belper Town / Alvechurch
26	Leek Town / Lincoln U	v	Kettering Town
27	Stourbridge	v	Basford United / Peterborough Sports
28	Hitchin Town	v	Cheshunt / Herne Bay
29	Dorking Wanderers	v	Ware
30	Northwood / Mald & Tip	v	Walt Cas / Canvey Is
31	Billericay Town	v	Tooting & Mitcham United
32	Leatherhead	v	AFC K'pston / Hythe Town
33	Ashford United / Sit'Bourne	v	Merstham
34	Bishop's Stortford	v	Greenwich B / Hanwell T
35	Needham Market	v	Arlesey Town
36	King's Lynn Town	v	Mildenhall Town
37	Hendon	v	Kings Langley
38	Aylesbury / Molesey	v	Harlow Town
39	Chipstead / Barking	v	Beaconsfield Town
40	Brentwood / South Park	v	VCD Ath / Bedford T
41	Tonbridge Angels	v	Heybridge S / Carshalton
42	Ramsgate / Bury Town	v	Phoenix Sports / Chalfont StP
43	Romford / Hastings U	v	Ashford T / Uxbridge
44	Metropolitan Police	v	AFC Sudbury / Aylesbury
45	Dunstable Town	v	East Grinstead Town / Lewes
46	Cor-Casuals / AFC D'stable	v	Hertford Town
47	Cray Wands / Horsham	v	Grays Ath / Norwich U
48	Worthing	v	Lowestoft Town
49	Staines Town	v	Margate
50	Waltham A / Faversham	v	Dulwich Hamlet
51	Thamesmead / AFC H'church	v	Brightlingsea Regent
52	Royston Town	v	Enfield Town
53	Potters Bar / Tilbury	v	Witham Town
54	Harrow Borough	v	Haringey B / Whyteleafe
55	Leiston	v	Folkestone Invicta
56	Burgess Hill Town	v	Marlow / Aveley
57	Bowers & P / Dereham	v	Egham Town / Shoreham
58	Biggleswade Town	v	Wingate & Finchley
59	Kingstonian	v	Thurrock
60	Hayes & Yead / Barton Rov	v	Chesham United
61	Taunton / AFC Totton	v	Merthyr Town
62	Dorchester Town	v	Basingstoke Town
63	Salisbury / Paulton R	v	Evesham / Cirencester
64	Gosport Borough	v	Bristol MF / Cinderford
65	Fleet Town / Yate Town	v	Moneyfields / Bideford
66	Mangotsfield / Thame Utd	v	North Leigh / Wimborne
67	B Cleeve / Larkhall	v	Farnborough
68	Swindon S / Barnstaple	v	Slimbridge / Hartley W
69	Hereford	v	Weymouth
70	Tiverton Town	v	Banbury United
71	Kidlington / Winchester	v	Slough Town
72	Shortwood U / Didcot Town	v	Frome Town

FAT1Q - Jack Wood, Aylesbury United captain (hoops), tangles with Jack Harris of Hastings United. Photo: Roger Turner.

FATP - The Herne Bay defenders appeal to the linesman is upheld, and Barton Rovers' 'goal' is disallowed. Bay went on to win by a single goal to progress to the next round. Photo: Gordon Whittington.

FAT3P - Action between Macclesfield Town and Forest Green Rovers. Photo: Peter Barnes.

FATP - Hopley (Witton) chips Taylor (Brighouse) for his second goal. Photo: Keith Clayton.

FAT3Q - Gloucester City's No.2 fires in a shot at the AFC Fylde goal. Photo: Peter Barnes.

#	Home		Away	Score	
1	Bridlington Town	v	Yorkshire Amateur (11/9)	6-0	129
2	Bedlington Terriers	v	Bishop Auckland	0-3	55
3	Albion Sports	v	Ashington	3-4	92
4	Knaresborough Town	v	Silsden	1-2	
5	Stockton Town	v	Eccleshill United	2-0	150
6	Blyth Town	v	Ryton & Crawcrook Albion	1-2	
7	Darlington Railway Athletic	v	Barnoldswick Town	0-4	39
8	Consett	v	Hebburn Town	5-1	
9	Daisy Hill	v	Garforth Town	4-1	67
10	Penrith	v	Durham City	5-3aet	114
11	Billingham Town	v	Willington	4-2	
12	West Allotment Celtic	v	Hall Road Rangers	0-2	85
13	Washington	v	Billingham Synthonia	0-1	
14	Easington Colliery	v	Thackley	2-1	72
15	AFC Darwen	v	Pickering Town	1-2	174
16	Nelson	v	Heaton Stannington	1-2	
17	West Auckland Town	v	Seaham Red Star	3-2aet	
18	Crook Town	v	Esh Winning	1-2	100
19	Carlisle City	v	Team Northumbria	1-2	45
20	Brandon United	v	Chester-Le-Street Town	0-7	53
21	Tow Law Town	v	Norton & Stockton Ancients	1-3	57
22	Whickham	v	Charnock Richard (11/9)	0-2	242
23	Thornaby	v	Liversedge	1-4	57
24	Newcastle Benfield	v	Alnwick Town	8-1	
25	City of Liverpool	v	Litherland Remyca (11/9)	1-2	711
26	Barton Town Old Boys	v	Grimsby Borough	0-2	
27	Staveley MW	v	Cheadle Town	1-0	
28	Maltby Main	v	Widnes	0-2	42
29	Alsager Town	v	Squires Gate	2-1	44
30	Ashton Town	v	Parkgate	4-2	45
31	Bootle	v	Maine Road	4-1	
32	St Helens Town	v	Chadderton	3-5	
33	Runcorn Town	v	Winsford United	4-1	
34	Dronfield Town	v	Glasshoughton Welfare	0-2	53
35	Pontefract Collieries	v	Hemsworth MW	2-4	
36	Irlam	v	Selby Town	1-0	75
37	Winterton Rangers	v	Penistone Church	1-5	
38	Ashton Athletic	v	Athersley Recreation	2-0	67
39	Armthorpe Welfare	v	Congleton Town	2-3	58
40	Barnton	v	Harworth Colliery	5-2aet	45
41	Black Country Rangers	v	Stafford Town (11/9)	1-0	71
42	Dudley Town	v	Wellington Amateurs	0-4	
43	FC Oswestry Town	v	Walsall Wood	1-3aet	70
44	Coton Green	v	Kirby Muxloe	1-3	
45	Ashby Ivanhoe	v	Pelsall Villa	2-1	93
46	Whitchurch Alport	v	Wellington	1-2aet	151
47	Highgate United	v	Lye Town	2-0	
	(at Lye Town FC)				
48	Bolehall Swifts	v	Heath Hayes	7-2	
49	Bromyard Town	v	Atherstone Town	2-6	52
	(at Bewdley Town FC)				
50	Cradley Town	v	Uttoxeter Town	1-4	47
51	Pershore Town	v	Bewdley Town	1-2	58
52	Chelmsley Town	v	Studley	3-2	46
53	Ellistown & Ibstock United	v	Bromsgrove Sporting	0-13	276
	(at Bromsgrove Sporting FC)				
54	Redditch Borough	v	Rocester (11/9)	2-5	
	(at Redditch United FC)				
55	AFC Bridgnorth	v	Boldmere St Michaels	0-5	
56	Shawbury United	v	Heather St Johns	3-1	68
57	Shifnal Town	v	Gornal Athletic	5-1	62
58	Barnt Green Spartak	v	Cadbury Athletic (9/9)	0-1	83
59	Racing Club Warwick	v	Coventry United	1-3	99
60	Malvern Town	v	Tividale	4-1	129
61	Bardon Hill	v	Littleton	1-5	30
62	Lutterworth Athletic	v	Stone Old Alleynians	0-2	
63	Brocton	v	Eccleshall	6-0	
64	Continental Star	v	Wolverhampton Casuals		
	(walkover for Wolverhampton Casuals – Continental Star withdrawn)				
65	Stourport Swifts	v	Smethwick	5-1	
66	Ellesmere Rangers	v	Pegasus Juniors	2-7aet	47
67	Clay Cross Town	v	Leicester Road	2-3	
68	Clifton All Whites	v	Oadby Town (13/9)	7-0	26
69	Borrowash Victoria	v	Bottesford Town	1-7	
70	Gedling MW	v	Oakham United	2-3aet	50
71	Loughborough University	v	Arnold Town	7-1	
72	Ollerton Town	v	Retford United	2-3	155
73	Pinxton	v	Harrowby United	4-0	
74	Rainworth MW	v	Heanor Town	1-4	85
75	Graham St Prims	v	Kimberley MW	2-5	
76	Teversal	v	Blidworth Welfare	0-1aet	43
77	Aylestone Park	v	Stapenhill	3-7	50
78	Belper United	v	Radford (9/9)	0-1	77
79	Barrow Town	v	St Andrews	0-3	64
80	Long Eaton United	v	South Normanton Athletic	2-0	56
81	Brigg Town	v	Harborough Town	0-4	
82	Holbrook Sports	v	Hinckley	0-2	90
83	Thetford Town	v	Framlingham Town	4-3	97
84	Yaxley	v	Eynesbury Rovers	7-0	53
85	Great Yarmouth Town	v	Bourne Town	3-0	
86	Wisbech Town	v	Mildenhall Town	2-2aet	
	Mildenhall Town	v	Wisbech Town (13/9)	4-0	166
87	Ely City	v	Kirkley & Pakefield	3-2aet	
88	Walsham Le Willows	v	Deeping Rangers	2-2aet	38
	Deeping Rangers	v	Walsham Le Willows (13/9)	3-3aet	87
	(Walsham Le Willows won 5-4 on kicks from the penalty mark)				
89	Gorleston	v	Wisbech St Mary	2-0	96
90	Diss Town	v	Team Bury	3-0	92
91	London Bari	v	Newbury Forest	3-0	14
92	FC Clacton	v	Enfield 1893	0-1	76
93	Wivenhoe Town	v	Wadham Lodge	1-2	72
94	FC Broxbourne Borough	v	Cornard United	3-2	45
95	Takeley	v	Tower Hamlets	7-2	30
96	Halstead Town	v	Hadley	3-2	86
97	Langford	v	Baldock Town	2-2aet	60
	(Baldock Town won 4-3 on kicks from the penalty mark)				
98	Stansted	v	Saffron Walden Town	1-2	188
99	Hadleigh United	v	Debenham LC	1-0	77
100	Burnham Ramblers	v	London Lions	2-1	26
101	Harpenden Town	v	Ilford	1-3aet	42
102	Whitton United	v	Biggleswade United	0-4	47
103	Woodbridge Town	v	Hatfield Town	4-1	256
104	Southend Manor	v	West Essex	7-0	30

FAV1P - Goal mouth action from the Lydney Town v AFC Porchester tie. Photo: Peter Barnes.

FAV1Q - Bexhill's Gordon Cuddington scores his sides second goal past Holesdale 'keeper Alfie George. Photo: Alan Coomes.

FAV3P - Bemusement on the faces of the Newport Pagnell defenders as London Colney's goal comes courtesy of a rebound off the post. Photo: Gordon Whittington.

FIRST QUALIFYING ROUND
SATURDAY 10 SEPTEMBER 2016 - WINNING CLUB TO RECEIVE £450 LOSING CLUB TO RECEIVE £150

105	Hertford Town	v	Clapton (20/9)	2-1	
	(10/9 - tie ordered to be replayed, 0-0aet)				
106	Sporting Bengal United	v	Stowmarket Town	2-1aet	83
107	Codicote	v	St Margaretsbury (11/9)	0-3	53
	(at Stotfold FC)				
108	Redbridge	v	Eton Manor	5-4aet	30
109	Raunds Town	v	Northampton On Chenecks	1-4	
110	Risborough Rangers	v	Broadfields United	0-3	68
111	Winslow United	v	Rushden & Higham United	6-4	44
112	Long Buckby	v	Hillingdon Borough	1-3	
113	Bedfont & Feltham	v	Sandhurst Town	3-0	
114	Ampthill Town	v	Northampton Sileby Rangers	2-3	
115	Rothwell Corinthians	v	Burton Park Wanderers	8-0	
116	AFC Hayes	v	Crawley Green	2-2aet	
	(Crawley Green won 4-1 on kicks from the penalty mark)				
117	Kensington Borough	v	Thrapston Town	0-2	
118	Brackley Town Saints	v	Leighton Town	3-3aet	74
	Leighton Town	v	Brackley Town Saints (13/9)	4-3	
119	Spelthorne Sports	v	Tring Athletic	0-0	48
	Tring Athletic	v	Spelthorne Sports (13/9)	2-0	57
120	Cranfield United	v	Southall	2-2aet	30
	Southall	v	Cranfield United (14/9)		
	(tie awarded to Southall – Cranfield United failed to fulfil fixture)				
121	Bicester Town	v	Potton United	3-2	22
122	FC Deportivo Galicia	v	Irchester United	0-1	
123	London Tigers	v	Cogenhoe United	3-1	
124	Daventry Town	v	Windsor	3-1	83
125	Stotfold	v	North Greenford United	2-2aet	53
	North Greenford United	v	Stotfold (13/9)	4-0	54
126	Bedford	v	CB Hounslow United	0-1	
127	Desborough Town	v	Woodford United	10-0	
128	Stewarts & Lloyds Corby	v	Wellingborough Whitworths	0-4	
129	Hanworth Villa	v	Bedfont Sports	0-4	
130	Amersham Town	v	Highmoor Ibis (11/9)	0-2	
131	AFC Stoneham	v	Malmesbury Victoria	3-0	
132	Buckingham Athletic	v	Binfield	2-3	38
133	Hook Norton	v	Bracknell Town (9/9)	1-5aet	
134	Shrivenham	v	Abbey Rangers	2-3aet	
135	Ash United	v	Tytherington Rocks	2-1	42
136	Thame United	v	Tadley Calleva (11/9)	5-1	76
137	Badshot Lea	v	Farnham Town (9/9)	3-1	68
138	Fairford Town	v	Chipping Sodbury Town	3-2	
139	Chertsey Town	v	Lydney Town	1-2	
140	AFC Portchester	v	Holyport	3-0	
141	Woodley United	v	Ardley United	0-4	
142	Cove	v	Buckingham Town	0-4	
143	Tunbridge Wells	v	Steyning Town	4-1	
144	Hailsham Town	v	Lingfield	0-3	50
145	Croydon	v	Loxwood	2-1	
146	Whitstable Town	v	Chichester City	2-2aet	
	Chichester City United	v	Whitstable Town (13/9)	3-2	
147	Broadbridge Heath	v	Crowborough Athletic	2-4	53
148	Southwick	v	FC Elmstead	1-2	
149	Bearsted	v	Pagham	0-1	
150	Cray Valley (PM)	v	Glebe (9/9)	0-1	138
151	St Francis Rangers	v	Ringmer	1-2	
152	Raynes Park Vale	v	Haywards Heath Town	1-2	
153	Arundel	v	Westfield	1-2	
154	Horley Town	v	Hassocks	4-2	67
155	Sevenoaks Town	v	Crawley Down Gatwick	3-1	47
156	Little Common	v	Erith Town	2-1aet	56
157	Redhill	v	Deal Town	1-2	89
	(at Deal Town FC)				
158	Guildford City	v	Eastbourne United	2-1	
	(tie awarded to Eastbourne United – Guildford City removed)				
159	Chessington & Hook United	v	Rochester United	3-3aet	64
	Rochester United	v	Chessington & Hook United (14/9)	2-1	68
160	Bexhill United	v	Holmesdale	2-3	46
	(at Holmesdale FC)				
161	Shoreham	v	Meridian VP	8-2	34
162	Mile Oak	v	Erith & Belvedere	2-1	35
163	Littlehampton Town	v	Saltdean United	2-0	57
164	Worthing United	v	Peacehaven & Telscombe+ (23/9)	0-2	
	(10/9 – tie abandoned after 70 mins, 2-0 – tie ordered to be replayed)				
165	Dorking	v	Beckenham Town (11/9)	1-4	
166	Bridon Ropes	v	Colliers Wood United	2-1	
167	Langney Wanderers	v	Selsey	4-4aet	45
	Selsey	v	Langney Wanderers (13/9)	4-1	74
168	Brockenhurst	v	Ringwood Town	5-0	
169	Corsham Town	v	United Services Portsmouth (11/9)	1-0	71
170	Westbury United	v	Folland Sports	2-1	57
171	New Milton Town	v	Horndean	1-5	
172	Oldland Abbotonians	v	Lymington Town	4-0	54
173	Whitchurch United	v	Laverstock & Ford	3-1	
174	Hamworthy United	v	Amesbury Town	3-5	
175	Cowes Sports	v	Cadbury Heath	4-2aet	
176	Andover New Street	v	Gillingham Town	1-3aet	40
177	Hallen	v	Fawley	3-2	43
178	Bournemouth	v	Verwood Town (13/9)	4-3	
179	Hythe & Dibden	v	Team Solent	1-2	
180	Bemerton Heath Harlequins	v	Downton	7-0	44
181	Romsey Town	v	Warminster Town	3-0	62
182	Christchurch	v	Swanage Town & Herston	2-1	39
183	Bridport	v	Cribbs	2-4	92
184	Alresford Town	v	Chippenham Park	5-1	43
185	Welton Rovers	v	Ashton & Backwell United	0-3	44
186	Liskeard Athletic	v	Portishead Town	1-2	
187	Hengrove Athletic	v	Camelford	3-2	50
188	AFC St Austell	v	Crediton United	3-2	169
189	Cullompton Rangers	v	Wincanton Town	3-2	105
190	Shepton Mallet	v	Tavistock	1-6	62
191	Radstock Town	v	Torpoint Athletic	3-6	50
192	Wellington AFC	v	Bishop Sutton	0-1	29
193	Keynsham Town	v	Ivybridge Town	4-2	71
194	Cheddar	v	Elburton Villa	2-1	

SECOND QUALIFYING ROUND

SATURDAY 24 SEPTEMBER 2016 - WINNING CLUB TO RECEIVE £600 LOSING CLUB TO RECEIVE £200

1	Northallerton Town	v	Jarrow Roofing Boldon CA	0-4	75
2	Whitley Bay	v	Stockton Town	0-2	322
3	West Auckland Town	v	Padiham	1-2aet	89
4	Heaton Stannington	v	Billingham Synthonia	0-1	134
5	Esh Winning	v	South Shields	0-4	266
6	Easington Colliery	v	Ashington	2-0	86
7	Birtley Town	v	Holker Old Boys	2-4	
8	Chester-Le-Street Town	v	Norton & Stockton Ancients	3-2	68
9	Bishop Auckland	v	Billingham Town (23/9)	1-2	310
10	Ryton & Crawcrook Albion	v	Sunderland Ryhope CW	0-5	57
11	Barnoldswick Town	v	Stokesley SC	7-1	
12	Bridlington Town	v	Daisy Hill (25/9)	5-2	138
13	Newcastle Benfield	v	Liversedge	3-0	88
14	Penrith	v	Team Northumbria	4-2	90
15	Silsden	v	Hall Road Rangers	3-4aet	63
16	Consett	v	Pickering Town	1-3	
17	Harrogate Railway Athletic	v	Charnock Richard	1-3	89
18	Westella VIP	v	Irlam	0-3	29
19	Atherton LR	v	Cammell Laird 1907	3-2	
20	Alsager Town	v	Stockport Town	0-3	44
21	AFC Liverpool	v	Abbey Hey	3-2aet	82
22	AFC Blackpool	v	Runcorn Town	0-2	80
23	Congleton Town	v	Bacup Borough	7-3aet	100
24	Ashton Athletic	v	AFC Emley	1-2	87
25	Hallam	v	Nostell MW	8-1	113
26	Staveley MW	v	Grimsby Borough	2-0	137
27	Rossington Main	v	Bootle	0-4	
28	Penistone Church	v	West Didsbury & Chorlton	3-2aet	121
29	Ashton Town	v	Barnton	3-2	43
30	Litherland Remyca	v	Vauxhall Motors	3-1	
31	Widnes	v	Chadderton	1-4	36
32	Glasshoughton Welfare	v	Hemsworth MW	2-2aet	116
	Hemsworth MW	v	Glasshoughton Welfare (27/9)	1-1aet	97
	(Hemsworth MW won 3-2 on kicks from the penalty mark)				
33	Hanley Town	v	Boldmere St Michaels	2-1	51
34	Uttoxeter Town	v	Wellington Amateurs	3-0	
35	Tipton Town	v	Bromsgrove Sporting	0-1	93
36	Birstall United	v	Malvern Town	2-2aet	
	Malvern Town	v	Birstall United (28/9)	3-2aet	145
37	Rocester	v	Black Country Rangers	1-0	
38	Willenhall Town	v	Haughmond	0-3	39
39	Walsall Wood	v	Pegasus Juniors	2-0	62
40	Stourport Swifts	v	Cadbury Athletic	0-1	93
41	Paget Rangers	v	Highgate United+	2-1	39
	(at Rushall Olympic FC)				
42	Coventry Copsewood	v	Atherstone Town+	2-1	78
43	Stone Old Alleynians	v	Ashby Ivanhoe	1-1aet	
	Ashby Ivanhoe	v	Stone Old Alleynians (28/9)	1-1aet	108
	(Ashby Ivanhoe won 3-1 on kicks from the penalty mark)				
44	Coventry United	v	Wednesfield	2-0	74
45	Kirby Muxloe	v	Littleton+	2-0aet	
46	Shawbury United	v	Coventry Sphinx	3-2	
47	Wolverhampton Casuals	v	Bilston Town	4-2	
48	Brocton	v	Chelmsley Town	0-2	67
49	Bolehall Swifts	v	Shifnal Town	0-2	
50	Westfields	v	Dudley Sports	8-0	
51	Wellington	v	Lichfield City	2-5	51
52	Bewdley Town	v	Wolverhampton SC	1-7	52
53	Leicester Road	v	West Bridgford	4-3	
54	Dunkirk	v	Bottesford Town	1-4	34
55	Heanor Town	v	Kimberley MW	2-2aet	
	Kimberley MW	v	Heanor Town (28/9)	0-2	
56	Anstey Nomads	v	Quorn	0-2	102
57	Oakham United	v	Retford United	1-0	
58	Harborough Town	v	Blaby & Whetstone Athletic	2-1	
59	Blidworth Welfare	v	Shirebrook Town	2-0	
60	Hucknall Town	v	Eastwood Community	5-0	
61	Pinxton	v	Loughborough University	4-2	
62	Greenwood Meadows	v	Hinckley	3-6	
63	Clipstone	v	Sherwood Colliery	1-3	
64	Stapenhill	v	Long Eaton United	2-3	
65	Clifton All Whites	v	Holwell Sports	1-2aet	39
66	AFC Mansfield	v	Radcliffe Olympic	4-2	49
67	New Mills	v	Radford	3-4	
68	St Andrews	v	Retford+	3-0	62
69	Yaxley	v	Newmarket Town	4-3aet	
70	Fakenham Town	v	Great Yarmouth Town+	1-3	60
71	Peterborough Northern Star	v	Blackstones	4-0	50
72	Thetford Town	v	Downham Town	2-0	96
73	Gorleston	v	March Town United	3-2	107
74	Ely City	v	Diss Town	4-2	86
75	Huntingdon Town	v	Swaffham Town	1-4	
76	Mildenhall Town	v	Peterborough Sports	1-3	
77	Boston Town	v	Walsham Le Willows	2-3	
78	Biggleswade United	v	Woodbridge Town	3-0	77
79	Colney Heath	v	Redbridge	2-1	
80	Takeley	v	Biggleswade	1-2aet	
81	Cockfosters	v	Hadley Wood & Wingate+	4-0	70
82	Waltham Forest	v	Hadleigh United	2-1	
83	Sporting Bengal United	v	Sawbridgeworth Town	3-2	
84	Hertford Town	v	Brantham Athletic	3-2	
85	Haverhill Borough	v	Haverhill Rovers (23/9)	1-0	
86	Wadham Lodge	v	Enfield 1893 (23/9)	3-1	102
87	Long Melford	v	Baldock Town	2-3	
88	Southend Manor	v	Canning Town+	0-0aet	
	(Canning Town won 5-4 on kicks from the penalty mark)				
89	Halstead Town	v	St Margaretsbury	1-4	101
90	London Bari	v	Barkingside	2-1aet	
91	FC Broxbourne Borough	v	Saffron Walden Town	1-2	48
92	Burnham Ramblers	v	Ilford	0-4	
93	Harefield United	v	Leverstock Green	0-4	
94	Wembley	v	Hillingdon Borough	2-1	
95	Daventry Town	v	Edgware Town	4-1	103
96	London Tigers	v	Southall	2-5	
97	North Greenford United	v	Oxhey Jets	1-2	56
98	Bicester Town	v	Broadfields United	2-3	
99	Holmer Green	v	Cricklewood Wanderers	3-0	47
100	Desborough Town	v	Wellingborough Whitworths	6-3aet	54
101	Northampton On Chenecks	v	Leighton Town	1-0	47
102	Bedfont & Feltham	v	Sun Sports	2-4	
103	Northampton Sileby Rangers	v	Rayners Lane+	5-0	36
104	LPOSSA	v	Crawley Green		
	(walkover for Crawley Green - LPOSSA withdrawn)				
105	Burnham	v	Highmoor Ibis	2-3aet	
106	Thrapston Town	v	CB Hounslow United+	3-1	
107	Winslow United	v	Tring Athletic	1-4	
108	Rothwell Corinthians	v	Irchester United	2-1	43
109	Wellingborough Town	v	Bedfont Sports+ (25/9)	0-2	142
110	Tuffley Rovers	v	Ardley United	4-1	47
111	Carterton	v	Brimscombe & Thrupp		
	(walkover for Brimscombe & Thrupp – Carterton withdrawn)				
112	Ash United	v	Milton United+	3-1	36
113	Frimley Green	v	Walton & Hersham	0-3	51
114	Fleet Spurs	v	Fairford Town+	1-3	
115	Alton Town	v	Henley Town	4-2	
116	Bashley	v	Highworth Town	0-4	
117	Melksham Town	v	New College Swindon (23/9)	4-0	65
118	Bracknell Town	v	Binfield (23/9)	2-1	351
	(at Binfield FC)				
119	Royal Wootton Bassett	v	Thame United	2-4	62
120	Buckingham Town	v	Eversley & California+	4-3aet	
121	Oxford City Nomads	v	Abingdon United	2-3	45
122	AFC Stoneham	v	Longlevens	3-1	53
123	Abbey Rangers	v	Badshot Lea	1-0	38

SECOND QUALIFYING ROUND
SATURDAY 24 SEPTEMBER 2016 - WINNING CLUB TO RECEIVE £600 LOSING CLUB TO RECEIVE £200

124	Lydney Town	v	AFC Portchester	2-0	97
125	Rochester United	v	Beckenham Town	1-2aet	40
126	Glebe	v	Deal Town	1-1aet	48
	Deal Town	v	Glebe (27/9)	1-3	
127	FC Elmstead	v	AFC Uckfield Town+	1-0	
128	Ringmer	v	Sporting Club Thamesmead	2-2aet	47
	Sporting Club Thamesmead	v	Ringmer (28/9)	6-1	40
129	Holmesdale	v	Banstead Athletic	1-4	30
130	Mile Oak	v	Croydon	1-3	41
131	Oakwood	v	Shoreham	0-10	43
132	Horley Town	v	Selsey	1-0	
133	Chichester City	v	Sheppey United	3-1	58
134	AC London	v	Littlehampton Town	1-1aet	
	Littlehampton Town	v	AC London (27/9)	1-5	
135	Little Common	v	Wick	0-2	52
136	Crowborough Athletic	v	Gravesham Borough	2-0	74
137	Corinthian	v	Sevenoaks Town	3-2	
138	Cobham	v	Lingfield	0-1	
139	Westfield	v	Haywards Heath Town	0-1	70
140	East Preston	v	Tunbridge Wells	1-4	125
141	Bridon Ropes	v	Rusthall	2-1aet	29
142	Eastbourne United	v	AFC Croydon Athletic	2-1	104
143	Tooting & Mitcham Wanderers	v	Seaford Town+	3-1	43
	(at Seaford Town FC)				
144	Canterbury City	v	Peacehaven & Telscombe (28/9)	8-0	63
145	Pagham	v	Horsham YMCA	0-1	
146	Westbury United	v	Cribbs	1-2	72
147	Whitchurch United	v	Amesbury Town	0-6	
148	Devizes Town	v	Corsham Town	2-1	102
149	Portland United	v	Almondsbury UWE	2-0	141
150	Shaftesbury Town	v	Fareham Town	5-1	59
151	Christchurch	v	Romsey Town	1-3	48
152	Hallen	v	Team Solent	1-3	37
153	Bournemouth	v	Brockenhurst	3-1	
154	Bitton	v	Gillingham Town	0-3	
155	Horndean	v	Oldland Abbotonians	2-0	
156	Calne Town	v	Roman Glass St George	4-3	44
157	Cowes Sports	v	Alresford Town	0-2	
158	Bemerton Heath Harlequins	v	Longwell Green Sports	3-0	36
159	East Cowes Victoria Athletic	v	Sherborne Town	0-4	27
160	Cullompton Rangers	v	Budleigh Salterton	4-1aet	81
161	Keynsham Town	v	Tavistock+	0-6	55
162	Clevedon Town	v	Cheddar	3-1aet	
163	AFC St Austell	v	Street	2-3	185
164	Exmouth	v	Witheridge	1-0	
165	Hengrove Athletic	v	Bishop Sutton	2-1	
166	Wells City	v	Torpoint Athletic	1-2	
167	Ashton & Backwell United	v	Willand Rovers	0-1	
168	Portishead Town	v	Helston Athletic	1-3aet	40
169	Brislington	v	Plymouth Parkway	0-1	64

FIRST ROUND PROPER
SATURDAY 22 OCTOBER 2016 - WINNING CLUB TO RECEIVE £675 LOSING CLUB TO RECEIVE £225

1	AFC Liverpool	v	Bootle (23/10)	0-6	247
2	1874 Northwich	v	Billingham Synthonia	1-0	231
3	Stockton Town	v	Sunderland Ryhope CW	1-3	
4	Penrith	v	Easington Colliery	3-1	
5	Guisborough Town	v	Padiham	0-3	110
6	Runcorn Town	v	Hallam	1-2	109
7	South Shields	v	Runcorn Linnets	2-1	1060
8	Charnock Richard	v	Barnoldswick Town	3-1aet	178
9	Atherton LR	v	Chester-Le-Street Town	0-3	
10	Ashton Town	v	Billingham Town	0-4	
11	AFC Emley	v	Chadderton	3-1	132
12	Newcastle Benfield	v	Irlam	3-1	71
13	Atherton Collieries	v	Jarrow Roofing Boldon CA	5-0	
14	Congleton Town	v	Hall Road Rangers	2-3	145
15	Bridlington Town	v	Pickering Town (23/10)	0-1	334
16	Holker Old Boys	v	Stockton Town	1-2	110
17	Litherland Remyca	v	Shildon	1-4	130
18	Shifnal Town	v	Quorn	1-4	55
19	Heanor Town	v	Blidworth Welfare	0-4	
20	St Andrews	v	Paget Rangers	1-2	74
21	Long Eaton United	v	Coventry United	2-1	
22	Wolverhampton Casuals	v	Chelmsley Town	2-1	
23	Ashby Ivanhoe	v	Hucknall Town	3-4aet	121
24	Handsworth Parramore	v	Shepshed Dynamo	3-4	108
25	Bromsgrove Sporting	v	Cadbury Athletic	5-3aet	505
26	Westfields	v	Walsall Wood	6-0	
27	Staveley MW	v	Pinxton	2-0	179
28	Holwell Sports	v	AFC Mansfield	0-2	65
29	Hinckley	v	Wolverhampton SC	3-1aet	
30	Lichfield City	v	Shawbury United	2-1	
31	Kirby Muxloe	v	Hemsworth MW	0-1	
32	Penistone Church	v	Sherwood Colliery	1-2	
33	Bottesford Town	v	Haughmond	0-2	77
34	Malvern Town	v	Worksop Town	1-2	
35	Rocester	v	Oakham United	8-1	107
36	Uttoxeter Town	v	Leicester Road	5-4	108
37	Radford	v	Harborough Town	3-1aet	85
38	Sporting Khalsa	v	Hanley Town	1-0	59
39	Coventry Copsewood	v	Holbeach United	0-2	98
40	Northampton Sileby Rangers	v	Oxhey Jets (25/10)	5-0	42
	(22/10 – tie abandoned after 15 mins due to serious injury to player, 1-0)				
41	Thetford Town	v	Great Yarmouth Town	2-1	101
42	Wadham Lodge	v	Hertford Town (23/10)	2-1	121
43	Sporting Bengal United	v	Southall	0-3	
44	Felixstowe & Walton United	v	Haverhill Borough	4-0	115
45	Broadfields United	v	London Bari	2-1	
46	Highmoor Ibis	v	Holmer Green	0-1	
47	Peterborough Sports	v	Swaffham Town	6-0	
48	Waltham Forest	v	Rothwell Corinthians	1-2	
49	Thrapston Town	v	Leverstock Green	3-7	
50	Canning Town	v	Biggleswade	4-5aet	70
51	Northampton On Chenecks	v	Ely City	1-3	35
52	Gorleston	v	Barking	2-0	118
53	Biggleswade United	v	Baldock Town	2-1	
54	Flackwell Heath	v	Cockfosters	0-3	70
55	Walsham Le Willows	v	Tring Athletic	0-1	
56	Crawley Green	v	Basildon United	1-2	
57	Colney Heath	v	Hoddesdon Town	1-4	
58	Daventry Town	v	Newport Pagnell Town	2-3	105
59	Godmanchester Rovers	v	London Colney	0-3	
60	Yaxley	v	Stanway Rovers	0-1	
61	St Margaretsbury	v	Ilford	3-2	
62	Peterborough Northern Star	v	Sun Sports	1-3	39
63	Welwyn Garden City	v	Saffron Walden Town	3-1	
64	Wembley	v	Desborough Town	5-2	
65	Banstead Athletic	v	Crowborough Athletic	1-3	
66	Wick	v	Haywards Heath Town	0-1	86
67	Bedfont Sports	v	Buckingham Town	5-4	
68	Canterbury City	v	Lydney Town	3-1	51
69	FC Elmstead	v	Sporting Club Thamesmead (21/10)	0-2	149
70	Abbey Rangers	v	Tunbridge Wells	3-0	138
71	Hollands & Blair	v	Ascot United	0-1	78
72	Walton & Hersham	v	Thame United	3-0	53
73	Croydon	v	Bracknell Town	4-1	

FAV1P- Lordswood 'keeper Ryan Chandler collects a corner against Newhaven. Photo: Alan Coomes.

FAV1Q - Cray Valley 'keeper Jack Bradshaw clears a Glebe corner. Photo: Alan Coomes.

FAV2Q - Heanor v Kimberley MW - Heanor's Ryan Seale (white shirt) nips in to win the ball. Photo: Bill Wheatcroft.

FAV4P - Crowborough's Henry Muggeridge beats two Eastbourne Town players to score. Photo: Roger Turner.

FIRST ROUND PROPER
SATURDAY 22 OCTOBER 2016 - WINNING CLUB TO RECEIVE £675 LOSING CLUB TO RECEIVE £225

No	Home	v	Away	Score	Att
74	Epsom & Ewell	v	Bridon Ropes	1-0	92
75	Horsham YMCA	v	Horndean	3-2	
76	Eastbourne United	v	Horley Town	2-0	138
77	Shoreham	v	Glebe	2-3	107
78	Beckenham Town	v	Lancing	1-3	
79	Eastbourne Town	v	Tooting & Mitcham Wanderers	9-0	
80	AC London	v	Highworth Town (23/10)	3-3aet	
	Highworth Town	v	AC London (2/11)	2-1	141
81	Fairford Town	v	Andover Town	1-2	101
82	Alton Town	v	Corinthian	0-2	
83	Ash United	v	Chichester City	0-4	73
84	Alresford Town	v	Lingfield	5-3	68
85	Lordswood	v	Newhaven	1-2	
86	Abingdon United	v	Thatcham Town	1-3	
87	Cribbs	v	Odd Down	1-1	55
	Odd Down	v	Cribbs (25/10)	2-1	39
88	Devizes Town	v	Gillingham Town	0-3	
89	Amesbury Town	v	Brimscombe & Thrupp	0-1	
90	Helston Athletic	v	Team Solent	1-2	
91	Street	v	Blackfield & Langley	0-2	102
92	Bournemouth	v	Melksham Town	0-3	50
93	Calne Town	v	Torpoint Athletic	0-2	78
94	Tuffley Rovers	v	Sherborne Town	4-0	99
95	Cullompton Rangers	v	Hengrove Athletic	1-0	105
96	Bemerton Heath Harlequins	v	Plymouth Parkway	2-2aet	40
	Plymouth Parkway	v	Bemerton Heath Harlequins	0-3	64
97	Sholing	v	Buckland Athletic	0-3	147
98	Clevedon Town	v	Willand Rovers	4-2aet	
99	Romsey Town	v	Portland United	2-3	101
100	Exmouth	v	Tavistock	3-2	
101	AFC Stoneham	v	Shaftesbury Town	1-3	60

SECOND ROUND PROPER
SATURDAY 12 NOVEMBER 2016 - WINNING CLUB TO RECEIVE £750 LOSING CLUB TO RECEIVE £250

No	Home	v	Away	Score	Att
1	Newton Aycliffe	v	Worksop Town	4-0	
2	Pickering Town	v	Shildon	0-5	
3	Padiham	v	Bootle	0-2	290
4	1874 Northwich	v	Atherton Collieries	0-3	283
5	Charnock Richard	v	Staveley MW (15/11)	2-4aet	
6	Billingham Town	v	Sunderland Ryhope CW	5-2	
7	Hallam	v	Morpeth Town	0-4	454
8	Hall Road Rangers	v	Bottesford Town	0-2	
9	Sunderland RCA	v	Stockton Town	1-0aet	
10	North Shields	v	Chester-Le-Street Town	2-0	
11	Dunston UTS	v	Hemsworth MW (29/11)	3-1	172
12	Newcastle Benfield	v	Penrith	0-1	148
13	South Shields	v	Marske United	2-0	1116
14	AFC Emley	v	Cleethorpes Town	1-2	215
15	Sleaford Town	v	Leicester Nirvana (16/11)	4-1	
16	Long Eaton United	v	Holbeach United	3-2	85
17	Wolverhampton Casuals	v	Nuneaton Griff	1-2	
18	Hucknall Town	v	Rocester	5-1	
19	Blidworth Welfare	v	AFC Mansfield	1-2	146
20	Paget Rangers	v	Hinckley	1-4	311
21	Westfields	v	Sherwood Colliery	3-2	134
22	Alvechurch	v	Sporting Khalsa	1-2	
23	Radford	v	Shepshed Dynamo	1-3	100
24	Uttoxeter Town	v	Coleshill Town	1-3	
25	Bromsgrove Sporting	v	Lichfield City	3-1	
26	Quorn	v	AFC Wulfrunians	3-1aet	98
27	Wadham Lodge	v	Ely City	0-3	
28	Rothwell Corinthians	v	Tring Athletic (16/11)	1-2	92
29	Leverstock Green	v	Welwyn Garden City	1-2	
30	St Margaretsbury	v	Stanway Rovers	4-2aet	77
31	Newport Pagnell Town	v	Broadfields United	2-1	
32	Berkhamsted	v	Hullbridge Sports	5-2	143
33	Gorleston	v	Northampton Sileby Rangers	2-1	140
34	Cockfosters	v	Wembley (15/11)	1-2	73
35	Peterborough Sports	v	Biggleswade	5-3	
36	London Colney	v	Holmer Green	3-0	85
37	Biggleswade United	v	Sun Sports	1-1aet	160
	Sun Sports	v	Biggleswade United (15/11)	1-1aet	
	(Sun Sports won 5-4 on kicks from the penalty mark)				
38	FC Romania	v	Ipswich Wanderers (16/11)	2-0	
39	Hoddesdon Town	v	Thetford Town	2-0	95
40	Basildon United	v	Felixstowe & Walton United	3-2	64
41	Eastbourne Town	v	Ashford United	2-1	
42	Sutton Common Rovers	v	Sporting Club Thamesmead	2-1	
43	Newhaven	v	Ascot United	2-1	81
44	Bedfont Sports	v	Haywards Heath Town	2-0	
45	Eastbourne United	v	Crowborough Athletic	0-1	121
46	Walton & Hersham	v	Glebe (15/11)	2-2aet	75
	(Glebe won 3-1 on kicks from the penalty mark)				
47	Camberley Town	v	Southall	0-4	
48	Croydon	v	Andover Town	2-1	61
49	Corinthian	v	Alresford Town	3-2	52
50	Lancing	v	Horsham YMCA	1-7	128
51	Chichester City	v	Canterbury City (16/11)	3-1aet	
52	Highworth Town	v	Knaphill	1-3	145
53	Epsom & Ewell	v	Abbey Rangers	2-3	
54	Portland United	v	Blackfield & Langley	1-2	261
55	Shaftesbury Town	v	Team Solent	1-3	
56	Brimscombe & Thrupp	v	Bradford Town	2-2aet	103
	Bradford Town	v	Brimscombe & Thrupp (16/11)	5-0	
57	Bristol Manor Farm	v	Odd Down	2-1	134
58	Moneyfields	v	Thatcham Town	0-4	
59	Cullompton Rangers	v	Bemerton Heath Harlequins	1-1aet	96
	(at Willand Rovers FC)				
	Bemerton Heath Harlequins	v	Cullompton Rangers (15/11)	3-2	
60	Hartley Wintney	v	Melksham Town (15/11)	1-2	131
61	Gillingham Town	v	Exmouth	0-1	
62	Buckland Athletic	v	Newport (IW)	1-0	
63	Torpoint Athletic	v	Clevedon Town	1-0	245
64	Tuffley Rovers	v	Bodmin Town	0-2	98

FAVQF - Action from the Bromsgrove Sporting v Buckland Athletic tie. Photo: Peter Barnes.

FAV5P - Coleshill 'keeper Paul Hathaway punches clear a Crowborough corner. Photo: Alan Coomes.

FAV2P - Midfield action from the Brimscombe & Thrupp v Bradford Town match. Photo: Peter Barnes.

THIRD ROUND PROPER
SATURDAY 3 DECEMBER 2016 - WINNING CLUB TO RECEIVE £975 LOSING CLUB TO RECEIVE £325

1	North Shields	v	Shildon	1-2	427
2	Newton Aycliffe	v	Morpeth Town	2-3	
3	Cleethorpes Town	v	Bootle	2-1	196
4	South Shields	v	Staveley MW	3-0	
5	Penrith	v	Atherton Collieries	0-3	
6	Dunston UTS	v	Sunderland RCA	1-3	186
7	Bottesford Town	v	Billingham Town	1-2	198
8	Hucknall Town	v	AFC Mansfield	1-2	
9	Nuneaton Griff	v	Bromsgrove Sporting	0-2	
10	Sporting Khalsa	v	Sleaford Town	5-5aet	70
	Sleaford Town	v	Sporting Khalsa (7/12)	0-3	124
11	Coleshill Town	v	Westfields	4-1	87
12	Hinckley	v	Quorn	2-1aet	
13	Long Eaton United	v	Shepshed Dynamo	2-4aet	106
14	Wembley	v	Peterborough Sports	0-4	
15	FC Romania	v	Tring Athletic	1-1aet	
	Tring Athletic	v	FC Romania (6/12)	2-1	
16	Newport Pagnell Town	v	London Colney	3-1	

17	Gorleston	v	Basildon United		
	(3/12 - tie abandoned after 89 minutes due to serious incident, 0-1)				
	(walkover for Gorleston – Basildon United withdrawn)				
18	St Margaretsbury	v	Berkhamsted	1-3	
19	Sun Sports	v	Hoddesdon Town	3-1	40
20	Welwyn Garden City	v	Ely City	2-3	151
21	Abbey Rangers	v	Eastbourne Town	1-2	80
22	Crowborough Athletic	v	Bedfont Sports	2-2aet	
	Bedfont Sports	v	Crowborough Athletic (7/12)	2-3	
23	Croydon	v	Glebe	3-2	
24	Knaphill	v	Southall	1-2	94
25	Newhaven	v	Chichester City	1-3	66
26	Sutton Common Rovers	v	Corinthian (4/12)	1-4	
27	Horsham YMCA	v	Buckland Athletic	0-3	135
28	Bemerton Heath Harlequins	v	Melksham Town	2-3	77
29	Team Solent	v	Bodmin Town	1-0	
30	Bradford Town	v	Torpoint Athletic	2-0	
31	Bristol Manor Farm	v	Thatcham Town	4-1	116
32	Exmouth	v	Blackfield & Langley	5-0	

FOURTH ROUND PROPER
SATURDAY 7 JANUARY 2017 - WINNING CLUB TO RECEIVE £1,500 LOSING CLUB TO RECEIVE £500

1	Shildon	v	Atherton Collieries	1-4	412
2	Billingham Town	v	Cleethorpes Town	1-2	384
3	AFC Mansfield	v	Sunderland RCA	0-1	140
4	South Shields	v	Morpeth Town	4-0	
	(at Morpeth Town FC) (7/1 - tie abandoned after 81 minutes due to floodlight failure, 2-4)				
5	Gorleston	v	Coleshill Town	0-3	226
6	Sun Sports	v	Bromsgrove Sporting	0-4	
7	Newport Pagnell Town	v	Peterborough Sports	3-2	80
8	Sporting Khalsa	v	Tring Athletic	1-0	

9	Ely City	v	Shepshed Dynamo	3-0	386
10	Hinckley	v	Berkhamsted	5-0	
11	Bradford Town	v	Southall	2-4aet	152
12	Bristol Manor Farm	v	Melksham Town	1-1aet	245
	Melksham Town	v	Bristol Manor Farm (14/1)	3-5	1215
13	Chichester City	v	Buckland Athletic	1-3	280
14	Team Solent	v	Croydon	3-0	
15	Exmouth	v	Corinthian	4-0	
16	Crowborough Athletic	v	Eastbourne Town	6-0	461

FIFTH ROUND PROPER
SATURDAY 28 JANUARY 2017 - WINNING CLUB TO RECEIVE £1,875 LOSING CLUB TO RECEIVE £625

1	Cleethorpes Town	v	Atherton Collieries	3-2	588
2	Southall	v	Exmouth (29/1)	4-2	
3	Bromsgrove Sporting	v	Bristol Manor Farm	2-1	1487
4	Crowborough Athletic	v	Coleshill Town	3-6	605

5	Hinckley	v	Buckland Athletic	3-4aet	418
6	Newport Pagnell Town	v	Sunderland RCA	3-2aet	764
7	Ely City	v	Sporting Khalsa	0-3	646
8	Team Solent	v	South Shields	2-5	638

SIXTH ROUND PROPER
SATURDAY 18 FEBRUARY 2017 - WINNING CLUB TO RECEIVE £3,375 LOSING CLUB TO RECEIVE £1,125

| 1 | South Shields | v | Newport Pagnell Town | 6-1 | 3161 |
| 2 | Southall | v | Cleethorpes Town | 2-5 | 348 |

| 3 | Bromsgrove Sporting | v | Buckland Athletic (19/2) | 2-0 | 2984 |
| 4 | Coleshill Town | v | Sporting Khalsa | 2-0 | 939 |

SEMI FINALS
WINNING CLUB TO RECEIVE £4,500 LOSING CLUB TO RECEIVE £1,500

11/03	Bromsgrove Sporting	v	Cleethorpes Town	1-1	3349
18/03	Cleethorpes Town	v	Bromsgrove Sporting	1-0	1154
	Cleethorpes Town 2-1 on aggregate.				4503

11/03	Coleshill Town	v	South Shields	1-2	1755
18/03	South Shields	v	Coleshill Town	4-0	3464
	South Shields 6-1 on aggregate.				5219

THE FINAL...

CLEETHORPES   0

SOUTH SHIELDS   4
(Finnigan 43 (pen), Morse 80, Foley 86, 89)
Wembley Stadium   **Att: 38,224***
*combined Trophy/Vase attendance

THE SQUADS

CLEETHORPES	SOUTH SHIELDS
Liam Higton	Liam Connell
Tim Lowe	Alex Nicholson
Peter Winn	Darren Lough
Liam Dickens	Jon Shaw
Matt Bloomer	Dillon Morse
Matty Coleman (sub 70)	Julio Arca
Liam Davis (sub 73)	Andrew Stephenson (sub 56)
Alex Flett	Wayne Phillips (sub 82)
Marc Cooper (sub 61)	Gavin Congdon
Brody Robertson	Carl Finnigan (sub 71)
Jon Oglesby	David Foley
Substitutes	**Substitutes**
Andy Taylor (61)	Robert Briggs (56)
Luke Mascall (70)	Michael Richardson (71)
Jack Richardson (73)	Barrie Smith (82)
Gary King	Louis Storey
Kieran Wressell	Darren Holden

Referee Darren England
Assisted by Matthew Jones and Marc Wilson
4th official, Robert Jones

So, yet again, The Vase has a winner from the north east, making it eight victories in the last nine years for a Northern League team. Even though they had the greatest distance to travel the 13,000 fans making the long trip from South Shields to cheer on The Mariners made up easily the largest contingent of the four teams appearing on Non-League Finals Day. Lifting their fourth trophy of the 2016/17 season they might well have counted themselves fortunate to have, earlier in the season, beaten the previous year's Vase victors Morpeth Town in the fourth round, for, having been behind when the first tie was abandoned with only 8 minutes left, they proceeded to win the replay 4-0. Unarguably they were the better team on this sunny Sunday, although the four goal deficit was a little unkind on a courageous Cleethorpes team who had rallied well after the first twenty minutes of the game had passed them by. During that period Shields had scorned several chances. In the second minute an effort was cleared off the Cleethorpes' line by a fortuitous defender, with vain cries for a penalty coming from some Mariners' players. Twice in the opening minutes Owls' goalkeeper Liam Higton came to the rescue, tipping one shot over and blocking

Wayne Phillips (South Shields) gets in his shot against Cleethorpes. Photo: Keith Clayton.

another after David Foley had put Carl Finnegan clear. All Cleethorpes had to show at that time was a booking for midfielder Liam Davis and one corner kick but they at last were able to move forward and threaten Liam Connell's goal. A Brody Robertson's shot saw Connell, at full stretch, conceding a corner and three minutes later Davis engineered a chance which unfortunately Marc Cooper, racing goalward, found frustratingly drifting away just behind him. Shields retaliated with another Foley drive which Peter Winn was able to block, enabling Higton to fall on the ball and eventually clear. Davis then repeated the feat when he blocked Darren Lough's shot.

Often these finals become dour affairs with more determination to halt the opposition rather than move forward positively. Interchanges are backwards or sideways so what a pleasure it was to witness two teams pressing towards the opposition goal at every opportunity. This was certainly the case here as both sides were intent on forging a chance to score. Even so, and despite the northern team forcing three corners on the trot, the scoresheet remained blank until minute 43 when Gavin Congdon was brought down by Tim Lowe as he scurried into the box. No arguments, all agreed, clear penalty. Up stepped Finnegan, Higton went left, ball went right and Shields were ahead. Indeed, as added time at the end of the half ticked away, the effervescent Congdon's shot was turned against the post by Higton with Congdon heading the rebound wide.

Half time discussion centred on how Cleethorpe's might react to going one down in the last minutes of the first half. Would their heads drop, since, after all, they had eventually found their feet in the latter twenty or so minutes after South Shields had clearly dominated the game's opening period? Would the late penalty be a precursor to a one sided second half? All agreed it had been enjoyable to see two teams playing with so much freedom from fear of losing and were looking to a continuation of the feast of open play.

In a repeat of the opening minutes the north easterners were again to the fore, with Congdon and Foley a threat with their dribbling skills. Goalkeeper Higton dealt well with a fierce Foley shot and just minutes later had to dive on a near post effort from Congdon who posed a constant threat whenever he had the ball at his feet within sight of goal. At the other end Robertson found himself with only Connell to beat but Alex Nicholson managed to stick out a limb and block the striker in the act of shooting. When Connell dropped a corner one of his defenders was

luckily on hand to boot away but increasingly Shields were threatening to extend their lead. Congdon, in another one on one chance he had largely forged himself, shot against Higton rather than past him but then, with ten minutes to go on the clock, defender Dillon Morse was left completely unmarked on the far post to head home despite Higton getting a hand on his effort.

Rather cruelly fate then permitted Shields to double that two goal gap in the closing minutes. The Lincolnshire lads stood waiting for an offside flag that never came and Foley was able to stroll through to score Shields third. The same player then completed his brace after Lough had put him clear to beat Higton at his near post.

There were no complaints from Cleethorpes at the final whistle. They acknowledged their opponents deserved victory. How good it was again, generally a hallmark of this competition, to witness the friendly, sporting reaction to each other of players, managements and officials at the end of a game which had been well played, enjoyable and entertaining throughout. Having gained and accepted promotion from their respective Step 5 Leagues both clubs will interestingly find themselves meeting in Step 4, Northern Premier Division One North come the new season. If the fixtures repeat this level of performance, bring them on.

Arthur Evans.

Some of the South Shields players celebrate their FA Vase win. Photo: Peter Barnes.

PAST FINALS

1975 HODDESDON TOWN 2 *(South Midlands)* EPSOM & EWELL 1 *(Surrey Senior)* **Att: 9,500**
Sedgwick 2 Wales Ref: Mr R Toseland
Hoddesdon: Galvin, Green, Hickey, Maybury, Stevenson, Wilson, Bishop, Picking, Sedgwick, Nathan, Schofield
Epsom & Ewell: Page, Bennett, Webb, Wales, Worby, Jones, O'Connell, Walker, Tuite, Eales, Lee

1976 BILLERICAY TOWN 1 *(Essex Senior)* STAMFORD 0 (aet) *(United Counties)* **Att: 11,848**
Aslett Ref: Mr A Robinson
Billericay: Griffiths, Payne, Foreman, Pullin, Bone, Coughlan, Geddes, Aslett, Clayden, Scott, Smith
Stamford: Johnson, Kwiatowski, Marchant, Crawford, Downs, Hird, Barnes, Walpole, Smith, Russell, Broadbent

1977 BILLERICAY TOWN 1 *(Essex Senior)* SHEFFIELD 1 (aet) *(Yorkshire)* **Att: 14,000**
Clayden Coughlan og Ref: Mr J Worrall
Billericay: Griffiths, Payne, Bone, Coughlan, Pullin, Scott, Wakefield, Aslett, Clayden,Woodhouse, McQueen. Sub: Whettell
Sheffield: Wing, Gilbody, Lodge, Hardisty, Watts, Skelton, Kay, Travis, Pugh, Thornhill,Haynes. Sub: Strutt
Replay BILLERICAY TOWN 2 SHEFFIELD 1 **Att: 3,482**
Aslett, Woodhouse Thornhill at Nottingham Forest
Billericay: Griffiths, Payne, Pullin, Whettell, Bone, McQueen, Woodhouse, Aslett, Clayden, Scott, Wakefield
Sheffield: Wing, Gilbody, Lodge, Strutt, Watts, Skelton, Kay, Travis, Pugh, Thornhill, Haynes

1978 NEWCASTLE BLUE STAR 2 *(Wearside)* BARTON ROVERS 1 *(South Midlands)* **Att: 16,858**
Dunn, Crumplin Smith Ref: Mr T Morris
Newcastle: Halbert, Feenan, Thompson, Davidson, S Dixon, Beynon, Storey, P Dixon, Crumplin, Callaghan, Dunn. Sub: Diamond
Barton Rovers: Blackwell, Stephens, Crossley, Evans, Harris, Dollimore, Dunn, Harnaman, Fossey, Turner, Smith. Sub: Cox

1979 BILLERICAY TOWN 4 *(Athenian)* ALMONDSBURY GREENWAY 1 *(Glos. Co)* **Att: 17,500**
Young 3, Clayden Price Ref: Mr C Steel
Billericay: Norris, Blackaller, Bingham, Whettell, Bone, Reeves, Pullin, Scott, Clayden,Young, Groom. Sub: Carrigan
Almondsbury: Hamilton, Bowers, Scarrett, Sulllivan, Tudor, Wookey, Bowers, Shehean, Kerr, Butt, Price. Sub: Kilbaine

1980 STAMFORD 2 *(United Counties)* GUISBOROUGH TOWN 0 *(Northern Alliance)* **Att: 11,500**
Alexander, McGowan Ref: Neil Midgeley
Stamford: Johnson, Kwiatkowski, Ladd, McGowan, Bliszczak I, Mackin, Broadhurst, Hall,Czarnecki, Potter, Alexander. Sub: Bliszczak S
Guisborough: Cutter, Scott, Thornton, Angus, Maltby, Percy, Skelton, Coleman, McElvaney,Sills, Dilworth. Sub: Harrison

1981 WHICKHAM 3 *(Wearside)* WILLENHALL 2 (aet) *(West Midlands)* **Att: 12,000**
Scott, Williamson, Peck og Smith, Stringer Ref: Mr R Lewis
Whickham: Thompson, Scott, Knox, Williamson, Cook, Ward, Carroll, Diamond, Cawthra,Robertson, Turnbull. Sub: Alton
Willenhall: Newton, White, Darris, Woodall, Heath, Fox, Peck, Price, Matthews, Smith,Stringer. Sub: Trevor

1982 FOREST GREEN ROVERS 3 *(Hellenic)* RAINWORTH M.W 0 *(Notts Alliance)* **Att: 12,500**
Leitch 2, Norman Ref: Mr K Walmsey
Forest Green: Moss, Norman, Day, Turner, Higgins, Jenkins, Guest, Burns, Millard, Leitch, Doughty. Sub: Dangerfield
Rainworth M.W: Watson, Hallam, Hodgson, Slater, Sterland, Oliver, Knowles, Raine, Radzi, Reah, Comerford. Sub: Robinson

1983 V.S. RUGBY 1 *(West Midlands)* HALESOWEN TOWN 0 *(West Midlands)* **Att: 13,700**
Crawley Ref: Mr B Daniels
VS Rugby: Burton, McGinty, Harrison, Preston, Knox, Evans, ingram, Setchell, Owen,Beecham, Crawley. Sub: Haskins
Halesowen Town: Coldicott, Penn, Edmonds, Lacey, Randall, Shilvock, Hazelwood, Moss, Woodhouse,P Joinson, L Joinson. Sub: Smith

1984 STANSTED 3 *(Essex Senior)* STAMFORD 2 *(United Counties)* **Att: 8,125**
Holt, Gillard, Reading Waddicore, Allen Ref: Mr T Bune
Stanstead: Coe, Williams, Hilton, Simpson,   Cooper, Reading, Callanan, Holt, Reevs,Doyle, Gillard. Sub: Williams
Stamford: Parslow, Smitheringate, Blades, McIlwain, Lyon, Mackin, Genovese, Waddicore,Allen, Robson, Beech. Sub: Chapman

1985 HALESOWEN TOWN 3 *(West Midlands)* FLEETWOOD TOWN 1 *(N W Counties)* **Att: 16,715**
L Joinson 2, Moss Moran Ref: Mr C Downey
Halesowen: Coldicott, Penn, Sherwood, Warner, Randle, Heath, Hazlewood, Moss (Smith),Woodhouse, P Joinson, L Joinson
Fleetwood Town: Dobson, Moran, Hadgraft, Strachan, Robinson, Milligan, Hall, Trainor, Taylor(Whitehouse), Cain, Kennerley

1986 HALESOWEN TOWN 3 *(West Midlands)* SOUTHALL 0 *(Isthmian 2 South)* **Att: 18,340**
Moss 2, L Joinson Ref: Mr D Scott
Halesowen: Pemberton, Moore, Lacey, Randle (Rhodes), Sherwood, Heath, Penn, Woodhouse, PJoinson, L Joinson, Moss
Southall: Mackenzie, James, McGovern, Croad, Holland, Powell (Richmond), Pierre,Richardson, Sweales, Ferdinand, Rowe

1987 ST. HELENS 3 *(N W Counties)*   **WARRINGTON TOWN** 2 *(N W Counties)*   Att: 4,254
Layhe 2, Rigby   Reid, Cook   Ref: Mr T Mills
St Helens: Johnson, Benson, Lowe, Bendon, Wilson, McComb, Collins (Gledhill), O'Neill,Cummins, Lay, Rigby. Sub: Deakin
Warrington: O'Brien. Copeland, Hunter, Gratton, Whalley, Reid, Brownville (Woodyer), Cook,Kinsey, Looker (Hill), Hughes

1988 COLNE DYNAMOES 1 *(N W Counties)*   **EMLEY** 0 *(Northern Counties East)*   Att: 15,000
Anderson   Ref: Mr A Seville
Colne Dynamoes: Mason, McFafyen, Westwell, Bentley, Dunn, Roscoe, Rodaway, Whitehead (Burke),Diamond, Anderson, Wood (Coates)
Emley: Dennis, Fielding, Mellor, Codd, Hirst (Burrows), Gartland (Cook), Carmody,Green, Bramald, Devine, Francis

1989 TAMWORTH 1 *(West Midlands)*   **SUDBURY TOWN** 1 (aet) *(Eastern)*   Att: 26,487
Devaney   Hubbick   Ref: Mr C Downey
Tamworth: Bedford, Lockett, Atkins, Cartwright, McCormack, Myers, Finn, Devaney, Moores,Gordon, Stanton. Subs: Rathbone, Heaton
Sudbury Town: Garnham, Henry, G Barker, Boyland, Thorpe, Klug, D Barker, Barton, Oldfield,Smith, Hubbick. Subs: Money, Hunt
Replay **TAMWORTH** 3   **SUDBURY TOWN** 0   Att: 11,201
Stanton 2, Moores   at Peterborough
Tamworth: Bedford, Lockett, Atkins, Cartwright, Finn, Myers, George, Devaney, Moores,Gordon, Stanton. Sub: Heaton
Sudbury Town: Garnham, Henry, G Barker, Boyland, Thorpe, Klug, D Barker, Barton, Oldfield,Smith, Hubbick. Subs: Money, Hunt

1990 YEADING 0 *(Isthmian 2 South)*   **BRIDLINGTON TOWN** 0 (aet) *(N Co East)*   Att: 7,932
    Ref: Mr R Groves
Yeading: Mackenzie, Wickens, Turner, Whiskey (McCarthy), Croad, Denton, Matthews, James(Charles), Sweates, Impey, Cordery
Bridlington: Taylor, Pugh, Freeman, McNeill, Warburton, Brentano, Wilkes (Hall), Noteman,Gauden, Whiteman, Brattan (Brown)
Replay **YEADING** 1   **BRIDLINGTON TOWN** 0   Att: 5,000
Sweales   at Leeds Utd FC
Yeading: Mackenzie, Wickens, Turner, Whiskey, Croad (McCarthy), Schwartz, Matthews,James, Sweates, Impey (Welsh), Cordery
Bridlington: Taylor, Pugh, Freeman, McNeill, Warburton, Brentano, Wilkes (Brown), Noteman,Gauden (Downing), Whiteman, Brattan

1991 GRESLEY ROVERS 4 *(West Midlands)*   **GUISELEY** 4 (aet) *(Northern Co East)*   Att: 11,314
Rathbone, Smith 2, Stokes   Tennison 2, Walling, A Roberts   Ref: Mr C Trussell
Gresley: Aston, Barry, Elliott (Adcock), Denby, Land, Astley, Stokes, K Smith, Acklam,Rathbone, Lovell (Weston)
Guiseley: Maxted, Bottomley, Hogarth, Tetley, Morgan, McKenzie, Atkinson (Annan),Tennison, Walling, A Roberts, B Roberts
Replay **GUISELEY** 3   **GRESLEY ROVERS** 1   Att: 7,585
Tennison, Walling, Atkinson   Astley   at Bramall Lane
Guiseley: Maxted, Annan, Hogarth, Tetley, Morgan, McKenzie (Bottomley), Atkinson,Tennison (Noteman), Walling, A Roberts, B Roberts
Gresley: Aston, Barry, Elliott, Denby, Land, Astley, Stokes (Weston), K Smith, Acklam, Rathbone, Lovell (Adcock)

1992 WIMBORNE TOWN 5 *(Wessex)*   **GUISELEY** 3 *(Northern Premier Div 1)*   Att: 10,772
Richardson, Sturgess 2, Killick 2   Noteman 2, Colville   Ref: Mr M J Bodenham
Wimborne: Leonard, Langdown, Wilkins, Beacham, Allan, Taplin, Ames, Richardson, Bridle,Killick, Sturgess (Lovell), Lynn
Guiseley: Maxted, Atkinson, Hogarth, Tetley (Wilson), Morgan, Brockie, A Roberts,Tennison, Noteman (Colville), Annan, W Roberts

1993 BRIDLINGTON TOWN 1 *(NPL Div 1)*   **TIVERTON TOWN** 0 *(Western)*   Att: 9,061
Radford   Ref: Mr R A Hart
Bridlington: Taylor, Brentano, McKenzie, Harvey, Bottomley, Woodcock, Grocock, A Roberts, Jones, Radford (Tyrell), Parkinson. Sub: Swailes
Tiverton Town: Nott, J Smith, N Saunders, M Saunders, Short (Scott), Steele, Annunziata, KSmith, Everett, Daly, Hynds (Rogers)

1994 DISS TOWN 2 *(Eastern)*   **TAUNTON TOWN** 1 *(Western)*   Att: 13,450
Gibbs (p), Mendham   Fowler   Ref: Mr K. Morton
Diss Town: Woodcock, Carter, Wolsey (Musgrave), Casey (Bugg), Hartle, Smith, Barth, Mendham, Miles, Warne, Gibbs
Taunton Town: Maloy, Morris, Walsh, Ewens, Graddon, Palfrey, West (Hendry), Fowler, Durham, Perrett (Ward), Jarvis

1995 ARLESEY TOWN 2 *(South Midlands)*   **OXFORD CITY** 1 *(Ryman 2)*   Att: 13,670
Palma, Gyalog   S Fontaine   Ref: Mr G S Willard
Arlesey: Young, Cardines, Bambrick, Palma (Ward), Hull, Gonsalves, Gyalog, Cox, Kane,O'Keefe, Marshall (Nicholls). Sub: Dodwell
Oxford: Fleet, Brown (Fisher), Hume, Shepherd, Muttock, Hamilton (Kemp), Thomas, Spittle, Sherwood, S Fontaine, C Fontaine. Sub: Torres

1996 BRIGG TOWN 3 *(N Co East)*   **CLITHEROE** 0 *(N W Counties)*   Att: 7,340
Stead 2, Roach   Ref: Mr S J Lodge
Brigg: Gawthorpe, Thompson, Rogers, Greaves (Clay), Buckley (Mail), Elston, C Stead, McLean, N Stead (McNally), Flounders, Roach
Clitheroe: Nash, Lampkin, Rowbotham (Otley), Baron, Westwell, Rovine, Butcher, Taylor (Smith), Grimshaw, Darbyshire, Hill (Dunn)

1997 WHITBY TOWN 3 *(Northern)*   **NORTH FERRIBY UTD.** 0 *(N Co East)*   Att: 11,098
Williams, Logan, Toman   Ref: Graham Poll
North Ferriby: Sharp, Deacey, Smith, Brentano, Walmsley, M Smith, Harrison (Horne), Phillips (Milner), France (Newman), Flounders, Tennison
Whitby Town: Campbell, Williams, Logan, Goodchild, Pearson, Cook, Goodrick (Borthwick), Hodgson, Robinson, Toman (Pyle), Pitman (Hall)

THE FA VASE

1998 TIVERTON TOWN 1 *(Western)*   **TOW LAW TOWN 0** *(Northern Division 1)*   **Att: 13,139**
Varley   **Ref: M A Riley**
Tiverton Town: Edwards, Felton, Saunders, Tatterton, Smith J, Conning, Nancekivell (Rogers), Smith K (Varley), Everett, Daly, Leonard (Waters)
Tow Law Town: Dawson, Pickering, Darwent, Bailey, Hague, Moan, Johnson, Nelson, Suddick, Laidler (Bennett), Robinson.

1999 TIVERTON TOWN 1 *(Western)*   **BEDLINGTON TERRIERS 0** *(Northern)*   **Att: 13, 878**
Rogers 88   **Ref: W. C. Burns**
Bedlington Terriers: O'Connor, Bowes, Pike, Boon (Renforth), Melrose, Teasdale, Cross, Middleton (Ludlow), Gibb, Milner, Bond. Subs:
Pearson, Cameron, Gowans
Tiverton Town: Edwards, Fallon, Saunders, Tatterton, Tallon, Conning (Rogers), Nancekivell (Pears), Varley, Everett, Daly, Leonard. Subs:
Tucker, Hynds, Grimshaw

2000 DEAL TOWN 1 *(Kent)*   **CHIPPENHAM TOWN 0** *(Western)*   **Att: 20,000**
Graham 87   **Ref: D Laws**
Deal Town: Tucker, Kempster, Best, Ash, Martin, Seager, Monteith, Graham, Lovell, Marshall, Ribbens. Subs: Roberts, Warden, Turner
Chippenham Town: Jones, James, Andrews, Murphy, Burns, Woods, Brown, Charity, Tweddle, Collier, Godley. Subs: Tiley, Cutler

2001 TAUNTON TOWN 2 *(Western)*   **BERKHAMPSTED TOWN 1** *(Isthmian 2)*   **(at Villa Park) Att: 8,439**
Fields 41, Laight 45   Lowe 71   **Ref: E. K. Wolstenholme**
Taunton Town: Draper, Down, Chapman, West, Hawkings, Kelly, Fields (Groves), Laight, Cann (Tallon), Bastow, Lynch (Hapgood).
Subs: Ayres, Parker
Berkhampsted Town: O'Connor, Mullins, Lowe, Aldridge, Coleman, Brockett, Yates, Adebowale, Richardson, Smith, Nightingale.
Subs: Ringsell, Hall, Knight, Franklin, Osborne

2002 WHITLEY BAY 1 *(Northern)*   **TIPTREE UNITED 0** *(Eastern)*   **(at Villa Park) Att: 4742**
Chandler 97   **Ref: A Kaye**
Whitley Bay: Caffrey, Sunderland, Walmsley, Dixon (Neil), Anderson, Locker, Middleton, Bowes (Carr), Chandler, Walton, Fenwick (Cuggy).
Subs: Cook, Livermore
Tiptree United: Haygreen, Battell, Wall, Houghton, Fish, Streetley (Gillespie), Wareham (Snow), Daly, Barefield, Aransibia (Parnell), Brady.
Subs: Powell, Ford.

2003 BRIGG TOWN 2 *(Northern Co.East)*   **A.F.C SUDBURY 1** *(Eastern Counties)*   **(at Upton Park) Att: 6,634**
Housham 2, Carter 68   Raynor 30   **Ref: M Fletcher**
Brigg Town:- Steer, Raspin, Rowland, Thompson, Blanchard, Stones, Stead (Thompson 41), Housham,
Borman (Drayton 87), Roach, Carter. Subs (not used) Nevis, Gawthorpe.
AFC Sudbury:- Greygoose, Head (Norfolk 63), Spearing, Tracey, Bishop, Anderson (Owen 73), Rayner,
Gardiner (Banya 79), Bennett, Claydon, Betson. Subs (not used) Taylor, Hyde.

2004 WINCHESTER CITY 2 *(Wessex)*   **A.F.C SUDBURY 0** *(Eastern Counties)*   **(at St Andrews) Att: 5,080**
Forbes 19, Smith 73 (pen)   **Ref: P Crossley**
Winchester City:- Arthur, Dyke (Tate 83), Bicknell, Redwood, Goss, Blake, Webber, Green, Mancey, Forbes (Rogers 70),
Smith (Green 90). Subs (not used) - Lang and Rastall.
AFC Sudbury:- Greygoose, Head, Wardley, Girling, Tracey, Norfolk, Owen (Banya 62), Hyde (Calver 57), Bennett, Claydon,
Betson (Francis 73n). Subs (not used) - Rayner, Nower.

2005 DIDCOT TOWN 3 *(Hellenic)*   **A.F.C SUDBURY 2** *(Eastern Counties)*(at White Hart Lane) **Att: 8,662**
Beavon (2), Wardley (og)   Wardley, Calver (pen)   **Ref: R Beeeby**
Didcot Town:- Webb, Goodall, Heapy, Campbell, Green, Parrott, Hannigan, Ward, Concannon (Jones 88), Beavon (Bianchini 90), Powell.
Subs (not used) – Cooper, Allen, Spurrett.
AFC Sudbury:- Greygoose, Girling, Wardley, Bennett, Hyde (Hayes 78), Owen (Norfolk 65), Claydon (Banya 59), Head, Calver, Betson,
Terry Rayner. Subs (not used) – Howlett, Nower.

2006 NANTWICH TOWN 3 *(NWC 1)*   **HILLINGDON BOROUGH 1** *(Spartan S.Mids P.)*(at St Andrews) **Att: 3,286**
Kinsey (2), Scheuber   Nelson
Nantwich Town:- Hackney, A.Taylor, T.Taylor, Smith, Davis, Donnelly, Beasley, Scheuber (Parkinson 69), Kinsey (Marrow 69),
Blake (Scarlett 86) and Griggs. Subs (not used): O'Connor and Read.
Hillingdon Borough:- Brown, Rundell (Fenton 80),Kidson, Phillips, Croft, Lawrence, Duncan (Nelson 46), Tilbury, Hibbs,
Wharton (Lyons 38). Subs (not used): O'Grady, White.

2007 TRURO 3 *(Western Division 1)*   **AFC TOTTON 1** *(Wessex Division 1)* **Att: 27,754 (New Vase record)**
Wills (2), Broad   Potter   **Ref: P Joslin**
AFC Totton: Brunnschweiler, Reacord, Troon (Stevens 60), Potter (Gregory 82), Bottomley, Austen, Roden, Gosney, Hamodu (Goss 89), Osman, Byres.
Subs not used: Zammit, McCormack.
Truro City: Stevenson, Ash, Power, Smith, Martin (Pope 84), Broad, Wills, Gosling, Yetton, Watkins, Walker (Ludlam 90).
Subs not used: Butcher, Routledge, Reski.

2008 KIRKHAM & WESHAM 2 *(North West Co. Div.2)*   **LOWESTOFT TOWN 1** *(Eastern Co. Premier)*   Att: 19,537
Walwyn (2)   Thompson (og)   Ref: A D'Urso
Kirkham and Wesham: Summerfield, Jackson (Walwyn 79), Keefe (Allen 55), Thompson, Shaw, Eastwood, Clark, Blackwell, Wane,
Paterson (Sheppard 90), Smith. Subs not used: Moffat and Abbott
Lowestoft Town: Reynolds, Poppy, Potter, Woodrow, Saunders, Plaskett (McGee 79), Godbold, Darren Cockrill (Dale Cockrill 46), Stock, Hough,
King (Hunn 55). Subs not used: McKenna and Rix.

2009 WHITLEY BAY 2 *(Northern Division One)*   **GLOSSOP NORTH END 0** *(North West Co. Prem)*   Att: 12,212
Kerr, Chow   Ref: K Friend
Whitley Bay: Burke, Taylor, Picton, McFarlane (Fawcett 60), Coulson, Ryan, Moore, Robson, Kerr, Chow (Robinson 73), Johnston (Bell 60).
Subs not used: McLean and Reay.
Glossop North End: Cooper, Young, Kay, Lugsden, Yates, Gorton, Bailey (Hind 57), Morris, Allen (Balfe 65), Hamilton (Bailey 72), Hodges.
Subs not used: Whelan and Parker.

2010 WHITLEY BAY 6 *(Northern Division One)*   **WROXHAM 1** *(Eastern Counties Premier Division)*   Att: 8,920
Chow 21(sec), Easthaugh 16 (og), Kerr, Johnston, Cook 12   Ref: A Taylor
Robinson, Gillies
Whitley Bay: Terry Burke, Craig McFarlane, Callum Anderson, Richard Hodgson, (sub Lee Picton 69th min), Darren Timmons, Leon Ryan,
Adam Johnston (sub Joshua Gillies 77th min), Damon Robson, Lee Kerr, Paul Chow (sub Phillip Bell 61st min), Paul Robinson.
Subs not used – Tom Kindley and Chris Reid.
Wroxham: Scott Howie, Gavin Pauling (sub Ross Durrant 57th min), Shaun Howes, Graham Challen, Martin McNeil (sub Josh Carus 46th min), Andy
Easthaugh (sub Owen Paynter 69th min), Steve Spriggs, Gavin Lemmon, Paul Cook, Danny White, Gary Gilmore.
Subs not used – Danny Self and Gareth Simpson.

2011 WHITLEY BAY 3 *(Northern Division One)*   **COALVILLE TOWN 2** *(Midland Alliance)*   Att: 8,778
Chow 28, 90, Kerr 61   Moore 58, Goodby 80   Ref: S Mathieson
Whitley Bay: Terry Burke, Craig McFarlane (sub Steve Gibson 90th min), Callum Anderson, Darren Timmons, Gareth Williams (sub David Coulson 68th
min), Damon Robson, Lee Kerr, Paul Chow, Paul Robinson, David Pounder (sub Brian Smith 68th min), Gary Ormston.
Subs not used – Kyle Hayes (gk) and Brian Rowe. Coalville Town: Sean Bowles, Ashley Brown (sub Matthew Gardner 88th min), Cameron Stuart, Adam
Goodby, Zach Costello, Lee Miveld,
Callum Woodward, Anthony Carney (sub Craig Attwood 90th min), Ryan Robbins (sub Ashley Wells 66th min), Matt Moore, Jerome Murdock.
Subs not used – Richard Williams (gk) and James Dodd.

2012 DUNSTON UTS 2 *(Northern Division One)*   **WEST AUCKLAND TOWN 0** *(Northern Division One)*   Att: 5,126
Bulford 32, 79   Ref: R East
Dunston UTS: Liam Connell, Ben Cattenach, Terry Galbraith, Michael Robson, Chris Swailes, Kane Young, Steven Shaw, Michael Dixon,
Stephen Goddard (sub Sreven Preen 84th min), Andrew Bulford (sub Danny Craggs 88th min), Lee McAndrew.
Subs not used – Andrew Clark (g/k), Ian Herron, Jack Burns.
West Auckland Town: Mark Bell, Neil Pattinson, Andrew Green, Jonny Gibson, John Parker, Mark Stephenson (sub Daniel Hindmarsh 76th min),
Stuart Banks, Mark Hudson, Mattie Moffatt, Michael Rae, Adam Nicholls (sub Martin Young 60th min).
Subs not used – Daryll Hall, Ross Preston, Matthew Coad.

2013 SPENNYMOOR TOWN 2 *(Northern Division One)*   **TUNBRIDGE WELLS 1** *(Kent League)*   Att: 16,751
Cogdon 18, Graydon 80   Stanford 78   Ref: M Naylor
Spennymoor Town: Robert Dean, Kallum Griffiths, Leon Ryan, Chris Mason, Stephen Capper, Keith Graydon, Lewis Dodds, Wayne Phillips (Anthony Peacock
64 min), Joe Walton (Andrew Stephenson 73 min), Mark Davison, (Michael Rae 76 min), Gavin Congdon.
Subs not used - David Knight (g/k), Steven Richardson.
Tunbridge Wells: Chris Oladogba, Jason Bourne, Scott Whibley, Perry Spackman, Lewis Mingle, Jon Pilbeam (Richard Sinden 85 min), Andy McMath,
Joe Fuller (Tom Davey 58 min), Andy Irvine, Carl Connell (Jack Harris 58 min), Josh Stanford.
Subs not used - Michael Czanner (gk), Andy Boyle.

2014 SHOLING 1 *(Wessex Premier Division - 1st)*   **WEST AUCKLAND TOWN 0** *(Northern Division One - 5th)*   Att: 5,432
McLean 71   Ref: D Coote
Sholing: Matt Brown, Mike Carter, Marc Diaper, Peter Castle (Dan Miller 53 min), Lee Bright, Tyronne Bowers (Kevin Brewster 75 min), Barry Mason,
Lewis Fennemore (Alex Sawyer 78 min), Lee Wort, Byron Mason, Marvin McLean.
Subs not used - Ashley Jarvis, Nick Watts.
West Auckland Town: Jordan Nixon, Neil Pattinson, Andrew Green (Jonathan Gibson 63 min), Daryll Hall, Lewis Galpin, Brian Close,
Shaun Vipond (Stuart Banks 76 min), Robert Briggs, Mattie Moffat (Steven Richardson 74 min). John Campbell, Dennis Knight.
Subs not used - Paul Garthwaite, Adam Wilkinson..

2015 NORTH SHIELDS 2 *(Northern Division One - 4th)*   **GLOSSOP NORTH END 1** *(North West Co. Premier - 1st)*   Att: 9,674
Bainbridge 80, Forster 96   Bailey 55   Ref: A Madley
North Shields: Christopher Bannon, Stuart Donnison, John Parker, Kevin Hughes, John Grey, James Luccock (Ryan Carr 59), Ben Richardson,
Mciahel McKeown, Dean Holmes (Adam Forster 69), Denver Morris, Gareth Bainbridge (Kieran Wrightson 107).
Subs not used - Curtis Coppen and Marc Lancaster.
Glossop North End: Greg Hall, Michael Bowler, Matthew Russell, Kevin Lugsden, Dave Young, Martin Parker, Lee Blackshaw (Samuel Grimshaw 69),
Samuel Hare (Samuel Hind 82), Tom Bailey, Kieran Lugsden, Eddie Moran (Daniel White 60).
Subs not used - Benjamin Richardson and Richard Gresty.

2016   **MORPETH TOWN** 4 *(Northern Division One - 4th)*   HEREFORD 1 *(Midland League - 1st)*   **Att: 46,781**

Swailes 34, Carr 47, Taylor 59, Bell 92   Purdie 2   *(Inaugural Non-League finals day)*

Ref: S Atwelly

Morpeth Town: Karl Dryden, Stephen Forster, James Novak, Ben Sayer, Chris Swailes, Michael Hall, Sean Taylor (sub Damien Mullen 78), Keith Graydon, Luke Carr (sub Shaun Bell 88), Michael Chilton (sub Steven Anderson 69), Jordan Fry.

Subs not used - Dale Pearson and Niall Harrison.

Hereford: Martin Horsell, Jimmy Oates, Joel Edwards, Rob Purdie, Ryan Green, Aaron Birch, Pablo Haysham, Mike Symons, Jamie Willets (sub John Mills 70), Joe Tumelty (sub Mustapha Bundu 55), Sirdic Grant.

Subs not used - Nathan Summers, Dylan Bonella and Ross Staley.

All Finals at Wembley unless otherwise stated.

FIRST QUALIFYING ROUND 2017-18
SATURDAY 9 SEPTEMBER 2017

1	Stokesley SC	v	Hebburn Town
2	Chester-Le-Street Town	v	Silsden AFC
3	Sunderland Ryhope CW	v	Guisborough Town
4	Seaham Red Star	v	Albion Sports
5	Whickham	v	Newton Aycliffe
6	Padiham	v	Thackley
7	Garforth Town	v	Holker Old Boys
8	Blyth AFC	v	West Allotment Celtic
9	Esh Winning	v	Penrith AFC
10	Heaton Stannington	v	Carlisle City
11	Tow Law Town	v	Crook Town AFC
12	Brandon United	v	Bishop Auckland
13	Ashington	v	Easington Colliery AFC
14	Northallerton Town	v	Alnwick Town
15	Marske United	v	Ryton & Crawcrook Albion
16	Barnoldswick Town	v	Dunston UTS
17	Darlington Railway Athletic	v	Harrogate Railway Athletic
18	Eccleshill United	v	Jarrow Roofing Boldon CA
19	Campion AFC	v	Bedlington Terriers
20	Widnes	v	Glasshoughton Welfare
21	Alsager Town	v	New Mills
22	Vauxhall Motors	v	1874 Northwich
23	Maltby Main	v	Cammell Laird 1907
24	Northwich Victoria	v	Stockport Town
25	Hallam	v	Abbey Hey
26	St Helens Town	v	Hemsworth MW
27	Selby Town	v	Charnock Richard
28	Rossington Main	v	Cheadle Town
29	Barnton	v	Penistone Church
30	Maine Road	v	Pontefract Collieries
31	Prestwich Heys	v	Liversedge
32	Atherton LR	v	Irlam
33	Litherland Remyca	v	Ashton Town AFC
34	Parkgate	v	Daisy Hill
35	Worsbrough Bridge Athletic	v	Dronfield Town
36	AFC Liverpool	v	Athersley Recreation
37	AFC Blackpool	v	West Didsbury & Chorlton AFC
38	Squires Gate	v	Congleton Town
39	Cadbury Athletic	v	Littleton
40	Pegasus Juniors	v	Droitwich Spa
41	Lutterworth Athletic	v	AFC Wulfrunians
42	Boldmere St Michaels	v	Coventry Alvis
43	Coventry United	v	Tipton Town
44	Bewdley Town	v	Rugby Town
45	Heather St Johns	v	Coventry Sphinx
46	Barnt Green Spartak	v	Walsall Wood
47	Westfields	v	Stapenhill
48	Wellington Amateurs	v	Dudley Town
49	Hereford Lads Club	v	Stone Old Alleynians
50	Studley	v	Long Buckby
51	Leicester Road	v	Racing Club Warwick
52	Malvern Town	v	Smethwick
53	Chelmsley Town	v	AFC Bridgnorth
54	Uttoxeter Town	v	Gornal Athletic
55	Ellesmere Rangers	v	Highgate United
56	Nuneaton Griff	v	Rocester
57	Ashby Ivanhoe	v	St Martins
58	Paget Rangers	v	Wolverhampton Casuals
59	Hanley Town	v	Lichfield City
60	Ellistown & Ibstock United	v	Eccleshall
61	Wolverhampton SC	v	FC Oswestry Town
62	Shawbury United	v	Wellington
63	Whitchurch Alport	v	Pershore Town
64	Cradley Town	v	Bromyard Town
65	Bilston Town	v	Bolehall Swifts
66	Coton Green	v	Heath Hayes
67	Tividale	v	Brocton
68	Long Eaton United	v	Rainworth MW
69	Hall Road Rangers	v	Gedling MW
70	Quorn	v	Oadby Town
71	Clifton All Whites	v	Harrowby United
72	Friar Lane & Epworth	v	Lutterworth Town
73	Kimberley MW	v	Barrow Town
74	South Normanton	v	Melton Town
75	Radcliffe Olympic	v	Belper United
76	Kirby Muxloe	v	Anstey Nomads
78	Leicester Nirvana	v	Graham St Prims
79	Loughborough University	v	Winterton Rangers
80	Worksop Town	v	Aylestone Park
81	Grimsby Borough	v	Shirebrook Town
82	Hucknall Town AFC	v	Clay Cross Town
83	Heanor Town	v	Holbrook Sports
84	Bottesford Town	v	West Bridgford
86	Birstall United	v	South Normanton Athletic
87	Skegness Town	v	Sleaford Town
88	Westella & Willerby	v	Arnold Town
89	Blaby & Whetstone Athletic	v	Blidworth Welfare
90	Raunds Town	v	Wellingborough Town
91	Stewarts & Lloyds AFC	v	Swaffham Town
92	Fakenham Town	v	Huntingdon Town
93	Downham Town	v	Biggleswade United
94	Histon	v	Blackstones
95	Potton United	v	Netherton United
96	Pinchbeck United	v	Holbeach United
97	Bourne Town	v	Harborough Town
98	March Town United	v	Peterborough Northern Star
99	Cogenhoe United	v	Rothwell Corinthians
100	Stansted	v	Wodson Park
101	Basildon United	v	St Margaretsbury
102	Barkingside	v	Southend Manor
103	Framlingham Town	v	Waltham Forest
104	Brimsdown	v	Debenham LC
105	FC Clacton	v	Coggeshall Town
106	Hadleigh United	v	Wadham Lodge
107	Ilford	v	Cornard United
108	Redbridge	v	Brantham Athletic
109	Enfield 1893	v	Haverhill Borough
110	Norwich CBS	v	Ipswich Wanderers
111	Saffron Walden Town	v	Sawbridgeworth Town
112	Enfield Borough	v	Canning Town
113	Tower Hamlets	v	Hackney Wick
114	Woodbridge Town	v	Hoddesdon Town
115	Stowmarket Town	v	Team Bury
116	Long Melford	v	Halstead Town
117	Great Yarmouth Town	v	FC Broxbourne Borough
118	Haverhill Rovers	v	Whitton United
119	Wivenhoe Town	v	Holland
120	Great Wakering Rovers	v	Sporting Bengal United
121	Wootton Blue Cross	v	London Lions
122	Welwyn Garden City	v	Brackley Town Saints
123	AFC Hayes	v	Hatfield Town
124	Hillingdon Borough	v	Marston Shelton Rovers
125	Malmesbury Victoria	v	Chipping Sodbury Town
126	New College Swindon	v	Ampthill Town
127	Baldock Town	v	Buckingham Town
128	North Greenford United	v	Harpenden Town
129	Oxford City Nomads	v	Woodley United
130	Royal Wootton Bassett Town	v	Fairford Town
131	Clanfield 85	v	Holmer Green
132	Colney Heath	v	Harefield United

133	Abingdon United	v	Highmoor Ibis
134	Hadley	v	Milton United
135	Edgware Town	v	Risborough Rangers
136	Cricklewood Wanderers	v	Stotfold
137	Crawley Green	v	Tuffley Rovers
138	Highworth Town	v	Easington Sports
139	Leighton Town	v	Brimscombe & Thrupp
140	Ardley United	v	Longlevens AFC
141	Lydney Town	v	Winslow United
142	Buckingham Athletic	v	Bedford
143	Broadfields United	v	Pitshanger Dynamo
144	Amersham Town	v	Langford
145	Rochester United	v	Lancing
146	Southwick	v	Broadbridge Heath
147	Hollands & Blair	v	Tooting & Mitcham Wanderers
148	AFC Croydon Athletic	v	Bearsted
149	Eastbourne United	v	Newhaven
150	Ringmer	v	AC London
151	Erith & Belvedere	v	Holmesdale
152	Glebe	v	Deal Town
153	East Preston	v	Forest Hill Park
154	Sheppey United	v	Loxwood
155	Oakwood	v	Langney Wanderers
156	FC Elmstead	v	Whitstable Town
157	Hailsham Town	v	Abbey Rangers
158	Banstead Athletic	v	Fisher
159	Westside	v	Steyning Town
160	Snodland Town	v	Horsham YMCA
161	Chessington & Hook United	v	Lydd Town
162	Worthing United	v	Horley Town
163	Colliers Wood United	v	K Sports
164	Bridon Ropes	v	Wick
165	FC Deportivo Galicia	v	Lewisham Borough (Community)
166	Walton & Hersham	v	Little Common
168	CB Hounslow United	v	Peacehaven & Telscombe
169	St Francis Rangers	v	Erith Town
170	Seaford Town	v	Saltdean United
171	Mile Oak	v	Chertsey Town
172	Arundel	v	Lordswood
173	Canterbury City	v	Sutton Common Rovers
174	Stansfeld	v	Bedfont & Feltham
175	Gravesham Borough	v	Cobham
176	Tooting Bec	v	Littlehampton Town

177	AFC Uckfield Town	v	Raynes Park Vale
178	Redhill	v	Chatham Town
179	Beckenham Town	v	Lingfield
180	Bedfont Sports	v	Three Bridges
181	Tadley Calleva	v	Andover New Street
182	Shaftesbury	v	Brockenhurst
183	Horndean	v	Andover Town
184	Windsor	v	Devizes Town
185	Hamble Club	v	Bemerton Heath Harlequins
186	Ascot United	v	Farnham Town
187	Hamworthy United	v	AFC Stoneham
188	Amesbury Town	v	New Milton Town
189	East Cowes Victoria Athletic	v	Calne Town
190	AFC Aldermaston	v	Romsey Town
191	Petersfield Town	v	Corsham Town
192	Swanage Town & Herston	v	Ash United
193	Cove	v	Westbury United
194	Warminster Town	v	Folland Sports
195	Knaphill	v	Sidlesham
196	Pewsey Vale	v	Chippenham Park
197	Newport (IW)	v	Fleet Spurs
198	Guildford City	v	Lymington Town
199	United Services Portsmouth	v	Verwood Town
200	Ringwood Town	v	Eversley & California
201	Laverstock & Ford	v	Fawley
202	Cowes Sports	v	Baffins Milton Rovers
203	Hythe & Dibden	v	Bagshot
204	Camelford	v	Helston Athletic
205	Cullompton Rangers	v	Torpoint Athletic
206	Wellington AFC	v	Wells City
207	Cheddar	v	Radstock Town
208	Bovey Tracey	v	Keynsham Town
209	Witheridge AFC	v	Cribbs
210	Plymouth Parkway	v	Sherborne Town
211	Axminster Town	v	Crediton United
212	Tavistock AFC	v	Hallen
213	Almondsbury UWE	v	Clevedon Town
214	Bitton AFC	v	Brislington
215	Welton Rovers	v	Willand Rovers
216	Bridport	v	Wincanton Town
217	AFC St Austell	v	Bishops Lydeard
218	Cadbury Heath	v	St Blazey
219	Roman Glass St George	v	Elburton Villa
220	Ashton & Backwell United	v	Godolphin Atlantic

SECOND QUALIFYING ROUND 2017-18
SATURDAY 23 SEPTEMBER 2017

1	Sunderland Ryhope CW / Guisborough	v	N'thallertn / Alnwick Town
2	Team Northumbria	v	Durham City
3	Stockton Town	v	Consett AFC
4	Garforth / Holker OB	v	Nelson
5	Stokesley / Hebburn T	v	Newcastle Benfield
6	Billingham Synthonia	v	Whitley Bay
7	Willington	v	Darl'ton RA / Harrogate R
8	Tow Law / Crook Town	v	Esh Winning / Penrith AFC
9	Heaton Stannington / Carlisle City	v	Thornaby
10	Marske / Ryton & CA	v	Seaham RS / Albion Sports
11	Whickham / Newton A	v	Blyth AFC / West Allot C
12	West Auckland Town	v	Chester-L-S / Silsden AFC
13	Padiham / Thackley	v	Ashington / Easington Colliery AFC
14	Barn'wick / Dunston UTS	v	Washington
15	Eccleshill / Jarr RBCA	v	Knaresborough Town
16	Campion AFC / Bedlington	v	Brandon / Bishop Auck
17	Rossington / Cheadle	v	Hallam / Abbey Hey
18	Litherland Remyca / Ashton T	v	Chadderton
19	Atherton LR / Irlam	v	Parkgate / Daisy Hill
20	Winsford United	v	Maine Road / Pontefract
21	Alsager / New Mills	v	Nostell MW
22	Vauxhall M / 1874 Northwich	v	Squires G / Congleton
23	AFC L'pool / Athersley Recreation	v	City of Liverpool
24	Sandbach United	v	AFC Emley
25	Ashton Athletic	v	Maltby Main / Cammell Laird 1907
26	Selby Town / Charnock Richard	v	Bacup Borough
27	Burscough	v	Armthorpe Welfare
28	AFC B'pool / West Didsbury & Chorlton AFC	v	Northwich / Stockport Town
29	Widnes / Glasshoughton	v	AFC Darwen
30	Worsbrough Bridge Athletic / Dronfield Town	v	Barnton / Penistone Church

31	St Helens T / Hemsworth	v	Prestwich Heys / Liversedge
32	Ellesmere / Highgate U	v	Whitchurch Alport / Pershore T
33	Bilston Town / Bolehall Swifts	v	Haughmond
34	Wellington Amateurs / Dudley Town	v	Atherstone Town
35	Shawbury U / Wellington	v	Cadbury Ath / Littleton
36	Chelmsley Town / AFC Bridgnorth	v	Lutterworth Athletic / AFC Wulf's
37	Dudley Sports	v	Tividale / Brocton
38	Shifnal Town	v	Pegasus J / Droitwich Spa
39	Cradley / Bromyard Town	v	Barnt Green Spartak / Walsall W
40	Ibstock U / Eccleshall	v	Wednesfield
41	Heather St Johns / Coventry S	v	Nuneaton G / Rocester
42	Westfields / Stapenhill	v	Daventry Town
43	Stourport Swifts	v	Paget Rangers / Wolv Cas
44	Malvern / Smethwick	v	Bewdley / Rugby Town
45	Stafford Town	v	Ashby Ivanhoe / St Martins
46	Studley / Long Buckby	v	Hanley Town / Lichfield City
47	Boldmere / Coventry Alvis	v	Worcester City
48	Leicester Road / RC Warwick	v	Coventry Copsewood
49	Coton Green / Heath Hayes	v	Wolv SC / Oswestry Town
50	Uttoxeter Town / Gornal Ath	v	Bardon Hill
51	Coventry United / Tipton Town	v	Hereford Lads Club / Stone Old Alleynians
52	Barton Town Old Boys	v	Clipstone
53	Retford United	v	Pinxton
54	Westella & Willerby / Arnold Town	v	Ollerton Town
55	Thurn Nirv / Gra St Prim	v	Radcliffe O / Belper United
56	Friar Lane / Lutterworth Town	v	Teversal
57	Grimsby B / Shirebrook	v	L Eaton U / Rainworth
58	Hall Rd'Ran / Gedling MW	v	Skegness Town / Sleaford
59	Hucknall T / Clay Cross Town	v	Eastwood Community
60	Holwell Sports	v	Dunkirk

61	South Normanton / Melton Town v	FC Bolsover
62	Heanor Town / Holbrook S	Quorn / Oadby Town
63	Blaby & Whetstone Athletic / Blidworth Welfare v	Bottesford / West Bridgford
64	Loughboro U / Winterton	Staveley MW
65	Worksop / Aylestone Park	Kirby Mux / Anstey N
66	Boston Town	Birstall United / South Normanton Ath
67	Sandiacre Town	Sherwood Colliery
68	Clifton All Whites / Harrowby United v	St Andrews
69	Radford	Kimberley MW / Barrow Town
70	Godmanchester Rovers	Raunds Town / W'Boro Twn
71	Northampton On Chenecks	Irchester United
72	Stew Llyd / Swaffham	Rushden & Higham United
73	Biggleswade	Northampton Sileby Rangers
74	Histon / Blackstones	Cogenhoe / Rothwell C
75	Potton U / Netherton United	March / Peterborough Northern Star
76	Bourne Town / Harborough Town v	Wisbech Town
77	Eynesbury Rovers	Burton Park Wanderers
78	Downham Town / Bigg'wade U	Thrapston Town
79	Pinchbeck United / Holbeach U v	Fakenham / Huntingdon T
80	Thetford Town	Oakham United
81	Wellingborough Whitworths	Wisbech St Mary
82	Redbridge / Brantham	FC Clacton / Coggeshall Town
83	Bethnal Grn / Hackney Wick	Little Oakley
84	Enfield Borough / Canning Townv	Woodbridge / Hoddesdon
85	Wroxham	Norwich CBS / Ipswich W
86	Basildon / St Marg	Walsham Le Willows
87	Barkingside / Southend M	Haverhill R / Whitton
88	L Melford / Halstead T	Stanway Rovers
89	West Essex	Gt Wakering / S Bengal U
90	Diss Town	Framlingham Town / Waltham F
91	Ilford / Cornard United	Hullbridge Sports
92	Kirkley & Pakefield	Burnham Ramblers
93	Gt Yarmouth / Broxbourne Borough v	Brimsdown / Debenham LC
94	Stansted / Wodson Park	Wivenhoe / Holland
95	Stowmarket / Team Bury	Enf'ld 1893 / Haverhill Borough
96	Hadleigh U / Wadham Lodge	Saff Wald / Sawbridgewth
97	Buckingham Athletic / Bedford v	AFC Hayes / Hatfield T
98	New College Swindon / Ampthillv	Clanfield / Holmer Grn
99	Highworth T / Easington Sports v	Burnham
100	Abingdon U / Highmoor Ibis	Welwyn GC / Brackley Town Saints
101	Broadfields United / Pitshanger Dynamo v	Holyport
102	Wantage Town	Lydney Town / Winslow United
103	Cricklewood Wanderers / Stotfold v	Rayners Lane
104	Hadley / Milton	Colney Hth / Harefield U
105	Hillngdon B / Marston Shelton Rovers v	N Greenford / Harpenden Town
106	Wallingford Town AFC	Oxhey Jets
107	Tytherington Rocks	Ardley Utd / Longlevens AFC
108	Oxford City Nomads / Woodley United v	Baldock Town / Buckingham Town
109	Wootton Bass / Fairford	Codicote
110	Wootton Blue / London Lions	Malmesbury Victoria / Chipping Sodbury Town
111	Amersham Town / Langford	Crawley Grn / Tuffley Rovers
112	Edgware Town / Risborough Rangers v	Henley Town
113	Leighton T / Brimscombe & Thrupp v	Leverstock Green
114	FC Elmstead / Whitstable	Rochester United / Lancing
115	Gravesham Borough / Cobham v	Bexhill United
116	Ringmer / AC London	Worthing United / Horley Town

117	Rusthall	Crawley Down Gatwick
118	Hassocks	Spelthorne Sports
119	Seaford Town / Saltdean United v	Stansfeld / Bedfont & Feltham
120	Balham	E Preston / Forest Hill Park
121	Snodland Town / Horsh YMCA	Oakwood / Langney Wanderers
122	Southwick / Broadbridge Heath v	AFC Croydon Athletic / Bearsted
123	Billingshurst	Arundel / Lordswood
124	Westside / Steyning Town	Bedfont Sp / Three Bdges
125	Sporting Club Thamesmead	Walt Hers / Little Common
126	Meridian VP	FC Deportivo Galicia / Lewisham Borough (Community)
127	Beckenham / Lingfield	Bridon Ropes / Wick
128	Erith & Bel / Holmesdale	Chessington / Lydd Town
129	Colliers W'd / K Sports	Hailsham T / Abbey Rangers
130	Redhill / Chatham	Kensington Borough
131	Tooting Bec / Littlehampton	Banstead / Fisher
132	Eastbourne United / Newhaven v	Hollands & Blair / Tooting & Mitcham Wanderers
133	Glebe / Deal Town	CB Hounslow United / P'Hav & Tel
134	St Francis / Erith Town	Mile Oak / Chertsey
135	Sheppey United / Loxwood	Tunbridge Wells
136	Canterbury City / Mole V	AFC U'field / Raynes Park
137	Newport IW / Fleet Spurs	Alresford Town
138	Badshot Lea	Frimley Green
139	AFC Aldermaston / Romsey Town v	Bournemouth
140	AFC Portchester	Tadley Calleva / Andover NS
141	Knaphill / Sidlesham	Horndean / Andover Town
142	Fareham Town	Binfield
143	Godalming Town	Shaftesbury / Brock'hurst
144	Alton Town	Amesbury Town / New Milt
145	Cowes / Baffins Milton Rovers	Selsey
146	Hamworthy / AFC Stoneham	Guildford C / Lymington
147	East Cowes Victoria Athletic / Calne Town v	Downton
148	Sandhurst Town	Ringwood / Eversley & California
149	Warminster Town / Folland Sports v	Ascot Utd / Farnham
150	Midhurst & Easebourne	United Services Portsmouth / Verwood
151	Swanage Town & Herston / Ash United v	Laverstock & Ford / Fawley
152	Windsor / Devizes	Whitchurch United
153	Cove / Westbury U	Christchurch
154	Bashley	Hythe & Dibden / Bagshot
155	Pewsey Vale / Chippenham Park v	Camberley Town
156	Hamble Club / Bemerton	Petersfield / Corsham
157	Welton / Willand	Saltash United
158	Odd Down	Oldland Abbotonians
159	Cheddar / Radstock T	Roman Glass St George / Elburton Villa
160	Hengrove Athletic	Ashton & Backwell United / Godolphin Atlantic
161	Cadbury H / St Blazey	Shepton Mallet AFC
162	Almondsbury / Clevedon	Wellington / Wells City
163	Bovey Tracey / Keynsham Town v	Bishop Sutton
164	AFC St Austell / Bishops Lydeard v	Bridgwater Town
165	Bridport / Wincanton Town	Plymouth Parkway / Sherborne
166	Tavistock / Hallen	Camelford / Helston Athletic
167	Cullompton / Torpoint	Witheridge / Cribbs
168	Portishead Town	Bodmin Town
169	Longwell Green Sports	Ivybridge Town
170	Axminster Town / Crediton United v	Bitton AFC / Brislington

THE FA YOUTH CUP

PRELIMINARY ROUND

1	Chester-Le-Street	v	Darlington 1883 (8/9)	2-5
2	Newcastle Benfield	v	Spennymoor Town (5/9)	3-2
3	Blyth Spartans	v	Hebburn Town (8/9)	5-3 302
4	Workington AFC	v	Ryton & Crawcrook Albion (8/9)0-4 44	
5	Skelmersdale United	v	Hyde United (7/9)	0-4
6	FC United of Manchester	v	Curzon Ashton (5/9)	3-0 391
7	AFC Blackpool	v	St Helens Town (8/9)	3-4 55
8	Prescot Cables	v	Clitheroe (8/9)	1-2 142
9	Altrincham	v	Stockport County (9/9)	3-2 203
10	Irlam	v	Radcliffe Borough (8/9)	6-0 68
11	Vauxhall Motors	v	Warrington Town (6/9)	2-1 77
12	Nelson	v	Lancaster City	

(walkover for Nelson – Lancaster City withdrawn)

13	Abbey Hey	v	Witton Albion (8/9)	3-1
14	Bootle	v	West Didsbury & Chorlton AFC	

(walkover for West Didsbury & Chorlton – Bootle withdrawn)

15	Burscough	v	Ashton Athletic (30/8)	1-4 45
16	Mossley AFC	v	Colne (8/9)	0-3 45
17	Sheffield	v	Maltby Main (7/9)	3-0 114
18	Harrogate Railway Athletic	v	Hemsworth MW (8/9)	3-1 33
19	Tadcaster Albion	v	Brighouse Town (5/9)	4-1 88
20	FC Halifax Town	v	Staveley MW (7/9)	4-0 145
21	Farsley Celtic	v	Goole AFC (8/9)	3-2
22	Ossett Town	v	Worksop Town (8/9)	5-7 53
23	Garforth Town	v	Silsden AFC (7/9)	3-2 64
24	Pontefract Collieries	v	Ossett Albion (5/9)	4-2 80
25	Hall Road Rangers	v	Selby Town (8/9)	7-4 57
26	AFC Emley	v	Stocksbridge Park Steels (5/9)1-2 93	
27	Kimberley MW	v	Bourne Town (7/9)	3-0 68
28	Leicester Nirvana	v	Lutterworth Athletic (7/9)	3-2
29	Stamford AFC	v	Ashby Ivanhoe (5/9)	1-2
30	Anstey Nomads	v	Loughborough Dynamo	

(walkover for Loughborough Dynamo – Anstey Nomads withdrawn)

31	Boston United	v	Lincoln United (7/9)	5-0 131
32	Grantham Town	v	Bottesford Town (8/9)	1-2 90
33	Leicester Road	v	Mickleover Sports (7/9)	3-0 45
34	Matlock Town	v	Dunkirk (8/9)	0-7
35	Alfreton Town	v	Aylestone Park (7/9)	3-2 79
36	Gresley	v	St Andrews (7/9)	0-3
37	Tamworth	v	Hednesford Town (9/9)	5-3aet 292
38	Wolverhampton Casuals	v	Highgate United (6/9)	3-0 63
39	Nuneaton Griff	v	Kidsgrove Athletic (7/9)	1-2 91
40	Hereford	v	Malvern Town (5/9)	8-0
41	Alvechurch	v	Sutton Coldfield Town (6/9)	7-1 58
42	Stourbridge	v	Redditch United (6/9)	3-1 65
43	Halesowen Town	v	Coton Green (7/9)	2-1 62
44	Ellesmere Rangers	v	Rugby Town (8/9)	4-2
45	Racing Club Warwick	v	Romulus (7/9)	1-10 85
46	Dudley Town	v	Nuneaton Town (5/9)	2-5 40
47	Leamington	v	Paget Rangers	

(walkover for Leamington – Paget Rangers withdrawn)

48	Coleshill Town	v	Dudley Sports (5/9)	2-0 44
49	Stratford Town	v	Bromsgrove Sporting (8/9)	1-2aet 56
50	Newcastle Town	v	Bilston Town (7/9)	6-0 96
51	St Ives Town	v	St Neots Town (5/9)	2-0 88

(at Huntingdon Town FC)

52	Desborough Town	v	Eynesbury Rovers (5/9)	4-1
53	Godmanchester Rovers	v	Northampton On Chenecks (6/9)1-3 39	
54	Corby Town	v	Brackley Town (8/9)	7-2 54
55	Kempston Rovers	v	Rothwell Corinthians (8/9)	3-0 73
56	Wellingborough Town	v	AFC Rushden & Diamonds (5/9)1-5 115	
57	Cogenhoe United	v	Rushden & Higham United (8/9)0-2	
58	Peterborough Sports	v	Peterborough Northern Star (7/9)1-2	
59	Wroxham	v	Felixstowe & Walton United (8/9)4-1	
60	Needham Market	v	Great Yarmouth Town (8/9)4-1aet 45	
61	Leiston	v	Hadleigh United (7/9)	5-3 32
62	Mildenhall Town	v	Woodbridge Town (7/9)	0-4 63
63	Fakenham Town	v	Newmarket Town (5/9)	3-5 72
64	Cornard United	v	Wisbech St Mary (8/9)	3-2
65	Cambridge City	v	King's Lynn Town (8/9)	2-1 74

(at Huntingdon Town FC)

66	Bury Town	v	Brantham Athletic (8/9)	1-1aet 58

(Bury Town won 5-4 on kicks from the penalty mark)

67	Dereham Town	v	Ely City (8/9)	1-2 61
68	Stowmarket Town	v	AFC Sudbury (8/9)	0-8 36

69	Swaffham Town	v	Walsham Le Willows (8/9)	1-5 53
70	Gorleston	v	Lowestoft Town	

(walkover for Gorleston – Lowestoft Town withdrawn)

71	Chelmsford City	v	Waltham Abbey (7/9)	2-1 64
72	Ilford	v	Clapton	

(walkover for Ilford – Clapton withdrawn)

73	Hullbridge Sports	v	AFC Hornchurch (8/9)	3-4 26
74	Heybridge Swifts	v	Brentwood Town (6/9)	2-4 51
75	Great Wakering Rovers	v	St Margaretsbury (8/9)	2-1 55
76	Saffron Walden Town	v	Barking (8/9)	2-1 81
77	Woodford Town	v	Bishop's Stortford	

(walkover for Bishop's Stortford – Woodford Town not accepted into the Competition)

78	Thurrock	v	Royston Town (8/9)	3-1
79	Ware	v	Brightlingsea Regent (8/9)	6-2
80	Aveley	v	Redbridge (8/9)	4-1 48
81	North Greenford United	v	Hatfield Town (8/9)	4-0 34
82	Hendon	v	Tring Athletic (7/9)	3-6 33
83	Potters Bar Town	v	Ashford Town (Middx) (8/9)	5-2 46
84	Bedfont Sports	v	Harrow Borough (5/9)	5-1 41
85	Colney Heath	v	Hitchin Town (8/9)	1-4 39
86	Spelthorne Sports	v	Hadley Wood & Wingate (7/9) 3-1	
87	Beaconsfield SYCOB	v	Staines Town (12/9)	3-1 48
88	Buckingham Athletic	v	Harefield United (8/9)	4-3 55
89	Hemel Hempstead Town	v	Uxbridge (8/9)	1-2
90	Chesham United	v	Sun Sports (8/9)	5-0 56
91	Hanwell Town	v	Welwyn Garden City	

(walkover for Hanwell Town – Welwyn Garden City withdrawn)

92	St Albans City	v	Hayes & Yeading United (8/9) 4-2	
93	Sporting Club Thamesmead	v	Croydon	

(walkover for Sporting Club Thamesmead – Croydon withdrawn)

94	Eastbourne Borough	v	Margate (9/9)	4-1 188
95	Bridon Ropes	v	Chipstead (8/9)	1-0 65
96	Tonbridge Angels	v	Whitstable Town	

(walkover for Tonbridge Angels – Whitstable Town withdrawn)

97	East Grinstead Town	v	Greenwich Borough (8/9)	1-3 24
98	Lewisham Borough (Community)	v	VCD Athletic	

(walkover for VCD Athletic – Lewisham Borough (Community) not accepted into the Competition)

99	Meridian VP	v	Faversham Town (7/9)	4-1 60
100	Thamesmead Town	v	Folkestone Invicta (5/9)	3-4 49
101	Eastbourne Town	v	Ebbsfleet United (8/9)	0-2
102	Dulwich Hamlet	v	Phoenix Sports (5/9)	1-2 118
103	Erith & Belvedere	v	Ramsgate	

(walkover for Ramsgate – Erith & Belvedere withdrawn)

104	AFC Croydon Athletic	v	Lordswood (8/9)	0-0aet 37

(Lordswood won 3-2 on kicks from the penalty mark)

105	Ashford United	v	Glebe (15/9)	1-0 33

(8/9 – tie abandoned after 7 mins due to floodlight failure, 0-0)

106	Carshalton Athletic	v	Dartford (9/9)	2-3
107	Chessington & Hook United	v	Mile Oak (5/9)	2-2aet

(Mile Oak won 5-4 on kicks from the penalty mark)

108	Pagham	v	Leatherhead (7/9)	3-4
109	Corinthian Casuals	v	Haywards Heath Town (7/9)	1-4 91
110	Worthing	v	Dorking (6/9)	7-0
111	Dorking Wanderers	v	Guildford City (8/9)	3-2aet
112	Whitehawk	v	Burgess Hill Town (5/9)	2-1 58
113	Metropolitan Police	v	Three Bridges (8/9)	3-1
114	Camberley Town	v	Lancing	

(walkover for Camberley Town – Lancing withdrawn)

115	Bognor Regis Town	v	Knaphill	

(walkover for Knaphill – Bognor Regis Town withdrawn)

116	Lewes	v	South Park (8/9)	2-1
117	Chertsey Town	v	Redhill (5/9)	10-0 49
118	Shoreham	v	Westfield (8/9)	2-3 30
119	Wick	v	Walton & Hersham	

(walkover for Wick – Walton & Hersham withdrawn)

120	Steyning Town	v	Arundel (7/9)	3-1 56

(at Lancing FC, Sussex FA County Ground)

121	Crawley Down Gatwick	v	Newhaven (4/9)	2-6 45
122	Ascot United	v	Carterton (8/9)	3-0 44
123	Hungerford Town	v	Kidlington (7/9)	5-2 59
124	Wantage Town	v	Thatcham Town (8/9)	4-3
125	Slough Town	v	Andover Town (6/9)	0-6
126	Didcot Town	v	Shrivenham (8/9)	3-2
127	Farnborough	v	Oxford City (7/9)	0-3 157
128	Fleet Town	v	Burnham	

(walkover for Burnham – Fleet Town withdrawn)

129 Thame United v Windsor (8/9) 0-2 25
130 Alton Town v Highmoor Ibis (5/9) 3-3aet 40
(Alton Town won 6-5 on kicks from the penalty mark)
131 Maidenhead United v Binfield (7/9) 2-1 76
132 Holmer Green v Marlow (8/9) 1-6 50
133 Salisbury v Wimborne Town (6/9) 4-2 104
134 Winchester City v Moneyfields (8/9) 5-3 21
135 Tadley Calleva v Hamworthy United (8/9) 1-5
136 Christchurch v Sholing (8/9) 1-2 101
137 Havant & Waterlooville v AFC Stoneham (8/9) 3-0 97
138 Yate Town v New College Swindon (7/9) 3-2 54
139 Cirencester Town v Oldland Abbotonians (8/9) 4-2 39
140 Chippenham Town v Bristol Manor Farm (7/9) 4-2aet 62
141 Bishop Sutton v Portishead Town (8/9) 1-0 45
142 Clevedon Town v Weston Super Mare (5/9) 2-4 73
143 Bridgwater Town v Paulton Rovers (8/9) 1-4 48
144 Odd Down v Bath City (8/9) 0-1 70
145 Radstock Town v Brislington (8/9) 6-2aet 57

FIRST ROUND QUALIFYING

1 Blyth Spartans v Durham City (22/9) 1-8 329
2 Shildon v Darlington 1883 (19/9) 1-2
3 South Shields v Newcastle Benfield (19/9) 1-2aet 50
4 Ryton & Crawcrook Albion v Kendal Town
(walkover for Ryton & Crawcrook Albion - Kendal Town withdrawn)
5 Vauxhall Motors v Altrincham 1-4 103
6 St Helens Town v Chadderton (21/9) 2-1
(at Chadderton FC)
7 Marine v Abbey Hey (22/9) 4-1 117
8 Ashton Athletic v Colne (20/9) 6-1 51
9 Clitheroe v Chorley (21/9) 1-0
10 Stalybridge Celtic v AFC Fylde (22/9) 0-5 35
(at Mossley FC)
11 West Didsbury & Chorlton AFC v Nantwich Town (20/9) 3-2
12 Ashton Town v FC United of Manchester (22/9) 2-4 125
13 AFC Darwen v Irlam (25/9) 2-2aet
(Irlam won 4-2 on kicks from the penalty mark)
14 Hyde United v Nelson (23/9) 1-0aet 87
15 Farsley Celtic v Nostell MW (21/9) 2-3 68
16 Rossington Main v Garforth Town (22/9) 0-3
17 Handsworth Parramore v Cleethorpes Town (19/9) 4-0 78
18 FC Halifax Town v Stocksbridge Park Steels (20/9)1-0 159
19 Worksop Town v Sheffield (22/9) 2-4 159
20 Harrogate Railway Athletic v Hall Road Rangers (22/9) 0-1 44
21 Barton Town Old Boys v Harrogate Town (22/9) 6-1 80
22 Pontefract Collieries v Tadcaster Albion (19/9) 3-2 107
23 Belper Town v Basford United (21/9) 4-3
24 Boston United v Leicester Nirvana (21/9) 1-0 87
25 St Andrews v Bottesford Town (22/9) 0-5 35
(at Quorn FC)
26 Kimberley MW v Leicester Road (21/9) 2-1 58
27 Ilkeston v Dunkirk (22/9) 1-3 119
28 Loughborough Dynamo v New Mills (22/9) 6-2
29 Ashby Ivanhoe v Alfreton Town (21/9) 1-6 110
30 Boldmere St Michaels v AFC Telford United (21/9) 4-5 78
(at Chasetown FC)
31 Kidderminster Harriers v Kidsgrove Athletic (22/9) 4-0
32 Romulus v Leamington (21/9) 8-0
33 Coleshill Town v Alvechurch (20/9) 5-3 33
34 Stourbridge v Newcastle Town (20/9) 0-1 85
35 Rushall Olympic v Leek Town (19/9) 6-0
36 Ellesmere Rangers v Worcester City
(walkover for Ellemere Rangers – Worcester City withdrawn)
37 Bromsgrove Sporting v Halesowen Town (21/9) 2-0 127
38 Nuneaton Town v Lye Town (19/9) 4-3aet 40
39 Evesham United v Hereford (19/9) 0-2 120
40 Pegasus Juniors v Bedworth United (22/9) 2-3aet 32
41 Tamworth v Wolverhampton Casuals (19/9)3-5 131
42 Peterborough Northern Star v Biggleswade Town (23/9) 1-2
43 Desborough Town v AFC Rushden & Diamonds (19/9) 0-3 82
44 Kempston Rovers v Kettering Town (22/9) 0-7 72
45 Northampton On Chenecksv v AFC Dunstable (22/9) 1-2aet
46 Yaxley v Rushden & Higham United (20/9) 4-5 43
47 St Ives Town v Corby Town (19/9) 3-2 56
(at Huntingdon Town FC)
48 Framlingham Town v Histon (22/9) 7-3

49 Cambridge City v Ely City (21/9) 0-1 87
(at Huntingdon Town FC)
50 Bury Town v Norwich United (21/9) 4-1 47
51 Wroxham v Gorleston (21/9) 1-2 47
52 Newmarket Town v AFC Sudbury (20/9) 1-9 73
53 Needham Market v Haverhill Rovers (22/9) 12-1 42
54 Woodbridge Town v Cornard United (22/9) 10-0 55
55 Leiston v Walsham Le Willows (22/9) 2-1 45
56 Whitton United v Ipswich Wanderers (22/9) 5-3
57 Bishop's Stortford v Great Wakering Rovers (21/9)3-2 121
58 AFC Hornchurch v Tower Hamlets (22/9) 3-1 44
59 Sawbridgeworth Town v Ware (22/9) 1-7
60 Barkingside v Concord Rangers (14/9) 3-4aet 48
61 Brentwood Town v Cheshunt (20/9) 2-5 68
62 Tilbury v Waltham Forest (22/9) 9-1 54
63 Aveley v Halstead Town (22/9) 4-1 38
64 FC Broxbourne Borough v Ilford (22/9) 2-1 15
65 Wadham Lodge v Saffron Walden Town (19/9)4-2aet
66 Chelmsford City v Thurrock (21/9) 2-1 99
67 CB Hounslow United v Beaconsfield SYCOB (19/9) 1-3
68 Spelthorne Sports v Potters Bar Town (21/9) 1-2 50
69 Uxbridge v Flackwell Heath (19/9) 6-2 127
70 Hanwell Town v Northwood (20/9) 5-1
71 Bedfont Sports v Chesham United (19/9) 3-2aet
72 Chalfont St Peter v Wealdstone (20/9) 0-1 73
73 Leverstock Green v Cockfosters (22/9) 1-6 47
74 North Greenford United v London Tigers (20/9) 10-1 25
75 Edgware Town v Hitchin Town (21/9) 2-2aet
(Hitchin Town won 3-0 on kicks from the penalty mark)
76 St Albans City v Tring Athletic (22/9) 4-2
77 Wingate & Finchley v Buckingham Athletic (22/9) 5-3aet
78 Lingfield v Meridian VP (21/9) 1-3
79 VCD Athletic v Bridon Ropes
(walkover for Bridon Ropes – VCD Athletic withdrawn)
80 Ebbsfleet United v Dartford (21/9) 1-0 181
81 Ramsgate v Hastings United (29/9) 0-4
(at Hastings United FC) (22/9 - tie abandoned after 105 mins due to floodlight failure, 2-1)
82 Tonbridge Angels v Phoenix Sports (19/9) 4-0
83 Ashford United v Little Common (22/9) 9-0
84 Corinthian v Cray Wanderers (21/9) 13-1 66
85 Sporting Club Thamesmead v Sevenoaks Town (22/9) 2-0 68
86 Tooting & Mitcham United v Greenwich Borough (19/9) 0-2 29
87 Lordswood v Eastbourne Borough (20/9)0-0aet
(Lordswood won 11-10 on kicks from the penalty mark)
88 Welling United v Folkestone Invicta (22/9) 1-3 121
89 Metropolitan Police v Dorking Wanderers (22/9) 1-0
90 Haywards Heath Town v Chichester City (22/9) 2-0 38
91 Molesey v Knaphill (23/9) 8-2
92 Chertsey Town v Westfield (19/9) 1-4 42
93 Worthing v Horley Town (19/9) 6-1 40
(at Horley Town FC)
94 Steyning Town v Hampton & Richmond Boro (21/9) 1-4 43
(at Lancing FC, Sussex FA County Ground)
95 Lewes v Wick (22/9) 6-1
96 Merstham v Leatherhead (19/9) 7-1 57
97 Newhaven v Whitehawk (22/9) 0-6 42
98 Mile Oak v Camberley Town (22/9) 1-3 43
99 Marlow v Basingstoke Town (21/9) 6-0 54
100 Didcot Town v Hungerford Town (22/9) 1-4 61
101 Maidenhead United v Oxford City (28/9) 3-6
(at Oxford City FC)
102 Ascot United v Burnham (22/9) 5-2 98
103 Bracknell Town v Windsor (21/9) 2-2aet
(at Windsor FC) (Bracknell Town won 4-3 on kicks from the penalty mark)
104 Andover Town v Hartley Wintney (21/9) 6-2 55
105 Wantage Town v Alton Town (22/9) 3-2 32
106 Fareham Town v Team Solent (21/9) 0-1 47
107 Havant & Waterlooville v Winchester City (19/9) 4-4aet 79
(Havant & Waterlooville won 4-1 on kicks from the penalty mark)
108 Cove v Poole Town (22/9) 0-10 53
109 Salisbury v Weymouth
(walkover for Salisbury – Weymouth withdrawn)
110 Gosport Borough v AFC Portchester (19/9) 2-1aet 110
111 Sholing v Ringwood Town (21/9) 1-0 70
112 Hamworthy United v AFC Totton (20/9) 2-2aet 65
(Hamworthy United won 4-3 on kicks from the penalty mark)

113	Chippenham Town	v Gloucester City (22/9)	0-7	121
114	Tuffley Rovers	v Yate Town (21/9)	1-9	49
115	Bradford Town	v Cirencester Town (20/9)	0-5	
116	Bitton	v Malmesbury Victoria (20/9)	3-0	
117	Ashton & Backwell United	v Weston Super Mare (20/9)	0-3	
118	Bath City	v Bishop Sutton (21/9)	9-0	76
119	Radstock Town	v Taunton Town (22/9)	4-1	50
120	Cullompton Rangers	v Welton Rovers (22/9)	4-2	36
121	Paulton Rovers	v Larkhall Athletic (22/9)	2-0	51

SECOND ROUND QUALIFYING

1	Darlington 1883	v Clitheroe (5/10)	2-1	
2	West Didsbury & Chorlton	v Irlam (5/10)	2-9	71
3	St Helens Town	v Newcastle Benfield (6/10)	1-2	48
	(at Liverpool FA County Ground)			
4	Southport	v Altrincham (5/10)	1-5	141
5	Ryton & Crawcrook Albion	v Marine (4/10)	4-0	101
6	Tranmere Rovers	v Durham City (5/10)	3-0	118
7	FC United of Manchester	v Gateshead (5/10)	3-0	164
8	AFC Fylde	v Barrow (6/10)	4-1	69
	(at Kellamergh Park)			
9	Hyde United	v Ashton Athletic (7/10)	2-1	49
10	Wrexham	v North Ferriby United (6/10)	2-1	59
11	York City	v Garforth Town (5/10)	6-0	
12	Pontefract Collieries	v Hall Road Rangers (3/10)	4-1	
13	Barton Town Old Boys	v Handsworth Parramore (3/10)	2-1aet	
14	Nostell MW	v Sheffield (3/10)	2-0	95
15	Guiseley	v FC Halifax Town (12/10)	2-3	
	(at FC Halifax Town) (6/10 - tie abandoned due to floodlight failure, 1-2)			
16	Belper Town	v Alfreton Town (5/10)	4-5	
17	Lincoln City	v Dunkirk (7/10)	4-5aet	71
18	Boston United	v Loughborough Dynamo (3/10)	3-1	126
19	Bottesford Town	v Kimberley MW (6/10)	0-2	63
20	Soihull Moors	v Coleshill Town (5/10)	2-1	70
21	Bedworth United	v Rushall Olympic (5/10)	3-3aet	
	(Bedworth United won 4-3 on kicks from the penalty mark)			
22	Newcastle Town	v Ellesmere Rangers (4/10)	3-2	77
23	Hereford	v Bromsgrove Sporting (4/10)	8-1	130
24	Wolverhampton Casuals	v AFC Telford United (6/10)	3-1	
25	Romulus	v Kidderminster Harriers (3/10)	3-1	
26	AFC Rushden & Diamonds	v Ely City (3/10)	1-3	
27	Biggleswade Town	v St Ives Town (5/10)	3-0	
28	Kettering Town	v Nuneaton Town (6/10)	3-2	23
29	AFC Dunstable	v Rushden & Higham United (6/10)	4-4aet	28
	(Rushden & Higham United won 4-2 on kicks from the penalty mark)			
30	Framlingham Town	v Gorleston (6/10)	5-4aet	55
31	Chelmsford City	v Leiston (5/10)	0-1	
32	Whitton United	v AFC Sudbury (6/10)	0-4	54
33	Bury Town	v Woodbridge Town (6/10)	0-5	64
34	Braintree Town	v Needham Market (5/10)	1-1aet	
	(Braintree Town won 3-2 on kicks from the penalty mark)			
35	Bishop's Stortford	v Ware (3/10)	1-2	135
36	Wadham Lodge	v Aveley (3/10)	1-2	64
37	FC Broxbourne Borough	v Concord Rangers (5/10)	3-2aet	68
38	AFC Hornchurch	v Tilbury (6/10)	4-0	57
39	Dagenham & Redbridge	v Cheshunt (6/10)	4-1	
40	Boreham Wood	v Hanwell Town (3/10)	5-1	
41	St Albans City	v Wealdstone (5/10)	1-3	73
42	Bedfont Sports	v Cockfosters (3/10)	1-0	41
43	Hitchin Town	v North Greenford United (5/10)	1-3	75
44	Wingate & Finchley	v Beaconsfield SYCOB (5/10)	2-3aet	
45	Uxbridge	v Potters Bar Town (3/10)	3-2aet	131
46	Maidstone United	v Bridon Ropes (3/10)	6-2	166
47	Tonbridge Angels	v Dover Athletic (3/10)	3-0	
48	Bromley	v Folkestone Invicta (6/10)	2-3	102
49	Greenwich Borough	v Ashford United (6/10)	1-4	
50	Sporting Club Thamesmead	v Meridian VP (4/10)	2-3	
51	Lordswood	v Ebbsfleet United (6/10)	1-2	
52	Hastings United	v Corinthian (6/10)	2-3	
53	Sutton United	v Molesey (5/10)	5-4aet	
54	Whitehawk	v Worthing (6/10)	0-1	
55	Westfield	v Hampton & Richmond Boro (5/10)	0-3	40
56	Merstham	v Lewes (3/10)	3-0	63
57	Camberley Town	v Woking (6/10)	2-5	129
58	Haywards Heath Town	v Metropolitan Police (6/10)	1-8	48
59	Wantage Town	v Bracknell Town (6/10)	1-4	40

60	Oxford City	v Ascot United (5/10)	4-4aet	
	(Oxford City won 6-5 on kicks from the penalty mark)			
61	Hungerford Town	v Marlow (5/10)	4-2	91
62	Eastleigh	v Havant & Waterlooville (5/10)	3-0	113
63	Andover Town	v Sholing (5/10)	2-1	63
64	Hamworthy United	v Poole Town (4/10)	1-7	112
	(at Poole Town FC)			
65	Team Solent	v Gosport Borough (5/10)	3-4	45
66	Aldershot Town	v Salisbury (5/10)	0-2	88
67	Gloucester City	v Cirencester Town (4/10)	4-1	
	(at Tuffley Rovers FC)			
68	Paulton Rovers	v Radstock Town (3/10)	1-2	133
69	Cullompton Rangers	v Bitton (6/10)	2-3	36
70	Yate Town	v Bath City (6/10)	0-7	86
71	Forest Green Rovers	v Weston Super Mare (4/10)	6-4aet	
BYE – Chester				

THIRD ROUND QUALIFYING

1	Altrincham	v Tranmere Rovers (23/10)	1-7	148
2	Hyde United	v Irlam (21/10)	2-0	100
3	York City	v Barton Town Old Boys (18/10)	9-0	160
4	Ryton & Crawcrook Albion	v Darlington 1883 (21/10)	4-2	162
5	Newcastle Benfield	v Chester (17/10)	0-8	
6	Pontefract Collieries	v Wrexham (17/10)	0-3	146
7	FC Halifax Town	v AFC Fylde (19/10)	4-1	143
8	Nostell MW	v FC United Of Manchester (17/10)	2-3	81
9	Romulus	v Kettering Town (19/10)	2-0	
	(at Castle Vale Town FC)			
10	Kimberley MW	v Boston United (19/10)	0-9	145
	(at Boston United FC)			
11	Dunkirk	v Alfreton Town (18/10)	2-1	
	(at Clifton All Whites FC)			
12	Hereford	v Newcastle Town (20/10)	2-1	43
13	Wolverhampton Casuals	v Solihull Moors (20/10)	4-3	
14	Ely City	v Bedworth United (20/10)	1-2	
15	Braintree Town	v Dagenham & Redbridge (19/10)	2-4aet	
16	Biggleswade Town	v Beaconsfield SYCOB (19/10)	0-2	
17	Woodbridge Town	v AFC Sudbury (19/10)	1-2aet	130
18	Uxbridge	v North Greenford United (17/10)	1-3	139
19	Aveley	v FC Broxbourne Borough (19/10)	0-3	31
20	AFC Hornchurch	v Rushden & Higham United (20/10)	5-0	56
21	Framlingham Town	v Leiston (20/10)	2-0	
22	Boreham Wood	v Wealdstone (17/10)	4-0	94
23	Ware	v Bedfont Sports (19/10)	3-0	
24	Hampton & Richmond Borough	v Metropolitan Police (19/10)	0-1	83
25	Ashford United	v Folkestone Invicta (20/10)	0-1	129
26	Tonbridge Angels	v Maidstone United (19/10)	5-5aet	
	(Maidstone United won 6-5 on kicks from the penalty mark)			
27	Sutton United	v Corinthian (19/10)	0-3	115
28	Worthing	v Meridian VP (20/10)	4-0	
29	Merstham	v Ebbsfleet United (20/10)	4-0	67
30	Eastleigh	v Hungerford Town (19/10)	2-1	132
31	Bath City	v Gloucester City (19/10)	0-2	88
32	Poole Town	v Bracknell Town (18/10)	9-0	83
33	Woking	v Radstock Town (20/10)	4-5	134
34	Salisbury	v Bitton (20/10)	3-2aet	98
35	Gosport Borough	v Andover Town (19/10)	0-3	
36	Forest Green Rovers	v Oxford City (19/10)	1-2	

FIRST ROUND PROPER

1	Bradford City	v Hartlepool United (1/11)	1-0	242
2	Chester	v Fleetwood Town (2/11)	1-0	413
3	Sheffield United	v Crewe Alexandra (1/11)	2-1	612
4	FC United of Manchester	v Carlisle United (1/11)	0-2	
5	Hyde United	v Morecambe (4/11)	1-4	140
6	Wrexham	v Accrington Stanley (2/11)	0-2	140
7	Bolton Wanderers	v Blackpool (2/11)	2-1aet	666
8	Scunthorpe United	v Grimsby Town (2/11)	2-0	310
9	Oldham Athletic	v Bury (1/11)	2-0	219
10	Tranmere Rovers	v Doncaster Rovers (1/11)	3-0	171
11	FC Halifax Town	v York City (2/11)	2-2aet	236
	(FC Halifax Town won 4-3 on kicks from the penalty mark)			
12	Rochdale	v Ryton & Crawcrook Albion (2/11)	7-0	236
13	Dunkirk	v Coventry City (4/11)	3-2aet	315
14	Notts County	v Romulus (1/11)	1-3	
15	Peterborough United	v Port Vale (27/10)	0-9	386
16	Shrewsbury Town	v Wolverhampton Casuals (1/11)	5-1	231
17	Bedworth United	v Mansfield Town (2/11)	0-3	
18	Chesterfield	v Walsall (3/11)	3-1	300
19	Boston United	v Hereford (2/11)	3-2	175
20	Boreham Wood	v Northampton Town (1/11)	1-0	144
21	Cambridge United	v Beaconsfield SYCOB (1/11)	4-1	158

22	Barnet	v Luton Town (1/11)	1-3	256
23	Southend United	v Leyton Orient (2/11)	0-6	298
24	Dagenham & Redbridge	v Colchester United (2/11)	7-3	155
25	AFC Sudbury	v Framlingham Town (3/11)	2-1	133
26	Milton Keynes Dons	v AFC Hornchurch (1/11)	6-1	400
27	Ware	v Stevenage (3/11)	2-4aet	
28	Charlton Athletic	v Maidstone United (1/11)	1-1aet	250
	(Charlton Athletic won 3-1 on kicks from the penalty mark)			
29	Millwall	v Worthing (7/11)	6-0	281
30	Gillingham	v Corinthian (1/11)	3-1	
31	Folkestone Invicta	v Merstham (3/11)	1-4	
32	AFC Wimbledon	v North Greenford United (1/11)	8-1	396
33	Gloucester City	v Poole Town (1/11)	0-4	
	(at Tuffley Rovers FC)			
34	Newport County	v Yeovil Town (4/11)	0-1	
	(at Spytty Park Stadium)			
35	Radstock Town	v Exeter City (1/11)	0-8	330
36	Oxford United	v Bristol Rovers (27/10)	0-2	228
	(at Abingdon United FC)			
37	Andover Town	v Oxford City (2/11)	2-3	90
38	Cheltenham Town	v Plymouth Argyle (1/11)	1-5	176
39	Salisbury	v Swindon Town (3/11)	2-3	237
40	Portsmouth	v Eastleigh (27/10)	5-0	758

BYE – FC Broxbourne Borough; Metropolitan Police

SECOND ROUND PROPER

1	FC Halifax Town	v Sheffield United (16/11)	1-5	
2	Rochdale	v Shrewsbury Town (16/11)	1-2	141
3	Chester	v Bolton Wanderers (16/11)	2-0	580
4	Morecambe	v Accrington Stanley (16/11)	2-4	156
5	Mansfield Town	v Dunkirk (15/11)	5-2	506
6	Chesterfield	v Carlisle United (15/11)	1-2aet	250
7	Bradford City	v Boston United (15/11)	2-1	305
8	Scunthorpe United	v Tranmere Rovers (15/11)	2-4	194
9	Romulus	v Oldham Athletic (15/11)	0-2	185
10	Poole Town	v Leyton Orient (15/11)	1-7	316
11	Swindon Town	v AFC Sudbury (19/11)	3-2aet	153
12	Plymouth Argyle	v Gillingham (15/11)	2-2aet	341
	(Gillingham won 4-2 on kicks from the penalty mark)			
13	Stevenage	v Charlton Athletic (15/11)	2-0	
14	Luton Town	v Dagenham & Redbridge (17/11)	4-3aet	408
15	Oxford City	v Peterborough United (16/11)	3-1	
16	Boreham Wood	v FC Broxbourne Borough (16/11)	1-2	157
17	Portsmouth	v Metropolitan Police (16/11)	2-0	573
18	Cambridge United	v Millwall (16/11)	2-0	164
19	Yeovil Town	v Merstham (15/11)	2-0	
20	AFC Wimbledon	v Bristol Rovers (23/11)	3-0	310
21	Exeter City	v Milton Keynes Dons (18/11)	3-1	

THIRD ROUND PROPER

1	Middlesbrough	v Rotherham United (13/12)	5-0	207
	(at Bishop Auckland FC)			
2	Liverpool	v Crystal Palace (17/12)	2-2aet	
	(at Tranmere Rovers FC) (Liverpool won 5-4 on kicks from the penalty mark)			
3	FC Broxbourne Borough	v Chester (7/12)	1-0aet	
4	Burnley	v Bradford City (13/12)	2-0	381
5	Watford	v Norwich City (29/11)	1-5	550
6	Gillingham	v Oxford City (30/11)	2-0	
7	Huddersfield Town	v AFC Wimbledon (17/12)	1-2	246
8	Reading	v Manchester City (15/12)	0-4	517
9	Swindon Town	v Queens Park Rangers (13/12)	1-3	235
10	Shrewsbury Town	v Accrington Stanley (3/11)	2-1	240
11	Portsmouth	v Newcastle United (9/12)	1-4	832
12	Leicester City	v Leyton Orient (14/12)	3-1	359
13	Brighton & Hove Albion	v Derby County (14/12)	2-0	
14	Exeter City	v Wigan Athletic (13/12)	1-2	
15	Arsenal	v Blackburn Rovers (16/12)	0-1	
	(at Boreham Wood FC)			
16	Preston North End	v Sheffield United (30/11)	1-0	345
17	Oldham Athletic	v Birmingham City (14/12)	1-4	242
18	Swansea City	v Wolverhampton Wanderers (16/12)	2-1	156
	(at Landore Training Ground)			
19	Sunderland	v Burton Albion (15/12)	4-1	206
	(at Eppleton CW FC)			
20	Fulham	v Mansfield Town (16/12)	3-1	
	(at Motspur Park)			

21	Cambridge United	v AFC Bournemouth (14/12)	2-1	406
22	Barnsley	v Carlisle United (16/12)	0-1	284
23	Chelsea	v Cardiff City (13/12)	5-0	210
	(at Aldershot Town FC)			
24	Everton	v Tranmere Rovers (8/12)	2-0	703
25	Stoke City	v West Ham United (22/11)	2-2aet	
	(Stoke City won 4-2 on kicks from the penalty mark)			
26	Nottingham Forest	v Ipswich Town (6/12)	4-2aet	366
27	West Bromwich Albion	v Yeovil Town (6/12)	2-3	218
28	Hull City	v Leeds United (6/12)	3-2aet	221
	(at North Ferriby United FC)			
29	Tottenham Hotspur	v Stevenage (30/11)	10-1	897
	(at Stevenage FC)			
30	Bristol City	v Aston Villa (6/12)	0-2	301
31	Sheffield Wednesday	v Luton Town (9/12)	4-0	315
32	Manchester United	v Southampton (13/12)	1-2	1943

FOURTH ROUND PROPER

				Res	Att
1	Preston North End	v Everton (18/1)		0-0aet	643
	(Preston North End won 7-6 on kicks from the penalty mark)				
2	AFC Wimbledon	v Hull City (10/1)		3-0	663
3	Stoke City	v Nottingham Forest (10/1)		4-1	549
4	Middlesbrough	v Fulham (13/1)		2-1	255
	(at Bishop Auckland FC)				
5	Blackburn Rovers	v Aston Villa (11/1)		0-0aet	824
	(Aston Villa won 7-6 on kicks from the penalty mark)				
6	Newcastle United	v Swansea City (9/1)		3-1	1307
7	Queens Park Rangers	v Tottenham Hotspur (10/1)		1-4	647
8	Wigan Athletic	v Southampton (11/1)		1-2	304
9	Manchester City	v Liverpool (18/1)		3-1	
	(at Academy Arena)				
10	Brighton & Hove Albion	v Cambridge United (13/1)		2-0	
11	Leicester City	v Carlisle United (18/1)		2-1	386
12	Birmingham City	v Chelsea (18/1)		0-5	
13	FC Broxbourne Borough	v Yeovil Town (11/1)		1-0	
14	Sheffield Wednesday	v Gillingham (6/1)		3-0	650
15	Burnley	v Norwich City (6/1)		0-4	527
16	Sunderland	v Shrewsbury Town (11/1)		3-1	235
	(at Eppleton CW FC)				

FIFTH ROUND PROPER

1	Manchester City	v Southampton (26/1)	4-0	
	(at Academy Arena)			
2	Chelsea	v Sheffield Wednesday (1/2)	4-0	234
	(at Aldershot Town FC)			
3	Aston Villa	v FC Broxbourne Borough (4/2)	7-0	901
4	Sunderland	v Newcastle United (25/1)	3-4	1009
	(at Eppleton CW FC)			
5	Tottenham Hotspur	v Norwich City (2/2)	2-0	698
	(at Stevenage FC)			
6	Stoke City	v Brighton & Hove Albion (3/2)	2-2aet	
	(Stoke City won 4-2 on kicks from the penalty mark)			
7	Middlesbrough	v Leicester City (3/2)	0-1aet	231
	(at Bishop Auckland FC)			
8	Preston North End	v AFC Wimbledon (1/2)	3-2aet	519

SIXTH ROUND PROPER

1	Leicester City	v Chelsea (15/2)	0-1	449
2	Newcastle United	v Tottenham Hotspur (27/2)	3-5	2847
3	Preston North End	v Stoke City (27/2)	1-3	1747
4	Aston Villa	v Manchester City (22/2)	1-2	964

FIRST ROUND

1	Nottinghamshire	v	Manchester (1/10)	4-2aet	
	(at Hucknall Rolls Royce Leisure FC)				
2	Lancashire	v	Isle Of Man (1/10)	2-1	
	(at Lancashire FA County Ground)				
3	Lincolnshire	v	West Riding		
	(walkover for West Riding – Lincolnshire withdrawn)				
4	Amateur Football Alliance	v	Oxfordshire (8/10)	1-3	
	(at Enfield Town FC)				
5	Devon	v	Berks & Bucks (8/10)	1-5	57
	(at Devon County FA, Coach Road)				
6	Suffolk	v	London (8/10)	4-1	47
	(at Woodbridge Town FC)				
7	Herefordshire	v	Essex (9/10)	0-1	

SECOND ROUND

1	West Riding	v	Leicestershire & Rutland (5/11)	1-2	
	(at West Riding County FA)				
2	Liverpool	v	Lancashire (26/11)	2-4	
	(at Liverpool Soccer Centre)				
3	Sheffield & Hallamshire	v	Northumberland (29/10)	3-2aet	
	(at Nostell Miners Welfare FC)				
4	Westmorland	v	Nottinghamshire (22/10)	0-1	55
	(at Kendal Town FC)				
5	Birmingham	v	North Riding (22/10)	2-3	
	(at Birmingham FA County Ground)				
6	Cumberland	v	Cheshire (29/10)	0-1	
	(at Penrith AFC)				
7	Durham	v	Staffordshire (29/10)	3-0	
	(at Billingham Synthonia FC)				
8	Wiltshire	v	Kent (5/11)	3-2aet	
	(at Amesbury Town FC)				
9	Suffolk	v	Hertfordshire (5/11)	4-3	48
	(at Woodbridge Town FC)				
10	Cambridgeshire	v	Essex (4/11)	0-3	62
	(at Histon FC)				
11	Bedfordshire	v	Norfolk (2/11)	0-1aet	
	(at Kempston Rovers FC)				
12	Gloucestershire	v	Cornwall (29/10)	0-7	60
	(at Gloucestershire FA, Oaklands Park)				
13	Northamptonshire	v	Middlesex (29/10)	0-3	45
	(at Cogenhoe United FC)				
14	Oxfordshire	v	Berks & Bucks (12/11)	5-3	
	(at Carterton FC)				
15	Jersey	v	Guernsey (5/11)	3-1	
	(at Springfield Stadium, Jersey)				
16	Somerset	v	Sussex (29/10)	1-3	40
	(at Frome Town FC)				

PREVIOUS TEN FINALS

2016	Liverpool	v	Sussex	2-0
2015	Cheshire	v	Middlesex	3-2
2014	Lancashire	v	Suffolk	3-2 aet
2013	Bedfordshire FA	v	Manchester FA	4-4 aet
(Bedfordshire FA won 4-2 on kicks from the penalty mark)				
2012	Essex FA	v	West Riding FA	4-2 aet
2011	Norfolk FA	v	Staffordshire FA	4-2
2010	Kent FA	v	Sheffield & Hallamshire	1-0
2009	Birmingham FA	v	Kent FA	2-1
2008	Suffolk FA	v	Cambridgeshire FA	2-1
2007	West Riding FA	v	Suffolk FA	1-1 aet, 4-3p

THIRD ROUND

1	Essex	v	Sussex	1-2	61
	(at Len Forge Centre)				
2	Oxfordshire	v	Nottinghamshire (8/1)	5-1	
	(at Kidlington FC)				
3	Jersey	v	Durham	1-2	
	(at Springfield Stadium, Jersey)				
4	Cheshire	v	Suffolk	2-1	
	(at Vauxhall Motors FC)				
5	North Riding	v	Wiltshire (3/12)	1-0	59
	(at North Riding FA, Stokesley FC)				
6	Leicestershire & Rutland	v	Norfolk	2-1	
	(at Holmes Park)				
7	Cornwall	v	Lancashire	5-2	
	(at St Blazey FC)				
8	Sheffield & Hallamshire	v	Middlesex	1-2	
	(at Stocksbridge Park Steels FC)				

FOURTH ROUND

1	Cornwall	v	Sussex (21/1)	2-1aet	130
	(at St Blazey FC)				
2	Cheshire	v	Oxfordshire (21/1)	0-3	
	(at Vauxhall Motors FC)				
3	Leicestershire & Rutland	v	Durham (28/1)	2-3aet	
	(at Holmes Park)				
4	Middlesex	v	North Riding (8/1)	4-2	70
	(at Uxbridge FC)				

SEMI FINALS

1	Cornwall	v	Durham (25/2)	2-1	230
	(at St Blazey FC)				
2	Oxfordshire	v	Middlesex (26/2)	2-7	
	(at Thame United FC)				

THE FINAL

SUNDAY 1 APRIL 2017

1	Middlesex	v	Cornwall	2-1	736
	(at Barnet FC)				

FA YOUTH CUP

SEMI FINALS

				1st Leg		2nd Leg	
1	Manchester City	v	Stoke City	6-0	3205	3-2	983
2	Tottenham Hotspur	v	Chelsea	1-2	2533	1-7	3314

THE FINAL

			1st Leg		2nd Leg	
Manchester City	v	Chelsea	1-1	3392	1-5	4892

PREVIOUS TEN FINALS

				Aggregate Score
2016	Chelsea	v	Manchester City	4-2
2015	Chelsea	v	Manchester City	5-2
2014	Chelsea	v	Fulham	7-6
2013	Norwich City	v	Chelsea	4-2
2012	Chelsea	v	Blackburn Rovers	4-1
2011	Manchester Utd	v	Sheffield United	4-1
2010	Chelsea	v	Aston Villa	3-2
2009	Arsenal	v	Liverpool	6-2
2008	Manchester City	v	Chelsea	4-2
2007	Liverpool	v	Manchester Utd	2-2* 4-3p

FIRST ROUND

1 Thornaby Village v Wrekenton Blue Star
   (walkover for Thornaby Village – Wrekenton Blue Star withdrawn)
   (16/10 – tie abandoned 45 mins, 2-1)

2 Amble Tavern v Witton Park Rose & Crown 0-2 50
   (at Morpeth Town FC)

3 Northallerton Police v Burradon & New Fordley
   (walkover for Burradon & New Fordley - Northallerton Police withdrawn)

4 Dawdon Welfare Park v Newton Aycliffe Locomotion 1-2 80
   (at Seaham Red Star FC)

5 FC Dovecot v Garston 4-1
   (at Anfield Sports & Community Centre)

6 Oyster Martyrs v Nicosia
   (walkover for Oyster Martyrs – Nicosia withdrawn)

7 Chapeltown Fforde Grene v Mayfair 1-2
   (at Yorkshire Amateur FC)

8 Oakenshaw v Ferrybridge Progressive (23/10) 0-7
   (at Field FC)

9 Woodman Sports Club v Seacroft WMC 0-3
   (at Carlton Athletic Sports Ground)

10 Neston Nomads v Poulton Royal 3-2aet 20
    (at Cammell Laird FC)

11 West Bowling v Queens Park 2-0
    (at Bradford (Park Avenue) FC)

12 Lobster v Seymour
    (walkover for Lobster – Seymour failed to fulfil fixture)

13 Olympic v The Molly
    (walkover for The Molly – Olympic withdrawn)

14 Custys v Millhouse 3-1
    (at The North Field, Jericho Lane)

15 St John Fisher OB v Pineapple 3-7
    (at Ossett Albion FC)

16 Lower Breck v Dengo United 0-3
    (at Prescot Cables FC)

17 New Sharlston Welfare v Colton
    (walkover for New Sharlston Welfare – Colton withdrawn)

18 Thornton United v Kennelwood 5-3aet
    (at Manningham Mills Sports)

19 AFC Blackburn Leisure v Allerton 1-10
    (at Blackburn Leisure Sports Club)

20 Austin Ex Apprentices v FC Brimington 5-2 109
    (at Pilkington XXX FC)

21 Frolesworth United v Alcester Town 4-3aet
    (at Lutterworth Athletic FC)

22 RHP Sports & Social v Halfway 3-0 104
    (at Newark Flowserve FC)

23 Attenborough Cavaliers v Sporting Dynamo 1-0 60
    (at Radford FC)

24 Wolverhampton Casuals (Sun) v Thomas Brothers
    (walkover for Wolverhampton Casuals FC – Thomas Brothers failed to fulfil fixture)

25 Enderby Social v OJM 0-1
    (at Huncote Sports & Social)

26 Birstall Stamford v Carlton Top Spot 4-3
    (at Birstall United FC)

27 Black Horse (Redditch) v Oadby Athletic 3-0 74
    (at Studley FC)

28 Nuthall v Hampton Blackwood 2-1
    (at Kimberley MW FC)

29 Weddington Thistle v Mowmacre & Hoskins 8-2 135
    (at Nuneaton Town FC)

30 Olympia v Falcons 0-2
    (at Cockfosters FC)

31 Gym United v Priory Sports 1-0
    (at Walsham Le Willows FC)

32 Omonia v Upshire (3.00) 2-1
    (at Haringey Borough FC)

33 NLO v FC Houghton (23/10) 3-2aet 18
    (at Chalfont St Peter FC)

34 Club Lewsey v British Airways HEW 4-2
    (at Arlesey Town FC)

35 St Josephs (Luton) v Brache Nation
    (walkover for St Josephs (Luton) – Brache Nation withdrawn)

36 Harpole v Doves United 3-2 110
    (at Harpole FC)

37 Broadfields United (Sunday) v North Wembley 2-0
    (at Harefield United FC)

38 Two Touch v AC Sportsman (23/10) 2-3
    (at Amersham Town FC)

39 Market Hotel v Broadwater 1-4 69
    (at Lydd Town FC)

40 Chessington United v London St Georges 2-1
    (at Leatherhead FC)

41 Wickham Wanderers v Portland 2-1
    (at Green Court Sports Club, Crockenhill)

42 Lebeqs Tavern Courage v Southall United 4-2
    (at Bristol Manor Farm FC)

43 Black Horse (Chesham) v Shire United
    (walkover for Shire United – Black Horse (Chesham) withdrawn)

44 FC Bengals v AFC Kumazi Strikers 4-2
    (at Brunel Sports Complex)

SECOND ROUND

1 Burradon & New Fordley v Mayfair (20/11) 5-3 86
   (at New Fordley FC)

2 Custys v Thornaby Village 4-1 14
   (at Heswall FC)

3 Dengo United v Hartlepool Lion Hillcarter 3-3aet 55
   (at St John Bosco College) (Dengo United won 4-2 on kicks from the penalty mark)

4 Home & Bargain v Allerton 5-0
   (at Alder Sports Club)

5 Canada v Black Bull 1-5
   (at Lower Breck Complex)

6 Newton Aycliffe Locomotion v West Bowling 4-1 98
   (at Shildon FC)

7 Ferrybridge Progressive v Thornton United 4-1
   (at Pontefract Collieries FC)

8 Witton Park Rose & Crown v New Sharlston Welfare 12-0 64
   (at Tow Law Town FC)

9 Neston Nomads v Alder (27/11) 3-0
   (tie reversed – at Alder Sports Club)

10 Pineapple v Seacroft WMC 4-0
    (at The North Field, Jericho Lane)

11 Oyster Martyrs v Campfield 3-1
    (at Skelmersdale United FC)

12 Hardwick Social v The Molly 3-1
    (at Stockton Town FC)

13 FC Dovecot v Wallsend New Rising Sun 2-3
    (at Litherland Sports Park)

14 Lobster v Leeds City Rovers 1-0
    (at Burscough FC)

15 Austin Ex Apprentices v Black Horse (Redditch) 3-2
    (at Pilkington XXX FC)

16 Wolverhampton Casuals (Sun) v Anstey Sports Bar Swifts 3-0
    (at Wolverhampton Casuals FC)

17 Gym United v Nuthall 3-1
    (at Walsham Le Willows FC)

18 Weddington Thistle v Quorn Royals 2008 4-2
    (at Nuneaton Town FC)

19 Attenborough Cavaliers v Stanleys (2.00) 5-2
    (at Radford FC)

20 Frolesworth United v Birtsall Stamford 3-4

(at Lutterworth Athletic FC)
21 Harpole v OJM 2-3
(at Harpole FC)
22 RHP Sports & Social v Riverside Rovers 5-0 57
(at Newark Flowserve FC)
23 St Josephs (Luton) v Wickham Wanderers 3-2
(at Arlesey Town FC)
24 New Salamis v Belstone (Sunday) 7-1
(at Cheshunt FC)
25 Falcons v Green Man (Luton) 4-1
(at Newmarket Town FC)
26 NLO v Omonia (20/11) 2-3
(at Hillingdon Borough FC)
27 AC Sportsman v FC Bengals 1-5 10
(at Dunstable Town FC)
28 Shire United v St Josephs (South Oxhey) (1.30)0-1
(at Osterley Sports Club)
29 Broadfields United (Sunday) v Club Lewsey 0-3
(at Harefield United FC)
30 Broadwater v Lebeqs Tavern Courage (2.00)0-2
(at Worthing United FC)
31 Lambeth All Stars v Barnes Albion (27/11) 1-4
(tie reversed – at Colliers Wood United FC)
32 Barnes AFC v Chessington United 3-3aet 22
(at Hanworth Villa FC) (Chessington United on 4-2 on kicks from the penalty mark)

THIRD ROUND

1 Wallsend New Rising Sun v Home & Bargain 2-3aet
(at Newcastle Benfield FC)
2 Lobster v Custys 3-1aet
(at Burscough FC)
3 Witton Park Rose & Crown v Burradon & New Fordley 2-1 68
(at Tow Law Town FC)
4 Neston Nomads v Black Bull 1-4
(at Cammell Laird 1907 FC)
5 Newton Aycliffe Locomotion v Hardwick Social (2.00) 0-4
(at Shildon FC)
6 Dengo United v Oyster Martyrs 2-4 95
(at St John Bosco College)
7 Ferrybridge Progressive v Pineapple 3-2
(at Pontefract Collieries FC)
8 Wolverhampton Casuals (Sun) v Gym United 4-3aet
(at Wolverhampton Casuals FC)
9 RHP Sports & Social v Weddington Thistle 1-4aet 31
(at Newark Flowserve FC)
10 Austin Ex Apprentices v Birstall Stamford 4-0
(at Pilkington XXX FC)
11 OJM v Attenborough Cavaliers (8/1)3-3aet
(Attenborough Cavaliers won 5-4 on kicks from the penalty mark)
(tie reversed – at Radford FC)
12 Falcons v FC Bengals (2.00) 2-3
(at Newmarket Town FC)
13 Chessington United v Lebeqs Tavern Courage (2.00)1-0
(at Leatherhead FC)
14 Club Lewsey v Omonia 0-1
(at Berkhamsted FC)
15 New Salamis v St Josephs (South Oxhey)
(walkover for New Salamis, St Josephs (South Oxhey) failed to fulfil fixture)
(at Haringey Borough FC)
16 St Josephs (Luton) v Barnes Albion 0-0aet
(St Josephs (Luton) won 4-2 on kicks from the penalty mark)
(at Arlesey Town FC)

FOURTH ROUND

1 Hardwick Social v Lobster 2-0
(at Stockton Town FC)
2 Ferrybridge Progressive v Oyster Martyrs (22/1) 1-0
(at Pontefract Collieries FC)
3 Witton Park Rose & Crown v Black Bull
(15/1 – tie abandoned after 70 mins, 3-0 – both Clubs removed – subject to appeal)
4 Attenborough Cavaliers v Home & Bargain (2.00) 0-4
(at Radford FC)
5 FC Bengals v Austin Ex Apprentices (29/1) 2-3
(tie reversed – at Pilkington XXX FC)
6 Omonia v St Josephs (Luton) (22/1) 4-2
(at New River Sports Stadium)
7 New Salamis v Weddington Thistle (3.00) 4-0
(at Haringey Borough FC)
8 Wolverhampton Casuals (Sun) v Chessington United (22/1) 3-0
(tie awarded to Chessington United – Wolverhampton Casuals (Sunday) removed)

FIFTH ROUND

1 Hardwick Social v Witton Park Rose & Crown or Black Bull
(walkover for Hardwick Social – Witton Park Rose & Crown and Black Bull removed)
2 Home & Bargain v Ferrybridge Progressive 2-1
(at Alder Sports Club)
3 Austin Ex Apprentices v New Salamis 0-4
(at Pilkington XXX FC)
4 Omonia v Chessington United 2-2aet
(Chessington United won 5-3 on kicks from the penalty mark - at New River Sports Stadium)

SEMI FINALS

1 New Salamis v Chessington United 6-2 203
(at Dagenham & Redbridge FC)
2 Home & Bargain v Hardwick Social 1-3 287
(at Guiseley AFC)

THE FINAL

SUNDAY 7 MAY 2017

Hardwick Social v New Salamis 1-1, 3-1p 575
(at Sheffield United FC)

PREVIOUS TEN FINALS

2016	New Salamis	v Barnes	1-1, 4-3p
2015	Campfield	v OJM	2-0
2014	Humbledon Plains Farm	v Oyster Martyrs	5-2
2013	Oyster Martyrs	v Barnes Albion	4-3
2012	Hetton Lyons C.C.	v Canada	5-1
2011	Oyster Martyrs	v Paddock	1-0
2010	Hetton Lyons C.C.	v Magnet Tavern	4-2
2009	Scots Grey	v Oyster Martyrs	4-3 aet
2008	Hetton Lyons C.C.	v Coundon Conservative	3-2
2007	Coundon Conservative	v Lebeq Tavern Courage	5-0

FIRST QUALIFYING ROUND

1	South Shields	v Gateshead Leam Rangers	2-0	25
2	Wigan Athletic	v MSB Woolton	1-0	

SECOND QUALIFYING ROUND

1	Wallsend Boys Club	v Boldon CA Villa	5-2	42
2	South Shields	v Cramlington United	1-1aet	30
	(South Shields won 4-2 on kicks from the penalty mark)			
3	South Park Rangers	v Kendal Town		
	(walkover for South Park Rangers – Kendal Town withdrawn)			
4	Penrith	v Bishop Auckland	1-0aet	
5	RACA Tynedale	v Rutherford		
	(walkover for RACA Tynedale – Rutherford withdrawn)			
6	Workington Reds	v Birtley Town (1.00)	2-1	
7	Norton & Stockton Ancients	v Carlisle United	7-0	150
8	Prudhoe Town	v Hartlepool United	0-9	50
9	Boldon CA	v Blyth Town Lions	3-1	
10	Ossett Albion	v Malet Lambert	1-0	39
11	Wakefield	v Farsley Celtic	0-7	
12	Bradford Park Avenue	v Sheffield United	1-8	
13	Sheffield Wednesday	v Brighouse Athletic	4-0	
14	Accrington	v Curzon Ashton	11-2	85
15	FC United Of Manchester	v Bolton Wanderers	2-1	
16	CMB	v Stockport County	0-4	
17	Burnley	v Wigan Athletic	0-7	
18	Merseyrail Bootle	v City of Manchester	4-1	
19	Chorltonians	v Warrington Wolverines	0-2	
20	Rise Park	v Arnold Town	0-0aet	
	(Arnold Town won 4-3 on kicks from the penalty mark)			
21	Leicester City Women Dev	v Winterton Rangers	3-0	
22	Dronfield Town	v Lincoln Moorlands Railway	4-4aet	15
	(Lincoln Moorlands Railway won 3-2 on kicks from the penalty mark)			
23	Nettleham	v Teversal	16-0	
24	Market Warsop	v AFC Leicester	5-1	
25	Stourbridge	v Stockingford AA Pavilion	2-1	68
26	Coundon Court	v Bilbrook	9-0	
27	Leamington Lions	v Wolverhampton Sporting Com	2-2aet	58
	(Leamington Lions won 5-4 on kicks from the penalty mark)			
28	Bedworth United	v Stone Dominoes	7-0	
29	Coleshill Town	v Coventry Ladies Development	0-3	59
30	Shrewsbury Town	v Wyrley	2-4	
31	Bradwell Belles	v Shrewsbury Juniors	1-5	70
32	Knowle	v Leek Town	1-2	
33	Crusaders	v Gornal	2-2aet	30
	(Gornal Ladies won 4-3 on kicks from the penalty mark)			
34	Burton Albion	v Lye Town	3-1	
35	Rubery	v Boldmere St Michaels	2-3aet	
36	Moulton	v Histon	2-5	
37	Riverside	v Woodford United	9-0	35
38	Oadby & Wigston	v Roade	2-0	100
39	Peterborough United	v Cambridge City	0-1	
40	Acle United	v Netherton United	2-0	75
41	ICA Sports	v Peterborough Northern Star		
	(walkover for Peterborough Northern Star – ICA Sports withdrawn)			
42	Newmarket Town	v Wymondham Town	2-7	
43	Park	v Northampton Town	0-14	
44	Kettering Town	v Thrapston Town	4-0	50
45	Colchester Town	v AFC Sudbury	0-3	

46	Brandon Town	v Great Wakering Rovers		
	(walkover for Brandon Town – Great Wakering Rovers withdrawn)			
47	Little Thurrock Dynamos	v Brentwood Town	1-2aet	
48	Harlow Town	v Billericay Town	2-3	
49	Writtle	v Leyton Orient	0-3	
50	Haringey Borough	v Chelmsford City (3.00)	12-0	
51	Bishop's Stortford	v Bungay Town (Sat 17 Sep 7.30)	1-3	
52	Hertford Town	v Garston		
	(walkover for Hertford Town – Garston withdrawn)			
53	Houghton Athletic	v Sherrardswood	2-1	
54	AFC Dunstable	v Sandy	8-0	
55	Colney Heath	v Royston Town	1-3	
56	Hemel Hempstead Town	v Bedford	2-1	60
57	Queens Park Rangers Dev	v Wargrave	5-0	
58	Marlow	v Oxford City	2-4aet	
59	Ascot United	v Milton Keynes City	3-2	60
60	Newbury	v Chinnor	6-2	
61	Brentford	v Chesham United	0-8	
62	Carshalton Athletic	v Aylesford	1-3	53
63	Meridian	v Eastbourne	2-0	
64	Haywards Heath & Wivelsfield	v Cowfold	1-5	
65	Burgess Hill Town	v Regents Park Rangers	0-4	
66	Long Lane	v Fulham Foundation	2-3	
67	Margate	v Bexhill United	1-9	
68	Herne Bay	v Parkwood Rangers (2.30)	1-1aet	82
	(Herne Bay won 3-1 on kicks from the penalty mark)			
69	London Corinthians	v Victoire (3.00)	6-0	
70	Abbey Rangers	v Crawley Wasps	1-7	
71	Worthing Town	v Rottingdean Village		
	(walkover for Worthing Town – Rottingdean Village withdrawn)			
72	Warsash Wasps	v Poole Town	1-2	
73	Fleet Town	v Team Solent	6-0	
74	New Milton Town	v AFC Bournemouth	1-0	
75	Bournemouth Sports	v Southampton	0-12	
76	Middlezoy Rovers	v Ilminster Town	2-2aet	
	(Ilminster Town won 2-0 on kicks from the penalty mark)			
77	AEK Boco	v Royal Wootton Bassett Town	3-1aet	
78	Buckland Athletic	v Cheltenham Civil Service		
	(walkover for Buckland Athletic – Cheltenham Civil Service withdrawn)			
79	Downend Flyers	v Pen Mill	7-1	
80	Keynsham Town Development	v Torquay United		
	(walkover for Torquay United – Keynsham Town Development withdrawn)			

THIRD QUALIFYING ROUND

1	Wallsend Boys Club	v Wigan Athletic	3-2	68
2	Norton & Stockton Ancients	v FC United Of Manchester	2-1	300
3	Leeds	v South Park Rangers	6-1	104
4	Farsley Celtic	v Merseyrail Bootle	2-4	
5	Penrith	v Boldon CA	4-2	
6	Lincoln Moorlands Railway	v Warrington Wolverines	1-6	
7	Crewe Alexandra	v Morecambe	3-3aet	
	(Crewe Alexandra won 4-2 on kicks from the penalty mark)			
8	Steel City Wanderers	v Sheffield Wednesday	1-4	
9	Mossley Hill	v Liverpool Marshall Feds	0-4	60
10	Guiseley AFC Vixens	v Rotherham United	7-2	
11	Chester-Le-Street Town	v Sheffield United	0-1	30
12	Hartlepool United	v Ossett Albion	7-1	
13	Accrington	v Tranmere Rovers	3-0	53
14	Stockport County	v Brighouse Town	1-2	40
15	Blackpool Wren Rovers	v Chorley	2-2aet	
	(Blackpool Wren Rovers won 5-3 on kicks from the penalty mark)			
16	Hull City	v South Shields	4-2aet	
17	Workington Reds	v RACA Tynedale	1-5	

18	Wyrley v Radcliffe Olympic	1-6	
19	Leamington Lions v Burton Albion	0-4	
20	Sporting Khalsa v Coundon Court	7-0	
21	Arnold Town v Coventry Ladies Dev	3-3aet	41
	(Coventry Ladies Development won 4-3 on kicks from the penalty mark)		
22	Bedworth United v Leicester City Women Dev	2-6	60
23	Leicester City v Birmingham & West Midlands	2-3	
24	Loughborough Foxes v Wolverhampton Wanderers	2-3	
25	Shrewsbury Juniors v The New Saints	2-6aet	50
26	Boldmere St Michaels v Long Eaton United	2-8	
27	Stourbridge v Gornal	1-2	109
28	Oadby & Wigston v Solihull Ladies	0-6	
29	Market Warsop v Nettleham	3-4	
30	Loughborough Students v Leek Town	1-3	
31	Norwich City v Riverside	10-0	
32	Lowestoft Town v Enfield Town	2-0	
33	Milton Keynes Dons v Actonians	4-0	
34	Histon v Peterborough Northern Star	0-5	
35	Northampton Town v Cambridge City	2-3	
36	Denham United v Ipswich Town	4-1	
37	Cambridge United v Wymondham Town	3-0	
38	AFC Sudbury v Luton Town	2-3	
39	Kettering Town v Brandon Town	6-0	60
40	Bungay Town v Acle United (7.00)	3-6	110
41	Hemel Hempstead Town v Herne Bay	2-0	65
42	AFC Dunstable v Meridian	4-1	
43	Houghton Athletic v Brentwood Town	0-3	
44	Haringey Borough v Chichester City (3.00)	2-8	
45	Crawley Wasps v Oxford City	0-2	
46	Newbury v Hertford Town	2-1	
47	Leyton Orient v Ascot United	16-0	
48	Billericay Town v Basingstoke Town	1-2	
50	Worthing Town v Stevenage	0-15	51
51	Cowfold v Aylesford	1-2	40
52	Chesham United v London Corinthians	2-1	
53	Bexhill United v AFC Wimbledon	0-6	
54	Royston Town v Regents Park Rangers	2-3	35
55	Gillingham v Maidenhead United	4-0	
56	Southampton Women v Fleet Town	5-1	
57	Shanklin v St Nicholas	3-2	
58	Buckland Athletic v Keynsham Town (1.00)	2-3	
59	Torquay United v Brislington	2-4	
60	Poole Town v AEK Boco	3-0	
61	Ilminster Town v Plymouth Argyle	0-4	
62	Southampton Saints v Downend Flyers	8-2	
63	Larkhall Athletic v Cheltenham Town	9-1	25
64	New Milton Town v Exeter City	1-2	

FOURTH QUALIFYING ROUND

1	Sheffield United v Merseyrail Bootle	3-1	
	(at Swallownest Miners Welfare FC)		
2	Penrith v Norton & Stockton Ancients	0-4	
	(at Penrith AFC)		
3	Guiseley AFC Vixens v Nettleham (2.00)	7-1	
	(at Guiseley AFC)		
4	Liverpool Marshall Feds v Warrington Wolverines	7-1	
	(at IM Marsh Campus)		
5	RACA Tynedale v Crewe Alexandra	2-1	
	(at Ryton & Crawcrook Albion FC)		
6	Brighouse Town v Blackpool Wren Rovers	5-0	
	(at Brighouse Town FC)		
7	Hartlepool United v Accrington	7-1	
	(at Grayfields Sports Pavillion)		

8	Hull City v Leeds (2.00)	6-0	
	(at Hull University)		
9	Wallsend Boys Club v Sheffield Wednesday	1-2	
	(at Wallsend Boys Club)		
10	Sporting Khalsa v Wolverhampton Wanderers	2-4aet	
	(at Sporting Khalsa FC)		
11	Solihull Ladies v Burton Albion (2.30)	3-0	
	(at Studley FC)		
12	Radcliffe Olympic v Gornal	8-0	
	(at Radcliffe Olympic FC)		
13	Leek Town v Leicester City Women Dev	1-2aet	
	(at Leek Town FC)		
14	The New Saints v Birmingham & West Midlands	2-5	
	(at TNS FC)		
15	Long Eaton United v Coventry Ladies Dev	7-1	
	(at Long Eaton United FC)		
16	Acle United v Brentwood Town	3-0	68
	(at Great Yarmouth Town FC)		
17	Norwich City v Lowestoft Town (20/11)	3-3aet	
	(Norwich City won 4-3 on kicks from the penalty mark)		
	(at Norwich United FC)		
18	Cambridge United v Stevenage (2.00)	3-0	
	(at Mildenhall Town FC)		
19	Kettering Town v Peterborough Northern Star	0-3	50
	(at Burton Park Wanderers FC)		
20	Leyton Orient v Cambridge City	3-1	
	(at Mile End Park Stadium)		
21	Luton Town v Oxford City	6-1	61
	(at Stockwood Park Athletics Stadium)		
22	Chesham United v Regents Park Rangers	2-4	
	(at Chesham United FC)		
23	Hemel Hempstead Town v AFC Dunstable	2-0	100
	(at Hemel Hempstead Town FC)		
24	AFC Wimbledon v Denham United (2.00)	4-2	
	(at Cobham FC)		
25	Aylesford v Gillingham (1.30)	0-7	
	(at Aylesford Recreation Ground)		
26	Queens Park Rangers Dev v Milton Keynes Dons (2.00)	1-6	
	(at Hanwell Town FC)		
27	Brislington v Poole Town	8-0	
	(at Brislington FC)		
28	Southampton Saints v Exeter City (2.00)	10-0	35
	(at Sholing FC)		
29	Larkhall Athletic v Newbury (2.00)	8-1	30
	(at Larkhall Athletic FC)		
30	Plymouth Argyle v Basingstoke Town (20/11)	3-1	43
	(at Elburton Villa FC)		
31	Shanklin v Southampton Women (2.00)	0-3	
	(at County Ground, Shanklin)		
32	Chichester City v Keynsham Town (20/11)	1-2	
	(at Chichester City FC)		

FIRST ROUND

1	Radcliffe Olympic (at Radcliffe Olympic FC)	v	Sheffield Wednesday	6-0	60
2	Sheffield United (at Sheffield United FC)	v	Leicester City Women Dev	2-0	
3	Bradford City Women's (at Eccleshill United FC)	v	Blackburn Rovers	0-1	*
4	Stoke City (Liverpool Marsh Feds won 4-2 on kicks from the penalty mark) (at Norton United FC)	v	Liverpool Marshall Feds	1-1aet	
5	Guiseley AFC Vixens (at Guiseley AFC)	v	Nottingham Forest	0-1	53
6	Wolverhampton Wanderersv (at Hednesford Town FC)		Solihull Ladies (2.00)	4-0	40
7	Birmingham & West Midlands v (at Vale Stadium, Castle Vale, Birmingham)		Leicester City	0-3	28
8	Middlesbrough (at Thornaby FC)	v	Hartlepool United	1-0	237
9	West Bromwich Albion (at Rushall Olympic FC)	v	Fylde Ladies	4-1	
10	Huddersfield Town (at Shelley FC)	v	Derby County	0-1	76
11	RACA Tynedale (at Ryton & Crawcrook Albion FC)	v	Newcastle United	0-3	
12	Norton & Stockton Ancients v (at Norton & Stockton Ancients FC)		Hull City	1-6	200
13	Long Eaton United (walkover for Long Eaton United – Nuneaton Town withdrawn)	v	Nuneaton Town		
14	Brighouse Town (at Brighouse Town FC)	v	Peterborough Northern Star	3-2	54
15	Southampton Saints (at Sholing FC)	v	Gillingham	1-7	
16	Acle United (at Great Yarmouth Town FC)	v	C&K Basildon	0-2	108
17	Cardiff City (at CCB Centre for Sporting Excellence, Caerphilly)	v	Larkhall Athletic (2.00)	6-0	105
18	Tottenham Hotspur (at Cheshunt FC)	v	Leyton Orient	1-0	51
19	Cambridge United (at Mildenhall Town FC)	v	Queens Park Rangers	3-1	
20	Milton Keynes Dons (at Newport Pagnell Town FC)	v	Hemel Hempstead Town	3-1	95
21	Plymouth Argyle (walkover for Plymouth Argyle – Forest Green Rovers withdrawn)	v	Forest Green Rovers		
22	Lewes (at Lewes FC)	v	Brislington (2.00)	5-0	60
23	West Ham United (at Thurrock FC)	v	Coventry United (2.00)	0-3	47
24	Crystal Palace (at Crystal Palace FC)	v	Charlton Athletic	1-2	562
25	Luton Town (at Stockwood Park Athletics Stadium)	v	Portsmouth	1-4	44
26	Norwich City (at Norwich United FC)	v	AFC Wimbledon	1-4	
27	Southampton Women (at Hamble Club FC)	v	Swindon Town (11/12)	2-0	
28	Regents Park Rangers (at Kew Association FC)	v	Keynsham Town	1-6	

SECOND ROUND

1	Long Eaton United (at Long Eaton United FC)	v	Brighouse Town	3-4	
2	Derby County	v	Sheffield United	3-2aet	240
	(at Mickleover Sports FC)				
3	West Bromwich Albion (at Rushall Olympic FC)	v	Radcliffe Olympic	4-0	
4	Nottingham Forest (at Basford United FC)	v	Wolverhampton Wanderers	4-0	
5	Middlesbrough (at Thornaby FC)	v	Leicester City	1-2aet	
6	Blackburn Rovers (at Bamber Bridge FC)	v	Hull City	5-0	
7	Liverpool Marshall Feds (at IM Marsh Campus)	v	Newcastle United	1-0	
8	Coventry United (at Coleshill Town FC)	v	Milton Keynes Dons	4-0	81
9	C&K Basildon (at Canvey Island FC)	v	Keynsham Town	1-3	
10	Lewes (at Lewes FC)	v	Cardiff City (2.00)	2-0	110
11	Tottenham Hotspur (at Cheshunt FC)	v	Gillingham	3-0	111
12	Plymouth Argyle (at Elburton Villa FC)	v	AFC Wimbledon	0-3	
13	Cambridge United (at Mildenhall Town FC)	v	Southampton Women	4-0	110
14	Charlton Athletic (at Charlton Athletic FC)	v	Portsmouth	5-0	

THIRD ROUND

1	Blackburn Rovers (at Bamber Bridge FC)	v	Tottenham Hotspur	1-2	
2	Charlton Athletic (at Sporting Club Thamesmead FC)	v	Sheffield FC Ladies	0-2	153
3	Aston Villa (at Tamworth FC)	v	Cambridge United	7-1	
4	Millwall Lionesses (at St Pauls Sports Ground)	v	London Bees	1-0	
5	Leicester City Women (at Riverside Pavilion)	v	Liverpool Marshall Feds	2-1	
6	Keynsham Town (at Keynsham Town FC)	v	Durham Women	0-7	138
7	Coventry United (at Coleshill Town FC)	v	Oxford United	2-0	189
8	West Bromwich Albion (at Rushall Olympic FC)	v	Lewes	3-1	
9	Doncaster Rovers Belles v (walkover for Doncaster Rovers Belles - Watford withdrawn)		Watford		
10	Derby County (at Mickleover Sports FC)	v	Nottingham Forest	0-1	633
11	Brighouse Town (at Brighouse Town FC)	v	Everton (3.00)	1-8	
12	AFC Wimbledon (at Sutton United FC)	v	Brighton & Hove Albion	1-4	550

FOURTH ROUND

1	Durham	v	Everton	2-2aet	365
	(Everton won 4-3 on kicks from the penalty mark) (at Durham City FC)				
2	Coventry United	v	Aston Villa	0-1	364
	(at Rugby Town FC)				
3	Millwall Lionesses	v	Nottingham Forest	3-1	
	(at St Pauls Sports Ground)				
4	West Bromwich Albion	v	Leicester City Women	2-1	
	(at Rushall Olympic FC)				
5	Tottenham Hotspur	v	Brighton & Hove Albion	1-0	127
	(at Cheshunt FC)				
6	Sheffield FC	v	Doncaster Rovers Belles	0-1	
	(at Sheffield FC)				

FIFTH ROUND

1	Notts County	v	Yeovil Town	3-2	443
	(at Eastwood Town CFC)				
2	Liverpool	v	Everton	2-1aet	728
	(at Select Security Stadium, Widnes)				
3	Arsenal	v	Tottenham Hotspur	10-0	1400
	(at Boreham Wood FC)				
4	Sunderland	v	Aston Villa	3-2	262
	(at The Hetton Centre)				
5	Birmingham City	v	West Bromwich Albion	2-0	1122
	(at Solihull Moors FC)				
6	Bristol City	v	Millwall Lionesses	5-0	466
	(at Stoke Gifford Stadium)				
7	Manchester City	v	Reading (18/3)	1-0	
	(at Academy Arena)				
8	Chelsea	v	Doncaster Rovers Belles	7-0	806
	(at Staines Town FC)				

SIXTH ROUND

1	Birmingham City	v	Arsenal	1-0	514
	(at Solihull Moors FC)				
2	Chelsea	v	Sunderland	5-1	682
	(at Staines Town FC)				
3	Bristol City	v	Manchester City	1-2	594
	(at Stoke Gifford Stadium)				
4	Liverpool	v	Notts County	2-0	302
	(at Select Security Stadium, Widnes)				

SEMI FINALS

1	Birmingham City	v	Chelsea	1-1aet	1425
	(Birmingham City won 4-2 on kicks from the penalty mark - at Solihull Moors FC)				
2	Manchester City	v	Liverpool	1-0	3453
	(at Academy Stadium)				

THE FINAL

Saturday 13 May - @ Wembley Stadium

Birmingham City	v	Manchester City	1-4	35,271

New record crowd for Women's FA Cup

FA County Youth Cup (R2) - Norfolk net their winning goal in the final minute of extra-time to leave Bedfordshire distraught. Photo: Gordon Whittington.

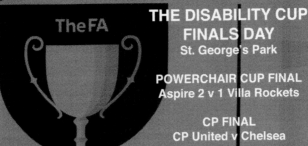

The FA

THE DISABILITY CUP FINALS DAY
St. George's Park

POWERCHAIR CUP FINAL
Aspire 2 v 1 Villa Rockets

CP FINAL
CP United v Chelsea

BLIND CUP FINAL
Merseyside 3 v 2 RNC Shrews

The FA

FOR ALL

Left: Merseyside Blind squad with action from the final below.

Above: Powerchair Cup winners Aspire and, right, in action against Villa Rockets.

Above: CP United after their victory in the CP Cup Final against Chelsea, and above them Foster puts United on their way to the win.

All photos by Keith Clayton.

COUNTY FOOTBALL ASSOCIATION CONTACTS

AMATEUR FOOTBALL ALLIANCE
Tel: 020 8733 2613 Fax: 020 7250 1338
Website: www.amateur-fa.com
Email: info@amateur-fa.com

ARMY FA
Tel: 01252 787 067 Fax: 01252 787 072
Website: www.armyfa.com
Email: info@armyfa.com

BEDFORDSHIRE FA
Tel: 01582 565 111 Fax: 01582 565 222
Website: www.bedfordshirefa.com
Email: info@bedfordshirefa.com

BERKS & BUCKS FA
Tel: 01367 242 099 Fax: 01367 242 158
Website: www.berks-bucksfa.com
Email: info@berks-bucksfa.com

BIRMINGHAM FA
Tel: 0121 357 4278 Fax: 0121 358 1661
Website: www.birminghamfa.com
Email: info@birminghamfa.com

CAMBRIDGESHIRE FA
Tel: 01223 209 025 Fax: 01223 209 030
Website: www.cambridgeshirefa.com
Email: info@cambridgeshirefa.com

CHESHIRE FA
Tel: 01606 871 166 Fax: 01606 871 292
Website: www.cheshirefa.com
Email: info@cheshirefa.com

CORNWALL FA
Tel: 01208 269010 Fax: 01208 892665
Website: www.cornwallfa.com
Email: info@cornwallfa.com

CUMBERLAND FA
Tel: 01900 872 310
Fax: 01900 616 470
Website: www.cumberlandfa.com
Email: info@cumberlandfa.com

DERBYSHIRE FA
Tel: 01332 361 422 Fax: 01332 360 130
Website: www.derbyshirefa.com
Email: info@derbyshirefa.com

DEVON FA
Tel: 01626 332 077 Fax: 01626 336 814
Website: www.devonfa.com
Email: info@devonfa.com

DORSET FA
Tel: 01202 682 375 Fax: 01202 666 577
Website: www.dorsetfa.com
Email: info@dorsetfa.com

DURHAM FA
Tel: 01913 872 929
Website: www.durhamfa.com
Email: info@durhamfa.com

EAST RIDING FA
Tel: 01482 221 158 Fax: 01482 221 169
Website: www.eastridingfa.com
Email: info@eastridingfa.com

ENGLISH SCHOOLS FA
Tel: 01785 785 970 Fax: 01785 785 971
Website: www.esfa.co.uk
Email: info@schoolsfa.com

ESSEX FA
Tel: 01245 465 271 Fax: 01245 393 089
Website: www.essexfa.com
Email: info@essexfa.com

GLOUCESTERSHIRE FA
Tel: 01454 615 888 Fax: 01454 618 088
Website: www.gloucestershirefa.com
Email: info@gloucestershirefa.com

GUERNSEY FA
Tel: 01481 200 443 Fax: 01481 200 451
Website: www.guernseyfa.com
Email: info@guernseyfa.com

HAMPSHIRE FA
Tel: 01256 853 000 Fax: 01256 357 973
Website: www.hampshirefa.com
Email: info@hampshirefa.com

HEREFORDSHIRE FA
Tel: 01432 342 179 Fax: 01432 279 265
Website: www.herefordshirefa.com
Email: info@herefordshirefa.com

HERTFORDSHIRE FA
Tel: 01462 677622 Fax: 01462 677624
Website: www.hertfordshirefa.com
Email: info@hertfordshirefa.com

HUNTINGDONSHIRE FA
Website: www.huntsfa.com
Email: info@huntsfa.com

ISLE OF MAN FA
Tel: 01624 615 576 Fax: 01624 615 578
Website: www.isleofmanfa.com
Email: info@isleofmanfa.com

JERSEY FA
Tel: 01534 730 433 Fax: 01534 500 029
Website: www.jerseyfa.com
Email: info@jerseyfa.com

KENT FA
Tel: Governance 01622 791850,
Development 01622 792140
Fax: 01622 790658
Website: www.kentfa.com
Email: info@kentfa.com

LANCASHIRE FA
Tel: 01772 624 000 Fax: 01772 624 700
Website: www.lancashirefa.com
Email: info@lancashirefa.com

LEICESTERSHIRE & RUTLAND FA
Tel: 0116 2 867 828
Website: www.leicestershirefa.com
Email: info@leicestershirefa.com

LINCOLNSHIRE FA
Tel: 01522 524 917 Fax: 01522 528 859
Website: www.lincolnshirefa.com
Email: info@lincolnshirefa.com

LIVERPOOL FA
Tel: 01515 234 488 Fax: 01515 234 477
Website: www.liverpoolfa.com
Email: info@liverpoolfa.com

LONDON FA
Tel: 020 7610 8360 Fax: 020 7610 8370
Website: www.londonfa.com
Email: info@londonfa.com

MANCHESTER FA
Tel: 01616 047 620 Fax: 01616 047 622
Website: www.manchesterfa.com
Email: info@manchesterfa.com

MIDDLESEX FA
Tel: 020 8515 1919 Fax: 020 8515 1910
Website: www.middlesexfa.com
Email: info@middlesexfa.com

NORFOLK FA
Tel: 01603 704 050 Fax: 01603 704 059
Website: www.norfolkfa.com
Email: info@norfolkfa.com

NORTHAMPTONSHIRE FA
Tel: 01604 670 741 Fax: 01604 670 742
Website: www.northamptonshirefa.com
Email: info@northamptonshirefa.com

NORTH RIDING FA
Tel: 01642 717 770 Fax: 01642 717 776
Website: www.northridingfa.com
Email: info@northridingfa.com

NORTHUMBERLAND FA
Tel: 01912 700 700 Fax: 01912 700 700
Website: www.northumberlandfa.com
Email: info@northumberlandfa.com

NOTTINGHAMSHIRE FA
Tel: 0115 983 7400 Fax: 0115 946 1977
Website: www.nottinghamshirefa.com
Email: info@nottinghamshirefa.com

OXFORDSHIRE FA
Tel: 01993 894400 Fax: 01993 772 191
Website: www.oxfordshirefa.com
Email: info@oxfordshirefa.com

RAF FA
Tel: 01993 895 704 Fax: 01993 895 545
Website: www.royalairforcefa.com
Email: info@royalairforcefa.com

ROYAL NAVY FA
Tel: 02392 722 671 Fax: 02932 724 923
Website: www.royalnavyfa.com
Email: info@navyfa.com

SHEFFIELD & HALLAMSHIRE FA
Tel: 0114 261 5500
Website: www.sheffieldfa.com
Email: info@sheffieldfa.com

SHROPSHIRE FA
Tel: 01743 362 769 Fax: 01743 270 494
Website: www.shropshirefa.com
Email: info@shropshirefa.com

SOMERSET FA
Tel: 01458 832359 Fax: 01458 835588
Website: www.somersetfa.com
Email: info@somersetfa.com

STAFFORDSHIRE FA
Tel: 01785 256 994 Fax: 01785 279 837
Website: www.staffordshirefa.com
Email: info@staffordshirefa.com

SUFFOLK FA
Tel: 01449 616 606 Fax: 01449 616 607
Website: www.suffolkfa.com
Email: info@suffolkfa.com

SURREY FA
Tel: 01372 373 543 Fax: 01372 361 310
Website: www.surreyfa.com
Email: info@surreyfa.com

SUSSEX FA
Tel: 01903 753 547 Fax: 01903 761 608
Website: www.sussexfa.com
Email: info@sussexfa.com

WESTMORLAND FA
Tel: 01539 730 946 Fax: 01539 740 567
Website: www.westmorlandfa.com
Email: info@westmorlandfa.com

WEST RIDING FA
Tel: 01132 821 222 Fax: 01132 821 525
Website: www.wrcfa.com
Email: info@wrcfa.com

WILTSHIRE FA
Tel: 01793 486 047 Fax: 01793 692 699
Website: www.wiltshirefa.com
Email: info@wiltshirefa.com

WORCESTERSHIRE FA
Tel: 01905 827 137 Fax: 01905 798 963
Website: www.worcestershirefa.com
Email: info@worcestershirefa.com

COUNTY & MISCELLANEOUS CUPS

A.F.A. Senior Cup
HOLDERS: West Wickham
Quarter-Finals

Old Wilsonians	v	Old Carthusians	1-1
Winchmore Hill	v	Nottsborough	0-4
Polytechnic	v	Old Parkonians	3-0
Old Meadonians	v	Old Parmiterians	3-0

Semi-Finals

Nottsborough	v	Old Carthusians	0-2
Old Meadonians	v	Polytechnic	1-3

Final

Polytechnic	v	Old Carthusians	4-1

A.F.A. Middlesex/Essex Senior Cup
HOLDERS: Polytechnic
Quarter-Finals

Actonians Association	v	Crouch End Vampires	3-1
NUFC Oilers	v	Old Parkonians	0-3
Old Hamptonians	v	Polytechnic	3-1
Old Manorians	v	Latymer Old Boys	1-2 aet

Semi-Finals

Old Parkonians	v	Actonians Association	2-5
Latymer Old Boys	v	Old Hamptonians	0-5

Final

Old Hamptonians	v	Actonians Association	0-2

A.F.A. Surrey/Kent Senior Cup
HOLDERS: Nottsborough
Quarter-Finals

West Wickham	v	Clapham Old Xaverians	1-3
Mickleham Old Boxhillians	v	Nottsborough	1-7
Old Thorntonians	v	Merton	2-1
Dorkinians	v	Old Wokingians	1-0

Semi-Finals

Clapham Old Xaverians	v	Old Thorntonians	1-3
Nottsborough	v	Dorkinians	5-0

Final

Nottsborough	v	Old Thorntonians	4-0

Arthur Dunn Cup
HOLDERS: Old Tonbridgians
Quarter-Finals

Old Salopians	v	Lancing Old Boys	2-1
Old Brentwoods	v	Old Reptonians	0-1
Old Chigwellians	v	Old Etonians	0-3
Old Berkhamstedians	v	Old Carthusians	0-3

Semi-Finals

Old Salopians	v	Old Reptonians	2-2
Old Reptonians	v	Old Salopians	2-1
Old Etonians	v	Old Carthusians	1-1
Old Carthusians	v	Old Etonians	1-0

Final

Old Reptonians	v	Old Carthusians	1-3

Bedfordshire Senior Challenge Cup
HOLDERS: Barton Rovers
Quarter-Finals

Dunstable Town	v	Crawley Green	1-1, 4-2p
Stotfold	v	Luton Town	1-2
AFC Dunstable	v	Bedford Town	3-1
Kempston Rovers	v	Arlesey Town	0-0, 5-4p

Semi-Finals

Kempston Rovers	v	AFC Dunstable	0-3
Dunstable Town	v	Luton Town	3-0

Final

Dunstable Town	v	AFC Dunstable	0-2

Bedfordshire Senior Trophy
HOLDERS: Ampthill Town
Quarter-Finals

The 61 FC (Luton)	v	Ampthill Town	1-0
Kempston Rovers U21	v	Flitwick Town	4-1
Shefford Town & Campton	v	AFC Kempston T. & Bedford Col.	0-1
Langford	v	Sharnbrook	3-1

Semi-Finals

AFC Kempston T. & Bedford Col.	v	Kempston Rovers U21	1-0
Langford	v	The 61 FC (Luton)	1-1, 4-5p

Final

AFC Kempston T. & Bedford Col.	v	The 61 FC (Luton)	1-1, 2-4p

Bedfordshire Intermediate Cup
HOLDERS: Sundon Park Rangers
Final

Potton United Res	v	AFC Dunstable U21	2-2, 6-7p

Bedfordshire Junior Cup
HOLDERS: Cople & Bedford S.A.
Final

Cranfield United Res	v	Riseley Sports	0-2

Berks & Bucks Senior Cup
HOLDERS: Aylesbury
Quarter-Finals

Slough Town	v	Milton Keynes Dons	3-0
Wantage Town	v	Hungerford Town	0-3
Marlow	v	Maidenhead United	1-2
Aylesbury	v	Chesham United	0-5

Semi-Finals

Maidenhead United	v	Slough Town	4-2
Chesham United	v	Hungerford Town	2-5

Final

Hungerford Town	v	Maidenhead United	0-1

Berks & Bucks Senior Trophy
HOLDERS: Flackwell Heath
Quarter-Finals

Binfield	v	Windsor	4-2
Newport Pagnell Town	v	Burnham	4-1
Bracknell Town	v	Holmer Green	2-0
Flackwell Heath	v	Highmoor Ibis	4-0

Semi-Finals

Flackwell Heath	v	Bracknell Town	1-2
Newport Pagnell Town	v	Binfield	3-6

Final

Bracknell Town	v	Binfield	2-0

Berks & Bucks Intermediate Cup
HOLDERS: Risborough Rangers
Final

Woodley United	v	Marlow United	2-1

Berks & Bucks Junior Cup
HOLDERS: Kintbury Rangers Res
Final

Olney Town Res	v	New Zealand FC (Aylesbury)	1-2

Birmingham Senior Cup
HOLDERS: Solihull Moors
Quarter-Finals

Sutton Coldfield Town	v	Birmingham City	3-1
Solihull Moor	v	Walsall	1-2
Burton Albion	v	Wolverhampton Wanderers	0-3
Leamington	v	Stratford Town	2-1

Semi-Finals

Sutton Coldfield Town	v	Wolverhampton Wanderers 2-2, 3-4p	
Leamington	v	Walsall	2-1

Final

Leamington	v	Wolverhampton Wanderers 1-1, 5-4p	

Birmingham Vase
HOLDERS: A E I Rugby
Final

Coton Green	v	Wednesfield	0-2

Birmingham Amateur Cup
HOLDERS: Cadbury Athletic Res
Final

Coventry United U21	v	Two Gates	4-0

Channel Islands - Muratti Vase
HOLDERS: Jersey
Final

Guernsey	v	Jersey	2-1

Break down of Muratti Vase Wins

Jersey	53	Guernsey	46	Shared 1	Alderney	1

Cheshire Senior Cup
HOLDERS: Stockport County
Quarter-Finals

Witton Albion	v	Warrington Town	1-3
Nantwich Town	v	1874 Northwich	3-1
Hyde United	v	Altrincham	2-1
Crewe Alexandra	v	Stockport County	2-1

Semi-Finals

Nantwich Town	v	Warrington Town	0-0, 5-3p
Hyde United	v	Crewe Alexandra	0-4

Final

Crwe Alexandra	v	Nantwich Town	3-2

Cornwall Senior Cup
HOLDERS: Bodmin Town
Quarter-Finals

Torpoint Athletic	v	Falmouth Town	2-3
Saltash United	v	Holman Sports Club	4-1
Ludgvan	v	Bodmin Town	3-3, 3-5p
Millbrook	v	Newquay	2-4

Semi-Finals

Falmouth Town	v	Saltash United	2-4
Newquay	v	Bodmin Town	2-5

Final

Bodmin Town	v	Saltash United	2-1

Cornwall Junior Cup
HOLDERS: Callington Town 3rds
Final

St Stephen	v	St Minver	1-3

Cumberland Senior Cup
HOLDERS: Workington
Quarter-Finals

Pirelli	v	Whitehaven	4-0
Carlisle City	v	Netherhall	3-0
Silloth	v	Penrith	1-1, 5-6p
Workington	v	Cleator Moor Celtic	5-1

Semi-Finals

Pirelli	v	Workington	1-1, 2-4p
Penrith	v	Carlisle City	1-1, 3-2p

Final

Penrith	v	Workington	1-2 aet

Derbyshire Senior Challenge Cup
HOLDERS: Alfreton Town
Quarter-Finals

Alfreton Town	v	Borrowash Victoria	3-0
Gresley	v	Glossop North End	3-1
Matlock Town	v	Chesterfield	4-2
Buxton	v	South Normanton Athletic	5-1

Semi-Finals

Gresley	v	Buxton	3-0
Matlock Town	v	Alfreton Town	3-3, 5-4p

Final

Matlock Town	v	Gresley	5-0

Devon St Lukes Cup
HOLDERS: Plymouth Argyle
Quarter-Finals

Tiverton Town	v	Bideford	3-1
Plymouth Parkway	v	Ivybridge Town	5-1
Cullompton Rangers	v	Exmouth Town	1-4
Willand Rovers	v	Exeter City	1-3

Semi-Finals

Exmouth Town	v	Exeter City	2-2, 4-1p
Plymouth Parkway	v	Tiverton Town	1-3

Final

Tiverton Town	v	Exmouth Town	3-1

Devon Premier Cup
HOLDERS: Appledore
Quarter-Finals

University of Exeter	v	Elmore	5-1
The Windmill	v	Stoke Gabriel	3-1
Newton	v	East Allington United	1-3
Crediton United	v	Braunton	3-1

Semi-Finals

University of Exeter	v	Crediton United	2-1
East Allington United	v	The Windmill	1-4

Final

University of Exeter	v	The Windmill	3-0

Devon Senior Cup
HOLDERS: University of Exeter Res
Quarter-Finals

Lakeside Athletic	v	Witheridge Res	4-2
Northam Lions	v	Cronies	1-8
Ilfracombe Town Res	v	University of Exeter Res	0-2
Alphington Res	v	Roselands	1-2

Semi-Finals

Cronies	v	University of Exeter Res	4-1
Roselands	v	Lakeside Athletic	4-0

Final

Roselands	v	Cronies	0-3

Devon Intermediate Cup
HOLDERS: Sporting Barum
Final

Chaddlewood Inn	v	Royal Oak	0-3

RISELEY SPORTS
Bedfordshire Junior Cup
Winners

MILL LANE
Hertfordshire Junior Cup
Winners

EATON SOCON RESERVES
Huntingdonshire Junior Cup
Winners

EATON SOCON
Huntingdonshire Intermediate Cup
Winners

JAMES KING BLISWORTH
Northants Junior Cup
Winners
(Also winners of the Northants Combination
Premier and Cup double)

Photos: Gordon Whittington

Dorset Senior Cup
HOLDERS: Weymouth
Quarter-Finals

Hamworthy United	v	Gillingham Town	1-3
Sherborne Town	v	Weymouth	0-4
Portland United	v	Swanage Town & Herston	3-4
Poole Town	v	Wimborne Town	3-4

Semi-Finals

Gillingham Town	v	Swanage Town & Herston	5-0
Weymouth	v	Wimborne Town	2-0

Final

Weymouth	v	Gillingham Town	1-0 aet

Dorset Senior Trophy
HOLDERS: Merley Cobham Sports
Quarter-Finals

Sherborne Town Res	v	Portland United Res	0-4
Wareham Rangers	v	Holt United	1-3
Shaftesbury Town Res	v	Parley Sports	3-6 aet
Blandford United	v	Merley Cobham Sports	2-0

Semi-Finals

Blandford United	v	Parley Sports	0-2
Holt United	v	Portland United Res	8-1

Final

Holt United	v	Parley Sports	2-2, 4-5p

Dorset Intermediate Cup
HOLDERS: Chickerell United Res
Final

Lower Parkstone CFC	v	Corfe Castle	4-1

Dorset Junior Cup
HOLDERS: Portland United Youth
Final

Halstock	v	Okeford United	1-3

Durham Senior Challenge Cup
HOLDERS: Newton Aycliffe
Final

Billingham Synthonia	v	South Shields	0-2

East Riding Senior Cup
HOLDERS: Bridlington Town
Quarter-Finals

Bridlington Town	v	Dunnington	2-0
Hull City	v	South Cave United	6-2
Pocklington Town	v	Crown	4-0
Hanson Jewellers	v	Hall Road Rangers	2-2, 0-3p

Semi-Finals

Hull City	v	Hall Road Rangers	4-1
Pocklington Town	v	Bridlington Town	1-3

Final

Bridlington Town	v	Hull City	4-2

Essex Senior Cup
HOLDERS: Concord Rangers
Quarter-Finals

Chelmsford City	v	Braintree Town	2-0
Billericay Town	v	Tilbury	1-1, 2-4p
East Thurrock United	v	Colchester United	2-0
Heybridge Swifts	v	Basildon United	2-0

Semi-Finals

Chelmsford City	v	Heybridge Swifts	4-0
East Thurrock United	v	Tilbury	3-2

Final

Chelmsford City	v	East Thurrock United	1-0

Essex Premier Cup
HOLDERS: Frenford Senior
Quarter-Finals

Rayleigh Town	v	May & Baker Eastbrook Comm.	1-3
Catholic United	v	Frenford Senior	3-1
Kelvedon Hatch	v	Leigh Ramblers	3-2
Harold Wood Athletic	v	Springfield	2-1

Semi-Finals

Kelvedon Hatch	v	Harold Wood Athletic	0-0, 5-6p
Catholic United	v	May & Baker Eastbrook Comm.	2-1

Final

Catholic United	v	Harold Wood Athletic	1-0

(Catholic United fielded an ineligible player; trophy awarded to Harold Wood Athletic)

Essex Junior Cup
HOLDERS: Chingford Athletic
Final

May & Baker Eastbrook C.	v	Wormingford Wanderers	1-1, 4-3p

Gloucestershire Senior Challenge Cup
HOLDERS: Forest Green Rovers
Quarter-Finals

Yate Town	v	Mangotsfield United	0-1
Cirencester Town	v	Shortwood United	1-0
Bristol City U23	v	Forest Green Rovers	1-0
Cinderford Town	v	Bristol Rovers U21/Res	6-1

Semi-Finals

Cinderford Town	v	Cirencester Town	1-3
Mangotsfield United	v	Bristol City U23	0-3

Final

Bristol City U23	v	Cirencester Town	02/08/17

Gloucestershire Challenge Trophy
HOLDERS: Bristol Manor Farm
Quarter-Finals

Lydney Town	v	Bristol Manor Farm	1-3
Brimscombe & Thrupp	v	Cirencester Town Dev.	5-0
Fairford Town	v	Chipping Sodbury Town	3-2
Cadbury Heath	v	Kingswood (North) AFC	4-2

Semi-Finals

Bristol Manor Farm	v	Fairford Town	1-3
Brimscombe & Thrupp	v	Cadbury Heath	2-3

Final

Cadbury Heath	v	Fairford Town	2-2, 4-3p

Hampshire Senior Cup
HOLDERS: Havant & Waterlooville
Quarter-Finals

Basingstoke Town	v	AFC Stoneham	2-0
Sholing	v	Winchester City	0-1
Gosport Borough	v	AFC Bournemouth	0-6
AFC Totton	v	Hartley Wintney	1-3

Semi-Finals

Basingstoke Town	v	Winchester City	3-1
Hartley Wintney	v	AFC Bournemouth	0-1

Final

Basingstoke Town	v	AFC Bournemouth	0-0, 7-6p

Herefordshire Challenge Cup
HOLDERS: Hereford
Quarter-Finals

Kington Town	v	Westfields	1-5
Leominster Town	v	Hereford Lads Club	1-4
Bromyard Town	v	Pegasus Juniors	0-3
Hereford	v	Holme Lacy	4-0

Semi-Finals

Westfields	v	Hereford Lads Club	1-1, 2-4p
Pegasus Juniors	v	Hereford	1-3

Final

Hereford Lads Club	v	Herefield	3-0

Herts Senior Challenge Cup
HOLDERS: Hitchin Town
Quarter-Finals

Cheshunt	v	Leverstock Green	4-2
Bishop's Stortford	v	Hoddesdon Town	2-2, 4-3p
Ware	v	Kings Langley	2-2, 3-1p
St Albans City	v	Hitchin Town	2-2, 3-5p

Semi-Finals

Hitchin Town	v	Cheshunt	3-1
Ware	v	Bishop's Stortford	3-7

Final

Hitchin Town	v	Bishop's Stortford	2-1

Hertfordshire Senior Centenary Trophy
HOLDERS: Bishop's Stortford Swifts
Quarter-Finals

Bishop's Stortford Swifts	v	Belstone	4-0
London Lions	v	Letchworth Garden City	4-0
Sandridge Rovers	v	Baldock Town	2-1
Sarratt	v	Wodson Park	2-7

Semi-Finals

London Lions	v	Bishop's Stortford Swifts	5-0
Sandridge Rovers	v	Wodson Park	0-1

Final

London Lions	v	Wodson Park	3-0

Herts Senior Challenge Cup
HOLDERS: Hadley A
Final

Mill Lane	v	Croxley Green CC	2-0

Huntingdonshire Senior Cup
HOLDERS: St Ives Town
Quarter-Finals

Yaxley	v	Godmanchester Rovers	1-2
Huntingdon Town	v	Eynesbury Rovers	0-4

Semi-Finals

St Neots Town	v	Godmanchester Rovers	1-1, 5-4p
Eynesbury Rovers	v	St Ives Town	2-0

Final

Eynesbury Rovers	v	St Neots Town	1-0

Huntingdonshire Intermediate Cup
HOLDERS: Brampton
Final

Peterborough ICA Sports	v	Eaton Socon	1-2

Huntingdonshire Junior Cup
HOLDERS: Houghton & Wyton
Final

Eaton Socon Res	v	Ramsey Town	2-1

Isle of Man FA Cup
HOLDERS: Peel
Quarter-Finals

Peel	v	Braddan	8-1
Foxdale	v	Douglas & District	2-1
St Georges	v	Rushden United	6-2 aet
Douglas Athletic	v	St Marys	4-3

Semi-Finals

Peel	v	Foxdale	2-1
St Georges	v	Douglas Athletic	5-1

Final

Peel	v	St Georges	2-3 aet

Kent Senior Cup
HOLDERS: Dartford
Quarter-Finals

Folkestone Invicta	v	Ramsgate	4-2
Welling United	v	Bromley	1-0
Margate	v	Charlton Athletic	1-2
Dover Athletic	v	VCD Athletic	4-0

Semi-Finals

Dover Athletic	v	Folkestone Invicta	3-0
Welling United	v	Cahrlton Atheltic	1-1, 2-0p

Final

Dover Athletic	v	Welling United	2-0

Kent Senior Trophy
HOLDERS: Sheppey United
Quarter-Finals

Deal Town	v	Sevenoaks Town	3-2 aet
Canterbury City	v	Glebe	1-0
Cray Valley	v	Lordswood	4-0
Whitstable Town	v	Ashford United	0-1

Semi-Finals

Deal Town	v	Cray Valley	2-2, 1-3p
Ashford United	v	Canterbury City	3-0

Final

Ashford United	v	Cray Valley	2-1

Kent Intermediate Cup
HOLDERS: Greenwich Borough Res
Final

Hollands & Blair Res	v	Faversham Town U21	1-0

Lancashire Senior Cup
HOLDERS: Everton
Quarter-Finals

Fleetwood Town	v	Morecambe	4-0
Southport	v	Blackburn Rovers	1-1, 2-3p
Barrow	v	Rochdale	1-3
Liverpool	v	Bolton Wanderers	3-1

Semi-Finals

Liverpool	v	Rochdale	6-0
Blackburn Rovers	v	Fleetwood Town	1-1, 3-4p

Final

Fleetwood Town	v	Liverpool	09/08/17

Lancashire Challenge Trophy
HOLDERS: Chorley
Quarter-Finals

Clitheroe	v	AFC Fylde	2-1
Ashton Athletic	v	Atherton Laburnum Rovers	3-0
Radcliffe Borough	v	West Disbury & Chorlton	1-1, 3-1p
Daisy Hill	v	Chorley	1-5

Semi-Finals

Radcliffe Borough	v	Clitheroe	2-1
Ashton Athletic	v	Chorley	1-1, 5-4p

Final

Ashton Athletic	v	Radcliffe Borough	2-1

Leicestershire Challenge Cup
HOLDERS: Leicester Nirvana
Quarter-Finals

Blaby & Whetstone Athletic	v	St Andrews	1-3
Harborough Town	v	Leicester Nirvana	4-0
Coalville Town	v	Ellistown & Ibstock United	HW
Shepshed Dynamo	v	Barwell	1-3

Semi-Finals

Harborough Town	v	Coalville Town	2-6 aet
Barwell	v	St Andrews	4-0

Final

Barwell	v	Coalville Town	3-1

Leicestershire Senior Cup
HOLDERS: Hinckley AFC
Quarter-Finals

Leicester Road	v	Barrow Town	3-2
Heather St John's	v	Ashby Ivanhoe Res	4-2
Melton Town	v	Holwell Sports	1-3
Aylestone Park Youth Sen.	v	Lutterworth Town	1-5

Semi Finals

Holwell Sports	v	Heather St John's	2-2, 4-1p
Leicester Road	v	Lutterworth Town	4-0

Final

Leicester Road	v	Holwell Sports	2-1

Lincolnshire Senior Cup
HOLDERS: Gainsborough Trinity
Quarter-Finals

Stamford	v	Grimsby Town	2-1
Grantham Town	v	Lincoln City	1-5
Lincoln United	v	Gainsborough Trinity	2-1
Boston United	v	Spalding United	0-1

Semi-Finals

Lincoln United	v	Lincoln City	2-0
Stamford	v	Spalding United	2-1

Final

Stamford	v	Lincoln United	2-3

Lincolnshire Senior Trophy
HOLDERS: Winterton Rangers
Quarter-Finals

Deeping Rangers	v	Blackstones	3-1
Boston Town	v	Holbeach United	3-2
Bottesford Town	v	Barton Town Old Boys	2-3
Winterton Rangers	v	Cleethorpes Town	2-7

Semi-Finals

Deeping Rangers	v	Boston Town	2-1
Cleethorpes Town	v	Barton Town Old Boys	6-1

Final

Cleethorpes Town	v	Deeping Rangers	1-0

Liverpool Senior Cup
HOLDERS: Everton
Quarter-Finals

Litherland Remyca	v	Everton	1-0
Tranmere Rovers	v	Bootle	2-2, 4-5p
Prescot Cables	v	AFC Liverpool	2-0
Widnes FC	v	Southport	1-3

Semi-Finals

Southport	v	Litherland Remyca	3-2
Bootle	v	Prescot Cables	1-5

Final

Prescot Cables	v	Southport	2-0

Liverpool Challenge Cup
HOLDERS: South Liverpool
Quarter-Finals

Waterloo Dock	v	Liverpool Nalgo	3-2
Maghull	v	MSB Woolton	1-2
Lower Beck	v	South Liverpool	0-2
Vulcan	v	Byrom	1-2

Semi-Finals

MSB Woolton	v	South Liverpool	0-2
Waterloo Dock	v	Byrom	2-3

Final

Byrom	v	South Liverpool	0-5

London Senior Cup
HOLDERS: Tooting & Mitcham United
Quarter-Finals

Cray Valley (PM)	v	AFC Wimbledon	2-1
Haringey Borough	v	Greenwich Borough	5-2
Wingate & Finchley	v	Met Police	1-2
Dulwich Hamlet	v	Tooting & Mitcham United	3-1

Semi-Finals

Met Police	v	Haringey Borough	3-2
Cray Valley (PM)	v	Dulwich Hamlet	3-2 aet

Final

Cray Valley (PM)	v	Met Police	2-1

London Senior Trophy
HOLDERS: Glebe
Quarter-Finals

Bridon Ropes	v	Barking Res	4-2
Glebe	v	South Kilburn	8-0
Newham United	v	FC Elmstead (1958)	1-0
Tooting Bec	v	Balham	0-4

Semi-Finals

Bridon Ropes	v	Balham	0-3
Glebe	v	Newham United	3-3, 4-3p

Final

Balham	v	Glebe	3-2

Manchester Premier Cup
HOLDERS: Mossley
Quarter-Finals

Stalybridge Celtic	v	Curzon Ashton	1-0
Glossop North End	v	West Didsbury & Chorlton AFC	2-4
Abbey Hey	v	FC United of Manchester	1-3
Hyde United	v	Salford City	3-3, 1-3p

Semi-Finals

Stalybridge Celtic	v	Salford City	2-1
FC United of Manchester	v	West Didsbury & Chorlton AFC	7-1

Final

FC United of Manchester	v	Stalybridge Celtic	1-0

Middlesex Senior Challenge Cup
HOLDERS: Northwood
Quarter-Finals

Enfield Town	v	Hendon	1-3
Edgware Town	v	Hampton & Richmond Boro	1-2
Harrow Borough	v	Wealdstone	0-1
Ashford Town (Middx)	v	Hanworth Villa	2-3

Semi-Finals

Hanworth Villa	v	Hampton & Richmond Boro	1-3
Hendon	v	Wealdstone	0-0, 1-3p

Final

Hampton & Richmond Boro	v	Wealdstone	1-0

Middlesex Premier Cup
HOLDERS: Woodford Town
Quarter-Finals

Staines Lammas	v	Broadfields United	1-4
Cockfosters Res	v	Rayners Lane	1-1, 4-5p
Kensington Borough	v	Hillingdon Borough	1-2
Harefield United	v	North Greenford United Res	5-4

Semi-Finals

Rayners Lane	v	Broadfields United	1-4
Hillingdon Borough	v	Harefield United	2-2, 5-4p

Final

Hillingdon Borough	v	Broadfields United	1-4

Norfolk Senior Cup
HOLDERS: Dereham Town
Quarter-Finals

Harleston Town	v	Norwich CEYMS	2-1
Norwich United	v	Long Stratton	1-0
King's Lynn Town	v	Wroxham	2-1
Diss Town	v	Fakenham Town	1-2

Semi-Finals

Harleston Town	v	Fakenham Town	1-1, 4-5p
King's Lynn Town	v	Norwich United	1-1, 5-4p

Final

King's Lynn Town	v	Fakenham Town	2-0

Northamptonshire Senior Cup
HOLDERS: AFC Rushden & Diamonds
Quarter-Finals

Desborough Town	v	Northampton Sileby Rangers	4-1
Kettering Town	v	Peterborough Sports	3-3, 4-2p
Cogenhoe United	v	Corby Town	2-2, 3-4p
Brackley Town	v	Wellingborough Town	5-1

Semi-Finals

Corby Town	v	Desborough Town	3-0
Kettering Town	v	Brackley Town	1-0

Final

Corby Town	v	Kettering Town	1-1, 6-7p

Northamptonshire Junior Cup
HOLDERS: Peterborough Sports
Final

Raunds Town	v	James King Blisworth	0-1

North Riding Senior Cup
HOLDERS: Middlesbrough U21/Res
Quarter-Finals

Whitby Town	v	York City	3-1
Pickering Town Community	v	Marske United	4-1
Middlesbrough U23/Res	v	Northallerton Town	4-0
Richmond Town	v	Scarborough Athletic	

Semi-Finals

Whitby Town	v	Middlesbrough U23/Res	4-3
Pickering Town Community	v	Scarborough Athletic	1-0

Final

Whitby Town	v	Pickering Town Community	3-1

Northumberland Senior Cup
HOLDERS: North Shields
Quarter-Finals

Morpeth Town	v	Newcastle United U21	2-3
Team Northumbria	v	Blyth Town	1-2
Blyth Spartans	v	Bedlington Terriers	11-1
North Shields	v	Heaton Stannington	3-0

Semi-Finals

Blyth Town	v	Blyth Spartans	2-5 aet
North Shields	v	Newcastle United U21	1-1, 10-9p

Final

Blyth Spartans	v	North Shields	3-2

Nottinghamshire Senior Cup
HOLDERS: Basford United
Quarter-Finals

West Bridgford	v	Teversal	1-2
Rainworth MW	v	Real United	9-1
Basford United	v	Kimberley Miners Welfare	5-1
Carlton Town	v	Sherwood Colliery	3-2 aet

Semi-Finals

Rainworth MW	v	Basford United	0-2
Carlton Town	v	Teversal	2-0

Final

Basford United	v	Carlton Town	1-4

Oxfordshire Senior Cup
HOLDERS: Oxford United
Quarter-Finals

Thame Youth Rangers	v	North Leigh	1-2
Oxford City	v	Thame United	0-0, 4-2p
Hook Norton	v	Banbury United	0-3
Kidlington	v	Oxford United	1-5

Semi-Finals

Oxford City	v	North Leigh	0-3
Oxford United	v	Banbury United	3-2 aet

Final

Oxford United	v	North Leigh	1-2

Sheffield & Hallamshire Senior Challenge Cup
HOLDERS: Frickley Athletic
Quarter-Finals

Penistone Church	v	Hallam	2-1 aet
Shaw Lane Association	v	Sheffield FC	3-0
Staveley Miners Welfare	v	Handsworth Parramore	0-2
Frickley Athletic	v	Frecheville C.A.	4-1

Semi-Finals

Handsworth Parramore	v	Frickley Athletic	0-2
Shaw Lane Association	v	Penistone Church	3-1

Final

Shaw Lane Association	v	Frickley Athletic	1-0

Shropshire Challenge Cup
HOLDERS: Shrewsbury Town
Semi-Finals

Market Drayton Town	v	AFC Telford United	0-4

Final

Shrewsbury Town	v	AFC Telford United	0-2

Somerset Premier Cup
HOLDERS: Wells City
Quarter-Finals

Taunton Town	v	Clevedon Town	3-1
Brislington	v	Ashton & Backwell United	4-0
Weston-Super-Mare	v	Bath City	3-0
Keynsham Town	v	Paulton Rovers	1-0

Semi-Finals

Brislington	v	Weston-Super-Mare	1-2
Keynsham Town	v	Taunton Town	1-2 aet

Final

Taunton Town	v	Weston-Super-Mare	4-2

Somerset Senior Cup
HOLDERS: Nailsea & Tickenham
Quarter-Finals

Clutton	v	Uphill Castle	3-1
Nailsea United	v	Odd Down (Bath) Res	3-3, 2-4p
Street Res	v	Fry Club	2-0
Hengrove Athletic Res	v	Berrow	3-1

Semi-Finals

Odd Down (Bath) Res	v	Street Res	4-1 aet
Clutton	v	Hengrove Athletic Res	1-0

Final

Odd Down (Bath) Res	v	Clutton	1-0

Staffordshire Senior Cup
HOLDERS: Rushall Olympic
Quarter-Finals

Hednesford Town	v	Wolverhampton Sporting Comm.	3-2
Stafford Rangers	v	Wolverhampton Casuals	0-2
Rushall Olympic	v	Stoke City	3-5
Chasetown	v	Newcastle Town	2-0

Semi-Finals

Hednesford Town	v	Chastown	0-4
Wolverhampton Casuals	v	Stoke City	0-3

Final

Chasetown	v	Stoke City	1-1, 3-4p

(Staffordshire) Walsall Senior Cup
HOLDERS: Rushall Olympic
Quarter-Finals

Romulus	v	Walsall	1-2
Wolverhampton Casuals	v	Boldmere St Michaels	3-1
Chasetown	v	Sporting Khalsa	3-3, 5-3p
Stafford Rangers	v	Rushall Olympic	3-0

Semi-Finals

Wolverhampton Casuals	v	Walsall	0-3
Chasetown	v	Stafford Rangers	1-2

Final

Walsall	v	Stafford Rangers	3-1

Suffolk Premier Cup
HOLDERS: Lowestoft Town
Quarter-Finals

Needham Market	v	AFC Sudbury	1-0
Leiston	v	Ipswich Town Youth	6-3
Felixstowe & Walton United	v	Lowestoft Town	2-3
Newmarlet Town	v	Haverhill Rovers	3-2

Semi-Finals

Needham Market	v	Leiston	4-4, 4-2p
Newmarket Town	v	Lowestoft Town	0-2

Final

Lowestoft Town	v	Needham Market	2-3

Suffolk Senior Cup
HOLDERS: Waveney
Quarter-Finals

Bramford United	v	Achilles	1-6
Woodbridge Town	v	Haverhill Borough	1-3
Capel Plough	v	Leiston St Margarets	2-0
Crane Sports	v	AFC Sudbury Res	1-1, 3-2p

Semi-Finals

Achilles	v	Capel Plough	2-0
Haverhill Borough	v	Crane Sports	1-4

Final

Crane Sports	v	Achilles	1-2

Surrey Senior Cup
HOLDERS: Merstham
Quarter Finals
Woking	v	Knaphill	3-1
Merstham	v	Whyteleafe	2-1
Chertsey Town	v	Dorking Wanderers	0-3
Guildford City	v	Raynes Park Vale	2-1
Semi-Finals
Guildford City	v	Woking	1-2
Dorking Wanderers	v	Merstham	2-3
Final
Woking	v	Merstham	4-0

Surrey Premier Cup
HOLDERS: Nottsborough
Quarter Finals
Corinthian-Casuals Res	v	Chessington & Hook United	4-0
Met Police Res	v	Nottsborough	1-1, 3-1p
Worcester Park	v	Bagshot	2-1
Banstead Athletic	v	Staines Lammas	4-2
Semi-Finals
Met Police Res	v	Banstead Athletic	2-3
Corinthian-Casuals Res	v	Worcester Park	1-2
Final
Worcester Park	v	Banstead Athletic	3-3, 4-3p

Surrey Intermediate Cup
HOLDERS: Horsley
Final
Ahmadiyya Muslim Youth	v	Chessington	0-5

Surrey Junior Cup
HOLDERS: Lyne
Final
Woodmansterne Hyde	v	Colliers Wood United Res	4-2

Sussex Senior Challenge Cup
HOLDERS: Eastbourne Borough
Quarter-Finals
Shoreham	v	Bognor Regis Town	1-3
Brighton & Hove Albion	v	Crowborough Athletic	2-0
Crawley Town	v	Whitehawk	3-1
Eastbourne Borough	v	Worthing	2-0
Semi-Finals
Bognor Regis Town	v	Crawley Town	2-3 aet
Eastbourne Borough	v	Brighton & Hove Albion	3-4
Final
Brighton & Hove Albion	v	Crawley Town	3-0 aet

Sussex Intermediate Cup
HOLDERS: Lewes U21
Final
Cowfold	v	Roffey	2-1

Sussex Junior Cup
HOLDERS: Sidley United
Final
Lancing United	v	Romans United	1-3

West Riding County Cup
HOLDERS: Bradford Park Avenue
Quarter-Finals
Brighouse Town	v	Ossett Town	2-0
Farsley Celtic	v	Guiseley	4-2
Tadcaster Albion	v	Silsden	4-1
Harrogate Town	v	Bradford Park Avenue	1-3
Semi-Finals
Bradford Park Avenue	v	Farsley Celtic	1-3
Brighouse Town	v	Tadcaster Albion	1-2
Final
Tadcaster Albion	v	Farsley Celtic	1-1, 2-4p

Westmorland Senior Challenge Cup
HOLDERS: Milnthorpe Corinthians
Quarter-Finals
Kirkoswald	v	Appleby	4-3aet
Kendal United	v	Milnthorpe Corinthians	3-4
Keswick	v	Wetheriggs United	5-2
Cartmel & District	v	Kendal County	1-0
Semi-Finals
Keswick	v	Milnthorpe Corinthians	4-4, 0-1p
Cartmel & District	v	Kirkoswald	5-1
Final
Cartmel & District	v	Milnthorpe Corinthians	0-3

Wiltshire Senior Cup
HOLDERS: Melksham Town
Quarter-Finals
Highworth Town	v	Bradford Town	2-0
Calne Town	v	Laverstock & Ford	1-0
Salisbury	v	Amesbury Town	2-1
Swindon Supermarine	v	Downton	6-1
Semi-Finals
Highworth Town	v	Salisbury	4-3
Calne Town	v	Swindon Supermarine	0-4
Final
Swindon Supermarine	v	Highworth Town	2-1

Wiltshire Junior Cup
HOLDERS: Stockton & Codford
Final
Luxol UK	v	Tawny Owl	3-2

Worcestershire Senior Invitation Cup
Quarter-Finals
Stourbridge	v	Kidderminster Harriers	0-1
Semi-Finals
Evesham United	v	Kidderminster Harriers	0-3
Worcester City	v	Redditch United	0-2
Final
Redditch United	v	Kidderminster Harriers	0-0, 2-4p

Worcestershire Senior Invitation Urn
HOLDERS: Alvechurch
Quarter-Finals
Dudley Sports	v	Malvern Town	2-4
Stourport Swifts	v	Alvechurch	1-1, 5-3p
Bewdley Town	v	Bromsgrove Sporting	2-2, 2-3p
Lye Town	v	Highgate United	1-1, 3-4p
Semi-Finals
Bromsgrove Sporting	v	Malvern Town	1-0
Highgate United	v	Stourport Swifts	3-1
Final
Highgate United	v	Bromsgrove Sporting	1-1, 5-4p

Worcestershire Junior Cup
HOLDERS: Droitwich Spa
Final
Montpellier	v	Worcester Raiders	0-1

1874 NORTHWICH — Winsford United FC, Wharton Road, Winsford, Cheshire CW7 3AE — 01606 558 447

M6 to junction 18, follow A54 through Middlewich for approx. 3 miles, bear right at round-a-bout at Winsford Railway Station, follow road for approx. 1 mile, turn right into Kingsway, ground is on the right.

Nearest Railway Station Winsford - 1.2km   **Bus Route** Wesley Court stop - 34m away

449

ABBEY HEY — The Abbey Stadium, Goredale Avenue, Gorton, Manchester M18 7HD — 0161 231 7147

M60 to junction 24, take A57 to Manchester City Centre for approx 1 mile, at first set of major traffic lights (MacDonalds on right) pass through for approx 300yards, turn left immediatley before overhead railway bridge (A.H.F.C. sign) into Woodland Avenue. Take first right, pass under railway bridge, turn first left into Goredale Avenue.

Nearest Railway Station Ryder Brow - 0.5km   **Bus Route** Ryder Brow Road stop - 124m away

449

ABBEY HULTON UNITED — Birches Head Road, Abbey Hulton, Stoke-on-Trent ST2 8DD

From the A500, take Leed Road A5009 towards Leek,
Turn left onto Birches Head Road.
Go over the narrow bridge, and continue past the junction with Redhills Road, then turn right into the ground. (if you go over the canal bridge you have gone too far)
For satnavs, use post code ST2 8DD for Trent Squash Club, which is next door to the football club.

Nearest Railway Station Stoke-on-Trent - 4.2km   **Bus Route** Woodhead Road stop - 262m away

449

ABBEY RANGERS — Addlestone Moor, Addlestone, KT15 2QH — 01932 422 962

From Junction 11 M25.
Exit A317 St. Peter's Way towards Chertsey, Addlestone and Weybridge.
At roundabout take 2nd exit towards Addlestonemoor.

Nearest Railway Station Addlestone   **Bus Route** No.461

384

ABINGDON UNITED — The Northcourt, Northcourt Road, Abingdon OX14 1PL — 01235 203 203

From the north – Leave A34 at Abingdon north turning. Ground on right at first set of traffic lights.
From the south – Enter Town Centre, leave north on A4183 (Oxford Road).
Ground on left after one mile.

Nearest Railway Station Radley - 2.5km   **Bus Route** Boundary House (Oxford Rd) stop - 215m

422

AC LONDON — Banstead Athletic FC, Merland Rise, Tadworth, Surrey KT20 5JG — 01737 350 982

From M25 Junction 8 Follow Signs To Banstead Sports Centre.

Nearest Railway Station Tattenham Corner.   **Bus Route** Metro 420 & 460

384

AFC ALDERMASTON — AWE, Aldermaston, Reading RG7 8UA — 01189 824 454

From A4 at Padworth, take A340 (Aldermaston/Tadley) to Calleva Park Roundabout. Take first left on A340, and then take next left at mini roundabout into AWE West Gate. Follow signs for Aldermaston Recreational Society. Car Park directly ahead. Enter ground through gate at end of car park. Ground is on right hand side.

Nearest Railway Station Midgham - 4km   **Bus Route** Calleva Park stop - 48m away

422

AFC BLACKPOOL — Mechanics Ground, Jepson Way, Common Edge Road, Blackpool, FY4 5DY — 01253 761 721

M6 to M55, exit at junction 4.
At roundabout turn left along A583 to traffic lights, turn right into Whitehill Road, to traffic lights (2 miles).
Go straight across the main road into Jepson Way, ground at top.

Nearest Railway Station Squires Gate - 2.2km   **Bus Route** Borough Boundary stop - 109m away

449

AFC BRIDGNORTH — Crown Meadow, Innage Lane, Bridgnorth WV16 4HS — 07748 302 650

Follow signs for Shrewsbury A458 over River Bridge on bypass. At next island turn right (Town Centre). At T Junction turn right, first left into Victoria Road. Turn right at crossroads by Woodberry Down. Follow road round to right. Club is on the right 300 yards from crossroads.

Bus Route Bus stops outside the ground.

553

AFC CROYDON ATHLETIC — Mayfield Stadium, off Mayfield Road, Thornton Heath CR7 6DN — 020 8689 5322

From M25: Exit at either Junction 6 and then take the A22 to Purley Cross and then join the A23 London Road and then directions below from Purley, or exit at Junction 7 and take the A23 London Road all the way. **From Streatham and Norbury:** Take the A23 London Road to the roundabout at Thornton Heath, continue down the A23 Thornton Road. Then take the 1st on the Right past the No Entry road (Fairlands Avenue), Silverleigh Road, 50 yards, at the fork, keep left (signposted Croydon Athletic FC) into Trafford Road, then Mayfield Road (which is a continuation of Trafford Road) Go to the end of Mayfield Road, then left at the last house. Follow the lane, passed allotments, past an open car park space and continue along the lane to our club car park.

505

AFC DARWEN — WEC Group Anchor Ground, Anchor Road, Darwen, Lancs BB3 0BB — 01254 776 193

M65 to junction 4. At traffic lights turn left onto A666 (signposted Darwen). After approx 1/2 mile turn left between Anchor Car sales and the Anchor Pub. Bear right and ground is on the left.

Nearest Railway Station Darwen - 1.7km   **Bus Route** Birch Hall Avenue stop - 256m away

449

AFC DUNSTABLE — Creasey Park, Creasey Park Drive, Brewers Hill Road LU6 1BB — 01582 891 433

From the South: When travelling north on the A5, go straight across the lights in the centre of Dunstable. Turn left at the next main set of lights into Brewers Hill Road. You will immediately pass the Fire Station on your left. Carry on until you hit the first roundabout. Go over the roundabout and take the immediate right into Creasey Park Drive. From North: When travelling south on the A5, go through the chalk cutting and over the first set of traffic lights. At the next set of lights turn right into Brewers Hill Road. Go over the roundabout and take the immediate right into Creasey Park Drive. Public Transport: Creasey Park is well served by buses. Arriva and Centrebus services from Luton, Houghton Regis Leighton Buzzard and Aylesbury all stop at the bottom of Brewers Hill Road. Some 24 services stop directly opposite Creasey Park Drive in Weatherby.

362

AFC EMLEY
The Welfare Ground, Off Upper Lane, Emley, nr Huddersfield HD8 9RE.　　**01924 849 392**

From M1 J38: Travel on road signposted to Huddersfield through the village of Bretton to the first roundabout. Take first exit off this roundabout signposted Denby Dale. After approximately one mile turn right at road signposted Emley. After 2 miles enter the village of Emley. Entrance to ground is opposite a white bollard in centre of road. (Narrow entrance).
From M1 J39: Travel on road signposted toward Denby Dale. Travel for approximately 3 miles up hill to first roundabout. Take 2nd exit and follow directions as above.

Nearest Railway Station Denby Dale - 5km　　　　**Bus Route** Upper Lane Church Street - stop 61m away

463

AFC FYLDE
Mill Farm, Coronation Way, Wesham, Preston PR4 3JZ　　**01772 682 593**

Access to the site via the A585 is less than 1 mile from the M55 Junction 3 to the north, which leads to Blackpool to the west and Preston and the M6 to the east. To the south, the A585 Fleetwood Road forms the Kirkham and Wesham Bypass and connects with the A583 Blackpool Road, a main route between Blackpool and Preston.

Nearest Railway Station Kirkham & Wesham half a mile away.　　　　**Bus Route** No. 61

14

AFC HAYES
Farm Park, Kingshill Avenue, Hayes UB4 8DD　　**020 8845 0110**

From the A40 McDonalds Target roundabout take A312 south towards Hayes.
At White Hart roundabout take third exit into Yeading Lane.
Turn right at first traffic lights into Kingshill Avenue.
Ground approx one miles on the right-hand side.

Nearest Railway Station Northholt or Haye & Harlington　　　　**Bus Route** No.90

384

AFC HORNCHURCH
The Stadium, Bridge Avenue, Upminster, Essex RM14 2LX　　**01708 220 080**

Bridge Avenue is off A124 between Hornchurch and Upminster.

Nearest Railway Station Upminster Bridge Underground - 0.4km

208

AFC LIVERPOOL
Marine FC, College Road, Crosby, Liverpool L23 3AS　　**0151 9241743 or 0151 286 9101**

M57/M58 take the A5036 signposted Bootle & Docks, at the roundabout under the flyover turn right onto the A565 following signs for Crosby and Marine AFC. After passing Tesco Express on the right, turn left at the traffic lights (by Merchants Taylors School) into College Road, ground is approx ½ mile on the left.

Nearest Railway Station Blundellsands & Crosby - 0.5km　　　　**Bus Route** Brompton Avenue stop - 175m away

449

AFC MANSFIELD
Forest Town Stadium, Clipstone Road West, Forest Town, Mansfield NG19 0EE　　**07973 491 739**

The ground is situated approximately 3 miles to the north east of Mansfield town centre and sits on the B6030 Clipstone Road West. Pedestrian access can be gained via gates on Clipstone Road West with vehicle access via Main Avenue and then the 2nd right, turning into Second Avenue.

Nearest Railway Station Mansfield - 2.7km　　　　**Bus Route** School - stop 64m away

463

AFC PORTCHESTER
Wicor Recreation Ground Cranleigh Road Portchester Hampshire PO16 9DP 01329 233 833 (Clubhouse)

Leave the M27 at Junction 11 and follow the signs to Portchester into Portchester Road. Carry on for approx 1 mile at the large roundabout, take the 3rd exit into Cornaway Lane and at the 'T' junction turn right in Cranleigh Road and follow the road to the end. Postcode for Satellite Navigation systems PO16 9DP

Nearest Railway Station Porchester - 15.km　　　　**Bus Route** Sandport Grove stop

541

AFC RUSHDEN & DIAMONDS
Kempston Rovers FC, Hillgrounds Leisure, Hill Grounds Road, Kempston MK42 8SZ　　**01234 852 346**

Take A421 Bedford by pass turning as indicated to Kempston onto A5140 Woburn Road. At roundabout turn left into St John's Street then right into Bedford Road. After the shops and park on the left turn immediately left into Hillgrounds Road. Ground is past the swimming pool on right hand side.

Nearest Railway Station Bedford - 1.3km　　　　**Bus Route** Prentice Gardens - stop 100m away

362

AFC STONEHAM
The HP Arena, Jubilee Park, Chestnut Avenue, Eastleigh SO50 9PF　　**07765 046 429**

Leave M27 at Junction 5. Turn into Stoneham Lane & pass the rear of Eastleigh Football Club. At end of Stoneham Lane (mini roundabout), turn left into Chestnut Avenue. Entrance to ground is on the left and shared with Chandlers Ford Golf Academy.

Nearest Railway Station Southampton Airport Parkway - 1.6km　　　　**Bus Route** Golf Driving Range stop

541

AFC SUDBURY
Wardale Williams Stadium, Brundon Lane, Sudbury CO10 7HN　　**01787 376 213**

From Braintree: Take A131 through Halstead to Sudbury. On descending hill into Sudbury turn left at first set of traffic lights (Kings Head), and then take the first right into Brundon Lane. The road narrows before reaching ground on the right hand sideFrom Colchester, Bury St Edmunds and Ipswich: Enter Sudbury and follow signs for Halstead/Chelmsford. Go aross the river bridge and go under the old rail bridge, then turn right at the traffic lights (Kings Head) into Bulmer Road and the first right again into Brundon Lane. The road narrows before reaching ground on the right hand side.

Nearest Railway Station Sudbury - 1.5km　　　　**Bus Route** Bulmer Road - stop 100m away

208

AFC SUDBURY RESERVES
The Wardale Williams Stadium, Brundon Lane, Sudbury CO10 7HN　　**01787 376 213**

From Colchester, Bury St Edmunds and Ipswich: Enter Sudbury and follow signs for Halstead/Chelmsford. Go aross the river bridge and go under the old rail bridge, then turn right at the traffic lights (Kings Head) into Bulmer Road and the first right again into Brundon Lane. The road narrows before reaching ground on the right hand side.

Nearest Railway Station Sudbury - 1.5km

402

AFC TELFORD UNITED
New Bucks Head Stadium, Watling Street, Wellington, Telford TF1 2TU　　**01952 640 064**

(Sat Nav follow TF1 2NW into Haybridge Road) From M54 Junction 6, A5223 towards Wellington, straight over first roundabout (retail park). Straight over second roundabout (B5067). Left at third roundabout (Furrows garage). Continue over railway bridge and follow road round to the right, then turn left into AFC Telford United Car Park.

Nearest Railway Station Wellington (Shropshire) - 20min walk to ground.　　　　**Bus Route** 44 - every 10 mins from Town centre.

64

AFC TOTTON
Testwood Stadium, Salisbury Road, Calmore, Totton SO40 2RW
02380 868 981

From the M27 Junction 2. From the east take the first exit at the roundabout or from the west take the third exit at the roundabout. Take the first left within 100 yards, signposted Totton Central.
At the T junction turn left and you will find the entrance to the ground approximately 1 mile on the left hand side, just before the Calmore Roundabout.

Nearest Railway Station Totton - 2.9km   **Bus Route** Cooks Lane - stop 300m away   373

AFC UCKFIELD TOWN
The Oaks, Old Eastbourne Road, Uckfield TN22 5QL
01825 890 905

Next to Radutt Restaurant on Old Eastbourne Road, south of Uckfield Town Centre

Nearest Railway Station Uckfield - 2.1km   495

AFC VARNDEANIANS
Withdean Stadium, Tongdean Lane, Brighton BN1 5JD

Heading south on the A23, turn right opposite Withdean Park into Togdean Lane, and go under railway bridge.

Nearest Railway Station Preston Park - 0.9km   **Bus Route** Bottom of Valley Drive - stop 91m away   495

AFC WULFRUNIANS
Castlecroft Stadium, Castlecroft Road, Wolverhampton WV3 8NA
01902 761410

Follow A454 (signposted Bridgnorth) and turn left at Mermaid Pub onto Windmill Lane. Turn right onto Castlecroft Avenue. Ground is straight across past Wightwick Cricket Ground.

Nearest Railway Station Wolverhampton - 5km   **Bus Route** Castlecroft Hotel stop - 218m away   436

ALBION SPORTS
Throstle Nest, Newlands, Farsley, Leeds, LS28 5BE.
0113 255 7292

Come off the M606 at the roundabout. Take fourth exit onto Rooley Lane which is the A6177, continue to follow A6177 through two roundabouts then turn right onto Leeds Road A647. Continue to follow A647, go through roundabout. At next roundabout, take second exit onto Bradford Road B6157. Follow for ½ mile before turning left onto New Street then turn right onto Newlands. Ground on left.

Nearest Railway Station New Pudsey - 1km   **Bus Route** Town St Slaters Rd - stop 340m away   463

ALDERSHOT TOWN
EBB Stadium, High street, Aldershot, GU11 1TW
01252 320 211

Exit from the M3 at junction 4 and take the A331 to Aldershot , after 3 miles take the 4th exit off the A331 and take the Town Centre route to Aldershot.
1.25 miles from the A331 junction the ground will be on your right hand side. Located on the High Street in Aldershot.

16

ALFRETON TOWN
The Impact Arena, North Street, Alfreton, Derbyshire DE55 7FZ
01773 830 277

From M1 Junction 28 Take A38 towards Derby for 2 miles.
Then take slip road onto B600 Turn right at Tjunction towards town centre.
At pedestrian crossing turn left into North Street and the ground is 150-yards down on the right hand side.

Nearest Railway Station Alfreton - Approx. 15min walk from the ground   66

ALMONDSBURY U.W.E.
The Field, Almondsbury, Bristol BS32 4AA
01454 612 240

Exit M5 at Junction 16. Arriving from the south take the left exit lane. Turn left at lights and ground is 150m on right hand side. Arriving from east take right hand lane on slip road. Take 3rd exit and ground is 150m on right hand side.

Nearest Railway Station Patchway - 2.9km   **Bus Route** Over Lane - stop 70m away   559

ALNWICK TOWN
St. Jame's Park, Weavers Way, Alnwick, Northumberland NE66 1BG
01665 603 162

M1, at exit 32, take slip road left for M18 toward The North / Doncaster / Hull, at exit 2, take slip road left for A1(M) toward the North, keep straight onto A1 / Doncaster By Pass, keep straight onto A1(M), take slip road for A1(M) / Aberford By Pass, road name changes to A1 / Leeming Lane, keep straight onto A1(M), keep left onto A1, take slip road left for A1068 toward Alnwick / Alnmouth, at roundabout, take 1st exit onto Willowburn Avenue, turn left, and then immediately turn left onto St James Estate, ground is on the right.

Nearest Railway Station Alnmouth - 4.1km   **Bus Route** Wagonway Road - stop 16m away   476

ALRESFORD TOWN
Arlebury Park, The Avenue, Alresford, Hants SO24 9EP
01962 735 100 or 07703 346

Alresford is situated on the A31 between Winchester and Alton. Arlebury Park is on the main avenue into Alresford opposite Perins School.
Postcode for Satellite Navigation systems SO24 9EP

Nearest Railway Station Alresford - 620m   **Bus Route** Bridge Road stop   541

ALSAGER TOWN
Woodpark Stadium, Woodland Court, Alsager ST7 2DP
07888 750 532

M6 to Junction 16, A500 towards Stoke, leave A500 at 2nd exit (A34 to Congleton) at 2nd set of traffic lights on A34 turn left for Alsager (B5077). After 500 yards (opposite Caradon/Twyfords Factory) turn right into Moorhouse Avenue. Ground is off West Grove 1/4 mile on right. Entrance to ground is down drive on the bottom right hand corner, between the houses.

Nearest Railway Station Alsager - 0.9km   **Bus Route** Curzon Avenue stop - 374m away   449

ALTON TOWN
Alton (Bass) Sports Ground, Anstey Road, Alton, Hants GU34 2RL
541

Leave the A31 at the B3004 signposted to Alton. Follow the road round to the left passing Anstey Park on the right, the ground is then immediately on the left – opposite the turning into Anstey Lane. Postcode for Satellite Navigation systems GU34 2RL

Nearest Railway Station Alton - 0.6km   **Bus Route** Anstey Lane - stop 32m away

ALTRINCHAM
The J Davidson Stadium, Moss Lane, Altrincham, Cheshire WA15 8AP

0161 928 1045

From M6 junction19, turn right towards Altrincham into town centre (approx 15 minutes). Turn down Lloyd Street, past Sainsburys on the right. Tesco Extra on left. Then follow signs for Altrincham F.C.

238

Nearest Railway Station Altrincham - Approx. 10min walk from the ground

Bus Route Arriva 263 & Stagecoach X41

ALVECHURCH
Lye Meadow, Redditch Road, Alvechurch B48 7RS

0121 445 2929

Exit M42 at junction 2, take the A441 dual carriageway towards Redditch. At the 1st island, take the B4120 to Alvechurch. The ground is approximately 1 mile of the right (car park entrance is before the ground)

298

Nearest Railway Station Alvechurch - 0.7km

Bus Route Bus stops at the ground.

AMESBURY TOWN
Bonnymead Park Recreation Road Amesbury SP4 7BB

01980 623 489

From Salisbury take A345 to Amesbury, turn left just past the bus station and proceed through the one way system, when road splits with Friar Tuck Café and Lloyds Bank on left turn left and follow road over the river bridge and when road bears sharp right turn left into Recreation Road.
From A303 at Countess Roundabout go into Amesbury, straight over traffic lights, at mini-roundabout turn right into one way system and follow directions as above. Postcode for Satellite Navigation systems SP4 7BB

541

Bus Route Mandalay Guest House - stop 600m away

AMPTHILL TOWN
Ampthill Park, Woburn Street, Ampthill MK45 2HX

01525 404 440

From the South, leave M1 at junction 12 Toddington. Turn right as signposted until you meet the junction with the Ampthill bypass. Go straight across until you meet a mini-roundabout at the town centre. Turn left into Woburn Street. The ground is about half a mile on the right, just past a lay-by. From the North, leave the M1 at J13 and turn left. At first set of traffic lights, turn right onto A507 Ridgmont bypass. Continue until you see the right-hand turning signposted for Ampthill. Ground is about a mile on the left, opposite the rugby ground.

516

Nearest Railway Station Flitwick - 3.1km. Millbrook - 3.4km

Bus Route Alameda Road - stop 117m away

ANDOVER NEW STREET
Foxcotte Park Charlton Andover Hampshire SP11 0TA

01264 358 358 (Weekends

From Basingstoke follow the A303 to Weyhill roundabout. At roundabout turn right and 2nd roundabout turn left on to A342. Approx 1/2 mile turn right into Short Lane, continue into Harroway Lane to the 'T' junction at the top. Turn right into Foxcotte Lane and continue for about 3/4 mile then turn left, this still Foxcotte Lane, to the top some 3/4 mile to the roundabout straight across into Foxcotte Park. Postcode for Satellite Navigation systems SP11 0TA.

541

Nearest Railway Station Andover - 2.4km

Bus Route Charlton Cemetery - stop 120m away

ANDOVER TOWN
Portway Stadium, West Portway, Portway Industrial Estate, Andover SP10 3LF

Leave A303 at Junction for A342 . If from the East cross back over A303. At large roundabout take A342 across the face of the Premier Hotel. First right into the Portway Industrial Estate then follow the one way system and after the road swings right at the bottom of the hill the ground is on the left.

541

Nearest Railway Station Andover - 1.8km

Bus Route Arkwright Gate - stop 130m away

ANSTEY NOMADS
Davidson Homes Park, Cropston Road, Anstey, Leicester LE7 7BP

07709 149 608

From A46 follow signs to Anstey and enter village by Leicester Road.
Proceed to roundabout in centre of village and take 3rd exit.
Pass Co-op store and car showroom and ground 100 metres on right.

396

Nearest Railway Station Leicester - 6.2km

ARDLEY UNITED
The Playing Fields, Fritwell Road, Ardley OX27 7PA

07711 009 198

From M40 travelling North. At the end of the slip road at junction 10 turn left onto B430. Take the first right and the ground is 10 yards on your right. **From M40 travelling South** at the end of the slip road at junction 10 turn right, cross the motorway keeping in the right hand lane follow signs for B430. Take the first right and the ground is 10 yards on the right. **From the A34.** Leave the A34 after the BP garage signed Middleton Stoney / Weston on the Green. Stay on this road some 10 miles to Ardley. After entering the village take the first left after passing the Fox and Hounds public house, and the ground is 10 yards on your right.

422

Nearest Railway Station Bicester North - 6.3km

Bus Route Water Lane stop - 121m away

ARLESEY TOWN
New Lamb Meadow, Hitchin Road, Arlesey SG15 6RS

01462 734 504

From the A1 exit at Baldock(J10) and follow the signs for Stotfold then Arlesey. You will enter Arlesey from the area known as Church End, this is the opposite end of Arlesey, but as there is only one main street just follow keep driving until you pass the Biggs Wall building and the ground is on your left.
Coming of the M1 at Luton and follow the signs for Hitchin, pass Hitchin Town FC on the Shefford Road and turn right into Turnpike Lane, this is Ickleford. Follow the road out of Ickleford and bear left away from the Letchworth turning, the ground is a little further on, on the right.

363

Nearest Railway Station Arlesey - 2.6km

Bus Route Prince of Wales - stop 100m away

ARMTHORPE WELFARE
Welfare Ground, Church Street, Armthorpe, Doncaster DN3 3AG

From the north, turn right at main roundabout in the centre of Doncaster and straight across at next roundabout on to Wheatley Hall Road. Turn right on to Wentworth Road, go to top of hill towards the Hospital on to Armthorpe Road. From the south, take the M18 to J4 on to the A630. At 2nd roundabout, turn left and proceed to next roundabout, then turn right. Ground 400 yards on left behind Netto.

463

Nearest Railway Station Kirk Sandall - 3.4km

Bus Route Beech Road - stop 13m away

ARNOLD TOWN
Eagle Valley, Oxton Road, Arnold, Nottingham NG5 8PS

0115 965 6000

From South: From Nottingham, take the A60 Mansfield road. At the first traffic island half a mile north of Arnold, join the A614 towards Doncaster. After 200 yards, go through traffic lights and, after 300 yards, take the next turn right. The ground entrance is 200 yards on the right. **From North:** A614 towards Nottingham. As you approach the first set of traffic lights, turn left 300 yards before the lights. The ground entrance is 200 yards on the right. **From M1:** Leave at Junction 27. Head towards Hucknall/Nottingham. After one mile, turn right at the first set of traffic lights. One mile, turn first left at island and stay on this road for two miles until junction with A60. Turn right and, at the next island, turn left onto the A614 towards Doncaster. After 200 yards, go through traffic lights and, after 300 yards, take the next right turn. The ground entrance is 200 yards on the right.

396

ARUNDEL
Mill Road, Arundel, W. Sussex BN18 9QQ

01903 882 548

On A27 from Worthing over railway bridge to roundabout.
Second exit into Queen St to Town Centre. Cross Bridge over river, and turn right at miniroundabout.
Enter pay and display car par on right. Ground entrance is located at the far left hand corner of the car park.

495

Nearest Railway Station Arundel - 1.6km

ASCOT UNITED — Ascot Racecourse, Car Park 10, Winkfield Rd, Ascot SL5 7RA — 01344 291 107

Directions to Racecourse – New postcode SL5 7LJ (If your sat nav does not have this postcode try SL5 7LN for A330 Winkfield Road) From Bracknell take A329 to Ascot. From Heatherwood Hospital roundabout take Ascot High Street. At first mini-roundabout go straight. At mini roundabout at end of High Street turn left along A330 Winkfield Road. Go under bridge and take first right signposted Car Park 7&8. Continue forwards past golf club, through gates and follow track to the end. Please arrive from Ascot High Street as some sat navs will direct you by a back road which ends in a locked gate and you will have to retrace your route.

Nearest Railway Station Ascot - 1.3km   **Bus Route** Hilltop Close (Cheapside Rd) stop - 934m

422

ASH UNITED — Shawfields Stadium, Youngs Drive off Shawfield Road, Ash, GU12 6RE. — 01252 320 385 / 345 757

FROM M3: Get off the M3 at J4, onto the A331: Take 3rd Exit off to Woking. Up to the roundabout turn left into Shawfields Road, follow road for about 500 yards, Football Ground is on the left, take next turning on your left into Youngs Drive where club is 50yards on. **FROM M25:** Get onto the A3 heading to Guildford/Portsmouth. Keep on this until you reach the A331(Hog's Back). Then go onto the A31 until you reach the exit for the A331 to Aldershot. Follow the signs for Aldershot, which will be the 1st exit off the A331.When you reach the r'about take the exit for Woking, which will be the 3rd exit off. Up to the r'about turn left into Shawfields Road, then as above.

Nearest Railway Station Ash or Ash Vale   **Bus Route** Stagecoach 20A, 550

384

ASHBY IVANHOE — NFU Sports Ground, Lower Packington Road, Ashby de la Zouch LE65 1TS — 01530 413 140

From A42 junction 12, follow signs for Ashby, pass golf club on the left, then pass car wash garage on right and take the second right onto Avenue Road.
Turn right at the end of the road onto Lower Packington Road, follow road around bends and the ground is on the right.

396

ASHFORD TOWN (MIDDLESEX) — Robert Parker Stadium, Stanwell, Staines TW19 7BH — 01784 245 908

M25 junction 13, A30 towards London,
third left at footbridge after Ashford Hospital crossroads,
ground sign posted after 1/4 mile on the right down Short Lane,
two miles from Ashford (BR) and Hatton Cross tube station.

Nearest Railway Station Heathrow Terminal 4 Underground - 1.5km   **Bus Route** Genesis Close - stop 400m away

363

ASHFORD UNITED — The Homelands, Ashford Road TN26 1NJ — 01233 611 838

Take Junction 10 off the M20 following signs for the A2070. Continue along A2070 eventually merging onto A2042. At the roundabout take first exit on to Avenue Jacques Faucheux. At the next roundabout take second exit onto Ashford Road. Ground will be on the right handside.

Nearest Railway Station Ham Street - 4.2km   **Bus Route** Smithfields Crossroads - stop 600m away

220

ASHINGTON — Woodhorn Lane, Ashington NE63 9FW — 01670 811 991

Leave the A1 at the junction with the A19 north of Newcastle. Go along the A19 eastwards untio the next roundabout . Here take the second exit (A189) signposted to Bedlington and Ashington.
Continue along A189 until reach Woodhorn roundabout, turn left onto A197. Turn left at first roundabout.
Just before the hospital car park entrance, turn right. Ground is on left.

Bus Route Wansbeck Hospital - stop 71m away

476

ASHTON & BACKWELL UNITED — The Lancer Scott Stadium, West Town Road, Backwell. BS48 3HQ — 01275 461 273

Off the main A370 in Backwell, travelling from Bristol the entrance is on the right, apprximately 500 metres after the crossroads. Travelling from Weston Super Mare the entrance to the ground is on the left approximately 500 metrs past the New Inn Pub and Restaurant.

Nearest Railway Station Nailsea & Backwell - 0.9km   **Bus Route** Spar (Rodney Rd) - stop 150m away

559

ASHTON ATHLETIC — Brocstedes Park, Downall Green, Ashton in Markerfield WN4 0NR — 01942 716 360

From South: M6 to junction 25, turn right onto A49, after 1/2 mile turn right into Soughers Lane, at T junction turn right into Downall Green Road, pass over M6 and turn 2nd right into Boothbrow Road, turn 2nd right in Brocstedes Road. From North: M6 to junction 24, rejoin north bound M6 to junction 25, directions as above.

Nearest Railway Station Bryn - 1.6km. Garswood - 1.7km.   **Bus Route** Cemetery stop - 430m away

449

ASHTON UNITED — Hurst Cross, Surrey Street, Ashton-u-Lyne OL6 8DY — 0161 339 4158

From the M62 (approx 7.5 miles) Exit at Junction 20, take A627M to Oldham exit (2.5 miles) Take A627 towards Oldham town centre At King Street Roundabout take Park Road Continue straight onto B6194 Abbey Hills Road Follow B6194 onto Lees Road Turn right at the stone cross memorial and 1st right into the ground. From the M60 (approx 2.5 miles); Exit at Junction 23, take A635 for Ashton town centre Follow by-pass to B6194 Mossley Road. At traffic lights turn left into Queens Road Continue onto B6194 Lees Road Turn left at the stone cross memorial and 1st right into the ground.

Nearest Railway Station Ashton-under-Lyne - 1.4km   **Bus Route** Kings Road - stop 50m away

240

ATHERSLEY RECREATION — Sheerien Park, Ollerton Road, Athersley North, Barnsley, S71 3DP — 07910 121 070

From M1 J38. Go down slip road, round roundabout and back under motorway. Take first left onto Haigh Lane, go to top of the hill and, at T-junction, turn right. At next T-junction, turn left onto Shaw Lane and go to bottom of hill. At T-junction of A61, turn right to Barnsley, go through first set of traffic lights and take first left onto Newstead Road. Follow to second roundabout and turn right onto Ollerton Road. Follow to second turn on left - do not take it but go past and entrance is between houses 123-125 Ollerton Road. Follow drive into ground.

Nearest Railway Station Barnsley - 3.4km   **Bus Route** Trowell Way - stop 80m away

463

ATHERSTONE TOWN — Sheepy Road, Atherston, Warwickshire CV9 3AD — 01827 717 829

Take M42 towards Atherstone. Exit at Junction 10. Travel southbound on A5 towards Nuneaton for approximately 4 miles. At third roundabout take first exit to Holly Lane Industrial Estate. Over railway bridge (Aldi HQ on left). At the next roundabout turn right onto Rowlands Way. Ground is 300 yards on the right. Car park and street parking in Rowlands Way.

Nearest Railway Station Atherstone - 0.6km   **Bus Route** Lister Road stop - 118m away

436

ATHERTON COLLIERIES — The Kensite Stadium, Alder Street, Atherton, Greater Manchester M46 9EY — 07968 548 056

M61 to junction 5, follow sign for Westhoughton, turn left onto A6, turn right onto A579 (Newbrook Road/Bolton Road) into Atherton. At first set of traffic lights turn left into High Street, then second left into Alder Street to ground.

Nearest Railway Station Atherton - 0.7km   **Bus Route** High Street - stop 100m away

286

ATHERTON L.R.
Crilly Park, Spa Road, Atherton, Manchester M46 9JX
01942 575 173

M61 to Junction 5, follow signs for Westhoughton, turn left onto A6, turn right at first lights into Newbrook Road, then turn right into Upton Road, passing Atherton Central Station. Turn left into Spa Road.

449

Nearest Railway Station Atherton - 0.3km   **Bus Route** Devonshire Rad stop - 97m away

AVELEY
Mill Field, Mill Road, Aveley, Essex RM15 4SJ
01708 865 940

London - Southend A1306, turn into Sandy Lane at Aveley.

209

Nearest Railway Station Purfleet - 2.4km

AYLESBURY
SRD Stadium, Haywood Way, Aylesbury, Bucks. HP19 9WZ
01296 431 655

When entering Aylesbury from all major routes, join the ring road and follow signposts for A41 Bicester and Waddesdon. leave the ring road at the roundabout by the Texaco Garage and Perry dealership. From the Texaco Garage cross straight over four roundabouts. At the fifth roundabout with the Cotton Wheel Pub on the right hand side, turn right into Jackson Road. Take the second left into Haywood Way, club is at the bottom of the road. If entering Aylesbury from Bicester (A41), turn left into Jackson Road by the Cotton Wheel Pub, and then second left into Haywood Way.

364

Nearest Railway Station Aylesbury Vale Parkway - 1.2km   **Bus Route** O'grady Way - stop 200m away

AYLESBURY UNITED
Chesham United FC, The Meadow, Amy Lane, Chesham HP5 1NE
01296 487 367 (Office)

From M25 Junction 20 take A41 (Aylesbury), leave A41 at turn-off for Chesham (A416), pass through Ashley Green into Chesham. Follow signs to Amersham, still on A416 pass two petrol stations opposite each other and at next roundabout take third exit into ground. From M1 Junction 8 follow signs for Hemel Hempstead then joining the A41 for Aylesbury, then as above.

364

Nearest Railway Station Chesham underground - 0.7km   **Bus Route** The Wild Rover Pub - stop 250m away

AYLESTONE PARK
Mary Linwood Recreation Ground, Saffron Lane, Leicester LE2 6TG
0116 278 5485

Leave the M1 at Junction 21.
Take Soar Valley Way (A563), over first set of traffic lights and turn right onto Saffron Lane at Southfields roundabout (B5366). Ground 400 metres on left.
From Leicester City Centre, take Saffron Lane to Southfield Roundabout and ground 400 metres on left.

396

Nearest Railway Station South Wigston - 1.1km

BACUP BOROUGH
Brian Boys Stadium, Cowtoot Lane, Blackthorn, Bacup, OL13 8EE
01706 878 655

From M62/M60: Follow onto M66, follow to end signed Rawtenstall. Continue for approx 4 miles to Bacup, turn left into Burnley Road, turn right before the Irwell Inn into Cooper Street. At top of hill turn right and second left into Cowtoot Lane. From M6/M65: To junction 9 (Halifax/ Burnley West) then take A679 and follow to Irwell Inn, turn left directions as above.

449

Bus Route Thorn Cp School stop - 119m away

BADSHOT LEA
Ash United, Shawfields Stadium, Youngs Drive off Shawfield Rd, Ash, GU12 6RE.
01252 320 385

FROM M3: Get off the M3 at J4, onto the A331: Take 3rd Exit off to Woking. Up to the roundabout turn left into Shawfields Road, follow road for about 500 yards, Football Ground is on the left, take next turning on your left into Youngs Drive where club is 50yards on. FROM M25: Get onto the A3 heading to Guildford/Portsmouth. Keep on this until you reach the A31(Hog's Back). Then go onto the A331 until you reach the exit for the A331 to Aldershot. Follow the signs for Aldershot, which will be the 1st exit off the A331.When you reach the r'about take the exit for Woking, which will be the 3rd exit off. Up to the r'about turn left into Shawfields Road, then as above.

384

Nearest Railway Station Ash or Ash Vale   **Bus Route** Stagecoach 20A, 550

BAFFINS MILTON ROVERS
The Kendall Stadium, Eastern Road, Portsmouth PO3 5LY

Travelling towards Portsmouth on the M27 continue onto A27. Take the A2030 (s) exit toward Portsmouth(E)/Southsea. At the roundabout, take the 4th exit onto Eastern Road/A2030. Turn left at Anchorage Road. Destination will be on the left. Travelling towards Portsmouth on the A3(M) merge onto A27. Take the A2030 exit toward Portsmouth(E)/Central Southsea. At the roundabout, take the 2nd exit onto Eastern Road/A2030. Turn left at Anchorage Road. Destination will be on the left.

541

Nearest Railway Station Hilsea - 1.3km   **Bus Route** Robinson Way - stop 420m away

BAGSHOT
Fleet Spurs FC, Kennels Lane, Southwood, Farnborough, Hants GU14 0ST

From the M3 Junction 4A take the A327 towards Farnborough/Cove. Left at the roundabout, over the railway line, left at the next roundabout Kennels Lane is on the right opposite the Nokia building, entrance is 100 yards on the left. Postcode for Satellite Navigation systems GU14 0ST

384

BALDOCK TOWN
Arlesey Town FC, Armadillo Stadium, Hitchin Road, Arlesey SG15 6RS
07968 215 395

From the A1 exit at Baldock(J10) and follow the signs for Stotfold then Arlesey. You will enter Arlesey from the area known as Church End, this is the opposite end of Arlesey, but as there is only one main street just follow keep driving until you pass the Biggs Wall building and the ground is on your left.
Coming of the M1 at Luton and follow the signs for Hitchin, pass Hitchin Town FC on the Shefford Road and turn right into Turnpike Lane, this is ckleford. Follow the road of Ickleford and bear left away from the Letchworth turning, the ground is a little further on, on the right.

516

Nearest Railway Station Arlesey - 2.6km   **Bus Route** Prince of Wales - stop 100m away

BALHAM
Colliers Wood Utd, Wibandune Sports Gd, Lincoln Green, Wimbledon SW20 0AA
020 8942 8062

On A3 Southbound 1 mile from Robin Hood Gate.

384

Nearest Railway Station Raynes Park   **Bus Route** London Transport 265

BAMBER BRIDGE
Sir Tom Finney Stadium, Brownedge Road, Bamber Bridge PR5 6UX
01772 909 690

Junction 29, A6 (Bamber Bridge by-pass)onto London Way. First roundabout take 3rd exit Brownedge Road (East) then take first right. Ground on left at the bottom of the road.

286

Nearest Railway Station Lostock Hall - 0.9km. Bamber Bridge - 0.9km   **Bus Route** Irongate - stop 100m away

BANBURY UNITED
The Banbury Plant Hire Community Stadium, off Station Road, Banbury OX16 5AD　　01295 263 354

From M40, Junction 11, head towards Banbury, over first roundabout, left at next roundabout into Concorde Avenue. Straight on at next roundabout, taking left hand lane, and turn left at traffic lights, turn first right into Station Approach. At station forecourt and car park, take narrow single track road on extreme right and follow to Stadium.

314

Nearest Railway Station Banbury - 0.2km

BANSTEAD ATHLETIC
Merland Rise, Tadworth, Surrey KT20 5JG　　01737 350 982

From M25 Junction 8 Follow Signs To Banstead Sports Centre.

384

Nearest Railway Station Tattenham Corner　　　**Bus Route** Metro 420 & 460

BARKING
Mayesbrook Park, Lodge Avenue, Dagenham RM8 2JR　　02032 440 069

Take the exit road from the A13 at Becontree Heath onto the A1153 Lodge Avenue turn off. We are approximately one mile down on the left. The 368 bus stops outside or opposite the ground - alternatively, buses 145,364 and number 5 are a short walk from the LIDL supermarket or from the A13 end get the 62 to the bottom of the hill and walk up Lodge Avenue. To reach us by train go to Upney station, turn left and at the bottom of the hill cross the road into the 'The Drive'. Go to the end of The Drive and enter Mayesbrook Park. Go to the left and the ground is about five minutes' walk and past the Sporthouse.

209

Nearest Railway Station Upney (District Line), 2 miles　　　**Bus Route** 368 (50 yards) 5, 145, 364 (400 yards)

BARKINGSIDE
Cricketfield Stadium, 3 Cricklefield Place, Ilford IG1 1FY　　020 8552 3995

Taking the A127, from the east travel towards London before coming to the traffic light controlled junction at Barley Lane, Goodmayes . Turn Left by taking the slip road and follow Barley Lane to its junction with the traffic light controlled High Road, Goodmayes (A118) (it is the first set of traffic control lights for traffic rather than pedestrians on that road). Turn Right and follow the road past Seven Kings station (which should be on your right) and on towards Ilford. The entrance to the ground is some 400 yards past the station with the Ilford Swimming Baths on the left being the point at which both coaches and those in cars or on foot should turn left into the car parks.

415

Nearest Railway Station Ilford (underground) / Seven Kings (BR) ½ mile　　**Bus Route** 86 outside ground

---

BARNOLDSWICK TOWN
Silentnight Stadium, West Close Road, Barnoldswick, Colne, BB18 5LJ　　07528 410 204

M65 to end (Colne), straight on at round-a-bout, through two sets of traffic lights to round-a-bout. Turn left to Barnoldswick. On entering Barnoldswick through traffic lights straight on at mini round-a-bout, through built up area. On leaving built up area turn right into Green Berfield Lane (Club signposted). Bear right on track to rear of ground and car park. From A56 Gisburn turn right signposted Barnoldswick. On entering built up area turn left onto Green Berfield lane, (Club signposted). Bear on track to rear of ground and car park.

449

Bus Route Greenberfield Road stop - 97m away

BARNSTAPLE TOWN
Mill Road, Barnstaple, North Devon EX31 1JQ　　01271 343 469

From M5 South, exit junction 27, take A361 to Barnstaple, stay on A361 signposted Ilfracombe over new bridge, at 2nd set of traffic lights turn right, signposted Town Centre. At next set of traffic lights turn right into Mill Road.

373

Nearest Railway Station Barnstaple - 1km

BARNTON
Townfield, Townfield Lane, Barnton, Cheshire CW8 4LH　　07484 793 822

Turn off the A533 (Northwich to Runcorn) at the Beech Tree Inn (Barnton Village) into Beech Lane. Turn right at the 'T' junction with Townfield Lane - the ground is 200 yards on the left signed Memorial Hall. Note parking restrictions well signed.

449

Nearest Railway Station Greenbank - 2.6km　　　**Bus Route** Crocus Street stop - 128m away

---

BARROW
Furness Building Society Stadium, Wilkie Road, Barrow-in-Furness LA14 5UW　　01299 823 061

M6 Junction 36, onto A590 signposted Barrow. Follow A590 all the way to the outskirts of Barrow (approx. 27 miles) entering via Industrial route. In a further 2 miles you pass the Fire Station on the right hand side, take next left into Wilkie Road, the ground is on the right.

18

Nearest Railway Station Barrow-in-Furness half a mile away.

BARROW TOWN
Riverside Park, Bridge Street, Quorn, Leicestershire LE12 8EN　　01509 620 650

Leave A6 south of Loughborough near Quorn. From A6 take Barrow/Quorn exit and follow signs to Barrow. Ground 400 metres on right.

From Nottingham: Take A60 and as you exit Hoton village follow signs for Prestwold and Barrow. On reaching Barrow go through village to roundabout at end of main street, turn right down hill and over river. Ground on left.

396

Nearest Railway Station Barrow upon Soar - 1.7km

BARTON ROVERS
Luton Road, Barton-le-Clay, Bedford MK45 4SD　　01582 707 772

Leave M1 at J12 head towards Harlington.
Follow signs through Sharpenhoe Village to Barton.
At T-junction in village turn right, continue 500 yards and turn right into ground on concrete roadway adjacent to playing fields.

365

Nearest Railway Station Harlington - 4.6km　　　**Bus Route** The Memorial - stop 200m away

---

BARTON TOWN
The Easy Buy Ground, Marsh Lane, Barton-on-Humber DN18 5JD　　01652 661 809

Approaching from the South on A15, Barton is the last exit before the Humber Bridge. Follow the A1077 into the town. Turn right at the mini roundabout at the bottom of the hill into Holydyke. Take second left onto George Street and then into King Street. Marsh Lane is opposite the junction of King Street and High Street. The ground is at the end of Marsh Lane, on the right, immediately after the cricket ground.

463

Nearest Railway Station Barton-on-Humber - 0.5km　　　**Bus Route** Butts Road - stop 133m away

---

BARWELL
Kirkby Road Sports Ground, Kirkby Road, Barwell LE9 8FQ　　07961 905 141

FROM M6 NORTH/M42/A5 NORTH: From M6 North join M42 heading towards Tamworth/Lichfield, leave M42 at Junction 10(Tamworth Services) and turn right onto A5 signposted Nuneaton. Remain on A5 for approx 11 miles, straight on at traffic lights at Longshoot Motel then at next roundabout take first exit signposted A47 Earl Shilton. In about 3 miles at traffic lights go straight on and in 1 mile at roundabout take first exit signposted Barwell. In about 1.5 miles, centre of village, go straight over mini roundabout and then in 20 metres turn right into Kirkby Road. Entrance to complex is 400 metres on right opposite park.
FROM M1 SOUTH: From M1 South Take M69 (Signposted Coventry) Take Junction 2 Off M69 (Signposted Hinckley) Follow signs to Hinckley . Go straight on at traffic lights with Holywell Pub on the right. The road bears to the right at next traffic lights turn right signposted Earl Shilton/Leicester. Keep on this road past golf club on right at Hinckley United Ground on left and at large roundabout take second exit signposted Barwell. In about 1.5 miles, centre of village, go straight over mini roundabout and then in 20 metres turn right into Kirkby Road. Entrance to complex is 400 metres on right opposite park.

242

BASFORD UNITED
Greenwich Avenue, off Bagnall Road, Basford, Nottingham NG6 0LD — 0115 924 4491

From M1 junction 26 take the A610 to Nottingham for 1.3 miles, turn left at the 2nd roundabout by the Gateway Hotel onto Cinderhill Road. After ¼ mile turn right onto Bagnall Road, take the 4th left onto Greenwich Avenue and the ground is at the end of the road. NB. This is the best route and the route via the A453 should be avoided if possible.

Nearest Railway Station Highbury Vale Tram Stop - 400m   **Bus Route** Christina Avenue - stop 150m away

298

BASHLEY
Bashley Road Ground, Bashley Road, New Milton, Hampshire BH25 5RY — 01425 620 280

Take the A35 from Lyndhurst towards Christchurch, turn left onto B3058 towards New Milton. The ground is on the left hand side in Bashley village.

Nearest Railway Station New Milton - 1.9km   **Bus Route** Village Store & PO - stop 230m away

541

BASILDON UNITED
The Stuart Bingham Stadium, Gardiners Close, Basildon SS14 3AW — 01268 520 268

Gardiners Close is sandwiched between the Southend Arterial Road (A127) and Cranes Farm Road (A1235). Take 5 bus from Basildon Town Centre get off at Jolly Friar pub. 400 yard walk.

Nearest Railway Station Basildon (C2C), 2 miles   **Bus Route** 5 (First), 400 metres from ground

415

BASINGSTOKE TOWN
The Ark Cancer Charity Stadium, Western Way, Basingstoke RG22 6EZ — 01256 327 575

Leave M3 at junction 6 and turn left onto South Ringway which is the A30. Straight over first roundabout. At second roundabout turn left into Winchester Road. Proceed past ground on right to roundabout. Take fifth exit into Western Way. Ground on right.

Nearest Railway Station Basingstoke - 2.6km   **Bus Route** Mansfield Road - 50m away

316

BATH CITY
Twerton Park, Twerton, Bath, Somerset BA2 1DB — 01225 423 087

Take Junction 18 off M4. 3rd exit off roundabout and follow A46 (10 miles) to Bath City Centre. Along Pulteney Road then right into Claverton Street and then follow A36 Lower Bristol Road (1.5 miles). Left under Railway bridge (signs Bath City FC) into Twerton High Street and ground is 2nd turning on left.

Nearest Railway Station Bath Spa - 2 miles from ground or Avon Street - 1 mile   **Bus Route** No.5 - every 12mins from Town Centre.

108

BEACONSFIELD SYCOB
Holloways Park, Windsor Road, Beaconsfield, Bucks HP9 2SE — 01494 676 868

Leave Junction 2 of M40, take A355 towards Slough, 50 yards off roundabout turn left and at next roundabout turn complete right, coming back towards A355 to continue across A355, then turn right and 150 yards on left is sign to club. Go through gate and clubhouse is 200 yards on right.

Nearest Railway Station Beaconsfield - 2.8km

365

BEARSTED
Otham Sports Club, Honey Lane, Otham, Maidstone ME15 8RG — 07860 360 280

Take A224 and A20 to the M20 in Swanley. Then for M20 for 22.8 miles then take exit 8 onto Ashford Road/A20 and then Green Hill, and turn into Honey Lane for the ground.

Nearest Railway Station Bearsted - 3.2km   **Bus Route** Arriva No.13

505

BECKENHAM TOWN
Eden Park Avenue, Beckenham Kent BR3 3JL — 07774 728 758

374 Eden Park Avenue, Beckenham, Kent BR3 3JL

Nearest Railway Station Eden Park - 0.3km

505

BEDFONT & FELTHAM
The Orchard, Hatton Road, Bedfont TW14 9QT — 020 8890 7264

Hatton Road runs alongside the A30 at Heathrow. Ground is opposite the Duke of Wellington Public House.

Nearest Railway Station Hatton Cross (Piccadilly Line)   **Bus Route** London Transport 203, H25, H26

384

BEDFONT SPORTS
Bedfont Sports Club, Hatton Road, Bedfont TW14 8JA — 0208 831 9067

From Junction 13, M25 – Staines. At Crooked Billet roundabout turn right onto the A30 Signposted C. London, Hounslow. At Clockhouse Roundabout take the 2nd exit onto the A315 Signposted Bedfont. Turn left onto Hatton Road. Arrive on Hatton Road, Bedfont Sports Club.

Nearest Railway Station Hatton Cross or Feltham BR   **Bus Route** London Transport 203, H25, H26

384

BEDFORD
McMullen Park, Meadow Lane, Cardington, Bedford, MK44 3SB — 07831 594 444

From the M1 Junction 13: take the A421 on to the Bedford Bypass, take the third exit onto the A603, the ground is 250 yards on the left. From the A1 at Sandy: take A603 to Bedford. The ground is on the right just before you reach the Bedford Bypass.

Nearest Railway Station Bedford St Johns - 3.8km   **Bus Route** Meadow Lane - stop 141m away

516

BEDFORD TOWN
The Eyrie, Meadow Lane, Cardington, Bedford MK44 3LW — 01234 831 558

From A1: Take A603 from Sandy to Bedford, go through Willington and ground is a mile and a half on right, signposted Meadow Lane. From M1: Off at Junction 13, take A421, carry on A421 onto Bedford Bypass and take A603 Sandy turn off. Ground is on left.

Nearest Railway Station Bedford St Johns - 3.8km   **Bus Route** Meadow Lane - stop 150m away

366

BEDLINGTON TERRIERS   Doctor Pitt Welfare Park, Park Road, Bedlington NE22 5AT   **07935 840 277**

From the A1:- Take the Seaton Burn turn off and at the roundabout take the second turn off (A1088). At the next roundabout, take the first turnoff to pass Aesica on the left. Straight over at the next roundabout. You will go down a dip, over a bridge and back up the other side, do not turn off, continue on the same road until you come into Bedlington. At the top of the bank there is a roundabout outside the Red Lion pub, go straight over. Down the hill there is another roundabout at the Netto shop, take the second turnoff (turning right). Follow the road past the Police station and Law courts and the road bends sharply to the left. Continue around the corner, take the second right. The ground is at the top of the street.

Nearest Railway Station Cramlington - 5km   **Bus Route** Allgood Terrace - stop 216m away

476

BEDWORTH UNITED   The Oval, Coventry Road, Bedworth CV12 8NN   **02476 314 752**

1.5 miles from M6 J3, take B4113 Coventry–Bedworth Road and after third set of traffic lights (Bedworth Leisure Centre).
Ground 200 yards off opposite cemetery.
Coaches to park in Leisure Centre.

Nearest Railway Station Bedworth - 0.5km   **Bus Route** Bus stops at the Leisure Centre

299

BELPER TOWN   The Marstons Stadium, Christchurch Meadow, Bridge Street, Belper DE56 1BA   **01773 825 549**

From North: Exit M1: Exit junction 28 onto A38 towards Derby. Turn off at A610 (signposted 'Ripley/Nottingham') 4th exit at roundabout towards Ambergate. At junction with A6 (Hurt Arms Hotel) turn left to Belper. Ground on right just past first set of traffic lights. Access to the ground is by the lane next to the church. From South: Follow A6 north from Derby towards Matlock. Follow A6 through Belper until junction with A517. Ground on left just before traffic lights at this junction. Access to the ground is by the lane next to the church.
NB. Please do not attempt to bring coaches into the ground – these can be parked outside

Nearest Railway Station Belper - 0.4km   **Bus Route** The Lion Hotel - stop 200m away

299

BELPER UNITED   Borrowash Victoria FC, Anderson Electrical Arena, Spondon, Derby DE21 7PH   **01332 669 688**

From M1 Junction 25 travel towards Derby on A52.
Take third turning left (directly under pedestrian footbridge) onto Borrowash Road.
Past golf driving range on left and in approximately 400 metres turn left into the Asterdale Sports Centre.

Nearest Railway Station Spondon - 1.2km

396

BEMERTON HEATH HARLEQUINS The Clubhouse, Western Way, Bemerton Heath Salisbury SP2 9DT   **01722 331 925**

Turn off the A36 Salisbury to Bristol road at Skew Bridge (right turn if coming out of Salisbury), 1st left into Pembroke Road for 1/2 mile, 2nd left along Western Way – Ground is 1/4 mile at the end of the road. 40 minutes walk fro Salisbury railway station. Bus service 51 or 52 from the city centre.
Postcode for Satellite Navigation systems SP2 9DP

Nearest Railway Station Salisbury - 2.1km   **Bus Route** Winding Way - stop 75m away

541

BERKHAMSTED   Broadwater, Lower Kings Road, Berkhamsted HP4 2AL   **01442 865 977**

Exit A41 onto A416. Go straight over the town centre traffic lights into Lower Kings Road. Go over the canal bridge and take first left into Broadwater. Follow the road to the left, going parallel to the canal. The ground is on the right hand side, sandwiched between the canal and the railway.

Nearest Railway Station Berkhamsted - 0.3km   **Bus Route** Castel Hill Avenue - stop 190m away

516

BEWDLEY TOWN   Ribbesford Meadows, Ribbesford, Bewdley, Worcs DY12 2TJ   **07739 626 169**

From Kidderminster follow signs to Bewdley on A456 past West Midlands Safari Park and follow signs to Town Centre at next Island. Go over River Bridge into Town and turn left at side of Church (High Street). Stay on this road for 1 ½ miles. Entrance to ground is on left.

Bus Route Burlish Farm - stop 1km away

553

BEXHILL UNITED   The Polegrove, Brockley Road, Bexhill on Sea TN39 3EX   **07791 368 049**

From west take A259, at Little Common roundabout take fourth exit into Cooden Sea Road, Turn Left at Cooden Beech Hotel into Cooden Drive. About 1½ miles further, turn right for Brockley Road. Ground at bottom on the right hand side

Nearest Railway Station Collington - 0.3km   **Bus Route** Polegrove - stop 91m away

495

BICESTER TOWN   Ardley United FC, The Playing Fields Fritwell Road Ardley OX27 7PA   **07711 009198**

From M40 travelling North. At the end of the slip road at junction 10 turn left onto B430. Take the first right and the ground is 10 yards on your right. From M40 travelling South at the end of the slip road at junction 10 turn right, cross the motorway keeping in the right hand lane follow signs for B430. Take the first right and the ground is 10 yards on the right. From the A34. Leave the A34 after the BP garage signed Middleton Stoney / Weston on the Green. Stay on this road some 10 miles to Ardley. After entering the village take the first left after passing the Fox and Hounds public house, and the ground is 10 yards on your right.

Nearest Railway Station Bicester North - 6.3km   **Bus Route** Water Lane stop - 121m away

422

BIDEFORD   The Sports Ground, Kingsley Road, Bideford EX39 2LH   **01237 474 974**

Exit M5 at J.27. A361 to Barnstaple. Turn left onto A39 to Bideford.
9 miles turn left into town.
Ground on right hand side as entering town centre.

Bus Route The Dairy - stop 100m away

374

BIGGLESWADE FC   Biggleswade Town FC, Langford Road, Biggleswade SG18 9JT   **01767 318 202**

From the south – up the A1, past the first roundabout (Homebase) signposted Biggleswade. At next roundabout (Sainsburys) turn right onto A6001. As you approach the Town Centre, go straight over the mini roundabout following signs for Langford (Teal Road). At traffic lights, turn right (still heading towards Langford). Continue along Hitchin Street over two mini roundabouts and as you pass under the A1, the ground entrance is 200 yards on the right. From the north – exit A1 at the Sainsburys roundabout and follow instructions as above.

Nearest Railway Station Biggleswade - 1km   **Bus Route** Eldon Way - stop 260m away

516

BIGGLESWADE TOWN   The Carlsberg Stadium, Langford Road, Biggleswade SG18 9JT   **01767 318 202 (Matchdays)**

From the south – up the A1, past the first roundabout (Homebase) signposted Biggleswade. At next roundabout (Sainsburys) turn right onto A6001. As you approach the Town Centre, go straight over the mini roundabout following signs for Langford (Teal Road). At traffic lights, turn right (still heading towards Langford). Continue along Hitchin Street over two mini roundabouts and as you pass under the A1, the ground entrance is 200 yards on the right. From the north – exit A1 at the Sainsburys roundabout and follow instructions as above.

Nearest Railway Station Biggleswade - 1km

318

BIGGLESWADE UNITED
Second Meadow, Fairfield Rd, Biggleswade, Beds SG18 0BS

07714 661 827

From A1 south take second roundabout (Sainsbury's NOT Homebase). Cross the river bridge and then take second left into Sun Street then take first left into Fairfield Road and travel to the very end and into lane. From A1 north, take first roundabout (Sainsbury's) and follow previous instructions.

516

Nearest Railway Station Biggleswade - 0.9km

Bus Route Fairfield Road - stop 85m away

BILLERICAY TOWN
New Lodge, Blunts Wall Road, Billericay CM12 9SA

01277 652 188

From the M25 (J29) take the A127 to the Basildon/Billericay (A176) turn-off, (junction after the Old Fortune of War r'about). Take second exit at r'about (Billericay is signposted). Then straight over (2nd exit) at the next roundabout. Continue along that road until you enter Billericay. At the first r'about take the first available exit. At the next r'about (with Billericay School on your left) go straight over (1st exit). At yet another r'about!, turn left into the one-way system. Keep in the left-hand lane and go straight over r'about. At first set of lights, turn left. Blunts Wall Road is the second turning on your right.

160

Nearest Railway Station Billericay - 1.4km

Bus Route London Road - stop 300m away

BILLINGHAM SYNTHONIA
Norton (Teesside) Sports Complex, Station Road, Norton TS20 1PE

01642 530 203

Norton Sports Complex is on Station Road, conveniently located just off the A19.
Travelling from the A19, take the A1027 signposted Norton. At the first roundabout take the 3rd exit onto Junction Road. At the first turning on the right take Station Road. The sports complex is on the left, just before the railway crossing.

476

Nearest Railway Station Billingham - 2.7km

Bus Route Jameson Road - stop 400m away

BILLINGHAM TOWN
Bedford Terrace, Billingham, Cleveland TS23 4AE

07873 794 768

Leave A19 on A1027 signed Billingham.
Turn left at third roundabout, into Cowpen Lane.
Go over a railway bridge, then first left into Warwick Crescent, then first left again into Bedford Terrace (follow one-way signs) to the ground.

476

Nearest Railway Station Billingham - 0.4km

Bus Route Warwick Crescent - stop 136m away

BILLINGSHURST
Jubilee Fields, Newbridge Road, Billingshurst, West Sussex. RH14 9HZ

01403 786 445

Follow A272 towards Petworth/Midhurst. When leaving the by-pass roundabout appr 50yds further on turn right to Jubilee Fields. (entrance to recycling tip) Follow Road Round.

495

Nearest Railway Station Billingshurst - 1.7km

Bus Route Hole Farm - stop 126m away

BILSTON TOWN COMMUNITY
Queen Street Stadium, Queen Street, Bilston WV14 7EX

07725 816 043

From M6 Junction 10 take A454 to Wolverhampton then pick up A563 to Bilston. Turn left at 2nd roundabout and left at mini roundabout by the ambulance station. under the by-pass bridge and first left into Queens Street. Ground is 500 yards on left

553

Nearest Railway Station Bilston Central - 550m

Bus Route Bus stops outside the ground

BINFIELD
Stubbs Lane off Hill Farm Lane, Binfield RG42 5NR

01344 860 822

From M4 Junction 10 take A329 signposted Wokingham & Binfield, at roundabout take 1st exit. Go through 1st set of traffic lights, turn left at 2nd set opposite Travel Lodge. Follow road through village over two mini-roundabouts, at 'T' junction with church in front of you turn right. Take left filter road after 150 yards into Stubbs Lane. Ground is on left at end of short lane.

422

Nearest Railway Station Bracknell - 3.9km

Bus Route Church Lane North stop - 628m

BIRSTALL UNITED SOCIAL
Meadow Lane, Birstall LE4 4FN

0116 267 1230

At junction 3, exit onto M1 toward Nottingham. At junction 21a, take the A46 exit to Braunstone Frith/Kirby Muxloe/B5380. Keep right at the fork, follow signs for A46/Leicester North/Newark. Continue onto Leicester Western Bypass/A46. Take the A6/Wanlip ramp to Leicester/Loughboro. At the roundabout, take the 2nd exit onto Wanlip. Turn right onto Fillingate. At the roundabout, take the 1st exit and stay on Fillingate. Fillingate turns slightly right and becomes Rectory Rd. Rectory Rd turns slightly left and becomes Wanlip Lane. Turn left onto Lambourne Road. Turn left onto Blenheim Road. Turn right onto Meadow Lane.

396

Nearest Railway Station Syston

BISHOP AUCKLAND
Heritage Park, Bishop Auckland, Co. Durham DL14 9AE

01388 604 605

North: From junction 60 of the A1 follow the A689 to Bishop Auckland. Go straight across the next 2 roundabouts. At the 3rd roundabout turn left onto the A688 and straight across the next 2 roundabouts. At the following roundabout turn left at Aldi and then go straight across at the next roundabout. The stadium is 200 yards on your right. **South:** From junction 58 from the A1, take the A68 towards Bishop Auckland. At the West Auckland by-pass, turn right at the roundabout. Go straight across the next roundabout and the stadium is located 500 yards on your left.

476

Nearest Railway Station Bishop Auckland - 2.2km

Bus Route Bus stops right outside the ground.

BISHOP SUTTON
Lakeview, Wick Road, Bishops Sutton, Bristol BS39 5XN.

07532 126 483

On main A368 Bath to Weston-Super-Mare road at rear of Butchers Arms Public House.

559

Bus Route Butchers Arms Pub - stop 50m away

BISHOP'S CLEEVE
Kayte Lane, Bishop's Cleeve, Cheltenham GL52 3PD

01242 676 166

From Cheltenham take A435 towards Evesham.
Pass racecourse, take right at traffic lights then first left into Kayte Lane.
Ground 1/2 mile on left.

374

Nearest Railway Station Cheltenham Spa - 4.9km

Bus Route Bus stops outside the ground

BISHOP'S STORTFORD
ProKit Uk Stadium, Woodside Park, Dunmow Road, Bishop's Stortford CM23 5RG

01279 306 456

Woodside Park is situated 1/4 mile from Junction 8 of M11.
Follow A1250 towards Bishop's Stortford Town Centre, entrance to the ground is signposted through Woodside Park Industrial Estate.

320

Nearest Railway Station Bishop's Stortford - 20 minute walk from ground.

BISHOPS LYDEARD
Cottlestone Road, Bishops Lydeard, Taunton, TA4 3BA　　07956 682 367

Exit M5 at Junction 25, take A358 towards Minehead. Once past Marine Camp
Go straight over roundabout and take first right turn into Bishops Lydeard. At T Junction turn right and
Head through village past the Co-Op. Continue for 1.5 Miles and club is on right hand side.

559

Nearest Railway Station Bishops Lydeard - 1.5km　　　　　**Bus Route** Darby Way - 80m away

BITTON
Rapid Solicitors Ground, Bath Road, Bitton, Bristol BS30 6HX.　　01179 323 222

From M4 leave at Junction 18. Take A46 towards Bath, at first roundabout take A420 for Wick / Bridgeyate. On approach to Bridgeyate
turn left at mini-roundabout onto A4175 and follow for 2.2 miles, then turn left for Bath on A431. The ground is 100 yards on the right.
From Bath take A431, go through Kelston and Bitton village. Ground is on the left. From Chippenham take A420 to Bristol and turn left at
mini-roundabout onto A4175 and follow as above.

559

Nearest Railway Station Bitton - 500m　　　　　**Bus Route** Cherry Garden Road - stop 50m away

BLABY & WHETSTONE ATHLETIC
Warwick Road, Whetstone, Leicester LE8 6LW　　0116 286 4852

From Junction of the M1 exit from roundabout onto A5460. At next roundabout take 4th exit onto B4114 for 1.3 miles then take first exit
at next roundabout onto B582 Blaby Road. Having crossed railway bridge take 1st right onto Victoria Road. At the min roundabout take
first exit onto High Street and at the next mini roundabout take 2nd exit onto Brook Street. At the next roundabout take 3rd exit onto
Cambridge Road and immediately right by corner shop onto Warwick Road. Ground on left.

396

Nearest Railway Station Narborough - 15 minute walk away　　　　　**Bus Route** 84 & 84A stops in Brook St. 5min walk away

BLACK COUNTRY RANGERS
Halesowen Town F C, The Grove, Old Hawne Lane, Halesowen B63 3TB　　07891 128 896

Get to Junction 3 of the M5. Head towards Kidderminster on the A458 for a mile or so to the first traffic island at the bottom of the hill. Turn right on to
the A459 towards Dudley (the cricket ground should now be on your left) and continue past where the road splits to the next island. Turn left here on to
the A456 towards Stourbridge until you get to the next island. Take the 3rd exit (Old Hawne Lane) and the ground is about 400 yards away, at the top of
the hill on the left.

553

Nearest Railway Station Old Hill - 1.8km　　　　　**Bus Route** Cranmoor Crescent - stop 50m away

BLACKFIELD & LANGLEY
Gang Warily Rec., Newlands Rd, Southampton SO45 1GA　　02380 893 603

Leave M27 at Junction 2 signposted A326 to Fawley. Head South along A326 through several roundabouts. Pass the Holbury P/H on
your right at roundabout take the right fork signposted Lepe and Fawley.At the 1st set of traffic lights turn left then turn left into the
ground, approx 200 yards. There is a sign at the traffic lights indicating Blackfield & Langley FC. Postcode for Satellite Navigation
systems SO45 1GA

541

Bus Route Gang Warily Leisure Centre - stop 50m away

BLACKSTONES
Lincoln Road, Stamford, Lincs PE9 1SH　　01780 757 835

From Stamford Centre take A6121 towards Bourne. Turn left into Lincoln Road. Ground on the right hand side.
Go into town on A16 from Spalding. Turn left at roundabout into Liquor Pond Street becoming Queen Street over railway crossing along
Sleaford Road. Turn right into Carlton Road then right at crossroads into Fydell Street. Over railway crossing and river take 2nd left
(sharp turn) into Tattershall Road. Continue over railway crossing, ground on left.

529

Nearest Railway Station Stamford - 1.5km　　　　　**Bus Route** Junction with Kesteven Rd - stop 75m away

BLYTH SPARTANS
Croft Park, Blyth, Northumberland NE24 3JE　　01670 352 373

From the Tyne Tunnel, take the A19 signposted MORPETH. At second roundabout take the A189 signposted ASHINGTON.
From A189 take A1061 signposted BLYTH. At 1st roundabout follow signs A1061 to BLYTH. Go straight across next two roundabouts
following TOWN CENTRE/SOUTH BEECH. At next roundabout turn left onto A193 go straight across next roundabout, and at the next
turn right into Plessey Rd and the ground is situated on your left. Team coach should the turn left into William St (3rd left) and reverse up
Bishopton St to the designated parking spot.

68

BLYTH TOWN
Off Sandringham Avenue, South Newsham, Blyth NE24 3PS　　07710 715045

From A1 North & South. Exit A1 at junction for A19/Tyne Tunnel/Cramlington. At the roundabout take 3rd exit staying on A19
At next roundabout (Moor Farm) take 2nd exit onto A189. After 2.2 miles take the exit to A192 Seaton Delaval/Cramlington. At
roundabout take 3rd exit onto A1061 Blyth. At next roundabout take 2nd exit A1061 Town Centre/South Beach. Go over the railway line and turn left at the traffic lights. South Newsham Pavilion is on your left.

476

Nearest Railway Station Cramlington - 5.2km　　　　　**Bus Route** Sandringham Drive roundabout - stop 145m

BODMIN TOWN
Priory Park, Bodmin, Cornwall PL31 2AE　　01208 78165

Situated in Priory Park through main car park. Use football car park on Saturdays.

488

Nearest Railway Station Bodmin General - 587m

BOGNOR REGIS TOWN
Nyewood Lane, Bognor Regis PO21 2TY　　01243 822 325

West along sea front from pier past Aldwick shopping centre then turn right into Nyewood Lane.

If walking from Bognor Railway Station - Walk along Linden Road until you reach Parklands Avenue, just after Parklands Avenue is a
footpath on your left (opposite Town Cross Avenue) that if followed leads all the way to the entrance of the football club.

110

Nearest Railway Station Bognor is within walking distance to the ground.

BOLDMERE ST. MICHAELS
Trevor Brown Memorial Ground, Church Road, Boldmere B73 5RY　　0121 373 4435

A38(M) from M6 junction 6 and A5127 from Birmingham to Yenton Traffic Lights.
Left on A452 Chester Road, then 6th.right into Church Road.
From M6 junction 5 A452 Brownhills to Yenton Traffic Lights. Straight on then 6th right into Church
Road.

436

Nearest Railway Station Chester Road - 0.9km　　　　　**Bus Route** Church Road stop - 106m away

BOLEHILL SWIFTS
Rene Road, Bolehall, Tamworth, Staffordshire B77 3NN　　07702 786 722

Exit M42 at Junction 10, take A5 towards Tamworth, exit A5 at 2nd exit (Glascote & Amington Industrial Estate). Turn right onto
Marlborough Way, at next island turn left (B5000), turn right into Argyle Street (opposite chip shop). At T-junction, turn left into Amington
Road, drive over the canal bridge, and turn 2nd right into Leedham Avenue. Take right fork into Rene Road. Club is situated 150 yards
on right immediately after school.

436

Nearest Railway Station Tamworth High Level/Tamworth - 0.9km　　　　　**Bus Route** The Ridings top - 356m away

BOOTLE
TDP Solicitors Stadium, Vestey Rd, Off Bridle Road, Bootle L30 1NY
0151 525 4796

At Liverpool end of M57 and M58 follow signs for Liverpool (A59 (S)), for 1 1/2 miles. At Aintree racecourse on left and Aintree Train Station on right ,turn right at lights into Park Lane. Turn left at second set of lights into Bridle Road. After 200 yards turn left at lights into Vestey Estate , ground 200 yards.

449

Nearest Railway Station Aintree - 0.5km

Bus Route Hereford Drive stop - 251m away

BOREHAM WOOD
Meadow Park, Broughinge Road, Boreham Wood WD6 5AL
0208 953 5097

From M25 – Exit J23, A1 Southbound to London. Exit slip road to Borehamwood join A5135, straight over two roundabouts, at third 3rd roundabout take 2nd exit into Brook Road, Broughinge Road is first turning on the right, after big car park.
From M1 Southbound – Exit J4 to Edgware onto A41 (Watford by pass), Keep going straight over at the roundabout and two sets of traffic lights until you hit Apex Corner, turn left towards A1, over Stirling Corner, exit slip road into Borehamwood join A5135 at the third roundabout take 2nd exit into Brook Road, Broughinge Road is first turning on the right, after big car park.

20

Nearest Railway Station Elstree & Boreham Wood.

BORROWASH VICTORIA
Anderson Electrical Arena, Borrowash Road, Spondon, Derby DE21 7PH
07726 683 957

From M1 Junction 25 travel towards Derby on A52. Take third turning left (directly under pedestrian footbridge) onto Borrowash Road. Past golf driving range on left and in approximately 400 metres turn left into the Asterdale Sports Centre.

396

Nearest Railway Station Spondon - 1.2km

BOSTON TOWN
DWB Stadium, Tattershall Road, Boston, Lincs PE21 9LR
01205 365 470

Go into town on A16 from Spalding. Turn left at roundabout into Liquor Pond Street becoming Queen Street over railway crossing along Sleaford Road. Turn right into Carlton Road then right at crossroads into Fydell Street. Over railway crossing and river take 2nd left (sharp turn) into Tattershall Road. Continue over railway crossing, ground on left.

529

Nearest Railway Station Boston - 1.6km

Bus Route Bus stops outside the ground

BOSTON UNITED
Jakemans Stadium, York Street, Boston PE21 6JN
01205 364 406

A1 to A17 Sleaford to Boston-Over Boston Railway Station crossing, bear right at the Eagle Public House-To light over Haven Bridge-straight along John Adams Way(Dual Carriageway) - Turn right at traffic lights into main ridge, then right again into York Street (This is opposite Eagle Fisheries) Ground is signposted after Railway crossing.

70

Nearest Railway Station Boston - less than 1 mile from the ground

---

BOTTESFORD TOWN
Birkdale Park, Ontario Road, Bottesford, Scunthorpe DN17 2TQ
01724 871 883

Exit M180 via M181-Scunthorpe. At circle (Berkeley Hotel), turn right into Scotter Road. At circle (Asda) straight ahead, 2nd left into South Park road then on to Sunningdale Road, turn right into Goodwood Road, Birch Park at end (right turn). Please note that Goodwood Road is not suitable for large vehicles. Instead, take 2nd right off Sunningdale Road which is Quebec Road, then 2nd right which is Ontario Road down to the bottom and ground is on the left.

463

Nearest Railway Station Scunthorpe - 3.6km

Bus Route Maple Leaf - stop 149m away

BOURNE TOWN
Abbey Lawn, Abbey Road, Bourne, Lincs PE10 9EN
07598 815 357

From Town Centre turn east on A151 towards Spalding into Abbey Road. Ground approximately half a mile on right.

529

Bus Route Nowells Lane - stop 105m away

BOURNEMOUTH
Victoria Park, Namu Road, Winton, Bournemouth BH9 2RA
01202 515 123

From the North and East – A338 from Ringwood. Take the 3rd exit signed A3060 Wimborne, going under the road you've just left. Stay on this road passing Castlepoint Shopping Centre (on your right), then the Broadway Hotel on your right, keep straight ahead passing the Horse & Jockey on your left, keep to the nearside lane. At roundabout take the 1st exit marked A347, pass Redhill Common on your right and the fire station on your left; continue on the A347 turning left at the filter with the pub – The Ensbury Park Hotel – immediately in front of you. 1st left into Victoria Avenue, and the third right into Namu Road, turning right at the end into the lane for the ground entrance. **From the West** – A35 from Poole. Take the A3049 Dorset Way passing Tower Park (which is hidden from view) on your right, at the next roundabout take the second exit, and then the first exit at the next roundabout, taking up a position in the outside lane. At the next roundabout (with a pub called the Miller and Carter Steakhouse on your right) take the third exit, Wallisdown Road A3049. Go through the shopping area of Wallisdown across two roundabouts and at the third one take the first exit, you will see the ground on your right as you approach the pelican crossing. Turn right into Victoria Avenue. then third right into Namu Road. turning right at the end into the lane for the ground entrance. Postcode for Satellite Navigation systems BH9 2RA

541

BOWERS & PITSEA
Len Salmon Stadium, Crown Avenue, Pitsea, Basildon SS13 2BE
01268 045 268

From A13, Take the turn off for Pitsea. At the roundabout take the first exit so that you pass Tesco's on your left. At the next roundabout take the third exit (Ashlyns). Go straight at the next roundabout (approx. 20 metres). Follow the road until the next roundabout and take the second exit and then take the first left into Kenneth Road. Follow the road to the end and turn right and then immediate left into the grounds. Visitors car park is at far end of clubhouse building. Access to clubhouse via pathway between clubhouse and football pitch then side door beside patio area. A130: Take the Canvey Island turn off and follow road to join A13 then follow above. Coming from A127 Take the Wickford turn off and take the third exit at roundabout. Follow road going straight over two roundabouts At third roundabout turn left (Ashlyns) then follow above.

210

Nearest Railway Station Pitsea - 1.7km

Bus Route Wilsner - stop 200m award

BRACKLEY TOWN
St James Park, Churchill Way, Brackley NN13 7EJ
01280 704 077

Take A43 from Northampton or Oxford, or A422 from Banbury to large roundabout south of town. Take exit marked Brackley (South) and follow towards the town (Tesco store on left). Pass the Locomotive public house and take first turning right, signposted Football Club, into Churchill Way - road leads into Club car park.

72

Nearest Railway Station Banbury - Approx. 10 miles from the ground.

Bus Route Stagecoach No. 500 from Banbury.

BRACKLEY TOWN SAINTS
St James Park, Churchill Way, Brackley, Northamptonshire, NN13 7EF
01280 704 077

Take A43 from Northampton or Oxford, or A422 from Banbury to large roundabout south of town. Take exit marked Brackley (South) and follow towards the town (Tesco store on left). Pass the Locomotive public house and take first turning right, signposted Football Club, into Churchill Way - road leads into Club car park.

422

Bus Route Tesco (Oxford Rd) stop - 38m away

BRACKNELL TOWN
Larges Lane Bracknell RG12 9AN
01344 412 305

Leave M4 at J10, take A329M signposted Wokingham & Bracknell. Follow road for 5 miles, over roundabout, pass Southern industrial estate (Waitrose etc.) on right to a 2nd roundabout with traffic lights; take 2nd exit and follow signposts for M3. At next roundabout take 1st exit. At next roundabout take 3rd exit, Church Road dual carriageway. This brings you to another roundabout with Bracknell & Wokingham college on right and Old Manor PH on left, take 5th exit for Ascot - A329. Go down hill on dual carriageway, London Road to next roundabout take 4th exit back up the dual carriageway, London Road, Larges Lane last left turn before reaching roundabout again. Ground 200 yards on right.

422

Nearest Railway Station Bracknell - 0.5km

Bus Route Larges Bridge Drive stop - 282m away

BRADFORD PARK AVENUE — Horsfall Stadium, Cemetery Road, Bradford, West Yorkshire BD6 2NG — 07710 446 485

M62 to junction 26. Join M606 leave at second junction. At the roundabout take 2nd exit (A6036 signposted Halifax) and pass Odsal Stadium on the left hand side. At next roundabout take the 3rd exit (A6036 Halifax, Horsfall Stadium is signposted). After approximately one mile turn left down Cemetery Road immediately before the Kings Head Public House. Ground is 150 yards on the left.

74

Nearest Railway Station Bradford Foster Square or Bradford Interchange   **Bus Route** From Interchange - 681 (682 Eve & Sun)

BRADFORD TOWN — Bradford Sports & Social Club, Trowbridge Rd, Bradford on Avon BA15 1EE — 07801 499 168

From Bath or Melksham on entering Bradford on Avon follow the signs for A363 to Trowbridge. The ground is after a mini roundabout and behind a stone wall on the right hand side. From Trowbridge, follow A363 to Bradford-on-Avon. The ground is just past shop on right, behind stone wall on left.

559

Nearest Railway Station Bradford-upon-Avon - 0.3km   **Bus Route** Junction Road _ stop 30m away

BRAINTREE TOWN — The Ironmongery Direct Stadium, off Clockhouse Way, Braintree CM7 3RD — 01376 345 617

Leave M11 at junction 8A (for Stansted Airport) and follow A120 towards Braintree and Colchester for 17 miles. At Gallows Corner roundabout (with WestDrive Kia on your right) take first exit into Cressing Road. Clockhouse Way and the entrance to the ground are three quarters of a mile on the left and are clearly sign-posted.

112

Nearest Railway Station Braintree - less than a mile from the ground.

BRAINTREE TOWN RESERVES — Stoneylands Stadium, New Road, Long Melford, Sudbury CO10 9JY — 01787 312 187

Leave M11 at junction 8A (for Stansted Airport) and follow A120 towards Braintree and Colchester for 17 miles. At Gallows Corner roundabout (with WestDrive Kia on your right) take first exit into Cressing Road. Clockhouse Way and the entrance to the ground are three quarters of a mile on the left and are clearly sign-posted.

402

Nearest Railway Station Sudbury - 4.6km

BRANDON UNITED — Welfare Park, Rear Commercial Street, Brandon DH7 7PL — 07555 586 305

Leave A1 on A690, go through Durham and continue on A690. Once at 'Langley Moor' (you go under a railway bridge), turn right at the "Lord Boyne" pub.
After 100 yards take the next left.
Go up the road for approx half a mile, and turn right at the newsagents.
Take the next left, and Brandon's ground is up a small track.

476

Nearest Railway Station Durham - 4.4km   **Bus Route** S Lukes Church - stop 52m away

BRANTHAM ATHLETIC — Brantham Leisure Centre, New Village, Brantham CO11 1RZ — 01206 392 506

Turn off the A12 heading towards East Bergholt, stay on the B1070 through East Bergholt and go straight across the roundabout with the A137. Turn left immediately at the T-junction and follow this road around the sharp curve to the right and turn right immediately before the Village Hall. Follow this road around the sharp left hand turn and the Social Club and the car park are on the right.

402

Nearest Railway Station Manningtree - 1.5km   **Bus Route** Temple Pattle (Brooklands Close) - 120m

BRENTWOOD TOWN — The Arena, Brentwood Centre, Doddinghurst Road, Brentwood CM15 9NN — 07768 006 370

From High Street (Wilson's Corner) turn north into Ongar Road.
Then at third mini roundabout turn right into Doddinghurst Road.

210

Nearest Railway Station Shenfield - 2.1km   **Bus Route** Leisure Centre - stop 150m away

BRIDGWATER TOWN — Fairfax Park, College Way, Bath Road, Bridgwater, Somerset TA6 4TZ — 01278 446 899

Southbound from Bristol M5 J.23- enter town on A39 from Glastonbury. Ground is between Bridgwater College and Rugby Ground by railway bridge.
Northbound from Taunton – M5 J.24- enter town on A38, follow signs for Glastonbury (A39). Ground is between Bridgwater College and Rugby Ground as you pass over railway bridge.

559

Nearest Railway Station Bridgwater - 0.7km

BRIDLINGTON TOWN — Neil Hudgell Law Stadium, Queensgate, Bridlington YO16 7LN — 01262 606 879

From South (Hull, Beeford, Barmston): Approach Bridlington on the A165, passing golf course on right and Broadacres Pub, Kingsmead Estate on left. Straight through traffic lights to Queensgate by B&Q. Turn right. At traffic lights turn left and over the railway bridge. At roundabout bear left and carry on heading north up Quay Road. After traffic lights turn right into Queensgate. Ground is 800 yards up the road on the right.
From South and West (Driffield, Hull, York): Approach Bridlington on A614. (This was formally the A166). Straight on at traffic lights (Hospital on right) and follow the road round the bend. At roundabout straight across to mini roundabout and bear right (second exit). Follow road around to right and to traffic lights. Straight on. At next traffic lights (just after Kwikfit) turn left into Queensgate. Ground is 800 yards up the road on the right.
From North (Scarborough): Approach Bridlington (Esso garage on right) at roundabout turn left then at mini roundabout second exit. Follow road around to right and to traffic lights. Straight on. At next traffic lights (just after Kwikfit) turn left into Queensgate. Ground is 800 yards up the road on the right.

463

BRIDON ROPES — Meridian Sports & Social Club, Charlton Park Lane, Charlton, London SE7 8QS — 0208 856 1923

Exit the M2/A2 (Coming from Kent) at the Sun in the Sands interchange, take third exit along Shooters Hill Road.
Take fifth left turn into Charlton Park Lane and follow road until a mini roundabout.
Take second exit and Meridian is situated on your right.

505

Nearest Railway Station Charlton - 1.3km

BRIDPORT — St Mary's Field, Bridport, Dorset DT6 5LN — 01308 423 834

Follow Bridport by-pass in any direction to the Crown Inn roundabout. Take exit to town centre, at first set of traffic lights (Morrisons) turn left. Ground is 200 yards on the right.

559

Bus Route Leisure Centre - stop 20m away

BRIGG TOWN — The Hawthorns, Hawthorn Avenue, Brigg DN20 8PG — 01652 409 137

From M180 (Exit 4 - Scunthorpe East) A18 to Brigg. Leave Town via Wrawby Road, following signs for Airport and Grimsby. 100 metres after Sir John Nelthorpe Lower School, and immediately after bus stop/shelter, turn left into Recreation ground (signposted "Football Ground") and follow road to club car park.

463

*SAT NAV postcode DN20 8DT
Nearest Railway Station Brigg - 0.9km   **Bus Route** Vale of Ancholme School - stop 189m away

BRIGHOUSE TOWN
Yorkshire Payments Stadium, St Giles Road, Hove Edge, Brighouse, HD6 2PN
01484 380 088

Leave M62 at jct 26 go onto A58 Halifax. Carry on to third set of traffic lights at Hipperholme. Turn left at lights onto A644 Brighouse past Brighouse Juniors pitch on right. Take next left in 100 metres then next left into Spout House Lane. Follow road past Old Pond PH road bears right, carry on and as road begins to bear left turn right into lane, gate 20 metres on left into car park.

287

Nearest Railway Station Brighouse - 2.5km

BRIGHTLINGSEA REGENT
North Road, Brightlingsea, Essex CO7 0PL
01206 304 199

Take exit 28 off M25, take slip road left for A12 toward Brentwood / Chelmsford / Romford, turn left onto slip road, merge onto A12, take slip road left for A120, take slip road left for A133, at roundabout, take 2nd exit, turn left onto B1029 / Great Bentley Road, turn right onto B1027 / Tenpenny Hill, and then immediately turn left onto B1029 / Brightlingsea Road, turn left to stay on B1029 / Ladysmith Avenue, bear left onto Spring Road, turn left onto North Road.

162

Nearest Railway Station Alresford - 4.8km   **Bus Route** Spring Chase - stop 300m away

---

BRIMSCOMBE & THRUPP
'The Meadow', London Road, Brimscombe Stroud, Gloucestershire GL5 2SH
07833 231 464

9 miles north of Cirencester on A419. 2 miles south of Stroud on A419

422

Nearest Railway Station Stroud - 2.9km   **Bus Route** Brewery Lane stop - 261m away

---

BRIMSDOWN
Haringey Borough FC, Coles Park, White Hart Lane, Tottenham, London N17 7JP
0208 889 1415

At junction 25 of the M25 or from the A406 (North Circular Road) turn south onto the A10 (Great Cambridge Road) towards Central London. At the junction of the A10 and White Hart Lane turn right (use slip road at traffic lights) into White Hart Lane and the ground is about 500 yards on the left, some 150 yards after a petrol station.

516

Nearest Railway Station White Hart Lane - 1.5km. Wood Green (UG) - 1.5km   **Bus Route** W3 stops outside the ground.

BRISLINGTON
Ironmould Lane, Brislington, Bristol BS4 4TZ
01179 774 030

On A4 Bristol to Bath road, about 500 yards on Bath side of Park & Ride. Opposite the Wyevale Garden Centre.

559

Nearest Railway Station Keynsham - 3km   **Bus Route** Ironmould Lane - stop 100m away

---

BRISTOL MANOR FARM
The Creek, Portway, Sea Mills, Bristol BS9 2HS
0117 968 3571

Leaving M5 at Junction 18, take A4 marked Bristol. U-turn on dual carriageway by Bristol and West Sports Ground and then ground is half-mile on left hand side!

375

Nearest Railway Station Sea Mills - 0.3km   **Bus Route** Riverleaze - stop 50m away

---

BRISTOL TELEPHONES
BTRA Sports Ground, Stockwood Lane, Stockwood, Bristol BS14 8SJ
01275 891 776

From Bristol: Leave Bristol via A37 Wells Road. At Whitchurch, turn left at traffic lights at Toby Carvery. Continue on this road, crossing two mini roundabouts, after the second the ground can be found on the right by BS14 Club. From Keynsham: Leave Keynsham towards Bristol. At 'Rest a While' cafe bear left to Stockwood Hill. Continue on past Stockwood Vale GC and across two mini roundabouts. The ground can be found on the left just past the entrance to BS14 Club.

559

Nearest Railway Station Keynsham - 3.6km   **Bus Route** Battson Road - stop 50m away

---

BROADBRIDGE HEATH
Broadbridge Leisure Centre, Wickhurst Lane Broadbridge Heath Horsham RH12 3YS
01403 211 311

Alongside A24, Horsham north/south bypass.
From the A24 Horsham Bypass, at the large roundabout/underpass take the Broadbridge Heath Bypass towards Guildford and then at the first roundabout turn left into Wickhurst Lane.

495

Nearest Railway Station Christs Hospital - 1.5km   **Bus Route** Tesco - stop 213m away

---

BROADFIELDS UNITED
Harefield United FC, Breakspear Road North, Harefield, Middlesex UB9 6NE
01895 823 474

From the M25 at Junction 16 turn left. At the roundabout turn right towards Denham and at the next roundabout turn left then right at the end of the road. Turn left by the Pub and follow the road over the canal and into the village. Go straight across the roundabout into Breakspear Road and the ground is approximately 800 metres on the right.

516

Nearest Railway Station Denham - 3km   **Bus Route** Wickham Close - stop 150m away

---

BROCKENHURST
Grigg Lane, Brockenhurst, Hants SO42 7RE
01590 623 544

Leave the M27 at Junction 1 and take the A337 to Lyndhurst. From Lyndhurst take the A337 signposted Brockenhurst, turn right at Careys Manor Hotel into Grigg Lane. Ground situated 200 yards on the right. Postcode for Satellite Navigation systems SO42 7RE

541

Nearest Railway Station Brockenhurst - 0.5km   **Bus Route** Brockenhurst College - stop 260m away

---

BROCTON
Silkmore Lane Sports Grd, Silkmore Lane, Stafford, Staffordshire ST17 4JH

From M6 J13 take A449 towards Stafford for 1.5 miles until reaching traffic lights by Esso petrol station. Turn right at traffic lights into Rickescote Road, follow road round over railway bridge to mini island, at island bear left into Silkmore Lane. At next mini island take 4th exit for entrance to ground. **From Lichfield/Rugeley.** After passing Staffs Police HQ at Baswick go downhill past BMW garage and pub to large island, take 1st exit into Silkmore Lane, at next mini island take 2nd exit into ground entrance. Do not turn into Lancaster Road or Silkmore Crescent as directed by Sat Navs **Hospitality:** Spittle Brook, Queensville Bridge. At end of driveway go over Splitter Island and turn right at mini island, at next island take 2nd exit (Stafford Town Centre). Go over Railway Bridge, at bottom of bridge turn immediately right, travelling back on yourself. Spittle Brook is 100 yds on left.

436

Nearest Railway Station Stafford - 2km   **Bus Route** Silkmore Crescent stop - 30m away

---

BROMLEY
The Stadium, Hayes Lane, Bromley, Kent BR2 9EF
020 8460 5291

From M25 Motorway: Leaving the M25 at Junction 4, follow the A21 to Bromley and London, for approximately 4 miles and then fork left onto the A232 signposted Croydon/Sutton. At the 2nd set of traffic lights turn right into Baston Road (B265), following it for about 2 miles as it becomes Hayes Street and then Hayes Lane. Bromley FC is on right hand side of road just after a mini roundabout. From the Croydon/Surrey areas use the A232, turn left into Baston Road (B265), following it for about 2 miles as it becomes Hayes Street and then Hayes Lane. From West London use the South Circular Road as far as West Dulwich and then via Crystal Palace, Penge, Beckenham and Bromley South areas. From North and East London use the Blackwall Tunnel and then the A20 road as far as Sidcup. Then use the A232 to Keston Common, turn right into Baston Road (B265), following it for about 2 miles as it becomes Hayes Street and then Hayes Lane.

22

BROMSGROVE SPORTING — The Victoria Ground, Birmingham Road, Bromsgrove, Worcs, B61 0DR — 01527 876949

From M5 - leave at Junction 4 and follow the signs for the the A38 towards Bromsgrove. Proceed across the M42 junction (you can use this junction if you are heading south for your return journey). After half a mile turn right at the first set of traffic lights onto the Birmingham Road. After three quarters of a mile the ground is on your right.
From M42: Leave at Junction 1 and take second roundabout exit onto A38 towards Bromsgrove. Continue as for M5.

Nearest Railway Station Bromsgrove - 2km

Bus Route All Saints Road stop - 214m away

436

BUCKINGHAM ATHELTIC — Stratford Fields, Stratford Road, Buckingham MK18 1NY — 01280 816 945 (MD)

From Oxford, Aylesbury or Bletchley: take the Buckingham ring road to the roundabout where the A422 from Stony Stratford/Deanshanger meet-turn left, towards town centre. The ground is situated on the left behind fir trees at the bottom of the hill where 30mph begins (opposite a recently-built block of luxury apartments). From Milton Keynes: Up A5 then (A422) to Buckingham-straight across roundabout towards the town centre-ground location as above. From M1: come off at junction 13 and follow A421 straight through, turning right where it meets the Buckingham ring road – then follow as above, turning left at the next-but-one roundabout.

Bus Route High Street - stop 206m away

516

BUCKINGHAM TOWN — Irish Centre, Manor Fields, Bletchley, Milton Keynes MK2 2HX — 01908 375 978

Take A413 out of Buckingham and continue on that road until entering Winslow. As you enter Winslow there is a garage on the right hand side. Take the 1st turn right past the garage (Avenue Road) and then the 1st turn right again into Park Road. Entrance at end of road through the blue gates. Bear left into the car park.

Nearest Railway Station Fenny Stratford - 0.6km

Bus Route Wharfside - stop 300m away

529

BUCKLAND ATHLETIC — Homers Heath, South Quarry, Kingskerswell Road, Newton Abbot TQ12 5JU — 01626 361 020

From Exeter: Take the A380 signposted Torquay and travel along this road until you reach Penn Inn roundabout. Take the right hand lane and follow the road around which takes you into the left lane and towards the town centre. Filter left at first set of traffic lights and go passed Sainsbury's, and you are now on the main road towards Decoy. Go under the railway bridge and follow this road to the next mini roundabout. Go straight across, passing the Keyberry Hotel on the left. Go up the hill and down the other side. The ground is situated on the right hand side, opposite Combined linen services. PLEASE NOTE Coaches will not be able to go under the railway bridge at Decoy. Please phone for these directions for alternative route. **Nearest Railway Station:** Newton Abbot - 1.6km.

559

BUGBROOKE ST MICHAELS — Birds Close, Gayton Road, Bugbrooke NN7 3PH — 01604 830 707

At M1 Junction 16 take A45 to Northampton.
At first roundabout follow signs to Bugbrooke.
Go straight through village, ground entrance immediately past last house on the left.

Bus Route Bakers Arms Pub - stop 500m away

529

BURGESS HILL TOWN — Leylands Park, Maple Drive, Burgess Hill, West Sussex RH15 8DL — 01444 254 832

Turn east from A273 London Road into Leylands Road,
take 4th left sign posted Leyland Park.
Nearest station is Wivelsfield.

Nearest Railway Station Wivelsfield - 0.4km

164

BURNHAM — The Gore, Wymers Wood Road, Burnham, Slough SL1 8JG — 01628 668 654

Approx. 2 miles from M4 junction 7 and 5 miles from M40 junction 2. From M40 take A4 towards Maidenhead until you reach roundabout with Sainsbury Superstore on left. Turn right into Lent Rise Road and travel approx 11/2 miles over 2 double roundabouts. 100 yards after second double roundabout fork right into Wymers Wood Road. Ground entrance on right.

Nearest Railway Station Taplow - 1.9km

Bus Route Pink Lane stop - 239m away

422

BURNHAM RAMBLERS — Leslie Fields Stadium, Springfield Road CM0 8TE — 01621 784 383

A12 Proceed along the A12 until you reach the turn off for Maldon. Carry on through Danbury and then follow the signs for Burnham on Crouch (B1010). *Just before you get to Burnham on Crouch there is a garage on the left-hand side. Springfield Road is about quarter of a mile past the garage on the right. Turn right into Springfield Road, then take the second turning on the right and then first right and drive through the gates of the ground. **A127** Proceed along the A127, and take the A130 turn off sign-posted to Chelmsford. At Rettendon Turnpike (a large roundabout), take the A132 to South Woodham Ferrers. Burnham on Crouch is sign-posted from there (B1012 and then B1010). Continue from * above. **A13** Proceed along A13 and take the A130 turn off sign-posted to Chelmsford. At Rettendon Turnpike (a large roundabout) take the A132 to South Woodham Ferrers. Burnham on Crouch is sign-posted from there (B1012 and B1010). Continue from * above.

Nearest Railway Station Burnham on Crouch (Greater Anglia)

Bus Route 31X (Eastern National)

415

BURSCOUGH — Victoria Park, Bobby Langton Way, Mart Lane, Burscough L40 0SD — 01704 896 776

M6 to J27. Follow signs for 'Parbold' (A5209), carry on through Newburgh into Burscough passing Briars Hall Hotel on left. Turn right at second mini-roundabout into Junction Lane (signposted 'Burscough & Martin Mere') into village, over canal. Take second left into Mart Lane to ground at end.

Nearest Railway Station Burscough Bridge - 0.2km

Bus Route Tesco stop - 105m away

449

BURTON PARK WANDERERS — Burton Park, Polwell Lane, Burton Latimer, Northants NN15 5PS — 07980 013 506

From A14 take J10 towards Burton Latimer, at Alpro roundabout turn right, then straight over roundabout next to Versalift then right at Morrisions. Follow the round around the top of Morrisions continue until you are past the small Alumasc building on the left. Entrance to ground is next left.

Nearest Railway Station Kettering - 4.1km

Bus Route Station Road - stop 120m away

529

BURY TOWN — Ram Meadow, Cotton Lane, Bury St Edmunds IP33 1XP — 01284 754 721

Follow signs to Town Centre from A14. At second roundabout take first left into Northgate Street then left into Mustow Street at T junction at lights and left again into Cotton Lane. Ground is 350 yards on the right.

Nearest Railway Station Bury St Edmunds - 0.7km

211

BUXTON — The Silverlands, Buxton, Derbyshire SK17 6QH — 01298 23197

FROM MANCHESTER (A6): Drop down hill into Buxton on the A6. Junction with A53 (Buxton) At mini-roundabout turn left (signposted Matlock) A6. At Safeway roundabout take 2nd exit (right) B5059 (not shown) (signposted Poole's Cavern and Country Park) Turn right onto High Street (London Road Lights) – A515. Turn right on Buxton Market at Joe Royle's shop. Turn left onto Concert Place (signposted for Police Station) then Hardwick Square South. Continue forward onto Silverlands. Ground on right after 400 metres.

Nearest Railway Station Higher Buxton - walking distance from the gorund.

244

CADBURY ATHLETIC
TSA Sports Ground, Eckersall Road, Kings Norton, Birmingham, B38 8SR   0121 4584 570

Exit M42 at junction 2, take the A441 dual carriageway towards Redditch. At the 1st island, take the B4120 to Alvechurch. The ground is approximately 1 mile of the right (car park entrance is before the ground).

436

Nearest Railway Station Kings Norton - 0.5km   **Bus Route** Meadow Hill Road stop - 266m away

CADBURY HEATH
Springfield, Cadbury Heath Road, Bristol BS30 8BX   07971 399 268

M5-M4-M32 Exit 1 follow signs for ring road, exit roundabout for Cadbury Heath left, 100m mini roundabout straight across, 400m mini roundabout turn right into Tower Road North, 150m turn right into Cadbury Heath Road, ground 50m on right via Cadbury Heath Social Club car park.

559

Nearest Railway Station Oldland - 1.2km   **Bus Route** The King William IV - stop 100m away

CALLINGTON TOWN
Ginsters Marshfield Parc PL17 7DR   01579 382 647

Ground is in the grounds of Callington Community College which is a quarter of a mile from the town centre.

488

CALNE TOWN
Bremhill View, Calne, Wiltshire SN11 9EE   07795 833 702

Take A4 to Calne from Chippenham, on approaching Calne turn left at the first roundabout on to A3102 Calne bypass. At the next roundabout turn right, next left and then right and right again.

559

Bus Route Northend - stop 80m away

CAMBERLEY TOWN
Krooner Park, Wilton Road, Camberley, Surrey GU15 2QW   01276 65 392

Exit M3 Motorway at Junction 4. At the end of the slip road take the right hand land signposted A331, immediately take the left hand lane signposted Frimley and Hospital (Red H Symbol) and this will lead you up onto the A325. Continue to the roundabout and turn left onto the B3411 (Frimley Road) Continue past Focus DIY store on Left and stay on B3411 for approx 1.5 miles. At the next Mini roundabout turn left into Wilton Road, proceed through industrial estate (past the Peugeot garage) and the entrance to the ground is right at the end.

384

Nearest Railway Station Camberley   **Bus Route** Stagecoach 1

CAMBRIDGE CITY
St Ives Town FC, Westwood Road, St Ives, Cambridgeshire PE27 6DT   01223 233 226

From the A14 (Junction 26) continue along London Road (A1096). On entering the Town of St Ives (avoiding Town Centre), continue over the first roundabout and over the by-pass (Harrison Way), continue over the next two roundabouts (still on Harrison Way). Turn left at the next two mini- roundabouts onto the A1123 (Needingworth Road/St Audrey Lane). Turn left at the cross roads onto Ramsey Road where Westwood Road can be found on the right hand side (opposite the Fire Station). Continue to the bottom of the road where the turning for the football club can be found on the right hand side before the St Ives Recreation Centre.

366

Bus Route Langley Close - stop 300m away

CAMELFORD
Trefew Park, PL32 9TS

From the South drive into Camelford up Victoria Road for 300 yards, turn left into Oakwood Rise.
Follow road around for approximately 300 yards. Entrance is on the right up the lane.
From the North as you enter Camelford turn right into Oakwood Rise then as above.

488

CAMMELL LAIRD
Kirklands, St Peter's Road, Rock Ferry, Birkenhead CH42 1PY   0151 645 3121

From Chester: M563/A41 towards Birkenhead, at New ferry signpost take the B5136 towards New ferry, approx 1 mile, turn right at traffic island into Proctor Road, ground at the bottom of Proctor Road. From Liverpool: Take the Birkenhead Tunnel, A41 for approx 1 mile, take the B5136 signposted New Ferry / Rock Ferry at big round-a-bout. Follow until the 2nd set of traffic lights, turn left, then first right into St Peters Road, ground at the bottom of the road on the left.

449

Nearest Railway Station Rock Ferry - 0.7km   **Bus Route** St Peters Road stop - 58m away

CAMPION
Scotchman Road, Bradford, BD9 5DB.   01274 491 919

Leave M62 at J26 to join M606. Stay until end and join A6177 Ring Road (East). Go past Asda supermarket and at first roundabout take first exit and join A650. Go past Leisure Exchange. Road becomes A6037. After approx ¾m turn left into Station Road. At junction, turn left and join A6177. At second set of lights, turn right into Manningham Lane, then turn left into Oak Lane at next lights. At second set of lights, turn right into Heaton Road. Ground is approx 500m on right.

463

Nearest Railway Station Frizinghall - 1.9km   **Bus Route** Toller Lane Masham Place - 109m away

CANTERBURY CITY
Deal Town FC, The Charles Sportsground, St Leonards Road, Deal CT14 9AU   01304 375 623

Come in on Queen Street, then right into London Road and over bridge, straight on into St Leonard's Road where London Road bears right, and entrance to ground is on left.

505

Nearest Railway Station Deal 3/4 mile away

CANVEY ISLAND
The Frost Financial Stadium, Park Lane, Canvey Island, Essex SS8 7PX   01268 682 991

A130 from A13 or A127 at Sadlers Farm roundabout.
One mile through Town Centre, first right past old bus garage.

211

Nearest Railway Station Leigh-on-Sea - 3.2km   **Bus Route** Transport Museum - stop 100m away

CARLISLE CITY
Gilford Park, Carlisle CA1 3AF   01228 523 777

M6 to junction 42, follow the A6 towards Carlisle for approx 2 miles, turn left into Petteril Bank Road, by the Aldi Store. Follow this road for about 1 mile and turn right into the ground. Access road just before the railway bridge.

449

Nearest Railway Station Carlisle - 1.9km   **Bus Route** Ridgemount Road stop - 321m away

CARLTON TOWN
Bill Stokeld Stadium, Stoke Lane, Gedling NG4 2QS
0115 940 3192

From M1 J26 take A610 to Nottingham Ring Road. Follow signs for Mansfield (A60) for approx 4 miles via 2 roundabouts until reaching junction with A60 at Arnold. Take right turn at Vale Hotel on to Thackerays Lane. Proceed to roundabout and take 3rd exit on to Arno Vale Road. Proceed through traffic lights to top of hill and continue straight on at next lights on to Arnold Lane. Continue past golf course, the old Gedling Colliery and church to mini roundabout. Continue straight on to the old junction with A612. (Southwell) must turn right here and at next set of lights turn left and follow the loop road to the next junction. Take left turn on to the new A612 Gedling By Pass and follow to the next set of traffic lights at Severn Trent Works. Turn left on to Stoke Lane. Entrance to Carlton Town is immediate right. **[Ground must be accessed via the new A612 between Netherfield and Burton Joyce. Football club is signposted in both directions on the approach to the ground).** *Sat Nav postcode NG4 2QW

Nearest Railway Station Carlton - 1.1km. Netherfield - 1.5km   **Bus Route** Stoke Lane - stop 50m away

300

CARSHALTON ATHLETIC
War Memorial Sports Ground, Colston Avenue, Carshalton SM5 2PN
020 8642 2551

Turn right out of Carshalton Station exit,
turn right again,
and then left into Colston Avenue.

Nearest Railway Station Carshalton - 0.3km

220

CB HOUNSLOW UNITED
Bedfont & Feltham FC, The Orchard, Hatton Road, Bedfont TW14 9QT
0208 890 7264

Hatton Road runs alongside the A30 at Heathrow.
Ground is opposite the Duke of Wellington Public House.

Nearest Railway Station Hatton Cross (Underground) Piccadilly Line   **Bus Route** London Transport 203, H25, H26

384

CHADDERTON
Andrew Street, Chadderton, Oldham, Greater Manchester OL9 0JT
07506 104 005 (MD)

M62 to junction 20, follow A627(M) towards Manchester. Motorway becomes a dual carriageway, turn left at first major traffic lights (A699) Middleton Road, then second left into Burnley Street, towards Asda Chadderton then second left past Chadderton Sports Centre into Andrew Street Chadderton FC ground on right at the end of Andrew St. Directions from M60 Junction 21 A663 towards Chadderton/Oldham Thru lights at Gorse St Thru lights at Whitegate Lane (McDonalds on left) Thru lights at Foxdenton Lane (garage on left & pub on right Pass new School on left Thru lights at Hunt Lane Right next lights A669 Middleton Road 2nd Left into Burnley St (towards Asda) 2nd left into Andrew St - ground entrance is 2nd on right.

Nearest Railway Station Freehold (Manc. Metrolink) - 1.1km   **Bus Route** Middleton Road stop - 133m away

449

CHALFONT ST PETER
Mill Meadow, Gravel Hill, Amersham Road, Chalfont St Peter SL9 9QX
01753 885 797

Follow A413 (Amersham Road).
The ground is adjacent to the Chalfont Community Centre off Gravel Hill which is part of the A413.
Players and officials can park inside the ground.
The A413 is the Denham to Aylesbury road.

Nearest Railway Station Gerrards Cross - 2.3km   **Bus Route** The Waggon & Horses Pub - stop 250m away

367

CHALFONT WASPS
Crossleys, Bowsridge Lane Chalfont, St Giles HP8 4QN
01494 875 050

From the A413 follow the signs to Chalfont St Giles village centre and after 300 yards, turn left into Bowsridge Lane. Travel 400 yards along Bowsridge Lane and turn right into Crossleys. The entrance to the car park is at the far end of Crossleys, through the height restriction barrier.

Nearest Railway Station Seer Green - 3.3km   **Bus Route** Milton Hill stop - 304m away

422

CHARD TOWN
Denning Sports Field, Zembard Lane, Chard, Somerset TA20 1JL
01460 61402

From A30 High Street, follow Swimming Pool/Sports Centre signs via Helliers road.
Turn right into Crimchard, turn left into Zembard Lane. Ground is on right hand side.

Bus Route Holyrood School - stop 100m away

559

CHARNOCK RICHARD
Mossie Park, Charter Lane, Charnock Richard, Chorley PR7 5LZ
01257 794 288

M6 to junction 28 (Leyland) at end of slip road turn right. Travel to the traffic lights and turn right onto the A49 towards Wigan, through Euxton and on to Charnock Richard. Pass the Bowling Green Pub on the right, continue for ¾ mile and turn left into Charter Lane. Turn first right into Charter lane, ground 500 yards on the right. M61 to junction 8 (Chorley) follow the signs for Southport on reaching the A49 follow signs for Wigan, through Charnock Richard directions then as above. PLEASE USE THE CLUB PARK. Do not park on the road.

Nearest Railway Station Euxton Balshaw Lane - 3km   **Bus Route** Leeson Avenue stop - 299m away

449

CHASETOWN
The Scholars, Church Street, Chasetown, Walsall WS7 3QL
01543 682 222

From the M42 junction10 towards Tamworth or from the M6 Junction 11 or 12 towards Cannock or the A38 southbound from Derby - follow signs for A5 towards Brownhills, At the traffic lights at the Terrace Restaurant turn towards Burntwood onto the A5195. Straight over first island towards Chasetown and Hammerwich, over toll road and at second island turn left into Haney Hay Road which leads into Highfields Road signposted Chasetown, up the hill to mini island, then straight on into Church Street past the church on left and school on right. Ground is on the left at end of road. If using M6 Toll exit at junction T6 Burntwood - turn left out of Toll booths and left at second island and follow over toll road as above.

Nearest Railway Station Hednesford - 6.4km   **Bus Route** Queen Street - stop 160m away

300

CHATHAM TOWN
Maidstone Road Sports Ground, Maidstone Road, Chatham ME4 6LR
01634 812 194

Exit the M2 at junction 3, and follow directions for Chatham & Town Centre. You will then pass a Homebase & Toys 'R' Us on the left hand side. Continue straight over the roundabout and then there is a split in the road, where you bear right for chatham this is Maidstone Road. Follow this, continuing straight over the cross roads and you will see a petrol station on the left. Bournville Road is opposite the petrol station on the left. Ground entrance is first left.

Nearest Railway Station Chatham - 1.4km   **Bus Route** Bus stops outside the ground.

505

CHEADLE TOWN
Park Road Stadium, Cheadle, Cheshire SK8 2AN
0161 428 2510

M60 to junction 2 (formerly M63 junction 11), follow A560 to Cheadle. Go through first main set of traffic lights and then first left after shops into Park Road. Ground at end of road.

Nearest Railway Station Gatley - 1.8km   **Bus Route** Stockport Road stop - 161m away

449

CHEDDAR
Bowdens Park, Draycott Road, Cheddar BS27 3RL
01934 707 271

FROM WELLS: Take the A371 (Weston Super Mare) through Draycott and Bowdens Park is on your left about half a mile past Cheddar Garden Centre (if you get to the church you've gone too far). FROM WESTON: Head towards Wells on the A371 and go through the village of Cheddar. The church is on your right as you come out of the village and Bowdens Park is 200 yards past the church on your right hand side.

Bus Route Church Street - stop 400m away

559

CHELMSFORD CITY
Melbourne Park Stadium, Salerno Way, Chelmsford CM1 2EH
01245 290 959

Leave A12 at J15 and head towards Chelmsford. At the roundabout turn left into Westway. Turn left onto the A1060 signposted Sawbridgeworth. At the second set of traffic lights turn right into Chignal Road. Turn right into Melbourne Avenue. Salerno Way is on your left. At the end of the football pitches and immediately before the block of flats, turn left at the mini roundabout in Salerno Way to enter the Stadium car park.

Nearest Railway Station Chelmsford - take bus or taxi to ground.   **Bus Route** No. 54 and 56 opposite the train station.

114

CHELMSLEY TOWN
Coleshill FC Pack Meadow, Packington Lane, Coleshill, B46 3JQ
07736 296 246

From M6 Junction 4 take A446 signposted Lichfield. Straight over 1st roundabout then immediately turn right across dual carriageway onto B4117 signposted Coleshill. After school on right, turn right into Packington Lane. Ground is ½ mile on left.

Nearest Railway Station Coleshill Parkway - 3.6km   **Bus Route** St Edwards Primary School stop - 258m away

436

CHELTENHAM SARACENS
Petersfield Park, Tewkesbury Road GL51 9DY
01242 584 134

Follow directions into Cheltenham following signs for railway station. At Station roundabout take Gloucester Road, in a Northerly direction for approx 2 miles. Turn left at lights past Tesco entrance onto Tewkesbury Road, follow road past 'The Range' store over railway bridge. Take 1st left and then 1st left again, then left into service road into car park.

Nearest Railway Station Cheltenham Spa - 1.4km   **Bus Route** Moors Avenue stop - 171m away

422

CHERTSEY TOWN
Alwyns Lane, Chertsey, Surrey KT16 9DW
01932 561 774

Leave M25 at junction 11, East on St. Peters Way (A317). Left at roundabout in Chertsey Road (A317). Left into Eastworth Road (A317). Straight on into Chilsey Green Road (A320), 3rd exit on roundabout (towards Staines) (A320). 1st right after car showrooms into St. Ann's Road (B375). Right at Coach & Horses in Grove Road (residential). Alwyns Lane is very narrow and not suitable for large motor coaches.

Nearest Railway Station Chertsey   **Bus Route** Abellio 446, 451, 461, 557

384

CHESHAM UNITED
The Meadow, Amy Lane, Amersham Road, Chesham HP5 1NE
01494 783 964

From M25 Junction 20 take A41 (Aylesbury), leave A41 at turn-off for Chesham (A416), pass through Ashley Green into Chesham. Follow signs to Amersham, still on A416 pass two petrol stations opposite each other and at next roundabout take third exit into ground. From M1 Junction 8 follow signs for Hemel Hempstead then joining the A41 for Aylesbury, then as above.

Nearest Railway Station Chesham underground - 0.7km   **Bus Route** The Wild Rover Pub - stop 250m away

322

CHESHUNT
Cheshunt Stadium, Theobalds Lane, Cheshunt, Herts EN8 8RU
01992 625 793

M25, junction 25 take A10 north towards Hertford.
Third exit at roundabout towards Waltham Cross A121.
First exit at roundabout towards Cheshunt B176.
Under railway bridge then left onto Theobalds Lane.
Ground is 800 yard on the right.
Nearest Railway Station Theobalds Grove - 0.6km

212

CHESSINGTON & HOOK UNITED
Chalky Lane, Chessington, Surrey KT9 2NF
01372 602 263

Chalky Lane is off A243 (Opposite Chessington World of Adventures) which leads to Junction 9 on M25 or Hook Junction on the A3.

Nearest Railway Station Chessington South   **Bus Route** London United 71, 465

384

CHESTER
Lookers Vauxhall Stadium, Bumpers Lane, Chester CH1 4LT
01244 371 376

Stay on the M56 until you reach a roundabout at the end of the motorway. Follow the signs to North Wales & Queensferry. After around one and a half miles you will reach a set of traffic lights where you need to bear left on to the A550 (signposted North Wales & Queensferry). Then from the A550, take the A548 towards Chester. Head straight through the first set of traffic lights and about passing a Vauxhall and then a Renault garage on your left, turn right at the next lights into Sovereign Way. Continue to the end of Sovereign Way and then turn right into Bumpers Lane and the entrance to the Club car park is just down on the right.

Nearest Railway Station Chester - 2.5 miles away.   **Bus Route** No.10A from City Centre Bus Exchange.

24

CHESTER-LE-STREET TOWN
Moor Park, Chester Moor, Chester-le-Street, Co.Durham DH2 3RW
07972 419 275

Leave A1M at junction 63 and take the A167 towards Chester Le Street and Durtham. Keep going along this road for a couple of miles. You will go under a railway bridge, and as the road begins to climb, you will see the Chester Moor pub on your left. Turn into the pub and the ground is accessed along a track at the rear of the pub car park.

Nearest Railway Station Chester-le-Street - 2.2km   **Bus Route** Inn (A167) - stop 69m away

476

CHICHESTER CITY
Oaklands Park, Chichester, W Sussex PO19 6AR
01243 533 368

Half a mile north of the city centre, adjacent to festival theatre.
Turn into Northgate car park and entrance to the ground is next to the Chichester Rackets Club.

Nearest Railway Station Chichester - 1.2km   **Bus Route** University - stop 182m away

495

CHINNOR
Station Road, Chinnor, Oxon OX39 4PX
01844 352 579

Leave the M40 at Junction 6 & follow the B4009 sign posted Princes Risborough. After 3 miles you will enter Chinnor. Turn left at The Crown P/H roundabout & the ground is 400 yards on the right opposite the Black Boy P/H.

Nearest Railway Station Princes Risborough - 4.9km   **Bus Route** Duck Square stop - 56m away

422

CHIPPENHAM PARK
Hardenhuish Park, Bristol Road, Chippenham SN14 6LR
01249 650 400

Exit 17 from M4. Follow A350 towards Chippenham for three miles to first roundabout, take second exit (A350); follow road to third roundabout (junction with A420). Turn left and follow signs to town centre. Ground is 1km on left hand side adjacent to pedestrian controlled traffic lights. Car/Coach park located adjacent to traffic lights.

Nearest Railway Station Chippenham - 1km   **Bus Route** Fenway Park - stop 170m away

559

CHIPPENHAM TOWN — Hardenhuish Park, Bristol Road, Chippenham SN14 6LR — 01249 650 400

Exit 17 from M4. Follow A350 towards Chippenham for three miles to first roundabout, take second exit (A350); follow road to third roundabout (junction with A420). Turn left and follow signs to town centre. Ground is 1km on left hand side adjacent to pedestrian controlled traffic lights. Car/Coach park next to traffic lights.

Nearest Railway Station Chippenham - 1km   **Bus Route** Bus stops within 200m of the ground.

116

CHIPPING SODBURY TOWN — The Ridings, Wickwar Road, Chipping Sodbury, Bristol BS37 6BQ

Travelling north and south M5 – Exit at junction 14, B4509 follow signs to WickWar, at roundabout take third exit onto B4058, turn left onto B4509, at "T" junction turn right onto Wickwar High Street B4060. At mini roundabout continue forward onto Sodbury Road. Road merges into the Wickwar Road, continue on this road for two miles. Ground is on the left hand side. Travelling east and west M4 – Exit at junction 18, A46 Bath Road, follow signs to Yate. At traffic lights bear left onto A432 Badminton Road, stay on this road for three miles. At roundabout take third exit Wickwar Road. Ground is on the right hand side.

Nearest Railway Station Yate - 2.7km   **Bus Route** Wickwar Road - stop 50m away

559

CHIPSTEAD — High Road, Chipstead, Surrey CR5 3SF — 01737 553 250

From the Brighton Road north bound,
go left into Church Lane and left into Hogcross Lane.
High Road is on the right.

Nearest Railway Station Chipstead - 2.1km

221

CHORLEY — Victory Park Stadium, Duke Street, Chorley, Lancashire PR7 3DU — 01257 230 007

M61 (Junc.6) follow A6 to Chorley, going past the Yarrow Bridge Hotel on Bolton Rd. Left at first set of traffic lights into Pilling Lane, first right into Ashley St. Ground 2nd entrance on left. **M6** (Junc.27) follow Chorley, left at lights, A49 continue for 2½ miles, right onto B5251. Drive through Coppull and into Chorley for about 2 miles. Entering Chorley turn right into Duke St. 200yds past Plough Hotel. Right into Ashley St. and first right into Ground.

Nearest Railway Station Chorley - half a mile from the ground.   **Bus Route** Bus station half a mile from the ground.

76

CHRISTCHURCH — Hurn Bridge S.C, Avon Causeway, Christchurch BH23 6DY — 01202 473 792

A338 from Ringwood turn off at sign for Bournemouth International Airport (Hurn) on left. At T junction turn right, continue through traffic lights, at the small roundabout in Hurn turn right away from the Airport, exit signed Sopley and 100 yards on the right is Hurn Bridge Sports Ground. Postcode for Sat. Nav. systems BH23 6DY

Nearest Railway Station Christchurch - 4.6km   **Bus Route** Post Office - stop 100m away

541

CINDERFORD TOWN — The Causeway, Hildene, Cinderford, Gloucestershire GL14 2QH — 07896 887 162

Take A40 west out of Gloucester, then A48 for 8 miles. Turn right at Elton Garage onto A4151 (Forest of Dean). Continue through Littledean, climb steep hill, turn right at crossroads (football ground), then second left into Latimer Road. Or if coming from Severn Bridge take A48 Chepstow through Lydney, Newnham then left at Elton Garage – then as above.

Bus Route Forest High School - stop 200m away

375

CIRENCESTER TOWN — The Corinium Stadium, Kingshill Lane, Cirencester GL7 1HS — 01285 654 543

Go along the dual carriageway, the Cirencester North-South outer bypass which links the M4 at Junction 15, Swindon, with the M5 at Junction 11a, Gloucester. That road is identified on the road signs and road maps as A419(T) from Swindon or A417(T) from the M5. It is about 20 or so minutes road time from both the M4 and the M5 junctions, traffic permitting. Come off the bypass at the Burford Road Junction (named on the road signs). There is a big services located there - fuel, food and a Travelodge. At that junction, go up the slip road to a roundabout. At the roundabout, turn away from Cirencester Town Centre, (If you are coming from the south, go over the bypass and straight over another roundabout) and up to the traffic lights. Turn right, and follow the road to a T-junction. Turn right, that road takes you back over the bypass, and then turn first left into Kingshill Lane. The Ground is half a mile on the right, past Kingshill School and the Council Playing Fields.   **Bus Route** Kingshill School - stop 150m away

376

CIRENCESTER TOWN DEV. — Corinium Stadium, Kingshill Lane, Cirencester Glos GL7 1HS — 01285 654 543

Leave bypass at Burford Road roundabout.
Aim for Stow, turn right at traffic lights, then right again at next junction, first left into Kingshill Lane.
Ground 500 yards on right.

Bus Route Kingshill School Grounds stop - 55m away

422

CITY OF LIVERPOOL — TDP Solicitors Stadium, Vesty Road, off Bridle Road, Bootle, Liverpool L30 1NY

At Liverpool end of M57and M58 follow signs for Liverpool (A59 (S)), for 1 1/2 miles. At Aintree racecourse on left and Aintree Train Station on right ,turn right at lights into Park Lane. Turn left at second set of lights into Bridle Road. After 200 yards turn left at lights into Vestey Estate , ground 200 yards.

Nearest Railway Station Aintree - 0.5km   **Bus Route** Arriva 15, 135 & 157

449

CLANFIELD 85 — Radcot Road, Clanfield OX18 2ST — 01367 810 314

Situated on A4095 at southern end of village, 8 miles west of Witney and 4 miles east of Faringdon.

Bus Route Carter Institute stop - 399m away

422

CLAPTON — The Old Spotted Dog, Upton Lane, Forest Gate E7 9NP — 07983 588 883

A13 to Plaistow junction (A112) follow A112 along Prince Regent's Lane straight across two sets of lights.
At 3rd set of lights, turn right onto Clegg St. Go straight across the next set of lights onto Upton Lane, (A114).
The Ground is approximately half a mile down on the left hand side.

Nearest Railway Station Forest Gate, 8-10 min walk or Plaistow (District Line), 5-7 min   **Bus Route** 325, stops outside ground

415

CLEETHORPES TOWN — The Bradley Football Development Centre Bradley Road, Grimsby, DN37 0AG — 01472 325 300

Head East along the M180/A180. Exit at the Great Coates Interchange. Travel back over motorway to first Roundabout. Take first exit and follow for two miles to Trawl Pub Roundabout. Take second exit, follow for two miles to Bradley Roundabout. Take second exit on to Bradley Road. The ground is approximately 500 yards on the left.

Nearest Railway Station Grimsby Town - 3km   **Bus Route** Crowland Avenue - stop 470m away

301

CLEVEDON TOWN
Hand Stadium, Davis Lane, Clevedon BS21 6TG

07768 100 632

Exit J20 from M5, at bottom of slip road, turn left at roundabout into Central Way.
At next roundabout turn left to Kenn Road.
Stay on Kenn Road out of town, cross river, take 1st left into Davis Lane, over motorway.
Ground 200m on right.

559

Nearest Railway Station Yatton - 4km   **Bus Route** Sercombe Park - stop 400m away

---

CLIFTON ALL WHITES
Green Lane, Clifton, Nottingham NG11 9AZ

07775 615 237

At junction 24 of the M1, take the A453 exit to Nottingham (S). Take Remembrance Way/A453 to Farnborough Rd in Clifton. Merge onto Kegworth Interchange. Turn right to stay on Kegworth Interchange. Continue straight onto Remembrance Way/A453. At Mill Hill Roundabout, take the 2nd exit onto Barton Ln/Remembrance Way/A453. At the roundabout, take the 2nd exit onto Clifton Ln/Remembrance Way/A453. At the roundabout, take the 2nd exit onto Green Lane.

396

Nearest Railway Station Beeston - 3.2km   Clifton Centre Tram Stop 426m from ground.

CLIPSTONE
Worksop Van Hire Stad, Clipstone Rd East, Clipstone Village NG21 9AB   01623 627 262 / 07937 143 685

From M1 J29, take exit signposted A617 Mansfield. At next roundabout, take third exit continuing on the A617. Keep going straight on until you get to the Mansfield ring road with Riley's snooker hall on your right and a miner's statue on your left. Follow the road round underneath a pedestrian bridge and take the next left onto the A6191 (Ratcliffe Gate). After around half a mile, turn left onto the B6030 (Carter Lane). Follow the B6030 for about 3 miles, go straight on at a roundabout and the ground will be on your left.

463

Nearest Railway Station Mansfield Woodhouse - 4.9km   **Bus Route** Station Road - stop 27m away

---

CLITHEROE
Shawbridge, off Pendle Road, Clitheroe, Lancashire BB7 1LZ

01200 423 344

M6 junction 31, A59 to Clitheroe (17 miles) at 5th roundabout turn left after half a mile at Pendle Road. Ground is one mile behind Bridge Inn on the right.

287

Nearest Railway Station Clitheroe - 0.6km   **Bus Route** Hayhurst Street - 50m away

---

COALVILLE TOWN
Owen Street Sports Ground, Owen St, Coalville LE67 3DA

01530 833 365

From the M42/A42 take the exit signposted Ashby and follow A511 to Coalville and Leicester. After approx. 3 miles and at the first roundabout take the second exit (A511). At the next roundabout take the 3rd exit into Coalville Town Centre. At the traffic lights go straight over to mini-roundabout then straight on for 50 meters before turn right into Owen Street. Ground is at the top of Owen Street on the left.

246

COBHAM
Leg O'Mutton Field, Anvil Lane, Cobham KT11 1AA

01932 866 386

From Cobham High Street, turn right into Downside Bridge Road and turn right into Leg of Mutton Field.

384

Nearest Railway Station Cobham   **Bus Route** Green Line 715

COCKFOSTERS
Cockfosters Sports Ground, Chalk Lane, Cockfosters, Herts EN4 9JG

0208 449 5833

Leaving the M25 motorway at junction 24 (Potters Bar), take the A111 signposted to Cockfosters. The ground is situated approximately 2 miles from the motorway on the right immediately before Cockfosters Underground Station. VEHICLE DRIVERS PLEASE BE AWARE THAT THE YELLOW LINES & PARKING RESTRICTIONS IN CHALK LANE ARE STRICTLY ENFORCED UP TO 6.30PM INCLUDING SATURDAYS.

516

Nearest Railway Station New Barnet - 1.5km   **Bus Route** Cockfosters - stop 200m away

---

CODICOTE
John Clementsts Memorial Ground, Bury Lane, Codicote SG4 8XY

01438 821 072

From A1 (M) junction 6, take the A1000 turn off at Welwyn then to Codicote via B656.
At Codicote turn right after the Bell Public house into Bury Lane.
The ground entrance is on the left opposite the church.

516

Nearest Railway Station Knebworth - 3.5km   **Bus Route** St Giles Church - stop 16m away

---

COGENHOE UNITED
Compton Park, Brafield Road, Cogenhoe NN7 1ND

01604 890 521

From A45 Northampton Ring Road turn as indicated to Billing/Cogenhoe.
Go over River Nene and up hill ignoring first turning on left to Cogenhoe.
Take next left and ground is on right hand side.

529

Bus Route Orchard Way - stop 190m away

COGGESHALL TOWN
The Crops, West Street, Coggeshall CO6 1NS

01376 562 843

From the M11 take junction 8, take the A120 exit to Stansted Airport/Colchester/B. Stortford.
At the roundabout, take the 1st exit onto Thremhall Ave/A120.
At Priory Wood Roundabout, take the 3rd exit onto the A120 ramp to Colchester.
Continue onto A120. At the roundabout, take the 2nd exit and stay on A120.
At the roundabout, take the 3rd exit onto Coggeshall Rd/A120. Turn right onto West Street.

402

Nearest Railway Station Kelvedon - 3.6km

COLESHILL TOWN
Pack Meadow, Packington Lane, Coleshill B46 3JQ

01675 463 259

From M6 Junction 4 take A446 signposted Lichfield. Straight over 1st roundabout then immediately turn right across dual carriageway onto B4117 signposted Coleshill. After school on right, turn right into Packington Lane. Ground is ½ mile on left.

436

Nearest Railway Station Coleshill Parkway - 3.6km   **Bus Route** St Edmunds Primary School - 258m away

---

COLLIERS WOOD UNITED
Wibandune Sports Ground, Lincoln Green, Wimbledon SW20 0AA

0208 942 8062

On A3 Southbound 1 mile from Robin Hood Gate.

384

Nearest Railway Station Raynes Park   **Bus Route** London Transport 265

COLNE
The XLCR Stadium, Harrison Drive, Colne, Lancashire BB9 9SL   **01282 862 545**

Follow M65 to end of motorway. Turn left and follow signs for Skipton and Keighley, continue to roundabout, take 1st left up Harrison Drive, across small roundabout, follow road to ground.

288

Nearest Railway Station Colne - 0.6km   **Bus Route** Tennyson Road - stop 100m away

---

COLNEY HEATH
The Recreation Ground, High St, Colney Heath, St Albans AL4 0NP   **01727 824 325**

From the A1, leave at junction 3 and follow A414 St. Albans. At long roundabout take the left into the village and ground is just past the school on left after 400 yards. **From the M25**, leave at junction 22 and follow B556 Colney Heath. On entering the village turn left at Queens Head PH (roundabout) and follow High Street for ½ mile. The ground is on the right just before the school.
From M1 going south; leave at junction 7. At Park Street roundabout follow A414 Hatfield. Continue on A414 past London Colney. Enter Colney Heath coming round the long roundabout and into village. The ground is past the school on the left after 400 yards.

516

Nearest Railway Station Welham Green - 3.6km   **Bus Route** Crooked Billet Ph - stop 50m away

---

COLWYN BAY
Llanelian Road, Old Colwyn, North Wales LL29 8UN   **01492 514 680**

From Queensferry take the A55 and exit at Junction 22 signposted Old Colwyn at end of slip road turn left, up the hill to the mini roundabout, straight across onto Llanelian Road, ground is approx half mile on the right.

288

Nearest Railway Station Colwyn Bay - 2.4km   **Bus Route** Bus stops outside the ground

---

CONCORD RANGERS
Aspect Arena, Thames Road, Canvey Island, Essex SS8 0HH   **01268 515 750**

Take the A13 to Sadlers Farm at Benfleet, follow the road onto Canvey Way signposted Canvey Island (A130) next r'about (Waterside Farm) take 3rd exit onto Canvey Island 1st exit, signposted seafront / Industrial area next r'about 1st exit, next r'about 1st exit. Next landmark is a set of traffic lights (King Canute Pub on the left, carry on through to a mini r/bout passing a school on the right turn right into Thorney Bay Road, Thames Road is the 3rd turning on the right, Concord Rangers is approx 1 mile along Thames Road.

118

Nearest Railway Station Benfleet - Approx. 3 miles from the ground.

CONGLETON TOWN
Ivy Gardens, Booth Street, Crescent Road, Congleton, Cheshire CW12 4DG   **01260 274 460**

On approach to Congleton from M6, past Waggon & Horses Pub, at 1st roundabout 2nd exit, past fire station, 2nd right into Booth Street. Ground at top of road.

449

Nearest Railway Station Congleton - 1.9km   **Bus Route** Booth Street stop - 75m away

---

CONSETT
Belle Vue Park, Ashdale Road, Consett DH8 7BF   **01207 588 886**

Take the A692 from the east into Consett. On the edge of the town, the A692 takes a left at a roundabout. Continue along the A692 for approx 100 yards, before turning right into Leadgate Road. Go along here for approx .25 mile, and turn right into Ashdale Road. There is a road sign for the Leisure Centre pointing into Ashdale Road. The ground is approx 200 yards along Ashdale Road on your right.

476

Bus Route Mortons Garage - stop 174m away

CORBY TOWN
Steel Park, Jimmy Kane Way, Rockingham Road, Corby NN17 2AE   **01536 406 640**

From A14, Exit at Jnc 7, Keep left, at first roundabout take A6003 Oakham/Uppingham stay on this road for approx. 7 miles (ignore signs for Corby to your right en route) straight over two roundabouts at second B.P. petrol station on right. At next roundabout approx 1 mile ahead turn right onto A6116 for 300 yards entrance to Ground between Rugby Club and Rockingham Forest Hotel (Great Western).

301

Nearest Railway Station Corby - 2.2km   **Bus Route** Dalton Road - stop 500m away

---

CORINTHIAN
Gay Dawn Farm, Valley Road, Longfield DA3 8LY   **01474 573 118**

From the station turn right and at once bear right into footpath alongside railway, and at end right into Ash Road, then up hill, right into Castle Hill, left into Valley Road, out of town and then left into Pennis Lane and ground is on left.

505

Nearest Railway Station Longfield - 1.5 miles away

CORINTHIAN-CASUALS
King George's Field, Queen Mary Close, Hook Rise South, KT6 7NA   **020 8397 3368**

The ground is situated just off the A3 not far from the Tolworth roundabout. If you are travelling from the M25 you can join the A3 at junction 10 towards London. Stay on the A3 until you reach the 50mph speed limit, continue under the Hook roundabout and move into the lefthand lane for ca. 174 yds. Bear LEFT onto Hook Rise North for 0.2 mile (Tolworth Junction). At roundabout, take the FOURTH exit (as if you were going to rejoin the A3 going towards Portsmouth) then almost immediately take slip road on left onto Hook Rise South for 0.5 mile. If you are travelling from London on the A3 take the Tolworth Junction exit. At roundabout, take the SECOND exit (as if you were going to rejoin the A3 going towards Portsmouth) then almost immediately take slip road on left onto Hook Rise South for 0.5 mile. Turn LEFT into Queen Mary Close. Ground and car park under railway bridge on right hand side. Youth Section pitches and changing rooms are in the park on the left.

221

Nearest Railway Station Tolworth - 0.6km

CORNARD UNITED
Backhouse Lane, Great Cornard, Sudbury, Suffolk CO10 0NL

Left off roundabout on A134 coming from Ipswich/Colchester into Sudbury, follow signs for Country Park - ground is immediately opposite along Blackhouse Lane.

402

Nearest Railway Station Sudbury - 2.2km

CORSHAM TOWN
Southbank Ground, Lacock Road, Corsham SN13 9HS   **07963 030 652**

A4 into Corsham, at Hare and Hounds Roundabout take the Melksham Road B3353 until the War Memorial, then Lacock Road. Ground a half a mile on the right side.

559

Nearest Railway Station Chippenham - 5.8km   **Bus Route** St Patrick's School - stop 50m away

---

COVE
Oak Farm Fields, 7 Squirrels Lane, Farnborough GU14 8PB   **01252 543 615**

From M3 junction 4, follow signs for A325, then follow signs for Cove FC.

384

Nearest Railway Station Farnborough Main

COVENTRY ALVIS — Alvis Sports & Social Club, Green Lane, Coventry, CV3 6EA — 07904 496 954

From roundabout on A45, Kenpas Highway/Stonebridge Highway, take B4113 into St Martin's Road.
Turn right into Green Lane South after the school.
The ground is on the left hand side.

436

Nearest Railway Station Coventry - 2.3km   **Bus Route** Gretna Road stop - 85m away

COVENTRY COPSEWOOD — Copsewood Sports & Social Club, Allard Way, Binley, Coventry CV3 1JP — 07884 585 440

M6 South: Leave at junction 2 and follow A4600 signs for City Centre. Go over 3 roundabouts and past 1 set of traffic lights, on reaching the 2nd set of traffic lights with Coventry Oak pub on left, turn left down Hipswell Highway. Follow road for 1 mile and reach another set of lights (Fire Station on left and Mill Pool pub on right). Go over lights and the ground is 300 yards on the left. **From M40:** Follow A46 signs to Coventry and Leicester, stay on this road until very end, you then reach a roundabout with a flyover, go round the roundabout following M69 signs. This road takes you past Asda and you reach a set of traffic lights with a roundabout, again following M69 signs. This is Allard Way and takes you past Matalan on left, Go under railway bridge and ground is 400 yards on the right. A45 from Birmingham Direction: Follow A45 until reaching a slip road signposted A46, this slip road has the Festival Pub on left side of it. It is after a roundabout with big Peugeot car showroom on left. Go down slip road and take 2nd exit . , this is another slip road leading to A46, signposted A4114 Coventry. Follow road until reaching roundabout with a flyover, and then follow as M40 directions above.

436

COVENTRY SPHINX — Sphinx Sports & Social Club, Sphinx Drive, Coventry CV3 1WA — 02476 451 361

From M6. Leave M6 at Junction 3 and take A444 towards Coventry. Continue to Binley Road (6 roundabouts) and turn left on A428 Binley Road towards Binley. Pass a row of shops on left and Bulls Head public house on right. After the Bulls Head, turn 1st right into Biggin Hall Crescent. Then take the 5th turn into Siddeley Avenue. Take 1st left into Sphinx Drive and the ground is at the end.
From M42 & A45. Follow A45 towards Coventry and take A4114 Coventry at Coventry Hill Hotel. At roundabout take 2nd exit to next roundabout and take 3rd exit onto Holyhead Road. After approx 2.5 miles you will come to Coventry Ring Road where you turn left and then get over to your right onto the ring road. Continue on Ring Road and leave at Junction is signposted M69 and Football Stadium. Follow signs for A428 Binley until you see Bulls Head public house on your right. Then follow the above instructions.

436

Nearest Railway Station Coventry - 2.6km   **Bus Route** Bulls Head Lane stop - 363m away

COVENTRY UNITED — Coventry RFC, Butts Park Arena, The Butts, Coventry CV1 3GE — 436

Head for Coventry Ring Road, once on the Ring Road come off at junction 7 (B4101/Earlsdon/Tile Hill).
At the next roundabout take the first exit onto Butts Road/B4101.

Nearest Railway Station Coventry - 1km   **Bus Route** Albany Road stop - 156m away

COWES SPORTS — Westwood Park Reynolds Close off Park Rd Cowes Isle of Wight PO31 7NT — 01983 718 277

Turn left out of the Cowes pontoon, 1st right up Park Road approx 1/2 mile take the 4th right into Reynolds Close. Postcode for Sat. Nav. systems PO31 7NT

541

Bus Route Parklands Avenue - stop 100m away

CRADLEY TOWN — The Beeches, Beeches View Avenue, Cradley, Halesowen B63 2HB — 07708 659 636

A456 Manor Way (SP Kidderminster). Straight on at first island, turn right (second exit) at second island into Hagley Road (B4183). Pass Foxhunt Inn on left and turn third (careful some might say second!!) left into Rosemary Road. Straight on into Lansdowne Road/Dunstall Road and turn left at T-junction into Huntingtree Road/Lutley Mill Road. Left again at next T-junction into Stourbridge Road (A458) and immediately left again into Beecher Road East. First left into Abbey Road and after 250 yards swing right up along Meres Road. Take first left into Hedgefield Grove go straight to the end where the ground entrance is almost opposite in Beeches View Avenue between house numbers 48 and 50.

553

Nearest Railway Station Cradley Heath - 2km   **Bus Route** Hedgefield Grove - stop 200m away

CRAWLEY DOWN GATWICK — The Haven Centre, Hophurst Lane, Crawley Down RH10 4LJ — 01342 717 140

From the North: Turn off the M23 at Junction 10 signposted East Grinstead At the roundabout at the Copthorne Hotel, take the 2nd exit, signed A264 East Grinstead. At the next roundabout (Duke's Head) take the 3rd exit, B2028 south, toward Turners Hill After approx. 1 mile turn left into Sandy Lane. (just after entering the 30mph zone and a telephone box on the layby on the right). At the end of Sandy Lane (war memorial on the right), turn left signed Felbridge. After a couple of bends pass the Haven Centre is on your left. **From the East:** Travel through East Grinstead on the A22 until the Junction with the A264 at the Felbridge Traffic lights. Turn left (Sign posted Crawley) and after 100 Meters take the Left Fork towards Crawley Down. Approx 1.5 Miles Haven Centre on Right. **From the South:** Travel North through Turners Hill on the B2028 after approx 2 Miles take the 2nd turning on your right (Vicarage Road). This is a Right fork and is sited just after passing over a small bridge. Follow Vicarage Road for approx 1/2 Mile past Junction with Sandy Lane and The Haven Centre is 200 Meters on your left.

495

CRAWLEY GREEN — Barton Rovers FC, Sharpenhoe Road, Barton Le Cay, Beds MK45 4SD — 01582 882 398

From M1 J12, turn right from South turn left from North, onto the A5120. After approximately 1.5 miles, take the second turning on the right signposted Harlington and Barton. Follow the road through Sharpenhoe to Barton. At mini-roundabout turn right and after about 400 yards, turn right into the ground. Ground entrance is in Luton Road.

516

Nearest Railway Station Harlington - 4.6km   **Bus Route** Sharpenhoe Road - stop 60m away

CRAY VALLEY PAPER MILLS — Badgers Sports, Middle Park Avenue, Eltham SE9 5HT — 07834 546 213

From A20 Kent - Sidcup bypass to 'Big Yellow Storage' roundabout. Take last exit (back on yourself), then 1st left onto Eltham Palace Rd. 1st left onto Middle Park avenue. Badgers Sports will be on your left.
From A2 Kent - To A205 exit, left onto Westhorne Avenue, to 'Yorkshire Grey' McDonalds roundabout. 2nd exit onto Middle Park Avenue. Badgers Sports will be on your right.

505

Nearest Railway Station Mottingham - 30min walk from ground   **Bus Route** 160 stops outside the ground.

CRAY WANDERERS — Bromley FC, Hayes Lane, Bromley, Kent BR2 9EF — 020 8460 5291

From M25: Leaving the motorway at junction 4, follow the A21 to Bromley and London, for approximately 4 miles and then fork left onto the A232 signposted Croydon/Sutton. At the second set of traffic lights, turn right into Baston Road (B265), following it for about two miles as it becomes Hayes Street and then Hayes Lane. Cray Wanderers FC is on the right hand side of the road just after the mini roundabout. There is ample room for coaches to drive down the driveway, turn round and park.

222

Nearest Railway Station Bromley South - 1km   **Bus Route** Hayes Road - stop 160m away

CRIBBS — The Lawns, Station Road, Henbury, Bristol BS10 7TB — 0117 950 2303

From M5 J17 follow signs to Bristol West & Clifton on the A4018 dual carriageway cross two roundabouts, at 3rd roundabout take fourth exit and follow signs to M5, take 1st turning left after car dealers, ground straight ahead.

559

Nearest Railway Station Pilning - 4.3km. Sea MIlls - 4.5km. Patchway - 4.5km   **Bus Route** Rugby Club - stop 400m away

CROCKENHILL — Wested Meadow Ground, Eynesford Road, Crockenhill, Kent BR8 8EJ — 07702 886 966

From M25 - Turn off at Junction 3, taking the B2173 London Road, Swanley exit. After 100 Yards turn left into Wested Lane. Continue over the narrow railway bridge into Eynsford Road, following the road for about 1 mile. The Ground and Car park is on the Right.
From London - Follow the A20 from London taking the M25 turn off. At the Roundabout take the 5th exit, then directions as above.
From Swanley - From Asda, follow the road out of Swanley towards the M25. At the first Roundabout take the right exit into Goldsel Road. Follow the road into the village turning left at the T Junction. Continue along the Eynsford Road for about 1 mile until you reach the Ground and Car Park on the left.

505

CROOK TOWN
The Sir Tom Cowie Millfield, West Road, Crook, Co.Durham DL15 9PW   **01388 762 959**

Leave the A1 at Junction 62, and take the A690 towards Durham. Keep on this road through Durham, Meadowfield, Willington and Helmington Row. When you arrive in Crook town centre keep going straight ahead, as the A690 becomes the A689. The ground is situated on this road on your right, approximately 300 yards from the town centre.

476

Bus Route Bus stops right outside the ground

CROWBOROUGH ATHLETIC
Crowborough Co. Stadium, Alderbrook Rec, Fermor Road, TN6 3DJ   **07879 434 467**

Walking or driving from the Town Centre to the football club - If you use the A26 you'll either turn left or right to get in to the High Street, at the traffic lights, depending if you've come from the Tunbridge Wells or Uckfield direction. Head down the High Street from the lights until you cross the zebra crossing after about 100 yards. Then you'll need to bear right and turn in to Croft Road, you'll go over another zebra crossing, carry straight on past the front of Waitrose and then you'll come to a mini roundabout which you go straight over. After 50 yards there's another mini roundabout, go straight over and follow the road round the 's' bend, an M&S Petrol Station will be on your right, and then head towards the next junction. At the junction of Myrtle Road on your left and Southview Road on your right, Croft Road changes in to Whitehill Road without you ever realising it so carry straight on. Go down the hill and there will be a public house on your right hand side called The Bricklayers, carry on past the pub then you'll come to another mini roundabout, take the first exit left, this is the start of Fermor Road and take the second right, this is Aldervale Cottages and turn immediately right again into The Crowborough Community Ground, known locally as Alderbrook Rec Ground.

505

CROYDON
Croydon Sports Arena, Albert Road, South Norwood SE25 4QL   **02086 545524 (CH-0208 6548555)**

From East Croydon head east on Addiscombe Road towards Addiscombe Grove. Follow Cherry Orchard Rd and B243 to Grasmere Rd in South Norwood. At the end of Grasmere Road, turn left into Albert Road and turn right into the entrance to Croydon FC Sports Arena which is about 100 yards on the right hand side. Drive up to the clubhouse which overlooks the Arena.

505

Nearest Railway Station Croydon Tramlink - 1/4 mile   **Bus Route** No.312

CULLOMPTON RANGERS
Speeds Meadow, Cullompton EX15 1DW   **01884 33090**

Leave M5 at junction 28, left at Town Centre, at Meadow Lane turn left past Sports Centre, at end of road turn right, then in 100 yards turn left into ground at end of lane.

488

CURZON ASHTON
Tameside Stadium, Richmond Street, Ashton-u-Lyme OL7 9HG   **0161 330 6033**

M60 (from Stockport) Junction 23 turn left off slip road, then get into the second from left lane to go through the lights onto the A6140 sign-posted Ashton. Keep on the A6140 until you come to a set of traffic lights with a cinema on your right, turn left at these lights, follow road over a bridge then over a mini-roundabout then turn left after the mini-roundabout. Ground is at the bottom.

78

Nearest Railway Station Ashton-under-Lyne - Approx. one mile from ground.   Also 5mins from Ashton West Metrolink.

DAGENHAM & REDBRIDGE
Chigwell Construction Stadium, Victoria Road, Dagenham, Essex RM10 7XL   **020 8592 1549**

If you are coming from the **North or West**, follow the M25 Clockwise until junction 27 and take the M11 towards London. Proceed along the M11 and as the road splits at the end of the motorway follow the signs for A406 South & A13. There are speed cameras along this road and the speed limit is 50 mph. After 5 miles, take the slip road on the left signposted A13 Dagenham, Tilbury and Southend. Go under the underpass and over the flyover and with the leisure complex on your right bear left onto the A1306 signposted Dagenham East. At the fifth set of lights with McDonalds in front of you, tern left onto the A1112, Ballards Road. The speed limit is 30mph and there is a speed camera on your left. At the Bull Roundabout bear left and go past Dagenham East Tube Station. Victoria Road is the fifth turning on the left. **South & East Via Dartford Crossing:** Follow signs for A13 to Dagenham/ Central London. Proceed along this road and take the turn off signposted Elm Park & Dagenham East and turn right at the roundabout at the bottom of the slip road. Proceed to the set of lights and turn left onto a dual carriageway. After about half a mile you will see a McDonalds on your right. Get into the right hand filter lane and turn right onto the A1112 Ballards Road, then as above.

26

DAISY HILL
New Sirs, St James Street, Westhoughton, Bolton BL5 2EB   **01942 818 544**

M61 to junction 5, A58 (Snydale Way/Park Road) for one and a half mile, left into Leigh Road (B5235) for 1 mile to Daisy Hill. Turn right into village 200 yards after mini roundabout, then left between church and school into St James Street. Ground 250 yards on left.

449

Nearest Railway Station Daisy Hill - 0.7km   **Bus Route** Hindley Road stop - 173m away

---

DARLINGTON 1883
Blackwell Meadows, Grange Road, Darlington DL1 5NR   **01325 363 777**

(SOUTH) From A1M exit at junction 57 , A66 (M) take slip road left towards Darlington & Airport. At the roundabout end of motorway, take first exit A66 Follow this to roundabout take 2nd exit A167 Darlington . Blackwell Meadows is on your right after approx. 400 yards.
(NORTH) From A1M junction 59, take the A167 towards the town centre, and when you reach the town centre in 5 miles, take the A167 to Northallerton along Grange Road. The ground is on your left after South Park. There is limited car parking at the ground, it is recommended to use the town centre car parks, a 10 minute walk away.

80

Nearest Railway Station Darlington - 1.5 miles away

DARLINGTON R.A.
Brinkburn Road, Darlington, Co. Durham DL3 9LF   **01325 468 125**

Leave A1(M) at junction 58 and follow the A68 into Darlington.
Continue along the road until you see the Brown Trout public house on your right.
Turn left at this point into Brinkburn Road, and the ground is 100 yards along on the left.

476

Nearest Railway Station North Road - 1.4km   **Bus Route** Brinkburn Road - stop 145m away

---

DARTFORD
Princes Park Stadium, Grassbanks, Darenth Road, Dartford DA1 1RT   **01322 299 991**

From M25 clockwise leave at Junction 1b to r'about controlled by traffic lights. Take third exit onto Princes Road, (A225) then second exit at next roundabout. Continue down hill to traffic lights (ground on your left), turn left into Darenth Road then second turning on your left into Grassbanks leading to car park. From M25 anti-clockwise leave at Junction 2 onto slip road A225 to r'about, then first exit, second exit at next r'about then down hill to traffic lights turn left into Darenth Road, then second turning on your left into Grassbanks.

120

Nearest Railway Station Dartford - bus ride away from the ground.   **Bus Route** Fasttrack B towards Bluewater/Dartford.

DAVENTRY TOWN
Communications Park, Browns Road, Daventry, Northants NN11 4NS   **01327 311 239**

From Northampton or J.16 of the M1, follow A45 westbound into Daventry, crossing the A5 on the way.
At first roundabout bear left along A45 Daventry Bypass.
At next roundabout go straight over onto Browns Road.
The Club is at the top of this road on the left.

529

Bus Route The Cherwell - stop 330m away

DEAL TOWN
Charles Sports Ground, St Leonards Road, Deal CT14 9AU   **01304 375 623**

Come in on Queen Street, then right into London Road and over bridge, straight on into St Leonard's Road where London Road bears right, and entrance to ground is on left.

505

Nearest Railway Station Deal - 3/4 mile away

DEBENHAM LC
Debenham Leisure Centre, Gracechurch Street, Debenham IP14 6BL
01728 861 101

Approach Ipswich along the A14. Turn left at junction 51 onto the A140 signposted towards Norwich.
After approx 4 miles turn right towards Mickfield and follow the road into Debenham turning left into Gracechurch Street.
Debenham Leisure Centre is approx 1 mile on the right hand side.

402

DEEPING RANGERS
The Haydon Whitham Stadium, Outgang Road, Market Deeping PE6 8LQ
01778 344 701

From Town Centre head north on B1524 towards Bourne. Turn right onto Towngate East at Towngate Tavern Pub. Go straight over mini roundabout onto Outgang Road. Ground 1/4 mile on left. From A16 by pass at roundabout with the A15 Bourne Road turn towards Deeping then left into Northfields Road, then left into Towngate/Outgang Road. Ground 1/4 mile on left.

529

Bus Route Buttercup Court - stop 720m away

DEREHAM TOWN
Aldiss Park, Norwich Road, Dereham, Norfolk NR20 3PX
01362 690 460

Take the A47 towards Swaffham & Dereham. Do not take first slip road into Dereham. Carry on along the by-pass and take the second slip road, onto the B1110, sign posted B1147 to Bawdeswell, Swanton Morley and the Dereham Windmill. Follow the slip road round and Aldiss Park is 500 yards on your right.

212

Bus Route Paget Adams Drive - stop 300m away

DESBOROUGH TOWN
Waterworks Field, Braybrooke Road, Desborough NN14 2LJ
01536 761 350

Take exit 3 marked Desborough off the A14 and follow bypass for 2 miles.
At roundabout turn right and ground is 200 yards on the left hand side.

529

Bus Route Bus stops outside the ground.

DEVIZES TOWN
Nursteed Road, Devizes, Wiltshire SN10 3DX
01380 722 817

Leave Devizes on A342 for Andover. Ground is on the right hand side opposite Eastleigh Road.

559

Bus Route Eastleigh Road - stop 80m away

DIDCOT TOWN
Draycott Engineering Loop Meadow Stadium, Bowmont Water, Didcot OX11 7GA
01235 813 138

From A34 take A4130 towards Didcot.
At first roundabout take first exit, at next roundabout take third exit, then straight across next two roundabouts.
At fifth roundabout turn right into Avon Way.
Follow Avon Way for 1/2 mile till you get to a mini roundabout.
Straight across it, ground is on the left after 100 yards, in Bowmont Water.

376

Nearest Railway Station Didcot Parkway - 0.4km

DIDCOT TOWN RESERVES
Loop Meadow Stadium, Bowmont Water, Didcot OX11 7GA
01235 813 138

From A34 take A4130 towards Didcot, at first roundabout take first exit, at next roundabout take third exit, then straight across next two roundabouts, at 5th roundabout turn right into Avon Way, ground is on the left. Also footpath direct from Didcot Railway Station.

422

Nearest Railway Station Didcot Parkway - 0.4km   **Bus Route** Ladygrove Park Primary School stop - 171m

---

DISS TOWN
Brewers Green Lane, Diss, Norfolk IP22 4QP
01379 651 223

Off B1066 Diss -Thetford road near Roydon school.

402

Nearest Railway Station Diss - 0.5 miles

DORCHESTER TOWN
The Avenue Stadium, Weymouth Avenue, Dorchester DT1 2RY
01305 262 451

The stadium is located at the junction of A35 Dorchester Bypass and the A354 to Weymouth, adjacent to Tesco. There is a coach bay for the team coach at the front of the stadium. Any supporters coach should park on the railway embankment side of the stadium.

324

Nearest Railway Station Dorchester South & West - 0.9km

DORKING WANDERERS
West Humble Playing Fields, London Road, Dorking, Surrey RH5 6AD
07500 006 240

From the M25 go off at junction 9, take the A243 exit to A24/Leatherhead/Dorking. At the roundabout, take the 3rd exit onto A243. At the roundabout, take the 2nd exit onto Leatherhead By-Pass Rd/A243. At the roundabout, take the 2nd exit onto Leatherhead By-Pass Rd/A24. At the roundabout, take the 2nd exit and stay on Leatherhead By-Pass Rd/A24. At the roundabout, take the 1st exit onto Dorking Rd/A24. Continue to follow A24. At the roundabout, take the 2nd exit onto London Rd/A24. At the roundabout, take the 4th exit and stay on London Rd/A24.

166

Nearest Railway Station Box Hill & Westhumble - 04.km

DOVER ATHLETIC
Crabble Athletic Ground, Lewisham Road, Dover, Kent CT17 0JB
01304 822 373

From outside of Kent, find your way to the M25, then take the M2/A2 (following the signs to Canterbury, then from Canterbury follow signs to Dover) as far as the Whitfield roundabout (there is a McDonald's Drive-Thru on the left). At the roundabout and follow this road until the first set of traffic lights. At the fourth exit at this roundabout, down Whitfield Hill. At the bottom of the hill turn left at the roundabout and follow this road until the first set of traffic lights. At the lights turn right (180 degrees down the hill) and follow the road under the railway bridge, the ground is a little further up the road on the left. There is no parking for supporters within the ground, although parking is available in the rugby ground, which is just inside the main entrance - stewards will direct you. If you have to take the M20/A20 leave the A20 in Folkestone (the exit immediately after the tunnel through the hill) and travel through the Alkham Valley (turn left at the roundabout at the end of the slip-road and then left again, following the signs for Alkham) which will eventually take you near Kearsney train station (turn right into Lower Road just before the railway bridge, before you get to the station).
Nearest Railway Station: Main line - Dover Priory 2 miles away. Kearsney Station is a 10-15 minute walk from the ground.

28

DOWNHAM TOWN
Memorial Field, Lynn Road, Downham Market PE38 9AU

One and a quarter miles from Downham Market (BR) - continue to town clock, turn left and ground is three quarters of a mile down Lynn Road.

402

Nearest Railway Station Downham Market - 1.25 miles

DOWNTON
Brian Whitehead Sports Ground Wick Lane Downton Wiltshire SP5 3NF
01725 512 162

The ground is situated 6 miles south of Salisbury on the A338 to Bournemouth. In the village – sign to the Leisure Centre (to west) – this is Wick Lane – football pitch and Club approx 1/4 mile on the left. Postcode for Satellite Navigation systems SP5 3NF

541

Bus Route The Bull - stop 180m away

DRONFIELD TOWN
Stonelow Playing Fields, Stonelow Road, Dronfield, S18 2EU

From South: At M1 J29, 2nd exit A617 Chesterfield. At roundabout, take 4th exit (A61 Sheffield), then 2nd and 3rd exits at next roundabout to stay on A61. Leave at first slip road signed Sheepbridge/Unstone. Right towards Unstone/Dronfield. Go across 1st mini roundabout, then right and immediate left at next mini roundabout onto Green Lane. Up hill, 2nd right onto Stonelow Road and 1st right onto Shireoaks. From North: At M1 J30, 3rd exit towards Renishaw. Through Renishaw and Eckington then right for Coal Aston. Left at first mini roundabout, keep on Green Lane, down steep hill and left onto Stonelow Road then take 1st right onto Shireoaks.

463

Nearest Railway Station Dronfield - 0.9km   **Bus Route** Oakhill Road Bottom - stop 270m away

---

DROYLSDEN
The Butchers Arms Ground, Market Street, Droylsden, M43 7AY
0161 370 1426

From junction 23 M60 follow signs A635 Manchester, then A662 signed Droylsden, at town centre traffic lights turn right into Market Street, through next set of lights and the main entrance to the ground is 75 yards on your left.

289

Nearest Railway Station Droylsden - 240m away   **Bus Route** Bus stops outside the ground

---

DUDLEY SPORTS
Hillcrest Avenue, Brierley Hill, West Mids DY5 3QH
01384 349 413

The Ground is situated in Brierley Hill, just off A461. It can be approached from Stourbridge off the Ring Road to Amblecote, turning right at third set of traffic lights or from Dudley passing through Brierley Hill Town centre.

553

Nearest Railway Station Lye - 2.1km Stourbridge - 2.5km Cradley Heath - 2.8km   **Bus Route** Lancaster Road - stop 60m away

---

DUDLEY TOWN
The Dell Stadium, Bryce Road, Brierley Hill, West Mids DY5 4NE
07986 549 675

From M5 Junction 4 follow signs for Stourbridge. From the Ring Road, take A491 sign posted Wolverhampton.
At the second set of lights, turn right onto Brettle Lane A461. After approx 6 miles you will approach Brierley Hill High Street. Turn left at lights onto bank Street. You will see Civic hall and Police Station. Carry on over small bridge and at next set of traffic lights you will see Bryce Road and Stadium is on your left.

553

Nearest Railway Station Lye - 3.7km Cradley Heath 3.9km Stourbridge - 4km   **Bus Route** Rookery Park - stop 200m away

---

DULWICH HAMLET
Champion Hill Stadium, Dog Kennell Hill, Edgar Kail Way SE22 8BD
020 7274 8707

East Dulwich station, 200 yards.
Denmark Hill station, 10 minutes walk.
Herne Hill station then bus 37 stops near ground.
Buses 40 & 176 from Elephant & Castle, 185 from Victoria.

168

Nearest Railway Station East Dulwich - 0.2km

DUNKIRK
Ron Steel Spts Ground, Lenton Lane, Clifton Bridge, Nottingham NG7 2SA
0115 985 0803

From M1 Junction 24 take A453 towards Nottingham, through Clifton and join A52 onto Clifton Bridge. Get in middle lane down the slip road onto the island under the flyover signposted Industrial Estate. Take immediate 1st left and 1st left again onto Lenton Lane. Follow the road past Greenwood Meadows and the ground is 200 yards on the right.

396

Nearest Railway Station Beeston - 2.3km

DUNSTABLE TOWN
Creasey Park Stadium, Brewers Hill Rd, Dunstable LU6 1BB
01582 891 433

From the south: When travelling on the A5, go straight across the lights in the centre of Dunstable. Turn left at the next main set of lights into Brewers Hill Road. You will immediately pass the Fire Station on your left. Carry on until you hit the first r'about, Go over the r'about and take the immediate right into Creasey Park Drive. From the north: When travelling south on the A5, go through the chalk cutting and over the first set of traffic lights. At the next set of lights, turn right into Brewers Hill Road. Then proceed as above. From the East: When coming into Dunstable, go straight across the first r'about you come to. Then turn left at the double mini-r'about into Drovers Way. Follow this road for about 1/2 mile as it bears to the right and becomes Brewers Hill Road. Go over two mini-r'abouts and just before you hit the larger r'about, turn left into Creasey Park Drive.

326

Bus Route Langridge Court - stop 100m away

DUNSTON UTS
UTS Stadium, Wellington Road, Dunston, Gateshead NE11 9JL
0191 493 2935

From south take Dunston/Whickham exit off A1M.
Turn right at top of slip road into Dunston Road and head down the bank.
As the road veers left, the road becomes Wellington Road, and the ground is situated on your left.

476

Nearest Railway Station Metrocentre - 0.9km. Dunston - 1km.   **Bus Route** Wellington Road - stop 24m away

---

DURHAM CITY
Belle View Staduim, Delves Lane, Consett, Co. Durham DH8 7BF
01207 588 886

Leave the A1M at J62 (signed Durham City) At the top of the slip road turn left.
After about 1/2 mile bear left (signed Belmont + Dragonville).
At the top of the slip road turn left.
At traffic lights turn left then take the 2nd left, the stadium is on your right.

476

Bus Route Mortons Garage - stop 174m away

EASINGTON COLLIERY
Memorial Avenue, Seaside Lane, Easington Colliery SR8 3PL

Travelling on the A1 (M) take the A168 exit toward A19/Thirsk/Teeside. Continue onto A19 and after approximately 41 miles take the A182/B1283 exit toward Houghton-le-Sprng/Easington.
At the next roundabout take the first exit onto Hall Walks/B1283. Continue for just under 2 miles and then turn right onto Memorial Avenue.

476

Bus Route Black Diamond - stop 43m away

EASINGTON SPORTS
Addison Road, Banbury OX16 9DH
01295 257 006

From North/South M40 – Leave M40 at J11, follow A422 to Banbury, 2nd roundabout take A4260 to Adderbury. Go through three sets of traffic lights, at top of hill at T-junction turn left. Take 3rd right into Addison Road.
From South West A361 – Entering Banbury take 1st right turning into Springfield Ave after 'The Easington' PH.
Follow road and take T-junction right into Grange Road, 1st right into Addison Road. Ground on left at end of road.

422

Nearest Railway Station Banbury - 1.6km   **Bus Route** Springfield Avenu stop - 117m away

EAST COWES VICTORIA ATHLETIC Beatrice Avenue Whippingham East Cowes Isle of Wight PO32 6PA   01983 297 165

From East Cowes ferry terminal follow Well Road into York Avenue until reaching Prince of Wells PH, turn at the next right into Crossways Road then turn left into Beatrice Avenue, from Fishbourne follow signs to East Cowes and Whippingham Church, ground is 200 yards from the church on Beatrice Avenue.
Postcode for Satellite Navigation systems PO32 6PA

541

                                                                                           Bus Route Osborne House - stop 400m away

---

EAST GRINSTEAD TOWN   The GAC Stadium, East Court, College Lane, East Grinstead RH19 3LS   01342 325 885

A264 Tunbridge Wells road (Moat Road) until mini roundabout at bottom of Blackwell Hollow,
turn immediately right by club sign then 1st left,
ground 200 yards down lane past rifle club on right.

222

Nearest Railway Station East Grinstead - 1.1km   **Bus Route** East Court - stop 100m away

---

EAST PRESTON   Roundstone Recreation Ground, Lashmar Road, East Preston BN16 1ES   01903 776 026

From Worthing proceed west for six miles on A259 to The Roundstone PH.
From the roundabout, take the first exit, signposted East Preston.
Turn left over the railway crossing. Turn left soon afterwards, and then first right into Roundstone Drive.
Turn left into Lashmar Road and the approach road to the ground is on the right.

495

Nearest Railway Station Angmering - 0.8km   **Bus Route** Windlesham Gardens - stop 209m away

---

EAST THURROCK UNITED   FutureFuel Stadium, Rookery Hill, Corringham, Essex SS17 9LB   01375 644 166

From M25 Junction 30. Take A13 towards Southend. Exit A13 at Stanford-le-hope exit (A1014), this is just after the BP garage.
Turn right at the roundabout (3rd exit) onto a1014. Straight over first roundabout. Through traffic lights.
Ground is 200 yards on your left.

122

Nearest Railway Station Stanford-le-Hope or Basildon.   **Bus Route** 100 - Stops 100 metres from the ground.

EAST YORKSHIRE CARNEGIE Dunswell Park, Dunswell HU6 0AA

463

EASTBOURNE BOROUGH   Langney Sports Club, Priory Lane, Eastbourne BN23 7QH   01323 766 265

From M25 take M23/A23 eastbound to A27 Polegate by pass pick up and follow signs for crematorium 50yds past crematorium turn right at mini roundabout into Priory Road.
Stadium 100yds on left.

124

Nearest Railway Station Pevensey & Westham - 15-20 mins walk.   **Bus Route** The LOOP Bus from the town centre.

EASTBOURNE TOWN   The Saffrons, Compton Place Road, Eastbourne BN21 1EA   01323 724 328

Come into Eastbourne following the signs for Eastbourne Railway Station. When arriving at the railway station mini-roundabout turn right into Grove Road, (opposite from the station) and carry on past the Police Station and Town Hall (the large clock building.) Go straight over at the junction past the Caffyns car showroom (you can see the ground on your right), then take the first right turn into Compton Place Road and the entrance to The Saffrons car park is 100 yards on the right.

495

Nearest Railway Station Eastbourne - 0.4km   **Bus Route** Saffrons Road Cricket Club - stop 100m away

---

EASTBOURNE UNITED   The Oval, Channel View Road, Eastbourne, BN22 7LN   01323 726 989

From A27 Polegate bypass follow new A22 (Golden Jubilee Way) and cross roundabout into Highfield Link.
At next roundabout take slip road left into Lottbridge Drive.
At second roundabout take third exit into Seaside. 4
00 yards turn left opposite 'Co-op' into Channel View Road.
Oval is second turning left.

495

Nearest Railway Station Eastbourne - 2km   **Bus Route** Desmond Road - stop 241m away

---

EASTLEIGH   The Silverlake Stadium 'Ten Acres', Stoneham Lane, Eastleigh SO50 9HT   02380 613 361

From junction 13 of M3, turn right into Leigh Road, turn right at Holiday Inn, at mini roundabout take second exit, at the next mini roundabout take second exit, then next mini roundabout take first exit. Then take the first turning right (signposted) ground 200 metres on the left.

30

EBBSFLEET UNITED   Stonebridge Road, Northfleet, Kent DA11 9GN   01474 533 796

Exit the M25 at Junction 2 and take the A2 signposted Canterbury. Leave the A2 at the Northfleet/Gravesend West junction. At roundabout, follow signs to Ebbsfleet International Station/A226 which will take you on to Thamesway and past Ebbsfleet International. The stadium is at the end of the road.

32

Nearest Railway Station Northfleet - 300 yards from the ground.   **Bus Route** 480/490 or FASTRACK 'B' Service

---

ECCLESHALL   Pershall Park, Chester Road, Eccleshall ST21 6NE   01785 851 351 (MD)

M6 to junction 15, follow signs for Eccleshall A519 (approx. 10 miles). Turn right towards Loggerheads B5026, continue passed church, cricket and tennis clubs until signpost for Pershall. Ground 100 yards on the right.

449

                                                                                           Bus Route Pershall Farm stop - 228m away

---

ECCLESHILL UNITED   Mitton Group Stadium, Kingsway, Wrose, Bradford, BD2 1PN   01274 615 739

M62 J26 onto M606, right onto Bradford Ring Road A6177, left on to A650 for Bradford at 2nd roundabout. A650 Bradford Inner Ring Road onto Canal Rd, branch right at Staples (Dixons Car showrooms on right), fork left after 30mph sign to junction with Wrose Road, across junction - continuation of Kings Rd, first left onto Kingsway. Ground is 200 yards on right.

463

Nearest Railway Station Frizinghall - 1.7km   **Bus Route** Kingsway Plumpton Drive - stop 97m away

EDGWARE TOWN
Silver Jubilee Park, Townsend Lane, London NW9 7NE
0208 205 1645

From Edgware tube station, turn left onto Station Road and then left onto Edgware Road. Go South for about two miles on Edgware Road, turn right onto Kingsbury Road. Turn first left onto Townsend Lane down to the bottom of the hill and then turn left into the park through the park barriers..

516

Nearest Railway Station Hendon - 1.1km   **Bus Route** Queensbury Road - stop 660m away

---

EGHAM TOWN
Runnymead Stadium, Tempest Road, Egham TW20 8XD
01784 435 226

From M25 - J13 - Take the A30, heading south. The road runs parallel with the M25 briefly, and sweeps round a sharp left hand bend, under the M25. Stay right, down to the r'about in front of you just the other side of the M25. Go round the r'about and back under the M25.This road is called The Causeway. Carry on down this road, over the small r'about at Sainsbury's and at the bigger r'about turn right (signposted B3376 - Thorpe, Chertsey, Woking). Proceed down Thorpe Rd, over a level crossing, to a mini r'about, go over, and on the left, after the green turn into Pond Road. Left into Wards Place then first right and you will see the entrance to the football ground.

367

Nearest Railway Station Egham - 1km   **Bus Route** Charta Road - stop 200m away

---

ELLESMERE RANGERS
Beech Grove, Ellesmere, Shropshire SY12 0BT
07947 864 357

Follow A5 Wellington and take A495 to Ellesmere. On Approaching Ellesmere, straight over at roundabout, then turn left into housing estate opposite Lakelands School. At crossroads, turn left and the 1st right down the lane to Beech Grove Playing Fields.

553

Bus Route Lakelands School - stop 50m away

ELY CITY
Unwin Sports Ground, Downham Road, Ely CB6 2SH
01353 662 035

Follow signs for Kings Lynn/Downham Market as you approach Ely. Don't go into the city centre. After the Little Chef roundabout (junction of A10/A142) continue for approx half a mile until the next roundabout. Turn left for Little Downham (the B1411). There is also a sign for A Golf Course. The Golf Course is part of a Sports Complex which includes the football club. After turning left at the roundabout take another left after only about 50 metres into the Sports Complex entrance. The football club is at the end of the drive past the rugby club and tennis courts.

402

Nearest Railway Station Ely - 2.5km

ENFIELD 1893 FC
The Harlow Arena, Elizabeth Way, Harlow, Essex CM19 5BE
07957 647 820

Exit M11 at Junction 7. Follow the A414 towards Harlow until the first set of traffic lights where you filter off to the left onto the A1169. Follow the A1169, signed for Roydon, over several mini roundabouts until you get to a large grassed roundabout where you turn right (2nd exit). Continue straight down the road until you meet another roundabout where you turn left (2nd exit). Keep going until you reach the GSK roundabout where you turn right, then keep going straight until you see the ground ahead of you at the Roydon Road roundabout. Go straight over the roundabout and the entrance to the ground is on the left. If coming into town from the west on the A414 turn right at the first roundabout (the old ground was straight ahead) signed Roydon A1169. Follow the A1169 for approx 1 mile and the entrance to the ground is on the right.

415

Nearest Railway Station Harlow Town, 1 mile

ENFIELD BOROUGH
Enfield Town FC, Donkey Lane, Enfield EN1 3PL
07493 377 484

From the M25: Head towards London on the A10 from junction 25. Turn right into Carterhatch Lane at the Halfway House pub. Donkey Lane is first left after the pub.

From London/North Circular Road: Head north up the A10 and turn left to Carterhatch Lane at the Halfway House pub. Donkey Lane is first left after the pub.

516

Nearest Railway Station Southbury - 1.2km

ENFIELD TOWN
Queen Elizabeth Stadium, Donkey Lane, Enfield EN1 3PL
07787 875 650

From the M25: Head towards London on the A10 from junction 25. Turn right into Carterhatch Lane at the Halfway House pub. Donkey Lane is first left after the pub.

From London/North Circular Road: Head north up the A10 and turn left to Carterhatch Lane at the Halfway House pub. Donkey Lane is first left after the pub.

170

Nearest Railway Station Southbury - 1.2km

EPSOM & EWELL
Chipstead FC, High Road, Chipstead, Surrey CR5 3SF
01737 553 250

From M25 Junction 8. Take the A217.
At 1st Roundabout take the 2nd Exit.
At the end of the Road Turn Left.
Ground is 2 Miles on the Right.

384

Nearest Railway Station Kingswood

ERITH & BELVEDERE
Park View Road, Welling DA16 1SY
07584 302 210

Take the M25 to Junction 2. At the roundabout, take the A2 towards Central London. Leave the A2 at the third exit (Danson Interchange, signposted A221 to Bexleyheath and Sidcup). Turn right (second exit) at the roundabout at the end of the slip road, and then turn right (third exit) at the next roundabout. Go under the A2 Bridge and up the slope to another roundabout. Take the second exit and follow the road (Danson Road) to the traffic lights at the end. Turn left at the lights onto Park View Road. The ground is on the left. There is no car park, but plenty of street parking is available.

505

Nearest Railway Station Welling - 1.1km

ERITH TOWN
Oakwood (VCD Ath FC), Old Road, Crayford Kent DA1 4DN
07877 766 794

Follow A2 until you reach the exit for A220/A223 towards Bexleyheath and Crayford. At the roundabout, take the second exit on to Bourne Road/A223. After just over half a mile, turn right onto the A207 London Road. Keep left at the fork, then turn left onto Crayford High Street/A2000. Where the A2000 bends right, go straight on to pick up Old Road, and the ground is on your right.

505

Nearest Railway Station Crayford - 0.9km

ESH WINNING
West Terrace, Waterhouse, Durham DH7 9BQ
07432 648 072

Leave the A1 at Junction 62, and take the A690 towards Durham. Keep on this road through Durham. Once you start to head down a bank on the A690, you will come to a roundabout. Take the right turn onto the B6302, which will be signposted towards Ushaw Moor. Keep on this road though Ushaw Moor (there is a staggered crossroads to negotiate), and carry on the B6302 into Esh Winning. Keep on going as the ground is not in Esh Winning, but the next village along, Waterhouses. When the road takes a sharp left you will see a track continuing straight ahead. The ground is along this track.

476

Bus Route Church (Russell St) - stop 158m away

EVERSLEY & CALIFORNIA
ESA Sports Complex, Fox Lane, Eversley RG27 0NS
0118 973 2400

Leave the M3 at junction 4a signposted Fleet/Farnborough. At the roundabout take the 2nd exit towards Yateley.
At the roundabout take the 2nd exit towards Yateley. At the roundabout take the 2nd exit towards Yateley.
At the roundabout take the 1st exit and proceed through Yateley on the Reading Road. At the roundabout take the 2nd exit and follow the road for about 1 mile. Turn right down the first turning for Fox Lane and then follow the road round to the right where the ground will be signposted.

384

Nearest Railway Station Fleet, Sandhurst

EVESHAM UNITED — Jubilee Stadium, Cheltenham Road, Evesham WR11 2LZ — 01386 442 303

FROM M5 NORTH: Leave M5 motorway at Junction 7 and follow B4084 through Pershore onto Evesham. At traffic lights in Evesham with River Avon and Bridge on left, take right hand lane and turn right into Cheltenham Road signposted A46, M5 Southbound, Oxford and Cheltenham. Continue through two sets of traffic lights passing Tesco Garage and Ambulance Station on left before reaching roundabout. Ground situated on right at roundabout. FROM M5 SOUTH: Leave M5 motorway at Junction 9 signposted Tewkesbury and Evesham. Take 3rd exit signposted Ashchurch and Evesham. Follow A46 (Evesham) through Beckford before reaching roundabout on outskirts of Evesham. Ground situated on left at roundabout. FROM M42: Leave M42 motorway at Junction 3 (A435) signposted Redditch and Evesham. Continue on A435 (Evesham) through Studley then A46 until reaching roundabout on outskirts of Evesham. Take left hand exit onto Evesham by-pass (A46), signposted M5 South, Cheltenham and Oxford. Proceed on by-pass going over three r'abouts before reaching ground, which is situated on 4th r'about at end of by-pass. **Nearest Railway Station:** Evesham - 2.9km. **Bus Route:** Lavender Walk - stop 400m away

377

EXMOUTH TOWN — King George V, Exmouth EX8 3EE — 01395 263 348

From Junction 30 of M5 take te A376 to Exmouth, on entering the town the ground is on your right, before the railway station.

Nearest Railway Station Exmouth - 0.6km   **Bus Route** Exeter Road - stop 143m away

488

EYNESBURY ROVERS — Alfred Hall Memorial Ground, Hall Road, Eynesbury, St Neots PE19 2SF — 07938 511 581uc

From the A1 take the A428 towards Cambridge. Turn left at the Tesco roundabout and continue on Barford Road for half a mile going straight on at 4 roundabouts. Turn left into Hardwick Road and left into Hall Road. Ground at end of road.

Nearest Railway Station St Neots - 2.1km   **Bus Route** Ernulf Academy Forecourt - stop 150m away

529

FAIRFORD TOWN — Cinder Lane, London Road, Fairford GL7 4AX — 01285 712 071

Take A417 from Lechlade, turn left down Cinder Lane 150 yards after 40 mph sign. From Cirencester take Lechlade Road, turn right down Cinder Lane 400 yards after passing the Railway Inn.

Bus Route Hatherop Lane stop - 124m

422

FAKENHAM TOWN — Clipbush Park, Clipbush Lane, Fakenham, Norfolk NR21 8SW — 01328 854 617

From Kings Lynn: Follow A148 from Kings Lynn towards Cromer. On approaching Fakenham, you will come to a roundabout, where the A148 and the A1065 join. Take the first exit, continuing on the A148, towards Cromer. continue to the next roundabout, and take the third exit into Clipbush Lane. continue to the next roundabout, and the entrance to the ground is the first exit, and is well signposted.
From Norwich: Those travelling from Norwich, will be approaching on the A1067, which will take you directly into Fakenham. At the first roundabout, turn right into Clipbush lane. Continue to the next r'about, and the entrance to the ground is the third exit from the roundabout, and is well signposted. **Bus Route** Sanders Coaches No.9

402

FALMOUTH TOWN — Bickland Park, Bickland Water Road, Falmouth TR11 4PB — 01326 375 156

Take Penryn by-pass from Asda roundabout. Leave by-pass at Hillhead roundabout, take first right and follow industrial estate signs. Around 1/2 mile on the left.

Nearest Railway Station Penmere - 1.3km   **Bus Route** Conway Road - stop 54m away

488

FAREHAM TOWN — Cams Alders, Palmerston Drive, Fareham, Hants PO14 1RH — 07445 805 122

Leave the M27 at Junction 11. Follow signs A32 Fareham – Gosport. Pass under the viaduct with Fareham Creek on your left, straight over at the roundabout then fork right – B3385 sign posted Lee-on-Solent. Over the railway bridge, Newgate Lane and turn immediately first right into Palmerston Business Park, follow the road to the ground. Postcode for Satellite Navigation systems PO14 1BJ

Nearest Railway Station Fareham - 0.9km   **Bus Route** Fairfield Avenue - stop 250m away

541

FARLEIGH ROVERS — Parsonage Field, Harrow Road, Warlingham CR6 9EX — 01883 626 483

From M25 junction 6 left at lights up Godstone Hill (Caterham bypass) to roundabout. Take fourth turning off of roundabout. Up Succombs Hill then right into Westhall Rd. Right at the green then second left into Farleigh Rd. Left at mini round about continue still on Farleigh Road. Right at the Harrow Pub. This is Harrow Road. Right at the end of the houses and the ground is behind the houses.

Nearest Railway Station Upper Warlingham   **Bus Route** Metro Bus 409

384

FARNBOROUGH — Rushmoor Community Stadium, Cherrywood Road, Farnborough, Hants GU14 8DU — 07957 936 436

Leave the M3 at Junction 4 and take the A331 towards Farnham, after a few hundred yards exit at the second slip road- signed A325 Farnborough, turn right at the roundabout and cross over the dual carriageway and small roundabout, passing the Farnborough Gate shopping centre on your left hand side, at the next roundabout turn left (first exit) onto the A325. Go over a pelican crossing and at the next set of lights take the right filter into Prospect Avenue. At the end of this road turn right at the roundabout into Cherrywood Road, the ground is half a mile on the right hand side.
Nearest Railway Station Frimley - 0.7km

328

FARNHAM TOWN — Memorial Ground, West Street, Farnham GU9 7DY — 01252 715 305

Follow A31 to Coxbridge roundabout (passing traffic lights at Hickleys corner. Farnham station to left.) At next roundabout take 3rd exit to Farnham town centre. At the mini roundabout take 2nd exit. The ground is to the left.

Nearest Railway Station Farnham   **Bus Route** Stagecoach 5, 14, 18, 19, 46, 64, 71, 536

384

FARSLEY CELTIC — Throstle Nest, Newlands, Pudsey, Leeds, LS28 5BE — 0113 255 7292

Farsley is sandwiched between Leeds and Bradford approximately 1 mile from the junction of the Leeds Outer Ring Road (A6110) and the A647 towards Bradford. At the junction, take the B6157 towards Leeds, passing the police station on the left hand side. At New Street (the junction cornered by Go Outdoors) turn left. Newlands is approximately 300 yards on the right. Throstle Nest is situated at the end of Newlands with parking available outside the ground.

Nearest Railway Station New Pudsey - 1km   **Bus Route** Town Street - stop 500m away

248

FAVERSHAM TOWN — Shepherd Neame Stadium, Salters Lane, Faversham Kent ME13 8ND — 01795 591 900

From the M25 continue onto M26 9.9 miles. Continue onto M20 8.1 miles. Exit onto Slip Road (M20 J7) 0.2 miles. Bear left 0.1 miles. Continue onto Sittingbourne Road A249 0.9 miles. Bear right onto Detling Hill A249 4.6 miles. Bear left 0.1 miles. Continue onto Slip Road (M2 J5) 0.4 miles. Continue onto M2 10.5 miles. Exit onto Slip Road (M2 J6) 0.1 miles. Turn left onto Ashford Road A251 0.5 miles. Turn right onto Canterbury Road A2 0.2 miles. Turn right onto Westwood Place 0.1 miles.

Nearest Railway Station Faversham - 0.6km

223

FAWLEY
Waterside Spts & Soc. club, 179 Long Lane, Holbury, Soto, SO45 2PA   **02380 893 750 (Club)**

Leave the M27 at Junction 2 and follow the A326 to Fawley/Beaulieu. Head south for approx 7 miles. The Club is situated on the right hand side 2/3 mile after crossing the Hardley roundabout. The Club is positioned directly behind the service road on the right hand side. Postcode for Satellite Navigation systems SO45 2PA

Nearest Railway Station Netley - 5.3km   **Bus Route** New Forest Academy - stop 100m away

541

FC BOLSOVER
Langwith Road Ground, Langwith Road, Shirebrook, NG20 8TF   **07950 682 973**

From M1 J29: At roundabout take the A617 towards Mansfield (for 3.5 miles). At next roundabout take 2nd exit B6407 Common Lane towards Shirebrook (1.8 miles). Go straight on at next roundabout (for 300 yards). At a staggered crossroads, turn right onto Main Street (for 1.1 miles). At T Junction turn right (for 100yards), take first road on your left (Langwith Road). Ground is 400 yards on the right.

Nearest Railway Station Shirebrook - 0.2km   **Bus Route** Langwith Road End - stop 36m away

463

FC BROXBOURNE BOROUGH
Broxbourne Borough V & E Club, Goffs Lane, Cheshunt, Herts EN7 5QN   **01992 624 281**

Leave M25 at Junction 25. Take A10 northbound. Turn first exit at roundabout. Straight over the next roundabout then 3rd exit at the next roundabout after that. Ground entrance is 50 yards on the right.

Nearest Railway Station Theobalds Grove - 2.3km   **Bus Route** Goffs School - stop 37m away

516

FC CLACTON
Rush Green Bowl, Rush Green Rd, Clacton-on-Sea CO16 7BQ   **07581 056 174**

Leave the A12 at junction 29, then at roundabout take the 1st exit, then merge onto the A120 (sign posted Clacton, Harwich). Branch left, then merge onto the A133 (sign posted Clacton). Continue along the A133 following signs to Clacton until St Johns Roundabout (tiled Welcome to Clacton sign) take the 4th exit onto St Johns Rd - B1027 (sign posted St Osyth) Entering Clacton On Sea B1027 (fire station on left). B1027 At second mini-roundabout turn left onto Cloes Lane (Budgens on left). Continue down Cloes Lane for about 1/2 mile, passing St.Clares School on your right, at traffic lights, turn right onto Rush Green Rd. Rush Green Bowl will then appear on the right after 1/4 mile.

Nearest Railway Station Clacton-on-Sea - 1.8km

402

FC DEPORTIVO GALICIA
Bedfont Sports, Hatton Road, Bedfont, Middlesex TW14 8JA   **020 8831 9067**

From Junction 13, M25 – Staines. At Crooked Billet roundabout turn right onto the A30 Signposted C. London, Hounslow. At Clockhouse Roundabout take the 2nd exit onto the A315 Signposted Bedfont. Turn left onto Hatton Road. Arrive on Hatton Road, Bedfont Sports Club.

Nearest Railway Station Hatton Cross or Feltham BR   **Bus Route** London Transport 203, H25, H26

384

FC ELMSTEAD
Holmesdale FC, Oakley Road, Bromley, Kent BR2 8HQ   **505**

Off the A232 on the A233.

Nearest Railway Station Hayes - 2.1km

FC HALIFAX TOWN
The Shay Stadium, Shay Syke, Halifax HX1 2YS   **01422 341 222**

From the North: Take the A629 to Halifax Town Centre, take the 2nd exit at the roundabout following signs for A629 (Huddersfield), then into Skircoat Road where you will find the ground. General: Take the M62 exiting at junction 24, follow signs for A629 Halifax into Skircoat Road, then onto Shaw hill where you will find the ground.

Nearest Railway Station Halifax - 5-10min walk from the ground.

34

FC OSWESTRY TOWN
The Venue, Burma Road, Oswestry, Shropshire SY11 4AS   **01691 684 840**

From Chester take the A483 towards Wrexham / Oswestry. Once entering Oswestry at the 2nd round-a-bout turn left and left again to ground.

Nearest Railway Station Gobowen - 2.1km   **Bus Route** Park Crescent Jct stop - 325m away

449

FC ROMANIA
Cheshunt FC, Theobalds Lane, Cheshunt, Herts EN8 8RU   **01992 625 793**

Exit the M25 at junction 25 and head north on the A10. At the next roundabout turn right onto the A121, Winston Churchill Way. At next roundabout turn left into the High Street. Pass under the railway bridge and take the next left into Theobalds Lane. The ground is 200 yards down this road on the right hand side. (NOTE: On exit, you can continue down Theobalds Lane and turn left onto the dual carriageway (A10), then straight over the roundabout for the M25)

Nearest Railway Station Theobalds Grove – 5 mins walk

415

FC UNITED OF MANCHESTER
Broadhurst Park, 310 Lightbowne Road, Moston, Manchester, M40 0FJ   **0161 769 2005**

From South leave M60 at J21 turn left and immediately right to Manchester City Centre A663. After 350 yards bear right onto A6104 to Manchester. At Greengate roundabout take first exit onto Lightbowne Road. Ground is half a mile on the left. **From North** leave M60 at J20, turn right onto A664 Blackley. After 700 yards turn left at lights onto A6104 Oldham. After 1.5 miles take 4th exit off Greengate roundabout onto Lightbowne Road.

Nearest Railway Station Moston - 11min walk from the ground.   **Bus Route** Matchday Special and Shuttle Bus

82

FELIXSTOWE & WALTON UNITED
Goldstar Ground, Dellwood Avenue, Felixstowe IP11 9HT   **01394 282 917**

The A12 meets the A14 (Felixstowe to M1/M6 trunk road) at Copdock interchange, just to the South of Ipswich. For Felixstowe take the A14 heading east over the Orwell Bridge. Follow the A14, for approx. 14 miles until you come to a large roundabout with a large water tower on your right, take the 1st exit off the roundabout, which is straight on. Take the first exit at the next roundabout, straight ahead again. At the next roundabout take the fourth exit onto Beatrice Avenue, take the first left into Dellwood Avenue. The ground is 100 yards down on the left behind tall wooden fencing.

Nearest Railway Station Felixstowe - 0.3km

402

FISHER
St Pauls Sports Ground, Salter Road, Rotherhithe, London SE16   **505**

The new stadium can be found around 100 yards from the old Surrey Docks Stadium on Salter Road.

The stadium is roughly 10 minutes walk from Rotherhithe Station on the London Overground, and 15 minutes walk from Canada Water Station for the Jubilee Line. The 381 and C10 buses both stop adjacent to the stadium. Nelson Dock Pier is 15 minutes walk away, served by River Bus 4 from Canary Wharf.

FLACKWELL HEATH
Wilks Park, Magpie Lane, Heath End Rd, Flackwell Hth HP10 9EA   **01628 523 892 / 07932 952 538**

Junction 4 of M40 Follow signs A404 (High Wycombe) Turn right at traffic lights halfway down Marlow Hill, signposted Flackwell Heath. Ground three (3) miles on left.

422

Nearest Railway Station Bourne End - 3km   **Bus Route** Fernlea Close stop - 106m

FLEET SPURS
Kennels Lane Southwood Farnborough Hampshire, GU14 0ST   **384**

From exit 4a on the M3, take the A327 towards Farnborough/Cove.Continuing on the A327 Filter Left at Traffic Lights - follow A327Take 1st exit at next roundabout into Summit Ave - A327Make a U turn around the next rounaboutKennels Lane is the first left. The grounds entrance is 250 yards on the left.

FLEET TOWN
Calthorpe Park, Crookham Road, Fleet, Hants GU51 5FA   **01252 623 804 Match day only**

Leave the M3 at Junction 4a, and follow the signs for Fleet. Head along the A3013, Fleet Road. Carry on along the street passing the main shopping street, through several pedestrian crossings for about 1 mile. When you get to the Oatsheaf Pub crossroads head straight across. Ground is 300yds down the hill on the right.

368

Nearest Railway Station Fleet - 2.1km   **Bus Route** Leawood Road - stop 150m away

FOLKESTONE INVICTA
The Fullicks Stadium, Cheriton Road CT19 5JU   **01303 257 461**

Leave the M20 motorway at junction 13, and head south onto the A20 (Cherry Garden Avenue). At the traffic lights, turn left onto the A2034 (Cheriton Road), pass the Harvey Grammar School and Stripes club - the ground is next left before Morrisons' supermarket; opposite the cemetery. Some car parking is available at Stripes.

172

Nearest Railway Station Folkestone West - 0.4km

FOLLAND SPORTS
Folland Park, Kings Ave, Hamble, Southampton SO31 4NF   **02380 452 173**

Leave the M27 at Junction 8 and take the turning for Southampton East At the Windhover roundabout take the exit for Hamble (B3397) Hamble Lane, proceed for 3 miles. Upon entering Hamble the ground is on the right via Kings Avenue, opposite the Harrier P/H. Postcode for Satellite Navigation systems SO31 4NF

541

Nearest Railway Station Hamble - 1km   **Bus Route** Verdon Avenue - stop 300m away

FOREST HILL PARK
Ladywell Arena, Silvermere Road, Catford, London SE6 4QX   **07774 294 236**

Either before or after Catford Railway Station (depending on which way you come in) turn in to Doggett Road off the South Circular. Continue along Doggett Road until arriving at Silvermead Road.

505

Nearest Railway Station Ladywell and Catford Bridge.   **Bus Route** 47, 54, 75, 136, 181, 185, 199, 208

FRAMLINGHAM TOWN
Framingham Sports Club, Badingham Road, Framlingham IP13 9HS

Via the A14, take the A140 ramp to Diss/Norwich/B1078. At the roundabout, take the 1st exit onto A140, Follow A1120 and B1119 to your destination in Framlingham. Turn right onto Stowmarket Rd/A1120, Continue to follow A1120. Turn right onto B1119. Turn right onto College Rd/B1116. At the roundabout, take the 2nd exit onto Well Cl Square/B1116, Continue to follow B1116. Turn left onto Fore St/B1119, Continue to follow B1119. Slight left onto Badingham Rd/B1120

402

FRICKLEY ATHLETIC
Westfield Lane, South Elmsall, Pontefract WF9 2EQ   **01977 642 460**

From North: Leave A1 to join A639, go over flyover to junction. Turn left and immediately right, signed South Elmsall. Continue to roundabout and take 2nd exit to traffic lights and turn left onto Mill Lane (B6474). Turn right at the T-junction and continue down hill to next T-junction. Turn right and immediately left up Westfield Lane. The ground is signposted to the left after about half a mile. **From South:** Exit M18 at J2 onto A1 (North). Leave A1 for A638 towards Wakefield. Continue on A638, going straight on at the first roundabout and turn left at next roundabout to traffic lights. Continue as above from South.

302

Nearest Railway Station South Elmsall - 0.7km. Moorthorpe - 0.9km   **Bus Route** Westfield Lane - stop 100m away

FRIMLEY GREEN
Frimley Green Rec. Ground, Frimley Green, Camberley GU16 6JY   **01252 835 089**

Exit M3 at junction 4 and follow the signs to Frimley High Street. At the mini roundabout in front of the White Hart public house turn into Church Road. At the top of the hill by the Church the road bends right and becomes Frimley Green Road. Follow the road for approx of a mile, go over the mini roundabout which is the entrance to Johnson's Wax factory, and the Recreation Ground is the second turning on the left, just past Henley Drive, which is on your right.

384

Nearest Railway Station Frimley   **Bus Route** Stagecoach 3, Arriva 49

FROME TOWN
The Special Effect Stadium, Badgers Hill, Berkley Road, Frome BA11 2EH   **01373 464 087**

From Bath, take A36 and then A361. At third roundabout, follow A361 and at fourth roundabout take A3098. Take first right and ground is one mile on left hand side. From south follow A36 (Warminster) and take A3098 to Frome. At T Junction turn right and take second exit at roundabout. Ground is first right and follow road for one mile on left hand side.

330

Nearest Railway Station Frome - 0.9km   **Bus Route** Bus stops outside the ground

GAINSBOROUGH TRINITY
The Gainsborough Martin & Co Arena, Gainsborough, Lincolnshire DN21 2QW   **01427 613 295**

The Northolme is situated on the A159, Gainsborough to Scunthorpe road, approximately a third of a mile north of the Town Centre. Public Car Park on the right 150 yards before the Ground. Any person parked illegally in the Streets around the Ground will be issued with a ticket from the Police.

84

Nearest Railway Station Gainsborough Central - less than half a mile away.

GARFORTH TOWN
Community Stadium, Cedar Ridge, Garforth, Leeds LS25 2PF   **0113 287 7567**

From North: travel south on A1 and join M1. Turn off at 1st junc (47). From South: M1 at junc 47. From Leeds area: join M1 at junc 44 or 46 and turn off at junc 47. From West: M62 to junc 29, join M1 and off at junc 47. From junc 47: take turning signe 'Garforth' (A642). Approx. 200 yds turn left into housing estate opposite White House. (Cedar Ridge). Stadium at end of lane. From the South (alternative): A1, turn off on to A63 signposted 'Leeds' immediately after 'Boot & Shoe' Public House. At 1st roundabout turn right on to A656 and follow to next roundabout. Take 1st left on to A642 (Garforth) and follow from M1 junc 47.

463

Nearest Railway Station East Garforth - 1km. Garforth - 1.2km.   **Bus Route** Aberford Road - stop 128m away

GATESHEAD
The International Stadium, Neilson Road, Gateshead NE10 0EF
01914 783 883

Travelling up on the A1, turn off at the junction with the A194 just north of the Washington Services. Follow the A194 until the roundabout junction with the A184, turn left onto this road. The International Stadium is on the right after approximately 3 miles.

36

Nearest Railway Station Gateshead Stadium Metro stop 5min walk away.

GEDLING MINERS WELFARE
Plains Social Club, Plains Road, Mapperley, Nottingham NG3 5RH
0115 926 6300

Situated on B684 in Mapperley.
From Nottingham the ground is approached via Woodborough Road.
From the north via A614 by Lime Lane Junction to Plains Road.

396

Nearest Railway Station Carlton - 3.5km

GLASSHOUGHTON WELFARE
Glasshoughton Centre, Leeds Road, Glasshoughton, Castleford WF10 4PF
01977 511 234

Leave the M62 J32, signposted Castleford/Pontefract (A639). At the bottom of the slip road take the A656, taking carer to pick up the middle lane for Castleford. After approx. ¼ mile, bear left at the first roundabout and, after a further ¼ mile, left at the next roundabout on to Leeds Road. Ground is then 200 yards on the right.

463

Nearest Railway Station Glasshoughton - 0.8km   **Bus Route** Leeds Road Carr Lane - stop 83m away

---

GLEBE
Foxbury Avenue, Chislehurst, Bromley BR7 6SD
07903 274 178

The club is located just off the A222 close to the Vauxhall Garage and a stone's throw away from the Sidcup bypass.

505

Nearest Railway Station Sidcup - 1.9km   **Bus Route** Nos. 269 & 260.

GLOSSOP NORTH END
Surrey Street, Glossop, Derbys SK13 7AJ
01457 855 469

From M67 follow A57 signposted Glossop/Sheffield. On approaching Town Centre turn left at traffic lights by Tesco Store into Glossop Brook Road, continue up the hill to the ground. For Sat/Nav enter Glossop Brook Road for easiest access to ground.

289

Nearest Railway Station Glossop - 0.4km   **Bus Route** St Mary's Road - stop 300m away

---

GLOUCESTER CITY
Cheltenham Town FC, The Abbey Business Stadium, Whaddon Road GL52 5NA
01242 573 558 (Cheltenham

M5 (J10) follow A4019 - Cheltenham, through lights until you reach a r'about, PC World on left, McDonalds on right, turn left. After 500yds you'll come to a double r'about, straight over, keep going for 300yds, turn right into Swindon Lane, go over the level crossing and 2 mini r'abouts until you come to a large r'about, straight over, past Racecourse and turn right into Albert Rd at the end turn left at r'about (Prestbury Rd) 200yds turn into Whaddon Road.

126

Nearest Railway Station Cheltenham Spa - 30/40 mins walk from the ground.   **Bus Route** D or P/Q from Station. Bus A from Bus Station

---

GODALMING TOWN
Wey Court, Meadrow, Guildford, Surrey GU7 3JE
01483 417 520

A3100 from Guildford, pass the Manor Inn on the left and then the petrol station on the right. Wey Court is 50 yards further along the road on the right hand side.
A3100 from Godalming, pass the Three Lions pub on the left and then turn left into Wey Court immediately after the Leathern Bottle pub.
Parking: Please note that the club car park is for players and officials only. Spectators are asked to use the public car park next door to the ground.

384

Nearest Railway Station Farncombe - 1/2 a mile from the ground.

GODMANCHESTER ROVERS
The David Wilson Homes Ground, Godmanchester, Huntingdon PE29 2LQ

From Junction 24 of the A14, take exit A1198 signposted Godmanchester, Wood Green Animal Shelter, Papworth, Royston. After approx 3/4 mile turn left into Bearscroft Lane where the ground is on the right hand side.

402

Nearest Railway Station Huntingdon - 3.1km

GODOLPHIN ATLANTIC AFC
Godolphin Way, Cornwall TR7 3BU

Off Henver Road turn into Godolphin Way and ground is then first entrance on the left.

488

Nearest Railway Station Newquay - 1.2km   **Bus Route** Brook House Inn - stop 136m away

---

GOOLE AFC
Victoria Pleasure Gardens, Marcus Road, Goole DN14 6TN
01405 762 794 (Match days)

Leave the M62 at Junction 36 and follow signs to Goole Town Centre.
Turn right at the 2nd set of traffic lights into Boothferry Road. Turn right again after 300 yards into Carter Street.
The Victoria Pleasure Grounds is at the end of the road. 366 Metres from Goole Railway Station.

290

Nearest Railway Station Goole - 0.5km   **Bus Route** Goole Newport Street - stop 200m away

---

GORLESTON
Emerald Park, Woodfarm Lane, Gorleston, Norfolk NR31 9AQ
01493 602 802

On Magdalen Estate follow signs to Crematorium, turn left and follow road to ground.

402

GOSPORT BOROUGH
Aerial Direct Stadium, Privett Park, Privett Road, Gosport, Hampshire PO12 0SX
023 9250 1042 (Match days

Leave the M27 at junction 11 and follow the signs "A32 Gosport". After approximately four miles you will reach two roundabouts in quick succession. Go straight ahead at the first and take the third exit (signposted Alverstoke, Stokes Bay, Privett Park) at the second. Follow this road (Military Road) until reaching the roundabout at the Cocked Hat pub. Take the first exit into Privett Road. The ground is signposted on the left after 300 yards. SatNav users should use **PO12 3SY** as the postcode for their destination.

332

Nearest Railway Station Portsmouth Harbour   **Bus Route** X5 (to Southampton) & 9/9A (to Fareham)

GRAHAM STREET PRIMS   Baytree Cars Arena, Borrowash Road, Spondon DE21 7PH
01332 332 092

From M1 Junction 25 travel towards Derby on A52. Take third turning left (directly under pedestrian footbridge) onto Borrowash Road. Past golf driving range on left and in approximately 400 metres turn left into the Asterdale Sports Centre.

396

Nearest Railway Station Spondon - 1.2km

GRANTHAM TOWN   South Kesteven Sports Stadium, Trent Road, Gratham NG31 7XQ
01476 402 224

FROM A1 NORTH: Leave A1 At A607 Melton Mowbray exit. Turn left at island on slip road into Swingbridge Lane. At T junction turn left into Trent Road ground is 100yds on right. **FROM A52 NOTTINGHAM:** Pass over A1 and at first island turn right into housing estate & Barrowby Gate. Through housing estate to T junction. Turn right and then immediately left into Trent road ground is 100 yards on the left. **FROM A607 MELTON MOWBRAY:** Pass under A1 and take next left A1 South slip road. At island turn right into Swingbridge Road then as for A1 North above. From all directions follow brown signs for Sports Complex, which is immediately behind the stadium.

250

Nearest Railway Station Grantham - 1.5km   **Bus Route** Meres Leisure Centre - stop 100m away

---

GRAVESHAM BOROUGH   Chatham Town FC, Maidstone Road, Chatham, Kent ME4 6LR

Exit the M2 at junction 3, and follow directions for Chatham & Town Centre. You will then pass a Homebase & Toys 'R' Us on the left hand side. Continue straight over the roundabout and then there is a split in the road, where you bear right for chatham this is Maidstone Road. Follow this, continuing straight over the cross roads and you will see a petrol station on the left. Bournville Road is opposite the petrol station on the left. Ground entrance is first left.

505

Nearest Railway Station Chatham - 1.4km   **Bus Route** Bus stops outside the ground.

GRAYS ATHLETIC   Aveley FC, Mill Field, Mill Field Road, Aveley RM15 4SJ
07738 355 619

London - Southend A1306, turn into Sandy Lane at Aveley.

213

Nearest Railway Station Purfleet - 2.4km   **Bus Route** Hanford Road - stop 100m away

---

GREAT WAKERING ROVERS   Burroughs Park, Little Wakering Hall Lane, Great Wakering SS3 0HH
01702 217 812

A127 towards Southend and follow signs for Shoeburyness for about four miles.
Turn left to Great Wakering on B1017 at Bournes Green.
Go down High Street for half a mile and ground is on the left.

.415

Nearest Railway Station Shoeburyness - 3.2km   **Bus Route** Barrow Hall Rd (Little Wakering Rd) - 631m

---

GREAT YARMOUTH TOWN   The Wellesley, Sandown Road, Great Yarmouth NR30 1EY
07873 861 983

Approaching Great Yarmouth on the A47 at the end of the single carriageway you will come to a roundabout where the A12 and A47 meet. Take the second exit onto the A149 towards the town centre. Continue to the next roundabout (Fuller's Hill roundabout) and take the second exit. Keep in the left hand lane and at the traffic lights turn left onto Northgate Street. Follow this road to the roundabout and take the second exit onto Kitchener Road. At the crossroads go straight ahead onto Sandown Road and you will see the Wellesley on the right.

402

Nearest Railway Station Great Yarmouth - 1/2 mile away.

GREENWICH BOROUGH   DGS Marine Stadium, Middle Park Avenue, Eltham SE9 5HP
07946 721 878

If coming in on the A2 (either north or south), head onto the South Circular s/p Catford. At the roundabout take the second exit into Middle Park Avenue. The entrance to the ground is on your right hand side. If coming in on the A20 then when you reach the Cliftons Roundabout (junction with A205 South Circular) go all the way around the roundabout and head back onto the A20 then turn left immediately down to Goals 5-a-side centre into Eltham Palace Road. At the end turn left at the roundabout and the entrance to the ground is on your left hand side. There is ample free parking at the ground.

223

Nearest Railway Station Mottingham - 15min walk away   **Bus Route** 160 stops at the ground

---

GRESLEY   The Moat Ground, Moat Street, Church Gresley, Derbyshire DE11 9RE
01283 215 316

From the South: Follow the M42 northbound to Junction 11, turn off onto the A444 toward Burton Upon Trent. Turn right onto the A514 (Castle Road) toward Gresley and follow the road up the hill to the traffic island at the top. Continue on the A514 over the island and take the second road on the left (School Street), the next left into Moat Street where the Moat Ground is located. **From the North-East:** Follow the M1 south to junction 23a, turn off on to the A42 southbound. Continue on the A42 to Ashby-de-la-Zouch then turn off onto the A511 toward Swadlincote. At Woodville turn off the A511 onto the A514 toward Church Gresley, follow the road signs to Gresley, the School Street turn off is second on the right after the Gresley island. Take the first turn on the left in School Street to take you to the ground. **From the North-West:** From Stoke-on-Trent follow the A50 toward Burton-Upon-Trent, turn on to the A511 and continue through Burton. Turn off the A511 onto the A444 toward Nuneaton. Follow the A444 until you reach the turn off for the A514. Turn left onto the A514 (Castle Road) toward Gresley and follow the road up the hill to the traffic island at the top. Continue on the A514 over the island and take the second road on the left (School Street), the next left into Moat Street where the Moat Ground is located. **Bus Route:** Church Street - stop 200m away.

302

GRIMSBY BOROUGH   The Bradley Football Development Centre, Bradley Road, Grimsby, DN37 0AG
07890 318 054

Head East along the M180/A180. Exit at the Great Coates Interchange. Travel back over motorway to first Roundabout. Take first exit and follow for two miles to Trawl Pub Roundabout. Take second exit, follow for two miles to Bradley Roundabout. Take second exit on to Bradley Road. The ground is approximately 500 yards on the left.

463

Nearest Railway Station Grimsby Town - 3km   **Bus Route** Crowland Avenue - stop 463m away

---

GUERNSEY   Footes Lane Stadium, St Peter Port, Guernsey GY1 2UL
01481 747 279

The ground is located centrally in the island, is easily accessible with parking for several hundred cars in the immediate vicinity and on a regular bus route stopping immediately outside the stadium. It is approximately three miles north easterly from Guernsey Airport and one mile west from St Peter Port, the island's capital.

224

Bus Route Bus stops outside the ground

GUILDFORD CITY   Spectrum Leisure Centre, Parkway, Guildford GU1 1UP
01483 443 322

From A3, exit at Guildford – follow signs to leisure centre.
From Guildford main line station, take no.100 shuttle bus to Spectrum.
From London Road Station walk via Stoke Park.

384

Nearest Railway Station Guildford Main Line (2 miles) & Guildford (London Rd) (1 mile)   **Bus Route** Arriva 100

GUISBOROUGH TOWN   King George V Ground, Howlbeck Road, Guisborough TS14 6LE
01287 636 925

Turn off the A19 into the A174, then come off at the second junction, turning right onto the A172. Follow this round until roundabout with 1043, take left exit to join the A1043. Take right at next roundabout to join the A171. At second roundabout turn right into Middlesbrough Road (will be signposted towards Guisborough) then take left turning at traffic lights into Park Lane. Take first left into Howlbeck Road, and the ground is at the end of the road.

476

Bus Route Howlbeck Road - stop 49m away

GUISELEY
Nethermoor Park, Otley Road, Guiseley, Leeds LS20 8BT   **01943 873 223 (Office) 872 872**

From the West M62, M606 then follow signs to A65 through Guiseley to Ground on Right. From South and East M1 and M621 towards Leeds City Centre. Continue on M621 to Junction 2, follow Headingly Stadium signs to A65 towards Ilkley then as above. From North West From Skipton, A65 Ilkley, via Burley By-pass A65 towards Leeds, Ground quarter of a mile on left after Harry Ramsden's roundabout From North/NE A1M, leave at A59, towards Harrogate, then A658 signed Leeds Bradford Airport, at Pool turn right onto A659 Otley, continue towards Bradford/Leeds, to Harry Ramsden roundabout then A65 Leeds ground quarter of a mile on left.
Nearest Railway Station Nethermoor is about 5 min walk away.   **Bus Route** There are two bus stops directly outside.

38

HACKNEY WICK
The Old Spotted Dog, Upton Lane, Forest Gate E7 9NP   **07960 384 338**

Five minute walk along Upton Lane from Romford Road.

Nearest Railway Station Wanstead Park, 10 min walk or Stratford, 25 min walk   **Bus Route** 25, 6 min walk from Woodgrange Pk bus stop

415

HADLEIGH UNITED
The Millfield, Tinkers Lane, Duke St, Hadleigh IP7 5NF   **01473 822 165**

On reaching Hadleigh High Street turn into Duke Street (right next to Library), continue on for approximately 150 metres and take left turn into narrow lane immediately after going over small bridge, continue to end of the lane where you will find the entrance to club car park.

402

HADLEY
Hadley Sports Ground, Brickfield Lane, Arkley, Barnet EN5 3LD   **07905 446 331**

From M25, exit junction 23 (South Mimms) go south on the A1 to Stirling Corner roundabout. Take the left exit onto Barnet Road and continue until the first set of traffic lights. Go straight over and then take the immediate first left opposite the Gate Oublic House into Brickfield Lane. The ground is approximately 75 yards on the left.

Nearest Railway Station Elstree & Borehamwood - 2.8km   **Bus Route** Brickfield Lane - stop 70m away

516

HAILSHAM TOWN
The Beaconfield, Western Road, Hailsham BN27 3JF   **01323 840 446**

Turn off A22 at Diplocks Way roundabout.
Ground on left (alleyway signposted opposite SETYRES WEALDEN) just before end of Diplocks Way.

Nearest Railway Station Polegate - 4.4km   **Bus Route** Bramble Drive - stop 190m away

495

HALESOWEN TOWN
The Grove, Old Hawne Lane, Halesowen B63 3TB   **0121 629 0727**

Get to Junction 3 of the M5. Head towards Kidderminster on the A458 for a mile or so to the first traffic island at the bottom of the hill. Turn right on to the A459 towards Dudley (the cricket ground should now be on your left) and continue past where the road splits to the next island. Turn left here on to the A456 towards Stourbridge until you get to the next island. Take the 3rd exit (Old Hawne Lane) and the ground is about 400 yards away, at the top of the hill on the left.

Nearest Railway Station Old Hill - 1.8km   **Bus Route** Cranmoor Crescent - stop 50m away

252

HALL ROAD RANGERS
Hawroth Park, Dawson Drive, Hull HU6 7DY

M62 to A63, turn left before Humber Bridge onto A164 to Beverley, after approx. 5 miles turn right onto A1079. In 2 miles, turn left at large roundabout to ground 20 yards on right signed 'Dene Park Sports & Social Club'.

Nearest Railway Station Cottingham - 3.5km   **Bus Route** Larard Avenue - stop 158m away

463

HALLAM
Sandygate Road, Crosspool, Sheffield S10 5SE   **0114 230 9484**

A57 Sheffield to Glossop Rd, left at Crosspool shopping area signed Lodge Moor on to Sandygate Rd. Ground half mile on left opposite Plough Inn. 51 bus from Crucible Theatre.

Nearest Railway Station Sheffield - 4.5km   **Bus Route** Ringstead Crescent - stop 19m away

463

HALLEN
Hallen Centre, Moorhouse Lane, Hallen Bristol BS10 7RU   **01179 505 559**

From Junction 17 M5 follow A4018 towards Bristol. At third roundabout turn right into Crow Lane. Proceed to T junction - turn right and right again at mini roundabout by Henbury Lodge Hotel. At next mini roundabout turn left into Avonmouth Way. Continue for 1.5 miles into Hallen village. At crossroads turn left into Moorhouse Lane

Nearest Railway Station St Andrews Road - 2.7km   **Bus Route** Moorhouse Park - stop 250m away

559

HALSTEAD TOWN
Rosemary Lane, Broton Industrial Estate, Halstead, Essex CO9 1HR   **01787 472 082**

From A1311 Chelmsford to Braintree road follow signs to Halstead.

402

HAMBLE CLUB
Hamble Community Facility, Hamble Lane SO31 4TS   **07977 324 923**

Travelling on the M27 leave at junction 8, take the A3024 exit to Southampton (E)/Hamble. At the roundabout, take the 3rd exit onto A3024. At the roundabout, take the 2nd exit onto Hamble Lane/A3025. At the roundabout, take the 2nd exit and stay on Hamble Lane/A3025. At the roundabout, take the 2nd exit and stay on Hamble Lane/A3025. Continue straight onto Hamble Lane/B3397. At the roundabout, take the 1st exit and stay on Hamble Lane/B3397. Turn right for Hamble Club.

Nearest Railway Station Hamble - 0.4km   **Bus Route** Hamble Lane School - stop 500m away

541

HAMPTON & RICHMOND BOROUGH
Beveree Stadium, Beaver Close, Station Road, Hampton TW12 2BX   **0208 979 2456**

Exit M25 at Junction 12 (M3 Richmond). Exit M3 at Junction 1 and take 4th exit (Kempton Park, Kingston).
After approximately 2 miles turn left into High Street, Hampton. Immediately turn left on to Station Road.
The entrance to the ground is 200 yards on the right hand side.

Nearest Railway Station Hampton - less than half a mile from the ground.

128

HAMWORTHY UNITED — The County Ground, Blandford Close, Hamworthy, Poole BH15 4BF
01202 674 974

From M27 to Cadnam – follow A31 to Ringwood – A347/A348 Ferndown - Bearcross – follow on this road until you pass the Mountbatten Arms on your left – turn right at next roundabout onto the A3049 and follow the signs to Dorchester and Poole. Continue on this dual carriageway over the flyover to the next roundabout – straight across and take the 2nd exit left off the dual carriageway to Upton / Hamworthy – go straight across 2 mini roundabouts and continue to Hamworthy passing the Co-op store on your left – then turn left at the 2nd set of traffic lights into Blandford Close.   Postcode for Satellite Navigation systems BH15 4BF

541

Nearest Railway Station Poole - 1.4km | **Bus Route** Carter School – stop 100m away

---

HANDSWORTH PARRAMORE — The Windsor Foodservice Stadium, Sandy Land, Worksop S80 1UJ
01909 479 955

From either the A1 or M1 J31, take the A57 towards Worksop. After approximately 7 miles, look out for the A60/Sandy Lane turnoff at the roundabout. Continue over two mini-roundabouts for ¾mile then turn left into the retail park and left again into the stadium car park.

463

Nearest Railway Station Worksop - 0.5km | **Bus Route** Grafton Street – stop 114m away

---

HANLEY TOWN — Abbey Lane, Bucknall, Stoke-on-Trent, Staffordshire ST2 8AJ
07875 137 482

From Stoke-on-Trent take the A52/Leek Road.
After almost 2 miles turn right onto Bucknall Road/A52, continue for just over half a mile and turn left onto Fellbrook Lane.
Continue onto Abbey Lane.

449

Nearest Railway Station Stoke-on-Trent - 3.2km | **Bus Route** Abbey Lane stop - 229m away

---

HANWELL TOWN — Reynolds Field, Preivale Lane, Perivale, Greenford, UB6 8TL
020 8998 1701

From West - Exit M25 at junction 16 and follow A40(M) towards London. Continue over Greenford Flyover and get into nearside lane, signposted Ealing & Perivale. Exit and turn right across the A40 and the ground is immediatley on the left.
From East - At Hanger Lane Giratory take the A40 exit towards Oxford. The first exit is signposted Perivale/Ealing. Take the slip road and then left at traffic lights . Take the first left again into Perivale Lane.

368

Nearest Railway Station Perivale Underground - 0.6km | **Bus Route** Perivale Lane - stop 200m away

---

HANWORTH VILLA — Rectory Meadows, Park Road, Hanworth TW13 6PN
020 8831 9391

From M25 and M3 once on the M3 towards London. This becomes the A316, take the A314 (Hounslow Rd) exit signposted Feltham & Hounslow. Turn left onto Hounslow Rd, at the second mini round about (Esso garage on the corner) turn left into Park Rd. Continue down Park Road past the Hanworth Naval Club on the right and Procter's Builders Merchants on the left. Follow the road around the 90 degree bend and continue to the end of the road past the Hanworth Village Hall. Once past the two houses next to the village hall turn left into Rectory Meadows.

384

Nearest Railway Station Feltham or Hampton | **Bus Route** London United 111 or H25

HARBOROUGH TOWN — Bowden's Park, Northampton Road, Market Harborough, Leics. LE16 9HF
01858 467 339

Half a mile south of Market Harborough on the A508. 4 miles north of the A14 junction 2 towards Market Harborough turn left towards Leisure Centre, but keep left passed inflatable dome on the right, then through large car park, club house straight in front, with parking area.

529

Nearest Railway Station Market Harborough - 1.5km | **Bus Route** Leisure Centre - stop 200m away

---

HAREFIELD UNITED — Preston Park, Breakespeare Road North, Harefield, UB9 6NE
01895 823 474

From the M25 at Junction 16 turn left. At the roundabout turn right towards Denham and at the next roundabout turn left then right at the end of the road. Turn left by the Pub and follow the road over the canal and into the village. Go straight across the roundabout into Breakspear Road and the ground is approximately 800 metres on the right.

516

Nearest Railway Station Denham - 3km | **Bus Route** Wickham Close - stop 150m away

---

HARINGEY BOROUGH — Coles Park, White Hart Lane, Tottenham, London N17 7JP
0208 889 1415 (Matchday)

At junction 25 of the M25 or from the A406 (North Circular Road) turn south onto the A10 (Great Cambridge Road) towards Central London. At the junction of the A10 and White Hart Lane turn right (use slip road at traffic lights) into White Hart Lane and the ground is about 500 yards on the left, some 150 yards after a petrol station. PUBLIC TRANSPORT: Bus W3 from Finsbury Park station to Northumberland Park station via Alexandra Palace station and Wood Green underground station passes ground. In other direction W3 can be boarded at White Hart Lane station).

213

Nearest Railway Station Wood Green Underground - 1.6km | **Bus Route** Bus stops outside the ground

---

HARLOW TOWN — The Harlow Arena, off Elizabeth Way, The Pinnacles, Harlow CM19 5BE
01279 443 196

Barrows Farm is situated on the western side of town just off of the Roydon Road (A1169) on the Pinnacles Industrial Estate.
If coming into Harlow from the M11 (North or South) exit at Junction 7 and follow the A414 until the first roundabout where you turn left onto the A1169. Follow the A1169 signed for Roydon until you see the ground ahead of you at the Roydon Road roundabout. Go straight over the roundabout and the entrance to the ground is on the right.
If coming into town from the west on a A414 turn right at the first roundabout (the old ground was straight ahead) signed Roydon A1169. Follow the A1169 for approx 1 mile and the entrance to the ground is on the right.

174

HARPENDEN TOWN — Rothamstead Park, Amenbury Lane, Harpenden AL5 2EF
07734700226/07702604771

Approaching Harpenden from St. Albans, turn left into Leyton Road at mini-roundabout by the Silver Cup and Fire Station. Coming from Luton, go through the town and as you leave (just past The George) turn right into Leyton Road. Turn left in Amenbury Lane and then left into car park after 300 yards. Entrance to the Club is up the pathway, diagonally across the car park in the far corner from the entrance. This is a pay-and-display car park up to 6.30pm.

516

Nearest Railway Station Harpenden - 0.6km | **Bus Route** Amenbury Lane - stop 250m away

---

HARROGATE RAILWAY ATH. — Station View, Starbeck, Harrogate, North Yorkshire HG2 7JA
01423 883 104

From All Areas I would suggest using the M1 A1 Link Road heading North. Once on the A1 North stay on it until Junction 47. Exit at Junction 47 and take the 1st Exit at the Roundabout A59 heading towards Knaresborough and Harrogate. At the next Roundabout take the 3rd exit A59 Knaresborough. Stay on the A59 through Knaresborough and on towards Harrogate, after approx 1 mile from Knaresborough you will enter Starbeck. Proceed through Starbeck over the Railway Crossing. Station View is the 1st Right after the Railway Crossing. The Ground is at the far end of Station View. If you are coming from Harrogate towards Knaresborough on the A59 turn left immediately prior to pelican crossing just before the Railway Crossing.

463

Nearest Railway Station Starbeck - 0.1km | **Bus Route** Henry Peacock - stop 134m away

---

HARROGATE TOWN — The CNG Stadium, Wetherby Road, Harrogate HG2 7SA
01423 210 600

A61 to Harrogate, turn right on to a A658, and at roundabout take A661, proceed through second set of lights (Woodlands pub) ground approx. 500 mtrs on the right. From A1 Wetherby. Leave A1 at Wetherby on to A661 to Harrogate. Stay on this road and when reaching Harrogate at Woodland pub lights, ground 500mtrs on the right.

86

Nearest Railway Station Harrogate - 25min walk from the ground. | **Bus Route** 770 / 771 TransDev from Town Centre.

HARROW BOROUGH — Earlsmead, Carlyon Avenue, South Harrow HA2 8SS — 0844 561 1347

From the M25 junction 16, take the M40 East towards Uxbridge and London. Continue onto A40, passing Northolt Aerodrome on the left hand side. At the Target Roundabout junction (A312) turn left towards Northolt. Just after passing Northolt Underground Station on the left hand side, turn left at the next set of traffic lights, onto Eastcote Lane, becoming Field End Road.
At next roundabout, turn right onto Eastcote Lane. At a small parade of shops, take the turning on the right into Carlyon Avenue. Earlsmead is the second turning on the right.
Nearest Railway Station Northolt Underground - 1.1km

176

HARROWBY UNITED — Dickens Road, Grantham NG31 9RB — 01476 401 201

From A1 take B6403, go past roundabout, to Ancaster and take road for Harrowby.
Follow the road into Grantham, ground on right opposite Tesco Express.

Nearest Railway Station Grantham - 2.6km   **Bus Route** St Wulframs School - stop 100m away

529

HARTLEPOOL UNITED — Victoria Park, Clarence Road, Hartlepool TS24 8BZT — 01429 272 584

Exit the A19 at signpost Hartlepool A689, Motorway A1(M). At r'about turn right (s/p Hartlepool A689) and continue on the A689 for 4.3 miles, through the village of Newton Bewley, to the r'about by the Owton Lodge pub. Go straight on (s/p Town Centre A689) and follow Town Centre signs for 2.8 miles, over two r'abouts. At the traffic lights just past the Blacksmiths Arms on your left, go straight on. At the next traffic lights go straight on again over the bridge into the new marina complex and straight on again at the r'about into Marina Way. This is the area for the Jackson's Wharf parking. To get to the ground itself continue to the next r'about and turn left (s/p The North A179, A1048). Turn left at the lights into Clarence Road to the ground.
Nearest Railway Station Hartlepool is about half a mile away.

40

HARTLEY WINTNEY — Memorial Playing Fields, Green Lane, Hartley Wintney RG27 8DL — 01252 843 586

On entering Hartley Wintney via the A30 take the turn at the mini roundabout signposted A323 Fleet. Take the 1st right turn, Green Lane, which has St John's Church on the corner. Continue down Green Lane for about 800 metres and turn right into car park, which has a shared access with Greenfields School. Turn left at St John's Church if coming down the A323 from Fleet.
Nearest Railway Station Winchfield - 1.9km   **Bus Route** Green Lane - stop 100m away

369

HASSOCKS — The Beacon, Brighton Road, Hassocks BN6 9NA — 01273 846 040

Off A273 Pyecombe Road to Burgess Hill.
Ground is 300 yards south of Stonepound crossroads (B2116) to Hurstpeirpoint or Hassocks.

Nearest Railway Station Hassocks - 1.2km   **Bus Route** Friars Oak Cottages - stop 211m away

495

HASTINGS UNITED — The Pilot Field, Elphinstone Road, Hastings TN34 2AX — 01424 444 635

From A1 turn left at third roundabout into St Helens Road.
Then left after one mile into St Helens Park Road leading into Downs Road.
Turn left at T-junction at the end of the road. Ground is 200 yards on the right.

Nearest Railway Station Ore - 0.9km. Hastings - 1.9km.

224

HATFIELD TOWN — Gosling Sport Park, Stanborough Rd, Welwyn Garden City, Herts AL8 6XE — 01707 384 300

From A1 (M) junction 4, take A414 towards Hertford/Welwyn Garden City.
At the roundabout take the 1st exit onto the A6129, heading to Stanborough/Wheathampstead.
At the next roundabout take the 2nd exit onto the A6129 Stanborough Road.
At the next roundabout take the 3rd exit into Gosling Sports Park.
Nearest Railway Station Welwyn Garden City - 1.3km   **Bus Route** Stanborough Close - stop 200m away

516

HAUGHMOND — Sundorne Sports Village, Sundorne Road, Shrewsbury. SY1 4RQ — 07785 531 754

Head in to Shrewsbury on the A5, at the Preston Island, take the 1st exit onto the A49.
At the next roundabout take the 1st exit onto Sundorne Road/B5062.
At the next roundabout take the 1st exit for the ground.

Nearest Railway Station Shrewsby - 2.6km   **Bus Route** Ta Centre stop - 109m away

436

HAVANT AND WATERLOOVILLE — Westleigh Park, Martin Road, West Leigh, Havant PO9 5TH — 02392 787 822

Ground is a mile and a half from Havant Town Centre. Take A27 to Havant then turn onto B2149 (Petersfield Road).
Turn right at next junction after HERON pub into Bartons Road then take first right into Martin Road.

Nearest Railway Station Havant - within 2 miles of the ground.

130

HAVERHILL BOROUGH — The New Croft, Chalkestone Way, Haverhill, Suffolk CB9 0BW — 01440 702 137

Take the A143 in to Haverhill and, at the roundabout by Tesco, turn left and then right in the one in front of the store. Carry on over the next roundabout past Aldi on the left and past the Sports Centre, Cricket Club and garage on the left. Just after the Workspace Office Solutions building take a right towards the town centre (towards Parking (South). The drive way into Hamlet Croft is a small turning on the left just after Croft Lane (look for the sign for Tudor Close).

402

HAVERHILL ROVERS — The New Croft, Chalkstone Way, Haverhill, Suffolk CB9 0BW — 01440 702 137

Take the A143 in to Haverhill and, at the roundabout by Tesco, turn left and then right in the one in front of the store. Carry on over the next roundabout past Aldi on the left and past the Sports Centre, Cricket Club and garage on the left. Just after the Workspace Office Solutions building take a right towards the town centre (towards Parking (South). The drive way into Hamlet Croft is a small turning on the left just after Croft Lane (look for the sign for Tudor Close).

402

HAYES & YEADING UNITED — SKYex Community Stadium, Beaconsfield Road, Hayes UB4 0SL — 0208 573 2075

From the M40/A40(M) Head eastbound towards London, take the Target Roundabout exit signposted Northolt, Harrow & Hayes. At the top of the slip road take the fourth exit (the first after the exit towards London) onto the A312 towards Hayes. The next roundabout (The White Hart) is about is about 1 mile and a half on. Here ignore signs to Yeading (third exit) instead take the second exit towards Hayes & Heathrow to stay on the A312 (Hayes-By - Pass). At the next roundabout again ignore signs to Yeading and carry straight over. Take the next exit signposted Southall and Uxbridge (A4020 Uxbridge Road). At the top of the slip road take the first exit towards Southall and follow the directions below Head eastbound along the (A4020) Uxbridge Road. Head eastbound along the (A4020) Uxbridge Road signposted towards Southall. Get into the far right hand lane as soon as you can and turn right into Springfield Road at the next set of Traffic Lights (There is a petrol station and a retail development with a Wickes on the corner of Springfield Road). Follow the road to the School, the Road bears left into Beaconsfield Road, and about 100 yards on your right is the entrance to the ground.

369

HAYWARDS HEATH TOWN — Hanbury Park Stadium, Haywards Heath RH16 4GL
01444 412 837

A272 to Haywards Heath Town Centre. At Sussex roundabout, north on B2708 (Hazelgrove Road) take first right into New England Road. Fourth right Allen Road leads to ground.
Allen Road is the only vehicular and pedestrian access to the ground.

495

Nearest Railway Station Haywards HEath - 1.9km   **Bus Route** Market Square - stop 84m away

---

HEADINGTON AMATEURS — Horspath Sports Ground, Oxford Rd, Horspath, Oxford OX4 2RR
07764 943 778

A4142 (Oxford Ring Road - BMW Plant) turn into Horspath Road, follow road for 0.5 miles, ground is on left.

422

Bus Route Horspath Road Ind. Est. stop - 416m away

HEANOR TOWN — The Town Ground, Mayfield Avenue, Heanor DE75 7EN
01773 713 742

From M1: J26, take A610 Ripley Road to end of dual carriageway then take A608 to Heanor via Langley Mill. At traffic lights at top of long hill take left lane signed Ilkeston. First right into Mundy Street, second left onto Godfrey Street. Ground on left where road forks.
From A608 Derby: Enter town and see Tesco on left. Turn right at roundabout to the Market Place. Turn right at end of square and at crossroads right again onto Mundy Street. Then left into Godfrey Street and ground on left where road forks.

436

Nearest Railway Station Langley Mill - 2km   **Bus Route** Sports Ground stop - 132m away

---

HEATH HAYES — Coppice Colliery Grd, Newlands Lane, Heath Hayes, Cannock, WS12 3HH
07969 203 063

From M6 Junction 11 take the A4601 towards Cannock and at the 1st island turn right onto the A460 signposted Rugeley/Cannock Business Parks. At the double island (A5) go straight on still on A460 and over two islands. At the 3rd island, turn right onto A5190 signposted Lichfield. Pass Texaco garage on the right and take the next right turn into Newlands Lane. Entrance to the ground is 50 yards down the lane on the left under the barrier.

436

Nearest Railway Station Cannock - 2.7km   **Bus Route** Five Ways Inn stop - 253m away

---

HEATHER ST. JOHN'S — St John's Park, Ravenstone Rd, Heather LE67 2QJ
01530 263 986

Exit M42 at Junction 11. Take the road towards Measham, pass the Car Auctions and go over the traffic lights. At 2nd mini island take 2nd exit onto Leicester Road. After approximately 3 miles you will enter Heather. At T junction turn left. At mini island take 2nd exit onto Ravenstone Road and go up the hill. Ground is 200 metres on the left.

436

Bus Route Holyoake Drive stop - 160m away

HEATON STANNINGTON — Grounsell Park, Newton Road, High Heaton, Newcastle upon Tyne NE7 7HP
0191 281 9230

The ground is a short distance from the Freeman Hospital.
Take the coast road A1058 left for Newcastle, and eventually turn right at traffic lights onto Newton Road.
For satnavers postcode NE7 7HP.

476

Nearest Railway Station Longbenton - 1.2km   **Bus Route** No.38 stops at the ground

---

HEBBURN TOWN — Hebburn Sports & Social, Victoria Rd West, Hebburn, Tyne & Wear NE31 1UN
0191 483 5101

Leave A1M on A194(M) (junction 65) and follow signs for Tyne Tunnel. Continue until fourth roundabout and turn left on to B1306 (Hebburn, Mill Lane). Right at traffic lights into Victoria Road. Ground 200 yards long this road on the left.

476

Nearest Railway Station Hebburn - 1km   **Bus Route** Victoria Road West - stop 74m away

---

HEDNESFORD TOWN — Keys Park, Park Road, Hednesford, Cannock WS12 2DZ
01543 422 870

Leave M6 at J11 and follow the signs for Cannock. At the next island take the third exit towards Rugeley (A460). On reaching the A5 at Churchbridge island, rejoin the A460 signposted Rugeley and follow this road over five traffic islands. At the sixth traffic island, by a Texaco petrol station, turn right past a McDonalds restaurant and follow this road to the next island which is 'Cross Keys Island'. Go over this island to the next small island and turn right. Keys Park football ground is on left.

254

Nearest Railway Station Hednesford - 1.6km   **Bus Route** Brickworks Road - stop 200m away

---

HELSTON ATHLETIC — Kellaway Park, Helston TR13 8PJ
01326 573742 (Clubhouse)

From Redruth, go across 5 roundabouts, final one by Tesco, then turn first left.

488

Bus Route Tesco - stop 101m away

HEMEL HEMPSTEAD TOWN — Vauxhall Road, Adeyfield Road, Hemel Hempstead HP2 4HW
01442 264 300

Leave at Junction 8, straight over (2nd exit) first roundabout, straight over (2nd exit) second roundabout at which point you need to get in the right hand lane - take first right across the dual carriageway which leads in to Leverstock Green Road. First left at mini-roundabout in to Vauxhall Road, the entrance to the ground is on the right hand side by an out of place looking roundabout.

132

Nearest Railway Station Hemel Hempstead - Taxi ride away from the ground   **Bus Route** 320 from Stop 'A' outside the station

---

HEMSWORTH M.W. — Yorkshire NuBuilds Stadium, Wakefield Road, Fitzwilliam, Pontefract WF9 5AJ
01977 614 997

From East/West: M62 to J32 towards Pontefract then follow A628 towards Hemsworth. At Ackworth roundabout (Stoneacre Suzuki Garage), take a right on to the A638 Wakefield Road. Travel half a mile to next roundabout then take first exit. Travel one mile to crossroads and turn left into Fitzwilliam. Pass a row of shops on your right and turn left after the bus shelter before an iron bridge. To ground.
From North: A1 South to M62 then follow above directions.
From South: A1(M) North to A638 Wakefield Road. Travel to Ackworth Roundabout (Stoneacre Suzuki Garage) and go straight across and follow the A638 to the next roundabout. Take first exit then to crossroads. Turn left into Fitzwilliam and pass row of shops on your right. Turn left after bus shelter before iron bridge and carry on to the ground.

463

Nearest Railway Station Fitzwilliam - 0.4km   **Bus Route** Wakefield Road - stop 22m away

---

HENDON — Silver Jubilee Park, Townsend Lane, Kingsbury, London NW9 7NE
020 8205 1645

From Staples Corner travel north along the A5, towards Edgware, through West Hendon, to the junction with Kingsbury Road (Red Lion public house on corner). Turn into Kingsbury Road and Townsend Lane is the 3rd turning on the left, at the top of the hill. The ground is in the bottom left hand corner of the Silver Jubilee Park.

178

Nearest Railway Station Hendon - 1.1km   **Bus Route** Queensbury Road - 700m away

HENGROVE ATHLETIC — Norton Lane, Whitchurch, Bristol BS14 9TB — 07884 492 217

Take A37 from Bristol through Whitchurch village past Maes Knoll pub, over hump bridge taking next turning on right, which is Norton Lane. Ground is immediately after Garden Centre.

Nearest Railway Station Bedminster - 2.5km **Bus Route** Wooton Park - stop 100m away

559

HENLEY TOWN — The Triangle Ground, Mill Lane, Henley RG9 4HB — 07758 376 369

From Henley Town centre take the A4155 towards Reading. Mill Lane is approx 1 mile from the Railway Station on the left approx 250 yards after passing the mini roundabout at the Newtown Industrial Estate.
From M4 Junction 11 head towards Reading on the A33 inner distribution road then follow the A4155 to Henley before turning right into Mill Lane after passing the roundabout to Tesco. The Ground and Car Park on your left over the Railway Bridge.

Nearest Railway Station Henley-on-Thames - 1km **Bus Route** Marsh Mills stop - 333m away

422

HEREFORD — Edgar Street, Hereford HR4 9JU — 01432 268 257

Edgar Street is part of the main A49 road running through the centre of Hereford. Coming from the M5, take junction 7 (Worcester South) and follow signs for A4103 Hereford. At Hereford follow the A4103 until it joins the A49. Follow the A49 to the ground on the left, turn left immediately after the ground into Blackfriars Street. Turn left into the Merton Meadow car park. The main Club entrance is ten yards after the turning on the left, the players entrance is midway down the main stand.

Nearest Railway Station Hereford - 0.6km

334

HEREFORD LADS CLUB — Hereford Lads Club, Widemarsh Common, Hereford HR4 9NA — 07837 665 745

Driving north through Hereford on the A49/Edgar Street, continue on A49 until road merges onto Newtown Road (first exit off roundabout). In less than half a mile turn left for the ground.
Driving South into Hereford on the A49/Holmer Road, continue on A49 until road merges onto Newtown Road. In less than half a mile turn right for the ground.

Nearest Railway Station Hereford - 1km **Bus Route** Priory Place - stop 150m away

553

HERNE BAY — Winch's Field, Stanley Gardens, Herne Bay CT6 5SG — 01227 374 156

From M25 exit onto Sittingbourne Rd/A249 toward Sheerness. Continue to follow A249. At the roundabout, take the 1st exit onto the M2 ramp to Canterbury/Dover/Ramsgate. Merge onto M2. Continue onto Thanet Way/A299. Continue to follow A299. Take the A291 exit toward Canterbury/Herne Bay. At the roundabout, take the 2nd exit onto A291. At the roundabout, take the 1st exit onto Canterbury Rd/B2205. Turn left onto Spenser Rd. Take the 1st left onto Stanley Gardens. Take the 1st left to stay on Stanley Gardens.

Nearest Railway Station Herne Bay - 0.8km

225

HERTFORD TOWN — Hertingfordbury Park, West Street, Hertford, SG13 8EZ — 01992 583 716

From the A1, follow the A414 from Hatfield to Hertford until you see the Gates Ford Dealership on the right. At the next roundabout take the 4th exit on your left (doubling back) and immediately past the Gates Ford dealership (now on your left), TURN LEFT into West Street, (Hertford Town FC signposted on the railings), continue along West Street until you pass the Scout hut on your right, just as the road begins to bear left there is a sign post bearing a brown tourist football sign, TURN RIGHT down the hill and over the bridge to the ground (situated at the bottom on the right). **From the A10,** from the roundabout at the top of the A10 slip road, continue on the dual carriageway (A414 signposted to Hatfield), over the next roundabout, (Mercedes dealership on your right) continue down the hill and TURN LEFT at the roundabout at the bottom (multi-storey car park on your right). You will pass All Saints Church on your left. Go straight across the next roundabout, and immediately past the Gates Ford dealership, then as above.

Nearest Railway Station Hertford North - 0.8km

214

HEYBRIDGE SWIFTS — The Texo Stadium, Scraley Road, Heybridge, Maldon, Essex CM9 8JA — 01621 852 978

Leave Maldon on the main road to Colchester,
pass through Heybridge then turn right at sign to Tolleshunt Major (Scraley Road).
The ground is on the right.

Bus Route Scylla Close - stop 1km away

214

HIGHGATE UNITED — The Coppice, Tythe Barn Lane, Shirley Solihull B90 1PH — (no number)

Take junction 3 off the M42 (A435/Birmingham (S)/Redditch/Evesham) take first exit off the roundabout.
Continue on the A435 until the next roundabout, take the 4th exit onto Station Road. Continue onto Norton Lane.
Take next left onto Lowbrook Lane and after just under half a mile turn left into Tilehouse Lane.
Just under a mile later turn right onto Tythe Barn Lane and the ground will be on the right.

Nearest Railway Station Whitlocks End - 0.4km **Bus Route** Whitlocks End stop - 302m away

436

HIGHMOOR IBIS — Scours Lane, Tilehurst, Reading RG30 6AY — 01189 453 999

Come off J12 of the M4 head along the A4 towards Reading, take a left onto Langley Hill and follow it all the way up onto Park Lane, continue onto School Road past the Tilehurst shops and then down onto Kentwood Hill. At the bottom of the hill take a right onto the Oxford Road towards Reading and just past the Waitrose Shop you need to take a left into an industrial estate and under the railway bridge and the ground will be in front of you to your right.

Nearest Railway Station Tilehurst - 1.2km **Bus Route** Cold Store stop - 277m away

422

HIGHWORTH TOWN — Elms Recreation Ground, Highworth SN6 7DD — 07939 032 451

From the A419 (Honda) roundabout travel in a North Easterly direction for 3.5 miles towards Highworth along the A361. Upon reaching Highworth, take the first exit at the Fox roundabout and immediately left into The Elms. After 100 yards, turn left into the Rec car park and the club is at the opposite end.

Bus Route Swindon Street stop - 90m away

422

HILLINGDON BOROUGH — Middlesex Stadium, Breakspear Rd, Ruislip HA4 7SB — 01895 639 544

From M40/A40 eastbound, leave the A40 at the Swakeleys roundabout, exit is sign-posted Ickenham & Ruislip and take the B467.
At the second mini-roundabout turn left into Breakspear Road South.
After approx 1 mile, turn right into Breakspear Road by the Breakspear Arms PH.
The ground is a further 1/2 mile on the left-hand side.

Nearest Railway Station Willow Lawn - 737m **Bus Route** Howletts Lane - stop 98m away

516

HINCKLEY AFC — St. John's Park, Ravenstone Road, Heather, Leicestershire, LE67 2QJ — 01530 263 986

Exit M42 at Junction 11. Take the road towards Measham, pass the Car Auctions and go over the traffic lights. At 2nd mini island take 2nd exit onto Leicester Road. After approximately 3 miles you will enter Heather. At T junction turn left. At mini island take 2nd exit onto Ravenstone Road and go up the hill. Ground is 200 metres on the left.

Bus Route Holyoake Drive stop - 160m away

436

HISTON — The Glassworld Stadium, Bridge Road, Impington, Cambridge CB24 9PH
01223 237 373

From the M11 (Northbound) Junc 14, take the A14 eastbound signed towards Newmarket. Take the first exit off the A14 and at the roundabout, take the first exit onto the B1049. Go straight over the traffic lights, past the Holiday Inn Hotel (on your right) and the entrance to the club is half a mile on your right.

Nearest Railway Station Cambridge - the following buses run every 20 minutes,   **Bus Route** Citi 8 and Guided Busway routes A, B and C

402

HITCHIN TOWN — Top Field, Fishponds Road, Hitchin SG5 1NU
01462 459 028 (match days

From East A1 to J8 onto A602 to Hitchin.
At Three Moorhens Pub roundabout, take third exit (A600) towards Bedford, over next roundabout and lights, turn right at next roundabout, turnstiles on left, parking 50 yards on.

Nearest Railway Station Hitchin - 1.3km   **Bus Route** Buss stops outside the ground

336

HODDESDON TOWN — Wodson Park, Wadesmill Road, Ware, Herts SG12 0UQ
01920 462 064

A10 off junction A602 and B1001 turn right at roundabout after 300 yards and follow Ware sign, past Rank factory. Turn left at main road onto A1170 (Wadesmill Road) Stadium is on the right after 3/4 mile.

Nearest Railway Station Ware - 1.9km   **Bus Route** Wodson Park - stop 90m away

516

HOLBEACH UNITED — Carters Park, Park Road, Holbeach, Lincs PE12 7EE
01406 424 761

Approaching Town Centre traffic lights from Spalding Direction take Second Left, or from Kings Lynn direction take sharp right, into Park Road. Ground is 300 yards on the left.

Bus Route Carter's Park - stop 70m away

529

HOLBROOK SPORTS — APC Sealants Ground, Shaw Lane, Holbrook, Derbyshire DE56 0TG
01332 880 259

Leave A38 at junction signposted Kilburn/Denby Pottery. From south turn left at end of slip road – from north turn rightFollow road through Kilburn to crossroads with traffic lights (Kilburn Toll Bar). Turn left and follow road under A38 to top of hill. Turn left (Hop Inn and Bulls Head).
Follow road through Bargate and go over painted island. At Holbrook village look out for 'rural' petrol station (Venture Garage) and turn right shortly after into Shaw Lane. Ground 50 yards on left.

Nearest Railway Station Belper - 2.3km and Duffield - 2.4km

396

HOLKER OLD BOYS — Rakesmoor, Rakesmoor Lane, Hawcoat, Barrow-in-Furness LA14 4QB
01229 828 176

M6 to junction 36, A590 to Barrow until you reach Kimberley-Clark Paper Mill. Turn 1st left into Bank Lane, signposted Hawcoat & and Barrow Golf Club, At the T junction turn left into Rakesmoor Lane. Ground 200 yards on the right.

Nearest Railway Station Barrow-in-Furness - 2.6km   **Bus Route** Dunmail Raise stop - 151m away

449

HOLLAND — Eastcliff Sports Ground, Dulwich Road, Holland-on-Sea CO15 5HP
07778 142 118

From Colchester, Get on A12 in Mile End from A134 and Via Urbis Romanae, Head south on Rotary Way. At the roundabout, take the 2nd exit and stay on Rotary Way. Turn left onto Westway/A134. At the roundabout, take the 5th exit and stay on Westway/A134. At the roundabout, take the 2nd exit and stay on Westway/A134. At Essex Hall Roundabout, take the 2nd exit onto A134. Turn left onto Turner Rd/A134. Continue to follow A134. Continue straight onto Via Urbis Romanae. At the roundabout, take the 2nd exit. At the roundabout, take the 3rd exit. At the roundabout, take the 2nd exit onto the A12 ramp to Ipswich/Felixstowe/A14/Harwich/A120. Take A120 and A133 to St John's Rd/B1027 in Clacton-on-Sea. Merge onto A12. Take the A120 ramp to Colchester North/A1232/Clacton Harwich. Keep right to continue on A120. At the roundabout, take the 1st exit onto Colchester Rd/A133. At the roundabout, take the 3rd exit onto A133. At the roundabout, take the 2nd exit and stay on A133. Go through 1 r'dabout. Continue on B1027. Drive to Dulwich Rd in Holland-on-Sea.

Nearest Railway Station Clacton-on-Sea - 1.7km

402

HOLLANDS & BLAIR — Star Meadow Sports Club, Darland Avenue, Gillingham, Kent ME7 3AN
01634 573839

Hollands & Blair FC's home ground can be found on Darland Avenue, Gillingham. The car park entrance is just after The Star Public House car park. The post code for Sat Nav is ME7 3AP.

505

HOLMER GREEN — Airedale Park, Watchet Lane, Holmer Green, Bucks HP15 6UF
01494 711 485

From Amersham on A404 High Wycombe Road. After approx 2 miles turn right into Sheepcote Dell Road. Continue until end of road at Bat & Ball pub. Turn right, then immediately left. Continue approx 1/2 mile until double mini-roundabouts. Turn left in front of the Mandarin Duck restaurant into Airedale Park 150 yards on the right

Nearest Railway Station Great Missenden - 4.3km   **Bus Route** Copners Drive - stop 350m away

516

HOLMESDALE — Holmesdale Sp.& Soc.Club, 68 Oakley Rd, Bromley BR2 8HG
020 8462 4440

Off the A232 on the A233.

Nearest Railway Station Hayes - 2.1km

505

HOLWELL SPORTS — Welby Road, Asfordby Hill, Melton Mowbray, Leicestershire LE14 3RD
01664 812 080

From Derby. Take A52 to M1 J24 then A6 to Loughborough. At Zouch take left on A6006 to Asfordby And Asfordby Hill. At island take left turn and ground 300 metres on left.
From Nottingham A52 to A6006, onto A46. Left onto A6006 and then as above.
From Leicester – turn off A46 at Six Hills Hotel, left at t-junction, right at cross roads and then as above.

Nearest Railway Station Melton Mowbray - 2.8km

396

HOLYPORT — Summerleaze Village SL6 8SP
07515 789 415

From the A4 Maidenhead take the B4447 towards Cookham after 1/4 mile turn right into Ray Mill Road West, at the T-junction turn left into Blackamoor Lane. As road bends sharply you will see the entrance to the ground on left, signposted Holyport FC. Please observe speed limit down track to the ground. Please note a new electric gate has been installed at the entrance to Summerleaze, it will automatically open upon approach on match days.

Nearest Railway Station Furze Platt - 1km   **Bus Route** Veterinary Hospital stop - 133m away

422

HOOK NORTON
The Bourne, Hook Norton OX15 5PB
01608 737 132

From Oxford – A44 to junction with A361 turn right, take 1st left to a 'T' junction, turn right & enter village, after 30 MPH turn left then 1st right into 'The Bourne', take 1st left into ground.

Bus Route The Pear Tree Inn stop - 233m away

HORLEY TOWN
The New Defence, Court Lodge Road, Horley RH6 8SP
01293 822 000

From centre of town go North up Victoria where it meets the A23, straight across to Vicarage Lane, 2nd left into Court Lodge Road follow it through estate and we are behind adult education centre.

384

Nearest Railway Station Horley
Bus Route Metrobus 100, 526

HORNDEAN
Five Heads Park Five Heads Road Horndean Hampshire PO8 9NZ
02392 591 363

Leave A3(M) at Junction 2 and follow signs to Cowplain. Take the slip road passing Morrisons store on the right crossing over the mini roundabout then continue to the set of traffic lights ensuring you are in the right hand lane signed Horndean. Turn right at these traffic lights and continue on for approximately 400 yards until you reach the Colonial Bar on your left, next junction on your left after the Colonial Bar is Five Heads Road, turn left into Five Heads Road and the ground is approx 1/4 mile along this road. Postcode for Satellite Navigation systems PO8 9NZ

541

Nearest Railway Station Rowlands Castle - 4.5km
Bus Route Horndean Com. School - stop 560m away

HORSHAM
Sussex FA Headquaters, Culver Road, Lancing West Sussex BN15 9AX
01403 252 689 / 07952 351 712

From Chichester along the A27 and head towards Worthing until you reach the roundabout at Lancing Leisure Centre. Turn right at the roundabout into Grinstead Lane. 500 yards on the right is The Harvester restaurant, turn right after the restaurant into Grinstead Avenue, left at the mini roundabout into North Road. Pass the shops until the next mini roundabout and turn right into Culver Road. From Eastbourne/Hastings take the A27 through Lewes, Brighton, Hove, Portslade & Shoreham until you reach the roundabout at Lancing Leisure Centre. Turn left at the roundabout into Grinstead Lane, then as above.

225

Nearest Railway Station Lancing - 5min walk from the ground.

HORSHAM YMCA
Gorings Mead, Horsham, West Sussex RH13 5BP
01403 252 689

Travel north on the A23, turning off onto the A272 at Bolney.
Continue on the A272 to Cowfold then follow the A281 to Horsham.
On entering the outskirts of the town, follow the A281 (Brighton Road) a short distance and Gorings Mead is a turning on the left. The entrance to the ground is at the bottom of Gorings Mead.

495

Nearest Railway Station Horsham - 0.9km
Bus Route Brighton Road - stop 205m away

HULLBRIDGE SPORTS
Lower Road, Hullbridge, Hockley Essex SS5 6BJ
01702 230 420

Leave the A127 and head towards Rayleigh on the A129. Turn left at the first mini roundabout and go down Crown Hill towards Rayleigh Station. Go past Rayleigh Station which will be on your left and the road bends round to the left and you will go under the railway bridge. Take the first turning the other side of the railway bridge which will be Down Hall Road. Continue to the end of Down Hall Road and turn left at the end into Hullbridge Rd. Follow Hullbridge Rd until it comes to an end and there will be a sharp right hand bend which goes in to Lower Rd. Continue along Lower Rd, straight over the mini r'about and up the hill. You will see Hilltop Avenue on your left hand side and the turning in to the football ground will be just after this on the right.

415

Nearest Railway Station Rayleigh, approx. 3 miles
Bus Route 20, bottom of the hill

HUNGERFORD TOWN
Bulpitt Lane, Hungerford RG17 0AY
01488 682 939

From M4 Junction, take A338 to Hungerford. First Roundabout turn right on to A4, next roundabout first left, 100 yards roundabout 1st left up High Street, go over three roundabouts, at fourth roundabout turn first left signposted 'Football Club'. Take second left into Bulpitt Lane, go over crossroads, ground on left.

134

Nearest Railway Station Hungerford - Approx. one mile from the ground.
Bus Route Priory Close stop - 120m away

HUNGERFORD TOWN RESERVES
Bulpit Lane, Hungerford RG17 0AY
01488 682 939

From M4 Junction, take A338 to Hungerford. First Roundabout turn right on to A4, next roundabout first left, 100 yards roundabout 1st left up High Street, go over three roundabouts, at fourth roundabout turn first left signposted 'Football Club'. Take second left into Bulpitt Lane, go over crossroads, ground on left.

Nearest Railway Station Hungerford - Approx. one mile from the ground.
Bus Route Priory Close stop - 120m away

HUNTINGDON TOWN
Jubilee Park, Kings Ripton Road,, Huntingdon, Cambridgeshire PE28 2NR
07974 664 818

At the A1 Brampton Hut roundabout, follow signs for A14 East until reaching the Spittals Interchange roundabout.
Follow the A141 towards St Ives/March and go over 3 roundabouts.
Take next left turn at traffic lights towards Kings Ripton and the ground is on the left.

529

Nearest Railway Station Huntingdon - 3.4km
Bus Route Newnham Close - stop 1km away

HYDE UNITED
Ewen Fields, Walker Lane, Hyde SK14 5PL
0161 367 7273

M60 (Manchester Orbital Motorway) to Junction 24, take the M67 (towards Sheffield) to junction 3 (Hyde/Dukinfield/Stalybridge). Once on exit slipway, keep to the right-hand lane heading for Hyde town centre. At the traffic lights at end of the slipway turn right, then at the second set of lights turn left (Morrisons on left) onto Mottram Road. Turn right at next lights onto Lumn Road. Left at Give Way sign onto Walker Lane. Ground entrance is on left, just after Hyde Leisure Pool, and is clearly signposted. Please note for Satnav, use SK14 5PL

290

Nearest Railway Station Newton for Hyde - 0.8km
Bus Route Walker Lane - stop 110m away

HYTHE & DIBDEN
Clayfields, Claypit Lane, Dibden SO45 5TN
07825 550 624

Travel along A326 and at the Dibden Roundabout take the first exit left into Southampton Road. Continue for approximately 1/2 mile and turn right into Claypits Lane just before the Shell Filling Station. The ground is 100 yards on the left and there is car parking in the ground.
Postcode for Satellite Navigation systems SO45 5TN

541

Nearest Railway Station Southampton Town Quay - 3.5km
Bus Route Drapers Copse - stop 200m away

HYTHE TOWN
Reachfields Stadium, Fort Road, Hythe CT21 6JS
01303 264 932 / 238 256

Leave the M20 at junction 11, then at the r'dabout take the 3rd exit onto the B2068, signposted Hastings, Hythe. At the next r'dabout take the 2nd exit onto Ashford Road, A20. Continue onto Ashford Road, A20. Entering Newingreen, at the T-junction turn left onto Hythe Rd, A261, signposted Hythe. Continue down London Rd, A261. Entering Hythe, continue at the traffic lights onto Scanlons Bridge Rd, A2008. Turn right at the next set of lights onto Dymchurch Rd, A259. Either take the 1st left down Fort Rd and turn right at the end of Fort Rd for the car-park, or after a few hundred yards turn left onto the Reachfields estate. Follow the road round and the stadium will be on your right.

226

Nearest Railway Station Hythe - 0.5km

ILFORD
Cricklefield Stadium, 486 High Road, Ilford, Essex IG1 1FY
020 8514 8352

Taking the A127, from the east travel towards London before coming to the traffic light controlled junction at Barley Lane, Goodmayes (B177) . Turn Left by taking the slip road and follow Barley Lane to its junction with the traffic light controlled High Road, Goodmayes (A118) (it is the first set of traffic control lights for traffic rather than pedestrians on that road). Turn Right and follow the road past Seven Kings station (which should be on your right) and on towards Ilford. The entrance to the ground is some 400 yards past the station with the Ilford Swimming Baths on the left being the point at which both coaches and those in cars or on foot should turn left into the car parks.

Nearest Railway Station Seven Kings (BR), approx. ½ mile   **Bus Route** 86, outside ground

415

ILKESTON TOWN
New Manor Ground, Awsworth Road, Ilkeston, Derbyshire DE7 8JF
0115 944 428

M1 Junction 26, take the A610 signed Ripley, leave at the first exit on to the A6096 signed Awsworth / Ilkeston, at the next island take the A6096 signed Ilkeston, keep on this road for about half a mile, then turn right into Awsworth Road, Signed Cotmanhay (Coaches can get down this road) the ground is about half a mile on the left hand side down this road. Car Parking available at the ground £1 per car.

436

IPSWICH WANDERERS
SEH Sports Centre, Humber Doucy Lane, Ipswich IP4 3NR
01473 720 691

Exit the M25 At junction 28, exit toward A12/Chelmsford E/A1023/Brentwood/London/Romford. Keep left at the fork, follow signs for C'ford/A12 and merge onto A12. Continue on A12. Drive to Humber Doucy Ln in Suffolk. Merge onto A12. At the r'about, take the 3rd exit onto the A14 (E) ramp to A12 (N)/Felixstowe/Lowestoft. Merge onto A14. At junction 57, exit onto Nacton Rd/A1189 toward Ipswich. At the r'about, take the 3rd exit onto Ransomes Way/A1189. At the r'about, take the 2nd exit and stay on Ransomes Way/A1189. At the r'about, take the 1st exit onto Felixstowe Rd/A1156. At the r'about, continue straight onto Bixley Rd/A1189. Continue to follow A1189. At the r'about, take the 2nd exit onto Woodbridge Rd E/A1214. Slight left toward Playford Rd. Continue onto Playford Rd. Turn left onto Humber Doucy Lane.   **Nearest Railway Station:** Derby Road (Ipswich) 2.1km.

402

IRCHESTER UNITED
Alfred Street, Irchester NN29 7DR
01933 312 877

From A509 Wellingborough/Newport Pagnell Road turn into Gidsy Lane to Irchester.
Turn left into Wollaston Road B659. Alfred Street is on left hand side with the ground at the end.

Nearest Railway Station Wellingborough - 3.1km   **Bus Route** Alfred Street - stop 100m away

529

IRLAM
Silver Street, Irlam, Manchester M44 6HR
07969 946 277

M60 to junction 10, take A57 to Irlam, then B5320 into Lower Irlam.
Turn right into Silver Street, Ground approx 300 yards on the right.

Nearest Railway Station Flixton - 2.3km   **Bus Route** Silver Street stop - 23m away

449

IVYBRIDGE TOWN
Erme Valley, Ermington Road, Ivybridge PL21 9ES
01752 896 686

From Plymouth-leave A38 at Ivybridge and follow signs towards Ermington.
Ground is immediately next to South Devon Tennis Centre.
From Exeter-leave A38 at Ivybridge. Ground is in front of you at the end of the slip road.

Nearest Railway Station Ivybridge - 1.8km   **Bus Route** Community Centre - stop 251m away

488

JARROW
Perth Green Community Assoc., Inverness Road, Jarrow NE32 4AQ
0191 489 3743

Take teh A168 exit off the A1 (M). Continue onto A19. After about 55 miles at the roundabout, take the 2nd exit and stay on A19. After 1.5 miles take the A194 slight exit to South Shields. At the next roundabout, take the 4th exit onto Leam Lane/A194, then at the next roundabout, take the 4th exit and stay on Leam Lane/A194, then turn left onto Edinburgh Road and then at the roundabout, take the 2nd exit onto Perth Avenue. Turn left onto Inverness Road.

Nearest Railway Station Brockley Whins - 530m   **Bus Route** Imverness Road-youth club - stop 75m away

476

JARROW ROOFING BOLDON C.A.
Boldon CA Sports Ground, New Road, Boldon Colliery NE35 9AL
07714 525 549

From south take A19 and follow signs for Tyne Tunnel. Turn right at junction marked Boldon Colliery (Testo Roundabout) on to the A184. Turn left at the next r'about, into the B1293, and head towards Asda. At second r'about, turn right at end of retail park. At the r'about at the entrance to Asda, take the "10 to" exit, and you will pass a large brick building on your right, known as The Shack. Turn right into the car park after this building, and at the far end of the car park there is a small lane that leads off left. Roofers ground is at the end of this track.

Nearest Railway Station Tyne & Wear Metro - 1km   **Bus Route** Boldon Asda - stop 59m away

476

K SPORTS
Cobdown Sports & Social Club, Station Road, Ditton, Aylesford, Kent ME20 6AU
08448 800 048

Station Road is off London Road / A20 close to the M20.

Nearest Railway Station Aylesford

505

KEMPSTON ROVERS
Hillgrounds Leisure, Hillgrounds Road, Kempston, Bedford MK42 8SZ
01234 852 346

Take A421 Bedford by pass turning as indicated to Kempston onto A5140 Woburn Road. At roundabout turn left into St John's Street then right into Bedford Road. After the shops and park on the left turn immediately left into Hillgrounds Road. Ground is past the swimming pool on right hand side.

Nearest Railway Station Bedford - 1.3km   **Bus Route** Prentice Gardens - stop 100m away

370

KENDAL TOWN
Pye Motors Stadium, Parkside Road, Kendal, Cumbria LA9 7BL
01539 727 472

M6 junction 36, via A590/591/A6 to Kendal (South). At first traffic lights turn right, left at roundabout, right into Parkside Road. Ground on right over brow of hill.

Nearest Railway Station Kendal - 1.3km   **Bus Route** Castle Circle - stop 200m away

291

KENSINGTON BOROUGH
Amersham Town FC, Spratleys Meadow, School Lane, Amersham HP7 0EL
0207 289 3395

From Beaconsfield and High Wycombe follow the signposts to Amersham Old Town. Turn left at the bottom of the hill (Tesco roundabout). Go straight on through the next roundabout. From London at the first roundabout take the second exit signposted Amersham Old Town. Go straight on through the second, third (Tesco) and fourth roundabout. At the roundabout in front of the old Market Hall turn right into Church Street. Go past the Church on your right and take the first left into School Lane. Go past the recreation ground on your left and the road on your left (Mill Lane). The ground is one hundred yards on your left past Mill Lane.

384

KENT FOOTBALL UNITED Glentworth Club, Lowfield Street, Dartford DA1 1JB 07860 654 558

Off the A225 - Lowfield Street.

505

Nearest Railway Station Dartford - 0.8 km

KETTERING TOWN Latimer Park, Burton Latimer, Kettering NN15 5PS 01536 217 006

From Jct 10 of the A14 turn due South at the roundabout onto Kettering Road (signposted Burton Latimer). After 200 yards turn right at the roundabout onto Attendiez Way. Go over the next roundabout and follow the road around Morrison's warehouse. The road becomes Polwell Lane and the entrance to Latimer Park is on the left just after Morrison's warehouse. **If approaching from the South**, take the A6 to its junction with the A14 and follow the directions above or, if travelling up the A509 turn right at the roundabout just after Isham (signposted Burton Latimer) onto Station Road and continue for half a mile past the Weetabix and Alumasc factories before turning left onto Polwell Lane. The entrance to Latimer Park is on the right after 50 yds.

338

Nearest Railway Station Kettering - 4.1km **Bus Route** Station Road - stop 150m away

---

KEYNSHAM TOWN AJN Stadium, Bristol Road, Keynsham BS31 2BE 07814 609 853

On A4175 off the Bristol to Bath A4. On left immediately after 30mph sign.

559

Nearest Railway Station Keynsham - 0.7km **Bus Route** Rugby Club - stop 50m away

---

KIDDERMINSTER HARRIERS Aggborough Stadium, Hoo Road, Kidderminster DY10 1NB 01562 823 931

From North M5 Junc 3 onto A456 to Kidderminster, From South M5 Junc 6 onto A449 to Kidderminster. Alternatively M40/42 Junc 1 onto A38 to Bromsgrove/A448 to Kidderminster. (All routes follow Brown signs to (SVR) Steam Railway then follow signs to Aggborough). Aggborough is signposted at either end of Hoo Road.

88

Nearest Railway Station Kidderminster - half a mile from the ground.

KIDLINGTON Yarnton Road, Kidlington, Oxford OX5 1AT 01865 849 777

From Kidlington Roundabout take A4260 into Kidlington. After 3rd set of traffic lights take 2nd left into Yarnton Road. Ground 300 yards on left, just past Morton Avenue.

377

Nearest Railway Station Oxford Parkway - 1.9km **Bus Route** Treeground Place - stop 100m away

---

KIDLINGTON RESERVES Yarnton Road, Kidlington, Oxford OX5 1AT 01865 849 777

From Kidlington roundabout (Sainsburys) take the A4260 into Kidlington, at the fifth set of lights turn left into Yarnton Road, ground is approx 300 metres on left, just past left turn to Morton Ave.

422

Nearest Railway Station Oxford Parkway - 1.9km **Bus Route** Treeground Place stop - 63m away

---

KIDSGROVE ATHLETIC The Novus Stadium, Hollinwood Road, Kidsgrove, Staffs ST7 1DH 01782 782 412

Leave the M6 at Junction 16, join the A500 towards Stoke-on-Trent. Take the 2nd exit signposted Newcastle & Kidsgrove. Top of the slip road, turn left onto A34 Kidsgrove/Congleton. Straight over at roundabout. At 1st set of traffic lights (by Caudwell Arms pub) turn right onto A34. Continue to next set of lights, turn right into Cedar Avenue. Continue then take 2nd right into Lower Ash Road. Take 3rd left into Hollinwood Road, Ground on left at top.

303

Nearest Railway Station Kidsgrove - 0.8km **Bus Route** Grove Avenue - stop 200m away

---

KIMBERLEY MINERS WELFARE Kimberley MWFC, The Stag Ground, Kimberley, Nottingham NG16 2NB 07803 267 825

Leave the M1 at Junction 26. Take A610 to Nottingham before you reach Nuthall Island.
As Island take first exit signposted B600 Kimberley.
Follow road for around 2 miles before you see Stag PH on the right hand side.
Continue down road for a further 200 yards, entrance to ground between HAMA Medical Centre and Roots Emporium.

396

Nearest Railway Station Ilkeston - 3.4km and Bulwell - 3.8km.

KING'S LYNN RESERVES The Walks Stadium, Tennyson Road, King's Lynn PE30 5PB. 01553 760 060

At the roundabout, at the junction of A47 and the A17, follow the A47, signposted King's Lynn and Norwich. Travel along the dual carriageway for approx. one and a half miles branching off left, following the signs for Town Centre, onto the Hardwick roundabout. Take the first exit, following the signs for Town Centre, travel through two sets of traffic lights until reaching a further set of traffic lights at the Southgates roundabout. Take the fourth exit onto Vancouver Avenue, and travel for approx. 300 metres, going straight across a mini roundabout, The Walks is a further 200 metres along on the left hand side, with car parking outside the ground. The changing rooms and hospitality suite are located at the rear of the main stand.

402

Nearest Railway Station King's Lynn - 5min walk away. **Bus Route** Serviced by Eastern Counties & Norfolk Green

---

KING'S LYNN TOWN The Walks Stadium, Tennyson Road, King's Lynn PE30 5PB 01553 760 060

At the roundabout, at the junction of A47 and the A17, follow the A47, signposted King's Lynn and Norwich. Travel along the dual carriageway for approx. one and a half miles branching off left, following the signs for Town Centre, onto the Hardwick roundabout. Take the first exit, following the signs for Town Centre, travel through two sets of traffic lights until reaching a further set of traffic lights at the Southgates roundabout. Take the fourth exit onto Vancouver Avenue, and travel for approx. 300 metres, going straight across a mini roundabout, The Walks is a further 200 metres along on the left hand side, with car parking outside the ground. The changing rooms and hospitality suite are located at the rear of the main stand.

340

Nearest Railway Station King's Lynn - 5min walk away. **Bus Route** Serviced by Eastern Counties & Norfolk Green

---

KINGS LANGLEY Gaywood Park, Hempstead Road, Kings Langley Herts WD4 8BS 07730 410 330

From M25 leave at Junction 20. Take A4251 to Kings Langley. Go over first roundabout and through village, past 'Young Pretender' Pub & restaurant on left. Go past Coniston Road on left and immediately indicate and move into 'turn right lane' in middle of road. Turn RIGHT into Ground. If car park is full, use lay-byes on road outside ground. Total distance from junction 20 :- 1.4 miles approx. From Hemel Hempstead, take A4251 through Apsley. Continue under railway bridge and ground is approx. a quarter of a mile on LEFT, immediately before lay-bye.

342

Nearest Railway Station Kings Langley - 1.6km

KINGSTONIAN Leatherhead FC, Fetcham Grove, Guildford Road, Leatherhead, Surrey KT22 9AS 020 8330 6869

M25 junction 9 to Leatherhead.
Follow signs to the Leisure Centre, ground adjacent.

180

Nearest Railway Station Leatherhead - half a mile away

KIRBY MUXLOE
Kirby Muxloe Sports Club, Ratby Lane LE9 2AQ
0116 239 2301

From M1 leave at JCTT 21A and follow the signposts for Kirby Muxloe. As you enter the village, at the roundabout take 2nd exit onto Ratby Lane. At mini Roundabout take 2nd exit and the ground is 200 yards on the right hand side. From A47 at Traffic lights turn right onto Colchester Road A563 Continue on A563 for approximately 6 miles turning onto A5630 Anstey Lane. After approximately 2 miles turn left on A46 towards M1 just before next left and then follow directions to Kirby Muxloe, as you enter the village, at the roundabout take 2nd exit onto Ratby Lane. At mini roundabout take 2nd exit and the ground is 200 yards on the right hand side.

529

Bus Route Kirby Corner - stop 55m away

KIRKLEY & PAKEFIELD
Walmer Road, Lowestoft NR33 7LE
01502 513 549

From A12 to Lowestoft town centre and go over roundabout at Teamways Garage and past Teamways Pub.
Take next left into Walmer Road.

402

Nearest Railway Station Oulton Broad South - 1.8km

KNAPHILL
Brookwood Country Park, Redding Way, Knaphill GU21 2AY
01483 475 150

From A3: A322 from Guildford through towards Worplesdon. At Fox Corner rounabout, take 2bd exit onto Bagshot Road, A322 signposted Bagshot. Pat West Hill Golf Club, at traffic lights turn right onto Brookwood Lye Road, A324 signposted Woking. Turn left into Hermitage Road on A324, up to roundabout, take 1st exit onto Redding Way, then 1st left entering driveway towards car park and ground.

384

Nearest Railway Station Brookwood or Woking
Bus Route Arriva 34, 35

KNARESBOROUGH TOWN
Manse Lane, Knaresborough, HG5 8LF
01423 548 896

From West/South Leeds Area: A658 or A61 towards Harrogate. Join A658 southern bypass towards York. At roundabout take left to Knaresborough. Turn left at second roundabout and travel over river bridge. Manse Lane is first on right alongside garage; From East Leeds Area: A58 or A1 to Wetherby. Join B6164 to Knaresborough then as above. From East on A59 from A1: Turn right at first roundabout. Manse Lane is first turn left after speed restriction sign.

463

Nearest Railway Station Knaresborough - 1.5km
Bus Route Aspin Park School - stop 168 away

LANCASTER CITY
Giant Axe, West Road, Lancaster LA1 5PE
01524 382 238

From the South: Exit M6 at Junction 33. At roundabout take the second exit onto the A6, pass through Galgate and then Lancaster University on the right until the next roundabout. Take the second main exit into Lancaster and follow signs for the railway station. At the traffic lights by Waterstones Bookshop turn immediately left. Take the second right onto Station Road and follow downhill on West Road and take the first right into the ground. **From the North:** Exit M6 at Junction 34 and turn left onto the A683. Follow signs for railway station into City around the one way system. Move over to the right hand side lane at the police station and through traffic lights. Manoeuvre into the left-hand lane until traffic lights at Waterstones Bookshop. Follow directions as from the south.

256

LANCING
Culver Road, Lancing, West Sussex BN15 9AX
01903 767 285

A27 to Manor Roundabout, south down Grinstead Lane, second right.
Left at mini-roundabout, next turning right Culver Road.
From railway 3rd turning on left (heading north) past Merry Monk public house.

495

Nearest Railway Station Lancing - 0.2km
Bus Route North Road Post Office - stop 123m away

LANGFORD
Forde Park, Langford Road, Henlow, Beds SG16 6AF
01462 816 106

From West along A57 to Henlow then north on A6001. Ground at north end of Henlow.
From North and East, leave A1 at Langford water tower then into Langford.
Turn left at Boot Restaurant. Follow A6001 round to the left. Club is 1/2 mile away.

516

Nearest Railway Station Arlesey - 1.9km
Bus Route Newtown (Langford Rd) - stop 24m away

LANGNEY WANDERERS
Langney Sports Club, Priory Lane, Eastbourne BN23 7QH
01323 766 265

From M25 take M23/A23 eastbound to A27 Polegate by pass pick up and follow signs for crematorium 50yds past crematorium turn right at mini roundabout into Priory Road.
Stadium 100yds on left.

495

Nearest Railway Station Pevensey & Westham - 15-20 mins walk.
Bus Route The LOOP Bus from the town centre.

LARKHALL ATHLETIC
Plain Ham, Charlcombe Lane, Larkhall, Bath BA1 8DJ
01225 334 952

Take the A4 east from Bath City Centre towards Chippenham/M4. After approximately 1 mile after Cleveland Bridge junction (keep straight ahead) fork left into St Saviours Road (turning is signposted 'Larkhall Local Shops'). In Larkhall Square take first left exit (Salisbury Road) and turn right at t-junction. Follow the road round to the left and up the hill. You are now on Charlcombe Lane. The ground is on the right, on a parallel lane, as Charlcombe Lane narrows. Continue for approximately 100 yards, turn around in Woolley Lane on the right and go back down the hill, this time keeping to the top lane on the left hand side. Plain Ham is on the left just past the junction with Charlcombe Lane.

378

Nearest Railway Station Bath Spa - 2.8km
Bus Route Charlcombe Lane - stop 200m away

LAUNCESTON
Pennygillam Ind. Est., Launceston PL15 7ED
01566 773 279

Leave A30 onto Pennygillam roundabout, turn into Pennygillam Industrial Estate.
Ground is 400 yards on the left.

488

LAVERSTOCK & FORD
The Dell, Church Road, Laverstock, Salisbury, Wilts SP1 1QX
01722 327 401

From Southampton – At the end of the carriageway from Southampton (A36) turn right at traffic lights for the Park & Ride by the Tesco store. Turn left at the traffic lights over the narrow bridge then take the next turning into Manor Farm Road. Take the next turning right into Laverstock Road, (do not turn left under the railway bridge). Keep left into Laverstock village, past the Church and the Club is situated on the left hand side directly opposite the Chinese takeaway and shop. From Bournemouth – Follow the A36 to Southampton past Salisbury College and straight across the Tesco roundabout take left at traffic lights into the Park & Ride (take the corner slowly, the road goes back on itself) then follow directions as above.

541

Nearest Railway Station Salisbury - 2.5km
Bus Route St Andrews School - stop 40m away

LEAMINGTON
Phillips 66 Community Stadium, Harbury Lane, Whitmarsh, Leamington CV33 9QB
01926 430 406

From West and North – M40 Southbound – Exit J14 and take A452 towards Leamington. Ahead at 1st island. Next island take 2nd exit A452 (Europa Way). Next island take 4th exit (Harbury Lane) signposted Harbury and Bishops Tachbrook. Next island take 3rd exit (Harbury Lane). At traffic lights continue straight ahead Harbury Lane. Ground is 1.5 miles on left.
From South – M40 northbound – Exit J13. Turn right onto A452 towards Leamington. At 1st island take 3rd exit A452 (Europa Way) and follow as above (Europa Way onwards).

90

Nearest Railway Station Leamington Spa - 3 miles away
Bus Route Nos. 65 & 66

LEATHERHEAD
Fetcham Grove, Guildford Road, Leatherhead, Surrey KT22 9AS — 01372 360 151

M25 junction 9 to Leatherhead,
follow signs to Leisure Centre,
ground adjacent.

Nearest Railway Station Leatherhead - half a mile away

182

LEEK TOWN
Harrison Park, Macclesfield Road, Leek, Cheshire ST13 8LD — 01538 399 278

From the South: Leave M6 at J15, over roundabout on to the A500, go over the flyover, up the slip road, onto the A50 and follow the signs to Leek. Go straight over the roundabout (Britannia Building on the left) to large set of lights. Go straight across St. Georges Street to top of road to junction, turn left, go down the hill for about a half a mile. The Ground is on the left. **From the North:** Leave M6 at J19. Take Macclesfield signs. Follow into Macclesfield then take A523 Leek/Buxton signs. Follow these to Leek. Ground is situated on the right as you come into Leek. From West Midlands: M6 J15. A500 towards Stoke, over flyover, take A50 past Brittania Stadium. After approx 3 miles join A53 signposted Leek. On entering the town, straight ahead up St Edwards St. (Remainder as above)

303

LEICESTER NIRVANA
Gleneagles Avenue, Leicester LE5 1LU — 01162 660 009

From M1—Exit at Jct 22 (A50/A511 to Leicester/Coalville).
Follow A50 to Leicester, until you reach signs for A563 (Glenfirth Way).
After Sainsbury's, turn right then immediately left in to Gleneagles Avenue. Entrance is at the bottom of the cul de sac.

Nearest Railway Station Syston - 3.9km   **Bus Route** Lakeview Chase - stop 70m away

529

LEICESTER ROAD
Leicester Road Stadium, Leicester Road, Hinckley, LE10 3DR — 01455

From North West: A5 Southbound at Dodwells roundabout (A5/A47) take 1st exit (Earl Shilton, A47 and Industrial Estates), straight over 3 roundabouts, straight over traffic lights, at next roundabout take the 3rd exit (B4668) towards Hinckley, the entrance is 200 yards on the right.
From M69, Junction 1: take A5 north (Tamworth/Nuneaton) then as above.

Nearest Railway Station Hinckley - 2.7km   **Bus Route** Leicester Road stop - 262m away

436

LEIGHTON TOWN
Lake Street, Leighton Buzzard, Beds LU7 1RX — 01525 373 311

Ground is situated just south of Town Centre on the A4146 Leighton Buzzard to Hemel Hemstead Road.
Entrance to car park and ground is opposite Morrisons Supermarket Petrol Station.
1/2 mile south of town centre.

Nearest Railway Station Leighton Buzzard - 1.3km   **Bus Route** Morrisons (Lake St) - stop 60m away

516

LEISTON
LTAA, Victory Road, Leiston IP16 4DQ — 01728 830 308

Take junction 28 off the M25, take the A12/A1023 exit to Chelmsford/Romford/Brentwood, keep left at the fork,
follow signs for Chelmsford/A12 (E) and merge onto A12, at the roundabout,
take the 3rd exit onto the A14 ramp, merge onto A14, at junction 58, exit toward A12, keep left at the fork,
follow signs for Lowestoft/Woodbridge/A12 (N) and merge onto A12, go through 7 roundabouts, turn right onto A1094,
turn left onto Snape Rd/B1069, continue to follow B1069, turn left onto Victory Rd, ground will be on the left.

Bus Route Alde Valley Sixth Form - stop 300m away

184

LEISTON RESERVES
The LTAA, Victory Road, Leiston, Suffolk IP16 4DQ — 01728 830 308

Take junction 28 off the M25, take the A12/A1023 exit to Chelmsford/Romford/Brentwood, keep left at the fork,
follow signs for Chelmsford/A12 (E) and merge onto A12, at the roundabout,
take the 3rd exit onto the A14 ramp, merge onto A14, at junction 58, exit toward A12, keep left at the fork,
follow signs for Lowestoft/Woodbridge/A12 (N) and merge onto A12, go through 7 roundabouts, turn right onto A1094,
turn left onto Snape Rd/B1069, continue to follow B1069, turn left onto Victory Rd, ground will be on the left.

402

LETCOMBE
Bassett Road, Letcombe Regis OX12 9JU — 07765 144 985

Take the B4507 from Wantage (Sign posted White Horse). Turn left after half a mile to Letcombe Regis. Ground on Far side of Village, on the right hand side of road.

Bus Route Church stop - 168m away

422

LEVERSTOCK GREEN
Pancake Lane, Leverstock Green, Hemel Hempstead, Herts HP2 4NQ — 01442 246 280

From M1 at Junction 8, Follow A414 to second roundabout turn left along Leverstock Green Way. Pancake Lane is on the left 300 yards past the Leather Bottle Public House. Ground is 300 yards on left. All visitors are requested to park inside the ground.

Nearest Railway Station Apsley - 3.2km   **Bus Route** Pancake Lane - stop 300m away

516

LEWES
The Dripping Pan, Mountfield Road, Lewes, East Sussex BN7 2XD — 01273 470 820

After leaving the M23, follow the A23 to Brighton. On the outskirts of Brighton join the A27 eastbound. Stay on the A27 for about 5 miles. At the roundabout take first exit into Lewes. Follow this road until you reach traffic lights outside Lewes Prison. Turn right at the lights and follow the road down the hill until you reach a mini roundabout outside the Swan public house. Turn left at roundabout into Southover High Street and continue over next mini roundabout outside the Kings Head public house. At the next roundabout go straight over into Mountfield Road. The Dripping Pan is on your right.

Nearest Railway Station Lewes - 0.3km   **Bus Route** Priory School - stop 100m away

226

LEWISHAM BOROUGH
Ladywell Arena, Silvermere Road, Catford, London SE6 4QX

Either before or after Catford Railway Station (depending on which way you come in) turn in to Doggett Road off the South Circular. Continue along Doggett Road until arriving at Silvermead Road.

Nearest Railway Station Ladywell and Catford Bridge.   **Bus Route** 47, 54, 75, 136, 181, 185, 199, 208

505

LEYTON ORIENT
Matchroom Stadium, Brisbane Road, Leyton, London E10 5NF — 0871 310 1883

Exit M25 at junction 27 and follow signs to 'London (NE), M11' onto the M11 southbound. After 7.1 miles where the road divides, bear right (s/p A406 N. Circ. Rd West, London N and W) onto the North Circular Road. Keep in left hand lanes and take first exit after 0.6 miles (s/p Walthamstow and City A104, then Whipps Cross A104, West End (A503)). At roundabout turn left (s/p Whipps Cross, Bakers Arms, Walthamstow A503) into Woodford New Road A104. At next roundabout (Whipps Cross) after 1.2 miles, take 2nd exit (s/p A104 Bakers Arms, Leyton) and follow road round to left, towards BP station, into Lea Bridge Road. After 0.5 miles, just after Esso station, turn left at lights (s/p Leyton, Stratford, then Leyton Leisure Lagoon) into Leyton Green Road. Filter left after 0.3 miles and turn left at T-junction in Leyton High Road. After 1.2 miles ground is down sidestreets on RHS. From South/South-East via Blackwall Tunnel: Out of tunnel, continue on A102 following signs to 'Stratford, Dalston'. Remain on the A102/A106 for 4.2 miles, following signs for Leyton, passing New Spitalfields Market and over a bridge. At lights just after Car Superstore, turn left into Oliver Road.
Nearest Railway Station: Leyton tube station on the Central Line.   **Bus Route:** Nos. 58, 69, 97 and 158 run along Leyton High Road.

41

LICHFIELD CITY
Brownsfield Park, Brownsfield Road, Lichfield, Staffs, WS13 6AY
01543 258 338

From M42 J10, follow A5 towards Brownhills, or J9 and follow A446 to Lichfield, then follow signs for A38 Lichfield/Derby. From Swinfen Roundabout take 3rd exit for A38 north and then take next off A38 onto A5192 (Cappers Lane). Follow A5192 through 2 islands onto Eastern Avenue. The Ground is on the right at the top of the hill next to Norgreen factory.
From M6 J12, follow A5 towards Lichfield then A38 to Lichfield Derby, then follow instructions as above. (Sat Nav: WS13 6RZ)

436

Nearest Railway Station Lichfield Trent Valley High Level/Lichfield Trent Valley - 1.4km   **Bus Route** Netherstowe Lane stop - 78m away

---

LINCOLN UNITED
Sun Hat Stadium, Ashby Avenue, Hartsholme, Lincoln LN6 0DY
01522 690 674

Along Lincoln Relief Road (A46) until reaching roundabout with exit for Birchwood. Take this exit which is Skellingthorpe Road for approximately 1 mile, at 30 mph sign turn right into Ashby Avenue. Entrance to ground is 200 yards on right.

304

Nearest Railway Station Hkeham - 2.1km   **Bus Route** Ecclesharе Court - stop 75m away

---

LINGFIELD
Sports Pavilion, Godstone Road, Lingfield, Surrey RH7 6BT
01342 834 269

A22 (London to Eastbourne Road) 4 miles north of East Grinstead, to Mormon Temple roundabout, take exit Lingfield (B2028) Newchapel Road for 1½ miles. Turn left at mini-roundabout. Ground ½ mile on left.

495

Nearest Railway Station Lingfield - 1.2km   **Bus Route** Godstone Road - stop 391m away

---

LITHERLAND REMYCA
Litherland Sports Park, Boundary Road, Litherland, Liverpool L21 7LA
0151 288 6288

End of M57/M58 Along Dunningsbridge Road towards Docks, turn right at Junction of Bootle Golf Course on the right hand side into Boundary Road, 2nd turning on the left into sports park.

449

Nearest Railway Station Aintree - 1.7km   **Bus Route** Moss Lane stop - 98m away

---

LITTLE COMMON
Little Common Recreation Ground, Green Lane, Bexhill on Sea TN39 4PH
01424 845 861

From the west take the A259, at Little Common roundabout take second exit into Peartree Lane and then left into Little Common Recreation Ground car park.

495

Nearest Railway Station Cooden Beach - 1.6km   **Bus Route** Green Lane - stop 183m away

---

LITTLE OAKLEY
War Memorial Club Ground, Harwich Road, Little Oakley, Harwich CO12 5ED
01255 880 370

Follow M5, M4 and M25 to Brentwood. Take exit 28 from M25 toward A12/Chelmsford E/A1023/Brentwood/London/Romford. Keep left at the fork, follow signs for C'ford/A12 and merge onto A12. Take the A120 ramp to Calchester North/A1232/Clacton Harwich. Keep right to continue on A120. At the roundabout, take the 2nd exit and stay on A120. Turn right at Main Rd/B1352. Slight left onto Church Hill/B1352. Turn right onto Mayes Lane. At the roundabout, take the 1st exit and stay on Mayes Lane. Turn right onto Harwich Rd/B1414

402

Nearest Railway Station Harwich International - 3.3km   **Bus Route** Mayes Lane stop - 173m away

---

LITTLEHAMPTON TOWN
St Flora Sportsfield, St Flora's Road, Littlehampton BN17 6BD
01903 716 390

Leave A259 at Waterford Business Park and turn into Horsham Road.
After Shell Garage turn left into St. Floras Road.
Ground is at the end of road on the left.

495

Nearest Railway Station Littlehampton - 1km   **Bus Route** Parkside Avenue - stop 79m away

---

LITTLETON
5 Acres, Pebworth Road, North Littleton, Evesham, Worcs, WR11 8QL
07765 224 290

Get on A46 and aim for Bidford-on-Avon, leave A46 at Bidford roundabout and follow signs for B439 (Bidford ½ mile). Come to roundabout in Bidford and take exit B4085 (Cleeve Prior), over a very narrow bridge controlled by traffic lights, straight over crossroads following sign to Honeybourne Broadway. Straight on for approximately 3 miles signpost right turn for the Littletons at crossroads, the ground is 1¼ miles on the right.

436

Nearest Railway Station Honeybourne - 3.1km   **Bus Route** The Ivy Inn stop - 1.2km away

---

LIVERSEDGE
Clayborn Ground, Quaker Lane, Hightown Road, Cleckheaton WF15 8DF
01274 862 108

M62 J26, A638 into Cleckheaton, right at lights on corner of Memorial Park, through next lights and under railway bridge, first left (Hightown Rd) and Quaker Lane is approx ¼mile on left and leads to ground. From M1 J40, A638 thru Dewsbury and Heckmondwike to Cleckheaton, left at Memorial Park lights then as above. Buses 218 & 220 (Leeds - Huddersfield) pass top of Quaker Lane.

463

Nearest Railway Station Low Moor - 4.5km   **Bus Route** Hightown Road - stop 142m away

---

LONDON COLNEY
Cotlandswick Playing Fields, London Colney, Herts AL2 1DW
01727 822 132

From M25 J22, follow the A1081 signposted to St Albans. At London Colney roundabout take A414, signposted Hemel Hempstead/Watford. There is a hidden turn into the ground after approximately 500 metres (just after lay-by) signposted Sports Ground and London Colney FC. Follow the ground around between the Rugby and Irish clubs to ground entrance.

516

Nearest Railway Station Park Street - 2.3km   **Bus Route** Leisure Centre - stop 430m away

---

LONDON LIONS
Rowley Lane Sports Ground, Rowley Lane, Barnet EN5 3HW
0208 441 6051

Exit the M25 at junction 23, take the A1(M)/A1081/A1 exit to Hatfield/Barnet/London. At the roundabout, take the 5th exit onto the A1 slip road to London (N&C)/Brent Cross. Continue on A1. Drive to Paddock Lane in Barnet, continue onto A1. In just under 2 miles take the A5135 exit towards Borehamwood/Barnet/Arkley/A411, then turn left onto Rowley Lane, sports ground will be on your right.

516

Nearest Railway Station Elstree & Borehamwood - 2.4km   **Bus Route** Buses stop on Rowley Lane.

LONDON TIGERS
Avenue Park, Western Avenue, Perivale, Greenford UB6 8GA
020 7289 3395 (10am-6pm)

Exit junction 16 of the M25 onto the A40 (M) towards London. After you pass the Target roundabout there will be a sharp left turn at the 200yard marker for the Greenford slip road from the A40 into Avenue Park, just past the overhead footbridge. If coming from Central London or Hangar Lane, drive up to the Target roundabout and do a U-turn onto the eastbound carriageway and turn left into Avenue Park after the footbridge. The nearest Tube station is Greenford on the Central Line, which is a 10-minute walk.

516

Nearest Railway Station Greenford Underground - 706m   **Bus Route** Henley Close - stop 330m away

LONG BUCKBY AFC
Station Road, Long Buckby NN6 7QA
07749 393 045

From the Village Centre turn into Station Road. Ground on left hand side.
Parking is available in South Close adjacent to the Rugby Club.
(do NOT park "half on half off" the pavement outside the ground).

Nearest Railway Station Long Buckby - 0.3km

Bus Route Watson Road - stop 70m away

529

LONG EATON UNITED
Grange Park, Station Rd, Long Eaton, Derbys NG10 2EG
0115 973 5700

M1 Junc 25, take A52 towards Nottingham, to island by Bardills Garden Centre, right onto B6003. Approx 2 miles to end of road to T-junction. At traffic lights, turn right A453 and take 2nd left into Station Road. Entrance on left down un-named road opposite disused car park next to Grange School.

Nearest Railway Station Attenborough - 1.9km

Bus Route School stop - 158m away

436

LONG MELFORD
Stoneylands Stadium, New Road, Long Melford, Suffolk CO10 9JY
01787 312 187

Turn down St Catherine Road off Hall St (Bury-Sudbury road) and then turn left into New Road.

Nearest Railway Station Sudbury - 4.6km

402

LONGLEVENS AFC
Saw Mills End, Corinium Avenue, Gloucester GL4 3DG
01452 530 388 (Clubhouse)

From South: From M5 Gloucester exit junction 11a, and bear left onto A417. At roundabout take 2nd exit continue on A417 for ½ mile. At next roundabout take 2nd exit (look for coroners court sign) for ½ mile then turn left on Sawmills End (Ibis Hotel). Ground is on the left just past hotel. **From North:** From M5 Gloucester exit junction 11, at roundabout take third exit onto A40 for approx 2 miles. At roundabout take 2nd exit (A417) for 1 mile. At roundabout take 3rd exit (look for coroners court sign) for ½ mile then turn left on Sawmills End (Ibis Hotel). Ground is on the left just past hotel.

Nearest Railway Station Gloucester - 1.9km

Bus Route Budgen's Garage stop - 146m away

422

LONGWELL GREEN SPORTS
Longwell Green Com. Centre, Shellards Road BS30 9AD
01179 323 722

Leave Junction 1 M32 follow signs for Ring Road (A4174). At Kingsfield roundabout turn into Marsham Way. At first set of traffic lights turn left into Woodward Drive. Continue to min roundabout and turn right into Parkway Road and continue to Shellards Road. Ground is situated to the rear of the Community Centre.

Nearest Railway Station Bitton - 1.4km

Bus Route Sally Barn Close - stop 500m away

559

LORDSWOOD
Martyn Grove, Northdane Way, Walderslade, ME5 8YE
01634 669 138

Take Junction 3 of the M2 (signposted Chatham). At the roundabout take the first exit, then turn right onto Walderslade Woods. At the next roundabout take the 2nd exit and follow the road. At the next roundabout take the 2nd exit onto Lordswood Lane, follow the road, and at the next roundabout take the 3rd exit onto Albemarle road. Follow the road all the way to the bottom and then turn left onto North Dane Way. Martin Grove is situated within the grounds of Lordswood Sports and Social Club and Lordswood Leisure Centre - the entrance is approx 400 yards on your left.

Nearest Railway Station Chatham - 4.8km

Bus Route Lords Wood Leisure Centre - stop 30m away

505

LOUGHBOROUGH DYNAMO
Nanpantan Sports Ground, Nanpantan Road, Loughborough LE11 3YE
01509 237 148

From M1: At Junction 23 turn towards Loughborough (A512). At 1st set of traffic lights turn right on to Snells Nook Lane.. At 1st crossroads ("Priory" pub on left) turn left on to Nanpantan Rd. Turn (1st) right after 0.75 miles on to Watermead Lane. The ground is at the end of the lane. **From Leicester (A6):** Turn left at 3rd roundabout on Epinal Way (Ring Road) on to Forest Road. After 2 miles turn (5th) left on to Watermead Lane. **From Nottingham (A60):** Turn right at 1st set of traffic lights in Loughborough. Go through next 4 sets of traffic lights. Turn left at the first roundabout on to Epinal Way straight on at next roundabout and then take the third exit at following r'about on to Forest Road. After 2 miles turn (5th) left on to Watermead Lane.

Nearest Railway Station Loughborough - 4.6km

Bus Route Nursery School - stop 500m away

304

LOUGHBOROUGH UNIVERSITY
Loughborough Uni Stadium, Holywell Sports Complex, Holywell Park LE11 3TU
01509 228 774

From M42/A42 exit at Junction 13 take the A512 towards Loughborough. After crossing Junction 23 of the M1 travel approx 3/4 mile to first traffic island. Turn right into University, following the signs for Holywell park & Holywell Sports Complex (Loughborough University Stadium). After entering the University through the Security barrier, keep straight on at both small islands. Bear left on entry to the large General Spectator Car park. Access to the ground which is on the left hand side of Car Park 'W' (available for spectator parking). Parking at the Stadium is limited to Officials/Team Coach as only a small number of cars can be accommodated. (Sat Nav users use LE11 3QF)

Nearest Railway Station Loughborough - 4km

Bus Route Wheatsheaf stop - 172m away

436

LOWESTOFT TOWN
Crown Meadow, Love Road, Lowestoft NR32 2PA
01502 567 280

Head for Lowestoft town centre. After crossing Bascule Bridge and railway station turn right at traffic lights (sp A12 Yarmouth) into Katwyck Way. After 300 yards take 1st exit at roundabout into Raglan Street. At 'T' junction turn left into Love Road and ground is about 100 yards on right.

Nearest Railway Station Lowestoft - 0.7km

186

LOXWOOD
Loxwood Sports Ass., Plaistow Road, Loxwood RH14 0RQ
07791 766 857

Leave A272 between Billinghurst and Wisborough Green and join the B2133 for 3.4 miles.
On entering Loxwood Village take 1st left into Plaistow Road, ground situated 100 yards on the left.

Bus Route Plaistow Road - stop 28m away

495

LUTTERWORTH ATHLETIC
Weston Arena, Hall Park, Hall Lane, Bitteswell, Lutterworth LE17 4LN
01455 554 046

Exit the M1 at junction 20 and take the first exit at the roundabout. Then take the third exit at the next roundabout and head into Lutterworth. Continue on through Lutterworth, and when you have left the town continue for half a mile before taking the first left. The ground is immediately on your left.

Bus Route Manor Farm - stop 1.5km away

529

LUTTERWORTH TOWN
Dunley Way, Lutterworth, Leicestershire, LE17 4NP
07855 836 489

Travelling North on the A426 turn left into Crescent Road. Follow this road until it merges into Dunley Way. Just before the bend where Dunley Way merges into Sherrier Way take the left. The ground is down the end of this road.
Travelling South on the A426 turn right into Central Avenue. At the T-juction turn right into Dunley Way. Just before the bend where Dunley Way merges into Sherrier Way take the left. The ground is down the end of this road.

Bus Route Elizabethan Way - stop 300m away

529

LYDD TOWN
The Lindsey Field, Dengemarsh Road, Lydd, Kent TN29 9JH

01797 321 904

Travelling along the B2075 into Lydd fork left onto Harden Road before entering the Lydd. Continue along Harden Road across rounadout onto Robin Hood Lane and eventually onto Dengemarsh Road.

505

LYDNEY TOWN
Lydney Recreation Ground, Swan Road, Lydney GL15 5RU

01594 844 523

From Gloucester – take Lydney road off A48 down Highfield Hill and into the town centre. Take 1st left into Swan Road after 2nd set of pelican lights.
From Chepstow – at by-pass roundabout take Lydney road. Go over railway crossing then take 2nd right into Swan Road.

422

Nearest Railway Station Lydney Town - 144m   **Bus Route** Forest Parade - 156m away

---

LYE TOWN
Sports Ground, Stourbridge Road, Lye, Stourbridge, West Mids DY9 7DH

01384 422 672

Situated on A458 Birmingham to Stourbridge RoadFrom M5 Junction 3, take road marked Kidderminster, as far as lights at the bottom of Hagley Hill. Turn right, then take the third turning off the first island. Carry straight on at the next island. Turn left at Lights/Crossroads, onto the A458. Ground approximately 400 yards on the left hand side.

436

Nearest Railway Station Lye - 0.5km   **Bus Route** Cemetery Road stop - 93m away

---

LYMINGTON TOWN
The Sports Ground, Southampton Road, Lymington SO41 9ZG

01590 671 305

From the North & East – Leave the M27 at Junction 1 (Cadnam/New Forest) and proceed via Lyndhurst then Brockenhurst on the A337. On the outskirts of Lymington proceed through main set of traffic lights with Royal Quarter Housing Development and the Police Station on your right hand side. Continue for just another 250 metres and turn left immediately into St Thomas's Park with he ground in front of you.
Alternatively, turn left at the traffic lights into Avenue Road then first right, Oberland Court, with the Lymington Bowling Club facing you.
If travelling from the direction of Christchurch & New Milton using the A337 pass the White Hart P/H on the outskirts of Pennington and proceed down and up Stanford Hill. Passing the Waitrose Supermarket on your left hand side, the ground is situated immediately on your right hand side sign posted St Thomas Park.

541

Nearest Railway Station Lymington Town - 0.6km   **Bus Route** Town Hall - Stop 110m away

---

MACCLESFIELD TOWN
Moss Rose Ground, London Road, Macclesfield SK11 7SP

01625 264 686

From North (M6), Exit Junction 19, Knutsford. Follow the A537 to Macclesfield. Follow signs for the Town Centre. The follow signs A523 Leek, the ground is a mile out of town. The ground is sign-posted from the Town Centre
From South (M6), Exit Junction 17 Sandbach. Follow A534 to Congleton. Then A536 to Macclesfield. After passing the Rising Sun on the left, less than a mile, turn right into Moss Lane. Follow this around and it will bring you to the rear of the ground.

42

Nearest Railway Station Macclesfield - roughly 20min walk away   **Bus Route** Nos. 9 & 14 from the bus station.

MAIDENHEAD UNITED
York Road, Maidenhead, Berkshire SL6 1SF

01628 636 314

The Ground is in the town centre.
200 yards from the station and two minutes walk from the High Street.
Access from M4 Junctions 7 or 8/9.

44

Nearest Railway Station Maidenhead - 200 yards from the ground.

MAIDSTONE UNITED
The Gallagher Stadium, James Whatman Way, Maidstone, Kent ME14 1LQ

01622 753 817

M20 (junction 6) and M2 (junction 3).
Follow signs to Maidstone on the A229.
At the White Rabbit roundabout, take the third exit on to James Whatman Way.

46

Nearest Railway Station Maidstone East & Maidstone Barracks a walk away   **Bus Route** Nos. 101 or 155 from the Mall Bus Station

---

MAINE ROAD
Brantingham Road, Chorlton-cum-Hardy M21 0TT

0161 861 0344

M60 junction 7, A56 towards Manchester, A5145 (Stockport), A6010 Wilbraham Road to Chorlton. Left at traffic lights into Withington Road, first left into Brantingham Road. Ground on left.

449

Nearest Railway Station Chorlton (Manc. Metrolink) - 768m   **Bus Route** Manley Road stop - 170m away

---

MALDON & TIPTREE
Wallace Binder Ground, Park Drive, Maldon CM9 5JQ

07817 499 540

From M25 junction 28 travel north on A12 until A414 to Maldon.
Turn right at Safeways roundabout, then over next two roundabouts.
Ground is on the right.

215

Bus Route Jersey Road - stop 50m away

MALMESBURY VICTORIA
Flying Monk Ground, Gloucester Road, SN16 0AJ

01666 822 141

At M4 Junction 14, take A429 to Cirencester, at priory roundabout take Second exit. At Wychurch roundabout take second exit, after 500 yards at roundabout take first exit B4014, after ½ mile at roundabout take first exit towards town centre. At bottom of hill club is behind the Supermarket. Entrance is via lane opposite the bus stop. Enter with caution as the lane is narrow and used by the general public.

559

Bus Route Bus stops outside the Supermarket

MALTBY MAIN
Muglet Lane, Maltby, Rotherham S66 7JQ.

07795 693 683

Exit M18 at Junc 1 with A631.
Two miles into Maltby, right at traffic lights at Queens Hotel corner on to B6427 Muglet Lane.
Ground ¾mile on left.

463

Nearest Railway Station Rotherham Central - 8 miles   **Bus Route** Duke Avenue - stop 78m away

---

MALVERN TOWN
HD anywhere Community Stadium, Lamgland Avenue, Malvern WR14 2EQ

07944 110 402

Leave M5 at Junction 7 and turn towards Worcester. Turn left at next roundabout onto A4440 towards Malvern. Straight over next two roundabouts and take left slip road onto A449 at next roundabout. When approaching Malvern, turn left onto B4208 signposted Welland. Straight over three roundabouts and then take the third left into Orford Way. Take the third left into Langland Avenue. Ground is 300 yards on left.

553

Nearest Railway Station Great Malvern - 1.2km. Malvern Link - 1.5km   **Bus Route** Bus stops outside the ground

MANGOTSFIELD UNITED — Cossham Street, Mangotsfield, Bristol BS16 9EN
0117 956 0119

Exit the M32 at Junction 1 and follow the A4174 towards Downend following signs to Mangotsfield.
Turn left into Cossham Street, the ground is approx 300 yards on the right.

378

Bus Route Cossham Street - stop 50m away

MARCH TOWN UNITED — GER Sports Ground, Robin Goodfellow Lane, March, Cambs PE15 8HS
01354 653 073

Follow signs for A14 E. Continue onto A14. At the roundabout, take the 2nd exit onto Thrapston Rd/A14. Continue to follow A14.
At the next roundabout, take the 2nd exit onto A141. Continue on the A141 until roundabout signposted B1099, take the 4th exit onto
Wisbech Rd/B1099. At the next roundabout, take the 1st exit onto Norwood Road. Turn right onto Maple Grove. Turn right onto
Robingoodfellow's Lane.

402

Nearest Railway Station March - 0.7km   **Bus Route** Darthill Road stop - 290m away

---

MARGATE — Hartsdown Park, Hartsdown Road, Margate, Kent CT9 5QZ
01843 221 769

From M25 continue onto M26 merge onto M20, at junction 7, exit onto Sittingbourne Rd/A249 toward Sheerness/Canterbury/Ramsgate,
continue to follow A249, take the ramp onto M2, continue onto A299 (signs for Margate/Ramsgate), turn right at the fork, at the
roundabout, take the 2nd exit onto Canterbury Rd (Birchington)/A28 continue to follow A28, turn right onto The Square/A28 continue to
follow A28, turn right onto George V Ave/B2052, turn right onto Hartsdown Rd/B2052, ground will be on the left.

188

Nearest Railway Station Margate - 0.7 miles from the ground.

MARINE — The Marine Travel Arena, College Road, Crosby, Liverpool L23 3AS
0151 924 1743

From the East & South: Leave the M62 at junction 6 and take the M57 to Switch Island at the end. At the end of the M57 take the A5036 (signposted
Bootle & Docks). At the roundabout, at the end of the road (by Docks), turn right onto the A565 following signs for 'Crosby' and 'Marine AFC' and follow
this road for 1 mile. After passing the Tesco Express on your right, turn left at the traffic lights (by Merchant Taylors' School) into College Road. The
ground is half a mile on your left. **From the North:** Leave the M6 at junction 26 and join the M58. Travel along the M58 to Switch Island at the end.
Take the A5036 (signposted Bootle & Docks) and follow directions above.

258

Nearest Railway Station Blunellsands & Crosby - 0.5km   **Bus Route** Brompton Avenue - stop 175m away

---

MARKET DRAYTON TOWN — Greenfields Sports Ground, Greenfields Lane, Market Drayton TF9 3SL
01630 661 780

Take the A41 to Ternhill Island, turn right on A53 for Newcastle-under-Lyne. Straight on at first island (by Muller factory). At next island
turn right to town centre (by Gingerbread Inn). Approx 200yds take 2nd right into Greenfields Lane. Ground 150 yards on right, car park
opposite.

From Stoke-on-Trent take A53 for Shrewsbury, at Gingerbread Inn turn left for town centre then as above.

305

Bus Route Cmetery Road Jct - stop 400m away

MARLOW — Alfred Davies Memorial Ground, Oak tree Road, Marlow SL7 3ED
01628 483 970

From M40 (Junction 4 High Wycombe) or M4 (Junction 8/9 Maidenhead) take A404, leave at the A4155 junction signposted Marlow.
Follow A4155 towards Marlow then turn right at Esso service station into Maple Rise.
At crossroads follow straight ahead into Oak Tree Road.
Ground 100 yards on left.

370

Nearest Railway Station Marlow - 1km   **Bus Route** Oak Tree Road - stop 100m away

---

MARSKE UNITED — GER Stad., Mount Pleasant Avenue, Marske by the Sea, Redcar TS11 7BW
07772 686 794

Leave A19 and join Parkway (A174) to Marske until Quarry Lane r'about. Take exit (A1085) into Marske. Take the next right after you
pass under a railway, into Meadow Rd. Take the next left into Southfield Rd and the entrance is on your left shortly before a T-junc.

476

Nearest Railway Station Marske - 0.4km   **Bus Route** Windy Hill Lane - stop 84m away

---

MATLOCK TOWN — DCJ Group Insurance Arena, Causeway Lane, Matlock, Derbyshire DE4 3AR
01629 583 866

On A615, ground is 500 yards from Town Centre and Matlock BR. Sat Nav users can enter DE4 3AR

260

Nearest Railway Station Matlock - 0.3km   **Bus Route** Causeway Lane - stop 100m away

---

MELKSHAM TOWN — Oakfield Stadium, Eastern Way, Melksham SN12 7GU

If you are travelling on the A3102 take the first exit at the roundabout situated after new road turning on your right. Continue on this road, going across
the next 2 roundabouts, the Stadium and complex will be on your left, there is a Drive way up to the ground opposite the Right hand turning for
Hawthorn Road. If you are travelling on the on the A365 take the 3rd exit at the Bowerhill roundabout, which will take you towards the town centre. At
the first roundabout you come to take the 3rd exit onto snowbery lane. Follow this road to the next round about and take the 3rd Exit onto Eastern
Way. After about 300 yards there is right hand turning into the new complex after you pass Hawthorn Road turning.

559

Nearest Railway Station Melksham - 2.7km   **Bus Route** New Road - stop 300m away

---

MELTON TOWN — Melton Sports Village, Burton Road, Melton Mowbray LE13 1DR
01664 480 576

From Town centre follow signs for A1/Oakham. 1/2 mile up Burton Road ground is on the left.

529

MERIDIAN VP — Meridian Sports & Social Club, 110 Charlton Park Lane, London SE7 8QS
0208 856 1923

Charlton Park Lane can be found off the South Circular.

505

Nearest Railway Station Charlton - 1.3km

MERSTHAM — Moatside Stadium, Weldon Way, Merstham, Surrey RH1 3QB
01737 644 046

Leave Merstham village (A23) by School Hill,
take 5th right (Weldon Way).
Clubhouse and car park on the right.
Ten minutes walk from Merstham BR.

190

Nearest Railway Station Merstham - 0.7km

MERTHYR TOWN
Loadlok Community Stadium, Penydarren Park, Park Terrace CF47 8RF

0772 567 302

Leave the M4 at Junction 32 and join the A470 to Merthyr Tydfil. After approx 22 miles at the fourth roundabout take 3rd exit. At next roundabout go straight on and go straight on through two sets of traffic lights. At third set turn left (ground signposted Merthyr Tydfil FC from here). After 50 yards take first right, then first right just after Catholic Church into Park Terrace. The ground is at the end of the road approx. 200 yards on.

344

Nearest Railway Station Merthyr Tydfil - 0.6km   **Bus Route** St Mary's Church - stop 100m away

---

METROPOLITAN POLICE
Imber Court, Ember Lane, East Molesey, Surrey KT8 0BT

020 8398 7358

From London A3 take A309 towards Scilly Isles roundabout then right into Hampton Court Way.
Left at first roundabout into Imber Court Road. Ground is in 300 yards.

192

Nearest Railway Station Thames Ditton - 0.8km

MICKLEOVER SPORTS
Don Arnott Arena, Mickleover Sports Club, Station Rd, Mickleover Derby DE3 9JG

01332 512 826

M1 NORTH - J28. A38 to Derby. At Markeaton Island right A52 Ashbourne, 2nd left Radbourne Lane, 3rd Left Station Road 50 yds.

M1 SOUTH – J25. A52 to Derby. Follow signs for Ashbourne, pick up A52 at Markeaton Island (MacDonalds) then as above.

FROM STOKE A50 – Derby. A516 to A38 then as above.

262

Nearest Railway Station Peartree - 5.1km   **Bus Route** Buxton Drive - stop 100m away

---

MIDHURST & EASEBOURNE
Rotherfield, Dodsley Lane, Easebourne, Midhurst GU29 9BE

01730 816 557

Ground one mile out of Midhurst on London Road (A286) opposite Texaco Garage. Ample car parking.

495

Bus Route Dodsley Grove - Stop 125m away

MILDENHALL TOWN
Recreation Way, Mildenhall, Suffolk IP28 7HG

01638 713 449

Next to swimming pool and car park a quarter of a mile from town centre.

215

Bus Route Maids Head - stop 250m away

MILE OAK
Mile Oak Recreation Ground, Chalky Road, Portslade BN41 2YU

01273 423 854

From A27 (Brighton Bypass) leave at A293 exit. Right at first roundabout. Ground 1 mile on right.
Parking in the Sports Centre opposite the ground (park) entrance.

495

Nearest Railway Station Fishersgate - 2.1km   **Bus Route** New England Rise - stop 11m away

---

MILTON UNITED
Potash Lane, Milton Heights, OX13 6AG

01235 832 999

Exit A34 at Milton, 10 miles south of Oxford & 12 miles north of junction 13 of M4. Take A4130 towards Wantage approximately 200 metres turn 1st left then right into Milton Hill. Ground 400 metres on the left.

422

Nearest Railway Station Didcot Parkway - 4.7km. Appleford - 5.9km   **Bus Route** The Pack Horse stop - 69m away

---

MOLESEY
412 Walton Road, West Molesey KT8 2JG

020 8979 4823

Take A3 towards Cobham/London & exit at Esher-Sandown turn. 1st exit at roundabout to A244 through Esher to Marquis of Granby Pub. 1st exit A309 at next roundabout. 1st exit at end of road turn right, follow until mini roundabout left into Walton Road after 1 mile ground on left.

227

Nearest Railway Station Hampton - 1.5km   **Bus Route** Grange Road - stop 150m away

---

MONEYFIELDS
Moneyfields Sports Ground, Moneyfield Ave, Copnor, Portsmouth PO3 6LA

02392 665 260

Leave the A27 from both West and East at the Southsea turn off (A2030) Head down the Eastern Road and turn right into Tangiers Road at the fourth set of traffic lights. Continue along this road until you pass the school and shops on your left and take the next right into Folkestone Road. This becomes Martins Road and the ground is directly in front of you at the end of the road.

371

Nearest Railway Station Hilsea - 1.6km   **Bus Route** Chichester Road - stop 400m away

---

MORPETH TOWN
Craik Park, Morpeth Common, Morpeth, Northumberland NE61 2YX

07425 135 301

From south. Turn off the A1 onto A197, sign posted Morpeth.
Turn left at sign pointing Belsay (B6524).
Take right turn just before bridge under the A1.
Ground is signposted and up a small track is on the right.

476

Nearest Railway Station Morpeth - 1.9km   **Bus Route** Whalton Road - stop 670m away

---

MOSSLEY
Seel Park, Market Street, Mossley, Lancashire OL5 0ES

01457 832 369

Exit M60 Junction 23 following A635 Ashton-under-Lyne. Take 3rd exit off roundabout then 3rd exit off next roundabout (Asda) and then 3rd exit off next roundabout signed Mossley A670. At junction turn right on to Mossley Rd through traffic lights. After approx 2.5 miles drop down hill entering Mossley town centre. Passing supermarket on left turn right before next traffic lights. Continue up the hill and left into Market Street. Ground is approx 200 yards on the left.

291

Nearest Railway Station Mossley - 0.3km   **Bus Route** Stamford Street - 200m away

---

NANTWICH TOWN
Weaver Stadium, Waterlode, Kingsley Fields, Nantwich, CW5 5BS

01270 621 771

M6 Jun 16 A500 towards Nantwich. Over 4 roundabouts onto A51 towards Nantwich Town Centre, through traffic lights and over railway crossing. Over next r/bout then left at next r/bout past Morrisons supermarket on right. Continue over r/bout through traffic lights. Ground on right at next set of traffic lights.
SATNAV Postcode: CW5 5UP

264

Nearest Railway Station Nantwich - 1.1km   **Bus Route** Malbank School - stop 150m away

| **NEEDHAM MARKET** | Bloomfields, Quinton Road, Needham Market IP6 8DA | 01449 721 000 |

Quinton Road is off Barretts Lane which in turn is off Needham Market High Street.

194

| Nearest Railway Station Needham Market - 0.6km | Bus Route Quinton Road stop - 38m away |

| **NEEDHAM MARKET RESERVES** | Bloomfields, Quinton Road, Needham Market IP6 8DA. | 01449 721 000 |

Quinton Road is off Barretts Lane which in turn is off Needham Market High Street.

402

| Nearest Railway Station Needham Market - 0.6km | Bus Route Quinton Road stop - 38m away |

| **NELSON** | Little Wembley, Lomeshaye Way, Nelson, Lancs BB9 7BN. | |

M65 to junction 13, take first exit towards Fence A6068, take second left towards nelson B6249, after ½ mile turn right (signposted Lomeshaye Village), ground 200 yards on the right.

449

| Nearest Railway Station Nelson - 1km | Bus Route Business Village stop - 83m away |

| **NEW BRADWELL ST PETER** | Recreation Ground, Bradwell Road, Bradville, Milton Keynes MK13 7AD | 01908 313 835 |

From M1 J14 go towards Newport Pagnell, turn left at first roundabout into H3 (A422 Monks Way). Go six roundabouts then turn right into V6 (Grafton Street). At first roundabout drive all the way around and then take the first left. At first mini-roundabout, turn left. Go 1/2 mile and straight across next mini-roundabout. Ground is then immediately on the left.
From Bushey Station, take Pinner Road (A4008) and continue along Oxhey Lane (towards Harrow). At the traffic lights turn right into Little Oxhey Lane. Altham Way is on left just after crossing Railway Bridge. Clubhouse is located next to swimming pool. Please park in the Pool/Jets overflow car park to avoid either blocking in cars, or being blocked in yourself.

| **NEW COLLEGE ACADEMY** | Supermarine S&S Club, Supermarine Drive, Swindon SN3 4BZ | 01793 824 828 |

Off main A361 Swindon – Highworth Road. 2 miles north East of Swindon leave a 419 at the a 361 junction and head to Highworth. Ground is on left after roundabout exit.

422

| Nearest Railway Station Swindon - 5.8km | Bus Route Stanton Fitzwarren Turn stop - 284m away |

| **NEW MILLS** | Church Lane, New Mills SK22 4NP | 01663 747 435 |

Via Buxton: Follow the A6 By-Pass, go straight through the roundabout, under railway bridge and about 1 mile further on turn right onto Marsh Lane (Past Furness Vale primary school), this road takes you straight to the ground. Coach drivers should proceed on the A6 a couple of miles turning right opposite the Swan.
From Chesterfield, take the A619 then the A623 and after the hair pin bend at Sparrow pit, proceed down the A623 turning right onto the A6 By-Pass, Follow directions as above.

449

| Nearest Railway Station New Mills Central - 0.7km | Bus Route School (Bus Park) stop - 72m away |

| **NEW MILTON TOWN** | Fawcetts Fields, Christchurch Road, New Milton BH25 6QB | 01425 628 191 |

Leave the M27 at Junction 2 and follow the signs to Lyndhurst. Carry on this road over four roundabouts and take the next slip road.At the traffic lights turn right to Lyndhurst. Go around the one way system and follow the signs to Christchurch (A35). After 10 miles at the Cat and Fiddle Public House turn left and continue towards the Chewton Glen Hotel. First exit at roundabout A337 to New Milton. The ground is one mile on the left. Postcode for Sat. Nav. systems BH25 6QB

541

| Nearest Railway Station New Milton - 1.1km | Bus Route Old Milton Green - stop 150m away |

| **NEWCASTLE BENFIELD** | Sam Smiths Park, Benfield Road, Walkergate NE6 4NU | 07525 275 641 |

Take the A1058 from either the Tyne Tunnel or central Newcastle. Turn off this road at the junction with Benfield Road. Turn south at this junction, and the Crosslings building will be on your left. Ground is around 400 metres on left, by taking the first turning after passing railway bridge. The ground is 100 yards along this road.

476

| Nearest Railway Station Walkergate - 492m | Bus Route Benfield Comprehensive School - 96m away |

| **NEWCASTLE TOWN** | Lyme Valley Stadium, Buckmaster Avenue, Clayton, ST5 3BX | 01782 662 350 |

FROM M6: Leave the M6 at Junction 15 and immediately turn left up the bank (signposted A519 Newcastle.) Go to the second roundabout and turn right into Stafford Avenue. Take the first left into Tittensor Road (signposted Newcastle Town FC.) Go to the end and the ground is below in the parkway. (Entrance through the gateway signposted Newcastle Town FC.) FROM A50 DERBY: Follow the A50 to the end and join the A500 (signposted M6 South) just past Stoke City Football Ground. Follow the A500 to the Motorway and at the roundabout turn right up the bank (A519 Newcastle.) Go to the second roundabout and turn right into Stafford Avenue. Take the first left into Tittensor Road (signposted Newcastle Town FC.) Go to the end and the ground is below in the parkway. (Entrance through the gateway signposted Newcastle Town FC.)

305

| **NEWHAVEN** | The Trafalgar Ground, Fort Road Newhaven East Sussex BN9 9DA | 01273 513 940 |

From A259, follow the one way system around the town of Newhaven.
Turn left into South Road (pass the Police Station) which becomes Fort Road.
The ground is visible on the right just past a small parade of shops and before the approach road to Newhaven Fort.
Postcode for Sat-nav users: BN9 9DA

495

| Nearest Railway Station Newhaven Harbour - 0.4km | Bus Route Court Farm Road - stop 20m away |

| **NEWMARKET TOWN** | Ridgeons Stadium, Cricket Field Road, Off Cheveley Rd, Newmarket CB8 8BT | 01638 663 637 |

Four hundred yards from Newmarket BR.Turn right into Green Road and right at cross roads into new Cheveley Road.
Ground is at top on left.

402

| Nearest Railway Station Newmarket - 0.4km | |

| **NEWPORT (I.O.W.)** | St George's Park, St George's Way, Newport PO30 2QH | 01983 525 027 |

From the Fishbourne Car Ferry Terminal take the A3054 towards Newport. At the large roundabout in the town centre take the A3020 towards Sandown, under the footbridge then 1st exit off the next roundabout. The ground is 200 yards on the left. Postcode for Satellite Navigation systems PO30 2QH

541

| | Bus Route St Georges Park - stop 70m away |

NEWPORT PAGNELL TOWN
Willen Road, Newport Pagnell MK16 0DF

01908 611 993

529

From the A422 Newport Pagnell by pass turn into Marsh End Road, then first right into Willen Road.

Bus Route Green Park Drive - stop 160m away

NEWQUAY
Mount Wise TR7 2BU

01637 872 935

488

From link road turn right onto Mount Wise, just past traffic lights turn Right into Clevedon Road.

Nearest Railway Station Newquay - 0.8km

Bus Route Windsor Court - stop 117m away

NEWTON AYCLIFFE
Moore Lane Park, Moore Lane, Newton Aycliffe, Co. Durham DL5 5AG

01325 312 768

476

From North, leave the A1 at junction 60, and travel west along the A689 towards Bishop Auckland. At the roundabout, turn left to join A167. Travel along here for a couple of miles, and at first traffic lights and turn right onto B6443 (Central Avenue). At first roundabout (Tesco's) turn left into Shafto Way then 3rd left into Gunn Way then right into Moore Lane.

Nearest Railway Station Newton Aycliffe - 2km

Bus Route Shafto Way - stop 271m away

NORTH FERRIBY UNITED
Eon Visual Media Stadium, Grange Lane, Church Road, North Ferriby HU14 3AB

01482 634 601

92

Main Leeds to Hull road A63 or M62. North Ferriby is approx. 8 miles west of Hull.
Proceed through village past the Duke of Cumberland Hotel.
Turn right down Church Road. Ground mile down on left.

Nearest Railway Station Ferriby - 5 min walk from the ground.

NORTH GREENFORD UNITED
Berkeley Fields, Berkley Avenue, Greenford UB6 0NX

0208 422 8923

384

A40 going towards London. At the Greenford Flyover come down the slip road, keep in the left hand lane, turn left onto the Greenford Road (A4127). At the third set of traffic lights, turn right into Berkeley Av. Go to the bottom of the road. There is a large car park. We are on the right hand side.

Nearest Railway Station Greenford or Sudbury Hill (Piccadilly Line).

Bus Route No.92

NORTH LEIGH
Eynsham Hall Park, North Leigh, Witney, Oxon OX29 6SL

07583 399 577

379

Ground is situated off A4095 Witney to Woodstock road, three miles east of Witney.
Entrance 300 yards east of main park entrance.

Nearest Railway Station Combe - 3.3km

NORTH LEIGH DEVELOPMENT
Eynsham Hall Park Sports Ground OX29 6SL.

01993 880 157

422

Ground entrance is on the A4095 Witney to Woodstock Road, three miles East of Witney. The entrance which is sign posted from both directions is 250 yards metres east of the entrance to the Eynsham Hall.

Nearest Railway Station Combe (Oxon) - 3.3km

Bus Route Park Road Garden Centre - 67m away

NORTH SHIELDS
Daren Persson Staduim, West Percy Road, Chirton, North Shields NE29 6UA

476

Continue north on the A19 after Tyne Tunnel. Take right exit at roundabout onto the A1058.
At next roundabout take third exit at Billy Mill, signed to North Shields.
At roundabout with A193, turn right, then take second left into Silkey's Lane.
Ground is 100 yards on left.

Nearest Railway Station Meadow Well - 392m

Bus Route Waterville Road - stop 29m away

NORTHALLERTON TOWN
The Calvert Stadium, Ainderby Road, Northallerton DL7 8HU

01609 778 337

476

Leave A1 at Leeming Bar (A684) and follow signs to Northallerton.
Approaching the town take the left turn B1333, signed Romanby.
Ground is on left after 50 yards in Romanby.

Nearest Railway Station Northallerton - 0.3km

Bus Route Chantry Road - stop 81m away

NORTHAMPTON O.N.C.
Old Northamptonians Sports Ground, Billing Road, NN1 5RT

01604 634 045

529

Leave A45 at exit marked Bedford A428 and Town Centre.
Take exit into Rushmere Road marked Abington, Kingsthorpe and County Cricket.
At first set of lights turn left into Billing Road, sports ground 250 yards on the right.

Nearest Railway Station Northampton - 2.7km

Bus Route School for Boys - stop 80m away

NORTHAMPTON S.R.
Fernie Fields Sports Ground, Moulton, Northampton NN3 6FR

01604 670 366

529

Approach from A43 (Kettering): From large roundabout with traffic lights, take the A5076 Talavera Way exit, signposted to Market Harborough, Moulton Park and Kingsthorpe. The entrance to the ground is about a quarter of a mile on the left. Approach from A45: Take exit to A43 Ring Road / Kettering / Corby. Go straight over 1 roundabout to large roundabout with traffic lights. Then follow directions above.

Nearest Railway Station Northampton - 5.5km

Bus Route Booth Rise - stop 205m away

NORTHWICH VICTORIA
Townfield Lane, Barnton, Cheshire CW8 4LH

01606 625 449

449

Turn off the A533 (Northwich to Runcorn) at the Beech Tree Inn (Barnton Village) into Beech Lane. Turn right at the 'T' junction with Townfield Lane - the ground is 200 yards on the left signed Memorial Hall. Note parking restrictions well signed.

Nearest Railway Station Northwich and Hartford.

Bus Route Warrington bus from Northwich Bus Terminal

NORTHWOOD
Northwood Park, Chestnut Avenue, Northwood, Middlesex HA6 1HR — 01923 827 148

M25 Junction 18, take A404 through Rickmansworth to Northwood. After passing under grey railway bridge, take first right into Chestnut Avenue. Ground is in grounds of Northwood Park, entrance is 400 metres on left.
(Ground is 20 minutes from J.18).

Nearest Railway Station Northwood Hills Underground - 0.7km

371

NORWICH CBS
Football Development Centre, Bowthorpe Park, Clover Hill Road, Norwich NR5 9ED — 07745 036 715

Follow A11 towards Norwich until roundabout with 2nd exit signposted A47 (Swaffham). Merge onto Norwich Southern Bypass/A47. Take the A1074 exit toward Norwich. At the next roundabout, take the 4th exit. At the next roundabout, take the 2nd exit onto Dereham Road/A1074. At the next roundabout, take the 3rd exit onto Wendene. Turn left onto Clover Hill Road.

Bus Route Breckland Road stop - 176m away

402

NORWICH UNITED
Plantation Park, Blofield, Norwich NR13 4PL — 01603 716 963

Follow A11 towards Norwich until A47 roundabout - take the 5th exit onto the A47 ramp to Gt Yarmouth/Ipswich/Lowestoft/A4146/A140. Continue on the A47 for just over ten miles until exit toward Blofield/Heath, take this exit.
Then turn right onto Shack Lane. Turn right onto Woodbastwick Road.
Turn left onto Plantation Road.

Nearest Railway Station Brundall - 2.1km   **Bus Route** Surgery (Plantation Rd) stop - 48m away.

216

NORWICH UNITED RESERVES
Plantatio Park, Blofield, Norwich NR13 4PL — 01603 716 963

Follow A11 towards Norwich until A47 roundabout - take the 5th exit onto the A47 ramp to Gt Yarmouth/Ipswich/Lowestoft/A4146/A140. Continue on the A47 for just over ten miles until exit toward Blofield/Heath, take this exit.
Then turn right onto Shack Lane. Turn right onto Woodbastwick Road.
Turn left onto Plantation Road.

Nearest Railway Station Brundall - 2.1km   **Bus Route** Surgery (Plantation Rd) stop - 48m away.

402

NOSTELL MINERS WELFARE
The Welfare Ground, Crofton Co. Centre, Middle Lane, New Crofton WF4 1LB — 01924 866 010

From M1 J39/M62 J31: Go towards Wakefield, take A638 Doncaster Road. After 2m, pass transport café/petrol station on right, go under bridge, turn right into Lodge Lane opposite Indian Restaurant. Go through Crofton Village, turn left at 'Slipper' PH, right on to Middle Lane, signposted 'Crofton Community Centre' about 400m; From A1: Take A638 towards Wakefield, turn left in Lodge Lane opposite Indian Restaurant, then as above.

Nearest Railway Station Streethouse - 2.9km   **Bus Route** The Slipper Pub - stop 372m away

463

NUNEATON GRIFF
The Pingles Stadium, Avenue Road, Nuneaton, Warwickshire CV11 4LX — 07944 457 250

From M5, M42 & M6: Take M6 south to junction 3 and leave by turning left onto A444 (Nuneaton). Stay on A444 through Bermuda Park, McDonalds and George Eliot Hospital roundabouts until reaching large roundabout with footbridge over road. Carry straight on (2nd exit) and downhill, taking right hand lane. At bottom of hill you reach Coton Arches Island, take 2nd exit (A4252 Avenue Road) and travel ½ mile to Cedar Tree Pub traffic lights, turn left into Stadium car park service road. It is unsuitable for coaches to turn around in. **From A5:** Travel south following signs for Nuneaton. After passing through Atherstone travel for 2½ miles until junction with A444. At this junction (Royal Red Gate Pub) turn right at staggered junction and continue on A444 through Caldecote and Weddington into Nuneaton. Join one-way system at Graziers Arms by turning left and immediately take right hand lane for 300 yards and follow A444 for Coventry. At Third Island turn left on to dual carriageway (Coton Road) for ½ mile and turn left at Coton Arches island on to A4252 (Avenue Road) then as above. **Hospitality:** Attleborough Liberal Club, Bull Street, Nuneaton. Leave ground, turn left at Cedar Pub traffic lights, take 3rd turn on right, club car park is 2nd on the right.

436

NUNEATON TOWN
Liberty Way, Nuneaton CV11 6RR — 024 7638 5738

From the South, West and North West, exit the M6 at Junction 3 and follow the A444 into Nuneaton. At the Coton Arches r'about turn right into Avenue Road which is the A4254 signposted for Hinckley. Continue along the A4254 following the road into Garrett Street, then Eastboro Way, then turn left into Townsend Drive. Follow the road round before turning left into Liberty Way for the ground.

Nearest Railway Station Nuneaton - approx. 35min walk from the ground.

94

OADBY TOWN
Freeway Park, Wigston Road, Oadby LE2 5QG — 01162 715 728

A14 Desborough, A6 towards Market Harborough. Follow A6 towards Leicester. Enter Oadby, go past Sainsbury's (traffic lights), next set of lights turn left. Signpost Oadby Town Centre, follow road over mini roundabout (St Peters Church in foreground) bear left towards Wigston. Follow road over roundabout, through the next lights, ground on the left.

Nearest Railway Station South Wigston - 3.6km   **Bus Route** Brabazon Road - stop 35m away

529

OAKHAM UNITED
Main Road, Barleythorpe, Oakham, Rutland, LE15 7EE — 01572 757 484

Oakham United Football Club is located on the main road running through the village of Barleythorpe (B640). The B640 links the town centre to the A606 Oakham bypass.

Nearest Railway Station Oakham - 1km   **Bus Route** Pasture Lane - stop 30m away

529

OAKWOOD
Tinsley Lane, Three Bridges, Crawley RH10 8AJ — 01293 515 742

From the South on M23, take junction 10 exit left onto A2011, next roundabout take fourth exit right, next roundabout second exit, take first right into Tinsley Lane. Ground entrance 100 metres on left.

Nearest Railway Station Three Bridges - 1.3km   **Bus Route** Maxwell Way - Stop 98m away

495

ODD DOWN (BATH)
Lew Hill Memorial Ground, Combe Hay Lane, Odd Down BA2 8PA — 01225 832 491

Situated behind Odd Down Park & Ride on main A367 Bath to Exeter road.

Nearest Railway Station Oldfield Park - 2.9km   **Bus Route** St Gregory's School - stop 50m away

559

OLDLAND ABBOTONIANS
Aitchison Playing Field, Castle Road, Oldland Common, Bristol BS30 9SZ — 01179 328 263

Exit M4 at Jct19 to M32. Exit M32 at Jct 1 after 400 yds and take 1st exit from roundabout for A4174. Straight over traffic lights to next roundabout continuing on A4174. Go over five roundabouts for approximately 4.8 miles. At next roundabout take 1st exit to Deanery Road (A420) and continue for 0.9 miles to Griffin Public house and turn right into Bath Road (A4175). Continue for 1.3 miles to Oldland Common High Street and look for Dolphin Public House. Turning for Castle Street is next left between Chinese Chip Shop and Post Office. Ground is at the end of Castle Road.

Nearest Railway Station Oldland - 400m   **Bus Route** The Clamp - stop 130m away

559

OLLERTON TOWN
The Lane, Walesby Lane, New Ollerton, Newark NG22 9UT
From north and south on the A614, take the A6075 from the Ollerton roundabout towards Ollerton Village. At the next roundabout, leave at the first exit and immediately take a left (30m from roundabout) onto Walesby Lane. After approx 600m, just after the school, the ground is on the left.

463

Nearest Railway Station Worksop   **Bus Route** Rosewood Centre - stop 214m away

OLNEY TOWN
Recreation Ground, East Street, Olney, Bucks MK46 4DW   01234 712 227
From the North enter via A509 Warrington Road then turn left into Midland Road and immediately right into East Street. Ground on left hand side after Fire Station. From Milton Keynes: Follow the A509 into Olney, over river bridge, 200 metres past the Swan Bistro and public house and take the first turning right onto the market square immediately before the traffic lights), follow road to the right onto a one way system into East Street. Follow East Street for 500 metres, the ootball Club is on the right hand side, car park entrance being the immediately following right turn.

529

Bus Route High Street - stop 220m away

OSSETT ALBION
Queens Terrace, Dimple Wells, Ossett, Yorkshire WF5 8JU   01924 273 746
From M1 Junction 40: Follow Wakefield signs for 200 yards. Turn right at traffic lights (Holiday Inn on the corner). At the end of Queens Drive turn right and then 2nd left onto Southdale Road. At the end of Southdale Road turn right then immediately left onto Dimple Wells Road, the ground is facing. NOTE: There is a weight limit on Southdale Road. Coaches will need to continue on Station Road to the end, turn left, then at the end left again. Take 1st right onto Priory Road following for 200 yards turning left twice.

292

Nearest Railway Station Dewsbury - 4km   **Bus Route** The Green Healey Road - 100m away

OSSETT TOWN
The 4G Voice & Data Stadium,Ingfield, Prospect Road, Ossett, Wakefield WF5 9HA   01924 272 960
From M1 Junction 40: Take A638 signposted Ossett Town Centre. Take first left off A638 onto Wakefield Road, sixth left turn into Dale Street (B6120) to traffic lights. Turn left at lights. The Ground is in front of you opposite the bus station. The entrance to the Ground is just before the Esso petrol station.

292

Nearest Railway Station Dewsbury - 3.9km   **Bus Route** Prospect Road - stop 50m away

OXFORD CITY
Court Place Farm, Marsh Lane, Marston, Oxford OX3 0NQ   01865 744 493
Follow the A40 to the Headington roundabout going straightover towards Banbury & Northampton A40. Within a mile a flyover is visible as the exit from the Ring Road. Turn left under the flyover and left again toward Marsh Lane. Turn right at the T Junction and the ground is on your left just before the Pedestrian Crossing.

136

Nearest Railway Station Oxford - three miles from the ground.   **Bus Route** 14A from the Station to the ground.

OXFORD CITY NOMADS
Court Place Farm Stadium, Marsh Lane, Marston OX3 0NQ   01865 744 493
From South: From Newbury travel along the A34 towards Oxford turn onto Ring Road heading towards London (East). Follow Ring Road over 5 roundabouts to the Green Road roundabout signposted London, M40 East. Go straight over towards Banbury. A fly-over is visible, turn left onto the slip road and follow road to Court Place Farm Stadium on left. **From North:** At the North Oxford roundabout, travel towards London M40 on the Eastern by-pass, turn off at the flyover, the ground is visible to the left as you go over bridge. All players and officials must park in the Stadium car park not the new Community Arena car park – unless the match is against the Nomads Development Team who will generally play on the artificial 3G pitch.

422

Nearest Railway Station Oxford - 3.4km   **Bus Route** Elms Drive stop - 52m away

OXHEY JETS
Boundary Stadium, Altham Way, South Oxhey, Watford WD19 6FW   020 8421 6277
From Bushey + Oxhey Station, take Pinner Road (A4008) and continue along Oxhey Lane towards Harrow. At the traffic lights turn right into Little Oxhey Lane. Altham Way is on left just after crossing a narrow railway bridge. Please park in the large swimming pool car park marked "Jets overflow parking" to avoid either blocking in cars, or being blocked in.

516

Nearest Railway Station Carpenders Park - 1km   **Bus Route** Lytham Avenue - stop 75m away

PADIHAM
Arbories Memorial Sports Ground, Well Street, Padiham BB12 8LE   01282 773 742
M65 to Junction 8, then follow A6068 signposted Clitheroe and Padiham. At traffic lights at bottom of hill turn right into Dean Range/Blackburn Road towards Padiham. At next junction turn into Holland Street opposite church, then into Well St at the side of Hare & Hounds Pub to ground.

449

Nearest Railway Station Hapton - 2.2km   **Bus Route** Memorial Park stop - 110m away

PAGET RANGERS
Trevor Brown Memorial Ground, Church Road, Boldmere, Birmingham, B73 5RY   07528 177 046
A38(M) from M6 junction 6 and A5127 from Birmingham to Yenton Traffic Lights.
Left on A452 Chester Road, then 6th.right into Church Road.
From M6 junction 5 A452 Brownhills to Yenton Traffic Lights. Straight on then 6th right into Church Road.

436

Nearest Railway Station Chester Road - 0.9km   **Bus Route** Church Road stop - 106m away

PAGHAM
Nyetimber Lane, Pagham, West Sussex PO21 3JY   01243 266 112
A27 to junction of A259 on the Chichester Bypass.
Exit to Pagham (Vinnetrow Road).
At the Bear Inn (right hand side) turn left into Nyetimber Lane. The ground is 200 metres on right.

495

Nearest Railway Station Bognor Regis - 4.3km   **Bus Route** The Bear Inn - stop 119m away

PARKGATE
Roundwood Sports Complex, Green Lane, Rawmarsh, S62 6LA   01709 826 600
From Rotherham A633 to Rawmarsh. From Doncaster A630 to Conisbrough, then A6023 through Swinton to Rawmarsh.
Ground at Green Lane - right from Rotherham, left from Conisbrough at the Crown Inn.
Ground 800yds on right.

463

Nearest Railway Station Swinton - 3.4km   **Bus Route** Roundwood Grove - stop 57m away

PAULTON ROVERS
Athletic Ground, Winterfield Road, Paulton, Bristol BS39 7RF   01761 412 907
From A39 at Farrington Gurney, follow A362 marked Radstock for two miles.
Turn left at roundabout, take B3355 to Paulton and ground is on the right.

379

Bus Route Alexandra Park - stop 150m away

PEACEHAVEN & TELSCOMBE The Sports Park, Piddinghoe Ave, Peacehaven, BN10 8RJ `01273 582 471`

From Brighton on A259, over roundabout & Piddinghoe Ave. is next left after 2nd set of lights-ground at end. From Newhaven, Piddinghoe Ave. is 1st right after 1st set of lights. 3 miles from Newhaven(BR). Peacehaven is served by Brighton to Newhaven & Eastbourne buses.

Nearest Railway Station Newhaven - 3.2km | **Bus Route** Slindon Avenue - stop 140m away

495

PEGASUS JUNIORS Old School Lane, Hereford HR1 1EX `07816 121 248`

pegasus juniors - Old School Lane hr1 1ex - 07980 456 995
Approach City on A4103 (from Worcester) at roundabout on outskirts take 2nd exit (A4103) over railway bridge, traffic light controlled. Take 2nd turning on left into Old School Lane, ground entrance 150 metre's on left.

Nearest Railway Station Hereford - 1.3km | **Bus Route** Bus stops outside the ground

553

PENISTON CHURCH Church View Road, Penistone, Sheffield S36 6AT `463`

From North: Leave M1 at J37, take 3rd exit A628 Manchester. After ½ mile take 2nd exit A628 Manchester. After approx 4 mile take 2nd exit A628 Manchester then at traffic lights turn left to Penistone Town Centre. On entering town centre after pelican crossing take 1st left Victoria Street then 2nd left. Ground is on your right. From South: Leave M1 at J35A at roundabout take 2nd exit A616 Manchester. At next roundabout take 2nd exit A616 Manchester then take 1st exit signed Penistone, Huddersfield A629. Follow this road through Wortley, Thurgoland and then take B6462 then travel under 3 railway bridges. Turn sharp left after 3rd bridge and follow road to the right onto Church View Road. Ground is approx 600 yards on left.

Nearest Railway Station Penistone - 0.2km | **Bus Route** Church View Road - stop 149m away

---

PENN & TYLERS GREEN French School Meadows, Elm Road, Penn, Bucks HP10 8LF `01494 815 346`

From West - 'M40 to High Wycombe leave at J4. Follow A404 to Amersham, via Wycombe. Stay on A404 up the hill past railway station approx. 3 miles at Hazlemere Crossroads turn right onto the B474 signposted to Penn and Beaconsfield. Continue for approx. one mile go past three new houses on left, turn into Elm Road, the ground is on the left.
From East -Leave M40 at Junction 2 and take the road signed Beaconsfield. From Beaconsfield follow the road through Penn towards Hazlemere, pass the pond on green and entrance to ground is on the right had side of road before the hill.

Nearest Railway Station High Wycombe - 3.9km | **Bus Route** The Red Lion stop - 85m away

422

PENRITH The Stadium, Frenchfield Park, Frenchfield, Penrith CA11 8UA `01768 865 990`

Turn off M6 at junction 40 then onto dual carriageway to Appleby and Scotch Corner. Take the A686 (signposted Alston), for approximately half a mile. Then take a right turn (opposite Carleton Road), and follow the track running parallel with the A66. Turn left into the sports complex and follow the road to the far end.

Nearest Railway Station Penrith North Lakes - 2.3km | **Bus Route** Oak Road - stop 727m away

476

PERSHORE TOWN King George V Playing Field, King George's Way, Pershore WR10 1QU

M5 Junction 7, take B4080 (formerly A44) to Pershore.
On entering the town turn left at 2nd set of traffic lights (signposted Leisure Centre).
The ground is 300 yards on the left hand side.

Nearest Railway Station Pershore - 2.1km | **Bus Route** Abbey Tea Rooms stop - 167m away

436

PETERBOROUGH NORTHERN STAR Branch Bros Stadium, Chestnut Avenue, Peterborough, Cambs PE1 4PE `01733 552 416`

From A1 turn on to A1139 Fletton Parkway. Follow signs for A47 Wisbech. Exit at Junction 7 (near Perkins Engines Site). At top of slip road turn left into Eastfield Road. At Traffic lights turn right into Newark Avenue and then first right in to Eastern Avenue. Take 2nd left in to Chestnut Avenue and the club is on the right behind steel Palisade Fencing.

Nearest Railway Station Peterborough - 2.6km | **Bus Route** Hawthorn Road - stop 35m away

529

PETERBOROUGH SPORTS Lincoln Road, Peterborough PE1 3HA `01733 308 993`

From the North - Come in on the A15 Southbound and cross the large A47 Roundabout just past Morrison's on your right. ***Take the left hand slip road at a set of traffic lights after approximately 400 yards and turn right at the T-Junction after 50 yards. The entrance to the ground is approx 400 yards down on your left in front of a church and before a zebra crossing where there is a sign to the health centre. If journeying from the East take the turning from the A47 signposted City Centre and follow instructions from *** above. If journeying from the South or West come in via the A47 and take the exit signposted City Centre. You go straight on at this roundabout (back up alongside A47) and then take the 3rd (right) at the large roundabout with the A15 and follow instructions from *** above.

306

PETERSFIELD TOWN ' Love Lane, Petersfield, Hampshire GU31 4BW `01730 233 416`

Off circulatory one-way system in the town centre. Approx 10 minutes walk from Petersfield train station. Postcode for Satellite Navigation systems GU31 4BW

Nearest Railway Station Petersfield - 0.8km | **Bus Route** Madeline Road - stop 140m away

541

PEWSEY VALE Recreation Ground, Kings Corner Ball Road, Pewsey SN9 5BS `01672 5629 090`

From Pewsey High Street/B3087 turn right into Ball Road, keep right to continue on Easterton Lane, turn right to stay on Easterton Lane, turn left and the ground will be on the left.
Park at the top end of the co-operative car park and walk along the path to the pitch.

Nearest Railway Station Pewsey - 0.9km | **Bus Route** Co-op stop - 316m away

422

PHOENIX SPORTS Phoenix Sports Ground, Mayplace Road East, Barnehurst, Kent DA7 6JT `01322 526 159`

Take A206/Bob Dunn Way towards Erith (Jct 1a off the A282). Continue on the A206 through five roundabouts, at the sixth take the second exit onto A2000/Perry Street. Follow the A2000 for half a mile and turn right onto Mayplace Road. At the next roundabout take the second exit and stay on Mayplace Road East. Ground will be on the left.

Nearest Railway Station Barnehurst - 1.1km | **Bus Route** Woodside Road - stop 50m away

227

PHOENIX SPORTS RESERVES Phoenix Sports Ground, Mayplace Road East, Barnehurst, Kent DA7 6JT `07895 182 927`

Mayplace Road can be found off the A2000.

Nearest Railway Station Barnehurst - 1.1km. Crayford - 1.2km

505

PICKERING TOWN — Recreation Club, off Mill Lane, Malton Road, Pickering YO18 7DB — 01751 473 317

A169 from Malton. On entering Pickering, take 1st left past Police Station and BP garage into Mill Lane, ground 200 yds on right.

463

Nearest Railway Station Pickering - 650m   **Bus Route** Millfield Close - stop 62m away

PINCHBECK UNITED — Sir Harley Stewart Field, Winfrey Avenue, Spalding, PE11 1DA — 07508 809 969

Follow signs to Spalding Town Centre. From the north drive south down Pinchbeck Road towards Spalding. At traffic lights turn right into Kings Road. At the next set of lights turn left into Winfrey Avenue. The Ground is on the left. From the south follow signs to The Railway station and Bus Stations. The Ground is opposite the Bus Station on Winfrey Avenue. There is parking outside the ground in a pay and display car park.

529

Nearest Railway Station Spalding - 0.2km   **Bus Route** Broad Street - stop 100m away

PLYMOUTH ARGYLE RESERVES — Coach Road TQ12 1EJ

Ground is located at the Devon County FA Head-Quarters in Newton Abbot.

488

Nearest Railway Station Newton Abbot - 0.9km   **Bus Route** Decoy Road - stop 373m away

PLYMOUTH PARKWAY AFC — Bolitho Park, St Peters Road, Manadon, Plymouth PL5 3JH

From Cornwall/Exeter exit at the Manadon/Tavistock junction off the Plymouth Parkway (A38), off roundabout into St Peters Road. Entrance is one mile on the right.

488

Nearest Railway Station St Budeaux Road - 2.8km   **Bus Route** St Peters Road - stop 10m away

PONTEFRACT COLLIERIES — Skinner Lane, Pontefract, WF8 4QE — 01977 600 818

M62 jct32 (Xscape) towards Pontefract.
Left at lights after roundabout for park entrance and retail park.
Traffic through town should follow racecourse signs through lights to roundabout and back to lights.

463

Nearest Railway Station pontefract Tanshelf - ¼ mile

POOLE TOWN — Tatnam Ground, Oakdale School, School Lane, Poole BH15 3JR — 01794 517 991

Follow the A35 into Poole and at the roundabout by the fire station take the second exit into Holes Bay Road (A350). At next roundabout take 1st exit onto Broadstone Way (A349) and turn right at Wessex Gate East traffic lights into Willis Way. Turn right into Fleets Way and continue until you see Poole Motor Cycles. Turn left into Palmer Road opposite Poole Motor Cycles and take first right into School Lane which will take you to the Club/School car park. The ground is on the right hand side.

138

Nearest Railway Station Poole - 3/4 mile from the ground.

PORTISHEAD TOWN — Bristol Road, Portishead, Bristol BS20 6QG — 01275 817 600

Leave M5 at Junction 19 and take road to Portishead. At outskirts of town take 1st exit from small roundabout signposted Clevedon and Police H.Q. Ground is 150 yds along road on left by bus stop.

559

Nearest Railway Station Avonmouth - 5.1km   **Bus Route** Glebe Road - stop 50m away

PORTLAND UNITED — New Grove Corner, Grove Road, Portland DT5 1DP — 01305 861 489

On entering the Island of Portland, stay on the main road (signposted for Easton) to the top of the Island (unmistakable - sharp steep hairpin bend with the Portland Heights Hotel in front of you). Continue towards Easton into Yeats Road and Easton Lane. 100 yards after passing the Drill Hall (Castle like building) turn left into Grove Road. New Grove Corner is 200-300 yards on the left.

541

Bus Route Clifton Hotel - stop 280m away

POTTERS BAR TOWN — Pakex Stadium, Parkfield, Watkins Rise, Potters Bar EN6 1QB — 01707 654 833

M25 junction 24 enter Potters Bar along Southgate Road (A111) turn right into High Street at first lights (A1000) then left into The Walk after half a mile. Ground is 200 yards on the right - opposite Potters Bar Cricket Club.

216

Nearest Railway Station Potters Bar - 0.9km

POTTON UNITED — The Hollow, Bigglewade Road, Potton, Beds SG19 2LU — 01767 261 100

From Sandy, take B1042 into Potton.
Head towards Potton Town Centre and take right turn towards Biggleswade (B1040).
The ground is on left hand side at foot of hill

529

Nearest Railway Station Sandy - 4.4km   **Bus Route** The Ridgewy - stop 11m away

PRESCOT CABLES — Valerie Park, Eaton Street, Prescot L34 6HD — 0151 430 0507

From North: M6 to Jct 26, onto M58 to Junction 3. Follow A570 to junction with A580 (East Lancs Road). (Approach junction in right hand lane of the two lanes going straight on). Cross A580 and take first road on right (Bleak Hill Road). Follow this road through to Prescot (2 miles). At traffic lights turn right, straight on at large r'about (do not follow route onto Prescot by-pass) and right at next lights. 100 yards turn right at Hope and Anchor pub into Hope Street. Club will be in sight at bottom of road. From South: M6 to Junction 21a (M62 Jct 10). Follow M62 towards Liverpool, to junction 7. Follow A57 to Rainhill and Prescot. Through traffic lights at Fusilier pub, 100 yards turn right at Hope and Anchor pub (as above). From East: Follow M62 as described in 'From South' or A580 East Lancs Road to Junction with A570 (Rainford by-pass), turn left and take first right. Follow route as 'From North'.

293

PRESTWICH HEYS — Adie Moran Park, Sandgate Road, Whitefield M45 6WG — 0161 7773 8888 (MD)

M60 to junction 17 towards Whitefield, turn right into Clyde Avenue continue over traffic lights onto Thatch Leach Lane, turn right at the Frigate Public House, over motorway bridge, ground on the left.

449

Nearest Railway Station Clifton - 3.5km   **Bus Route** Sandgate Road stop - 73m away

PUNJAB UNITED   Elite Venue, Hawkins Avenue, Dunkirk Close, Gravesend, Kent DA12 5ND   **01474 323 817**

Go onto Valley Drive off the A2. Turn left onto Scott Road. Continue on Scott Road T-juction, turn left and then first right until T-juction, turn right ontol Wilberforce Way. Follow Wilberforce Way until Palmer Avenue, take left onto Hawkins Avenue, then first left onto Christian Fields Avenue and then left onto Dunkirk Close at the T-junction.

505

Nearest Railway Station Gravesend - 2.7km

QUORN   Farley Way Stadium, Farley Way, Quorn, Leicestershire LE12 8RB   **01509 620 232**

Exit Junction 24 M1 Southbound on A6 through Kegworth, continue on A6 signposted Leicester/Loughborough bypass. Through Loughborough and at first roundabout take 2nd exit signposted Quorn. Turn left at traffic lights 200 yards from island and the ground is situated just inside on the left.

436

Nearest Railway Station Quorn & Woodhouse - 1.5km   **Bus Route** Alexander Road stop - 189m away

---

RACING CLUB WARWICK   Townsend Meadow, Hampton Road, Warwick, Warwickshire CV34 6JP   **01926 495 786**

M40 Junction 15, signposted Warwick. At roundabout with traffic lights take A429 to Warwick. Follow this road for ½ mile and you will come to houses on your left. Take the 2nd turn on the left into Shakespeare Avenue. Follow to T-junction. Turn right into Hampton Road. Entrance to ground is 50 yards on left.

436

Nearest Railway Station Warwick Parkway - 1.4km   **Bus Route** Shakespeare Avenue stop - 131m away

---

RADCLIFFE BOROUGH   Stainton Park, Pilkington Road, Radcliffe, Lancashire M26 3PE   **0161 724 8346**

M62 junction 17 – follow signs for 'Whitefield' and 'Bury'.
Take A665 to Radcliffe via by-pass to Bolton Road. Signposted to turn right into Unsworth Street opposite Turf Hotel.
The Stadium is on the left approximately half a mile turning Colshaw Close East.

293

Nearest Railway Station Radcliffe - 1.3km   **Bus Route** Lowe Street - 100m away

---

RADCLIFFE OLYMPIC   The Recreation Ground, Wharfe Lane, Radcliffe on Trent, Nottingham NG12 2AN   **07500 804 057**

A1M- A1-A614-A6097 to the island on the A46. Go south towards Leicester, at next island turn tight on the A52 to Nottingham. At Radcliffe on Trent turn right at traffic lights, through the village to the church, turn right down Wharf Lane, ground is 250 yards on the left hand side, turn left down road before play area. **M1 from the south** to Junction 24 or from the north at Junction 26. Follow the Nottingham signs for A52. Radcliffe on Trent is approx. 5 miles outside of Nottingham, then turn left at the lights next to the RSPCA shelter and follow road to the church. Turn left down Wharf Lane, then as above.

396

Nearest Railway Station Radcliffe (Notts) - 0.4km

RADFORD   Selhurst Street, Off Radford Road, Nottingham NG7 5EH   **0115 942 3250**

Leave the M1 at junction 26 (signposted Nottingham, Ilkeston), at roundabout take the 1st exit onto the A610 (signposted Nottingham) At r'about take the 3rd exit onto the A610 (signposted Nottingham) Entering Nottingham. At next r'about take the 2nd exit onto Nuthall Road - A610 (signposted Nottingham, Arnold), at traffic signals continue forward onto Nuthall Rd - A610 (signposted City Centre) At traffic signals turn left onto Western Boulevard - A6514 (signposted Ring Road, Mansfield) Turn immediately right onto Wilkinson St; go to top of street, past Tram Depot, follow tram line towards Nottingham At top of hill, (traffic lights turn right onto Radford Road – 4th turning on the right onto Selhurst St - Ground immediately on right.

396

Nearest Railway Station Nottingham - 2.8km

RADSTOCK TOWN   Southfields Recreation Ground, Southfields, Radstock BA3 2NZ   **01761 435 004**

The town of Radstock is situated 15 miles south east of Bristol and 8 miles southwest of Bath on the A367. At the double roundabout in Radstock town centre take the A362 towards Frome. The ground is on the right hand bend, third turning. Turn right into Southfield, ground is 200 yards ahead.

559

Bus Route Withies Park - stop 80m away

RAINWORTH M.W.   Welfare Ground, Kirklington Road, Rainworth, Mansfield NG21 0JY   **01623 792 495**

From M1 (Junction 29) – take A617. At Pleasley turn right onto the new Mansfield Bypass road which is still the A617 and follow to Rainworth. At roundabout with B6020 Rainworth is off to the right, but it is better to go straight over onto the new Rainworth Bypass and then right at the next roundabout (the ground can be seen on the way along the Bypass) At mini roundabout, turn right onto Kirklington Road and go down the hill for ¼ mile – ground and car park on the right Alternatively you can reach the new A617 Bypass from the A38 via Junction 28 on the M1. From A614 at roundabout, take the A617 to Rainworth for 1 mile. Left at 1st r'about into village. At mini r'about right into Kirklington road – ¼ mile down hill as above.

463

Nearest Railway Station Mansfield - 4¼ miles   **Bus Route** Garden Avenue - stop 24m away

---

RAMSBOTTOM UNITED   The Harry Williams Stadium, Acrebottom (off Bridge Street) BL0 0BS.   **01706 822 799**

From South,M66(north) to junction1,take the A56 towards Ramsbottom, after 1 mile turn left at traffic lights down Bury New Road follow the road towards the centre then turn left just before the railway crossing, ground runs parallel with the railway line.

From the North leave the A56 (Edenfield by pass) at the start of the M66, follow the signs for Ramsgate into the centre turn left down Bridge street then after 100 yards turn immediately right after the railway level crossing ground parallel with railway line.

294

RAMSGATE   Southwood Stadium, Prices Avenue, Ramsgate, Kent CT11 0AN   **01843 591 662**

Approach Ramsgate via A299 (Canterbury/London) or A256 (Dover/Folkestone) to Lord of Manor roundabout.
Follow the signpost to Ramsgate along Canterbury Road East, counting via 2nd exit of the 1st roundabout.
At the 2nd roundabout, continue towards Ramsgate on London Road (2nd exit).
Take the 3rd turning on the left, into St Mildred's Avenue, then 1st left into Queen Bertha Road.
After the right hand bend, take left into Southwood Road, and 1st left into Prices Ave. The stadium is at the end of Prices Avenue.

228

Nearest Railway Station Ramsgate - 1km

RAUNDS TOWN   Kiln Park, London Road, Raunds, Northants NN9 6EQ   **01933 623 351**

From North, East or West, take A14 J13 and follow A45 signs to Raunds.
Turn left at roundabout by BP garage.
From South follow A45 towards Thrapston.
Turn right at roundabout by BP garage. Ground on left.

529

Bus Route Bus stops outside the ground.

RAYNERS LANE   Tithe Farm Social Club, Rayners Lane, South Harrow HA2 0XH   **0208 868 8724**

From A40 Polish War Memorial turn left into A4180 (West End Road), approximately 500 metres turn right into Station Approach, at traffic lights turn right into Victoria Road. At next roundabout continue straight on to traffic lights at junction with Alexandra Avenue (Matrix Bar &taurant on left). Continue straight on over traffic lights and take second turning on left into Rayners Lane. Ground is approximately half a mile on the left.

516

Nearest Railway Station Rayners Lane underground - 680m   **Bus Route** Clitheroe Avenue - stop 64m away

RAYNES PARK VALE
Prince George's Playing Field, Raynes Park SW20 9NB
0208 540 8843

Exit Raynes Park station into Grand Drive cross Bushey Road at the traffic lights continue up Grand Drive for 400 yards entrance on the left follow drive to clubhouse. From the A3. Onto Bushey Road towards South Wimbledon. Grand Drive on the right, ground in Grand Drive on the left hand side.

384

Nearest Railway Station Raynes Park

Bus Route London Buses 152 & 163

REDBRIDGE
Oakside Stadium, Station Road, Barkingside, Essex IG6 1NB
0208 550 8989

Take junction 26 off the M25, exit toward A121/Loughton/Waltham Abbey. Take A121, A1168, A113 and A123 to Station Road in Ilford.
Having turned off onto the A123 take the 2nd exit the next roundabout onto Craven Gardens.
Then turn left onto Carlton Drive, turn left to stay on Carlton Drive.
Slight right onto Station Road.

415

Nearest Railway Station Barkingside Underground - 186m

Bus Route Barkingside - 395m away

REDDITCH UNITED
Valley Stadium, Bromsgrove Road, Redditch B97 4RN
01527 67450

M42 J2, at island first exit onto the A441 for 2 miles, next island first exit onto Birmingham Road A441 for 1.2 miles then at island third exit onto Middlehouse Lane B4184 for 0.3 miles. At traffic lights (next to fire station) turn left onto Birmingham Road for 0.2 miles then turn right into Clive Road for 0.3 miles. At island take first exit onto Hewell Road for 0.2 miles then at 'T' junction right onto Windsor Street for 0.1 miles. At traffic lights (next to bus station) continue straight ahead onto Bromsgrove Road for 0.3 miles and at the brow of the hill, turn right into the ground's entrance.

346

Nearest Railway Station Redditch - 0.4km

Bus Route Bus stops outside the ground

REDHILL
Kiln Brow, Three Arch Road, Redhill, Surrey RH1 5AE
01737 762 129

On left hand side of A23 two and a half miles south of Redhill.

384

Nearest Railway Station Redhill (mainline) Earlswood

Bus Route 100, 400, 420, 430, 435, 460

RETFORD UNITED
Cannon Park, Leverton Road, Retford, Notts DN22 6QF
01777 710 300

Leave the A1 at Ranby and follow the A620 towards Retford. Go past Ranby prison and go straight on at the next 2 mini roundabouts. At the 3rd roundabout take the 3rd exit signposted Gainsborough. Passing Morrisons on the left, go through the traffic lights and move into the right hand lane. Turn right at the traffic lights. Turn left at the traffic lights by the Broken Wheel Public House into Leverton Road. Go past the Masons Arms Public House and go over 2 hump backed bridges. The ground is signposted and is on the right.

463

Nearest Railway Station Retford - 1.6km

Bus Route Claters Close - stop 185m away

RINGMER
Caburn Ground, Anchor Field, Ringmer BN8 5QN
01273 812 738

From Lewes road turn right into Springett Avenue, opposite Ringmer village.

495

Nearest Railway Station Glynde - 3.7km

Bus Route Primary School - stop 205m away

RINGWOOD TOWN
The Canotec Stadium, Long Lane, Ringwood, Hampshire BH24 3BX
01425 473 448

Travel to Ringwood via the A31 (M27). From Ringwood town centre travel 1 mile on the B3347 towards Christchurch. At the Texaco petrol station turn into Moortown Lane and after 200 yards turn right into Long Lane. The ground is situated 250 yards on your left. Postcode for Satellite Navigation systems BH24 3BX

541

Bus Route Crow Crossroads - stop 100m away

RISBOROUGH RANGERS
" Windsors" Horsenden Lane, Princes Risborough. Bucks HP27 9NE
07849 843632 (MD only)

On entering Prices Risborough from Aylesbury, turn left at first roundabout.
At the second roundabout turn right. Go pass Esso petrol station on left hand side.
After approximately 400 yards take the right fork. Take second turn on left (Picts Lane).
At junction turn right over the railway bridge and then immediately right again.
Ground is approximately 200 yards on the right hand side.

516

Nearest Railway Station Princes Rosborough - 0.2km

Bus Route Railway Station - stop 0.2km away

ROCESTER
Hillsfield, Mill Street, Rocester, Uttoxeter ST14 5JX
01889 591 301

From Uttoxeter take the B5030, signposted Ashbourne/Alton Towers After 3 miles turn right opposite the JCB factory over humpback bridge into Rocester village. Turn right at mini island into Mill Street, ground is 500 yards on the left immediately past the JCB Academy.

436

Bus Route Ashbourne Road Garage stop - 152m away

ROCHESTER UNITED
Rochester United Sports Ground, Rede Court Road, Strood, Kent ME2 3TU
07775 735 543

Rochester's ground can be accessed via the A2 in Strood.

505

Nearest Railway Station Strood - 2.1km

ROMAN GLASS ST GEORGE
Oaklands Park, Gloucester Road, Alomndsbury BS32 4AG
01454 612 220

Exit M5 at Junction 16. Arriving from the south take the left exit lane.
Turn left at lights and ground is 100m on left hand side.
Arriving from east take right hand lane on slip road. Take 3rd exit nd ground is 100m on left hand side.

559

Nearest Railway Station Patchway - 2.6km

Bus Route Alondsbury Depot - stop 100m away

ROMFORD
Thurrock FC, South Way, Ship Lane, Aveley RM19 1YN
01708 865 492

Approaching the ground from the North - along the M25 in a clockwise direction. Leave the motorway at junction 30. At the roundabout take the second exit and stay in the left hand lane. This leads to a large roundabout controlled by traffic lights. The fifth exit is Ship Lane and the ground is approximately 50 yards on the right hand side. Approaching the ground from the South - anti-clockwise on the M25. When going through the Dartford Tunnel take the left hand bore. On coming out of the tunnel take the first exit - junction 31. This leads to a large roundabout controlled by traffic lights. Take the third exit which is Ship Lane. The ground is situated approximately 50 yards on the right hand side. **Nearest Railway Station:** Chafford Hundred - 1.6km. **Bus Route:** Back Lane - stop 200m away

217

ROMSEY TOWN — The By-Pass Ground, South Front, Romsey SO51 8GJ — 01794 516 691

The ground is situated on the south of the town on the A27/A3090 roundabout (Romsey by pass), adjacent to the Romsey Rapids and Broadlands Estate.
Postcode for Satellite Navigation systems SO51 8GJ

Nearest Railway Station Romsey - 0.5km   **Bus Route** Linden Road - stop 100m away

541

ROMULUS — Sutton Coldfield FC, Central Ground, Coles Lane B72 1NL — 0121 354 2997

From M42 Junc 9, take A4097 (Minworth sign). At island, follow signs to Walmley Village. At traffic lights turn right (B4148). After shops turn left at traffic lights into Wylde Green Road. Over railway bridge turn right into East View Road, which becomes Coles Lane.

Nearest Railway Station Sutton Coldfield - 1.1km   **Bus Route** Douglas Road - stop 80m away

306

ROSSINGTON MAIN — Welfare Ground, Oxford Street, Rossington, Doncaster, DN11 0TE — 01302 865 524 (MD)

Enter Rossington and go over the railway crossings.
Passing the Welfare Club, Oxford Street is the next road on the right.
The ground is at the bottom of Oxford Street.

Nearest Railway Station Doncaster - 6.4km   **Bus Route** Grantham Street - stop 149m away

463

ROTHWELL CORINTHIANS — Sergeants Lawn, Desborough Road, Rothwell NN14 6JR — 01536 711 706

A14 to Rothwell. Take B669 towards Desborough. Ground on right at rear of cricket field opposite last houses on the left.
arking on verge or in adjacent field if gate open. Access to ground via footpath.

Nearest Railway Station Kettering - 5.6km

529

ROYAL WOOTTON BASSETT — Gerrard Buxton Sports Ground Malmesbury Rd Royal Wootton Bassett SN4 8DS — 01793 853 880

Exit A417 AT Burford Road Junction and follow signs for Cirencester Town FC.

Bus Route The Farm stop - 69m

422

ROYSTON TOWN — Garden Walk, Royston, Herts, SG8 7HP — 01763 241 204

From A505 (Town Bypass) take A10 towards town centre (signposted London).
Go straight on at next roundabout.
Garden Walk is on the left after the 3rd set of pedestrian lights (opposite Catholic Church).
Entrance to ground is approx 75 metres on left.

Nearest Railway Station Royston - 0.7km   **Bus Route** St Mary's School - stop 150m away

348

RUGBY TOWN — Butlin Road, Rugby, Warwicks CV21 3SD — 01788 844 806

From M6 J.1 North and South, take A426 signed Rugby at third island turn left into Boughton Road.
Continue along Boughton Road after passing under viaduct turn right at traffic lights, B5414 up the hill take second left at mini island into Butlin Road.

Nearest Railway Station Rugby - 1km   **Bus Route** Jolly Brewers stop - 127m away

436

RUNCORN LINNETS — Millbank Linnets Stadium, Murdishaw Ave, Runcorn, Cheshire WA7 6HP — 07050 801733 (Clubline)

A533 Queensway take ramp to Daresbury Expressway follow A533 to roundabout take 1st exit onto Murdishaw Avenue to ground.

Nearest Railway Station Runcorn East - 1.2km   **Bus Route** Halton Arms stop - 62m away

449

RUNCORN TOWN — Pavilions Sports Complex, Sandy Lane, Weston Point, Runcorn WA7 4EX — 01928 590 508

M56 J12. Head towards Liverpool. Come off at fourth exit (Runcorn Docks), turn left at the top of slip road, left at T-Junction, then left into Pavilions. ;M62 J7. Head towards Runcorn. When crossing Runcorn Bridge, stay in the right hand lane. Follow road around and come off at second exit (Runcorn Docks). Turn right at the top of slip road, left at T-Junction, then left into Pavilions.

Nearest Railway Station Runcorn - 1.6km   **Bus Route** South Parade stop - 69m away

449

RUSHALL OLYMPIC — Dales Lane off Daw End Lane, Rushall, Nr Walsall WS4 1LJ — 01922 641 021

M6 J10 follow signs for Walsall stay on this dual carriage way for about four miles until you come to the Walsall Arboretum and turn left following signs for Lichfield A461. Go under the bridge and you will come to McDonald's on your right, turn right into Daw End Lane. Go over the canal bridge and turn right opposite the Royal Oak Public House and the ground is on the right.
Alternative: From the A38 to it's junction with the A5 (Muckley Corner Hotel) take the A461 to Walsall after about five miles you will reach some traffic lights in Rushall by Mcdonald's, turn left into Daw End Lane go over the canal bridge and turn right opposite The Royal Oak Public House the ground is on the right. **Nearest Railway Station:** Walsall - 3km. **Bus Route:** Royal Oak - stop 50m away

266

RUSHDEN & HIGHAM UNITED — Hayden Road, Rushden, Northants NN10 0HX — 01933 410 036

From A6/A45 (Chowns Mill Roundabout) take Higham / Rushden bypass at 3rd roundabout, take the 3rd exit onto Newton Road, then immediately right after Newton Road School into Cromwell road this then leads into Hayden Road. Ground is approx. 100 yards on left hand side. From Bedford (A6) take Rushden / Higham Bypass and at the 1st roundabout take the 1st exit onto Newton Road, then turn immediately right after Newton Road School into Cromwell road this leads into Hayden Road. Ground is approx. 100 yards on the left hand side.

Bus Route Ashwell Road - stop 60m away

529

RUSTHALL — Jockey Farm, Nellington Road, Rusthall, Tunbridge Wells, Kent TN4 8SH — 07897 427 522

Follow Rusthall High Street through Rusthall and eventually you'll dive onto Nellington Road.

Nearest Railway Station High Rocks - 1.5km

505

RYHOPE CW
Ryhope Recreation Park, Ryhope Street, Ryhope, Sunderland SR2 0AB

07901 545 760

From the A1 exit onto A168 toward A19/Thirsk/Teesside. Continue onto A19. Take the A1018 ramp to Sunderland. At the roundabout, take the 2nd exit onto Stockton Rd/A1018. Continue to follow Stockton Road. Go through 2 roundabouts. Slight left onto Ryhope Street S/B1286. Ground will be on the left.

476

Nearest Railway Station Sunderland - 3.8km   **Bus Route** Ryhope Street-post office - stop 79m away

---

RYTON & CRAWCROOK ALBION
Kingsley Park, Stannerford Road, Crawcrook NE40 3SN

0191 413 4448

Leave the A1 at the south side of the River Tyne (A694). At the roundabout take the A695 (sign posted Blaydon). At Blaydon take the B6317 through Ryton to reach Crawcrook. Turn right at the traffic lights (sign posted Ryton/Clara Vale). Kingsley Park is situated approximately 500 meters on the right.

476

Nearest Railway Station Wylam - 1.5km   **Bus Route** Stannerford Road - stop 121m away

---

SAFFRON WALDEN TOWN
The Meadow, 1 Catons Lane, Saffron Walden, Essex CB10 2DU

01799 520 980

Into Castle Street off Saffron-Walden High Street.
Then left at T-junction and first left by Victory Pub.

402

Nearest Railway Station Audley End - 3.5km

SALFORD CITY
Moor Lane, Kersal, Salford, Manchester M7 3OZ

0161 792 6287

M62 to Junction 17 (Prestwich, Whitefield). Take A56 Bury New Road towards Manchester. Continue through four sets of traffic lights. Turn right into Moor Lane. Ground 500 yards on left. Take first left after ground (Oaklands Road), first left again into Nevile Road and follow along to main entrance.

96

Nearest Railway Station Manchester Victoria - 3 miles from the ground.   **Bus Route** First Bus No.98 from Manchester Victoria.

SALISBURY
Raymond McEnhill Stadium, Partridge Way, Old Sarum SP4 6PU

07803 247 874

From North/East/West: Leave A303 at Countess roundabout at Amesbury and take A345 towards Salisbury until Park and Ride roundabout from where the ground is signposted. From South: Proceed to A345 and then follow directions to Amesbury until Park and Ride roundabout from where the ground is signposted.

380

Nearest Railway Station Salisbury - 4km   **Bus Route** Bus stops outside the ground

---

SALTASH UNITED
Kimberley Stadium, Callington Road, Saltash PL12 6DX

01752 845 746

At the top of Town Centre fork right at mini-roundabout.
Ground is situated 400m ahead on the left-hand side next to Leisure Centre and Police Station.

488

Nearest Railway Station Saltash - 0.9km   **Bus Route** Callington Road St Annes - stop 40m away

---

SALTDEAN UNITED
Hill Park, Coombe Vale Saltdean Brighton East Sussex BN2 8HJ

01273 309 898

From Brighton Pier proceed east along coast road to Rottingdean.
Straight through Rottingdean lights then after ¼ mile turn left at Saltdean Lido.
Proceed inland for approx. ½ mile then bear left down bridleway to Clubhouse.

495

Nearest Railway Station Southease - 5km   **Bus Route** Saltdean Vale Shops - stop 175m away

---

SANDBACH UNITED
Sandbach Community Football Centre, Hind Heath Road, Sandbach CW11 3LZ

01270 768 389

M6 to junction 17, take the A534 towards Sandbach, travel to traffic lights and go straight across, travel to round-a-bout, take the 2nd exit, travel to nest round-a-bout and take the 1st exit onto Crewe Road. Dtay on this roard for 1 mile and turn right at the traffic lights into Hind Heath Road ground approx ¾ mile on the right.

449

Nearest Railway Station Sandbach - 1.4km   **Bus Route** Salt Line Way stop - 260m away

---

SANDHURST TOWN
Bottom Meadow, Memorial Ground, Yorktown Rd, GU47 9BJ

01252 878 460

Coming from Camberley: Once on the A321 (Yorktown Road), drive past the pitches and memorial park on your left, continue past the large car parks. Turn left in to a small car park opposite Park Road. There is a café (Pistachios in the Park), some skateboard ramps and a large barrier/gate. Drive through the gate and park on the grass area on the right-hand side. The Stadium itself is about 50 yards further down the track (it is visible in the corner). **Coming from Sandhurst Village:** Once on the A321 (Yorktown Road), driving away from the village shops, continue until you see a petrol station on your right. Continue for a further 50 yards where you need to turn right in to a small car park opposite Park Road. There is a café (Pistachios in the Park), some skateboard ramps and a large barrier/gate. Drive through the gate and park on the grass area on the right-hand side. The Stadium itself is about 50 yards further down the track (it is visible in the corner).

422

Nearest Railway Station Sandhurst - 0.9km   **Bus Route** Wellington Arms stop - 194m away

---

SAWBRIDGEWORTH TOWN
Crofters End, West Road, Sawbridgeworth CM21 0DE

01279 722 039

From junction 7 of M11 take the A414 towards Harlow and go through three roundabouts. At the 4th roundabout take the 3rd exit onto Cambridge Rd (A1184). Continue on A1184 and at the roundabout take the 1st exit onto West Road. Turn right onto Crofters and ground will be facing.

415

Nearest Railway Station Sawbridgeworth, approx. ½ mile   **Bus Route** 510 & 511, approx. ½ mile

---

SCARBOROUGH ATHLETIC
Flamingo Land Stadium, Scarborough Leisure Village, Ashburn Rd YO11 2JW

01723 379 113

From the A64 turn right onto Valley Road, at the next roundabout take teh second exit, continue along Valley Road until right turn into Ashburn Road.

294

Nearest Railway Station Scarborough - 1km

SEAFORD TOWN
The Crouch, Bramber Road, Seaford BN25 1AG

01323 892 221

A259 to Seaford. At mini roundabout by station, turn left (coming from Newhaven) or RIGHT (from Eastbourne).
At end of Church Street, across junction, then left at end. After 500m turn left up Ashurst Road Bramber Road is at the top.

495

Nearest Railway Station Seaford - 0.6km   **Bus Route** Seaford Head Lower School - stop 168m away

SEAHAM RED STAR
Seaham Town Park, Stockton Road, Seaham. Co.Durham SR7 0HY

Leave A19 on B1404 slip road. Follow signs to Seaham/Ryhope. Turn right at traffic lights on to the B1285. Then left at Red Star social club approximately 200 yards after the traffic lights. There is a car park at the next roundabout behind their social club The ground is a short walk at the top of the park.

476

Nearest Railway Station Seaham - 1.5km   **Bus Route** Mill Inn (Stockton Rd) - stop 201m away

---

SELBY TOWN
The Fairfax Plant Hire Stadium, Richard Street, Scott Road, Selby YO8 4BN   **01757 210 900**

From Leeds, left at main traffic lights in Selby down Scott Rd, then 1st left into Richard St. From Doncaster, go straight across main traffic lights into Scott Rd then 1st left. From York, right at main traffic lights into Scott Rd and 1st left. NB: From Feb 14th, roadworks on the A19 mean there are different directions from York - on the A19 travel to the Greencore roundabout and take the first exit onto the Selby bypass. Travel over the new swing bridge and, at the first roundabout, take the third exit and continue to the traffic lights at Selby Abbey. Turn left and travel through town turning right at the end of town into Scott Road. Then, take first left.

463

Nearest Railway Station Selby - 0.8km   **Bus Route** Leisure Centre - stop 73m away

---

SELSEY
The Bunn Leisure Stadium, High Street, Selsey, Chichester, PO20 0QH   **01243 603 420**

Entering Selsey go straight over roundabout and straight over to mini-roundabout to traffic lights.
Turn sharp right at lights, through supermarket car park to ground.

495

Bus Route Medical Centre - stop 92m away

SELSTON
Parish Hall, Mansfield Road, Selston, Nottinghamshire NG16 6EE   **01773 812 540**

Follow M1 to Nottinghamshire. Take exit 27 from M1. Continue on Mansfield Rd/A608.
Take B600 to Mansfield Rd/B6018 in Selston
At the roundabout, take the 1st exit onto Mansfield Rd/A608. Turn right onto Sandhill Road.
Turn right onto Alfreton Rd/B600. Continue to follow B600.
Turn right onto Mansfield Rd/B6018. Ground will be on the left.

396

Nearest Railway Station Kirkby in Ashfield - 4.5km

SEVENOAKS TOWN
Greatness Park, Seal Road, Sevenoaks TN14 5BL   **07876 444 274**

Sevenoaks Town's ground can be accessed from the A25 (Seal Road).

505

Nearest Railway Station Bat & Ball - 0.4km

SHAFTESBURY
Cockrams, Coppice Street, Shaftesbury SP7 8PF   **07917 652 438**

Travelling South on the A350 into Shaftesbury, at the roundabout, take the 2nd exit onto Little Content Lane/A30/A350. Continue to follow A30/A350. Go through one roundabout. Turn right onto Coppice Street. Destination will be on the right. Travelling North on the A350 into Shaftesbury, at the roundabout, take the 2nd exit onto Christy's Lane/A30/A350. Turn left onto Coppice Street. Destination will be on the right.

541

Bus Route Linden Park - stop 100m away

SHAW LANE AFC
Athersley Rec. FC, Sheerien Park, Ollerton Road, Athersley North, Barnsley, S71 3DP   **01226 203 509**

From North: M1 J38. Go down slip road, round roundabout and back under motorway. Take first left onto Haigh Lane, to top of the hill and, at T-junction, turn left onto Shaw Lane and go to bottom of hill. At T-junction of A61, turn right to Barnsley, go through first set of traffic lights and take first left onto Newstead Road. Follow to second roundabout and turn right onto Ollerton Road. Follow to second turn on left - do not take it but go past and entrance is between houses 123-125 Ollerton Road. Follow drive into ground.

268

Nearest Railway Station Barnsley - 3.4km   **Bus Route** Trowell Way - stop 80m away

---

SHAWBURY UNITED
Butler Sports Ground, Bowensfield, Wem, Shrewsbury SY4 5AP   **01939 233 287**

shawbury united - Butler Sports Ground, Bowensfield, Wem, Shrewsbury. SY4 5AP Tel: 01939-233287
From the A5 Shrewsbury by-pass, take the A49 heading towards Whitchurch. Go through the villages of Hadnall & Preston Brockhurst and then take a left turn at crossroads under the B5063 sign posted Wem. At next junction turn right under Railway Bridge on to the B5476 into Mill Street. At next Junction by Church turn right into High Street, take the next left after pedestrian crossing into New Street and then next left by the Public House into Pyms Road. Take the 2nd left into Bowens Field and ground is 100 yards straight ahead.

436

Nearest Railway Station Wem - 0.6km   **Bus Route** Adams School stop - 161m away

---

SHEERWATER
Sheerwater Recreation Ground, Blackmore Crescent, Woking GU21 5NS

From M25(J11) take the A320 towards Woking, At Six Cross roundabout take the exit to Monument Road.
At the lights turn left into Eve Road for Sheerwater Estate.
First left is Blackmore Crescent, Entrance is Quarter of a mile on left.

384

Nearest Railway Station Woking or West Byfleet   **Bus Route** Arriva 436 and Abellio 446

SHEFFIELD
Home of Football Stadium, Sheffield Road, Dronfield S18 2GD   **0114 362 7016**

From the South – M1 to Junc 29, A617 into Chesterfield. At Roundabout follow A61 Sheffield. This is a dual carriageway passing over 2 roundabouts. At the 3rd roundabout take the 3rd exit signposted Dronfield. The Coach and Horses Public House is at the bottom of the hill on the right and the BT Local Business Stadium directly behind it. Entrance to the ground is by turning right at the traffic lights and immediate right into the Club Car Park. **From the East** - M18 to M1 north to Junc 33 (Sheffield). Turn towards Sheffield and take the 3rd exit from dual carriageway signposted 'Ring Road / Chesterfield'. Go straight on at traffic island so that you are travelling alongside dual carriageway for a short period. At the junction turn left onto A61 Chesterfield. This is a dual carriageway passing through numerous traffic lights and two traffic islands. Follow Chesterfield sign at all times. After passing Graves Tennis centre on your left, turn left at next traffic island (still signposted Chesterfield). At next traffic island take 2nd exit signposted Dronfield The Coach and Horses Public House is at the bottom of the hill on the right and the BT Local Business Stadium directly behind it. Entrance to the ground is by turning right at the traffic lights and immediate right into the Club Car Park. **Nearest Railway Station:** Dronfield - 1.1km

307

SHEPPEY UNITED
Havill Stadium, Holm Park, Queenborough Road ME12 3DB   **01795 669 547**

Exit the M2 at Junction 5 (Sheerness, Maidstone) and at the roundabout take the first exit onto the A249 Northbound. Stay on the A249 over the Sheppey Crossing until you reach a roundabout. Take the first exit at the roundabout. At the next roundabout take the 2nd exit until you come to a set of traffic lights. At the traffic lights turn right. At the next traffic lights keep straight on. This is the Queenborough Road. Follow the Queenborough Road until you see a church on the right (this is St Peter's Church). Turn left onto St Peter's Close and the ground is a short distance down the road to the left (the ground is signposted as "Sheppey United FC" on the Queenborough Road). The club have a car park at the ground and use of an overflow car park opposite the ground (Holm Sports Football Ground).

505

SHEPSHED DYNAMO
The Dovecote, Butt Hole Lane, Shepshed, Leicestershire LE12 9BN   **01509 650 992**

From M1: Leave at Junction 23 and take A512 (Ashby). At first traffic lights turn right into Leicester Road and continue to garage on right. Turn right at mini roundabout into Forest Street and continue to Black Swan pub on left. Turn right into Butt Hole Lane, ground 100 yards. **From M6:** Leave at Junction 15 (Stoke-on-Trent) and take A50 to join M1 at Junction 24 South. At Junction 23 leave M1 and continue as above.

436

Bus Route Market Place stop - 229m away

SHEPTON MALLET
Playing Fields, Old Wells Road, West Shepton, Shepton Mallet BA4 5XN
01749 344 609

From the town take B3136 (Glastonbury Road) for approximately 1/2 mile. Turn right at junction of Old Wells Road near King William Public House. Approximately 300 yards up the Old Wells Road turn left into the playing fields.

559

Bus Route West Lodge - stop 180m away

SHERBORNE TOWN
Raleigh Grove, Terrace Playing Field, Sherborne DT9 5NS
01935 816 110

From Yeovil take A30 - marked Sherborne. On entering town turn right at traffic lights, over next traffic lights and at the next junction turn right. Go over bridge, take second left marked 'Terrace Pling Fields'. Turn into car park, football club car park is situated in the far right-hand corner.

559

Nearest Railway Station Sherborne - 0.5km

Bus Route Sherborne Station - stop 0.5km away

SHIFNAL TOWN
Phoenix Park, Coppice Green Lane, Shifnal, Shrops TF11 8PD
07986 563 156

Via the M6 get on to the M54 and follow signs for Wales/Telford/Wolverhampton/Shrewsbury/A5. At junction 3, take the A41 exit to Whitchurch/Weston.
Continue on Newport Road/A41. Turn left and continue onto Stanton Road. Turn right onto Curriers Lane. Turn right onto High Street/B4379. Continue to follow B4379. Turn right onto Drayton Road. Turn right onto Cornwallis Drive.

553

Nearest Railway Station Shifnal - 0.8km

Bus Route Green (Barn Rd) - stop 100m away

SHILDON
Dean Street, Shildon, Co. Durham DL4 1HA
01388 773 877

Leave A1M at junction 58. Follow A68 signed Bishop Auckland, turn right at roundabout onto A6072. At Shildon turn right at second roundabout (onto B6282) , then left into Byerley Rd (still the B6282). Right at Timothy Hackworth pub into Main St., then at the top of the bank, left into Dean Street.

476

Nearest Railway Station Shildon - 1.2km

Bus Route St. Johns Church - stop 149m away

SHIREBROOK TOWN
Langwith Road, Shirebrook, Mansfield, NG20 8TF
01623 742 535

Depart M1 at Junction 29, at roundabout take A617 towards Mansfield (for 3.5 miles), at next roundabout take 2nd Exit B6407 Common Lane towards Shirebrook (or 1.8 miles), go straight on at next roundabout (for 300 yards), at staggered crossroads turn right onto Main Street (for 1.1 miles), at T Junction turn right (for 100 yards), take the first road on your left (Langwith Road). The ground is 400 yards on the right.

463

Nearest Railway Station Shirebrook - 0.2km

Bus Route Langwith Road End - stop 36m away

SHOLING
The Universal Stadium, Portsmouth Road, Sholing, SO19 9PW
02380 403 829

side and continue towards Hamble. At the next mini roundabout take the 2nd exit and after 150 yards turn right into Portsmouth Road (Woolston). Continue for approximately 1/2 mile and the ground is situated on the right hand side opposite a lay-by entrance.

541

Nearest Railway Station Netley - 1.9km

Bus Route Bus stop outside the ground.

SHOREHAM
Middle Road, Shoreham-by-Sea, West Sussex, BN43 6GA
01273 454 261

Take the A27 to Shoreham. At the Holmbush Roundabout take the exit towards Southlands Hospital. Immediately before the hospital, turn left down Hammy Lane, then right at the mini roundabout into Middle Road. The entrance to the ground is at the far end of the recreation ground immediately at the end.

228

Nearest Railway Station Shoreham-by-Sea - 1.1km

Bus Route Hammy Lane - stop 150m away

SHORTWOOD UNITED
Meadowbank, Shortwood, Nailsworth GL6 0SJ
01453 833 936

When entering Nailsworth from Stroud turn right at mini roundabout, when coming from Cirencester go straight over roundabout, and when from Bath turn left at mini roundabout.
Proceed up Spring Hill 30 yards turn left at Raffles Wine Warehouse, straight through town turn left at Brittannia Pub carry on for 1 mile until you come to Shortwood village you will see sign post on fork in the road keep to the left follow on for quarter of a mile ground opposite church.

380

Bus Route Homefield Turn - stop 250m away

SHORTWOOD UNITED RESERVES
Meadowbank, Shortwood, Nailsworth GL6 0SJ
01453 833 936

12 miles west of Cirencester head for Cirencester, proceed up Spring Hill for 30 yards turn left through the Car Park, then left at Brittania Inn. Proceed up hill for approx ¾ mile to Shortwood. Ground is on the left hand side opposite the Church.

422

Bus Route Homefield Turn stop - 209m away

SHRIVENHAM
The Recreation Ground, Barrington Park, Shrivenham SN6 8BJ
07775 933 076

Shrivenham village is signposted off A420 Oxford to Swindon road, six miles east of Swindon, four miles west of Faringdon. Drive through village turn into Highworth Road, ground is on right, parking is before the ground on the left Martens Rd, No parking allowed by the ground.

422

Bus Route Green (Townsend Rd) stop - 268m away

SILSDEN
Keighley Road, Keighley Road, Silsden BD20 0EH
01535 958 850

A629 Skipton to Keighley road, take A6034, ground in on the left after the golf driving range.

449

Nearest Railway Station Steeton & Silsden - 1.1km

Bus Route Keighley Road stop - 55m away

SITTINGBOURNE
Woodstock Park, Broadoak Road, Sittingbourne ME9 8AG
01795 410 777

From the M2 exit at Junction 5, take A249 towards Sheerness, leave A249 at 1st junction, raised section to Key Street roundabout, take A2 to Sittingbourne. One way system to town centre, first right into Park Road, Follow signs to Kent Science Park, Park Road becomes Gore Court Road, Gore Court Road becomes Woodstock Road, Woodstock Road becomes Ruins Barn Road.
When houses disappear approximately half a mile, take left as signposted Kent Science Park/Sittingbourne Research Centre into Broadoak Road, down hill passed Research Centre on right, carry on up hill, take left into car park Woodstock Park.

229

Nearest Railway Station Sittingbourne - 3.1km

Bus Route Kent Science Park - stop 500m away

SKELMERSDALE UNITED — Prescot Cables FC, Valerie Park, Eaton Street, Prescot L34 6HD — 01695 722 123

From North: M6 to Jct 26, onto M58 to Jct 3. Follow A570 to junction with A580 (East Lancs Road). (Approach junction in right hand lane of the two lanes going straight on). Cross A580 and take first road on right (Bleak Hill Road). Follow this road through to Prescot (2 miles). At traffic lights turn right, straight on at large r'about (do not follow route onto Prescot by-pass) and right at next lights. 100 yards turn right at Hope and Anchor pub into Hope Street. Club will be in sight at bottom of road. **From South:** M6 to Jct 21a (M62 junction 10). Follow M62 towards Liverpool, to junction 7. Follow A57 to Rainhill and Prescot. Through traffic lights at Fusilier pub, 100 yards turn right at Hope and Anchor pub (as above). **From East:** Follow M62 as described in 'From South' or A580 East Lancs Road to Junction with A570 (Rainford by-pass), turn left and take first right. Follow route as 'From North'.

295

SLEAFORD TOWN — Eslaforde Park, Boston Road, Sleaford, Lincs NG34 9GH — 01529 415 951

15 Sleaford By-pass, roundabout to A17 Holdingham Roundabout third exit towards Boston on A17.
Take second exit of A17 towards Sleaford ground is 1 mile on right hand side before you enter Sleaford.

Nearest Railway Station Sleaford - 1.4km   **Bus Route** Eslaforde Park - stop 90m away

529

SLIMBRIDGE — Thornhill Park, Cambridge, Glos GL2 7AF — 07702 070 229

From the A38 take the A4135 to Dursley. The ground is 100 yards on the left.

Nearest Railway Station Cam & Dursley - 0.8km   **Bus Route** Wisloe Road - stop 300m away

381

SLOUGH TOWN — Arbour Park, Stoke Road, SLough SL2 5AY — 07792 126 124

From the M4: Exit at Junction 5 (signposted Colnbrook/Datchet/Langley) and head west on London Road (A4). Pass the Sainsbury's Superstore on your right hand side and drive straight over the roundabout, continuing on London Road. Pass the Tesco Slough Extra store and then the turning to Slough Rail station on your right and at the next junction, turn right onto Stoke Road (B416). Continue along Stoke Road for 0.7 miles, going straight ahead at the crossroads with Shaggy Calf Lane and Elliman Avenue (following the signpost to Slough Cemetery & Crematorium, Wexham Park Hospital and Stoke Poges). The entrance to Arbour Park is a few hundred yards further on the right hand side.

Nearest Railway Station Slough   **Bus Route** First Group 1, 13, 12, 14, 353.

350

SMETHWICK — Hillcrest Avenue, Brierley Hill, West Mids. DY5 3QH — 01384 826 420

The Ground is situated in Brierley Hill, just off A461. It can be approached from Stourbridge off the Ring Road to Amblecote, turning right at third set of traffic lights or from Dudley passing through Brierley Hill Town centre.

Nearest Railway Station Lye - 2.1km Stourbridge 2.5km Cradley Heath - 2.8km   **Bus Route** Lancaster Road - stop 60m away

553

SNODLAND TOWN — Potyns Field, Paddlesworth Road, Snodland ME6 5DP — 07702 808 883

Coming south on the A228 turn right onto Holborough Road. Follow until a right turn onto Birling Road, take second right onto Constitution Hill. Follow until Paddlesworth Road.
Coming North on the A228 towards Snodland turn left onto Malling Road, take first left onto Hollow Lane. Turn left at the T-junction onto Snodland Road then first right onto St Benedict Road. Continue on this road until T-juction, turn left onto Constitution Hill/Paddlesworth Road.

Nearest Railway Station Snodland - 1.3km

505

SOHAM TOWN RANGERS — Julius Martin Lane, Soham, Ely, Cambridgeshire CB7 5EQ — 01353 720 732

Take the turning off the A14 for Soham/Ely. Join the A142 following signs for Ely/Soham. On approaching Soham at the Q8 Petrol Station, continue down the Soham by-pass for approx. 1.5 miles. Turn left after the Bypass Motel, continue bearing left across the Common into Bushel Lane, at end of road, turn right into Hall Street. Julius Martin Lane is 2nd left.

Bus Route Julius Martin Lane - stop 200m away

217

SOLIHULL MOORS — The Automated Technology Group Stadium, Damson Park, Damson Parkway, Solihull B91 2PP 0121 705 6770

Leave the M42 at Junction 6 and take the A45 towards Birmingham, after approximately 2 miles, at the traffic lights, take the left hand filter lane onto Damson Parkway. Follow the road for approximately 1 mile where the Autotech Stadium is situated on the right hand side, continue over the traffic lights (for the Land Rover factory entrance) to the traffic island and come back on yourself to find the entrance to the Football Club on the left just after the traffic lights. Use B92 9EJ as the postcode for SatNav purposes.

Nearest Railway Station Solihull & Birmingham within 3 miles away.   **Bus Route** Nos. X12 or 966 from Town Centre.

48

SOUTH NORMANTON ATHLETIC — J Robinson Structures Arena, Lees Lane South Normanton, Derby DE55 2AD — 07834 206 253

M1 Junction 28 take B6019 to Alfreton, turn right onto Market Street at the Shell petrol station, then take the 5th turning on the left onto Lees Lane opposite Ladbrooks. The ground is at the end of the lane.

Nearest Railway Station Alfreton - 1.8km   **Bus Route** Market Street stop - 105m away

436

SOUTH PARK — King George's Field, Whitehall Lane, South Park RH2 8LG — 01737 245 963

From junction 8 of the M25, take A217 and follow signs to Gatwick. Follow through the one way system via Reigate town centre and continue on until traffic lights and crossroads by The Angel public house, turn right at these lights, into Prices Lane, and continue on road. After a sharp right bend into Sandcross Lane past Reigate Garden Centre. Take next left after school into Whitehall Lane.

Nearest Railway Station Reigate - 2km   **Bus Route** Sandcross Lane - stop 200m away

229

SOUTH PARK RESERVES — King George's Field, Whitehall Lane, South Park, Reigate, Surrey RH2 8LG — 01737 245 963

From junction 8 of the M25, take A217 and follow signs to Gatwick. Follow through the one way system via Reigate town centre and continue on until traffic lights and crossroads by The Angel public house, turn right at these lights, into Prices Lane, and continue on road. After a sharp right bend into Sandcross Lane past Reigate Garden Centre. Take next left after school into Whitehall Lane.

Nearest Railway Station Reigate   **Bus Route** Metrobus 430, 435

384

SOUTH SHIELDS — Mariners Park, Shaftesbury Avenue, Jarrow, Tyne & Wear NE32 3UP — 0191 4547800

The ground is within walking distance of Bede Metro Station. Alight at the station and go down the stairs before turning right if you have departed a train heading for South Shields, or turning left if departing a train going towards Newcastle. At the next junction you come to, turn right, and there is then a short walk along Shaftesbury Avenue to reach the ground.

Nearest Railway Station Bede - 0.2km   **Bus Route** Taunton Avenue - stop 200m away

295

SOUTHALL
Hanwell Town FC, Perivale Lane, Perivale, Greenford, Middlesex UB6 8TL **0208 998 1701**

From West, junction 16 M25 and follow A40 (M) towards London.
Go over the Greenford flyover and get into the nearside lane signposted Ealing & Perivale.
Exit and turn right across the A40. The ground is immediately on the left.
Turn left into Perivale Lane and the entrance is 200 yards on the left.
Nearest railway station is Perivale (London Underground – Central Line).
Nearest Railway Station Perivale Underground - 580m   **Bus Route** Perivale Lane - stop 178m away

516

SOUTHEND MANOR
The Arena, Southchurch Park, Northumberland Crescent, Southend SS1 2XB **07788 580 360**

Take junction 29 off the M25, merge onto Southend Arterial Road/A127. At the rnext oundabout, take the 3rd exit onto Prince Ave/A127. At the next roundabout, take the 2nd exit onto Priory Cres/A1159. Continue to follow A1159. Go through 1 roundabout then at the next roundabout, take the 2nd exit onto Eastern Ave/A1159. At the next roundabout, take the 3rd exit onto Hamstel Road. Go through 1 roundabout then continue onto Lifstan Way, in less than half a mile turn right onto Woodgrange Drive. Then turn third left at the 3rd cross street onto Marlborough Road, Northumberland Crescent will be at the end of this road.
Nearest Railway Station Southend East (C2C), ½ mile to ground   **Bus Route** 7 & 8 (Arriva) to Woodgrange Drive, ¼ mile

415

SOUTHPORT
Merseyrail Community Stadium, Haig Avenue, Southport, Merseyside PR8 6JZ **01704 533 422**

Leave M6 at junction 26. Join M58 to junction 3. Join A570 signposted Southport, follow A570 through Ormskirk Town Centre following signs for Southport. At the big roundabout (McDonalds is on the left) take the fourth exit. Proceed along this road until you reach the 2nd set of pedstrian lights and take the next left into Haig Avenue.

Nearest Railway Station Meols Cop - 1mile away. Southport - 1.5miles away.   **Bus Route** 44 Arriva from the Southport Station.

98

SOUTHWICK
Old Barn Way, Southwick BN42 4NT **01273 701 010**

A27 from Brighton take first left after Southwick sign to Leisure Centre. Ground adjacent.
Five minutes walk from Fishergate or Southwick stations.

Nearest Railway Station Fishersgate - 0.4km   **Bus Route** Old Barn Way - stop 151m away

495

SPALDING UNITED
Sir Halley Stewart Playing Fields, Winfrey Avenue, Spalding PE11 1DA **01775 712 047**

From the North follow the A52 and pick up the A16 south, as you near Spalding follow A16 By-pass past the New Power Station (on right). Carry on the by-pass to Springfields Roundabout, (McDonalds is on the left) turn right. Follow signs to Spalding Town Centre over Fulney Bridge on the Holbeach Road and travel approx ¾ mile from by-pass. Turn right over second bridge forming the roundabout then straight over into West Elloe Avenue. Continue down to traffic lights (Approx 400 yards). Turn left into Pinchbeck Road. After approx 300 yards turn right at the traffic lights. Turn left at the next set of traffic lights into Winfrey Avenue. The Ground is on the left.
Nearest Railway Station Spalding - 0.2km   **Bus Route** Broad Street - stop 100m away

307

SPELTHORNE SPORTS
Spelthorne Sports Club, 296 Staines Rd West, Ashford Common, TW15 1RY **01932 961 055**

From M25 (J13) take the A30 exit to London (W)/Hounslow/Staines. At the roundabout, take the 1st exit onto Staines Bypass/A30 heading to London(W)/Hounslow/Staines/Kingston/A308. Turn left onto Staines Bypass/A308. Continue to follow A308. Go through one roundabout. Make a U-turn at Chertsey Rd. Ground will be on the left.

Nearest Railway Station Sunbury   **Bus Route** 290 to outside the club.

384

SPENNYMOOR TOWN
The Brewery Field, Durham Road, Spennymoor DL16 6JN **01388 827 248**

Leave the A1(M) at junction 59, then at roundabout take the 1st exit onto the A167. At roundabout take the 2nd exit onto the A167. At Rushyford roundabout take the 3rd exit onto the A167. At roundabout take the 3rd exit onto the A167. At Thinford Roundabout take the 1st exit onto the A688. At roundabout take the 1st exit onto the A688. At roundabout take the 3rd exit onto Saint Andrew's Lane. At roundabout take the 1st exit onto Saint Andrew's Lane. At mini roundabout take 2nd exit onto King Street. At mini roundabout take 2nd exit onto King Street/Durham Road. Bear right onto Durham Road. Take 3rd exit on left onto Wood Vue.

100

SPORTING BENGAL UNITED
Mile End Stadium, Rhodeswell Rd, Off Burdett Rd E14 7TW **020 8980 1885**

Come off the Great West Road/A4 onto Earls Court Road/A3220. Continue straight to stay on Earls Ct Rd/A3220. Turn left onto Cremorne Rd/A3220. Continue onto Cheyne Walk/A3212. Turn right onto Peckham - Camberwell - Vauxhall - Westminster Hwy/A202. Continue straight onto Kennington Ln/Peckham - Camberwell - Vauxhall - Westminster Hwy/A202/A3204. Turn left onto Kennington Ln/A3, A3 turns slightly right and becomes Elephant and Castle. Continue onto New Kent Rd/A201. Keep left to continue on New Kent Rd. At the r'about, take the 2nd exit onto Tower Bridge Rd/A100. Turn right onto Abbey St/B202. Turn right onto Jamaica Rd/A200. At the r'about, take the 2nd exit onto Rotherhithe Tunnel/A101. Continue to follow A101. Slight left onto Yorkshire Rd. Turn right onto Salmon Ln. Continue onto Rhodeswell Rd. Keep right to continue on Turners Rd. Turn right onto St Paul's Way/B140. Turn left onto Burdett Rd/A1205. Turn left and then right again.
Nearest Railway Station Mile End – approx. 5 mins walk   **Bus Route** 277, 309, D6, D7 – outside ground

415

SPORTING CLUB THAMESMEAD
Sporting Club Thamesmead, Bayliss Avenue, Thamesmead, London SE28 8NJ **0208 320 4488**

Sporting Club Thamesmead can be accessed via Eastern Way.

Nearest Railway Station Abbey Wood - 1.8km

505

SPORTING KHALSA
Aspray Arena, Noose Lane, Willenhall WV13 3BB **01902 219 208**

From M6 junction 10, take 2nd exit onto A454 to Wolverhampton/Dudley A463. Take the A454 exit towards Wolverhampton. At Keyway junction take 2nd exit onto the Keyway A454 and continue on A454 going through one roundabout. At next traffic lights make a u turn at Nechells Lane. Turn left into Noose Lane and over roundabout. Ground is located on your left.

Nearest Railway Station Wolverhampton - 3.9km   **Bus Route** Fibbersley Bridge stop - 125m away

436

SQUIRES GATE
Brian Addison Stadium, School Road, Marton, Blackpool, Lancs FY4 5DS **01253 348 512**

M55 to junction 4, turn left onto the A583, at first set of traffic lights turn right (Whitehill Road) follow sign for airport, at round-a-bout thake Lytham St Annes exit.
Ground approx. 11/2 on right.

Nearest Railway Station Squires Gate - 2.4km   **Bus Route** St Nicholas School stop - 75m away

449

ST ALBANS CITY
Clarence Park, York Road, St. Albans, Herts AL1 4PL **01727 848 914**

M25 (Clockwise) exit at junc. 21A(A405). Follow signs to St. Albans from slip road. At Noke Hotel r'about, bear right on A405 and stay on A405 until London Colney r'about (traffic light controlled). Turn left onto A1081. Follow road for approx 1 mile until mini r'about (Great Northern pub on left). Turn right into Alma Rd. At traffic lights turn right into Victoria St. and continue to junction with Crown pub. Go straight across into Clarence Rd, ground is first on left. M25 (C-clockwise) exit at junc. 22 (A1081). Follow signs to St. Albans. At London Colney r'about exit onto A1081. Then as above.

Nearest Railway Station St. Albans City - 5-10 minute walk from the ground.

140

ST HELENS TOWN
Ruskin Drive Sportsground, Ruskin Drive, Dentons Green, St Helens WA10 6RP — **01942 716 360**

From South: M6 to junction 25, turn right onto A49, after 1/2 mile turn right into Soughers Lane, at T junction turn right into Downall Green Road, pass over M6 and turn 2nd right into Boothbrow Road, turn 2nd right in Brocstedes Road. (Ashton Athletic FC)

449

Nearest Railway Station St Helens Central - 1.9km **Bus Route** Ruskin Drive stop - 153m away

---

ST MARGARETSBURY
Recreation Ground, Station Road, St Margarets SG12 8EH — **01920 870 473**

A10 to Cambridge. Exit at A414 Harlow & Chelmsford.
Proceed 400 yards to Amwell roundabout and take 3rd exit (B181) to Stanstead Abbotts.
Ground is 1/2 mile on the right-hand side.

516

Nearest Railway Station St Margarets - 0.3km **Bus Route** St Nary's Church - stop 170m away

---

ST. ANDREWS
Canal Street, Aylestone, Leicester LE2 8LX — **0116 283 9298**

From the north to J21 of the M1. 1st left at roundabout and on to next roundabout. 2nd exit and follow A5460 towards Leicester. At 1st set of traffic lights turn right onto Braunstone Lane East. After approximately 1 mile turn left at T-junction and follow Aylestone Road towards Leicester. Take 3rd road on the left. Turn right at T-Junction and turn left at No Entry Signs over the canal bridge and left into ground.

529

Nearest Railway Station South Wigston - 3km

ST. AUSTELL
Poltair Park, Trevarthian Road, St Austell PL25 4LR — **01726 66099**

Near Poltair School and St Austell Brewery (5 minutes from St Austell Rail Station).

488

Nearest Railway Station St Austell - 0.3km **Bus Route** Poltair Road - stop 33m away

---

ST. FRANCIS RANGERS
Colwell Ground, Princess Royal Hospital, Lewes Rd, Haywards Hth RH16 4EX — **01444 474 021**

Enter through the main Hospital at mini-roundabout bear right and follow one way system.
On reaching Sports Complex sign- straight ahead pass bowling green, tennis courts and swimming pool.
Turn left through gate down unmade path to ground and parking.

495

Nearest Railway Station Haywards Heath - 1.9km

ST. IVES TOWN
Pro-Edge Stadium, Westwood Road, St. Ives PE27 6DT — **01480 463 207**

From A1123 Houghton Road rurn right at traffic lights into Ramsey Road. After Fire Station turn right into Westwood Road. Ground at end of road on right hand side immediately before St Ivo Recreation Centre Car Park.

352

ST. NEOTS TOWN
Rowley Park, Kester Way, Cambridge Road, St Neots, PE19 6SN — **01480 470 012**

From St Neots town centre, take the B1428 Cambridge Road, after going under the railway bridge, turn left at the first roundabout into Dramsell Rise. Follow the road up the hill to Kester Way and the ground. If approaching from Cambridge on the A428, turn right at the first roundabout as you approach St Neots onto the Cambridge Road. At the second roundabout, turn right into Dramsell Rise and follow as above. If travelling via the A1, follow signs for the A428 Cambridge. Go straight over roundabout with Tescos on left hand side, then turn left at next roundabout. Follow final instructions above as if approaching from Cambridge.

354

Nearest Railway Station St Neots - 06.km

ST. NEOTS TOWN RESERVES
St. Neots Town FC, Kester Way, St. Neots PE19 6SN — **01480 470 012**

From St Neots town centre, take the B1428 Cambridge Road, after going under the railway bridge, turn left at the first roundabout into Dramsell Rise. Follow the road up the hill to Kester Way and the ground. If approaching from Cambridge on the A428, turn right at the first roundabout as you approach St Neots onto the Cambridge Road. At the second roundabout, turn right into Dramsell Rise and follow as above. If travelling via the A1, follow signs for the A428 Cambridge. Go straight over roundabout with Tescos on left hand side, then turn left at next roundabout. Follow final instructions above as if approaching from Cambridge.

516

Nearest Railway Station St Neots - 06.km

STAFFORD RANGERS
Marston Road, Stafford ST16 3BX — **01785 602 430**

M6 Junction 14. Follow signs for Uttoxeter and Stone. Straight over at 1st and 2nd (A34) islands, 3rd right sign posted Common Road and Astonfields Road Ind. Estate. The ground is straight ahead after three quarters of a mile. The route from the Motorway is highlighted by the standard football road signs.
*Sat Nav ST16 3UF

270

Nearest Railway Station Stafford - 1.8km **Bus Route** Co-operative Strret - stop 200m away

---

STAFFORD TOWN
Evans Park, Riverway, Stafford ST16 3TH — **07789 110 923**

From M6 junction 13, take A449 towards Stafford for 1½ miles until reaching traffic lights by an Esso petrol station. Turn right at the lights into Rickerscote Road, follow the road round over railway bridge to a mini island. At the island bear left into Silkmore Lane, after approximately 600 yards take the 2nd exit at the mini island and carry on until a large island, take the 2nd exit towards Stafford town centre (A34 Lichfield Road). Go over the railway bridge with Alstrom factory on the left hand side. Straight on at 1st set of traffic lights, then bear left at next set of lights (A518 Uttoxeter) and follow road round with B&Q and Argos on your left hand side. At the roundabout (with KFC and Pizza Hut in front of you) take the 2nd exit (A518 Uttoxeter) and follow to traffic lights. Go straight over lights into Riverway, the ground entrance is approximately 80 yards on the right hand side. Follow the driveway behind the cricket pavilion to the stadium entrance.

436

Nearest Railway Station Stafford - 1.1km **Bus Route** Hatherton Street stop - 99m away

---

STAINES LAMMAS
The Lucan Pavilion, The Boradway, Laleham, Staines, Middlesex TW18 1RZ — **01784 465 204**

Leave M25 at junction 11 and take A317 towards Chertsey. At first roundabout keep left following A317. As the road straightens move into the right hand lane to the lights and straight on to the B387 Fordwater Road. Follow that road to the end and at the lights turn right onto Chertsey Bridge Road – B375. Go over Chertsey Bridge and continue to next roundabout and turn left onto Littleton Lane (Signed Laleham/Staines).Follow that road to the end and then turn left onto Shepperton Road B376.

384

Nearest Railway Station Staines

STAINES TOWN
Wheatsheaf Park, Wheatsheaf Lane, Staines TW18 2PD — **01784 469 240**

Leave M25 at Junction 13. If coming from the North (anticlockwise), bear left onto A30 Staines By-Pass; if coming from the South (clockwise), go round the roundabout and back under M25 to join By-Pass. Follow A30 to Billet Bridge roundabout, which you treat like a roundabout, taking last exit, A308, London Road towards Town Centre. At 3rd traffic lights, under iron bridge, turn left into South Street, passing central bus station, as far as Thames Lodge (formerly Packhorse). Turn left here, into Laleham Road, B376, under rail bridge. After 1km, Wheatsheaf Lane is on the right, by the traffic island. Ground is less than 100 yds on left. Please park on the left.

196

Nearest Railway Station Staines - 1.3km **Bus Route** Penton Hook Road - stop 100m away

STALYBRIDGE CELTIC
Bower Fold, Mottram Road, Stalybridge, Cheshire SK15 2RT
0161 338 2828

Via the B6174 (Stalybridge Road). At a mini r'about, turn left (exit 1 of 5) onto Roe Cross Road (A6018). Follow for 1 3/4 miles passing the Roe Cross Inn on the right and through the cutting (the road is now called Mottram Road). When you pass the Dog and Partridge on the right, you will be almost there. Bower Fold is on the left opposite a sharp right turn next to the Hare and Hounds pub. If the car park is full, parking can be found on the streets.

Nearest Railway Station Stalybridge - 1.5 miles from the ground.

272

STAMFORD
Zeeco Stadium, Ryhall Road, Stamford. PE9 1US
01780 751 471

From the North using the A1: Leave the A1 at the B1081 exit signposted Stamford. Continue into Great Casterton. Turn left at the crossroads (signposted Ryhall) for about 2.5 miles. At the end of the road turn right and immediately right again. Continue for about 1.5 miles across several mini roundabouts and the stadium is on the right. **From the South using the A1:** Leave A1 at A606 exit signposted Oakham. Turn right over the A1 then left as if going back onto A1 south. Then, before joining the south bound carriageway, take the first right signposted Great Casterton for 0.5 mile. Turn left for one mile into Great Casterton (ignore first turning right for Little Casterton) then turn right at the crossroads (signposted Ryhall) for about 2.5 miles. At the end of the road turn right and immediately right again. Continue for about 1.5 miles across several mini roundabouts and the stadium is on the right. **From the West using the A43:** Join A1 north as you approach Stamford. Then follow directions as A1 from the South. **From the East using the A1175:** Go straight over roundabout for Morrisons. At the mini-roundabout, take the 3rd exit and follow road. You will pass Sainsbury's and then Travis Perkins on your right. The stadium is on your left at bottom of dip. Sat Nav PE9 4QN. **Nearest Railway Station:** Stamford - 2.1km. **Bus Route:** Gush Way - stop 300m away.

308

STANSFELD
Glebe FC, Foxbury Avenue, Chislehurst, Bromley BR7 6HA
07861 885 590

The club is located just off the A222 close to the Vauxhall Garage and a stone's throw away from the Sidcup bypass.

Nearest Railway Station Sidcup - 1.9km

505

STANSTED
Hargrave Park, Cambridge Road, Stansted CM24 8BX
07921 403 842

Exit M11 at junction 8, take A120 west and cross first roundabout. At next roundabout take right exit, follow road into Stansted Mountfitchet. Once in Stansted Mountfitchet look for Esso Petrol Station on your left. Drive past and ground entrance is approx. 200 yards on the left.

Nearest Railway Station Stansted Mountfitchet - ¼ mile   **Bus Route** 301 100 yards from ground

415

STANWAY ROVERS
Hawthorns, New Farm Road, Stanway, Colchester CO3 0PG
01206 578 187

Leave A12 at Jct 26 to A1124. Turn right(from London)or left from Ipswich onto Essex Yeomanry Way.
A1124 towards Colchester 1st right into Villa Road, then left into Chaple Road, and left into New Farm Road.
Ground 400 yds on left.

Nearest Railway Station Colchester - 3.7km

402

STAPENHILL
Edge Hill, Maple Grove, Stapenhill DE15 9NN.
01283 516 433

From North: Exit A38 at Clay Mills and follow A5018 towards Burton. Follow A444 (Nuneaton). At Swan junction traffic lights turn right onto Stapenhill Road. At roundabout go straight over – 6th left onto Sycamore Road. Ground 500 yards on Maple Grove

From South: Follow A511 to Burton on Trent, at Swan junction traffic lights turn left onto Stapenhill Road. At roundabout go straight over – 6th left onto Sycamore Road. Ground 500 yards on Maple Grove
Nearest Railway Station Burton-on-Trent - 3km

396

STAVELEY MINERS WELFARE
Inkersall Road, Staveley, Chesterfield, S43 3JL
01246 471 441

From M1 J29A, follow the signs to Staveley.
Go past Poolsbrook Country Park and turn left onto Cemetry Road then right onto Inkersall Road.
The ground is on the left on the brow of a hill.

Nearest Railway Station Chesterfield - 5,4km   **Bus Route** Market Street - stop 156m away

463

STEWARTS & LLOYDS CORBY
Recreation Ground, Occupation Road, Corby NN17 1EH
01536 401 497

From the Oundle/Weldon Road turn at roundabout into A6086 Lloyds Road and continue to roundabout. Take second exit going over railway line along Rockingham Road. Continue over speed bumps then turn left into Occupation Road and first right into Cannock Road. Ground is beyond the British Steel Club and Rugby pitch.

Nearest Railway Station Corby - 1.2km   **Bus Route** The Game Bird Pub - stop 110m away

529

STEYNING TOWN
The Shooting Field, Steyning, West Sussex BN44 3RQ
01903 814 601

Entering Steyning from the west. Take 1st left in the High St (Tanyard Lane) Follow into Shooting Field estate, ground is 4th turn on the left. Entering Steyning from the east. From the High St., turn right into Church St..
Turn left by Church into Shooting Field estate.
NB Coaches MUST park in Church Street Car Park.

Bus Route Middle Mead - stop 52m away

495

STICKER
Burngullow Park PL26 7EN
01726 71003

From A390 follow signs to Sticker, in the centre of the Village take St Stephen Road (between pub & post office).
After 0.75 miles at cross roads turn Right and ground entrance on your right in 200 meters.

Nearest Railway Station St Austell - 4.4km   **Bus Route** Hewas Inn (Fore St) - stop 1.1km away

488

STOCKPORT COUNTY
Edgeley Park, Hardcastle Road, Stockport SK3 9DD
0161 286 8888

Via the M60, exit at Junction 1 ('sign-posted 'Stockport Town Centre and West'). At the r'about turn right and continue through to the second set of lights and turn left (ignoring the sign directing you to Stockport Co.) and follow the road to the left, which is Chestergate. At the lights turn right up King Street, past the fire station on the right to the top of the hill, turn right at the r'about signed Edgeley. Continue down Hardcastle street turning left after the bus stop signed Caroline Street.

Nearest Railway Station Stockport - Approx. half a mile from the ground.

102

STOCKPORT TOWN
Lambeth Grove, Woodley, Stockport SK6 1QX
0161 494 3146

Stockport Town Football Club is located at Stockport Sports Village, Lambeth Grove Woodley, SK6 1QX. The ground lies a short distance from the M60. To reach us from the motorway, you should leave at Junction 25, which is signposted for Bredbury. Follow signs from here for the A560 towards Bredbury and Sheffield. Just after passing the McDonalds Drive-Thru, take a left at the traffic lights and proceed down Stockport Road towards Woodley, passing both Morrisons and Homebase on your left before passing under the railway bridge at Bredbury Railway Station.

Nearest Railway Station Woodley - 0.7km. Bredbury - 0.8km.   **Bus Route** Hyde Road stop - 414m away

449

STOCKSBRIDGE PARK STEELS Look Local Stadium, Bracken Moor Lane, Stocksbridge, Sheffield S36 2AN 0114 288 8305 (Match days)

From the West onto A616. Immediately you reach the Stocksbridge bypass turn Right signed (Stocksbridge West), then continue until you reach the shopping centre approx 1.5 miles. 300 yards past the centre you will see Gordons Autos on your left. Turn right directly opposite signed (Nanny Hill) and continue up the hill for Approx 500 yds, Ground is on the Left. **From M1**- From North Junction 36 on to A61 Sheffield to McDonalds Roundabout. **From South** Junction 35a on to A616 Manchester to McDonalds Roundabout. From McDonalds roundabout on A616 Manchester for approx 6 miles then take Stocksbridge West exit, then continue until you reach the shopping centre approx 1.5 miles. 300yds past the centre you will see Gordons Autos on your Left. Turn right directly opposite signed (Nanny Hill) and continue up the hill for Approx 500yds, ground on Left.

308

STOCKTON TOWN Bishopton Road West, Stockton-on-Tees TS19 0QD **01642 604 915**

From A19: Take the A1027 (towards Stockton/Norton). Take 2nd Exit at first roundabout and 2nd Exit at the second roundabout. At lights (near Sainsburys) turn right onto Bishopton Road West.
From A66: Take the A135 (Yarm Rd) towards Stockton, at 2nd set of lights turn left onto A1027 (Hartburn Lane). Travel along past Park (on right) and as road bears left, get into filter to turn right to follow A1027. At roundabout take 2nd exit, at 2nd set of lights (near Sainsburys) turn left onto Bishopton Road West.

Nearest Railway Station Stockton - 1.4km   **Bus Route** Whitehouse Drive - stop 101m away

476

STOKE GABRIEL G J Churchward Memorial TQ9 6RR **01803 782 913**

At Tweenaway Cross turn Right, after quarter of a mile turn Left at the Parkers Arms Inn.
After approx 1 mile ground entrance is signposted on your right, before the village itself.

Nearest Railway Station Paignton - 4.3km   **Bus Route** Ramslade Touring Park - stop 344m away

488

STONE OLD ALLEYNIANS Wellbeing Park, Yarnfield Lane, Yarnfield ST15 0NF **07813 553 087**

From the South Junction 14 (M6), take A34 towards Stone. Carry on A34 until you see Wayfarer Public House on left. Immediately after Pub, turn left towards Yarnfield. Follow road and once over the motorway bridge, continue for ½ mile. Ground is on left.

Nearest Railway Station Norton Bridge - 2.8km   **Bus Route** Labour-in-Vain Pub - stop 650m away

553

STORRINGTON Recreation Ground, Pulborough Road, Storrington RH20 4HJ **01903 745 860**

Turn west on A283 (off A24).
Ground opposite pond to west of village centre.

Nearest Railway Station Pulborough - 5.6km   **Bus Route** Brow Close - stop 238m away

495

STOTFOLD Roker Park, The Green, Stotfold, Hitchin, Herts SG5 4AN **01462 730 765**

At A1 junction 10, take the A507 to Stotfold and right into town. Proceed along High Street and at traffic lights turn right (from Hitchin – straight over traffic lights) towards Astwick Turn right at the Crown pub into The Green.
The ground is set back from The Green on the left.

Nearest Railway Station Arlesey - 2.9km   **Bus Route** The Green - stop 80m away

516

STOURBRIDGE War Memorial Athletic Ground, High Street, Amblecote DY8 4HN **01384 394 040**

From M6: Leave the M5 Southbound at Junction 3 and take the A456 towards Kidderminster. Upon entering Hagley (following a long downhill approach), take the right hand filter lane at the traffic lights (Signposted A491 Stourbridge). Continue to follow the A491 towards Stourbridge Town Centre and continue to follow the Ring Road (watching the Speed Camera), and take the A491 exit now signposted Wolverhampton. The ground is on the left hand side of the road immediately after the 3rd set of traffic lights (approximately 500 yards) and opposite the Vets for Pets. Please note that Parking is Extremely Limited on the Ground. **From M42:** Leave the M5 Northbound at Junction 4 and follow the A491 towards Stourbridge and in Hagley, take the left hand filter lane to continue on the A491 and proceed as above. **Nearest Railway Station:** Stourbridge - 1km

274

STOURPORT SWIFTS Walshes Meadow, Harold Davis Drive, Stourport on Severn DY13 0AA **01299 825 188**

Follow the one way system through Stourport Town Centre signposted 'Sports Centre'.
Go over river bridge and turn left into Harold Davies Drive.
Ground is at rear of Sports Centre.

Nearest Railway Station Hartlebury - 4.2km   **Bus Route** Swimming Pool stop - 104m away

436

STOWMARKET TOWN Greens Meadow, Bury Road, Stowmarket, Suffolk IP14 1JQ **01449 612 533**

Exit the A14 at junction 49 signposted Haughley/Stowmarket.
Take the 2nd exit towards Stowmarket. Follow the road all the way until you go under the A14 and reach another roundabout.
At this roundabout take the 1st exit and you will see the club to your immediate left.

Nearest Railway Station Stowmarket - 1km

402

STRATFORD TOWN The DCS Stadium, Knights Lane, Tiddington, Stratford Upon Avon CV37 7BZ **01789 261 037**

From Town Centre follow signs for Banbury (A422) and Oxford (A3400). Cross Clopton Bridge and turn immediately left onto B4086 towards Wellesbourne. After approx 1 mile you enter the village of Tiddington. Turn 1st right into Knights Lane. Ground is approx 800 yards on right (100 yards after school).

Nearest Railway Station Stratford-upon-Avon - 2.8km   **Bus Route** Alveston Primary School - stop 50m away

356

STREET The Tannery Ground, Middlebrooks, Street BA16 0TA **01458 445 987**

Ground is signposted from both ends of A39 and B3151.

Bus Route Green Lane Ave - stop 220m away

559

STUDLEY The Beehive, Abbeyfields Drive, Studley B80 7BF **01527 853 817**

From M42 Junction 3, take exit towards Redditch (A435).
Head South for 5 miles, Abbeyfield Drive is on the left hand side ½ mile past "The Boot" Public House, adjacent to a sharp left hand bend.

Nearest Railway Station Redditch - 4.6km   **Bus Route** Red Hill Close stop - 49m away

436

SUN SPORTS
Sun Postal Sports Club, Bellmountwood Avenue, Watford, Herts WD17 3BN
01923 227 453

From Watford town centre take the A411 (Hempstead Road) away from the Town Hall towards Hemel Hempstead. At 2nd set of traffic lights turn left into Langley Way. At the next roundabout, where there is a parade of shops on the left and the "Essex Arms" on the right, take the third exit into Cassiobury Drive. Then take the first turn left into Bellmountwood Avenue then at the left hand bend turn right into the Club entrance.

516

Nearest Railway Station Watford Underground - 1.1km   **Bus Route** Langley Way - stop 250m away

SUNDERLAND RYHOPE C.A.
Meadow Park, Beachbrooke, Stockton Rd, Ryhope, Sunderland SR2 0NZ
07802 523 533

From the A19, leave at the junction with the A690, but on that roundabout take the B1286 through Doxford Park. Continue along this road for some time (there are number of roundabouts), but there are signposts to Ryhope along this road. You will eventually come to a T-junction at the end of the B1286, and turn right onto the A1018. After 200 yards you will come to another roundabout, here take a right turn. Then take the next right into a new housing estate. There is a board at the entrance pointing you to Meadow Park, the home of R. C.A. The ground is at the far end of the estate.

476

Nearest Railway Station Seaham - 3.3km   **Bus Route** Ryhope Hospital - 94m away

SUTTON ATHLETIC
London Hire Stadium, Lower Road, Hextable, Kent BR8 7RZ
01322 665 377

London Road can be accessed via the B258.

505

Nearest Railway Station Swanley - 2.4km

SUTTON COLDFIELD TOWN
Central Ground, Coles Lane, Sutton Coldfield B72 1NL
0121 354 2997

From M42 Junc 9, take A4097 [Minworth sign]. At island, follow signs to Walmley Village. At traffic lights turn right [B4148]. After shops turn left at traffic lights into Wylde Green Road. Over railway bridge turn right into East View Road, which becomes Coles Lane.

276

Nearest Railway Station Sutton Coldfield - 1.1km   **Bus Route** Douglas Road - stop 100m away

SUTTON COMMON ROVERS
Sutton United FC, Gander Green Lane, Sutton. Surrey SM1 2EY
020 8644 4440

Travel along the M25 to junction 8. Then north on the A217 for about 15-20 minutes. Ignoring signs for Sutton itself, stay on the A217 to the traffic lights by the Gander Inn (on the left), turn right into Gander Green Lane. The Borough Sports Ground is about 200 yards up this road on the left hand side, if you reach West Sutton station you have gone too far.

384

Nearest Railway Station West Sutton   **Bus Route** 413

SUTTON UNITED
Borough Sports Ground, Gander Green Lane, Sutton, Surrey SM1 2EY
0208 644 4440

Travel along the M25 to junction 8. Then north on the A217 for about 15-20 minutes. Ignoring signs for Sutton itself, stay on the A217 to the traffic lights by the Gander Inn (on the left), turn right into Gander Green Lane. The Borough Sports Ground is about 200 yards up this road on the left hand side, if you reach West Sutton station you have gone too far.

50

Nearest Railway Station West Sutton a few minutes walk from the ground.

SWAFFHAM TOWN
The Pavillion, Shoemakers Lane, Swaffham, Norfolk PE37 7NT
01760 722 700

Follow A11 until roundabout signposted A134, take first exit.
At the next roundabout, take the 3rd exit onto Swaffham Road/A1065.
Continue to follow A1065. At the next roundabout, take the 1st exit onto Brandon Road/A1065.
Continue to follow A1065. Turn left onto Haspalls Road.
Turn right onto Cley Road. Turn left onto Shoemakers Lane.

402

Bus Route Greenhoe Place (Haspalls Rd) stop - 212m away

SWALLOWNEST
Rotherham Road, Sheffield S26 4UR.
0114 287 2510

From M1 J31: Take 3rd exit from north or 1st exit from south. Go a mile on dual carriageway to a second roundabout. Take 3rd exit, Chesterfield Road. Go through traffic lights and Swallownest Miners Welfare is 50 metres on your left.

463

Nearest Railway Station Woodhouse - 2.2km   **Bus Route** Park Street - stop 61m away

SWINDON SUPERMARINE
The Webbswood Stadium, South Marston, Swindon SN3 4BZ
01793 828 778

From M5 Junction 11a, take the A417 to Cirencester, then A419 Swindon. At the A361 junction by Honda Factory take road to Highworth. After one mile Club is on 4th roundabout.
From M4 Junction 15, take A419 towards Swindon Cirencester, take A361, then as above .
From A420 Swindon take A419 to Cirencester, near Honda factory take A361, then as above.

381

Nearest Railway Station Swindon - 5.8km   **Bus Route** Stanton Fitzwarren Turn - stop 300m away

TADCASTER ALBION
i2i Stadium, Ings Lane, Tadcaster LS24 9AY
01904 606 000

From A64 follow Tadcaster signs (A659) either from the west or east. From the west, on reaching John Smiths Brewery turn right down Centre Lane or New Street. From the east, go over the river bridge, turn left after pedestrian lights and down New Street.

296

Nearest Railway Station Ulleskelf - 4.3km   **Bus Route** John Smith's Brewery - stop 300m away

TADLEY CALLEVA
Barlows Park Silchester Road Tadley Hampshire RG26 3PX
07787 501 028

From M3 Basingstoke Junction 6 take the A340 to Tadley, travel through Tadley and at the main traffic lights turn right into Silchester Road, proceed for 0.5 mile then turn left into the car park. Postcode for Satellite Navigation systems RG26 3PX

541

Nearest Railway Station Midgham - 5.1km   **Bus Route** Tadley Common Road - stop 60m away

TAKELEY
Station Road, Takeley, Bishop's Stortford CM22 6SQ
01279 870 404

Take the A120 (W) exit from the M11.
Follow Dunmow Road/B1256 after 3 miles turn right into Station Road/B183.
Ground will be on your left.

415

Nearest Railway Station Stansted Airport (overground) Epping (underground)   **Bus Route** from Stansted Airport to Four Ashes Pub.

TAMWORTH
The Lamb Ground, Kettlebrook, Tamworth, Staffordshire B77 1AA — 01827 657 98

M42 Junction 10.
Take A5/A51 to Town centre.
Then follow the signs for Kettlebrook and Tamworth FC.

Nearest Railway Station Tamworth - within walking distance of the ground.

104

TAUNTON TOWN
The Viridor Stadium, Wordsworth Drive, Taunton, Somerset TA1 2HG — 01823 254 909

From M5 Junction 25 follow signs to Town Centre.
Proceed along Toneway then bear left at roundabout into Chritchard Way.
At traffic lights proceed into Wordsworth Drive and the ground is on the left.

Nearest Railway Station Taunton - 1.4km   **Bus Route** Milford Road - stop 20m away

382

TAVISTOCK
Langsford Park, Red & Black Club, Crowndale Road, Tavistock PL19 8JR — 01822 614 447

Take signs for Tavistock College and Sports Centre, go past the College and the ground entrance is a further 100 meters on your left hand side.

Nearest Railway Station Gunnislake - 4.9km   **Bus Route** Canons Way - stop 694m away

488

TEAM BURY
Bury Town FC, Ram Meadow, Cotton Lane, Bury St Edmunds IP33 1XP — 01284 754 721

From the M11: Take junction 9 for the A11. Follow this road and make sure you get into the outside lane for the A14 signed Bury St Edmunds. Leave the A14 Junction 43, signposted to central Bury St Edmunds. Once clear of the exit roundabout, follow the signs to Town Centre. Take the first exit at the next roundabout (after 300 yards) into Northgate Street. At the second set of traffic lights (T - Junction), turn left into Mustow Street and first left into Cotton Lane, past the Hawkes garage and the Drive Car Showroom. Carry on down to the bottom of Cotton Lane and turn right in the council car park. The ground is at the far end of the car park, situated on the left hand side.

Nearest Railway Station Bury St Edmunds - 0.7km   **Bus Route** Schoolhall Lane (Northgate St) - 106m away

402

TEAM NORTHUMBRIA
Coach Lane, Benton, Newcastle upon Tyne NE7 7XA — 0191 215 6575

Take the A1058 from either the A19 or central Newcastle. Turn off this road at the junction with Benfield Road. Turn north at large Crosslings warehouse into Red Hall Drive, this then becomes Coach Lane. The ground is on the right just past Newcastle University halls of residence.

Nearest Railway Station Four Lane Ends - 976m   **Bus Route** Coach Lane Campus - stop 97m away

476

TEAM SOLENT
Test Park, Lower Broomhill Road, Southampton SO16 9BP

Leave the M27 at junction 3 for the M271. Take the first slip road off the M271 and then first exit off the roundabout on to Lower Broomhill Road. Carry on to the next roundabout and take the last exit, (coming back on yourself) into Redbridge lane and the entrance to Test Park is approx. 500m on right.
From City centre take the Millbrook road to the M271, first slip road off on to roundabout, 3rd exit on to Lower Broomhill Way and then as above. Postcode for Satellite Navigation systems SO16 9QZ

Nearest Railway Station Redbridge - 1.2km   **Bus Route** The Saints - stop 450m away

541

TEVERSAL
Teversal Grange Spts and So.Centre, Carnarvon St, Teversal, NG17 3HJ — 01623 554 924

From North: Travel South on the M1 to junc 29 take the A6175 to Heath and Holmewood. Travel through Holmewood, and at the r'dabout take the B6039 to Hardstaft and Tibshelf. At the T-junction in Tibshelf (pub on your left) turn left onto B6014 travelling over the motorway into Teversal. Follow the road round passing the Carnarvon Arms pub and under a bridge, take 2nd left onto Coppywood Close, travel to the top and following the road round with the ground at the top. **From South:** From the M1 junc 28, take the A38 to Mansfield. Travel through a number of sets of traffic lights and after passing the Kings Mill Reservoir you will come to a major junction (King & Miller Pub and McDonalds on your left). Travel straight on taking the A6075 towards Mansfield Woodhouse, at the next set of lights turn left onto the B6014 to Stanton Hill. You will come to a r'dabout with a Co-op on your left, continue on the B6014 towards Tibshelf. Take the second right onto Coppywood Close, then as above.

Nearest Railway Station Sutton Parkway - 4.5km

396

THACKLEY
Dennyfield, Ainsbury Avenue, Thackley, Bradford BD10 0TL — 01274 615 571

Via M606 (or M62 Junction 27 and A650) — A6177 (Bradford Ring Road eastbound) and A658 (Harrogate Road) to Greengates traffic lights by (Roebuck Inn). Take 657 towards Shipley and at Thackley corner (beyond "S" bend) turn right into Thackley Road. At crossroads beyond Methodist Church , veer into Ainsbury Avenue and Dennyfield is 200 yards ahead. Alternatively via M621 (Junction 1). A6110 (Leeds Ring Road westbound), A647 to New Pudsey Station – then A6120 to Rodleyand via A657 as above.

Nearest Railway Station Baildon - 1.4km   **Bus Route** Thackley Road - stop 200m away

463

THAME RANGERS
Meadow View Park, Tythrop Way, Thame OX9 3RN — 01844 214 401

From the west: At the Oxford Road roundabout on the edge of Thame take the first left (sign posted Aylesbury) and follow the by-pass. At the next roundabout take the third exit on to Tythrop Way. The ground is 200 yards on the left.
From the east: Leave the M40 at Junction 6 and follow the signposts to Thame. On arriving in Thame, take the first right on to Wenman Road (B4012). Stay on the B4012 as it by-passes Thame, going straight over two roundabouts. The ground is on the right, directly off the by-pass, approximately half a mile after you pass Chinnor Rugby Club.

Nearest Railway Station Haddenham & Thame Parkway - 2.9km   **Bus Route** Queens Close stop - 309m away

422

THAME UNITED
The ASM Stadium, Meadow View Park, Tythrop Way, Thame, Oxon OX9 3RN — 01844 214 401

From the west: At the Oxford Road roundabout on the edge of Thame take the first left (sign posted Aylesbury) and follow the by-pass. At the next roundabout take the third exit on to Tythrop Way. The ground is 200 yards on the left.
From the east: Leave the M40 at Junction 6 and follow the signposts to Thame. On arriving in Thame, take the first right on to Wenman Road (B4012). Stay on the B4012 as it by-passes Thame, going straight over two roundabouts. The ground is on the right, directly off the by-pass, approximately half a mile after you pass Chinnor Rugby Club.

Nearest Railway Station Haddenham & Thame Parkway - 2.9km   **Bus Route** Queens Close - stop 350m away

372

THAMESMEAD TOWN
Dartford FC, Princes Park, Grassbanks, Darenth Road, Dartford DA1 1RT — 01322 299 991

From M25 clockwise leave at Junction 1b to r'about controlled by traffic lights. Take third exit onto Princes Road, (A225) then second exit at next roundabout. Continue down hill to traffic lights (ground on your left), turn left into Darenth Road then second turning on your left to Grassbanks leading to car park. From M25 anti-clockwise leave at Junction 2 onto slip road A225 to r'about, then first exit, second exit at next r'about then down hill to traffic lights turn left into Darenth Road, then second turning on your left into Grassbanks.

Nearest Railway Station Dartford - 1.4km   **Bus Route** Fasttrack B towards Bluewater/Dartford.

230

THATCHAM TOWN
Waterside Park, Crookham Hill, Thatcham, Berks RG18 4QR — 01635 862 016

From North, follow A34/A339 towards Newbury. Then follow A4 signposted Thatcham, continue on A4 through Thatcham until you come to a roundabout with a signpost to the Railway Station off to the right (Pipers Way). Continue to the station and go over the level crossing, ground is approximately 250m on left.
From West leave the M4 at junction 13 then follow the directions above. From the East, leave the M4 at junction 12 and follow A4 towards Newbury/Thatcham then follow directions above to the Railway station.

Nearest Railway Station Thatcham - 1.6km   **Bus Route** Vincent Road stop - 287m away

422

THETFORD TOWN
Recreation Ground, Mundford Road, Thetford, Norfolk IP24 1NB
01842 766 120

Take M4, M25 and M11 to A11 in Cambridgeshire. Follow A11, Newmarket Bypass and A11 to Rutherford Way in Thetford. Continue onto A11. Continue onto Newmarket Bypass/A14. Slight left onto Newmarket Bypass (signs for A11/Thetford/Norwich). Continue onto A11. At the roundabout, take the 3rd exit onto London Rd/A11. Continue to follow A11. At the roundabout, take the 2nd exit onto Thetford Bypass/A11. At the roundabout, take the 2nd exit and stay on Thetford Bypass/A11. At the roundabout, take the 3rd exit onto Mundford Road/A1066.

Nearest Railway Station Thetford - 0.5km

402

THORNABY
Teesdale Park, Acklam Road, Thornaby, Stockton on Tees TS17 7JU
01642 672 896

Turn off A19 onto A1130 and head towards Thornaby.
Continue along Acklam Road for about half a mile.
Ground is signposted from the main road- on the right up a track between houses after half a mile.

Nearest Railway Station Thornaby - 1.2km   **Bus Route** Millfield Close - stop 143m away

476

THRAPSTON TOWN
Chancery Lane, Thrapston, Northants NN14 4JL
01832 732 470

Exit A14 at A605 roundabout, travel towards Peterborough till 1st roundabout (approx 700 metres).
Take first exit into Thrapston.
At traffic lights turn into Oundle Road adjacent to Masons Arms Pub.
Turn left into Devere Road and ground at bottom of hill.

Bus Route Library - stop 170m away

529

THREE BRIDGES
Jubilee Walk, Three Bridges Road, Crawley, RH10 1LQ
01293 442 000

Leave the M23 at Junction 10 heading towards Crawley on the A2011 (Crawley Avenue). At the roundabout take the first left heading towards Three Bridges Train Station (Hazelwick Avenue). Pass Tesco on your left and head straight over the roundabout (second exit). As you approach the traffic lights remain in the right hand side lane. After turning right in to Haslett Avenue at these lights move immediately in to the right turn lane at the next set of lights. Turn right at these lights in to Three Bridges Road. Follow the road round to the left then turn left after one hundred yards in to Jubilee Walk (directly opposite the Plough Pub). Follow the road to the end and turn right (still Jubilee Walk) and head straight on where Three Bridges Jubilee Field Stadium is at the far end.   **Nearest Railway Station:** Three Bridges - 0.4km   **Bus Route** Jubilee Walk - stop 71m away

495

THURROCK
South Way, Ship Lane, Grays, Essex RM19 1YN
01708 865 492

Approaching the ground from the North - along the M25 in a clockwise direction. Leave the motorway at junction 30. At the roundabout take the second exit and stay in the left hand lane. This leads to a large roundabout controlled by traffic lights. The fifth exit is Ship Lane and the ground is approximately 50 yards on the right hand side. Approaching the ground from the South - anti-clockwise on the M25. When going through the Dartford Tunnel take the left hand bore. On coming out of the tunnel take the first exit - junction 31. This leads to a large roundabout controlled by traffic lights. Take the third exit which is Ship Lane. The ground is situated approximately 50 yards on the right hand side.

Nearest Railway Station Chafford Hundred - 1.6km   **Bus Route** Back Lane - stop 200m away

198

TILBURY
Chadfields, St Chads Road, Tilbury, Essex RM18 8NL
01375 843 093

A13 Southend bound go left at Chadwell St Mary's turning, then right after 400 metres and right again at roundabout (signed Tilbury).
Right into St Chads Road after five miles, first right into Chadfields for ground.

Nearest Railway Station Tilbury Town - 1.1km   **Bus Route** Raphael Avenue - stop 75m away

218

TIVERTON TOWN
Ladysmead, Bolham Road, Tiverton, Devon EX16 6SG
01884 252 397

M5 Junction 27, follow A361 to Tiverton's second exit at roundabout, turning left.
Continue for about 400 yards, crossing roundabout until reaching mini-roundabout.
Carry on straight across. Ground is 200 yards on right.

Nearest Railway Station Tiverton Parkway - 2km   **Bus Route** Park Road - stop 300m away

358

TIVIDALE
The Beeches, Packwood Road, Tividale, West Mids B69 1UL
01384 211 743

M5 Junction 2. Take A4123 towards Dudley. After approx 1.5 miles and after footbridge, take left up Trafalgar Road. Take 2nd right into Elm Terrace and then 1st left into Birch Crescent. Take 1st right into Packwood Road and ground is at end of road.

Nearest Railway Station Dudley Port - 1.6km   **Bus Route** Regent Road - stop 100m away

553

TONBRIDGE ANGELS
Longmead Stadium, Darenth Avenue, Tonbridge, Kent TN10 3JF
01732 352 417

From M25. Take A21 turning at Junction 5 to junction with A225/b245 (signposted Hildenborough). After passing Langley Hotel on left make slightly hidden left turn into Dry Hill Park Road. Left again at mini roundabout into Shipbourne Road (A227) and then left again at next roundabout into Darenth Avenue' Longmead stadium can be found at the bottom of the hill at the far end of the car park.

Nearest Railway Station Tonbridge - 3.1km   **Bus Route** Heather Walk - stop 250m away

200

TOOTING & MITCHAM UNITED
KNK Stadium, Imperial Fields, Bishopsford Road, Morden, Surrey SM4 6BF
020 8685 6193

M25 Jct 8, take the A217 northbound, this goes through Tadworth and Cheam. It's dual carriageway most of the way, although long stretches have a 40mph speed limit. This leads to a major roundabout with lights (Rose Hill). Take the third exit (Mitcham A217), this is Bishopsford Road and the ground is a mile further on. Go through two sets of lights, the road dips, and the entrance is on the right opposite a petrol station.
From the South: M25 Jct 7, M23 then A23 northbound. Turn left onto the A237 after passing under a railway bridge at Coulsdon South station. Through Hackbridge and Beddington, then turn left onto the A239. Turn left at lights by Mitcham Cricket Green into the A217, the ground is 800 yards on the left.

Nearest Railway Station Mitcham Tram Stop - 0.5km

202

TORPOINT ATHLETIC
The Mill, Mill Lane, Carbeile Road, Torpoint PL11 2RE
01752 812 889

Take turning at Carbeile Inn onto Carbeille Road and first turning on the right into Mill Lane.

Nearest Railway Station Dockyard (plymouth) - 2.5km   **Bus Route** Carbeile Inn - stop 338m away

488

TORQUAY UNITED
Plainmoor, Torquay, Devon TQ1 3PS
01803 328 666

BY ROAD FROM THE NORTH/EAST (A30/M5): At the junction of the A30/M5 take A38 signposted Plymouth. After 3 miles take left fork on A380 signposted Torquay. After a further 10 miles at Penn Inn roundabout take 2nd exit to Torquay. At Kerswell Gardens take the A3022 to Torquay. At Lowes Bridge turn left into Hele Rd (B3199) and continue until a double roundabout is reached. Turn left and immediately right onto Westhill Road. Take the fifth turning on the right (St Marychurch Rd) then second left into St Paul's Rd. Continue on into St Paul's Crescent and the ground is on the left. Main entrance from Westlands Lane.

Nearest Railway Station Torre, 25 mins away. Main Torquay 2+ miles away.

52

TOTTON & ELING — Millers Park, Little Tesrwood Farm Salisbury Road Totton SO40 2RW — 07545 182 379

Leave M27 at Junction.2 and take A326 exit signposted Totton/Fawley. Almost immediately leave A326 onto slip road signposted Totton Town Centre which will meet the A36 (Salisbury Road). Turn left on to A36 and proceed for approx. three quarters of a mile and the ground entrance is on the left just before the Calmore Roundabout.

541

Nearest Railway Station Totton - 2.9km

Bus Route Cooks Lane - stop 280m away

TOW LAW TOWN — Ironworks Ground, Tow Law, Bishop Auckland DL13 4EQ — 01388 731 443

Leave the A1 at junction 58 and turn on to A68. Follow signs for Tow Law/Corbridge.
Ground is at far end of Tow Law on the left side.
The ground is situated on Ironworks Road, which is the first left after a sharp left hand bend on the A68 in Tow Law.

476

Nearest Railway Station Wolsingham - 4.8km

TOWER HAMLETS — Mile End Stadium, Rhodeswell Rd, Poplar E14 7TW — 020 8980 1885

From A12(A406/M11), leave A12 at junction with A11/A118 and turn right onto A11 (signposted Central London, Bow, Mile End). Keep driving along Bow Road until you come to Mile End Station. At this junction, turn left onto A1205 Burdett Road (signposted Rotherhithe Tunnel, Poplar). Keep going down this road until you come to a railway bridge, go under that and at the next junction do a right onto St Pauls Way. Go through the lights and bear right onto Rhodeswell Road, the ground/car park are on the right.
From A13, pass through Poplar along the East India Dock Road. At big junction turn right onto A1205 Burdett Road (signposted Mile End). Continue up this road up until you arrive at a junction and turn left onto St Pauls Way. Go through the lights and bear right onto Rhodeswell Road, the ground/car park are on the right.

415

Nearest Railway Station Mile End (Central, Dist, Hammersmith & City Lines), 5mins walk.

Bus Route 309, D6, D7, 277

TRAFFORD — First Point, Shawe View, Pennybridge Lane, Flixton Urmston M41 5AQ — 0161 747 1727

Anti-Clockwise exit at J10 (Trafford Centre) and turn right towards Urmston B5214. Straight across two roundabouts. First lights turn right into Moorside Road, at next roundabout take second exit in to Bowfell Road. At next lights turn sharp left then immediately right in to Pennybridge Lane next to Bird In Hand Pub, parking on left 100 yards. Or Leave M60 at J8, taking A6144 towards Lymm, Partington, Carrington. At second set of traffic lights turn right on B5158 towards Flixton. Remain on B5158 crossing railway bridge at Flixton Station and turn right at next set of traffic lights. Passing Bird in Hand Pub take immediate right in to Pennybridge Lane. Parking on left 100 yards.

Nearest Railway Station Urmston - 0.3km

TRANMERE ROVERS — Prenton Park, Prenton Road West, Birkenhead, Merseyside, CH42 9PY — 03330 144 452

North: From Liverpool city centre, travel through the Kingsway (Wallasey) Mersey Tunnel and after the toll booths (there is a £1.70 charge for cars), continue on the M53 to Junction 3. Take the first exit (signposted Birkenhead) and continue for approximately 1 mile passing Sainsbury's on the left hand side (keep in right hand lane). Turn right at the traffic lights at the Halfway House (pub), continue for 500 yards to the next set of traffic lights and turn left into Prenton Road West. The ground appears in front of you. South / East: M6, M56 and M53 to J4. Take the fourth exit from the roundabout onto the B5151 (Mount Road). Continue for 2.5 miles when Mount Road becomes Storeton Road and turn right onto Prenton Road West at traffic lights. The ground is on the righthand side in 200 yards.

54

TRING ATHLETIC — Grass Roots Stadium, Pendley Sports Centre, Cow Lane, Tring HP23 5NS — 01442 891 144

From M25 take A41 to Aylesbury. At roundabout at junction take last exit sign-posted Berkhamsted.
Turn next left into Cow Lane. Stadium is on the right at end of Cow Lane.

516

Nearest Railway Station Tring - 1.5km

Bus Route Bus stops at the ground.

TRURO CITY — Treyew Road, Truro, Cornwall TR1 2TH — 01872 225 400

On arriving at Exeter, leave the M5 at junction 31 and join the A30. Travel via Okehampton, Launceston, and Bodmin.. At the end of the dual carriageway (windmills on right hand side) take left hand turning signposted Truro. After approximately 7 miles turn right at traffic lights, travel downhill crossing over three roundabouts, following signs for Redruth. Approximately 500 metres after third roundabout signed 'Arch Hill', ground is situated on left hand side.

142

Nearest Railway Station Truro - 10min walk from the ground.

TUFFLEY ROVERS — Glevum Park Lower Tuffley Lane, Tuffley, Gloucester GL2 5DT — 07545 492 261

From the motorway junction 12 of the M5 motorway head towards Gloucester for a short distance on the B4008 down to a roundabout. At this roundabout take the second exit A38 towards Gloucester. After 1/2 mile you will reach another roundabout with a Holiday Inn on your right. Take the first exit continuing along the A38 on towards Gloucester until you reach a large traffic light junction at the end of the dual carriageway (approx 1.5 miles). At these lights continue straight over ignoring sign for Tuffley to the right. Once through this first set of lights keep in the right hand keep in the right filter lane to the next lights. Turn right here and head towards City Centre and Historic Docks along the Old Bristol Road. Just after the newly shaped road straightens along the old road take the turning right in to Lower Tuffley Lane. Continue along Lower Tuffley Lane almost to the end and the entrance to the ground is on the left through a gateway directly after the commercial premises of Marshall Langston and opposite a large transport depot.

422

Nearest Railway Station Gloucester - 3.5km

Bus Route Pearce Way stop - 197m away

TUNBRIDGE WELLS — Culverden Stadium, Culverden Down, Tunbridge Wells TN4 9SG — 07900 243 508

You can access Culverden Down via the A26 / St John's Road.

505

Nearest Railway Station Tunbridge Wells 1.5km. High Brooms - 1.8km

---

TYTHERINGTON ROCKS — Hardwicke Playing Field, Woodlands Road, Tytherington Glos GL12 8UJ — 07837 555 776

From M5 Junction 14 take A38 for Bristol. Tytherington turn-off is approx three (3) miles. Enter village, ground is signposted.

422

Bus Route Stowell Hill Road stop - 102m away

UNITED SERVICES PORTSMOUTH — Victory Stadium HMS Temeraire Burnaby Road Portsmouth PO1 2HB — 02392 573 041 (Gr'sman)

Leave the M27 at Junction 12 and join the M275 to Portsmouth. Follow the signs to Gunwharf, turn right at the traffic lights into Park Road, then at the next set of lights turn left into Burnaby Road and the ground entrance is at the end of the road on your right. Entrance is via HMS Temeraire.

541

Nearest Railway Station Portsmouth Harbour - 0.7km

Bus Route University - stop 120m away

UTTOXETER TOWN — Oldfields Sports Ground, Springfield Road, Uttoxeter, ST14 7JX — 01889 564 347

Exit M6 at junction 15 onto A500, head for Uttoxeter, then turn onto A50 following signs for Uttoxeter
Turn right at B5030 onto Ashbourne Road then continue onto Cheadle Road.
At Smithfield Hotel mini roundabout turn right onto Smithfield Road., then turn right onto Springfield Road.
The ground is on the left with parking in front.

436

Nearest Railway Station Uttoxeter - 1.1km

Bus Route Smithfield Road stop - 178m away

UXBRIDGE
Honeycroft Road, West Drayton, Middlesex UB7 8HX

01895 443 557

M4 to Junction 4 (Heathrow),
take A408 towards Uxbridge for 1 mile,
turn left into Horton Road.
Ground 1/2 mile on right.

372

Nearest Railway Station West Drayton - 1km

VCD ATHLETIC
Oakwood, Old Road, Crayford DA1 4DN

01322 524 262

Follow A2 until you reach the exit for A220/A223 towards Bexleyheath and Crayford. At the roundabout, take the second exit on to Bourne Road/A223. After just over half a mile, turn right onto the A207 London Road. Keep left at the fork, then turn left onto Crayford High Street/A2000. Where the A2000 bends right, go straight on to pick up Old Road, and the ground is on your right.

230

Nearest Railway Station Crayford - 0.9km

VERWOOD TOWN
Potterne Park Potterne Way Verwood Dorset BH21 6RS

01202 814 007

Turn off the A31 at Verwood/Matchams junctions just West of Ringwood Town centre exit (immediately after garage if coming from the East) to join the B3081. Follow the B3081 through the forest for approximately 4 miles coming into Verwood itself. At the second set of traffic lights turn left into Black Hill. At the roundabout take the 1st exit left into Newtown Road. At the end of Newtown Road turn left and then 1st left into Potterne Way. Note: Along Black Hill on the left you will pass Bradfords Building Merchants and the entrance to the Verwood Sports & Social Club where post match refreshments are made available.

541

Bus Route Potterne Bridge - stop 280m away

VIRGINIA WATER
Windsor FC, Stag Meadow, St Leonards Road Windsor SL4 3DR

01753 860 656

Exit M4 at Junction 6 – follow signs for Windsor – now on Royal Windsor Way relief road (A355/A322) – continue down this road over the River Thames and the flyover – until reaching a very large roundabout – take the 3rd exit into Imperial Road (signposted M3, Ascot and Legoland) until reaching T Junction with traffic lights – turn left at lights in St Leonards Road - after approx. a quarter of a mile take a right where the PREMIER (bright YELLOW signage) shop is. Ground entrance/car park is 200 metres.

422

Nearest Railway Station Windsor & Eton Central - 1.5km   **Bus Route** Stag Meadow stop - 131m away

WADHAM LODGE
Wadham Lodge Sports Ground, Kitchener Road, Walthamstow E17 4JP

07903 061 692

From North and West London - Use the M25 or any other means to get onto the North Circular Road (A406). Leave A406 at Crooked Billet roundabout slip road. At roundabout take the 4th turn off signposted Leyton/Walthamstow. After 300 yards you will see a church on your left. Turn left here into Brookscroft Road. Follow the road until you are forced to turn left. Turn left into Kitchener Road and you will see the gates to the ground and car park on your right. **From East London** - From the M11/A406 junction, follow road flow onto the Southend Road. Exit when you see sign for the A112. This takes you to the Crooked Billet Roundabout. Take the first exit to Walthamstow, then turn left into Brookscroft Road and follow directions above. **From South London** - The easiestway is through Blackwall Tunnel then follow signs for Stansted Airport until you get onto the M11 link road. You'll come through to Leytonstone and the Redbridge roundabout. Keep left until you flow onto the North Circular Road (A406). Take the A406, then follow the instructions for East London.B

415

Nearest Railway Station Walthamstow Central - Victoria Line/London Overground, 1.4 miles   **Bus Route** 34,97, 215, 357, approx. 1/4 mile

WALLINGFORD TOWN
Wallingford Sports Park, Hithercroft Road, Wallingford OX10 9RB

01491 835 044

N, S & E A4130 Wallingford Ring Road, signposted Didcot. Right at Hithercroft Road roundabout (signposted Hithercroft Industrial Estate). Ground 200 yds on left. West A4130 signs for Reading taking Ring Road (right first roundabout) along Calvin Thomas Way. Left 2nd roundabout Hithercroft Road. Ground on left. Wallingford centre East along High Street past Waitrose car park. Left 1st mini roundabout to Croft Road. Next mini roundabout right into Hithercroft Road. Ground is 0.5 miles on the right.

422

Nearest Railway Station Wallingford - 366m   **Bus Route** Moses Winter Way stop - 58m away

WALSALL WOOD
Oak Park, Lichfield Road, Walsall Wood, Walsall WS9 9NP

01922 ...

From North - Leave M6 at Junction 12 and take A5 until big island just outside Brownhills (next island after 'The Turn' pub on left). Take A452 Chester Road North through Brownhills High Street to traffic lights at Shire Oak (Pub at junction on right hand side). Turn left here into Brookscroft Road. Follow the road until you are forced to cross over and turn right immediately onto Oak Park Leisure Centre Car park (rear of Kentucky Fried Chicken). Proceed diagonally over car park and follow road round to ground entrance. **From South using M5/M6 motorways** - M5 North past Junction 1 onto M6 North. Leave at Junction 9 (Wednesbury turn off) and take A4148 to Walsall. Proceed for about 2 miles over several islands until going down a hill alongside the Arboretum. At big island at bottom, turn right onto A461 for Lichfield. Take A461 for about 4 miles and go through Walsall Wood village (after Barons Court Hotel on right) up the hill after village, Oak Park is on the left opposite Fitness First. Turn left and go diagonally across Oak Park Leisure Centre car park. Follow road round to ground entrance.

436

WALSHAM-LE-WILLOWS
The Meadow, Summer Road, Walsham-le-Willows IP31 3AH

01359 259 298

From Stanton heading to Diss on the A143 carry on till you pass the Duke of Malborough Public House, after 100yds take the next right which will be Summer Road and follow this road for about 2-3 miles, ground will be on the right hand side of the road.

402

WALTHAM ABBEY
Capershotts, Sewardstone Road, Waltham Abbey, Essex EN9 1NX

01992 711 287

Exit M25 at junction 26 and take 2nd left at roundabout into Honey Lane (A121).
At the Sewardstone roundabout, take third right into Sewarstone Road which takes you over the M25.
Ground is first right before cemetery.

218

Nearest Railway Station Waltham Cross - 2km   **Bus Route** Catersfield - stop 100m away

WALTHAM FOREST
Wadham Lodge, Kitchener Road, Walthamstow E17 4JP

07715 640 171

From the Crooked Billet roundabout (A406 North Circular Road) head south onto the A112 (Chingford Road) towards Walthamstow.
Take the 1st left into Brookscroft Road (St John's Church on the corner).
Follow this road to the end where it turns left into Kitchener Road and the ground is on the right.
Using postcode E17 4LJ should direct you correctly.

415

Nearest Railway Station Walthamstow Central - Victoria Line/London Overground.   **Bus Route** 34,97, 215, 357 – approx. 1/4 mile

WALTON & HERSHAM
Sports Ground, Stompond Lane, Walton-on-Thames KT12 1HF

01932 245 263

From Walton Bridge - On leaving bridge, follow sign to Esher (A244), keeping in middle-lane at traffic lights. Proceed along New Zealand Ave., through pedestrian lights (Sainsbury's on left) and traffic lights by Waror (Homebase on right). Keep in left lane at next lights (by pub), bear right at one-way system by war memorial, then carry on straight past cinema on left, still on A244 to Esher. Proceed along Hersham Road until the first mini-roundabout, turning right there in to Stompond Lane. The ground is immediately on the left and the main car park is on the left a little further on down Stompond Lane.

384

Nearest Railway Station Walton-on-Thames less a mile from the ground.

WALTON CASUALS
Elmbridge Sports Hub, Waterside Drive, Walton-on-Thames, Surrey KT12 2JP

07927 222 010

Follow A308 towards Staines/Kingston/Sunbury, continue until roundabout with second exit taking you onto Hampton Court Way/A309. Continue onto A3050, follow the A3050 via Bridge Road and Riverbank. After travelling along the latter for just over 3 miles take the second exit off the roundabout onto Waterside Drive. Follow until Sports Hub appears on the right.

231

Nearest Railway Station Both Walton and Hersham stations about 43min walk.   **Bus Route** Nos. 461 & 459 stop nearest the hub.

WANTAGE TOWN
Alfredian Park, Manor Road, Wantage OX12 8DW
01235 764 781

Proceed to Market Square. Take road at southeast corner (Newbury Street signposted to Hungerford). Continue for approximately a quarter of a mile take right turning into the ground. Clearly marked 'Wantage Town FC'.

422

Bus Route King Alfreds School stop - 423m away

WARE
Wodson Park, Wadesmill Road, Ware, Herts SG12 0UQ
01920 462 064

A10 off junction A602 and B1001 turn right at roundabout after 300 yards and follow Ware sign, past Rank factory. Turn left at main road onto A1170 (Wadesmill Road) Stadium is on the right after 3/4 mile.

219

Nearest Railway Station Ware - 1.9km   **Bus Route** Wodson Park - stop 100m away

WARMINSTER TOWN
Weymouth Street, Warminster BA12 9NS
01985 217 828

A36 from Salisbury, head for town centre, turn left at traffic lights in the town centre signposted A350 Shaftesbury. Club is situated approx. 400 yards on left hand side at top of Weymouth Street.

559

Nearest Railway Station Warminster - 0.9km   **Bus Route** Glebe Field - stop 80m away

WARRINGTON TOWN
Cantilever Park, Common Lane, Latchford, Warrington WA4 2RS
01925 653 044

From M62 Junction 9 Warrington Town Centre: Travel 1 mile south on A49, turn left at traffic lights into Loushers Lane, ground ½ mile on right hand side. From M6 North or South Junction 20: Follow A50 (Warrington signs) for 2 miles, cross Latchford Swingbridge, turn immediate left into Station Road, ground on left.

278

Nearest Railway Station Warrington Central - 2.3km   **Bus Route** Fairfield Gardens - stop 200m away

WASHINGTON
Nissan Sports Complex, Washington Road Sunderland SR5 3NS
0746 541 461

Leave the A19 on slip road marked "Nissan Offices" as you pass Sunderland travelling north. This is the A1290. Continue to follow "Nissan Offices" signs. Left at traffic lights, then right at roundabout into complex. Ground is at far end of the plant.

476

Nearest Railway Station East Boldon - 4.2km   **Bus Route** Ferryboat Lane - 453m away

WEALDSTONE
Grosvenor Vale, Ruislip, Middlesex HA4 6JQ
07790 038 095 / 01895 637 487

From the M1: Follow Signs for Heathrow Airport on the M25. Come off at Junction 16 onto the A40, come off at The Polish War Memorial junction A4180 sign posted to Ruislip, continue on West End Road, right into Grosvenor Vale after approx 1.5 miles, the ground is at the end of the road.
From the M25: Follow Take Junction 16 Off M25 onto A40. Then come off at The Polish War Memorial junction A4180 sign posted to Ruislip, continue on West End Road, right into Grosvenor Vale after approx 1.5 miles, the ground is at the end of the road.

144

Nearest Railway Station Ruislip and Ruislip Gardens both walking distance.   **Bus Route** E7

WEDNESFIELD
Cottage Ground, Amos Lane, Wednesfield WV11 1ND
07807 868 763

Going south, leave M6 at Junction 11 onto A460 towards Wolverhampton. After approx. 3 miles turn left at the Millhouse Public House into Pear Tree Lane. Continue on across mini-island into Knowle Lane. Continue across mini-island into Long Knowle Lane. Continue across mini-island into Amos Lane. Ground is about ½ mile along on left hand side.
Going north, leave M6 at Junction 10A onto M54. Leave M54 at Junction 1 onto A460 towards Wolverhampton. Turn left at Millhouse Public House and continue as above.

553

Nearest Railway Station Wolverhampton - 3km   **Bus Route** Cottages Homes - stop 20m away

WELLING UNITED
Park View Road Ground, Welling, Kent DA16 1SY
0208 301 1196

M25 to Dartford then A2 towards London.
Take Bexleyheath/Blackfen/Sidcup, turn off (six miles along A2) then follow A207 signed welling.
Ground is 1 mile From A2 on main road towards Welling High Street.

146

Nearest Railway Station Welling - 15-20 minute walk from the ground.   **Bus Route** Numbers 89, 486 and B16.

WELLINGBOROUGH TOWN
Victoria Mill Ground, London Road, Wellingborough NN8 2DP
01933 441 388

Leave A.45 at Wellingborough turn-off, pass Tesco's Store on left-hand side, up to roundabout. Take first exit to town centre. Ground is 300 yards on right-hand side. Entry just past the Dog & Duck public house adjacent to entry to Whitworths ground.

529

Nearest Railway Station Wellingborough - 1.2km   **Bus Route** The Dog & Duck Pub - stop 50m away

WELLINGBOROUGH WHITWORTH
Victoria Mill Ground, London Road, Wellingborough NN8 2DP
07825 632 545

Leave A.45 at Wellingborough turn-off, pass Tesco's Store on left-hand side, up to roundabout. Take first exit to town centre. Ground is 300 yards on right-hand side. Entry just past the Dog & Duck public house adjacent to entry to Whitworths ground.

529

Nearest Railway Station Wellingborough - 1.2km   **Bus Route** The Dog & Duck Pub - stop 50m away

WELLINGTON
Wellington Playing Field, North Street, Wellington TA21 8LY
01823 664 810

Leave the M5 motorway at Junction 26 and follow directions to Wellington. At town centre traffic lights take turning into North Street. Take the next left adjacent to the Fire Station and signposted 'Car Park'. The ground is in the corner of the car park.

559

Bus Route Nth St Police Station - stop 150m away

WELLINGTON
Wellington Playing Field, Wellington, Hereford HR4 8AZ
07842 186 643 (MD)

The Ground is situated in Wellington, behind School and opposite the Church. Wellington is 8 miles South of Leominster or 6 miles North of Hereford on the A49. At the Hereford end of the dual carriageway take the turn for Wellington.

553

Bus Route Wellington Village - stop 270m away

WELLINGTON AMATEURS — Fortis Stadium, School grove, Oakengates, Telford, Shrops TF2 6BQ

07738 715 038

From M54 take Junction 5. At roundabout take first left onto Rampart Way. At traffic lights take the first left onto A442 (Eastern Primary). Leave A442 at next junction. At roundabout (Greyhound Interchange), take the second exit onto B5061 (Holyhead Road). Just after red brick Church on right, turn right onto Vicar Street. Take the next left into School Grove. Continue to the end of the street and proceed up the slope onto the Car Park.

553

Nearest Railway Station Oakengates - 0.5km **Bus Route** School grove - stop 70m away

WELLS CITY — Athletic Ground, Rowdens Road, Wells, Somerset BA5 1TU

01749 679 971

From North & Southwest - Follow A39 to Strawberry Way to roundabout, follow A371 East Somerset Way and take right turn into Rowdens Road. Ground is on left. From East - Follow A371 from Shepton Mallet. After approximately 5 miles on East Somerset Way take left turn into Rowdens Road. Ground is on left.

559

Bus Route The Police Station - stop 20m away

WELTON ROVERS — West Clewes, North Road, Midsomer Norton, Bath BA3 2QD

02762 412 097

The ground is on the main A362 in Midsomer Norton.

559

Bus Route Elm View - 50m away

WELWYN GARDEN CITY — Herns Lane, Welwyn Garden City, Herts AL7 1TA

01707 329 358

Best Route to the Ground: From A1 (M) follow Welwyn Garden City signpost A1000.
Take second exit off one-way system, sign-posted Panshanger. Ground is 400 yards on left.

516

Nearest Railway Station Welwyn Garden City - 1.9km **Bus Route** Hernes Way - stop 160m away

WEMBLEY — Vale Farm, Watford Road, Sudbury, Wembley HA0 3HG.

0208 904 8169

Wembley FC is relatively close to both the A440 and the M1.
From Sudbury Town Station 1km along Watford Road.

516

Nearest Railway Station Sudbury Town Underground - 1km Sudbury & Harrow Road **Bus Route** Butlers Green - stop 150m away

WEST ALLOTMENT CELTIC — Druid Park, Callerton Lane, Woolsington, Newcastle Upon Tyne NE13 8DF

0191 250 7008

2 minutes drive from the A1 and only 200yds from Callerton Parkway Metro.
There is free parking on site for circa 100 cars with extra parking at Callerton Park Metro

476

Nearest Railway Station Callerton Parkway - 116m **Bus Route** Bus stops 70m from the ground.

WEST AUCKLAND TOWN — Darlington Road, West Auckland, Co. Durham DL14 9AQ

07951 292 036

Leave A1 at junction 58 on to the A68. Follow signs to W. Auckland/Corbridge.
On entering village, ground is behind factory on left side.
Ground is up a track on the left side of road next to Oakley Grange Farm.

476

Nearest Railway Station Bishop Auckland - 4.1km **Bus Route** Oakley Grange Farm - stop 128m away

WEST BRIDGFORD — Regatta Way, Gamston, West Bridgford, Nottingham NG2 5AT

07791 633 221

Follow M5 and M42 to A42 in Leicestershire. Continue on A42 to your destination in Nottinghamshire. Continue onto A42 after 13.7miles Keep left at the fork, follow signs for A453/A6/Nott'm(S)/Derby/East Midlands Airport. At Finger Farm Roundabout, take the 3rd exit onto Ashby Rd/A453. Ashby Rd/A453 turns slightly left and becomes Kegworth Interchange. Turn right to stay on Kegworth Interchange. Continue straight onto Remembrance Way/A453. At the roundabout, take the 2nd exit onto Clifton Ln/Remembrance Way/A453. At the roundabout, take the 2nd exit onto Clifton Ln/Remembrance Way/A453. At the roundabout, take the 1st exit and stay on Clifton Ln/Remembrance Way/A453. At The Farnborough Rd Roundabout, take the 2nd exit onto Clifton Ln/A453. Take the Newark (A46) exit toward Melton (A606)/Grantham (A52). At the roundabout, take the 1st exit onto Clifton Ln/B679. At the roundabout, take the 2nd exit onto the A52 ramp to A606/A46/Grantham/Melton/Newark/Tollerton. Merge onto Clifton Blvd/A52. At the roundabout, take the 2nd exit onto A52. At Wheatcroft Island, take the 2nd exit onto Gamston Lings Bar Rd/A52. Continue to follow A52. At Gamston Roundabout, take the 1st exit onto Radcliffe Rd/A6011. Turn right onto Regatta Way. **Nearest Railway Station:** Nottingham - 2.7km.

396

WEST DIDSBURY & CHORLTON — The Recreation Ground, End of Brookburn Road, Chorlton, Manchester M21 8FF

07891 298 441

From the M60 take junction 5 onto Princess Road towards city centre. Turn left at Christie Fields offices/Premier Inn onto Barlow Moor Road and continue past Chorlton Park to Chorlton bus station. Turn left into Beech Road, then 2nd left into Reynard Road and continue past the Chorltonville sign passing over 5 speed ramps as far as Brookburn Primary School. Turn left into Brookburn Road and continue to the end of the cul de sac, through the gateway and down the tarmac access which leads into the ground. From Stretford follow Edge Lane and turn right into St Clements Road at church. Continue through Chorlton Green and pass graveyard on left and then Bowling Green PH. Go past school and turn immediately right and continue to end of Brookburn Road as above. There is car parking within the grounds of the club, but restricted access for coaches.

449

WEST ESSEX — Barking FC, Mayesbrook Park, Lodge Avenue, Dagenham RM8 2JR

07956 557 438

Take the exit road from the A13 at Becontree Heath onto the A1153 Lodge Avenue turn off. We are approximately one mile down on the left. The 368 bus stops outside or opposite the ground - alternatively, buses 145,364 and number 5 are a short walk from the LIDL supermarket or from the A13 end get the 62 to the bottom of the hill and walk up Lodge Avenue. To reach us by train go to Upney station, turn left and at the bottom of the hill cross the road into the 'The Drive'. Go to the end of The Drive and enter Mayesbrook Park. Go to the left and the ground is about five minutes' walk and past the Sporthouse.

415

Nearest Railway Station Upney (District Line) 2 miles **Bus Route** 368 (50 yards) 5, 145, 364 (400 yards)

WESTBURY UNITED — Meadow Lane, Westbury, Wiltshire BA13 3QA

01373 764 197

From town centre proceed along Station Road towards rail station.
At double mini roundabout turn right. Ground is 300 metres on left hand side opposite Fire Station.

559

Nearest Railway Station Westbury - 1.1km **Bus Route** Sprinfield Road - stop 200m away

WESTFIELD — Woking Park, off Elmbridge Lane, Kingfield, Woking GU22 9BA

01483 771 106

Follow signs to Woking Leisure Centre on the A247.

384

Nearest Railway Station Woking **Bus Route** Arriva 34, 35

WESTFIELDS
Allpay Park, Widemarsh Common, Hereford HR4 9NA
07860 410 548

On reaching the outskirts of Hereford from Worcester, continue along A4103, over roundabout signposted Holmer and Leisure Centre. Proceed for 1 mile to large roundabout by the "Starting Gate Inn" and turn left towards Hereford. Proceed for ½ mile, past Hereford Leisure Centre and at mini roundabout, turn right. Proceed 150 yards and bear left around the Common, in front of Cricket Pavilion and immediately turn right into the driveway for Allpay Park.

Nearest Railway Station Hereford - 1km

Bus Route Priory Place stop - 165m away

436

WESTON-SUPER-MARE
Woodspring Stadium, Winterstoke Road, Weston-super-Mare BS24 9AA
01934 621 618

Leave the M5 at Junction 21, take the dual carriageway A370 and continue straight until the 4th roundabout with ASDA on the right. Turn left into Winterstoke Road, bypassing a mini roundabout and continue for 1/2 mile. Woodspring Stadium is on the right.

Nearest Railway Station Weston-Super-Mare - 25-30 minute walk away.

148

WEYMOUTH
Bob Lucas Stadium, Radipole Lane, Weymouth DT4 9XJ
01305 785 558

Approach Weymouth from Dorchester on the A354.
Turn right at first roundabout onto Weymouth Way, continue to the next roundabout then turn right (signposted Football Ground).
At the next roundabout take third exit into the ground.

Nearest Railway Station Weymouth - 2.2km

Bus Route Bus stops outside the ground

360

WEYMOUTH RESERVES
Bob Lucas Stadium, Radipole Lane, Weymouth DT4 9XJ
01305 785 558

Approach Weymouth from Dorchester on the A354.
Turn right at first roundabout onto Weymouth Way, continue to the next roundabout then turn right (signposted Football Ground).
At the next roundabout take third exit into the ground.

Nearest Railway Station Weymouth - 2.2km

Bus Route Bus stops at the ground.

541

WHICKHAM
Glebe Sports Club, Rectory Lane, Whickham NE11 9NQ
0191 4200 186

From A1M take the A692 junction, and travel in the direction signed to Consett. At top of the back the road forks left towards Consett, but you should take the right fork along the B6317 to Whickham. Follow this road for 1.5 miles, left turn into Rectory Lane (B6316). Take first right into Holme Avenue, and then first left. The ground is at top of lane. More car parking can be found further along Rectory Lane, take the next right. Walk past the cricket pitch to access the football club.

Nearest Railway Station Metrocentre - 2.1km

Bus Route Whaggs Lane-south - stop 105m away

476

WHITBY TOWN
Turnbull Ground, Upgang Lane, Whitby, North Yorks YO21 3HZ
Office: 01947 604847 CH:

On entering Whitby from both the A169 and A171 roads, take the first fork and follow signs for the "West Cliff".
Then turn left at the Spa Shop and Garage, along Love Lane to junction of the A174.
Turn right and the ground is 600 yards on the left.

Nearest Railway Station Whitby - 1km

Bus Route Argyle Road - 120m away

280

WHITCHURCH ALPORT
Yockings Park, Black Park Road, Whitchurch SY13 1PG
449

From the North either A41 or A49 into town. At main set of traffic lights turn first left (sign posted Whitchurch Alport FC) into Talbot Street, follow a long to Black Park Road, ground on the left. From the East A525 into Whitchurch, under the railway bridge and turn right into Queens Road, first left into Sainsbury Road then first right into Talbot Street than as above.

Nearest Railway Station Whitchurch - 0.4km

Bus Route Railway Station stop - 501m away

WHITCHURCH UNITED
Longmeadow Winchester Road Whitchurch Hampshire RG28 7RB
01256 892 493

From the South – take the A34 (North), 2 miles north of Bullington Cross take the Whitchurch exit. Head for Whitchurch Town Centre. The ground is 500 yards on your right. Postcode for Satellite Navigation systems RG28 7RB

Nearest Railway Station Whitchurch - 1.7km

Bus Route Charcot Close - stop 100m away

541

WHITEHAWK
The Enclosed Ground, East Brighton Park, Wilson Avenue, Brighton BN2 5TS
01273 609 736

From N (London) on M23/A23 – after passing Brighton boundary sign & twin pillars join A27 (sp Lewes); immediately after passing Sussex University (on L) leave A27 via slip rd at sp B2123, Falmer, Rottingdean; at roundabout at top of slip rd turn R onto B2123 (sp Falmer, Rottingdean); in 2m at traffic lights in Woodingdean turn R by Downs Hotel into Warren Road; in about 1m at traffic lights turn L into Wilson Ave, crossing racecourse; in 1¼m turn L at foot of hill (last turning before traffic lights) into East Brighton Park; follow lane for the ground.

Nearest Railway Station Brighton Central - two & half miles from the ground.

Bus Route B&H Bus No.7 or 27

150

WHITLEY BAY
Hillheads Park, Rink Way, Whitley Bay NE25 8HR
0191 291 3637

Leave the A19 on the A191, and turn eastwards towards Whitely Bay. Continue along New York Road (A191) which then becomes Rake Lane (A191). Pass hospital on right & then into Shields Rd. and Hillheads Rd (both A191). Ground is to the right, floodlights can be seen from miles away! It is next to an ice rink.

Nearest Railway Station Monkseaton - 768m

Bus Route Whitley Bay Ice Rink - stop 149m away

476

WHITSTABLE TOWN
The Belmont Ground, Belmont Road, Belmont, Whitstable CT5 1QP
01227 266 012

Approach East Kent on the M2 from the London direction towards Margate. Continue to the end of the motorway at Faversham. Proceed onto the A299 Thanet Way. (signposted Margate and Ramsgate). Continue on the A299 for approx 6 miles (passing Seasalter marshes on your left). Take the Whitstable turn off A2990. Continue until you reach the Long Reach roundabout and go straight ahead (second exit). Turn left at the second roundabout (Tesco). Descend Millstrood Hill. After passing the cemetery on your right, turn left into Grimshill Road. The entrance to the Belmont Ground is on the right, 140 yards along Grimshill Road. (SAT NAV - CT5 4LN)

Nearest Railway Station Whitstable 400 yards away

505

WHITTON UNITED
King George V Playing Fields, Old Norwich Road, Ipswich IP1 6LE
01473 464 030

Located just off the busy A1156 Bury Road into Ipswich.

Nearest Railway Station Westerfield - 2.9km

Bus Route Maypole (Old Norwich Rd) - 52m away

402

WHYTELEAFE
15 Church Road, Whyteleafe, Surrey CR3 0AR — 0208 660 5491

FROM THE M25 AND THE SOUTH: From Junction 6 of the M26 head north along the A22 (signposted to London, Croydon and Caterham). At Wapses Lodge Roundabout, the Ann Summers building is clearly visible opposite, take the third exit. Take the first left adjacent to Whyteleafe South railway station and cross the level crossing. Fork right after 200 yards into Church Road. The ground is a quarter of a mile down the road on the right. FROM THE NORTH: From Purley Cross (where the A23 crosses the A22), head south signposted to Eastbourne and the M25. Pass 'My Old China' (Chinese restaurant) on your right and continue under a railway bridge. Follow the A22 through Kenley and into Whyteleafe. At the first roundabout (with Whyteleafe Tavern opposite), turn right and cross a level crossing adjacent to Whyteleafe Station. Take first left into Church Road keeping St Luke Church to your right. The ground is a quarter of a mile up the road on the left.

Nearest Railway Station Whyteleafe South - 0.4km

231

WICK
Crabtree Park, Coomes Way, Wick, Littlehampton, W Sussex BN17 7LS — 01903 713 535

A27 to Crossbush. A284 towards Littlehampton.
After one mile over level crossing left into Coomes Way next to Locomotive pub. Ground at end.

Nearest Railway Station Littlehampton - 1.7km   **Bus Route** Seaton Road - stop 250 m away

495

WIDNES
Select Security Stadium, Lower House Lane, Widnes, Cheshire WA8 7DZ — 0151 510 6000

From the M62 - Exit at Junction 7, take A568 dual carriageway towards Widnes (Following brown signs to Halton Stadium). Keep right after junction onto Ashley Way (A562). Take 2nd exit off roundabout (McDonald's on the right). Take 2nd exit off mini-roundabout into Lowerhouse Lane. From Runcorn & the South: Cross Widnes/Runcorn Bridge (A533). Follow signs to Widnes (A562). At roundabout take 3rd exit towards Widnes Town Centre. Take first left following brown signs to Halton Stadium(McDonald's on the right). Take 2nd exit off mini-roundabout into Lowerhouse Lane.

Nearest Railway Station Widnes - 1.5km   **Bus Route** Cricketers Arms stop - 121m away

449

WILLAND ROVERS
Silver Street, Willand, Collumpton, Devon EX15 2RG — 01884 33885

Leave M5 Junction 27 and take first left at roundabout. Follow signs to Willand. After passing Halfway House pub on right, go straight over mini-roundabout (signposted to Cullompton) ground is 400 metres on left hand side.

Nearest Railway Station Tiverton Parkway - 3.2km   **Bus Route** Garage (Silver St) - stop 50m away

559

WILLINGTON
Hall Lane, Willington, Co. Durham DL15 0QG — 01388 745 912

The ground is situated off the A690 in Willington.

Bus Route Police House - stop 129m away

476

WIMBORNE TOWN
The W+S Stadium, Cowgrove Road, Wimborne, Dorset BH21 4EL — 01202 884 821

On the Wimborne To Blandford Road (B3082), turn left into Cowgrove Road just past Victoria Hospital.

Bus Route First School - stop 400m away

382

WINCANTON TOWN
Wincanton Sports Ground, Moor Lane, Wincanton. BA9 9RA — 01963 31815

Travelling to Wincanton on the A357 via Sturminster Newton turn right at the roundabout after passing under the A303 into Laurence Hill and follow the road across three further roundabouts into Southgate Road. Traffic from the A303 will also enter Southgate Road when following the signs to the town. At the junction turn right in the direction of Buckhorn Weston going under the A303 again before entering Moor Lane. Wincanton Sports Centre is on the left.

Nearest Railway Station Templecombe - 4.9km   **Bus Route** Balsam Lane - stop 1.2km away

559

WINCHESTER CITY
The Simplyhealth City Ground, Hillier Way, Winchester SO23 7SR — 07768 848 905

From Junction 9 on the M3 take the A33/A34 for one mile then follow A33 for a further mile.
Take the first left into Kings Worthy and follow the road for about three miles.
When you enter the 30mph zone take the second left, first right, then left into Hillier Way, Ground is on the right.

Nearest Railway Station Winchester - 0.9km   **Bus Route** Simonds Court - stop 250m away

383

WINDSOR
Stag Meadow, St Leonards Road, Windsor, Berks SL4 3DR — 01753 860 656

Exit M4 at Junction 6, follow dual carriageway (signposted Windsor) to large roundabout at end, take third exit into Imperial Road, turn left at T-junction into St Leonards Road. Ground approx ½ mile on right opposite Stag & Hounds public house.

Nearest Railway Station Windsor & Eton - 1.5km   **Bus Route** Stag Meadow stop - 131m away

422

WINGATE & FINCHLEY
Maurice Rebak Stadium, Summers Lane, Finchley N12 0PD — 020 8446 2217

The simplest way to get to The Harry Abrahams Stadium is to get on to the A406 North Circular Road.
If coming from the West (eg via M1), go past Henlys Corner (taking the left fork after the traffic lights) and then drive for about 1 mile. The exit to take is the one immediately after a BP garage. Take the slip road and then turn right at the lights onto the A1000. If coming from the East (eg via A10, M11) take the A1000 turn off. At the end of the slip road turn left at the lights. Go straight over the next set of lights. Then after 100m pass through another set of lights, then at the next set of lights turn right into Summers Lane. The stadium is a few hundred metres down on the right hand side. **Nearest Railway Station:** New Southgate - 2.3km

204

WINSFORD UNITED
The Barton Stadium, Kingsway, Winsford, Cheshire CW7 3AE — 01606 558 447

M6 to junction 18, follow A54 through Middlewich for approx. 3 miles, bear right at round-a-bout at Winsford Railway Station, follow road for approx. 1 mile, turn right into Kingsway, ground is on the right.

Nearest Railway Station Winsford - 1.2km   **Bus Route** Wesley Court stop - 34m away

449

WINSLOW UNITED
The Recreation Ground, Elmfields Gate, Winslow, Bucks MK18 3JG — 01296 713 057

Best Route to the Ground: A413 from Aylesbury to Winslow, turn right from High Street into Elmfields Gate. Ground is 100 yards on left. X21 Milton Keynes to Buckingham, turn left through Great Horwood to Winslow. Turn left from High Street into Elmfields Gate. PLEASE PARK IN PUBLIC CAR PARK OPPOSITE GROUND IF POSSIBLE.

Bus Route Elmside - stop 210m away

516

WINTERTON RANGERS — West Street, Winterton, Scunthorpe DN15 9QF. 01724 732 628

From Scunthorpe - Take A1077 Barton-on-Humber for 5 miles.
On entering Winterton take 3rd right (Eastgate), 3rd left (Northlands Rd) and 1st Right (West St).
Ground 200 yards on left.

463

Nearest Railway Station Scunthorpe - 6¼ miles   **Bus Route** Post Office - stop 150m away

---

WISBECH ST MARY — Wisbech St Mary Playing Fields, Beechings Close, Wisbech St Mary PE13 4SS 01945 411 777

Follow A47 towards Wisbech. Just before Ring's End turn left onto Gull Road/B1187.
Then turn right onto Gull Road.
Gull Road turns slightly left and becomes High Road, follow for just over 4 miles and then turn left onto Station Road.
Then turn left onto Beechings Close less than half a mile later.

402

Bus Route St Mary's Close (High Rd) stop - 362m away

WISBECH TOWN — The Elgoods Fenland Stadium, Lynn Road, Wisbech PE14 7AL 01945 581 511

From A1 follow signs for Wisbech (A47). At the outskirts of Wisbech, take 2nd exit off roundabout, signposted A47. After 1.5 miles, go straight over at the next roundabout. At next roundabout (another 3.1 miles on, Total Garage on right) take first exit (signposted B198 West Walton/Walsoken). Cross over next roundabout (which is new, so not marked on some maps and sat navs) and follow road for just over a mile. The entrance to the stadium is on the right via the right turn lane.

529

Bus Route Pumping Station - stop 370m away

WITHAM TOWN — Village Glass Stadium, Spa Road, Witham CM8 1UN 01376 511 198

From M25: At junction 28, take the A12/A1023 exit to Chelmsford/Romford/Brentwood.
At the roundabout, take the 1st exit onto the A12 ramp to Chelmsford/Harwich/A120.
Merge onto A12. At junction 21, exit onto Hatfield Rd/B1389 toward Witham.
Go through 2 roundabouts. Turn left onto Spinks Lane. Turn right onto Highfields Road.
Turn left ground will be on the right.

219

Nearest Railway Station Witham - 1.1km   **Bus Route** Cuppers Close - stop 200m away

---

WITHERIDGE — Edge Down Park, Fore Street, Witheridge EX16 8AH 01884 861 511

B3137 Tiverton to Witheridge, on entering the village football pitch is on the right-hand side before the Fire Station and School.

488

Bus Route School (B3137) - stop 174m away

WITTON ALBION — Wincham Park, Chapel Street, Wincham, CW9 6DA 01606 430 08

M6 Junction 19: Follow A556 for Northwich for three miles, through two sets of traffic lights. Turn right at the beginning of the dual carriageway onto A559. After ¾ mile turn right at traffic lights by Slow & Easy Public House, still following A559. After a further ¾ mile turn left a Black Greyhound Public House (signposted). Follow the road through the industrial estate for about ½ mile. Turn left immediately after crossing the canal bridge (signposted) **From M56 Junction 10:** Follow the A558 (Northwich Road) towards Northwich for approximately 6 miles. Turn right at the crossroads by the Black Greyhound Public House (signposted). Follow the road through the industrial estate for about ½ mile. Turn left immediately after crossing the canal bridge (signposted). **Nearest Railway Station:** Northwich - 1.2km

282

WIVENHOE TOWN — Maple Tree Cars Stadium, Broad Lane, Elmstead Road, Wivenhoe CO7 7HA

The ground is situated off the B1027 on the junction of Elmstead Road and Brightlingsea Road to the north of Wivenhoe.

40

Nearest Railway Station Wivenhoe - 2.4km.   **Bus Route** No.62.

WODSON PARK — Woodson Park Sports Centre, Wadesmill Road, Herts SG12 0UQ 01920 487 091

From the South: leave the M25 at junction 25 and take the A10 north past Cheshunt and Hoddesdon. After crossing the Lea Valley with Ware below and to your right, leave the A10 at the junction for the A1170 (signposted for Wadesmill and Thundridge). The slip road comes off the A10 onto a roundabout. Turn left (first exit) onto Wadesmill Road (A1170) and come back over the A10 to a second roundabout. Go straight over and take the first turn on the left into Wodson Park Sports Centre. The football ground is on the far left of the car park. From the North: Leave the A10 at the Ware North turn off (A1170). The slip road takes you to a r'about. Turn right (3rd exit) into Wadesmill Road and take the first left into Wodson Park Sports Centre.

516

Nearest Railway Station Ware - 2.1km   **Bus Route** Wodspn Park - stop 557m away

---

WOKING — The Laithwaite Community Stadium, Kingfield Road, Woking, Surrey GU22 9AA 01483 772 470

The ground is situated on the A247, opposite the entrance to Woking Park, midway between the town centre and Old Woking. Leave the M25 at either junctions 10 (Wisley) or 11 (Chertsey) and follow the signs towards Woking. When nearing the town centre follow the brown signs showing Heathside car park. The ground is about 15 minutes' walk from the car park. Come out of the car park and follow the signs for Woking FC. Travelling supporters are requested to use Heathside car park as there are no parking areas around the Stadium.

56

Nearest Railway Station Woking - about 15 mins from the ground.

WOKINGHAM & EMMBROOK — Lowther Road Wokingham RG41 1JB 01189 780 209

From M4 – exit J10 – take left slip road signposted Reading . After 100 yds exit to Winnersh Triangle /Earley . As you approach traffic lights go through both sets bearing right towards Earley/Winnersh /Wokingham . Continue to next set of traffic lights and keep left bearing left under Railway Bridge . Keep left and bear left at next set of traffic lights to Winnersh/Wokingham on A329 –Reading Road . Continue straight ahead to traffic lights – go straight ahead and continuing on A329 – Reading Road passing Sainsbury's on your right . Continue through next lights, under bridge and past BP garage on the left . Once past the garage take next left into Old Forest Road . Go over the bridge to next turn on the right hand side into Lowther Road and immediately right into the Emmbrook Sports and Social Club.

42

Nearest Railway Station Winnersh - 1.6km   **Bus Route** Toutley Close stop - 154m away

---

WOLVERHAMPTON CASUALS — Brinsford Stadium, Brinsford Lane, Wolverhampton WV10 7PR 07870 737 229

Turn onto M54 off M6 Northbound. Take Junction 2 and turn right onto A449 to Stafford. Go to next island and come back on yourself towards M54. Brinsford Lane is approximately ½ mile from island on left. Ground is 200 yards on left in Brinsford Lane.

55

Nearest Railway Station Billbrook - 4.8km   **Bus Route** Old Heath House - stop 350m away

---

WOLVERHAMPTON SPORTING CFC — Pride Park, Hazel Lane, Great Wyrley, Staffs WS6 6AA 07966 505 425

Going south, leave M6 at Junction 11 onto A460 towards Wolverhampton. After approx. 3 miles turn left at the Millhouse Public House into Pear Tree Lane. Continue on across mini-island into Knowle Lane. At Red Lion Public House continue across mini-island into Long Knowle Lane. Continue across mini-island into Amos Lane. Ground is about ½ mile along on left hand side. Going north, leave M6 at Junction 10A onto M54. Leave M54 at Junction 1 onto A460 towards Wolverhampton. Turn left at Millhouse Public House and continue as above.

55

Nearest Railway Station Ladywood - 1km   **Bus Route** Hazel Lane - stop 270m away

WOODBRIDGE TOWN
Notcutts Park, Fynn Road, Woodbridge IP12 4LS
01394 385 308

Get on A14 from A137.
Follow A14 and A12 to Ipswich Road/B1438.
Continue on Ipswich Road/B1438.
Drive to Fynn Road in Woodbridge.

Nearest Railway Station Woodbridge - 1.7km

Bus Route Ashton House (California) - 201m away

402

WOODLEY UNITED
Rivermoor Stadium, Scours Lane, Reading, Berkshire, RG30 6AY
0118 9453 555

Come off J12 of the M4 head along the A4 towards Reading, take a left onto Langley Hill and follow it all the way up onto Park Lane, continue onto School Road past the Tilehurst shops and then down onto Kentwood Hill. At the bottom of the hill take a right onto the Oxford Road towards Reading and just past the Waitrose Shop you need to take a left into an industrial estate and under the railway bridge and the ground will be in front of you to your right.

Nearest Railway Station Tilehurst - 1.2km

Bus Route Cold Store stop - 277m away

422

WOODSTOCK TOWN
New Road, Woodstock OX20 1PD
07748 1522 246

A44 from Oxford, turn right opposite The Crown into Hensington Road. After half a mile road bends to right, take 1st turning right into New Road. Ground on left.

Nearest Railway Station Hanborough - 2.9km

Bus Route Hensington Road stop - 118m away

422

WORCESTER CITY
The Victoria Ground, Birmingham Road, Bromsgrove B61 0DR
01905 23003

From M5 J4 take A38 to Bromsgrove, after island at M42 J1, take 1st right at Traffic Lights (signposted Bromsgrove North).
Ground is 1000 metres on right (opposite Tesco Garage).
From M42 J1, follow above directions from islands.

Nearest Railway Station Bromsgrove - two miles from the ground.

Bus Route 144/144a from Crowngate Bus Station

436

WORCESTER PARK
Skinners Field, Green Lane, Worcester Park, Surrey KT4 8AJ
0208 337 4995

From M25, come off at A3 turn off and head towards London, then come off at Worcester Park turn off, stay on this road until you pass station on your left and go under bridge, then take first left which is Green Lane, ground is 500 yards on the left.

Nearest Railway Station Worcester Park

Bus Route 151, 213, X26

384

WORKINGTON
Borough Park, Workington, Cumbria CA14 2DT
01900 602 871

A66 into Workington. At traffic lights at bottom of hill (HSBC opposite), turn left towards town centre. Approach traffic lights in centre lane (Washington Central Hotel on your right) and turn right. Continue on this road, passing over a mini roundabout, a pedestrian crossing and a further set of traffic lights. You will come to the Railway Station (facing you), carry on through the junction and bear right, passing the Derwent Park Stadium (Rugby League/speedway), then left and Borough Park becomes visible ahead of you.

Nearest Railway Station Workington - 0.6km

Bus Route Tesco - stop 100m away

284

WORKSOP TOWN
The Windsor Foodservice Stadium, off Sandy Lane, Worksop S80 1UJ
01909 479 955

From M1 junc 31 take A57 Worksop after 7 miles carry on to by-pass at 3rd roundabout take 1st exit Sandy Lane industrial estate Ground 1ml on left at side of Tyre Centre.
From A1 junc34 take B6045 Blyth, then take A57 Worksop at 1st set of lights go straight on pass the Hospital on the left,next set of lights straight on, at the next set go under the bridge,the next set of lights turn right,100mts up the road 1st right then turn first left into the ground.

Nearest Railway Station Worksop - 0.5km

Bus Route Grafton Street - stop 114m away

463

WORSBROUGH BRIDGE ATHLETIC
Park Road, Worsbrough Bridge, Barnsley S70 5LJ
01226 284 452

From M1 J36: Travel on the A61 towards Barnsley. The ground is approx. 2 miles from the junc. next to Worsbrough Mill Museum Car Park; From Doncaster: Travel on the A635 to Stairfoot roundabout, then take 2nd exit (B6100) signposted 'Worsbrough' The ground is 2 miles from the roundabout as you reach the A61.

Nearest Railway Station Barnsley - 3.1km

Bus Route West Street - stop 29m away

463

WORTHING
Woodside Road, Worthing, West Sussex BN14 7HQ
01903 233 444

A24 or A27 to Grove Lodge roundabout.
A24 (Town Centre exit) and right into South Farm Road.
Over five roundabouts take last on right (Pavilion Road) before level crossing.
Woodside Road on right, ground on left. 1/2 mile from BR.

Nearest Railway Station Worthing - 0.6km

206

WORTHING UNITED
The Robert Albon Memorial Ground, Lyons Way BN14 9JF
01903 234 466

From the West past Hill Barn roundabout to second set of traffic lights, turn left into Lyons Way.
From East first set of traffic lights at end of Sompting bypass, turn right into Lyons Way.

Nearest Railway Station East Worthing - 1.9km

Bus Route Lyons Farm Sainsbury's - stop 203m away

495

WREXHAM
Racecourse Ground, Mold road, Wrexham LL11 2AH
01978 891 864

From Wrexham by-pass (A483) exit at Mold junction (A451).
Follow signs for Town Centre and football ground is half a mile on the left hand side.

Nearest Railway Station Wrexham General is right next to the ground.

58

WROXHAM
Trafford Park, Skinners Lane, Wroxham NR12 8SJ
01603 783 536

Head North East from Norwich on the A1151 (Wroxham Road).
Over the railway bridge and straight over the mini roundabout.
Take the next left after the petrol station into Castle Street.
Over another railway bridge and turn left into Skinners Lane.
The entrance to the football ground is at the end on the left hand side.

Nearest Railway Station Hoveton & Wroxham - 1.6km

Bus Route 722, 724 and 717.

402

YATE TOWN

Jelf Stadium, Lodge Road, Yate, Bristol BS37 7LE

01454 228 103

From East: leave M4 J18, enter Yate on A432 via Chipping Sodbury bypass. Turn right at first small roundabout (Link Road), straight over next roundabout into Goose Green Way, over more roundabouts and 2 major sets of traffic lights. Turn right at third set of lights (by The Fox), then immediately left into Lodge Road. Ground 200m on right. From North: M5 (South) exit J14, B4509/B4060 into Chipping Sodbury. Turn right into Chipping Sodbury High Street, down Bowling Hill and right at first roundabout into Goose Green Way – then as above. From South: leave M5 at J15, then join M5. Leave M4 at J19, take second exit onto M32. Leave M32 at J1, at roundabout take first exit onto A4174. Continue on A4174 over traffic lights, then at roundabout take first exit onto A432. Enter Yate on A432, at traffic lights turn left into Stover Road (B4059), then at roundabout take second exit – still on B4059. Left at traffic lights (Fox PH) and immediately left into Lodge Road.

Nearest Railway Station Yate - 1km

Bus Route North Road - stop 100m away

383

YAXLEY

In2itive Park, Leading Drove, Holme Road, Yaxley, Peterborough PE3 7NA

01733 244 928

Leave A1 at Norman Cross and travel towards Peterborough. Turn off A15 at traffic lights. Bear immediately right and go past cemetery. At bottom of hill turn right into Main Street then left into Holme Road. After short distance go over small bridge and turn left between a bungalow and house into Leading Drove. Ground on left hand side.

Bus Route Churhc Street stop 300m away

529

YORK CITY

Bootham Crescent, York YO30 7AQ

01904 624 447

From Tadcaster (A64) take left turning onto A1237 (Outer Ringroad) continue for approx 5 miles to A19 and then turn right into York. Continue for just over 1 mile and turn left into Bootham Crescent opposite Grange Hotel.

Nearest Railway Station York - 20 min walk away.

106

YORKSHIRE AMATEUR

Bracken Edge, Roxholme Road, Leeds, LS8 4DZ (Sat. Nav. LS7 4JG)

0113 289 2886

M621 J2: A58 (Wetherby), up Roundhay Road to Fforde Green Hotel. Keep to right hand lane, through lights, double back at next set of lights. When back at first set of lights, right into Harehills Lane. Go uphill to 6th right turn (Sycamore Ave). Left at top. Entrance on right; A1 Nth: Exit at Wetherby junction. A58 towards Leeds. At outer Ring Road, cross roundabout, road becomes dual carriageway (Easterly Road). Cross roundabout. Take right lane until 2nd lights then right into Harehills Lane and as above; A1 Sth: Exit on A64. At Ring Road roundabout, right and at next roundabout left into Wetherby Road and Easterly Road, then as above.

Nearest Railway Station Leeds - 3.5km

Bus Route Harehills Ln Roxholme Ave - stop 168m away

463

Team	Page	Team	Page	Team	Page	Team	Page
AFC Junction (Normanton)	677	AFC Santander	666	Alconbury Res	577	Alphington Res	649
AFC Kempston Tn & Bedford Coll 'A'	574	AFC Scholes	680	Alder	600	Alresford Colne Rangers	583
AFC Kempston Tn & Bedford Coll Res	573	AFC Shifnal	662	Alderbury	672	Alresford Colne Rangers Res	583
AFC Kempston Town & Bedford College	573	AFC Solihull	436	Alderholt	643	Alsager Town Res	620
AFC Kesgrave	621	AFC Solihull Res	642	Alderholt Res	643	Alston Moor Sports Club	649
AFC Kesgrave Res	622	AFC Somers	642	Alderney FC	655	Altarnun	651
AFC Kilburn	665	AFC Sparta	644	Alemite Athletic	643	Altofts	631
AFC Kilburn Res	665	AFC Spelthorne Sports	623	Alemite Athletic Res	643	Altofts Res	632
AFC Kirkby	600	AFC Stanground Sports	614	Alexandra Park	672	Alton	637
AFC Laffans	637	AFC Stanground Sports 'A'	615	Alexandra Park 10th	674	Altrincham Hale	602
AFC Laffans Res	637	AFC Stanground Sports 'B'	615	Alexandra Park 3rd	673	Altrincham Hale	637
AFC Lewisham	595	AFC Stanground Sports Res	614	Alexandra Park 4th	673	Altrincham Hale Res	603
AFC Lindley	657	AFC Station	672	Alexandra Park 5th	673	Altrincham Res	580
AFC Liverpool Res	601	AFC Staverton	671	Alexandra Park 6th	673	Altrincham-Hale A	637
AFC Lynn	668	AFC Testwood	672	Alexandra Park 7th	673	Alumni	600
AFC Macclesfield	580	AFC Top Valley	669	Alexandra Park 8th	673	Alvaston United	665
AFC Mangotsfield	644	AFC Tyldesley	680	Alexandra Park 9th	674	Alveston	675
AFC Mangotsfield	645	AFC Uckfield Town II	664	Alexandra Park Res	673	Alvis Sporting Club	436
AFC Mangotsfield 'A'	646	AFC Uckfield Town III	664	Alexton & New Parks Dev	598	Alwoodley FC	681
AFC Mangotsfield B	646	AFC Uckfield Town IV	664	Alfold	495	Alwoodley FC Res	681
AFC Mangotsfield Res	646	AFC United	604	Alfold Res	678	Amanah	642
AFC Monton	602	AFC Varndeanians II	663	Alford Town	652	Ambassadors	678
AFC Monton Res	602	AFC Varndeanians III	664	Alford Town Res	652	Ambleside Town	679
AFC Morzinga	594	AFC Ventora	670	Alkerton Rangers	675	Ambleside Utd	679
AFC Mottingham	594	AFC Vesey	642	All-Star Panthers	652	Ambleside Utd Res	679
AFC Nailsea	679	AFC Villa	669	Allendale	650	Amersham Town	518
AFC Nailsea Res	680	AFC Walcountians	670	Allendale A	651	Amory Green Rovers	650
AFC Newbiggin	609	AFC Wednesbury	553	Allendale Res	651	Amory Green Rovers 2nds	650
AFC North	653	AFC Wembley	604	Allenton United	665	Ampthill Town Res	573
AFC North Leatherhead	658	AFC Westend	654	Aller Park Rangers	680	AMS - Men	640
AFC North Res	653	AFC Westend Res	654	Allestree	665	Anchor	643
AFC Oaklands	591	AFC Wootton	658	Allexton & New Parks	598	Andover Lions	589
AFC Oakley M&DH	573	AFC YourShirts	622	Alleyn Old Boys	672	Andoversford	647
AFC Oakley M&DH Res	574	AGC - Men	640	Alleyn Old Boys 3rd	673	Andoversford Res	647
AFC Oldham 2005	659	Aigburth Peoples Hall	600	Alleyn Old Boys 4th	673	Andoversford Thirds	647
AFC Oldsmiths	672	Aimbry	657	Alleyn Old Boys 5th	674	Angmering FC	678
AFC Oldsmiths 3rd	673	Ainsworth	659	Alleyn Old Boys 6th	674	Angmering Seniors	678
AFC Oldsmiths Res	673	Ainsworth Res	660	Alleyn Old Boys 7th	674	Angmering Seniors Res	679
AFC Orchard	652	Aintree Villa	600	Alleyn Old Boys Res	673	Annfield Plain	626
AFC Orton	615	Albanian	637	Alliance	664	Anstey Nomads Res	598
AFC Par	651	Albanian II	637	Allscott	553	Anstey Town	598
AFC Penistone Church	616	Albanian III	638	Almondbury WMC	657	Ansty Sports & Social Club	664
AFC Pennington	643	Albanian IV	639	Almondbury Woolpack	657	Ansty Sports & Social Club II	664
AFC Petersfield	589	Albrighton FC	662	Almondsbury UWE A	646	APBS	640
FC Phoenix	675	Albury	643	Almondsbury UWE Res	646	Apollo Rangers	653
FC Phoenix XI	672	Alcester Town	436	Alnmouth United	609	Apollo Tavern	655
FC Renegades	647	Alcester Town Res	675	Alpha & Omega	604	Apperley	647
FC Ringmer	663	Alcombe Rovers	676	Alphington 3rds	650	Apperley Res	647
FC Ringmer II	664	Alconbury	576	Alphington AFC	488	Appleby	679

Name	No.	Name	No.	Name	No.	Name	No.
Appleby Frodingham	578	Ashtonians Res	660	Aylesford	595	Barcombe	664
Appleby Res	679	Ashurst Wood	664	Aylestone Park OB Res	598	Barcombe II	664
Appledore AFC	488	Ashurst Wood II	664	Aylsham	571	Bardon Hill	598
Appledore Lions	667	Ashurst Wood III	664	Aylsham A	667	Bardsey	656
Appledore Res	667	Ashville	628	Aylsham Res	572	Barham Athletic	622
Ardingly	664	Ashville Res	628	Ayre United	657	Barham Athletic Res	622
Ardingly II	664	Askam United	629	Azaad Sports	553	Barkham Athletic	625
Ardington & Lockinge	665	Askam United Res	654	B.K.S. Sports	674	Barlestone St Giles	598
Arlingham	675	Askern	578	Babbacombe Corinthians	671	Barlestone St Giles Res	598
Arnold Saints	669	Aslockton Cranmers	611	Babbacombe Corinthians 2nds	671	Barlick Wanderers	649
Arnold Samba	669	Astley & Tyldesley FC	659	Bacton	667	Barmby Moor	634
Art Eternal	661	Astley & Tyldesley FC Res	660	Bacton United '89	621	Barnard Castle Glaxo Rangers	649
Arun Church	679	Aston	642	Bacton United '89 'A'	622	Barnet and Harrow	605
Asfordby	598	Aston Clinton	518	Bacton United '89 Res	622	Barnetby United	670
Ash Rangers	676	Aston Clinton Dev	435	Baddow Athletic	662	Barnetby United Res	671
ASHA FC	665	Aston United	611	Badsey United	675	Barnham Trojans	678
Ashbourne	620	Athersley Recreation Res	616	Bagshot Res	637	Barnham Trojans Res	679
Ashbrooke Belford House	626	Atherton Town	602	Baildon Trinity Athletic	631	Barnoldswick Barons	649
Ashburton	671	Atherton Town A	603	Bakewell Town	656	Barnoldswick Town	660
Ashburton 2nd	671	Atherton Town Res	602	Bakewell Town Res	657	Barns Green	678
Ashby Ivanhoe Res	598	Athletico Romsey	672	Balcombe	663	Barns Green Res	679
Ashby RAOB	670	Athletico Romsey A	672	Balcombe II	664	Barnslake	658
Ashby Road	660	Athletico Romsey Res	672	Baldock Town Res	591	Barnstaple FC	666
Ashcott	680	Atletico Corinthians	643	Ball Haye Green	620	Barnstaple FC Res	667
Ashcott A	681	Atletico Europa	574	Balsham	576	Barnston	583
Ashcott Res	680	Attenborough	611	Balti Sports	582	Barnston Res	583
Ashdon Villa	576	Attleborough Town	571	Balti Sports Res	651	Barnt Green Spartak	436
Ashfield FC	665	Attleborough Town A	646	Baltonsborough	663	Barnton Wanderers	649
Ashford	595	Attleborough Town Res	572	Bamber Bridge	660	Barnwood United	675
Ashford Ath Res	663	Audley & District	620	Bamford	657	Barnwood United Res	675
Ashingdon A	674	Audley & District Res	620	Bampton	650	Barrington	577
Ashingdon B	674	Avondale Rangers	643	Bampton 2nds	650	Barrington	669
Ashingdon Res	674	Avonmouth	645	BANBURY CROSS	641	Barrow Celtic	653
Ashington Colliers	609	Avonmouth 'A'	646	Banbury Galaxy	641	Barrow Celtic Res	654
Ashington Rovers	678	Avonmouth Res	646	Banbury Sports	641	Barrow Town Res	598
Ashland Rovers	611	Avonvale United	675	Banbury United Youth	641	Barrow Wanderers	654
Ashley	645	AVRO	602	Bank of England	672	Barsham	661
Ashley Res	645	AVRO Res	602	Bank of England 3rd	673	Bartestree	448
Ashover FC	656	Awliscombe United	650	Bank of England 4th	674	Bartestree	656
Ashridge Park	625	Awsworth Villa	611	Bank of England 5th	674	Bartestree Res	656
Ashton & Backwell United Res	619	Awsworth Villa Res	611	Bank of England Res	673	Bartley Green Continental	642
Ashton Athletic	660	Axbridge Town	679	Bankfield Old Boys	600	Bartley Reds United	642
Ashton Keynes	648	Axbridge Town Res	680	Banks Harbour	653	Barton Athletic	671
Ashton Keynes Res	648	Axminster Town 2nds	650	Banwell	619	Barton Athletic 2nds	671
Ashton United	645	Axminster Town 3rds	650	Banwell A	680	Barton Mills	577
Ashton United	660	Axminster Town AFC	488	Banwell Res	679	Barton United	436
Ashton United Res	646	Axmouth United	649	Bar 33	646	Bartons Willows	622
Ashton Villa	680	Aylesbury Dynamos	640	Bar Hill	576	Barwick & Stoford	680
Ashtonians	659	Aylesbury Dynamos Res	641	Bar Hill Res	577	Basford Utd Community	611

Team	No.	Team	No.	Team	No.	Team	No.
Basford Utd Community Res	611	Beer Albion	649	Beverley Town	593	Bishop Auckland Res	652
Basildon Town	586	Beer Albion 2nds	650	Beverley Town Academy	653	Bishops Cleeve FC Thirds	647
Basildon Town Res	586	Beesands Rovers	671	Beverley Town Res	652	Bishops Cleeve Res	587
Basingstoke Athletic	641	Beeston AFC	611	Beversbrook FC	633	Bishops Itchington	641
Basingstoke Labour	641	Beeston Juniors	681	Bewdley Town Res	553	Bishops Itchington Res	641
Basingstoke Royals	641	Beeston Juniors Res	681	Bexley	594	Bishops Lydeard Colts	676
Baslow	656	Beeston Old Boys Association	665	Bexley Res	595	Bishops Lydeard Res	676
Bassett Bulldogs	676	Beeston Res	611	Bexlians	594	Bishops Lynn	668
Bassingbourn	577	Beeston Rylands	669	Bibury	654	Bishops Stortford Swifts	585
Bassingbourn Res	577	Beeston St Anthony's	631	Bicester United	641	Bishops Stortford Swifts Res	586
Baston	614	Beeston St. Anthony's	681	Bickerstaffe	680	Bishops Waltham Dynamo's	672
Bath Villa	663	Beeston St. Anthony's Res	632	Bickleigh	649	Bishops Waltham Dynamos	670
Battersea Ironsides	623	Belgrave	660	Bickleigh 2nds	650	Bishopsteignton United	671
Bawtry Town FC	617	Belgrave	669	Bideford CAFC Res	667	Bishopsteignton United 2nds	671
Beacon Hill Rovers	586	Belgrave 2nd	670	Bideford Community AFC	666	Bishopthorpe United	634
Beacon Hill Rovers	662	Belgrave Wanderers	655	Biggleswade Res	573	Bisterne United	643
Beacon Hill Rovers Res	662	Belgrave Wanderers	655	Bilborough Town	611	Bisterne United Res	643
BEADS FC	606	Belle Vue Social Club	583	Bilborough United	611	Bitton Res	645
Bealonians	637	Belper Town Res	647	Bildeston Rangers	622	BKS Sports A	674
Bealonians II	637	Belper Utd Res	647	Billinge	580	Blaby & Whetstone Athletic Res	598
Bealonians III	638	Belrose	663	Billinge Community	680	Black Bull	680
Bealonians IV	639	Belstone	591	Billingham	652	Black Swan (Luton)	574
Bealonians VI	639	Belton	572	Billingham Town Res	606	Blackburn Eagles	643
Bealonians VII	639	Belton Res	661	Billingshurst 3rds	678	Blackburn Elite	643
Beaminster	669	Belton Villa	668	Billingshurst Res	678	Blackburn Olympic	643
Bearwood Athletic	642	Belvedere	595	Bilsthorpe	578	Blackburn United	643
Beaulieu Park	662	Bembridge	657	Bilsthorpe Res	611	Blackburn United Res	643
Beaumont Park	678	Bembridge Res	658	Bingham Town	611	Blackhill & Ebbchester	652
Beaumont Town	660	Bendix	644	Bingham Town Res	611	Blackpool Wren Rovers	629
Beaumont Town Res	660	Benfleet	586	Bingley Town First	648	Blackpool Wren Rovers Res	629
Beccles Caxton	572	Bengal Tigers	645	Bingley Town Res	649	Blackrod Town	659
Beccles Caxton Res	661	Bengeo Trinity	591	Binstead & COB	657	Blackrod Town Res	660
Beccles Town	571	Benhall St Mary	621	Binstead & COB	658	Blacon Youth FC	647
Beccles Town Res	572	Benhall St Mary Res	622	Birchover Park	611	Blacon Youth Res FC	648
Beckwithshaw Saints	656	Benson Lions	665	Birchwood	668	Blakeney	667
Beckwithshaw Saints Res	656	Benwick Athletic	577	Birchwood Res	668	Blakeney Res	668
Bedale Town	656	Benwick Athletic Res	577	Birkenhead Town FC	647	Blandford United	582
Bedale Town Res	656	Berinsfield	665	Birmingham Citadel	642	Blandford United Res	650
Bedford Albion	574	Berinsfield Res	665	Birmingham Irish	642	Blazing Rag	656
Bedford Albion Res	574	Berkeley Town	654	Birmingham Medics A	642	Blewbury	665
Bedgrove Dynamos	640	Berkeley Town Res	675	Birmingham Medics B	642	Blidworth Welfare	578
Bedgrove Dynamos Res	641	Berks County FC	624	Birmingham Tigers	448	Blidworth Welfare Red	665
Bedgrove United	641	Berks County FC Rovers	625	Birmingham Tigers	642	Blockley Sports	676
Bedgrove United Res	641	Berks County Res	625	Birstall Old Boys	668	Blofield United	571
Bedians AFC	659	Berrow	618	Birstall RBL	660	Blofield United Res	572
Bedlington Town	609	Berrow & Highbridge Town Res	677	Birstall United Res	598	Bloxbury Athletic	641
Bedminster Cricketers	646	Berrow Res	679	Birtley Town	609	Bloxham	641
Beechfield United	602	Berry Brow	657	Biscovey	651	Bloxham Res	641
Beehive FC	648	Beston	669	Bishop Auckland Hogans	649	Bloxwich Town	436

Name	No.	Name	No.	Name	No.	Name	No.
Bluebird United	669	Bottesford FC Res	668	Bradworthy	666	Bridgemarsh Res	674
Bluepool	642	Bottesford Town Res	670	Bradworthy Res	667	Bridgerule	667
Blunsdon FC	648	Bottisham	577	Braintree & Bocking United	662	Bridgeway	675
Bluntisham Rangers	576	Bounty United	641	Braintree & Bocking United Res	662	Bridgford United	665
Bluntisham Rangers Res	577	Bourne Blades	654	Braishfield	672	Bridgham Utd.	646
Blyth FC	609	Bournemouth Electric	643	Braishfield Res	672	Bridgwater Grasshoppers	676
Blyth Spartans Res	609	Bournemouth Electric Res	643	Braithwaite	679	Bridgwater Sports	676
Blyth Town A	609	Bournemouth Manor	643	Bramford United	621	Bridgwater Sports Colts	677
BNJS	642	Bournemouth Manor A Team	643	Bramford United Res	622	Bridgwater Sports Res	676
Boca Seniors	666	Bournemouth Manor Res	643	Bramham	635	Bridgwater Town FC Res	618
Bodicote Sports	641	Bournemouth Sports	643	Bramhope	656	Bridgwater Wolves	676
Bodicote Sports Res	641	Bournemouth Sports Res	643	Brampton	575	Bridlington SC County	652
Bohemians	655	Bourton Rovers	435	Brampton Res	577	Bridlington SC County Res	653
Bohemians Res	655	Bourton Rovers Thirds	647	Brandesburton	593	Bridlington Town County	653
Boldmere Sports & Social 'A'	642	Bovey Tracey	488	Brandesburton Res	653	Bridlington Town Res	593
Boldmere Sports & Social Falcons	436	Bovey Tracey 2nds	671	Brandon Sports	646	Bridon Ropes Res	595
Boldon CA	626	Bovingdon	591	Brandon Town	572	Bridport A	651
Boldre Royals	643	Bovingdon Res	592	Brandon Town Res.	646	Bridport Res	582
Bolney Rovers	664	Bovington Res	592	Bransgore United	643	Brigg Town FC Res	661
Bolton County	602	Bow Amateur Athletic Club	649	Brantham Athletic 'A'	583	Briggensians	671
Bolton County Res	603	Bowes	649	Brantham Athletic Res	583	Brighouse Athletic	657
Bolton Lads & Girls Club Res	603	Bowthorpe Rovers	646	Braunton	666	Brighouse Old Boys	631
Bolton Lads Club	660	Boxgrove	679	Braunton Fourths	667	Brighouse Old Boys Res	632
Bolton Nomads	659	Boxted Lodgers	583	Braunton Res	666	Brighouse Sports AFC	655
Bolton United	663	Boxted Lodgers Res	583	Braunton Thirds	667	Brighouse Town	660
Bolton Wyresdale	659	Boynton Sports	617	Bravehearts	650	Brighstone	657
Bolton Wyresdale A	660	Boys Brigade Old Boys	644	Braybrooke	625	Brighstone Res	658
Bolton Wyresdale Res	660	Brackley Sports	666	Bream Amts	667	Brightlingsea Regent A	583
Bookham	654	Brackley Sports Res.	666	Bream Amts Res	667	Brighton & Sussex Medical School	664
Boothstown	602	Braddan	657	Bredon	654	Brighton Electricity	644
Boothstown Res	603	Bradenham Wanderers	571	Bredon Res	647	Brill United	641
Bootle	653	Bradenham Wanderers Res	572	Breightmet United	602	Brimpton	625
Bootle Res	654	Bradfield Rovers	583	Breightmet United Res	603	Brimscombe & Thrupp Res	435
Bootle Res	628	Bradfield Rovers Res	583	Brent	638	Brimsham Green	644
Borden Village	594	Bradford Abbas	680	Brent II	639	Brinsworth Whitehill	616
Border Wanderers	678	Bradford FC	678	Brent III	639	Brislington Res	618
Border Wanderers Res	678	Bradford RIASA	660	Brentham	604	Bristol Barcelona	644
Boreham	662	Bradford Town Youth FC	677	Brentham Res	605	Bristol Barcelona 'A'	645
Boro Rangers	606	Brading Town	657	Brentwood Athletic	662	Bristol Barcelona Res	644
Boroughbridge	631	Brading Town A	658	Brentwood Athletic Res	662	Bristol Bilbao	645
Boroughbridge A	656	Brading Town Res	658	Brentwood Town Res	586	Bristol Eagles	645
Boroughbridge Res	632	Bradley	648	Brentwood United	670	Bristol Manor Farm Res	645
Boscastle	651	Bradley Res	649	Brereton Social	620	Bristol Spartak	646
Boscastle Res	652	Bradley Stoke Town	644	Bretforton Old Boys	676	Bristol Spartak Res	646
Boscombe Polonia	650	Bradley Stoke Town 'A'	645	Bretton North End	615	Bristol Telephones	587
Bosham	495	Bradley Stoke Town Res	644	Brhoden United	681	Bristol Telephones Res	646
Botanic	600	Bradninch	650	Bridge Hill	662	Briston	667
Botley Village	672	Bradwell	656	Bridge United	654	Britannia	653
Bottesford FC	668	Bradwell Res	657	Bridgemarsh	674	Britannia Res	654

Carshalton 3rd	673	Chagford 2nds	650	Cheadle Town	620	Chipperfield Corinthians Res	592
Carshalton 4th	674	Chagossian & Mauritian Association	664	Cheadle Town Res	580	Chipping Sodbury Town 'A'	644
Carshalton 5th	674	Chalfont Wasps Res	435	Cheadle Town Res	620	Chipping Sodbury Town Res	645
Carshalton 6th	674	Chalford	654	Checkemlads U18	601	Chipstead	594
Cartworth Moor	657	Chalford 3rds	675	Cheddar A	680	Chipstead Res	670
Cashes Green	675	Chalford Res	675	Cheddar Res	619	Chiseldon	676
Cask	657	Chalgrove	613	Chelmsley Wood	642	Chittlehampton	666
Castle Acre Swifts	572	Chalgrove Res	613	Cheltenham Civil Service	587	Chivenor	666
Castle Acre Swifts Res.	646	Chalk Lane	593	Cheltenham Civil Service 3rds	647	Chobham Burymead	676
Castle Cary	618	Chalke Valley	670	Cheltenham Civil Service 4ths	647	Chorley	660
Castle Cary Res	680	Chalvey (WMC) Sports A	652	Cheltenham Civil Service Res	647	Chorltonians	659
Castle Donington	668	Chalvey (WMC) Sports Res	652	Cheltenham Saracens Res	647	Chorltonians Res	659
Castle Donington Cobras	665	Chalvey Sports	435	Cheltenham United	647	Christchurch	674
Castle Donington Res	668	Chamberlayne Athletic	672	Cheriton Fitzpaine	650	Christians in Sport	661
Castle Hill	659	Chantry Grasshoppers	622	Cherry Bees	643	Christians in Sport 2nd XI	661
Castle Rising	668	Chantry Grasshoppers Res	622	Cherry Hinton	575	Christleton Celtic FC	647
Castle Vale Town	436	Chapel	678	Cherry Hinton A	577	Chudleigh Athletic	671
Castlecroft Rangers	642	Chapel Swifts	652	Cherry Hinton Res	576	Chudleigh Athletic 2nds	671
Castletown	657	Chapel Town	602	Chertsey Curfews	676	Chudleigh Athletic 3rds	671
Castletown Utd	679	Chapel Town Res	603	Chertsey Old Salesians	654	Church Fenton FC	634
Caterpillar	598	Chard Rangers	669	Cheshire Lines	628	Church Fenton Res	635
Caterpillar FC	668	Chard Rangers Res	669	Cheshire Lines Res	628	Church Stretton	553
Caterpillar FC Res	668	Chard United All Stars	669	Cheshunt U21s	592	Church Stretton	662
Catholic United	586	Chard Utd.	669	Chessington KC	623	Churchill Club 70	619
Catholic United Res	586	Chard Utd. Res	669	Chessington KC	659	Churchill Club 70 Res	679
Cavalry Arms	657	Charfield	675	Chester Argyle FC	648	Churwell Lions	681
Cavendish	648	Charfield Res	675	Chester Nomads	627	Churwell Lions FC	677
Cavendish Res	648	Charlton	613	Chester Nomads III FC	647	Cinque Port	583
Cawood	634	Charlton	680	Chester Nomads Res	628	Citigroup	638
CC Sport	595	Charlton & District	641	Chesterfield Town	665	City Colts	666
Cedars Park	622	Charlton & District Second	641	Chesterton	620	City Life	577
Cedars Park 'A'	622	Charlton Res	613	Chesterton	641	City of Liverpool Res	601
Cedars Park Res	622	Charlton Rovers	654	Chew Magna	619	City of Liverpool Res	628
Centenary Park	605	Charlton Rovers Res	647	Chew Magna Res	663	City of London	638
Central Ajax	676	Charlton Rovers Thirds	647	Chickerell United	650	City of London II	639
Central FC	650	Charlwood	670	Chickerell United A	651	City of London III	639
Central FC 2nds	650	Charmouth	669	Chickerell Utd Res	651	Civil Service	634
Centrals	655	Charnock Richard	660	Chiddingfold	676	Civil Service	656
Cestrian Alex FC	647	Chasewell Park	641	Chilcompton Sports	618	Civil Service	672
CFA FC	661	Chasewell Park Res	641	Chilcompton Sports Res	663	Civil Service 3rd	673
CGB Humbertherm	661	Chatburn	648	Chilcompton United	663	Civil Service 4th	673
Chacombe	641	Chatteris Fen Tigers	577	Childs Ercall	662	Civil Service 5th	673
Chadderton EDS	603	Chatteris Fen Tigers Res	577	Childwall Valley U18	601	Civil Service 6th	674
Chadderton Park	659	Chatteris Town	575	Chineham Sat	641	Civil Service 7th	674
Chadderton Res	602	Chatteris Town A	577	Chingford Athletic	586	Civil Service 8th	674
Chaddertonians	659	Chatteris Town B	577	Chinley	657	Civil Service Res	673
Chaddlewood Inn	670	Chatteris Town Res	576	Chinnor FC Res	613	CK Dons	668
Chaddlewood Miners Old Boys	669	Cheadle Hulme Athletic	659	Chippenham Park Dev	633	Clanfield	589
Chagford	649	Cheadle SMU	620	Chipperfield Corinthians	591	Clanfield Res	655

Clapham Old Xaverians	637	Cockers	646	Congresbury A	680	Corinthians 12	658
Clapham Old Xaverians II	638	Cockfield United	622	Congresbury Res	679	Corinthians Res	674
Clapham Old Xaverians III	639	Cockfield United Res	622	Coniston	654	Corinthians U21	653
Clapham Old Xaverians IV	639	Coddenham Athletic	622	Coniston Res	654	Corner Pin	669
Clapton in Gordano	679	Codsall High Old Boys	642	Connaught Red Star	583	Corsham Town Res	633
Clare Town	577	Coggeshall Town Res	583	Cononley Sports	649	Cosby United	660
Clare Town Res	577	Colby	657	Continental Star	436	Cosby United Res	660
Claverdon AFC	675	Colchester Athletic	583	Continental Star Res	448	Cosmos	646
Clay Cross Town	578	Colden Common	589	Cookham Dean	624	Cosmos Res	646
Claydon	621	Coldfield Rangers	642	Cookham Dean Res	624	Cossington Saints	668
Claydon Res	622	Coldham United	577	Cople & Bedford SA	573	Costessey Sports	572
Clayton Park Rangers	643	Coldham United Res	577	Coplestonians	621	Cote Heath	656
Clean Slate	518	Coldlands U21	642	Coplestonians 'A'	622	Cotgrave	611
Clean Slate Res	666	Coleford Athletic	663	Coplestonians Res	622	Cotham Old Boys	645
Cleator Moor Celtic	626	Coleford Athletic Res	663	Copley United	655	Coton Green	436
Clee Hill United	662	Coleford Town	667	Copmanthorpe	634	Coton Green Res	448
Cleethorpes Town 'A'	652	Coleford Town Res	667	Copmanthorpe Res	635	Cotswold Rangers	675
Cleeve West Town	618	Coleshill North Warwick	642	Copperas Hill	600	Cotswold Rangers Res	675
Cleeve West Town A	679	Coleshill United	665	Coppull United	629	Cottenham United	576
Cleeve West Town Res	679	Coleshill United Res	666	Coppull United Res	629	Cottenham United A	577
Clevedon United	618	Colkirk	646	Copthorne	663	Cottenham United Res	577
Clevedon United Res	619	College Wanderers	670	Copthorne II	664	Cottesmore Amateurs	598
Cliffe	634	Collegians	681	Copthorne III	664	Cottesmore Amateurs Res	598
Clifford FC	635	Collier Row U21	653	Copthorne IV	664	Cottingham Rangers	653
Clifton	574	Collingham	578	Corby Eagles	607	Countess Wear Dynamoes	650
Clifton All Whites	611	Collingham Juniors OB	681	Corby Hellenic Fisher	608	County Hall	598
Clifton All Whites Res	611	Colne	660	Corby Kingswood	607	Courtland Raiders	653
Clifton Rockets	645	Colne Athletic	583	Corby Kingswood Res	608	Coven Utd	662
Clifton Rockets Res	645	Colne Engaine	583	Corby Locos	607	Coventrians	436
Clifton St Vincents	645	Colne Valley	657	Corby Pegasus	607	Cowes Sports Res	657
Clifton St Vincents A Team	645	Colton Athletic	681	Corby Pegasus Res	607	Cowfold	495
Clifton St Vincents B Team	645	Colton Athletic Res	681	Corby Ravens	608	Cowfold 3rds	678
Clifton St Vincents Res	645	Colyton	649	Corby Ravens Res	608	Cowfold Res	678
Clifton Vale	645	Colyton 2nds	650	Corby S&L Khalsa	607	Cowling	648
Club AZ	637	Combe A	669	Corby Siam	608	Cowling Res	649
Club Corinthians	645	Combe Martin	666	Corby Strip Mills	607	Coxhoe Athletic	626
Club Langley	594	Combe Martin Res	667	Corby Strip Mills Res	608	CPA 1sts	642
Clubbies AFC	647	Combe Res	669	Corby Trades & Labour	608	CPA 2nds	642
Clutton	618	Combe St Nicholas	618	Corby United	608	Crackenedge	677
Clutton Res	663	Comberton United	576	Corby United Res	608	Cramlington Town	609
Clymping	495	Comberton United Res	577	Core Construction	676	Cramlington United	609
Clymping Res	678	Compton	672	Corfe Castle	651	Cranborne	582
Clyst Valley	649	Compton	665	Corfe Castle Res	651	Cranbrook	650
Clyst Valley 2nds	650	Compton Res	672	Corfe Mullen United	650	Crane Sports	621
CMB	629	Comrades	672	Corfe Mullen United Res	651	Cranes Sports Res	622
CMB	629	Comrades Res	672	Corinthian Sports	646	Cranfield United	573
CMB Res	629	Congleton Rovers	620	Corinthian Sports Res	646	Cranfield United Res	574
Coal Exchange	678	Congleton Vale	580	Corinthians	657	Cranford Park	605
Coalville Town Dev	598	Congresbury	618	Corinthians	674	Cranleigh	676

Name	No.	Name	No.	Name	No.
Cranmer Arms	669	Crowland Town Res	614	Dartmouth AFC	671
Craven Arms Town	662	Crowle Town Colts	670	Dartmouth AFC 2nd	671
Crawley Athletic	664	Crown F.M.N	642	Darwen Alexandra	643
Crawley Devils	664	Crown FC	593	Daten	580
Crawley GreenRes	573	Crown Gawthorpe	677	Daten 3rd	680
Crawley Panthers	664	Croxley Community	591	Daten 4th	680
Crawley United	664	Croydon BR FC	671	Daventry Drayton Grange	607
Crayford Arrows	595	Croydon BR Res	672	Daventry Rangers	608
Crediton United	488	Crusaders	661	Daventry Rangers Res	608
Crediton United 2nds	650	Crusaders	642	Davy FC	616
Creech FC	676	CS Rovers	574	Davy FC Res	617
Cresconians	642	CT 66	662	Dawlish	649
Cressing United	583	CT 66 Res	662	Dawlish United	649
Crewe	580	CT Shush	448	DC Auto Repairs	669
Crewkerne Rangers	669	CT Shush	642	DC UK	641
Crewkerne Rangers Res	669	CT Shush	642	DCK Maidenbower	664
Cribbs 'A'	644	CT Shush U21	663	DCK Maidenbower II	664
Cribbs 'B'	644	Cuckfield	664	De Veys	645
Cribbs Res	645	Cuckfield Developement	664	De Veys Res	644
Cricklade Town	633	Cuckfield II	664	Deal Community Sports	594
Cricklewood Wanderers	604	Cuckfield Town	664	Deal Sports Res	595
Croftlands Park	653	Cuffley	591	Deal Town Rangers	595
Crofton Sports	677	Cuffley Res	591	Deal Town Res	595
Crofton Sports Res	677	Cullercoats	609	Deanshanger Athletic	666
Cromer Town	571	Cullompton Rangers 2nds	649	Deanshanger Athletic Res.	666
Cromer Youth Old Boys	667	Culm United	650	Debden	576
Cromford	665	Cumberworth	657	Debden Sports	586
Cronies	649	Cumnor Minors	666	Debenham LC Res	622
Crook Town Wanderers	649	Curzon Ashton Dev	660	Deddington Town	641
Crooklands Casuals	629	Custy's	600	Deddington Town Res	641
Crooklands Casuals Res	654	Cutters Friday	618	Dedham Old Boys	583
Cropredy	613	Cutters Friday	644	Dedham Old Boys Res	583
Crosby Colts	670	Cuxton 91	595	Deepcut Community	654
Crosby Colts Res	671	D R G (Frenchay)	645	Deeping Rangers Res	614
Cross Hills	648	D.I.UTD	670	Deers Leap	676
Cross Hills Res	649	D.R.A.M. Community FC	677	Deighton FC	657
Crosscourt United	644	DAC Beachcroft	645	Del United	679
Crossway FC	648	Dagenham United	586	Delabole United	651
Crossways Spitfires	651	Dale	657	Delaford	652
Croston Sports	629	Dalton Athletic	656	Denaby Main	616
Croston Sports Res	629	Dalton Dynamos	657	Denaby United	616
Crouch End Vampires	672	Dalton United	629	Denholme United	655
Crouch End Vampires 3rd	673	Dalton United A	654	Denso	662
Crouch End Vampires 4th	673	Dalton United Res	654	Dent	679
Crouch End Vampires 5th	673	Danson Sports	672	Denton Town	580
Crouch End Vampires 6th	674	Darkside	658	Denver	668
Crouch End Vampires Res	673	Darlaston Town (1874)	553	Derby Singh Brothers	665
Croughton	641	Darley Dale Lions	656	Derbyshire Amateurs	665
Crowland Town	614	Darlington Res	626	Dereham Taverners	646
		Darlington Travellers Rest	649		

Dereham Taverners Res.	646
Dersingham Rovers	571
Dersingham Rovers Res	572
Desborough & Rothwell United	607
Desborough & Rothwell United Res	608
Desford	598
Desford Res	598
Desi	642
Devizes Town Res	633
Devonport FC	670
Dewsbury Rangers FC	681
Dewsbury Rangers FC Res	681
DHSOB	657
Didcot Eagles	666
Didmarton	675
Didsbury FC	659
Didsbury FC Second	659
Diggle	657
Digmoor	680
Dimple	665
Dinamo Flitwick	574
Dinnington Town	578
Ditchling	663
Ditchling II	664
Dittisham United	671
Ditton Minors	663
Diverse	641
Diversity United	644
Dobwalls	488
Dobwalls Res	651
Docking	668
Doddington United	577
Dodworth MWFC	617
Donhead Utd	651
Donyatt United	669
Dorchester	665
Dorchester Res	665
Dorchester Sports	582
Dorchester Sports Res	650
Dore Valley	656
Dorkinians	637
Dorkinians II	638
Dorkinians III	638
Dorkinians IV	639
Dorkinians V	639
Dorkinians VI	639
Dormansland Rockets	663
Dormansland Rockets II	664
Dosthill Rovers	642

Name	Page
Douglas & District	657
Douglas Athletic	657
Douglas Royal	657
Dove Holes	656
Dove Holes Res	656
Dowlish & Donyatt	669
Down Ampney	648
Downend	645
Downham Town Res	572
Dowty Dynamos	647
Dowty Dynamos Res	647
Draycott	679
Drayton	665
Drayton Town	670
Dreams & Peterborough Rangers	615
DRG Frenchay Res	644
Driffield Evening Institute	593
Driffield Evening Institute Res	653
Driffield Town	653
Drighlington FC	681
Drighlington FC Res	681
Dringhouses	634
Dringhouses Res	635
Droitwich Spa	436
Dronfield Old Boys	656
Dronfield Town A	656
Dronfield Town Res	578
Dronfield Woodhouse	657
Drummond Athletic	595
Dukinfield Town	602
Dukinfield Town Res	602
Dulverton Town	676
Dulwich Village	595
Dunkeswell Rovers	650
Dunmow Rhodes	662
Dunmow Rhodes Res	662
Dunnington	634
Dunnington Res	635
Dunsfold	654
Dunton & Broughton Dev	661
Dunton & Broughton Utd	660
Dunton & Broughton Utd Res	661
Durdham Down Rangers	645
Durham City Res	652
Durkar	677
Durley	672
Durley Res	672
Durning	662
Dursley Town	654
Dursley Town Res	675
Dussindale Rovers	572
Dussindale Rovers	668
Duston Dynamo's	666
Duxford United	576
Duxford United Res	577
Dynamo Kingston	658
E F Lakers	643
E.C.S.	657
E.C.S. Res	658
Eagle Sports	580
Eagley	629
Eagley Res	629
Ealandians	681
Ealandians III	681
Ealandians Res	681
Ealing Casuals	605
Earby Town	648
Earby Town Res	649
Earith United	577
Earl Shilton Albion	598
Earls Barton United	607
Earls Barton United Res	608
Earls Colne	583
Earls Colne Res	583
Earls Hall United	674
Earlswood Town	436
Earsham	572
Earsham Res	668
Easington Sports Res	435
Easington United	593
Easington United Casuals	653
Easington United Res	653
Easingwold Town	634
East Allington United	671
East Allington United 2nd	671
East Ardsley Wanderers	681
East Barnet Old Grammarians	672
East Barnet Old Grammarians 3rd	673
East Barnet Old Grammarians 4th	673
East Barnet Old Grammarians 5th	673
East Barnet Old Grammarians Res	673
East Bergholt United	621
East Bergholt United 'A'	622
East Bergholt United Res	622
East Budleigh	650
East Budleigh 2nds	650
East Coast	661
East Coker	680
East Court	664
East Cowes Vics Res	658
East Dean	678
East Drayton	670
East End Park	631
East End Park Res	632
East Grinstead Meads	664
East Grinstead Town III	664
East Harling	572
East Harling Res	572
East Hendred AFC	665
East Kent College	594
East Leake FC	668
East Leake Robins	668
East Manchester	602
East Manchester Academy	603
East Riding Rangers	593
East Riding Rangers 3rds	653
East Riding Rangers 4ths	653
East Riding Rangers Res	653
East Row First	664
East Ruston	667
East Villa	600
East Yorkshire Carnegie	593
Eastbourne Rangers II	664
Eastcombe	675
Eastcombe Res	675
Eastern Raiders	653
Eastham Athletic FC	647
Eastmoor	677
Easton	572
Easton Cowboys	645
Easton Cowboys A	646
Easton Cowboys Res	646
Easton Res	572
Eastrington Village	653
Eastwood Community	578
Eastwood Community Res	647
Eastwood Hanley	620
Eaton Socon	575
Eaton Socon A	577
Eaton Socon Res	576
Eccles	663
Eccles Res	663
Ecclesfield	680
Ecclesfield Red Rose 1915	616
Eccleshall Res	620
Eccleston & Heskin	663
Economicals	637
Economicals II	637
Economicals III	638
Economicals IV	638
Eden Thistle	679
Edgcumbe FC	651
Edge Hill Boys Club Old Boys	600
Egbertian II	638
Egbertian III	639
Egerton	580
Egham Athletic	676
Ekco Whitecaps	674
Elburton Villa	488
Eldon Celtic	624
Eli Lilly	600
Elland Allstars	655
Ellesmere Port FC	647
Ellesmere Port Town	628
Ellesmere Port Town FC A	647
Ellesmere Port Town Res	628
Ellingham	661
Ellwood Res	667
Elm Bank	635
Elmer FC	678
Elmhurst	640
Elmore	649
Elmore 2nds	650
Elmswell	622
Elstead	654
Elstow Abbey	573
Eltham Town	672
Elton Athletic FC	647
Elton Rigger FC	648
Elton Vale	602
Elton Vale Res	602
Ely City Res	576
Ely Crusaders	577
Ely Crusaders Res	577
Emerald Athletic	553
Emeronians	662
Endmoor KGR	679
Endmoor KGR Res	679
Enfield Borough	518
Enfield Old Grammarians	637
Enfield Old Grammarians II	638
Enfield Old Grammarians III	639
Enfield Old Grammarians IV	639
English Bicknor	654
English Bicknor Res	667
Enville Athletic	436

Name	No.	No.	Name	Name	No.
Epping	586	664	FC FotoGold	608	Felsted Rovers Res	662

Name	No.	No.	Name	Name	No.
Epping	586	664	FC FotoGold	Felsted Rovers Res	662
Epsom Casuals	659	572	FC Geordie	Feltham Rangers	658
Epworth Colts Blues	671	647	FC Georgies Bar	Feniton	649
Epworth Town	670	652	FC Graceholme	Feniton 2nds	650
Epworth Town Colts	670	668	FC Hamlets	Feniton 3rds	650
Epworth Town Res	670	647	FC Headingley	Fenstanton	576
Equalizers	667	648	FC Hodnet	Fenstanton Res	577
Erith 147 Sports	594	601	FC Imaan Lions	Fernhurst Sports	678
Erpingham United	667	615	FC Independence	Fernhurst Sports Res	678
Erpingham United Res	667	670	FC Khalsa GAD	Ferring	495
Eton Wick	652	435	FC Kokan	Ferring Res	644
Eton Wick Res	652	666	FC Lakeside	Ferryhill Town	649
Eunice Huntingdon	615	665	FC Lakeside Res	Field	631
Euro Garages	643	661	FC Lemsford	Field Res	632
Euroglaze FC	617	661	FC Lozells	Fieldhead Hospital	677
Euxton Villa	629	676	FC Mandeville	Filby & Runham	655
Euxton Villa Res	629	672	FC Mandeville Res	Filton Athletic	645
Evenwood Town	649	594	FC MSR All Stars	Filton Athletic Res	646
Evercreech Rovers	663	595	FC Oswestry Res	Finchampstead Res.	625
Evergreen	591	654	FC Peterborough	Finedon Volta	607
Evergreen	604	654	FC Peterborough A	Finedon Volta Res	608
Evergreen	645	654	FC Peterborough Rese	Finmere	641
Evergreen Res	592	681	FC Plummet Line	Finmere Res	641
Ewhurst	678	681	FC Polonia	Finn Harps U18	601
Ewhurst Res	678	663	FC Polonia	Fintan	647
Ewyas Harold	656	681	FC Prince	Fintan Res	647
Ewyas Harold Res	656	681	FC Slough	Fire United Christian	604
Exmoor Rangers	676	669	FC Spandits	First & Last	661
Exmouth Amateurs	649	669	FC St Helens	First Tower Utd	658
Exmouth Amateurs 2nds	650	594	FC Staines	Fishburn Park	606
Exmouth Spartans	650	595	FC Stratford	Fishponds Old Boys	646
Exmouth Town Res	649	604	FC Stratford A	Fishponds Old Boys Res	646
Exning United	576	643	FC Trunk	FISSC	675
Extreme United	662	654	FC UBER	FISSC Res	676
Exwick Villa	488	647	FC United Knaresborough	Fittleworth	678
Exwick Village	650	647	FC United of Manchester	Fittleworth Res	679
Eyam	656	654	FC Wickhamford	Fitzwilliam Old Boys	637
Eye United	615	652	Featherstone Colliery	Flackwell Heath Res	435
Eynsham	613	642	Feckenham	Flamengo	642
Eynsham Res	613	578	Feckenham Res	Fleckney Athletic	660
F C Stafford	553	647	Feeder	Fleet Spurs A	637
F1 Racing	634	611	Feeder Res	Fleet Spurs Res	637
Failsworth Dynamos	659	583	Felbridge	Fleet Spurs Vet	637
Failsworth Dynamos Res	659	668	Felixstowe Harpers United	Fleetdown United	594
Fairbank United	681	553	Felixstowe Rangers	Fleetdown United Res	595
Fairfield	664	604	Felling Magpies	Fleetlands	589
Fairfield FC	657	605	Felmingham	Fleetlands Res	655
Fairfield Villa	436	676	Felpham Colts	Fleetwood Hesketh	663
Fairford Town Res'	435	595	Felsted Rovers	Fletching	664
Fairwarp II	586				
Fakenham Town Res	659				
Falcons	671				
Falcons	670				
Falcons FC	670				
Falcons Res	670				
Falmouth Town Res	667				
Fantail	594				
Farcet United	667				
Fareport Town	667				
Faringdon Town	652				
Faringdon Town 'A'	652				
Faringdon Town Res	615				
Farley Boys	661				
Farley Boys 2nd X1	661				
Farnborough North End	676				
Farnborough O.B.G. 'A'	672				
Farnborough OB Guild	594				
Farnborough OB Guild Res	595				
Farncombe Athletic	654				
Farncombe Athletic A	654				
Farncombe Athletic Res	654				
Farnley Sports	681				
Farnley Sports Res	681				
Farrington Gurney	663				
Farsley Celtic Juniors	681				
Farsley Celtic Juniors Res	681				
Farway Res	669				
Farway United	669				
Faversham Strike Force Seniors	594				
Faversham Town Res	595				
FC Assyria	649				
FC Barolo	576				
FC Barometrics	662				
FC Barometrics Res	488				
FC Barometrics Thirds	650				
FC Barrow Island	656				
FC Beaconsfield	615				
FC Birmingham	613				
FC Bolsover	613				
FC Brizen	553				
FC Cavaliers	634				
FC Clacton Res	659				
FC Coalville	659				
FC Darlaston	681				
FC Deportivo Galicia	664				
FC Deportivo Galicia Res	657				
FC Dorcan	436				
FC Elmstead Res	435				

Fletching II	664	Freethorpe Res	572	Garden House Rangers	642	Globe Rangers	637
Flitch United	583	Fremington	666	Garforth Crusaders	681	Gloster Rovers	675
Flitch United Res	662	Fremington Res	667	Garforth Rangers	631	Gloucester Elmleaze	647
Flitwick Town	573	Frenford Senior	585	Garforth Rangers	681	Glyn Old Boys	637
Flitwick Town 'A'	574	Frenford Senior Res	586	Gargrave	648	Glyn Old Boys II	638
Flitwick Town Res	574	Frenford Senior U21	653	Garsington	613	Glyn Old Boys III	639
Flixton AFC	637	Freshford United	677	Garsington Res	613	Glyn Old Boys IV	639
Flockton FC	657	Friar Lane & Epworth	598	Garstang	629	GNG	598
Florence	620	Friar Lane & Epworth Res	598	Garstang Res	629	GNG Res	598
Foley Meir	620	Friary Vaults	670	Garswood United	580	GNP Sports	448
Foley Meir Res	620	Frilsham & Yattendon	624	Gas Recreation	583	Gobowen Celtic	662
Folsom	642	Frimley Select	637	Gas Recreation Res	583	Godalming & Farncombe Athletic	623
Fordham	576	Frome Collegians	663	Gatcliffe FC	670	Godmanchester Rovers Res	576
Fordham Res	577	Frome Town Sports	618	Gateshead FC A	609	Godolphin Atlantic Res	651
Fordingbridge Turks	643	Frome Town Sports Res	663	Gateshead Leam Rangers	626	Golborne Sports	580
Fordingbridge Turks Res	643	Frontline	652	Gateshead Redheugh 1957	609	Golcar United	677
Forest East	661	Frontline Res	652	Gateshead Rutherford	609	Golcar United Res	677
Forest Edge Rovers	672	Fry Club	618	Gayton United	572	Golcar Utd	657
Forest Glade U21	653	Fry Club Res	619	Gayton United A	668	Golden Lion	671
Forest Hall	609	Fry's Club OB	646	Gayton United Res	572	Goldenhill Wanderers	620
Forest Park	669	Fry's Club OB Res	646	Gedling Southbank	611	Goole United	593
Forest Row	663	Frys Club 'A'	644	Gedling Southbank A	669	Goonhavern Athletic	648
Forest Row II	664	Frys Club 'B'	644	Gedling Southbank Colts	669	Goose Green United	680
Forton Rangers	669	Fulbourn Institute	575	Geneva U18	601	Goring Cricket Club Res	644
Forton Rangers Res	669	Fulbourn Institute A	577	Gentlemens Club	661	Goring St Theresas	644
Fothergill-Whittles	657	Fulbourn Institute Res	576	Georgeham & Croyde	666	Goring United	625
Four Marks	589	Fulford FC	634	Georgeham & Croyde Res	667	Goring Utd Res	625
Four Marks Res	655	Fulham Compton Old Boys	637	Gerrans & St Mawes Utd	651	Goring-by-Sea Cricket Club	644
Fowlmere	575	Fulham Compton Old Boys II	638	Gidlow Athletic	680	Gorleston Res	572
Fowlmere Res	577	Fulham Compton Old Boys III	639	Gidlow Athletic Res	680	Gornal Colts	553
Fownhope	656	Fulwood Amateurs	629	Gilberdyke Phoenix	653	Gorran	651
Fownhope Res	656	Fulwood Amateurs Res	629	Gildersome Spurs OB	681	Gosfield United	662
Fox & Hounds (Batley)	677	Fulwood Amateurs Res A	629	Gillingham Town Res	582	Gosfield United Res	662
Foxdale	657	Furnace Green Rovers	664	Gillway Boys U21	642	Gosforth Bohemians	609
Foxhole Stars	651	Furness Cavaliers	629	Gimingham United	667	Govan Athletic	602
Foxhole Stars Res	651	Furness Cavaliers Res	653	Gimingham United Res	667	Govan Athletic A	637
Foxton	575	Furness Rovers	629	Girton United	576	Govan Athletic Res	603
Foxton Res	577	Furness Rovers Res	653	Girton United Res	577	Governors Athletic	657
Framlingham Town Res	622	Furness Vale	656	Glastonbury	618	Grainger Park B C	609
Frampton Athletic	645	Furngate	664	Glastonbury Res	663	Grampound	651
Frampton Athletic Res	644	Gala Wilton	587	Glen Villa	660	Grampound Res	651
Frampton United	587	Gala Wilton Fourths	647	Glen Villa Res	661	Grangefield OB	681
Frampton United 3rds	675	Gala Wilton Thirds	647	Glenfield Town	660	Grangetown Boys Club	606
Frampton United Res	675	Galleywood	586	Glenfield Town Res	661	Grappenhall Sports	580
Franklyn's FC	647	Galleywood Res	586	Glenside 5 Old Boys	646	Grassington Utd	648
Frecheville CA FC	616	Galmington Dragons	676	Glenside 5 Old Boys Res	646	Grassington Utd Res	649
Freeland	613	Galmpton United	488	Glinton & Northborough	614	Great Baddow	586
Freeland Res	613	Gamlingay United	575	Glinton & Northborough Res	615	Great Baddow Res	662
Freethorpe	572	Gamlingay United Res	577	Globe Bullough Park	643	Great Bentley	583

Name	No.	Name	No.	Name	No.	Name	No.
Great Bentley Res	583	GSK Ulverston Rangers Res	653	Hamble Utd Res	672	Hardwicke 3rds	675
Great Chishill	576	Gt Yarmouth Town Res	572	Hambledon	676	Hardwicke Res	675
Great Doddington	608	Guilden Morden	577	Hambledon A	654	Harefield St Mary's	652
Great Harwood Town	643	Guildford Barbarians	654	Hambrook	645	Harefield United Res	591
Great Horwood	666	Guildford Park	654	Hambrook Res	644	Harleston Town	571
Great Horwood Res.	666	Guildford Park Res	654	Hamilton Athletic Foxes	677	Harleston Town Res	572
Great Leighs Athletic	662	Guildford United	676	Hammer United	678	Harlington	574
Great Linford	666	Guisborough Three Fiddles	606	Hampstead Heath	591	Harlow Hill	656
Great Linford Res.	666	Gunnislake	651	Hampstead Heathens	638	Harold Hill	585
Great Milton	641	Gunthorpe Harriers	615	Hampsthwaite HC	656	Harold Hill Res	586
Great Paxton	576	Guru Nanak	594	Hampsthwaite United	656	Harold Hill U21	653
Great Paxton Res	577	Guru Nanak Res	595	Hampsthwaite United Res	656	Harold Wood Athletic	585
Great Preston	631	Guyhirn	577	Hampton	615	Harold Wood Athletic A	662
Great Shelford	575	Gymnasium	657	Hampton	436	Harold Wood Athletic B	662
Great Shelford Res	577	H T Dons	650	Hampton	642	Harold Wood Athletic Res	586
Great Yarmouth Town Hall	655	H.V.Academicals	657	Hamworthy Recreation	582	Harpole	607
Greenalls Padgate St Oswalds	580	Hackney Wick	604	Hamworthy Recreation Res	643	Harpole Res	608
Greenhill YC	668	Haddenham United	640	Hamworthy United Res	582	Harrison Signs FC	634
Greenhill YC 'A'	668	Haddenham United Res	640	Handcross Village	664	Harrow Bhoys	605
Greenhill YC Res	668	Hade Edge	657	Handcross Village II	664	Harrow Hill	654
Greens Park Rangers	645	Hadley A	592	Handcross Village III	664	Harrow Hill A	667
Greenways	594	Hadley Res	592	Handley Sports	651	Harrow Hill B	668
Greenwood Meadows Res	611	Hag Fold	680	Handsworth GSOB 'A'	642	Harrow Hill Res	667
Greetland AFC	655	Hagbourne United	665	Handsworth GSOB 'D'	642	Harrow Rangers	605
Greetland AFC Res	655	Haisboro Athletic	667	Handsworth GSOB B	642	Harston Bostocks	577
Grendon Rangers	518	Hale	628	Handsworth GSOB C	642	Harston Bostocks Res	577
Grendon Rangers Res.	666	Hale End Athletic	637	Handsworth Parramore Res	616	Hartcliffe	644
Greshams	667	Hale End Athletic II	637	Hangleton	644	Hartfield	664
Gresley Res	448	Hale End Athletic III	638	Hangleton FC Res	644	Harting	678
Gressenhall Res.*	646	Hale Leys United	518	Hanham Abbotonians	645	Harting Res	679
Gretton	607	Hale Rovers	637	Hanham Athletic	587	Hartland	666
Greyfriars Athletic	645	Halebank	580	Hanham Athletic Res	644	Hartland Clovelly Res	667
Greyfriars Athletic 'A'	644	Halesowen	642	Hanley Swan	647	Hartland Clovelly Thirds	667
Greyfriars Athletic 'B'	645	Halesworth Town	622	Hanley Town Res	620	Hartlepool FC	626
Greyfriars Athletic Res	644	Halesworth Town Res	622	Hannakins Farm	585	Hartley Wintney A	637
Greyhounders	611	Hall Green United	631	Hanney 66 Club	666	Harton and Westoe CW	626
Greystoke	679	Hall Green United	642	Hanney United	665	Hartshead	631
Griffin Athletic	653	Hall Green United Res	632	Hanslope	666	Hartshead Res	632
Grimethorpe Sports	616	Hall Road Rangers Res	593	Hanslope Res.	666	Harwell Village	665
Grimsby Borough Dev	652	Hallen Res	645	Hanson Jewellers	593	Harwich & Parkeston	583
Grimsby Borough Res	661	Halls AFC	594	Hanson Jewellers Res	653	Harwich Rangers	648
Grindleford	656	Halls AFC Res	595	Harbertonford	671	Harworth C	578
Grindleton	648	Halstead United	594	Harbertonford 2nd	671	Harworth CI Res	647
Grouville	658	Halstock	669	Harchester Hawks	625	Haslingden St Marys	629
Grouville Res	658	Haltemprice	653	Harchester Hawks Res	625	Haslingden St Marys Res	629
Grove Rangers	665	Halton Moor	677	Harchester United	653	Hatfield Heath	643
Grove Rangers Res	666	Halwill	649	Hardwick	575	Hatfield Peverel	583
Grundisburgh	621	Halwill 2nds	650	Hardwick Res	576	Hatfield Peverel Res	583
GSK Ulverston Rangers	629	Hamble Utd	672	Hardwicke	587	Hatfield Social	591

Imperial	618	Jersey Rangers	645	Kentisbeare	650	Kingskerswell & Chelston 2nds	671
Imperial Res	646	Jersey Rangers Res	645	Kentisbeare 2nds	650	Kingsmere United	641
Ince Central	680	Jersey Scottish	658	Kesgrave Kestrels	622	Kingstanding Celtic	642
Indian Gymkhana Club	604	John Fisher Old Boys	639	Kesgrave Kestrels Res	622	Kingsteignton Athletic	671
Indian Gymkhana Club Res	605	John Fisher Old Boys II	639	Keswick	679	Kingsteignton Athletic 2nds	671
Inf Men	640	Johnson & Phillips	595	Keswick Res	679	Kingston Albion	658
Infinity	589	Johnson and Philips Res	672	Kettering Nomads	607	Kingston Hull	653
Ingles	598	Jorvik Blades	634	Kettering Nomads Res	608	Kingstone Rovers	656
Ingles Res	598	JTC Jersey Wanderers	658	Kettering Orchard Park	607	Kingsway Rangers	660
Ingoldisthorpe	668	JTC Jersey Wanderers C	658	Ketton	614	Kingsway Rovers	675
Ingoldisthorpe Res	668	JTC Jersey Wanderers Res	658	Ketton Res	614	Kingsway Rovers Res	675
Inkberrow	436	Jubilee Sports	616	Kew Association	672	Kingswood	587
Inkberrow A	676	Junction	657	Kew Association 3rd	674	Kingswood	646
Inkberrow Res	676	Junction Inn	655	Kew Association Res	673	Kingswood Res	675
Inmar	672	K Sports Res	594	Kewstoke Lions	619	Kington Town	553
INT CORPS	640	K V F C	679	Kewstoke Lions Res	679	Kington Town Res	656
Intel FC	648	K.G.C	658	Keymer & Hassocks	664	Kinja FC	592
Interhound,	663	K&M Polonia Exeter	650	Keynsham Town A	646	Kintbury Rangers	665
Ipplepen Athletic	671	Kartel Sports	637	Keynsham Town Res	618	Kintbury Rangers Res	665
Ipplepen Athletic 2nds	671	KEA	641	Keyworth United	578	Kinver	642
Ipswich Athletic	621	KEA Res	641	Keyworth United Res	611	Kippax	631
Ipswich Athletic Res	622	Kedington	577	Kibworth Town	660	Kippax Res	632
Ipswich Exiles	621	Keele University	620	Kibworth Town Res	661	Kirby Muxloe Res	598
Ipswich Valley Rangers	621	Keele University Res	620	Kidlington Res	435	Kirk Deighton Rangers	656
Ipswich Wanderers Res	583	Keens Park Rangers	676	Kilkhampton	666	Kirk Deighton Rangers Res	656
IQRA	661	Kegworth Imperial	668	Killingworth Town	609	Kirkburton	657
Irlam Steel	602	Keinton Park Rangers	680	Killingworth YPC	609	Kirkby Athletic	665
Irlam Steel Res	603	Keinton Park Rangers Res	681	Kimberley Miners Welfare Res	611	Kirkby Athletic II	665
Iron Acton	644	Kellaway Rangers	646	Kings	647	Kirkby Malzeard	656
Iron Acton Res	644	Kellaway Rangers Res	646	Kings Cliffe	614	Kirkby Malzeard Res	656
Iron Tugboat City	672	Kellingley Welfare	631	Kings Cliffe Res	615	Kirkby Town Railway	628
Irthlingborough Rangers	608	Kelsall FC	647	Kings College Wimbledon	640	Kirkby United	653
Irthlingborough Town	608	Kelvedon Hatch	585	Kings College Wimbledon II	640	Kirkby United Res	654
Isleham United	577	Kelvedon Hatch Res	586	Kings College Wimbledon III	640	Kirkbymoorside	634
Isleham United Res	577	Kelvedon Social	583	Kings Heath Old Boys	642	Kirkheaton Rovers	657
Islington	643	Kelvedon Social A	662	Kings Hill	594	Kirkley & Pakefield 'A'	661
Iver Heath Rovers	652	Kelvedon Social Res	583	Kings Hill Res	663	Kirkley & Pakefield B	661
Iver Heath Rovers Res	652	Kempston Athletic	574	Kings Old Boys	637	Kirkley & Pakefield Res	571
Ivybridge Town 2nd	671	Kempston Hammers Sports	574	Kings Old Boys II	638	Kirkoswald	679
J L Rovers	604	Kempston Rovers Dev	573	Kings Res	647	Kirkoswald Res	679
J.M.C. Athletic	674	Kendal County	629	Kings Stanley	675	Kirton Brickworks	611
Jamaica Bell	645	Kendal County Res	679	Kings Stanley Res	675	Kislingbury JLB FC	608
James King Blisworth	607	Kendal Utd	679	Kings Sutton	641	Kitto FC	670
Jarrow FC	626	Kendal Utd Res	679	Kings Sutton Res	641	Kiveton Park	617
Jarvis Brook	495	Kennington	594	Kingsbridge & Kellaton United	671	Knaphill Athletic	676
Jarvis Brook II	664	Kennington Athletic	613	Kingsbury	669	Knaphill Athletic A	654
Jedenastka	661	Kensington Dragons	604	Kingsdale	671	Knaresborough Celtic	656
Jersey Portuguese	658	Kensington Dragons Res	605	Kingshill Sports	648	Knaresborough Celtic Res	656
Jersey Portuguese Res	658	Kenson	662	Kingskerswell & Chelston	671	Knaresborough Town	631

Name	No.	Name	No.	Name	No.	Name	No.
Littlehampton Town Athletic	679	Long Sutton Athletic Res	615	Ludgvan	648	Maidenhead Magpies Res	625
Littleover Dazzlers	665	Long Wittenham Athletic	665	Ludlow	553	Maidenhead Town	624
Littleport Town	576	Long Wittenham Athletic Res	665	Ludlow Colts	656	Maidenhead Town Res	625
Littleport Town Res	577	Longford	675	Lunesdale Utd	679	Maidstone Athletic	663
Littletown	677	Longford Res	675	Luton Aces	661	Malborough United	671
Littletown Res	678	Longham	646	Luton Leagrave AFC	661	Maldon Saints	662
LIV Supplies AFC	593	Longhope	667	Luton Leagreave	574	Malew	657
Liver Academy	600	Longlevens 3rds	675	Lutterworth Athletic Dev	661	Malgo	663
Liverpool Baltic	601	Longlevens 4ths	675	Lutterworth Town	598	Mallaby	627
Liverpool Medics	601	Longlevens 5ths	675	Lutterworth Town Res	598	Malmesbury Victoria Dev	633
Liverpool Nalgo	600	Longlevens Res	654	Luxol St Andrews FC	677	Malpas	580
Liversedge	660	Longridge Town	629	Lydbrook Athletic	654	Malt Shovel	635
Liverton U18	601	Longshaw	643	Lydbrook Athletic A	667	Malt Shovel Hawthorn	653
Liverton United	488	Longstanton	577	Lydbrook Athletic Res	667	Maltby Main Res	617
Liverton United 2nd	671	Longwell Green Res	645	Lydd Town Res	594	Malton & Norton	634
Lloyds Warren 3rd	674	Longwell Green Sports 'A'	644	Lydiard Millicent	633	Malton & Norton Res	635
LNER	605	Looe Town Res	652	Lydney Town A	667	Malvern Town Res	553
LNER Builders	635	Lord Raglan	643	Lydney Town B	668	Malvern Vale	647
Locking Park	679	Lostock Gralam	580	Lydney Town Res	654	Malvern Vale Res	647
Locking Park Res	679	Lostock St Gerards	629	Lyme Regis	649	Manby	652
Lockleaze Community	646	Lostock St Gerards Res	629	Lyme Regis 2nds	650	Manchester Central	602
Locks Heath	589	Lostwithiel	651	Lyme Rovers	669	Manchester Gregorians	602
Loddiswell Athletic	671	Lostwithiel Res	652	Lymm	660	Manchester Gregorians Res	602
Loddon United	571	Loughborough Emmanuel	668	Lymm A	660	Manchester Polonia	659
Loddon United Res (W)	572	Loughborough FC	598	Lymm Res	660	Manea United	576
Lodge Bar FC	647	Loughborough FC 'A'	668	Lympstone	649	Manford Way	585
Lodgefield Park	642	Loughborough FC Res	598	Lynch Pin	435	Manford Way Res	586
Lodsworth Res	679	Loughborough United	668	Lyndhurst	589	Mangotsfield Sports	645
London Airways	672	Loughborough United Res	668	Lyne Seniors	676	Mangravet	663
London APSA	586	Loughton Manor	518	Lyneham	676	Manningham Allstars JFC	648
London Hospital Old Boys	639	Louth Old Boys	652	Lynton & Lynmouth	667	Manor Athletic	680
London Lawyers	637	Louth Old Boys Vets	652	Lytchett and Upton Red Triangle	651	Manor Farm Saints	655
London Lions	591	Louth Town	661	Lytham Town	629	Manor FC	665
London Welsh	638	Louth Town Res	652	Lytham Town Res	629	Manor Hotel	617
London Welsh II	639	Lower Breck	600	M.C United	658	Manorcroft United	676
Long Ashton	619	Lower Breck Res	600	M&DH Clapham Sports	573	Mansfield Hosiery Mills	611
Long Ashton 'A'	646	Lower Green	658	Mablethorpe Athletic	652	Mansfield Rd	613
Long Ashton Res	646	Lower Hopton	677	Made for Ever	644	Mansfield Rd Res	613
Long Crendon	640	Lower Hopton Res	678	Madeley Sports	662	Manzur	655
Long Crendon Res	641	Lower Parkstone CFC	643	Madeley Sports Res	662	Manzur	655
Long Dog Soldiers	641	Lower Stratton	676	Magdala Amateurs	611	Mapperley	669
Long Lane	594	Lower Street	643	Maghull	627	March Rangers	577
Long Lane Res	595	LPOSSA	604	Maghull Res	628	March Rangers Res	577
Long Marston	640	LPOSSA Res	605	Magna 73	660	March Soccer School	577
Long Marston Res	641	Ludford Rovers	652	Magna 73 Res	661	March Town United Res	576
Long Riston	653	Ludgershall	640	Magna Exteriors	641	Marcham	665
Long Stratton	571	Ludgershall Res	641	Magpies (Saturday)	643	Marcham Res	666
Long Stratton Res	572	Ludgershall Sports	633	Maiden Newton & Cattistock	651	Marchester United	577
Long Sutton Athletic	614	Ludgvan	488	Maidenhead Magpies	624	Marconi Athletic	662

Name	No.	Name	No.	Name	No.	Name	No.
Marconi Athletic Res	662	MBNA FC	647	Merton 6th	674	Millbrook	488
Marden Minors	663	McCadam	675	Merton 7th	674	Millmead	676
Maresfield Village II	664	Meadow Rangers	663	Merton Res	673	Millmoor Juniors	616
Marham Wanderers	646	Meadowbrook Athletic	671	Methley United	681	Millmoor Juniors Dev	617
Mariners	655	Measham Welfare	668	Metrogas	594	Millmoor Juniors Res	616
Marist Rovers	653	Medbourne	607	Metrogas Res	595	Millom	629
Maristow	669	Medbourne Res	608	Mevagissey Res	651	Millom A	654
Maristow 2nd	670	Melbourn	577	Michael United	657	Millom Res	653
Market Bosworth	668	Melbourne Dynamo	665	Michelmersh & Timsbury	589	Millwey Rise	650
Market Drayton Tigers	620	Melbourne Dynamo Res	665	Michelmersh & Timsbury	672	Millwey Rise 2nds	650
Market Drayton Town Res	553	Melbourne Inn	670	Michelmersh & Timsbury Res	655	Milnthorpe Corinthians	629
Market Rasen Dev	652	Meldreth	577	Mickleham Old Boxhillians	638	Milnthorpe Corinthians Res	629
Market Rasen Town	661	Melksham Town 'A'	677	Mickleham Old Boxhillians II	639	Milton	576
Market Weighton United	653	Melksham Town 'B' FC	677	Mickleover RBL	578	Milton	607
Market Weighton United Res	653	Melksham Town Res	633	Mickleover RBL Res	647	Milton	659
Marks Tey	648	Mellor	659	Mickleover Sports Res	647	Milton A	577
Marlborough Res	676	Mellor Res	659	Middlestone Moor Masons Arms	649	Milton Keynes Academy	435
Marlborough Town	633	Mells & Vobster Utd	663	Middleton Cheney	613	Milton Res	576
Marlow United	624	Mells & Vobster Utd Res	663	Middleton Cheney	641	Milton United	620
Marnhull	651	Meltham Athletic	657	Middleton Old Boys	677	Milton United Res	620
Marnhull Res	651	Meltis Albion	573	Middleton Park	631	Milverton Rangers	676
Marown	657	Meltis Albion	573	Middleton Park	681	Minchinhampton	675
Marsden	657	Melton Town Dev	598	Middleton Rovers	653	Minchinhampton Res	675
Marsh Gibbon	666	Mendip Broadwalk	619	Middlewich Town	580	Minehead AFC	618
Marsh Gibbon Res.	666	Mendip Broadwalk 'A'	644	Middlezoy Athletic	677	Minehead Res	676
Marshalls	628	Mendip Broadwalk Res	644	Middlezoy Rovers	618	Minety	648
Marshalls Res	628	Mendlesham	621	Middlezoy Rovers Res	676	Misterton	669
Marshland Saints	668	Mendlesham Res	622	Midgley United	655	Misterton Res	669
Marston Shelton Rovers	573	Mepal Sports	577	Midgley United Res	655	Mistley	648
Marston Shelton Rovers Res	574	Mercian United	652	Midway	644	Mitcheldean	654
Marston Sts	613	Mere Town	582	Milborne Port	650	Mitcheldean A	668
Marston Sts Res	613	Mere Town Res	651	Milborne Port A	681	Mitcheldean Res	667
Martham	572	Mereway	607	Milborne Port Res	651	MK Gallactico Res.	666
Martham Res	572	Meridian VP Res	595	Mildenhall Town Res	576	MK Gallacticos	518
Martock United	680	Merley Cobham Sports	582	Mildenhall United	577	MK Wanderers	666
Martock United Res	681	Merley Cobham Sports Res	643	Mile End Park Rangers	604	MK Wanderers Res.	666
Mary Dendy	649	Merriott Dynamos	669	Milford	643	MMU Cheshire	620
Matlock Town ADS	665	Merriott Rovers	669	Milford & Witley	676	Moira United	665
Matlock Town Res	578	Merrow	623	Milkwall	667	Monkseaton	609
Matlock United	665	Merrow A	654	Milkwall Res	668	Montacute	680
Mattishall	571	Mersea Island	583	Mill Hill St Peters	629	Montefiore Halls	672
Mattishall Res	572	Mersey Batteries U18	601	Mill Hill St Peters Res	629	Montpelier Villa	495
May & Baker E.C.	585	Mersey Royal	628	Mill Hill Village	638	Montpelier Villa AFC II	664
May & Baker E.C. Res	586	Mersey Valley	580	Mill Hill Village II	639	Montpelier Villa AFC III	664
May & Baker E.C. U21	653	Merton	666	Milland	678	Montpelier	436
Maybridge	644	Merton	672	Milland Res	679	Moor Lane	634
Mayfield	665	Merton 3rd	673	Millbridge	669	Moors Academy	436
Mayfield Athletic	638	Merton 4th	674	Millbridge 2nd	669	Moorside	657
Mayland Village	662	Merton 5th	674	Millbridge 3rd	670	Moorside Rangers	659

Morchard Bishop	650	Mytchett Athletic	637	New Romney	594	Newton Road	622
Moredon	676	N P L	623	New Romney Res	595	Newton Rovers	671
Moreton Rangers	435	N.P.L	658	New Star Soccer FC	670	Newton Rovers 2nds	671
Morganians	676	N.P.L Res	659	New Town All Stars	676	Newton St Cyres	649
Morganians Res	677	Nailsea & Tickenham	618	New Zealand	640	Newton St Cyres 2nds	650
Morley Rangers	669	Nailsea & Tickenham Res	619	New-Magdalen AFC	638	Newton United	671
Morley Town AFC	681	Nailsea United	618	Newark Flowserve	611	Newton United 2nd	671
Morley Town AFC III	681	Nailsea United Res	619	Newark Town	578	Newtown	649
Morley Town AFC Res	681	Nailsea Utd A	679	Newburgh Harrock United	680	Newtown 2nds	649
Morley United	681	Nailsea Utd B	680	Newbury FC	624	Newtown AFC	680
Morley Village	646	Narborough	572	Newbury FC Res	625	Newtown Villa	678
Morley Village Res.	646	Narborough Foxes	661	Newbury Forest	586	Newtown Villa Res	678
Mortimer	624	Narborough Res.	646	Newbury Forest Res	586	Nicholas Wanderers	644
Mortimer Res	624	National Westminster Bank	638	Newcastle Chemfica	609	Nicholas Wanderers 'A'	645
Morwenstow Res	667	Nayland Rangers	648	Newcastle Town Res	620	Nicholas Wanderers Res	644
Mossley Hill Athletic	627	NCSF United	645	Newcastle University	609	Nirvana Athletic	661
Mossley Hill Athletic Res	628	Necton	572	Newchurch	658	Niton Community	658
Moston Brook	659	Necton Res.	646	Newdigate	678	Niton Community Res	658
Moston Brook Res	659	Needham Market Phoenix	622	Newdigate Res	678	NKF Burbage	436
Mostonians	659	Needingworth United	576	Newent Town	654	Nomads	595
Mostonians Res	659	Needingworth United Res	577	Newent Town A	667	Nomads A	670
Mott MacDonald	577	Neston Nomads	628	Newent Town Res	667	Nomads Res	670
Moulton	607	Neston Nomads III FC	647	Newhall United	665	Nomansland & Landford	672
Moulton Harrox	614	Neston Nomads Res	628	Newham United	586	Normalair	680
Moulton Harrox Res	614	Nether Stowey	677	Newick	664	Norman Wanderers	668
Moulton Res	608	Netherbury	669	Newlands Athletic FC	647	Normandy	637
Mount	657	Netherfield Albion	611	Newman College	663	Norristhorpe	681
Mount Athletic	600	Netherfield Seniors	669	Newnham Utd	668	Norristhorpe Res	681
Mount Gould FC	669	Netherley Woodlane Legion	600	Newport IOW A	658	Norsemen	672
Mount St. Mary's	681	Netherton	657	Newport Town	553	Norsemen 4th	673
Mountsorrel Amateurs	668	Netherton United	614	Newport Town Res	662	Norsemen 5th	673
Mountsorrel Amateurs Res	668	Netherton United 'A'	614	Newquay Res	648	Norsemen 6th	673
Mountsorrel FC	668	Netherton United 'B'	615	Newsome	657	Norsemen 7th	674
Mousehole	488	Netherton United Res	614	Newsome FC	677	Norsemen Res	673
MSB Woolton	600	Netley Central Sports	589	Newton	627	North A C	655
Mudeford Mens	643	Nettleham	661	Newton	647	North AC	655
Mudford	680	New Bohemians	617	Newton	659	North Bristol Trust	646
Mulbarton Wanderers	571	New Bradwell St Peter	518	Newton Abbot 66	671	North Bristol Trust Res	646
Mulbarton Wanderers A	646	New Carlton	677	Newton Abbot 66 2nd	671	North Bristol United	646
Mulbarton Wanderers Res	572	New Ferry Rangers FC	647	Newton Abbot Spurs	488	North Cave	652
Mullion	648	New Field	583	Newton Abbot Spurs 2nd	671	North Cotes	652
Mundford	571	New Field	648	Newton Athletic FC	647	North Curry	677
Mundford Res	572	New Field Res	648	Newton Aycliffe Navy Club	649	North Elmham	646
Mundon Vics	662	New Fordley	609	Newton Flotman	572	North Ferriby Athletic	593
Mundon Vics Res	662	New Hanford	604	Newton Heath	659	North Ferriby United Academy	652
Mursley United	518	New Holland Villa	670	Newton Heath 2nd Team	659	North Gawber Colliery	616
Mushet & Coalway Utd	667	New Milton Eagles	643	Newton Poppleford	650	North Hill	651
Mushet & Coalway Utd Res	667	New Parks Social 2015	660	Newton Poppleford 2nds	650	North Kilworth	661
Mutford & Wrentham	661	New Pot Oil	677	Newton Res	659	North Kilworth Res	661

North Leeds	681	Nottingham Community	669	Old Bancroftians AFC	640	Old Cliftonians Res	645
North Leeds Res	681	Nottingham Riverside United	669	Old Barkabbeyans	586	Old Colfeians	672
North Molton Sports Club	666	Nottingham Trent University	611	Old Barkabbeyans Res	586	Old Cothamians	646
North Molton Sports Club Res	667	Nottinghamshire FC	665	Old Batelians	681	Old Cothamians Res	646
North Nibley	675	Nottinghamshire FC II	665	Old Batelians Res	681	Old Crosbeians	638
North Oxford	665	Nottsborough	672	Old Bemrosians	665	Old Eastbournians	640
North Oxford Res	665	Nottsborough 3rd	673	Old Berkhamstedians	640	Old Elizabethans	645
North Petherton	676	Nottsborough 4th	673	Old Blackburnians	659	Old Elizabethans	665
North Petherton Res	677	Nottsborough Res	673	Old Blackburnians A	660	Old Elizabethans Res	645
North Petherwin	651	NUFC Oilers	672	Old Blackburnians Res	660	Old Epsomians	640
North Petherwin Res	651	NUFC Oilers Res	673	Old Blues	672	Old Etonians	640
North Shields Athletic	609	Nunthorpe Ath	606	Old Blues 3rd	673	Old Etonians II	640
North Somercotes United	652	Nursling	672	Old Blues 4th	674	Old Finchleians	672
North Somercotes United Res	652	Nutfield	670	Old Blues Res	673	Old Finchleians 3rd	673
North Sundon Wanderers	661	Nutfield Res	670	Old Boilers	638	Old Finchleians 4th	673
North Swindon WMC	676	Nutley	664	Old Boltonians	659	Old Finchleians 5th	673
North Tawton	650	Nutley II	664	Old Boltonians A	660	Old Finchleians 6th	673
North Thoresby	652	Nyetimber Pirates	678	Old Boltonians B	660	Old Finchleians 7th	673
North Walsham Town	571	Nyetimber Pirates Res	678	Old Boltonians Res	659	Old Finchleians Res	673
North Walsham Town A	667	Oadby Town Res	598	Old Bradfieldians	640	Old Foresters	640
North Walsham Town Res	572	Oakengates Athletic	662	Old Bradwell United	518	Old Foresters II	640
North Weald	643	Oakengates Rangers	662	Old Bradwell United Res	573	Old Foresters III	640
Northam Lions	666	Oakfield	657	Old Brentwoods	640	Old Garchonians	672
Northam Lions Res	667	Oakfield Res	658	Old Brentwoods II	640	Old Garchonians 3rd	673
Northampton Spartak	607	Oakham United Res	614	Old Brentwoods III	640	Old Garchonians 4th	673
Northbank Carlisle	609	Oakington Vikings	577	Old Bromleians	595	Old Garchonians Res	673
Northbrook	644	Oaksey	648	Old Bromleians Res	672	Old Georgians	645
Northerners	655	Ockham Res	654	Old Bromleians Res	595	Old Georgians Res	646
Northfield Athletic	675	Odcombe	680	Old Carthusians	640	Old Grantonians	639
Northfield Emerald 2013	661	Odcombe Res	681	Old Carthusians II	640	Old Guildfordians	638
Northfield Town	436	Odd Down (BATH) Res	618	Old Carthusians III	640	Old Guildfordians II	639
Northolt	643	Offord United	577	Old Centralians	631	Old Haberdashers	640
Northowram	655	Offwell Rangers	650	Old Centralians	681	Old Hall	655
Northowram Res	655	Okeford United	651	Old Centralians Res	632	Old Hamptonians	637
Northway	613	Okehampton Argyle	649	Old Centralians Res	681	Old Hamptonians II	638
Northwood St Johns	658	Old Aldenhamians	640	Old Challoners	639	Old Hamptonians III	639
Northwood St Johns Res	658	Old Aldenhamians II	640	Old Challoners II	639	Old Harrovians	640
Norton Athletic	661	Old Alleynians AFC	640	Old Chelmsfordians	586	Old Harrovians II	640
Norton Athletic	620	Old Alleynians AFC II	640	Old Chelmsfordians A	662	Old Harrovians III	640
Norton Athletic Res	661	Old Aloysians	637	Old Chelmsfordians B	662	Old Hill	642
Norton Canes	642	Old Aloysians II	637	Old Chelmsfordians Res	586	Old Horns	642
Norton Fitzwarren	676	Old Aloysians III	638	Old Chigwellians	640	Old Ignatians	637
Norton Fitzwarren Res	677	Old Aloysians IV	639	Old Chigwellians II	640	Old Ignatians II	637
Norwich CEYMS	571	Old Altrinchamians	602	Old Chigwellians III	640	Old Ignatians III	638
Norwich CEYMS Res	572	Old Altrinchamians	637	Old Cholmeleians	640	Old Ignatians IV	639
Norwich Eagles	668	Old Altrinchamians Res	603	Old Cholmeleians II	640	Old Ignatians V	639
Norwich Medics	668	Old Amplefordians	640	Old Cholmeleians III	640	Old Isleworthians	638
Nostell Miners Welfare	631	Old Ashtonians	659	Old Citizens	640	Old Johnians FC	640
Nostell Miners Welfare	677	Old Aylestone	660	Old Cliftonians	645	Old Kingsburians	638

Name	Page	Name	Page	Name	Page	Name	Page
Old Kingsburians II	639	Old Parkonians 6th	673	Old St Marys	638	Old Wilsonians 5th	674
Old Kingsburians III	639	Old Parkonians 7th	673	Old St Marys II	638	Old Wilsonians 6th	674
Old Kingsburians IV	639	Old Parkonians 8th	673	Old St Marys III	639	Old Wilsonians 7th	674
Old Lyonians	672	Old Parkonians 9th	673	Old Stationers	672	Old Wilsonians 8th	674
Old Lyonians 3rd	673	Old Parkonians Res	673	Old Stationers 3rd	673	Old Wilsonians 9th	674
Old Lyonians 4th	673	Old Parmiterians	592	Old Stationers Res	673	Old Wilsonians Res	673
Old Lyonians 5th	674	Old Parmiterians	637	Old Stoics	640	Old Wimbledonians	658
Old Lyonians Res	673	Old Parmiterians II	638	Old Strand Academicals	638	Old Windsor	652
Old Magdalenians	638	Old Parmiterians III	638	Old Stretfordians	659	Old Wokingians	637
Old Malton	634	Old Parmiterians IV	638	Old Suttonians	637	Old Wokingians II	638
Old Malton Res	635	Old Parmiterians V	638	Old Suttonians II	638	Old Wokingians III	638
Old Malvernians	640	Old Parmiterians VI	639	Old Suttonians III	638	Old Wokingians IV	639
Old Malvernians II	640	Old Parmiterians VII	639	Old Suttonians IV	638	Old Wokingians V	639
Old Mancunians	659	Old Parmiterians VIII	639	Old Suttonians SV	640	Old Wokingians VI	639
Old Mancunians A	660	Old Pauline	637	Old Suttonians V	639	Old Wokingians VII	639
Old Mancunians B	660	Old Pauline II	638	Old Suttonians VI	639	Old Wokingians VIII	639
Old Mancunians Res	660	Old Pauline III	638	Old Suttonians VII	639	Old Woodhouseians	637
Old Manorians	637	Old Pauline IV	639	Old Tenisonians	637	Old Woodhouseians II	638
Old Manorians II	638	Old Pegasonians	639	Old Tenisonians II	638	Old Woodhouseians III	639
Old Manorians III	638	Old Radleians	640	Old Tenisonians III	639	Old Woodhouseians IV	639
Old Manorians IV	639	Old Reptonians	640	Old Thorntonians	637	Old Wulfrunians	553
Old Manorians V	639	Old Richians	675	Old Thorntonians II	638	Old Wulfrunians 'A'	642
Old Marlburians	640	Old Richians Res	675	Old Thorntonians III	638	Old Wulfrunians B	642
Old Meadonians	637	Old Roan	594	Old Thorntonians IV	638	Old Wykehamists	640
Old Meadonians II	637	Old Rugbeians	640	Old Thorntonians V	639	Old Wykehamists II	640
Old Meadonians III	638	Old Rutlishians	659	Old Thorntonians VI	639	Old Xaverians	600
Old Meadonians IV	638	Old Salesians	672	Old Tiffinians	638	Old Xaverians Res	600
Old Meadonians IX	639	Old Salesians	676	Old Tiffinians II	639	Old Xaverians U18	601
Old Meadonians V	638	Old Salesians 3rd	674	Old Tiffinians III	639	Oldbury FC	646
Old Meadonians VI	638	Old Salesians Res	674	Old Tiffinians IV	639	Oldbury FC Res	646
Old Meadonians VII	639	Old Salopians	640	Old Tollingtonians	637	Oldbury United	553
Old Meadonians VIII	639	Old Salopians II	640	Old Tollingtonians II	639	Oldham Hulmeians	659
Old Merchant Taylors	640	Old Salvatorians	637	Old Tollingtonians III	639	Oldham Hulmeians A	660
Old Merchant Taylors II	640	Old Salvatorians II	637	Old Tonbridgians	640	Oldham Hulmeians B	660
Old Millfieldians	640	Old Salvatorians III	638	Old Tonbridgians II	640	Oldham Hulmeians Res	659
Old Minchendenians	637	Old Salvatorians IV	639	Old Town United	676	Oldham Victoria	659
Old Minchendenians II	638	Old Salvatorians V	639	Old Trafford and Gorse Hill	659	Oldland Abbotonians Res	645
Old Minchendenians III	638	Old Sedcopians	637	Old Uffingtonians	638	Olney	666
Old Minchendenians IV	639	Old Sedcopians II	638	Old Vaughanians	638	Olton Ravens U21	642
Old Newton United	621	Old Sedcopians III	639	Old Vaughanians II	639	Olveston United	645
Old Newton United Res	622	Old Sedcopians IV	639	Old Vaughanians III	639	Olveston United Res	644
Old Owens	672	Old Sennockians	640	Old Wellingtonians	640	Onchan	657
Old Owens 3rd	673	Old Sodbury	645	Old Westminsters	640	Ongar Town	586
Old Owens 4th	673	Old Sodbury Res	644	Old Westminsters II	640	Orange Athletic Chester FC	648
Old Owens 5th	674	Old Southendian	586	Old Whitgiftian	638	Orchard Park	653
Old Parkonians	672	Old Southendian A	674	Old Whitgiftian II	639	Orchard Park Res	653
Old Parkonians 3rd	673	Old Southendian B	674	Old Wilsonians	672	Origin Headley	641
Old Parkonians 4th	673	Old Southendian Res	586	Old Wilsonians 3rd	673	Orleton Colts	656
Old Parkonians 5th	673	Old Southendian U21	653	Old Wilsonians 4th	674	Orleton Colts Res	656

Name	No.	Name	No.	Name	No.	Name	No.
Polytechnic Res	673	Premium	669	R Sigs	640	Ravenstone United	668
Pond Park Rangers	640	Prescot Cables Res	628	RAC - Men	640	Rawcliffe	634
Pontefract Sports & Social	677	Prestbury Rovers	647	Radcliffe Boys	660	Rawdon Old Boys	631
Ponteland United	609	Prestbury Rovers Res	647	Radcliffe Boys Res	660	Rayleigh Town	585
Pool	631	Preston Wanderers	663	Radcliffe JFC	659	Rayleigh Town A	662
Pool A	656	Prestwich	659	Radcliffe Olympic	611	Rayleigh Town Res	586
Pool Res	632	Prestwich Heys Res	602	Radcliffe St Mary's	659	Rayners Lane Res	592
Poole Borough	650	Prince of Wales (OCR)	677	Radcliffe St Mary's Res	660	RBFC A	655
Poole Borough Res	643	Princes Villa FC	648	Radcliffe Town	659	RBFC B	655
Poppleton United	634	Princetown	669	Radcliffe Town A	660	RE	640
Poringland Wanderers	572	Princetown 2nd	670	Radcliffe Town B	660	Reading YMCA	624
Poringland Wanderers Res	572	Priory	650	Radcliffe Town Res	660	Reading YMCA Rapids	624
Porlock	676	Priory Rovers	672	Radford Res	647	Real Moor	677
Porlock Res	676	Project Clapham	623	Radstock Town A	663	Real Riverside A	642
Port of Bristol	646	Prostar Windows	655	Radstock Town Res	619	Real Riverside B	642
Port of Bristol Res	646	Prudhoe Town	626	Railway Academicals	674	Real Saracens	652
Portcastrian	643	Prudhoe Youth Club Seniors	609	Railway Academicals A	674	Real Thornbury	645
Portchester Rovers	670	Pucklechurch Sports	644	Railway Academicals Res	674	Real Thornbury Res	644
Portesham United Res	651	Pucklechurch Sports Res	644	Railway FC	656	Real United	611
Portesham Utd	651	Pulborough	678	Railway Social Club	670	Real Vikings U18	601
Porthleven	488	Pulborough Patriots	679	Rainford United	680	Reckitts AFC	593
Porthleven Res	648	Pulrose United	657	Rainhill Town	627	Reckitts Res	653
Portishead Caledonian Thistle	679	Puma FC	667	Rainhill Town Res	628	Red Lion Alverthorpe	677
Portishead Town A	679	Punchbowl	680	Ramblers	675	Red Lions	680
Portishead Town B	680	Punjab United	594	Rame Peninsula FC	651	Red Lodge	576
Portishead Town Colts	680	Punjab United	665	Rampant Horse	646	Red Row Welfare	609
Portishead Town Res	618	Purnell Sports	618	Ramsbury	676	Red Rum	600
Portland Old Boys	645	Purnell Sports A	663	Ramsden Scotia	586	Red Star Alma	620
Portland Old Boys Res	645	Purnell Sports Res	663	Ramsey	657	Red Velvet	595
Portland Town	651	Putford	666	Ramsey Hill	583	Red Velvet	671
Portland Town A	651	Pymore	669	Ramsey Pavilion	577	Redbridge U21	653
Portland Town B	651	QK Southampton	589	Ramsey Town	614	Redbrook Rovers	667
Portland United Res	650	QK Southampton Res	655	Ramsey Town Res	615	Redbrook Rovers Res	667
Portland United Youth	651	Quainton	640	Randwick	675	Redcar Athletic	626
Porton Sports	670	Quainton Res	641	Randwick 3rds	675	Redcar Newmarket	606
Portslade Athletic	663	Quedgeley Wanderers	654	Randwick Res	675	Redcar Town	606
Portslade Athletic II	664	Quedgeley Wanderers 3rds	675	Rangers	655	Redcliffe Raiders	645
Potterspury	666	Quedgeley Wanderers Res	675	Rangers	655	Redditch Borough	436
Potterspury Res.	666	Queen Mary College Old Boys	637	Rangeworthy	644	Redgate	676
Potton Town	574	Queen Mary College Old Boys II	638	Rangeworthy Res	644	Redgate Clayton	620
Poulton	629	Queen Mary College Old Boys III	638	Rank Outsiders	667	Redgate Clayton Res	620
Poulton	648	Queens County	653	Rank Outsiders Res	668	Redgate Rangers	572
Poulton Res	629	Queens Head	650	Ransomes Sports	621	Redgate Rangers Res	572
Poulton Royal	628	Queens Park Athletic	643	Ransomes Sports Res	622	Redgate Rangers Res	668
Poynton	580	Queens Park Crescents	573	RAPTC	640	Redgate Rovers	627
Predators	678	Queens Rangers	651	Ratby Sports	598	Redgate Rovers Res	628
Prees	662	Queniborough	660	Ravenscroft Old Boys	639	Redgrave Rangers	646
Premiair	615	Queniborough Res	661	Ravenshead	611	Redhouse Farm	609
Premiair Res	615	Quinton	675	Ravenshead II	665	Redlynch and Woodfalls	643

Name	Page	Name	Page	Name	Page	Name	Page
Redlynch and Woodfalls Res	643	Riverside	614	Roffey III	664	Royston Cross	677
Redmarley	667	Riverside Res	615	Rogate 08 FC	678	Royston Town A	576
Redruth United	648	Rivets Sports	640	Rogate 08 FC Res	679	Royton Town	602
Redwood United	661	Rivets Sports Res	641	Rolls	648	Royton Town Res	602
Reepham Town	571	Riviera United	671	Rolls Res	648	Rozel Rovers	658
Reepham Town Res	572	Riviera United 2nds	671	Rolls-Royce Leisure	665	Rozel Rovers Res	658
Regency Town	647	RLC	640	Rolvenden	594	RR Athletic	646
Regency Town Res	647	RNAS Culdrose	648	ROMA	600	RSG	647
Reigate OB	670	Roach Dynamos	659	Roman Glass St George 'A'	644	Ruardean Hill Rangers	654
Reigate Priory	623	Roade	607	Roman Glass/St George Res	645	Ruardean Hill Rangers A	667
Reigatians	637	Roade Res	607	Romans United	644	Ruardean Hill Rangers Res	667
Reigatians II	638	Robertswood	652	Romulus Res	448	Ruardean Utd	667
Reigatians III	638	Robin Hood Athletic	631	Roos	653	Ruddington Village	611
Reigatians IV	639	Robin Hood Athletic Res	632	Ropley	637	Ruddington Village Res	611
Reigatians V	639	Robin Hood Colts	665	Rose and Crown	657	Rudgwick	678
Reigatians VI	639	Roborough	669	Roselands	671	Rudgwick Res	678
REME	640	Roby & Waterloo GSOB Res	601	Roselands 2nds	671	Rudheath Social	580
Renhold United	573	Rocester Res	448	Rosemont Athletic U18	601	Rufforth United	634
Renhold United Res	574	Rochdale Sacred Heart	602	Rosemont U18	601	Rugby Borough	598
Renishaw Rangers	617	Rochdale Sacred Heart A	603	Ross Juniors	656	Ruislip	605
Retainers	645	Rochdale Sacred Heart Res	602	Ross Juniors	667	Runton United	667
Retainers Res	645	Rochdale St Clements	659	Rossendale FC	659	Runwell Sports	586
Retford	578	Rochdale St Clements A	660	Rossendale FC Res	660	Runwell Sports Res	586
RH Athletic A	670	Rochdale St Clements B	660	Rotherfield	663	Rushen Utd	657
RIASA East	660	Rochdale St Clements Res	659	Rotherfield II	664	Rushmoor Community	637
RIASA South	660	Rochdale Town	602	Rotherfield United	624	Rusthall Res	595
Ribble Wanderers	663	Rochdalians AFC	659	Rotherfield United Res	625	Rustington	495
Riccall United	634	Rochdalians AFC Second	659	Rothwell	631	Ruston Sports	661
Richings Park	624	Roche Res	651	Rothwell	681	Ryan F.C.	586
Richings Park	652	Rochester City	595	Rothwell Res	681	Ryburn United	655
Richings Park Res	652	Rochford Town	586	Rottingdean Village	495	Ryburn United Res	655
Richmond Raith Rovers	627	Rochford Town A	674	Route One Rovers	677	RYCOB	657
Richmond Town	626	Rochford Town Res	674	Rovers AC	655	Ryde Saints	657
Richmond Town Res	656	Rock Inn	677	Rovers AC	655	Ryde Saints A	658
Ridgewood	664	Rock Rivers	553	Rovers AC	655	Ryde Saints Res	658
Ridings FC	652	Rock Rovers	662	Rowfant Village	678	Ryhill	677
Ridings High	646	Rockland Utd.	646	Rowhedge	583	Rylands	580
Ridings High Res	646	Rockland Utd. Res.	646	Rowsley 86	665	Ryton and Crawcrook Albion A	609
Ringmer III	664	Rockleaze Rangers	587	Rowsley 86 Res	665	S C Birchanger	643
Ripley Town Res	665	Rockleaze Rangers 'A'	646	Royal Artillery	640	Saffron Crocus	577
Ripley Village	623	Rockleaze Rangers B	646	Royal Bank of Scotland	638	Saffron Crocus Res	577
Ripon City	631	Rockleaze Rangers Res	646	Royal Bank of Scotland II	638	Saffron Dynamo	598
Ripon City Res	656	Rocquaine Pirates	655	Royal Holloway Old Boys	623	Saffron Dynamo Res	598
Riseley Sports	574	Rodborough Old Boys	675	Royal Holloway Old Boys	676	Saffron Dynamos	577
Rishton Rovers	643	Rodborough Old Boys 3rds	675	Royal Oak	650	Saintbridge	675
Rishton United	643	Rodborough Old Boys Res	675	Royal Oak	662	Saints Old Boys	645
River Lane Rangers	668	Rodillian	681	Royal Sun Alliance	639	Saints Old Boys A Team	645
Riverbank Athletic	648	Roffey	495	Royal Wootton Bassett Town Res	633	Saints Old Boys B Team	645
Riverside	662	Roffey II	664	Roydon	586	Saints Old Boys Res	645

Salcombe Town	671	Saxton Rovers	665	Shamblehurst	672	Sherburn White Rose	631
Sale Amateurs	637	Saxton Rovers Res	665	Shamwickshire Rovers	666	Sherburn White Rose Res	632
Sale UNT	637	Scamblesby	652	Shamwickshire Rovers Res	666	Sheringham	571
Salem	655	Scaynes Hill	664	Shankhouse	609	Sheringham Res	572
Salem Res	655	Scaynes Hill II	664	Shanklin	657	Sherston	648
Salford Victoria	659	Scholes	657	Shanklin Res	658	Sherwin Athletic	665
Salford Victoria Res	659	Scissett	657	Shap	679	Sherwood Colliery	578
Salisbury Athletic	600	Scole United	571	Shape Changers	671	Sherwood Colliery Res	647
Saltash United Fourths	651	Scole United Res	572	Sharnbrook	573	Shevington	680
Saltash United Thirds	651	Scot	666	Sharpness	654	Shifnal United 97	662
Saltford	619	Scotter United	670	Sharpness 3rds	675	Shildon Railway	649
Saltford Res	663	Scotter United Res	671	Sharpness Res	675	Shillingstone	651
Salts	677	Sculcoates Amateurs	593	Shebbear United	666	Shipdham	646
Salts	649	Sculcoates Amateurs Res	652	Shebbear United Res	667	Shipham	680
Salts Res	678	Scunthonians	670	Sheering	643	Shipston Excelsior	436
Salts Res	649	Sea Mills Park	645	Sheering Res	643	Shipston Excelsior Colts	676
Salvation Army	622	Sea Mills Park 'A'	645	Sheffield Bankers	616	Shipston Excelsior Res	675
Sampford Peverell	650	Sea Mills Park Res	644	Sheffield Bankers Res	617	Shire Academics	681
Sandal Wanderers	681	Seaham Red Star Res	626	Sheffield Lane Top	617	Shire Academics III	681
Sandbach Curshaws	649	Seaton Burn	609	Sheffield Medics	617	Shire Academics IV	681
Sandbach Town	649	Seaton Delaval AFC	609	Shefford Town & Campton	573	Shire Academics Res	681
Sandford	650	Seaton Town	649	Shefford Town & Campton 'A'	574	Shirebrook Rangers	665
Sandford 2nds	650	Seaton Town 2nds	650	Shefford Town & Campton Res	573	Shirebrook Wanderers	665
Sandhurst Sports	637	Seaview	658	Shelf FC	655	Shirehampton	618
Sandhurst Town Res	435	Seaview Res	658	Shelf United	655	Shirehampton Res	644
Sandiacre Town	611	Sedbergh Wanderers	679	Shelf United Res	655	Shirley Town	672
Sandon Royals	662	Sedbergh Wanderers Res	679	Shelley	631	Shobdon	656
Sandown	658	Sedbury Utd	668	Shelley	657	Shoebury Town	586
Sandown Res	658	Segensworth FC	670	Shelley Res	632	Shoebury Town A	674
Sandridge Rovers	591	Seghill	609	Shelthorpe Dynamo	598	Shoebury Town Res	674
Sandridge Rovers Res	592	Selby Olympia	634	Shelthorpe Dynamo	668	Shotley	622
Sandy	573	Selkirk Utd	680	Shene Old Grammarians	637	Shottermill & Haslemere	676
Sandy Albion	574	Selston	578	Shene Old Grammarians II	639	Shrewsbury Juniors	662
Sandy Res	574	Selston Res	611	Shene Old Grammarians III	639	Shrewton United	633
Santon	671	Semington Magpies	677	Shene Old Grammarians IV	639	Shrivenham Res	435
Santos	659	Settle Utd	648	Shenfield A.F.C.	586	Shurdington Rovers	647
Sarratt	591	Settle Utd Res	649	Shenfield A.F.C. Res	586	Siddington	648
Sarratt Res	592	Settle Utd 3rds FC	649	Shenstone Pathfinder	620	Sidlesham	495
Sartan United	645	Seven Acre Sports	672	Shenstone Pathfinder	553	Sidlesham Res	678
Sartan United Res	646	Seven Stars Kennford	650	Shepborough United	668	Sidmouth Town	488
Sarum Youth (Sen)	670	Seymour United	645	Shepley	657	Sidmouth Town 3rds	650
Sawston Rovers	576	Seymour United 'A'	645	Sheppey United Res	595	Sidmouth Town Res	649
Sawston Rovers Res	577	Seymour United Res	644	Shepshed Amateurs	668	Signal Box Frankfort 2nd	670
Sawston United	575	Shaftesbury Crusade	645	Shepshed Amateurs Res	668	Signal Box Frankfort 3rds	670
Sawston United A Team	577	Shaftesbury Crusade Res	645	Shepton Beauchamp	669	Signal Box Oak Villa	669
Sawston United Res	576	Shaftesbury Town Res	650	Shepton Mallet Res	618	Signcraft FC	652
Sawtry	614	Shaftsbury Youth FC	647	Shepton Res	669	Signol Athletic	659
Sawtry Res	615	Shalford	654	Sherborne Harriers	648	Sikh Hunters	553
Saxmundham Sports	622	Shalford Res	654	Sherborne Town Res	582	Sileby Town	598

Sileby Town Res	598	Sneinton Town Pythian	669
Sileby Victoria	668	Snettisham	668
Sileby Victoria Res	668	Sneyd Park	645
Silhill 'A'	642	Sneyd Park A Team	645
Silhill B	642	Sneyd Park B Team	645
Silhill C	642	Sneyd Park Res	645
Silhill D	642	Snodland Town Res	595
Silhill E	642	Snydale Athletic	677
Silkstone United	616	Snydale Athletic Res	677
Silksworth Colliery Welfare	626	Soccer Ed	605
Silsden	660	Soham Town Rangers Res	576
Silsden Whitestar	648	Soham United	576
Silsden Whitestar Res	649	Soham United Res	577
Silver End United	662	Som Academy	605
Silver End United Res	662	Somer Valley Sports	663
Silverdale Athletic	620	Somersham	622
Silverstone	666	Somersham Res	622
Silverstone Res.	666	Somersham Town	576
Silverton	650	Somersham Town 'A'	577
Sinclair Utd	641	Somersham Town Res	577
Sinjuns Grammarians	638	Somerton Town	618
Sinjuns Grammarians II	638	Somerton Town Res	680
Sinjuns Grammarians III	639	Somerville Old Boys	638
Sittingbourne Lions	663	Sompting	644
Skegby United	669	Soton Medics	672
Skegness Town	661	Soudley	667
Skegness United	652	Soundwell Victoria	644
Skelmanthorpe	657	South Bank Cuaco	672
Skipton LMS	648	South Bank Cuaco 3rd	673
Skipton Town	648	South Bank Cuaco 4th	674
Skipton Town Res	649	South Bank Cuaco 5th	674
Skirlaugh	653	South Bank Cuaco 6th	674
Skirlaugh Res	653	South Bank Cuaco Res	673
Slaithwaite Utd	657	South Cave	593
Sleaford Sports Amateurs	661	South Cave Utd Res	653
Sleaford Town Res	661	South Cerney	648
Slinfold	678	South Cheriton United	651
Slinfold Res	679	South Creake	668
Sling	668	South Darenth	594
Sloane	637	South East Athletic	595
Slough Heating Laurencians	652	South East Athletic Res	595
Slough Heating Laurencians Res	652	South Garston	600
Slyne with Hest	629	South Godstone	670
Smallfield	663	South Kilburn	604
Smethwick Vaults	642	South Kilburn Res	605
Smiths Athletic	654	South Kirkby Colliery	616
Smiths Athletic Res	647	South Kirkby Colliery Res	617
Smithswood Firs	436	South Liverpool	627
Snaresbrook	586	South Liverpool Res	628
Sneinton Town	669	South Manchester	659

South Manchester Res	659	Southport Hesketh	629
South Milford	634	Southport Trinity	628
South Molton	667	Southrepps	667
South Normanton	578	Southrepps Res	667
South Park A	670	Southsea Utd	670
South Park B	670	Southside Star	654
South Park Rangers	653	Southside Star FC Res	647
South Park Rangers	679	Southwater	678
South Park Rangers Res	680	Southwater 3rds	679
South Petherton	669	Southwater Res	678
South Petherton Res	669	Southwater Royals	679
South Reading	625	Southwell City	578
South Redditch Athletic	675	Southwell City Res	611
South Sefton Borough	600	Southwich Rangers Res	644
South Shields Res	626	Southwick Rangers	644
South Walsham	572	Southwold Town	661
South Walsham Res	572	Sowerby Bridge	655
South Wonston Swifts	589	Sowerby Bridge Res	655
South Woodham Ferrers United	662	Sowerby United	655
South Zeal United	650	Sowerby United Res	655
Southall Res	604	Spalding Town	614
Southampton University	672	Spalding United A	615
Southcott Village R.A.	666	Spalding United Res	614
Southcott Village R.A. Res.	666	Spaniards	637
Southend Collegians	674	Spartan Youth	604
Southend Collegians A	674	Spartan Youth	623
Southend Collegians Res	674	Spartans	637
Southend Manor U21	653	Spectrum	676
Southend Rangers	674	Spexhall	661
Southend Rangers Res	674	Spexhall Res	661
Southend Sports	586	Spittal Rovers	609
Southend Sports A	674	Spixworth	571
Southend Sports B	674	Sporle	646
Southend Sports Res	586	Sport 4 Pinehurst	676
Southgate County	637	Sporting '87	621
Southgate County II	638	Sporting '87 'A'	622
Southgate County III	639	Sporting '87 Res	622
Southgate Olympic	637	Sporting Academics	658
Southgate Olympic II	637	Sporting Academics Res	658
Southgate Olympic III	638	Sporting Barum	666
Southgate Olympic IV	638	Sporting Club Thamesmead	595
Southgate Olympic V	639	Sporting Greyhound	645
Southgate Olympic VI	639	Sporting Greyhound Res	645
Southgate Olympic VII	639	Sporting Hackney	604
Southgate Seniors	652	Sporting Knavesmire	634
Southmead CS Athletic	587	Sporting Lewsey Park	661
Southmead Hospital	645	Sporting Lindfield	664
Southminster St Leonards	662	Sporting Markfield	668
Southminster St Leonards Res	662	Sporting Rebels	648
Southport & Ainsdale Amateurs	663	Sporting Sandwell	642

Club	No.	Club	No.	Club	No.	Club	No.
Sporting Wessex	672	St Georges United	662	St Stephen Res	662	Staveley MW Res	647
Sporting Weston	679	St Georges Warriors	642	St Teath	651	Staveley Utd	679
Sporting Weston Res	680	St Helens BS	658	St. Bedes AFC	681	Stedham United	678
Sportsco A	642	St Ives Rangers	576	St. Bedes AFC Res	681	Stedham United Res	678
Sportz Central	676	St Ives Rangers Res	577	St. Marys C.O.B.	643	Steeple Aston	641
Spratton	607	St Ives Town	648	St. Neots Town Res	518	Steeple Aston Res	641
Spratton Res	608	St James' Old Boys	673	St. Nicholas	681	Steeple Bumpstead	576
Springfield	585	St James' Old Boys Res	673	St. Pancras	645	Steeple Bumpstead Res	577
Springfield Res	586	St John	658	St.Judes	680	Steeple Claydon	666
Springhead	602	St John Res	658	Staddiscombe Colts	670	Steeple Claydon Res.	666
Springhead A	603	St Johns Utd	657	Staffordshire LA	620	Steeple Morden	576
Springhead Res	602	St Josephs	661	Staffordshire Moorlands	620	Steeple Morden A	577
Sproughton Sports	622	St Just	648	Staines Lammas Res	654	Steeple Morden Res	577
Sproughton Sports Res	622	St Lawrence	658	Staithes Athletic	606	Steeton	677
Sproughton United	622	St Lawrence Res	658	Stalbridge	651	Steeton Res	677
Sprowston Athletic	572	St Martins	488	Stalham Town	571	Stevenage Community	591
Spurley Hey	659	St Martins	553	Stalham Town A	667	Steventon	665
Square FC	661	St Martins	658	Stalham Town Res	572	Steventon Res	666
Square FC 2nd X1	661	St Martins 2nds	650	Staly Lions	659	Stevington	573
St Agnes	648	St Martins 3rds	650	Stalybridge Celtic	660	Stevington Res	574
St Aldhelms	645	St Martins AC	655	Stamford Belvedere	614	Stewkley	666
St Aldhelms A	646	St Martins FC	655	Stamford Belvedere Res	615	Stewkley Res.	666
St Aldhelms Res	646	St Martins Village	662	Stamford Bridge	634	Sticker	488
St Andrews	571	St Mary's Yarm	606	Stamford Lions	614	Sticker Res	651
St Andrews	645	St Marys	644	Stamford Lions 'A'	615	Stillington S&C (Beckett)	635
St Andrews Res	572	St Marys	657	Stamford Lions Res	614	Stilton United	614
St Andrews Res	598	St Mawgan	651	Standish St.Wilfrids	663	Stock United	662
St Anns Chapel	652	St Mawgan Res	651	Standon and Puckeridge	591	Stockbridge	589
St Brelade	658	St Merryn	651	Stanford	661	Stockport County	660
St Brelade Res	658	St Minver	651	Stanford-in-The-Vale	665	Stockport Georgians	602
St Breward	651	St Minver Res	651	Stanford-in-The-Vale Res	665	Stockport Georgians Res	602
St Briavels	667	St Newlyn East	651	Stanhope Town S&S Club	649	Stocksbridge Park Steels Res	616
St Cleer	651	St Nicholas	605	Stanion United	607	Stocksbridge PS Dev	617
St Clement	658	St Nicholas Old Boys	675	Stanion United Res	608	Stockton & Codford FC	677
St Clement C	658	St Ouen	658	Stanley United	677	Stockton West End	606
St Clement Res	658	St Ouen C	658	Stanley United	681	Stockwood Green	618
St Clements	635	St Ouen Res	658	Stanningley OB	681	Stockwood Green Res	619
St Clere's	662	St Patricks	661	Stansfeld (Oxford & Bermondsey)	594	Stockwood Wanderers	618
St Columb Major	651	St Patricks Res	661	Stansfeld (O & B) Res	594	Stockwood Wanderers Res	646
St Columbas	655	St Paul's	658	Stanton	621	Stoconians	659
St Day	648	St Paul's Res	658	Stanwick Rovers	608	Stogursey	676
St Dennis	488	St Pauls Church FC	680	Staplegrove	618	Stoke	680
St Dennis Res	651	St Pauls United	647	Staplegrove Res	677	Stoke by Nayland	648
St Dennis Thirds	651	St Peter	658	Staplehurst Monarchs United	594	Stoke Climsland	651
St Dominick	651	St Peter C	658	Staplehurst Monarchs United Res	595	Stoke Fleming & Strete	671
St Eval Spitfires	652	St Peter Res	658	Stapleton	644	Stoke Gabriel	488
St George (EIG)	679	St Peter's Iver	652	Stapleton Res	644	Stoke Gabriel 2nd	671
St George (EIG) Res	680	St Peters	644	Starcross Generals	650	Stoke Gabriel 3rds	671
St George's FC	652	St Saviours FC	648	Staunton & Corse	647	Stoke Gifford United	645
St Georges	657	St Stephen	651	Staunton & Corse Res	647	Stoke Gifford United Res	646

Stoke Hammond Wanderers	666	Sun Sports Res	591	SWIS	641	Templecombe Rovers	680
Stoke Heath	662	Sunderland Hall Farm Glasshus	652	SWIS Res	641	Tenbury Town	656
Stoke Hill	650	Sunderland West End	626	Sydenham Sports	595	Tenbury United	656
Stoke Old Alleynians Res	620	Sundon Park Rovers	574	Syresham	666	Tenterden Town	595
Stoke Poges Saints FC	652	Sungate	586	T D Shipley	678	Terrington	668
Stoke Poges Saints FC Res	652	Sungate Res	586	T D Shipley Res	678	Tetbury Town	675
Stoke Res	681	Surbiton Eagles	658	T V R United	678	Tetbury Town 3rds	675
Stokenchurch	435	Surrey Athletic	654	Tacket Street BBOB	622	Tetbury Town Res	675
Stokesley SC	626	Susies Star's	652	Tacolneston	572	Tetney Rovers	652
Stone Dominoes	620	Sutton	649	Tacolneston	646	Tetsworth	641
Stoneclough	629	Sutton Athletic FC	648	Tacolneston Res.	646	Tetsworth Res	641
Stoneclough Res	629	Sutton Athletic Res	594	Tadcaster Magnets	634	Teversal Res	578
Stonehouse Town	587	Sutton Bonington	668	Tadcaster Magnets Res	635	Tewkesbury Town	647
Stonehouse Town 3rds	675	Sutton Bonington Academicals	668	Tadley Calleva A Team	641	Thackley	660
Stonehouse Town 4ths	675	Sutton Bridge United	614	Talbot Knowle United	644	Thakeham Village	678
Stonehouse Town Res	675	Sutton Celtic	658	Talbot Knowle Utd	645	Thame Rangers	518
Stones	664	Sutton Courtenay	665	Talbot Rise United	643	Thame United Res	435
Stones II	664	Sutton Courtenay Res	666	Tangmere	678	Thames Borough	671
Stonewall	604	Sutton Heath Saxons	622	Tanner Athletic	680	Thaxted Rangers	577
Stonewall Res	605	Sutton Junction	680	Taplow United	624	Thaxted Rangers Res	577
Stoney Middleton	657	Sutton Junction Res	680	Taplow United "A"	625	The 61 FC (Luton) Res	573
Stonham Aspal	622	Sutton Rovers	652	Taplow United Res	625	The 61FC (Luton)	518
Stonham Aspal 'A'	622	Sutton Rovers Res	652	Tarporley Victoria	580	The Beeches	648
Stonham Aspal Res	622	Sutton Travellers	665	Tarporley Victoria Res	649	The Butchers Arms	670
Stony Stratford Town	518	Sutton United	436	Tarvin	649	The Celts	628
Stony Stratford Town	666	Sutton United 'C'	642	Tattenhoe	666	The Crown	661
Stony Stratford Town Res.	666	Sutton United A	642	Tattenhoe Res.	666	The Crown FC	678
Stowupland Falcons	621	Sutton United B	642	Tattingstone United	622	The Crown Res	661
Stowupland Falcons 'A'	622	SuttonTown	658	Taverham	668	The Eagle	577
Stowupland Falcons Res	622	Swaffham Town Res	572	Tavern	648	The Hop Leaf	625
Stratton Juniors	676	Swallownest FC	616	Taverners	654	The Ivy House FC	655
Stratton United	648	Swanage RBL	651	Taverners Res	675	The Ivy Veterans	643
Stratton United	666	Swanage Town & Herston	582	Tavistock Community	669	The Lecturn	644
Street Res	618	Swanage Town & Herston Res	651	Tavistock Rovers	670	The Lion	643
Strelley Rose	669	Swanwick Pentrich Road	578	Tawny Owl	676	The Navy Inn	669
Strensall	634	Swanwick Pentrich Road Res	647	TC Sports	646	The Raj FC	634
Stroud Harriers	654	Swarthmoor	629	Team DNF	611	The Stiffs	677
Stroud Harriers Res	675	Swarthmoor Social Res	653	Team Dudley	553	The Swan FC	652
Stroud United	675	Swavesey Institute	576	Tebby AFC	645	The Tache FC	652
Stroud United Res	675	Sway	589	Tebby AFC Res	645	The Unicorn	678
Studley Rangers	676	Sway Res	643	Tedburn St Mary	650	The View	644
Studley United	675	Swillington Saints	631	Tedburn St Mary 2nds	650	The Village Inn	680
Studs FC	660	Swindon AFC	676	Teddington	658	The Warren Res	673
Studs FC Res	661	Swindon Centurians	676	Teign Village	671	The Wilberforce Wanderers	604
Sturminster Marshall	651	Swindon Spitfires	676	Teignmouth	671	The Windmill FC (Devon)	669
Sturminster Newton	582	Swinley Forest	654	Teignmouth 2nd	671	Thetford Rovers	572
Sturminster Newton United Res	651	Swinton	659	Telford Juniors	553	Thetford Rovers Res	572
Styal	580	Swinton AFC	635	Tempest United	629	Thirsk Falcons	656
Sudbury Court	605	Swinton Athletic	616	Tempest United Res	629	Thornaby Dubliners	606
Suffolk Punch Haverhill	577	Swinton Athletic Res	617	Temple Cloud	663	Thornbury Town	587

Thornbury Town Res	675	Tiptree Heath	583	Trawden Celtic Res	649	UCL Academicals V	639
Thorncombe	669	Tiptree Jobserve	583	Tredworth Tigers	675	UCL Academicals VI	639
Thorncombe Res	669	Tiptree Jobserve Res	583	Tredworth Tigers Res	675	UEA	572
Thorne Colliery	578	Tiptree Park	583	Tregony	651	UEA A	668
Thornesians	681	Tiptree Park Res	648	Tregrehan Mills	651	UEA Res	572
Thornesians AFC	677	Tisbury	651	Trent Vineyard	665	Uffington United	665
Thornesians III	681	Tivvy Park Rangers	650	Trident	675	Uffington United Res	666
Thornesians Res	681	Toby	586	Trimley Athletic	621	Ufford Sports	622
Thorney	614	Toby Res	586	Trimley Athletic Res	622	Ufford Sports Res	622
Thornham	668	Tockwith AFC	634	Trimley Red Devils	621	Uley	675
Thornhill United	657	Tollesbury	583	Trimley Red Devils Res	622	Uley 3rds	675
Thornleigh	659	Tollesbury	648	Tring Corinthians	518	Uley Res	675
Thornleigh A	660	Tollesbury Res	583	Tring Town AFC	518	Ullswater Utd	679
Thornleigh B	660	Tonbridge Invicta	595	Trinity	658	Underwood Villa	611
Thornleigh Res	660	Tooting & Mitcham Wanderers	604	Trinity & All Saints COB	681	Underwood Villa Res	611
Thornton Cleveleys	629	Tooting Bec	623	Trinity & All Saints COB Res	681	Unicorn Athletic	637
Thornton Cleveleys Res	629	Topsham Town	649	Trinity Res	658	Union Mills	657
Thornton Heath	659	Torbay Police	671	Trowbridge Town	633	Unite MK	518
Thornton United	677	Torbay Police 2nds	671	Trowbridge Town ‘A’ FC	677	United Approach	669
Thornton United Res	678	Tormarton	644	Trowbridge Town Res	677	United Chelmsford Churches	662
Thorpe United	634	Toros	656	Trowbridge Wanderers Dev18	677	United Chelmsford Churches Res	662
Thorpe United Res	635	Torpedo	645	Tuddenham 08	577	United F C	655
Thorpe Village	572	Torpedo A Team	645	Tudor Rose	661	United Worksop	665
Thorpe Wood Rangers	615	Torpedo B Team	645	Tudor Sports	671	Unity	611
Thorverton	650	Torpedo Res	645	Tuffley Rovers 3rds	675	Unity	624
Three Daggers FC	677	Torpoint Athletic Thirds	651	Tuffley Rovers 4ths	675	Unity Res	611
Thringstone MW	668	Torquay Town	671	Tuffley Rovers 5ths	675	Unity Res	625
Thundersley Athletic	674	Torridgeside AFC	488	Tuffley Rovers Res	654	University 3rds	649
Thurcroft Miners Institute	617	Torridgeside Res	666	Tunley Athletic	619	University 4ths	650
Thurlaston	660	Torridgeside Thirds	667	Tunstall Town	620	University 5ths	650
Thurnby Rangers	598	Torrington	666	Turton	629	University of Buckingham	666
Thurnby Rangers	660	Torrington Res	667	Turton Res	629	University of Essex	583
Thurston	622	Totnes & Dartington	488	Twentyten	641	University of Essex Res	583
Tibberton United	675	Totnes & Dartington 2nds	671	Twentyten Res	641	University of Exeter	488
Tidenham	667	Tottenham Hale Rangers	604	Two Gates	642	University of Exeter Res	649
Tidenham Res	668	Totterdown United	645	Twyford & Ruscombe	625	University of Hertfordshire	638
Tideswell United	578	Totterdown United Res	644	Twyford United	666	University of Hertfordshire II	639
Tideswell United Res	656	Totternhoe	518	Tydd St Mary	614	University of Kent	595
Tilburg Regents	638	Totternhoe Res	573	Tydd St Mary Res	615	University of Plymouth	669
Tillingham Hotspur	662	Tottington United	659	Tyersal	677	University of Plymouth 2nds	670
Timsbury Athletic	618	Tottington United A	660	Tyersal Res	678	University of Surrey	676
Timsbury Athletic Res	663	Tottington United Res	660	Tyldesley United	680	University of Surrey A	654
Tingley Athletic	678	Towcester Town	666	Tysoe United	676	University of Surrey B	654
Tintagel	651	Towcester Town Res.	666	UCF Sylvans	655	Upham	589
Tintwistle Athletic	659	Town Malling Club	663	UCF Sylvans	655	Upham Res	672
Tintwistle Athletic Res	603	Town Mead	643	UCF Sylvans	655	Uphill Castle	618
Tipton St John	649	Townmead	652	UCL Academicals	637	Uphill Castle A	680
Tipton Town	553	Traco Athletic	637	UCL Academicals II	637	Uphill Castle Res	679
Tipton Town Res	448	Trafford United	659	UCL Academicals III	638	Uplowman Athletic	650
Tipton Youth	553	Trawden Celtic	648	UCL Academicals IV	638	Uplyme	669

West Farleigh	595	Westhill Sports Res	663	White Notley	583	Willingdon Athletic	663
West Farleigh Res	663	Westland Sports	582	White Notley Res	662	Willingdon Athletic II	664
West Haddon Albion	607	Westland Sports Res	650	Whitecroft	667	Willingdon Athletic III	664
West Haddon Albion Res	608	Westminster	665	Whitecroft & Barton	657	Willington Quay Saints	609
West Hoathly	664	Weston	592	Whitecroft & Barton Sports Res	658	Willington Sports	665
West Hoathly II	664	Weston	656	Whitecroft A	667	Willington W.M.C.	649
West Horton	677	Weston	663	Whitecroft Res	667	Willow Wanderers	652
West Howe Saturday	643	Weston	667	Whitehaven	629	Wilmslow Albion	602
West Hull Amateurs	653	Weston St Johns	619	Whitkirk Wanderers	631	Wilmslow Albion Res	602
West Kirby	627	Westoning	573	Whitkirk Wanderers Res	632	Wilsden Athletic	648
West Kirby Res	628	Westoning	574	Whitley Bay A	609	Wilstead	573
West Lynn	668	Westonzoyland	676	Whitley Bay Boys Club Seniors	609	Wilstead Res	574
West SL Benfica	605	Westover Bournemouth	643	Whitminster Res	675	Wilts Calne Town	633
West Totton	672	Westover Bournemouth Res	643	Whittington	620	Wimblington	577
West Town United	645	Westside	623	Whittington	642	Wimblington Res	577
West Wickham	672	Westwood United	624	Whittington U21	642	Wincanton Town A	651
West Wickham 3rd	673	Westwood United Res	625	Whittlesey Athletic 'A'	614	Wincanton Town Res	650
West Wickham 4th	674	Wetherby Athletic	631	Whittlesey Athletic 'B'	615	Winchcombe Town	654
West Wickham 5th	674	Wetherby Athletic B	635	Whittlesey Athletic 'C'	615	Winchcombe Town Res	647
West Wickham 6th	674	Wetheriggs Utd	679	Whittlesey Athletic Res	614	Winchester	650
West Wickham Res	673	Wetheriggs Utd Res	679	Whittlesford United	576	Winchester Castle	589
West Wight	657	Wey Valley	637	Whittlesford United Res	577	Winchester Castle Res	655
West Wight Res	658	Wey Valley Res	637	Whitworth Valley	659	Winchmore Hill	672
West Wratting	575	Weymouth A	651	Whitworth Valley Res	660	Winchmore Hill 3rd	673
West Wratting Res	576	Weysiders	676	Why United	678	Winchmore Hill 4th	673
Westbrook YMCA	677	Whaddon United	654	Why United Res	679	Winchmore Hill 5th	673
Westbury	666	Whaddon United Res	647	Wibsey	677	Winchmore Hill 6th	673
Westbury Sports Club	602	Whaley Bridge	580	Wick	645	Winchmore Hill 7th	673
Westbury Sports Club Res	603	Whalley Range	659	Wick 'A'	644	Winchmore Hill 8th	673
Westbury Town	677	Whalley Range Res	659	Wick Res	644	Winchmore Hill 9th	674
Westbury United Res	677	Whaplode Drove	615	Wicken	577	Winchmore Hill Res	673
Westbury Utd	667	Wheatley Hill WMC	652	Wicken Sports	666	Windermere SC	679
Westbury Utd Res	667	Wheatsheaf	648	Wickersley	616	Windermere SC Res	679
Westcott 1935 FC	678	Wheelwright OB	681	Wickham Market	621	Windlesham & Lightwater	676
Westcott 1935 FC Res	679	Wheldrake	635	Wickham Market Res	622	Windlesham & Lightwater A	654
Westella & Willerby	593	Whelley	680	Wickhambrook	577	Window Doctor AFC	653
Westend	657	Whetstone Athletic	661	Wickwar Wanderers	675	Windscale FC	626
Westend	679	Whinney Banks YCC	606	Widbrook Utd	670	Windsor Great Park	652
Westerfield United	621	Whipton & Pinhoe	650	Wideopen and District	609	Windyridge Rovers	647
Westerfield United Res	622	Whiston Juniors U18	601	Wigan Rovers	680	Wing Village	666
Westerleigh Sports	644	Whitburn Athletic	609	Wigan Rovers Res	680	Wing Village Res	666
Western Athletic	605	Whitby Athletic FC	647	Wigginton Grasshoppers	634	Wingrave	640
Westfield	618	Whitchurch Alport Juniors	662	Wigginton Grasshoppers Res	635	Wingrave Res	641
Westfield	495	White Eagles	574	Wilberfoss	634	Winklebury Wizards	641
Westfield A	663	White Eagles	625	Wilby	608	Winkleigh	650
Westfield Res	663	White Eagles	676	Willand Rovers Res	649	Winlaton Vulcans	609
Westfields Res	656	White Eagles	677	Willaston	628	Winnington Avenue	649
Westhamians	586	White Eagles Res	625	Willen	666	Winnington Avenue 1994	649
Westhamians U21	653	White Ensign	585	Willen Res.	666	Winscombe	618
Westhill Sports	663	White Ensign Res	586	Willesborough Athletic	595	Winscombe A	679

Winscombe Res	619	Woking Tigers	654	Woolavington	676	Writtle Saturday	662
Winsford Saxons FC	649	Wokingham & Emmbrook Res	624	Wooldale Wanderers	657	Wrockwardine Wood	662
Winsford United Res	649	Wokingham & Emmbrook Res	435	Woolsery	667	Wroughton FC	633
Winsham	669	Wollaston Victoria	607	Woolverstone United	622	Wroughton Res	676
Winsham Res	669	Wollaston Victoria Res	608	Wootton Blue Cross	573	Wroxall	658
Winstanley St.Aidans	680	Wollaton	611	Wootton St George	607	Wroxham Res	571
Winstanley Warriors	680	Wollaton Hall & Bramcote	669	Wootton Village	574	Wroxton Sports	641
Winstanley Warriors Res	680	Wollaton III	665	Woottons (The)	668	Wroxton Sports Res	641
Winterbourne United	645	Wollaton IV	665	Woottons (The) Res	668	Wyberton	661
Winterbourne United Res	644	Wollaton Res	611	Worcester College Old Boys	637	Wyke Wanderers	631
Wirksworth Ivanhoe	665	Wolsingham	649	Worcester Raiders	553	Wyke Wanderers Res	632
Wirksworth Ivanhoe Res	665	Wolstanton United	620	Working Wonders	617	Wymering	670
Wirksworth Town	665	Wolverhampton SC U21	620	Workington	660	Wymeswold FC	668
Wirksworth Town Res	665	Wolverhampton United	553	Worle	619	Wymondham Town	571
Wirral SB	628	Wolviston FC	626	Worle Rangers	679	Wymondham Town Res	572
Wisbech St Mary A	577	Wombwell Main	616	Worle Rangers Res	679	Wyre Villa	629
Wisbech St Mary B	577	Wombwell Main Dev	617	Worle Res	679	Wyre Villa Res	629
Wisbech St Mary C	577	Wonder Vaults	553	Wormingford Wanderers	583	Wyrley	553
Wisbech St Mary Res	576	Wood Green Old Boys	638	Wormingford Wanderers Res	583	Wythenshawe Amateur	637
Wisbech Town Acorns U21	615	Wood Green Old Boys II	639	Wormingford Wanderers Res	648	Wythenshawe Amateurs	602
Wisbech Town Res	614	Wood Green Old Boys III	639	Wormley Rovers	591	Wythenshawe Amateurs Res	602
Wisborough Green	678	Wood Wanderers	642	Wormley Rovers Res	592	Wythenshawe Town	580
Wisborough Green Res	678	Woodbury	649	Worplesdon Phoenix	676	Yapton	678
Wisdom Sports	664	Woodbury 2nds	650	Worplesdon Phoenix A	654	Yapton Res	678
Wistow	635	Woodchester	675	Worrall Hill	667	Yardley Gobion	666
Witan	638	Woodcote Stoke Row	624	Worsbrough Bridge Athletic Dev	617	Yardley Gobion Res.	666
Witan II	639	Woodcote Stoke Row Res	625	Worth Avenue	643	Yarmouth & Calb	658
Witchampton United	650	Woodford	670	Wortham	622	Yarmouth & Calb Res	658
Witchford 96	576	Woodford United	641	Worthian Town Leisure 3	644	Yarnton	613
Witchford 96 Res	577	Woodford Wolves	607	Worthing BCOB	644	Yarnton Res	613
Witheridge 3rds	650	Woodhouse Imperial	668	Worthing BCOB Res	644	Yate Athletic	644
Witheridge Res	649	Woodhouse Imperial Res	668	Worthing Borough	678	Yate Athletic Res	644
Withernsea	653	Woodhouse Moor Methodists	681	Worthing Dynamos	644	Yateley United	623
Withernsea Res	653	Woodingdean Wanderers	644	Worthing Leisure	678	Yateley United A	637
Withington	656	Woodkirk Valley	681	Worthing Town Leisure	495	Yateley United B	637
Witnesham Wasps	622	Woodkirk Valley Mens Res	681	Wortley	681	Yatton Ath Res	679
Witnesham Wasps Res	622	Woodley United "A"	625	Wortley Res	681	Yatton Athletic	618
Wittering Harriers	614	Woodley United "B"	625	Wotton Rovers	654	Yaxham	646
Wittering Harriers Res	615	Woodley United Res	624	Wotton Rovers Res	675	Yelvertoft	608
Wittering Res	615	Woodley United Royals	624	Wraysbury Village	624	Yelverton	572
Witton Albion Dev	660	Woodmansterne Hyde	670	Wrecclesham	654	Yelverton Res	572
Wivelsfield Green Pilgrims	664	Woodmansterne Hyde Res	670	Wrecclesham Res	654	York RI	634
Wixams	574	Woodnesborough	595	Wrens Nest	553	York St Johns University	634
WMOV DRDE Trust	669	Woodthorpe Park Rangers	669	Wright & Unity Sports	624	Yorkley	667
WMOV DRDE Trust 2nd	670	Woofferton	656	Wrington Red Hill Res	679	Yorkley Res	667
Wodson Park	592	Wool & Winfrith	651	Wrington Redhill	618	Yorkshire Amateur	660
Woking & Horsell	676	Wool & Winfrith A	651	Wrington Redhill A	680	Youlgrave United	656
Woking & Horsell A	654	Wool & Winfrith Res	651	Writtle A	662	Zeals FC	677
Woking & Maybury	654	Woolaston	654	Writtle Res	662	Zubry Oxford FC	613
Woking Corinthians	654	Woolaston Res	667	Writtle Manor	662		